S0-AJD-370

Handbook of Stem Cells

Volume 2

Adult and Fetal

EDITORIAL BOARD

Handbook of Stem Cells

Volume 2

Adult and Fetal

EDITORS

Robert Lanza
Helen Blau
Douglas Melton
Malcolm Moore
E. Donnall Thomas (Hon)
Catherine Verfaillie
Irving Weissman
Michael West

ELSEVIER
ACADEMIC
PRESS

AMSTERDAM • BOSTON • HEIDELBERG • LONDON
NEW YORK • OXFORD • PARIS • SAN DIEGO
SAN FRANCISCO • SINGAPORE • SYDNEY • TOKYO

Elsevier Academic Press
200 Wheeler Road, 6th Floor, Burlington, MA 01803, USA
525 B Street, Suite 1900, San Diego, California 92101-4495, USA
84 Theobald's Road, London WC1X 8RR, UK

This book is printed on acid-free paper. ♾

Library of Congress Cataloging-in-Publication Data
Application submitted

British Library Cataloguing in Publication Data
A catalogue record for this book is available from the British Library

ISBN: 0-12-436643-0 (set)
ISBN: 0-12-436642-2 (volume 1)
ISBN: 0-12-436641-4 (volume 2)
ISBN: 0-12-436644-9 (CD-Rom)

For all information on all Academic Press publications
visit our Web site at www.books.elsevier.com

Printed in the United States of America

04 05 06 07 08 09 9 8 7 6 5 4 3 2 1

Contents

PART TWO
Early development

PART THREE
Ectoderm

PART FOUR
Mesoderm

Contributors

Numbers in parentheses indicate the chapter to which the author contributed.

Alaa Adassi, MD (27)
Stem Cell Institute and Division of Hematology, Oncology and Transplantation, Department of Medicine, University of Minnesota Medical School, Minneapolis, MN

Iva Afrikanova, PhD (36)
Department of Pathology and Immunology, Washington University School of Medicine, St. Louis, MO

Koichi Akashi, MD, PhD (34)
Associate Professor, Cancer Immunology and AIDS, Dana-Farber Cancer Institute, Harvard Medical School, Boston, MA

Piero Anversa, MD (64)
Director, Cardiovascular Research Institute, Professor and Vice Chairman, Department of Medicine, New York Medical College, Valhalla, NY

Anthony Atala, MD (16, 50)
The William Boyce Professor and Director, Wake Forest Institute for Regenerative Medicine, Wake Forest University, Winston-Salem, NC

Scott T. Avecilla, BS (35)
Research Associate, Department of Genetic Medicine, Cornell University Medical College, New York, NY

Dolores Baksh, PhD (59)
NIAMS, National Institutes of Health, Bethesda, MD

Yann Barrandon, MD, PhD (69)
Laboratory of Stem Cell Dynamics, Swiss Institute of Technology (EPFL), Lausanne University Hospital (CHUV), 1015 Lausanne, Switzerland

Stephen H. Bartelmez (10)
The Basic Research Laboratory, Center for Cancer Research, National Cancer Institute-Frederick, Frederick, MD

Steven R. Bauer, PhD (73)
Chief, Laboratory of Stem Cell Biology, Division of Cellular and Gene Therapies, Office of Cellular, Tissue, and Gene Therapies, Center for Biologics Evaluation and Research, Food and Drug Administration, Bethesda, MD

Prosper Benhaim, MD (40)
Associate Professor, Orthopedic Surgery, UCLA, Los Angeles, CA

Paolo Bianco, MD (39, 71)
Professor of Pathology, Department of Experimental Medicine and Pathology, La Sapienza University, Rome, Italy

Helen M. Blau, PhD (37)
Professor and Director, Baxter Laboratory in Genetic Pharmacology, Department of Microbiology and Immunology, Stanford University School of Medicine, Stanford, CA

Hans Bode (4)
Department of Developmental and Cell Biology, University of California, Irvine, CA

Susan Bonner-Weir, PhD (66)
Associate Professor/Senior Investigator, Harvard Medical School, Boston, MA

Corinne A. Boulanger, MS (25)
Mammary Biology and Tumorigenesis Laboratory, Center for Cancer Research, Bethesda, MD

Mairi Brittan, BSc (47)
Histopathology Unit, London Research Institute, Cancer Research UK, London, United Kingdom

Marianne Bronner-Fraser, PhD (19)
California Institute of Technology, Division of Biology, Beckman Institute, Pasadena, CA

Hal E. Broxmeyer, PhD (17)
Chairman and Mary Margaret Walther Professor, Microbiology/Immunology, Professor of Medicine, Scientific Director of the Walther Oncology Center, Indiana University School of Medicine, Indianapolis, IN

Richard K. Burt, MD (68)
Associate Professor, Division of Immunotherapy, Department of Medicine, Northwestern University Feinberg School of Medicine, Chicago, IL

Maeve A. Caldwell, PhD (52)
Centre for Brain Repair, University Forvie Site, Cambridge, United Kingdom

Fernando D. Camargo (31)
Baylor College of Medicine, Houston, TX

Arnold I. Caplan, PhD (28)
Professor of Biology, Director of Skeletal Research Center, Department of Biology, Case Western Reserve University, Cleveland, OH

Peter Carmeliet, MD, PhD (42)
Professor of Medicine, Adjunct Director Center for Transgene Technology and Gene Therapy, Flanders Interuniversity Institute for Biotechnology (VIB), University of Leuven, Campus Gasthuisberg, Leuven, Belgium

Elena Cattaneo, PhD (62)
Department of Pharmacological Sciences and Center of Excellence on Neurodegenerative Diseases, University of Milano, Milan Italy

Siddharthan Chandran MD, PhD (52)
Department of Clinical Neurosciences, University of Cambridge, Forvie Site, Cambridge, United Kingdom

Howard Y. Chang, MD, PhD (57)
Department of Dermatology and Biochemistry, Stanford University, Stanford, CA

Xin Chen, PhD (57)
Department of Biopharmaceutical Sciences, University of California, San Francisco, San Francisco, CA

Tao Cheng, MD (6)
Director of Stem Cell Biology, University of Pittsburgh Cancer Institute, Pittsburgh, PA

Richard W. Childs, MD (67)
Senior Investigator, National Heart, Lung, and Blood Institute, National Institutes of Health, Bethesda, MD

Kyunghee Choi, PhD (36)
Associate Professor, Department of Pathology and Immunology, Washington University School of Medicine, St. Louis, MO

Dipanjan Chowdhury (8)
Rosenstiel Basic Medical Sciences Research Center, Department of Biology, Brandeis University, Waltham, MA

Yun Shin Chung, PhD (36)
Department of Pathology and Immunology, Washington University School of Medicine, St. Louis, MO

Philippe Collas, PhD (13)
Professor, Department of Biochemistry, Institute of Basic Medical Sciences, University of Oslo, Oslo, Norway

Gay M. Crooks, MD (33)
Associate Professor of Pediatrics, Department of Pediatrics, USC Keck School of Medicine, Division of Research Immunology/BMT, The Saban Research Institute of Childrens Hospital Los Angeles, Los Angeles, CA

Giulio Cossu, MD (65)
Professor of Histology and Embryology, Stem Cell Research Institute, Dibit, H. San Raffaele, Milan, Italy, Institute of Cell Biology and Tissue Engineering, San Raffaele Biomedical Science Park of Rome, University of Rome "La Sapienza", Rome, Italy

Brian R. Davis, PhD (72)
Senior Scientist, Institute for Inherited Disease Research, Newtown, PA

Gabriella Cusella De Angelis, MD, PhD (65)
Stem Cell Research Institute, Dept. of Exptl. Med., Human Anatomy, University of Pavia, Pavia, Italy

Sharon Y.R. Dent (formerly Sharon Y. Roth) (9)
Associate Professor, Department of Biochemistry and Molecular Biology, University of Texas M.D. Anderson Cancer Center, Houston, TX

John E. Dick, PhD (58)
Canada Research Chair in Stem Cell Biology, Toronto General Research Institute, Princess Margaret Hospital, University Health Network, Professor, Department of Medical Genetics and Microbiology, University of Toronto, Toronto, Ontario, Canada

Natalie Direkze, MB, BS, MRCP (47)
Histopathology Unit, London Research Institute, Cancer Research UK, London, United Kingdom

Yuval Dor, PhD (46)
Harvard University, Cambridge, MA

Ryan R. Driskell (48)
Department of Anatomy and Cell Biology, University of Iowa, Iowa City, IA

Catherine Dulac, PhD (22)
Professor of Molecular and Cellular Biology, Investigator, Howard Hughes Medical Institute, Department of Molecular and Cellular Biology, Harvard University, Cambridge, MA

Cynthia E. Dunbar, MD (53)
Head of Molecular Hematopoiesis, Section Hematology Branch, National Institutes of Health, Bethesda, MD

Hideo Ema, MD, PhD (30)
Associate Professor, Laboratory of Stem Cell Therapy, Center for Experimental Medicine, Institute of Medical Science University of Tokyo, Tokyo, Japan

John F. Engelhardt, PhD (48)
Professor, Director, Center for Gene Therapy, Department of Anatomy and Cell Biology, University of Iowa, Iowa City, IA

Tariq Enver, PhD (7)
Professor of Stem Cell Biology, MRC Molecular Haematology Unit, Weatherall Institute of Molecular Medicine, John Radcliffe Hospital, Headington, Oxford, England

Yvonne A. Evrard, PhD (9)
Department of Biochemistry and Molecular Biology, University of Texas M.D. Anderson Cancer Center, Houston, TX

Valentina M. Factor (45)
Laboratory of Experimental Carcinogenesis, Center for Cancer Research, National Cancer Institute, National Institutes of Health, Bethesda, MD

K. Rose Finley (60)
Division of Hematology/Oncology, Children's Hospital, Dana-Farber Cancer Institute, and Harvard Medical School, Boston, MA

Jennifer C. Fletcher, PhD (56)
Plant Gene Expression Center, USDA/UC Berkeley, Albany, CA

Elaine Fuchs, PhD (24)
Rebecca C. Lancefield Professor, Investigator of the Howard Hughes Medical Institute, Laboratory of Mammalian Cell Biology and Development, The Rockefeller University, New York, NY

Margaret T. Fuller, PhD (5)
Professor, Departments of Developmental Biology and Genetics, Stanford University School of Medicine, Stanford, CA

Amiela Globerson, PhD (32)
Department of Immunology, Weizmann Institute of Science, Rehovot, Israel, Director, Center for Multidisciplinary Research in Aging, Ben Gurain University of the Negev, Beer Sheva, Israel

Victor M. Goldberg, MD (70)
Case Western Reserve University, University Hospitals of Cleveland, Cleveland, OH,

Margaret A. Goodell, PhD (31, 38)
Associate Professor, Center for Cell and Gene Therapy, Baylor College of Medicine, Houston, TX

Berthold Göttgens, DPhil (29)
Leukaemia Research Fund Lecturer, Department of Haematology, Cambridge Institute for Medical Research, University of Cambridge, Cambridge, United Kingdom

Elizabeth Gould, PhD (20)
Professor, Department of Psychology, Program in Neuroscience, Princeton University, Princeton, NJ

Anthony Richard Green, PhD, FRCP, FRCPath, FMedSci (29)
Professor of Haemato-Oncology, Head of Department of Haematology, Department of Haematology, University of Cambridge, Cambridge Institute for Medical Research, Cambridge, United Kingdom

Joe W. Grisham (45)
Laboratory of Experimental Carcinogenesis, Center for Cancer Research, National Cancer Institute, National Institutes of Health, Bethesda, MD

Markus Grompe, MD (44)
Director, Oregon Stem Cell Center, Professor, Department of Medical and Molecular Genetics, Department of Pediatrics, Oregon Health and Science University, Portland, OR

David N. Haylock, PhD (55)
Stem Cell Research Laboratory, Peter MacCallum Cancer Centre, Melbourne,Victoria, Australia

Anne L. Hazlehurst (74)
Center for Biochemical Engineering, Brown University, Providence, RI

Marc H. Hedrick, MD (40)
Adjunct Associate Professor, Department Surgery and Pediatrics, University of California, Los Angeles, Los Angeles, CA

Marko E. Horb, PhD (12)
Laboratory of Molecular Organogenesis, Institut de Recherches Cliniques de Montreal (IRCM), Montreal, Quebec, Canada

Jerry I. Huang, MD (70)
Case Western Reserve University, University Hospitals of Cleveland, Cleveland, OH

H. David Humes, MD (43)
Professor, Division of Nephrology, Department of Internal Medicine, University of Michigan School of Medicine, Ann Arbor, Michigan

Haruhiko Ishii (8)
Rosenstiel Basic Medical Sciences Research Center, Department of Biology, Brandeis University, Waltham, MA

David K. Jin, MD, PhD (35)
Department of Genetic Medicine, Cornell University Medical College, New York, NY

D. Leanne Jones, PhD (5)
Department of Developmental Biology, Stanford University School of Medicine, Stanford, CA

Jan Kajstura, PhD (64)
Cardiovascular Research Institute, New York Medical College, Valhalla, NY

Anne Kessinger, MD (61)
Professor, Department of Internal Medicine, University of Nebraska Medical Center, Omaha, NE

Chris Kintner, PhD (18)
Professor, Molecular Neurobiology Laboratory, The Salk Institute for Biological Studies, La Jolla, CA

Naoko Koyano-Nakagawa, PhD (18)
Department of Neuroscience, University of Minnesota, Minneapolis, MN

Robb Krumlauf, PhD (19)
Scientific Director, Stowers Institute for Medical Research, Kansas City, MO

Thomas Küntziger, PhD (13)
Professor, Institute of Basic Medical Sciences, Department of Biochemistry, University of Oslo, Oslo, Norway

Mark A. LaBarge, PhD (37)
Department of Life Sciences, Lawrence Berkeley National Laboratory, Berkeley, CA

Peter M. Lansdorp, MD, PhD (11)
Professor of Medicine, University of British Columbia, Senior Scientist, Terry Fox Laboratory, BC Cancer Research Center, Vancouver, British Columbia, Canada

Robert Lanza, MD (Preface)
Vice President, Medical and Scientific Development, Advanced Cell Technology, Adjunct Professor of Surgical Sciences, Institute of Regenerative Medicine, Wake Forest University School of Medicine, Winston-Salem, NC

Ihor Lemischka, PhD (3)
Professor, Department of Molecular Biology, Princeton University, Princeton, NJ

Annarosa Leri (64)
Associate Professor, New York Medical College, Valhalla, NY

Joseph J. Lucas, PhD (14)
Department of Pediatrics, National Jewish Medical and Research Center, Denver, CO

Aernout Luttun, PhD (42)
Center for Transgene Technology and Gene Therapy, Flanders Interuniversity Institute for Biotechnology, Department of Medicine, University of Leuven, Leuven, Belgium

Michael J. Lysaght, PhD (74)
Professor and Director, Center for Biomedical Engineering, Brown University, Providence, RI

Gerard J. Madlambayan, PhD (59)
University of Toronto, Institute of Biomaterials and Biomedical Engineering, Toronto, Ontorio, Canada

Gillian May, PhD (7)
MRC Molecular Haematology Unit, Weatherall Institute of Molecular Medicine, John Radcliffe Hospital, Headington, Oxford, United Kingdom

Joby L. McKenzie, BSc (58)
Molecular and Medical Genetics, University of Toronto/University Health Network, Toronto, Ontario, Canada

Shannon McKinney-Freeman, PhD (38)
Children's Hospital Boston, Boston, MA

Douglas A. Melton, PhD (Foreword, 46)
Thomas Dudley Cabot Professor in the Natural Sciences, Department of Molecular and Cellular Biology, Harvard University, Investigator, Howard Hughes Medical Institute, Cambridge, MA

Christian Mirescu, PhD (20)
Department of Psychology, Princeton University, Princeton, NJ

Malcolm A.S. Moore, PhD (15)
Enid A. Haupt Professor of Cell Biology, Head, James Ewing Laboratory of Developmental Hematopoiesis, Memorial Sloan-Kettering Cancer Center, New York, NY

Yo-hei Morita, BA (30)
Laboratory of Stem Cell Therapy, Center for Experimental Medicine, Institute of Medical Science, University of Tokyo, Tokyo, Japan

Bernardo Nadal-Ginard, MD, PhD (64)
Cardiovascular Research Institute, New York Medical College, Valhalla, NY

Hiromitsu Nakauchi, MD, PhD (30)
Professor, Laboratory of Stem Cell Therapy, Center for Experimental Medicine, Institute of Medical Science, University of Tokyo, Tokyo, Japan

Donald Orlic, PhD (53)
Associate Investigator, Genetics and Molecular Biology Branch, National Human Genome Research Institute, NIH, Bethesda, Maryland

Christopher S. Potten, PhD, DSc (1)
Professor, EpiStem Limited, Manchester, United Kingdom

Sean Preston, MB, BS, MRCP (47)
Histopathology Unit, London Research Institute, Cancer Research UK, London, United Kingdom

Darwin J. Prockop, MD, PhD (Foreword)
Director, Center for Gene Therapy, Professor of Biochemistry, Tulane University Health Sciences Center, New Orleans, LA

Nicole L. Prokopishyn, PhD (72)
Fund for Inherited Disease Research, Newtown, PA

Shahin Rafii, MD (35)
Professor of Genetic Medicine, Hematology-Oncology and Genetic Medicine, Cornell University Medical College, New York, NY

Carlos Almeida Ramos, MD (31)
Oncology/Hematology Fellow, Memorial Sloan-Kettering Cancer Center, New York, NY

Pamela A. Raymond, PhD (63)
Professor, Cell and Developmental Biology, University of Michigan Medical School, Ann Arbor, MI

Pamela Gehron Robey, PhD (39)
Chief, Craniofacial and Skeletal Diseases Branch, National Institute of Dental and Craniofacial Research, National Institutes of Health, Bethesda, MD

Ariane Rochat, PhD (69)
Project Leader, Laboratory of Stem Cell Dynamics, Swiss Institute of Technology (EPFL) and Lausanne, University Hospital (CHUV), Lausanne, Switzerland

Hans-Reimer Rodewald, PhD (49)
Professor, Head of Department, Department of Immunology, University Clinics Ulm, Ulm, Germany

Nadia Rosenthal, PhD (41)
Head, EMBL Mouse Biology Programme, European Molecular Biology Laboratory, Monterotondo Scalo (Rome), Italy

Ferdinando Rossi, MD, PhD (62)
Professor of Neuroscience, Rita Levi Montalcini Centre for Brain Repair, Department of Neuroscience, University of Turin, Turin, Italy

Francis W. Ruscetti, PhD (10)
Head, Leukocyte Biology Section, Center for Cancer Research, National Cancer Institute-Frederick, Frederick, MD

Maurilio Sampaolesi, PhD (65)
Stem Cell Research Institute, Dept. of Exptl. Med., Human Anatomy, University of Pavia, Pavia, Italy

Maria Paola Santini, Laurea (41)
EMBL Mouse Biology Programme, European Molecular Biology Laboratory, Monterotondo Scalo (Rome), Italy

David T. Scadden, MD (6)
Professor of Medicine, Harvard University, Massachusetts General Hospital, Boston, MA

Ruth Seggewiss, MD (53)
Section Hematology Branch, National Institutes of Health, Bethesda, MD

Ranjan Sen (8)
Rosenstiel Basic Medical Sciences Research Center, Department of Biology, Brandeis University, Waltham, MA

J. Graham Sharp (61)
University of Nebraska Medical Center, Omaha, Nebraska

Sergey V. Shmelkov, MD (35)
Department of Genetic Medicine, Cornell University Medical College, New York, NY

Mohummad Minhaj Siddiqui, BS (16)
Wake Forest Institute for Regenerative Medicine, Wake Forest University School of Medicine, Winston-Salem, NC

Paul J. Simmons, PhD (55)
Program Head in Stem Cell Biology, Stem Cell Biology Laboratory, Peter MacCallum Cancer Centre, East Melbourne, Australia

William B. Slayton, MD (54)
Assistant Professor, Pediatric Hematology/Oncology, University of Florida College of Medicine, Gainesville, FL

Gilbert H. Smith, PhD (25)
Mammary Biology and Tumorigenesis Laboratory, Center for Cancer Research, Bethesda, MD

Lukas Sommer, PhD (21)
Assistant Professor in Cell and Developmental Biology, Institute of Cell Biology, Swiss Federal Institute of Technology, Zurich, Switzerland

Gerald Spangrude, PhD (54)
Professor of Medicine, Division of Hematology, University of Utah, Salt Lake City, UT

Ramaprasad Srinivasan, MD, PhD (67)
Staff Physician, Urologic Oncology Branch, National Cancer Institute, Bethesda, MD

Mark S. Szczypka, PhD (43)
Director of Research, Research Division, Nephros Therapeutics Inc., Ann Arbor, MI

Yoshiyuki Takahashi, MD, PhD (67)
Hematology Branch, National Heart Lung and Blood Institute/NIH, Bethesda, MD

Rafael Tejada, (35)
Research Associate, Department of Genetic Medicine, Cornell University Medical College, New York, NY

Naohiro Terada, MD, PhD (14)
Associate Professor, Department of Pathology, University of Florida, Gainesville, FL

E. Donnall Thomas, (Hon) (Foreword)
Member, Fred Hutchinson Cancer Research Center, Professor of Medicine, Emeritus, University of Washington, Seattle, WA

James A. Thomson, VMD, PhD, Dipl ACVP (57)
John D. MacArthur Professor, Department of Anatomy, University of Wisconsin-Madison Medical School, The Wisconsin National Primate Research Center, Madison, WI

Snorri S. Thorgeirsson (45)
Laboratory of Experimental Carcinogenisis, Center for Cancer Research, National Cancer Institute, National Institutes of Health, Bethesda, MD

Marc Tjwa, MD (42)
Center for Transgene Technology and Gene Therapy, Flanders Interuniversity Institute for Biotechnology (VIB), University of Leuven, Campus Gasthuisberg, Leuven, Belgium

David Tosh, PhD (12)
Biology and Biochemistry, University of Bath, Bath, United Kingdom

Paul A. Trainor, PhD (19)
Stowers Institute for Medical Research, Kansas City, MO

David Traver, PhD (34)
Department of Cell and Developmental Biology, University of California, San Diego, La Jolla, CA

Tudorita Tumbar, PhD (24)
Laboratory of Mamalian and Cell Biology, The Rockefeller University, New York, NY

Joseph P. Vacanti, MD (26)
Chief, Pediatric Surgery, Massachusetts General Hospital, Director, Laboratory for the Tissue Engineering and Organ Fabrication, Massachusetts General Hospital, Boston, MA

Larissa Verda, MD, PhD (68)
Research Associate, Division of Immunotherapy, Department of Medicine, Northwestern University Feinberg School of Medicine, Chicago, IL

Catherine M. Verfaillie, MD (2, 27)
Director, Stem Cell Institute, Professor, Department of Medicine, University of Minnesota, Minneapolis, MN

Fiona M. Watt, DPhil (23)
Head, Keratinocyte Laboratory, Cancer Research UK London Research Institute, London, United Kingdom

Gordon C. Weir, MD (66)
Professor of Medicine, Harvard Medical School, Head, Section on Islet Transplantation and Cell Biology, Diabetes Research and Wellness Foundation Chair, Joslin Diabetes Center, Boston, MA

James W. Wilson, PhD (1)
Research Centre for Gastroenterology, Institute for Cell and Molecular Science, Barts and The London Queen Mary's School of Medicine and Dentistry, London, United Kingdom

Nicholas A. Wright MA, DSc, MD, PhD, FRCPath, FRCS, FRCP, FmedSci (47)
Histopathology Unit, London Research Institute, Cancer Research UK, London, United Kingdom

Zipora Yablonka-Reuveni, PhD (51)
Research Professor, Department of Biological Structure, University of Washington, Seattle, WA

Pamela C. Yelick, PhD (26)
Staff Member, Department of Cytokine Biology, The Forsyth Institute, Department of Oral and Developmental Biology, Harvard School of Dental Medicine, Boston, MA

Jung U. Yoo, MD (70)
Case Western Reserve University, University Hospitals of Cleveland, Cleveland, OH

Peter W. Zandstra, PhD (59)
Associate Professor, Institute of Biomaterials and Biomedical Engineering, University of Toronto, Toronto, Ontario, Canada

Lisa Zakhary (22)
Department of Molecular and Cellular Biology, Harvard University, Cambridge, MA

Wen Jie Zhang, PhD (36)
Department of Pathology and Immunology, Washington University School of Medicine, St. Louis, MO

Leonard I. Zon, MD (60)
Grousbeck Professor of Pediatrics, HMS, Investigator, HHMI, Children's Hospital Boston, Boston, MA

Patricia A. Zuk PhD (40)
Research Director, Regenerative Bioengineering and Repair Laboratory, David Geffen School of Medicine at UCLA, Los Angeles, CA

Preface

New discoveries in the field of stem cells increasingly dominate the news and scientific literature. Wave upon wave of papers has led to an avalanche of new knowledge and research tools that may soon lead to new therapies for cancer, heart disease, diabetes, and a wide variety of other diseases that afflict humanity. The *Handbook of Stem Cells* integrates this exciting area of biology, combining in two volumes the prerequisites for a general understanding of adult and embryonic stem cells; the tools, methods, and experimental protocols needed to study and characterize stem cells and progenitor populations; as well as a presentation by the world's experts of what is currently known about each specific organ system. No topic in the field of stem cells is left uncovered, including basic biology/mechanisms, early development, ectoderm, mesoderm, endoderm, methods (such as detailed descriptions of how to derive and maintain animal and human embryonic stem cells), application of stem cells to specific human diseases, regulation and ethics, and patient perspectives from Mary Tyler Moore (diabetes) and Christopher Reeve (spinal cord injury). The result is a comprehensive two-volume reference that will be useful for students and experts alike. It represents the combined effort of 12 editors and more than 300 scholars and scientists whose pioneering work has defined our understanding of stem cells.

Robert Lanza, M.D.
Boston, Massachusetts

Foreword

Almost everything we know about cell transplantation dates to the end of World War II. It was found that mice could be protected against otherwise lethal irradiation by an injection of spleen or marrow cells. At first it was hypothesized that the protection was caused by a humerol factor in the spleen or marrow preparations. That the protection might be caused by living cells seemed to be ruled out by several experiments. However, cytogenetic and skin transplant studies made it clear that the cellular hypothesis rather than the humoral hypothesis was the explanation for the irradiation protection phenomenon.

The early investigators recognised that there must be some kind of seed cell or cells in the spleen or marrow preparations that generated the repopulated marrow. These cells came to be called stem cells, but the search for the elusive stem cell became a long and complicated one. There followed thousands of experiments in inbred mice that clarified the requirements for successful cell transplants and described the immunological phenomena involved. The dog became a model for bridging the gap of knowledge between inbred mice and outbred species. As is often the case, physicians were driven to attempt to alleviate human disease by the application of knowledge gained from studies of animal systems. Application of this knowledge to human marrow transplantation began to produce results in patients with fatal disorders such as immunodeficiency disease, leukemia, and aplastic anemia. By the end of the twentieth century, transplantation of hematopoietic cells from marrow, blood, or cord blood had taken its place in the therapeutic armamentarium against an ever-increasing number of diseases.

As work continued, stem cells were isolated and characterized. Despite many studies, the expansion of human stem cells by *in vitro* culture proved to be difficult. Gene therapy of human stem cells remained an attractive but elusive goal. It had long been assumed that hematopoietic stem cells would produce only hematopoietic cells, but intriguing data began to suggest that marrow stem cells might generate other tissues such as a liver, a heart, or even a central nervous system. These and other tissues and organs seemed to have their own stem cells, and these stem cells might not be lineage specific. The plasticity of stem cells, or transdifferentiation, became a major subject of study. Techniques for obtaining stem cells form embryonic tissues were developed and seemed to offer even greater utility. Application of these stem cells to a variety of otherwise incurable human diseases became a possibility.

Thus, at the beginning of the twenty-first century, the stage was set for this work, *Handbook of Stem Cells*. This two-volume book is a much-needed attempt to bring together the cumulative work of many investigators in widely diverse aspects of stem cell studies. Clearly, this field is a work in progress. Much more work will be needed to fulfill the exciting promise of stem cell research. This handbook provides essential information for those who undertake this challenge.

E. Donnall Thomas, (Hon)

Embryonic Stem Cells Versus Adults Stem Cells: Some Seemingly Simple Questions

As reflected by the contributions to this volume, we have been making tremendous strides in research on stem cells. As the same time, it has been surprisingly difficult to answer several seemingly simple questions.

How Do You Define a Stem Cell?

The textbook definition is that a stem cell is a cell that divides to generate one daughter cell that is a stem cell and another daughter cell that produces differentiated descendants. The definition readily fits a newly fertilized egg but begins to unravel as we move along the pathway of development. Totipotent embryonic stem (ES) cells can readily be recovered from the inner cell mass or the germinal ridge of embryos. But the window of time for recovering ES cells from the embryo is narrow—about day 4 to 6 for the inner cell mass and slightly later for the germinal ridge in mouse embryos. Where do the daughter cells that are immortal stem cells go after the window closes? One possible answer is that we may have been misled by the observation that ES cells are immortal if cultured under the appropriate conditions. *In vivo* they may have a limited life span, and they may gradually disappear as the embryo develops. A simpler and more appealing answer is that they probably become both the stem cells of the hematopoietic system and the more recently identified stem-like cells found in essentially every nonhematopoietic tissue of adult vertebrates.

What Are the Differences Between Stem-like Cells in Adult Tissues and ES Cells?

One answer is that ES cells can readily be shown to differentiate into essentially all cell phenotypes, whereas most isolates of adult stem cells from sources such as bone marrow stroma, fat, muscle, and nervous tissue have a more limited potential for differentiation. Also, most but not all isolates of adult stem cells have a more limited life span in culture than ES cells have. These distinctions, however, are valid only if we assume that the scientists who have worked with adult stem cells have been clever enough to devise all the experimental conditions for testing their potentials for differentiation and expansion. But are we that clever? What about the nuclear transfer experiments in which the nucleus of any completely differentiated cell can be reprogrammed to generate an ES cell if it is inserted into an enucleated embryo? Many nuclear transfer experiments fail, but the successful experiments say that any cell can become a stem cell if we are clever enough to send the correct signals from the cytoplasm to the nucleus. Therefore, the progression from a fertilized egg to an ES cell to an adult stem cell to a differentiated cell may be a continuum in which few if any steps are irreversible. If this concept is correct, the differences among ES cells, adult stem cells, and fully differentiated cells come down to questions of how many steps need to be reversed and how difficult they are to reverse to re-create a totipotent and immortal stem cell.

Are ES Cells or Adult Stem Cells Better Suited to Medical Therapies or Tissue Engineering?

Several distinguished scientists have offered simple answers to this question, some favoring ES cells and others adult stem cells. As time passes, it seems clear that we need far more research to answer it. Use of ES cells is hindered by the tumorigenicity of the cells and the danger of immune responses if they are used heterologously. Adult stem cells have not shown any tendency to becoming malignant, and several kinds of adult stem cells can be obtained in adequate amounts for autologous therapy. However, it is unlikely that one kind of stem cell will be ideal for all practical applications envisioned. ES cells may prove to be ideal for creating new organs through new protocols that will circumvent the current ethical and technical minefields. Adult stem cells may be more useful for repairing damage to tissues by trauma, disease, or perhaps uncomplicated aging. Recent observations are providing increasing evidence for the concept that adult stem cells are part of a natural system for tissue repair. The initial response to tissue injury appears to be proliferation and differentiation of stem-like cells endogenous to the tissue. After the endogenous stem-like cells are exhausted, non-hematopoietic stem cells from the bone marrow are recruited to the site of injury. Moreover, the data indicate that the adult stem cells that home to injured tissues repair the damage by two or three mechanisms: by differentiating into the appropriate cell phenotype, by providing cytokines and other factors to enhance recovery of endogenous cells, and perhaps by cell fusion, a process that may provide a rapid mechanism for differentiation of the stem cells.

Summary

We are at a remarkable stage in research with both ES and adult stem cells. One report after another destroys the dogmas of biology that still fill textbooks. There are limits on the potentials of the cells and their practical applications. But we are far from knowing the limits, particularly since we still cannot precisely define their critical features and we still depend on complex biological systems for testing them.

Darwin J. Prockop, MD, PhD

"Stemness": Definitions, Criteria, and Standards

Introduction

Stem cells have recently generated more public and professional interest than almost any other topic in biology. One reason stem cells capture the imagination of so many is the promise that understanding their unique properties may provide deep insights into the biology of cells as well as a path toward treatments for a variety of degenerative illnesses. And although the field of stem cell biology has grown rapidly, there exists considerable confusion and disagreement as to the nature of stem cells. This confusion can be partly attributed to the sometimes idiosyncratic terms and definitions used to describe stem cells. Although definitions can be restrictive, they are useful when they provide a basis for mutual understanding and experimental standardization. With this intention, I present explanations of definitions, criteria, and standards for stem cells. Moreover, I highlight a central question in stem cell biology, namely the origin of these cells. I also suggest criteria or standards for identifying, isolating, and characterizing stem cells. Finally, I summarize the notion of "stemness" and describe its possible application in understanding stem cells and their biology.

What Is a Stem Cell?

Stem cells are defined functionally as cells that have the capacity to self-renew as well as the ability to generate differentiated cells.[1,2] More explicitly, stem cells can generate daughter cells identical to their mother (self-renewal) as well as produce progeny with more restricted potential (differentiated cells). This simple and broad definition may be satisfactory for embryonic or fetal stem cells that do not perdure for the lifetime of an organism. But this definition breaks down in trying to discriminate between transient adult progenitor cells that have a reduced capacity for self-renewal and adult stem cells. It is therefore important when describing adult stem cells to further restrict this definition to cells that self-renew throughout the life span of the animal.[3] Another parameter that should be considered is potency: Does the stem cell generate to multiple differentiated cell types (multipotent), or is it only capable of producing one type of differentiated cell (unipotent)? Thus, a more complete description of a stem cell includes a consideration of replication capacity, clonality, and potency. Some theoretical as well as practical considerations surrounding these concepts are considered in this chapter.

SELF-RENEWAL

Stem cell literature is replete with terms such as "immortal," "unlimited," "continuous," and "capable of extensive proliferation," all used to describe the cell's replicative capacity. These rather extreme and vague terms are not very helpful, as it can be noted that experiments designed to test the "immortality" of a stem cell would by necessity outlast authors and readers alike. Most somatic cells cultured *in vitro* display a finite number of (less than 80) population doublings prior to replicative arrest or senescence, and this can be contrasted with the seemingly unlimited proliferative capacity of stem cells in culture.[4–8] Therefore, it is reasonable to say that a cell that can undergo more than twice this number of population doublings (160) without oncogenic transformation can be termed "capable of extensive proliferation." In a few cases, this criteria has been met, most notably with embryonic stem (ES) cells derived from either humans or mice as well as with adult neural stem cells (NSCs).[2,9] An incomplete understanding of the factors required for self-renewal *ex vivo* for many adult stem cells precludes establishing similar proliferative limits *in vitro*. In some cases, a rigorous assessment of the capacity for self-renewal of certain adult stem cells can be obtained by single-cell or serial transfer into acceptable hosts, an excellent example of which is adult hematopoietic stem cells (HSCs).[10,11] Adult stem cells are probably still best defined *in vivo,* where they must display sufficient proliferative capacity to last the lifetime of the animal. Terms such as "immortal" and "unlimited" are probably best used sparingly if at all.

CLONALITY

A second parameter, perhaps the most important, is the idea that stem cells are clonogenic entities: single cells with the capacity to create more stem cells. This issue has been exhaustively dealt with elsewhere and is essential for any definitive characterization of self-renewal, potential, and lineage.[1] Methods for tracing the lineage of stem cells are described in subsequent chapters. Although the clonal "gold standard" is well understood, there remain several confusing practical issues. For instance, what constitutes a cell line? The lowest standard would include any population of cells that can be grown in culture, frozen, thawed, and subsequently repassaged *in vitro*. A higher standard would be a clonal or apparently homogenous population of cells with these characteristics, but it must be recognized that cellular preparations that do not derive from a single cell may be a mixed population containing stem cells and a separate population of "supportive" cells required for the propagation of the purported stem cells. Hence, any reference to a stem cell line should be made with an explanation of their derivation. For example, it can be misleading to report on stem cells or "stem cell lines" from a tissue if they are cellular preparations containing of a mixed population, possibly contaminated by stem cells from another tissue.

POTENCY

The issue of potency maybe the most contentious part of a widely accepted definition for stem cells. A multipotent stem cell sits atop a lineage hierarchy and can generate multiple types of differentiated cells, the latter being cells with distinct morphologies and gene expression patterns. At the same time, many would argue that a self-renewing cell that can only produce one type of differentiated descendant is nonetheless a stem cell.[12] A case can be made, for clarity, that a unipotent cell is probably best described as a progenitor. Progenitors are typically the descendants of stem cells, only they more constrained in their differentiation potential or capacity for self-renewal and are often more limited in both senses.

DEFINITION

In conclusion, a working definition of a stem cell is a clonal, self-renewing entity that is multipotent and thus can generate several differentiated cell types. Admittedly, this definition is not applicable in all instances and is best used as a guide to help describe cellular attributes.

Where Do Stem Cells Come From?

The origin or lineage of stem cells is well understood for ES cells; their origin in adults is less clear and in some cases controversial. It may be significant that ES cells originate before germ layer commitment, raising the intriguing possibility that this may be a mechanism for the development of multipotent stem cells, including some adult stem cells. The paucity of information on the developmental origins of adult stems cells leaves open the possibility that they too escape lineage restriction in the early embryo and subsequently colonize specialized niches, which function to both maintain their potency as well as restrict their lineage potential. Alternatively, the more widely believed, though still unsubstantiated, model for the origin of adult stem cells assumes that they are derived after somatic lineage specification, whereupon multipotent stem cells–progenitors arise and colonize their respective cellular niches. In this section, I briefly summarize the origin of stem cells from the early embryo and explain what is known about the ontogeny of adult stem cells focusing attention on HSCs and NSCs.

STEM CELLS OF THE EARLY EMBRYO

Mouse and human ES cells are derived directly from the inner cell mass of preimplantation embryos after the formation of a cystic blastocyst.[13] This population of cells would normally produce the epiblast and eventually all adult tissues, which may help to explain the developmental plasticity exhibited by ES cells. In fact, ES cells appear to be the *in vitro* equivalent of the epiblast, as they have the capacity to contribute to all somatic lineages and in mice to produce germ line chimeras.

By the time the zygote has reached the blastocyst stage, the developmental potential of certain cells has been restricted. The outer cells of the embryo have begun to differentiate to form trophectoderm, from which a population of embryonic trophoblast stem cells has also been derived in mice.[14] These specialized cells can generate all cell types of the trophectoderm lineage, including differentiated giant trophoblast cells.

At the egg cylinder stage of embryonic development (embryonic day (E) 6.5 in mice), a population of cells near the epiblast (Figure 1) can be identified as primordial germ cells (PGCs), which are subsequently excluded from somatic specification or restriction.[15] PGCs migrate to and colonize the genital ridges, where they produce mature germ cells and generate functional adult gametes. PGCs can be isolated either prior or subsequent to their arrival in the genital ridges and, when cultured with appropriate factors *in vitro,* can generate embryonic germ (EG) cells.[16,17] EG cells have many of the characteristics of ES cells with respect to their differentiation potential and their contribution to the germ line of chimeric mice.[18,19] The most notable difference between ES and EG cells is that the latter may display (depending upon the developmental stage of their derivation) considerable imprinting of specific genes.[20–22] Consequently, certain EG cell lines are incapable of producing normal chimeric mice.

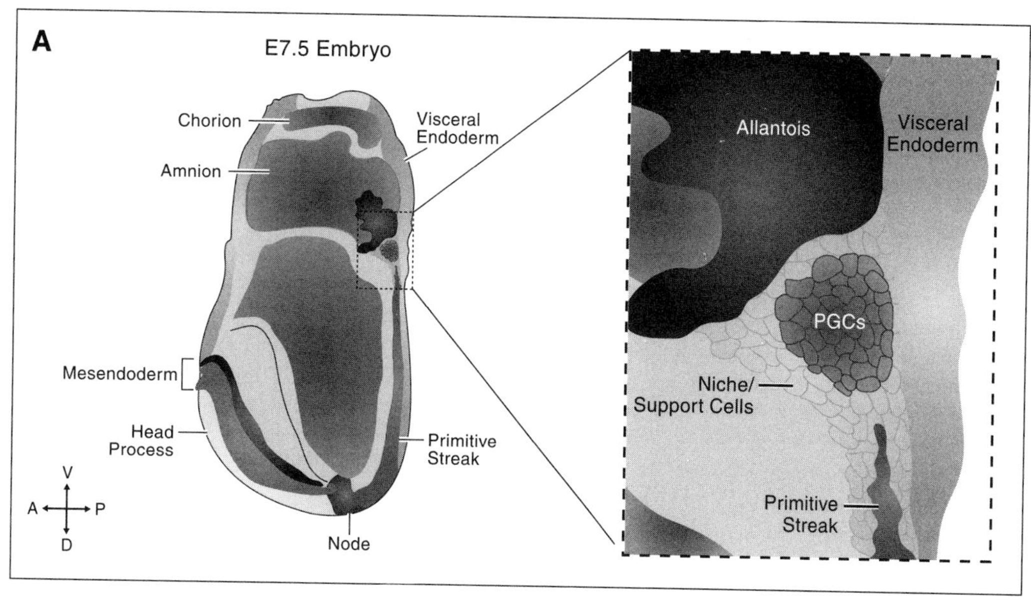

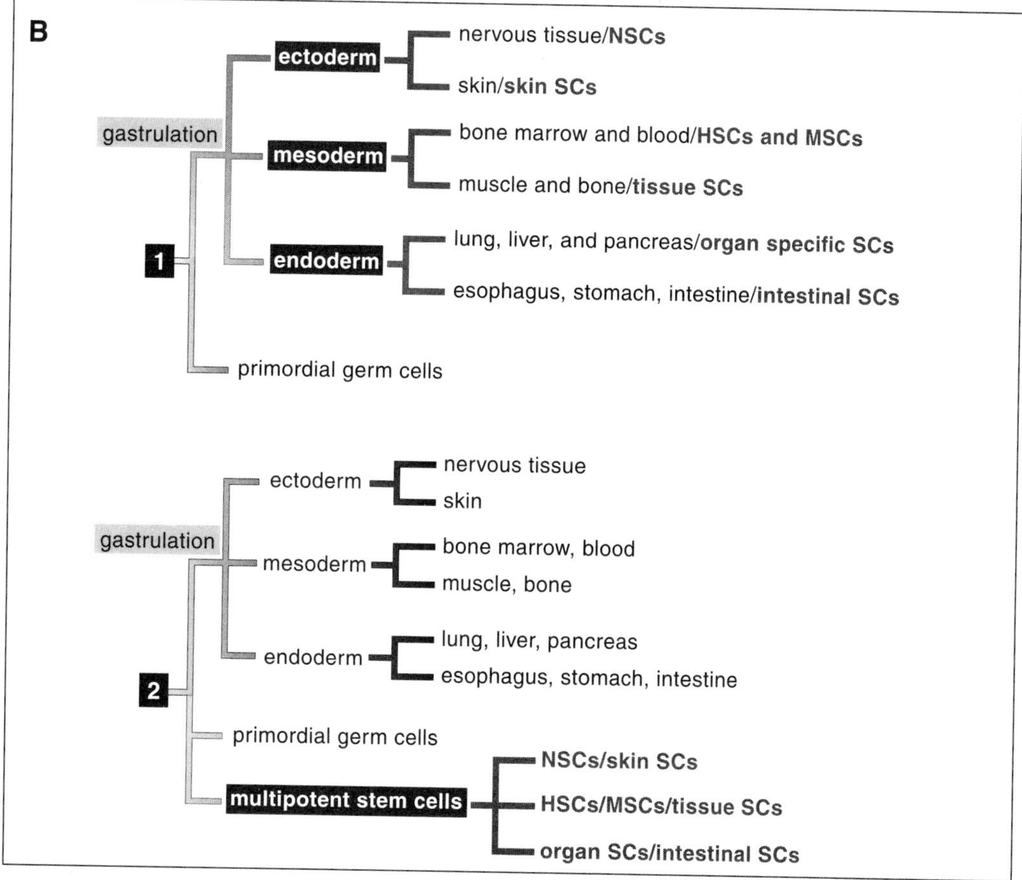

Figure 1. (A) Development of primordial germ cells. A schematic of an embryonic day 7.5 mouse embryo highlights the position of the developing primordial germ cells (PGCs) proximal to the epiblast. The expanded view on the right serves to illustrate the point that PGCs escape lineage commitment/restriction by avoiding the morphogenetic effects of migrating through the primitive streak during gastrulation. (B) Putative developmental ontogeny of stem cells. In lineage tree 1, the development of stem cells occurs after the formation of germ layers. These stem cells are thus restricted by germ layer commitment to their respective lineage (e.g., mesoderm is formed, giving rise to hematopoietic progenitors that become hematopoietic stem cells). Lineage tree 2 illustrates the idea that stem cells might develop similarly to PGCs, in that they avoid the lineage commitments during gastrulation and subsequently migrate to specifc tissue and organ niches.

Importantly, no totipotent stem cell has been isolated from the early embryo. ES and EG cells generate all somatic lineages as well as germ cells but rarely if ever contribute to the trophectoderm, extraembryonic endoderm, or extraembryonic mesoderm. Trophectoderm stem (TS) cells have been isolated, and these only generate cells of the trophectoderm lineage. It remains to be seen whether cells can be derived and maintained from totipotent embryonic stages.

Although our understanding of cell fates in the early embryo is incomplete, it appears that the only pluripotent stem cells found after gastrulation are PGCs (with the possible exceptions of multipotential adult progenitor cells[23] and teratocarcinomas). It may be that PGCs escape germ layer commitment during gastrulation by developing near the epiblast and subsequently migrate to positions inside the embryo proper. This developmental strategy may not be unique to PGCs, and it raises the interesting possibility that other stem cells might have similar developmental origins. Alternatively, it may be the case that adult stem cells are derived from PGCs. Although intriguing, it is important to stress that this idea lacks experimental evidence.

ONTOGENY OF ADULT STEM CELLS

The origin of most adult stem cells is poorly understood. With the issue of adult stem cell plasticity at the forefront, as described in this section, studies designed to elucidate the ontogeny of adult stem cells may help to reveal their specific lineage relationships and shed light on their plasticity and potential. Information on the origins of adult stem cells would also help to define the molecular programs involved in lineage determination, which may in turn provide insights into methods for manipulating their differentiation. To this end, I summarize what is known about the development of adult stem cells within the context of the hematopoietic and neural systems.

The development of hematopoietic cells in mice occurs soon after gastrulation (E7.5), although HSCs with the same activities as those in the adult have only been observed and isolated at midgestational stages (E10.5).[24–26] These observations suggest that the embryo has a unique hematopoietic lineage hierarchy, which may not be founded by an adult-type HSC. Thus, hematopoiesis appears to occur at multiple times or in successive waves within the embryo, and the emergence of an HSC may not precede or be concomitant with the appearance of differentiated hematopoietic cells.

The first site of hematopoiesis in the mouse is the extraembryonic yolk sac, soon followed by the intraembryonic aorta–gonad–mesonephros (AGM) region. Which of these sites leads to the generation of the adult hematopoietic system and, importantly, HSCs is still unclear. Results from nonmammalian embryo-grafting experiments, with various findings in the mouse, suggest that the mammalian embryo, specifically the AGM, generates the adult hematopoietic system and HSCs.[27–29] Interestingly, the midgestational AGM is also the region that harbors migrating PGCs and is thought to produce populations of mesenchymal stem cells, vascular progenitors, and perhaps hemangioblasts.[30–34] In the absence of studies designed to clonally evaluate the lineage potential of cells from the AGM, and without similarly accurate fate mapping of this region, it remains possible that all of the adult stem cell types thought to emerge within the AGM arise from a common unrestricted precursor. This hypothetical precursor could help to explain reports of nonfusion-based adult stem cell plasticity. The observed lineage specificity of most adult stem cells could likewise be attributed to the high-fidelity lineage restriction imposed on them by the specific niche they colonize or are derived from. Simple ideas such as these have not been ruled out by experimental evidence, underscoring both the opportunity and the necessity for further study of the developmental origins of adult stem cells.

A key lesson from studies of the developing hematopoietic system is that the appearance of differentiated cells does not tell us where or when the corresponding adult stem cells originate. Definitive lineage tracing, with assays of clonogenic potential, remains the method of choice for identifying the origin of stem cells. Another potential pitfall revealed by these studies is that the definition of the stem cell can make all the difference in its identification.

The development of NSCs begins with the formation of nervous tissue from embryonic ectoderm following gastrulation. Induction of the neural plate is thought to coincide with the appearance of NSCs as well as restricted progenitor types.[35] The exact frequency and location of stem cells within the developing neuroepithelium remains unknown; specific markers must be discovered to fully unravel this question. An emerging view in the field is that embryonic neuroepithelia generate radial glial that subsequently develop into periventricular astrocytes and that these cells are the embryonic and adult NSCs within the central nervous system.[36–39] Developing and adult NSCs also appear to acquire positional and temporal information. For example, stem cells isolated from different neural regions generate region-appropriate progeny.[40–42] In addition, several studies suggest that temporal information is encoded within NSCs, that earlier stem cells give rise more frequently to neurons, and that more mature stem cells preferentially differentiate into glia.[35,43,44] Moreover, more mature NSCs appear incapable of making cells appropriate for younger stages when transplanted into the early cerebral cortex.[45] Thus, the nervous system appears to follow a classical lineage hierarchy, with a common progenitor cell generating most if not all differentiated cell types in a regional- and temporal-specific manner. There may also be rare stem cells in the nervous system, perhaps not of neural origin, that have greater plasticity in terms of producing diverse somatic cell types and lacking temporal and spatial constraints.[26,35]

There are several caveats that must be considered when describing the developmental origins of NSCs. First, disrupting the neuroepithelia to purify NSCs may have the undesirable effect of dysregulating spatial patterning acquired by these cells. Second, growth of purified NSCs in culture may reprogram the stem cells through exposure to nonphysiological *in vitro* culture conditions. Both of these problems can be addressed either by *in vivo* lineage tracing or by prospectively isolating NSCs and transplanting them into acceptable hosts without intervening culture. Carefully designed experiments promise to answer questions important not only for stem cell biology but also for neuroembryology and development. These include which features of the developmental program are intrinsic to individual cells, which differentiation or patterning signals act exclusively to instruct specific cell fates, and how developmental changes in cell-intrinsic programs restrict the responses of progenitors to cell-extrinsic signals.

How Are Stem Cells Identified, Isolated, and Characterized?

How stem cells are identified, isolated, and characterized are the key methodological questions in stem cell biology, so much so that subsequent chapters are devoted to addressing these problems in detail. Here, I briefly outline standards and criteria that may be employed when approaching the challenge of identifying, isolating, and characterizing a stem cell.

EMBRYONIC STEM CELLS

The basic characteristics of an ES cell include self-renewal, multilineage differentiation *in vitro* and *in vivo,* clonogenicity, a normal karyotype, extensive proliferation *in vitro* under well-defined culture conditions, and the ability to be frozen and thawed. In animal species, *in vivo* differentiation can be assessed rigorously by the ability of ES cells to contribute to all somatic lineages and produce germ line chimerism. These criteria are not appropriate for human ES cells; consequently, these cells must generate embryoid bodies and teratomas containing differentiated cells of all three germ layers. Moreover, as a stringent *in vivo* assessment of pluripotency is impossible, human ES cells must be shown to be positive for well-known molecular markers of pluripotent cells. These markers are defined as factors expressed consistently, and enriched, in human ES cells.[46] As a substitute for whole-animal chimerism, human ES cells could be tested for their contributions to specific tissues when transplanted in discrete regions of nonhuman adults or embryos. A complementary analysis might include transplanting human ES cells into nonhuman blastocysts and evaluating their contribution to various organs and tissues, though this experiment has raised ethical concerns in some quarters. Finally, a practical consideration is the passage number of ES cells. Although it is important to establish the capacity of ES cells to proliferate extensively, it is equally important that low-passage cells are evaluated experimentally to guard against any artifacts introduced through *in vitro* manipulation.

ADULT STEM CELLS

The basic characteristics of an adult stem cell are a single cell (clonal) that self-renews and generates differentiated cells. The most rigorous assessment of these characteristics is to prospectively purify a population of cells (usually by cell surface markers), transplant a single cell into an acceptable host without any intervening *in vitro* culture, and observe self-renewal and tissue, organ, or lineage reconstitution. Admittedly, this type of *in vivo* reconstitution assay is not well defined for many types of adult stem cells. Thus, it is important to arrive at an accurate functional definition for cells whose developmental potential is assessed *in vitro* only. Above all, clonal assays should be the standard by which fetal and adult stem cells are evaluated because this assay removes doubts about contamination with other cell types.

Two concepts about the fate or potential of stem cells have moved to the forefront of adult stem cell research. The first is plasticity, the idea that restrictions in cell fates are not permanent but are flexible and reversible. The most obvious and extreme example of reversing a committed cell fate comes from experiments in which a terminally differentiated somatic cell generates to another animal following nuclear transfer or cloning.[47,48] Nuclear transfer experiments show that differentiated cells, given the appropriate conditions, can be returned to their most primal state. Thus, it may not be surprising if conditions are found for more committed or specified cells to dedifferentiate and gain a broader potential. A related concept is that of transdifferentiation. Transdifferentiation is the generation of functional cells of a tissue, organ, or lineage that is distinct from that of the founding stem cell.[49,50] Important issues here are whether the cells proposed to transdifferentiate are clonal and whether the mechanism by which they form the functional cell requires fusion.[51–54] Experiments designed to carefully evaluate these possibilities will yield insight into the nature of stem cells.

Stemness: Progress Toward a Molecular Definition of Stem Cells

Stemness refers to the common molecular processes underlying the core stem cell properties of self-renewal and the generation of differentiated progeny. Although stems cells in different cellular microenvironments or niches will by necessity have different physiological demands and therefore distinct molecular programs, there are likely certain genetic characteristics specific to and shared by all stem cells. Through transcriptional profiling, many of the genes enriched in ES cell, TS cell, HSC, and NSC populations have been identified.[55–60] By extending this approach to other stem cells and more organisms, it may be possible to develop a molecular fingerprint for stem cells. This fingerprint could be used as the basis for a molecular definition of stem cells that, when combined with their functional definition, would provide a more comprehensive set of criteria for understanding their unique biology. Perhaps more importantly, these types of studies could be used to help identify and isolate new stem cells. This goal is far from being accomplished, but the preliminary findings for specific stem cells have been described.

The transcriptional profiling of stem cells has suggested that they share several distinct molecular characteristics. Stem cells appear to have the capacity to sense a broad range of growth factors and signaling molecules and to express many of the downstream signaling components involved in the transduction of these signals. Signal transduction pathways present and perhaps active in stem cells include TGFβ, Notch, Wnt, and Jak/Stat family members. Stem cells also express many components involved in establishing their specialized cell cycles, either related to maintaining cell cycle arrest in G_1

(for most quiescent adult stem cells) or connected to progression through cell cycle checkpoints promoting rapid cycling (as is the case for ES cells and mobilized adult stem cells).[61,62] Most stem cells also express molecules involved in telomere maintenance and display elevated levels of telomerase activity. There is also considerable evidence that stem cells have significantly remodeled chromatin acted upon by DNA methylases or transcriptional repressors of histone deacetylase and Groucho family members. Another common molecular feature is the expression of specialized posttranscriptional regulatory machinery regulated by RNA helicases of the Vasa type. Finally, a shared molecular and functional characteristic of stem cells appears to be their resistance to stress, mediated by multidrug resistance transporters, protein-folding machinery, ubiquitin, and detoxifier systems.

Although in its infancy, the search for a molecular signature to define stem cells continues. We have begun to understand in general terms what molecular components are most often associated with stem cells. In the future, it may be possible to precisely define stem cells as a whole and individually by their telltale molecular identities. Until that time, stemness remains a concept of limited utility with tremendous potential.

ACKNOWLEDGEMENTS

I would like to thank Jayaraj Rajagopal and Kevin Eggan for helpful discussion and suggestions. I apologize to those authors whose work was inadvertently overlooked or omitted because of space limitations.

Douglas A. Melton, PhD
Chad Cowan, PhD

REFERENCES

1. Weissman, I.L., Anderson, D.J., and Gage, F. (2001). Stem and progenitor cells: Origins, phenotypes, lineage commitments, and transdifferentiations. *Annu. Rev. Cell Dev. Biol.* **17,** 387–403.
2. Smith, A.G. (2001). Embryo-derived stem cells: of mice and men. *Annu. Rev. Cell Dev. Biol.* **17,** 435–462.
3. van der Kooy, D., and Weiss, S. (2000). Why stem cells? *Science* **287,** 1439–1441.
4. Houck, J.C., Sharma, V.K., and Hayflick, L. (1971). Functional failures of cultured human diploid fibroblasts after continued population doublings. *Proc. Soc. Exp. Biol. Med.* **137,** 331–333.
5. Hayflick, L. (1973). The biology of human aging. *Am. J. Med. Sci.* **265,** 432–445.
6. Hayflick, L. (1974). The longevity of cultured human cells. *J. Am. Geriatr. Soc.* **22,** 1–12.
7. Sherr, C.J., and DePinho, R.A. (2000). Cellular senescence: mitotic clock or culture shock? *Cell* **102,** 407–410.
8. Shay, J.W., and Wright, W.E. (2000). Hayflick, his limit, and cellular ageing. *Nat. Rev. Mol. Cell Biol.* **1,** 72–76.
9. Morrison, S.J., Shah, N.M., and Anderson, D.J. (1997). Regulatory mechanisms in stem cell biology. *Cell* **88,** 287–298.
10. Allsopp, R.C., and Weissman, I.L. (2002). Replicative senescence of hematopoietic stem cells during serial transplantation: does telomere shortening play a role? *Oncogene* **21,** 3270–3273.
11. Iscove, N.N., and Nawa, K. (1997). Hematopoietic stem cells expand during serial transplantation *in vivo* without apparent exhaustion. *Curr. Biol.* **7,** 805–808.
12. Slack, J.M. (2000). Stem cells in epithelial tissues. *Science* **287,** 1431–1433.
13. Papaioannou, V. (2001). Stem cells and differentiation. *Differentiation* **68,** 153–154.
14. Tanaka, S., *et al.* (1998). Promotion of trophoblast stem cell proliferation by FGF4. *Science* **282,** 2072–2075.
15. Saitou, M., Barton, S.C., and Surani, M.A. (2002). A molecular program for the specification of germ cell fate in mice. *Nature* **418,** 293–300.
16. Matsui, Y., Zsebo, K., and Hogan, B.L. (1992). Derivation of pluripotential embryonic stem cells from murine primordial germ cells in culture. *Cell* **70,** 841–847.
17. Resnick, J.L., *et al.* (1992). Long-term proliferation of mouse primordial germ cells in culture. *Nature* **359,** 550–551.
18. Labosky, P.A., Barlow, D.P., and Hogan, B.L. (1994). Mouse embryonic germ (EG) cell lines: transmission through the germ line, and differences in the methylation imprint of insulin-like growth factor 2 receptor *(Igf2r)* gene compared with embryonic stem (ES) cell lines. *Development* **120,** 3197–3204.
19. Stewart, C.L., Gadi, I., and Bhatt, H. (1994). Stem cells from primordial germ cells can reenter the germ line. *Dev. Biol.* **161,** 626–628.
20. Surani, M.A. (1998). Imprinting and the initiation of gene silencing in the germ line. *Cell* **93,** 309–312.
21. Surani, M.A. (2001). Reprogramming of genome function through epigenetic inheritance. *Nature* **414,** 122–128.
22. Howell, C.Y., *et al.* (2001). Genomic imprinting disrupted by a maternal effect mutation in the *Dnmt1* gene. *Cell* **104,** 829–838.
23. Jiang, Y., *et al.* (2002). Pluripotency of mesenchymal stem cells derived from adult marrow. *Nature* **418,** 41–49.
24. Orkin, S.H. (1996). Development of the hematopoietic system. *Curr. Opin. Genet. Dev.* **6,** 597–602.
25. Dzierzak, E. (2002). Hematopoietic stem cells and their precursors: developmental diversity and lineage relationships. *Immunol. Rev.* **187,** 126–138.
26. Weissman, I.L. (2000). Stem cells: units of development, units of regeneration, and units in evolution. *Cell* **100,** 157–168.
27. Kau, C.L., and Turpen, J.B. (1983). Dual contribution of embryonic ventral blood island and dorsal lateral plate mesoderm during ontogeny of hemopoietic cells in *Xenopus laevis*. *J. Immunol.* **131,** 2262–2266.
28. Medvinsky, A.L., *et al.* (1993). An early preliver intraembryonic source of CFU-S in the developing mouse. *Nature* **364,** 64–67.
29. Medvinsky, A., and Dzierzak, E. (1996). Definitive hematopoiesis is autonomously initiated by the AGM region. *Cell* **86,** 897–906.
30. Molyneaux, K.A., *et al.* (2001). Time-lapse analysis of living mouse germ cell migration. *Dev. Biol.* **240,** 488–498.
31. Minasi, M.G., *et al.* (2002). The mesoangioblast: a multipotent, self-renewing cell that originates from the dorsal aorta and differentiates into most mesodermal tissues. *Development* **129,** 2773–2783.
32. Alessandri, G., *et al.* (2001). Human vasculogenesis *ex vivo:* Embryonal aorta as a tool for isolation of endothelial cell progenitors. *Lab. Invest.* **81,** 875–885.
33. Hara, T., *et al.* (1999). Identification of podocalyxin-like protein 1 as a novel cell surface marker for hemangioblasts in the murine aorta–gonad–mesonephros region. *Immunity* **11,** 567–578.

34. Munoz-Chapuli, R., *et al.* (1999). Differentiation of hemangioblasts from embryonic mesothelial cells? A model on the origin of the vertebrate cardiovascular system. *Differentiation* **64,** 133–141.
35. Temple, S. (2001). The development of neural stem cells. *Nature* **414,** 112–117.
36. Alvarez-Buylla, A., Garcia-Verdugo, J.M., and Tramontin, A.D. (2001). A unified hypothesis on the lineage of neural stem cells. *Nat. Rev. Neurosci.* **2,** 287–293.
37. Tramontin, A.D., *et al.* (2003). Postnatal development of radial glia and the ventricular zone (VZ): a continuum of the neural stem cell compartment. *Cereb. Cortex* **13,** 580–587.
38. Doetsch, F., *et al.* (1999). Subventricular zone astrocytes are neural stem cells in the adult mammalian brain. *Cell* **97,** 703–716.
39. Gaiano, N., and Fishell, G. (2002). The role of notch in promoting glial and neural stem cell fates. *Annu. Rev. Neurosci.* **25,** 471–490.
40. Kalyani, A.J., *et al.* (1998). Spinal cord neuronal precursors generate multiple neuronal phenotypes in culture. *J. Neurosci.* **18,** 7856–7868.
41. He, W., *et al.* (2001). Multipotent stem cells from the mouse basal forebrain contribute GABAergic neurons and oligodendrocytes to the cerebral cortex during embryogenesis. *J. Neurosci.* **21,** 8854–8862.
42. Anderson, D.J., *et al.* (1997). Cell lineage determination and the control of neuronal identity in the neural crest. *Cold Spring Harb. Symp. Quant. Biol.* **62,** 493–504.
43. Qian, X., *et al.* (2000). Timing of CNS cell generation: a programmed sequence of neuron and glial cell production from isolated murine cortical stem cells. *Neuron* **28,** 69–80.
44. White, P.M., *et al.* (2001). Neural crest stem cells undergo cell-intrinsic developmental changes in sensitivity to instructive differentiation signals. *Neuron* **29,** 57–71.
45. Desai, A.R., and McConnell, S.K. (2000). Progressive restriction in fate potential by neural progenitors during cerebral cortical development. *Development* **127,** 2863–2872.
46. Brivanlou, A.H., *et al.* (2003). Stem cells: setting standards for human embryonic stem cells. *Science* **300,** 913–916.
47. Solter, D. (2000). Mammalian cloning: advances and limitations. *Nat. Rev. Genet.* **1,** 199–207.
48. Rideout, W.M., 3rd, Eggan, K., and Jaenisch, R. (2001). Nuclear cloning and epigenetic reprogramming of the genome. *Science* **293,** 1093–1098.
49. Liu, Y., and Rao, M.S. (2003). Transdifferentiation: fact or artifact. *J. Cell Biochem.* **88,** 29–40.
50. Blau, H.M., Brazelton, T.R., and Weimann, J.M. (2001). The evolving concept of a stem cell: Entity or function? *Cell* **105,** 829–841.
51. Medvinsky, A., and Smith, A. (2003). Stem cells: Fusion brings down barriers. *Nature* **422,** 823–835.
52. Terada, N., *et al.* (2002). Bone marrow cells adopt the phenotype of other cells by spontaneous cell fusion. *Nature* **416,** 542–545.
53. Wang, X., *et al.* (2003). Cell fusion is the principal source of bone marrow-derived hepatocytes. *Nature* **422,** 897–901.
54. Ying, Q.L., *et al.* (2002). Changing potency by spontaneous fusion. *Nature* **416,** 545–548.
55. Ivanova, N.B., *et al.* (2002). A stem cell molecular signature. *Science* **298,** 601–604.
56. Ramalho-Santos, M., *et al.* (2002). "Stemness": transcriptional profiling of embryonic and adult stem cells. *Science* **298,** 597–600.
57. Tanaka, T.S., *et al.* (2002). Gene expression profiling of embryo-derived stem cells reveals candidate genes associated with pluripotency and lineage specificity. *Genome Res.* **12,** 1921–1928.
58. Anisimov, S.V., *et al.* (2002). SAGE identification of gene transcripts with profiles unique to pluripotent mouse R1 embryonic stem cells. *Genomics* **79,** 169–176.
59. Luo, Y., *et al.* (2002). Microarray analysis of selected genes in neural stem and progenitor cells. *J. Neurochem.* **83,** 1481–1497.
60. Park, I.K., *et al.* (2002). Differential gene expression profiling of adult murine hematopoietic stem cells. *Blood* **99,** 488–498.
61. Burdon, T., *et al.* (1999). Signaling mechanisms regulating self-renewal and differentiation of pluripotent embryonic stem cells. *Cells Tiss. Organs* **165,** 131–143.
62. Savatier, P., *et al.* (2002). Analysis of the cell cycle in mouse embryonic stem cells. *Methods Mol. Biol.* **185,** 27–33.

1

Development of Epithelial Stem Cell Concepts

Christopher S. Potten and James W. Wilson

Stem cell concepts have evolved dramatically over the last few years from the simple ideas in the literature of the mid-twentieth century. This has culminated in a rapid expansion of interest in both embryonic and adult tissue stem cells in the last five years, with the development of interest in gene therapy and tissue engineering. This chapter explores the evolution of stem cell concepts as applied to adult epithelial tissues. These tissues are characterised by a high degree of polarisation and very distinct cell maturation and migration pathways, which permit the identification of specific locations in the tissues that represent the origins of all this cell movement. Cells at the origin of the migratory pathways must represent the cells upon which the tissue is dependent and the cells that have a long-term (permanent) residence in the tissue, i.e., the stem cells. A variety of cell kinetic studies, with lineage tracking experiments, have indicated that in the intestine, on the dorsal surface of the tongue, and in the interfollicular epidermis, the proliferative compartment of the tissue is divided into discrete units of proliferation, each with its own stem cell compartment. In the skin, the evolving stem cell studies suggest at least three distinct stem cell populations that provide a source of cells for the epidermis and growing hair follicle and a reserve, regenerative, highly potent population in the upper follicle region. In the small intestine, there are indications that the stem cell compartment itself is hierarchical, with a commitment to differentiation occurring 2 to 3 generations down the lineage, resulting in a population of actual stem cells that perform their function in steady state and a population of potential stem cells that can be called into action if the actual stem cells are killed. Until recently, there have been no reliable markers for adult intestinal stem cells; however, recent developments have indicated ways in which these cells may be identified. Cancer is rare in the small intestinal epithelium, which is surprising since this tissue represents a large mass with many stem cells dividing many times. This suggests that effective genome protective mechanisms have evolved, and some aspects of these have been identified.

Handbook of Stem Cells
Volume 2

Concept of Stem Cells in Adult Mammalian Tissues

In the 1950s and 1960s all proliferating cells in the renewing tissues of the body were regarded as having equal potential for self-maintenance; one daughter cell on average from each division of a proliferative cell was retained within the proliferative compartment. Thus all proliferating cells were regarded as stem cells. It proved difficult to displace this concept; however, a groundbreaking paper by Till and McCulloch in 1961[1] provided the first clear evidence that for one of the replacing tissues of the body, the bone marrow, not all proliferative cells are identical. They studied cells capable of repopulating haemopoietic tissues following cellular depletion of the tissue by exposure to a cytotoxic agent, i.e., radiation. Specifically, mice were irradiated to deplete their bone marrow of endogenous, functional haemopoietic precursors; then they were injected with bone marrow–derived precursors obtained from another animal. The exogenous cells were subjected to a variety of treatments prior to transplant. It was found that the haemopoietic precursors circulated in the host and seeded cells into various haemopoietic tissues including the spleen. Cells that seeded into the spleen and possessed extensive regenerative and differentiative potential grew by a process of clonal expansion to form macroscopically visible nodules of haemopoietic tissue 10–14 days after transplant. By appropriate genetic or chromosome tracking (marking), it could be shown that these nodules were derived from single cells, i.e., that they were clones, and that further clonogenic cells were produced within the clones. The colonies were referred to as spleen colonies, and the cells that form the colonies were called colony-forming units–spleen (CFU-S). These experiments provided the theoretical basis for subsequent human bone marrow transplant studies. Through a variety of preirradiation manipulations and pre- and post-transplantation variables, this technique led to our understanding of the bone marrow hierarchies, or cell lineages, and their stem cells. These studies showed that this tissue contained undifferentiated self-maintaining precursor cells that generated dependent lineages that were able to differentiate down a range of different pathways, generating a variety of cell types. Recent studies have suggested that CFU-S are not the ultimate haemopoietic stem cells but are part of a stem cell hierarchy in the bone marrow.

Such clonal regeneration approaches have been subsequently developed for a variety of other tissues, notably the imaginative approaches adopted by Rod Withers for epidermis, intestine, kidney, and testis. These clonal regeneration approaches were summarised and collected in a book produced in 1985,[2] but readers are specifically referred to Withers and Elkind,[3] which deals with the gut, and Withers,[4] for studies on the epidermis. These approaches[2] implicated hierarchical organisations within the proliferative compartments of many tissues. The stringency of the criteria defining a clone varied enormously depending as it did on the number of cell divisions required to produce the detectable clones. For epidermis and intestine, the stringency was high because the clones could be large and macroscopic, containing many cells resulting from many cell divisions, and were similar in appearance to the spleen colony nodules.

One difficulty with the interpretation and generality of application to stem cell populations based on these clonal regeneration studies is that to see the regenerating clones, the tissue has to be disturbed, generally by exposure to a dose of radiation. This disturbance may alter the cellular hierarchies that one wishes to study and will certainly alter the nature (cell cycle status, responsiveness to signals, susceptibility to subsequent treatment, etc.) of the stem cell compartment. This has been referred to as the biological equivalent of the Heisenberg uncertainty principle in quantum physics. However, these clonal regeneration assays still provide a valuable and, in some places, unique opportunity to study aspects of stem cell biology *in vivo,* i.e., by using this approach to look at stem cell survival and functional competence under a variety of conditions.

Definition for Stem Cells

There have been relatively few attempts to define what is meant by the term *stem cells,* which has resulted in some confusion in literature and the use of a variety of terms, the relationship between which sometimes remain obscure. These include precursors, progenitors, and founder cells. The concept is further complicated by the use of terms such as committed precursors or progenitors and by the sometimes confusing use or implication of the term differentiation. One of the difficulties in defining stem cells is that the definitions are often context dependent and, hence, different criteria are brought into the definition by embryologists, haematologists, dermatologists, gastroenterologists, etc. In 1990, in a paper in *Development,*[5] we attempted to define a stem cell. This definition was, admittedly, formulated within the context of the gastrointestinal epithelium, but we felt it had a broader application. The definition still largely holds and can be summarised as follows: Within adult replacing tissues of the body, stem cells can be defined as a small subpopulation of the proliferating compartment, consisting of relatively undifferentiated proliferative cells that maintain their population size when they divide and produce progeny that enter a dividing transit population. Within this population, further rounds of cell division and differentiation events occur, resulting in the production of the various differentiated functional cells required of the tissue. The stem cells persist throughout the animal's lifetime in the tissue, dividing many times. As a probable consequence of this large division potential, these cells are the most efficient repopulators of the tissue following injury. If this repopulation requires a reestablishment of the full stem cell compartment, the self-maintenance probability of the stem cells at division will be raised from the steady-state value of 0.5 to a value between 0.5 and 1, which enables the stem cell population to be reestablished and maintains the production of differentiated cells to ensure the functional integrity of the tissue.

The consequences of this definition are obvious, namely that stem cells are rare cells in the tissue, vastly outnumbered by the dividing transit population; the cells upon which the entire lineage and ultimately the tissue are dependent; the only permanent long-term residents of the tissue; and the cells at the origin of any cell lineages or migratory pathways that can be identified in the tissue.

The concept of differentiation enters into the definition of stem cells. This also often leads to confusion. In our view, differentiation is a qualitative and relative phenomenon. Cells tend to be differentiated relative to other cells. Hence, adult tissue stem cells may or may not be differentiated relative to embryonic stem cells (a current point of debate, bearing in mind the controversy in the literature concerning bone marrow stem cell *plasticity*). Stem cells produce progeny that may differentiate down a variety of pathways leading to the concepts of *totipotency* and *pluripotency* of stem cells in terms of their differentiation. This is a strange concept to apply to a stem cell since it is their progeny that differentiate, not the stem cells themselves. The fact that the progeny can differentiate down more than one differentiated lineage is obviously the case in the bone marrow. As a result, bone marrow stem cells are referred to as pluripotent, and the initial dividing transit cells that initiate a lineage that leads to specific differentiated cells can be thought of as committed precursors for that lineage.

Some of the instructive signals for differentiation in the haemopoietic cell lineage are well understood, but such signals for other tissues organised on a cell lineage basis have yet to be determined. There is much debate in literature concerning the extent to which stem cells may be instructed to produce progeny of specific differentiated types and whether this is limited or unlimited. This is a topic referred to as the degree of plasticity for stem cells. There are two distinct issues here:

- The first is whether a stem cell, such as a bone marrow stem cell, is ever instructed by its environment in nature, or in laboratory or clinical situations, to make an apparently unrelated tissue cell type such as a liver, intestinal, or skin cell and whether it can regenerate these tissues if they are injured. A subsidiary question to this is not whether this happens normally in nature, but whether we, as experimentalists or clinicians, can provide the necessary instructions or environment for this to happen in a controlled situation.

- The second issue relates not only to the stem cells but also to the early progeny of stem cells from, for example, the bone marrow, and whether these cells, which circulate around the body and may end up in a distant tissue, can end up expressing differentiation markers unrelated to the bone marrow cell lineages but specific to the tissue in which the cell resides.

The former is an issue of plasticity of the bone marrow stem cells, and the latter may be an issue of the plasticity of the bone marrow–derived cell lineages. If a bone marrow stem cell can ever be instructed to be a gastrointestinal stem cell, it should be capable of undertaking all the functional duties of a gastrointestinal stem cell, including the regeneration of the gastrointestinal epithelium if it is injured. The cloning of animals, by nuclear transfer technology into egg cytoplasm, clearly demonstrates that all nuclei of the body contain a full complement of DNA and that, under the right environmental conditions, this can be reprogrammed (or unmasked) by environmental signals to make all the tissues of the body. It should, however, be remembered that cloning experiments such as Dolly the sheep are rare and inefficiently produced events. Nevertheless, they clearly indicate enormous potential if we can provide the necessary instructive reprogramming signals. It should enable us to reproducibly instruct any adult tissue stem cell to make any tissue of the body. If and when this becomes the case, the distinction between embryonic stem cells and adult tissue stem cells may disappear.

Hierarchically Organised Stem Cell Populations

What determines the difference between a dividing transit cell and a stem cell, and is that transition abrupt or gradual? One can think of this transition as being a differentiation event that distinguishes a dividing transit cell from a stem cell. This is an old argument. Do differentiation signals act on preexisting stem cells, removing on average half the cells produced by previous symmetric divisions? Or do the stem cells divide asymmetrically to produce a differentiated progeny and a stem cell? One possibility is that this distinction is made when a stem cell divides. Do they need to divide to differentiate? In this case, such divisions must be regarded as asymmetric, with the dividing stem cell producing one stem cell (i.e., for self-maintenance) and one dividing transit cell. This type of asymmetric division may occur in tissues such as the epidermis. However, if this is the case, the stem cell must retain the potential to alter its self-maintenance probability, which for an asymmetric division is 0.5 in steady state, and to adopt a higher value if stem cells are killed and require repopulation. The current view regarding the bone marrow stem cells is that the transition between a stem cell and a dividing transit cell is a gradual one that occurs over a series of divisions within a cell lineage, which inevitably implies that one has a population of stem cells with a varying degree of "stemness" or, conversely, a varying degree of differentiation. For the bone marrow, one issue is whether experimentalists have ever identified the presence of the truly ancestral bone marrow stem cell. The difficulty may be one of identifying and extracting such cells, the location of which is probably in the bone, where they will be present in increasingly diminishing numbers as one looks for the increasingly primitive cells.

Our model for the gastrointestinal cellular organisation, based on an attempt to accommodate as much experimental data as possible, is that the commitment to differentiation producing dividing transit cells does not occur at the level of the ultimate stem cell in the lineage but at a position two or three generations along the cell lineage. If such a concept is drawn as a cell lineage diagram, the proliferative units in the intestine, the crypts, each contain 4 to 6 cell lineages and, hence, 4 to 6 lineage ancestor stem cells but up to 30 second- and third-tier stem cells. Under steady-state circumstances, these second- and third-tier stem cells are inevitably displaced and moved toward the dividing transit compartment, but if damage occurs in one or more ultimate stem cells, they can assume the mantle of the ultimate stem cell and repopulate the lineage.[6–8] This leads to the concept of actual and potential stem cells (see Fig. 1–1), discussed later in this chapter.

An analogy can be drawn to the hierarchical organisation within an organisation such as the army, a concept discussed when we were formulating the text for the *Development* paper in which we defined stem cells.[5] On a military battlefield, the hierarchically organised army is under the control and dependent upon the highly trained (or so one hopes) General. If the General is killed on the battlefield, there may be a reasonably well-trained Captain who can take command and assume the insignia, uniform, and function of the General. If the Captain also is killed, there may be lesser-trained officers who will attempt to assume the mantle of command. The majority of the troops, the Privates, would be insufficiently trained or experienced to adopt the functional role of the Commander. However, the Dolly the sheep scenario suggests that, occasionally, a Private given a crash course in military strategy might function as the officer in command. The analogy could be taken further to relate to the apoptosis sensitivity seen in the gastrointestinal ultimate stem cells. These cells appear to adopt a strategy of intolerance to genetic damage and a reluctance to undertake repair. Because this repair may be associated with inherent genetic risk, they will commit an altruistic suicide: the General who undergoes a nervous breakdown or serious injury and needs to be removed from command.

In the small intestinal crypts, no useful markers permitted the stem cells to be identified and, hence, studied. However, such markers are now being identified. In the absence of markers, the small intestine proved an invaluable biological model system to study stem cells because the cells of the intestinal cell lineage are arranged spatially along the long axis of the crypt. This can be demonstrated by cell migration tracking and mutational marker studies. As a consequence, the stem cells are known to be located at specific positions in the tissue (crypts): at the fourth or fifth cell position from the crypt base in the small intestine, and at the base of the crypt in the mid-colon of the large intestine (See Fig. 1–2).[6–8]

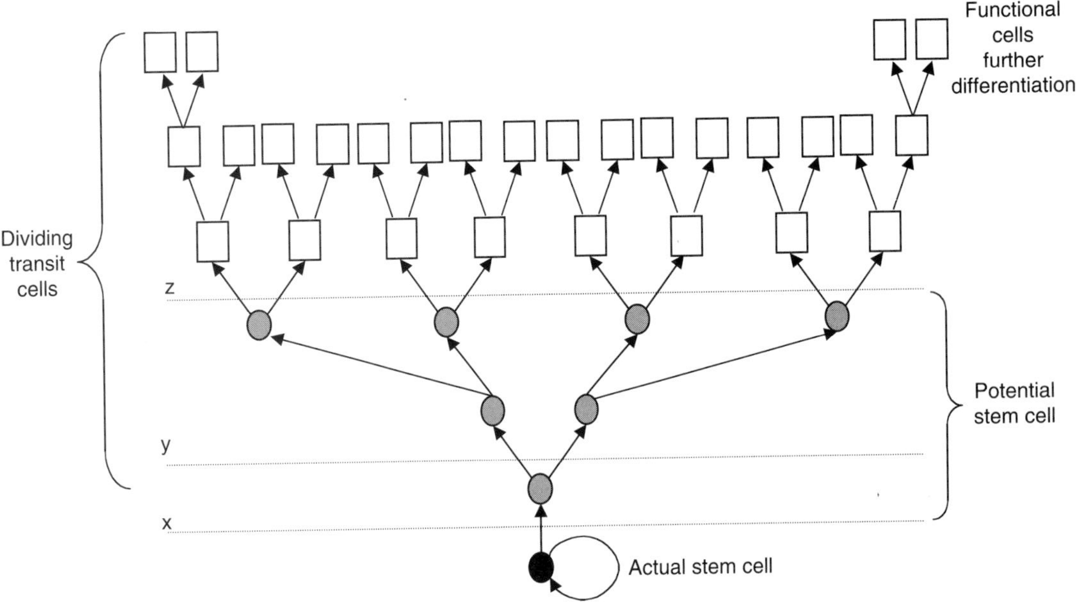

Figure 1–1. Typical stem cell–derived lineage that may be applicable to most epithelial tissues of the body. The lineage is characterised by a self-maintaining, lineage ancestor, actual stem cell (black), which divides and produces a progeny that enters a dividing transit population. The number of cell generations in the dividing transit population varies from tissue to tissue. The commitment to differentiation, which separates the stem cell from the dividing transit population, can occur at the point of actual stem cell division (X). In such a case, the stem cells are dividing asymmetrically on average. However, this commitment may be delayed to point Y or Z, generating a population of potential stem cells that can replace the actual stem cell if it is killed. Under normal steady-state circumstances, the potential stem cells form part of the dividing transit population and are gradually displaced down the lineage. They undergo further differentiation events, if required, to produce the functional, mature cells of the tissue.

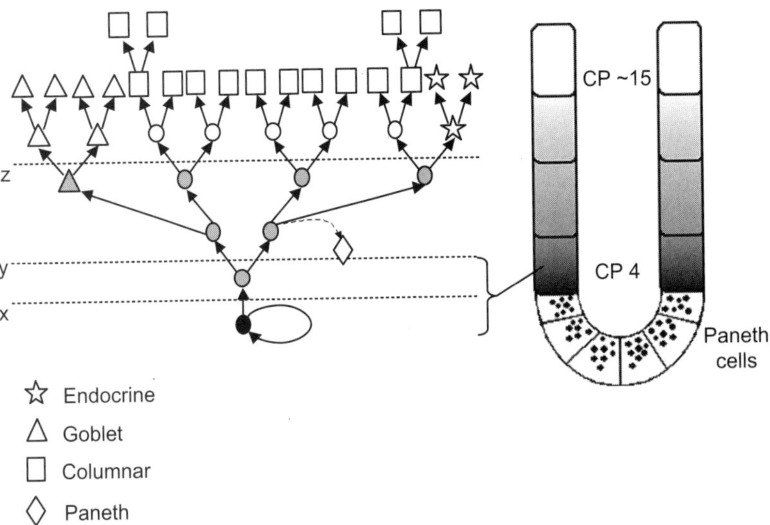

Figure 1–2. Cell lineage for the small intestinal crypts. It is postulated that each crypt contains 4 to 6 such lineages and, hence, 4 to 6 lineage ancestor actual stem cells. There are about six cell generations in each lineage, producing at least four distinct differentiated cell types. The attractive feature of this as a cell biological model system is that the position of a cell in a lineage can be related to its topographical position in a longitudinal section through the crypt, as shown on the right.

Skin Stem Cells

The first suggestion that the proliferative compartment of the epidermis, the basal layer, was heterogeneous and contained only a small subpopulation of stem cells came with the development of the skin macrocolony clonal regeneration assay developed by Withers.[4] This was soon combined with other cell kinetic and tissue organisation data to formulate the epidermal proliferative unit (EPU) concept[9] (see Fig. 1–3). This suggested that the basal layer consisted of a series of small groups of cells related by function and cell lineage, with a spatial organisation that related directly to the superficial functional cells of the epidermis, the stratum corneum. The concept indicated that the epidermis should be regarded as being made up of a series of functional proliferative units, each unit having a centrally placed self-maintaining stem cell and a short stem cell–derived cell lineage (with three generations). The differentiated cells produced at the end of the lineage migrated out of the basal layer into the suprabasal layers in an ordered fashion. In the suprabasal layers, further maturation events occurred, eventually producing the thin, flat, cornified cells at the skin surface that were stacked into columns (like a pile of plates), with cell loss occurring at a constant rate from the surface of the column (Fig. 1–3). Such an organisation is evident in the body skin epidermis and ears of the mouse, and a modified version of the proliferative unit can be identified on the dorsal surface of the tongue.[10] Debate continues about whether this concept applies to human epidermis. It is clear that in many sites of the human body, a similar columnar organisation can be seen in the superficial corneal layers of the epidermis. What is more difficult in humans is to relate this superficial structure to a spatial organisation in the basal layer. However, the spatial organisation seen in the superficial layers must have an organising system at a level lower in the epidermis, and it does not seem unreasonable to assume that this is in the basal layer, as it is in the mouse epidermis.

A macroscopic, clonal regeneration assay for mouse epidermis was developed by Withers[4]; it generates nodules similar in appearance to spleen colonies. Subsequently, Al-Barwari developed a microscopic clonal assay[11] that required a shorter time interval between irradiation and tissue sampling. Both techniques are labour intensive; neither has been used extensively. Together, these clonal regeneration assays were interpreted to indicate that only 10% (or less) of the basal cells have regenerative capacity, i.e., are stem cells.

The epidermal proliferative unit (EPU) stem cells must have an asymmetric division mode under steady-state cell kinetics since there is only one such cell per EPU. The epidermal microcolony assay developed by Al-Barwari suggests that following injury such as irradiation, surviving EPU stem cells can change their division mode from asymmetric to symmetric for a period of time to repopulate the epidermis (i.e., change their self-maintenance probability from 0.5 to a higher value). Al-Barwari's observations also indicated that a significant contribution to reepithelialisation could come from the upper regions of the hair follicles. It was clear from studies on the structural organisation of the epidermis following injury that to reestablish the spatial distribution of stem cells, the epidermis undergoes a reorganisation involving hyperplasia. During this, stem cells are redistributed; they eventually establish their EPU spatial configurations.

The skin contains another important stem cell population, namely, that associated with the growing hair follicles. Hair is produced over a protracted period by rapid divisions in the germinal region of the growing hair follicle (termed an anagen

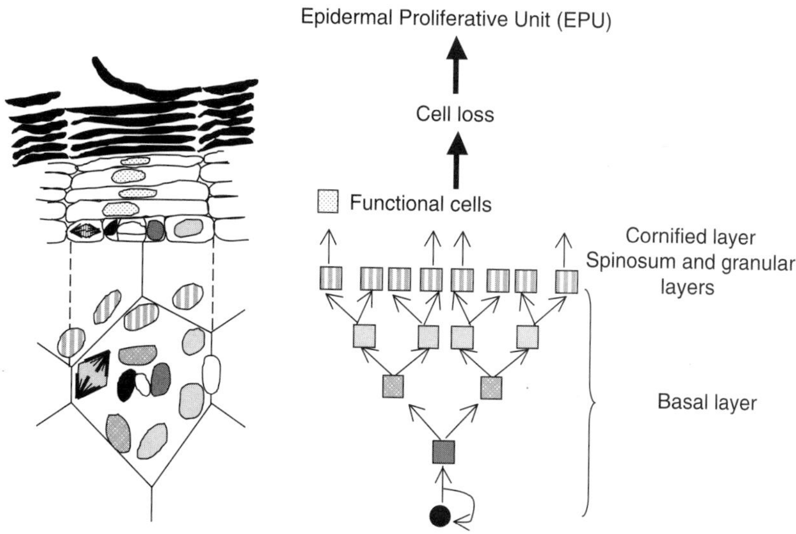

Figure 1–3. Diagram of the cell lineage seen in the interfollicular epidermis and the relationship between the cell lineage and the spatial organisation characterised as the epidermal proliferative unit (EPU), as seen in section view (upper left portion of the figure) and in surface view in epidermal sheets (lower left portion of the figure).

follicle). This hair growth may be maintained for long periods: three weeks in a mouse (in which the average cell cycle may be 12 hours), months to years in man, and indefinite periods for some animal species, such as Angora rabbits, some strains of dog, and Moreno sheep. This high level of cell division in the germinal matrix of the follicle, which has a considerable spatial polarity like the intestinal crypt, must have a fixed stem cell population residing in the lowest regions of the germinal matrix that can maintain the cell production for the required period. Little is known about these stem cells. The complication with hair follicles is that in mouse and man, the growing follicles eventually contain a mature hair, and cell proliferation activity ceases. The follicle shrinks and becomes quiescent (a telogen follicle). The simplest explanation is that the telogen follicle, which consists of fewer total cells than a growing follicle, contains a few quiescent hair follicle stem cells that can be triggered back into proliferation at the onset of a new hair growth cycle. However, as discussed later, there is some controversy concerning this concept.

It is now clear that the skin contains a third stem cell compartment, located in the upper outer sheath of the hair follicle below the sebaceous glands. This is sometimes identifiable by a small bulge in the outer root sheath, so this population of cells has been referred to as the *bulge cells.* What is evident from a series of extremely elegant but complicated experiments is that these bulge cells possess the ability, under specialised conditions, to reform the hair follicle if it is damaged and to contribute to the reepithelialisation of the epidermis. Cells from this region of the follicle were probably responsible for the epidermal re-epithelialisation from follicles seen by Al-Barwari. Cells from the bulge can make follicles during development of the skin and reestablish the follicles if they are injured. The controversy concerns the issue of whether bulge stem cells, predominantly quiescent cells, contribute to the reestablishment of an anagen follicle under normal undamaged situations. The simplest interpretation is that these cells are not required for this process; for this to happen, complex cell division and cell migratory pathways have to be inferred. This goes against the concept of stem cells being fixed or anchored and against the concept of keratinising epithelia being a tightly bound strong and impervious barrier. What seems likely for the skin is that the EPU stem cell and the hair follicle stem cell have a common origin during the development of the skin from the bulge stem cells, which then become quiescent and are present as a versatile reserve stem cell population that can be called into action if the skin is injured and requires reepithelialisation (see Figs. 1–4 and 1–5).[12]

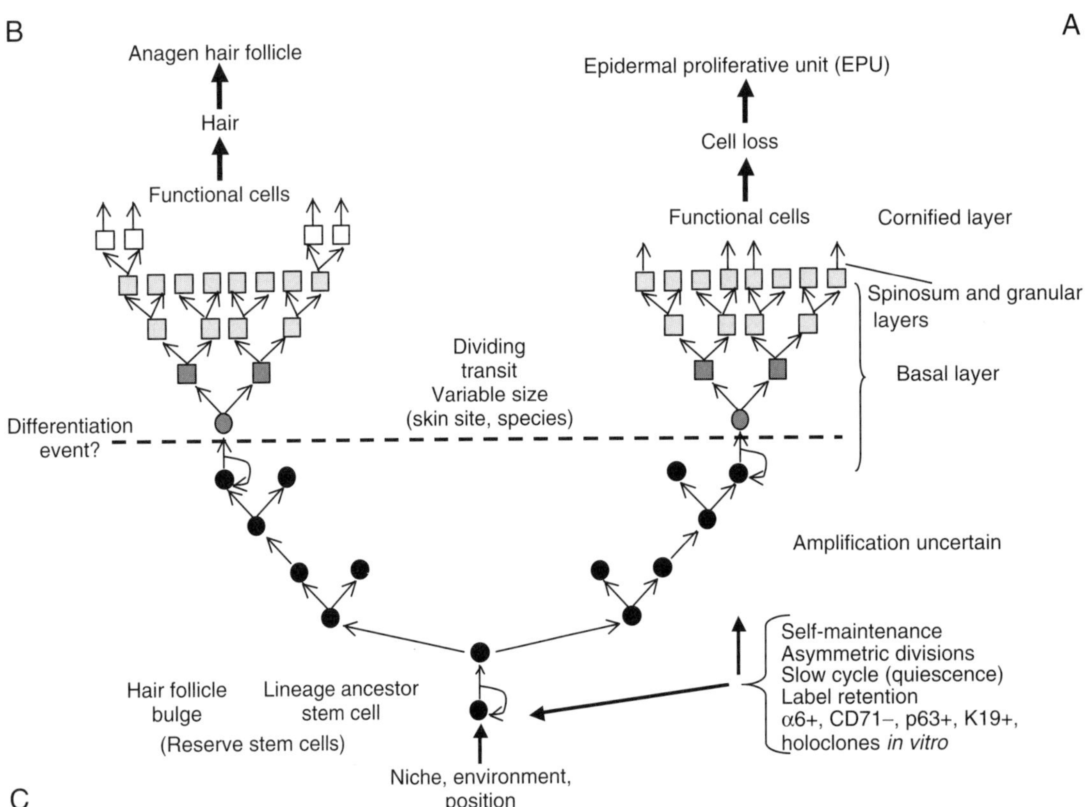

Figure 1–4. Complexity of the stem cell populations in mammalian skin as characterised in the mouse. A distinct cell lineage is proposed (a) for the interfollicular epidermis (EPU), (b) another for the matrix region of the growing hair follicle (anagen follicle), and (c) a potent reserve, regenerative stem cell compartment, which resides in the upper or outer root sheath or bulge region of the hair follicle. The stem cells in the bulge region can regenerate the epidermis, the hair follicle, and probably other structures such as the sebaceous glands.

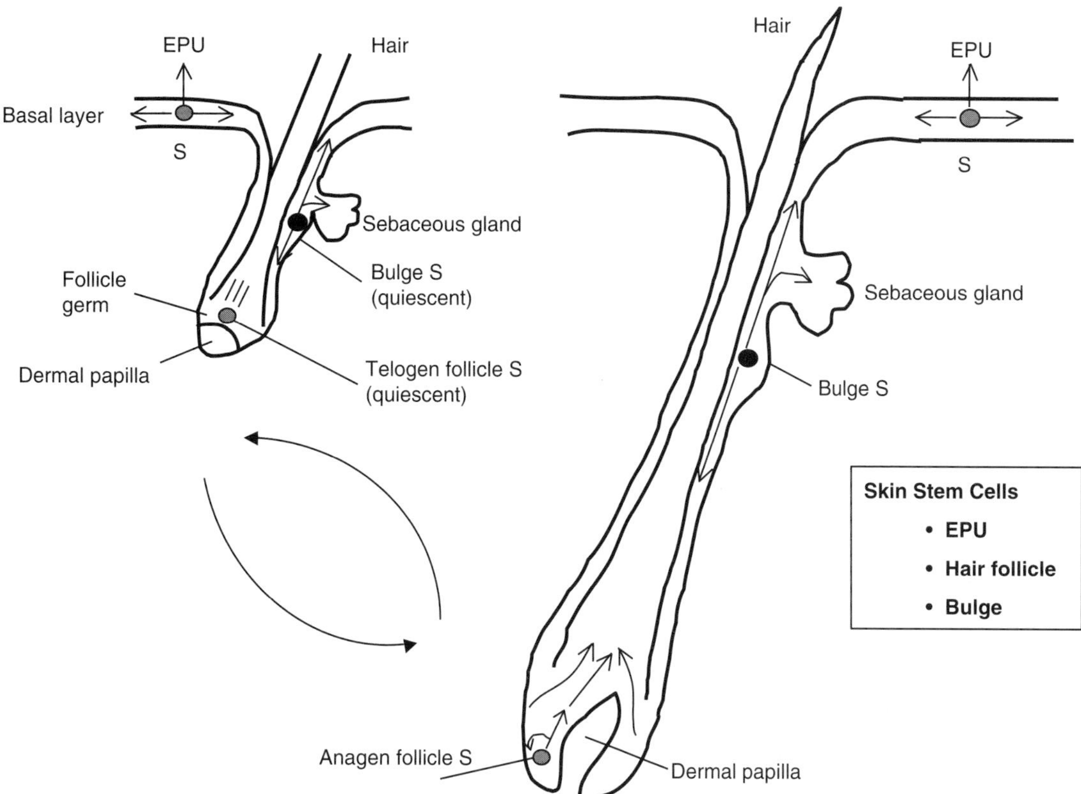

Figure 1–5. Diagram of a growing anagen hair follicle and a resting, or quiescent, telogen follicle. It shows the spatial distribution for the stem cell (S) compartments shown in Fig. 4.

Intestinal Stem Cell System

The intestinal epithelium, like all epithelia, is highly polarised and divided into discrete units of proliferation and differentiation. In the small intestine, the differentiated units are the finger-like villi protruding into the lumen of the intestine. These structures are covered by a simple columnar epithelium consisting of thousands of cells, which perform their specific function, wear out, and are shed, predominantly from the tip of the villus. There is no proliferation on the villus. The cell loss from the villus tip is precisely balanced in steady state by cell proliferation in units of proliferation at the base of the villi, called crypts. Each villus is served by about six crypts, and each crypt can produce cells that migrate onto more than one villus. The crypts in the mouse contain about 250 cells, 150 of which are proliferating rapidly and have an average cell cycle of 12 hours. The cells move from the mouth of the crypt at a velocity of about one cell diameter per hour. All this movement can be traced, in the small intestine, back to a cell position about four cell diameters from the base of the crypt. The very base of the crypt, in mice and humans, is occupied by a small population of functional differentiated cells, called Paneth cells. Cell migration tracking and innumerable cell kinetic experiments suggest that the stem cells that represent the origin of all this cell movement are located at the fourth position from the base of the crypt in the small intestine and at the base of the crypt in some regions of the large bowel. The crypt is a flask-shaped structure with about 16 cells in the circumferential dimensions. Mathematical modelling suggests that each crypt contains about five cell lineages and, hence, five cell lineage ancestor stem cells. Under steady-state kinetics, these cells are responsible for all the cell production, producing daughters that enter a dividing transit lineage between six and eight generations in the small and large bowel, respectively (see Figs. 1–1 and 1–2). The stem cells in the small intestine divide with a cycle of approximately 24 hours and, hence, in the lifetime of a laboratory mouse, divide about 1000 times. It is assumed that these cells are anchored or fixed in a microenvironmental niche that helps determine their function and behaviour. The attractive feature of this model system, from a cell biological point of view, is that in the absence of stem cell-specific markers, the behaviour, characteristics, and response to treatment of these crucial lineage ancestor cells can be studied by studying the behaviour of cells at the fourth position from the bottom of the crypt in the small intestine. When this is done, one feature seems to characterise a small population of cells at this position (about five cells): They express an exquisite sensitivity to genotoxic damage, such as that delivered by small doses of radiation.[13–15] They appear to tolerate no DNA damage and activate a p53-dependent altruistic suicide (apoptosis). It is believed that this is part of the genome protection mechanisms that operate in the small intestine and account for the low incidence of cancer in this large mass of rapidly proliferating tissue.

Clonal regeneration techniques, also developed by Withers,[3] have been used extensively. These techniques suggest the presence of a second compartment of clonogenic or potential stem cells (about 30 per crypt) that possess a higher radioresistance and a good ability to repair DNA damage. These observations, with others, suggest a stem cell hierarchy of the sort illustrated in Figs. 1–1 and 1–2, with the commitment to differentiation that distinguishes dividing transit cells from stem cells occurring about three generations along the lineage. Virtually identical lineage structures can be inferred for the colonic crypts.[16]

There has been an absence of stem cell-specific markers in the past; however, current work suggests that some may be available. Antibodies to Musashi-1, an RNA-binding protein identified as playing a role in asymmetric division control in neural stem cells, appears to be expressed in early lineage cells in the small intestine (see Fig. 1–6).[17]

Recent studies indicated that the ultimate stem cells in the crypt possess the ability to selectively segregate old and new strands of DNA at division, retain the old template strands in the daughter cell destined to remain a stem cell, and pass the newly synthesised strands, which may contain replication-induced errors, to the daughter cell destined to enter the dividing transit population and to be shed from the tip of the villus 5–7 days after birth from division.[18] This selective DNA segregation process provides a second level of genome protection for the stem cells[19] in the small intestine, protecting them from replication-induced errors and providing further protection against carcinogenic risk and an explanation for the low cancer incidence in this tissue (see Table 1–1). This mechanism of selective DNA segregation allows the template strands to be labelled with DNA synthesis markers at stem cell expansion, i.e., during late tissue development and during tissue regeneration after injury. The incorporation of a label into the template strands persists (label-retaining cells), providing a truly specific marker for the lineage ancestor cells (see Fig. 1–6). This figure also illustrates other ways in which intestinal stem cells may be distinguished from their rapidly dividing progeny.

TABLE 1–1
Why Do Small Intestinal Stem Cells Not Develop More Cancers?

Consider that the tissue, compared with the large intestine:

- is 3–4 times greater in mass (length)
- is 1.5 times more rapidly proliferating
- has 2–3 times the total stem cells
- has 3–4 times the stem cell divisions in a lifetime.

However, the small intestine has 70 times fewer cancers.

Stem Cell Organisation in Filiform Papillae on the Dorsal Surface of the Tongue

Oral mucosae are keratinising, stratified epithelia similar to epidermis in their structural organisation. The dorsal surface of the tongue is composed of many small, filiform papillae that have a uniform shape and size. Detailed histological investigations and cell kinetic studies performed by Hume[10] showed that each papilla is composed of four columns of cells, two dominant and two buttressing. The dominant anterior and posterior columns represent modified versions of EPUs and are called tongue proliferative units. The cell migratory pathways were mapped (like the studies in the intestinal crypts), enabling the position in the tissue from which all migration originated to be identified. This position was the presumed location of the stem cell compartment. The lineage characterising this epithelium is similar to that seen in the dorsal epidermis of the mouse, i.e., self-replacing asymmetrically dividing stem cells, occurring at a specific position in the tissue, producing a cell lineage that has approximately three generations (Fig. 1–7). The stem cells here have a pronounced circadian rhythm.[20]

Generalised Scheme

It appears that for the major replacing tissues of the body, hierarchical or cell lineage schemes explain the cell replacement processes. These schemes may involve isolated, single stem cells that under steady-state circumstances must be presumed to divide asymmetrically, producing a dividing transit population. The size of the dividing transit population differs dramatically from tissue to tissue. The number of generations defines the degree of amplification that the transit population provides each stem cell division, and this is related inversely to the frequency that stem cells will be found within the proliferating compartment (see Fig. 1–8). For some systems, such as the bone marrow and the intestine, the commitment to differentiation that separates the dividing transit compartment from the stem cell compartment appears to be delayed a few generations along the lineage. This generates a stem cell hierarchy with cells of changing (decreasing) "stemness" or, conversely, increasing commitment, leading to the concept of committed precursor cells. In the small intestine, this delay in the commitment to differentiation to a dividing transit population provides the tissue with a reserve population of potential stem cells that can repopulate the tissue if the lineage ancestor cells are destroyed—an added level of tissue protection in this extremely well-protected tissue. With regard to the bone marrow, committed precursors, or even earlier cells, appear to circulate in the blood and may lodge in various tissues. Given appropriate microenvironments and local signals, some lodged cells may be instructed to differentiate down unusual pathways. This has prompted research into using such cells to repopulate the liver of patients with specific gene defects that result in life-threatening, hepatic, metabolic deficiencies. Although the transdifferention theory is attractive, recent research indicates that the apparent plasticity of

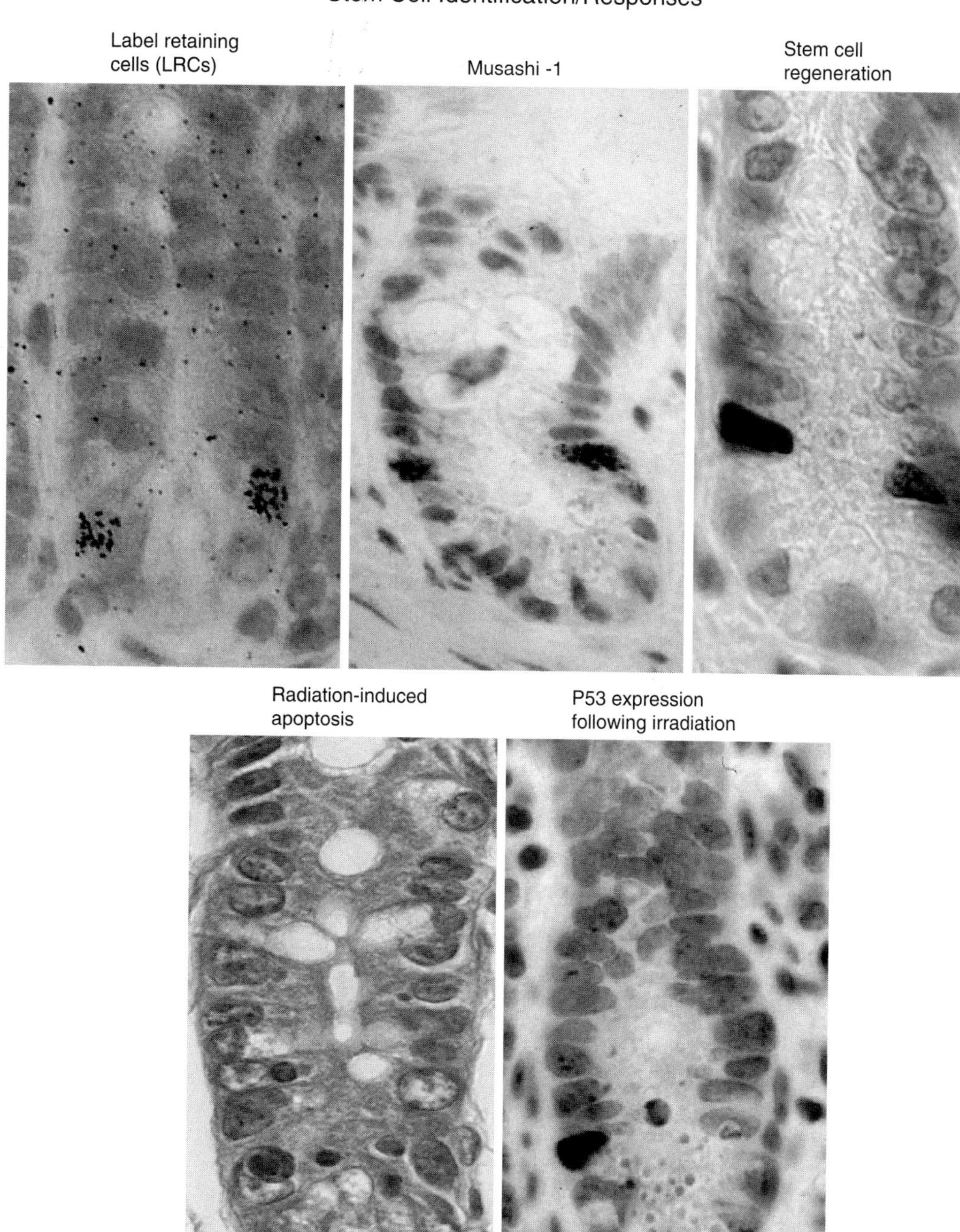

Figure 1–6. Photomicrographs of longitudinal sections of the small intestinal crypts from the mouse, illustrating possible ways of identifying the stem cell compartment. Using the selective strand segregation hypothesis, strands of DNA can be labelled, generating label-retaining cells at the fourth position from the bottom of crypts. Musashi-1, an RNA-binding protein, is expressed in early lineage cells and under some labelling conditions can show specificity for individual cells around cell position 4. Part of the regenerative or potential stem cell compartment can be seen by S phase labelling (bromodeoxyuridine labelling) at critical phases following cytotoxic injury when these cells are called into regenerative mode. This example is a labelling pattern at 24 hours after two doses of 5-fluorouracil, when the only cells in S phase are a few cells scattered around the fourth position from the base of the crypt. As part of the genome protective mechanism, it is postulated that the ultimate lineage-ancestor stem cells have an exquisite sensitivity to radiation and the induction of genome damage. When this happens, the cells commit suicide by apoptosis, which can be easily recognised and occurs about the fourth position from the base of the crypt. These cells do not express p53 protein, at least at the times studied and as detectable by immunohistochemistry. However, some cells express p53 protein at high levels following radiation exposure. It is postulated that these are the surviving potential stem cells in cell cycle arrest to allow for repair prior to entering rapid regenerative cell cycles. Under appropriate immunohistochemical preparative procedures, individual wild-type p53 protein-expressing cells can be seen around cell position 4.

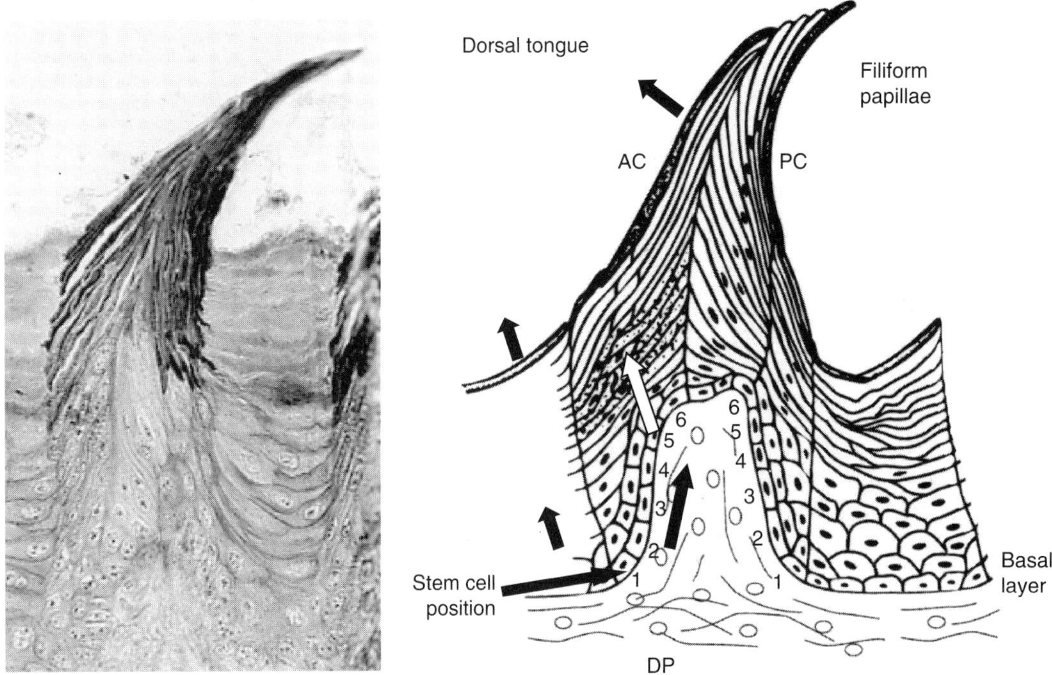

Figure 1-7. Histological section through the dorsal surface of the tongue (left panel), and a diagrammatic representation of this tissue showing the tongue proliferative units (the dominant anterior column, AC, and the posterior column, PC). Cell migratory pathways have been identified based on cell positional analyses, and cell marking and the location of the stem cells have been identified in the basal layer. The stem cells in this tissue express one of the strongest circadian rhythms in proliferation seen in the body.

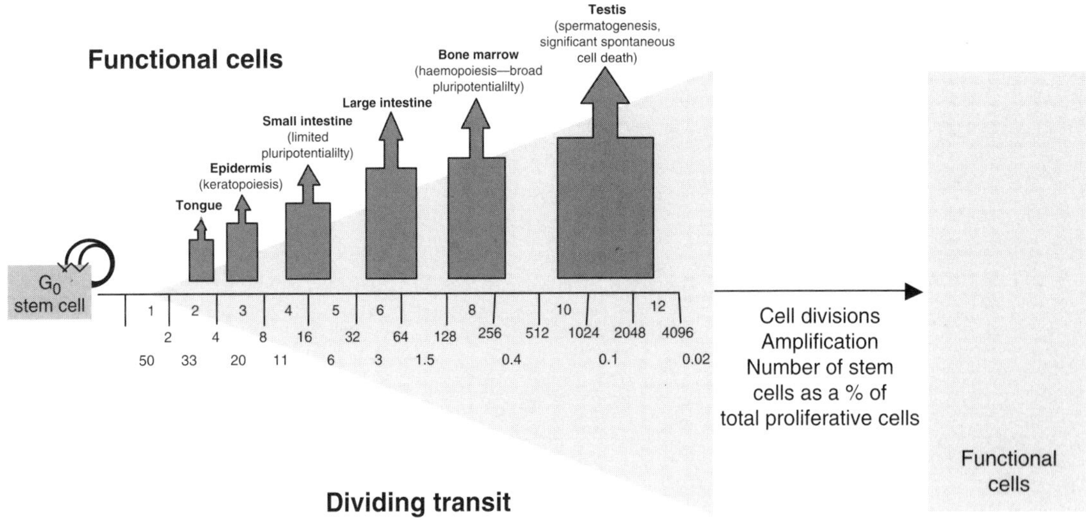

Figure 1-8. Diagrammatic representation of a stem cell–derived cell lineage, showing the approximate positions for the number of cell generations in the dividing transit population for a range of murine tissues. Stratified keratinising epithelia such as the tongue and epidermis tend to have the shortest lineages; the bone marrow and the testis tend to have the longest lineages. Also shown is the degree of theoretical amplification that the dividing transit lineage provides for each stem cell division and the inverse relationship between the degree of amplification and the proportion of the proliferative compartment that the stem cells occupy.

stem cells may be less clear-cut. Transplantation experiments in mice with specific gene disorders suggest that transplanted bone marrow cells may "fuse" with liver cells and hence, compliment any gene deficiency in the hepatocytes.[21] These hybrid cells will be viable and undergo clonal expansion. Experimental findings show that cells forming functional liver tissue in gene-deficient animals have specific genetic markers for both the donor and the host animal. Our concepts of stem cells clearly require further development and refinement.

REFERENCES

1. Till, J.E., and McCulloch, E.A. (1961). A direct measurement of the radiation sensitivity of normal bone marrow cells. *Rad. Res.* **14,** 213.
2. Potten, C.S., and Hendry, J.H. (1985). The micro-colony assay in mouse small intestine. *In* "Cell clones: manual of mammalian cell techniques" (C.S. Potten and J.H. Hendry, eds.). pp. 50–60. Churchill Livingstone, Edinburgh.
3. Withers, H.R., and Elkind, M.M. (1970). Micro-colony survival assay for cells of mouse intestinal mucosa exposed to radiation. *Int. J. Rad. Biology* **17,** 261.
4. Withers, H.R. (1967). The dose survival relationship for irradiation of epithelial cells of mouse skin. *Brit. J. of Radiology* **40,** 187.
5. Potten, C.S., and Loeffler, M. (1990). Stem cells: attributes, cycles, spirals, pitfalls, and uncertainties. Lessons for and from the crypt. *Development* **110,** 1001–1020.
6. Potten, C.S. (1998). Stem cells in gastrointestinal epithelium: numbers, characteristics, and death. Philos. *Trans. R. Soc. Lond. B. Biol. Sci.* **353,** 821–830.
7. Potten, C.S., Booth, C., and Pritchard, D.M. (1997). The intestinal epithelial stem cell: the mucosal governor. *Int. J. Exp. Pathol.* **78,** 219–243.
8. Marshman, E., Booth, C., and Potten, C.S. (2002). The intestinal epithelial stem cell. *Bioessays* **24,** 91–98.
9. Potten, C.S. (1974). The epidermal proliferative unit: the possible role of the central basal cell. *Cell Tissue Kinet.* **7,** 77–88.
10. Hume, W.J, and Potten, C.S. (1976). The ordered columnar structure of mouse filiform papillae. *J. Cell Sci.* **22,** 149–160.
11. Al-Barwari, S.E., and Potten, C.S. (1976). Regeneration and dose-response characteristics of irradiated mouse dorsal epidermal cells. *Int. J. Radiat. Biol. Relat. Stud. Phys. Chem. Med.* **30,** 201–216.
12. Potten, C.S., and Booth, C. (2002). Keratinocyte stem cells: a commentary. *J. Invest. Dermatol.* **119,** 888–899.
13. Potten, C.S. (1977). Extreme sensitivity of some intestinal crypt cells to X and gamma irradiation. *Nature* **269,** 518–521.
14. Hendry, J.H., Potten, C.S., Chadwick, C., and Bianchi, M. (1982). cell death (apoptosis) in the mouse small intestine after low doses: effects of dose-rate, 14.7 MeV neutrons, and 600 MeV (maximum energy) neutrons. *Int. J. Radiat. Biol. Relat. Stud. Phys. Chem. Med.* **42,** 611–620.
15. Potten, C.S., and Grant, H.K. (1998). The relationship between ionizing radiation-induced apoptosis and stem cells in the small and large intestine. *Br. J. Cancer* **78,** 993–1003.
16. Cai, W.B., Roberts, S.A., Bowley, E., Hendry, J.H., and Potten, C.S. (1997). Differential survival of murine small and large intestinal crypts following ionizing radiation. *Int. J. Radiat. Biol.* **71,** 145–155.
17. Potten, C.S., Booth, C., Tudor, G.L., Booth, D., Brady, G., Hurley, P., Ashton, G., Clarke, R., Sakakibara, S., and Okano, H. (2003). Identification of a putative intestinal stem cell and early lineage marker: Musashi-1. *Differentiation* **71,** 28–41.
18. Potten, C.S., Owen, G., and Booth, D. (2002). Intestinal stem cells protect their genome by selective segregation of template DNA strands. *J. Cell Sci.* **115,** 2381–2388.
19. Cairns, J. (1975). Mutation selection and the natural history of cancer. *Nature* **255,** 197–200.
20. Potten, C.S., Al-Barwari, S.E., Hume, W.J., and Searle, J. (1977). Circadian rhythms of presumptive stem cells in three different epithelia of the mouse. *Cell Tissue Kinet.* **10,** 557–568.
21. Medvinsky, A., and Smith, A. (2003). Fusion brings down barriers. *Nature* **422,** 823–825.

2

"Adult" Stem Cells: Tissue Specific or Not?

Catherine M. Verfaillie

Stem Cells: Definition

Stem cells are defined by the following three criteria: First, a stem cell undergoes self-renewing cell divisions, i.e., it can create at least one identical daughter cell, a characteristic required to maintain the stem cell pool. Second, a stem cell undergoes lineage commitment and differentiation, resulting in differentiated progenitors, precursor cells, and, ultimately, terminally differentiated cells. Differentiation is the acquisition of cell type–specific morphological, phenotypic, and functional features. When differentiation is not restricted to a given tissue, stem cells are pluripotent. Most adult stem cells are multipotent, i.e., they differentiate into multiple cell types that are, however, restricted to a given tissue. Third, stem cells robustly repopulate a give tissue *in vivo.* This requires stem cells to home to a given tissue, where they respond to specific cues to differentiate into cell types of that tissue. These types can take over the function of that tissue.

That stem cells exist in postnatal tissues has been recognized since the 1960s, with the first conceptual proof that blood or bone marrow (BM) contains cells that can rescue humans and animals from BM failure.[1,2] Full characterization of hematopoietic stem cells (HSCs) was not accomplished until the last decade, during which the phenotype of murine[3,4] and, to a lesser extent, human HSCs[5] were defined. Proof has been obtained that even a single murine HSC can fully reconstitute all blood cell types following transplantation in lethally irradiated animals and that the progeny of such cells can reconstitute the hematopoietic system in secondary lethally irradiated recipients.[4] HSCs therefore fulfill all characteristics of stem cells. Although HSCs are commonly obtained from postnatal tissues, such as BM and those circulating in the blood,[6] they can be obtained from prenatal tissues, including the umbilical cord blood,[7] BM, liver,[8] the aorta-gonad mesonephros region,[9,10] and the yolk sac.[11] Although the degree of self-renewal may differ for cells from ontogenically earlier or later HSCs, all HSCs, irrespective of ontogeny, have the same functional characteristics.[8,12]

Since then, several other tissue-specific stem cells have been defined, as described elsewhere in this book. For instance, neural stem cells (NSCs) can be found in the postnatal and prenatal brain in several neurogenic areas, including the subventricular zone and the rostromigratory pathway.[13,14] Human NSCs, like HSCs, can be prospectively identified by selecting cells based on cell surface determinants, including AC133 and CD24.[15] Culture of single AC133/CD24$^+$ cells leads to the formation of neurospheres that differentiate into neurons, astrocytes, and oligodendrocytes, and transplantation *in vivo* in immunodeficient animals leads to differentiation to the same cell types. No data exist that show whether these cells can functionally reconstitute areas of the brain. Therefore, human NSCs do not fulfill the criteria for stem cells. However, murine or rat NSCs can functionally reconstitute some compartments of the brain, such as the dopamine-producing cells in the substantia nigra,[16] or can result in remyelination in shiverer mice, caused by the deletion of an animal model for demyelinating diseases.[17]

Mesenchymal stem cells (MSCs), also called marrow stromal cells (MSCs), have been isolated from multiple tissues—foremost from BM aspirates,[18] but also from subcutaneous adipose tissue[19] and fetal lung.[20] MSCs were first described by Fridenshtein[21] as cells capable of creating fibroblast-like colonies that could differentiate into osteocytes and adipocytes. Since then, the phenotype of MSCs in bone tissue and BM and of cultured human MSCs has been elucidated,[18,22] and antigenic determinants have been defined that allow the selection of MSCs from rodent and human BM to almost homogeneity.[23] Using single-cell sorting and ring cloning, investigators have shown that MSCs differentiate not only into osteocytes and adipocytes but also into chondrocytes, skeletal myocytes, and smooth muscle myocytes.[18,24] In addition, grafting of MSC in animals with cartilaginous or bone defects results in engraftment and tissue-specific differentiation *in vivo.*[25]

Usually stem cells produce at least two differentiated cell types. However, some stem cells, such as endothelial[26,27] and corneal[28] stem cells, produce only one differentiated cell type. Recent studies have suggested that endothelial "stem cells" may persist into adult life, when they contribute to the formation of new blood vessels in a process known during embryonal development as vasculogenesis,[29] not solely in angiogenesis,[30] known as the formation of new blood vessels sprouting from preexisting vessels. As for HSCs and NSCs, the phenotype and the *in vitro* and *in vivo* differentiation potential of angioblasts, which can be isolated from BM and peripheral blood, have been characterized.[26,27]

Adult Stem Cells: Plasticity

Most tissue-specific stem cells are thus thought to be multipotent, but no longer pluripotent, like embryonic stem cells (ESC).

Handbook of Stem Cells
Volume 2

Indeed, "adult" stem cells are generated during development beyond the stage of gastrulation. During gastrulation, pluripotent cells become mesoderm, endoderm, and ectoderm; subsequently, tissue-specific fate decisions are made. Therefore, adult stem cells have lost pluripotency and acquired tissue-specific, restricted differentiation abilities. However, in the past few years, more than 200 reports have suggested that presumed tissue-restricted stem cells may possess developmental capabilities resembling those of more immature, pluripotent cells, such as ESC.[31–50] Although the recent reports of greater potency of adult stem cells have met great enthusiasm from the lay and scientific community, they have also met a mostly healthy dose of skepticism. If the concept was true, this would suggest that our previous understanding of lineage commitment and restriction of the differentiation potential of stem cells acquired during development may not be correct. Thus, it may challenge the dogmas developed in biology over the past century.

In this book, individual chapters describe the findings of apparent plasticity of adult tissue-specific stem cells. It is therefore unnecessary to describe the individual studies in detail. Rather, I will try to put the studies, pitfalls, and possible explanations for these observations into perspective.

CRITICISMS AND PITFALLS

The major criticism of the claim that stem cells are more potent than previously thought is that most studies describing plasticity do not fulfill the criteria commonly used to describe stem cells: (1) self-renewing single cells that (2) differentiate into functional progeny and (3) reconstitute a damaged organ *in vivo.* Furthermore, several potential technical difficulties in determining the donor origin of the presumed lineage-switched cells plague the interpretation of some findings.

Criticisms

To demonstrate clonality *in vitro,* several methods can be used, including limiting dilution analysis, isolation of cells using cloning rings, single-cell deposition using either fluorescence-activated cell sorting or micromanipulators, and retroviral marking and characterization of the viral insertion site in the host cell genome. As the chance for integration of a retrovirus in the same location in the host cell genome is less than 1/100,000, this method represents the most stringent assessment of the clonal origin of differentiated progeny.[51–53] Single-cell deposition by fluorescence-activated cell sorter or using micromanipulators are generally also considered full proof of single-cell derivation of cell progeny, even though it is theoretically possible that two closely attached cells may be codeposited.[54] In contrast, the isolation of single cells by limiting dilution or cloning rings always includes the risk that two or more cells were isolated. For *in vivo* studies, single-cell transplantation or viral marking studies represent the only means of determining single-cell derivation of differentiated progeny. Most studies published to date have not definitively proven that the greater potency of adult stem cells can be ascribed to a single cell capable of differentiation into the tissue of origin. Therefore, they do not prove true stem cell plasticity. Notable exceptions include the study by Krause *et al.*[39] in which a single-homed HSC was shown to yield not only hematopoietic chimerism but also cells in epithelium of lung, liver, gastrointestinal tract, and skin. The level of contribution to the nonhematopoietic system by the progeny of a single cell in the Krause study far exceeded that seen in a study by Wagers *et al.,*[45] in which a single HSC obtained by prospective phenotypic isolation from fresh murine BM reconstituted the hematopoietic system, but far fewer cells were detected in epithelial tissues. Differences in the HSCs used for grafting may explain these differences, in view of the notion that will be discussed later: that even highly purified stem cell populations may be heterogeneous and represent a spectrum of potentialities. Grant *et al.* showed that transplantation of a single HSC into irradiated recipients results not only in the reconstitution of the hematopoietic system, but also endothelial cells, provided that injury was induced in the retinal capillary bed.[46] Another example is the study by Jiang *et al.,* showing that a single BM-derived, multipotent cell injected into the blastocyst contributed to most, if not all, tissues of the ensuing mouse.[43]

The nature of a differentiated cell is characterized by morphological, phenotypic, and functional features. Most published studies have, however, only shown that a cell acquires morphological and phenotypic characteristics of a novel cell type. Because cell surface or intracellular antigenic determinants are not necessarily associated with a single cell type, these criteria alone do not suffice to identify differentiated cells. For instance, although CD34 represents an antigen on hematopoietic cells,[55] it has become clear that CD34 can also be found on angioblasts[56] or on progenitor cells from the liver.[57] Moreover, expression is not stable, and cells commonly thought to express certain antigens may lose this expression following cell activation or cell proliferation.[58,59] Spurious expression of antigens—or absorption of proteins from a culture medium[60,61] and, therefore, possibly *in vivo* from a serum or the microenvironment—in or on cells may interfere with interpretation of lineage switch. Better proof that differentiation in a tissue-specific manner has occurred is obtained if donor cells express a marker transgene, such as green fluorescent protein (GFP) or β-galactosidase (β-Gal) expressed from a tissue-specific promoter, as has been used to demonstrate muscle differentiation from BM cells.[31,62] However, unlike the saying "it looks like a duck, walks like a duck, and quacks like a duck," proof of differentiated cell function is required to claim lineage switch. Such proof has only been achieved in a few studies claiming stem cell plasticity. Lagasse and colleagues showed that transplantation of highly enriched HSC leads to restoration of liver function in hereditary tyrosinemia type I (HT-I) mice that have the fumarylacetoacetate hydrolase *(FAH)* gene deleted, which leads to liver failure unless the animals are maintained on NTBC.[63] They demonstrated that grafting of highly enriched HSCs leads to independence of NTBC because of the generation of *FAH* expressing hepatic parenchymal cells.[50]

As mentioned earlier, Grant *et al.* showed that a single HSC can create functioning endothelial cells.[46] Likewise, the study by Reyes *et al.* showed that a single MSC from human BM differentiates into functioning endothelial cells,[49] and Schwartz *et al.* demonstrated that such a single MSC can differentiate *in vitro* in cells with morphological, phenotypic, and functional characteristics of hepatocytes.[48]

Final proof for greater potency of adult stem cells is that the second cell type can robustly and functionally restore an organ *in vivo*. Some would say that this needs to be achieved in the absence of tissue damage.[64] HSC can engraft in the absence of BM damage, provided that very large doses of HSC are transplanted.[65] Poor engraftment in the absence of irradiation is partly related to an issue of "space" (i.e., a lack of stem cell niches available for engraftment) and may partly result from a lack of cytokine and other signals needed for robust clonal expansion of HSC. Because space- and tissue-specific cues are more abundant in the presence of tissue damage, engraftment may improve under circumstances of tissue damage. This was illustrated by Grant *et al.*,[46] as engraftment of HSC-derived cells in the endothelial capillary bed of the retina was only seen following vascular damage. Aside from space and proliferative signals, engraftment requires stem cells to be specifically attracted to the tissue in a process described as stem cell homing in hematopoietic transplantation.[66,67] This is the result of chemokines and cytokines generated by the tissue and the expression of the correct complement of adhesive ligands to which the engrafting cell can adhere. These increase when the tissue is inflamed.[67,68] Nevertheless, even in the setting of tissue damage such as lethal irradiation, or inflammatory and degenerative damage to muscle or other tissues, reported levels of engraftment of BM cells, enriched HSC, or other stem cells in tissues other than the tissue of origin have been low. The exceptions are the papers by Lagasse *et al.*[50] and Krause *et al.*,[39] in which significant tissue damage represented sufficient pressure for clonal expansion, and the paper by Sampaolesi *et al.*, in which inflammation was key for donor stem cells to get access to the muscle tissue.[69] One possibility is that the low numbers of lineage-switched cells are a reflection not of plasticity at the stem cell level but of transdifferentiation of mature cells.[70] If that is the case, plasticity will not have clinical implications. A second possibility is that the cues for clonal expansion are insufficient. Better understanding of those signals emanated by the microenvironment might lead to clinically useful plasticity. Although significant progress has been made in understanding factors responsible for inducing self-renewal and differentiation of stem cells in their niche in lower species, such as in spermatogenesis in drosophila,[71] the nature of the niche and the nature of factors that govern self-renewal, lineage commitment, and differentiation of mammalian stem cells is still unknown, even for the best-characterized HSC.

Technical Difficulties

Most studies suggesting that plasticity exists have been done in rodent models or using retrospective analyses of human tissues following BM or organ transplantation. Demonstration of the donor origin of cells in numerous rodent studies and most human studies has depended on the presence of the Y-chromosome in presumed lineage-switched cells. Although hybridization with Y-chromosome probes has been widely accepted to detect donor cells in grafted animal and human tissues,[72] when it is used to evaluate engraftment in tissue slices, care needs to be taken that specific hybridization is accomplished and that a signal ascribed to one cell nucleus is not the result of detecting a second nucleus in a plane underneath or above the specified cell nucleus.

For rodent studies, the presence of marker genes in donor cells, including β-*Gal* and enhanced green fluorescent protein (EGFP), has been used to demonstrate donor origin of presumed lineage-switched cells.[73,74] Although β-*Gal* is theoretically easy to use as a transgene, endogenous galactosidase in the lysosomes of mammalian cells may interfere with the specificity of donor cell detection, even though endogenous mammalian β-*Gal* has activity detectable at pH 6, whereas bacterial enzyme works well at a higher pH, and most staining protocols readily distinguish endogenous galactosidase activity.[73,74] Although detection of GFP fluorescence is simple because of autofluorescence of certain cell types, specific detection of GFP fluorescence may be difficult.[73,74] One novel development in the use of transgenes has been that the β-*Gal* or the GFP gene can be expressed from tissue-specific promoters, allowing detection not only of the donor origin of the cell but also of tissue-specific differentiation.[31,62]

In analogy to HSC transplantation studies that extensively use the polymorphism in the *Ly5* gene[3] or the glucosephosphate isomerase gene[76] to detect donor cells, studies describing plasticity have used donor cells expressing a cell surface marker missing on recipient cells, such as CD26 on liver cells.[32] Alternatively, one could exploit differences in major histocompatibility antigens between donor and recipient cells, although this is only applicable in the setting of allogeneic transplantation.

POSSIBLE EXPLANATIONS

To many, "stem cell plasticity" may be a new concept. However, the idea is almost a century old. For instance, in the late 1800s, it was recognized that epithelial changes occur in tissues in response to different stresses,[77] which was called metaplasia. For instance, a change from squamous epithelium to columnar epithelium because of gastric reflux occurs in Barrett's esophagus.[78] Furthermore, numerous examples exist of lineage switch in lower species. In drosophila, undifferentiated cells in imaginal discs are the precursors for legs and wings.[79] When cells from one imaginal disc are transferred to another imaginal disc, positional identity is sometimes lost, and the cells acquire the identity of the new location, a phenomenon known as transdetermination.[79] Young urodeles can regenerate whole limbs,[80] thought to be the result of reactivation of specific homeobox genes in the regenerating blastema, such as msx1.[81] When msx1 is expressed in murine myotubes, these tubes undergo dedifferentiation and can redifferentiate not only into myoblasts but also into osteoblasts, chondrocytes, and adipocytes.[81] And there is "Dolly."[82,83]

Then, what are the mechanisms underlying the observed plasticity? Four plausible explanations may exist. First, there is evidence that stem cells or progenitor cells for a given organ may exist in a distant organ. It is well known that HSCs exist not only in the BM but also circulate in the blood[84] and can be harvested from distant organs such as muscle.[85,86] Obviously, hematopoietic reconstitution following transplantation of non-purified or partially purified cells from muscle or other tissues contaminated with HSCs cannot be defined as plasticity.

Second, apparent plasticity can be the result of fusion between donor cells and recipient cells. That this is possible has long been established in the laboratory, since the creation of heterokaryons.[87] This technique is commonly used for antibody production. During the last 1–2 years, this phenomenon has come to the forefront in the field of stem cell plasticity as fusion between cells *in vitro* and cells *in vivo* has been shown. This may explain some of the observations. In 2002, Ying *et al.*[88] and Terada *et al.*[89] showed that coculture of ESC with either BM cells or NSCs can lead to fused, tetraploid, and aneuploid cells that function like ESC and maintain expression of some genes from BM cells or NSCs. The frequency of the fusion event was low ($1/10^4$–$1/10^5$), and this required considerable selectable pressure. The resultant ESC could form embryoid bodies *in vitro* and could contribute to some tissues when injected in the blastocyst. More recently, Wang *et al.*[90] and Vassilopoulos *et al.*[91] found that the remarkable tissue replacement following HSC or BM transplantation into HT-I mice, described by Lagasse *et al.*,[50] is largely the result of fusion between HSC-derived cells and parenchymal hepatocytes, providing the hepatocytes with the missing *FAH* gene and allowing them survive in the absence of NTBC. The frequency of fusion events was low ($1/10^5$ cells), and the cells only expanded *in vivo* in the setting of selectable pressure, i.e., removal of NTBC led to the death of nonfused cells but the survival of fused cells. Interestingly, Wang *et al.* showed that the genetic program of the HSC-derived cell was silenced and that the donor nucleus had started to transcribe hepatic genes. Therefore, this demonstration of nuclear reprogramming from one cell fate to another could be considered plasticity. However, what was not shown is that this happens at the stem cell level and that a hepatic stem cell was generated from an HSC. Although one might consider cell fusion a method for genetically correcting tissues, the fact that the fused cells were tetraploid and aneuploid, as described for the fused cells *in vitro*, gives one pause.

How widespread is the fusion phenomenon in the field of stem cell plasticity? No studies have definitively shown that a donor stem cell fuses with a recipient stem cell, resulting in reprogramming at the stem cell level with subsequent clonal growth of the fused stem cell. However, most investigators that have demonstrated stem cell plasticity are reevaluating the phenomenon to address this question. As fused cells contain more than 2N DNA, plasticity would be expected more often in tissues in which multinucleated cells are common. These include multinucleated skeletal myotubes generated through cell fusion. Although it is likely that BM-to-skeletal muscle transdifferentiation may be caused by this phenomenon, a paper by LaBarge *et al.* showed that BM-derived cells can create mononucleated muscle satellite cells, the progenitor for myoblasts that subsequently fuse with resident muscle fibers.[44] As the etiology of the cell contributing to the satellite compartment was not identified, it is not clear whether this constitutes stem cell plasticity or the transfer of satellite cells in the BM graft. Other tissues include cardiac muscle that becomes multinucleated by endoduplication,[92] hepatic cells,[93] and, within the hematopoietic tissue, macrophages. It is thus possible that macrophages generated by hematopoietic cells can fuse with cells of other tissues. Then, no new stem cells would be generated. Rather, one would find individual cells outside presumed stem cell niches in different organs, as described in several studies demonstrating plasticity. Whether the single donor-derived cells detected in numerous epithelia tissues, where they apparently acquired characteristics of the novel tissue, are the result of transdifferentiation or cell fusion is not known. Recent studies have elegantly shown that cells can be definitively shown or eliminated by exploiting the ability of the recombinase gene *Cre* to excise DNA marked by flanking Lox-P sites. In these studies, *Cre* expressed in the grafted cells from a universal promoter or a tissue-specific promoter can only activate, for instance, GFP, placed between Lox-P sites in recipient cells, if cell fusion occurs.[94]

A third explanation for the observed plasticity is that different stem cell populations may be more heterogenous than previously thought. Over the last decade, it has become clear that even the best-characterized stem cell population, namely HSCs, is more heterogenous than previously thought. For instance, investigators have identified cell subpopulations in mouse and humans HSCs that are responsible for long-term hematopoietic repopulation, short-term hematopoietic repopulation, or cells that can repopulate the lymphoid or the myeloid lineage.[95–97] It is therefore conceivable that, aside from cells committed to long-term hematopoietic repopulation, earlier stem cells committed to a hemangioblast or mesodermal fate or even earlier, truly pluripotent cells may persist within the so-called HSC population and be copurified using similar cell surface antigenic determinants. Then, differentiation would be to the hematopoietic lineage when the cell persists in its BM niche, but cells could differentiate into endothelium,[46,98] other mesodermal cell lineages, or even ectodermal or endodermal cell types[43] when transferred into appropriate microenvironments. If that were the case, then this would not constitute plasticity; rather, it would constitute the persistence of more pluripotent stem cells.

The final possibility is that stem cells can truly be reprogrammed in a manner similar to that observed during metaplasia,[77,78] as is seen in lower species,[79,80] or in nuclear transplantation.[82,83] To prove this, and to eliminate the possibility that plasticity is the reflection of heterogeneity at the stem cell level, lineage tracing of individual stem cells will be required.[99]

Potential Uses of Adult Stem Cells

What speaks most to the imagination is that stem cells can one day be used to replace defective body parts by *in vivo* infusion or by the creation of bioartificial tissues. Although this may be possible in the future, the immediate potential benefit of stem cells is that they constitute powerful tools to study cell self-renewal and differentiation. Investigators have used HSCs and, more recently, other defined stem cell populations and their intermediate committed progeny cells to identify the growth factor requirement of their development. This has yielded clinically used cytokines: erythropoietin, granulocyte colony stimulating factor, keratinocyte growth factor, and many more. With the completion of the human and mouse genome projects, stem cells and their differentiated progeny can now be used to define genetic programs that need to be activated or inactivated for cell differentiation to occur, leading to further insight into their developmental programs and to the creation of protein growth factors or small molecules that can activate such programs.

If stem cell plasticity is cause by de- and redifferentiation, understanding the genetic mechanisms underlying these processes will be invaluable. "Cell reprogramming" is already under way in the clinical setting—for instance, by using demethylation agents and histone deacetylases to reactivate fetal hemoglobin in patients with hemoglobinopathies.[100] Insights into processes that reprogram one tissue-specific stem cell into another may then enhance the level of plasticity and may perhaps make it clinically relevant.

Hematopoietic disorders and patients with other malignancies undergoing intensive chemo- or radiation-therapy have been treated for 2 to 3 decades with HSCs. With progress in defining the nature and the differentiation potential of stem cell populations for other tissues, such as NSC, keratinocyte stem cells, and corneal stem cells, stem cell therapy may become a mainstay for treatment of inherited or acquired defects in these tissues. If studies indicating that adult stem cells may have greater differentiation potential can be confirmed, adult stem cells may be used to treat degenerative or genetic disorders of many organs. Adult stem cells might then be used without prior differentiation *in vitro,* as there is, so far, no evidence that undifferentiated adult stem cells will cause tumor formation. Adult stem cells might also be used as autologous grafts, even though such personalized therapies may be prohibitively expensive. Furthermore, for acute illnesses such as myocardial infarctions or for immune-based diseases such as diabetes, allogeneic therapy may be needed, which will then require strategies to be developed to overcome immune rejection.

REFERENCES

1. Pillow, R.P., Epstein, R.B., Buckner, C.D., Giblett, E.R., and Thomas, E.D. (1966). Treatment of bone-marrow failure by isogeneic marrow infusion. *N. Engl. J. Med.* **275,** 94–97.
2. Gatti, R.A., Meuwissen, H.J., Allen, H.D., Hong, R., and Good, R.A. (1968). Immunological reconstitution of sex-linked lymphopenic immunological deficiency. *Lancet* **2,** 1366–1369.
3. Spangrude, G., Heimfeld, S., and Weissman, I. (1988). Purification and characterization of mouse hematopoietic stem cells. *Science* **241,** 58.
4. Ogawa, M., Hanada, K., Hamada, H., and Nakauchi, H. (1996). Long-term lymphohematopoietic reconstitution by a single 34-low/negative hematopoietic stem cell. *Science* **273,** 242–245.
5. Mazurier, F., Doedens, M., Gan, O.I., and Dick, J.E. (2003). Characterization of cord blood hematopoietic stem cells. *Ann N.Y. Acad. Sci.* **996,** 67–71.
6. Siena, S., Bregni, M., Brando, B., Ravagnani, F., Bonadonna, G., and Gianni, A.M. (1989). Circulation of CD34+ hematopoietic stem cells in the peripheral blood of high-dose cyclophosphamide treated patients: enhancement by intravenous recombinant human granulocyte-macrophage colony stimulating factor. *Blood* **74,** 1905–1914.
7. Wagner, J.E., Rosenthal, J., Sweetman, R., Shu, X.O., Davies, S.M., Ramsay, N.K., McGlave, P.B., Sender, L., and Cairo, M.S. (1996). Successful transplantation of HLA-matched and HLA-mismatched umbilical cord blood from unrelated donors: analysis of engraftment and acute graft-versus-host disease. *Blood* **88,** 795–802.
8. Holyoake, T.L., Nicolini, F.E., and Eaves, C.J. (1999). Functional differences between transplantable human hematopoietic stem cells from fetal liver, cord blood, and adult marrow. *Exp. Hematol.* **27,** 1418–1427.
9. Peault, B. (1996). Hematopoietic stem cell emergence in embryonic life: developmental hematology revisited. *J. Hematother.* **5,** 369.
10. Tavian, M., Coulombel, L., Luton, D., Clemente, H., Dieterlen-Lievre, F., and Peault, B. (1996). Aorta-associated CD34+ hematopoietic cells in the early human embryo. *Blood* **87,** 67.
11. Yoder, M., Hiatt, K., and Mukherjee, P. (1997). *In vivo* repopulating hematopoietic stem cells are present in the murine yolk sac at day 9.0 postcoitus. *Proc. Nat. Acad. Sci. USA* **94,** 6776.
12. Rebel, V.I., Miller, C.L., Eaves, C.J., and Lansdorp, P.M. (1996). The repopulation potential of fetal liver hematopoietic stem cells in mice exceeds that of their liver adult bone marrow counterparts. *Blood* **87,** 3500–3507.
13. Vescovi, A.L., Paraati, E.A., Gritti, A., Poulin, P., Ferrario, M., Wanke, E., Frölichsthal-Schoeller, P., Cova, L., Arcellana-Panlilio, M., Colombo, A., *et al.* (1999). Isolation and cloning of multipotential stem cells from the embryonic human CNS and establishment of transplantable human neural stem cell lines by epigenetic stimulation. *Exper. Neurol.* **156,** 71–83.
14. Johansson, C.B., Momma, S., Clarke, D.L., Risling, M., Lendahl, U., and Frisen, J. (1999). Identification of a neural stem cell in the adult mammalian central nervous system. *Cell* **96,** 25–34.
15. Uchida, N., Buck, D.W., He, D., Reitsma, M.J., Masek, M., Phan, T.V., Tsukamoto, A.S., Gage, F.H., and Weissman, I.L. (2000). Direct isolation of human central nervous system stem cells. *Proc. Nat. Acad. Sci. USA* **97,** 14,720–14,725.
16. Studer, L., Tabar, V., and McKay, R.D. (1998). Transplantation of expanded mesencephalic precursors leads to recovery in parkinsonian rats. *Nat. Neurosci.* **1,** 290–295.
17. Yandava, B.D., Billinghurst, L.L., and Snyder, E.Y. (1999). "Global" cell replacement is feasible via neural stem cell transplantation: evidence from the dysmyelinated shiverer mouse brain. *Proc. Nat. Acad. Sci. USA* **96,** 7029–7034.
18. Pittenger, M.F., Mackay, A.M., Beck, S.C., Jaiswal, R.K., Douglas, R., Mosca, J.D., Moorman, M.A., Simonetti, D.W., Craig, S., and Marshak, D.R. (1999). Multilineage potential of adult human mesenchymal stem cells. *Science* **284,** 143–147.
19. Zuk, P.A., Zhu, M., Mizuno, H., Huang, J., Futrell, J.W., Katz A, J., Benhaim, P., Lorenz, H.P., and Hedrick, M.H. (2001). Multilineage cells from human adipose tissue: implications for cell-based therapies. *Tissue Eng.* **7,** 211–228.

20. Noort, W.A., Kruisselbrink, A., in't Anker, P., Kruger, M., van Bezooijen, R., de Paus, R., Heemskerk, M., Lowik, C., Falkenburg, J., Willemze, R., *et al.* (2002). Mesenchymal stem cells promote engraftment of human umbilical cord blood-derived CD34(+) cells in NOD/SCID mice. *Exp. Hematol.* **30,** 870–878.
21. Fridenshtein, A. (1982). Stromal bone marrow cells and the hematopoietic microenvironment. *Arkh. Patol.* **44,** 3–11.
22. Haynesworth, S.E., Barber, M.A., and Caplan, I.A. (1992). Cell surface antigens on human marrow-derived mesenchymal cells are detected by monoclonal antibodies. *Bone* **13,** 69–80.
23. Gronthos, S., Zannettino, A.C., Hay, S.J., Shi, S., Graves, S.E., Kortesidis, A., and Simmons, P.J. (2003). Molecular and cellular characterization of highly purified stromal stem cells derived from human bone marrow. *J. Cell Sci.* **116,** 1827–1835.
24. Wakitani, S., Saito, T., and Caplan, A. (1995). Myogenic cells derived from rat bone marrow mesenchymal stem cells exposed to 5-azacytidine. *Muscle Nerve* **18,** 1417–1426.
25. Gao, J., Dennis, J.E., Solchaga, L.A., Awadallah, A.S., Goldberg, V.M., and Caplan, A.I. (2001). Tissue-engineered fabrication of an osteochondral composite graft using rat bone marrow-derived mesenchymal stem cells. *Tissue Eng.* **7,** 363–371.
26. Lin, Y., Weisdorf, D.J., Solovey, A., and Hebbel, R.P. (2000). Origins of circulating endothelial cells and endothelial outgrowth from blood. *J. Clin. Invest.* **105,** 71–77.
27. Asahara, T., Murohara, T., Sullivan, A., Silver, M., van der Zee, R., Li, T., Witzenbichler, B., Schatteman, G., and Isner, J. (1997). Isolation of putative progenitor endothelial cells for angiogenesis. *Science* **275,** 964–967.
28. Daniels, J.T., Dart, J.K., Tuft, S.J., and Khaw, P.T. (2001). Corneal stem cells in review. *Wound Repair Regen.* **9,** 483–494.
29. Ribatti, D., Vacca, A., Nico, B., Roncali, L., and Dammacco, F. (2001). Postnatal vasculogenesis. *Mech. Dev.* **100,** 157–163.
30. Carmeliet, P. (2000). Mechanisms of angiogenesis and arteriogenesis. *Nat. Med.* **6,** 389–395.
31. Ferrari, G., Cusella-De Angelis, G., Coletta, M., Paolucci, E., Stornaiuolo, A., Cossu, G., and Mavilio, F. (1998). Muscle regeneration by bone marrow-derived myogenic progenitors. *Science* **279,** 528–530.
32. Petersen, B.E., Bowen, W.C., Patrene, K.D., Mars, W.M., Sullivan, A.K., Murase, N., Boggs, S.S., Greenberger, J.S., and Goff, J.P. (1999). Bone marrow as a potential source of hepatic oval cells. *Science* **284,** 1168–1170.
33. Gussoni, E., Soneoka, Y., Strickland, C., Buzney, E., Khan, M., Flint, A., Kunkel, L., and Mulligan, R. (1999). Dystrophin expression in the mdx mouse restored by stem cell transplantation. *Nature* **401,** 390–394.
34. Jackson, K., Mi, T., and Goodell, M.A. (1999). Hematopoietic potential of stem cells isolated from murine skeletal muscle. *Proc. Nat. Acad. Sci. USA* **96,** 14,482–14,486.
35. Woodbury, D., Schwarz, E.J., Prockop, D.J., and Black, I.B. (2000). Adult rat and human bone marrow stromal cells differentiate into neurons. *J. Neurosci. Res.* **15,** 364–370.
36. Brazelton, T.R., Rossi, F.M.V., Keshet, G.I., and Blau, H.E. (2000). From marrow to brain: expression of neuronal phenotypes in adult mice. *Science* **290,** 1775–1779.
37. Mezey, E., Chandross, K.J., Harta, G., Maki, R.A., and McKercher, S.R. (2000). Turning blood into brain: cells bearing neuronal antigens generated *in vivo* from bone marrow. *Science* **290,** 1779–1782.
38. Theise, N.D., Nimmakayalu , M., Gardner, R., Illei, P.B., Morgan, G., Teperman, L., Henegariu, O., and Krause, D.S. (2000). Liver from bone marrow in humans. *Hepatology* **32,** 11–16.
39. Krause, D.S., Theise, N.D., Collector, M.I., Henegariu, O., Hwang, S., Gardner, R., Neutzel, S., and Sharkis, S.I. (2001). Multi-organ, multi-lineage engraftment by a single bone marrow-derived stem cell. *Cell* **105,** 369–377.
40. Clarke, D.L., Johansson, C.B., Wilbertz, J., Veress, B., Nilsson, E., Karlstrom, H., Lendahl, U., and Frisen, J. (2000). Generalized potential of adult neural stem cells. *Science* **288,** 1660–1663.
41. Bjornson, C., Rietze, R., Reynolds, B., Magli, M., and Vescovi, A. (1999). Turning brain into blood: a hematopoietic fate adopted by adult neural stem cells *in vivo. Science* **283,** 354–357.
42. Jiang, Y., Vaessen, B., Lenvik, T., Blackstad, M., Reyes, M., and Verfaillie, C.M. (2002). Multipotent progenitor cells can be isolated from post-natal murine bone marrow, muscle and brain. *Exp. Hematol.* **30,** 896–904.
43. Jiang, Y., Jahagirdar, B., Reyes, M., Reinhardt, R.L., Schwartz, R.E., Chang, H.C., Lenvik, T., Lund, T., Blackstad, M., Du, J., Aldrich, S., Lisberg, A., Low, W.C., Largaespada, D.A., and Verfaillie, C.M. (2002). Pluripotent nature of adult marrow derived mesenchymal stem cells. *Nature* **418,** 41–49.
44. LaBarge, M.A., and Blau, H.M. (2001). Biological progression from adult bone marrow to mononucleate muscle stem cell to multinucleate muscle fiber in response to injury. *Cell* **111,** 589–601.
45. Wagers, A.J., Sherwood, R.I., Christensen, J.L., and Weissman, I.L. (2002). Little evidence for developmental plasticity of adult hematopoietic stem cells. *Science* **297,** 2256–2259.
46. Grant, M.B., May, W.S., Caballero, S., Brown, G.A., Guthrie, S.M., Mames, R.N., Byrne, B.J., Vaught, T., Spoerri, P.E., Peck, A.B., and Scott, E.W. (2002). Adult hematopoietic stem cells provide functional hemangioblast activity during retinal neovascularization. *Nat. Med.* **8,** 607–612.
47. Reyes, M., Lund, T., Lenvik, T., Aguiar, D., Koodie, L., and Verfaillie, C.M. (2001). Purification and *ex vivo* expansion of postnatal human marrow mesodermal progenitor cells. *Blood* **98,** 2615–2625.
48. Schwartz, R.E., Reyes, M., Koodie, L., Jiang, Y., Blackstad, M., Johnson, S., Lund, T., Lenvik, T., Hu, W.S., and Verfaillie, C.M., (2002). Multipotent adult progenitor cells from bone marrow differentiate into functional hepatocyte-like cells. *J. Clin. Invest.* **96,** 1291–1302.
49. Reyes, M., Dudek, A., Jahagirdar, B., Koodie, K., Marker, P.H., and Verfaillie, C.M. (2002). Origin of endothelial progenitors in human post-natal bone marrow. *J. Clin. Invest.* **109,** 337–346.
50. Lagasse, E., Connors, H., Al-Dhalimy, M., Reitsma, M., Dohse, M., Osborne, L., Wang, X., Finegold, M., Weissman, I.L., and Grompe, M. (2000). Purified hematopoietic stem cells can differentiate into hepatocytes *in vivo. Nat. Med.* **6,** 1229–1234.
51. Szilvassy, S.J., Fraser, C.C., Eaves, C.J., Lansdorp, P.M., Eaves, A.C., and Humphries, R.K. (1989). Retrovirus-mediated gene transfer to purified hemopoietic stem cells with long-term lympho-myelopoietic repopulating ability. *Proc. Nat. Acad. Sci. USA* **86,** 8798–8802.
52. Jordan, C., McKearn, J., and Lemischka, I. (1990). Cellular and developmental properties of fetal hematopoietic stem cells. *Cell* **61,** 953–963.
53. Nolta, J., Dao, M., Wells, S., Smogorzewska, E., and Kohn, D. (1996). Transduction of pluripotent human hematopoietic stem cells demonstrated by clonal analysis after engraftment in immune-deficient mice. *Proc. Nat. Acad. Sci. USA* **93,** 2414–2419.
54. Terstappen, L., Huang, S., Safford, M., Lansdorp, P., and Loken, M. (1991). Sequential generations of hematopoietic colonies derived from single nonlineage-committed CD34$^+$ CD38$^-$ progenitor cells. *Blood* **77,** 1218.

55. Sutherland, D., and Keating, A. (1992). The CD34 antigen: structure biology and potential clinical applications. *J. Hematother.* **1,** 115.
56. Peichev, M., Naiyer, A.J., Pereira, D., Zhu, Z., Lane, W.J., Williams, M., Oz, M.C., Hicklin, D.J., Witte, L., Moore, M.A., and Raffii, S. (2000). Expression of VEGFR-2 and AC133 by circulating human CD34(+) cells identifies a population of functional endothelial precursors. *Blood* **95,** 952–958.
57. Paku, S., Schnur, J., Nagy, P., and Thorgeirsson, S.S. (2001). Origin and structural evolution of the early proliferating oval cells in rat liver. *Am. J. Pathol.* **158,** 1313–1323.
58. Ito, T., Tajima, F., and Ogawa, M. (2001). Developmental changes of CD34 expression by murine hematopoietic stem cells. *Exp. Hematol.* **28,** 1269–1273.
59. Sato, T., Laver, J., and Ogawa, M. (1999). Reversible expression of CD34 by murine hematopoietic stem cells. *Blood* **94,** 2548–2554.
60. Lumelsky, N., Blondel, O., Laeng, P., Velasco, I., Ravin, R., and McKay, R. (2001). Differentiation of embryonic stem cells to insulin-secreting structures similar to pancreatic islets. *Science* **292,** 1389–1394.
61. Rajagopal, J., Anderson, W.J., Kume, S., Martinez, O.I., and Melton, D.A. (2003). Insulin staining of ESC progeny from insulin uptake. *Science* **299,** 363.
62. Asakura, A., Komaki, M., and Rudnicki, M. (2001). Muscle satellite cells are multipotential stem cells that exhibit myogenic, osteogenic, and adipogenic differentiation. *Differentiation* **68,** 245–253.
63. Grompe, M., Lindstedt, S., Al-Dhalimy, M., Kennaway, N.G., Papaconstantinou, J., Torres-Ramos, C.A., Ou, C.N., and Finegold, M. (1995). Pharmacological correction of neonatal lethal hepatic dysfunction in a murine model of hereditary tyrosinaemia type I. *Nat. Genet.* **10,** 453–460.
64. Anderson, D.J., Gage, F.H., and Weissman, I.L. (2001). Can stem cells cross lineage boundaries? *Nat. Med.* **7,** 393–395.
65. Quesenberry, P.J., Crittenden, R.B., Lowry, P., Kittler, E.W., Rao, S., Peters, S., Ramshaw, H., and Stewart, F.M. (1994). *In vitro* and *in vivo* studies of stromal niches. *Blood Cells* **2,** 97.
66. Hardy, C. (1995). The homing of hematopoietic stem cells to the bone marrow. *Am. J. Med. Sci.* **309,** 260.
67. Papayannopoulou, T., and Craddock, C. (1997). Homing and trafficking of hemopoietic progenitor cells. *Acta. Haematol.* **97,** 97.
68. Campbell, J.J., and Butcher, E.C. (2000). Chemokines in tissue-specific and microenvironment-specific lymphocyte homing. *Curr. Opin. Immunol.* **12,** 336–341.
69. Sampaolesi, M., Torrente, Y., Innocenzi, A., Tonlorenzi, R., D'Antona, G., Pellegrino, M.A., Barresi, R., Bresolin, N., De Angelis, M.G., Campbell, K.P., Bottinelli, R., and Cossu, G., (2003). Cell therapy of alpha-sarcoglycan null dystrophic mice through intra-arterial delivery of mesoangioblasts. *Science* **301,** 487–492.
70. Hematti, P., Sloand, E.M., Carvallo, C.A., Albert, M.R., Yee, C.L., Fuehrer, M.M., Blancato, J.K., Kearns, W.G., Barrett, J.A., Childs, R.W., Vogel, J.C., and Dunbar, C.E. (2002). Absence of donor-derived keratinocyte stem cells in skin tissues cultured from patients after mobilized peripheral blood hematopoietic stem cell transplantation. *Exp. Hematol.* **30,** 943–949.
71. Kiger, A.A., White-Cooper, H., and Fuller, M.T. (2002). Somatic support cells restrict germline stem cell self-renewal and promote differentiation. *Nature* **407,** 750–754.
72. Schwartz, S., Depinet, T.W., Leana-Cox, J., Isada, N.B., Karson, E.M., Park, V.M., Pasztor, L.M., Sheppard, L.C., Stallard, R., Wolff, D.J., Zinn, A.B., Zurcher, V.L., and Zackowski, J.L. (1977). Sex chromosome markers, characterization using fluorescence *in situ* hybridization and review of the literature. *Am. J. Med. Genet.* **71,** 1–7.
73. Hadjantonakis, A.K., and Nagy, A. (2001). The color of mice: in the light of GFP-variant reporters. *Histochem. Cell Biol.* **115,** 49–58.
74. Franco, D., de Boer, P.A., de Gier-de Vries, C., Lamers, W.H., and Moorman, A.F. (2001). Methods on *in situ* hybridization, immunohistochemistry and beta-galactosidase reporter gene detection. *Eur. J. Morphol.* **39,** 169–191.
75. Sanchez-Ramos, J., Song, S., Dailey, M., Cardozo-Pelaez, F., Hazzi, C., Stedeford, T., Willing, A., Freeman, T.B., Saporta, S., Zigova, T., Sanberg, P.R., and Snyder, E.Y. (2000). The X-gal caution in neural transplantation studies. *Cell Transplant* **9,** 647–667.
76. Ploemacher, R.E., and Brons, N.H. (1988). Isolation of hemopoietic stem cell subsets from murine bone marrow: II. Evidence for an early precursor of day-12 CFU-S and cells associated with radioprotective ability. *Exp. Hematol.* **16,** 27–32.
77. Cotran, R.S. (1999). "Pathologic Basis of Disease," pp. 31–38 and 266–268. Saunders, Philadelphia.
78. Cotran, R.S. (1999). "Pathologic Basis of Disease," pp. 710–712. Saunders, Philadelphia.
79. Maves, L., and Schubiger, G. (1999). Cell determination and transdetermination in Drosophila imaginal discs. *Curr. Top. Dev. Biol.* **43,** 115–51.
80. Brockes, J.P. (1997). Amphibian limb regeneration: rebuilding a complex structure. *Science* **276,** 61–67.
81. Odelberg, S.J., Kollhoff, A., and Keating, M.T. (2000). Dedifferentiation of mammalian myotubes induced by msx1. *Cell* **103,** 1099–1109.
82. Campbell, K.H., McWhir, J., Ritchie, W.A., and Wilmut, I. (1996). Sheep cloned by nuclear transfer from a cultured cell line. *Nature* **380,** 64–66.
83. Wilmut, I., Schnieke, A.E., McWhir, J., Kind, A.J., and Campbell, K.H. (1997). Viable offspring derived from fetal and adult mammalian cells. *Nature* **385,** 810–813.
84. Bensinger, W.I., Weaver, C.H., Appelbaum, F.R., Rowley, S., Demirer, T., Sanders, J., Storb, R., and Buckner, C.D. (1995). Transplantation of allogeneic peripheral blood stem cells mobilized by recombinant human granulocyte colony-stimulating factor. *Blood* **85,** 1655–1664.
85. McKinney-Freeman, S.L., Jackson, K.A., Camargo, F.D., Ferrari, G., Mavilio, F., and Goodell, M.A. (2002). Muscle-derived hematopoietic stem cells are hematopoietic in origin. *Proc. Nat. Acad. Sci. USA* **99,** 1341–1346.
86. Kawada, H., and Ogawa, M. (2001). Bone marrow origin of hematopoietic progenitors and stem cells in murine muscle. *Blood* **98,** 2008–2013.
87. Kikyo, N., and Wolffe, A.P. (2000). Reprogramming nuclei: insights from cloning, nuclear transfer and heterokaryons. *J. Cell Sci.* **113,** 11–20.
88. Ying, Q.Y., Nichols, J., Evans, E.P., and Smith, A.G. (2002). Changing potency by spontaneous fusion. *Nature* **416,** 545–548.
89. Terada, N., Hamazaki, T., Oka, M., Hoki, M., Mastalerz, D.M., Nakano, Y., Meyer, E.M., More, L.L., Petersen, B.E., and Scott, E.W. (2002). Bone marrow cells adopt the phenotype of other cells by spontaneous cell fusion. *Nature* **416,** 542–545.
90. Wang, X., Al-Dhalimy, M., Lagasse, E., Finegold, M., and Grompe, M. (2001). Liver repopulation and correction of metabolic liver disease by transplanted adult mouse pancreatic cells. *Am. J. Pathol.* **158,** 1–9.
91. Vassilopoulos, G., Wang, P.R., and Russell, D.W. (2003). Transplanted bone marrow regenerates liver by cell fusion. *Nature* **422,** 901–904.
92. Clubb, F.J., Jr., and Bishop, S.P. (1984). Formation of binucleated myocardial cells in the neonatal rat. An index for growth hypertrophy. *Lab. Invest.* **50,** 571–577.

93. Gupta, S. (2000). Hepatic polyploidy and liver growth control. *Semin. Cancer Biol.* **10,** 161–171.
94. Ianus, A., Holz, G.G., Theise, N.D., and Hussain, M.A. (2003). *In vivo* derivation of glucose-competent pancreatic endocrine cells from bone marrow without evidence of cell fusion. *J. Clin. Invest.* **111,** 843–850.
95. Manz, M.G., Miyamoto, T., Akashi, K., and Weissman, I.L. (2002). Prospective isolation of human clonogenic common myeloid progenitors. *Proc. Nat. Acad. Sci. USA* **99,** 11,872–11,877.
96. Kondo, M., Weissman, I.L., and Akashi, K. (1997). Identification of clonogenic common lymphoid progenitors in mouse bone marrow. *Cell* **91,** 661–672.
97. Glimm, H., Eisterer, W., Lee, K., Cashman, J., Holyoake, T.L., Nicolini, F., Shultz, L.D., von Kalle, C., and Eaves, C.J. (2001). Previously undetected human hematopoietic cell populations with short-term repopulating activity selectively engraft NOD/SCID-beta2 microglobulin-null mice. *J. Clin. Invest.* **107,** 199–206.
98. Choi, K. (1998). Hemangioblast development and regulation. *Biochem. Cell Biol.* **76,** 947–956.
99. Gu, G., Brown, J.R., and Melton, D.A. (2003). Direct lineage tracing reveals the ontogeny of pancreatic cell fates during mouse embryogenesis. *Mech. Dev.* **120,** 35–43.
100. Dover, G.J., Charache, S.H., Boyer, S.H., Talbot, C.C., Jr., and Smith, K.D. (1983). 5-Azacytidine increases fetal hemoglobin production in a patient with sickle cell disease. *Prog. Clin. Biol. Res.* **134,** 475–488.

3

(Post) Genomic Stem Cell

Ihor Lemischka

Introduction and Goals

The completion of numerous genome sequences and the development of technologies for the acquisition of global gene expression profiles from different tissues and cell types offer unprecedented opportunities to redefine and address classical biological questions in new ways. We can now identify the complete "parts lists" of living entities and can observe how these parts lists are organized and put into play. Thus, biological processes—developmental cell fate determination, the cell cycle, tumor progression, and many others—can be studied as spatially and temporally controlled deployments of gene expression programs. Genetic control of biological processes has been studied for a long time; however, it has not been possible to observe the coordinated workings of entire genomes. The hope is that we will soon have a framework for a true understanding of how a cell "works" according to its genetically encoded regulatory mechanisms. Much has been written recently about such "systems biology" ways of thinking about and addressing biological questions.[1–5]

The modern genomic era has had an affect on stem cell biology. In contrast to other biological systems, comprehensive molecular analyses of stem cells are in their infancy. However, the time is appropriate to assess what has been learned and to put it in the context of the rich traditions of this field. At the same time, it is valuable to discuss a stem cell as a biological entity ripe for comprehensive molecular studies and systems biology approaches. In this regard, it is useful to seriously consider how stem cell biology will proceed into the twenty-first century and in step with other systems about which similar questions are being addressed. This chapter is an attempt to accomplish these goals. The focus of this chapter is not the detailed technical issues that accompany genomic and postgenomic approaches. A general familiarity with these is assumed, and this chapter stresses more biological and stem cell–specific points. Where possible, this chapter refers to studies in more mature biological systems to highlight possible directions for stem cell research.

Handbook of Stem Cells
Volume 2

What Is a Stem Cell?

To begin, several conceptual and practical issues, as well as questions unique to stem cells, need to be mentioned and perhaps reformulated. As a first step, it is important to reevaluate what a stem cell is. This will have a profound contextual effect on the information that can be acquired and on how it is to be interpreted. The term *stem cell* has made numerous appearances in the popular press, in many cases without adequate justification. A solid conceptual and generally accepted definition of a "generic" stem cell is necessary to provide a solid biological basis for any genomic and mechanistic studies. In this context, it will be possible to precisely define those functional aspects of stem cells that we eventually wish to understand. Having a firm set of definitions will also facilitate fruitful "dialogue" with other, often more experimentally tractable systems from which valuable lessons can be learned.

It is agreed that a stem cell is an entity that can effectively balance a decision to self-renew or to produce differentiated progeny. A further property of most stem cells is their high proliferative potential, defined as an ability to produce large clones of differentiated progeny. Numerous reviews have summarized the experimental foundations that define stem cell properties.[6–8] An excellent in depth primer covering many aspects of stem cell biology can be found online: http://www.nih.gov/news/stemcell/primer.htm.

A convenient segregation of stem cells into two basic classes is useful. First, there are stem cells responsible for the completion of the embryonic development and the establishment of the germ line. Model systems representative of these cells are mouse and human embryonic stem (ES) cells.[9–10] Although useful experimentally, and possibly as future therapeutics, ES cells are derived, and defined *in vitro*. Their status as *bona fide* stem cells that function in normal organisms is unclear. Second, there are stem cells that exist in mature organisms, whose role is to replenish tissues and organs composed of mature cells with finite half-lives. These somatic stem cells suggest a definition for "true" stem cells—that is, a requisite and clearly demonstrable physiological function in a normal organism. Physiological stem cell function may be a continuous homeostatic replenishment of mature cells or a replenishment dependent predominantly on tissue injury or stress.

Somatic stem cells can be viewed as products of developmental processes that specify different organ and tissue systems. As such, cell fate decision mechanisms in somatic stem cells and in ES or other stem cells in an embryo may be fundamentally different. Exciting, though controversial, results have suggested that somatic stem cells can have differentiation abilities that are not limited to their tissue of origin.[11–14] Much of the controversy surrounding such reports of stem cell "plasticity" has resulted from inadequate definitions of stem cell populations, and this has often produced data comparisons of an apples-and-oranges nature. Whatever the outcome of this controversy, it is nevertheless true that in the normal organism, the contribution of stem cells to mature cell populations is largely (if not exclusively) limited to their tissue of origin.

Somatic stem cells have been identified in numerous adult tissues. These include the hematopoietic system, skin, hair follicle, gut, muscle, liver, testes, breast, and the central as well as peripheral nervous systems.[15–29] It is tempting to suggest that most, if not all, adult tissues may contain stem cells capable of at least some stress- or injury-induced regenerative capacity.

For obvious experimental reasons, the best characterized and defined stem cells are those responsible for the replenishment of tissues with a high and continuous demand for mature cells. The precision with which a stem cell population is defined is of paramount importance when contemplating comprehensive genome-level analyses. As mentioned previously, the loose application of the term stem cell is a major cause of the existing confusion in the field, and this confusion will only be magnified when attempting to interpret genomewide datasets without adequate biological foundations. Without a rigorous definition of the stem cell in question, the value of genome scale datasets and analyses is dubious, at best, and misleading, at worst. In simple terms, the power of genomic technologies is only as great as the biological definition of the system to be studied. To highlight the various issues pertinent to stem cell definition as a necessary basis for genomic studies, this chapter will largely focus on the hematopoietic stem cell. I apologize for this "hematocentric" point of view; however, hematopoietic stem cells have a long history and are by far the best-characterized somatic stem cell population. In addition, they are the only stem cell population (with the possible exception of skin stem cells) with a proven record of clinical application. As such, hematopoietic stem cells are ideally suited as a vehicle for illustrating points pertinent to stem cells in general.

Hematopoietic Stem Cells

RETROSPECTIVE DEFINITION OF A HEMATOPOIETIC STEM CELL

Five decades of studies have defined the hematopoietic stem cell retrospectively (as a functional unit giving rise to at least 10 lineages of mature cells) and prospectively (as a rare cell that can be physically purified). It is precisely this large body of historical studies that provides a qualitative and quantitative set of definitions compatible with the current resolution of genomewide molecular technologies. It is useful to consider the properties of hematopoietic stem cells in more detail and to highlight how they affect genomic studies.

It is clear that hematopoietic stem cells residing in the adult bone marrow have a requisite physiological function throughout adult life. In both mouse and human, the total and lineage-specific daily outputs of mature blood cells have been accurately measured. The ability of single stem cells to clonally contribute to multiple distinct lineages was well established by studies from the 1960s and 1970s.[30,31] Classical studies also provided an estimate for the frequency of stem cells in the steady-state adult bone marrow.[32,33] An early study also suggested that the functional life span of hematopoietic stem cells may far exceed the life span of the intact organism.[34] Other studies, some dating from the mid-1960s, provided a direct demonstration that self-renewal and differentiation activities are balanced at the level of single stem cells and at least partly by cell autonomous mechanisms.

It is noteworthy that most hallmark properties of mouse hematopoietic stem cells were already established using the simple strategy of transplanting appropriately marked donor cells into radiation or genetically ablated host mice. The early studies used genetic or radiation-induced karyotypic abnormalities to clearly demonstrate self-renewal and multipotential differentiation properties.[30] More recent studies exploiting the largely random integration properties of retroviruses have confirmed and extended the classical observations.[35–37] With retroviral marking, it was shown that a single stem cell is both necessary and sufficient for the lifelong sustenance of an intact blood cell system. Further, the self-renewal ability of these durable single cells was directly demonstrated by retransplantation into secondary host animals. The high efficiency of retroviral marking also provided insights into the dynamic behavior of individual stem cell clones over time *in vivo*. Retroviral markers have also been used to define the properties of human hematopoietic stem cells in xenogeneic transplant contexts.[38,39] An important and still valid point emerged from all retrospective studies, that is, that the only definitive measurement of the existence and the properties of hematopoietic stem cells is their behavior following *in vivo* transplantation. I will return to this point later; however, it could be argued that *in vivo* functional ability should be demonstrated for any population of somatic cells that one wishes to call stem cells.

The collective retrospective studies thus defined a hematopoietic stem cell as a highly proliferative activity that can be transplanted and that can produce large clonal populations of all blood cell types over long time frames. A lower limit to the developmental abilities of single stem cells was also defined. There are other undifferentiated cell populations in the bone marrow that in the correct circumstances can produce sizeable clones, often containing multiple distinct cell lineages.[40,41] It is important to distinguish these progenitor cells from the true stem cells. First, defined retrospectively as bone marrow entities that can produce colonies *in vivo* or *in vitro*, these progenitor cells have limited self-renewal, proliferative, and multilineage differentiation potentials. The relevant issue here is that true stem cells, as well as their more numerous progenitor progeny, were traditionally defined as distinct activities by simple combinations of retrospective *in vivo* and *in vitro* assays. In many reports describing primitive and clonogenic cell populations in other tissues, there is neither effort nor, in most cases, means to distinguish such distinct stem and progenitor compartments. This should be kept firmly in mind when contemplating or evaluating genomic analyses of these cell populations.

Taken together, the various purely retrospective hematopoietic studies defined a biological system with a hierarchical precursor–product organization, initiating from a rare stem cell, progressing through more numerous progenitor populations limited in self-renewal and differentiation, and terminating in all mature cells in the blood. Conceptually (though clearly not in as much detail), the hematopoietic stem and progenitor cell hierarchy functionally resembles developmental fate maps generated for invertebrate organisms. With such a hematopoietic fate map in hand, it should be possible to define not only the genetic programs operating in the stem cells but also the dynamics of genetic programs as they are implemented and modified during key developmental decision points.

PROSPECTIVE DEFINITION OF A HEMATOPOIETIC STEM CELL

Retrospective studies provide a general, useful overview of the hematopoietic stem and progenitor cell hierarchy. However, from these studies, we only know that stem and progenitor cells exist and possess certain properties, because we can observe large progeny populations of mature cells. To proceed into the realm of genomic (or other direct) studies, the various stages of this system need to be defined prospectively. That is, one needs physically defined, highly enriched cell populations that represent the distinct biological activities, previously defined only retrospectively. A functionally defined stem cell activity needs to be redefined as a cellular entity with a set of well-characterized physical properties. Moreover, in the ideal case, all of the intermediate stages of the hierarchical system should be similarly redefined. Such physically defined stem and progenitor cell populations must always be shown to contain the exact complement of functionally defined biological activities. In essence, a physically defined hematopoietic hierarchy must display a one-to-one mapping to its functionally defined counterpart. Early estimates suggested that stem cells occur with a frequency of 1 in 10, or a 100,000 intact bone marrow cell population.[32,33] This frequency has been confirmed by more recent *in vivo* studies using alternate and more quantitative analytical techniques to evaluate transplant recipients.[42] From these estimates, it is clear that a prospective definition and the isolation of such cells is a daunting task.

Many years of work, from numerous laboratories, have provided prospective definitions for the hematopoietic stem and progenitor system. Two pioneering examples of prospective stem cell purification date from the mid-1980s.[43,44] Several alternative, and more refined, isolation strategies for the true stem cell have been developed. Most of these strategies have focused on the bone marrow, although some have been developed for hematopoietic stem cells found in mid-gestation fetal liver. Specific strategies will be described in a subsequent section. There exists also at least a provisional "road map" that organizes several physically defined cell populations representative of various functionally defined biological activities into a hierarchical branching diagram. Each of these cell populations can be evaluated on a single-cell basis for its complement of hematopoietic potentials. Careful bookkeeping has shown that the physically defined stem cells account for all of the stem activity in the organism.[45] Although the most rigorous prospective definitions of hematopoietic stem cells are in the mouse, similar procedures have been developed for the human system.[46]

Most importantly, from the point of view of stem cell analyses, single, prospectively isolated murine stem cells can function *in vivo* their entire lives.[47] These cells also yield progeny capable of function after retransplantation. It is clear, therefore, that at least an approximate one-to-one mapping is possible for retrospectively and prospectively defined true hematopoietic stem cells. An important issue arises at this point; that is, how accurate is the mapping? In other words, and, of practical relevance, how pure are the prospectively defined stem cells? This is important because the various genomic approaches (e.g., microarrays) commonly used to define global gene expression programs are often accurate to within a factor of two. Therefore, to be meaningful, such genomic technologies must be applied to cell populations in which the biological activities are also resolvable on a per cell basis to within a factor of two. The observation that single hematopoietic stem cells can generate an intact blood cell system must now be recast at the level of the entire population of purified cells. Specifically, an accurate frequency estimate for such cells in the purified cell population needs to be obtained. This is a complex issue because it concerns the difference between absolute and relative degrees of prospective stem cell activity enrichments. There are conceptual and technical sides to this issue, and both require some discussion.

It is relatively straightforward to provide a quantitative estimate for the relative prospective enrichment of stem cells. The transplantable activity in a given amount of starting material (for example, whole bone marrow) is compared to the activity in graded, progressively decreasing numbers of purified cells. A variety of specific *in vivo* transplantation systems are compatible with statistically sound limiting dilution analysis.[42,48–50] In this sense, stem cell purification is similar to the purification of an enzyme, where the activity in the purified population can be expressed as a specific activity relative to the starting material. Before embarking on expensive and labor-intensive genomic studies, one should make every effort to arrive at such a statistically rigorous specific activity measure. With accurate relative enrichment values, it is possible to arrive at correlations between expression levels of genes and relative stem cell-specific activities in the purified cell populations. However, these correlations may alternatively reflect gene expression in copurifying contaminant cell populations not related to the actual stem cells. More will be said about this later.

Ideally, a stem cell population should be pure; that is, each cell in the purified population should be capable of sustained *in vivo* function. Is this a realistic goal? The answers to this question are complex. The only reliable measure of stem cell activity is by *in vivo* transplantation. The practical difficulties of introducing single purified cells into ablated whole animals are not trivial. Traditional studies have suggested that a "seeding factor" dictates that only a portion of transplanted stem cells assume hematopoietic function.[51] Generally, the seeding factor values hover around 10 to 20%. In other words, if only 1-in-5 to 1-in-10 single transplanted stem cells produces durable hematopoiesis, then with the seeding factor, this represents a homogeneously pure stem cell population. One study has suggested that transplanted stem cells assume hematopoietic function with absolute efficiency and no seeding factor complications.[52] This is an unresolved issue.

In general, studies in which quantitative assessments have been made suggest that the functional frequency of stem cell activity in most purified populations is approximately 1 in 10. In several cases, it has been shown that this frequency can be increased to 1 in 5.[47,53] Recently, unpublished results suggested a further improvement to 1 in 3 or 1 in 2. It is clear that the issue of absolute stem cell homogeneity has reached a state of diminishing returns and that the situation will not improve significantly. However, the actual situation is more complex. Other complications obscure the issue of stem cell purity. Among these, the exact experimental design of the *in vivo* transplantation assay is significant. Twofold or greater differences in experimentally measured stem cell purity can easily be consequences of the recipient system, the choice of "carrier," more mature hematopoietic cells, and other details. In addition, positive stem cell engraftment and resulting hematopoietic function can be defined in various ways. Some laboratories consider a 1% contribution to mature cell populations in a transplant recipient to be indicative of stem cell function; other investigators are more stringent and require a much higher level of contribution. Similarly, the accepted temporal durability of the donor-derived graft (as indicative of stem cell function) can vary among individual laboratories. These differences in assay systems and interpretations can complicate comparisons of genomic datasets between individual laboratories.

Given all of these uncertainties, it is of paramount importance to arrive at a set of standard biological criteria with which to evaluate the degree of stem cell enrichment, at least within a single laboratory, and to adhere to these criteria for all subsequent experiments. It is also important to measure the biological activity of each individual sample to be used for genomic studies. Some studies in which gene expression profiles have been defined for alleged hematopoietic stem cell populations simply accept physical criteria as demonstrative of stem cell content in the purified cell populations. This is not adequate, given the numerous studies that clearly show physical phenotype is not necessarily predictive of functional hematopoietic potential.[54–56]

Somewhat ironically, it is the very difficulty in assessing the absolute homogeneity of purified stem cells that provides a possible means to perform genomic studies reflective of actual stem cells. Over the years, many protocols have been developed to purify *in vivo* functional stem cells.[36,47,53,55–62] Some of these use very different physical purification parameters, ranging from cell surface marker distributions to vital dye retention/efflux properties. In addition, hematopoietic stem cells with similar functional activities can be isolated from different fetal and adult sources. These populations are comparable because they behave similarly in the context of the same recipient hosts. Because the fetal liver and the bone marrow have different bulk hematopoietic cell populations, it is likely that purified stem cells from these sources will have different contaminants. Direct genomic comparisons of fetal and adult hematopoietic stem cells, which have similar specific activity functional values, should filter out irrelevant noise components. A similar rationale applies to comparisons of stem cells from the same source but purified according to different physical parameters. The stem cell populations should contain similar degrees of biological activity and, ideally, should be purified by maximally different strategies. Care should be taken that the stem cell populations to be compared do not contain similar populations of non–stem cell entities. This is a significant issue given that many purification procedures do not adequately distinguish between true stem cells and at least some classes of primitive progenitor cells. In some purification strategies, this issue has been specifically addressed. However, in other purification methods, particularly the dye efflux-based procedures, this can be a complication depending on the exact parameters of the purification procedure.

A clear demonstration of stem cell enrichment without significant copurification of progenitor cells is dependent on the assay system. Specifically, stem cells are measured by *in vivo* transplantation, whereas progenitor cells are commonly defined by their ability to form colonies in stromal monolayer-supported and cytokine-supported culture systems.A problem arises because at least some true stem cells can also produce colonies in certain *in vitro* systems.[48,50] The exact relationship on a per cell basis between cells that proliferate *in vitro* and those that function *in vivo* is difficult to assess, although, in certain stromal-dependent systems, it is likely that the majority of *in vivo* transplantable stem cells will proliferate.[63] Therefore, to provide an accurate definition of stem cells versus progenitor cells, it is necessary to use purification procedures in which at least one cell population is capable of *in vitro* proliferation but not of *in vivo* function. Even here, complications can arise. For example, *in vitro* studies have shown that the ability of stem cells to function *in vivo* can fluctuate with the cell cycle. *In vivo* activity in these cultures displays a periodic behavior that correlates with the cell cycle stage.[64–66] Other studies suggest that the expression levels of the cell surface markers used to separate stem cells capable of durable *in vivo* function from transiently functional stem cells can fluctuate.[61,67,68] In some contexts, these molecules are positive markers of the most primitive stem cell; in others, they define a more committed cell population. The reasons for such fluctuations reflect stem cell activation status, although other factors may be important. Taken together, these considerations reinforce the necessity of careful quantitative evaluation of any given candidate stem cell population to be used for genomic analyses. They also suggest caution in designing the exact gene expression comparisons: true stem cells versus progenitor cells, true stem cells versus terminally mature cells, and numerous others. I will return to this issue.

As discussed previously, it may be possible to circumvent absolute stem cell homogeneity as a prerequisite for genomic analyses. However, there is a requirement, at least with certain genomic technologies, for a minimal absolute level of enrichment. This reflects the sensitivity of the technology used. For example, if the actual stem cell frequency in a starting cell population is only 1%, then a microarray strategy will not detect genes expressed in this minor cell population. If, on the other hand, the frequency is 10% or greater, then microarrays may be a reasonable technology. Other technologies, such as cDNA subtraction, may be applicable even to suboptimally enriched stem cell populations. The relative merits of different genomic technologies will be discussed in a subsequent section.

PROSPECTIVE DISSECTION OF THE HEMATOPOIETIC STEM–PROGENITOR CELL HIERARCHY

Ideally, a prospectively defined set of cell populations representative of all major compartments in the hematopoietic hierarchy is desirable. With such a well-ordered set of cell populations, it should be possible to monitor global changes in gene expression as a function of biological transitions in the hematopoietic hierarchy. Can such a set of cell populations be obtained? Although complicated by certain conceptual issues, a provisional lineage map defined by physically purified mouse bone marrow cell populations has been derived. In this map, the long-term *in vivo* functional stem cell is defined as Thy1lo Lin^- c-kit^+ Sca-1^+ (Flk-2^-).[59] Importantly, this rare cell population contains the only bone marrow cells capable of robust, durable *in vivo* function. A related, more abundant population with transient multilineage *in vivo* abilities is defined as Thy1lo Mac-1lo (negative for other Lin markers) c-kit^+ Sca-1^+.[69,70] This cell population is suggested to represent the immediate products of commitment decisions taken at the most primitive stem cell level. A third, even more numerous population with multilineage *in vivo* abilities is defined as Thy1lo Mac-1lo CD4lo Sca-1+ c-kit^+ (negative for other Lin markers). This cell population represents multipotent cells with limited self-renewal ability. It is important to stress that each of these cell populations has been assigned its exact biological activities in the context of the same *in vivo* assay system. Moreover, the precursor–product relationships of these three cell populations have been rigorously established.[69,70] Genomewide comparisons of gene expression in these three cell populations may provide insights into the molecular regulation of the self-renewal process. At least three other physical separation strategies have successfully segregated bone marrow populations with durable versus transient *in vivo* activities. The first strategy uses the ability of the most primitive stem cell to exclude or efflux the vital dye rhodamine. These two cell populations are defined as (Thy1lo) Lin^- c-kit^+ Sca-1^+ Rholo and (Thy1lo) Lin^- c-kit^+ Sca-1^+ rhohi, respectively.[55] The most primitive durable stem cells actively efflux this dye; less primitive transient stem cells retain this dye. A second, conceptually similar strategy uses the Hoechst vital dye in addition to, or in place of, rhodamine.[60,62,71] This strategy takes advantage of differential CD34 surface antigen expression on durable versus transient stem cells (see the previous cautionary note). Durable and transient stem cells are defined as Lin^- c-kit^+ Sca-1^+ $CD34^-$/lo, and Lin^- c-kit^+ Sca-1^+ $CD34^+$/hi, respectively.[47,53] A third purification strategy takes advantage of differential elutriation properties.[56–58] In essentially identical *in vivo* assay systems, the relative contents of stem cell activity in all of the previously mentioned cell populations are essentially the same. In all cases, the purifications segregate the durable from the transient *in vivo* activities. Both of these stem cell subsets have approximately the same spectrum of multilineage differentiation abilities. If (as seems reasonable) durable versus transient functional abilities represent differences in self-renewal potential, then all three purification strategies could be used in parallel to refine a molecular analysis of the self-renewal process.

Similar purification procedures have been developed to prospectively identify progenitor cell populations that have discrete subsets of the total differentiation potential in multipotent stem cells. The common lymphoid progenitor (CLP) and common myeloid progenitor (CMP) have been defined in the bone marrow.[72–75] A genomic comparison of these entities with multipotent stem cells would, in principle, shed light on the lineage commitment process. Prospectively isolated progenitors that are within several cell divisions of terminal maturation have also been defined.[76,77] The biological properties of these progenitor cells have been measured at the level of single cells, using a variety of *in vitro* culture systems. In the fetal hematopoietic hierarchy, the existence of CLPs and CMPs is still incompletely defined.[78,79]

IS THE HEMATOPOIETIC HIERARCHY COMPOSED OF DISCRETE CELLULAR STAGES?

So far, an unspoken assumption has been that the development of the hematopoietic system can be described as an ordered progression through a series of discrete and deterministic stages. These stages would have a distinct set of physical properties that facilitate their isolation. An additional assumption is that these stages represent irreversible developmental transitions. Finally, at least for committed progenitor cells, it is assumed that their complement of differentiation activities is revealed by the given *in vitro* culture systems. Although there is little doubt that the differentiation process is at least operationally irreversible after some period of time, in the post-Dolly era, this notion needs to be carefully reexamined. This is particularly important when considering the primitive cell compartments closely related to stem cells. Developmental reversibility or flexibility of apparently committed hematopoietic progenitor cells has been documented in mice carrying mutations of the Pax5 transcriptional regulator and in studies using immortalized progenitor cell lines.[80–83] In one particularly elegant study, a conditional deletion of Pax5 from pre–B-cells growing in culture further argues that developmental reversibility can occur even in cells traditionally considered to be far along in their differentiation.[84] Furthermore, it has been shown that CLP cells can be "converted" to produce myeloid progeny.[79] Whether such reversibility occurs *in vivo,* and if so, to what extent, are important questions. When designing genomic comparisons between closely related cell populations, these are important considerations. The previously mentioned fluctuation of biological properties may complicate the interpretation of gene expression results. For example, it could be that the observed nondurability of some transient stem cell populations is simply caused by their inability to lodge in an appropriate bone marrow niche that can nurture a self-renewal process. This could be because of differences in cell adhesion molecule expression levels; otherwise, these cells could be identical to their durably functional counterparts. Would it be reasonable to consider modulation of adhesion molecule expression as the molecular events responsible for a commitment versus a self-renewal decision? Would genomic comparisons in this situation provide fundamental insights into cell fate decision mechanisms? There are no simple answers to these questions.

The issue of whether the hematopoietic hierarchy can be described by physically discrete cell populations can also be considered on a philosophic level. Much literature suggests stochastic components in mechanisms responsible for hematopoietic cell fate decisions.[85–87] A consistent interpretation of the Hoxb4 transcriptional regulator's ability to enhance the developmental abilities of stem cells is that this molecule shifts a self-renewal probability function.[88,89] The possibility that self-renewal probabilities can change has been demonstrated in studies from the 1980s.[90] It has also been suggested that lineage partitions can be regulated by stochastic mechanisms.[91,92] The full implications of stochasticity in cell fate regulation are beyond the scope of this chapter. However, it should be kept in mind that if stochastic regulation is prevalent in the hematopoietic system, then it is most accurate to view the different "classes" of stem cells in terms of probabilistically distributed functional continua. It may be that only the extreme "ends" of such continua can be discretely isolated using conventional markers and physical properties. Functional continua may not be revealed by the assay systems used to measure the properties of these cells; however, it may complicate the interpretation of molecular data. When working with sizeable purified populations of stem cells, stochastic effects may be less problematic. In these cases, any molecular description of genetic programs would reflect an average stem cell state and would be of value. The relative functional homogeneity of the given population would be reflected by a consensus pattern in the global gene expression profile. However, if the goal is to use individual stem cells for gene expression analyses, then stochastic distributions become a significant problem.[93] An interesting analysis would be to compare gene expression patterns in single stem cells from a population that has a one-in-two or one-in-three ability for *in vivo* function. For example, if 10 distinct patterns of gene expression were defined in 10 individual stem cells, then one would have to question the existence of a distinct stem cell gene expression state. At this point, the issue of stem cell assay systems arises again. An alternate explanation for an observed diversity of gene expression patterns in a functionally homogeneous stem cell population might be that the precision of molecular analyses has outstripped the resolution of the *in vivo* assays. The discrete gene expression patterns might reflect subtle functional differences that cannot be discerned in a standard transplantation experiment. In spite of this complication, one would still expect that at least a substantial proportion of the gene expression patterns would correlate among the individual stem cells. Refinements in the temporal and quantitative resolution of *in vivo* assay systems will also be important. In particular, mathematically sound analyses and models of stem cell function should provide useful insights for defining distinct *in vivo* biological behaviors.[94] In summary, if the hematopoietic hierarchy can be accurately described by discrete biological stages, then gene expression profile "snapshots" for each stage will be adequate. However, if the stages exist as overlapping continua of developmental states, then an accurate description of gene expression patterns would need to take the form of a "movie," with continuous, rather than discrete, gene expression shifts.

MOLECULAR PARTS LIST OR GENOMIC STATE OF A STEM CELL: CONCEPTUAL ISSUES

Returning to the most primitive hematopoietic stem cell population, how useful would a genetic profile or molecular parts list of such cells be? Optimistically, such a parts list should set the stage for an eventual description and understanding of the molecular networks and mechanisms responsible for regulating stem cell fate decisions.[95,96] One would like to believe that the biological properties of the stem cell would be a function of the contents of the parts lists and of the architecture of their interacting assemblies. The biological nature of the stem cell "state" would be mirrored by the molecular, or gene expression state, and its global organization. In essence, one would like to understand the genetic "program" of a stem cell and how it runs. This presupposes that the behavior of stem cells is genetically determined and, at least to an extent, is "hardwired." As with all developmental processes, it is natural to assume that this is the case. Experimental evidence for such hardwiring in the hematopoietic system derives from clear, mouse strain-specific genetic variation in the functional properties of stem cells.[97–101] Recent data suggest that quantitative variations in the ability of single stem cells to produce myeloid and lymphoid progeny may also be hardwired.[102] In addition, at the level of transcription, many examples from genetic knockout and other experiments document the crucial roles of individual transcriptional regulators.[103,104]

What is the biological state of a stem cell as it might relate to a gene expression state? By its intrinsic abilities to balance self-renewal and commitment decisions, the state of a stem cell must be poised between at least two alternative fates.

for human stem cells, it is not clear that they measure the same population of cells that can be defined in the mouse.

As mentioned previously, a reliable global gene expression profile of hematopoietic stem cells will result from comparisons of datasets obtained from numerous independent efforts that use different stem cell purification procedures, as well as different profiling strategies. Although this collective effort is incomplete, it is clear that at least a provisional molecular definition of mouse hematopoietic stem cells is available. This provisional definition will need to be substantially refined. For a biologist, the amount of gene expression data appears large, but to a statistician, even the most extensive existing genomic analyses of stem cells have exceedingly sparse data. This is an important point because one aspect of collecting datasets suitable for sophisticated statistical and pattern extraction techniques will be extensive repetition and replication of studies already performed. This will require discipline to resist moving on to what may seem to be more interesting studies without completing an adequate molecular definition.

The first global definition of a stem cell molecular parts list was obtained for mouse fetal liver hematopoietic stem cells using high-throughput sequencing of a subtracted cDNA library.[144] The library was constructed from stem cells defined as AA4.1$^+$ Lin$^-$ c-kit$^+$ Sca-1$^+$ and was depleted of gene products expressed in terminally differentiated AA4.1$^-$ cells. Therefore, the resulting dataset contains gene products preferentially expressed in stem cells and possibly in primitive progenitor cells. Several thousand previously assigned and novel gene products were identified. A preliminary comparison to gene expression in bone marrow stem cells was performed; it suggested a high degree of molecular similarity between fetal and adult stem cells. These studies relied extensively on sophisticated bioinformatics techniques to facilitate the "mining" of the sequence data. An innovative aspect of these efforts was the creation of the Stem Cell Database (SCDb) as an online, interactive resource containing all of the raw data as well as the results of the analyses (http://stemcell.princeton.edu). SCDb also contains a large volume of functional data documenting the properties of the stem cell populations used for molecular studies. The integration of functional, cellular, and genomic information within a single resource will permit a quantitative mapping to relate biological properties to potential regulatory mechanisms. Access to SCDb is unrestricted, and it has been visited by thousands of individuals. SCDb is designed to be an evolving resource and will incorporate datasets from numerous independent stem cell genomics and functional genomics efforts. To date, SCDb contains approximately 8000 nonredundant cDNA clusters assembled from about 40,000 individual sequenced clones. The subtracted sequence sets in SCDb include collections from bone marrow Rholo Lin$^-$ c-kit$^+$ Sca-1$^+$ cells and Rholo Holo Lin$^-$ c-kit$^+$ Sca-1$^+$ cells. Different molecular comparisons—for example, between stem cells and mature cells or between durable stem cells and transient stem cells or progenitor cells—are also included in SCDb.

Complementary datasets included in SCDb derive from more recent oligonucleotide microarray-based analyses of stem cells and other stages in the hematopoietic hierarchy.[145] These microarray studies represent the first in-depth comparisons of mouse fetal liver and adult bone marrow stem cells and provide a "signature" genomic profile common to these two sources of stem cells. Additionally, a comparison of mouse and human stem cells has shown that a large proportion (approximately 40%) of the stem cell signature is conserved. Extensive standard and real-time reverse transcriptase-polymerase chain reaction analyses have confirmed the microarray observations. Because these studies use commercially available microarrays representative of most murine and human genes, they also provide molecular signatures for more committed stages of the hierarchy. It is possible to correlate these signatures with similarities and differences among the biological properties characteristic of each developmental stage. For example, molecular components shared between durable and transient stem cells might be involved in the maintenance of multipotentiality, but those that are not shared might play differential roles in the self-renewal process.

A valuable feature of SCDb is the ability to compare datasets obtained in different laboratories or by different genomic approaches. Microarray analyses of hematopoietic stem cells isolated by the Hoechst efflux side population (SP) procedure have been reported.[147] A 60% overlap with the bone marrow stem cell signature explained previously can be demonstrated. Although these types of comparisons are only the beginning, their value in refining a stem cell parts lists is already apparent.

Many other global genomic studies focused on hematopoietic stem cells have been reported.[146,148,160–164] Each of these has unique features. One study attempted to combine stem cell genomic analyses with mouse strain-specific genetic variations in stem cell properties.[161] Others provided transcriptome data from stem cells as well as committed lymphoid and myeloid progenitors.[146] A third study provided a comparison of gene expression in hematopoietic and neural stem or progenitor cells.[164] Finally, a correlative analysis of gene expression in stem cells as a function of biological fluctuations has been performed.[162] Of great interest will be direct comparisons among the different datasets. Unfortunately, at this point, it is not trivial to readily compare datasets derived according to different genomic technology platforms. This is a general problem, and there are efforts to address it. Ultimately, global gene expression profiles of hematopoietic stem cells will need to be correlated to quantitative contents of biological activities in the purified cell populations. Just as retrospectively and prospectively characterized stem cell properties can display a one-to-one mapping, a similar mapping of gene expression profiles with stem cell properties should be an attainable goal. For example, distinct hematopoietic stem cell populations that contain the same relative level of *in vivo* activity should share a core panel of expressed gene products.

CURRENT STATUS OF MOLECULAR PARTS LISTS FROM NONHEMATOPOIETIC STEM CELLS

It is likely that consensus genomic parts lists correlated with distinct stages of the hematopoietic hierarchy will soon be available. How far along are similar efforts in other stem cell systems? A clear answer to this question is difficult. A major problem is the lack of sufficiently rigorous methods for retrospective and prospective definitions of nonhematopoietic stem cell populations. In particular, the segregation of stem cells and progenitor cells has been problematic. With few exceptions, *in vivo* transplantation systems to measure the durable or transient clonogenic properties of candidate stem cell populations are not available. When it is possible to perform transplantations, the resolution of the particular systems does not permit an accurate measure of biological function on a per cell basis.

Prospective bulk isolation procedures for candidate stem cells in the central and peripheral nervous systems, the skin, and the liver have been described.[23–26,165–167] However, it is not possible to state with any certainty that these cell populations share the spectrum of biological properties characteristic of their hematopoietic counterparts. Certain candidate stem cell populations have been defined by their ability to proliferate *in vitro*. For example, neurosphere-initiating cells have been equated to neural stem cells. However, the exact relationship between these cells has not been established. A second, instructive example of these complications comes from the epidermal stem cell area. Recently, a quantitative *in vivo* competitive repopulation assay for these cells has been developed. With this assay, the frequency of these cells has been measured at 1 in about 10 to 30,000, a value close to the frequency of hematopoietic stem cells and much lower than previous estimates.[168]

It has been suggested that the ability to retain low levels of Hoechst dye may be a generic physical property of most, if not all, stem cells. If this were rigorously demonstrated, then the SP purification procedure would be applicable to stem cell compartments of many tissues.[60] More extensive studies will clarify this issue. Although bulk purifications of nonhematopoietic stem cells are not sufficiently developed, in some cases, the anatomical geography of a tissue permits the identification of the stem cell compartment. This is true for the intestine, the hair follicle, and the skin. A geographical organization also permits the identification of intermediate and terminally mature differentiation stages. Laser capture technology could be used to isolate various cell populations. A recent study used laser capture for a genomic analysis of intestinal stem cells, and similar studies can be expected.[169] The identification of label-retaining nonrapidly cycling cells in the skin is also a promising approach to defining the stem cell population.[170] With respect to distinct anatomical geography and slow cell cycling status, there are similarities with the hematopoietic system.[171,172] In this regard, it will be important to determine the biological, cellular, and molecular properties of stem cell niches or microenvironments. One genomic effort to define the hematopoietic stem cell microenvironment has produced an analog of SCDb, the Stromal Cell DataBase (StroCDB). Similar to SCDb, StroCDB (http://stromalcell.princeton.edu) is a comprehensive and unrestricted online resource.[173]

Genomic analyses using nonhematopoietic stem or progenitor cells are only beginning. Two of these compared gene expression profiles in hematopoietic, neural (neurosphere), and embryonic stem cells.[145,147] Similarly, a comparison of gene expression in prospectively isolated neural stem cells and ES cells has been reported.[165] One study compared gene expression in cultured undifferentiated and differentiated neural progenitors.[174] As mentioned previously, a genomic profile of intestinal stem cells has been reported.[169] Comprehensive microarray analyses of embryos and ES cells are also under way.[175] The near future will certainly bring many similar analyses.

Although these issues may complicate comparative analyses designed to reveal such a generic stem cell molecular signature, it may also be that the expectation of global and extensive similarities in the biological properties of stem cells from different tissues is partially naive. Without extensive documented biological similarities, there would be little reason to expect extensive conservation of molecular profiles. To illustrate this point, the reasons that hematopoietic stem cells are endowed with remarkable self-renewal abilities are their rare frequency and their requisite rate of mature cell production. When the frequencies of tissue-specific stem cells are higher, a much lower degree of self-renewal potential may be adequate. The self-renewal activity of such stem cells may resemble that of hematopoietic progenitor cells. The most relevant genomic comparisons of stem cells or progenitors from different tissues will be difficult to determine in the absence of consensus biological definitions for the distinct developmental stages of each stem cell system.

Two studies mentioned previously have defined a molecular signature or "stemness" profile of several hundred gene products shared by hematopoietic, neural, and ES cells.[145,147] On the surface, the cell populations used in the two studies are similar, but there is a disappointingly small degree of gene sequence overlap. A careful comparison of the experimental details specific to these two studies reveals numerous differences at many levels—most importantly, in the actual cell populations, representative of the different stem cell populations, and in the computational tools used to analyze the data. Only one of the two studies used hematopoietic stem cells with exactly defined biological properties.[145] As explained previously, when the comparisons are restricted to *bona fide* stem cells, the two datasets are similar. Does this mean that a core set of "generic" stem cell regulatory mechanisms reflected by shared sets of gene products exist and can be defined? This is a complex question, and, on one level, the answer is clearly yes. Abundant evidence, some mentioned previously, has implicated the same signaling pathways regulating the properties of distinct stem cell populations. However, it must be stressed that these shared pathways may simply represent triggering modules used to activate different genetic programs. These genetic programs may well be specific to distinct stem cells.

On another level, it is important to ask if direct, gene sequence–based comparisons are adequate to reveal mechanistic similarities. A biological process–based or pathways-based comparative strategy may be more appropriate. One example of this is the comparison of Wnt pathway components among different stem cell populations. The individual components of this pathway are often encoded by members of multigene families. Thus, each type of stem cell may express a unique Frizzled Wnt receptor, a unique Tcf/Lef downstream transcriptional regulator, a unique Wnt ligand, and unique individual members of protein families that represent other components of the pathway. Clearly, an intact functional Wnt pathway can be shared, yet this would not necessarily be revealed by exact sequence homology comparisons. Similarly, different stem cell populations could be compared with respect to global cellular processes, such as the cell cycle, apoptosis, or chromatin remodeling. In all of these, multiple individual gene products can serve similar functions in overall regulation. It is important to reiterate the danger of ascribing, for example, specific self-renewal control functions to molecules that constitute the more generic cellular context within which self-renewal occurs. A useful strategy would be to identify stem cell–specific gene products that represent "interfaces" with general cellular contexts. An elegant example of this approach is the recent identification of Nucleostemin, a molecule expressed preferentially in stem cells and a likely component of cell cycle control machinery.[176]

ASSEMBLING THE MOLECULAR PARTS OF A STEM CELL INTO REGULATORY NETWORKS

Of what value would a complete molecular definition of stem cells be? On the one hand, the answer is straightforward because of the numbers of gene products that will emerge as appropriate candidates for experimental manipulation. Indeed, early efforts to define stem cell–specific gene products have yielded important functional insights into hematopoietic biology.[177–179] From a deeper point of view, an answer to this question is more complex and requires a more global outlook.

A complete description of the molecular parts list of a stem cell sets the stage for efforts to assemble the individual parts into interacting genetic programs or networks. These types of efforts are at the core of post–genome systems biology and have been undertaken in a variety of biological systems. It is worth considering such efforts and what we can learn from them. A key point is that it is not possible to understand the workings of a complex system solely by the definition and analysis of individual parts. In hematopoietic stem cell biology, a good example of this point is the mouse W-mutant.[180] The hematopoietic stem cell population in these mutants is compromised. Much is known about the molecular biology of W-mutants; the genetic lesions have been shown to reside in the receptor tyrosine kinase c-kit locus, many biochemical details of c-kit kinase signaling are known, and provisional signaling pathways are beginning to be elucidated.[181] It is tempting to say, therefore, that the nature of the stem cell defect in the W-mutant is fairly well understood. Yet, on a deeper level, the question of why stem cells deficient in c-kit are also compromised in their functional abilities remains almost completely unanswered. It is unlikely that the answer will come from continued analyses of c-kit kinase substrates, static signaling pathway organization, or an identification of the genomic targets controlled by the c-kit pathway. What will be necessary is a global perspective that somehow links the dynamic function of an entire signaling pathway to its ultimate biological outcome. There are no complete answers to these types of questions, even in biological systems as traditionally well defined as bacteriophage lambda. However, there are several pioneering examples in which this type of thinking has provided novel, and often unexpected, insights into developmental processes. Some of these are briefly described in the following section.

After infecting a bacterium, phage lambda makes a decision to replicate, and eventually lyse the host, or to insert its DNA into the host chromosome, and assume the (temporary) status of a benign parasite. The molecular machinery responsible for this cell fate choice is better defined than almost any other biological system and constitutes a genetic switch. The workings of this switch from the level of individual molecules activating and repressing gene expression to the ultimate biological outcome are beginning to be understood through an integrative approach that combines traditional molecular experimentation with computational modeling efforts.[182,183] It may seem that an analogy from prokaryotic biology is a far stretch in terms of relevance to stem cells. However, genetic switches are precisely that, and they will be implemented using similar components and conceptual paradigms wherever they occur in the biological realm. In addition, cell fate choices made by stem cells represent the outcomes of molecular decision processes that must be controlled at some level by switch-like circuits. On a philosophical note, it is relevant to ask precisely where in a genetic network the decision resides. Regarding stem cells, one can ask, for example, where the apparent irreversibility of a commitment decision resides.

Recent studies in which the properties of genetic networks have been explored include more directly relevant eukaryotic systems. In Drosophila, the circuits regulating segmentation, morphogen signaling, circadian rhythms, EGF-receptor signaling, and the Notch lateral inhibition process have been extensively explored.[184–188] In all of these, the parts lists, as well as circuit architectures, were defined through genetic techniques. Functional interactions among the individual parts were defined by epistasis and other approaches. True insights into how such regulatory circuits may function to produce biological results were obtained through the integration of genetic and molecular techniques with computational approaches. The latter allows one to model how a circuit functions in space and time and in ways impossible to ascertain by intuition alone. Several excellent review articles have been published that describe both the overall and the detailed aspects of such integrated approaches.[1–3,182,189–197]

There is a tradition of modeling in biology; however, what distinguishes the more recent studies is their focus on using biologically "real" and empirically determined parameters in the construction of the individual models. Recent studies have applied a similar overall approach to the p53 tumor suppressor regulatory circuit, NF kappa B signaling and vertebrate somitogenesis.[198–201] These kinds of efforts are not limited to transcriptional regulatory circuits; they have also focused on biochemical signaling circuits such as the mitogen-activated protein kinase pathway, bacterial chemotaxis, and the cell cycle.[195,202–204] More extensive efforts that incorporate signaling circuit analysis with cellular architecture are being pursued in the area of lymphocyte antigen recognition and response.[205]

These are interesting examples; however, it is not obvious how to proceed in a similar manner in the area of stem cell biology. Elegant analyses that more directly affect stem cells are efforts to describe and understand tissue specification during sea urchin development. In this organism, there is no ability for high-throughput, standard genetic approaches; therefore, the tools are directly related to those used in genomic studies of mammalian stem cells. A provisional genetic network that regulates sea urchin endomesoderm specification was assembled using a combination of global differential gene expression screens, extensive *in situ* hybridization studies, perturbation analyses using antisense techniques, and identification of candidate genetic regulatory DNA sequences by interspecies comparisons.[1,190,206] These are all technologies available in mammalian stem cell research. To underscore the relevance of these studies, a similar integrative strategy has yielded a provisional regulatory network for T-cell development in the mouse.[207,208] In both the sea urchin and the lymphoid systems, the provisional regulatory networks are not yet complete. However, even in their present states, they provide a valuable road map that can suggest the most prudent course for further experimentation. The results from these experiments can then be used to refine the existing networks. It is precisely this type of interplay between model building and experimentation that will become increasingly important to gain an understanding of complex biological phenomena.

What have these types of network studies contributed to an understanding of biological phenomena? In particular, do any of the insights suggest mechanistic paradigms for phenomena well described in stem cells? One prevalent feature uncovered in many networks is their robustness, or relative resistance to perturbations in individual components.[186–189,195,202,209] One might clearly imagine that such robustness would be a desirable property of stem cell regulatory mechanisms, particularly in systems such as the blood, the skin, or the intestine, where the proliferative output is extremely large. Given that at least certain tumors result from alterations in the regulation of stem cells, it is highly likely that these self-renewing cells are regulated by "buffered" robust regulatory mechanisms.[210] It is clear that the property of robustness emerges from the architecture and the dynamics of networks, rather than from individual network components. Hematopoietic, and possibly other, stem cells must also be able to respond in distinct ways to different physiological demands. This necessitates that stem cell regulatory mechanisms must be flexible in addition to being robust. Interestingly, the topological organization of many networks can accommodate such an apparently paradoxical situation. The overall topology can yield a perturbation resistant system; individual, highly connected nodes can serve to rapidly and dramatically shift global network properties.[211–213] Stem cells may also need to respond in an all-or-none manner to certain demands and in a graded, rheostat-like manner to others. Similarly, the system may need to "remember" its previous history of activity. Signaling networks can exhibit such a range of properties. As mentioned in a previous section, there is evidence for a strong stochastic component to certain stem cell fate decisions. Stochastic mechanisms imply an ability to amplify low amounts of noise to suprathreshold levels to yield a change in a system's state. Certain architectures and dynamic properties can produce such noise-based, stochastic switches.[214–216]

How is one to proceed in assembling candidate genetic networks responsible for stem cell regulation? Gene expression profiles characteristic of distinct developmental stages in a stem and progenitor cell hierarchy will necessarily play important roles. They provide the parts lists, and by correlation with successive developmentally related cellular entities and functions, they give an idea of the genomic shifts that may be responsible for cell fate decisions. It is important to realize, however, that these are steady-state, static portraits of intrinsically dynamic processes. As such, they may be developmentally far removed from the gene expression changes that mediate the actual cell fate decisions. What is necessary is an ability to monitor gene expression changes as they occur with changes in the cell fates. This raises the important issue of how an actual alteration in the developmental fate of a cell can be recognized. As with other issues complicated by retrospective versus prospective definitions, there are no simple solutions to the conundrum that a cell's fate or potential activity can, to date, only be determined by what it can produce in the appropriate assay systems. At the least, it will be crucial to embark on gene expression analyses in well-defined populations as they are induced to change in controlled settings. Clearly, this is not possible *in vivo*, and therefore, these efforts will require defined *in vitro* systems. Ideally, such a system should facilitate the controlled generation of an entire stem and progenitor cell hierarchy, starting with homogeneous stem cells. In the hematopoietic system, there have been numerous efforts to expand stem cells and various progenitor classes in both cytokine- and stromal monolayer-supported cultures. Although some reasonable degree of *ex vivo* stem cell expansion has recently been achieved using defined growth factor combinations, these efforts suffer from the complication that expansion is accompanied by vigorous and possibly random generation of more committed progenitor cell populations. Therefore, the expanded stem cells lose the advantage of purity and resemble the mixed populations representative of the entire primitive portion of the hematopoietic hierarchy.

One attractive system for the establishment of the hematopoietic hierarchy from highly purified stem cells is dependent on the AFT024 supportive stromal cell line.[63,173] Not only is the input stem cell activity (measurable by *in vivo* transplantation) qualitatively and quantitatively maintained for prolonged periods, but more committed primitive progenitor populations are produced and dramatically expanded. These progenitor populations are heterogeneous in terms of their myeloid and lymphoid potentials. Thus, during the culture period, the starting stem cell populations become numerically minor.

It should be feasible to monitor changes in stem cell gene expression profile over time, and any changes would effectively correlate with the loss of net stem cell activity in the whole population. Several studies have shown that single, prospectively isolated, hematopoietic stem cells can display limited clonal growth supported by defined cytokine combinations without complete loss of their undifferentiated state.[48,50] It is also possible to use vital dyes to monitor the division history of cultured stem cells.[217] With this technology, correlations could be established among changes in biological properties, gene expression profiles, and cell division. It should be possible to define molecular and cell fate changes that have occurred during the course of a single cell cycle. It would be useful to begin with stem cells labeled with fluorescent proteins expressed from stem cell-specific transcriptional regulatory regions. Such approaches have been elegantly employed in the ES cell system. For example, fluorescent proteins have been expressed in the context of the Oct-4 locus, whose activity is required for self-renewal and is down-regulated with differentiation. It seems, in summary, that carefully controlled, high-resolution *in vitro* systems to measure changes in stem cell gene expression as these cells lose their stem cell functional properties are both possible and feasible. A cell cycle-dependent periodicity of stem cell functional abilities has been mentioned previously. Therefore, these types of experiments will need to be designed and evaluated with great care.

A major goal of these dynamic studies is to measure gene expression changes as they occur precisely with biological alterations. This critically depends on the quantitative measurement of the latter. For hematopoietic stem cells (with the caveats discussed previously), this is feasible in quantitative *in vivo* transplantation designs. In the context of the previously mentioned experiments, loss of net stem cell activity would be straightforward to document. It is nevertheless important to keep in mind that failure to read out an *in vivo* assay may not reflect a developmental cell fate change. The other side of the coin, measuring the production of primitive committed progenitors destined for subsets of hematopoietic lineages, represents a more difficult situation. The main problem is that in most, if not all, *in vitro* systems, such cell populations are heterogeneous. A loss of gene expression characteristics can represent the commitment process; however, positive gene expression changes that may act to control commitment to distinct primitive compartments would not be easily detectable. Clearly, accurate measurements of both negative and positive gene expression state changes are necessary for a complete description of a developmental system. A solution to this problem would be the availability of "commitment reporter" mice with fluorescent proteins, such enhanced green fluorescent protein (EGFP) expressed by progenitor cells immediately after their specification. Animals with reporters expressed by promoters whose expression correlates with late stages of lineage-specific differentiation, although useful otherwise, are not necessarily appropriate for these purposes.[218,219] The definition of gene expression profiles characteristic of transient multipotent stem cells, as well as the common lymphoid or myeloid progenitor cells, should yield appropriate regulatory regions. For example, one would like to identify genes whose expression is transient in the common lymphoid progenitor and is not found in their more committed progeny dedicated to the individual B- or T-cell lineages. The neural and ES cell systems offer useful examples of reporter animals that use the regulatory regions of nestin, Sox2, and brachyury as tools to identify postspecification neural and mesodermal precursors.[165,220] In the hematopoietic system, EGFP expressed from the Rag1 locus may be a useful reporter for commitment to lymphoid lineages, although it continues to be expressed at later stages.[221] As gene products specifically expressed in the most primitive stem cells are identified, the generation of reporter mice where a fluorescent marker is turned off as a consequence of commitment should be possible. Ultimately, compound transgenic animals in which combinations of fluorescent colors simultaneously define gains and losses of various developmental properties will be most useful.

The availability of commitment reporter mice would allow one to address several important questions. For example, there exist fluorescent protein variants that change their emission spectrum color as a function of time after their initial synthesis.[222] An outstanding question in stem cell biology is, when a developmental commitment state or decision is irreversibly "locked in," is there a time window after initiation of the commitment process during which the cell retains flexibility? It may be possible to ask how soon after a commitment reporter gene is turned on the actual commitment decision occurs by isolating color variant cells and measuring their biological properties. A prediction from studies with cell lines is that differentiation processes proceed through transient states with "mixed" patterns of gene expression.[81,223] It will be important to define similar kinetics in primary cells. In addition, recent modeling studies suggest that kinetics, rather than steady-state expression levels, may be critical in mediating changes in cell fates. These observations underscore the necessity of high-resolution and well-defined approaches to analyzing the dynamics of gene expression profile alterations as a function of changes in biological properties.

Temporally ordered changes in global gene expression, or in the expression of other molecular species, can be used to infer functional connectivity. Mathematical and computational tools for this can be co-opted from engineering disciplines.[224,225] In biology, this is a vigorous and exciting area of research. The underlying logic is simple to intuit and relies on the cascade-like organization of many biological processes and systems. Other approaches to infer network connectivity rely on a combination of controlled system perturbations and computational techniques.[226–228] For example, in yeast, systematic perturbation combined with genomic and proteomic analyses has been applied to the galactose metabolic pathway.[229] A particularly elegant study in yeast that analyzes global transcriptional regulation takes advantage of tagged transcription factors and selective identification of DNA-binding targets. In this and other cases, the controlled perturbations are represented by collections of yeast strains, where each transcription factor (one per strain) carries an epitope tag, or where each gene is deleted and replaced by a "bar code" tag.[230, 231]

Clearly, these types of studies are not yet feasible in mammalian stem cell systems. Nevertheless, it should be possible to approach a similar level of resolution by other means. One extremely promising technology is inhibitory RNA (RNAi).[232] By judicious choice of oligonucleotides and target sequences, it appears possible to substantially down-regulate the expression level of any chosen gene product. Moreover, it is feasible to deliver the inhibitory molecules using standard retroviral or lentiviral technology. Several recent studies provide proof of principle for the feasibility of this strategy in stem cell systems.[233–235] Conceptually, this approach is similar to the use of antisense strategies in organisms such as the zebra fish. Using pseudo-typed, high-titer lentiviral vectors, it is fairly straightforward to genetically modify entire populations of purified hematopoietic stem cells. These vectors are not prone to silencing phenomena, and therefore, it should be possible to coordinately down-regulate the expression of numerous stem cell genes in at least a semi–high-throughput manner. The development of inducible RNAi vectors will provide a further level of control and resolution. Needless to say, gain-of-function high-throughput approaches are also feasible with the lentivirus systems, in particular with inducible vector designs.

An ability to down-regulate (or up-regulate) panels of gene products may have important conceptual advantages over the more traditional germ line knockout strategies. In a standard knockout animal, the given gene product is absent during the entire developmental period. Therefore, if the mutation has a subtle phenotype, it is not possible to tell whether the gene product is largely disposable for a given process or the system has adapted to its absence by putting into play compensatory mechanisms. In the numerous knockout strategies that permit conditional deletions, this complication is avoided. It is difficult to target the conditional mutation event to a stem or progenitor cell population, although the human CD34 and mouse Scl transcriptional regulatory elements may provide useful transgenic approaches for targeted mutagenesis.[236,237] As the various genomic analyses of stem cells progress, other appropriate transcriptional elements are likely to emerge. There may also be advantages to quantitatively down-regulating genes, rather than deleting them entirely. Self-renewal versus differentiation regulation in ES cells is exquisitely sensitive to the quantitative amount of the Oct-4 transcriptional regulator. Similarly, the PU.1 transcriptional regulator alternately promotes macrophage or B-cell development in a dose-dependent manner, and subtle changes in transcription factor amounts appear to mediate the development of eosinophils versus macrophages.[238–240] In these cases, and likely in many others, it may be more informative to modulate the quantitative levels of regulatory factors.

In contemplating semi–high-throughput loss or gain-of-function approaches, a crucial decision must be made as to which panel of gene products should be chosen for perturbations in stem cells. There is no correct or incorrect decision; however, there are some ideas that will facilitate the definition of regulatory networks. It seems reasonable that transcriptional regulators and chromatin-modifying proteins would represent suitable targets. By systematically targeting these gene families, it should be possible to at least approximate a description of which regulators regulate others. The outcomes of such analyses could play important roles in assembling networks, such as those for sea urchin or T-cell development. The latter is particularly important because it already provides a framework within which to evaluate the effectiveness of particular approaches. In addition, much work has defined roles for transcriptional regulators such as Gata2, PU.1, Ikaros, Pax5, and Hoxb4 in primitive aspects of hematopoietic development.[82,88,103,104,208,241] These would provide important starting points, with possible predicted results. Stem cells isolated from the W-series of mutants may be useful, given the wide range of severity observed with different alleles. Functional alterations in stem cells have been defined in p21cip1/waf1 and p27Kip1 cell cycle regulator mutants.[114,115] The analysis of these mutants may provide important insights into the coupling of stem cell properties with cell cycle regulatory networks. The representation of known cell-signaling pathway components can also be analyzed in stem cell genomic profiles. Components that are preferentially expressed in primitive cells would be good candidates for perturbation experiments. The architectural features of biological networks may also suggest good starting points—in particular, highly connected nodes in signaling pathways or nodes in which several pathways intersect. As with other issues discussed previously, any perturbation studies will rely on the resolution of the biological assays. With this is mind, all of the suggested tools, such as reporter mice, would be of great importance.

Several recent reports present interesting computational methods that may be useful in extracting functional network connectivity patterns from gene perturbation experiments.[225–227] Although these methods have generally been applied in model or simple systems, they suggest some exciting possibilities. Foremost of these is that it may not be necessary to perform vast numbers of individual gene perturbations to dramatically narrow the range of possible network architectures. In a modeling study, the reported algorithms successfully extracted the previously defined Drosophila segmentation network architecture from a vast number of possibilities in the simulations. Therefore, there is hope that similar approaches will be useful in complex developmental systems.

Because many properties of stem cells will be under the control of numerous regulatory gene products, perturbations of individual gene products may not be an optimal experimental strategy. A similar situation is encountered in many human disease traits, where simple Mendelian segregation has not identified clear-cut causal genetic loci. It would be useful to identify all genes (and only those genes) whose expression correlates with a given genetically defined biological property. An approach termed *genetical genomics* has recently been proposed, in which genetic segregation of a given trait is analyzed in conjunction with global gene expression profiles.[242] Each gene product on a microarray is considered a Mendelian trait, and its expression levels are correlated with traits that segregate during standard genetic crosses. In this way, it is possible to identify panels of genes regulated in trans by a given genetic locus, as well as those that map directly to that locus. A recent study in yeast illustrates the power of this approach.[243] In the area of stem cells, the genetical genomics approach is beginning to be used to understand mouse strain-specific differences in stem cell number and proliferative status. Standard quantitative trait locus genetic studies using recombinant inbred (RI) lines of mice generated from two parental strains that differ in stem cell properties have identified several candidate genetic loci.[244] More recently, the genetic analyses have been combined with global genomic studies.[161] The elegance of this approach resides in the combination of retrospective and prospective measurement of stem cell properties, mouse genetics, and genomewide expression analyses. It is straightforward to combine the genetical genomics strategy to the numerous other high-throughput studies of gene expression in stem cells. For example, the expression levels of genes in the stem cell, or in the progenitor cell signature datasets described previously, could be examined in the series of RI strains with defined differences in stem and progenitor cell properties.

Building Artificial Regulatory Circuits in Stem Cells

This chapter has focused on "top down" approaches to define regulatory networks in stem cells. It is also possible that important questions can be addressed using a complementary "bottom up" strategy. In the end, both avenues will be synergistic. It can be stated, perhaps a bit naively, that a true understanding of biological regulation will enable the *de novo* construction of regulatory mechanisms in these cells from defined components.[2] These regulatory "constructs" would function in similar ways to the endogenous switches that mediate cell fate choices. Not only would this permit a detailed exploration of the many parameters that dictate switch functions; in addition, this reverse engineering approach would have a profound affect on the clinical use of stem cells.[245] Bottom-up reverse engineering of regulatory circuits in stem cell will require several things. First, the candidate gene products that regulate the various cell fate choices will need to be identified. It is anticipated that this will be one of the outcomes of the ongoing genomic studies. It is likely, given results from other biological systems, that such regulators will be identified. Two pertinent examples are the Oct-4 and Nanog gene products that play crucial roles in regulating self-renewal in ES cells. Importantly, the Nanog gene product appears near the top of published lists of gene products characteristic of undifferentiated ES cells. Second, it will be necessary to have a firm knowledge of how different functional characteristics of switching circuits can be implemented. This is true on both the theoretical level and the practical level. On the theoretical level, many years of work have defined the various ways in which switches that display bistability, toggle, continuous input, hysteresis, noise resistance, and other basic properties can be implemented. In general, the successful design of such switches employs a judicious use of positive and negative feedback loops. Given the switch-like nature of many cell fate decisions, it is perhaps not surprising that feedback circuits abound in biology.

Several excellent review articles targeting biologists have summarized the basic principles of switch circuit design.[246,247] From a practical point of view, it is important to understand the biochemical and molecular nature of the actual components from which such regulatory circuits need to be constructed. It is also important to keep in mind that because the constructed circuits will be required to function inside living cells, it will not be possible to take into account all of the parameters that may influence successful designs. Therefore, the circuits designed from first engineering principles will likely require extensive *in vivo* optimization and fine-tuning. Artificial circuit design in living cells is a new discipline. Nevertheless, there have been several dramatic successes that provide useful paradigms. For example, bistable toggle switches, noise-resistant switches, noise-amplifying switches, and oscillators have been implemented from well-characterized prokaryotic transcriptional regulatory components.[192–195,215,246,248] There have also been interesting studies in which biological logic-gate decision circuits have been implemented in living cells.[249,250] In most cases, these have been implemented in bacteria; however, there are examples in yeast and mammalian cells.[214,251,252] In principle, therefore, it should be feasible to consider similar implementations in stem cells.

It seems clear that to attempt a bottom-up construction of cell fate switches in hematopoietic stem cells is still premature. The ES cell system, although not necessarily representative of true stem cells, seems ready for such efforts. Self-renewal in ES cells is regulated by a well-characterized signaling pathway activated by leukemia inhibitory factor. In addition, three necessary transcriptional regulators—Stat3, Oct-4, and Nanog—have been defined; each is necessary for the maintenance of the undifferentiated state. ES cells are easy to propagate and genetically modify. RNAi technology could be used to down-regulate the expression of the endogenous regulators. These could be replaced by the introduction of the same regulators with silent mutations that render them immune to the RNAi effects. The exogenous regulators would be introduced in inducible or repressible contexts controlled by artificial switching components. In essence, it should be possible to "replace" an endogenous regulatory circuit or network with an engineered circuit that contains the biologically relevant cell fate regulating proteins in artificially controllable contexts. Ultimately, it should be possible to construct networks in which each molecular node can be rapidly activated or inactivated at the protein level—for example, by using estrogen receptor fusions or artificial dimerization techniques. Such strategies are beginning to be applied to hematopoietic regulation.[253,254] These would be powerful systems in which to address fundamental questions relevant to self-renewal versus commitment decision making.

What kinds of information can be expected from engineering stem cell regulatory circuits? Many open issues involve the kinetics with which a decision occurs. How long must a signal be active to mediate the decision? Can the signal be removed for a period of time and subsequently reinstated without a loss of biological properties? Is it possible to directly demonstrate that a stochastic switch can yield deterministic cell fate outcomes? How do graded amounts of a signal influence the biological outcome, or how does an analogue signal yield a digital response? How are multiple signal inputs integrated to produce distinct biological outcomes? When multipotent stem cells begin to differentiate, do they progress through discrete intermediate stages in an obligate manner, or can these cells directly produce single lineages of mature cells? For example, must hematopoietic stem cells always progress through the CLP or CMP stages in producing lymphoid or myeloid cell populations? Very little information concerning these issues is available in the stem cell field; however, there are promising signs of progress.[255,256]

Road Forward for Stem Cell Biology

Modern biological research brings surprises at every turn. Therefore, it is dangerous to speculate in detail about what will be possible in stem cell research. Nevertheless, several areas are worth thinking about and are ripe for the initiation of pilot experimental efforts. The first and perhaps most important of these is the integration of stem cells with their microenvironments, or *niches,* as a unified experimental system. Developmental cell fate decisions rely on the complex interplay of cell-autonomous and instructive regulatory pathways. The cellular and molecular definitions of mammalian stem cell microenvironments are, in most cases, almost completely lacking. As a consequence, it should be kept in mind that genomic information acquired from stem cells in isolation may not reflect reality. It is possible that this information will represent molecular pathways and gene expression programs that result from a "relaxation" of a dynamic system to some default steady state. This is potentially a large problem that is only partially surmountable, given the necessity of system perturbations that accompany isolation procedures and other manipulations. One comprehensive effort to define the cellular and global molecular profiles of hematopoietic stem cell microenvironments was described previously.[63,173] Global genomic analyses of stem cells and their microenvironments will facilitate higher-order studies to define the molecular "cross talk" that occurs between these cell populations. These would involve allowing the cells to interact and measuring the functional, cellular, and molecular changes that occur as a consequence of such interactions. It will also be crucial to explore the interactions of stem cells and microenvironments in their normal *in vivo* context. In the hematopoietic system, this should be possible with the available range of markers and newly developed *in vivo* imaging capabilities.[257,258] The actual biological functions of stem cells will also need to be measured in largely unmanipulated *in vivo* contexts. Although individual hematopoietic stem cells can clearly produce all blood cell lineages after transplantation, it is possible that these same cells are instructed to produce only certain cell types when resident in normal niches. The challenge will be to devise highly quantitative single cell–based assays that can be performed in unmanipulated animals. A potential basis for such assays may be the generation of transgenic animals with fluorescent reporters that can be reversibly activated *in vivo* in specific stages of the hematopoietic hierarchy.

A second area that needs to be considered is posttranscriptional and translational regulation of gene expression in stem cells. Ideally, a most useful definition of regulatory networks will be at an integrated genomic and proteomic level. Currently, global proteomic analyses of the limited numbers of stem cells that can be readily obtained are not feasible. This situation will likely improve. The initiation of transcription to the production of the ultimate protein products is a time-consuming process. Stem cells may need to respond quickly to systemic demands. Therefore, it is possible that cell fate decisions that occur during the course of a single cell cycle will be controlled by posttranscriptional mechanisms. These processes need to be defined in stem cells. The key role of translational regulation has been demonstrated in many developmental systems.[259] It seems likely that such control modes will exist in mammalian stem cells. It is also likely that micro-RNA-mediated regulation will play a role in stem cell biology. Examples of ES cell–specific micro-RNAs have recently been described.[260] In addition, micro-RNA–mediated translational control of the Notch pathway component, Hes1, has been described.[261] Other modes of regulation, such as alternative splicing, selective mRNA transport, and regulation of mRNA and protein stabilities, are also likely to play important roles in stem cells. Novel approaches to monitoring alternative splicing at the level of single transcripts are being developed.[262] Similarly, the localization of transcription from numerous genes in single cells is becoming possible.[263] Technologies such as these will clearly have an effect on stem cell biology.

A third area ripe for exploration is epigenetic regulation in stem cells. Clearly, the issue of nuclear programming, as well as reprogramming, lies at the heart of cell fate decision processes. Recent animal cloning results suggest the remarkable flexibility of the epigenetic state of terminally differentiated somatic cells.[264,265] This ability to "wind back" the developmental clock will have a profound effect on future biomedical research and potential clinical applications.[266] An understanding of epigenetic regulation will also shed light on somatic stem cell plasticity phenomena. Virtually nothing is known about the structure and dynamics of chromatin in stem cells. Because only small numbers of stem cells can be obtained from somatic tissues, progress in this area will depend on the development of novel techniques. Traditional and more recent techniques, such as the detection of DNaseI hypersensitivity sites and chromatin immunoprecipitation, will need to be adapted, ultimately to the level of a few hundred cells. In addition, novel methods of visualizing chromatin dynamics in single living cells will need to be developed. An ability to observe changes in chromatin during a cell fate decision process occurring in real time would have a major effect.

Finally, signaling processes occurring in stem cells will need to be defined in the context of cell biology. This will require methods of identifying signaling complexes, and their dynamic behavior in living stem cells, with cell fate decision processes. Valuable lessons can be learned from immunology, in which such methods have been successfully employed. Ultimately, it will be necessary to observe how a regulatory network functions at the level of single, interacting protein components. This will require the integration of molecular, biophysical, cell biological, and computational approaches.

Summary

In this chapter, I have attempted to place stem cells in the post–genomic era by building conceptual and practical "bridges" between the rich, and sometimes old, traditions in the field and the remarkable possibilities offered by sophisticated technologies, genome projects, and novel ways of thinking. A theme that emerges is the necessity for integrative approaches that draw on tradition as an invaluable framework and on contemporary efforts in other systems as a source of novel ways forward. A second theme is the necessity of integrating "wet bench" experimentation with computational biology, modeling, and even paradigms from engineering disciplines. Such integration may not always be possible in an individual laboratory and will require a new appreciation and establishment of effective collaborative ventures.

REFERENCES

1. Davidson, E.H., McClay, D.R., and Hood, L. (2003). Regulatory gene networks and the properties of the developmental process. *Proc. Natl. Acad. Sci. U. S. A.* **100,** 1475–1480.
2. Hartwell, L.H., Hopfield, J.J., Leibler, S., and Murray, A.W. (1999). From molecular to modular cell biology. *Nature* **402,** C47– C52.
3. Kitano, H. (2002). Computational systems biology. *Nature* **420,** 206–210.
4. Hood, L., and Galas, D. (2003). The digital code of DNA. *Nature* **421,** 444–448.
5. Ideker, T., Galitski, T., and Hood, L. (2001). a new approach to decoding life: Systems biology. *Annu. Rev. Genomics Hum. Genet.* **2,** 343–372.
6. Fuchs, E., and Segre, J.A. (2000). Stem cells: a new lease on life. *Cell* **100,** 143–155.
7. Morrison, S.J., Shah, N.M., and Anderson, D.J. (1997). Regulatory mechanisms in stem cell biology. *Cell* **88,** 287–298.
8. Weissman, I.L. (2000). Stem cells: Units of development, units of regeneration, and units in evolution. *Cell* **100,** 157–168.
9. Evans, M., and Hunter, S. (2002). Source and nature of embryonic stem cells. *C.R. Biol.* **325,** 1003–1007.
10. Thomson, J.A., and Odorico, J.S. (2000). Human embryonic stem cell and embryonic germ cell lines. *Trends Biotechnol.* **18,** 53–57.
11. Blau, H.M., Brazelton, T.R., and Weimann, J.M. (2001). The evolving concept of a stem cell: entity or function? *Cell* **105,** 829–841.
12. Lemischka, I. (2002). A few thoughts about the plasticity of stem cells. *Exp. Hematol.* **30,** 848–852.
13. Lemischka, I. (2002). Rethinking somatic stem cell plasticity. *Nat. Biotechnol.* **20,** 425.
14. Weissman, I.L., Anderson, D.J., and Gage, F. (2001). Stem and progenitor cells: origins, phenotypes, lineage commitments, and transdifferentiations. *Annu. Rev. Cell Dev. Biol.* **17,** 387–403.
15. Alonso, L., and Fuchs, E. (2003). Stem cells of the skin epithelium. *Proc. Natl. Acad. Sci. U. S. A.* **100** Suppl., 11,830–11,835.
16. Asakura, A., Seale, P., Girgis-Gabardo, A., and Rudnicki, M.A. (2002). Myogenic specification of side population cells in skeletal muscle. *J. Cell Biol.* **159,** 123–134.
17. Brinster, R.L. (2002). Germline stem cell transplantation and transgenesis. *Science* **296,** 2174–2176.
18. Gage, F.H. (2000). Mammalian neural stem cells. *Science* **287,** 1433–1438.
19. Kondo, M., Wagers, A.J., Manz, M.G., Prohaska, S.S., Scherer, D.C., Beilhack, G.F., Shizuru, J.A., and Weissman, I.L. (2003). Biology of hematopoietic stem cells and progenitors: implications for clinical application. *Annu. Rev. Immunol.* **21,** 759–806.
20. Marshman, E., Booth, C., and Potten, C.S. (2002). The intestinal epithelial stem cell. *Bioessays* **24,** 91–98.
21. Oshima, H., Rochat, A., Kedzia, C., Kobayashi, K., and Barrandon, Y. (2001). Morphogenesis and renewal of hair follicles from adult multipotent stem cells. *Cell* **104,** 233–245.
22. Temple, S. (2001). The development of neural stem cells. *Nature* **414,** 112–117.
23. Suzuki, A., and Nakauchi, H. (2002). Identification and propagation of liver stem cells. *Semin. Cell Dev. Biol.* **13,** 455–461.
24. Morrison, S.J., White, M., Zock, C., and Anderson, D.J. (1999). Prospective identification, isolation by flow cytometry, and *in vivo* self-renewal of multipotent mammalian neural crest stem cells. *Cell* **96,** 737–749.
25. Uchida, N., Buck, D.W., He, D., Reitsma, M.J., Masek, M., Phan, T.V., Tsukamoto, A.S., Gage, F.H., and Weissman, I.L. (2000). Direct isolation of human central nervous system stem cells. *Proc. Natl. Acad. Sci. U. S. A.* **97,** 14,720–14,725.
26. Wang, X., Foster, M., Al-Dhalimy, M., Lagasse, E., Finegold, M., and Grompe, M. (2003). The origin and liver repopulating capacity of murine oval cells. *Proc. Natl. Acad. Sci. U. S. A.* **100** Suppl., 11,881–11,888.
27. Watt, F.M. (2001). Stem cell fate and patterning in mammalian epidermis. *Curr. Opin. Genet. Dev.* **11,** 410–417.
28. Weissman, I.L. (2002). The road ended up at stem cells. *Immunol. Rev.* **185,** 159–174.
29. Welm, B.E., Tepera, S.B., Venezia, T., Graubert, T.A., Rosen, J.M., and Goodell, M.A. (2002). Sca-1(pos) cells in the mouse mammary gland represent an enriched progenitor cell population. *Dev. Biol.* **245,** 42–56.
30. Abramson, S., Miller, R.G., and Phillips, R.A. (1977). The identification in adult bone marrow of pluripotent and restricted stem cells of the myeloid and lymphoid systems. *J. Exp. Med.* **145,** 1567–1579.
31. Wu, A.M., Siminovitch, L., Till, J.E., and McCulloch, E.A. (1968). Evidence for a relationship between mouse hemopoietic stem cells and cells forming colonies in culture. *Proc. Natl. Acad. Sci. U. S. A.* **59,** 1209–1215.
32. Boggs, D.R., Boggs, S.S., Saxe, D.F., Gress, L.A., and Canfield, D.R. (1982). Hematopoietic stem cells with high proliferative potential: assay of their concentration in marrow by the frequency and duration of cure of W/Wv mice. *J. Clin. Invest.* **70,** 242–253.
33. Harrison, D.E. (1980). Competitive repopulation: a new assay for long-term stem cell functional capacity. *Blood* **55,** 77–81.
34. Harrison, D.E. (1979). Mouse erythropoietic stem cell lines function normally 100 months: loss related to number of transplantations. *Mech. Ageing Dev.* **9,** 427–433.
35. Jordan, C.T., and Lemischka, I.R. (1990). Clonal and systemic analysis of long-term hematopoiesis in the mouse. *Genes Dev.* **4,** 220–232.

36. Jordan, C.T., McKearn, J., and Lemischka, I.R. (1990). Cellular and developmental properties of fetal hematopoietic stem cells. *Cell* **61,** 953–963.
37. Lemischka, I.R. (1992). What we have learned from retroviral marking of hematopoietic stem cells. *Curr. Top. Microbiol Immunol.* **177,** 59–71.
38. Guenechea, G., Gan, O.I., Dorrell, C., and Dick, J.E. (2001). Distinct classes of human stem cells that differ in proliferative and self-renewal potential. *Nat. Immunol.* **2,** 75–82.
39. Mazurier, F., Gan, O.I., McKenzie, J.L., Doedens, M., and Dick, J.E. (2003). Lentivector-mediated clonal tracking reveals intrinsic heterogeneity in the human hematopoietic stem cell compartment and culture-induced stem cell impairment. *Blood* **103,** 545–552.
40. Magli, M.C., Iscove, N.N., and Odartchenko, N. (1982). Transient nature of early hematopoietic spleen colonies. *Nature* **295,** 527–529.
41. Van Zant, G. (1984). Studies of hematopoietic stem cells spared by 5-fluorouracil. *J. Exp. Med.* **159,** 679–690.
42. Harrison, D.E., Jordan, C.T., Zhong, R.K., and Astle, C.M. (1993). Primitive hemopoietic stem cells: direct assay of most productive populations by competitive repopulation with simple binomial, correlation, and covariance calculations. *Exp. Hematol.* **21,** 206–219.
43. Spangrude, G.J., Heimfeld, S., and Weissman, I.L. (1988). Purification and characterization of mouse hematopoietic stem cells. *Science* **241,** 58–62.
44. Visser, J.W., Bauman, J.G., Mulder, A.H., Eliason, J.F., and de Leeuw, A.M. (1984). Isolation of murine pluripotent hemopoietic stem cells. *J. Exp. Med.* **159,** 1576–1590.
45. Uchida, N., and Weissman, I.L. (1992). Searching for hematopoietic stem cells: evidence that Thy-1.1lo Lin– Sca-1+ cells are the only stem cells in C57BL/Ka-Thy-1.1 bone marrow. *J. Exp. Med.* **175,** 175–184.
46. Baum, C.M., Weissman, I.L., Tsukamoto, A.S., Buckle, A.M., and Peault, B. (1992). Isolation of a candidate human hematopoietic stem-cell population. *Proc. Natl. Acad. Sci. U. S. A.* **89,** 2804–2808.
47. Osawa, M., Hanada, K., Hamada, H., and Nakauchi, H. (1996). Long-term lymphohematopoietic reconstitution by a single CD34-low/negative hematopoietic stem cell. *Science* **273,** 242–245.
48. Ema, H., Takano, H., Sudo, K., and Nakauchi, H. (2000). *In vitro* self-renewal division of hematopoietic stem cells. *J. Exp. Med.* **192,** 1281–1288.
49. Szilvassy, S.J., Humphries, R.K., Lansdorp, M., Eaves, A.C., and Eaves, C.J. (1990). Quantitative assay for totipotent reconstituting hematopoietic stem cells by a competitive repopulation strategy. *Proc. Natl. Acad. Sci. U. S. A.* **87,** 8736–8740.
50. Trevisan, M., Yan, X.Q., and Iscove, N.N. (1996). Cycle initiation and colony formation in culture by murine marrow cells with long-term reconstituting potential *in vivo. Blood* **88,** 4149–4158.
51. Till, J.E., and McCulloch, E.A. (1972). The "f-factor" of the spleen-colony assay for hemopoietic stem cells. *Ser. Haematol.* **5,** 15–21.
52. Benveniste, P., Cantin, C., Hyam, D., and Iscove, N.N. (2003). Hematopoietic stem cells engraft in mice with absolute efficiency. *Nat. Immunol.* **4,** 708–713.
53. Zhao, Y., Lin, Y., Zhan, Y., Yang, G., Louie, J., Harrison, D.E., and Anderson, W.F. (2000). Murine hematopoietic stem cell characterization and its regulation in BM transplantation. *Blood* **96,** 3016–3022.
54. Uchida, N., Fleming, W.H., Alpern, E.J., and Weissman, I.L. (1993). Heterogeneity of hematopoietic stem cells. *Curr. Opin. Immunol.* **5,** 177–184.
55. Spangrude, G.J., and Johnson, G.R. (1990). Resting and activated subsets of mouse multipotent hematopoietic stem cells. *Proc. Natl. Acad. Sci. U. S. A.* **87,** 7433–7437.
56. Uchida, N., Jerabek, L., and Weissman, I.L. (1996). Searching for hematopoietic stem cells. II. The heterogeneity of Thy-1.1(lo)Lin(-/lo)Sca-1+ mouse hematopoietic stem cells separated by counterflow centrifugal elutriation. *Exp. Hematol.* **24,** 649–659.
57. Jones, R.J., Wagner, J.E., Celano, P., Zicha, M.S., and Sharkis, S.J. (1990). Separation of pluripotent hematopoietic stem cells from spleen colony-forming cells. *Nature* **347,** 188–189.
58. Krause, D.S., Theise, N.D., Collector, M.I., Henegariu, O., Hwang, S., Gardner, R., Neutzel, S., and Sharkis, S.J. (2001). Multiorgan, multilineage engraftment by a single bone marrow-derived stem cell. *Cell* **105,** 369–377.
59. Christensen, J.L., and Weissman, I.L. (2001). Flk-2 is a marker in hematopoietic stem cell differentiation: a simple method to isolate long-term stem cells. *Proc. Natl. Acad. Sci. U. S. A.* **98,** 14,541–14,546.
60. Goodell, M.A., Brose, K., Paradis, G., Conner, A.S., and Mulligan, R.C. (1996). Isolation and functional properties of murine hematopoietic stem cells that are replicating *in vivo. J. Exp. Med.* **183,** 1797–1806.
61. Szilvassy, S.J., and Cory, S. (1993). Phenotypic and functional characterization of competitive long-term repopulating hematopoietic stem cells enriched from 5-fluorouracil-treated murine marrow. *Blood* **81,** 2310–2320.
62. Wolf, N.S., Kone, A., Priestley, G.V., and Bartelmez, S.H. (1993). *In vivo* and *in vitro* characterization of long-term repopulating primitive hematopoietic cells isolated by sequential Hoechst 33342-rhodamine 123 FACS selection. *Exp. Hematol.* **21,** 614–622.
63. Moore, K.A., Ema, H., and Lemischka, I.R. (1997). *In vitro* maintenance of highly purified, transplantable hematopoietic stem cells. *Blood* **89,** 4337–4347.
64. Berrios M., Dooner, G.J., Nowakowski, G., Frimberger, A., Valinski, H., Quesenberry, J., and Becker, S. (2001). The molecular basis for the cytokine-induced defect in homing and engraftment of hematopoietic stem cells. *Exp. Hematol.* **29,** 1326–1335.
65. Colvin, G.A., Lambert, J.F., Carlson, J.E., McAuliffe, C.I., Abedi, M., and Quesenberry, J. (2002). Rhythmicity of engraftment and altered cell cycle kinetics of cytokine-cultured murine marrow in simulated microgravity compared with static cultures. *In Vitro Cell Dev. Biol. Anim.* **38,** 343–351.
66. Quesenberry, P., Colvin, G., Lambert, J.F., Abedi, M., Cerny, J., Dooner, M., Moore, B. McAuliffe, C., Demers, D., Greer, D., Parent, A., Badiavas, E., Lum, L., and Falanga, V. (2003). Marrow stem cell potential within a continuum. *Ann. N.Y. Acad. Sci.* **996,** 209–221.
67. Ito, T., Tajima, F., and Ogawa, M. (2000). Developmental changes of CD34 expression by murine hematopoietic stem cells. *Exp. Hematol.* **28,** 1269–1273.
68. Tajima, F., Deguchi, T., Laver, J.H., Zeng, H., and Ogawa, M. (2001). Reciprocal expression of CD38 and CD34 by adult murine hematopoietic stem cells. *Blood* **97,** 2618–2624.
69. Morrison, S.J., Wandycz, A.M., Hemmati, H.D., Wright, D.E., and Weissman, I.L. (1997). Identification of a lineage of multipotent hematopoietic progenitors. *Development* **124,** 1929–1939.
70. Morrison, S.J., and Weissman, I.L. (1994). The long-term repopulating subset of hematopoietic stem cells is deterministic and isolatable by phenotype. *Immunity* **1,** 661–673.

71. Nadin, B.M., Goodell, M.A., and Hirschi, K.K. (2003). Phenotype and hematopoietic potential of side population cells throughout embryonic development. *Blood* **102,** 2436–2443.
72. Akashi, K., Kondo, M., Cheshier, S., Shizuru, J., Gandy, K., Domen, J., Mebius, J., Traver, D., and Weissman, I.L. (1999). Lymphoid development from stem cells and the common lymphocyte progenitors. *Cold Spring Harb. Symp. Quant. Biol.* **64,** 1–12.
73. Akashi, K., Reya, T., Dalma-Weiszhausz, D., and Weissman, I.L. (2000). Lymphoid precursors. *Curr. Opin. Immunol.* **12,** 144–150.
74. Akashi, K., Traver, D., Miyamoto, T., and Weissman, I.L. (2000). A clonogenic common myeloid progenitor that gives rise to all myeloid lineages. *Nature* **404,** 193–197.
75. Kondo, M., Weissman, I.L., and Akashi, K. (1997). Identification of clonogenic common lymphoid progenitors in mouse bone marrow. *Cell* **91,** 661–672.
76. Na Nakorn, T., Traver, D., Weissman, I.L., and Akashi, K. (2002). Myeloerythroid-restricted progenitors are sufficient to confer radioprotection and provide the majority of day 8 CFU-S. *J. Clin. Invest.* **109,** 1579–1585.
77. Nakorn, T.N., Miyamoto, T., and Weissman, I.L. (2003). Characterization of mouse clonogenic megakaryocyte progenitors. *Proc. Natl. Acad. Sci. U. S. A.* **100,** 205–210.
78. Mebius, R.E., Miyamoto, T., Christensen, J., Domen, J., Cupedo, T., Weissman, I.L., and Akashi, K. (2001). The fetal liver counterpart of adult common lymphoid progenitors gives rise to all lymphoid lineages, $CD45^+CD4^+CD^{3-}$ cells, as well as macrophages. *J. Immunol.* **166,** 6593–6601.
79. Yokota, T., Kouro, T., Hirose, J., Igarashi, H., Garrett, K., Gregory, S.C., Sakaguchi, N., Owen, J.J., and Kincade, W. (2003). Unique properties of fetal lymphoid progenitors identified according to RAG1 gene expression. *Immunity* **19,** 365–375.
80. Graf, T. (2002). Differentiation plasticity of hematopoietic cells. *Blood* **99,** 3089–3101.
81. Kulessa, H., Frampton, J., and Graf, T. (1995). GATA-1 reprograms avian myelomonocytic cell lines into eosinophils, thromboblasts, and erythroblasts. *Genes Dev.* **9,** 1250–1262.
82. Nutt, S.L., Heavey, B., Rolink, A.G., and Busslinger, M. (1999). Commitment to the B-lymphoid lineage depends on the transcription factor Pax5. *Nature* **401,** 556–562.
83. Rolink, A.G., Nutt, S.L., Melchers, F., and Busslinger, M. (1999). Long-term *in vivo* reconstitution of T-cell development by Pax5-deficient B-cell progenitors. *Nature* **401,** 603–606.
84. Mikkola, I., Heavey, B., Horcher, M., and Busslinger, M. (2002). Reversion of B-cell commitment upon loss of Pax5 expression. *Science* **297,** 110–113.
85. Abkowitz, J.L., Catlin, S.N., and Guttorp, P. (1996). Evidence that hematopoiesis may be a stochastic process *in vivo*. *Nat. Med.* **2,** 190–197.
86. Abkowitz, J.L., Golinelli, D., Harrison, D.E., and Guttorp, P. (2000). *In vivo* kinetics of murine hemopoietic stem cells. *Blood* **96,** 3399–3405.
87. Korn, A.P., Henkelman, R.M., Ottensmeyer, F., and Till, J.E. (1973). Investigations of a stochastic model of hemopoiesis. *Exp. Hematol.* **1,** 362–375.
88. Sauvageau, G., Thorsteinsdottir, U., Eaves, C.J., Lawrence, H.J., Largman, C., Lansdorp, M., and Humphries, R.K. (1995). Overexpression of Hoxb4 in hematopoietic cells causes the selective expansion of more primitive populations *in vitro* and *in vivo*. *Genes Dev.* **9,** 1753–1765.
89. Thorsteinsdottir, U., Sauvageau, G., and Humphries, R.K. (1999). Enhanced *in vivo* regenerative potential of Hoxb4-transduced hematopoietic stem cells with regulation of their pool size. *Blood* **94,** 2605–2612.
90. Schofield, R., Lord, B.I., Kyffin, S., and Gilbert, C.W. (1980). Self-maintenance capacity of CF-S. *J. Cell Physiol.* **103,** 355–362.
91. Ogawa, M. (1993). Differentiation and proliferation of hematopoietic stem cells. *Blood* **81,** 2844–2853.
92. Ogawa, M. (1999). Stochastic model revisited. *Int. J. Hematol.* **69,** 2–5.
93. Brail, L.H., Jang, A., Billia, F., Iscove, N.N., Klamut, H.J., and Hill, R. (1999). Gene expression in individual cells: analysis using global single cell reverse transcription polymerase chain reaction (GSC RT-PCR). *Mutat. Res.* **406,** 45–54.
94. Loeffler, M., and Roeder, I. (2002). Tissue stem cells: definition, plasticity, heterogeneity, self-organization and models—a conceptual approach. *Cells Tissues Organs* **171,** 8–26.
95. Lemischka, I. (1999). Searching for stem cell regulatory molecules: some general thoughts and possible approaches. *Ann. N.Y. Acad. Sci.* **872,** 274–287; discussion 287–288.
96. Lemischka, I. (2001). Stem cell dogmas in the genomics era. *Rev. Clin. Exp. Hematol.* **5,** 15–25.
97. Chen, J., Astle, C.M., Muller-Sieburg, C.E., and Harrison, D.E. (2000). Primitive hematopoietic stem cell function *in vivo* is uniquely high in the CXB-12 mouse strain. *Blood* **96,** 4124–4131.
98. de Haan, G., Nijhof, W., and Van Zant, G. (1997). Mouse strain-dependent changes in frequency and proliferation of hematopoietic stem cells during aging: Correlation between life span and cycling activity. *Blood* **89,** 1543–1550.
99. Morrison, S.J., Qian, D., Jerabek, L., Thiel, B.A., Park, I.K., Ford, S., Kiel, M.J., Schork, N.J., Weissman, I.L., and Clarke, M.F. (2002). A genetic determinant that specifically regulates the frequency of hematopoietic stem cells. *J. Immunol.* **168,** 635–642.
100. Muller-Sieburg, C.E., Cho, R.H., Sieburg, H.B., Kupriyanov, S., and Riblet, R. (2000). Genetic control of hematopoietic stem cell frequency in mice is mostly cell autonomous. *Blood* **95,** 2446–2448.
101. Phillips, R.L., Reinhart, A.J., and Van Zant, G. (1992). Genetic control of murine hematopoietic stem cell pool sizes and cycling kinetics. *Proc. Natl. Acad. Sci. U. S. A.* **89,** 11,607–11,611.
102. Muller-Sieburg, C.E., Cho, R.H., Thoman, M., Adkins, B., and Sieburg, H.B. (2002). Deterministic regulation of hematopoietic stem cell self-renewal and differentiation. *Blood* **100,** 1302–1309.
103. Shivdasani, R.A., and Orkin, S.H. (1996). The transcriptional control of hematopoiesis. *Blood* **87,** 4025–4039.
104. Sieweke, M.H., and Graf, T. (1998). A transcription factor party during blood cell differentiation. *Curr. Opin. Genet. Dev.* **8,** 545–551.
105. Mikkola, H.K., Klintman, J., Yang, H., Hock, H., Schlaeger, T.M., Fujiwara, Y., and Orkin, S.H. (2003). Hematopoietic stem cells retain long-term repopulating activity and multipotency in the absence of stem-cell leukemia SCL/tal-1 gene. *Nature* **421,** 547–551.
106. Heyworth, C., Pearson, S., May, G., and Enver, T. (2002). Transcription factor-mediated lineage switching reveals plasticity in primary committed progenitor cells. *EMBO J.* **21,** 3770–3781.

107. Hu, M., Krause, D., Greaves, M., Sharkis, S., Dexter, M., Heyworth, C., and Enver, T. (1997). Multilineage gene expression precedes commitment in the hemopoietic system. *Genes Dev.* **11,** 774–785.
108. Joshi, C., and Enver, T. (2003). Molecular complexities of stem cells. *Curr. Opin. Hematol.* **10,** 220–228.
109. Miyamoto, T., Iwasaki, H., Reizis, B., Ye, M., Graf, T., Weissman, I.L., and Akashi, K. (2002). Myeloid or lymphoid promiscuity as a critical step in hematopoietic lineage commitment. *Dev. Cell* **3,** 137–147.
110. Lessard, J., and Sauvageau, G. (2003). Bmi-1 determines the proliferative capacity of normal and leukemic stem cells. *Nature* **423,** 255–260.
111. Lessard, J., and Sauvageau, G. (2003). Polycomb group genes as epigenetic regulators of normal and leukemic hemopoiesis. *Exp. Hematol.* **31,** 567–585.
112. Ohta, H., Sawada, A., Kim, J.Y., Tokimasa, S., Nishiguchi, S., Humphries, R.K., Hara, J., and Takihara, Y. (2002). Polycomb group gene rae28 is required for sustaining activity of hematopoietic stem cells. *J. Exp. Med.* **195,** 759–770.
113. Park, I.K., Qian, D., Kiel, M., Becker, M.W., Pihalja, M., Weissman, I.L., Morrison, S.J., and Clarke, M.F. (2003). Bmi-1 is required for maintenance of adult self-renewing hematopoietic stem cells. *Nature* **423,** 302–305.
114. Cheng, T., Rodrigues, N., Dombkowski, D., Stier, S., and Scadden, D.T. (2000). Stem cell repopulation efficiency but not pool size is governed by p27(kip1). *Nat. Med.* **6,** 1235–1240.
115. Cheng, T., Rodrigues, N., Shen, H., Yang, Y., Dombkowski, D., Sykes, M., and Scadden, D.T. (2000). Hematopoietic stem cell quiescence maintained by p21cip1/waf1. *Science* **287,** 1804–1808.
116. Domen, J., Cheshier, S.H., and Weissman, I.L. (2000). The role of apoptosis in the regulation of hematopoietic stem cells: overexpression of Bcl-2 increases both their number and repopulation potential. *J. Exp. Med.* **191,** 253–264.
117. Lee, S.S., Kennedy, S., Tolonen, A.C., and Ruvkun, G. (2003). DAF-16 target genes that control *C. elegans* life-span and metabolism. *Science* **300,** 644–647.
118. Reya, T., Duncan, A.W., Ailles, L., Domen, J., Scherer, D.C., Willert, K., Hintz, L., Nusse, R., and Weissman, I.L. (2003). A role for Wnt signaling in self-renewal of hematopoietic stem cells. *Nature* **423,** 409–414.
119. Willert, K., Brown, J.D., Danenberg, E., Duncan, A.W., Weissman, I.L., Reya, T., Yates, J.R., 3rd, and Nusse, R. (2003). Wnt proteins are lipid-modified and can act as stem cell growth factors. *Nature* **423,** 448–452.
120. Alonso, L., and Fuchs, E. (2003). Stem cells in the skin: waste not, Wnt not. *Genes Dev.* **17,** 1189–1200.
121. Korinek, V., Barker, N., Moerer, P., van Donselaar, E., Huls, G., Peters, P.J., and Clevers, H. (1998). Depletion of epithelial stem-cell compartments in the small intestine of mice lacking Tcf-4. *Nat. Genet.* **19,** 379–383.
122. Merrill, B.J., Gat, U., DasGupta, R., and Fuchs, E. (2001). Tcf3 and Lef1 regulate lineage differentiation of multipotent stem cells in skin. *Genes Dev.* **15,** 1688–1705.
123. Polesskaya, A., Seale, P., and Rudnicki, M.A. (2003). Wnt signaling induces the myogenic specification of resident $CD45^+$ adult stem cells during muscle regeneration. *Cell* **113,** 841–852.
124. Theodosiou, N.A., and Tabin, C.J. (2003). Wnt signaling during development of the gastrointestinal tract. *Dev. Biol.* **259,** 258–271.
125. Bhatia, M., Bonnet, D., Wu, D., Murdoch, B., Wrana, J., Gallacher, L., and Dick, J.E. (1999). Bone morphogenetic proteins regulate the developmental program of human hematopoietic stem cells. *J. Exp. Med.* **189,** 1139–1148.
126. de Haan, G., Weersing, E., Dontje, B., van Os, R., Bystrykh, L.V., Vellenga, E., and Miller, G. (2003). *In vitro* generation of long-term repopulating hematopoietic stem cells by fibroblast growth factor-1. *Dev. Cell* **4,** 241–251.
127. Fortunel, N.O., Hatzfeld, J.A., Monier, M.N., and Hatzfeld, A. (2003). Control of hematopoietic stem–progenitor cell fate by transforming growth factor-beta. *Oncol. Res.* **13,** 445–453.
128. Karanu, F.N., Murdoch, B., Miyabayashi, T., Ohno, M., Koremoto, M., Gallacher, L., Wu, D., Itoh, A., Sakano, S., and Bhatia, M. (2001). Human homologues of Delta-1 and Delta-4 function as mitogenic regulators of primitive human hematopoietic cells. *Blood* **97,** 1960–1967.
129. Larsson, J., Blank, U., Helgadottir, H., Bjornsson, J.M., Ehinger, M., Goumans, M.J., Fan, X., Leveen, P., and Karlsson, S. (2003). TGF-{beta} signaling-deficient hematopoietic stem cells have normal self-renewal and regenerative ability *in vivo* despite increased proliferative capacity *in vitro. Blood* **102,** 3129–3135.
130. Ohishi, K., Katayama, N., Shiku, H., Varnum-Finney, B., and Bernstein, I.D. (2003). Notch signaling in hematopoiesis. *Semin. Cell Dev. Biol.* **14,** 143–150.
131. Varnum-Finney, B., Brashem-Stein, C., and Bernstein, I.D. (2003). Combined effects of Notch signaling and cytokines induce a multiple log increase in precursors with lymphoid and myeloid reconstituting ability. *Blood* **101,** 1784–1789.
132. Dyer, M.A., Farrington, S.M., Mohn, D., Munday, J.R., and Baron, M.H. (2001). Indian hedgehog activates hematopoiesis and vasculogenesis and can respecify prospective neurectodermal cell fate in the mouse embryo. *Development* **128,** 1717–1730.
133. Guss, K.A., Nelson, C.E., Hudson, A., Kraus, M.E., and Carroll, S.B. (2001). Control of a genetic regulatory network by a selector gene. *Science* **292,** 1164–1167.
134. Mann, R.S., and Carroll, S.B. (2002). Molecular mechanisms of selector gene function and evolution. *Curr. Opin. Genet. Dev.* **12,** 592–600.
135. Yang, Y.C., Piek, E., Zavadil, J., Liang, D., Xie, D., Heyer, J., Pavlidis, P., Kucherlapati, R., Roberts, A.B., and Bottinger, E. (2003). Hierarchical model of gene regulation by transforming growth factor β. *Proc. Natl. Acad. Sci. U. S. A.* **100,** 10,269–10,274.
136. Bolouri, H., and Davidson, E.H. (2003). Transcriptional regulatory cascades in development: Initial rates, not steady state, determine network kinetics. *Proc. Natl. Acad. Sci. U. S. A.* **100,** 9371–9376.
137. Levsky, J.M., and Singer, R.H. (2003). Gene expression and the myth of the average cell. *Trends Cell Biol.* **13,** 4–6.
138. Brenner, S., Johnson, M., Bridgham, J., Golda, G., Lloyd, D.H., Johnson, D., Luo, S., McCurdy, S., Foy, M., Ewan, M., Roth, R., George, D., Eletr, S., Albrecht, G., Vermaas, E., Williams, S.R., Moon, K., Burcham, T., Pallas, M., DuBridge, R.B., Kirchner, J., Fearon, K., Mao, J., and Corcoran, K. (2000). Gene expression analysis by massively parallel signature sequencing (MPSS) on microbead arrays. *Nat. Biotechnol.* **18,** 630–634.
139. Okazaki, Y., Furuno, M., Kasukawa, T., Adachi, J., Bono, H., Kondo, S., Nikaido, I., Osato, N., Saito, R., Suzuki, H., Yamanaka, I., Kiyosawa, H., Yagi, K., Tomaru, Y., Hasegawa, Y., Nogami, A., Schonbach, C., Gojobori, T., Baldarelli, R., Hill, D.,

Bult, C., Hume, D.A., Quackenbush, J., Schriml, L.M., Kanapin, A., Matsuda, H., Batalov, S., Beisel, K.W., Blake, J.A., Bradt Brusic, D., Chothia, C., Corbani, L.E., Cousins, S., Dalla, E., Dragani, T.A., Fletcher, C.F., Forrest, A., Frazer, K.S., Gaasterland, T., Gariboldi, M., Gissi, C., Godzik, A., Gough, J., Grimmond, S., Gustincich, S., Hirokawa, N., Jackson, I.J., Jarvis, E.D., Kanai, A., Kawaji, H., Kawasawa, Y., Kedzierski, R.M., King, B.L., Konagaya, A., Kurochkin, I.V., Lee, Y., Lenhard, B., Lyons, A., Maglott, D.R., Maltais, L., Marchionni, L., McKenzie, L., Miki, H., Nagashima, T., Numata, K., Okido, T., Pavan, W.J., Pertea, G., Pesole, G., Petrovsky, N., Pillai, R., Pontius, J.U., Qi, D., Ramachandran, S., Ravasi, T., Reed, J.C., Reed, D.J., Reid, J., Ring, B.Z., Ringwald, M., Sandelin, A., Schneider, C., Semple, C.A., Setou, M., Shimada, K., Sultana, R., Takenaka, Y., Taylor, M.S., Teasdale, R.D., Tomita, M., Verardo, R., Wagner, L., Wahlestedt, C., Wang, Y., Watanabe, Y., Wells, C., Wilming, L.G., Wynshaw-Boris, A., Yanagisawa, M., *et al.* (2002). Analysis of the mouse transcriptome based on functional annotation of 60,770 full-length cDNAs. *Nature* **420,** 563–573.

140. Velculescu E., Vogelstein, B., and Kinzler, K.W. (2000). Analyzing uncharted transcriptomes with SAGE. *Trends Genet.* **16,** 423–425.
141. Cheung, G., Morley, M., Aguilar, F., Massimi, A., Kucherlapati, R., and Childs, G. (1999). Making and reading microarrays. *Nat. Genet.* **21,** 15–19.
142. Duggan, D.J., Bittner, M., Chen, Y., Meltzer, P., and Trent, J.M. (1999). Expression profiling using cDNA microarrays. *Nat. Genet.* **21,** 10–14.
143. Lipshutz, R.J., Fodor, S., Gingeras, T.R., and Lockhart, D.J. (1999). High density synthetic oligonucleotide arrays. *Nat. Genet.* **21,** 20–24.
144. Phillips, R.L., Ernst, R.E., Brunk, B., Ivanova, N., Mahan, M.A., Deanehan, J.K., Moore, K.A., Overton, G.C., and Lemischka, I.R. (2000). The genetic program of hematopoietic stem cells. *Science* **288,** 1635–1640.
145. Ivanova, N.B., Dimos, J.T., Schaniel, C., Hackney, J.A., Moore, K.A., and Lemischka, I.R. (2002). A stem cell molecular signature. *Science* **298,** 601–604.
146. Park, I.K., He, Y., Lin, F., Laerum, O.D., Tian, Q., Bumgarner, R., Klug, C.A., Li, K., Kuhr, C., Doyle, M.J., Xie, T., Schummer, M., Sun, Y., Goldsmith, A., Clarke, M.F., Weissman, I.L., Hood, L., and Li, L. (2002). Differential gene expression profiling of adult murine hematopoietic stem cells. *Blood* **99,** 488–498.
147. Ramalho-Santos, M., Yoon, S., Matsuzaki, Y., Mulligan, R.C., and Melton, D.A. (2002). "Stemness": transcriptional profiling of embryonic and adult stem cells. *Science* **298,** 597–600.
148. Terskikh, A.V., Miyamoto, T., Chang, C., Diatchenko, L., and Weissman, I.L. (2003). Gene expression analysis of purified hematopoietic stem cells and committed progenitors. *Blood* **102,** 94–101.
149. Bassett, D.E., Jr., Eisen, M.B., and Boguski, M.S. (1999). Gene expression informatics: it's all in your mine. *Nat. Genet.* **21,** 51–55.
150. Churchill, G.A. (2002). Fundamentals of experimental design for cDNA microarrays. *Nat. Genet.* **32** Suppl., 490–495.
151. Holloway, A.J., van Laar, R.K., Tothill, R.W., and Bowtell, D.D. (2002). Options available—from start to finish—for obtaining data from DNA microarrays II. *Nat. Genet.* **32** Suppl., 481–489.
152. Quackenbush, J. (2001). Computational analysis of microarray data. *Nat. Rev. Genet.* **2,** 418–427.
153. Slonim, D.K. (2002). From patterns to pathways: Gene expression data analysis comes of age. *Nat. Genet.* **32** Suppl., 502–508.
154. Kacharmina, J.E., Crino, B., and Eberwine, J. (1999). Preparation of cDNA from single cells and subcellular regions. *Methods Enzymol.* **303,** 3–18.
155. Chiang, M.K., and Melton, D.A. (2003). Single-cell transcript analysis of pancreas development. *Dev. Cell* **4,** 383–393.
156. Brazma, A., Hingamp, P., Quackenbush, J., Sherlock, G., Spellman, P., Stoeckert, C., Aach, J., Ansorge, W., Ball, C.A., Causton, H.C., Gaasterland, T., Glenisson, P., Holstege, F.C., Kim, I.F., Markowitz, V., Matese, J.C., Parkinson, H., Robinson, A., Sarkans, U., Schulze-Kremer, S., Stewart, J., Taylor, R., Vilo, J., and Vingron, M. (2001). Minimum information about a microarray experiment (MIAME): toward standards for microarray data. *Nat. Genet.* **29,** 365–371.
157. Stoeckert, C.J., Jr., Causton, H.C., and Ball, C.A. (2002). Microarray databases: standards and ontologies. *Nat. Genet.* **32 Suppl.,** 469–473.
158. Rebel I., Miller, C.L., Eaves, C.J., and Lansdorp, M. (1996). The repopulation potential of fetal liver hematopoietic stem cells in mice exceeds that of their liver adult bone marrow counterparts. *Blood* **87,** 3500–3507.
159. Rebel I., Miller, C.L., Thornbury, G.R., Dragowska, W.H., Eaves, C.J., and Lansdorp, M. (1996). A comparison of long-term repopulating hematopoietic stem cells in fetal liver and adult bone marrow from the mouse. *Exp. Hematol.* **24,** 638–648.
160. Akashi, K., He, X., Chen, J., Iwasaki, H., Niu, C., Steenhard, B., Zhang, J., Haug, J., and Li, L. (2003). Transcriptional accessibility for genes of multiple tissues and hematopoietic lineages is hierarchically controlled during early hematopoiesis. *Blood* **101,** 383–389.
161. de Haan, G., Bystrykh, L.V., Weersing, E., Dontje, B., Geiger, H., Ivanova, N., Lemischka, I.R., Vellenga, E., and Van Zant, G. (2002). A genetic and genomic analysis identifies a cluster of genes associated with hematopoietic cell turnover. *Blood* **100,** 2056–2062.
162. Lambert, J.F., Liu, M., Colvin, G.A., Dooner, M., McAuliffe, C.I., Becker, S., Forget, B.G., Weissman, S.M., and Quesenberry, J. (2003). Marrow stem cells shift gene expression and engraftment phenotype with cell cycle transit. *J. Exp. Med.* **197,** 1563–1572.
163. Ma, X., Husain, T., Peng, H., Lin, S., Mironenko, O., Maun, N., Johnson, S., Tuck, D., Berliner, N., Krause, D.S., and Perkins, A.S. (2002). Development of a murine hematopoietic progenitor complementary DNA microarray using a subtracted complementary DNA library. *Blood* **100,** 833–844.
164. Terskikh, A.V., Easterday, M.C., Li, L., Hood, L., Kornblum, H.I., Geschwind, D.H., and Weissman, I.L. (2001). From hematopoiesis to neuropoiesis: evidence of overlapping genetic programs. *Proc. Natl. Acad. Sci. U. S. A.* **98,** 7934–7939.
165. D'Amour, K.A., and Gage, F.H. (2003). Genetic and functional differences between multipotent neural and pluripotent embryonic stem cells. *Proc. Natl. Acad. Sci. U. S. A.* **100** Suppl., 11,866–11,872.
166. Suzuki, A., Nakauchi, H., and Taniguchi, H. (2003). *In vitro* production of functionally mature hepatocytes from prospectively isolated hepatic stem cells. *Cell Transplant* **12,** 469–473.
167. Tamaki, S., Eckert, K., He, D., Sutton, R., Doshe, M., Jain, G., Tushinski, R., Reitsma, M., Harris, B., Tsukamoto, A., Gage, F., Weissman, I., and Uchida, N. (2002). Engraftment of sorted/expanded human central nervous system stem cells from fetal brain. *J. Neurosci. Res.* **69,** 976–986.

168. Schneider, T.E., Barland, C., Alex, A.M., Mancianti, M.L., Lu, Y., Cleaver, J.E., Lawrence, H.J., and Ghadially, R. (2003). Measuring stem cell frequency in epidermis: a quantitative *in vivo* functional assay for long-term repopulating cells. *Proc. Natl. Acad. Sci. U. S. A.* **100,** 11,412–11,417.
169. Stappenbeck, T.S., Mills, J.C., and Gordon, J.I. (2003). Molecular features of adult mouse small intestinal epithelial progenitors. *Proc. Natl. Acad. Sci. U. S. A.* **100,** 1004–1009.
170. Braun, K.M., Niemann, C., Jensen, U.B., Sundberg, J.P., Silva-Vargas, V., and Watt, F.M. (2003). Manipulation of stem cell proliferation and lineage commitment: visualization of label-retaining cells in wholemounts of mouse epidermis. *Development* **130,** 5241–5255.
171. Bradford, G.B., Williams, B., Rossi, R., and Bertoncello, I. (1997). Quiescence, cycling, and turnover in the primitive hematopoietic stem cell compartment. *Exp. Hematol.* **25,** 445–453.
172. Cheshier, S.H., Morrison, S.J., Liao, X., and Weissman, I.L. (1999). *In vivo* proliferation and cell cycle kinetics of long-term self-renewing hematopoietic stem cells. *Proc. Natl. Acad. Sci. U. S. A.* **96,** 3120–3125.
173. Hackney, J.A., Charbord, P., Brunk, B., Stoeckert, C.J., Lemischka, I.R., and Moore, K.A. (2002). A molecular profile of a hematopoietic stem cell niche. *Proc. Natl. Acad. Sci. U. S. A.* **99,** 13,061–13,066.
174. Karsten, S.L., Kudo, L.C., Jackson, R., Sabatti, C. Kornblum, H.I., and Geschwind, D.H. (2003). Global analysis of gene expression in neural progenitors reveals specific cell-cycle, signaling, and metabolic networks. *Dev. Biol.* **261,** 165–182.
175. Tanaka, T.S., Kunath, T., Kimber, W.L., Jaradat, S.A., Stagg, C.A., Usuda, M., Yokota, T., Niwa, H., Rossant, J., and Ko, M.S. (2002). Gene expression profiling of embryo-derived stem cells reveals candidate genes associated with pluripotency and lineage specificity. *Genome Res.* **12,** 1921–1928.
176. Tsai, R.Y., and McKay, R.D. (2002). A nucleolar mechanism controlling cell proliferation in stem cells and cancer cells. *Genes Dev.* **16,** 2991–3003.
177. Mackarehtschian, K., Hardin, J.D., Moore, K.A., Boast, S., Goff, S., and Lemischka, I.R. (1995). Targeted disruption of the Flk-2/Flt-3 gene leads to deficiencies in primitive hematopoietic progenitors. *Immunity* **3,** 147–61.
178. Matthews, W., Jordan, C.T., Gavin, M., Jenkins, N.A., Copeland, N.G., and Lemischka, I.R. (1991). A receptor tyrosine kinase cDNA isolated from a population of enriched primitive hematopoietic cells and exhibiting close genetic linkage to c-kit. *Proc. Natl. Acad. Sci. U. S. A.* **88,** 9026–9030.
179. Matthews, W., Jordan, C.T., Wiegand, G.W., Pardoll, D., and Lemischka, I.R. (1991). A receptor tyrosine kinase specific to hematopoietic stem and progenitor cell-enriched populations. *Cell* **65,** 1143–1152.
180. Russell, E.S. (1979). Hereditary anemias of the mouse: a review for geneticists. *Adv. Genet.* **20,** 357–459.
181. Lyman, S.D., and Jacobsen, S.E. (1998). C-kit ligand and Flt3 ligand: stem–progenitor cell factors with overlapping yet distinct activities. *Blood* **91,** 1101–1134.
182. Gilman, A., and Arkin, A. (2002). Genetic "code": representations and dynamical models of genetic components and networks. *Annu. Rev. Genomics Hum. Genet.* **3,** 341–369.
183. McAdams, H.H., and Shapiro, L. (1995). Circuit simulation of genetic networks. *Science* **269,** 650–656.
184. Shvartsman, S.Y., Muratov, C.B., and Lauffenburger, D.A. (2002). Modeling and computational analysis of EGF receptor-mediated cell communication in Drosophila oogenesis. *Development* **129,** 2577–2589.
185. Van Gelder, R.N., Herzog, E.D., Schwartz, W.J., and Taghert, H. (2003). Circadian rhythms: in the loop at last. *Science* **300,** 1534–1535.
186. Eldar, A., Dorfman, R., Weiss, D., Ashe, H., Shilo, B.Z., and Barkai, N. (2002). Robustness of the BMP morphogen gradient in Drosophila embryonic patterning. *Nature* **419,** 304–308.
187. Meir, E., von Dassow, G., Munro, E., and Odell, G.M. (2002). Robustness, flexibility, and the role of lateral inhibition in the neurogenic network. *Curr. Biol.* **12,** 778–786.
188. von Dassow, G., Meir, E., Munro, E.M., and Odell, G.M. (2000). The segment polarity network is a robust developmental module. *Nature* **406,** 188–192.
189. Bhalla, U.S., and Iyengar, R. (1999). Emergent properties of networks of biological signaling pathways. *Science* **283,** 381–387.
190. Bolouri, H., and Davidson, E.H. (2002). Modeling transcriptional regulatory networks. *Bioessays* **24,** 1118–1129.
191. de Jong, H. (2002). Modeling and simulation of genetic regulatory systems: a literature review. *J. Comput. Biol.* **9,** 67–103.
192. Hasty, J., Isaacs, F., Dolnik, M., McMillen, D., and Collins, J.J. (2001). Designer gene networks: toward fundamental cellular control. *Chaos* **11,** 207–220.
193. Hasty, J., McMillen, D., and Collins, J.J. (2002). Engineered gene circuits. *Nature* **420,** 224–230.
194. Hasty, J., McMillen, D., Isaacs, F., and Collins, J.J. (2001). Computational studies of gene regulatory networks in numero molecular biology. *Nat. Rev. Genet.* **2,** 268–79.
195. Tyson, J.J., Chen, K., and Novak, B. (2001). Network dynamics and cell physiology. *Nat. Rev. Mol. Cell Biol.* **2,** 908–916.
196. Smolen, P., Baxter, D.A., and Byrne, J.H. (2000). Mathematical modeling of gene networks. *Neuron* **26,** 567–580.
197. Smolen, P., Baxter, D.A., and Byrne, J.H. (2000). Modeling transcriptional control in gene networks: methods, recent results, and future directions. *Bull. Math. Biol.* **62,** 247–292.
198. Hoffmann, A., Levchenko, A., Scott, M.L., and Baltimore, D. (2002). The IkappaB-NF-kappaB signaling module. temporal control and selective gene activation. *Science* **298,** 1241–1245.
199. Lev Bar-Or, R., Maya, R., Segel, L.A., Alon, U., Levine, A.J., and Oren, M. (2000). Generation of oscillations by the p53-Mdm2 feedback loop: a theoretical and experimental study. *Proc. Natl. Acad. Sci. U. S. A.* **97,** 11,250–11,255.
200. Lewis, J. (2003). Autoinhibition with transcriptional delay: A simple mechanism for the zebra fish somitogenesis oscillator. *Curr. Biol.* **13,** 1398–1408.
201. Monk, N.A. (2003). Oscillatory expression of Hes1, p53, and NF-kappaB driven by transcriptional time delays. *Curr. Biol.* **13,** 1409–1413.
202. Alon, U., Surette, M.G., Barkai, N., and Leibler, S. (1999). Robustness in bacterial chemotaxis. *Nature* **397,** 168–171.
203. Bhalla, U.S., Ram, T., and Iyengar, R. (2002). MAP kinase phosphatase as a locus of flexibility in a mitogen-activated protein kinase signaling network. *Science* **297,** 1018–1023.
204. Novak, B., Pataki, Z., Ciliberto, A., and Tyson, J.J. (2001). Mathematical model of the cell division cycle of fission yeast. *Chaos* **11,** 277–286.
205. Delon, J., and Germain, R.N. (2000). Information transfer at the immunological synapse. *Curr. Biol.* **10,** R923–R933.

206. Davidson, E.H., Rast, J., Oliveri, Ransick, A., Calestani, C., Yuh, C.H., Minokawa, T., Amore Hinman, G., Arenas-Mena, C., Otim, O., Brown, C.T., Livi, C.B., Lee, Y., Revilla, R., Rust, A.G., Pan, Z., Schilstra, M.J., Clarke, P.J., Arnone, M.I., Rowen, L., Cameron, R.A., McClay, D.R., Hood, L., and Bolouri, H. (2002). A genomic regulatory network for development. *Science* **295,** 1669–1678.
207. Anderson, M.K., Hernandez-Hoyos, G., Dionne, C.J., Arias, A.M., Chen, D., and Rothenberg, E.V. (2002). Definition of regulatory network elements for T-cell development by perturbation analysis with PU.1 and GATA-3. *Dev. Biol.* **246,** 103–121.
208. Rothenberg, E.V., and Anderson, M.K. (2002). Elements of transcription factor network design for T-lineage specification. *Dev. Biol.* **246,** 29–44.
209. Csete, M.E., and Doyle, J.C. (2002). Reverse engineering of biological complexity. *Science* **295,** 1664–1669.
210. Reya, T., Morrison, S.J., Clarke, M.F., and Weissman, I.L. (2001). Stem cells, cancer, and cancer stem cells. *Nature* **414,** 105–111.
211. Albert, R., Jeong, H., and Barabasi, A.L. (2000). Error and attack tolerance of complex networks. *Nature* **406,** 378–382.
212. Barabasi, A.L., and Bonabeau, E. (2003). Scale-free networks. *Sci. Am.* **288,** 60–69.
213. Ravasz, E., and Barabasi, A.L. (2003). Hierarchical organization in complex networks. *Phys. Rev. E. Stat. Nonlin. Soft Matter Phys.* **67,** 026112.
214. Blake, W.J., Kaern, M., Cantor, C.R., and Collins, J.J. (2003). Noise in eukaryotic gene expression. *Nature* **422,** 633–637.
215. Hasty, J., Pradines, J., Dolnik, M., and Collins, J.J. (2000). Noise-based switches and amplifiers for gene expression. *Proc. Natl. Acad. Sci. U. S. A.* **97,** 2075–2080.
216. Rao, C.V., Wolf, D.M., and Arkin, A. (2002). Control, exploitation, and tolerance of intracellular noise. *Nature* **420,** 231–237.
217. Oostendorp, R.A., Audet, J., Miller, C., and Eaves, C.J. (1999). Cell division tracking and expansion of hematopoietic long-term repopulating cells. *Leukemia* **13,** 499–501.
218. Faust, N., Varas, F., Kelly, L.M., Heck, S., and Graf, T. (2000). Insertion of enhanced green fluorescent protein into the lysozyme gene creates mice with green fluorescent granulocytes and macrophages. *Blood* **96,** 719–726.
219. Heck, S., Ermakova, O., Iwasaki, H., Akashi, K., Sun, C.W., Ryan, T.M., Townes, T., and Graf, T. (2003). Distinguishable live erythroid and myeloid cells in beta-globin ECFP × lysozyme EGFP mice. *Blood* **101,** 903–906.
220. Fehling, H.J., Lacaud, G., Kubo, A., Kennedy, M., Robertson, S., Keller, G., and Kouskoff, V. (2003). Tracking mesoderm induction and its specification to the hemangioblast during embryonic stem cell differentiation. *Development* **130,** 4217–4227.
221. Igarashi, H., Gregory, S.C., Yokota, T., Sakaguchi, N., and Kincade, W. (2002). Transcription from the RAG1 locus marks the earliest lymphocyte progenitors in bone marrow. *Immunity* **17,** 117–130.
222. Terskikh, A., Fradkov, A., Ermakova, G., Zaraisky, A., Tan, P., Kajava, A.V., Zhao, X., Lukyanov, S., Matz, M., Kim, S., Weissman, I., and Siebert, P. (2000). "Fluorescent timer": protein that changes color with time. *Science* **290,** 1585–1588.
223. McNagny, K.M., and Graf, T. (2003). E26 leukemia virus converts primitive erythroid cells into cycling multilineage progenitors. *Blood* **101,** 1103–1110.
224. D'Haeseleer, P., Liang, S., and Somogyi, R. (2000). Genetic network inference: from coexpression clustering to reverse engineering. *Bioinformatics* **16,** 707–726.
225. Liang, S., Fuhrman, S., and Somogyi, R. (1998). Reveal, a general reverse engineering algorithm for inference of genetic network architectures. *Pac. Symp. Biocomput.* 18–29.
226. Gardner, T.S., di Bernardo, D., Lorenz, D., and Collins, J.J. (2003). Inferring genetic networks and identifying compound mode of action via expression profiling. *Science* **301,** 102–105.
227. Tegner, J., Yeung, M.K., Hasty, J., and Collins, J.J. (2003). Reverse engineering gene networks: integrating genetic perturbations with dynamical modeling. *Proc. Natl. Acad. Sci. U. S. A.* **100,** 5944–5949.
228. Wagner, A. (2001). How to reconstruct a large genetic network from n gene perturbations in fewer than n(2) easy steps. *Bioinformatics* **17,** 1183–1197.
229. Ideker, T., Thorsson, V., Ranish, J.A., Christmas, R., Buhler, J., Eng, J.K., Bumgarner, R., Goodlett, D.R., Aebersold, R., and Hood, L. (2001). Integrated genomic and proteomic analyses of a systematically perturbed metabolic network. *Science* **292,** 929–934.
230. Lee, T.I., Rinaldi, N.J., Robert, F., Odom, D.T., Bar-Joseph, Z., Gerber, G.K., Hannett, N.M., Harbison, C.T., Thompson, C.M., Simon, I., Zeitlinger, J., Jennings, E.G., Murray, H.L., Gordon, D.B., Ren, B., Wyrick, J.J., Tagne, J.B., Volkert, T.L., Fraenkel, E., Gifford, D.K., and Young, R.A. (2002). Transcriptional regulatory networks in Saccharomyces cerevisiae. *Science* **298,** 799–804.
231. Shoemaker, D.D., Lashkari, D.A., Morris, D., Mittmann, M., and Davis, R.W. (1996). Quantitative phenotypic analysis of yeast deletion mutants using a highly parallel molecular bar-coding strategy. *Nat. Genet.* **14,** 450–456.
232. Dykxhoorn, D.M., Novina, C.D., and Sharp, A. (2003). Killing the messenger: Short RNAs that silence gene expression. *Nat. Rev. Mol. Cell Biol.* **4,** 457–467.
233. Hemann, M.T., Fridman, J.S., Zilfou, J.T., Hernando, E., Paddison, J., Cordon-Cardo, C., Hannon, G.J., and Lowe, S.W. (2003). An epi-allelic series of p53 hypomorphs created by stable RNAi produces distinct tumor phenotypes *in vivo*. *Nat. Genet.* **33,** 396–400.
234. Kunath, T., Gish, G., Lickert, H., Jones, N., Pawson, T., and Rossant, J. (2003). Transgenic RNA interference in ES cell-derived embryos recapitulates a genetic null phenotype. *Nat. Biotechnol.* **21,** 559–561.
235. Rubinson, D.A., Dillon, C., Kwiatkowski, A.V., Sievers, C., Yang, L., Kopinja, J., Rooney, D.L., Ihrig, M.M., McManus, M.T., Gertler, F.B., Scott, M.L., and Van Parijs, L. (2003). A lentivirus-based system to functionally silence genes in primary mammalian cells, stem cells and transgenic mice by RNA interference. *Nat. Genet.* **33,** 401–406.
236. Gottgens, B., Nastos, A., Kinston, S., Piltz, S., Delabesse, E.C., Stanley, M., Sanchez, M.J., Ciau-Uitz, A., Patient, R., and Green, A.R. (2002). Establishing the transcriptional program for blood: The SCL stem cell enhancer is regulated by a multiprotein complex containing Ets and GATA factors. *EMBO J.* **21,** 3039–3050.
237. Huettner, C.S., Koschmieder, S., Iwasaki, H., Radomska, H.S., Akashi, K., and Tenen, D.G. (2003). Inducible expression of BCR/ABL using human CD34 regulatory elements results in a megakaryocytic myeloproliferative syndrome. *Blood* **102,** 3363–3370.
238. Dahl, R., and Simon, M.C. (2003). The importance of PU.1 concentration in hematopoietic lineage commitment and maturation. *Blood Cells Mol. Dis.* **31,** 229–233.

239. DeKoter, R.P., and Singh, H. (2000). Regulation of B lymphocyte and macrophage development by graded expression of PU.1. *Science* **288,** 1439–1441.
240. McNagny, K., and Graf, T. (2002). Making eosinophils through subtle shifts in transcription factor expression. *J. Exp. Med.* **195,** F43– F47.
241. Georgopoulos, K. (2002). Hematopoietic cell fate decisions, chromatin regulation, and Ikaros. *Nat. Rev. Immunol.* **2,** 162–174.
242. Jansen, R.C. (2003). Studying complex biological systems using multifactorial perturbation. *Nat. Rev. Genet.* **4,** 145–151.
243. Brem, R.B., Yvert, G., Clinton, R., and Kruglyak, L. (2002). Genetic dissection of transcriptional regulation in budding yeast. *Science* **296,** 752–755.
244. Geiger, H., True, J.M., de Haan, G., and Van Zant, G. (2001). Age- and stage-specific regulation patterns in the hematopoietic stem cell hierarchy. *Blood* **98,** 2966–2972.
245. Zandstra, W., and Nagy, A. (2001). Stem cell bioengineering. *Annu. Rev. Biomed. Eng.* **3,** 275–305.
246. Ferrell, J.E., and Xiong, W. (2001). Bistability in cell signaling: How to make continuous processes discontinuous, and reversible processes irreversible. *Chaos* **11,** 227–236.
247. Tyson, J.J., Chen, K.C., and Novak, B. (2003). Sniffers, buzzers, toggles, and blinkers: dynamics of regulatory and signaling pathways in the cell. *Curr. Opin. Cell Biol.* **15,** 221–231.
248. Elowitz, M.B., and Leibler, S. (2000). A synthetic oscillatory network of transcriptional regulators. *Nature* **403,** 335–338.
249. Guet, C.C., Elowitz, M.B., Hsing, W., and Leibler, S. (2002). Combinatorial synthesis of genetic networks. *Science* **296,** 1466–1470.
250. Yokobayashi, Y., Weiss, R., and Arnold, F.H. (2002). Directed evolution of a genetic circuit. *Proc. Natl. Acad. Sci. U. S. A.* **99,** 16,587–16,591.
251. Becskei, A., Seraphin, B., and Serrano, L. (2001). Positive feedback in eukaryotic gene networks: Cell differentiation by graded to binary response conversion. *EMBO J.* **20,** 2528–2535.
252. Rossi, F.M., Kringstein, A.M., Spicher, A., Guicherit, O.M., and Blau, H.M. (2000). Transcriptional control: rheostat converted to on/off switch. *Mol. Cell* **6,** 723–728.
253. Ezoe, S., Matsumura, I., Nakata, S., Gale, K., Ishihara, K., Minegishi, N., Machii, T., Kitamura, T., Yamamoto, M., Enver, T., and Kanakura, Y. (2002). GATA-2/estrogen receptor chimera regulates cytokine-dependent growth of hematopoietic cells through accumulation of p21(WAF1) and p27(Kip1) proteins. *Blood* **100,** 3512–3520.
254. Zeng, H., Masuko, M., Jin, L., Neff, T., Otto, K.G., and Blau, C.A. (2001). Receptor specificity in the self-renewal and differentiation of primary multipotential hemopoietic cells. *Blood* **98,** 328–334.
255. Lee, S.H., Lumelsky, N., Studer, L., Auerbach, J.M., and McKay, R.D. (2000). Efficient generation of midbrain and hindbrain neurons from mouse embryonic stem cells. *Nat. Biotechnol.* **18,** 675–679.
256. Viswanathan, S., Benatar, T., Rose-John, S., Lauffenburger, D.A., and Zandstra, W. (2002). Ligand/receptor signaling threshold (LIST) model accounts for gp130-mediated embryonic stem cell self-renewal responses to LIF and HIL-. *Stem Cells* **20,** 119–138.
257. Hadjantonakis, A.K., Dickinson, M.E., Fraser, S.E., and Papaioannou, V.E. (2003). Technicolor transgenics: imaging tools for functional genomics in the mouse. *Nat. Rev. Genet.* **4,** 613–625.
258. Modo, M., Cash, D., Mellodew, K., Williams, S.C., Fraser, S.E., Meade, T.J., Price, J., and Hodges, H. (2002). Tracking transplanted stem cell migration using bifunctional, contrast agent-enhanced, magnetic resonance imaging. *Neuroimage* **17,** 803–811.
259. Kuersten, S., and Goodwin, E.B. (2003). The power of the 3' UTR: Translational control and development. *Nat. Rev. Genet.* **4,** 626–637.
260. Houbaviy, H.B., Murray, M.F., and Sharp, A. (2003). Embryonic stem cell-specific MicroRNAs. *Dev. Cell* **5,** 351–358.
261. Kawasaki, H., and Taira, K. (2003). Hes1 is a target of microRNA-23 during retinoic-acid-induced neuronal differentiation of NT2 cells. *Nature* **423,** 838–842.
262. Zhu, J., Shendure, J., Mitra, R.D., and Church, G.M. (2003). Single molecule profiling of alternative pre-mRNA splicing. *Science* **301,** 836–838.
263. Levsky, J.M., Shenoy, S.M., Pezo, R.C., and Singer, R.H. (2002). Single-cell gene expression profiling. *Science* **297,** 836–840.
264. Hochedlinger, K., and Jaenisch, R. (2002). Monoclonal mice generated by nuclear transfer from mature B and T donor cells. *Nature* **415,** 1035–1038.
265. Hochedlinger, K., and Jaenisch, R. (2002). Nuclear transplantation: lessons from frogs and mice. *Curr. Opin. Cell Biol.* **14,** 741–748.
266. Rideout, W.M., 3rd, Hochedlinger, K., Kyba, M., Daley, G.Q., and Jaenisch, R. (2002). Correction of a genetic defect by nuclear transplantation and combined cell and gene therapy. *Cell* **109,** 17–27.

4

Evolution of Stem Cells

Hans Bode

With the expanding efforts to understand stem cells, it is becoming clear that an increasing number of the tissues in mammals contain stem cells. These efforts have shown, not too surprisingly, that stem cells exist in similar tissues in other vertebrates, such as chicks, zebra fish, and *Xenopus,* as well as more generally in bilaterians. Stem cells have been identified in more primitive deuterostomes such as the ascidian *Botryllus schlosseri,*[1] as well as in protostomes such as drosophila and planaria. These findings suggest that stem cells probably first appeared among the diploblasts. There is evidence for them in sponges[2,3] as well as in hydra, a cnidarian. Among the diploblasts, hydra is the most extensively understood in terms of its development. One of the prominent characteristics of the animal is that the adult consists of three cell lineages, each of which is a stem cell lineage. The stem cells of these three lineages have characteristics found in the stem cells of many organisms. However, there are some differences, suggesting that changes in the characteristics of stem cell lineages may have occurred during metazoan evolution.

Hydra: An Introduction

An adult hydra has a simple structure consisting of a single axis with radial symmetry (Fig. 4–1). The body column is a cylindrical shell made up of two epithelial layers, the ectoderm and the endoderm, surrounding a gastric cavity. The two tissue layers, which are separated by the mesoglea, a typical basement membrane, extend into the head at the apical end and into a foot at the basal end. The head consists of two parts. The upper half is the hypostome, or mouth region; the lower half is the tentacle zone from which a set of 5 to 7 evenly spaced tentacles emerge. Each epithelial layer is a stem cell lineage consisting of stem cells and three differentiation products.

All of the other somatic cells are part of the interstitial cell lineage and reside among the epithelial cells of one or both layers. These consist of the interstitial cells, a subset of which are multipotent stem cells. The three classes of somatic differentiation products are neurons, secretory cells, and nematocytes, the stinging cells characteristic of cnidarians. In addition, when hydra enters a sexual state, the interstitial cells also generate two types of unipotent stem cells, each of which give rise to one type of gamete, oocyte, or sperm. Thus, cells of this lineage make up about 80% of the cells in an adult hydra, and the multipotent stem cells generate at least 18 different cell types.

TISSUE DYNAMICS

In vertebrate adults, stem cell lineages such as those of the epidermis or the intestine are in an active steady state of production and loss of cells. Other tissues or organs are quiescent. In hydra, all three stem cell lineages are in a highly active steady state of production and loss of cells.

All epithelial cells of the body column are continuously in the mitotic cycle.[4] To balance this constant production and to maintain a steady-state size, cells are lost from an adult hydra in three ways (Fig. 4–1). Tissue in the upper third of the body column is displaced apically into the tentacle zone, from there primarily onto and along the tentacles, and eventually sloughed at the tentacle tips.[5] A small fraction (<10%) of the endodermal tissue is displaced into the hypostome and subsequently shed at the apex of the hypostome. In contrast, ectodermal tissue of the hypostome is a separate compartment. Ectodermal cells at the base of the hypostome divide, are displaced apically, and shed at the apex.[6] Tissue in the lower two-thirds of the body column is displaced basally.[5] In the peduncle, the lower quarter of the body column, tissue is displaced into the foot and sloughed. Loss at the extremities accounts for about 15% of the loss.[7]

The remaining 85% is lost during bud formation, hydra's form of asexual reproduction. In the budding zone, located 60–70% down the body column from the head (Fig. 4–1), a new bud appears as an evagination of the two epithelial layers. The evagination extends into a cylindrical protrusion, which subsequently forms a head at the distal end and a foot at the proximal end. When mature, it detaches, and when fed, it will grow into an adult in 4 to 6 days.

The cell populations of the interstitial cell lineage are also in a steady state of production and loss that matches that of the epithelial cells. As described in a later section, the dynamics of this steady state are a little more complex. Thus, the tissues of the entire adult hydra are in a steady state of production and loss.

Handbook of Stem Cells
Volume 2

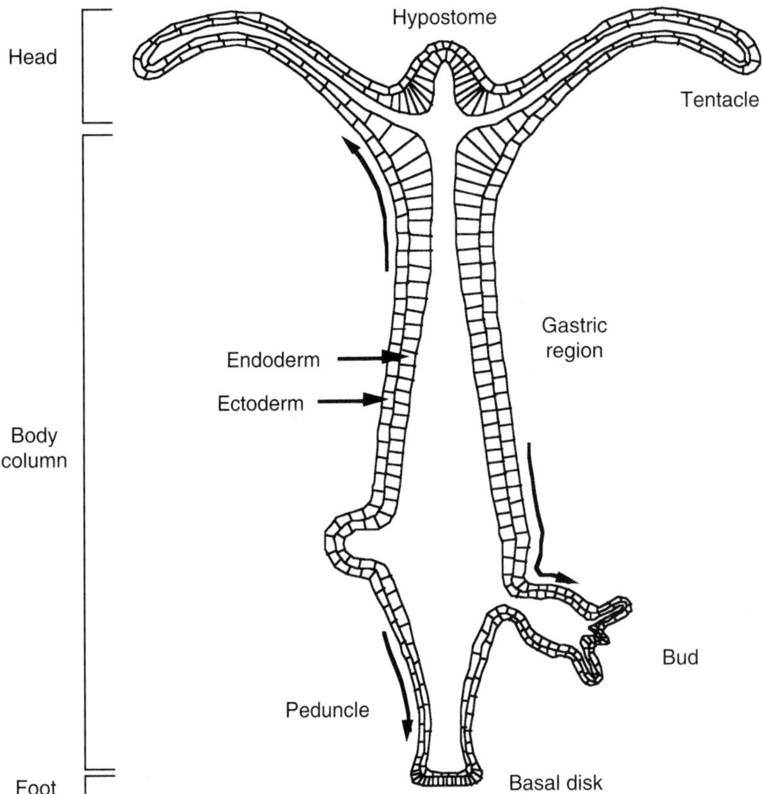

Figure 4-1. Longitudinal cross-section of an adult hydra. The regions and the two tissue layers are indicated. The protrusions from the body column are early and later stages of bud development, hydra's asexual form of reproduction. The arrows indicate the directions of tissue displacement. (Reprinted with permission of the editor of Integrative and Comparative Biology).

Each Epithelial Cell Lineage Is a Stem Cell Lineage

Several aspects of the epithelial cells of each of the two layers of the body column suggest that many, if not all of them, are stem cells.

PROLIFERATION CAPACITY

One characteristic is their extensive capacity for cell division. In an attempt to define the lifetime of a hydra, Martinez[8] fed and maintained 45 individual animals for 4 years. By the end of that period, each animal had produced on average 450 buds and was no different than at the beginning of the experiment. There was no sign of aging. A comparison of the maximum lifetime versus the age of first reproduction, or size, of a large number of animals indicates a fairly linear relationship.[8] The larger the animal, the longer it lives. Hydra is an exception; its lifetime is at least 20 times longer than animals with the same age of first reproduction.[8] Because the experiment was stopped after 4 years, no defined limit to the proliferation capacity of the epithelial cells is known.

Since all the epithelial cells in the body column are continuously in the mitotic cycle,[4] it is plausible that some or all are stem cells. That the stem cells in the epithelial layers are located throughout the body column is illustrated by the use of the regeneration capacity of a hydra. Isolation of a ring of body column tissue amounting to 1/10th of the body column leads to the regeneration of a head at the apical end and a foot at the basal end. When fed, the regenerate grows into a normal animal that propagates by budding indefinitely. The same result is obtained with rings of tissue isolated from any part of the body column except the lowest 1/10th, next to the foot. A similar experiment was carried out with excised pieces, each about 2% of the body column.[9,10] Here, too, complete animals regenerated from the small pieces and, when fed, grew into normal animals that could propagate indefinitely by budding. These results indicate that epithelial stem cells are distributed throughout at least 90% of the body column.

In summary, many of the epithelial cells have an apparently unlimited proliferation capacity, characteristic of stem cells. Because the ectoderm and endoderm always grow in concert in all of these experimental situations, similar numbers of stem cells exist in both layers. Whether all or only a fraction of the epithelial cells are stem cells remains unclear, although the apparently unlimited proliferation capacity of the epithelial cells suggests most, if not all, are stem cells.

DIFFERENTIATION CAPACITY

Epithelial cells of both layers divide throughout the animal until they are displaced into an extremity: the apical half of the hypostome, the tentacles, or the foot. When epithelial cells of either layer reach any of these extremities, they cease cell division and differentiate. Since an epithelial cell of the body column may end up in any of the three extremities, it can differentiate into one of three different cell types. This capacity is illustrated for the ectodermal epithelial cells in the following manner.

Tissue in the peduncle is invariably displaced onto the foot (Fig. 4–1), and the epithelial cells differentiate into the basal disk cells of the foot. Bisection of the body column below the budding zone invariably leads to the regeneration of a head at the apical end of the isolated peduncle + foot. Thus, the cells of the peduncle that normally will form a foot can also form the battery cells of the tentacles and the cells at the apex of the hypostome. A similar situation occurs during bud formation, when tissue that would otherwise be displaced into the peduncle, and eventually into the foot, becomes part of an evaginating bud (Fig. 4–1). When displaced onto a developing bud, tissue at the distal end of the emerging bud forms the tentacles and hypostome of the developing head.

Conversely, tissue of the upper third of the body column is invariably displaced into the head. Yet, when the animal is bisected in the upper quarter of the body column, a foot regenerates at the basal end of this piece. Hence, ectodermal epithelial cells destined to form cells of the tentacles can differentiate into basal disk cells. A similar set of events occurs in the endoderm. Thus, many, if not all, epithelial cells of the body column have the characteristics of a multipotent stem cell: they divide indefinitely and can differentiate into any of three different types of cells.

As tissue moves from the body column into an extremity, it shifts from a cell with stem cell-like qualities into a differentiated cell in two distinct steps. This is well documented for cells ending up in the tentacles and in the foot.

Differentiation of Epithelial Stem Cells into Battery Cells

In the upper part of the animal, the first step occurs at the head–body column border. When tissue is displaced apically from the body column into the tentacle zone, the epithelial cells continue to divide, but their differentiation capacity is restricted. Bisection directly below the head does not result in the regeneration of a foot. Instead, either a tentacle forms in the healed area or no structure forms. While traversing the tentacle zone, the epithelial cells continue to divide until they reach the tentacle zone–tentacle (TZ–T) border (Fig. 4–2a). Once having crossed the border, they cease dividing[11] and differentiate into battery cells, the differentiated cells of the tentacle ectoderm.

Several molecular markers indicate that the TZ–T border is sharp and that the transition is essentially from one cell to the next. *Cnox-3* and *Cnotx,* hydra orthologues of *labial* and *otx,*[12,13] as well as *Hym-301,* a gene encoding a peptide,[14] are all expressed in the tentacle zone but not in the tentacles (Fig. 4–2d). *Cnox-3* expression drops drastically[12] and *Hym-301* expression vanishes shortly below the head–body column border (Fig. 4–2d), providing molecular markers for changes in the cells as they are displaced from the body column into the tentacle zone. These changes could involve the reduction of the differentiation choices described in the regeneration experiments.

Another set is expressed along the length of the entire tentacle but not in the tentacle zone (Fig. 4–2b). These include TS-19, a monoclonal antibody that recognizes an unidentified cell surface antigen of the ectodermal cells of the tentacles[15]; the hydra laminin β-1 gene; and *HHMP,* a hydra matrix metalloprotease.[16] The sharpness of the border is most readily seen with the TS-19 antibody. The antigen is not expressed in the last cell on the tentacle zone side of the TZ–T border, but it is strongly expressed in the neighboring cell on the tentacle side of the border.[15] The sharp transition at the border occurs in both cell layers because some of these markers are expressed only in the ectoderm (*Cnox-3, Cnotx, Hym-301,* and TS-19); others are only in the endoderm (laminin β-1 and *HHMP*).

A third set of genes are expressed in a band that is 4 to 8 cells wide and overlaps the TZ–T border (Fig.4–2c). *HyAlx,* an *aristaless* orthologue,[17] is expressed in the ectoderm, and four others are expressed in the endoderm. These include pedibin, which encodes a peptide[18]; a hydra IQGAP gene[19]; HECE, which encodes an endothelin-converting enzyme[16]; and *HyBMP5-8b,* a BMP5-8b orthologue.[20] The expression pattern of these genes suggests a role for each in the transition of epithelial cells from the tentacle zone to the tentacle. This view is supported by the expression of these genes during *de novo* head formation. During head regeneration and bud formation, four of the five genes are expressed in a ring of spots in the developing tentacle zone. Subsequently, the center of each spot fades, and a tentacle emerges through each spot, resulting in the adult pattern. Hence, any of these genes may play a role in either tentacle morphogenesis or the transition from dividing to differentiating cells.

Using functional assays, the roles of two of the several genes expressed in the vicinity of the TZ–T border have been further delineated. *Hym-301,* expressed in the tentacle zone, plays a role in determining the number of tentacles formed around the circumference of the tentacle zone. When the peptide, HYM-301, is added to decapitated animals, an increased number of tentacles form.[14] Using RNAi by introducing Hym-301 dsRNA into an early-stage developing bud by electroporation, the number of tentacles formed was decreased. Application of the RNAi technique using HyAlx dsRNA resulted in a significant delay in the emergence of tentacles during bud formation.[17] This indicates that the gene plays a role in either tentacle morphogenesis or differentiation, or possibly both.

Differentiation of Epithelial Stem Cells into Foot Cells

A similar two-step transition exists at the peduncle–foot (P–F) border (Fig. 4–3a). Epithelial cells displaced basally beyond the budding zone continue to divide but shift from cylindrical to a flatter shape. When they reach the lower eighth to tenth of

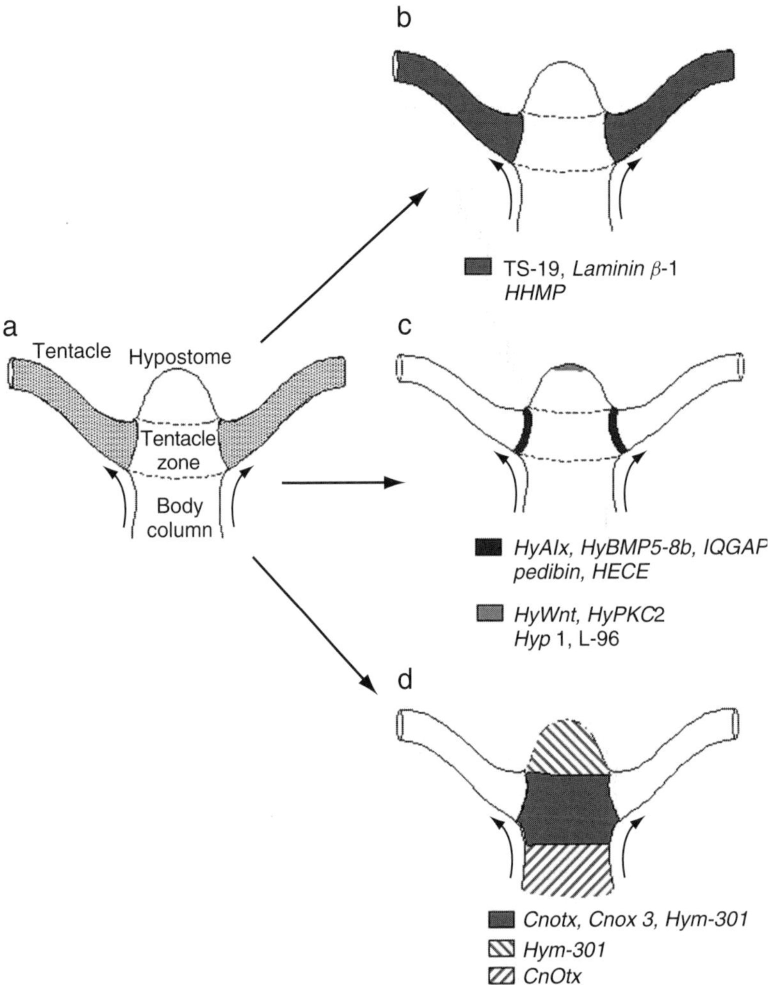

Figure 4–2. Expression patterns of genes that border the tentacle zone–tentacle (TZ–T) border, showing (a) regions of the head. The TZ–T border is the transition point from the clear area of the tentacle zone to the dotted region of the tentacle. Expression patterns of genes are expressed (b) in the tentacle, (c) at the TZ–T border, and (d) in the tentacle zone. Genes expressed in the apex of the hypostome are also indicated in (c).

the body column, the tissue is no longer capable of head regeneration. An animal bisected in this basal region of the body column does not regenerate a head, which indicates that the differentiation capacity of this region has been restricted to basal disk formation. Upon crossing the P–F border (Fig. 4–3a), the cells cease dividing and differentiate into the basal disk cells of the foot.

Here, too, there are three sets of genes expressed specifically in one of three regions of the lower part of the animal associated with the P–F border. The first set consists of genes whose expression is very high in the peduncle tissue as it is displaced basally toward the P–F border but stops abruptly at the border (Fig. 4–3b). These include *CnNK-2,* a hydra *NK-2* orthologue[21] as well as three genes expressed in the T–TZ region: *pedibin,*[18] *laminin β-1,*[16] and *HyBMP5-8b.*[20] The second set is expressed in a band of tissue spanning the border (Fig. 4–3c). The three genes are *manacle,* a paired-like gene; *shinguard,* a receptor tyrosine kinase[22]; and an insulin receptor gene.[23] Finally, *ppod1,* a gene encoding a foot-specific peroxidase,[24] and *HECE*[16] are expressed strongly all over the foot, but expression stops abruptly at the P–F border. *HyPKC2,* a hydra PKC orthologue, is expressed strongly at the base of the foot, fading out by the P–F border.[25] Here, too, some of them are expressed in the ectoderm (manacle, shinguard, and ppod1), and others are expressed in the endoderm (*CnNK-2,* PKC2, *pedibin, HECE,* and *laminin β-1*).

Thus, the sharp TZ–T and P–F borders of expression of three sets of genes indicate that a sudden transition in cell behavior occurs. This is tightly coupled with the abrupt cessation of cell division and the initiation of cell differentiation as cells cross each of these borders. Whether a similar phenomenon exists at the division–differentiation border in

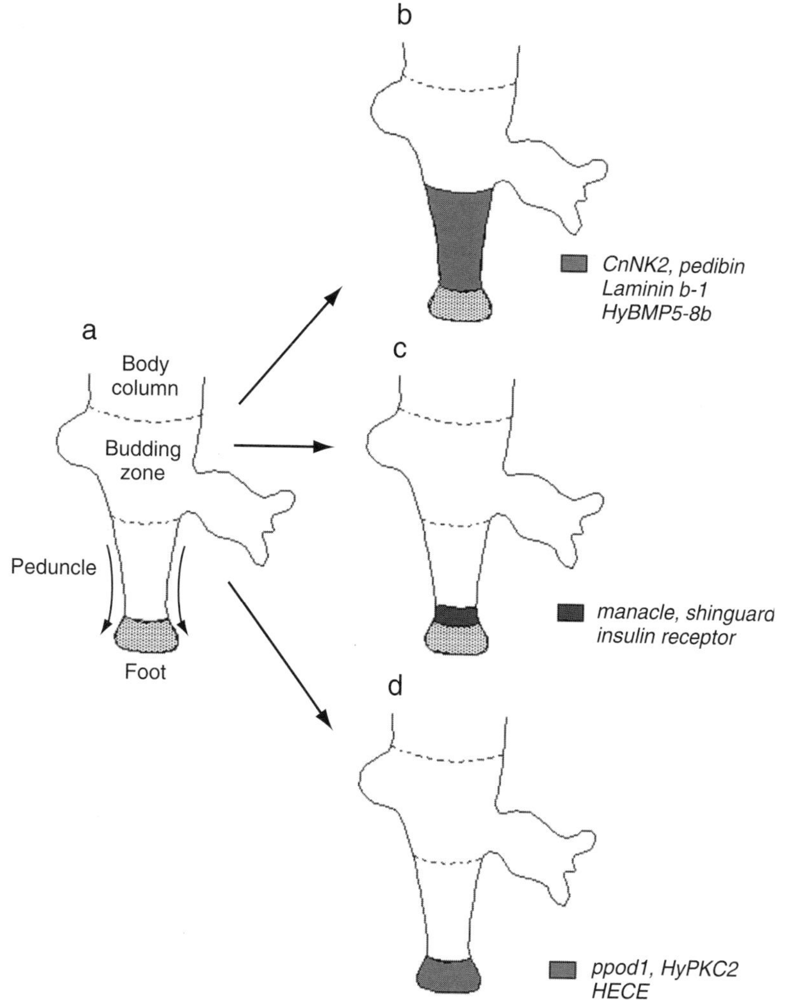

Figure 4–3. Expression patterns of genes that border the peduncle–foot (P–F) border, showing (a) regions of the lower body column. The P–F border separates the dotted region of the foot from the clear region of the peduncle. Expression patterns of genes are expressed (b) in the peduncle, (c) at the P–F border, and (d) in the foot.

the apical part of the hypostome occurs is not clear. However, the fact that four genes are expressed in either the ectoderm or the endoderm of the hypostome apex (Fig. 4–2c) suggests a similar situation. These genes are *HyWnt,* a hydra Wnt homologue[26]; *HyPKC2,* the same gene as expressed in the foot[25]; *Hyp1,* which encodes a peptide[27]; and L96, an antibody that recognizes an antigen in these differentiated cells.[28]

DIFFERENTIATION OF EPITHELIAL STEM CELLS IS CONTROLLED BY AXIAL PATTERNING PROCESSES

The behavior of the epithelial cells is clearly position dependent. Epithelial cells in the body column are in the mitotic cycle; those near the head or foot become restricted in their differentiation potential and then differentiate when displaced into an extremity. The morphology of the adult is in a similar situation. The morphology of the body column is continuously converted to that of the head when tissue is displaced apically and to that of the foot when displaced basally. These morphological changes are controlled by axial patterning processes. Normally in animal embryos, axial patterning processes set up, for example, the regions of the animal along the anterior–posterior and dorsal–ventral axes. Similarly, such processes set up the three regions (head, body column, and foot) of the oral–aboral axis in a hydra embryo. However, in hydra, these processes remain active in the adult to maintain this axis in the context of the tissue dynamics. Most likely, these axial patterning processes affect the behavior of the epithelial stem cells.

The critical elements of the axial patterning mechanism are the following: The head organizer in the hypostome produces two signals that are transmitted to the body column.[29] One signal sets up a morphogenetic gradient along the oral–aboral axis with a maximum in the head. This is a gradient of head formation capacity, which has been referred to as a gradient of positional value,[30] a source density gradient,[31,32] or a head activation gradient.[33] It is this gradient that provides the body column with the capacity for head regeneration.

The second signal, the head inhibition signal, is also graded down the body column and prevents this tissue from forming a head.[34] Because this signal has a short half-life, decapitation leads to a rapid decay of head inhibition, thereby allowing the head formation capacity of the body column to initiate head regeneration. To maintain the steady state of the adult, the organizer continuously produces both signals, which maintain the graded distributions of both head activation and head inhibition. Although not as well understood, there is evidence for foot activation[35] and inhibition gradients.[36]

It is likely that the behavior of the epithelial cells in the upper part of the body column is coupled with the head activation gradient. As tissue is displaced up the column, the level of head activation in the tissue rises. Upon reaching the tentacle zone, the level surpasses a threshold value, thereby specifying the cells for differentiation into cells of the tentacle and the tissue for tentacle morphogenesis.

This view is supported by treatment of hydra with diacylglycerol or 2 mM LiCl, which raises the head activation gradient throughout the body column as measured by transplantation experiments.[37,38] A gradient increase would be expected to shift the threshold level for tentacle formation down the body column. Animals treated with 2 mM LiCl form ectopic tentacles in the upper third of the body column,[39] indicating that this has occurred. The expression pattern of two genes supports this view. *Hym-301* is normally expressed in the head but not the body column (Fig. 4–2d). Following LiCl treatment, it is expressed throughout most of the body column,[14] suggesting that the body column has taken on the characteristic of the tentacle zone to form tentacles. Conversely, *Cnox-2,* the hydra orthologue of the ParaHox gene, *GSX,* is normally expressed throughout the body column but not in the head.[40] After treatment with diacylglycerol, *Cnox-2* expression is restricted to the lower part of the body column,[40] indicating that the upper part has taken on characteristics of the head.

In addition, *HyAlx,* expressed as spots just prior to the emergence of tentacle buds in a developing head, is also expressed in spots on the body column shortly before the appearance of ectopic tentacles.[17] Finally, the ectopic tentacles that form express battery cell-specific markers, such as TS-19, indicate that the epithelial cells on these tentacles have undergone the normal pattern of differentiation.[41] These results indicate that tentacle formation and, hence, the differentiation of ectodermal epithelial stem cells into battery cells are controlled by the axial patterning processes. Although the other switches from division to differentiation have not been examined in the same detail, it is likely that they too are controlled by these patterning processes.

In summary, the two epithelial layers have characteristics of cell lineages containing stem cells. Epithelial cells in the body column of both layers have characteristics of multipotent stem cells. They have an unlimited capacity for cell proliferation and the capability to differentiate into three types of cells. Cells approaching an extremity continue to divide, but they have a reduced range of differentiation capacity; those in the extremities are differentiated cells.

Interstitial Cell Lineage

As described previously, all of the nonepithelial cells are part of the third cell lineage, the interstitial cell lineage. In the asexual adult, the lineage consists of multipotent stem cells and three classes of somatic cell differentiation products (Fig. 4–4). These will be described in the context of the tissue dynamics of an adult hydra.

INTERSTITIAL CELLS

Because of the continuous expansion and displacement of the epithelial tissues in the body column, the stem cells of the interstitial cell lineage are constantly in the process of producing differentiated cells to maintain the cell composition of the animal in a steady state. The interstitial cells are scattered among the epithelial cells of both layers of the hypostome, tentacle zone, and body column, but they are absent in the tentacles and foot.[42] Stem cells among these interstitial cells are also distributed along the length of the body column, as shown with regeneration experiments. As mentioned previously, a whole hydra will regenerate from 1/10th of the body column isolated from any part of the upper 90% of the body column. Such regenerates have and maintain a normal distribution of cells of the interstitial cell lineage.

Of critical importance is the maintenance of this stem cell population. They would be expected to be continuously dividing to maintain their own density and population size in the context of the ever-dividing epithelial cells. Continuous labeling experiments have shown that the entire population of interstitial cells is constantly in the mitotic cycle with a cell cycle time of ~24 h,[43] which is consistent with this expectation.

INTERSTITIAL CELLS ARE MULTIPOTENT

The approach was similar to that demonstrating the presence of multipotent stem cells in the hematopoietic cell lineage of mice,[44] and it used an aggregation technique. Hydra can be dissociated into a suspension of viable cells, and the cells pelleted. The resulting pellet, or aggregate, of cells will develop into one or more normal animals, depending on how large the aggregate is.[45] The process involves the sorting out of epithelial cells to the appropriate layer to form a two-layer, spherical shell. The cells of the interstitial lineage settle among the epithelial cells of the appropriate layer. Then, patterning processes take place, setting up one or more equally spaced head organizers, which then organize surrounding tissue into one or more complete animals.

To demonstrate the range of the differentiation capacity of interstitial cells, aggregates were made that combined cells from two kinds of animals. Most cells were derived from animals in which the interstitial cells had been eliminated by treatment with nitrogen mustard cells, while small numbers of normal animals provided the interstitial cells.[46] About 20% of the aggregates exhibited a single clone containing interstitial cells and differentiation products. The remaining aggregates did not contain clones and were devoid of interstitial cells 10–14 days after the aggregates were formed. Each clone contained interstitial cells, neurons, nematocytes, and

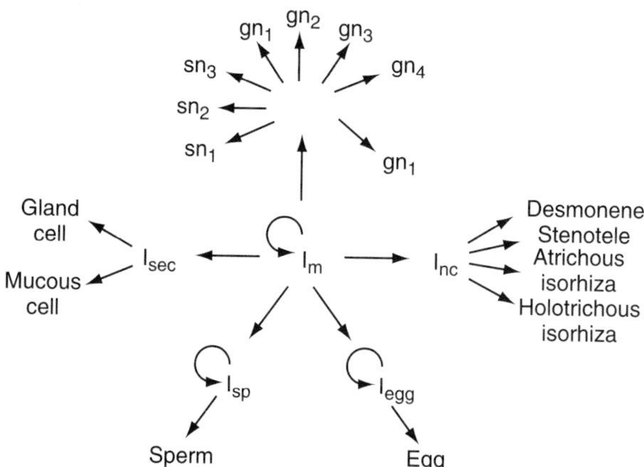

Figure 4–4. Interstitial cell lineage. Among the interstitial cells are multipotent stem cells (I_m), unipotent stem cells for sperm and egg (I_{sp} and I_{egg}), and cells committed to the differentiation of secretory cells (I_{sec}), neurons (I_{nv}), and nematocytes (I_{nc}). The two types of secretory cells and four types of nematocytes are named. Among the neurons are three types of sensory cells (sn) and >7 ganglionic cells.

secretory cells.[46] More direct evidence was provided by pulse-labeling the cells of aggregates several days after formation with 3H-TdR.[46] Those few aggregates that contained labeled interstitial cells also contained labeled interstitial cell differentiation products. These results indicate that a single interstitial cell can produce the several cell types associated with the interstitial cell lineage and is, thus, multipotent. Similar experiments carried out later resulted in clones containing oocytes, providing more direct evidence that the multipotent stem cell also produces gametes.[47]

One last point is that the stem cells among the interstitial cells are confined to the ectoderm, as shown in the following way: Aggregates were made involving endoderm cells of normal animals and ectoderm cells of animals in which all cells of the interstitial cell lineage had been removed. The aggregates developed into normal animals, but they lacked interstitial cells, nematocytes, or neurons.[48] Hence, there are no interstitial stem cells in the endoderm.

THREE CLASSES OF SOMATIC DIFFERENTIATION PRODUCTS

Because each of the three classes of differentiation products (neurons, secretory cells, and nematocytes) has a distinct distribution within the animal, the processes involved in maintaining each class are slightly different.

Neurons

The neurons are the most diverse class of the differentiated cell types (Fig. 4–4). Ganglionic neurons located near the base of each epithelial layer form a net that extends throughout the animal. Neuronal processes weave through the basement membrane between the two epithelial layers, connecting the neurons. There are at least seven ganglionic cell types based on the combination of neuropeptides or neuronal prehormone genes expressed in a particular ganglion cell.[49] Each type has a particular regional distribution throughout the animal. In addition, sensory cells are located at the surface among the epithelial cells in a random pattern and are connected into the net. The population of each of the three types of sensory neurons has specific locations: head ectoderm, foot ectoderm, or body column endoderm.[50–53]

The nerve net in the body column has a fairly constant density. As the epithelial cells divide, the neuron density decreases. To balance the continuous cell division of all the epithelial cells, interstitial cells continuously differentiate into neurons, many of which are spliced into the neighboring net to maintain the density.

Another aspect of maintaining the net deals with the higher density of neurons in the extremities. The density of the nerve net is 6–10 times higher in the head and 3–4 times higher in the foot than in the body column.[42] The difference is caused by the immigration of neuron differentiation intermediates into the extremities.[54,55] In the upper body column, many of the neuron precursors migrate into the head, differentiate, and splice into the net. The remaining precursors differentiate in place and are integrated into neighboring parts of the net in the body column. Similarly, in the lower body column, some neuron precursors migrate preferentially toward the foot, differentiate, and integrate; the rest differentiate and splice into the net in the body column.[55] Hence, the migration of precursors plays a significant role in the maintenance of the higher neuron density in the extremities.

Secretory Cells

The second class consists of two kinds of secretory cells, the gland cells and the mucous cells (Fig. 4–4). They are located among the endodermal epithelial cells and face the gastric cavity. The gland cells, which release digestive enzymes, are located in the body column, while the mucous cells are primarily in the hypostome and are involved in the ingestion of food into the gastric cavity. Stem cells committed to secretory cell differentiation migrate radially from the ectoderm into the endoderm, differentiate, move to the surface, and link to neighboring epithelial cells. As with the neurons in the body column, the stem cells continuously produce gland cells and mucous cells to maintain their density in the expanding endoderm.

Nematocytes

The third class of somatic cell differentiation products are the nematocytes, of which there are four types in hydra (Fig. 4–4). These are the stinging cells characteristic of cnidarians. The main feature of the cell is an organelle, termed the nematocyst, which consists of a capsule containing a tightly coiled thread. Each nematocyte is embedded in a pocket of an ectodermal epithelial cell of the body column or in a battery cell of the tentacle ectoderm. Emerging from the pocket into the surrounding medium is a sensory hair, or cnidocil, connected to the capsule. Interaction with the cnidocil violently releases the thread, resulting in the capture of prey or the warding off of predators.

The primary factor in maintaining the normal distribution of nematocytes throughout the animal involves long-distance migration of freshly differentiated nematocytes. About 90% of the nematocytes are mounted in the ectodermal battery cells of the tentacles, where each battery cell contains 15–20 embedded nematocytes.[55] With the continuous sloughing of battery cells at the tentacle tips, there is a continuous loss of nematocytes. Since nematocyte differentiation takes place in the body column, maintenance of the nematocyte populations in the tentacles takes place by the migration. Newly differentiated nematocytes migrate apically among the ectodermal epithelial cells, along the body column, and into the tentacles. They become mounted primarily in ectodermal epithelial cells recently displaced onto tentacles.[56]

Thus, the maintenance of the several populations of interstitial cell differentiation products in the context of hydra's tissue dynamics occurs primarily in one, or both, of two ways. One is maintaining a local density of a differentiated cell type by continuous differentiation of stem cells to match the continuous division of the epithelial cells. This occurs primarily for the neurons and the secretory cells of the body column. The other involves continuous production of differentiated cell types coupled with migration to maintain high densities of the differentiated cell types in an extremity. The maintenance of the nematocyte populations in the tentacles is the most dramatic example. The increased density of neurons in both head and foot is also maintained in this manner.

AXIAL LOCATION IS A MAJOR FACTOR AFFECTING DIFFERENTIATION DECISIONS

Because the interstitial cell lineage consists of three classes of somatic cell types, which include >18 of differentiation products, the number of factors affecting commitment decisions could be large. A major factor influencing these decisions is the axial location of the stem cell or a cell further down a differentiation pathway. This is true for all three classes.

For nematocytes, the type of nematocyst capsule being differentiated is recognizable during an intermediate stage in the differentiation pathway.[57] This provides a means for identifying the type being formed. The axial distributions vary for each type. Desmonemes are formed predominantly in the upper half of the body column, stenoteles in the lower half, and the two types of isorhizas fairly uniformly throughout the body column.[58] These differences indicate that the type of nematocyte formed by a stem cell committed to nematocyte differentiation is influenced by its axial location in the body column.

A few hints as to the basis of these differences are known. The head produces an inhibitor of stenotele formation,[59] which is transmitted to the body column and could reduce the number of interstitial cells committed to stenotele formation in the upper half of the animal. Or, it could prevent the differentiation of stem cells committed to stenotele formation. Inhibition mechanisms related to axial location play additional roles in nematocyte differentiation. Interstitial cells differentiate into neurons and secretory cells but not into nematocytes in the head. When head tissue is dissociated, and aggregates are formed, the resulting animals contain nematoblast nests.[60] This indicates that interstitial cells capable of nematocyte differentiation are in the head. Whether these are stem cells prevented from commitment to nematocytes or they are committed interstitial cells prevented from differentiation is unclear. There is evidence for the latter possibility. As head regeneration takes place following bisection in the mid-body column, all nematocyte differentiation intermediates rapidly disappear.[61]

Similar axial influences exist for the secretory and neuron classes. Stem cells committed to secretory cell formation migrate radially from the ectoderm into the endoderm, undergo differentiation, and are inserted among the epithelial cells facing the gastric cavity.[48,62] Stem cells committed to secretory cell formation differentiate into gland cells in the body column and into mucous cells in the head, reflecting an axial-dependent choice of type.

For neurons, the decision as to type may take place further down the differentiation pathway. Neuron differentiation occurs from the head down to the foot. Different subsets of neurons are associated with specific axial locations as defined by antibodies against neuropeptides or other neuron antigens.[49] As mentioned previously, the higher neuron density in the head and foot arises from a combination of localized neuron differentiation coupled with the immigration of neuron differentiation intermediates from the body column. That the type of neuron formed is dependent on its axial location was demonstrated in the following manner: in the lower body column, neuron precursors migrate into the foot and form foot-specific neurons.[54] When the lower part of the body column is transplanted to the upper body column, the neuron precursors will migrate into the head and form head-specific neurons.[63] This implies that the neuron precursor is reacting to signals from its immediate surroundings as to the type of neuron formed.

Changes in Cell Type as Cell Changes Axial Location

Another aspect in which axial location-dependent factors play a significant role in the differentiated state of neurons and secretory cells is related to tissue displacement. Once cells of either class are differentiated and inserted into the nerve net or among epithelial cells, they are displaced up or down the body column with their neighboring epithelial cells. Thus, neurons inserted into the nerve net in the upper third of the body column will be displaced into the head. Such neurons will change their phenotype from one type of neuron to another. For example, a subset of neurons that exhibit a FMRF amide-like immunoreactivity (FLI+) and illustrate this point is located in the head but not in the upper body column.[64] When animals in which the interstitial cells and all differentiation intermediates have been removed are decapitated, they will regenerate a head that contains FLI+ neurons.[65] Most likely FLI– neurons were converted into FLI+ neurons. In this case, the axial dependence of neuron type can be attributed to the head activation gradient, which, as described previously, plays a major role in axial patterning. When animals are treated with diacylglycerol, the level of head activation rises throughout the body column.[37] In such animals, the lower boundary of the FLI+ subset is displaced down into the body column, suggesting that FLI+ neurons appear above a threshold level of head activation. Normally, that level is in the head, but in diacylglycerol-treated animals, it has been displaced down the body column.

A similar situation exists for the secretory cells. When body column tissue is displaced into the tentacle zone, the gland cells disappear and mucous cells appear. By the time the tissue has reached the hypostome, there are large numbers of mucous cells but no gland cells. This could reflect a position-dependent conversion of gland cells into mucous cells. Or, it could reflect a position-dependent differentiation of mucous cells coupled with the loss of gland cells. Certainly the latter occurs in most of the endodermal tissue as it is displaced into the tentacles, which are devoid of gland cells.[42]

Thus, axial location-dependent influences can control the type of cell formed as well as subsequent switching of the type within a class. Although the head activation gradient is the most likely of the axial-dependent influences, and plausibly an important one, there must be multiple influences. The example of the stenotele inhibitor is one. In general, stem cells differentiate into cells of each class at all axial locations in the body column. What varies is the fraction of interstitial cells committed to a particular type within a class.

Evolutionary Context

In summary, all of the cells of an adult hydra belong to three cell lineages, each of which contains a multipotent stem cell that creates several differentiation products. These hydra lineages have some characteristics of bilaterian lineages containing stem cells as well as some characteristics not found in those lineages. Commonly, such a lineage contains a stem cell with a large and indefinite proliferation potential as well as the capacity to differentiate into one or more differentiation products. The stem cell has no physiological function such as that of a blood cell or muscle cell.

The interstitial cell lineage has similar characteristics. The stem cells among the interstitial cells have a large, and probably indefinite, potential for cell division because there is no known lifetime for a hydra, and if fed, the interstitial cells divide continuously. In addition, these stem cells have no known functions other than to divide and to differentiate. They have no known physiological function. Because the interstitial cells and the differentiation products are all single cells that remain in a mesenchymal state, this cell lineage, in its characteristics, is reminiscent of the hematopoietic stem cell lineage.

The two epithelial stem cell lineages of hydra share some characteristics with bilaterian epithelial stem cell lineages, but there are also some differences. In the skin or the lining of the gut in vertebrates, the differentiated cells face the external environment, and the stem cells at the base of the tissue layer are sequestered from the environment. In hydra, the geometry is different, but the situation is similar. The stem cells of the two epithelial layers are in the body column, and the differentiated cells are in the extremities, where interaction with the environment, the substrate for the foot, and the surrounding world for the tentacles and hypostome is more pronounced. Like the stem cells of epithelial layers, those of the ectoderm and endoderm in hydra have an apparently endless capacity for cell division.

However, there is a significant difference. The epithelial stem cells of both layers in the body column of hydra have physiological functions. The ectodermal epithelial cells act as a protective layer, as would the keratinocytes of an epidermis. Because there is no physical barrier to the surrounding aqueous medium, these cells are also involved in osmoregulation. Water is continuously transported from the external medium into vacuoles within the ectodermal epithelial cells and is subsequently transported into the gut. In the endoderm, the epithelial cells function as digestive cells. Further, all epithelial cells of both layers have muscle processes that control contraction of the body column along the axis.

The fact that the epithelial cells have more than one function may reflect the simple structure of a hydra. It has few cell types, and hence, unlike more complex metazoans with many cell types, a specific cell type probably has to take on more than one function. Thus, the epithelial cells of the body column of a hydra act not only as stem cells but also carry out one or more physiological functions.

Some of these characteristics are also in the Placozoa and sponges, more primitive diploblasts and plausibly the evolutionary ancestors of the cnidarians. Although not well understood, *Trichoplax adhaerens,* the one known member of the phylum Placozoa, has four cell types that appear to divide indefinitely.[66] The small, pancake-shaped creature maintains its limited size by periodically undergoing binary fission. Thus, these cells have the high proliferation capacity associated with stem cells, but each cell type also carries out a physiological function. Little is known about the differentiation capacity or origin of any of these cells.

The members of the phylum Porifera, or sponges, are more complex, consisting of 12 or more cell types.[2,3] The major classes are the epithelial cells, contractile cells, and skeletal cells that make up the structure of the sponge. The archaeocytes are multipotent stem cells that continuously divide and generate most of the somatic cells as well as the gametes.[3] Because sponges grow indefinitely, these stem cells are probably continuously generating the three cell types. Interestingly, the archaeocytes also have a physiological function because they act as digestive cells.

The characteristics of the cells in these primitive diploblasts suggest that stem cells may have evolved in the following manner: In early metazoans, most cells apparently had a large, if not unlimited, capacity for proliferation coupled with one or more physiological functions. Then, as the complexity of the animal increased and more physiological functions arose, some cells acquired the stem cell characteristic of serving as a source for nondividing differentiated cells. Yet these cells retained one or more physiological functions. The archaeocytes of sponges and the body column epithelial cells of hydra are examples. As the complexity increased further, the next step was the loss of the physiological function of the stem cells so that they adopted the characteristics commonly associated with stem cells in bilaterians: an unlimited capacity for proliferation and the source of one or more types of differentiated cells. The interstitial cell lineage of hydra appears to be an example of this last transition.

REFERENCES

1. Laird, D., and Weissman, I.L. (2002). Somatic stem cells in a protochordate. Keystone Symposium, "Stem cells: Origins, fates, and functions," pp. 80.
2. Simpson, T.L. (1984). "The Cell Biology of Sponges." Springer-Verlag, New York.
3. Harrison, F.W., and De Vos, L. (1991). Porifera. *In* "Microscopic Anatomy of Invertebrates," (F.W. Harrison and J.A. Westfall, eds.), Vol. 2, pp. 29–90. John Wiley & Sons, New York.
4. David, C.N., and Campbell, R.D. (1972). Cell cycle kinetics and development of *Hydra attenuata:* I. Epithelial cells. *J. Cell Sci.* **11,** 557–568.
5. Campbell, R.D. (1967). Tissue dynamics of steady state growth in *Hydra littoralis:* II. Patterns of tissue movement. *J. Morphol.* **121,** 19–28.
6. Dubel, S. (1989). Cell differentiation in the head of hydra. *Differentiation* **41,** 99–109.
7. Otto, J.J., and Campbell, R.D. (1977). Tissue economics of hydra: regulation of cell cycle, animal size, and development by controlled feeding rates. *J. Cell Sci.* **28,** 117–132.
8. Martinez, D.Z. (1998). Mortality patterns suggest lack of senescence in hydra. *Experimental Gerontology* **33,** 217–225.
9. Bode, P.M., and Bode, H.R. (1980). Formation of pattern in regenerating tissue pieces of *Hydra attenuata:* I. Head-body proportion regulation. *Dev. Biol.* **78,** 484–496.
10. Shimizu, H., Sawada, Y., and Sugiyama, T. (1993). Minimum tissue size required for hydra regeneration. *Dev. Biol.* **155,** 287–296.
11. Holstein, T.W., Hobmayer, E., and David, C.N. (1991). Pattern of epithelial cell cycling in hydra. *Dev. Biol.* **148,** 602–611.
12. Bode, H.R. (2001). The role of Hox genes in axial patterning in hydra. *Amer. Zool.* **41,** 621–628.
13. Smith, K.M., Gee, L., Blitz, I.L., and Bode, H.R. (1999). Cnotx, a member of the otx gene family, has a role in cell movement in hydra. *Dev. Biol.* **212,** 392–404.
14. Takahashi, T., Hatta, M., Yum, S., Koizumi, O., Kobayakawa, Y., Ohtani, M., Fujisawa, T., and Bode, H.R. (In preparation). A novel epitheliopeptide, Hym-301, plays a role in tentacle formation in hydra.
15. Bode, P.M., Awad, T.A., Koizumi, O., Nakashima, Y., Grimmelikhuijzen, C.J., and Bode, H.R. (1988). Development of the two-part pattern during regeneration of the head in hydra. *Development* **102,** 223–235.
16. Sarras, M.P., Jr., Yan, L., Leontovich, A., and Zhang, J.S. (2002). Structure, expression, and developmental function of early divergent forms of metalloproteinases in hydra. *Cell Res.* **12,** 163–176.
17. Smith, K.M., Gee, L., and Bode, H.R. (2000). HyAlx, an aristaless-related gene, is involved in tentacle formation in hydra. *Development* **127,** 4743–4752.
18. Hoffmeister-Ullerich, S.A. (2001). The foot formation stimulating peptide pedibin is also involved in patterning of the head in hydra. *Mech. Dev.* **106,** 37–45.
19. Venturelli, C.R., Kuznetsov, S., Salgado, L.M., and Bosch, T.C.G. (2000) An IQGAP-related gene is activated during tentacle formation in the simple metazoan hydra. *Dev. Genes Evol.* **210,** 458–463.
20. Reinhardt, B., Broun, M., Blitz, I.L., and Bode, H.R. (2004). HyBMP5-8b, a BMP5-8 orthologue, acts during axial patterning and tentacle formation in hydra. *Dev. Biol.* **267,** 43–59.
21. Grens, A., Gee, L., Fisher, D.A., and Bode, H.R. (1996). CnNK-2, an NK-2 homeobox gene, has a role in patterning the basal end of the axis in hydra. *Dev. Biol.* **180,** 473–488.
22. Bridge, D.M., Stover, N.A., and Steele, R.E. (2000). Expression of a novel receptor tyrosine kinase gene and a paired-like homeobox gene provides evidence of differences in patterning at the oral and aboral ends of hydra. *Dev. Biol.* **220,** 253–262.
23. Steele, R.E., Lieu, P., Mai, N.H., Shenk, M.A., and Sarras, M.P., Jr. (1996). Response to insulin and the expression pattern of a gene encoding an insulin receptor homologue suggest a role for an insulin-like molecule regulating growth and development in hydra. *Dev. Genes Evol.* **206,** 247–259.
24. Hoffmeister-Ullerich, S.A., Herrmann, D., Kielholz, J., Schweizer, M., and Schaller, H.C. (2002). Isolation of a putative peroxidase, a target for factors controlling foot-formation in the coelenterate hydra. *Eur. J. Biochem.* **269,** 4597–4606.
25. Hassel, M., Bridge, D.M., Stover, N.A., Kleinholz, H., and Steele, R.E. (1998). The level of expression of a protein kinase C gene may be an important component of the patterning process in hydra. *Dev. Genes. Evol.* **207,** 502–514.
26. Hobmayer, B., Rentzsch, F., Kuhn, K., Happel, C.M., von Laue, C.C., Snyder, P., Rothbacher, U., and Holstein, T.W. (2000). Wnt signaling molecules act in axis formation in the diploblastic metazoan hydra. *Nature* **407,** 186–189.
27. Hermans-Borgmeyer, I., Schinke, B., Schaller, H.C., and Hoffmeister-Ullerich, S.A. (1996). Isolation of a marker for head-specific cell differentiation in hydra. *Differentiation* **61,** 95–101.
28. Technau, U., and Holstein, T.W. (1995). Head formation in hydra is different at the apical and basal levels. *Development* **121,** 1273–1282.
29. Broun, M., and Bode, H.R. (2002). Characterization of the head organizer in hydra. *Development* **129,** 875–884.
30. Wolpert, L. (1971). Positional information and pattern formation. *Curr. Top. Dev. Biol.* **6,** 183–224.
31. Gierer, A., and Meinhardt, H. (1972). A theory of biological pattern formation. *Kybernetik* **12,** 30–39.
32. Meinhardt, H. (1993). A model for pattern formation of hypostome, tentacles, and foot in hydra: How to form structures close to each other, how to form them at a distance. *Dev. Biol.* **157,** 321–333.
33. MacWilliams, H.K. (1983). Hydra transplantation phenomena and the mechanism of hydra head regeneration: II. Properties of the head activation. *Dev. Biol.* **96,** 239–257.
34. MacWilliams, H.K. (1983). Hydra transplantation phenomena and the mechanism of hydra head regeneration: I. Properties of the head inhibition. *Dev. Biol.* **96,** 217–238.
35. Hicklin, J., and Wolpert, L. (1973). Positional information and pattern regulation in hydra: formation of the foot end. *J. Embryol. Exp. Morphol.* **30,** 727–740.
36. Cohen, J.E., and MacWilliams, H.K. (1975). The control of foot formation in transplantation experiments with *Hydra viridis. J. Theor. Biol.* **50,** 87–105.
37. Muller, W.A. (1990). Ectopic head and foot formation in hydra: diacylglycerol-induced increase in positional value and assistance of the head in foot formation. *Differentiation* **42,** 131–143.
38. Maggiore, C., and Bode, H.R. (Unpublished results).

39. Hassel, M., Albert, K., and Hofheinz, S. (1993). Pattern formation in *Hydra vulgaris* is controlled by lithium-sensitive processes. *Dev. Biol.* **156,** 362–371.
40. Shenk, M.A., Gee, L., Steele, R.E., and Bode, H.R. (1993). Expression of Cnox-2, a Hom/Hox gene, is suppressed during head formation in hydra. *Dev. Biol.* **160,** 108–118.
41. Broun, M., and Bode, H.R. (Unpublished results).
42. Bode, H.R., Berking, S., David, C.N., Gierer, A., Schaller, C.H., and Trenkner, E. (1973). Quantitative analysis of cell types during growth and morphogenesis in hydra. *Wilhelm Roux's Arch. Dev. Biol.* **171,** 269–285.
43. Campbell, R.D., and David, C.N. (1974). Cell cycle kinetics and development of *Hydra attenuata:* II. Interstitial cells. *J. Cell Sci.* **16,** 349–358.
44. Till, J.E., McCulloch, E.A., and Siminovitch, L. (1964). A stochastic model of stem cell proliferation based on the growth of spleen colony-forming units. *Proc. Nat. Acad. Sci. USA* **51,** 29–36.
45. Gierer, A., Berking, S., Bode, H., David, C.N., Flick, K., Hansmann, G., Schaller, H., and Trenkner, E. (1972). Regeneration of hydra from reaggregated cells. *Nat. New Biol.* **239,** 98–101.
46. David, C.N., and Murphy, S. (1977). Characterization of interstitial stem cells in hydra by cloning. *Dev. Biol.* **58,** 372–383.
47. Bosch, T.C.G., and David, C.N. (1986). Stem cells of *Hydra magnipapillata* can differentiate somatic cells and germ line cells. *Dev. Biol.* **121,** 182–191.
48. Smid, I., and Tardent, P. (1986). The potentialities of endoderm interstitial cells in *Hydra attenuata. Dev. Biol.* **117,** 672–675.
49. Hansen, G.N., Williamson, M., and Grimmelikhuijzen, C.J. (2002). A new case of neuropeptide coexpression (RGamide and LWamides) in hydra, found by whole-mount, two-color double-labeling *in situ* hybridization. *Cell Tissue Res.* **308,** 157–165.
50. Epp, L., and Tardent, P. (1978). The distribution of nerve cells in *Hydra attenuata Pall. Wilhelm Roux's Arch. Dev. Biol.* **185,** 185–193.
51. Westfall, J.A., and Kinnamon, J.C. (1978). A second sensory–motor–interneuron with neurosecretory granules in hydra. *J. Neurocytol.* **7,** 365–379.
52. Westfall, J.A., Argast, D.R., and Kinnamon, J.C. (1983). Numbers, distribution, and types of neurons in the pedal disk of hydra based on a serial reconstruction from transmission electron micrographs. *J. Morphol.* **178,** 95–103.
53. David, C.N., and Hager, G. (1994). Formation of a primitive nervous system: nerve cell differentiation in the polyp hydra. *Perspect. Dev. Neurobiol.* **2,** 135–140.
54. Teragawa, C.K., and Bode, H.R. (1995). Migrating interstitial cells differentiate into neurons in hydra. *Dev. Biol.* **171,** 286–293.
55. Slautterback, D.B., and Fawcett, D.W. (1959). The development of the cnidoblasts of hydra: an electron microscopic study of cell differentiation. *J. Biophys. Biochem. Cytol.* **5,** 441–452.
56. Bode, H.R., and Flick, K.M. (1976). Distribution and dynamics of nematocyte populations in Hydra attenuata. *J. Cell Sci.* **21,** 15–34.
57. David, C.N. (1973). A quantitative method for maceration of hydra tissue. *Wilhelm Roux's Arch. Dev. Biol.* **171,** 259–268.
58. Bode, H.R., and Smith, G.S. (1977). Regulation of interstitial cell differentiation in Hydra attenuata: II. Correlation of axial position of the interstitial cell with nematocyte differentiation. *Wilhelm Roux's Arch. Dev. Biol.* **181,** 203–213.
59. Fujisawa, T. (1987). An endogenous inhibitor if position-dependent stenotele differentiation in hydra. *Dev. Biol.* **122,** 210–216.
60. Rubin, D., and Bode, H.R. (Unpublished results).
61. Yaross, M.S., and Bode, H.R. (1978). Regulation of interstitial cell differentiation in Hydra attenuata: V. Inability of regenerating head to support nematocyte differentiation. *J. Cell Sci.* **34,** 39–52.
62. Bode, H.R., Heimfeld, S., Chow, M.A., and Huang, L.W. (1987). Gland cells arise by differentiation from interstitial cells in Hydra attenuata. *Dev. Biol.* **122,** 577–585.
63. Teragawa, C.K., and Bode, H.R. (1990). Spatial and temporal patterns of interstitial cell migration in Hydra vulgaris. *Dev. Biol.* **138,** 63–81.
64. Grimmelikhuijzen, C.J., Dockray, G.J., and Schot, L.P. (1982). FMRFamide-like immunoreactivity in the nervous system of hydra. *Histochemistry* **73,** 499–508.
65. Koizumi, O., and Bode, H.R. (1986). Plasticity in the nervous system of adult hydra: I. The position-dependent expression of FMRFamide-like immunoreactivity. *Dev. Biol.* **116,** 407–421.
66. Grell, K., and Ruthmann, A. (1991). Placozoa. *In* "Microscopic Anatomy of Invertebrates," (F.W. Harrison and J.A. Westfall, eds.), Vol. 2, pp. 13–28. John Wiley & Sons, New York.

these cells, may also serve as a source for candidate molecules that will be important components of the HSC niche in the bone marrow.[52]

Recent studies have shown that signaling through the canonical Wnt pathway can direct HSC self-renewal *in vitro* and *in vivo*.[53,54] Wnt is a secreted growth factor that binds to members of the Frizzled (Fz) family of cell surface receptors. The β-catenin molecule serves as a positive regulator of the pathway by mediating transcription in cooperation with members of the Lef–TCF transcription factor family. In the absence of a Wnt signal, cytoplasmic β-catenin is quickly degraded through the ubiquitin–proteasome pathway (reviewed by Huelsken *et al.*[55]).

Reya *et al.* have demonstrated that transduction of HSCs with a retrovirus encoding a constitutively active β-catenin molecule results in self-renewal and expansion of HSCs in culture for at least 4 weeks and in some cases as long as 1–2 months under conditions in which control HSCs do not survive in culture beyond 48 hours. The cultured cells resemble HSCs morphologically and phenotypically and are capable of reconstituting the entire hematopoietic system of lethally irradiated mice when transplanted in limiting numbers.[53] Proliferation of wild type HSCs cultured in the presence of growth factors was blocked by a soluble form of the ligand-binding domain of the Fz receptor, suggesting that Wnt signaling is required for the proliferation response of HSCs to cytokines within their niche. Because no other cell types were present in these cultures, this result raises the possibility that a Wnt secreted from HSCs may act as an autocrine signal to promote HSC proliferation.[53]

The cell–cell and cell–ECM adhesion molecules involved in anchoring HSCs within the bone marrow have not yet been identified. Interestingly, HSCs are mobile and detectable in the peripheral blood, spleen, and liver, suggesting that HSCs can migrate out of the niche.[56] Although circulating HSCs and progenitor cells are quickly cleared from the peripheral blood, the number of bloodborne HSCs is fairly stable, suggesting that the flux of HSCs into and out of the blood is roughly equivalent.[56] The mechanisms that recruit HSCs back into the niche after migration or homing of HSCs to the bone marrow after transplantation have not been clearly elucidated, although cellular adhesion molecules and chemokine receptors are likely involved.[57] However, the mobility of HSCs suggests that adhesion between HSCs and niche cells may be highly regulated.

MAMMALIAN EPIDERMIS

The mammalian epidermis is comprised primarily of keratinocytes, a subpopulation of which are stem cells. Epidermal stem cells are multipotential; they produce progeny that differentiate into interfollicular epidermis and sebocytes and contribute to all the differentiated cell types involved in the formation of the hair follicle, including the outer root sheath, inner root sheath, and hair shaft.[58,59]

It is not yet understood whether one "primordial" epidermal stem cell creates the stem–progenitor cell populations that maintain the interfollicular epidermis, the hair follicle, and sebaceous gland or whether the stem cells that maintain each of these specific cell types are equivalent, with their fate determined by the local environment.[58–60] However, accumulating evidence supports a model whereby the microenvironment, or niche, affects differentiation toward particular lineages.[61] For example, cultured rat dermal papillae cells can induce hair follicle formation by rat footpad epidermis, in which follicles are not normally found.[61,62] These data suggest that stem cells that normally maintain the interfollicular epidermis can be reprogrammed to act as hair follicle stem cells by signals emanating from the surrounding microenvironment. For this chapter, we consider the stem cells that generate the hair follicle and the interfollicular epidermis separately.

Hair Follicle

After placement and formation of the hair placode during mammalian embryonic development, the lower portion of the hair follicle cycles through periods of growth (anagen), regression (catagen), and quiescence (telogen). The proliferative cells that generate the inner root sheath and hair shaft are called matrix cells, a transiently dividing population of epithelial cells at the base of the hair follicle that engulfs a pocket of specialized mesenchymal cells, called the dermal papilla[63] (Fig. 5–3A).

Using multiple strategies, a stem cell niche for the mammalian epidermis has been located along the upper portion of the hair follicle in a region called the bulge.[58,59] Specifically, the bulge is located along the outer root sheath, which is contiguous with the interfollicular epidermis (Fig. 5–3A). As the hair follicle regresses during catagen, the dermal papilla comes into close proximity with the follicular bulge. It has been suggested that one or more signals from the dermal papilla may cause stem cells, transit-amplifying cells, or both in the bulge to migrate out and begin proliferating to regenerate the hair follicle.[63]

Both in human and in mouse epidermis, β1 integrin expression is enriched in cells within the bulge region of the outer root sheath. Targeted disruption of the β1 integrin gene in the outer root sheath cells did not disrupt the first hair cycle; however, proliferation of matrix cells was severely impaired, resulting in progressive hair loss and dramatic hair follicle abnormalities.[64] Proliferation of interfollicular keratinocytes was also significantly reduced, and by 7 weeks, these mice completely lacked hair follicles and sebaceous glands, suggesting that β1 integrin function is required for normal epidermal proliferation.[64] It is possible that one role of β1 integrin is to anchor stem cells within the bulge, close to self-renewal signals.[63]

To date, no candidate growth factors that might be secreted by cells in and around the bulge to control stem cell self-renewal have been definitively identified. However, both the Sonic hedgehog (Shh) and the Wnt/β-catenin signaling pathways have been shown to affect some aspects of cell proliferation and differentiation in the epidermis and epidermal appendages. Shh signaling appears to specify hair follicle placement and growth during embryogenesis, as well as postnatal follicle regeneration (for review, see Callahan *et al.*[65]).

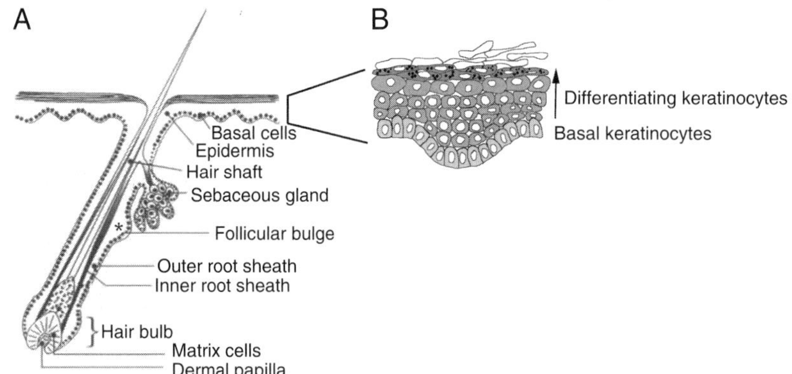

Figure 5-3. (A) Schematic of the components of a hair follicle (modified from Gatt *et al.*[66]). The follicular bulge (asterisk) has been proposed to act as a stem cell niche, which houses cells that can contribute to all the differentiated cell types involved in the formation of the hair follicle, including the outer root sheath, inner root sheath, and hair shaft. Stem cells within the bulge can also generate sebocytes and the cells that maintain the interfollicular epidermis. The bulge is located along the outer root sheath, which is contiguous with the interfollicular epidermis (dotted line). (B) Drawing of a cross-section of the interfollicular epidermis. The stem cells that maintain the interfollicular epidermis are within the basal layer of the epidermis and divide to produce the transit-amplifying cells, which undergo a process of terminal differentiation as they migrate toward the surface of the skin. Dead squamae are shed from the surface of the skin. Interfollicular epidermal stem cells are found in patches, surrounded by transit-amplifying cells that form an interconnecting network between the stem cell clusters.[67] (Please see CD-ROM for color version of this figure.)

Shh is expressed at the distal portion of the growing hair follicle, along one side of the matrix closest to the skin surface[66] (Fig. 5–3A). Interestingly, fibroblast growth factors (FGFs) and BMPs, expressed in the dermal papilla, affect hair follicle growth by regulating *Shh* expression in matrix cells[6, 65, 67] (Fig. 5–3A).

Loss of *Shh* function leads to disruption in hair follicle growth while ectopic expression of Shh target genes induces follicular tumors.[65] In addition, basal cell carcinomas, caused by mutations in downstream components of the Shh pathway, are composed of cells similar to hair follicle precursor cells.[68] Shh expression in the epithelium results in the expression of target genes such as *Patched (Ptc)* in both the proliferating matrix cells and the adjacent dermal papilla.[65,66] Because Shh targets are expressed in both the epidermis and the underlying dermal tissue, it is unclear whether the effect of Shh on epithelial cell proliferation is direct or indirect.

Wnt signaling also plays an important role in the formation of hair follicles during embryogenesis and postnatal specification of matrix-derived cells into follicular keratinocytes. Overexpression of a stabilized form of β-catenin in murine skin leads to the formation of ectopic hair follicles and hair follicle–derived tumors.[66] Alternatively, a skin-specific knockout of β-catenin attenuated hair germ formation during embryogenesis and dramatically restricted specification of cell fates by the multipotent bulge stem cells after completion of the initial hair cycle. At the initiation of the second growth phase, β-catenin–deficient stem cells were incapable of differentiating into follicular epithelial cells and were restricted to producing interfollicular keratinocytes.[69]

Several members of the Lef1–Tcf family, as well as numerous Wnts, are expressed in the skin. Cells within the bulge and the lower outer root sheath express *Tcf3,* while *Lef1* is highly expressed in the proliferative matrix cells and differentiating hair-shaft precursor cells.[70] Experiments suggest that Tcf3 may act as a repressor to maintain characteristics of the bulge and the lower outer root sheath cells and may do so independently of binding to β-catenin.[70,71] This implies that Tcf3 likely acts in a Wnt independent manner to direct the differentiation of cells within the bulge and lower outer root sheath. Lef1, on the other hand, requires binding to β-catenin and presumably activation by one or more Wnts to mediate its effects on hair follicle differentiation.[70–72] Although these data reemphasize a role for Wnt signaling in hair follicle generation, there is still no evidence that Wnts directly control the proliferation, maintenance, or self-renewal of epidermal stem cells.

Recent studies by Jamora *et al.* elegantly demonstrated that the stabilization of β-catenin through Wnt signaling in concert with the activation of *Lef1* transcription by repression of BMP signaling by noggin acted to repress E-cadherin expression and to drive follicle morphogenesis.[73] Conditional removal of α-catenin also resulted in the arrest of hair follicle formation and the subsequent failure of sebaceous gland formation. Together, these results highlight the importance of Wnt signaling and of the regulation of adherens junction formation in the development and maintenance of hair follicles.[73]

Interfollicular Epidermis

Stem cells in the bulge can migrate superficially to maintain the interfollicular epidermis. The stem cells that maintain the interfollicular epidermis are within pockets in the basal layer of the epidermis and divide to generate the transit-amplifying definitive studies in the stem cell compartment have not been reported, likely because of the early lethality of the Rb null embryo. Instead, INK4 proteins closely associated with Rb have been studied in the context of stem cell biology. These studies include a recent report indicating that Bmi-1, an upstream inhibitor of $p16^{INK4AINKIdffdsddasdfda}$ (p16) and $p19^{INK4D}$ (p19), expression, is critical for HSC self-renewal.[110] In the absence of Bmi-1, self-renewal of HSCs and neural stem cells is diminished, an effect dependent on the expression of p16. In mice engineered to be devoid of p16, a complex HSC phenotype has been observed with a decreased number of stem cells in younger mice but enhanced self-renewal in serially transplanted animals.[111]

The INK4 family member, $p18^{INK4C}$ (p18 hereafter), is expressed in multiple tissue types including hematopoietic cells,[83] the loss of which in mice results in organomegaly with higher cellularity and an increase in the incidence of tumors with advanced age or in the presence of carcinogens.[63,112,113] Furthermore, p18 has been suggested to be involved in the symmetric division of precursor cells in mouse developing brain.[83] Recently, it has been reported that the absence of p18 increases HSCs. Similar to the p21 null setting, but unlike p21, an increase in stem cell self-renewal is observed.[114]

Systematic evaluation of proximate molecular regulators of cell cycling are, therefore, yielding a complex picture of how each influences primitive cell function. Different members of the CKI subfamilies appear to play distinct roles in stem or progenitor cell populations. The function of these different CKIs appears to be highly differentiation-stage specific and confers an important level of regulation in stem or progenitor cells to maintain homeostasis. Cooperative effects between members of the two CKI subfamilies are likely with evidence of such interplay between p15 and p27 now documented.[101,115] How the CKIs exert distinct effects and the pathways converging on these regulators are the subject of ongoing study and will potentially provide further insight for manipulation of stem and progenitor populations. Whether these pathways are shared among primitive populations of cells in all tissues is not yet clear but preliminary data are suggestive that such is the case.[116]

RELATION BETWEEN CYCLIN-DEPENDENT KINASE INHIBITORS AND TRANSFORMING GROWTH FACTOR β-1

TGFβ-1 has been documented to have varied effects on hematopoietic cells including enhancement of granulocytes proliferation in response to granulocyte-macrophage colony-stimulating factor[117] or inhibition of progenitor cell responsiveness to other growth promoting cytokines.[118] The detailed roles of TGFβ-1 in signaling pathways and in hematopoiesis have been extensively reviewed elsewhere.[119–121] TGFβ-1 has been extensively characterized as a dominant negative regulator of hematopoietic cell proliferation including inhibiting primitive progenitor cells.[44,49,121,122] Antisense TGFβ-1 or neutralizing antibodies of TGFβ-1 have been used to induce quiescent stem cells into the cell cycle and to augment retroviral gene transduction in conjunction with downregulation of p27 in human $CD34^+$ subsets.[44,50,101] Based on the roles of CKIs in hematopoietic cells as described previously, the link between TGFβ-1 and CKIs in stem cell regulation has been recently addressed. TGFβ-1-induced cell cycle arrest has been shown to be mediated through p15, p21, or p27 in multiple cell lines or cell types, including human epithelial cell lines,[123,124] fibroblast cells,[125] and colon[126] and ovary cancer cell lines.[127] Recently, it was proposed that p21 and p27 are key downstream mediators for TGFβ-1 in hematopoietic cells,[121,128] and a recent study examined whether p21 or p27 was a proximal mediator for TGFβ-1 induced cell cycle exit in primary hematopoietic cells. Using fine mapping of gene expression in individual cells, TGFβ-1 and p21 were documented to be upregulated in quiescent, cytokine-resistant HSCs and also in terminally differentiated mature blood cells as compared with immature, proliferating progenitor cell populations. Type II TGFβ-1 receptors were expressed ubiquitously in these subsets of cells without apparent modulation. To provide further biochemical analysis of whether the coordinate regulation of TGFβ-1 and p21 or p27 represented a dependent link between them, the cytokine-responsive 32D cell line was analyzed for p21 or p27 upregulation following cell cycle synchronization and release in the presence or absence of TGFβ-1. Despite marked antiproliferative effects of TGFβ-1, neither the transcription of p21 mRNA nor the expression of p21 or p27 was altered. To corroborate these observations in primary cells, bone marrow mononuclear cells derived from mice engineered to be deficient in p21 or p27 were assessed. Both progenitor and primitive cell function was inhibited by TGFβ-1 equivalently in knockout and wild-type littermate controls. This data indicated that TGFβ-1 exerts its inhibition on cell cycling independent of p21 and p27 in primitive hematopoietic cells. Other data have recently reported examining the Cip/Kip CKI family member p57 in hematopoietic progenitors.[129] The absence of p57 was associated with a lack of responsiveness to TGFβ, failing to arrest cell cycling. Furthermore TGFβ was noted to induce p57 expression arguing for a direct link between TGFβ and the cell cycle regulatory function of p57. In addition, Dao *et al.*[115] reported that blocking TGFβ-1 could downregulate p15 expression in human $CD34^+$ cells and that TGFβ-1 may act through the INK4 family and the Cip/Kip family in hematopoietic cells. However, extensive biochemical analysis in primary hematopoietic cell subsets is needed to further address this question.

CKIs AND NOTCH

Notch1 has been well defined as a mediator of decisions at multiple steps in the hematopoietic cascade including stem cell self-renewal versus differentiation.[38] Variable effects on cell cycling have been reported including inhibition of proliferation and, in contrast, maintenance of proliferation but with a decreased interval in the G_1 phase of the cell cycle.[130] The latter observation has been followed up by more extensive analysis of an interaction between Notch1 and CKI regulation. It has been reported that the basis for Notch influencing G_1 may be through alteration in G_1–S checkpoint regulator stability, specifically affecting the proteasome degradation of CKI, p27.[131] The links of receptor-mediated effectors of stem cell function and cell cycle regulators are, therefore, beginning to emerge and provide an essential component of the larger regulatory network.

Summary and Future Directions

Further therapeutic potential of stem cells is envisioned to be broadened if the biology of the stem cells can be exploited to permit efficient *ex vivo* manipulation and enhance repopulation *in vivo.* Given the relative quiescence of HSCs that has not been satisfactorily overcome by cytokine manipulation *in vitro,* direct intervention in the control of the cell cycle has been sought as an approach to disassociate cell proliferation from cell differentiation thereby potentially bypassing a major hurdle in current stem cell expansion strategies. CKIs appear to be compelling candidates for the latter approach. In particular, we have learned that p21 and p27 govern the pool size of hematopoietic stem or progenitor cells, respectively, and their inhibitory roles in hematopoietic cells are not dependent on the action of TGFβ-1. Therefore, targeting specific CKIs together with TGFβ-1 may provide complementary strategies for enhancing hematopoietic stem or progenitor cell expansion and gene transduction. Controlled manipulation of specific CKIs directly or through their upstream mediators may also be relevant for the expansion or possible regeneration of other non-HSC pools.

As the roles of cell cycle regulators in the molecular control of stem cells are explored, many issues remain to be addressed. Much work is needed to delineate the roles of individual members of the cell cycle machinery within the context of tissue specific stem cell types. Furthermore, how these relate to one another and to signal transduction pathways that operate uniquely in specific stem cell populations are yet to be elucidated. Coupling extrinsic signals to cycle control will be essential first steps before understanding how a stem responds to the complicated setting of its microenvironment. Piecing together the components and their interactions by either a reductionist or systems approach will offer targets for a more rational manipulation of the stem cell.

ACKNOWLEDGMENTS

This work was supported by National Institutes of Health (NIH) grants DK02761, HL70561 (T.C.), HL65909, and DK50234; the Burroughs Wellcome Foundation; and the Doris Duke Charitable Foundation (D.T.S.). Because of the limited space and the targeted topic, many related publications cannot be cited in this chapter; we very much appreciate the important contributions from many other investigators in the field. We thank Mathew Boyer for his assistance in preparation of this manuscript.

REFERENCES

1. Blau, H.M., Brazelton, T.R., and Weimann, J.M. (2001). The evolving concept of a stem cell: entity or function? *Cell* **105,** 829–841.
2. D'Urso, G., Marraccino, R.L., Marshak, D.R., and Roberts, J.M. (1990). Cell cycle control of DNA replication by a homologue from human cells of the p34cdc2 protein kinase. *Science* **250,** 786–791.
3. Pardee, A.B. (1989). G1 events and regulation of cell proliferation. *Science* **246,** 603–608.
4. Sherr, C.J. (1996). Cancer cell cycles. *Science* **274,** 1672–1677.
5. Sherr, C.J., and Roberts, J.M. (1999). CDK inhibitors: positive and negative regulators of G1-phase progression. *Genes Dev.* **13,** 1501–1512.
6. Sherr, C.J. (2000). The Pezcoller lecture: cancer cell cycles revisited. *Cancer Res.* **60,** 3689–3695.
7. Oostendorp, R.A., Audet, J., and Eaves, C.J. (2000). High-resolution tracking of cell division suggests similar cell cycle kinetics of hematopoietic stem cells stimulated in vitro and in vivo. *Blood* **95,** 855–862.
8. Pawliuk, R., Eaves, C., and Humphries, R.K. (1996). Evidence of both ontogeny and transplant dose-regulated expansion of hematopoietic stem cells in vivo. *Blood* **88,** 2852–2858.
9. Harrison, D.E., and Lerner, C.P. (1991). Most primitive hematopoietic stem cells are stimulated to cycle rapidly after treatment with 5-fluorouracil. *Blood* **78,** 1237–1240.
10. Uchida, N., Friera, A.M., He, D., Reitsma, M.J., Tsukamoto, A.S., and Weissman, I.L. (1997). Hydroxyurea can be used to increase mouse c-kit+Thy-1. 1(lo)Lin-/loSca- 1(+) hematopoietic cell number and frequency in cell cycle in vivo. *Blood* **90,** 4354–4362.
11. Cheng, T., Rodrigues, N., Dombkowski, D., Stier, S., and Scadden, D.T. (2000). Stem cell repopulation efficiency but not pool size is governed by $p27^{kip1}$. *Nat. Med.* **6,** 1235–1240.
12. Cheng, T., Rodrigues, N., Shen, H., Yang, Y., Dombkowski, D., Sykes, M., and Scadden, D.T. (2000). Hematopoietic stem cell quiescence maintained by p21cip1/waf1. *Science* **287,** 1804–1808.
13. Bradford, G.B., Williams, B., Rossi, R., and Bertoncello, I. (1997). Quiescence, cycling, and turnover in the primitive hematopoietic stem cell compartment. *Exp. Hematol.* **25,** 445–453.
14. Cheshier, S.H., Morrison, S.J., Liao, X., and Weissman, I.L. (1999). In vivo proliferation and cell cycle kinetics of long-term self-renewing hematopoietic stem cells. *Proc. Natl. Acad. Sci. USA* **96,** 3120–3125.
15. Abkowitz, J.L.C.S. and Guttorp, P. (1996). Evidence that hematopoiesis may be a stochastic process in vivo. *Nat. Med.* **2,** 190–197.
16. Mahmud, N., Devine, S.M., Weller, K.P., Parmar, S., Sturgeon, C., Nelson, M.C., Hewett, T., and Hoffman, R. (2001). The relative quiescence of hematopoietic stem cells in nonhuman primates. *Blood* **97,** 3061–3068.
17. Lemischka, I.R., Raulet, D.H., and Mulligan, R.C. (1986). Developmental potential and dynamic behavior of hematopoietic stem cells. *Cell* **45,** 917–927.
18. Harrison, D.E., Astle, C.M., and Lerner, C. (1988). Number and continuous proliferative pattern of transplanted primitive immunohematopoietic stem cells. *Proc. Natl. Acad. Sci. USA* **85,** 822–826.
19. Loeffler, M., and Potten, C.S. (1997). Stem cells and cellular pedigrees—a conceptual introduction. *In* "Stem Cells." (Potten, C.S., ed.), pp. 1–27. Academic Press, London.
20. Quesenberry, P.R., Colvin, G.A., and Lambert, J.F. (2002). The chiaroscuro stem cell: a unified stem cell theory. *Blood* **100,** 4266–4271.
21. Bonfanti, L., Gritti, A., and Vesscoui, A.L. (2001). Multipotent stem cells in the adult central nervous system. *In* "Stem Cells and

CNS Development" (Rao, M.S., Ed.), pp. 31–48. Humana Press, Totowa, NJ.
22. Palmer, T.C. (2001). Mobilizing endogenous stem cells. *In* "Stem Cells and CNS Development" (Rao M.S., Ed.). Humana Press, Totowa, NJ.
23. Doetsch, F., Caille, I., Lim, D.A., Garcia-Verdugo, J.M., and Alvarez-Buylla, A. (1999). Subventricular zone astrocytes are neural stem cells in the adult mammalian brain. *Cell* **97,** 703–716.
24. Morshead, C.M., Reynolds, B.A., Craig, C.G., McBurney, M.W., Staines, W.A., Morassutti, D., Weiss, S., and van der Kooy, D. (1994). Neural stem cells in the adult mammalian forebrain: a relatively quiescent subpopulation of subependymal cells. *Neuron* **13,** 1071–1082.
25. Horner, P.J., and Gage, F.H. (2000). Regenerating the damaged central nervous system. *Nature* **407,** 963–970.
26. Dunnwald, M., Chinnathambi, S., Alexandrunas, D., and Bickenbach, J.R. (2003). Mouse epidermal stem cells proceed through the cell cycle. *J. Cell Physiol.* **195,** 194–201.
27. Verfaillie, C.M. (2002). Hematopoietic stem cells for transplantation. *Nat. Immunol.* **3,** 314–317.
28. Dunbar, C.E., Tisdale, J., Yu, J.M., Soma, T., Zujewski, J., Bodine, D., Sellers, S., Cowan, K., Donahue, R., and Emmons, R. (1997). Transduction of hematopoietic stem cells in humans and in nonhuman primates. *Stem Cells* **15(Suppl 1),** 135–139, discussion 139–140.
29. Wu, T., Kim, H.J., Sellers, S.E., Meade, K.E., Agricola, B.A., Metzger, M.E., Kato, I., Donahue, R.E., Dunbar, C.E., and Tisdale, J.F. (2000). Prolonged high-level detection of retrovirally marked hematopoietic cells in nonhuman primates after transduction of CD34+ progenitors using clinically feasible methods. *Mol. Ther.* **1,** 285–293.
30. Kohn, D.B., Hershfield, M.S., Carbonaro, D., Shigeoka, A., Brooks, J., Smogorzewska, E.M., Barsky, L.W., Chan, R., Burotto, F., Annett, G., Nolta, J.A., Crooks, G., Kapoor, N., Elder, M., Wara, D., Bowen, T., Madsen, E., Snyder, F.F., Bastian, J., Muul, L., Blaese, R.M., Weinberg, K., and Parkman, R. (1998). T lymphocytes with a normal ADA gene accumulate after transplantation of transduced autologous umbilical cord blood CD34+ cells in ADA-deficient SCID neonates. *Nat. Med.* **4,** 775–780.
31. Peters, S.O., Kittler, E.L., Ramshaw, H.S., and Quesenberry, P.J. (1996). Ex vivo expansion of murine marrow cells with interleukin-3 (IL-3), IL- 6, IL-11, and stem cell factor leads to impaired engraftment in irradiated hosts. *Blood* **87,** 30–37.
32. Orschell-Traycoff, C.M., Hiatt, K., Dagher, R.N., Rice, S., Yoder, M.C., and Srour, E.F. (2000). Homing and engraftment potential of Sca-1(+)lin(−) cells fractionated on the basis of adhesion molecule expression and position in cell cycle. *Blood* **96,** 1380–1387.
33. Szilvassy, S.J., Bass, M.J., Van Zant, G., and Grimes, B. (1999). Organ-selective homing defines engraftment kinetics of murine hematopoietic stem cells and is compromised by ex vivo expansion. *Blood* **93,** 1557–1566.
34. Conneally, E., Cashman, J., Petzer, A., and Eaves C. (1997). Expansion in vitro of transplantable human cord blood stem cells demonstrated using a quantitative assay of their lympho-myeloid repopulating activity in nonobese diabetic-*scid/scid* mice. *Proc. Natl. Acad. Sci. USA* **94,** 9836–9841.
35. Miller, C.L., and Eaves, C.J. (1997). Expansion in vitro of adult murine hematopoietic stem cells with transplantable lympho-myeloid reconstituting ability. *Proc. Natl. Acad. Sci. USA* **94,** 13648–13653.
36. Ema, H., Takano, H., Sudo, K., and Nakauchi, H. (2000). In vitro self-renewal division of hematopoietic stem cells. *J. Exp. Med.* **192,** 1281–1288.
37. Antonchuk, J., Sauvageau, G., and Humphries, R.K. (2002). HOXB4-induced expansion of adult hematopoietic stem cells ex vivo. *Cell* **109,** 39–45.
38. Stier, S., Cheng, T., Dombkowski, D., Carlesso, N., and Scadden, D.T. (2002). Notch1 activation increases hematopoietic stem cell self-renewal in vivo and favors lymphoid over myeloid lineage outcome. *Blood* **99,** 2369–2378.
39. Varnum-Finney, B., Xu, L., Brashem-Stein, C., Nourigat, C., Flowers, D., Bakkour, S., Pear, W.S., and Bernstein, I.D. (2000). Pluripotent, cytokine-dependent, hematopoietic stem cells are immortalized by constitutive notch1 signaling. *Nat. Med.* **6,** 1278–1281.
40. Reya, T., Duncan, A.W., Ailles, L., Domen, J., Scherer, D.C., Willert, K., Hintz, L., Nusse, R., and Weissman, I.L. (2003). A role for Wnt signalling in self-renewal of haematopoietic stem cells. *Nature* **423,** 409–414.
41. Willert, K., Brown, J.D., Danenberg, E., Duncan, A.W., Weissman, I.L., Reya, T., Yates, J.R., 3rd., and Nussem R. (2003). Wnt proteins are lipid-modified and can act as stem cell growth factors. *Nature* **423,** 448–452.
42. Austin, T.W., Solar, G.P., Ziegler, F.C., Liem, L., and Matthews, W. (1997). A role for the Wnt gene family in hematopoiesis: Expansion of multilineage progenitor cells. *Blood* **89,** 3624–3635.
43. Broxmeyer, H.E., Sherry, B., Lu, L., Cooper, S., Oh, K.O., Tekamp-Olson, P., Kwon, B.S., and Cerami, A. (1990). Enhancing and suppressing effects of recombinant murine macrophage inflammatory proteins on colony formation in vitro by bone marrow myeloid progenitor cells. *Blood* **76,** 1110–1116.
44. Hatzfeld, J., Li, M.L., Brown, E.L., Sookdeo, H., Levesque, J.P., O'Toole, T., Gurney, C., Clark, S.C., and Hatzfeld, A. (1991). Release of early human hematopoietic progenitors from quiescence by antisense transforming growth factor beta 1 or Rb oligonucleotides. *J. Exp. Med.* **174,** 925–929.
45. Keller, J.R., Mantel, C., Sing, G.K., Ellingsworth, L.R., Ruscetti, S.K., and Ruscetti, F.W. (1988). Transforming growth factor beta 1 selectively regulates early murine hematopoietic progenitors and inhibits the growth of IL-3-dependent myeloid leukemia cell lines. *J. Exp. Med.* **168,** 737–750.
46. Ruscetti, F.W., Jacobsen, S.E., Birchenall-Roberts, M., Broxmeyer, H.E., Engelmann, G.L., Dubois, C., and Keller, J.R. (1991). Role of transforming growth factor-beta 1 in regulation of hematopoiesis. *Ann. NY Acad. Sci.* **628,** 31–43.
47. Keller, J.R., McNiece, I.K., Sill, K.T., Ellingsworth, L.R., Quesenberry, P.J., Sing, G.K., and Ruscetti, F.W. (1990). Transforming growth factor beta directly regulates primitive murine hematopoietic cell proliferation. *Blood* **75,** 596–602.
48. Migdalska, A., Molineux, G., Demuynck, H., Evans, G.S., Ruscetti, F., and Dexter, T.M. (1991). Growth inhibitory effects of transforming growth factor-beta 1 in vivo. *Growth Factors* **4,** 239–245.
49. Cardoso, A.A., Li, M.L., Batard, P., Hatzfeld, A., Brown, E.L., Levesque, J.P., Sookdeo, H., Panterne, B., Sansilvestri, P., Clark, S.C., and Hatzfeld, J. (1993). Release from quiescence of CD34+ CD38- human umbilical cord blood cells reveals their potentiality to engraft adults. *Proc. Natl. Acad. Sci. USA* **90,** 8707–8711.
50. Hatzfeld, A., Batard, P., Panterne, B., Taieb, F., and Hatzfeld, J. (1996). Increased stable retroviral gene transfer in early hematopoietic progenitors released from quiescence. *Hum. Gene Ther.* **7,** 207–213.

51. McManus, M.T., and Sharp, P.A. (2002). Gene silencing in mammals by small interfering RNAs. *Nat. Rev. Genet.* **3,** 737–747.
52. Hartwell, L.H., and Weinert, T.A. (1989). Checkpoints: Controls that ensure the order of cell cycle events. *Science* **246,** 629–634.
53. Vogelstein, B.K.K. (1992). p53 function and disfunction. *Cell* **70,** 523–526.
54. Sherr, C.J. (1994). G1 phase progression: cycling on cue. *Cell* **79,** 551–555.
55. Sherr, C.J., and Roberts, J.M. (1995). Inhibitors of mammalian G1 cyclin-dependent kinases. *Genes Dev.* **9,** 1149–1163.
56. Classon, M., and Harlow, E. (2002). The retinoblastoma tumour suppressor in development and cancer. *Nat Rev Cancer* **2,** 910–917.
57. Bartek, J., and Lukas, J. (2001). Pathways governing G1/S transition and their response to DNA damage. *FEBS Lett.* **490,** 117–122.
58. Morgan, D.O. (1995). Principles of CDK regulation. *Nature* **374,** 131–134.
59. Nakanishi, M., Adami, G.R., Robetorye, R.S., Noda, A., Venable, S.F., Dimitrov, D., Pereira-Smith, O.M., and Smith, J.R. (1995). Exit from G0 and entry into the cell cycle of cells expressing p21Sdi1 antisense RNA. *Proc. Natl. Acad. Sci. USA* **92,** 4352–4356.
60. Rivard, N., L'Allemain, G., Bartek, J., and Pouyssegur, J. (1996). Abrogation of p27Kip1 by cDNA antisense suppresses quiescence (G0 state) in fibroblasts. *J. Biol. Chem.* **271,** 18337–18341.
61. Brugarolas, J., Chandrasekaran, C., Gordon, J.I., Beach, D., Jacks, T., and Hannon, G.J. (1995). Radiation-induced cell cycle arrest compromised by p21 deficiency. *Nature* **377,** 552–557.
62. Nakayama, K., Ishida, N., Shirane, M., Inomata, A., Inoue, T., Shishido, N., Horii, I., Loh, D.Y., and Nakayama, K. (1996). Mice lacking p27(Kip1) display increased body size, multiple organ hyperplasia, retinal dysplasia, and pituitary tumors. *Cell* **85,** 707–720.
63. Franklin, D.S., Godfrey, V.L., Lee, H., Kovalev, G.I., Schoonhoven, R., Chen-Kiang, S., Su, L., and Xiong, Y. (1998). CDK inhibitors p18(INK4c) and p27(Kip1) mediate two separate pathways to collaboratively suppress pituitary tumorigenesis. *Genes Dev.* **12,** 2899–2911.
64. Conlon, I., and Raff, M. (1999). Size control in animal development. *Cell* **96,** 235–244.
65. Cunningham, J.J., and Roussel, M.F. (2001). Cyclin-dependent kinase inhibitors in the development of the central nervous system. *Cell Growth Differ.* **12,** 387–396.
66. Cheng, T., and Scadden, D.T. (2002). Cell cycle entry of hematopoietic stem and progenitor cells controlled by distinct cyclin-dependent kinase inhibitors. *Int. J. Hematol.* **75,** 460–465.
67. Nabel, E.G. (2002). CDKs and CKIs: Molecular targets for tissue remodelling. *Nat. Rev. Drug Discov.* **1,** 587–598.
68. Aladjem, M.I., Spike, B.T., Rodewald, L.W., Hope, T.J., Klemm, M., Jaenisch, R., and Wahl, G.M. (1998). ES cells do not activate p53-dependent stress responses and undergo p53-independent apoptosis in response to DNA damage. *Curr. Biol.* **8,** 145–155.
69. Prost, S., Bellamy, C.O., Clarke, A.R., Wyllie, A.H., and Harrison, D.J. (1998). p53-independent DNA repair and cell cycle arrest in embryonic stem cells. *FEBS Lett.* **425,** 499–504.
70. Burdon, T., Smith, A., and Savatier, P. (2002). Signalling, cell cycle and pluripotency in embryonic stem cells. *Trends Cell Biol.* **12,** 432–438.
71. Berardi, A.C., Wang, A., Levine, J.D., Lopez, P., and Scadden, D.T. (1995). Functional isolation and characterization of human hematopoietic stem cells. *Science* **267,** 104–108.
72. Shen, H., Cheng, T., Preffer, F.I., Dombkowski, D., Tomasson, M.H., Golan, D.E., Yang, O., Hofmann, W., Sodroski, J.G., Luster, A.D., and Scadden, D.T. (1999). Intrinsic human immunodeficiency virus type 1 resistance of hematopoietic stem cells despite coreceptor expression. *J. Virol.* **73,** 728–737.
73. Becker, P.S., Nilsson, S.K., Li, Z., Berrios, V.M., Dooner, M.S., Cooper, C.L., Hsieh, C.C., and Quesenberry, P.J. (1999). Adhesion receptor expression by hematopoietic cell lines and murine progenitors: Modulation by cytokines and cell cycle status. *Exp. Hematol.* **27,** 533–541.
74. Roy, V., and Verfaillie, C.M. (1999). Expression and function of cell adhesion molecules on fetal liver, cord blood and bone marrow hematopoietic progenitors: implications for anatomical localization and developmental stage specific regulation of hematopoiesis. *Exp. Hematol.* **27,** 302–312.
75. de Nooij J.C.M.L., and Hariharan, I.K. (1996). A cyclin-dependent kinase inhibitor, Dacapo, is necessary for timely exit from the cell cycle during Drosphilia embryogenesis. *Cell* **87,** 1237–1247.
76. de Nooij, J.C.I.H. (1995). Uncoupling cell fate determination from patterned cell division in the Drosphilia eye [see comments]. *Science* **270,** 983–985.
77. Topley, G.I., Okuyama, R., Gonzales, J.G., Conti, C., and Dotto, G.P. (1999). p21(WAF1/Cip1) functions as a suppressor of malignant skin tumor formation and a determinant of keratinocyte stem-cell potential. *Proc. Natl. Acad. Sci. USA* **96,** 9089–9094.
78. Durand, B., Fero, M.L., Roberts, J.M., and Raff, M.C. (1998). p27kip1 alters the response of cells to mitogen and is part of a cell- intrinsic timer that arrests the cell cycle and initiates differentiation. *Curr. Biol.* **8,** 431–440.
79. Lowenheim, H., Furness, D.N., Kil, J., Zinn, C., Gultig, K., Fero, M.L., Frost, D., Gummer, A.W., Roberts, J.M., Rubel, E.W., Hackney, C.M., and Zenner, H.P. (1999). Gene disruption of p27(Kip1) allows cell proliferation in the postnatal and adult organ of corti. *Proc. Natl. Acad. Sci. USA* **96,** 4084–4088.
80. Levine, E.M., Close, J., Fero, M., Ostrovsky, A., and Reh, T.A. (2000). p27(Kip1) regulates cell cycle withdrawal of late multipotent progenitor cells in the mammalian retina. *Dev. Biol.* **219,** 299–314.
81. Taniguchi, T., Endo, H., Chikatsu, N., Uchimaru, K., Asano, S., Fujita, T., Nakahata, T., and Motokura, T. (1999). Expression of p21(Cip1/Waf1/Sdi1) and p27(Kip1) cyclin-dependent kinase inhibitors during human hematopoiesis. *Blood* **93,** 4167–4178.
82. Yaroslavskiy, B., Watkins, S., Donnenberg, A.D., Patton, T.J., and Steinman, R.A. (1999). Subcellular and cell-cycle expression profiles of CDK-inhibitors in normal differentiating myeloid cells. *Blood* **93,** 2907–2917.
83. Tschan, M.P., Peters, U.R., Cajot, J.F., Betticher, D.C., Fey, M.F., and Tobler, A. (1999). The cyclin-dependent kinase inhibitors p18INK4c and p19INK4d are highly expressed in CD34+ progenitor and acute myeloid leukaemic cells but not in normal differentiated myeloid cells. *Br. J. Haematol.* **106,** 644–651.
84. Marone, M., Pierelli, L., Mozzetti, S., Masciullo, V., Bonanno, G., Morosetti, R., Rutella, S., Battaglia, A., Rumi, C., Mancuso, S., Leone, G., Giordano, A., and Scambia, G. (2000). High cyclin-dependent kinase inhibitors in Bcl-2 and Bcl-xL-expressing CD34+-proliferating haematopoietic progenitors. *Br. J. Haematol.* **110,** 654–662.
85. Cheng, T., Shen, H., Rodrigues, N., Stier, S., and Scadden, D.T (2001). Transforming growth factor beta 1 mediates cell-cycle arrest of primitive hematopoietic cells independent of p21(Cip1/Waf1) or p27(Kip1). *Blood* **98,** 3643–3649.
86. Stier, S.C.T., Forkert, R., Lutz, C., Dombkowski, D.M., Zhang, J.L., and Scadden, D.T. (2003). Ex vivo targeting of p21Cip1/Waf1 permits relative expansion of human hematopoietic stem cells. *Blood* **102,** 1260–1266.

87. Liu, Y., Martindale, J.L., Gorospe, M., and Holbrook, N.J. (1996). Regulation of p21WAF1/CIP1 expression through mitogen-activated protein kinase signaling pathway. *Cancer Res.* **56,** 31–35.
88. Braun, S.E., Mantel, C., Rosenthal, M., Cooper, S., Liu, L., Robertson, K.A., Hromas, R., and Broxmeyer, H.E. (1998). A positive effect of p21cip1/waf1 in the colony formation from murine myeloid progenitor cells as assessed by retroviral-mediated gene transfer. *Blood Cells Mol. Dis.* **24,** 138–148.
89. LaBaer, J., Garrett, M.D., Stevenson, L.F., Slingerland, J.M., Sandhu, C., Chou, H.S., Fattaey, A., and Harlow, E. (1997). New functional activities for the p21 family of CDK inhibitors. *Genes Dev.* **11,** 847–862.
90. Cheng, M., Olivier, P., Diehl, J.A., Fero, M., Roussel, M.F., Roberts, J.M., and Sherr, C.J. (1999). The p21(Cip1) and p27(Kip1) CDK 'inhibitors' are essential activators of cyclin D-dependent kinases in murine fibroblasts. *EMBO J.* **18,** 1571–1583.
91. Mantel, C., Luo, Z., Canfield, J., Braun, S., Deng, C., and Broxmeyer, H.E. (1996). Involvement of p21cip-1 and p27kip-1 in the molecular mechanisms of steel factor-induced proliferative synergy in vitro and of p21cip-1 in the maintenance of stem/progenitor cells in vivo. *Blood* **88,** 3710–3719.
92. Wang, J., and Walsh, K. (1996). Resistance to apoptosis conferred by Cdk inhibitors during myocyte differentiation. *Science* **273,** 359–361.
93. Steinman, R.A., Hoffman, B., Iro, A., Guillouf, C., Liebermann, D.A., and el-Houseini, M.E. (1994). Induction of p21 (WAF-1/CIP1) during differentiation. *Oncogene* **9,** 3389–3396.
94. Steinman, R.A., Huang, J., Yaroslavskiy, B., Goff, J.P., Ball, E.D., and Nguyen, A. (1998). Regulation of p21(WAF1) expression during normal myeloid differentiation. *Blood* **91,** 4531–4542.
95. Ellisen, L.W., Carlesso, N., Cheng, T., Scadden, D.T., and Haber, D.A. (2001). The Wilms tumor suppressor WT1 directs stage-specific quiescence and differentiation of human hematopoietic progenitor cells. *EMBO J.* **20,** 1897–1909.
96. el-Deiry, W.S. (1998). p21/p53, cellular growth control and genomic integrity. *Curr. Top. Microbiol. Immunol.* **227,** 121–137.
97. el-Deiry, W.S., Kern, S.E., Pietenpol, J.A., Kinzler, K.W., and Vogelstein, B. (1992). Definition of a consensus binding site for p53. *Nat. Genet.* **1,** 45–49.
98. Hirabayashi, Y., Matsuda, M., Aizawa, S., Kodama, Y., Kanno, J., and Inoue, T. (2002). Serial transplantation of p53-deficient hemopoietic progenitor cells to assess their infinite growth potential. *Exp. Biol. Med. (Maywood)* **227,** 474–479.
99. Wlodarski, P., Wasik, M., Ratajczak, M.Z., Sevignani, C., Hoser, G., Kawiak, J., Gewirtz, A.M., Calabretta, B., and Skorski, T. (1998). Role of p53 in hematopoietic recovery after cytotoxic treatment. *Blood* **91,** 2998–3006.
100. Tong, X., and Srour, E.F. (1998). TGF-b suppresses cell division of Go CD34+ cells while maintaining primitive hematopoietic potential. *Exp. Hematol.* **26,** 684.
101. Dao, M.A., Taylor, N., and Noltam J.A. (1998). Reduction in levels of the cyclin-dependent kinase inhibitor p27(kip-1) coupled with transforming growth factor beta neutralization induces cell-cycle entry and increases retroviral transduction of primitive human hematopoietic cells. *Proc. Natl. Acad. Sci. USA* **95,** 13006–13011.
102. Coats, S., Flanagan, W.M., Nourse, J., and Roberts, J.M. (1996). Requirement of p27Kip1 for restriction point control of the fibroblast cell cycle. *Science* **272,** 877–880.
103. Kiyokawa, H., Kineman, R.D., Manova-Todorova, K.O., Soares, V.C., Hoffman, E.S., Ono, M., Khanam, D., Hayday, A.C., Frohman, L.A., and Koff, A. (1996). Enhanced growth of mice lacking the cyclin-dependent kinase inhibitor function of p27(Kip1). *Cell* **85,** 721–732.
104. Fero, M.L., Rivkin, M., Tasch, M., Porter, P., Carow, C.E., Firpo, E., Polyak, K., Tsai, L.H., Broudy, V., Perlmutter, R.M., Kaushansky, K., and Roberts, J.M. (1996). A syndrome of multiorgan hyperplasia with features of gigantism, tumorigenesis, and female sterility in p27(Kip1)-deficient mice. *Cell* **85,** 733–744.
105. Karnezis, A.N., Dorokhov, M., Grompe, M., and Zhu, L. (2001). Loss of p27(Kip1) enhances the transplantation efficiency of hepatocytes transferred into diseased livers. *J. Clin. Invest.* **108,** 383–390.
106. Doetsch, F., Verdugo, J.M., Caille, I., Alvarez-Buylla, A., Chao, M.V., Casaccia-Bonnefil, P. (2002). Lack of the cell-cycle inhibitor p27Kip1 results in selective increase of transit-amplifying cells for adult neurogenesis. *J. Neurosci.* **22,** 2255–2264.
107. Jacks, T., Fazeli, A., Schmitt, E.M., Bronson, R.T., Goodell, M.A., and Weinberg, R.A. (1992). Effects of an Rb mutation in the mouse. *Nature* **359,** 295–300.
108. Lee, E.Y., Chang, C.Y., Hu, N., Wang, Y.C., Lai, C.C., Herrup, K., Lee, W.H., and Bradley, A. (1992). Mice deficient for Rb are nonviable and show defects in neurogenesis and haematopoiesis. *Nature* **359,** 288–294.
109. Clarke, A.R., Maandag, E.R., van Roon, M., van der Lugt, N.M., van der Valk, M., Hooper, M.L., Berns, A., and te Riele, H. (1992). Requirement for a functional Rb-1 gene in murine development. *Nature* **359,** 328–330.
110. Park, I.K., Qian, D., Kiel, M., Becker, M.W., Pihalja, M., Weissman, I.L., Morrison, S.J., and Clarke, M.F. (2003). Bmi-1 is required for maintenance of adult self-renewing haematopoietic stem cells. *Nature* **423,** 302–305.
111. Forkert, R.C.T., Sharpless, N.E., Adams, G.B., Rodrigues, N.E., Depinho, R.A., and Scadden, D.T. (2002). Cyclin dependent kinase inhibitor, p16INK4a, differentially affects hematopoietic stem cells under homeostatic versus stress conditions. The American Society of Hematology.
112. Franklin, D.S., Godfrey, V.L., O'Brien, D.A., Deng, C., and Xiong, Y. (2000). Functional collaboration between different cyclin-dependent kinase inhibitors suppresses tumor growth with distinct tissue specificity. *Mol. Cell Biol.* **20,** 6147–6158.
113. Bai, F., Pei, X.H., Godfrey, V.L., and Xiong, Y. (2003). Haploinsufficiency of p18(INK4c) sensitizes mice to carcinogen-induced tumorigenesis. *Mol. Cell Biol.* **23,** 1269–1277.
114. Yuan, Y., Shen, H., Franklin, D.S., Scadden, D.T., and Cheng, T. (2004). *In vivo* self-renewing divisions of hematopoietic stem cells are increased in the absence of one early G1-phase inhibitor, p18INK4C. *Nat. Cell. Biol.* **6,** 436–442.
115. Dao, M.A., Hwa, J., and Nolta, J.A. (2002). Molecular mechanism of transforming growth factor beta-mediated cell-cycle modulation in primary human CD34(+) progenitors. *Blood* **99,** 499–506.
116. Qui, J., Takagi, Y., Harada, J., Teramoto, T., Rodrigues, N., Moskowitz, M., Scadden, D.T., and Cheng, T. (2004). Regenerative response in ischemic brain restricted by p21cipl/waf1. *J. Exp. Med.* **199,** 937–945.
117. Keller, J.R., Jacobsen, S.E., Sill, K.T., Ellingsworth, L.R., and Ruscetti, F.W. (1991). Stimulation of granulopoiesis by transforming growth factor beta: synergy with granulocyte/macrophage-colony-stimulating factor. *Proc. Natl. Acad. Sci. USA* **88,** 7190–7194.

118. Jacobsen, S.E., Ruscetti, F.W., Dubois, C.M., Lee, J., Boone, T.C., and Keller, J.R. (1991). Transforming growth factor-beta transmodulates the expression of colony stimulating factor receptors on murine hematopoietic progenitor cell lines. *Blood* **77,** 1706–1716.
119. Massague, J., Blain, S.W., and Lo, R.S. (2000). TGFbeta signaling in growth control, cancer, and heritable disorders. *Cell* **103,** 295–309.
120. Massague, J., and Chen, Y.G. (2000). Controlling TGF-beta signaling. *Genes Dev.* **14,** 627–644.
121. Fortunel, N.O., Hatzfeld, A., and Hatzfeld, J.A. (2000). Transforming growth factor-beta: pleiotropic role in the regulation of hematopoiesis. *Blood* **96,** 2022–2036.
122. Cashman, J.D., Clark-Lewis, I., Eaves, A.C., and Eaves, C.J. (1999). Differentiation stage-specific regulation of primitive human hematopoietic progenitor cycling by exogenous and endogenous inhibitors in an in vivo model. *Blood* **94,** 3722–3729.
123. Datto, M.B., Li, Y., Panus, J.F., Howe, D.J., Xiong, Y., and Wang, X.F. (1995). Transforming growth factor beta induces the cyclin-dependent kinase inhibitor p21 through a p53-independent mechanism. *Proc. Natl. Acad. Sci. USA* **92,** 5545–5549.
124. Landesman, Y., Bringold, F., Milne, D.D., and Meek, D.W. (1997). Modifications of p53 protein and accumulation of p21 and gadd45 mRNA in TGF-beta 1 growth inhibited cells. *Cell Signal* **9,** 291–298.
125. Miyazaki, M., Ohashi, R., Tsuji, T., Mihara, K., Gohda, E., and Namba, M. (1998). Transforming growth factor-beta 1 stimulates or inhibits cell growth via down- or up-regulation of p21/Waf1. *Biochem. Biophys. Res. Commun.* **246,** 873–880.
126. Li, C.Y., Suardet, L., and Little, J.B. (1995). Potential role of WAF1/Cip1/p21 as a mediator of TGF-beta cytoinhibitory effect. *J. Biol. Chem.* **270,** 4971–4974.
127. Elbendary, A., Berchuck, A., Davis, P., Havrilesky, L., Bast, R.C., Jr., Iglehart, J.D., and Marks, J.R. (1994). Transforming growth factor beta 1 can induce CIP1/WAF1 expression independent of the p53 pathway in ovarian cancer cells. *Cell Growth Differ.* **5,** 1301–1307.
128. Ducos, K., Panterne, B., Fortunel, N., Hatzfeld, A., Monier, M.N., and Hatzfeld, J. (2000). p21(cip1) mRNA is controlled by endogenous transforming growth factor-beta1 in quiescent human hematopoietic stem/progenitor cells. *J. Cell Physiol.* **184,** 80–85.
129. Scandura, J.M.B., and Nimer, S.D. (2002). TGFb induced growth arrest of human hematopoietic cells requires p57KIP2 upregulation. The American Society of Hematology.
130. Carlesso, N., Aster, J.C., Sklar, J., and Scadden, D.T. (1999). Notch1-induced delay of human hematopoietic progenitor cell differentiation is associated with altered cell cycle kinetics. *Blood* **93,** 838–848.
131. Sarmento, L.C.M., Scadden, D.T., and Carlesso, N. (2001). Notch promotes cell cycle entry by decreasing the CDK inhibitors P21cip1 and P27kip1. The American Society of Hematology.

7

The Genetic Regulation of Stem Cell Fate

Gillian May and Tariq Enver

In this chapter we review the transcriptional programs of stem cells with a particular, although not exclusive, emphasis on stem and progenitor cells of the hemopoietic system. We initially make some general comments on stem cells then consider the cell fate options open to them and how growth factors and transcription factors may influence their outcome. A large part of the review is concerned with how the molecular groundstate of stem cells is configured to afford or facilitate cell fate decision making and on the experimental programming and reprogramming of cell fate. The implications of these findings for leukemia and stem cell plasticity is also discussed.

Stem Cell Potentials and Plasticity

Although the stem cell concept has been an organizing principle of developmental biology for more than a century, in the last few years the field of stem cell biology has had something of a renaissance.[1] So what then is a stem cell? Broadly speaking any cell that has the ability to self-renew and to give rise to more differentiated progeny could be considered to have stem cell properties. In the context of transplantation, stem cell definitions are more stringent and the standard used is the ability to reconstitute an entire tissue system and maintain it for an extended period and preferably for the lifetime of the organism. Although such a definition is appropriate for the clinical setting of transplantation, it is perhaps worth pointing out that this operational definition is a reflection of what some stem cells can do under extreme and rather artificial circumstances and may therefore exclude a number of cells that exhibit bona fide stem cell functionality in the normal biologic situation.

One can perhaps draw an analogy with early operational definitions of transcriptional enhancers that demanded that they "enhance" transcription in an orientation independent manner when placed either upstream or downstream of a gene in the context of an episomal plasmid construct. Although a valuable indicator of a regulatory element's potential, the true functionality of *cis*-regulatory elements is only revealed in assays that test their potential in the context of the endogenous "native" locus.

Handbook of Stem Cells
Volume 2

In embryogenesis, stem cells function as units of organogenesis and tissue formation, whereas in adulthood stem cells are perhaps more appropriately considered as units of tissue maintenance or regeneration. The blood system provides an example where stem cells provide a critical maintenance function. In this system there is a tremendous daily turnover of mature cells, which in the case of erythroid cells and neutrophils accounts for billions of cells per day. Other examples of this include the epidermis, the epithelial lining of the gut, and the testis. Stem cells in adult muscle may function in repair, as may stem cells in the liver, kidney, pancreas, and central nervous system. The discovery of stem cells in the central nervous system has been both relatively recent and somewhat surprising and contributed to the new excitement surrounding stem cells.[1] However, two other discoveries have also fueled the stem cell renaissance. One is the scientifically controversial phenomenon of adult or somatic stem cell plasticity (reviewed in reference 2), and the other is the ethically contentious derivation of human embryonic stem cells.[3,4]

These cells, derived from the inner cell mass of *in vitro* fertilization (IVF) embryos surplus to requirements exhibit pluripotent differentiation *in vitro*. As such they in principle provide a source of cells for replenishing any tissue in the body. Immunocompatibility issues will require the generation of banks of different lines for therapeutic transplantation purposes, or, alternatively, autologous transplantation could be achieved by use of patient-matched, embryonic stem (ES) cells derived from therapeutic cloning. In such a scheme, the nucleus of an egg would be replaced by the diploid nucleus of a somatic cell and subsequently allowed to develop to an inner cell mass stage from which an ES cell line could be derived and appropriately differentiated. Embryonic stem cells are the subject of a companion handbook and are therefore not discussed in detail any further.

Adult, or somatic, stem cells have historically been considered to be stringently tissue-restricted in their differentiation potential. However, results reported over the last 5 years or so lead to an alternative view that adult stem cells may possess the kind of developmental plasticity more often associated with the developing embryo.[2] Early indicators that these cells may possess a wider degree of differentiation potential than initially thought were provided by studies on the contribution of transplanted bone marrow cells to the muscle compartment of mice.[5]

These studies have been followed by a spate of publications in which a plethora of stem cells of one tissue origin were reported to be able to give rise to differentiated cells of another. A classic early example of this type was the so-called brains to blood study in which neurosphere-derived neural stem cells (NSCs) were reported to contribute to hemopoiesis in a murine transplantation model thereby crossing not only tissue but also germ layer boundaries.[6] Although early interpretation of these kinds of findings generally focused on transdifferentiation as the mechanism underlying novel cellular output, alternative explanations require consideration. These include (1) cellular heterogeneity in the graft (i.e., the possibility of the existence within tissue A of stem cells for tissue B). Very few studies have been performed at the level of single cells or demonstrated clonality. Indeed, recent studies from Wagers *et al.*[7] showed that a single marked and transplanted hemopoietic stem cell (HSC) could restore hemopoiesis both in recipients and their parabiotic partners but could not make any functional contribution to other tissue types, even after injury. These results led the authors to conclude that transdifferentiation of HSC at least, if it occurs at all, is a very rare event. (2) It is possible that cells in the graft take on the phenotype and properties of a different tissue by virtue of cell fusion with host cells. This possibility was first raised in the context of *in vitro* cultures containing ES and bone marrow (BM)[8,9] cells but now has been demonstrated as the mechanism underlying the apparent transdifferentiation of bone marrow–derived cells contributing to liver regeneration.[10,11] (3) It is possible in some instances that cells became reprogrammed through genetic or epigenetic modification during *in vitro* manipulation. This may possibly have been the explanation for the blood-to-brain transition alluded to previously.[6,12] (4) Increased tissue differentiation potential may not reflect transdifferentiation at all but rather result from the postnatal persistence of bona fide multipotent stem cells generated during ontogeny. Cossu and colleagues suggest that postnatal stem cells residing within mesoderm-derived tissues might be residual mesangioblastic stem cells of embryonic origin.[13] If such populations do exist postnatally, one might expect them to be at their highest number in infancy, thus perhaps suggesting that cord blood may be worthy of continued serious examination in this regard.

Despite these reservations and early setbacks it seems likely that adult stem cells can under certain experimental conditions exhibit an unanticipatedly wide and therapeutically important range of developmental potentials, and work in this area continues apace. For example, recent studies from Cao *et al.* have identified muscle-derived stem cells (MDSCs) that appear not to be hemopoietic in origin but do possess the ability to repopulate the bone marrow of lethally irradiated mice in a dystrophic model.[14] MDSC clones retain myogenic potential after transplantation and thus contribute to muscle development when isolated from the bone marrow of primary recipients and engrafted into secondary hosts. The low passage number and lack of tumorigenicity of these MDSC cultures encourages the view that their potential is not necessarily an artefact of extensive cell culture.

Perhaps the most striking, and for that matter most convincing, example of adult stem cell plasticity is provided by mesenchymal stem cells. Verfaille and colleagues initially devised conditions for deriving postnatal mesodermal progenitor cells from bone marrow.[15]

Although the derivation of such clones was a low-frequency event these cells sparked interest because they exhibit multitissue differentiation potential *in vitro.* Similar cells derived from mouse and rat and termed multipotent adult progenitor cells (MAPCs) were subsequently shown to maintain telomere length over 120 doublings in culture and to give rise to multiple tissues types (1) when differentiated *in vitro,* (2) during ontogeny after injection into murine blastocysts, and (3) after transplantation into adult immunocompromised recipients.[16] The extensive self-renewal and differentiation potential of these cells invites comparison with embryoid cells with which they share something of a physical resemblance.

Stem Cell Fate Decisions

Figure 7–1 summarizes the cell fate decisions that impinge on adult stem cell compartments. Adult stem cells must presumably themselves derive from differentiation of other cells during ontogeny. Information regarding the precise developmental origins of adult stem cells is, by and large, rather limited. In the specific case of blood stem cells, however, much has been learned over the past few years. It is now generally accepted that the first adult HSC of the vertebrate arise intraembryonically in the aorta–gonads–mesonephros (AGM) region and its developmental anlage, the para-aortic splanchnopleura.[17] Studies in the frog *Xenopus laevis* indicate that from as early as the 32 cell stage of embryonic development the origins of adult and embryonic blood may be traced to different blastomeres.[18]

Similarly, evidence from Cossu and colleagues suggests that the developmental origins of another mesodermal derivative, namely muscle, during ontogeny may be distinct from those of adult-type muscle stem cells that, like blood stem cells, also arise in the AGM and "seed" adult muscle tissue during secondary myogenesis.[19]

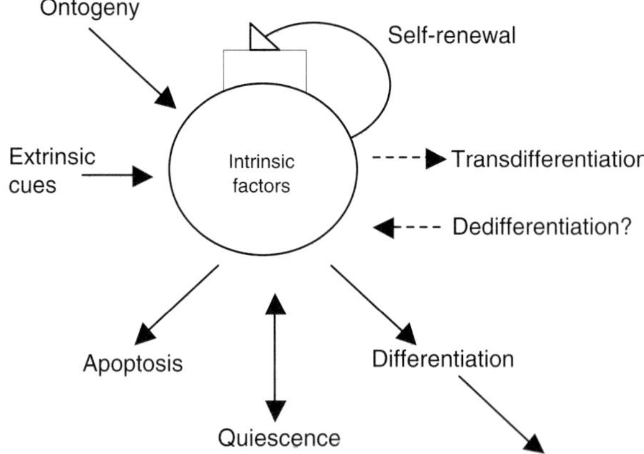

Figure 7–1. *Stem cell fates.* The cell fate issues surrounding the adult stem compartment of the hemopoietic system are diagrammed. In principle this applies to all stem cell compartments, although some may have a limited or only a single lineage output. In such systems the distinction between differentiation and lineage specification may be inappropriate.

Once formed, HSC must service a lifetime's demand for the mature effector cells of the bloodstream. Similar demands are faced by other adult stem cells, for example, the epithelial stem cells of the gut[20] and skin.[21] Meeting such demands requires the fine balancing of stem cell self-renewal and differentiation. In adult stem cell–based systems like the blood, which are composed of many different cell types, lineage specification is an additional feature of the differentiation process. However, the extent to which these processes are coupled or independent at a mechanistic level remains unclear. Similarly, the relative extent to which intrinsic and extrinsic factors influence the decision between self-renewal and differentiation has been hotly debated.[22] In the case of blood, several extrinsic factors that have well characterized activities in early developmental processes have recently been shown to affect self-renewal of the adult stem cell compartment. These include members of the wnt, bmp, Notch, and sonic hedgehog families.[23–26]

Ultimately the functional output of growth factor signals is determined by the cellular context in which they are perceived. Because the formation of stable transcription factor complexes at key *cis*-regulatory elements is an essential feature of the regulation of gene expression, transcription factors are likely to represent a key molecular component of "context" in this regard. Much attention has therefore been focused on the role of transcription factors in the ontogeny, self-renewal, and differentiation/lineage commitment of stem cells. Focusing on blood stem cells as a paradigm, key transcriptional regulators have been identified in two main ways. One, as alluded to previously, is by virtue of their binding to key regulatory elements. An example is provided by GATA1, an erythroid, megakaryocytic, and mast cell associated transcription factor, isolated originally on the basis of its binding to the promoter and enhancer regions (see reference 27 and refs therein) of globin genes. Many other key transcription factors have been identified by virtue of their involvement in leukemia-associated translocations or rearrangements. These involve both deregulation of expression and the production of novel or chimeric gene products through chromosomal translocation.[28] The various transcriptional factors identified by these and other routes are likely to represent only a subset of transcription factors involved in regulation of the stem cell compartment. This caveat aside, the use of homologous recombination strategies to ablate their function in murine model systems has already yielded considerable insight into the stages at which various transcription factors are required.[29] The application of conditional gene ablation strategies in particular has revealed the extent to which individual factors play critical and often distinct roles at different levels of the hemopoietic hierarchy. For example, GATA2 is required for the survival and proliferation of pluripotent stem cells but also plays a role later on in hemopoiesis in the development of the mast cell and platelet lineages.[30] Many factors have been shown to be important for the appropriate development of given lineages, but, more often than not, the defects appear to lie downstream of lineage commitment per se.[31] A number of factors however have been shown to be important in either the generation of stem cells during ontogeny or in the maintenance of the adult stem compartment. These include AML-1/RUNX1, SCL/TAL-1, Lmo-2/Rbtn-2, Mll, Tel, and the aforementioned GATA2.[29] The extent to which factors involved in stem cell ontogeny are also required for stem cell maintenance is an interesting one that was raised some time ago[32] and recently has been addressed experimentally by Mikkola *et al.*[33] Using a conditional knockout approach they showed that the SCL gene, although required for the formation of blood stem cells during ontogeny, was dispensable for HSC engraftment and self-renewal. Although it remains to be seen whether this distinction can be made for some of the other factors discussed previously, it is interesting to note that the biologic imperatives of stem cell ontogeny and stem cell maintenance/self-renewal are quite distinct both in terms of the frequency with which both events occur and the number of cells generated in the two processes.

In terms of self-renewal, two other cell-intrinsic factors are worthy of mention. Enforced expression of the homeobox factor Hox B4 has been shown to enhance self-renewal of hemopoietic stem cells,[34–36] although abrogation of its function appears to have only modest effects on the stem cell compartment *in vivo*.[37] More recently two groups have identified the transcriptional repressor Bmi-1 as a regulator of hemopoietic stem cell self-renewal. Bmi-1 deficient stem cells only transiently sustain hemopoiesis when transplanted into primary recipients and fail to engraft secondary recipients.[38,39] In addition, Bmi-1 has been linked to the self-renewal capacity of leukemic cells, emphasizing the close relationship between cancer cells and stem cells[40] and tabling Bmi-1 as a novel therapeutic target.[38]

In summary, we have accumulated a substantial amount of information about the role of several transcription factors within hemopoiesis. However, the key question of how to initiate a lineage-specific program of gene activity remains unanswered. In principle at least this must be a question of program accessibility. One approach to examining this issue is to analyze the chromatin structure within stem cells of key *cis*-acting regulatory elements of stem cell and unilineage-affiliated genes.

Multilineage Priming

Early studies in this area were facilitated by the availability of factor-dependent cell lines that retained multipotential differentiation capacity in response to physiologic cues such as cytokines and stroma. Analyses of these cell lines showed that many *cis*-regulatory elements of unambiguously lineage-affiliated genes are nuclease-sensitive and presumably therefore available to DNA-binding proteins in multipotent cell populations before unilineage commitment.[32] These include, for example, core elements of the erythroid-affiliated β-globin locus control region[41]; the immunoglobulin heavy chain enhancer (B-lymphoid)[42]; the CD3δ enhancer (T-lymphoid)[42]; and the enhancer of the myeloperoxidase gene (granulocyte-affiliated).[43] In a similar vein, analyses of loci encoding regulatory molecules such as the erythroid-affiliated cytokine receptor EPO-R[44] and transcription factor GATA1[45] also provided evidence for accessibility in multipotent cells.

In some cases this accessibility of regulatory elements could be demonstrated to be effective at the level of transcription, and transcripts for a number of different lineage-affiliated transcription factors, cytokine-receptors, and effector genes could be detected by reverse transcriptase polymerase chain reaction (RT-PCR) and/or Northern blot analysis.[46–48] The levels of transcription observed were significantly lower than those observed in the appropriate corresponding committed populations possibly reflecting (1) that not all *cis*-regulatory elements for the lineage-specific expression of a given gene are available in multipotent cells[41,44] and (2) that the transcription factors actually bound at accessible sites may be "stand in" factors that mark "territory" but will ultimately need to be replaced by alternative factors in committed cells to achieve full-scale activation.[41,43]

Studies conducted at the population level leave open the possibility that the accessibility of these lineage-affiliated programs is a reflection of the coexistence of subpopulations of covertly committed cells within the multipotential cell pool. However, coexpression of different lineage-affiliated programs was observed in individual cells, using single-cell RT-PCR analyses.[48] These results, obtained both in cell lines and in primary $CD34^+$, lin^- cells freshly isolated from the bone marrow were interpreted to indicate that, in multipotential cells, components of alternative or competing lineage pathways are simultaneously available both in terms of chromatin accessibility and in some instances gene expression, albeit at low level.[48] The combination of accessibility of multiple programs and general hemapoietic "noise" provided by low-level and heterogeneous expression of lineage-affiliated regulatory molecules may facilitate initiation of lineage-affiliated circuits of gene expression. Interaction or indeed competition between these circuits at some level could result in the consolidation and up-regulation of one program alongside the shutdown of other programs that conflict with the lineage pathway selected.

This model of the molecular groundstate of HSCs (Fig. 7–2) has been dubbed the multilineage-priming model.[32,48] The mechanisms underlying the initiation of multilineage priming in HSCs remain unclear, but the process appears to be intimately associated with the registration of

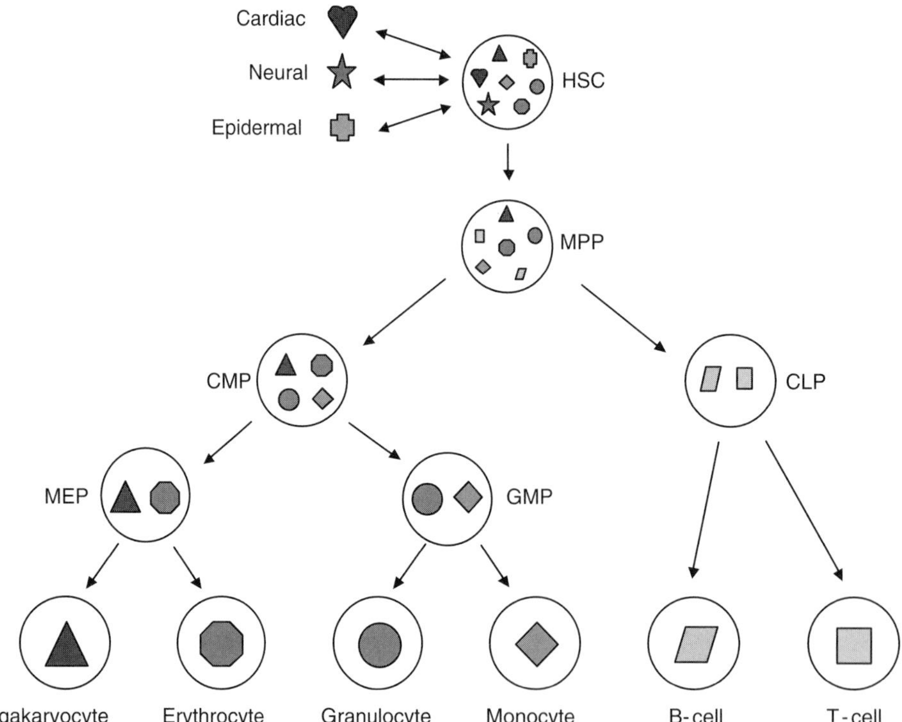

Figure 7–2. *The multilineage priming model for hemopoiesis.* Hemopoietic stem cells (HSCs) show low-level expression of molecules characteristic of multiple hemopoietic lineages, with the exclusion of those associated with lymphoid cells. Also expressed are molecules associated with a variety on nonhemopoietic cell fates perhaps reflecting the recently described phenomenon of adult stem cell plasticity. Transition to the multipotential progenitor (MPP) stage is accompanied by activation of lymphoid programs and repression of nonhemopoietic ones, perhaps indicating that cells from this compartment are unlikely to possess nonhemopoietic potential. Commitment to common myeloid progenitors (CMPs) and common lymphoid progenitors (CLPs) is associated with the consolidation of myeloid and lymphoid programs, respectively, and repression of the lymphoid program in CMPs and the myeloid program in CLPs. This theme of consolidating appropriate programs and repressing those no longer required for the pathway selected continues throughout the remainder of the hemopoietic hierarchy.

hemopoietic potential during ontogeny because coexpression of erythroid and myeloid gene expression programs is observed in AGM-derived HSC.[49] Curiously, evidence for priming of lymphoid-affiliated programs of gene expression was not obtained. This may have been due to the limited number of lymphoid genes examined, although recent studies from Miyamoto *et al.* have recently arrived at a similar conclusion.[50] These investigators demonstrated expression of myeloid genes in HSCs and common myeloid progenitors (CMPs) but not in common lymphoid progenitors (CLPs). Lymphoid genes were found to be expressed in CLPs but not CMPs or HSCs. If true, this myeloid, as opposed to lymphoid, predisposition of HSCs may be interpreted to reflect the relatively late emergence of lymphoid lineages during evolution.

Additional support for the multilineage priming hypothesis comes from the analysis of Pax5-deficient pro-B cells.[51,52] Pax5 encodes a B-cell specific transcription factor that is expressed throughout B-cell development. Abrogation of its function by gene targeting results in differentiation arrest at the pro-B cell stage. Although incompetent to differentiate further down the B-cell pathway, under appropriate conditions *in vitro* and *in vivo,* these cells exhibit multilineage differentiation potential that includes both myeloid cells and T lymphocytes. This apparent reversion to a stem cell state is accompanied by the reactivation of expression of a variety of lineage-affiliated genes in a manner reminiscent of multilineage priming seen in bona fide multipotential stem and progenitor cells. Strikingly, conditional ablation of Pax5 function in mature B cells leads to reactivation of multilineage potential albeit at a lower frequency.[53] Recent studies of normal B lymphopoiesis have led to the identification of early B cells that are yet to express Pax5, and, intriguingly, these cells also display aspects of multipotentiality.[54] Two additional and closely related experiments also support the notion of multilineage priming. First, after integration of a herpes thymidylate kinase gene into the megakaryocyte-specific locus of the integrin α_{IIb3} gene, treatment with an antiherpetic drug reduced the growth of a number of stem cells.[55] These results demonstrate that activation of megakaryocyte gene loci occurs before lineage commitment. Using a related approach, Miyamoto *et al.* demonstrated (1) that CLPs expressing the pre-T cell receptor α gene could give rise to normal numbers of B cells and (2) that CMPs with an activated lysozyme locus produced normal numbers of myeloerythroid colonies.[50] Finally, recent chromatin studies from Bonnifer and colleagues using highly sensitive *in vivo* footprinting techniques have demonstrated "premarking" of the c-fms and lysozyme loci ahead of unilineage commitment and full-scale activation.[56,57]

Transcription Factor Networks and Cross Antagonism

So how does a hemopoietic stem cell that is transcriptionally primed to initiate any of several lineage programs escape the status quo to commit to and execute a given lineage program? Whatever the extrinsic and intrinsic signals involved in this process, the decisions must ultimately be effected through altering the balance of transcription factor activities within the cell, and an emerging theme is the degree to which there is cross-talk between different transcription factors (Fig. 7–3).

Thus, as well as activating the appropriate pattern of lineage-specific gene expression, lineage-affiliated transcription factors simultaneously inhibit alternative lineage programs by directly antagonizing the activity of other transcription factors. One of the best characterized examples involves the erythroid-affiliated transcription factor GATA1 interacting with PU.1. PU.1 is a member of the Ets family of transcription factors and is essential for the development of monocytes, granulocytes, and lymphoid cells.[58–60] An antagonistic relationship between GATA1 and PU.1 in promoting erythroid and myeloid differentiation, respectively, has been indicated by a number of different studies. Deregulation of PU.1 in erythroid cells either by proviral insertion or in transgenic animals[61,62] results in erythroleukemia, suggesting that an elevated level of PU.1 is incompatible with the execution of an erythroid differentiation program. Conversely, enforced expression of GATA1 in a myelomonocytic cell line or in prospectively isolated primary granulocyte-monocyte progenitors alters their differentiation output.[63,64] Several studies have reported that PU.1 and GATA1 physically interact with each other and cross-antagonize their activities, although the mechanisms by which the two factors achieve this are different. It seems that GATA1 inhibits PU.1 function by preventing it from interacting with its co-activator molecule c-Jun, while PU.1 inhibits GATA1 function by disrupting its DNA-binding activity.[65–68] The observation that overexpression of PU.1 in *Xenopus laevis* embryos blocks erythropoiesis and that this block can in turn be overcome by elevated GATA1 expression suggests that the developmental outcome is determined primarily by the stoichiometry of these two factors.[66] An additional level of complexity is added to the PU.1–GATA1 relationship by the fact that both factors are also capable of positive autoregulation of their own expression.[69,70] The importance of this autoregulation is indicated by a recent study showing that targeted deletion of a high-affinity GATA-binding site in the GATA1 promoter leads to selective loss of the eosinophil lineage *in vivo.*[71]

More recently, it has been shown that GATA2 and PU.1 also interact functionally to cross-regulate each other's activity.[72] Using restoration of conditionally active PU.1 activity to PU.1-null hemopoietic progenitors, the authors showed that PU.1 antagonizes GATA2 expression during macrophage differentiation but functions co-operatively with GATA2 to specify mast cell fate, perhaps through co-regulation of target genes that require binding of both factors to their regulatory regions for optimal expression.

Additional examples of cross-antagonism between lineage-specific transcription factors, or their cofactors, have been reported. For example, Graf and colleagues showed that the myelomonocytic transcription factor MafB binds directly to ETS1 and inhibits expression of the transferrin receptor gene that is, in turn, required for erythroid differentiation.[73] In addition, there appears to be an antagonistic relationship

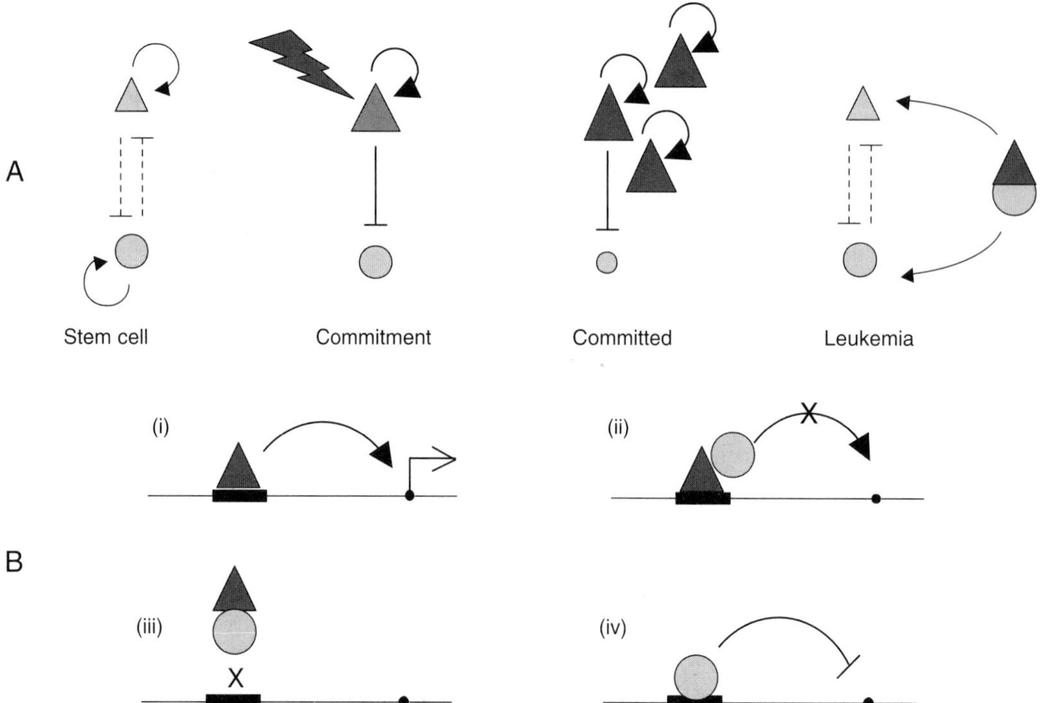

Figure 7–3. *Transcription factor thresholds and cross-antagonism.* (A) Schematic of changes in transcription factor activities during lineage specification. The expression level of a factor is depicted by symbol size and transactivation potential by the intensity of shading. Within a stem cell, transcription factors associated with conflicting lineages (▲ and ●) are coexpressed at low level and may both positively and negatively regulate their own and each other's expression. During commitment, the relative activity of one factor increases in response to intrinsic and/or extrinsic signals leading to a committed cell with high levels of the appropriate lineage factor (▲) and low levels of factors of competing lineages (●). In leukemia, the presence of a chimeric transcription factor generated by chromosomal translocation may block the relative up-regulation of one lineage relative to others and result in a cell stalled in a precommitment state. (B) The various transcriptional consequences of transcription factor cross-antagonism are diagrammed. (i) Positive transactivation of an appropriate lineage-affiliated gene by a transcription factor (▲) bound upstream of the gene promoter, in the absence of conflicting factors. (ii) Direct protein–protein interaction with an antagonistic factor (●) blocks the transactivation function of the DNA-bound factor. (iii) Interaction with an antagonistic factor blocks DNA binding. (iv) Direct transcriptional inhibition of lineage-affiliated genes by a transcription factor of an opposing lineage.

between the myeloid transcription factor C/EBP-β and FOG1, originally identified as a cofactor of GATA1 (Friend of GATA1).[74,75] Forced expression of C-EBPβ in avian myb-ets transformed multipotential hemopoietic progenitors, which normally express high levels of FOG mRNA, results in induction of eosinophil differentiation concomitant with rapid down-regulation of FOG expression. Conversely, forced expression of FOG inhibits C/EBP-β-induced eosinophil differentiation and also causes an eosinophilic cell line to revert to a more multipotent phenotype. The antagonism between FOG and C/EBP-β appears to be at the transcriptional level with C/EBP-β repressing transcription of the FOG gene, whereas FOG acts as a co-repressor for GATA1 to inhibit transcription of C/EBP-β target genes.

Achieving Lineage Dominance

Thus, a range of mechanisms are available whereby one transcription factor can modulate the activity of others, but the question remains how the balance of transcription factor activities within a multipotential progenitor cell is tipped such that dominance of one lineage at the expense of all other possible lineages is achieved (Fig. 7–3). Stochastic events may allow for this, pushing a key transcriptional activator or a lineage-affiliated loop of gene activity past some critical threshold level.[32,76] In addition, extrinsic signals such as the microenvironment, cytokines, and growth factors may stabilize or destabilize an incipient commitment decision. The possibilities of regulation by stochastic or by extrinsic events are not mutually exclusive. The fact that experimental manipulation of the expression level of a single transcriptional regulator such as GATA1 can alter the output of multipotential cells and indeed respecify the fate of myeloid-committed primary cells[63] indicates that quite small changes in the transcriptional complement of a cell may be sufficient to ensure one lineage outcome over another. Similarly, Weissman and colleagues[77] showed that ectopic receptor-mediated signaling at the cell surface can initiate a program of altered lineage output from lymphoid-committed progenitors. Taken together, these studies in primary cells suggest that the committed state of myeloid and lymphoid progenitors is not irrevocably fixed, as was once thought, but can be reprogrammed with relative ease, arguing for substantial lineage flexibility throughout the hematopoietic system.

This general scheme of an initial phase of multilineage priming followed by the emergence of specific lineage-affiliated themes through the interplay of extrinsic signals and cross-antagonistic transcriptional regulators provides a framework for thinking not only about normal unilineage commitment processes but also about more "plastic" scenarios.

It is also evident that events that prevent the achievement of lineage dominance may play a role in the normal maintenance of multipotentiality and in the development of leukemia. An example of the latter was referred to previously, whereby elevated levels of the myeloid transcription factor PU.1 within erythroid cells results in erythroleukemia. It should come as no surprise, therefore, that chimeric transcription factors have been implicated in leukemia and many of the most critical factors dysregulated in this way have been shown by gene knockout studies to be involved in early hemopoietic stem cell development or function.

Postgenomics and Gene Discovery

The studies described so far have concentrated on a limited number of molecules. Importantly many of these have been selected on the basis of genetic experiments or mutations in relevant disease states and therefore have impeccable credentials. Nevertheless, the advent of postgenomic high-throughput technologies has afforded the possibility of profiling total transcriptional output and these approaches, although in their infancy, are beginning to provide early insights into the very nature of stemness at a molecular level (see reference 78 for review).

A landmark study in this area was conducted by Lemischka and colleagues who mounted the first comprehensive attempt to define the global transcriptional profile of hemopoietic stem cells,[79] the results of which appear in an online form in the stem cell database (SCDb). Using subtractive hybridization of cDNA libraries generated from HSC-enriched and HSC-depleted murine fetal liver cells, these workers identified some 5735 HSC-enriched clones of which 2119 represented nonredundant gene products. Among these are included a number of transcriptional factors (161), membrane-associated/cell surface molecules (174), and signaling molecules (147). In a rather more limited analysis, these workers drew attention to potentially important differences in the transcriptomes of fetal liver–derived and adult HSCs. Using a not dissimilar strategy, Park *et al.* compared HSC with multipotential progenitors (MPPs).[80] HSC and MPP-derived cDNA libraries were first depleted for clones expressed in more mature lineage-committed hemopoietic cells and then arrayed on glass slides and simultaneously probed with independently labeled cDNAs from both HSCs and MPPs. This comparative study revealed several interesting differences in gene expression between long-term reconstituting HSCs and MPPs including genes like Notch and the breast cancer susceptibility gene BRCA2. Many of the genes identified in this study also feature in the SCDb. Human CD34-selected cells from bone marrow have also been compared with their granulocyte colony-stimulating factor (G-CSF)-mobilized counterparts.[81] Although CD34-positive cells represent a heterogeneous population, some clear differences in gene expression were noted; many of these were related to cell cycle. Akashi *et al.* have recently performed a comprehensive comparison of murine HSC, MPP, CMP, and CLP populations.[82] This study was done using Affymetrix microarrays with no prior use of subtractive approaches to pre-enrich in any way for stage-specific transcripts. Given limiting cell numbers, probe amplification was necessary and sample replication minimal. These points not withstanding, this study provides an unbiased and global view of the transcriptomes of these different stem and progenitor cell compartments. Interestingly, these studies provide strong evidence in support of the multilineage priming hypothesis alluded to previously. Thus, multipotent progenitors coexpress genes characteristic of a number of different myeloid and lymphoid cell types. This multilineage priming is restricted as MPPs progress to CLPs or CMPs that exclusively express lymphoid or myeloid genes, respectively. HSCs only express myeloid and not lymphoid genes, reminiscent of previous data obtained in AGM-derived HSCs that has already been discussed.[49] Strikingly, however, HSCs appear to express genes characteristic of a variety of nonhemopoietic lineages including those associated with neuronal, pancreatic, liver, hair, heart, endothelial, epithelial, and kidney cell types.[82] This broad range of multitissue priming is intriguing and may mechanistically underlie the phenomenon of stem cell plasticity. These data might suggest that the alternative cell fate potentials are a genuine, if low frequency, property of these cells rather than reflecting a reprogramming or transdifferentiation event.

The studies described so far have exclusively focused on the blood system. However, stem or stem-like cells from other tissues have also been examined in terms of their global gene expression profile. Several studies have looked at gene expression in NSCs.[83–85] One common theme that emerges from these is the apparent overlap in transcripts expressed in NSCs and HSCs hinting perhaps at a common molecular basis for stem cell identity or "stemness." Recent studies profiling human mammary stem/progenitor cells have also revealed overlaps in genetic programs with other stem and progenitor cell types.[86] Attention has also been focused on MAPCs, given reports of their extensive self-renewal capacity *in vitro* and their wide range of developmental potentials exhibited both *in vitro* and *in vivo*. Global transcriptional profiling of MAPC cell populations obtained from bone marrow, muscle, and brain indicated that these cells differed very little from each other with less than 1% of genes being differentially expressed between the different cell types.[87] At face value, the lack of a clear tissue imprint on MAPC cells of different origins might argue for a common developmental origin for these cells as opposed to their arising from more mature cells of these different tissue types by virtue of a transdifferentiation or dedifferentiation reprogramming-type of mechanism. Because MAPCs and ES cells appear to share many functional characteristics it is interesting to speculate that these may reflect a common or similar molecular groundstate. The expression by MAPCs of the ES-associated molecules Oct-4 and Rex-1 goes someway to supporting such a notion. Changes in gene expression in ESC populations differentiating in response to retinoic acid have been documented,[88] as have comparisons between ESCs and trophoblast-derived stem cells.[89] Formal comparison, if possible, of the data obtained with MAPCs would be of interest.

Ideally one would wish to compare the transcriptional profiles of any number of cell types of interest. Unfortunately, data compatibility, or rather lack of it, currently remains a major stumbling block in the field. Two groups have, however, recently directly tested the hypothesis that stem cells of different types may share a common transcriptional program.

Briefly, through comparisons of stem cells with their more differentiated counterparts Ivanova *et al*[90] and Ramalho-Santos *et al*[91] identified sets of HSC, NSC, and ESC enriched genes. Comparisons of these three sets of genes were then performed to identify a common gene expression signature for stemness. In one case, this identified 283 genes in common and in the other 216 genes (Fig. 7–4). Unfortunately, the comparison of these two signatures reveals only a handful of genes in common. This may reflect issues of data compatibility, differences in the provenance of the cells used in the different studies, or both. It should also be pointed out that both lists may be equally valid, and, therefore, it may be more appropriate to add rather than subtract these two largely different signatures. Validation by other methods will be required to discriminate between these two possibilities.

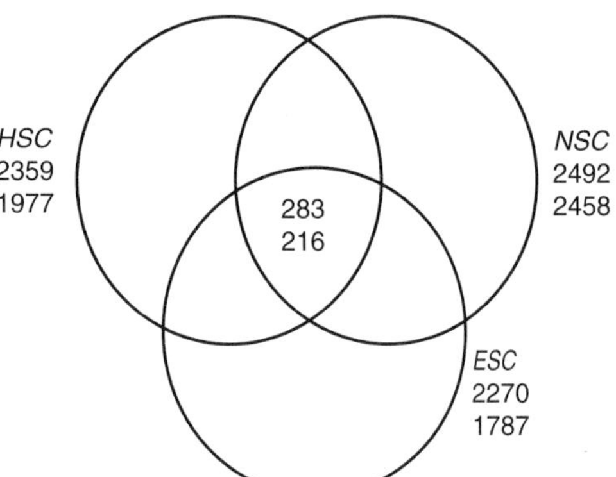

Figure 7–4. *Stem-cell-specific gene-expression profiles.* Global profiling techniques were used to generate lists of hemopoietic stem (HS) cells, neural stem (NS) cells , and embryonic stem (ES) cell specific genes. These different gene lists were then compared to identify a set of genes whose expression was common to all three stem cell types. In one study (red) this resulted in the identification of 283 genes[90] and in a similar study (blue) this yielded 216 genes.[91] These lists represent the first comprehensive attempt to produce a molecular signature of "stemness."

In conclusion, although microarray-based strategies have already provided valuable information and will undoubtedly continue to do so, improvements in technologic and statistical robustness are certainly required. This is particularly true with respect to measuring low levels of gene expression and small changes in gene expression between different cell types or with one cell type in response to receipt of intrinsic or extrinsic cues. The biologic relevance of these is already understood. For example, receptor densities as low as 50 molecules per cell, which are neither detectable by antibody staining nor revealed by binding of radiolabeled ligand, are known to initiate functionally relevant responses in cells on addition of their cognate ligands.[48] Similarly, changes in transcription factor levels in the two-fold range are known to be relevant in the context of haploinsufficient disease states and experimentally have been shown to alter cell fate outcomes in, for example, ES cell differentiation.[92] The development of global profiling strategies with the sensitivity and precision to accommodate these requirements poses a considerable challenge, although recent indications suggest that massively parallel signature sequencing may provide one platform with just such a capability.[93] A final point to consider is that most studies so far have examined cell populations. Many reports allude to the heterogeneity of stem cell compartments and most recently there have been indications that these populations may also be subject to circadian-dependent phenotypic changes.[94] The data so far therefore have been, by and large, average data, which take no account of cell to cell variations that are likely to be important, at least in early decision-making stages. However, reports have been recently published that apply array technology to the study of single cells,[95] and importantly Iscove *et al.* have developed robust probe amplification techniques for single cells.[96] The combination of these approaches together with genetic manipulation of key candidate regulators hold great promise for solving the rather refractory puzzle of how a stem cell decides what to do!

REFERENCES

1. Fuchs, E., and Segre, J.A. (2000). Stem cells: a new lease on life. *Cell* **100,** 143–155.
2. Joshi, C.V., and Enver, T. (2002). Plasticity revisited. *Curr. Opin. Cell Biol.* **14,** 749–755.
3. Draper, J.S., and Andrews, P.W. (2002). Embryonic stem cells: advances toward potential therapeutic use. *Curr. Opin. Obstet. Gynecol.* **14,** 309–315.
4. Smith, A.G. (2001). Embryo-derived stem cells: of mice and men. *Annu. Rev. Cell Dev. Biol.* **17,** 435–462.
5. Ferrari, G., Cusella-De Angelis, G., Coletta, M., Paolucci, E., Stornaiuolo, A., Cossu, G., and Mavilio, F. (1998). Muscle regeneration by bone marrow-derived myogenic progenitors. *Science* **279,** 1528–1530.
6. Bjornson, C.R., Rietze, R.L., Reynolds, B.A., Magli, M.C., and Vescovi, A.L. (1999). Turning brain into blood: a hematopoietic

fate adopted by adult neural stem cells in vivo. *Science* **283,** 534–537.
7. Wagers, A.J., Sherwood, R.I., Christensen, J.L., and Weissman, I.L. (2002). Little evidence for developmental plasticity of adult hematopoietic stem cells. *Science* **297,** 2256–2259.
8. Terada, N., Hamazaki, T., Oka, M., Hoki, M., Mastalerz, D.M., Nakano, Y., Meyer, E.M., Morel, L., Petersen, B.E., and Scott, E.W. (2002). Bone marrow cells adopt the phenotype of other cells by spontaneous cell fusion. *Nature* **416,** 542–545.
9. Ying, Q.L., Nichols, J., Evans, E.P., and Smith, A.G. (2002). Changing potency by spontaneous fusion. *Nature* **416,** 545–548.
10. Vassilopoulos, G., Wang, P.R., and Russell, D.W. (2003). Transplanted bone marrow regenerates liver by cell fusion. *Nature* **422,** 901–904.
11. Wang, X., Willenbring, H., Akkari, Y., Torimaru, Y., Foster, M., Al-Dhalimy, M., Lagasse, E., Finegold, M., Olson, S., and Grompe, M. (2003). Cell fusion is the principal source of bone-marrow-derived hepatocytes. *Nature* **422,** 897–901.
12. Morshead, C.M., Benveniste, P., Iscove, N.N., and van der Kooy, D. (2002). Hematopoietic competence is a rare property of neural stem cells that may depend on genetic and epigenetic alterations. *Nat. Med.* **8,** 268–273.
13. Minasi, M.G., Riminucci, M., De Angelis, L., Borello, U., Berarducci, B., Innocenzi, A., Caprioli, A., Sirabella, D., Baiocchi, M., De Maria, R.., Boratto, R., Jaffredo, T., Broccoli, V., Bianco, P., and Cossu, G. (2002). The meso-angioblast: a multipotent, self-renewing cell that originates from the dorsal aorta and differentiates into most mesodermal tissues. *Development* **129,** 2773–2783.
14. Cao, B., Zheng, B., Jankowski, R. J., Kimura, S., Ikezawa, M., Deasy, B., Cummins, J., Epperly, M., Qu-Petersen, Z., and Huard, J. (2003). Muscle stem cells differentiate into haematopoietic lineages but retain myogenic potential. *Nat. Cell Biol.* **5,** 640–646.
15. Reyes, M., Lund, T., Lenvik, T., Aguiar, D., Koodie, L., and Verfaillie, C.M. (2001). Purification and ex vivo expansion of postnatal human marrow mesodermal progenitor cells. *Blood* **98,** 2615–2625.
16. Jiang, Y., Jahagirdar, B.N., Reinhardt, R.L., Schwartz, R.E., Keene, C.D., Ortiz-Gonzalez, X.R., Reyes, M., Lenvik, T., Lund, T., Blackstad, M., Du, J., Aldrich, S., Lisberg, A., Low, W.C., Largaespada, D.A., and Verfaillie, C.M. (2002). Pluripotency of mesenchymal stem cells derived from adult marrow. *Nature* **418,** 41–49.
17. Dzierzak, E. (2003). Ontogenic emergence of definitive hematopoietic stem cells. *Curr. Opin. Hematol.* **10,** 229–234.
18. Ciau-Uitz, A., Walmsley, M., and Patient, R. (2000). Distinct origins of adult and embryonic blood in Xenopus. *Cell* **102,** 787–796.
19. De Angelis, L., Berghella, L., Coletta, M., Lattanzi, L., Zanchi, M., Cusella-De Angelis, M. G., Ponzetto, C., and Cossu, G. (1999). Skeletal myogenic progenitors originating from embryonic dorsal aorta coexpress endothelial and myogenic markers and contribute to postnatal muscle growth and regeneration. *J. Cell Biol.* **147,** 869–878.
20. Booth, C., and Potten, C.S. (2000). Gut instincts: thoughts on intestinal epithelial stem cells. *J. Clin. Invest.* **105,** 1493–1499.
21. Niemann, C., and Watt, F.M. (2002). Designer skin: lineage commitment in postnatal epidermis. *Trends Cell Biol.* **12,** 185–192.
22. Enver, T., Heyworth, C.M., and Dexter, T. M. (1998). Do stem cells play dice? *Blood* **92,** 348–351; discussion 352.
23. Bhardwaj, G., Murdoch, B., Wu, D., Baker, D.P., Williams, K.P., Chadwick, K., Ling, L.E., Karanu, F.N., and Bhatia, M. (2001). Sonic hedgehog induces the proliferation of primitive human hematopoietic cells via BMP regulation. *Nat. Immunol.* **2,** 172–180.
24. Reya, T., Duncan, A.W., Ailles, L., Domen, J., Scherer, D.C., Willert, K., Hintz, L., Nusse, R., and Weissman, I. L. (2003). A role for Wnt signalling in self-renewal of haematopoietic stem cells. *Nature* **423,** 409–414.
25. Varnum-Finney, B., Brashem-Stein, C., and Bernstein, I.D. (2003). Combined effects of Notch signaling and cytokines induce a multiple log increase in precursors with lymphoid and myeloid reconstituting ability. *Blood* **101,** 1784–1789.
26. Willert, K., Brown, J.D., Danenberg, E., Duncan, A.W., Weissman, I.L., Reya, T., Yates, J.R. 3rd, and Nusse, R. (2003). Wnt proteins are lipid-modified and can act as stem cell growth factors. *Nature* **423,** 448–452.
27. Orkin, S.H., and Zon, L.I. (1997). Genetics of erythropoiesis: induced mutations in mice and zebrafish. *Annu. Rev. Genet.* **31,** 33–60.
28. Rabbitts, T.H. (1999). Perspective: chromosomal translocations can affect genes controlling gene expression and differentiation–why are these functions targeted? *J. Pathol.* **187,** 39–42.
29. Cantor, A.B., and Orkin, S.H. (2002). Transcriptional regulation of erythropoiesis: an affair involving multiple partners. *Oncogene* **21,** 3368–3376.
30. Tsai, F.Y., Keller, G., Kuo, F.C., Weiss, M., Chen, J., Rosenblatt, M., Alt, F.W., and Orkin, S.H. (1994). An early haematopoietic defect in mice lacking the transcription factor GATA-2. *Nature* **371,** 221–226.
31. May, G., and Enver, T. (2001). The lineage commitment and self renewal of blood stem cells. *In* "Hematopoiesis: A Developmental Approach" (L. Zon, ed.), pp. 61–81. Oxford University Press, Oxford, UK.
32. Enver, T., and Greaves, M. (1998). Loops, lineage, and leukemia. *Cell* **94,** 9–12.
33. Mikkola, H.K., Klintman, J., Yang, H., Hock, H., Schlaeger, T.M., Fujiwara, Y., and Orkin, S.H. (2003). Haematopoietic stem cells retain long-term repopulating activity and multipotency in the absence of stem-cell leukaemia SCL/tal-1 gene. *Nature* **421,** 547–551.
34. Antonchuk, J., Sauvageau, G., and Humphries, R.K. (2002). HOXB4-induced expansion of adult hematopoietic stem cells ex vivo. *Cell* **109,** 39–45.
35. Buske, C., Feuring-Buske, M., Abramovich, C., Spiekermann, K., Eaves, C.J., Coulombel, L., Sauvageau, G., Hogge, D.E., and Humphries, R.K. (2002). Deregulated expression of HOXB4 enhances the primitive growth activity of human hematopoietic cells. *Blood* **100,** 862–868.
36. Sauvageau, G., Thorsteinsdottir, U., Eaves, C.J., Lawrence, H.J., Largman, C., Lansdorp, P.M., and Humphries, R.K. (1995). Overexpression of HOXB4 in hematopoietic cells causes the selective expansion of more primitive populations in vitro and in vivo. *Genes Dev.* **9,** 1753–1765.
37. Bjornsson, J.M., Larsson, N., Brun, A.C., Magnusson, M., Andersson, E., Lundstrom, P., Larsson, J., Repetowska, E., Ehinger, M., Humphries, R.K., and Karlsson, S. (2003). Reduced proliferative capacity of hematopoietic stem cells deficient in Hoxb3 and Hoxb4. *Mol. Cell Biol.* **23,** 3872–3883.
38. Lessard, J., and Sauvageau, G. (2003). Bmi-1 determines the proliferative capacity of normal and leukaemic stem cells. *Nature* **423,** 255–260.

39. Park, I.K., Qian, D., Kiel, M., Becker, M.W., Pihalja, M., Weissman, I.L., Morrison, S.J., and Clarke, M.F. (2003). Bmi-1 is required for maintenance of adult self-renewing haematopoietic stem cells. *Nature* **423,** 302–305.
40. Reya, T., Morrison, S. J., Clarke, M.F., and Weissman, I.L. (2001). Stem cells, cancer, and cancer stem cells. *Nature* **414,** 105–111.
41. Jimenez, G., Griffiths, S.D., Ford, A.M., Greaves, M.F., and Enver, T. (1992). Activation of the beta-globin locus control region precedes commitment to the erythroid lineage. *Proc. Natl. Acad. Sci. U. S. A.* **89,** 10618–10622.
42. Ford, A.M., Bennett, C.A., Healy, L.E., Navarro, E., Spooncer, E., and Greaves, M.F. (1992). Immunoglobulin heavy-chain and CD3 delta-chain gene enhancers are DNase I-hypersensitive in hemopoietic progenitor cells. *Proc. Natl. Acad. Sci. U. S. A.* **89,** 3424–3428.
43. Ford, A.M., Bennett, C.A., Healy, L.E., Towatari, M., Greaves, M.F., and Enver, T. (1996). Regulation of the myeloperoxidase enhancer binding proteins Pu1, C-EBP alpha, -beta, and -delta during granulocyte-lineage specification. *Proc. Natl. Acad. Sci. U. S. A.* **93,** 10838–10843.
44. Heberlein, C., Fischer, K.D., Stoffel, M., Nowock, J., Ford, A., Tessmer, U., and Stocking, C. (1992). The gene for erythropoietin receptor is expressed in multipotential hematopoietic and embryonal stem cells: evidence for differentiation stage-specific regulation. *Mol. Cell Biol.* **12,** 1815–1826.
45. Ronchi, A., Ciro, M., Cairns, L., Basilico, L., Corbella, P., Ricciardi-Castagnoli, P., Cross, M., Ghysdael, J., and Ottolenghi, S. (1997). Molecular heterogeneity of regulatory elements of the mouse GATA-1 gene. *Genes Funct.* **1,** 245–258.
46. Cross, M.A., Heyworth, C.M., Murrell, A.M., Bockamp, E.O., Dexter, T.M., and Green, A.R. (1994). Expression of lineage restricted transcription factors precedes lineage specific differentiation in a multipotent haemopoietic progenitor cell line. *Oncogene* **9,** 3013–3016.
47. Ford, A.M., Healy, L.E., Bennett, C.A., Navarro, E., Spooncer, E., and Greaves, M.F. (1992). Multilineage phenotypes of interleukin-3-dependent progenitor cells. *Blood* **79,** 1962–1971.
48. Hu, M., Krause, D., Greaves, M., Sharkis, S., Dexter, M., Heyworth, C., and Enver, T. (1997). Multilineage gene expression precedes commitment in the hemopoietic system. *Genes Dev.* **11,** 774–785.
49. Delassus, S., Titley, I., and Enver, T. (1999). Functional and molecular analysis of hematopoietic progenitors derived from the aorta-gonad-mesonephros region of the mouse embryo. *Blood* **94,** 1495–1503.
50. Miyamoto, T., Iwasaki, H., Reizis, B., Ye, M., Graf, T., Weissman, I.L., and Akashi, K. (2002). Myeloid or lymphoid promiscuity as a critical step in hematopoietic lineage commitment. *Dev. Cell* **3,** 137–147.
51. Nutt, S.L., Heavey, B., Rolink, A.G., and Busslinger, M. (1999). Commitment to the B-lymphoid lineage depends on the transcription factor Pax5. *Nature* **401,** 556–562.
52. Rolink, A.G., Nutt, S.L., Melchers, F., and Busslinger, M. (1999). Long-term in vivo reconstitution of T-cell development by Pax5-deficient B-cell progenitors. *Nature* **401,** 603–606.
53. Horcher, M., Souabni, A., and Busslinger, M. (2001). Pax5/BSAP maintains the identity of B cells in late B lymphopoiesis. *Immunity* **14,** 779–790.
54. Reynaud, D., Lefort, N., Manie, E., Coulombel, L., and Levy, Y. (2003). In vitro identification of human pro-B cells that give rise to macrophages, natural killer cells, and T cells. *Blood* **101,** 4313–4321.
55. Tronik-Le Roux, D., Roullot, V., Poujol, C., Kortulewski, T., Nurden, P., and Marguerie, G. (2000). Thrombasthenic mice generated by replacement of the integrin alpha(IIb) gene: demonstration that transcriptional activation of this megakaryocytic locus precedes lineage commitment. *Blood* **96,** 1399–1408.
56. Kontaraki, J., Chen, H.H., Riggs, A., and Bonifer, C. (2000). Chromatin fine structure profiles for a developmentally regulated gene: reorganization of the lysozyme locus before trans-activator binding and gene expression. *Genes Dev.* **14,** 2106–2122.
57. Tagoh, H., Himes, R., Clarke, D., Leenen, P.J., Riggs, A.D., Hume, D., and Bonifer, C. (2002). Transcription factor complex formation and chromatin fine structure alterations at the murine c-fms (CSF-1 receptor) locus during maturation of myeloid precursor cells. *Genes Dev.* 16, 1721–1737.
58. Hromas, R., Orazi, A., Neiman, R.S., Maki, R., Van Beveran, C., Moore, J., and Klemsz, M. (1993). Hematopoietic lineage- and stage-restricted expression of the ETS oncogene family member PU.1. *Blood* **82,** 2998–3004.
59. McKercher, S.R., Torbett, B.E., Anderson, K.L., Henkel, G.W., Vestal, D.J., Baribault, H., Klemsz, M., Feeney, A.J., Wu, G.E., Paige, C.J., and Maki, R.A. (1996). Targeted disruption of the PU.1 gene results in multiple hematopoietic abnormalities. *EMBO J.* **15,** 5647–5658.
60. Scott, E.W., Simon, M.C., Anastasi, J., and Singh, H. (1994). Requirement of transcription factor PU.1 in the development of multiple hematopoietic lineages. *Science* **265,** 1573–1577.
61. Moreau-Gachelin, F., Ray, D., Mattei, M.G., Tambourin, P., and Tavitian, A. (1989). The putative oncogene Spi-1: murine chromosomal localization and transcriptional activation in murine acute erythroleukemias. *Oncogene* **4,** 1449–1456.
62. Moreau-Gachelin, F., Wendling, F., Molina, T., Denis, N., Titeux, M., Grimber, G., Briand, P., Vainchenker, W., and Tavitian, A. (1996). Spi-1/PU.1 transgenic mice develop multistep erythroleukemias. *Mol. Cell Biol.* **16,** 2453–2463.
63. Heyworth, C., Pearson, S., May, G., and Enver, T. (2002). Transcription factor-mediated lineage switching reveals plasticity in primary committed progenitor cells. *EMBO J.* **21,** 3770–3781.
64. Kulessa, H., Frampton, J., and Graf, T. (1995). GATA-1 reprograms avian myelomonocytic cell lines into eosinophils, thromboblasts, and erythroblasts. *Genes Dev.* **9,** 1250–1262.
65. Nerlov, C., Querfurth, E., Kulessa, H., and Graf, T. (2000). GATA-1 interacts with the myeloid PU.1 transcription factor and represses PU.1-dependent transcription. *Blood* **95,** 2543–2551.
66. Rekhtman, N., Radparvar, F., Evans, T., and Skoultchi, A. I. (1999). Direct interaction of hematopoietic transcription factors PU.1 and GATA-1: functional antagonism in erythroid cells. *Genes Dev.* **13,** 1398–1411.
67. Zhang, P., Behre, G., Pan, J., Iwama, A., Wara-Aswapati, N., Radomska, H.S., Auron, P. E., Tenen, D.G., and Sun, Z. (1999). Negative cross-talk between hematopoietic regulators: GATA proteins repress PU.1. *Proc. Natl. Acad. Sci. U. S. A.* **96,** 8705–8710.
68. Zhang, P., Zhang, X., Iwama, A., Yu, C., Smith, K.A., Mueller, B.U., Narravula, S., Torbett, B.E., Orkin, S.H., and Tenen, D.G. (2000). PU.1 inhibits GATA-1 function and erythroid differentiation by blocking GATA-1 DNA binding. *Blood* **96,** 2641–2648.
69. Chen, H., Ray-Gallet, D., Zhang, P., Hetherington, C. J., Gonzalez, D.A., Zhang, D.E., Moreau-Gachelin, F., and Tenen, D.G. (1995). PU.1 (Spi-1) autoregulates its expression in myeloid cells. *Oncogene* **11,** 1549–1560.

70. Tsai, S.F., Strauss, E., and Orkin, S.H. (1991). Functional analysis and in vivo footprinting implicate the erythroid transcription factor GATA-1 as a positive regulator of its own promoter. *Genes Dev.* **5,** 919–931.
71. Yu, C., Cantor, A.B., Yang, H., Browne, C., Wells, R.A., Fujiwara, Y., and Orkin, S.H. (2002). Targeted deletion of a high-affinity GATA-binding site in the GATA-1 promoter leads to selective loss of the eosinophil lineage in vivo. *J. Exp. Med.* **195,** 1387–1395.
72. Walsh, J.C., DeKoter, R.P., Lee, H.J., Smith, E.D., Lancki, D.W., Gurish, M.F., Friend, D.S., Stevens, R.L., Anastasi, J., and Singh, H. (2002). Cooperative and antagonistic interplay between PU.1 and GATA-2 in the specification of myeloid cell fates. *Immunity* **17,** 665–676.
73. Sieweke, M.H., Tekotte, H., Frampton, J., and Graf, T. (1996). MafB is an interaction partner and repressor of Ets-1 that inhibits erythroid differentiation. *Cell* **85,** 49–60.
74. Querfurth, E., Schuster, M., Kulessa, H., Crispino, J.D., Doderlein, G., Orkin, S.H., Graf, T., and Nerlov, C. (2000). Antagonism between C/EBPbeta and FOG in eosinophil lineage commitment of multipotent hematopoietic progenitors. *Genes Dev.* **14,** 2515–2525.
75. Tsang, A.P., Visvader, J.E., Turner, C.A., Fujiwara, Y., Yu, C., Weiss, M.J., Crossley, M., and Orkin, S.H. (1997). FOG, a multitype zinc finger protein, acts as a cofactor for transcription factor GATA-1 in erythroid and megakaryocytic differentiation. *Cell* **90,** 109–119.
76. McAdams, H.H., and Arkin, A. (1997). Stochastic mechanisms in gene expression. *Proc. Natl. Acad. Sci. U. S. A.* **94,** 814–819.
77. Kondo, M., Scherer, D.C., Miyamoto, T., King, A.G., Akashi, K., Sugamura, K., and Weissman, I.L. (2000). Cell-fate conversion of lymphoid-committed progenitors by instructive actions of cytokines. *Nature* **407,** 383–386.
78. Joshi, C., and Enver, T. (2003). Molecular complexities of stem cells. *Curr. Opin. Hematol.* **10,** 220–228.
79. Phillips, R.L., Ernst, R.E., Brunk, B., Ivanova, N., Mahan, M.A., Deanehan, J.K., Moore, K.A., Overton, G.C., and Lemischka, I.R. (2000). The genetic program of hematopoietic stem cells. *Science* **288,** 1635–1640.
80. Park, I.K., He, Y., Lin, F., Laerum, O.D., Tian, Q., Bumgarner, R., Klug, C.A., Li, K., Kuhr, C., Doyle, M.J., Xie, T., Schummer, M., Sun, Y., Goldsmith, A., Clarke, M.F., Weissman, I.L., Hood, L., and Li, L. (2002). Differential gene expression profiling of adult murine hematopoietic stem cells. *Blood* **99,** 488–498.
81. Steidl, U., Kronenwett, R., Rohr, U.P., Fenk, R., Kliszewski, S., Maercker, C., Neubert, P., Aivado, M., Koch, J., Modlich, O., Bojar, H., Gattermann, N., and Haas, R. (2002). Gene expression profiling identifies significant differences between the molecular phenotypes of bone marrow-derived and circulating human CD34+ hematopoietic stem cells. *Blood* **99,** 2037–2044.
82. Akashi, K., He, X., Chen, J., Iwasaki, H., Niu, C., Steenhard, B., Zhang, J., Haug, J., and Li, L. (2003). Transcriptional accessibility for genes of multiple tissues and hematopoietic lineages is hierarchically controlled during early hematopoiesis. *Blood* **101,** 383–389.
83. Geschwind, D.H., Ou, J., Easterday, M.C., Dougherty, J.D., Jackson, R.L., Chen, Z., Antoine, H., Terskikh, A., Weissman, I.L., Nelson, S.F., and Kornblum, H.I. (2001). A genetic analysis of neural progenitor differentiation. *Neuron* **29,** 325–339.
84. Suslov, O.N., Kukekov, V.G., Ignatova, T.N., and Steindler, D.A. (2002). Neural stem cell heterogeneity demonstrated by molecular phenotyping of clonal neurospheres. *Proc. Natl. Acad. Sci. U. S. A.* **99,** 14506–14511.
85. Terskikh, A.V., Easterday, M.C., Li, L., Hood, L., Kornblum, H.I., Geschwind, D.H., and Weissman, I.L. (2001). From hematopoiesis to neuropoiesis: evidence of overlapping genetic programs. *Proc. Natl. Acad. Sci. U. S. A.* **98,** 7934–7939.
86. Dontu, G., Abdallah, W.M., Foley, J.M., Jackson, K.W., Clarke, M.F., Kawamura, M.J., and Wicha, M.S. (2003). In vitro propagation and transcriptional profiling of human mammary stem/progenitor cells. *Genes Dev.* **17,** 1253–1270.
87. Jiang, Y., Vaessen, B., Lenvik, T., Blackstad, M., Reyes, M., and Verfaillie, C.M. (2002). Multipotent progenitor cells can be isolated from postnatal murine bone marrow, muscle, and brain. *Exp. Hematol.* **30,** 896–904.
88. Kelly, D.L., and Rizzino, A. (2000). DNA microarray analyses of genes regulated during the differentiation of embryonic stem cells. *Mol. Reprod. Dev.* **56,** 113–123.
89. Tanaka, T.S., Kunath, T., Kimber, W.L., Jaradat, S.A., Stagg, C.A., Usuda, M., Yokota, T., Niwa, H., Rossant, J., and Ko, M.S. (2002). Gene expression profiling of embryo-derived stem cells reveals candidate genes associated with pluripotency and lineage specificity. *Genome Res.* **12,** 1921–1928.
90. Ivanova, N.B., Dimos, J.T., Schaniel, C., Hackney, J.A., Moore, K.A., and Lemischka, I.R. (2002). A stem cell molecular signature. *Science* **298,** 601–604.
91. Ramalho-Santos, M., Yoon, S., Matsuzaki, Y., Mulligan, R.C., and Melton, D.A. (2002). "Stemness": transcriptional profiling of embryonic and adult stem cells. *Science* **298,** 597–600.
92. Niwa, H., Miyazaki, J., and Smith, A.G. (2000). Quantitative expression of Oct-3/4 defines differentiation, dedifferentiation or self-renewal of ES cells. *Nat. Genet.* **24,** 372–376.
93. Brenner, S., Johnson, M., Bridgham, J., Golda, G., Lloyd, D.H., Johnson, D., Luo, S., McCurdy, S., Foy, M., Ewan, M., Roth, R., George, D., Eletr, S., Albrecht, G., Vermaas, E., Williams, S.R., Moon, K., Burcham, T., Pallas, M., DuBridge R.B., Kirchner J., Fearon, K., Mao, J., and Corcoran, K. (2000). Gene expression analysis by massively parallel signature sequencing (MPSS) on microbead arrays. *Nat. Biotechnol.* **18,** 630–634.
94. Lambert, J.F., Liu, M., Colvin, G.A., Dooner, M., McAuliffe, C.I., Becker, P.S., Forget, B.G., Weissman, S.M., and Quesenberry, P.J. (2003). Marrow stem cells shift gene expression and engraftment phenotype with cell cycle transit. *J. Exp. Med.* **197,** 1563–1572.
95. Tietjen, I., Rihel, J.M., Cao, Y., Koentges, G., Zakhary, L., and Dulac, C. (2003). Single-cell transcriptional analysis of neuronal progenitors. *Neuron* **38,** 161–175.
96. Iscove, N.N., Barbara, M., Gu, M., Gibson, M., Modi, C., and Winegarden, N. (2002). Representation is faithfully preserved in global cDNA amplified exponentially from sub-picogram quantities of mRNA. *Nat. Biotechnol.* **20,** 940–943.

8

Transcription Regulation in B-cell Development

Haruhiko Ishii, Dipanjan Chowdhury, and Ranjan Sen

The recently completed sequence of the human genome has been dubbed the blueprint for a human being from which, we hope, will arise ways to improve the human condition. The basis for this optimism is that the sequence does indeed contain the very basic information about all the possible components of a human being. However, the human is much more than an assemblage of all parts encoded in the genome. Only a fraction of all the information potentially available within the nucleus is expressed in cells, and differences in gene expression profiles between cell types form the basis for specialized cell function. Gene expression is regulated at various levels. Transcription regulation determines which genes in the genome will be read out as messenger RNA, and thus it is essential to establish tissue-specific patterns of gene expression. Once a gene is transcribed, other forms of regulation such as RNA turnover, differential splicing, and regulated translation determine whether a protein will be expressed and the nature of the expressed protein. Finally, proteins are subject to additional forms of regulation such as stability, post-translational modifications and associations with other proteins. In this chapter we discuss transcriptional regulatory mechanisms that promote B-lymphocyte differentiation.

Lymphocytes arise continuously during the lifetime of mammals starting from a self-renewing population of bone marrow-derived hematopoietic stem cells (HSCs).[1–3] Although HSCs are capable of long-term hematopoietic reconstitution, bone marrow progenitor populations have been isolated that reconstitute only subsets of hematopoietic lineages.[4,5] These cells with more limited differentiation potential do not reconstitute long term, suggesting that they lack the property of self-renewal. Extensive analysis by Weissman and colleagues has led to a scheme for hematopoiesis in which there are two major progenitor intermediates. The common lymphoid precursor (CLP) is the cell population that repopulates lymphoid, natural killer, and dendritic cells in irradiated mice.[3,6] The second intermediate, termed the common myeloid precursor (CMP), differentiates into granulocytes, megakaryocytes, monocytes, and erythrocytes.[7] It is interesting to note that these early intermediates retain developmental flexibility as shown by the ability of CLPs to redirect to the myeloid differentiation pathway with a strong cytokine signal.[2,8] This flexibility may also be manifest *in vivo* because bone marrow cells with lymphoid and myeloid bipotential have also been isolated.[9] Furthermore, CLPs and CMPs express many genes of the "wrong" lineage, consistent with the idea that these are not irreversibly committed progenitors.[10,11]

Handbook of Stem Cells
Volume 2

Transcription Factors Implicated in the Lymphoid–Myeloid Choice

The transcription factor PU.1 is an ETS-domain containing DNA binding protein[12,13] that is required for the generation of both lymphoid and myeloid lineages.[14] Singh and colleagues have proposed that PU.1 levels may dictate the choice between the two lineages. Bone marrow cell cultures from PU.1-deficient mice skewed toward myeloid differentiation *in vitro* in the presence of high levels of ectopically expressed PU.1.[15] In contrast, lower levels of PU.1 expression favored differentiation to the B-lymphocyte lineage. The dosage effect may, in part, be due to the effects of PU.1 on expression of the gene encoding the α chain of the receptor for interleukin 7 (IL-7Rα), a cytokine essential for B-lymphocyte differentiation. Low levels of PU.1 were found to be permissive for IL-7Rα expression in bone marrow cultures, whereas no IL-7Rα expression was evident in high PU.1 expressing cells. A second transcription factor family of GATA proteins has been implicated in the myeloid–lymphoid fate choice.[16,17] GATA1 and GATA2 are essential for generation of erythroid and megakaryocyte lineages,[18–20] respectively, whereas GATA3 is essential for T-lymphocyte development.[21] Several studies suggest that PU.1 and GATA proteins may be mutually antagonistic at the level of transcription activation, either by direct protein–protein interaction or by titration of associated factors such as the co-activator CBP.[22–24] Thus, activation of GATA proteins in precursor cells may tilt the balance in favor of myeloid–erythroid differentiation.

Brief Overview of B-cell Differentiation

IL-7Rα has been shown to be essential for B- and T-cell development.[25,26] CLPs were identified on the basis of IL-7Rα expression as bipotential precursors to both lymphocyte lineages. However, recent studies suggest that a different precursor population that lacks IL-7Rα called early lymphocyte precursors (ELPs) may be the point at which B–T divergence occurs[27,28] (Fig. 8–1). Moreover, an early T lymphocyte

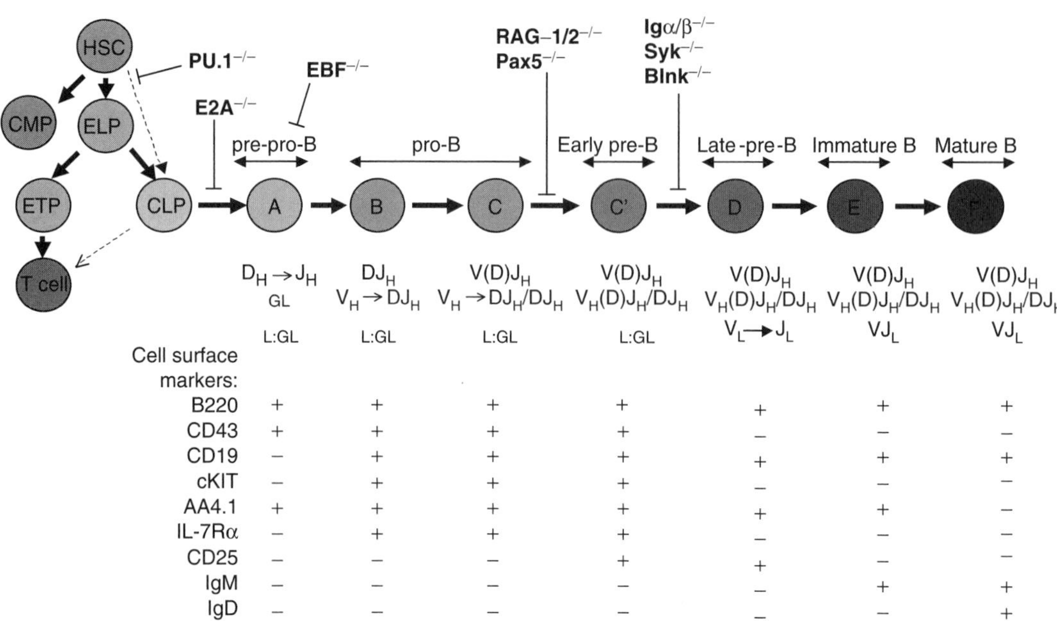

Figure 8–1. *Schematic representation of B-cell differentiation.* Hardy classification of B-cell development with a list of surface markers in the lower panel used to distinguish the different stages. (+) indicates medium or high expression, and (–) indicates low or no expression. D_H to J_H recombination is initiated in fraction A but occurs primarily in fraction B, where V_H to DJ_H recombination is also initiated. Recombination at the IgH locus stops after fraction C with light chain recombination taking place in fraction D. B-cell differentiation is blocked at different stages (as indicated) in the absence of transcription factors (PU.1, E2A, EBF, and Pax5), signaling molecules (Igα/β, Syk, Blnk), and other factors like RAG1/2. (Please see CD-ROM for color version of this figure.)

precursor (ETP) population that lacks IL-7Rα expression has been isolated from blood.[29] In this scheme ELPs are precursors of both ETPs and CLPs, with CLPs being more restricted to B-lineage differentiation. These observations are consistent with IL-7/IL-7Rα signals being crucial for adult B lymphopoiesis[30–32] but are substitutable with Bcl-2 mediated survival signals for significant reconstitution of T lymphopoeisis.[33,34]

Antigen-independent stages of B-cell differentiation are guided by the objective of producing B cells that express functional immunoglobulin molecules on the cell surface. This is accomplished sequentially with Ig heavy chains being expressed first followed by Ig light chains. Because antigen receptor genes are spread out as gene segments in the germline, gene assembly via genomic recombination is a hallmark of all antigen receptor loci. Gene recombination requires the lymphocyte-specific components RAG1 and RAG2 and antigen receptor loci that are accessible to the recombinase machinery.[35–37] Locus accessibility is an important concept because it provides a framework for lineage- and differentiation stage-specific regulation of antigen receptor gene rearrangements by a common enzymatic machinery. For example, B-cell antigen receptor loci are made accessible only in B-lineage cells, whereas T-cell antigen receptor loci are accessible in T-lineage precursors but not in B-cell precursors. Although features that distinguish accessible from inaccessible loci remain obscure, recent studies implicate histone modifications and chromatin remodeling as essential features of accessible loci.[38–43]

Immunoglobulin heavy chain gene rearrangements occur in two steps, before significant light chain gene rearrangements, during B-cell ontogeny.[35,36] At the pro-B cell stage one of several D_H gene segments rearranges to one of 4 J_H gene segments to produce DJ_H recombined alleles (Fig. 8–2). There is no direct evidence whether D_H to J_H recombination occurs sequentially or simultaneously on both alleles. This is followed by recombination of one of several hundred V_H genes to the recombined DJ_H alleles to produce "complete" V_HDJ_H rearrangements. Because of the error-prone nature of the V(D)J recombinase machinery, however, only a fraction of the completed rearrangements will encode a functional IgH protein. Because cells that do not express IgH need to be weeded out from differentiating further, the cellular milieu in which IgH recombination takes place must be such that it can "sense" the production of a functionally recombined allele. A functional IgH protein is sensed in the context of the pre-B cell receptor (pre-BCR), which is a complex of IgH together with surrogate light chains λ5 and V-pre-B,[44,45] and the integral membrane proteins Igα and Igβ[46,47] that facilitate transport of the pre-BCR to the cell surface as well as serve as signal transducing modules of the pre-BCR. Pre-BCR expression triggers several rounds of cell division and differentiation to small resting pre-B cells. The bulk of Ig light chain gene recombination occurs in these cells. Each of these developmental stages can be identified in bone marrow populations characterized by Hardy and colleagues on the basis of cell surface marker expression (Fig. 8–1).

2. Kondo, M., Scherer, D.C., Miyamoto, T., King, A.G., Akashi, K., Sugamura, K., and Weissman, I.L. (2000). Cell-fate conversion of lymphoid-committed progenitors by instructive actions of cytokines. *Nature* **407,** 383–386.
3. Akashi, K., Reya, T., Dalma-Weiszhausz, D., and Weissman, I.L. (2000). Lymphoid precursors. *Curr. Opin. Immunol.* **12,** 144–150.
4. Katsura, Y., and Kawamoto, H. (2001). Stepwise lineage restriction of progenitors in lympho-myelopoiesis. *Int. Rev. Immunol.* **20,** 1–20.
5. Kondo, M., Scherer, D.C., King, A.G., Manz, M.G., and Weissman, I.L. (2001). Lymphocyte development from hematopoietic stem cells. *Curr. Opin. Genet. Dev.* **11,** 520–526.
6. Kondo, M., Weissman, I.L., and Akashi, K. (1997). Identification of clonogenic common lymphoid progenitors in mouse bone marrow. *Cell* **91,** 661–672.
7. Akashi, K., Traver, D., Miyamoto, T., and Weissman, I.L. (2000). A clonogenic common myeloid progenitor that gives rise to all myeloid lineages. *Nature* **404,** 193–197.
8. Iwasaki-Arai, J., Iwasaki, H., Miyamoto, T., Watanabe, S., and Akashi, K. (2003). Enforced granulocyte/macrophage colony-stimulating factor signals do not support lymphopoiesis, but instruct lymphoid to myelomonocytic lineage conversion. *J. Exp. Med.* **197,** 1311–1322.
9. Katsura, Y. (2002). Redefinition of lymphoid progenitors. *Nat. Rev. Immunol.* **2,** 127–132.
10. Miyamoto, T., Iwasaki, H., Reizis, B., Ye, M., Graf, T., Weissman, I.L., and Akashi, K. (2002). Myeloid or lymphoid promiscuity as a critical step in hematopoietic lineage commitment. *Dev. Cell* **3,** 137–147.
11. Akashi, K., He, X., Chen, J., Iwasaki, H., Niu, C., Steenhard, B., Zhang, J., Haug, J., and Li, L. (2003). Transcriptional accessibility for genes of multiple tissues and hematopoietic lineages is hierarchically controlled during early hematopoiesis. *Blood* **101,** 383–389.
12. Macleod, K., Leprince, D., and Stehelin, D. (1992). The ets gene family. *Trends Biochem. Sci.* **17,** 251–256.
13. Janknecht, R., and Nordheim, A. (1993). Gene regulation by Ets proteins. *Biochim. Biophys. Acta* **1155,** 346–356.
14. Lloberas, J., Soler, C., and Celada, A. (1999). The key role of PU.1/SPI-1 in B cells, myeloid cells and macrophages. *Immunol. Today* **20,** 184–189.
15. DeKoter, R.P., and Singh, H. (2000). Regulation of B lymphocyte and macrophage development by graded expression of PU.1. *Science* **288,** 1439–1441.
16. Warren, L.A., and Rothenberg, E.V. (2003). Regulatory coding of lymphoid lineage choice by hematopoietic transcription factors. *Curr. Opin. Immunol.* **15,** 166–175.
17. Orkin, S.H., Shivdasani, R.A., Fujiwara, Y., and McDevitt, M.A. (1998). Transcription factor GATA-1 in megakaryocyte development. *Stem Cells* **16 (Suppl. 2),** 79–83.
18. Pevny, L., Lin, C.S., D'Agati, V., Simon, M.C., Orkin, S.H., and Costantini, F. (1995). Development of hematopoietic cells lacking transcription factor GATA-1. *Development* **121,** 163–172.
19. Tsai, F.Y., and Orkin, S.H. (1997). Transcription factor GATA-2 is required for proliferation/survival of early hematopoietic cells and mast cell formation, but not for erythroid and myeloid terminal differentiation. *Blood* **89,** 3636–3643.
20. Shivdasani, R.A., Fujiwara, Y., McDevitt, M.A., and Orkin, S.H. (1997). A lineage-selective knockout establishes the critical role of transcription factor GATA-1 in megakaryocyte growth and platelet development. *EMBO J.* **16,** 3965–3973.
21. Ting, C.N., Olson, M.C., Barton, K.P., and Leiden, J.M. (1996). Transcription factor GATA-3 is required for development of the T-cell lineage. *Nature* **384,** 474–478.
22. Nerlov, C., Querfurth, E., Kulessa, H., and Graf, T. (2000). GATA-1 interacts with the myeloid PU.1 transcription factor and represses PU.1-dependent transcription. *Blood* **95,** 2543–2551.
23. Hong, W., Kim, A.Y., Ky, S., Rakowski, C., Seo, S.B., Chakravarti, D., Atchison, M., and Blobel, G.A. (2002). Inhibition of CBP-mediated protein acetylation by the Ets family oncoprotein PU.1. *Mol. Cell Biol.* **22,** 3729–3743.
24. Yamagata, T., Mitani, K., Oda, H., Suzuki, T., Honda, H., Asai, T., Maki, K., Nakamoto, T., and Hirai, H. (2000). Acetylation of GATA-3 affects T-cell survival and homing to secondary lymphoid organs. *EMBO J.* **19,** 4676–4687.
25. Peschon, J.J., Morrissey, P.J., Grabstein, K.H., Ramsdell, F.J., Maraskovsky, E., Gliniak, B.C., Park, L.S., Ziegler, S.F., Williams, D.E., Ware, C.B., et al. (1994). Early lymphocyte expansion is severely impaired in interleukin 7 receptor-deficient mice. *J. Exp. Med.* **180,** 1955–1960.
26. He, Y.W., and Malek, T.R. (1996). Interleukin-7 receptor alpha is essential for the development of gamma delta + T cells, but not natural killer cells. *J. Exp. Med.* **184,** 289–293.
27. Medina, K.L., Garrett, K.P., Thompson, L.F., Rossi, M.I., Payne, K.J., and Kincade, P.W. (2001). Identification of very early lymphoid precursors in bone marrow and their regulation by estrogen. *Nat. Immunol.* **2,** 718–724.
28. Igarashi, H., Gregory, S.C., Yokota, T., Sakaguchi, N., and Kincade, P.W. (2002). Transcription from the RAG1 locus marks the earliest lymphocyte progenitors in bone marrow. *Immunity* **17,** 117–130.
29. Allman, D., Sambandam, A., Kim, S., Miller, J.P., Pagan, A., Well, D., Meraz, A., and Bhandoola, A. (2003). Thymopoiesis independent of common lymphoid progenitors. *Nat. Immunol.* **4,** 168–174.
30. Miller, J.P., Izon, D., DeMuth, W., Gerstein, R., Bhandoola, A., and Allman, D. (2002). The earliest step in B lineage differentiation from common lymphoid progenitors is critically dependent upon interleukin 7. *J. Exp. Med.* **196,** 705–711.
31. Maraskovsky, E., Peschon, J.J., McKenna, H., Teepe, M., and Strasser, A. (1998). Overexpression of Bcl-2 does not rescue impaired B lymphopoiesis in IL-7 receptor-deficient mice but can enhance survival of mature B cells. *Int. Immunol.* **10,** 1367–1375.
32. Kondo, M., Akashi, K., Domen, J., Sugamura, K., and Weissman, I.L. (1997). Bcl-2 rescues T lymphopoiesis, but not B or NK cell development, in common gamma chain-deficient mice. *Immunity* **7,** 155–162.
33. Maraskovsky, E., O'Reilly, L.A., Teepe, M., Corcoran, L.M., Peschon, J.J., and Strasser, A. (1997). Bcl-2 can rescue T lymphocyte development in interleukin-7 receptor-deficient mice but not in mutant rag-1-/- mice. *Cell* **89,** 1011–1019.
34. Akashi, K., Kondo, M., von Freeden-Jeffry, U., Murray, R., and Weissman, I.L. (1997). Bcl-2 rescues T lymphopoiesis in interleukin-7 receptor-deficient mice. *Cell* **89,** 1033–1041.
35. Hesslein, D.G., and Schatz, D.G. (2001). Factors and forces controlling V(D)J recombination. *Adv. Immunol.* **78,** 169–232.
36. Gellert, M. (2002). V(D)J recombination: RAG proteins, repair factors, and regulation. *Annu. Rev. Biochem.* **71,** 101–132.
37. Krangel, M.S. (2003). Gene segment selection in V(D)J recombination: accessibility and beyond. *Nat. Immunol.* **4,** 624–630.
38. McMurry, M.T., and Krangel, M.S. (2000). A role for histone acetylation in the developmental regulation of VDJ recombination. *Science* **287,** 495–498.
39. Mathieu, N., Hempel, W.M., Spicuglia, S., Verthuy, C., and Ferrier, P. (2000). Chromatin remodeling by the T cell receptor (TCR)-beta gene enhancer during early T cell development: Implications for the control of TCR-beta locus recombination. *J. Exp. Med.* **192,** 625–636.

40. Chowdhury, D., and Sen, R. (2001). Stepwise activation of the immunoglobulin mu heavy chain gene locus. *EMBO. J.* **20,** 6394–6403.
41. Ye, S.K., Agata, Y., Lee, H.C., Kurooka, H., Kitamura, T., Shimizu, A., Honjo, T., and Ikuta, K. (2001). The IL-7 receptor controls the accessibility of the TCRgamma locus by Stat5 and histone acetylation. *Immunity* **15,** 813–823.
42. Sikes, M.L., Meade, A., Tripathi, R., Krangel, M.S., and Oltz, E.M. (2002). Regulation of V(D)J recombination: A dominant role for promoter positioning in gene segment accessibility. *Proc. Natl. Acad. Sci. U.S.A.* **99,** 12309–12314.
43. Tripathi, R., Jackson, A., and Krangel, M.S. (2002). A change in the structure of Vbeta chromatin associated with TCR beta allelic exclusion. *J. Immunol.* **168,** 2316–2324.
44. Martensson, I.L., Rolink, A., Melchers, F., Mundt, C., Licence, S., and Shimizu, T. (2002). The pre-B cell receptor and its role in proliferation and Ig heavy chain allelic exclusion. *Semin. Immunol.* **14,** 335–342.
45. Melchers, F., ten Boekel, E., Seidl, T., Kong, X.C., Yamagami, T., Onishi, K., Shimizu, T., Rolink, A.G., and Andersson, J. (2000). Repertoire selection by pre-B-cell receptors and B-cell receptors, and genetic control of B-cell development from immature to mature B cells. *Immunol. Rev.* **175,** 33–46.
46. Meffre, E., Casellas, R., and Nussenzweig, M.C. (2000). Antibody regulation of B cell development. *Nat. Immunol.* **1,** 379–385.
47. Pike, K.A., and Ratcliffe, M.J. (2002). Cell surface immunoglobulin receptors in B cell development. *Semin. Immunol.* **14,** 351–358.
48. Kee, B.L., Quong, M.W., and Murre, C. (2000). E2A proteins: Essential regulators at multiple stages of B-cell development. *Immunol. Rev.* **175,** 138–149.
49. Greenbaum, S., and Zhuang, Y. (2002). Regulation of early lymphocyte development by E2A family proteins. *Semin. Immunol.* **14,** 405–414.
50. Hsu, L.Y., Lauring, J., Liang, H.E., Greenbaum, S., Cado, D., Zhuang, Y., and Schlissel, M. S. (2003). A conserved transcriptional enhancer regulates RAG gene expression in developing B cells. *Immunity* **19,** 105–117.
51. Bain, G., Robanus Maandag, E.C., te Riele, H.P., Feeney, A.J., Sheehy, A., Schlissel, M., Shinton, S.A., Hardy, R.R., and Murre, C. (1997). Both E12 and E47 allow commitment to the B cell lineage. *Immunity* **6,** 145–154.
52. Lin, H., and Grosschedl, R. (1995). Failure of B-cell differentiation in mice lacking the transcription factor EBF. *Nature* **376,** 263–267.
53. O'Riordan, M., and Grosschedl, R. (2000). Transcriptional regulation of early B-lymphocyte differentiation. *Immunol. Rev.* **175,** 94–103.
54. Reya, T., and Grosschedl, R. (1998). Transcriptional regulation of B-cell differentiation. *Curr. Opin. Immunol.* **10,** 158–165.
55. Sigvardsson, M., O'Riordan, M., and Grosschedl, R. (1997). EBF and E47 collaborate to induce expression of the endogenous immunoglobulin surrogate light chain genes. *Immunity* **7,** 25–36.
56. O'Riordan, M., and Grosschedl, R. (1999). Coordinate regulation of B cell differentiation by the transcription factors EBF and E2A. *Immunity* **11,** 21–31.
57. Schebesta, M., Heavey, B., and Busslinger, M. (2002). Transcriptional control of B-cell development. *Curr. Opin. Immunol.* **14,** 216–223.
58. Urbanek, P., Wang, Z.Q., Fetka, I., Wagner, E.F., and Busslinger, M. (1994). Complete block of early B cell differentiation and altered patterning of the posterior midbrain in mice lacking Pax5/BSAP. *Cell* **79,** 901–912.
59. Hesslein, D.G., Pflugh, D.L., Chowdhury, D., Bothwell, A.L., Sen, R., and Schatz, D.G. (2003). Pax5 is required for recombination of transcribed, acetylated, 5′ IgH V gene segments. *Genes Dev.* **17,** 37–42.
60. Nutt, S.L., Urbanek, P., Rolink, A., and Busslinger, M. (1997). Essential functions of Pax5 (BSAP) in pro-B cell development: difference between fetal and adult B lymphopoiesis and reduced V-to-DJ recombination at the IgH locus. *Genes Dev.* **11,** 476–491.
61. Nutt, S.., Heavey, B., Rolink, A.G., and Busslinger, M. (1999). Commitment to the B-lymphoid lineage depends on the transcription factor Pax5. *Nature* **401,** 556–562.
62. Rolink, A.G., Nutt, S.L., Melchers, F., and Busslinger, M. (1999). Long-term in vivo reconstitution of T-cell development by Pax5-deficient B-cell progenitors. *Nature* **401,** 603–606.
63. Schaniel, C., Bruno, L., Melchers, F., and Rolink, A.G. (2002). Multiple hematopoietic cell lineages develop in vivo from transplanted Pax5-deficient pre-B I-cell clones. *Blood* **99,** 472–478.
64. Barberis, A., Widenhorn, K., Vitelli, L., and Busslinger, M. (1990). A novel B-cell lineage-specific transcription factor present at early but not late stages of differentiation. *Genes Dev.* **4,** 849–859.
65. Hardy, R.R., and Hayakawa, K. (2001). B cell development pathways. *Annu. Rev. Immunol.* **19,** 595–621.
66. Mikkola, I., Heavey, B., Horcher, M., and Busslinger, M. (2002). Reversion of B cell commitment upon loss of Pax5 expression. *Science* **297,** 110–113.
67. Nutt, S.L., Morrison, A.M., Dorfler, P., Rolink, A., and Busslinger, M. (1998). Identification of BSAP (Pax-5) target genes in early B-cell development by loss- and gain-of-function experiments. *EMBO. J.* **17,** 2319–2333.
68. Hayashi, K., Yamamoto, M., Nojima, T., Goitsuka, R., and Kitamura, D. (2003). Distinct signaling requirements for Dmu selection, IgH allelic exclusion, pre-B cell transition, and tumor suppression in B cell progenitors. *Immunity* **18,** 825–836.
69. Schebesta, M., Pfeffer, P.L., and Busslinger, M. (2002). Control of pre-BCR signaling by Pax5-dependent activation of the BLNK gene. *Immunity* **17,** 473–485.
70. Maier, H., and Hagman, J. (2002). Roles of EBF and Pax-5 in B lineage commitment and development. *Semin. Immunol.* **14,** 415–422.
71. Fitzsimmons, D., Hodsdon, W., Wheat, W., Maira, S.M., Wasylyk, B., and Hagman, J. (1996). Pax-5 (BSAP) recruits Ets proto-oncogene family proteins to form functional ternary complexes on a B-cell-specific promoter. *Genes Dev.* **10,** 2198–2211.
72. Souabni, A., Cobaleda, C., Schebesta, M., and Busslinger, M. (2002). Pax5 promotes B lymphopoiesis and blocks T cell development by repressing Notch1. *Immunity* **17,** 781–793.
73. Eberhard, D., Jimenez, G., Heavey, B., and Busslinger, M. (2000). Transcriptional repression by Pax5 (BSAP) through interaction with corepressors of the Groucho family. *EMBO. J.* **19,** 2292–2303.
74. DeKoter, R.P., Lee, H.J., and Singh, H. (2002). PU.1 regulates expression of the interleukin-7 receptor in lymphoid progenitors. *Immunity* **16,** 297–309.
75. Mills, F.C., Fisher, L.M., Kuroda, R., Ford, A.M., and Gould, H.J. (1983). DNase I hypersensitive sites in the chromatin of human mu immunoglobulin heavy-chain genes. *Nature* **306,** 809–812.
76. Ford, A.M., Watt, S.M., Furley, A.J., Molgaard, H.V., and Greaves, M.F. (1988). Cell lineage specificity of chromatin configuration around the immunoglobulin heavy chain enhancer. *EMBO. J.* **7,** 2393–2399.

77. Jenuwein, T., Forrester, W.C., Qiu, R.G., and Grosschedl, R. (1993). The immunoglobulin mu enhancer core establishes local factor access in nuclear chromatin independent of transcriptional stimulation. *Genes Dev.* **7,** 2016–2032.
78. Forrester, W.C., van Genderen, C., Jenuwein, T., and Grosschedl, R. (1994). Dependence of enhancer-mediated transcription of the immunoglobulin mu gene on nuclear matrix attachment regions. *Science* **265,** 1221–1225.
79. Jenuwein, T., Forrester, W.C., Fernandez-Herrero, L.A., Laible, G., Dull, M., and Grosschedl, R. (1997). Extension of chromatin accessibility by nuclear matrix attachment regions. *Nature* **385,** 269–272.
80. Oltz, E.M., Alt, F.W., Lin, W.C., Chen, J., Taccioli, G., Desiderio, S., and Rathbun, G. (1993). A V(D)J recombinase-inducible B-cell line: role of transcriptional enhancer elements in directing V(D)J recombination. *Mol. Cell Biol.* **13,** 6223–6230.
81. Fernex, C., Capone, M., and Ferrier, P. (1995). The V(D)J recombinational and transcriptional activities of the immunoglobulin heavy-chain intronic enhancer can be mediated through distinct protein-binding sites in a transgenic substrate. *Mol. Cell Biol.* **15,** 3217–3226.
82. Serwe, M., and Sablitzky, F. (1993). V(D)J recombination in B cells is impaired but not blocked by targeted deletion of the immunoglobulin heavy chain intron enhancer. *EMBO. J.* **12,** 2321–2327.
83. Sakai, E., Bottaro, A., Davidson, L., Sleckman, B.P., and Alt, F.W. (1999). Recombination and transcription of the endogenous Ig heavy chain locus is effected by the Ig heavy chain intronic enhancer core region in the absence of the matrix attachment regions. *Proc. Natl. Acad. Sci. U. S. A.* **96,** 1526–1531.
84. Calame, K., and Sen, R. (2003). *In* "Immunoglobulin Genes (F. Alt, T. Honjo, eds.).
85. Jenuwein, T., and Grosschedl, R. (1991). Complex pattern of immunoglobulin mu gene expression in normal and transgenic mice: nonoverlapping regulatory sequences govern distinct tissue specificities. *Genes Dev.* **5,** 932–943.
86. Birshtein, B.K., Chen, C., Saleque, S., Michaelson, J.S., Singh, M., and Little, R.D. (1997). Murine and human 3′IgH regulatory sequences. *Curr. Top. Microbiol. Immunol.* **224,** 73–80.
87. Khamlichi, A.A., Pinaud, E., Decourt, C., Chauveau, C., and Cogne, M. (2000). The 3′ IgH regulatory region: A complex structure in a search for a function. *Adv. Immunol.* **75,** 317–345.
88. Manis, J.P., van der Stoep, N., Tian, M., Ferrini, R., Davidson, L., Bottaro, A., and Alt, F.W. (1998). Class switching in B cells lacking 3′ immunoglobulin heavy chain enhancers. *J. Exp. Med.* **188,** 1421–1431.
89. Pinaud, E., Khamlichi, A.A., Le Morvan, C., Drouet, M., Nalesso, V., Le Bert, M., and Cogne, M. (2001). Localization of the 3′ IgH locus elements that effect long-distance regulation of class switch recombination. *Immunity* **15,** 187–199.
90. Nelsen, B., Tian, G., Erman, B., Gregoire, J., Maki, R., Graves, B., and Sen, R. (1993). Regulation of lymphoid-specific immunoglobulin mu heavy chain gene enhancer by ETS-domain proteins. *Science* **261,** 82–86.
91. Scheidereit, C., Heguy, A., and Roeder, R.G. (1987). Identification and purification of a human lymphoid-specific octamer-binding protein (OTF-2) that activates transcription of an immunoglobulin promoter *in vitro*. *Cell* **51,** 783–793.
92. Clerc, R.G., Corcoran, L.M., LeBowitz, J.H., Baltimore, D., and Sharp, P.A. (1988). The B-cell-specific Oct-2 protein contains POU box- and homeo box-type domains. *Genes Dev.* **2,** 1570–1581.
93. Muller, M.M., Ruppert, S., Schaffner, W., and Matthias, P. (1988). A cloned octamer transcription factor stimulates transcription from lymphoid-specific promoters in non-B cells. *Nature* **336,** 544–551.
94. Staudt, L.M., Clerc, R.G., Singh, H., LeBowitz, J.H., Sharp, P.A., and Baltimore, D. (1988). Cloning of a lymphoid-specific cDNA encoding a protein binding the regulatory octamer DNA motif. *Science* **241,** 577–580.
95. Luo, Y., Fujii, H., Gerster, T., and Roeder, R.G. (1992). A novel B cell-derived coactivator potentiates the activation of immunoglobulin promoters by octamer-binding transcription factors. *Cell* **71,** 231–241.
96. Luo, Y., and Roeder, R.G. (1995). Cloning, functional characterization, and mechanism of action of the B-cell-specific transcriptional coactivator OCA-B. *Mol. Cell Biol.* **15,** 4115–4124.
97. Gstaiger, M., Knoepfel, L., Georgiev, O., Schaffner, W., and Hovens, C.M. (1995). A B-cell coactivator of octamer-binding transcription factors. *Nature* **373,** 360–362.
98. Strubin, M., Newell, J.W., and Matthias, P. (1995). OBF-1, a novel B cell-specific coactivator that stimulates immunoglobulin promoter activity through association with octamer-binding proteins. *Cell* **80,** 497–506.
99. Nelsen, B., Kadesch, T., and Sen, R. (1990). Complex regulation of the immunoglobulin mu heavy-chain gene enhancer: MicroB, a new determinant of enhancer function. *Mol. Cell Biol.* **10,** 3145–3154.
100. Lenardo, M., Pierce, J.W., and Baltimore, D. (1987). Protein-binding sites in Ig gene enhancers determine transcriptional activity and inducibility. *Science* **236,** 1573–1577.
101. Ephrussi, A., Church, G.M., Tonegawa, S., and Gilbert, W. (1985). B lineage-specific interactions of an immunoglobu-lin enhancer with cellular factors in vivo. *Science* **227,** 134–140.
102. Church, G.M., Ephrussi, A., Gilbert, W., and Tonegawa, S. (1985). Cell-type-specific contacts to immunoglobulin enhancers in nuclei. *Nature* **313,** 798–801.
103. Merrell, K., Wells, S., Henderson, A., Gorman, J., Alt, F., Stall, A., and Calame, K. (1997). The absence of the transcription activator TFE3 impairs activation of B cells in vivo. *Mol. Cell Biol.* **17,** 3335–3344.
104. Erman, B., Cortes, M., Nikolajczyk, B.S., Speck, N.A., and Sen, R. (1998). ETS-core binding factor: a common composite motif in antigen receptor gene enhancers. *Mol. Cell Biol.* **18,** 1322–1330.
105. Speck, N.A., and Gilliland, D.G. (2002). Core-binding factors in haematopoiesis and leukaemia. *Nat. Rev. Cancer* **2,** 502–513.
106. Okuda, T., van Deursen, J., Hiebert, S.W., Grosveld, G., and Downing, J.R. (1996). AML1, the target of multiple chromosomal translocations in human leukemia, is essential for normal fetal liver hematopoiesis. *Cell* **84,** 321–330.
107. Wang, Q., Stacy, T., Binder, M., Marin-Padilla, M., Sharpe, A.H., and Speck, N.A. (1996). Disruption of the Cbfa2 gene causes necrosis and hemorrhaging in the central nervous system and blocks definitive hematopoiesis. *Proc. Natl. Acad. Sci. U. S. A.* **93,** 3444–3449.
108. Wang, Q., Stacy, T., Miller, J.D., Lewis, A.F., Gu, T.L., Huang, X., Bushweller, J.H., Bories, J.C., Alt, F.W., Ryan, G., Liu, P.P., Wynshaw-Boris, A., Binder, M., Marin-Padilla, M., Sharpe, A.H., and Speck, N.A. (1996). The CBFbeta subunit is essential for CBFalpha2 (AML1) function in vivo. *Cell* **87,** 697–708.

109. Sasaki, K., Yagi, H., Bronson, R.T., Tominaga, K., Matsunashi, T., Deguchi, K., Tani, Y., Kishimoto, T., and Komori, T. (1996). Absence of fetal liver hematopoiesis in mice deficient in transcriptional coactivator core binding factor beta. *Proc. Natl. Acad. Sci. U. S. A.* **93,** 12359–12363.
110. Kadesch, T., Zervos, P., and Ruezinsky, D. (1986). Functional analysis of the murine IgH enhancer: evidence for negative control of cell-type specificity. *Nucleic Acids Res.* **14,** 8209–8221.
111. Erman, B., and Sen, R. (1996). Context dependent transactivation domains activate the immunoglobulin mu heavy chain gene enhancer. *EMBO. J.* **15,** 4565–4575.
112. Tian, G., Erman, B., Ishii, H., Gangopadhyay, S.S., and Sen, R. (1999). Transcriptional activation by ETS and leucine zipper-containing basic helix-loop-helix proteins. *Mol. Cell Biol.* **19,** 2946–2957.
113. Dang, W., Sun, X.H., and Sen, R. (1998). ETS-mediated cooperation between basic helix-loop-helix motifs of the immunoglobulin mu heavy-chain gene enhancer. *Mol. Cell Biol.* **18,** 1477–1488.
114. Dang, W., Nikolajczyk, B.S., and Sen, R. (1998). Exploring functional redundancy in the immunoglobulin mu heavy-chain gene enhancer. *Mol. Cell Biol.* **18,** 6870–6878.

mutants. However, TRRAP is also part of other H4-specific HAT complexes,[79] and loss of TRRAP likely abrogates functions of those activities as well. The TRRAP knockout does suffer severe and very early embryonic death,[80] consistent with loss of multiple HAT functions. Interestingly, TRAPP deficient cells have mitotic defects, supporting a role for HATs and histone acetylation in mitotic checkpoints and normal cell cycle progression.

The only other HAT family that has been studied by targeted deletion in mice at this writing is the p160 family of steroid receptor co-activators, SRC1, TIF2 (also known as GRIP1 or SRC-2), and p/CIP (also known as ACTR, AIB1, RAC3, TRAM-1, or SRC-3). Both SRC1 and ACTR contain intrinsic HAT activity.[29,30] The p160 family members also appear to act as platforms for multiple other chromatin modifying factors including CBP/p300, PCAF, and CARM1, a histone arginine methyltransferase.[29,30,81] Targeted deletion of SRC1 in mice resulted in only mild phenotypes. Both males and females are viable and fertile, but they display a partial resistance to several hormones including estrogen, progestin, androgen, and thyroid hormone.[82,83] This moderate phenotype is thought to be due to the overlapping expression of the other SRC proteins. TIF2, on the other hand, is essential for full fertility in both males and females.[84] Loss of p/CIP caused a phenotype distinct from the other p160 family members. Mice null for p/CIP displayed dwarfism, delayed puberty, poor female reproductive function, and defective mammary gland development.[85] Thus all of the p160 knockouts show nuclear hormone signaling-related defects. Additional studies are required to determine whether the loss of HAT activity of these co-activators, versus another function of these proteins, plays a role in the phenotypic defects that are seen in the null animals.

Histone Deacetylase Knockouts

One cannot fully understand the role of histone acetylation in development without examining the expression and functions of both HATs and HDACs. Currently, at least 13 mammalian HDACs have been identified and these are classified as type I or type II based on overall sequence characteristics.[86,87] A separate class of NAD$^+$-dependent HDACs share homology with the yeast Sir2 protein. Class I HDACs appear to reside permanently in the nucleus, whereas class II HDACs are able to shuttle in and out of the cytoplasm in response to specific signaling pathways.[87] HDACs serve important roles as co-repressors for a number of developmental factors, such as Ikaros and Aiolos (lymphoid development[88]), eed (hox gene repression[89,90]), and Mef2 (cardiac growth and development[91,92]). However, only two HDAC gene disruptions, for HDAC1 and HDAC9, in mouse have been reported thus far in the literature.

HDAC1 was the first mammalian HDAC to be identified.[93] This class I HDAC is homologous to the yeast Rpd3 HDAC. Targeted deletion of HDAC1 in mouse results in severe growth retardation and embryonic lethality by E10.5 because of a decrease in proliferation.[94] Further analyses of HDAC1 null ES cells indicated that the decreased proliferation is due to an increase in the cyclin dependent kinase (cdk) inhibitors p21 and p27. Expression of these cdk inhibitors was also observed in HDAC1 null embryos. Interestingly, levels of HDAC2 and HDAC3 were increased in the HDAC1 deficient cells, but these HDACs were not able to compensate for loss of HDAC1 or prevent global increases in acetylation of H3 and H4. HDAC1, then, has a unique role in restricting expression of cdk inhibitors to regulate cell proliferation.

HDAC9 and its splice variant, MITR, regulate the size of adult cardiac myocytes as well as the expression of fetal cardiac genes through affects on the MEF2 transcriptional activator. MITR is the predominant splice variant of HDAC9 in the heart and it lacks an HDAC catalytic domain. However, MITR interacts with MEF2 and inhibits MEF2 activator functions by recruiting additional co-repressor activities. Both MITR and HDAC9 (and other class II HDACs) possess two conserved CaMK (calcium/calmodulin-dependent protein kinase) phosphorylation sites in their amino terminal domains.[95,96] On phosphorylation of these sites, 14-3-3 proteins bind to the HDACs, triggering their export from the nucleus and relief of MEF2 repression. When active, MEF2 activates fetal cardiac genes, inducing the fetal muscle program.[57] Limitation of MEF2 functions is apparently important to the prevention of cardiac hypertrophy, because HDAC9 knockout mice, which do not express either HDAC9 or MITR, develop age-dependent cardiac hypertrophy and exhibit stress-dependent cardiomegaly.[95] The hypertrophy observed in the HDAC9 knockout animals is an interesting contrast to the cardiac hypoplasia observed in the CBP- and p300-deficient embryos. These two phenotypes highlight the importance of a balance of HAT and HDAC activities for normal heart development and growth.

Other Histone Modifications and Development

Although histone acetylation and deacetylation may be the most studied post-translational modifications to date, the body of research on several additional histone modifications is rapidly expanding. Enzymes involved in histone methylation, phosphorylation, and ubiqutylation have all been identified in recent years. Study of the functions and expression of these enzymes alongside with those of specific HATs and HDACs has become increasingly important because of the interdependence and cross regulation of different modification events. Loss of one HAT or HDAC activity might well affect the occurrence of other types of modifications, and loss of other enzymatic activities might affect levels and patterns of histone acetylation. This is an area of research that clearly needs more study, as highlighted by the phenotypes of the mouse knockouts described previously and in the following paragraphs.

Several mammalian histone methyltransferases (HMTs) have been identified, including Suv39h1/Suv39h2,[97] G9a,[98] Set9,[99] and mDOT1L.[100] Knockouts of Suv39h1 and Suv39h2 are both phenotypically normal.[101] Expression analysis shows that these two HMTs overlap in expression during embryogenesis, which may reflect a redundancy in function during early development. Double Suv39h1/2 null mice have impaired viability, with only 30% of the embryos surviving to adulthood. These double null animals have a global loss of methylated H3-K9, an increased tumor risk, and aberrant chromosomal interactions during male meiosis.[101] In contrast to the Suv39h1/2 knockouts, G9a deficient mice die by E12.5 and exhibit severe growth retardation. These embryos also have a global loss of methylated H3-K9, but in addition exhibit increased apoptosis.[102] The fourth HMT, mDOT1L, was identified only recently. At the β-globin locus, this HMT appears to enrich methylated H3-K79 in active regions of chromatin. In *Saccharomyces cervisiae,* methylation of K79 by Dot1p in active regions prevents the binding of silencing proteins, and loss of Dot1 functions actually decreases silencing at telomeric loci because of titration of silencing factors away from these regions. The role of mDot1L in gene activation and/or silencing in stem cells and embryonic development awaits the creation of mice null for this enzyme.

Less is known about histone kinases and enzymes required for histone ubiquitylation. Thus far, two nonmitotic, putative histone H3 kinases, MSK1/2 and RSK1,[99,103] have been identified in mammalian cells. H3 is apparently phosphorylated during mitosis by AIM1, a mammalian homologue of the Ipl1/aurora kinases.[104] Both MSK1/2 and RSK1 appear to be recruited to genes during transcriptional activation to mediate H3-S10 phosphorylation, while overexpression of AIM1 leads to mitotic hyperphosphorylation of H3-S10. Further studies in these areas through *in vitro* studies and gene knockouts need to be done to elucidate the potential roles of these enzymes in development, although these analyses are likely to be complicated because these kinases potentially have many substrates.

Outstanding Questions

One of the most promising and ambitious aspects of stem cell research is the potential to direct these totipotent cells along specific pathways of differentiation to create tissues and organs at will. The previous studies clearly indicate that chromatin remodeling and histone modification is important to differentiation, but we still know very little about how these events are controlled or coordinated. Histone deacetylation, for example, may simply set the stage for methylation of certain lysine residues. Conversely, acetylation of lysines would prevent their methylation and might well affect other modifications at surrounding sites. Unlike acetylation, however, histone methylation appears to be a very stable mark, because of the apparent absence of demethylating enzymes. As such, histone methylation has been proposed to afford a heritable "memory" function for cell transcription patterns. Do stem cells lack such memory? Or are certain histone modification patterns erased and rewritten as differentiation progresses? Can treatment of cells, or embryos, with deacetylase inhibitors reverse or create a new histone code, a new cellular memory? If so, then understanding the nature and the regulation of such epigenetic codes may allow a more controlled direction of cell fates, cell proliferation, and cell growth *in vitro.*

REFERENCES

1. Luger, K., Mader, A.W., Richmond, R.K., Sargent, D.F., and Richmond, T.J. (1997). Crystal structure of the nucleosome core particle at 2.8 A resolution. *Nature* **389,** 251–260.
2. Horn, P.J., and Peterson, C.L. (2002). Molecular biology. Chromatin higher order folding—wrapping up transcription. *Science* **297,** 1824–1827.
3. Narlikar, G.J., Fan, H.Y., and Kingston, R.E. (2002). Cooperation between complexes that regulate chromatin structure and transcription. *Cell* **108,** 475–487.
4. Wolffe, A.P., and Guschin, D. (2000). Review: chromatin structural features and targets that regulate transcription. *J. Struct. Biol.* **129 (2–3),** 102–122.
5. Martinez, E. (2002). Multi-protein complexes in eukaryotic gene transcription. *Plant Mol. Biol.* **50,** 925–947.
6. Hsiao, P.W., Deroo, B.J., and Archer, T.K. (2002). Chromatin remodeling and tissue-selective responses of nuclear hormone receptors. *Biochem. Cell Biol.* **80,** 343–351.
7. Gregory, P.D., Wagner, K., and Horz, W. (2001). Histone acetylation and chromatin remodeling. *Exp. Cell Res.* **265,** 195–202.
8. Strahl, B.D., and Allis, C.D. (2000). The language of covalent histone modifications. *Nature* **403,** 41–45.
9. Cheung, P., Tanner, K.G., Cheung, W.L., Sassone-Corsi, P., Denu, J.M., and Allis, C.D. (2000). Synergistic coupling of histone H3 phosphorylation and acetylation in response to epidermal growth factor stimulation. *Mol. Cell* **5,** 905–915.
10. Lo, W.S., Trievel, R.C., Rojas, J.R., Duggan, L., Hsu, J.Y., Allis, C.D., Marmorstein, R., and Berger, S.L. (2000). Phosphorylation of serine 10 in histone H3 is functionally linked in vitro and in vivo to Gcn5-mediated acetylation at lysine 14. *Mol. Cell* **5,** 917–926.
11. Clayton, A.L., Rose, S., Barratt, M.J., and Mahadevan, L.C. (2000). Phosphoacetylation of histone H3 on c-fos- and c-jun-associated nucleosomes upon gene activation. *EMBO J.* **19,** 3714–3726.
12. Sun, Z.W., and Allis, C.D. (2002). Ubiquitination of histone H2B regulates H3 methylation and gene silencing in yeast. *Nature* **418,** 104–108.
13. Dover, J., Schneider, J., Tawiah-Boateng, M.A., Wood, A., Dean, K., Johnston, M., and Shilatifard, A. (2002). Methylation of histone H3 by COMPASS requires ubiquitination of histone H2B by Rad6. *J. Biol. Chem.* **277,** 28368–28371.
14. Allfrey, V.G., Faulkner, R. and Mirsky, A.E. (1964). Acetylation and methylation of histones and their possible role in the regulation of RNA synthesis. *Proc. Natl. Acad. Sci. U. S. A.* **51,** 786–794.
15. Struhl, K. (1998). Histone acetylation and transcriptional regulatory mechanisms. *Genes Dev.* **12,** 599–606.
16. Wang, L., Liu, L., and Berger, S.L. (1998). Critical residues for histone acetylation by Gcn5, functioning in Ada and SAGA complexes, are also required for transcriptional function *in vivo. Genes Dev.* **12,** 640–653.
17. Kuo, M.H., Brownell, J.E., Sobel, R.E., Ranalli, T.A., Cook, R.G., Edmondson, D.G., Roth, S.Y., and Allis, C.D. (1996). Transcription-linked acetylation by Gcn5p of histones H3 and H4 at specific lysines. *Nature* **383,** 269–272.
18. Wolffe, A.P. (1996). Histone deacetylase: a regulator of transcription. *Science* **272,** 371–372.
19. Wolffe, A.P., and Pruss, D. (1996). Hanging on to histones. Chromatin. *Curr. Biol.* **6,** 234–237.
20. Kuo, M.H., Zhou, J., Jambeck, P., Churchill, M.E., and Allis, C.D. (1998). Histone acetyltransferase activity of yeast Gcn5p is required for the activation of target genes in vivo. *Genes Dev.* **12,** 627–639.

21. Brownell, J.E., Zhou, J., Ranalli, T., Kobayashi, R., Edmondson, D.G., Roth, S.Y., and Allis, C.D. (1996). Tetrahymena histone acetyltransferase A: a homolog to yeast Gcn5p linking histone acetylation to gene activation. *Cell* **84,** 843–851.
22. Yang, X.J., Ogryzko, V.V., Nishikawa, J., Howard, B.H., and Nakatani, Y. (1996). A p300/CBP-associated factor that competes with the adenoviral oncoprotein E1A. *Nature* **382,** 319–324.
23. Ogryzko, V.V., Schiltz, R.L., Russanova, V., Howard, B.H., and Nakatani, Y. (1996). The transcriptional coactivators p300 and CBP are histone acetyltransferases. *Cell* **87,** 953–959.
24. Bannister, A.J., and Kouzarides, T. (1996). The CBP co-activator is a histone acetyltransferase. *Nature* **384,** 641–643.
25. Mizzen, C.A., Yang, X.J., Kokubo, T., Brownell, J.E., Bannister, A.J., Owen-Hughes, T., Workman, J., Wang, L., Berger, S.L., Kouzarides, T., Nakatani, Y., and Allis, C.D. (1996). The TAF(II)250 subunit of TFIID has histone acetyltransferase activity. Cell 87, 1261–1270.
26. Wittschieben, B.O., Otero, G., de Bizemont, T., Fellows, J., Erdjument-Bromage, H., Ohba, R., Li, Y., Allis, C.D., Tempst, P., and Svejstrup, J.Q. (1999). A novel histone acetyltransferase is an integral subunit of elongating RNA polymerase II holoenzyme. *Mol. Cell* **4,** 123–128.
27. Winkler, G.S., Kristjuhan, A., Erdjument-Bromage, H., Tempst, P., and Svejstrup, J.Q. (2002). Elongator is a histone H3 and H4 acetyltransferase important for normal histone acetylation levels in vivo. *Proc. Natl. Acad. Sci. U. S. A.* **99,** 3517–3522.
28. Hawkes, N.A., Otero, G., Winkler, G.S., Marshall, N., Dahmus, M.E., Krappmann, D., Scheidereit, C., Thomas, C.L., Schiavo, G., Erdjument-Bromage, H., Tempst, P., and Svejstrup, J.Q. (2002). Purification and characterization of the human elongator complex. *J. Biol. Chem.* **277,** 3047–3052.
29. Spencer, T.E., Jenster, G., Burcin, M.M., Allis, C.D., Zhou, J., Mizzen, C.A., McKenna, N.J., Onate, S.A., Tsai, S.Y. Tsai, M.J., and O'Malley, B.W. (1997). Steroid receptor coactivator-1 is a histone acetyltransferase. *Nature* **389,** 194–198.
30. Chen, H., Lin, R.J., Schiltz, R.L., Chakravarti, D., Nash, A., Nagy, L., Privalsky, M.L., Nakatani, Y., and Evans, R.M. (1997). Nuclear receptor coactivator ACTR is a novel histone acetyltransferase and forms a multimeric activation complex with P/CAF and CBP/p300. *Cell* **90,** 569–580.
31. Lorch, Y., Beve, J., Gustafsson, C.M., Myers, L.C., and Kornberg, R.D. (2000). Mediator-nucleosome interaction. *Mol. Cell* **6,** 197–201.
32. Iizuka, M., and Stillman, B. (1999). Histone acetyltransferase HBO1 interacts with the ORC1 subunit of the human initiator protein. *J. Biol. Chem.* **274,** 23027–23034.
33. Kawasaki, H., Schiltz, L., Chiu, R., Itakura, K., Taira, K., Nakatani, Y., and Yokoyama, K.K. (2000). ATF-2 has intrinsic histone acetyltransferase activity which is modulated by phosphorylation. *Nature* **405,** 195–200.
34. Neal, K.C., Pannuti, A., Smith, E.R., and Lucchesi, J.C. (2000). A new human member of the MYST family of histone acetyl transferases with high sequence similarity to Drosophila MOF. *Biochim. Biophys. Acta* **1490,** 170–174.
35. Lahn, B.T., Tang, Z.L., Zhou, J., Barndt, R.J., Parvinen, M., Allis, C.D., and Page, DC. (2002). Previously uncharacterized histone acetyltransferases implicated in mammalian spermatogenesis. *Proc. Natl. Acad. Sci. U. S. A.* **99,** 8707–8712.
36. Gu, W., and Roeder, R.G. (1997). Activation of p53 sequence-specific DNA binding by acetylation of the p53 C-terminal domain. *Cell* **90,** 595–606.
37. Boyes, J., Byfield, P., Nakatani, Y., and Ogryzko, V. (1998). Regulation of activity of the transcription factor GATA-1 by acetylation. *Nature* **396,** 594–598.
38. Espinosa, J.M., and Emerson, B.M. (2001). Transcriptional regulation by p53 through intrinsic DNA/chromatin binding and site-directed cofactor recruitment. *Mol. Cell* **8,** 57–69.
39. Soutoglou, E., Katrakili, N., and Talianidis, I. (2000). Acetylation regulates transcription factor activity at multiple levels. *Mol. Cell* **5,** 745–751.
40. Schultz, R.M., Davis Jr W., Stein, P., and Svoboda, P. (1999). Reprogramming of gene expression during preimplantation development. *J. Exp. Zool.* **285,** 276–282.
41. Dimitrov, S., Dasso, M.C., and Wolffe, A.P. (1994). Remodeling sperm chromatin in *Xenopus laevis* egg extracts: the role of core histone phosphorylation and linker histone B4 in chromatin assembly. *J. Cell Biol.* **126,** 591–601.
42. Smith, R.C., Dworkin-Rastl, E, and Dworkin, M.B. (1988). Expression of a histone H1-like protein is restricted to early Xenopus development. *Genes Dev.* **2,** 1284–1295.
43. Nightingale, K., Dimitrov, S., Reeves, R., and Wolffe, A.P. (1996). Evidence for a shared structural role for HMG1 and linker histones B4 and H1 in organizing chromatin. *EMBO J.* **15,** 548–561.
44. Fu, G., Ghadam, P., Sirotkin, A., Khochbin, S., Skoultchi, A.I., and Clarke, H.J. (2003). Mouse oocytes and early embryos express multiple histone H1 subtypes. *Biol. Reprod.* **68,** 1569–1576.
45. Clarke, H.J., McLay, D.W., and Mohamed, O.A. (1998). Linker histone transitions during mammalian oogenesis and embryogenesis. *Dev. Genet.* **22,** 17–30.
46. Thompson, E.M., Legouy, E., and Renard, J.P. (1998). Mouse embryos do not wait for the MBT: chromatin and RNA polymerase remodeling in genome activation at the onset of development. *Dev. Genet.* **22,** 31–42.
47. McGraw, S., Robert, C., Massicotte, L., and Sirard, M.A. (2003). Quantification of histone acetyltransferase and histone deacetylase transcripts during early bovine embryo development. *Biol. Reprod.* **68,** 383–389.
48. Keohane, A.M., Lavender, J.S., O'Neill, L.P., and Turner, B.M. (1998). Histone acetylation and X inactivation. *Dev. Genet.* **22,** 65–73.
49. Avner, P., and Heard, E. (2001). X-chromosome inactivation: counting, choice and initiation. *Nat. Rev. Genet.* **2,** 59–67.
50. Jeppesen, P., and Turner, B.M. (1993). The inactive X chromosome in female mammals is distinguished by a lack of histone H4 acetylation, a cytogenetic marker for gene expression. *Cell* **74,** 281–289.
51. Belyaev, N., Keohane, A.M., and Turner, B.M. (1996). Differential underacetylation of histones H2A, H3 and H4 on the inactive X chromosome in human female cells. *Hum. Genet.* **97,** 573–578.
52. Boggs, B.A., Cheung, P., Heard, E., Spector, D.L., Chinault, A.C., and Allis, C.D. (2002). Differentially methylated forms of histone H3 show unique association patterns with inactive human X chromosomes. *Nat. Genet.* **30,** 73–76.
53. Heard, E., Rougeulle, C., Arnaud, D., Avner, P., Allis, C.D., and Spector, D.L. (2001). Methylation of histone H3 at Lys-9 is an early mark on the X chromosome during X inactivation. *Cell* **107,** 727–738.
54. O'Neill, L.P., Keohane, A.M., Lavender, J.S., McCabe, V., Heard, E., Avner, P., Brockdorff, N., and Turner, B.M. (1999). A developmental switch in H4 acetylation upstream of Xist plays a role in X chromosome inactivation. *EMBO J.* **18,** 2897–2907.
55. Zhang, Y., Ng, H.H., Erdjument-Bromage, H., Tempst, P., Bird, A., and Reinberg, D. (1999). Analysis of the NuRD subunits reveals a histone deacetylase core complex and a connection with DNA methylation. *Genes Dev.* **13,** 1924–1935.
56. Fournier, C., Goto, Y., Ballestar, E., Delaval, K., Hever, A.M., Esteller, M., and Feil, R. (2002). Allele-specific histone lysine

methylation marks regulatory regions at imprinted mouse genes. *EMBO J.* **21,** 6560–6570.

57. McKinsey, T.A., Zhang, C.L., and Olson, E.N. (2002). Signaling chromatin to make muscle. *Curr. Opin. Cell Biol.* **14,** 763–772.
58. Rupp, R.A., Singhal, N., and Veenstra, G.J. (2002). When the embryonic genome flexes its muscles. *Eur. J. Biochem.* **269,** 2294–2299.
59. Puri, P.L., Sartorelli, V., Yang, X.J., Hamamori, Y., Ogryzko, V.V., Howard, B.H., Kedes, L., Wang, J.Y., Graessmann, A., Nakatani, Y., and Levrero, M. (1997). Differential roles of p300 and PCAF acetyltransferases in muscle differentiation. *Mol. Cell* **1,** 35–45.
60. Missero, C., Calautti, E., Eckner, R., Chin, J., Tsai, L.H., Livingston, D.M., and Dotto, G.P. (1995). Involvement of the cell-cycle inhibitor Cip1/WAF1 and the E1A-associated p300 protein in terminal differentiation. *Proc. Natl. Acad. Sci. U. S. A.* **92,** 5451–5455.
61. Eckner, R., Yao, T.P., Oldread, E., and Livingston, D.M. (1996). Interaction and functional collaboration of p300/CBP and bHLH proteins in muscle and B-cell differentiation. *Genes Dev.* **10,** 2478–2490.
62. Puri, P.L., and Sartorelli, V. (2000). Regulation of muscle regulatory factors by DNA-binding, interacting proteins, and post-transcriptional modifications. *J. Cell Physiol.* **185,** 155–173.
63. Xu, W., Edmondson, D.G., Evrard, Y.A., Wakamiya, M., Behringer, R.R., and Roth, S.Y. (2000). Loss of Gcn5l2 leads to increased apoptosis and mesodermal defects during mouse development. *Nat. Genet.* **26,** 229–232.
64. Polesskaya, A., Naguibneva, I., Fritsch, L., Duquet, A., Ait-Si-Ali, S., Robin, P., Vervisch, A., Pritchard, L.L., Cole, P., and Harel-Bellan, A. (2001). CBP/p300 and muscle differentiation: No HAT, no muscle. *EMBO J.* **20,** 6816–6825.
65. Sartorelli, V., Puri, P.L., Hamamori, Y., Ogryzko, V., Chung, G., Nakatani, Y., Wang, J.Y., and Kedes, L. (1999). Acetylation of MyoD directed by PCAF is necessary for the execution of the muscle program. *Mol. Cell* **4,** 725–734.
66. Mal, A., Sturniolo, M., Schiltz, R.L., Ghosh, M.K., and Harter, M.L. (2001). A role for histone deacetylase HDAC1 in modulating the transcriptional activity of MyoD: inhibition of the myogenic program. *EMBO J.* **20,** 1739–1753.
67. Zhang, W., and Bieker, J.J. (1998). Acetylation and modulation of erythroid Kruppel-like factor (EKLF) activity by interaction with histone acetyltransferases. *Proc. Natl. Acad. Sci. U. S. A.* **95,** 9855–9860.
68. Weston, K. (1998). Myb proteins in life, death and differentiation. *Curr. Opin. Genet. Dev.* **8,** 76–81.
69. Sano, Y., and Ishii, S. (2001). Increased affinity of c-Myb for CREB-binding protein (CBP) after CBP-induced acetylation. *J. Biol. Chem.* **276,** 3674–3682.
70. Yao, T.P., Oh, S.P., Fuchs, M., Zhou, N.D., Ch'ng, L.E., Newsome, D., Bronson, R.T., Li, E., Livingston, D.M., and Eckner, R. (1998). Gene dosage-dependent embryonic development and proliferation defects in mice lacking the transcriptional integrator p300. *Cell* **93,** 361–372.
71. Giordano, A., and Avantaggiati, M.L. (1999). p300 and CBP: partners for life and death. *J. Cell Physiol.* **181,** 218–230.
72. Kung, A.L., Rebel, V.I., Bronson, R.T., Ch'ng, L.E., Sieff, C.A., Livingston, D.M., and Yao, T.P. (2000). Gene dose-dependent control of hematopoiesis and hematologic tumor suppression by CBP. *Genes Dev.* **14,** 272–277.
73. Kasper, L.H., Boussouar, F., Ney, P.A., Jackson, C.W., Rehg, J., van Deursen, J.M., and Brindle, P.K. (2002). A transcription-factor-binding surface of coactivator p300 is required for haematopoiesis. *Nature* **419,** 738–743.
74. Yamauchi, T., Yamauchi, J., Kuwata, T., Tamura, T., Yamashita, T., Bae, N., Westphal, H., Ozato, K., and Nakatani, Y. (2000). Distinct but overlapping roles of histone acetylase PCAF and of the closely related PCAF-B/GCN5 in mouse embryogenesis. *Proc. Natl. Acad. Sci. U. S. A.* **97,** 11303–11306.
75. Xu, W., Edmondson, D.G., and Roth, S.Y. (1998). Mammalian GCN5 and P/CAF acetyltransferases have homologous amino-terminal domains important for recognition of nucleosomal substrates. *Mol. Cell Biol.* **18,** 5659–5669.
76. Geschwind, D.H., Ou, J., Easterday, M.C., Dougherty, J.D., Jackson, R.L., Chen, Z., Antoine, H., Terskikh, A., Weissman, I.L., Nelson, S.F., and Kornblum, H.I. (2001). A genetic analysis of neural progenitor differentiation. *Neuron* **29,** 325–339.
77. Park, I.K., He, Y., Lin, F., Laerum, O.D., Tian, Q., Bumgarner, R., Klug, C.A., Li, K., Kuhr, C., Doyle, M.J., Xie, T., Schummer, M., Sun, Y., Goldsmith, A., Clarke, M.F., Weissman, I.L., Hood, L., and Li, L. (2002). Differential gene expression profiling of adult murine hematopoietic stem cells. *Blood* **99,** 488–498.
78. Roth, S.Y., Denu, J.M., and Allis, C.D. (2001). Histone acetyltransferases. *Annu. Rev. Biochem.* **70,** 81–120.
79. Allard, S., Utley, R.T., Savard, J., Clarke, A., Grant, P., Brandl, C.J., Pillus, L., Workman, J.L., and Cote, J. (1999). NuA4, an essential transcription adaptor/histone H4 acetyltransferase complex containing Esa1p and the ATM-related cofactor Tra1p. *EMBO J.* **18,** 5108–5119.
80. Herceg, Z., Hulla, W., Gell, D., Cuenin, C., Lleonart, M., Jackson, S., and Wang, Z.Q. (2001). Disruption of Trrap causes early embryonic lethality and defects in cell cycle progression. *Nat. Genet.* **29,** 206–211.
81. Yao, T.P., Ku, G., Zhou, N., Scully, R., and Livingston, D.M. (1996). The nuclear hormone receptor coactivator SRC-1 is a specific target of p300. *Proc. Natl. Acad. Sci. U. S. A.* **93,** 10626–10631.
82. Weiss, R.E., Xu, J., Ning, G., Pohlenz, J., O'Malley, B.W., and Refetoff, S. (1999). Mice deficient in the steroid receptor co-activator 1 (SRC-1) are resistant to thyroid hormone. *EMBO J.* **18,** 1900–1904.
83. Xu, J., Qiu, Y., DeMayo, F.J., Tsai, S.Y., Tsai, M.J., and O'Malley, B.W. (1998). Partial hormone resistance in mice with disruption of the steroid receptor coactivator-1 (SRC-1) gene. *Science* **279,** 1922–1925.
84. Gehin, M., Mark, M., Dennefeld, C., Dierich, A., Gronemeyer, H., and Chambon, P. (2002). The function of TIF2/GRIP1 in mouse reproduction is distinct from those of SRC-1 and p/CIP. *Mol. Cell Biol.* **22,** 5923–5937.
85. Xu, J., Liao, L., Ning, G., Yoshida-Komiya, H., Deng, C., O'Malley, B.W. (2000). The steroid receptor coactivator SRC-3 (p/CIP/RAC3/AIB1/ACTR/TRAM-1) is required for normal growth, puberty, female reproductive function, and mammary gland development. *Proc. Natl. Acad. Sci. U. S. A.* **97,** 6379–6384.
86. Bertos, N.R., Wang, A.H., and Yang, X.J. (2001). Class II histone deacetylases: structure, function, and regulation. *Biochem. Cell Biol.* **79,** 243–252.
87. De Ruijter, A.J., Van Gennip, A.H., Caron, H.N., Kemp, S., and Van Kuilenburg, A.B. (2003). Histone deacetylases (HDACs): characterization of the classical HDAC family. *Biochem. J.* **370,** 737–749.
88. Cortes, M., Wong, E., Koipally, J., and Georgopoulos, K. (1999). Control of lymphocyte development by the Ikaros gene family. *Curr. Opin. Immunol.* **11,** 167–171.

89. Wang, J., Mager, J., Schnedier, E., and Magnuson, T. (2002). The mouse PcG gene eed is required for Hox gene repression and extraembryonic development. *Mamm. Genome* **13,** 493–503.
90. Wang, J., Tie, F., Jane, E., Schumacher, A., Harte, P.J., and Magnuson, T. (2000). Mouse homolog of the Drosophila Pc-G gene esc exerts a dominant negative effect in Drosophila. *Genesis* **26,** 67–76.
91. Lu, J., McKinsey, T.A., Zhang, C.L., and Olson, E.N. (2000). Regulation of skeletal myogenesis by association of the MEF2 transcription factor with class II histone deacetylases. *Mol. Cell* **6,** 233–244.
92. McKinsey, T.A., Zhang, C.L., Lu, J., and Olson, E.N. (2000). Signal-dependent nuclear export of a histone deacetylase regulates muscle differentiation. *Nature* **408,** 106–111.
93. Taunton, J., Hassig, C.A., and Schreiber, S.L. (1996). A mammalian histone deacetylase related to the yeast transcriptional regulator Rpd3p. *Science* **272,** 408–411.
94. Lagger, G., O'Carroll, D., Rembold, M., Khier, H., Tischler, J., Weitzer, G., Schuettengruber, B., Hauser, C., Brunmeir, R., Jenuwein, T., and Seiser, C. (2002). Essential function of histone deacetylase 1 in proliferation control and CDK inhibitor repression. *EMBO J.* **21,** 2672–2681.
95. Zhang, C.L., McKinsey, T.A., Chang, S., Antos, C.L. Hill, J.A., and Olson, E.N. (2002). Class II histone deacetylases act as signal-responsive repressors of cardiac hypertrophy. *Cell* **110,** 479–488.
96. Zhang, C.L., McKinsey, T.A., and Olson, E.N. (2001). The transcriptional corepressor MITR is a signal-responsive inhibitor of myogenesis. *Proc. Natl. Acad. Sci. U. S. A.* **98,** 7354–7359.
97. Rea, S., Eisenhaber, F., O'Carroll, D., Strahl, B.D., Sun, Z.W., Schmid, M., Opravil, S., Mechtler, K., Ponting, C.P., Allis, C.D., and Jenuwein, T. (2000). Regulation of chromatin structure by site-specific histone H3 methyltransferases. *Nature* **406,** 593–599.
98. Tachibana, M., Sugimoto, K., Fukushima, T., and Shinkai, Y. (2001). Set domain-containing protein, G9a, is a novel lysine-preferring mammalian histone methyltransferase with hyperactivity and specific selectivity to lysines 9 and 27 of histone H3. *J. Biol. Chem.* **276,** 25309–25317.
99. Martens, J.H., Verlaan, M., Kalkhoven, E., and Zantema, A. (2003). Cascade of distinct histone modifications during collagenase gene activation. *Mol. Cell Biol.* **23,** 1808–1816.
100. Im, H., Park, C., Feng, Q., Johnson, K.D., Kiekhaefer, C.M., Choi, K., Zhang, Y., and Bresnick, E.H. (2003). Dynamic regulation of histone H3 methylated at lysine 79 within a tissue-specific chromatin domain. *J. Biol. Chem.* **278,** 18346–18352.
101. Peters, A.H., O'Carroll, D., Scherthan, H., Mechtler, K., Sauer, S., Schofer, C., Weipoltshammer, K., Pagani, M., Lachner, M., Kohlmaier, A., Opravil, S., Doyle, M., Sibilia, M., and Jenuwein, T. (2001). Loss of the Suv39h histone methyltransferases impairs mammalian heterochromatin and genome stability. *Cell* **107,** 323–337.
102. Tachibana, M., Sugimoto, K., Nozaki, M., Ueda, J., Ohta, T., Ohki, M., Fukuda, M., Takeda, N., Niida, H., Kato, H., and Shinkai, Y. (2002). G9a histone methyltransferase plays a dominant role in euchromatic histone H3 lysine 9 methylation and is essential for early embryogenesis. *Genes Dev.* **16,** 1779–1791.
103. Sassone-Corsi, P., Mizzen, C.A., Cheung, P. Crosio, C., Monaco, L., Jacquot, S., Hanauer, A., and Allis, C.D. (1999). Requirement of Rsk-2 for epidermal growth factor-activated phosphorylation of histone H3. *Science* **285,** 886–891.
104. Ota, T., Suto, S., Katayama, H., Han, Z.B., Suzuki, F., Maeda, M., Tanino, M., Terada, Y., and Tatsuka, M. (2002). Increased mitotic phosphorylation of histone H3 attributable to AIM-1/Aurora-B overexpression contributes to chromosome number instability. *Cancer Res.* **62,** 5168–5177.
105. Tomita, A., Towatari, M., Tsuzuki, S., Hayakawa, F., Kosugi, H., Tamai, K., Miyazaki, T., Kinoshita, T., and Saito, H. (2000). c-Myb acetylation at the carboxyl-terminal conserved domain by transcriptional co-activator p300. *Oncogene* **19,** 444–451.
106. Chen, H., Lin, R.J., Xie, W., Wilpitz, D., and Evans, R.M. (1999). Regulation of hormone-induced histone hyperacetylation and gene activation via acetylation of an acetylase. *Cell* **98,** 675–686.
107. Wolf, D., Rodova, M., Miska, E.A., Calvet, J.P., and Kouzarides, T. (2002). Acetylation of beta-catenin by CREB-binding protein (CBP). *J. Biol. Chem.* **277,** 25562–25567.
108. Lu, Q., Hutchins, A.E., Doyle, C.M., Lundblad, J.R., and Kwok, R.P. (2003). Acetylation of CREB by CBP enhances CREB- dependent transcription. *J. Biol. Chem.* **278,** 15727–15734.
109. Gaughan, L., Logan, I.R., Cook, S., Neal, D.E., and Robson, C.N. (2002). Tip60 and histone deacetylase 1 regulate androgen receptor activity through changes to the acetylation status of the receptor. *J. Biol. Chem.* **277,** 25904–25913.

10

Cell Cycle Control and Check Points in Hematopoietic Stem Cells

Francis W. Ruscetti and Stephen H. Bartelmez

The hematopoietic stem cell (HSC) uses numerous cell fate options to initially create then maintain the hematopoietic organ. Three major options are quiescence versus cell cycle entry, self-renewal versus differentiation, and differentiation versus apoptosis. HSC cell fate options can be modulated, in part, by a balance between positive and negative signals that can be delivered either as autocrine or paracrine signals. Under normal conditions of cycling, cells proceed through the cell cycle without interruption. HSCs have the ability to pause at least five places in the cell cycle, G_0, restriction point (R), G_1/S, S, and G_2/M. These temporary pauses at checkpoints are caused by factors such as nutrient depletion, genotoxic damage, absence of positive signals, and/or regulation by negative factors. The cell cycle kinase inhibitor p21 can function at all five checkpoints. Similarly, the cytokine, transforming growth factor-β1 (TGFβ1) is an autocrine and paracrine pleiotropic regulator of all stages of hematopoiesis. Depending on the stage of the target cell, the local environment and the TGFβ concentration, TGFβ can be proliferative or antiproliferative, apoptotic, or differentiative. TGFβ and p21 are major regulators of HSC quiescence. Thus, the actions of TGFβ and p21 can serve as paradigms for cell cycle checkpoint control in HSCs.

Hematopoietic Stem Cell Quiescence

HSCs are defined as possessing long-term repopulation activity (LTRA) following transplantation. During the past 2 decades, many other characteristics of stem cells have been clarified. HSCs have no ability to generate short-term protection of the host from radiation-induced death.[1] A common myeloid progenitor has been identified as the cell conferring short-term radioprotection.[2] Alternatively, HSC-enriched blood subsets often are defined and separated on the basis of their immunophenotype.[3] More primitive subsets selected for the absence of lineage markers (lin^-) and positive for $CD34^+$ (human) or Sca-1 (murine) antigen expression are enriched for higher numbers of quiescent (G_0 phase) cells with high LTRA.[4] G_0 cells are defined by 2N DNA content using Höechst 33242 staining and by low metabolic rates (pyronin, or Py^{low})[5] or by low mitochondrial activity (rhodamine 123, Rh^{low}).[6,7] The presence of significant proportions of immunophenotypically isolated stem cell candidates in G_0 phase provided evidence that most stem cells remained out of the cell cycle, with successive contributions of a portion of these cells to hematopoiesis. Retroviral marking experiments lend support to the clonal succession hypothesis of stem cell activity.[8] However, this theory has been challenged by the results of long-term *in vivo* BrdU labeling experiments that indicate that in mice $Hö^{low}/Rho^{low}$ HSCs are constantly and slowly cycling with an average turnover time of 30 days.[9,10] Similar results using immunophenotypically isolated murine HSCs found that 99% of HSCs divided every 57 days, on average. Seventy-six percent of these cells were in G_0-phase at any given time, and roughly 8% of the cells asynchronously entered the cell cycle daily.[11] Similar experiments in baboons found that BrdU was incorporated into 56 to 83% of $CD34^+$ cells but into only 10 to 30% of the lin^- $Hö^{low}/Rho^{low}$ HSCs at 1 year, supporting the existence of both long-term quiescent and very slowly cycling HSC pools in primates.[12] Because murine HSCs enter the cell cycle at a higher frequency than do primate HSCs, an unanswered question is whether similar molecular controls of quiescence are involved in both species. Using phenotypic characterization, HSCs can be heterogeneous either $CD34^+$ or $CD34^-$[13,14] or c-Kit^+ or c-Kit^-.[15] Also, stem cell antigen (Sca)-1, is present on all murine HSCs, and is functionally important because Sca-1 null mice have several defects[16]; however, Sca-1 is absent on primate HSCs. Furthermore, murine $Hö^{low}/Rho^{low}$ HSCs are CD34 negative,[17] whereas quiescent human HSCs appear to be CD34 high.[18] In humans, the relationship between quiescent CD34 high and CD34 negative HSCs remains to be elucidated,[19] but one must be cautious in extrapolating between human and mouse. Furthermore, most of the studies cited here on checkpoint control were done on cell lines or non-HSC primary cells and remain to be done on primary HSCs.

AUTOCRINE TGFβ-1 REGULATES HSC QUIESCENCE

Because the murine adult HSC compartment is slowly cycling, a rigorously define quiescent population must be used to determine the effects of TGFβs on HSC quiescence *in vitro*. $CD34^-$ lin^- $Hö^{low}/Rho^{low}$ HSCs that give long-term donor repopulation with one to five cells[7] are in G_0 phase and

Handbook of Stem Cells
Volume 2

have no radioprotection activity. In single-cell assays, the continuous presence of exogenous TGFβ-1 at 10 ηg/ml directly inhibits the *in vitro* cell division of essentially all lin⁻ Hö^{low}/Rho^{low} HSCs.[20] The addition of TGFβ-1 neutralizing antibodies as late as 3 days after the addition of TGF-β-1 preserved the ability of 80% of the cells to form macrocolonies, indicating that the effects of exogenous TGFβ-1 were reversible and not markedly apoptotic to HSCs in the context of other cytokines. Similar results were observed using lin⁻ Sca-1⁺ cells. Recently, human CD34^{High+}, CD38⁻, c-kit^{low}, IL-6R^{low}, and Mpl^{low} cells (designated HPP-Q) were shown to possess many of the characteristics of the murine lin⁻ Hö^{low}/Rho^{low} HSCs. These quiescent cells can be stimulated to form high proliferative potential (HPP) colonies.[21,22] In single-cell assays, these cells can be growth arrested by TGFβ. Recently, we found a quiescent CD34⁻ counterpart of the HPP-Q, which can proliferate in a combination of thrombopoietin (TPO), Flt-3 ligand (Flt-3), stem cell factor (SCF), interleukin-3 (IL-3), and interleukin-6 (IL-6). This proliferation is also inhibited by TGFβ (F.W.R., unpublished results).

The fact that proliferation of both human and murine quiescent primitive cells can be rapidly growth arrested by TGFβ suggests that treatment with TGFβ can maintain the stem cell nature of these cells. Although Hö^{low}/Rho^{low} HSCs cultured for 5 days with a SCF, IL-3, and IL-6 mixture showed LTRA with 15% donor chimerism compared with 60% using the same number of uncultured cells, the same cells treated for 5 days with cytokines and TGFβ had no LTRA activity.[22a] Lin⁻Hö^{low}/Rho^{low} HSCs stimulated to divide and then growth arrested with TGFβ showed markedly reduced engrafting potential.[23] In human and murine gene transfer experiments, when TGFβ was used to growth arrest the cells after retroviral infection, the cells were severely impaired in their ability to repopulate.[24] However, TGFβ arrests cytokine-induced growth at the G_1/S transition; this is clearly not the same as G_0 quiescence. Throughout the G_1/S transition, the synthetic machinery makes new mRNAs and proteins resulting in the loss of "stemness" in these cells even in the presence of TGFβ1.

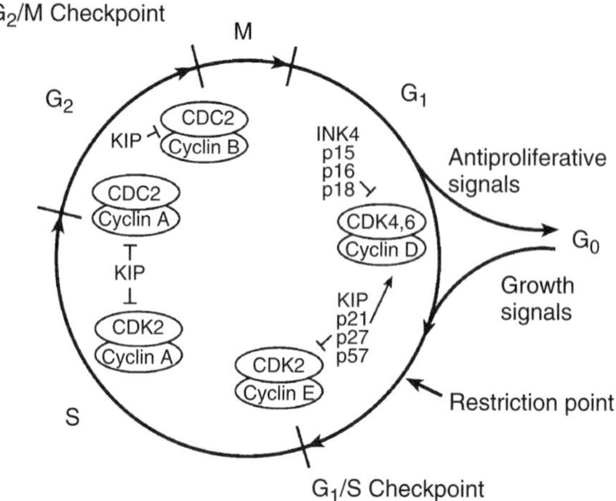

Figure 10–1. Schematic representation of the checkpoints in relation to the cell cycle machinery.

Hematopoietic Stem Cell Cycle Progression

CELL CYCLE PROGRESSION TO G_1 RESTRICTION POINT (R)

Many molecular events controlling cell cycle progression and checkpoint functions have been elucidated. The central players are protein complexes that contain regulatory proteins (referred to as a cyclins) and protein kinases with catalytic activity (referred to as a cyclin-dependent kinases or Cdk). Different cyclin/Cdk complexes are assembled and activated at different checkpoints in the cell cycle (Fig. 10–1).[25,26]

When mitogens bind to their transmembrane receptors, a series of molecular events occur involving activation of the receptor's kinase activity and recruitment and activation of molecules that control proliferation such as ras and myc.[27,28] Thus, mitogens stimulate commitment of the cell to entry in the cell cycle. In contrast, activation of the TGFβ signaling pathway allows the cell to remain in G_0.[21] These mitogen-activated early G_1 events are mediated by the induction of the D-type cyclins and subsequent phosphorylation of the retinoblastoma protein (Rb). D-type cyclins have a relatively short half-life of roughly 20 minutes and rapidly disappear with the removal of growth factors[29] or the appearance of antiproliferative signals such as the cell cycle kinase inhibitor p15.[30] Mitogens also regulate the stabilization and accumulation of D cyclin proteins, their nuclear translocation, and assembly with Cdk4/6.[31,32]

In late G_1 there occurs a point, referred to as the restriction point R,[33] where withdrawal of external growth factors fails to block progression and the cell is irreversibly committed to progression through the cycle. Thus, R could be considered a checkpoint. Although checkpoints are mostly concerned with repairing DNA damage, R is related to correcting the consequences of mitogen deprivation, one of which is oxidative stress that leads to DNA damage.[34] Cyclin D/Cdk4/6 complexes proteins promote the transition of cells from early to mid G_1 phase, transducing mitogenic signals from the external environment to a point in the cell cycle where external stimuli are no longer needed (Fig. 10–1).

In addition, cyclin D proteins play an important role in the progression through G_1 and entry into S phase. In continually dividing cell populations, levels of D-type cyclins do not usually change throughout the cell cycle.[35] Microinjection of anti-cyclin D antibodies and/or anti-sense cyclin D plasmid DNA into G_1 fibroblasts blocked S phase entry but failed to block S phase entry in cells near the G_1/S phase border.[36,37] Of the mammalian isoforms of cyclin D, most cell types express cyclin D2 and either cyclin D1 or D3 with HSCs expressing D2 and D3.[38]

MOLECULAR EVENTS AT RESTRICTION POINT CONFERRING MITOGEN INDEPENDENCE

The ability of D-type cyclins/Cdk4/6 complexes to phosphorylate and inactivate the Rb protein family members (Rb, p130, and p107[39]) makes events that follow mitogen independent. Cyclin D function is not required for G_1 progression in Rb null cells,[40] and triple Rb, p130, and p107 null cells cannot growth arrest.[41] Rb family members function by sequestering and thereby inactivating a number of factors necessary for S phase progression including E2F protein family, which consists of a number of transcription factors that are bound to and sequestered by the hypophosphorylated form of pRb.[42] On phosphorylation of pRb by cyclin D/Cdk4/6 complexes, E2F proteins are released and can associate with other proteins, such as the DP-1 family of proteins, to form complexes that act as transcriptional activators for several genes required in S phase. Among these genes are thymidine kinase,[43] cyclin E,[44] DNA polymerase α, E2F1,[45] proliferating cell nuclear antigen (PCNA),[46] Cdc2,[47] Rb, and p107.[48]

Cyclin D/CDK4 does not completely phosphorylate Rb; the downstream cyclin E/CDK2 complex completes the phosphorylation[49]; thus, cyclins D and E complexes appear to function cooperatively in phosphorylating pRb. Selective inactivation of either Cdk4/6 or Cdk2 resulted in an inability of cyclin D/Cdk4/6 complexes to completely phosphorylate pRb.[50] Similarly, the cyclin E/Cdk2 complex was unable to phosphorylate pRb unless pRb had been previously acted on by cyclin D/Cdk4/6 complexes. It is important to note that G_1/S transition is highly nonlinear with several feedback loops leading to downstream events also lying upstream. For example, c-myc expression is downstream from p21, Cdks, and E2F; however, it is an upstream regulator of p21 and Cdks.[51] Cyclin E is downstream from E2F and Rb because the cyclin E gene is induced by E2F; however, cyclin E phosphorylates Rb to release E2F.[52] Rb and p107 levels increase as cells go through S phase because of E2F binding sites in their promoters.[52]

Complexes of distinct Rb-E2F family members act as repressors at different stages of the cell cycle. E2F/p130 maintains cells in G_0 including human T cells[53] and CD34$^+$ lin$^-$ cells.[54] In early G_1, phosphorylation of p130 by cyclin D-CDK4 complexes targets p130 for degradation by proteosomes leaving high levels of free E2F-4 throughout the cell cycle.[55] This allows the formation of repressor p107/E2F-4 and Rb/E2F-4 complexes. E2F-1, E2F-2, and E2F-3 transcriptional activators are released at the R point by Rb phosphorylation; Rb-E2F-3 is the dominant complex necessary for G_1/S transition.[56] Thus, a combination of cyclin D complexes, cyclin E complexes, Rb phosphorylation, and E2F activation are all necessary for growth factor independent traverse of the R point leading to passage into S phase.[57]

INHIBITION OF G_1/S TRANSITION: CONVERGENCE OF TGFβ AND CDKI

The slow cycling by HSCs begs the question of what mitogen or combinations of mitogens stimulates the induction of the appropriate cell cycle machinery to effect passage into and through G_1 phase. Individual quiescent HSCs express transcripts for cyclins D2 and D3 (but not D1).[11] If the cyclin D proteins are produced in these cells primarily in G_0 phase, why do HSCs enter the cycle so slowly? One possibility is that stochastic progression into the cell cycle depends on permissible combinations of cell cycle activators and inhibitors afforded by the (random) fluctuation of individual protein levels and activities. Alternatively, the entrance of the HSC in to the cell cycle depends on exceeding a threshold number of activating signals and/or attenuating signals with many different possible combination of events leading to the same outcome.[58]

In the growth of isolated Sca$^+$Lin$^-$Thy-1^{low} cells, SCF plus IL-3 promoted maximum cloning efficiency in single-cell assays (roughly 38 colonies in 300 single cells), and TGF$β inhibits >90% of the proliferation. The addition of five factors (IL-1, IL-6, granulocyte-macrophage colony-stimulating factor [GM-CSF], macrophage colony-stimulating factor [M-CSF], and granulocyte colony-stimulating factor [G-CSF]) to the combination of SCF plus IL-3 does not increase the overall cloning efficiency of single Lin$^-$Thy-1^{low} cells.[59] However, this combination of cytokines reduced TGF$β inhibition to 25%, regardless of the TGFβ concentration. Thus, multiple cytokines can cooperate to partially override the inhibitory effects of TGFβ. In this regard, it is noteworthy that G-CSF, which down-modulates cyclins D2 and D3 in differentiating cells, appears to augment cyclin D-mediated cell cycle progression in HSCs.[60]

Similarly, multiple inhibitors, such as tumor necrosis factor α (TNF-α) and interferon-γ (IFN-γ), can directly cooperate with TGFβ to inhibit the proliferation of Sca$^+$Lin$^-$Thy-1^{low} cells. The addition of TNF-α or INF-γ as single inhibitors to these cells stimulated by the seven-factor combination, resulted in only minimal inhibition. The addition of INF-γ, TNF-α, plus TGFβ increased the inhibition observed with TGFβ from 25 to 76% inhibition of single-cell growth.[59] Thus, HSC growth is regulated by a balance of opposing positive and negative growth regulators. One can imagine intracellular mediators acting cooperatively to maintain HSC quiescence.

The activity of cyclin-Cdks is opposed by Cdk-inhibitors (CdkIs) of the INK4a class (p15, 16, 18) that inhibit cyclin D-Cdk4/6 complexes or the KIP/CIP family (p21, p27 and p57), which inhibit several types of cyclins-Cdks but have greatest inhibitory activity against cyclin E-Cdk2 complexes[61] (Fig. 10–1). The selective binding of INK4 inhibitors to Cdk4/6 complexes prevents p21 and p27 sequestration by those complexes. This results in greater p21 and p27 binding to Cdk2 complexes with resultant growth arrest. Interestingly, there is some evidence indicating that cyclin A-Cdk2 also plays a role in G_1 to S progression because overexpression of cyclin A in G_1 cells results in premature S phase entry.[62]

TGFβ arrests cells at the G_1/S phase through regulation of CdkIs. It stimulates the transcription of p15, which displaces p21 and p27 from the cyclin-Cdk complexes and inhibits cyclin E/Cdk2 and cyclin A/Cdk2 kinase activity. It is more complex because p21 and p27 are essential activators of cyclin D-Cdk4/6 complexes.[63] Inhibition of proteosomal activity relieves TGFβ induced G_1/S arrest leading to S phase entry.[64]

The number and activity of cyclin D/Cdk4/6 complexes were increased, although higher levels of p27 bound to the complexes, which stimulated enough Rb phosphorylation to drive S phase entrance despite the fact the kinase activity of cyclin E-Cdk2 complexes was still inhibited. In cells resistant to growth arrest by TGFβ, continued assembly and accumulation of cyclin D/Cdk4/6-p27 complexes leading to increased cyclin E/Cdk2 kinase activity was seen,[65] indicating that altered p27 function alters the effect of TGFβ on the cell cycle. The roles of cyclins, Cdk, CdkI, and Rb/E2F families in G_1S regulation are summarized in Fig. 10–2.

How are high levels of p15 and p21 induced and maintained in HSCs that are deciding to become and remain quiescent? The mechanisms by which TGFβ exerts growth arrest fall into two general categories. One includes TGFβ-induced repression of growth promoting transcription factors, most notably c-myc. c-myc null rat fibroblasts have a greatly elongated (five-fold) G_1 phase.[66] The factor c-myc can also act as a direct inhibitor of p15 and p21 transcription,[67–69] which would greatly retard growth arrest. As previously noted, free E2F4 can complex with p107 as p107 increases throughout the cell cycle. It has been recently shown that Smad3, an intracellular mediator of TGFβ signals, can exist as a preformed complex with p107-E2F4, and on TGFβ stimulation Smad4 translocates the complex to the nucleus where it binds to the TIE region of the c-myc promoter repressing transcription.[70] As a result, myc can no longer bind to the Inr of the p15 promoter allowing Smad3 and Smad4 to bind p300 coactivator now attached to the Inr through Miz-1.[68,69] TGFβ is then able to stimulate the transcription of both p15 and p21 through either the Smad or MAP kinase pathway in $CD34^+$ cells[71] and in nonhematopoietic cells.[72] Although myc repression has not been described for HSCs, it is noteworthy that TGFβ have been shown to use p107 in myeloid cells,[73] whereas p107 null Balb/c mice have myeloid hyperplasia[74] and E2F4 null mice have an accumulation of myeloid precursors among other defects.[75]

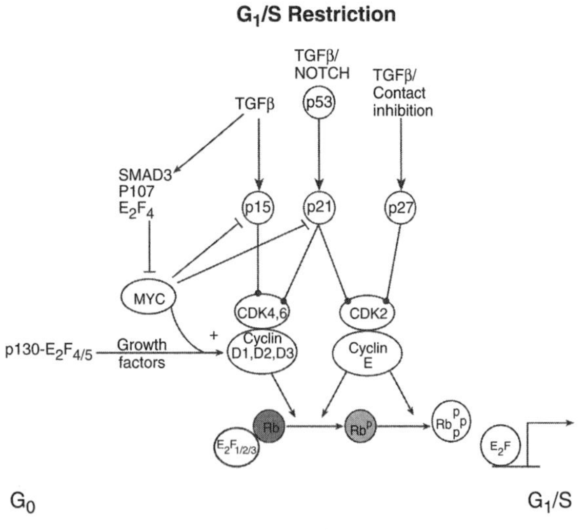

G_1/S Restriction

Figure 10–2. Schematic representation of the cell cycle machinery regulating G_1/S progression.

CDKI Null Mice and Hematopoietic Stem Cell Function

The CdkIs are attractive candidates for proteins that maintain HSC quiescence and oppose HSC cell cycle progression. Both CdkIs p15 and p21 have been implicated as playing roles in maintaining hematopoietic stem cell quiescence both in mouse and humans. In murine lin^- $Hö^{low}/Rho^{low}$ HSCs, high levels of p15 were seen, which disappear after one to two cycles of division.[75a] In p15 null mice, it has been reported that extramedullary hematopoiesis predominates in the B-cell compartment.[76] A functional significance for p21 in HSC function has been established.[77] An increase in stem cell cycling in p21 knockout mice, accompanied by an increased susceptibility of the stem cell compartment to 5-fluorouracil (5-FU)-induced cell death and to subtle stem cell exhaustion seen after four serial transplants, give compelling evidence that p21 is required for stem cell quiescence. In addition, p21 is uniformly expressed in primitive human $CD34^+$ lin^- cells.[71] The mechanism by which p21 promotes HSC quiescence is not known. Because cyclin D is expressed in quiescent HSCs, it may involve the ability of p21 to inhibit the activity of cyclin D/CDK4/6 complex. One would then expect p27 to have an effect on stem cell cycling, which does not appear to be the case.[78] If maintaining stable p130/E2F-4 association is necessary for quiescent HSCs in the same manner as quiescent T cells,[53] then perhaps, the ability of p21 to disrupt cdk2 from p130/E2F-4 complexes is functionally important.[79] The individual absence of p15, p21, or p27 has no effect on the ability of TGFβ to inhibit growth arrest in hematopoietic cells[76–78] indicating the presence of compensating pathways. TGFβ mediated repression of Cdc25A has been shown to lead to growth arrest in p15 negative cells.[80] Following TGFβ treatment, the activation of the protein phosphatase 2A (PP2A) by the release of its Bα subunit from the TGFβ receptor leads to the inhibition of p70S6 kinase, which is sufficient for G_1 growth arrest in some cells in the absence of Smad activity.[81] It is not known whether this PP2A mediated pathway is operational in HSCs, however, the role of PP2A in regulating Smad activation in hematopoietic cell differentiation has recently been reported.[82]

TGFβ NULL MICE

Homozygous TGFβ1 knockout mice have progressive wasting; death occurs by 5 weeks because of systemic cell-dependent inflammatory syndrome.[83] Major histocompatibility complex (MHC) class II-dependent autoimmune disease also occurs. Defective hematopoiesis, resulting in plasmacytosis, myeloid hyperplasia, and a lack of Langerhans dendritic cells, was correlated with the absence of TGFβ1,[83] because the mice still make adequate amounts of TGFβ2 and TGFβ3 showing that *in vivo* the isoforms are not equal in function. The double TGFβ1/MHC class II knockout mice lose the proinflammatory and autoimmune defects, but some mice still retain the myeloproliferative syndrome.[84] The phenotype of TβR-II knockout mice was indistinguishable from that of TGFβ1 knockout mice.[85] Attempts at isolating the quiescent lin^- $Hö^{low}/Rho^{low}$

c-kit+ HSCs from the TGFβ knockout mice has shown a >90% reduction indicating that autocrine TGFβ1 is a major regulator of stem cell quiescence.[85a]

Cell Cycle Checkpoint Function

HSCs in particular need continual monitoring of entrance into and progression through the cell cycle. Unrestrained self-renewal of HSCs will lead to stem cell exhaustion and progressive genetic instability. Cells are acutely sensitive to DNA damage. Reactive oxygen species (ROS) are a major source of intrinsic DNA damage. The high reactivity of DNA to ROS leads to more than 100 modifications of the genome per day.[86] External DNA damaging agents such as ultraviolet light (UV) or ionizing radiation (IR) alter the structure and function of DNA in several ways depending on the dose and duration of the stimuli. Many chemical agents also are mutagenic or carcinogenic affecting the integrity and replication of DNA. As a result, chemotherapeutic agents at high doses are used to initiate apoptosis in cancer treatment. The molecular sensors used to regulate cell cycle progression, detect DNA damage, and generate a pause in certain stages of the cell cycle in response to this damage are termed checkpoints.[87,88] Cells damaged in early to mid G_1 phase will pause at the G_1/S checkpoint. However, cells damaged in late G_1 will enter S phase and initiate DNA synthesis, although more slowly than undamaged cells. Similarly, cells damaged in early to mid G_2 will pause in the G_2/M checkpoint. However, cells that are damaged in late G_1 or G_2 will move more slowly into S and M phases, respectively, never really pausing. Because these checkpoints are closely linked to the cell cycle, these pauses often involve a suppression of cyclin-Cdk activity.[89,90] p21 inhibits the activities of cyclin E-Cdk2 and cyclin A-Cdk2 and to a lesser extent cyclin B-Cdc2[91] and has effects on all checkpoints.

THE G_1/S CHECKPOINT

At the G_1/S border, cyclin E-associated kinase activity is greatest.[92] Cyclin E/Cdk2 complexes have a wider substrate specificity than cyclin D/Cdk complexes and are phosphorylating a variety of proteins in addition to pRb.[93] Cyclin E-Cdk2 is also different than cyclin D complexes in that its activity is required for S progression in Rb null cells, indicating that cyclin E complexes function as the main sensor for G_1/S transition.

After DNA damage by agents such as IR, UV, radiomimetic chemicals, chemotherapeutic drugs, and ROS, two PI3K related protein kinases, ataxia telangiectasia mutated (ATM) and ATM-Rad3 related (ATR), are activated as the most proximal signal molecules.[94,95] ATR (UV) and ATM (IR) operate in parallel pathways to induce p53 and/or checkpoint kinase1 (Chk1) and checkpoint kinase2 (Chk2), which can target p53 and Cdc25c. Chk2 is found throughout the cell cycle, whereas Chk1 is short lived, appearing at the G_1/S boundary and reaching a peak in S and G_2. Chk1 mRNA production seems to be controlled by the Rb-E2F pathway.[96] The nuclear presence of Chk2 in murine bone marrow along with its ability to be activated throughout the mammalian cell cycle after DNA damage[97] makes Chk2 an attractive candidate for signaling the repair of DNA damage in HSCs. The maintenance of the G_1 checkpoint depends on increased expression, activation, and stabilization of the p53 gene product, a tumor suppressor transcription factor that senses external stimuli and translates them into internal signals.[98,99] p53 normally has a short cellular half-life (about 15 minutes), but it is activated and stabilized through post-translational mechanisms in response to DNA damage.[100,101] However, G_1 cells lacking functional p53 activity fail to arrest in G_1 and enter S phase regardless of the IR dose[102]; thus, p53 protein acts as a "sensor" for DNA damage. Cells from individuals with ataxia telangiectasia (AT) exhibit poor p53 induction and a poor G_1 checkpoint response after IR exposure.[103,104] The p53 response to DNA damage can lead to either G_1 arrest or apoptosis (Fig. 10–3).

After its induction, p53 transcriptionally activates a number of genes including p21,[105] GADD45,[106] and MDM2.[107] MDM2-p53 complexes inhibit p53 mediated transcriptional activity.[108] IR induces p53 phosphorylation, which blocks MDM2 binding stabilizing p53 and increasing its transcriptional activity.[109,110] Although IR induces p21 via p53 induction, basal p21 expression is p53 independent. Similarly, p21 may also be induced independently of p53 in HSCs by several transcription factors (see later discussion) and such events such as self-renewal, differentiation, and TGFβ stimulation. Overexpression of p21 results in G_1 arrest, whereas p21-deficient fibroblasts exposed to IR show a defective but not ablated G_1 checkpoint response.[111] Although p21 has homology to the Cdk inhibitor proteins p27 and p57, it is the only

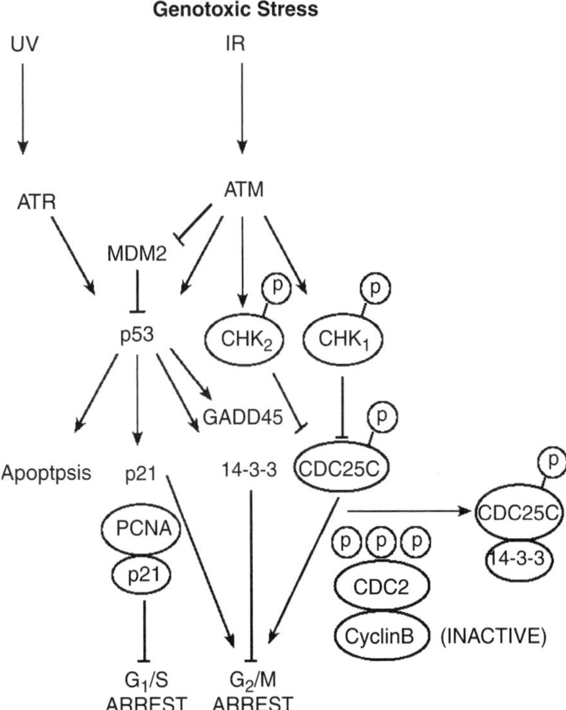

Figure 10–3. Schematic representation of the molecular events activated by genotoxic stress that result in checkpoint arrest.

family member important in DNA damage-induced G_1 arrest. Among its unique features, only p21 can bind to PCNA, blocking DNA replication.[112] Several other motifs of the p21 molecules are also necessary for G_1 arrest.[113] In 21 null mice, HSCs are much more sensitive to the lethal effects of 5-FU.[77]

In a manner similar to the inhibitory phosphorylations that inactivate cyclin B-Cdc2 (see later discussion), the G_1 checkpoint response is also regulated by inhibitory phosphorylations of G_1 Cdks. Like Cdc2, Cdk2 is phosphorylated on Thr-14 and Tyr-15 during the cell cycle.[114] Treatment of human B-cell lymphoma cells with interferon-α resulted in a rapid G_0-like arrest and the elimination of Cdc25A phosphatase, which is required for removal of Cdk2 tyrosine inhibitory phosphorylations.[115] The induction of Tyr-17 phosphorylation on Cdk4 by UV is important in the G_1 checkpoint response because transfection of cells with a mutant Cdk4 that could not be Tyr-17 phosphorylated resulted in a loss of the UV-induced G_1 checkpoint response.[116] These results indicate that G_1 Cdks are partially regulated by the addition and removal of inhibitory phosphorylations. Furthermore, INK4 family member proteins contribute to the G_1/S checkpoint response. Support for this comes from the observation that overexpression of p16 leads to G_1 arrest in $pRb^{+/+}$ cells but not in $pRb^{-/-}$ cells.[117] Rb null cells do not undergo an IR induced G_1 arrest.[118] Rb transcriptional repression by p21 is essential for this DNA damage response.

THE S PHASE CHECKPOINT

Less is known about the S phase checkpoint response. Similar to the G_1 and G_2 checkpoint responses, the S checkpoint response is stereotypic for a wide variety of DNA damages.[119] DNA-damaging carcinogenic agents known to trigger the S phase response include IR, UV-B, UV-C, and methylmethane sulfonate (MMS), as well as chemotherapeutic agents such as etoposide and amsacrine. Exposure of cells to cisplatin causes the accumulation of dephosphorylated Rb causing a prolonged arrest in S phase cells.[120] Rb null murine embryonic fibroblasts (MEF) do not arrest in S phase. IR strongly suppresses the activity of cyclin A/Cdk2,[121] which is thought to be required for S phase progression and DNA synthesis. However, this suppression does not occur in cells from individuals with AT, indicating that ATM may be an upstream regulator of cyclin A/Cdk2 activity.[121]

THE G_2/M CHECKPOINT

During the S and G2 phases, cyclin B/cdc2 complexes are inactivated by inhibitory phosphorylations of Cdc2 on Thr-14 and Tyr-15 by Weel and Myt1 kinases.[122,123] The complexes accumulate in the cytoplasm. The conversion to an active complex requires dephosphorylation by Cdc25C phosphatase.[124] Most if not all of the early nuclear mitotic events are then catalyzed by active cyclin B/Cdc2. TGFβ treatment caused phosphorylation of Cdc2 in the TGFβRII receptor-cyclin B-Cdc2 complex in human monocytic THP-1 cells[125] suggesting that G_1/S arrest may be assisted by preventing entry in G_2/M phase. Agents such as UV or MMS stimulate the production of the three members of GADD45 family (126). GADD45α and GADD45β each can disrupt and inactivate cyclin B-Cdc2 complexes, whereas all three GADD45s inhibit Cdc2 kinase activity.[126] In contrast, agents such as IR and etoposide trigger a G_2 checkpoint response that results in a delay in the activation of cyclin B/Cdc2 kinase activity at the G_2/M border because of an accumulation of Thr-14/Tyr-15 phosphorylated Cdc2, which results in inhibition of cyclin B/Cdc2 activity.[127] Activation of cyclin B/Cdc2 occurs through the action of the Cdc25C phosphatase, which removes the Thr-14/Tyr-15 phosphorylations. Hyperphosphorylation of Cdc25C correlates with increased activity near G_2/M, and this hyperphosphorylation does not occur in cells arrested in G_2 by DNA damage.[128] Similarly, the cyclin B/Cdc2 complex and Cdc5C, which normally associate at G_2/M, do not in DNA damaged cells. In hematopoietic cell lines, IR activates Lyn, a member of the Src kinase family that localizes to the nucleus, binds, and phosphorylates cdc2 on Tyr-15 suggesting that Lyn is important in the G_2 checkpoint response in HSCs.[129]

The association between the cyclin B/Cdc2 complex and Cdc25C may be blocked through the actions of the Chk1 and Chk2 kinases. Both kinases phosphorylate Cdc25C on serine 216, which results in it being bound by 14-3-3 proteins and its apparent cytoplasmic sequestration from the cyclin B-Cdc2 complex.[130] Chk2 is phosphorylated in IR-treated ATM normal but not nulls cells,[131] and the G_2 checkpoint response is lacking in ATM cells after IR.[132,133]

Recent studies indicate that p53 and p21 are necessary to sustain a G_2/M arrest following DNA damage because tumor cells lacking these proteins proceed through M phase with more rapid kinetics. In colorectal cells, p53 transactivates 14-3-3σ in response to DNA damage, and 14-3-3σ binds to and thus sequesters cyclin B/Cdc2 complexes in the cytoplasm, preventing mitotic entry.[130] In addition, in some IR-treated S phase cells, p53 acts as transcriptional repressor to reduce cyclin B and cdc2 levels.[134] This requires Rb because blocking RB function does not repress cyclin B levels and accelerates M phase passage.[134] Rb is necessary for the maintenance of G_2 arrest because Rb null MEF continue the checkpoint either to proliferate or die depending on the IR dose.[135] IR can induce PP2A, which can dephosphorylates all the Rb family members.[136] Finally, p21 can associate with the cyclin B/Cdc2 complex but with lower affinity than with other complexes.[50,51] Cells in which p53-dependent p21 expression is abrogated result in increased cyclin A and B associated kinase activity and enter G_2 phase more rapidly than normal cells.[137] Thus, p21 may act by inhibiting cyclin A/Cdk2 activity, delaying cyclin B/Cdc2 activation, and, thus, contributing to the G_2 checkpoint response.[138]

HEMATOPOIETIC CYTOKINES AND "OVERRIDING THE CHECKPOINT"

The arrest at the G_1 and G_2 checkpoint responses is thought to occur to allow DNA damaged cells time to either repair the damage, particularly to DNA, or alternatively undergo apoptosis or senescence. Support for this hypothesis comes from the ability of hematopoietic cytokines, such as IL-3, SCF, and erythropoietin (EPO), to prevent G_1 and G_2 checkpoint delays after exposures to IR and chemotherapeutic agents.[139] Treatment of bone marrow cells with both IL-3 and DNA-damaging agents prevents cells from undergoing apoptosis. In hematopoietic cell lines, apoptosis and G_2/M arrest induced by IR can be rescued by cytokines through distinct JAK kinase signaling pathways.[140] In contrast, DNA damage induced G_1 arrest in these same cells is alleviated by cytokine-mediated PI3K-dependent activation of Cdk2.[141] It would be predicted that the lack of checkpoint delay might greatly increase cell death. Continuous cytokine activation of PI3K in the presence of IR and cisplatin DNA damage results in greatly enhanced lethality of the DNA-damaging agent in hematopoietic cells.[142,143] Furthermore, in the autosomal recessive disease AT, the loss of ATM function results in attenuation of the G_1, S, and G_2 checkpoint functions in response to IR.[144] Cells from individuals with AT are hypersensitive to the killing effects of IR and display 3- to 10-fold increased frequencies in genetic instability.[145]

Effect of Abrogation of CDKI Regulators on Hematopoietic Stem Cell Function

Addition of anti-TGFβ1 to single HSC cultures in the absence of added growth factors results in 40% of HSCs surviving 14 days compared with limited survival (3–5 days) in medium alone.[146,147] Essentially all anti-TGFβ treated cells in the presence of cytokines began cell cycle progression (time to first division) more rapidly. Similar results were seen with human CD34$^+$ cells.[148] Unexpectedly, a substantial proportion of the surviving cells retained their LTRA in a competitive repopulation assay.[147] The competitive repopulating units indicated that there was a relative enrichment of HSCs treated with anti-TGFβ compared with normal HSCs. Even a short exposure of highly purified quiescent HSCs to a neutralizing anti-TGFβ antibody dramatically reduced the time required for engraftment of HSCs.[149] Also, an overnight treatment of antisense oligonucleotides (AS) to TGFβ or TGFβ-RII induces HSC cycling, reduces the number of HSCs required for hematopoietic repopulation, and decreases the time to engraftment.[149] Overnight treatment with the antisense, but not with the antibody, stimulated cell cycle entry. One hundred lin$^-$ Hö^{low}/Rho^{low} HSCs treated with TGFβ AS for 16 hours engrafted rapidly to reach donor cell chimerism of 50 to 60% by 3 weeks (neutrophils) and 70 to 85% by 1.5 months (T and B cells). The induction of rapid engraftment of HSCs by TGFβ MAS or antibody did not require any support cells or did not impair their LTRA as measured by sustained high percentage of donor chimeras 1 year post-transplant. Finally, blocking of endogenous TGFβ in HSCs markedly reduced the number of HSCs required to rescue a lethally irradiated congenic recipient; although more than >1200 control HSCs per mouse were required for hematopoietic rescue, as few as 60 TGFβ AS treated cells would rescue a recipient.[149]

The mechanisms by which blocking autocrine TGFβ functions in quiescent HSCs remains unclear. The maintenance of high levels of p15 and p21 expression in HSCs probably results in part from autocrine production of TGFβ1 by HSCs[21,150] and from paracrine production by marrow stromal cells.[151] Neutralizing autocrine TGFβ1 has been shown to rapidly down-regulate p21[71] and p15[150] expression in quiescent human HSCs. However, neutralization of TGFβ-1 alone has not been sufficient to promote cycling of either quiescent murine[148] or human HSCs.[150]

Recently, the interruption of p21 in human CD34$^+$ CD38$^-$ cells by using antisense lentiviral vectors resulted in *ex vivo* expansion of stem cell numbers.[152] This suggests that other factors are likely to sustain p21 levels in these quiescent cells. Although several transcription factors present in primitive hematopoietic cells are capable of up-regulating p21, including MLL[153] and Rb/E2F,[21] a role for these factors in preventing HSC cycling has not yet been established. Presumably, the p21 checkpoints are overcome by cytokines in responsive HSCs and by developmental regulators of cell fate such as Notch[154] and hoxB4[155] that sustain the pluripotentiality of HSCs while promoting cell cycling. Furthermore, the self-renewing HSCs are regulated by the relative contribution of repressive (eed-containing) and enhancing (Bmil-containing) complexes.[156,157] In addition, a role for wnt signaling in self-renewal of HSCs has just been published.[158] The ability of these pathways to suppress p21 during stem cell expansion is not clear.

Because anti-TGFβ treatment of 60 quiescent HSCs rescued a mouse from lethal irradiation, HSCs must generate short-term repopulating cells as well as self-renew to create an HSC pool. Although other mechanisms such as blocking apoptosis or better homing to the marrow space may play a role, considerable cell division must have occurred *in vivo* despite the presence of autocrine TGFβ in the progeny. Translation of any of these *ex vivo* methods to human stem cell transplants could reduce the time to engraft plus lower the number of stem cells required for a durable graft. With few exceptions,[21,149] blockage of autocrine TGFβ in human primitive hematopoietic cells has not led to cell cycle progression.[148,149] However, using a combination of anti-p27/anti-TGFβ[159] or antisense vectors to completely suppress p21 expression[152] provides evidence that blocking negative cell cycle regulators may be useful in *ex vivo* stem cell expansion, particularly in combination with positive regulators like thrombopoietin.[160] Whether, short-term *ex vivo* exposure to replicate HSCs or more substantial *ex vivo* stem cell expansion is more useful therapeutically will substantially depend on how each process regulates the genotoxic stress on HSCs.

ACKNOWLEDGMENTS

The authors thank Sandra Ruscetti and Salem Akel for contributing useful suggestions in editing the manuscript and Lin Grove for technical assistance.

This project has been funded in whole or in part with Federal funds from the National Cancer Institute, National Institutes of Health, under Contract No. NO1-CO-56000 and N.I.H. grant DK48708 awarded by National Institute of Diabetes, Digestive and

Kidney Diseases. The content of this publication does not reflect the views or policies of the Department of Health and Human Services, nor does mention of trade names, commercial products, or organizations imply endorsement by the U.S. Government.

REFERENCES

1. Jones, R.J., Collector, M.I., Barber, J.P., Vala, M.S., Fackler, M.J., May, W.S., Griffin, C.A., Hawkins, A.L., Zehnbauer, B.A., Hilton, J., Colvin, O.M., and Sharkis, S.J. (1996). Characterization of mouse lymphohematopoietic stem cells lacking spleen colony-forming activity. *Blood* **88,** 487–491.
2. Na Nakorn, T., Traver, D., Weissman, I.L., and Akashi, K. (2002). Myeloerythroid-restricted progenitors are sufficient to confer radioprotection and provide the majority of day 8 CFU-S. *J. Clin. Invest.* **109,** 1579–1585.
3. Kondo, M., Wagers, A.J., Manz, M.G., Prohaska, S.S., Scherer, D.C., Beilhack, G.F., Shizuru, J.A., and Weissman, I.L. (2003). Biology of hematopoietic stem cells and progenitors: implications for clinical application. *Annu. Rev. Immunol.* **21,** 759–806.
4. Morrison, S.J., and Weissman, I.L. (1994). The long-term repopulating subset of hematopoietic stem cells is deterministic and isolatable by phenotype. *Immunity* **1,** 661–673.
5. Gothot, A., Pyatt, R., McMahel, J., Rice, S., and Srour, E.F. (1997). Functional heterogeneity of human CD34(+) cells isolated in subcompartments of the G0/G1 phase of the cell cycle. *Blood* **90,** 4384–4393.
6. Bertoncello, I., Bradley, T.R., Hodgson, G.S., and Dunlop, J.M. (1991). The resolution, enrichment, and organization of normal bone marrow high proliferative potential colony-forming cell subsets on the basis of rhodamine-123 fluorescence. *Exp. Hematol.* **19,** 174–178.
7. Wolf, N.S., Kone, A., Priestley, G.V., and Bartelmez, S.H. (1993). In vivo and in vitro characterization of long-term repopulating primitive hematopoietic cells isolated by sequential Hoechst 33342-rhodamine 123 FACS selection. *Exp. Hematol.* **21,** 614–622.
8. Jordan, C.T., and Lemischka, I.R. (1990). Clonal and systemic analysis of long-term hematopoiesis in the mouse. *Genes Dev.* **4,** 220–232.
9. Bradford, G.B., Williams, B., Rossi, R., and Bertoncello, I. (1997). Quiescence, cycling, and turnover in the primitive hematopoietic stem cell compartment. *Exp. Hematol.* **25,** 445–453.
10. Pietrzyk, M.E., Priestley, G.V., and Wolf, N.S. (1985). Normal cycling patterns of hematopoietic stem cell subpopulations: an assay using long-term in vivo BrdU infusion. *Blood* **66,** 1460–1462.
11. Cheshier, S.H., Morrison, S.J., Liao, X., and Weissman, I.L. (1999). In vivo proliferation and cell cycle kinetics of long-term self-renewing hematopoietic stem cells. *Proc. Natl. Acad. Sci. U. S. A.* **96,** 3120–3125.
12. Mahmud, N., Devine, S.M., Weller, K.P., Parmar, S., Sturgeon, C., Nelson, M.C., Hewett, T., and Hoffman, R. (2001). The relative quiescence of hematopoietic stem cells in nonhuman primates. *Blood* **97,** 3061–3068.
13. Osawa, M., Hanada, K., Hamada, H., and Nakauchi, H. (1996). Long-term lymphohematopoietic reconstitution by a single CD34-low/negative hematopoietic stem cell. *Science* **273,** 242–245.
14. Bhatia, M., Bonnet, D., Murdoch, B., Gan, O.I., and Dick, J.E. (1998). A newly discovered class of human hematopoietic cells with SCID-repopulating activity. *Nat. Med.* **4,** 1038–1045.
15. Ortiz, M., Wine, J.W., Lohrey, N., Ruscetti, F.W., Spence, S.E., and Keller, J.R. (1999). Functional characterization of a novel hematopoietic stem cell and its place in the c-Kit maturation pathway in bone marrow cell development. *Immunity* **10,** 173–182.
16. Ito, C.Y., Li, C.Y., Bernstein, A., Dick, J.E., and Stanford, W.L. (2003). Hematopoietic stem cell and progenitor defects in Sca-1/Ly-6A-null mice. *Blood* **101,** 517–523.
17. Goodell, M.A., Rosenzweig, M., Kim, H., Marks, D.F., DeMaria, M., Paradis, G., Grupp, S.A., Sieff, C.A., Mulligan, R.C., and Johnson, R.P. (1997). Dye efflux studies suggest that hematopoietic stem cells expressing low or undetectable levels of CD34 antigen exist in multiple species. *Nat. Med.* **3,** 1337–1345.
18. Hao, Q.L., Thiemann, F.T., Petersen, D., Smogorzewska, E.M., and Crooks, G.M. (1996). Extended long-term culture reveals a highly quiescent and primitive human hematopoietic progenitor population. *Blood* **88,** 3306–3313.
19. Goodell, M.A. (1999). Introduction: focus on hematology. CD34(+) or CD34(−): does it really matter? *Blood* **94,** 2545–2547.
20. Sitnicka, E., Ruscetti, F.W., Priestley, G.V., Wolf, N.S., and Bartelmez, S.H. (1996). Transforming growth factor beta 1 directly and reversibly inhibits the initial cell divisions of long-term repopulating hematopoietic stem cells. *Blood* **88,** 82–88.
21. Fortunel, N., Batard, P., Hatzfeld, A., Monier, M.N., Panterne, B., Lebkowski, J., and Hatzfeld, J. (1998). High proliferative potential-quiescent cells: a working model to study primitive quiescent hematopoietic cells. *J. Cell Sci.* **111** (Pt 13), 1867–1875.
22. Fortunel, N.O., Hatzfeld, A., and Hatzfeld, J.A. (2000). Transforming growth factor-beta: pleiotropic role in the regulation of hematopoiesis. *Blood* **96,** 2022–2036.
23. Wiesmann, A., Kim, M., Georgelas, A., Searles, A.E., Cooper, D.D., Green, W.F., and Spangrude, G.J. (2000). Modulation of hematopoietic stem/progenitor cell engraftment by transforming growth factor beta. *Exp. Hematol.* **28,** 128–139.
24. Yu, J., Soma, T., Hanazono, Y., and Dunbar, C.E. (1998). Abrogation of TGF-beta activity during retroviral transduction improves murine hematopoietic progenitor and repopulating cell gene transfer efficiency. *Gene Ther.* **5,** 1265–1271.
25. Nigg, E.A. (2001). Cell cycle regulation by protein kinases and phosphatases. *Ernst Schering Res. Found. Workshop* **34,** 19–46.
26. Steinman, R.A. (2002). Cell cycle regulators and hematopoiesis. *Oncogene* **21,** 3403–3413.
27. Eisenman, R.N. (2001). Deconstructing myc. *Genes Dev.* **15,** 2023–2030.
28. Aktas, H., Cai, H., and Cooper, G.M. (1997). Ras links growth factor signaling to the cell cycle machinery via regulation of cyclin D1 and the Cdk inhibitor p27KIP1. *Mol. Cell Biol.* **17,** 3850–3857.
29. Matsushime, H., Roussel, M.F., Ashmun, R.A., and Sherr, C.J. (1991). Colony-stimulating factor 1 regulates novel cyclins during the G1 phase of the cell cycle. *Cell* **65,** 701–713.
30. Sherr, C.J., and Roberts, J.M. (1999). CDK inhibitors: positive and negative regulators of G1-phase progression. *Genes Dev.* **13,** 1501–1512.
31. Diehl, J.A., Cheng, M., Roussel, M.F., and Sherr, C.J. (1998). Glycogen synthase kinase-3beta regulates cyclin D1 proteolysis and subcellular localization. *Genes Dev.* **12,** 3499–3511.
32. Cheng, M., Sexl, V., Sherr, C.J., and Roussel, M.F. (1998). Assembly of cyclin D-dependent kinase and titration of p27Kip1 regulated by mitogen-activated protein kinase kinase (MEK1). *Proc. Natl. Acad. Sci. U. S. A.* **95,** 1091–1096.
33. Pardee, A.B. (1974). A restriction point for control of normal animal cell proliferation. *Proc. Natl. Acad. Sci. U. S. A.* **71,** 1286–1290.

11

Telomeres and Telomerase Regulation

Peter M. Lansdorp

Chromosome ends or telomeres are composed of guanine-rich repeat sequences and associated proteins. A minimum number of repeats is essential for proper telomere function and to avoid sustained activation of DNA damage pathways that may result in replicative senescence or cell death. The length of telomere repeats decreases with replication and as an indirect result of damage to telomeric DNA. To maintain their ability to divide, stem cells require *de novo* synthesis of telomere repeats, typically achieved by the reverse transcriptase telomerase. Telomerase is expressed at high levels in proliferative cells of the germ line and in early embryonic (stem) cells, allowing apparent immortal growth of such cells. Telomerase levels in hematopoietic stem cells and most other somatic cells appear to be lower and insufficient to balance the loss of telomeric DNA. As a result, the overall telomere length in most cells declines with proliferation and age, and their replicative potential becomes increasingly restricted. That telomerase nevertheless has a crucial role in human hematopoietic stem cells is strikingly illustrated by patients with the rare genetic disease dyskeratosis congenita (DKC). Patients with an autosomal dominant form of DKC have mutations in the telomerase RNA template gene. As expected, the cells from such patients show modestly reduced telomerase levels, yet they typically die from marrow failure or infections before the age of 50. In contrast, complete removal of the telomerase RNA gene from the germ line of laboratory mice is tolerated for up to six generations. Strict control of telomerase levels and telomere length appears to limit the proliferation of somatic (stem) cells in long-lived species and could provide an additional barrier to tumor growth. Here, the critical role of telomeres and telomerase in stem cell proliferation is reviewed.

Structure and Function of Telomeres

The ends of linear chromosomes are called telomeres and consist, in all vertebrates, of tandem repeats of $(TTAGGG/CCCTAA)_n$ sequences and associated proteins.[1,2] Telomeres distinguish normal chromosome ends from double-strand breaks and protect normal ends against fusion, recombination, and degradation.[3] The length of telomere repeats varies among chromosomes and among species. In humans, the average length of telomere repeats ranges from a few to 20 kilobases depending on the tissue type, the age of the donor, and the replicative history of the cells. Individual chromosome ends in human cells are remarkably heterogenous in length,[4] and chromosome 17p typically has a short track of telomere repeats.[5] Telomeres contain DNA-binding proteins specific for double-strand telomeric DNA. These include TRF1, TRF2,[6] and POT1, a protein specific for the single-strand, guanine-rich telomeric DNA.[7] Many other proteins are known to indirectly bind to telomeres, for example, using TRF1 and TRF2 (reviewed by De Lange[2]).

The single-strand overhang at the 3′ end of telomeres folds back onto duplex telomeric DNA to form a protective telomere "T loop."[8] In T-loops, the 3′ overhang associates with telomere repeats using TRF2 in a way that is incompletely understood but appears important for telomere stability and function.[9,10] The electron microscopy data supporting the T-loop structure as the typical chromosome-end structure in murine and human cells have highlighted the complexity of the molecular interactions and processing steps involved in telomere formation and telomere function. Although many details still need to be elucidated, it appears that following each round of replication, the ends of chromosomes must be processed and refolded into a stable structure before cells can proceed to the next step in the cell cycle. Most likely, free chromosome ends such as single-strand ends or blunt ends trigger a DNA damage response resolved by recruitment of DNA repair proteins, processing, and T-loop formation (Fig. 11–1). The need to remodel free ends into functional telomeres following replication requires efficient DNA damage responses and DNA repair reactions, and the molecular interactions involved may provide continuous selective pressure for the molecules involved in both double-strand break repair and telomere function. Whether each end needs to be folded into a T-loop before checkpoint signals are sufficiently resolved (and cells can continue to divide) is not known. It is possible that, depending on the magnitude and the efficiency of DNA damage responses in a particular cell, one or a few "loose ends" are tolerated, putting these chromosome ends at risk for fusion events and other chromosomal abnormalities.

The success of forming a stable telomere structure depends partly on the length of the double-strand telomere repeat sequences. A reasonable model is that the length of telomere double-strand repeats determines the local concentration of proteins required for the processing steps involved

Handbook of Stem Cells
Volume 2

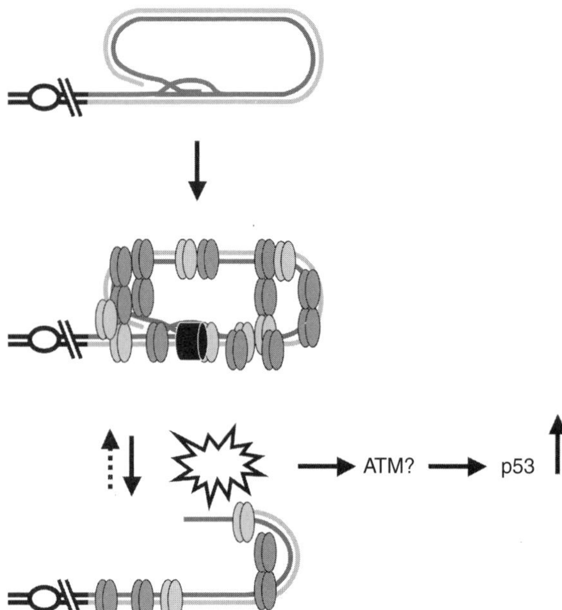

Figure 11-1. *Telomere function Is linked to telomere length.* (top) Following replication and processing, a chromosome end with a G-rich, single-strand overhang is created and folded back into a T-loop structure.[8] (middle) Telomere-binding proteins including TRF1 and TRF2 (indicated by light and dark gray circles) and POT1[7] (indicated by the cylinder in the T-loop), which binds to the 3′ single-strand overhang, are critical for the formation of a T-loop structure. (bottom) When the length of telomere repeats, the length of the single-strand overhang, or both[11] are (too) short, T-loop structures can no longer form, and an uncapped telomere[104] is exposed. The exposed telomere will result in a DNA damage response, which typically will involve up-regulation of p53,[105] most likely through phosphorylation by activated ATM.[106]

in telomere formation. To some extent telomerase expression or overexpression can decrease or bypass this length requirement.[11] Most likely, cells that express or overexpress telomerase can generate single-strand 3′ overhangs required for T-loop formation even when telomeres are very short.

Telomere repeats are lost with each round of replication by a variety of mechanisms (detailed later in this chapter). Most somatic cells express insufficient telomerase to compensate for the loss of telomere repeats. As a result, most somatic cells show a gradual decline in telomere length with proliferation and with age. This may increase DNA damage signals from telomeres as cells try to fold increasingly short ends into stable structures. Such signals (e.g., elevated levels of p53) may be additive with other forms of acute and accumulated (nontelomeric) DNA damage. As a result, cells could gradually increase their sensitivity to genotoxic stress. Little information on the role of DNA damage signals originating from telomeres versus other triggers of apoptosis or senescence in cells is available. Studies in this area are of interest in relation to the aging of stem cells but are complicated by difficulties in obtaining information about telomere length and about the replicative history of small numbers of cells. As well, DNA damage responses are known to be different in different (stem) cell types.[12]

Telomere Length Regulation

The length of telomere repeats at individual chromosome ends in cells is determined by many factors. The basic substrate for these factors is the unique telomere length profile of the 92 telomeres inherited in the fertilized ovum (Fig. 11–2). Studies of telomere length in cells following nuclear transfer into enucleated eggs have shown that telomeres can be elongated during embryonic development.[13] Whether such elongation depends on the cloning technique, species, or other unknown variables is not known.[14] Embryonic stem cells express high levels of telomerase and are capable of apparent immortal growth. Whether this is true for other human stem cell types remains to be seen. Mouse embryonic stem cells show highly variable telomere length[15] and are functionally p53 deficient.[12] Further studies on the role of p53 in relation to telomerase action and telomere structure are warranted. Throughout life, inherited telomere length appears to remain a critical determinant of the telomere length in somatic cells. For example, the average telomere length in nucleated blood cells from monozygotic twins, even in old age, was found to be similar in contrast to highly variable values observed in the general population.[16–18] Although genetic factors are clearly important determinants of telomere length in cells, some understanding of the various factors that shorten and elongate telomeres in human cells is important for several reasons. First, when describing the "self-renewal" and replicative potential of (stem) cells, it is important to understand that few normal diploid human cells have immortal growth properties and are capable of maintaining a constant telomere length. A basic

Figure 11-2. *Factors that determine telomere length in somatic cells.* The primary factor that determines telomere length in cells is the chromosome-specific telomere length profile in the parental haploid genomes that fuse to become the fertilized egg. At early stages of embryonic development (which may differ for the various lineages), telomerase levels become limiting and increasingly insufficient to counter the loss of telomeric DNA incurred in different ways (detailed in the text and Fig. 11–3). As a result, an increasingly heterogeneous telomere length profile is encountered in somatic cells at later stages of development.

understanding of the factors that cause telomere attrition is important when considering ways of manipulating the replicative potential of cells *in vitro* and *in vivo*. Second, different factors may be at work to elongate or shorten telomeres in different cell types. A basic appreciation of telomere attrition and elongation mechanisms may help to clarify fundamental differences among cells. Although much has been learned about telomeres over the past decade or two, primarily from studies of model organisms,[19–24] it is clear that we are only beginning to understand the full complexity of the molecules and molecular interactions involved in human telomere function. A more complete picture will need to take into account differences in gene and protein expression and molecular interactions during various stages of the cell cycle as well as differences in human (stem) cell types.

TELOMERE SHORTENING

Telomeric DNA is lost in human cells through several mechanisms related to DNA replication, remodeling, and repair (Fig. 11–3). Some of these processes occur at every chromosome end in every cell cycle, whereas others may occur infrequently (e.g., as a result of DNA damage or replicative errors). The sporadic nature of telomere loss resulting from DNA replication errors, aberrant recombination events, and chemical lesions complicates the study of such events and, as a result, is often ignored.

Loss of Telomere Repeats with Replication

Based on studies in yeast,[25] it is believed that telomeres are replicated from internal replication origins. According to this model, replication forks are expected to move toward the ends of chromosomes as shown in Fig. 11–3. The discontinuous nature of DNA replication will result in the 5' template strand being replicated by leading strand synthesis and the 3' template strand being replicated by discontinuous, lagging-strand DNA synthesis. The latter involves deposition of RNA primers along the 3' template strand. The position of the last RNA primer to be deposited on the 3' template strand is unlikely to be precisely controlled. This position will dictate the length of the newly formed 5' strand relative to the 3′ template strand. The RNA primer will also be removed, resulting in a short gap. Together, the inevitable loss of nucleotides resulting from lagging-strand DNA synthesis of linear chromosomes (shown by the boxes in Fig. 11–3A) was recognized as the "end replication problem" in the early 1970s.[26,27]

Processing of the blunt ends produced by leading-strand DNA synthesis is required to create a single-strand 3′ overhang (and to allow T-loop formation; see Fig. 11–1). Such exonuclease processing must be tightly controlled but will result in a variable degree of telomere shortening[28–30] (shown by the boxes in Fig. 11–3B). It has been suggested that processing of the 3′ ends of chromosomes varies among cell types[31] and that such differences may be important to prevent replicative senescence.[11]

The notion that fundamentally different steps are involved in the processing of 3' and 5' template ends following replication is compatible with observations showing the preferential involvement of "leading" versus "lagging" telomeres in fusion events triggered by the dislocation of specific telomere-binding proteins.[32]

Oxidative Damage and Recombination

That telomeres shorten as a result of oxidative damage has only recently been realized. It has been shown that telomeric

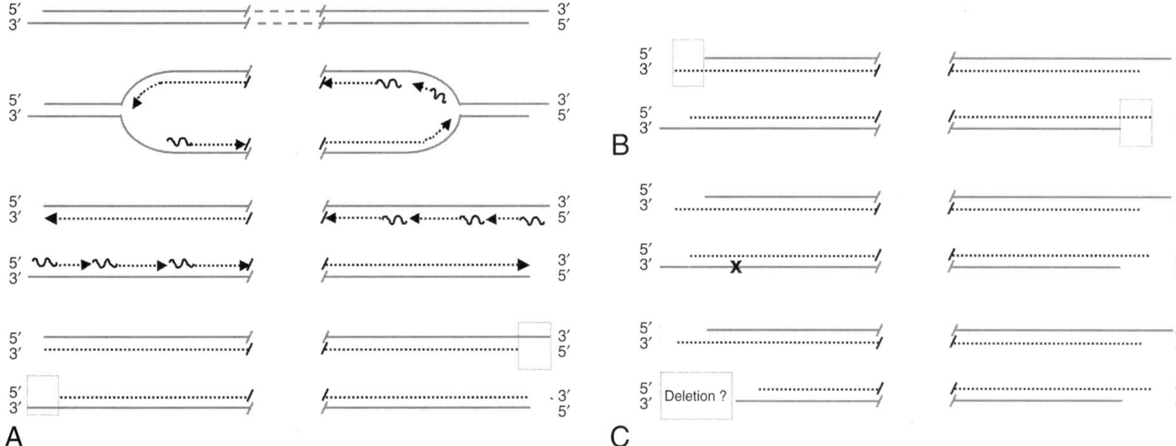

Figure 11–3. *Loss of telomere repeats Is linked to replication.* It is believed that telomeres are replicated from internal replication origins. According to this model, replication forks are expected to move toward the end of chromosomes. The discontinuous nature of DNA replication results in the 5′ template strand being replicated by leading strand synthesis and the 3′ template strand being replicated by discontinuous, lagging-strand DNA synthesis. The latter involves deposition of multiple short RNA primers (indicated by squiggles) along the 3′ template strand to initiate synthesis of short DNA "Okazaki" fragments eventually ligated to form a continuous strand. The position of the last RNA primer to be deposited on the 3′ template strand dictates the length of the newly formed 5′ strand. (A) The inevitable loss of nucleotides (box) resulting from lagging-strand DNA synthesis of linear chromosomes was recognized as the "end replication problem" in the early1970s.[26,27] Processing of the 5′ end of the blunt ends produced by leading-strand DNA synthesis by a 5′ to 3′ exonuclease is required to create a single-strand 3′ overhang (and to subsequently allow T-loop formation; see Fig. 11–1). (B) Such exonuclease processing will also result in telomere shortening[28] (box). (C) Finally, stalling of the lagging-strand replication fork (a lesion indicated by an X) may result in the loss of repeats because the newly formed 3′ strand (templated on the 5′ strand) will not be available for (bypass) repair reactions once the replication fork has reached the chromosome terminus and leading- and lagging-strand synthesis are no longer physically linked.

DNA, with its G-rich repeats, is 5- to 10-fold more vulnerable to oxidative damage than nontelomeric, genomic DNA.[33,34] Repair of oxidative damage to nucleotides is typically achieved using nucleotide excision repair pathways, which may involve a DNA polymerase template switch.[35] This essential mechanism may encounter problems with lesions near chromosome ends as the 3' ends of chromosomes may interfere with correct recombination reactions. Alternatively, oxidative lesions such as single-strand breaks may result in loss of telomeric DNA.[36] The contribution of oxidative lesions to telomere shortening could vary over time (e.g., as a function of the amount of oxygen radicals produced or the redox state of the cells). The role of telomeric DNA damage in telomere shortening and the mechanisms preventing such damage remain to be precisely defined.

Despite the repetitive nature of telomeric DNA in various species, telomeres appear to be remarkable resistant to recombination events. Nevertheless, intrachromatid recombination has been described as a mechanism to control the size of telomeres in yeast.[37] Similar mechanisms may trim telomeres in human cells. Finally, it is known that single-stranded telomeric DNA can adopt intramolecular G-quadruplex structures *in vitro.*[38,39] If similar structures exist *in vivo,* special processing (e.g., by specialized helicases) will be required to process such secondary structures at chromosome ends and at sites of internal telomere repeats. An example of a helicase-like protein required to unwind secondary structures of G-rich DNA postulated to occur sporadically during lagging-strand synthesis is the DOG-1 protein, which was recently described in *C. elegans.*[40] Recent studies have shown that the RTEL protein in the mouse, which is similar to the DOG-1 protein in *C. elegans*, is the major regulator of telomere length in the mouse.[40a]

TELOMERE ELONGATION

To avoid activation of DNA damage pathways triggered by critically short telomeres, cells must counter the loss of telomere repeats from various causes (described previously) and synthesize telomeric DNA *de novo* using telomerase or by copying repeats from existing telomeric DNA using recombination pathways (Fig. 11–4). Most normal and malignant cells maintain telomeres using telomerase, whereas few tumor cells use recombination pathways (reviewed by Neumann and Reddel[41]).

Telomerase

Telomerase is a ribonucleoprotein containing the reverse transcriptase telomerase protein (hTERT) and the telomerase RNA template (hTERC) as essential components.[42] In addition, several proteins have been described that are important for telomerase assembly, nuclear localization, and stability (reviewed by Collins and Mitchel[43]). Telomerase is capable of adding telomere repeats (templated by the telomerase RNA component) onto the 3′ single-strand end of telomeres. Telomerase levels are typically high in immortal cells that maintain a constant telomere length, such as the stem cells of the germ line in the testis and embryonic stem cells. In contrast, the overall length of telomeres decreases in hematopoietic stem cells and most other somatic cells with proliferation and with age.

Transcriptional Regulation and Alternative Splicing of TERT RNA. Telomerase transcription and telomerase protein expression is regulated at the level of transcription and alternative splicing in ways only partially understood. The level of full-length hTERT transcripts appears to be limiting in some cell types as is exemplified by the "immortalization" of primary human fibroblasts by overexpression of full-length hTERT.[44,45] Transcription of the *hTERT* gene is up-regulated by Myc[46,47] and by estrogens.[48] More information is also becoming available on the factors that suppress telomerase transcription.[49] In general, the complex control of *TERT* gene expression is increasingly recognized.[50] The levels of functional TERT protein and telomerase activity are also regulated by expression of inactive or dominant-negative forms of the hTERT protein, resulting from alternative splicing of hTERT transcripts.[51–55] Apart from basic transcription levels and alternative splicing of primary hTERT transcripts, the levels of functional telomerase complexes are controlled not only by levels of telomerase RNA but also by molecules required to assemble functional telomerase ribonucleoprotein complexes, subcellular localization of such complexes, and access to the 3' single strand of the telomeric DNA.

Expression of Telomerase RNA and Assembly of Telomerase Complexes. Recent observations with cells from patients with the rare genetic disorder DKC support the idea that levels of telomerase RNA, like levels of full-length hTERT transcripts, limit the amount of functional telomerase in human stem cells. It was found that patients with the autosomal dominant form of DKC have one normal and one mutated copy of the telomerase RNA template gene *hTERC.*[56] Not surprisingly, the telomerase RNA haploinsufficient lymphocytes from such patients show modestly reduced

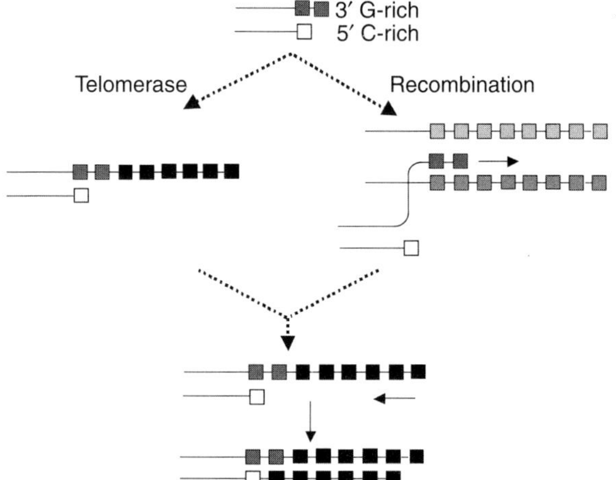

Figure 11–4. *Two ways to elongate telomeres.* Critically short telomeres need to be elongated to avoid being recognized as a double-strand break and triggering a DNA damage response. The most common mechanism is elongation by the reverse transcriptase telomerase. Telomerase will extend the 3′ ends of chromosomes using an RNA template encoding TTAGGG repeats and a reverse transcriptase. In the absence of telomerase, short telomeres can be elongated by invading, neighboring longer repeats if the processes that normally prevent recombination between telomeric repeats are being compromised.

levels of telomerase activity. Yet, patients with autosomal dominant DKC typically suffer from progressive aplastic anemia, immune deficiencies, or cancer and rarely live past the age of 50.[43,56–58] Subsequent affected generations have a more severe phenotype because of the inheritance of shortened telomeres from one parent, a phenomenon known as "anticipation."[59] These findings contrast with those in the mouse, where *mTERC* haploinsufficiency has no reported phenotype, and complete lack of telomerase activity and progressive telomere shortening is tolerated for up to six generations.[60] Nevertheless, a recent study suggests that even in the mouse, telomerase RNA may be limiting *in vivo*.[61] Levels of telomerase RNA and functional telomerase are more severely reduced in patients with the X-linked form of DKC involving the *dyskerin* gene. The DKC1 protein binds to the box H/ACA small nucleolar RNAs and the RNA component of telomerase. Surprisingly, mice with defects in *dyskerin* recapitulate the clinical features of DKC in the first and second generations even before reductions in telomere length are observed.[62] These results suggest that both impaired ribosome function and telomere shortening are capable of producing DKC symptoms and that, in the mouse, the ribosome dysfunction is the primary defect. The phenotypic differences between mice and man resulting from haploinsufficiency or complete loss of telomerase RNA and the *dyskerin* gene have highlighted the caution that should be exercised in directly extrapolating findings regarding telomere biology in mice to humans. One interpretation of these differences is that telomere shortening evolved to act as a tumor suppressor mechanism in long-lived species such as humans but did not assume this function in rodents.[24] This idea is supported by the relative ease by which cell lines can be produced from primary rodent tissues and the difficulty of obtaining human cell lines from normal and even malignant tissues.[63]

Cellular Localization and Nuclear Import of Telomerase. Recent data suggest that the assembly of telomerase occurs in the nucleolus.[64,65] However, it has been shown that human telomerase has a regulated intranuclear localization dependent on cell cycle stage, transformation, and DNA damage.[66] Little is known about the (posttranslational?) factors that regulate such trafficking of functional telomerase in and out of the nucleus. Given the low levels of functional telomerase in telomerase-competent cells, it can easily be imagined that such processes can affect telomere length regulation.

Telomerase Access to Telomeres and the Role of Telomere-Binding Proteins. Important mechanisms that regulate telomerase action and telomere length are related to the interaction of telomerase with its substrate, the 3' single-strand overhang typically found at chromosome ends. As mentioned, the 3' single strand is typically folded back into a T-loop. It is assumed that the closed T-loop structure is a poor substrate for telomerase. Indeed, the "window of opportunity" for telomerase appears to be during DNA replication when the T-loop is opened by the replication machinery. This notion is in agreement with findings in model organisms showing that telomerase is physically linked with the chromosome replication machinery.[67] The hPOT1 protein that interacts with the single-strand 3' end is a prime candidate to mediate interactions between telomeric DNA and telomerase.[7] Interestingly, different splice forms (with different affinities for telomeric DNA) of hPOT1 have been described, indicating another possible layer of telomere length regulation.[68] The hEST1A and hEST1B molecules are also capable of interacting with single-strand telomeric DNA as well as telomerase and could compete with POT1 for binding to single-strand telomeric DNA, providing yet another entry point for telomere length regulation.[69,70]

In general, many mysteries related to the role of telomerase in telomere length regulation and the immortalization and replicative senescence of cells remain. For example, the average telomere length in cells from outbred mice is typically short and becomes longer upon breeding in captivity over multiple generations.[71] In cells from inbred laboratory mice, the level of the telomerase reverse transcriptase and the level of telomerase RNA are critical factors that determine the overall telomere length.[61,72] In the absence of telomerase, the relatively long, average telomere length in rodent cells may facilitate rescue of short telomeres by recombination pathways[73] (as shown in Fig. 11–4). Furthermore, long telomeres may mask the presence of functionally important short telomeres.[74] The latter could accumulate with age even in rodents.[75]

Recombination

The role of so-called alternative lengthening of telomere (ALT) pathways in the elongation, maintenance, or both of telomeres in normal human cells, including hematopoietic cells, is not clear.[41] Recent data support the model shown in Fig. 11–4, in which a single-strand telomeric DNA from a critically short telomere invades a longer neighboring telomere and is subsequently elongated by conventional DNA polymerases.[76] This model of break-induced replication[77] requires that cells are recombination competent and that free ends are not captured by molecules that must typically prevent recombination at chromosome ends. One hallmark of ALT cells is that telomeres are heterogeneous in length, ranging from very short to very long and including telomeres several times the size encountered in cells that express telomerase. Most likely, ALT pathways are suppressed or inefficient in elongating telomeres in normal cells that express telomerase. However, recombination could play a role in the maintenance of short telomeres in primary human fibroblasts prior to replicative senescence.[78,79] The overall loss of telomere repeats in most human somatic cells with replication and with age indicates that the lengthening of telomeres through telomerase, ALT, or both typically cannot keep up with the rate of telomere attrition. Progressive telomere shortening limits the proliferation of most somatic stem cells and lymphocytes and may have evolved to suppress tumor growth.[80,81]

Loss of Telomeres in Cells of the Hematopoietic System

Since the important original observation that the length of telomeric restriction fragments in adult blood leukocytes is significantly shorter than in germ line material (sperm) from the same donor,[82] the decline of somatic telomeres has been documented in three ways: The original observation was confirmed,[83,84] it was shown that telomeres in various tissues were shorter in older donors,[85,86] and telomere shortening was documented during *in vitro* culture of human cells.[85,87] In the decade that followed these initial reports, many papers have appeared that greatly refined our understanding of telomere shortening in human nucleated blood cells (reviewed by Ohyashiki *et al.*[88]).

TELOMERE LENGTH DYNAMICS IN HUMAN NUCLEATED BLOOD CELLS

Studies in this general area have been facilitated by the development of quantitative fluorescence *in situ* hybridization (FISH) techniques to measure telomere length in suspension cells using flow cytometry. [89,90] With this technique, it was shown that the age-related decline in telomere length in lymphocytes is more pronounced than in granulocytes and that rapid telomere shortening early in life is followed by a gradual decline thereafter.[17,91]

A striking observation is that the average telomere length in comparable cells (such as blood neutrophilic granulocytes) in humans at any given age is heterogeneous (Fig. 11–5). This variation appears to be primarily genetic.[16] For example, monozygous twins over 70 years of age were shown to have similar telomere length in both granulocytes and lymphocytes; cells from dizygotic twins showed differences that were larger than in the monozygous twins (particularly in lymphocytes) but were smaller than in unrelated individuals.[17] Using further refinements in the flow FISH method,[90] it was recently shown[81] that the rapid decline in telomere length early in life is followed by a slow decline until 50–60 years, after which the decline again accelerates (Fig. 11–5). The decline in both granulocytes and lymphocytes is nonlinear, and both curves show a highly significant fit with a cubic function.

TELOMERE SHORTENING: WHAT DOES IT MEAN?

The pronounced decline in telomere length observed early in life presumably reflects a high turnover of (stem) cells, increasing cell numbers and body mass. The explanation for the accelerated decline late in life is not clear. It is possible that this also reflects an overall increase in proliferative activity, perhaps because the proportion of cells that exit the proliferative compartment because of accumulated genetic damage, including telomere shortening, increases in a nonlinear fashion. Alternatively, the accelerated decline could reflect the selective expansion of abnormal cells that can grow or survive with short telomeres because they express higher levels of telomerase or because apoptotic pathways are suppressed (e.g., by overexpression of Bcl-2). The increased skewing of X-chromosome inactivation patterns in females over 60,[92,93] and the increasingly oligoclonal immune response in the elderly[94] support this idea. It is also possible that the age-related decline in mitochondrial function[95,96] increases production of oxygen radicals and increased oxidative damage to telomeres. Finally, other factors or the combination of the factors proposed previously could be important.

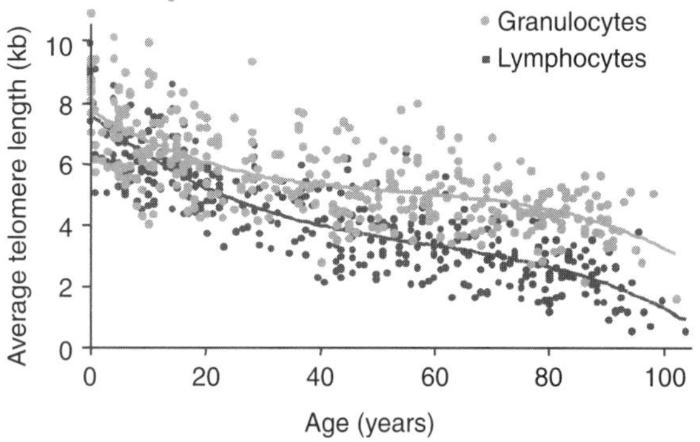

Figure 11–5. *Decline in telomere length with age is more pronounced in lymphocytes than in granulocytes.* Shown is the calculated telomere length for both cell types extracted from several hundred measurements over the entire age range.[107] Note the considerable variation in telomere length values among individuals at any age. Both granulocytes and lymphocytes show a highly significant decline, best described by a cubic function.

A recent paper described an association between telomere length in blood and mortality in 143 normal, unrelated individuals 60 years or older.[97] Those with shorter telomeres in blood DNA had poorer survival, attributable partly to a three-fold higher mortality rate from heart disease and an eight-fold higher mortality rate from infectious disease. These results lend support to the hypothesis that telomere shortening in human beings contributes to mortality in many age-related diseases and that measurements of telomere length in blood cells provides a surrogate marker for the telomere length in the stem cells of various tissues. Alternatively, these results suggest that tissue-specific stem cell subsets are replenished from circulating precursors.

TELOMERES AND THE REPLICATIVE POTENTIAL OF HEMATOPOIETIC STEM CELLS

Current data support the idea that the total production of blood cells from a single hematopoietic stem cell is primarily determined by differentiation of stem and progenitor cells and not by replicative senescence. Furthermore, the occasional loss of stem cells or progenitor cells because of telomere shortening is not expected to affect overall hematopoiesis (or overall telomere length in granulocytes) in the presence of a large excess of hematopoietic stem cells. That normal hematopoietic stem cells and tissues have extensive replicative potential has been confirmed by their successful use over almost four decades in both allogeneic and autologous stem cell transplantation. Nevertheless, telomeres shorten in hematopoietic stem cells, as indicated by the age-related loss of telomeres in granulocytes (Fig. 11–5), the (modest) loss of telomeres following allogeneic transplantation,[88,98] and the aplastic anemia that follows partial telomerase deficiency.[43] Telomere length data can be informative in the study of marrow failure (Table 11–1). Acute toxic insults to the stem cell compartment (e.g., as a result of viral infection of stem cells) would not be expected to alter the telomere length in circulating nucleated cells. However, if the damage to the stem cell compartment is prolonged and sustained, residual stem cells will be triggered to undergo a variable number of

TABLE 11–1
Telomere Length Profile of Marrow Failure Syndromes

	Telomere Length
Acute toxicity (e.g., viral infection)	Normal
Sustained, increased turnover (e.g., autoimmune destruction, DNA repair deficiencies)	Short to very short
Inherited (e.g., telomerase deficiencies)	Very short

additional cell divisions. The extent of such compensatory proliferation in the stem cell compartment is expected to result in short or very short telomeres in circulating nucleated cells. Interestingly, the telomere length in granulocytes from patients with aplastic anemia who recovered after immunotherapy did not differ markedly from controls, whereas immunotherapy nonresponders showed significant telomere shortening.[99] Finally, the telomere length in cells from patients with DKC is usually very short. Such patients are expected to inherit one (haploid) set of chromosomes with short telomeres (Fig. 11–2). The telomerase deficiency is expected to further limit the replicative potential in DKC stem cells, which, in turn, will place a larger demand on the proliferation of residual stem cell clones. The net result appears to be true cellular exhaustion, particularly in cells of the hematopoietic system, before the age of 50.

The number of mature "end" cells, such as granulocytes produced by individual stem cells,[100] is most likely highly variable and primarily determined by the processes that regulate self-renewal versus differentiation at the level of individual stem cells. Even a limited number of additional self-renewal divisions in a stem cell will greatly increase the overall output of cells. As a result, individual stem cells can produce staggering numbers of cells. This is illustrated by disorders characterized by clonal proliferation such as paroxysmal nocturnal hemoglobinuria and chronic myeloid leukemia (CML). However, even in CML, clonally expanded Philadelphia-positive stem cells eventually appear to encounter critical telomere shortening.[101] Unfortunately, with a large number of cells to select from, the genetic instability triggered by the loss of functional telomeres appears to favor the selection of subclones with additional genetic abnormalities and greater malignant potential.

Not all cells in the hematopoietic system are programmed to encounter the telomere checkpoint. Some memory B-cells appear to be a particularly interesting exception since the telomere length in B-cells is increasingly heterogenous with age. Apparently, some B-cells express sufficient telomerase (and/or other factors) to effectively elongate telomeres. Perhaps the many cell divisions required for effective selection and "affinity maturation" of antibody responses has favored the selection of mechanisms that result in telomere maintenance and elongation. It is tempting to speculate that B-cells are, as a result, at a greater risk of tumor development, possibly explaining the much higher incidence of B- versus T-cell lymphoma in the human population.

Telomeres, Stem Cells, and Aging

The field of stem cell biology is in its infancy. Despite several decades of intense research, the answers to many fundamental questions about stem cells remain elusive. Examples of pertinent questions are as follows: How many stem cells are there for various tissues? How often do and can these cells divide? Are stem cells lost with age, and how important is the loss of stem cells in the biology of aging? How do stem cells generate diverse progenitors (divide asymmetrically)? What intrinsic and extrinsic factors control self-renewal and differentiation?[102] Do stem cells have immortal DNA strands?[103] Do stem cells avoid accumulation of damage to genomic and mitochondrial DNA? More specific questions are: Does the age-related telomere shortening in leukocytes reflect a gradual decline in all stem cells or an increasing dominance of stem cells with short telomeres? If stem cells with long telomeres exist in the marrow, why do they not appear to contribute to hematopoiesis? Could the potential of such cells be harnessed in a therapeutically meaningful way?

The rapidly expanding knowledge in all areas of science and the increasing specialization and "industrialization" of biomedical sciences (exemplified by the large scale genome and proteome projects) may have discouraged basic questions about stem cells. Public perception about progress in science as well as competition for limited funds are strong incentives to focus on progress and trivialize ignorance. Yet, as always, studies that focus on basic questions offer the greatest potential for advancement.

Summary

Based on observations from several areas, telomeres have emerged as important regulatory elements that control the number of times normal human somatic cells can divide. Activation of DNA damage responses and cell cycle checkpoints that result from replicative loss of telomeric DNA and from oxidative insults to telomeric DNA may increase the sensitivity of cells to genomic DNA damage (Fig. 11–6). The DNA damage response triggered by critically short telomeres can be resolved by telomere elongation pathways that involve telomerase or recombination. However, in most somatic cells, including hematopoietic stem cells, the capacity of such telomere repair pathways appears limited, and telomere shortening effectively limits the proliferative potential of such cells. Telomere shortening most likely evolved as a tumor suppressor mechanism in long-lived species. The function of telomeres in stem cells may help explain poorly understood aspects of stem cell biology, including stem cell "exhaustion" in aplastic anemia and other proliferative disorders. Cells may bypass the DNA damage signals derived from critically short telomeres by expressing high levels of telomerase or by inactivating downstream signaling events (e.g., by loss of p53 function). Some cells, including

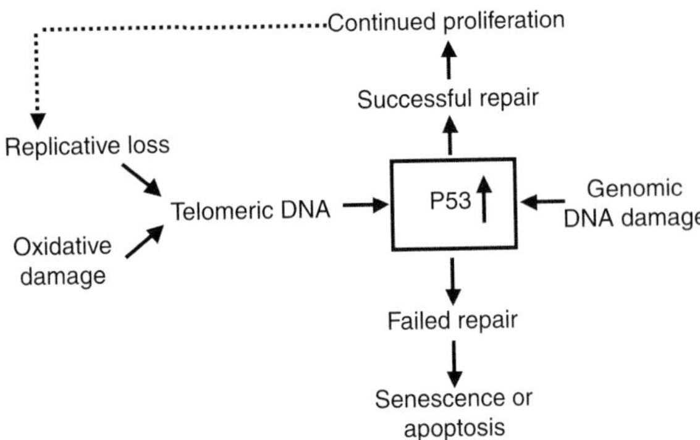

Figure 11–6. *Increased levels of p53 are triggered by progressive telomere shortening and accumulated damage to genomic DNA.* Initially, p53 levels are transiently up-regulated; this is followed by cell cycle arrest and DNA repair. Progressive telomere shortening and accumulated damage to genomic DNA increase levels of p53. Eventually, after a variable number of cell divisions, a threshold in DNA damage signals involving p53 is reached, triggering apoptosis or senescence. Increasing evidence suggests that p53[108] and DNA repair[109] are important in organismal aging. Mice with "hyperactive" p53 are cancer resistant, have shortened longevity, and have aging phenotypes consistent with a model in which aging is driven partly by gradual depletion of stem cell functional capacity.[110] Studies of recombinant inbred mice also support a connection among stem cells, DNA repair, and longevity.[111]

B-cell subsets, may avoid telomere shortening, and high levels of telomerase could make such B-cells more vulnerable to tumor development. Loss of p53 function also inactivates DNA damage responses triggered by critically short telomeres. This is expected to be a rare event, as both copies of the normal p53 allele in a cell must typically be lost or mutated to continue proliferation in the presence of many short and dysfunctional telomeres.[5] Loss of p53 function results in chromosome fusions and breakage that drives genetic instability and facilitates malignant progression. Genetic instability driven by loss of telomere function appears to be involved in most human cancers. A striking example is CML, in which the onset of blast crisis is inversely correlated with the length of telomeres in the chronic phase cells.[101]

ACKNOWLEDGMENTS

Work in my laboratory is supported by grants from the National Institutes of Health (AI29524), the Canadian Institutes of Health Research (MOP38075), and the National Cancer Institute of Canada (with support from the Terry Fox Run). Part of this work was previously published[81] and is used with permission. I thank Matthew Greenwood and Gerry Krystal for critical reading of the manuscript.

REFERENCES

1. Moyzis, R.K., Buckingham, J.M., Cram, L.S., Dani, M., Deaven, L.L., Jones, M.D., Meyne, J., Ratliff, R.L., and Wu, J.R. (1988). A highly conserved repetitive DNA sequence, $(TTAGGG)_n$, present at the telomeres of human chromosomes. *Proc. Natl. Acad. Sci. U. S. A* **85,** 6622–6626.
2. De Lange, T. (2002). Protection of mammalian telomeres. *Oncogene* **21,** 532–540.
3. Blackburn, E.H. (2001). Switching and signaling at the telomere. *Cell* **106,** 661–673.
4. Lansdorp, P.M., Verwoerd, N.P., van de Rijke, F.M., Dragowska, V., Little, M.T., Dirks, R.W., Raap, A.K., and Tanke, H.J. (1996). Heterogeneity in telomere length of human chromosomes. *Hum. Mol. Genet.* **5,** 685–691.
5. Martens, U.M., Zijlmans, J.M., Poon, S.S.S., Dragowska, W., Yui, J., Chavez, E.A., Ward, R.K., and Lansdorp, P.M. (1998). Short telomeres on human chromosome 17p. *Nat. Genet.* **18,** 76–80.
6. Smogorzewska, A., van Steensel, B., Bianchi, A., Oelmann, S., Schaefer, M.R., Schnapp, G., and de Lange, T. (2000). Control of human telomere length by TRF1 and TRF2. *Mol. Cell. Biol.* **20,** 1659–1668.
7. Baumann, P., and Cech, T.R. (2001). Pot1, the putative telomere end-binding protein in fission yeast and humans. *Science* **292,** 1171–1175.
8. Griffith, J.D., Comeau, L., Rosenfield, S., Stansel, R.M., Bianchi, A., Moss, H., and de Lange, T. (1999). Mammalian telomeres end in a large duplex loop. *Cell* **97,** 503–514.
9. Karlseder, J., Broccoli, D., Dai, Y., Hardy, S., and de Lange, T. (1999). p53- and ATM-dependent apoptosis induced by telomeres lacking TRF2. *Science* **283,** 1321–1325.
10. Zhu, X.D., Kuster, B., Mann, M., Petrini, J.H., and Lange, T. (2000). Cell cycle-regulated association of RAD50/ MRE11/NBS1 with TRF2 and human telomeres. *Nat. Genet.* **25,** 347–352.
11. Stewart, S.A., Ben Porath, I., Carey, V.J., O'Connor, B.F., Hahn, W.C., and Weinberg, R.A. (2003). Erosion of the telomeric single-strand overhang at replicative senescence. *Nat. Genet.* **33,** 492–496.
12. Aladjem, M.I., Spike, B.T., Rodewald, L.W., Hope, T.J., Klemm, M., Jaenisch, R., and Wahl, G.M. (1998). ES cells do not activate p53-dependent stress responses and undergo p53- independent apoptosis in response to DNA damage. *Curr. Biol.* **8,** 145–155.
13. Lanza, R.P., Cibelli, J.B., Blackwell, C., Cristofalo, V.J., Francis, M.K., Baerlocher, G.M., Mak, J., Schertzer, M., Chavez, E.A., Sawyer, N., Lansdorp, P.M., and West, M.D. (2000). Extension of cell life span and telomere length in animals cloned from senescent somatic cells. *Science* **288,** 665–669.
14. Giles, J., and Knight, J. (2003). Dolly's death leaves researchers woolly on clone ageing issue. *Nature* **421,** 776.
15. Lansdorp, P.M. (Unpublished observations).
16. Slagboom, P.E., Droog, S., and Boomsma, D.I. (1994). Genetic determination of telomere size in humans: a twin study of three age groups. *Am. J. Hum. Genet.* **55,** 876–882.
17. Rufer, N., Brummendorf, T.H., Kolvraa, S., Bischoff, C., Christensen, K., Wadsworth, L., Schultzer, M., and Lansdorp, P.M. (1999). Telomere fluorescence measurements in granulocytes and T-lymphocyte subsets point to a high turnover of hematopoietic stem cells and memory T-cells in early childhood. *J. Exp. Med.* **190,** 157–167.
18. Graakjaer, J., Bischoff, C., Korsholm, L., Holstebroe, S., Vach, W., Bohr, V.A., Christensen, K., and Kolvraa, S. (2003). The pattern of chromosome-specific variations in telomere length in humans is determined by inherited, telomere-near factors and is maintained throughout life. *Mech. Ageing Dev.* **124,** 629–640.
19. Zakian, V.A. (1996). Structure, function, and replication of *Saccharomyces cerevisiae* telomeres. *Annu. Rev. Genet.* **30,** 141–172.

20. Greider, C.W. (1996). Telomere length regulation. *Annu. Rev. Biochem.* **65,** 337–365.
21. McEachern, M.J., Krauskopf, A., and Blackburn, E.H. (2000). Telomeres and their control. *Annu. Rev. Genet.* **34,** 331–358.
22. Price, C.M. (1999). Telomeres and telomerase: broad effects on cell growth. *Curr. Opin. Genet. Dev.* **9,** 218–224.
23. McKnight, T.D., Riha, K., and Shippen, D.E. (2002). Telomeres, telomerase, and stability of the plant genome. *Plant Mol. Biol.* **48,** 331–337.
24. Chang, S., Khoo, C., and DePinho, R.A. (2001). Modeling chromosomal instability and epithelial carcinogenesis in the telomerase-deficient mouse. *Semin. Cancer Biol.* **11,** 227–239.
25. Wellinger, R.J., Wolf, A.J., and Zakian, V.A. (1993). Origin activation and formation of single-strand TG1-3 tails occur sequentially in late S phase on a yeast linear plasmid. *Mol. Cell Biol.* **13,** 4057–4065.
26. Watson, J.D. (1972). Origin of concatameric T4 DNA. *Nat. New Biol.* **239,** 197–201.
27. Olovnikov, A.M. (1973). A theory of marginotomy: the incomplete copying of template margin in enzymic synthesis of polynucleotides and biological significance of the phenomenon. *J. Theor. Biol.* **41,** 181–190.
28. Lingner, J., Cooper, J.P., and Cech, T.R. (1995). Telomerase and DNA end replication: no longer a lagging strand problem? *Science* **269,** 1533–1534.
29. Wellinger, R.J., Ethier, K., Labrecque, P., and Zakian, V.A. (1996). Evidence for a new step in telomere maintenance. *Cell* **85,** 423–433.
30. Makarov, V.L., Hirose, Y., and Langmore, J.P. (1997). Long G tails at both ends of human chromosomes suggest a C-strand degradation mechanism for telomere shortening. *Cell* **88,** 657–666.
31. Cimino-Reale, G., Pascale, E., Battiloro, E., Starace, G., Verna, R., and D'Ambrosio, E. (2001). The length of telomeric G-rich strand 3'-overhang measured by oligonucleotide ligation assay. *Nucleic Acids Res.* **29,** E35.
32. Bailey, S.M., Cornforth, M.N., Kurimasa, A., Chen, D.J., and Goodwin, E.H. (2001). Strand-specific postreplicative processing of mammalian telomeres. *Science* **293,** 2462–2465.
33. Henle, E.S., Han, Z., Tang, N., Rai, P., Luo, Y., and Linn, S. (1999). Sequence-specific DNA cleavage by Fe^{2+}-mediated Fenton reactions has possible biological implications. *J. Biol. Chem.* **274,** 962–971.
34. Oikawa, S., and Kawanishi, S. (1999). Site-specific DNA damage at GGG sequence by oxidative stress may accelerate telomere shortening. *FEBS Lett.* **453,** 365–368.
35. Hoeijmakers, J.H.J. (2001). Genome maintenance mechanisms for preventing cancer. *Nature* **411,** 366–374.
36. Proctor, C.J., and Kirkwood, T.B. (2002). Modeling telomere shortening and the role of oxidative stress. *Mech. Ageing Dev.* **123,** 351–363.
37. Bucholc, M., Park, Y., and Lustig, A.J. (2001). Intrachromatid excision of telomeric DNA as a mechanism for telomere size control in *Saccharomyces cerevisiae. Mol. Cell Biol.* **21,** 6559–6573.
38. Sen, D., and Gilbert, W. (1988). Formation of parallel four-stranded complexes by guanine-rich motifs in DNA and its implications for meiosis. *Nature* **334,** 364–366.
39. Haider, S.M., Parkinson, G.N., and Neidle, S. (2003). Structure of a G-quadruplex-ligand complex. *J. Mol. Biol.* **326,** 117–125.
40. Cheung, I., Schertzer, M., Rose, A., and Lansdorp, P.M. (2002). Disruption of *dog-1* in *Caenorhabditis elegans* triggers deletions upstream of guanine-rich DNA (Letter). *Nat. Genet.* **31,** 405–409.
40a. Ding, H., Schertzer, M., Wu, X., Gertsensein, M., Selig, S., Kammori, M., Pourvali, R., Poon, S., Vulto, I., Chavez, E., Tam, P.P.L., Nagy, A., and Lansdorp, P.M. (2004). Regulation of murine telomere length by Rtel: An essential gene encoding a helicase-like protein. *Cell Volume* **117.**
41. Neumann, A.A., and Reddel, R.R. (2002). Telomere maintenance and cancer: look, no telomerase. *Nat. Rev. Cancer* **2,** 879–884.
42. Weinrich, S.L., Pruzan, R., Ma, L., Ouellette, M., Tesmet, V.M., and Hull, S.E. (1997). Reconstitution of human telomerase with the template RNA component hTR and the catalytic protein subunit hTRT. *Nat. Genet.* **17,** 498–502.
43. Collins, K., and Mitchell, J.R. (2002). Telomerase in the human organism. *Oncogene* **21,** 564–579.
44. Vaziri, H., and Benchimol, S. (1998). Reconstitution of telomerase activity in normal human cells leads to elongation of telomeres and extended replicative life span. *Curr. Biol.* **8,** 279–282.
45. Bodnar, A.G., Ouellette, M., Frolkis, M., Holt, S.E., Chiu, C.P., Morin, G.B., Harley, C.B., Shay, J.W., Lichtsteiner, S., and Wright, W.E. (1998). Extension of life span by introduction of telomerase into normal human cells. *Science* **279,** 349–353.
46. Wang, J., Xie, L.Y., Allan, S., Beach, D., and Hannon, G.J. (1998). Myc activates telomerase. *Genes Dev.* **12,** 1769–1774.
47. Wu, K.J., Grandori, C., Amacker, M., Simon-Vermot, N., Polack, A., Lingner, J., and Dalla-Favera, R. (1999). Direct activation of TERT transcription by c-MYC. *Nat. Genet.* **21,** 220–224.
48. Misiti, S., Nanni, S., Fontemaggi, G., Cong, Y.S., Wen, J., Hirte, H.W., Piaggio, G., Sacchi, A., Pontecorvi, A., Bacchetti, S., and Farsetti, A. (2000). Induction of hTERT expression and telomerase activity by estrogens in human ovary epithelium cells. *Mol. Cell Biol.* **20,** 3764–3771.
49. Szutorisz, H., Lingner, J., Cuthbert, A.P., Trott, D.A., Newbold, R.F., and Nabholz, M. (2003). A chromosome 3-encoded repressor of the human telomerase reverse transcriptase *(hTERT)* gene controls the state of *hTERT* chromatin. *Cancer Res.* **63,** 689–695.
50. Aisner, D.L., Wright, W.E., and Shay, J.W. (2002). Telomerase regulation: not just flipping the switch. *Curr. Opin. Genet. Dev.* **12,** 80–85.
51. Kilian, A., Bowtell, D.D.L., Abud, H.E., Hime, G.R., Venter, D.J., Keese, P.K., Duncan, E.L., Reddel, R.R., and Jefferson, R.A. (1997). Isolation of a candidate human telomerase catalytic subunit gene, which reveals complex splicing patterns in different cell types. *Hum. Mol. Genet.* **6,** 2011–2019.
52. Wick, M., Zubov, D., and Hagen, G. (1999). Genomic organization and promoter characterization of the gene encoding the human telomerase reverse transcriptase *(hTERT). Gene* **232,** 97–106.
53. Cerezo, A., Kalthoff, H., Schuermann, M., Schafer, B., and Boukamp, P. (2002). Dual regulation of telomerase activity through c-Myc-dependent inhibition and alternative splicing of hTERT. *J. Cell Sci.* **115,** 1305–1312.
54. Colgin, L.M., Wilkinson, C., Englezou, A., Kilian, A., Robinson, M.O., and Reddel, R.R. (2000). The hTERT-α splice variant is a dominant negative inhibitor of telomerase activity. *Neoplasia* **2,** 426–432.
55. Yi, X., White, D.M., Aisner, D.L., Baur, J.A., Wright, W.E., and Shay, J.W. (2000). An alternate splicing variant of the human telomerase catalytic subunit inhibits telomerase activity. *Neoplasia* **2,** 433–440.
56. Vulliamy, T., Marrone, A., Goldman, F., Dearlove, A., Bessler, M., Mason, P.J., and Dokal, I. (2001). The RNA component of telomerase is mutated in autosomal dominant *dyskeratosis congenita. Nature* **413,** 432–435.

57. Mitchell, J.R., Wood, E., and Collins, K. (1999). A telomerase component is defective in the human disease *dyskeratosis congenita*. *Nature* **402,** 551–555.
58. Dokal, I. (2001). *Dyskeratosis congenita:* a disease of premature ageing. *Lancet* **358 (Suppl.),** S27.
59. Mason, P.J. (2003). Stem cells, telomerase, and *dyskeratosis congenita*. *Bioessays* **25,** 126–133.
60. Blasco, M.A., Lee, H.W., Hande, M.P., Samper, E., Lansdorp, P.M., DePinho, R.A., and Greider, C.W. (1997). Telomere shortening and tumor formation by mouse cells lacking telomerase RNA. *Cell* **91,** 25–34.
61. Hathcock, K.S., Hemann, M.T., Opperman, K.K., Strong, M.A., Greider, C.W., and Hodes, R.J. (2002). Haploinsufficiency of mTR results in defects in telomere elongation. *Proc. Natl. Acad. Sci. U. S. A.* **99,** 3591–3596.
62. Ruggero, D., Grisendi, S., Piazza, F., Rego, E., Mari, F., Rao, P.H., Cordon-Cardo, C., and Pandolfi, P.P. (2003). *Dyskeratosis congenita* and cancer in mice deficient in ribosomal RNA modification. *Science* **299,** 259–262.
63. Newbold, R.F. (2002). The significance of telomerase activation and cellular immortalization in human cancer. *Mutagenesis* **17,** 539–550.
64. Etheridge, K.T., Banik, S.S., Armbruster, B.N., Zhu, Y., Terns, R.M., Terns, M.P., and Counter, C.M. (2002). The nucleolar localization domain of the catalytic subunit of human telomerase. *J. Biol. Chem.* **277,** 24764–24770.
65. Teixeira, M.T., Forstemann, K., Gasser, S.M., and Lingner, J. (2002). Intracellular trafficking of yeast telomerase components. *EMBO Rep.* **3,** 652–659.
66. Wong, J.M., Kusdra, L., and Collins, K. (2002). Subnuclear shuttling of human telomerase induced by transformation and DNA damage. *Nat. Cell Biol.* **4,** 731–736.
67. Ray, S., Karamysheva, Z., Wang, L., Shippen, D.E., and Price, C.M. (2002). Interactions between telomerase and primase physically link the telomere and chromosome replication machinery. *Mol. Cell Biol.* **22,** 5859–5868.
68. Baumann, P., Podell, E., and Cech, T.R. (2002). Human Pot1 (protection of telomeres) protein: cytolocalization, gene structure, and alternative splicing. *Mol. Cell Biol.* **22,** 8079–8087.
69. Reichenbach, P., Hoss, M., Azzalin, C.M., Nabholz, M., Bucher, P., and Lingner, J. (2003). A human homolog of yeast est1 associates with telomerase and uncaps chromosome ends when overexpressed. *Curr. Biol.* **13,** 568–574.
70. Snow, B.E., Erdmann, N., Cruickshank, J., Goldman, H., Gill, R.M., Robinson, M.O., and Harrington, L. (2003). Functional conservation of the telomerase protein est1p in humans. *Curr. Biol.* **13,** 698–704.
71. Hemann, M.T., and Greider, C.W. (2000). Wild-derived inbred mouse strains have short telomeres. *Nucleic Acids Res.* **28,** 4474–4478.
72. Liu, Y., Snow, B.E., Hande, M.P., Yeung, D., Erdmann, N.J., Wakeham, A., Itie, A., Siderovski, D.P., Lansdorp, P.M., Robinson, M.O., and Harrington, L. (2000). The telomerase reverse transcriptase is limiting and necessary for telomerase function *in vivo*. *Curr. Biol.* **10,** 1459–1462.
73. Lansdorp, P.M. (1997). Lessons from mice without telomerase. *J. Cell Biol.* **139,** 309–312.
74. Hemann, M.T., Strong, M.A., Hao, L.Y., and Greider, C.W. (2001). The shortest telomere, not average telomere length, is critical for cell viability and chromosome stability. *Cell* **107,** 67–77.
75. Cherif, H., Tarry, J.L., Ozanne, S.E., and Hales, C.N. (2003). Ageing and telomeres: a study into organ- and gender-specific telomere shortening. *Nucleic Acids Res.* **31,** 1576–1583.
76. Henson, J.D., Neumann, A.A., Yeager, T.R., and Reddel, R.R. (2002). Alternative lengthening of telomeres in mammalian cells. *Oncogene* **21,** 598–610.
77. Kraus, E., Leung, W.Y., and Haber, J.E. (2001). Break-induced replication: a review and an example in budding yeast. *Proc. Natl. Acad. Sci. U. S. A.* **98,** 8255–8262.
78. Martens, U.M., Chavez, E.A., Poon, S.S.S., Schmoor, C., and Lansdorp, P.M. (2000). Accumulation of short telomeres in human fibroblasts prior to replicative senescence. *Exp. Cell Res.* **256,** 291–299.
79. Lansdorp, P.M. (2000). Repair of telomeric DNA prior to replicative senescence. *Mech. Ageing Dev.* **118,** 23–34.
80. Artandi, S.E., and DePinho, R.A. (2000). A critical role for telomeres in suppressing and facilitating carcinogenesis. *Curr. Opin. Genet. Dev.* **10,** 39–46.
81. Verfaillie, C.M., Pera, M.F., and Lansdorp, P.M. (2002). Stem cells: Hype and reality. *In* "Hematology 2002: American Society of Hematology Education Program," pp. 369–391. The American Society of Hematology, Washington, DC.
82. Cooke, H.J., and Smith, B.A. (1986). Variability at the telomeres of the human X–Y pseudoautosomal region. *Cold Spring Harb. Symp. Quant. Biol.* **51,** 213–219.
83. Allshire, R.C., Gosden, J.R., Cross, S.H., Cranston, G., Rout, D., Sugawara, N., Szostak, J.W., Fantes, P.A., and Hastie, N.D. (1988). Telomeric repeat from *T. thermophila* cross-hybridizes with human telomeres. *Nature* **332,** 656–659.
84. De Lange, T., Shiue, L., Myers, R., Cox, D.R., Naylor, S.L., Killery, A.M., and Varmus, H.E. (1990). Structure and variability of human chromosome ends. *Mol. Cell Biol.* **10,** 518–527.
85. Harley, C.B., Futcher, A.B., and Greider, C.W. (1990). Telomeres shorten during ageing of human fibroblasts. *Nature* **345,** 458–460.
86. Hastie, N.D., Dempster, M., Dunlop, M.G., Thompson, A.M., Green, D.K., and Allshire, R.C. (1990). Telomere reduction in human colorectal carcinoma and with ageing. *Nature* **346,** 866–868.
87. Counter, C.M., Avilion, A.A., LeFeuvre, C.E., Stewart, N.G., Greider, C.W., Harley, C.B., and Bacchetti, S. (1992). Telomere shortening associated with chromosome instability is arrested in immortal cells, which express telomerase activity. *EMBO J.* **11,** 1921–1929.
88. Ohyashiki, J.H., Sashida, G., Tauchi, T., and Ohyashiki, K. (2002). Telomeres and telomerase in hematologic neoplasia. *Oncogene* **21,** 680–687.
89. Rufer, N., Dragowska, W., Thornbury, G., Roosnek, E., and Lansdorp, P.M. (1998). Telomere length dynamics in human lymphocyte subpopulations measured by flow cytometry. *Nat. Biotechnol.* **16,** 743–747.
90. Baerlocher, G.M., and Lansdorp, P.M. (2003). Telomere length measurements in leukocyte subsets by automated multicolor flow-FISH. *Cytometry* **55A,** 1–6.
91. Frenck, R.W., Jr., Blackburn, E.H., and Shannon, K.M. (1998). The rate of telomere sequence loss in human leukocytes varies with age. *Proc. Natl. Acad. Sci. U. S. A.* **95,** 5607–5610.
92. Busque, L., Mio, R., Mattioli, J., Brais, E., Blais, N., Lalonde, Y., Maragh, M., and Gilliland, D.G. (1996). Nonrandom X-inactivation patterns in normal females: lyonization ratios vary with age. *Blood* **88,** 59–65.
93. Gale, R.E., Fielding, A.K., Harrison, C.N., and Linch, D.C. (1997). Acquired skewing of X-chromosome inactivation patterns in

myeloid cells of the elderly suggests stochastic clonal loss with age. *Br. J. Haematol.* **98,** 512–519.

94. Wedderburn, L.R., Patel, A., Varsani, H., and Woo, P. (2001). The developing human immune system: T-cell receptor repertoire of children and young adults shows a wide discrepancy in the frequency of persistent oligoclonal T-cell expansions. *Immunology* **102,** 301–309.
95. Ames, B.N., Shigenaga, M.K., and Hagen, T.M. (1993). Oxidants, antioxidants, and the degenerative diseases of aging. *Proc. Natl. Acad. Sci. U. S. A.* **90,** 7915–7922.
96. Wallace, D.C. (1999). Mitochondrial diseases in man and mouse. *Science* **283,** 1482–1488.
97. Cawthon, R.M., Smith, K.R., O'Brien, E., Sivatchenko, A., and Kerber, R.A. (2003). Association between telomere length in blood and mortality in people aged 60 years or older. *Lancet* **361,** 393–395.
98. Rufer, N., Brummendorf, T.H., Chapuis, B., Helg, C., Lansdorp, P.M., and Roosnek, E. (2001). Accelerated telomere shortening in hematological lineages is limited to the first year following stem cell transplantation. *Blood* **97,** 575–577.
99. Brummendorf, T.H., Holyoake, T.L., Rufer, N., Barnett, M.J., Schulzer, M., Eaves, C.J., Eaves, A.C., and Lansdorp, P.M. (2000). Prognostic implications of differences in telomere length between normal and malignant cells from patients with chronic myeloid leukemia measured by flow cytometry. *Blood* **95,** 1883–1890.
100. Antonchuk, J., Sauvageau, G., and Humphries, R.K. (2002). *HoxB4*-induced expansion of adult hematopoietic stem cells *ex vivo*. *Cell* **109,** 39–45.
101. Brummendorf, T.H., Mak, J., Baerlocher, G.M., Sabo, K., Abkowitz, J.L., and Lansdorp, P.M. (2000). Longitudinal studies of telomere length in feline blood cells point to a rapid turnover of stem cells in the first year of life. *Blood* **96,** 455a(Abstract).
102. Lansdorp, P.M. (1997). Self-renewal of stem cells. *Biol. Blood Marrow Transplant.* **3,** 171–178.
103. Potten, C.S., Owen, G., and Booth, D. (2002). Intestinal stem cells protect their genome by selective segregation of template DNA strands. *J. Cell Sci.* **115,** 2381–2388.
104. Blackburn, E.H. (2000). Telomere states and cell fates. *Nature* **408,** 53–56.
105. Wong, K.K., Maser, R.S., Bachoo, R.M., Menon, J., Carrasco, D.R., Gu, Y., Alt, F.W., and DePinho, R.A. (2003). Telomere dysfunction and ATM deficiency compromises organ homeostasis and accelerates ageing. *Nature* **421,** 643–648.
106. Bakkenist, C.J., and Kastan, M.B. (2003). DNA damage activates ATM through intermolecular autophosphorylation and dimer dissociation. *Nature* **421,** 499–506.
107. Baerlocher, G.M., and Lansdorp, P.M. (Unpublished observations).
108. Donehower, L.A. (2002). Does p53 affect organismal aging? *J. Cell Physiol.* **192,** 23–33.
109. Hasty, P., Campisi, J., Hoeijmakers, J., van Steeg, H., and Vijg, J. (2003). Aging and genome maintenance: lessons from the mouse? *Science* **299,** 1355–1359.
110. Tyner, S.D., Venkatachalam, S., Choi, J., Jones, S., Ghebranious, N., Igelmann, H., Lu, X., Soron, G., Cooper, B., Brayton, C., Hee Park, S., Thompson, T., Karsenty, G., Bradley, A., and Donehouwer, L.A. (2002). P53 mutant mice that display early ageing-associated phenotypes. *Nature* **415,** 45–53.
111. Geiger, H., and Van Zant, G. (2002). The aging of lymphohematopoietic stem cells. *Nat. Immunol.* **3,** 329–333.

12

How Cells Change Their Phenotype

David Tosh and Marko E. Horb

Introduction

Until recently, it was thought that once a cell had acquired a stable differentiated state it could not change its phenotype. We now know this is not the case, and over the past few years there has been a plethora of well-documented examples whereby already differentiated cells or tissue-specific stem cells have been shown to alter their phenotype to express functional characteristics of a different tissue. In this chapter, we examine evidence for these examples, comment on the underlying cellular and molecular mechanisms, and speculate about possible directions of research.

METAPLASIA AND TRANSDIFFERENTIATION: DEFINITIONS AND THEORETICAL IMPLICATIONS

Metaplasia is defined as the conversion of one cell type to another and can include conversions between tissue-specific stem cells.[1,2] Transdifferentiation, on the other hand, refers to the conversion of one differentiated cell type to another[3,4] and should therefore be considered a subset of metaplasia. Historically, metaplasia has been the term used by pathologists,[2,5] but in recent years transdifferentiation has become the favoured term, even when discussing the conversion of tissue-specific stem cells to unexpected lineages.[6–10] Within the medical community, the idea of metaplasia is not controversial, but in the scientific community, some scepticism still surrounds the phenomenon of transdifferentiation[11–15]—it being attributed to tissue culture artefacts or cell fusion.[16,17] Nevertheless, it is important to study metaplasia and transdifferentiation to gain a better understanding about the regulation of cellular differentiation, which may lead to new therapies for a variety of diseases, including cancer.

WHY STUDY TRANSDIFFERENTIATION?

Irrespective of which definition is applied, we consider the study of transdifferentiation and metaplasia to be important for four reasons. First, it allows us to understand the normal developmental biology of the tissues that interconvert. Most transdifferentiations occur in tissues that arise from neighbouring regions in the developing embryo and are therefore likely to differ in the expression of only one or two transcription factors.[5] If the genes involved in transdifferentiation can be identified, then this might shed some light on the developmental differences that exist among adjacent regions of the embryo. Second, metaplasia is important to study because it predisposes to certain pathological conditions, such as Barrett's metaplasia (see later sections for further details). In this condition, the lower end of the oesophagus contains cells characteristic of the intestine, and there is a strong predisposition to adenocarcinoma. Therefore, understanding the molecular signals in the development of Barrett's metaplasia will help to identify the key steps in neoplasia and may provide us with potential therapeutic targets as well as diagnostic tools. Third, understanding transdifferentiation will help to identify the master switch genes and thus allow us to reprogram stem cells or differentiated cells for therapeutic purposes. The fourth reason is that we will be able to identify the molecular signals for inducing regeneration and therefore to promote regeneration in tissues that otherwise do not regenerate (e.g., limb regeneration).[18]

Handbook of Stem Cells
Volume 2

Examples of the Phenomenon

Despite the controversy surrounding transdifferentiation, there are numerous examples that exist in both humans and animals; we focus on a select few. The examples we have chosen to examine in detail include the conversions of pancreas to liver, liver to pancreas, oesophagus to intestine, iris to lens, and bone marrow to other cell types. Other chapters in this book describe some of these as well as additional examples in more detail.

PANCREAS TO LIVER

The conversion of pancreas to liver is one well-documented example of transdifferentiation.[19–21] This type of conversion is not surprising since both organs arise from the same region of the endoderm[22] and Zaret and colleagues have clearly described the bipotential nature of the foregut endoderm.[23,24] In addition, the organs share many transcription factors, displaying their close developmental relationship.[25] The appearance of hepatocytes in the pancreas can be induced by different protocols, including feeding rats a copper-deficient diet with the copper chelator Trien,[26,27] overexpressing keratinocyte growth factor in the islets of the pancreas,[28] or feeding animals a methionine-deficient diet and exposing them to a carcinogen.[29] It has also been observed naturally in a primate, the vervet monkey.[30] Although the functional nature of the hepatocytes has been examined in detail, until recently, the molecular and cellular basis of the switch from pancreas to liver was poorly understood.

We have produced two *in vitro* models for the transdifferentiation of pancreas to liver.[31] This has been reviewed extensively elsewhere,[1,19,32] so we will not go into much detail here. The first model uses the pancreatic cell line AR42J, and the second uses mouse embryonic pancreas tissue in culture; both rely on the addition of glucocorticoid to induce transdifferentiation. AR42J cells are amphicrine cells derived from azaserine-treated rats,[33,34] and they express both exocrine and neuroendocrine properties—that is, they are able to synthesise digestive enzymes and express neurofilament. The dual nature of this cell line is evident in that when exposed to glucocorticoid, they initially enhance the exocrine phenotype by producing more amylase,[35] but when cultured with hepatocyte growth factor and activin A, the cells convert to insulin-secreting β-cells.[36,37] These properties of the AR42J cells suggest that they are an endodermal progenitor cell type with the potential to become exocrine or endocrine cell types.

The transdifferentiated hepatocytes formed from pancreatic AR42J cells express many of the proteins normally found in adult liver—for example, albumin, transferrin, and transthyretin. They also function as normal hepatocytes; in particular, they are able to respond to xenobiotics (e.g., they increase their catalase content after treatment with the peroxisomal proliferator, ciprofibrate, and express CYP3A1).[38,39] Although the mouse embryonic pancreas also expresses liver proteins after culture with dexamethasone, it is not clear whether the same cellular and molecular mechanisms are in operation as in the AR42J cells. It is possible that, rather than the hepatocytes arising from already differentiated cell types, the liver-like cells are derived from a subpopulation of pancreatic stem cells.

To determine the cell lineage of hepatocyte formation from pancreatic AR42J cells, we performed a lineage experiment based on the perdurance of green fluorescent protein (GFP) and used the pancreatic elastase promoter. After the transdifferentiation, some cells that expressed GFP also contained liver proteins (e.g., glucose-6-phosphatase). This result suggests that the nascent hepatocytes must have once had an active elastase promoter; therefore, they were differentiated exocrine cells. To elucidate the molecular basis of the switch in cell phenotype, we determined the expression of several liver-enriched transcription factors. Following treatment with dexamethasone, C/EBPβ became induced, the expression of the exocrine enzyme amylase was lost, and liver genes (e.g., glucose-6-phosphatase) were induced. These properties of C/EBPβ make it a good candidate to be an essential factor involved in the transdifferentiation of pancreas to liver. Indeed, C/EBPβ is sufficient to transdifferentiate AR42J cells to hepatocytes. Therefore, C/EBPβ appears to be a good candidate for the master switch gene distinguishing liver and pancreas.

LIVER TO PANCREAS

The numerous examples of pancreas-to-liver transdifferentiation suggest that the reverse switch should also occur readily; nevertheless, examples of this type of conversion are infrequent. The presence of pancreatic tissue in an abnormal location is known as heterotopic, accessory, or aberrant pancreas, and the frequency has been reported to range from 0.6 to 5.6%.[40,41] In most cases (70–90%), the heterotopic pancreas is found in the stomach or intestine and is considered to be an embryological anomaly.[40,41] In contrast, intrahepatic pancreatic heterotopia has only been reported in six individuals, comprising less than 0.5% of all cases of heterotopic pancreas.[42–46] In general, heterotopic pancreatic tissue can be composed of exocrine, endocrine, or both types of cells. In almost every case of pancreatic heterotopia in the liver, however, only exocrine cells are present; only one case describes the presence of endocrine cells.[44] Unlike the other cases of accessory pancreas, these rare incidents of intrahepatic pancreatic tissue cannot be explained as the result of a developmental error. In fact, in most of these cases, the patients were diagnosed with cirrhosis, suggesting that the heterotopic pancreas arose as a metaplastic process. Results with the animal models concur.

In other animals, pancreatic exocrine tissue can be induced in the liver by feeding rats polychlorinated biphenyls or by exposing trout to various carcinogens, such as diethylnitrosamine, aflatoxin B_1, or cyclopropenoid fatty acid.[47–50] In these examples, the hepatic exocrine tissue is most often associated with tumours or injury, such as hepatocellular carcinomas (that arise from hepatocytes), cholangiolar neoplasms (that arise from the bile duct), or adenofibrosis. Much like the human cases, these results suggest that during carcinogenesis, a metaplastic event occurs that generates pancreatic tissue. Indeed, pancreatic metaplasia in trout can be inhibited by the addition of the glucosinolate indole-3-carbinol, a known anticancer agent.[49] Whether inhibiting metaplasia prevents neoplasia remains to be determined. The ability of one cell (liver) to transdifferentiate into another (pancreas), no matter how rare, suggests that it should be possible to identify the molecular signals involved in switching a cell's phenotype and thus to learn how to control and direct this conversion for therapeutic purposes.

Two recent reports have shown that it is possible to experimentally convert liver cells into pancreatic cells.[51,52] Each has used a different approach to bring about transdifferentiation—by changing either the extracellular or the intracellular environment. In the first example, hepatic oval cells were isolated and maintained in tissue culture media supplemented with leukaemia inhibitory factor (LIF).[51] Upon the removal of LIF and the addition of high concentrations of glucose (23 mM) in the medium, the oval cells transdifferentiated to pancreatic cells. The oval cells were converted into a variety of pancreatic cell types, including glucagon, insulin, and pancreatic polypeptide-expressing cells. Functionally, these oval cell–derived endocrine cells were able to reverse hyperglycaemia in streptozotocin-induced diabetes. The mechanism whereby glucose induces the transdifferentiation is not known, though previously it was shown that glucose can promote the growth and differentiation of β-cells in the normal pancreas; perhaps a similar mechanism operates here.[53]

In the second example, hepatic cells (either *in vivo* or *in vitro*) were induced to transdifferentiate by overexpression

50. Hendricks, J.D., Meyers, T.R., and Shelton, D.W. (1984). Histological progression of hepatic neoplasia in rainbow trout *(Salmo gairdneri)*. *Nat. Cancer Inst. Monogr.* **65,** 321–336.
51. Yang, L., Li, S., Hatch, H., Ahrens, K., Cornelius, J.G., Petersen, B.E., and Peck, A.B. (2002). *In vitro* transdifferentiation of adult hepatic stem cells into pancreatic endocrine hormone-producing cells. *Proc. Natl. Acad. Sci. U. S. A.* **99,** 8078–8083.
52. Horb, M.E., Shen, C.N., Tosh, D., and Slack, J.M.W. (2003). Experimental conversion of liver to pancreas. *Curr. Biol.* **13,** 105–115.
53. Bonner-Weir, S. (1994). Regulation of pancreatic β-cell mass *in vivo*. *Recent Prog. Horm. Res.* **49,** 91–104.
54. McKinnon, C.M., and Docherty, K. (2001). Pancreatic duodenal homeobox-1, PDX-1, a major regulator of β-cell identity and function. *Diabetologia* **44,** 1203–1214.
55. Jonsson, J., Carlsson, L., Edlund, T., and Edlund, H. (1994). Insulin-promoter factor 1 is required for pancreas development in mice. *Nature* **371,** 606–609.
56. Offield, M.F., Jetton, T.L., Labosky, P.A., Ray, M., Stein, R.W., Magnuson, M.A., Hogan, B.L., and Wright, C.V. (1996). PDX-1 is required for pancreatic outgrowth and differentiation of the rostral duodenum. *Development* **122,** 983–995.
57. Stoffers, D.A., Zinkin, N.T., Stanojevic, V., Clarke, W.L., and Habener, J.F. (1997). Pancreatic agenesis attributable to a single nucleotide deletion in the human *IPF1* gene coding sequence. *Nat. Genet.* **15,** 106–110.
58. Ferber, S., Halkin, A., Cohen, H., Ber, I., Einav, Y., Goldberg, I., Barshack, I., Seijffers, R., Kopolovic, J., Kaiser, N., and Karasik, A. (2000). Pancreatic and duodenal homeobox gene 1 induces expression of insulin genes in liver and ameliorates streptozotocin-induced hyperglycaemia. *Nat. Med.* **6,** 568–572.
59. Sadowski, I., Ma, J., Triezenberg, S., and Ptashne, M. (1988). GAL4-VP16 is an unusually potent transcriptional activator. *Nature* **335,** 563–564.
60. Emerson, B.M. (2002). Specificity of gene regulation. *Cell* **109,** 267–270.
61. Naar, A.M., Lemon, B.D., and Tjian, R. (2001). Transcriptional coactivator complexes. *Ann. Rev. Biochem.* **70,** 475–501.
62. Featherstone, M. (2002). Coactivators in transcription initiation: here are your orders. *Curr. Opin. Genet. Dev.* **12,** 149–155.
63. Carey, M. (1998). The enhanceosome and transcriptional synergy. *Cell* **92,** 5–8.
64. Flint, J., and Shenk, T. (1997). Viral transactivating proteins. *Annu. Rev. Genet.* **31,** 177–212.
65. Memedula, S., and Belmont, A.S. (2003). Sequential recruitment of HAT and SWI/SNF components to condensed chromatin by VP16. *Curr. Biol.* **13,** 241–246.
66. Ikeda, K., Stuehler, T., and Meisterernst, M. (2002). The H1 and H2 regions of the activation domain of herpes simplex virion protein 16 stimulate transcription through distinct molecular mechanisms. *Genes Cell* **7,** 49–58.
67. Hall, D.B., and Struhl, K. (2002). The VP16 activation domain interacts with multiple transcriptional components as determined by protein–protein cross-linking *in vivo*. *J. Biol. Chem.* **277,** 46,043–46,050.
68. Ferber, S. (2000). Can we create new organs from our own tissues? *Isr. Med. Assoc. J.* **2,** 32–36.
69. Nevado, J., Gaudreau, L., Adam, M., and Ptashne, M. (1999). Transcriptional activation by artificial recruitment in mammalian cells. *Proc. Natl. Acad. Sci. U. S. A.* **96,** 2674–2677.
70. Yaghmai, R., and Cutting, G.R. (2002). Optimized regulation of gene expression using artificial transcription factors. *Mol. Ther.* **5,** 685–694.
71. Falk, G.W. (2002). Barrett's oesophagus. *Gastroenterology* **122,** 1569–1591.
72. Beck, F., Tata, F., and Chawengsaksophak, K. (2000). Homeobox genes and gut development. *Bioessays* **22,** 431–441.
73. Traber, P.G., and Silberg, D.G. (1996). Intestine-specific transcription. *Ann. Rev. Physiol.* **58,** 275–297.
74. Beck, F., Chawengsaksophak, K., Waring, P., Playford, R.J., and Furness, J.B. (1999). Reprogramming of intestinal differentiation and intercalary regeneration in Cdx2 mutant mice. *Proc. Natl. Acad. Sci. U. S. A.* **96,** 7318–7323.
75. Silberg, D.G., Sullivan, J., Kang, E., Swain, G.P., Moffett, J., Sund, N.J., Sackett, S.D., and Kaestner, K.H. (2002). Cdx2 ectopic expression induces gastric intestinal metaplasia in transgenic mice. *Gastroenterology* **122,** 689–696.
76. Eda, A., Osawa, H., Satoh, K., Yanaka, I., Kihira, K., Ishino, Y., Mutoh, H., and Sugano, K. (2003). Aberrant expression of CDX2 in Barrett's epithelium and inflammatory oesophageal mucosa. *J. Gastroenterol.* **38,** 14–22.
77. Bianco, P., and Robey, P.G. (2001). Stem cells in tissue engineering. *Nature* **414,** 118–121.
78. Tsonis, P.A. (2002). Regenerative biology: the emerging field of tissue repair and restoration. *Differentiation* **70,** 397–409.
79. Eguchi, G. (1988). Cellular and molecular background of Wolffian lens regeneration. *Cell. Differ. Dev.* **25,** 147–158.
80. Park, C.M., and Hollenberg, M.J. (1993). Growth factor-induced retinal regeneration *in vivo*. *Int. Rev. Cytol.* **146,** 49–74.
81. Del Rio-Tsonis, K., and Tsonis, P.A. (2003). Eye regeneration at the molecular age. *Dev. Dyn.* **226,** 211–224.
82. Bosco, L., Venturini, G., and Willems, D. (1997). *In vitro* lens transdifferentiation of *Xenopus laevis* outer cornea induced by fibroblast growth factor (FGF). *Development* **124,** 421–428.
83. Poulsom, R., Alison, M.R., Forbes, S.J., and Wright, N.A. (2002). Adult stem cell plasticity. *J. Pathol.* **197,** 441–456.
84. Jiang, Y., Vaessen, B., Lenvik, T., Blackstad, M., Reyes, M., and Verfaillie, C.M. (2002). Multipotent progenitor cells can be isolated from postnatal murine bone marrow, muscle, and brain. *Exp. Hematol.* **30,** 896–904.
85. Li, H., and Edlund, H. (2001). Persistent expression of Hlxb9 in the pancreatic epithelium impairs pancreatic development. *Dev. Biol.* **240,** 247–253.

13

Transdifferentiation

Thomas Küntziger and Philippe Collas

Novel ways of redirecting the fate of differentiated somatic cells, a process known as transdifferentiation, are actively being investigated. This chapter addresses the transdifferentiation potential of somatic cells and illustrates the functional reprogramming of somatic cells using extracts derived from another somatic cell type. Reprogramming cells *in vitro* might create new opportunities in the area of cell replacement therapy and might constitute a powerful tool for examining the molecular mechanisms of nuclear reprogramming.

Introduction

Epigenetic modifications—sequence-independent alterations of DNA—allow differentiated cells to perpetuate the molecular memory needed for the cells to retain their identity. These modifications are heritable, but they can also be experimentally reverted, as evidenced in the cloning of animals by the transplantation of somatic cell nuclei into oocytes or in cell hybridization studies. Nevertheless, reversion of the somatic cell nucleus to totipotency by nuclear transplantation is an inefficient process[1] with a high incidence of embryo lethality. Possible reasons for the low efficiency of nuclear transplantation may include errors generated during epigenetic remodeling accompanying dedifferentiation and the absence of functional centrosomes in recipient eggs, which are essential for normal embryonic cell divisions.[2] Methods for transdifferentiating somatic cells (i.e., directly turning their program into that of another somatic cell type) would circumvent difficulties associated with nuclear transplantation and potentially be beneficial for producing replacement cells for therapeutic applications. In this chapter, we briefly review the transdifferentiation potential of adult stem cells. We also address examples of somatic cell transdifferentiation and describe a recently developed *in vitro* somatic cell reprogramming strategy.

Transdifferentiation Potential of Adult Stem Cells

Tissue-specific stem cells reside in adult tissues including blood, skin, the central nervous system, the liver, the gastrointestinal tract, adipose tissue, and skeletal muscle.[3] Adult stem cells are responsible for regenerating damaged tissue and maintaining tissue homeostasis, as in the physiological replenishment of skin and blood cells. In contrast to the pluripotent embryonic stem (ES) cells, the differentiation and regenerative potential of adult stem cells has long been thought to be restricted to the tissues in which they reside. However, many reports argue that adult stem cells have broad differentiation ability: They can exhibit sufficient plasticity to differentiate into cell types outside their predicted developmental lineage and can even cross germ-layer boundaries.[4]

The hype emerging from the transdifferentiation potential of adult stem cells should not preclude caution in the interpretation of observations. Alterations in stem cell fate *in vivo* are rare occurrences.[5] Moreover, it should be demonstrated that the transdifferentiated cells are derived from the stem cells of the donor tissue and not from a contaminating subpopulation of cells already committed to differentiation. Additionally, the diploid state of the transdifferentiated stem cells should be verified. Indeed, coculture of somatic cells or adult stem cells with ES cells leads to occasional cell fusion events resulting in hyper-diploid hybrids that display an ES cell–like phenotype[6,7] (see Chapter 14). Cell fusion might therefore provide an explanation for how bone marrow cells or progenitor cells of the central nervous system can produce non–bone marrow or nonneural derivatives. Recently however, De Bari *et al.*[8] observed that mesenchymal stem cells from human synovial membranes, which are similar to mesenchymal–marrow stromal stem cells from bone marrow, differentiated to muscle cells while monitoring for these specific pitfalls.

Transdifferentiation Potential of Somatic Cells

Transdifferentiation can be defined as a direct switch of an already differentiated cell to another type of differentiated cell. Accordingly, transdifferentiation does not involve dedifferentiation—a resetting of the developmental clock. For a cell to reach a transdifferentiated state, several criteria should be fulfilled. Specific sets of genes must be turned on; other sets of genes must be turned off.[9–12] If this transition takes place rapidly, then the products of both sets of genes may be transiently coexpressed in the cell.[13] If the transdifferentiation process is slow, there might in theory be a stage in which the original genes are turned off before the new sets of genes are activated.[13] Transdifferentiated cells should acquire a new, characterized phenotype that is stably expressed.

Handbook of Stem Cells
Volume 2

If used in transplantation studies, the cells should be genetically labeled to ensure their traceability in the host organism. Furthermore, we should be able to withdraw the transplanted cells, eliciting the reoccurrence of symptoms. This would demonstrate that the rescue of a phenotype is a consequence of engraftment of the transdifferentiated cells.

TRANSDIFFERENTIATION BY CELL TRANSPLANTATION INTO A NEW MILIEU

Somatic cells can alter their phenotype and function when placed into a new environment. In *Drosophila,* imaginal discs—non–stem cell larval structures determined to form specific adult body parts—can switch fate after regenerative cell divisions.[14] Transdetermination of disc cells also occurs after transplantation into a new tissue, such that leg cells can switch to antenna, antenna to wing, etc. Transdetermination is believed to involve misregulation of key genes, including *Hox* genes.[15] In amphibians, cells from the cornea can form a new lens after the original lens is removed during tadpole stages.[16,17] Transdifferentiation in this situation is controlled by factors secreted by the neural retina. This type of lens regeneration also occurs in the chick embryo.[18]

Transdifferentiation can also take place after transplantation into ectopic sites in mammals. Injection of endothelial cells into damaged heart tissue causes their transdifferentiation into cardiomyocytes.[19] Pancreatic epithelial progenitor cells can also differentiate into hepatocytes.[20] Thus the microenvironment, including contact with surrounding cells, the extracellular matrix, the local milieu, and growth and differentiation factors, plays a key role in redirecting cell fate. These factors may also influence stem cell fate as these cells migrate and enter other organs.

PARALLELS BETWEEN MAMMALIAN STEM CELL FATE ALTERATION AND TRANSDETERMINATION

Although transdetermination in *Drosophila* does not involve stem cells, several parallels exist between mammalian stem cell fate change and disc cell transdetermination. First, both processes take place under regenerative proliferation. Second, progenitor cells, which can differentiate into mature effector cells, are involved. Third, cell fate changes in both situations do not lead to intermediate cell types but follow a normal pattern of differentiation. Lastly, *Hox* genes, implicated in transdetermination, are preferentially expressed in adult stem cells and regulate stem cells.[21]

TRANSDIFFERENTIATION OF SOMATIC CELLS IN CULTURE

Transdifferentiation of mammalian somatic cells has been achieved in coculture or by manipulation of cell culture conditions. Myoblasts transdifferentiate into mature adipocytes by ectopic expression of adipogenic transcription factors under conditions permissive for adipogenesis.[22] Induction of a hepatic transcription factor in pancreatic cells also causes their conversion into hepatocytes.[23] Inhibition of gap-junctional communication among cultured osteoblasts leads to an adipocytic phenotype.[24] Furthermore, embryonic or neonatal umbilical vein endothelial cells transdifferentiate into beating cardiomyocytes when cocultured with neonatal rat cardiomyocytes.[19] Interestingly, endothelial cells derived from adults do not transdifferentiate in this system, suggesting that this kind of plasticity is age dependent.

EPIGENETIC REPROGRAMMING BY CELL HYBRIDIZATION

During nuclear reprogramming, epigenetic modifications of the somatic nucleus must occur for pluripotency to be achieved. This presumably occurs after transplantation of a somatic nucleus into an oocyte. A differentiated nucleus can also be reprogrammed to a pluripotent state by the fusion of a somatic cell with a stem cell. When mouse thymic lymphocytes are fused to embryonic germ (EG) cells, methylation of imprinted or nonimprinted genes and repetitive sequences is erased and the lymphocyte nuclei acquire pluripotential stem cell–like properties.[25] Reversion of lymphocyte nuclei also occurs after fusion with ES cells; however, the methylation pattern of imprinted genes is maintained.[26] Nevertheless, such fusions reactivate a silent transgene (the ES cell–specific gene *Oct-4*) in the lymphocyte nucleus. Thus, factors in ES or EG cells can mediate some stage of epigenetic reprogramming.

New Strategies for Transdifferentiation

CELL REPROGRAMMING EXTRACT

Extracts from gametes or somatic cells have been used to investigate nuclear processes such as chromosome condensation, nuclear envelope breakdown or reformation,[27–31] and chromatin remodeling.[32,33] Cell extracts useful for manipulating gene expression in exogenous nuclei or cells have recently been developed.[11,33] The assay consists of incubating purified somatic nuclei or permeabilized cells in a nuclear and cytoplasmic extract from a different (target) cell type. Extracts are prepared by cell sonication and sedimentation of the coarse material.[11,33] The extract provides nuclear regulatory components that mediate alterations in the gene expression profile of the target genome, whereas cytoplasmic components are used to promote transport of the nuclear regulatory components from the extract to the nucleus of the permeabilized cells.

The extract is capable of eliciting changes in chromatin organization and composition. We demonstrated anchoring and activity of the nucleosome remodeling complex, BAF, within nuclei of exogenous fibroblasts incubated in a T-cell extract.[11] The extract elicits a β-actin–dependent ATPase activity of the chromatin-remodeling BAF complex, suggestive of induction of energy-dependent chromatin-remodeling activities. Furthermore, chromatin immunoprecipitation studies showed that the extract promotes histone H4 acetylation at the interleukin-2 *(IL2)* promoter in the genome of exogenous fibroblast nuclei.[11]

REPROGRAMMING FIBROBLAST FUNCTION IN SOMATIC CELL EXTRACT

Our *in vitro* cell reprogramming approach is illustrated in Fig. 13–1. The plasma membrane of "donor" cells is

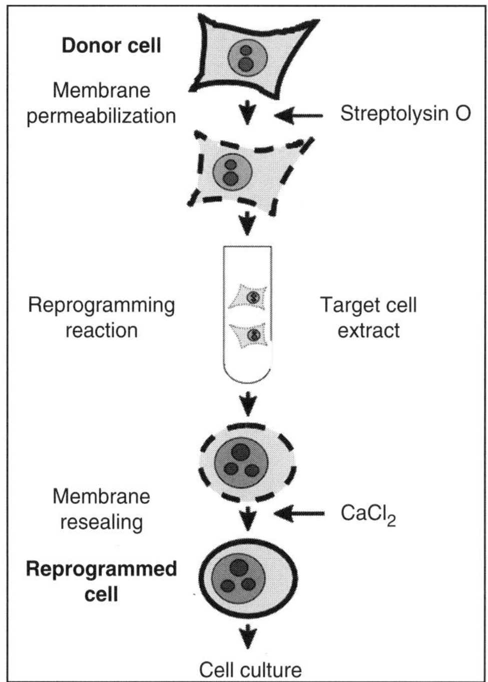

Figure 13–1. *In vitro cell reprogramming strategy.* Somatic "donor" cells (e.g., fibroblasts) are reversibly permeabilized; reprogrammed in a test tube containing an extract of, for example, T-cells; resealed; and cultured.

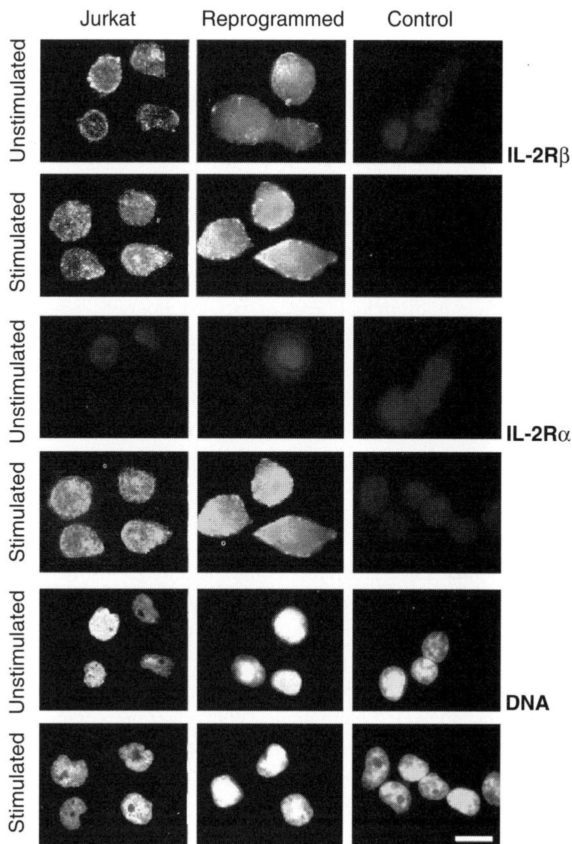

Figure 13–2. *Induction of a T-cell-specific signaling pathway in in vitro-reprogrammed cells.* The T-cell receptor–CD3 pathway was stimulated in Jurkat cells, 293T cells exposed to a 293T cell extract (Control), or 293T cells exposed to a Jurkat cell extract (Reprogrammed). In a resting state (Unstimulated), the reprogrammed cells express IL-2Rβ. However, stimulation (Stimulated) results in the synthesis and membrane targeting of the IL-2Rα subunit. This contributes to forming a functional IL-2R on the surface of the reprogrammed cells. Bar = 10 μm.

reversibly permeabilized with the bacterial toxin Streptolysin O. Donor cell function is reprogrammed by incubation of the permeabilized cells in a target cell extract as described previously. At the end of incubation, the cells are resealed and cultured. Analyses of cells incubated in a T-cell extract revealed the appearance of T-cell–like properties, which seemed to be stable for at least several weeks.

CHANGES IN GENE EXPRESSION PROFILE

293T cells exposed to a T-cell extract alter their gene expression pattern, as shown by cDNA macroarray analyses.[11] Compared with 293T cells permeabilized and exposed to a 293T extract, expression of >120 genes was modified as a result of reprogramming. Hematopoietic genes, including interleukin and interleukin receptors, cytokines and cytokine receptors, and cell surface molecules were activated or up-regulated, whereas genes for fibroblast growth factors, adhesion molecules, and cytoskeletal proteins were down-regulated. Levels of housekeeping gene mRNAs were not altered, indicating that detected changes in transcription profile resulted from reprogramming.

EXPRESSION OF CELL SURFACE MOLECULES

The reprogrammed cells express T-cell–specific surface receptors,[11] including the IL-2Rβ chain (Fig. 13–2). Morphological changes were also evident within the first few days of reprogramming: The fibroblasts appeared smaller and rounder, and they resembled T-cells. Curiously, morphological changes were distinct for approximately 2 weeks, after which the cells reverted to a fibroblast-like shape, although they continued to express T-cell–specific surface markers. The basis for this transient morphological alteration is being investigated.

INDUCTION OF A COMPLEX INTRACELLULAR REGULATORY FUNCTION

As a functional marker of cell reprogramming, we assessed the induction of a T-cell–specific pathway in the reprogrammed cells.[11] As mentioned previously, like T-cells, the reprogrammed cells expressed the low-affinity IL-2Rβ subunit (Fig. 13–2). Upon intracellular stimulation of the TCR–CD3 pathway in the reprogrammed cells (which normally occurs upon T-cell activation), synthesis of the IL-2Rα chain took place, which presumably contributed to assemble a functional high-affinity IL-2R (Fig. 13–2). This is a clear illustration of induction of a complex T-cell–specific function in the reprogrammed cells. These observations predict that it may be possible to induce other complex (e.g., secretory) functions in cells reprogrammed into other cell types.

Role of Master Switch Genes in Transdifferentiation

Studies on transdifferentiation of somatic cells raise the hypothesis that activation or suppression of so-called master genes may be essential for the transition from one cell type to another. Long-term *in vivo* reconstitution of T-cell development in B-cells by knocking out the *Pax5* gene has been reported, suggesting that *Pax5* is a master gene important for commitment to the B-cell lineage.[34,35] *Pax5*$^{-/-}$ pre–B-cells express genes of different lineage-associated programs, whereas restoration of *Pax5* activity represses lineage-promiscuous transcription. Similarly, the homeobox gene *Pdx1* has been proposed to be a master switch for initiating development of insulin-producing β-cells in the pancreas. *Pdx1* is essential for pancreas development and islet cell function.[36] *In vivo* expression of a *Pdx1* transgene into mouse or frog liver was sufficient to convert a subpopulation of hepatocytes into insulin-producing β-like cells[12,37] (see Chapter 12), and suppression of *Pdx1* leads to a complete absence of the pancreas in Pdx1 knockout mice. These observations suggest that *Pdx1* may be a master gene controlling β-cell function. However, the transcription factor Foxa2 acts upstream of *Pdx1* in the *Pdx1* regulatory cascade and thereby controls expression of *Pdx1*.[38] This argues that searching for master genes may be no easy task. If such genes exist, their identification might allow a more efficient transdifferentiation approach, provided that we find ways of manipulating their activity.

Prospects

INNOVATIVE ASPECTS OF *IN VITRO* CELL REPROGRAMMING

Should *in vitro* cell reprogramming prove functional on a large scale, it would present innovative technological, commercial, and societal benefits. Current strategies for cell reprogramming or controlled differentiation (such as directed differentiation of stem cells) are based on a receptor-mediated approach. *In vitro* reprogramming uses permeabilized cells; thus, "reprogramming factors" access the cellular interior directly. This not only may render the strategy more effective but also has the advantage of being useful without having a great deal of prior knowledge of regulatory mechanisms controlling cell function. *In vitro* reprogramming may be applied to many cell types; thus, it has potential for treating many diseases. It may allow for the production of isogenic (the patient's own) cells for transplantation. Unlike reprogramming by nuclear transplantation into oocytes, somatic cells are used as a source of reprogramming material. Unlike eggs, these can be grown in large numbers and, if necessary, can be transformed to produce a consistent supply of reprogramming material. Lastly, ethical and legal issues regarding human cloning and production of ES cells from human embryos would be avoided.

Despite the promising results, it would be biased to say that everything is perfect. Our reprogramming assay involves extensive cell manipulation. Thus, application of this technology to produce replacement cells for therapeutic purposes requires significant developments, and a large body of data is needed before this system can be applied to the generation of cells used for therapy.

THERAPEUTIC CELL CONCEPT?

It is clear from our observations that the reprogramming of 293T cells into T-cells is not complete. Only a subset of genes is up- or down-regulated and, to date, the reprogrammed cells do not express a pure T-cell–specific phenotype. Nevertheless, for cell replacement therapeutic applications, we may not need to produce a fully reprogrammed cell. For instance, for treating type 1 diabetes, it may be sufficient to engineer a cell that secretes regulated levels of insulin in response to glucose stimulation, much like a pancreatic β-cell. However, the replacement cell may not need to be a β-cell. This hypothesis is purely speculative and will require extensive genetic and functional investigations. Nevertheless, we tentatively propose a concept that a partially reprogrammed cell that displays the necessary therapeutic properties, or therapeutic cells, may be what it takes to treat certain diseases.

USING *IN VITRO* REPROGRAMMING AS A TOOL

Several laboratories have reported the transdifferentiation of stem cells or somatic cells into cells types beyond their predicted developmental lineage. This underlines how little we know about genome plasticity and illustrates the limitations of reprogramming cell lineages without understanding the underlying molecular processes. Our reprogramming assay may provide a powerful system for analyzing nuclear reprogramming processes, at least as they occur *in vitro*. It will be exciting to apply similar methods to the analysis of other systems, such as ES or EG cells, and to the identification of molecules central to biological processes as diverse as the establishment of pluripotency or the regulation of differentiation. A clearer understanding of nuclear reprogramming not only will lead to a better appreciation of differentiation, (de)differentiation, cloning, or stem cell biology but also will be relevant to the aberrant programming that occurs in cancer and other pathological situations.

ACKNOWLEDGMENTS

Our work is supported by the Research Council of Norway, the Norwegian Cancer Society, the European Union, and Nucleotech.

REFERENCES

1. Byrne, J.A., Simonsson, S., and Gurdon, J.B. (2002). From intestine to muscle: nuclear reprogramming through defective cloned embryos. *Proc. Natl. Acad. Sci. U. S. A.* **99,** 6059–6063.
2. Stearns, T. (2001). Centrosome duplication: A centriolar pas de deux. *Cell* **105,** 417–420.
3. Blau, H.M., Brazelton, T.R., and Weimann, J.M. (2001). The evolving concept of a stem cell: entity or function? *Cell* **105,** 829–841.

4. Håkelien, A.M., and Collas, P. (2003). Teaching cells new tricks. *Trends Biotechnol.* **21,** 354–361.
5. Wagers, A.J., Sherwood, R.I., Christensen, J.L., and Weissman, I.L. (2002). Little evidence for developmental plasticity of adult hematopoietic stem cells. *Science* **297,** 2256–2259.
6. Terada, N., Hamazaki, T., Oka, M., Hoki, M., Mastalerz, D.M., Nakano, Y., Meyer, E.M., Morel, L., Petersen, B.E., and Scott, E.W. (2002). Bone marrow cells adopt the phenotype of other cells by spontaneous cell fusion. *Nature* **416,** 542–545.
7. Ying, Q.L., Nichols, J., Evans, E.P., and Smith, A.G. (2002). Changing potency by spontaneous fusion. *Nature* **416,** 545–548.
8. De Bari, C., Dell'Accio, F., Vandenabeele, F., Vermeesch, J.R., Raymackers, J.M., and Luyten, F.P. (2003). Skeletal muscle repair by adult human mesenchymal stem cells from synovial membrane. *J. Cell Biol.* **160,** 909–918.
9. Ross, S.E., Hemati, N., Longo, K.A., Bennett, C.N., Lucas, P.C., Erickson, R.L., and MacDougald, O.A. (2000). Inhibition of adipogenesis by Wnt signaling. *Science* **289,** 950–953.
10. Yang, L., Qin, X.F., Baltimore, D., and Van Parijs, L. (2002). Generation of functional antigen-specific T-cells in defined genetic backgrounds by retrovirus-mediated expression of TCR cDNAs in hematopoietic precursor cells. *Proc. Natl. Acad. Sci. U. S. A.* **99,** 6204–6209.
11. Håkelien, A.M., Landsverk, H.B., Robl, J.M., Skålhegg, B.S., and Collas, P. (2002). Reprogramming fibroblast function in cell-free extracts. *Nat. Biotechnol.* **20,** 460–466.
12. Horb, M.E., Shen, C.N., Tosh, D., and Slack, J.M. (2003). Experimental conversion of liver to pancreas. *Curr. Biol.* **13,** 105–115.
13. Slack, J.M., and Tosh, D. (2001). Transdifferentiation and metaplasia—switching cell types. *Curr. Opin. Genet. Dev.* **11,** 581–586.
14. Wei, G., Schubiger, G., Harder, F., and Muller, A.M. (2000). Stem cell plasticity in mammals and transdetermination in *Drosophila:* common themes? *Stem Cells* **18,** 409–414.
15. Schneuwly, S., Klemenz, R., and Gehring, W.J. (1987). Redesigning the body plan of *Drosophila* by ectopic expression of the homoeotic gene *Antennapedia. Nature* **325,** 816–818.
16. Henry, J.J., and Elkins, M.B. (2001). Cornea-lens transdifferentiation in the anuran, *Xenopus tropicalis. Dev. Genes Evol.* **211,** 377–387.
17. Schaefer, J.J., Oliver, G., and Henry, J.J. (1999). Conservation of gene expression during embryonic lens formation and cornea-lens transdifferentiation in *Xenopus laevis. Dev. Dyn.* **215,** 308–318.
18. Eguchi, G., and Kodama, R. (1993). Transdifferentiation. *Curr. Opin. Cell Biol.* **5,** 1023–1028.
19. Condorelli, G., Borello, U., De Angelis, L., Latronico, M., Sirabella, D., Coletta, M., Galli, R., Balconi, G., Follenzi, A., Frati, G., Cusella De Angelis, M.G., Gioglio, L., Amuchastegui, S., Adorini, L., Naldini, L., Vescovi, A., Dejana, E., and Cossu, G. (2001). Cardiomyocytes induce endothelial cells to transdifferentiate into cardiac muscle: implications for myocardium regeneration. *Proc. Natl. Acad. Sci. U. S. A.* **98,** 10,733–10,738.
20. Dabeva, M.D., Hwang, S.G., Vasa, S.R., Hurston, E., Novikoff, P.M., Hixson, D.C., Gupta, S., and Shafritz, D.A. (1997). Differentiation of pancreatic epithelial progenitor cells into hepatocytes following transplantation into rat liver. *Proc. Natl. Acad. Sci. U. S. A.* **94,** 7356–7361.
21. Sauvageau, G., Thorsteinsdottir, U., Eaves, C.J., Lawrence, H.J., Largman, C., Lansdorp, P.M., and Humphries, R.K. (1995). Overexpression of HOXB4 in hematopoietic cells causes the selective expansion of more primitive populations *in vitro* and *in vivo. Genes Dev.* **9,** 1753–1765.
22. Hu, E., Tontonoz, P., and Spiegelman, B.M. (1995). Transdifferentiation of myoblasts by the adipogenic transcription factors PPAR-γ and C/EBP-α. *Proc. Natl. Acad. Sci. U. S. A.* **92,** 9856–9860.
23. Shen, C.N., Slack, J.M., and Tosh, D. (2000). Molecular basis of transdifferentiation of pancreas to liver. *Nat. Cell Biol.* **2,** 879–887.
24. Schiller, P.C., D'Ippolito, G., Brambilla, R., Roos, B.A., and Howard, G.A. (2001). Inhibition of gap-junctional communication induces the transdifferentiation of osteoblasts to an adipocytic phenotype *in vitro. J. Biol. Chem.* **276,** 14,133–14,138.
25. Tada, M., Tada, T., Lefebvre, L., Barton, S.C., and Surani, M.A. (1997). Embryonic germ cells induce epigenetic reprogramming of somatic nucleus in hybrid cells. *EMBO J.* **16,** 6510–6520.
26. Tada, M., Takahama, Y., Abe, K., Nakatsuji, N., and Tada, T. (2001). Nuclear reprogramming of somatic cells by *in vitro* hybridization with ES cells. *Curr. Biol.* **11,** 1553–1558.
27. Martins, S., Eikvar, S., Furukawa, K., and Collas, P. (2003). HA95 and LAP2-β mediate a novel chromatin-nuclear envelope interaction implicated in initiation of DNA replication. *J. Cell Biol.* **160,** 177–188.
28. Martins, S.B., Eide, T., Steen, R.L., Jahnsen, T., Skålhegg, B.S., and Collas, P. (2000). HA95 is a protein of the chromatin and nuclear matrix regulating nuclear envelope dynamics. *J. Cell Sci.* **113,** 3703–3713.
29. Poccia, D.L., and Collas, P. (1996). Transforming sperm nuclei into male pronuclei *in vivo* and *in vitro. Curr. Topics Dev. Biol.* **34,** 25–88.
30. Steen, R.L., Cubizolles, F., Le Guellec, K., and Collas, P. (2000). A-kinase anchoring protein (AKAP)-95 recruits human chromosome-associated protein (hCAP)-D2/Eg7 for chromosome condensation in mitotic extract. *J. Cell Biol.* **149,** 531–536.
31. Steen, R.L., Martins, S.B., Tasken, K., and Collas, P. (2000). Recruitment of protein phosphatase 1 to the nuclear envelope by A-kinase anchoring protein AKAP149 is a prerequisite for nuclear lamina assembly. *J. Cell Biol.* **150,** 1251–1262.
32. Kikyo, N., Wade, P.A., Guschin, D., Ge, H., and Wolffe, A.P. (2000). Active remodeling of somatic nuclei in egg cytoplasm by the nucleosomal ATPase ISWI. *Science* **289,** 2360–2362.
33. Landsverk, H.B., Håkelien, A.M., Küntziger, T., Robl, J.M., Skålhegg, B.S., and Collas, P. (2002). Reprogrammed gene expression in a somatic cell-free extract. *EMBO Rep.* **3,** 384–389.
34. Nutt, S.L., Heavey, B., Rolink, A.G., and Busslinger, M. (1999). Commitment to the B-lymphoid lineage depends on the transcription factor Pax5. *Nature* **401,** 556–562.
35. Rolink, A.G., Nutt, S.L., Melchers, F., and Busslinger, M. (1999). Long-term *in vivo* reconstitution of T-cell development by Pax5-deficient B-cell progenitors. *Nature* **401,** 603–606.
36. Jonsson, J., Carlsson, L., Edlund, T., and Edlund, H. (1994). Insulin-promoter factor 1 is required for pancreas development in mice. *Nature* **371,** 606–609.
37. Ferber, S., Halkin, A., Cohen, H., Ber, I., Einav, Y., Goldberg, I., Barshack, I., Seijffers, R., Kopolovic, J., Kaiser, N., and Karasik, A. (2000). Pancreatic and duodenal homeobox gene 1 induces expression of insulin genes in liver and ameliorates streptozotocin-induced hyperglycemia. *Nat. Med.* **6,** 568–572.
38. Lee, C.S., Sund, N.J., Vatamaniuk, M.Z., Matschinsky, F.M., Stoffers, D.A., and Kaestner, K.H. (2002). Foxa2 controls *Pdx1* gene expression in pancreatic β-cells *in vivo. Diabetes* **51,** 2546–2551.

14

Spontaneous Cell Fusion

Joseph J. Lucas and Naohiro Terada

"Cell fusion" has become a phenomenon of renewed interest in stem cell biology. It has been proposed as an important alternative mechanism to explain the apparent plasticity, or "transdifferentiation," of mammalian cells observed in many recent studies. Cell fusion is categorized as one form of membrane fusion widely observed in nature. Indeed, spontaneous cell fusion, including that between types not normally seen to fuse in an animal, has been observed for decades both in culture dishes and in mammals. In this chapter, we present a historical overview and describe recent findings of spontaneous cell fusion, focusing on its significance within the context of recent debates about adult stem cell plasticity.

Membrane Fusion

Membrane fusion is a natural occurrence in nature. As reviewed recently by Jahn *et al.*,[1] there are three major types of membrane fusion events. First, pathogens employ membrane fusion to introduce themselves or their genomes into host cells. This process has been most intensively studied for infection of animal cells by enveloped viruses, which contain glycoproteins capable of inducing fusion between the cell membrane and the viral envelope. Although the exact mechanism of fusion has not been fully elucidated, it appears that the viral fusion proteins can serve as bridges pulling two membranes together and facilitating lipid mixing.[2–4] Second, organelles within cells fuse to each other. Except for the fusion of mitochondria and peroxisomes,[5,6] all intracellular fusions appear to occur by similar processes. In brief, the complex chain of events leading to fusion includes the recognition and the attachment of two membranes, with Rab proteins serving as anchors, followed by membrane fusion, mediated by SNARE family proteins in reactions regulated at least partly by SM family proteins.[1,7] Although a picture of intracellular membrane fusion is clearly emerging from recent data, many details of the process for specific organelles remain to be determined. As noted by Jahn *et al.*,[1] the complexity of the process is suggested by the human genome, which encodes more than 60 Rabs,[8] more than 35 SNAREs,[9] and at least 7 SMs.[1,10] Third, under special circumstances, eukaryotic cells fuse to each other. Some notable examples in animals are the fusion of egg and sperm during fertilization, the formation of syncytiotrophoblast in the placenta, the formation of multinucleated myotubes by the fusion of myoblasts, and the generation of osteoclasts by the fusion of mononuclear phagocytic precursor cells. Cell fusion may also be observed under pathological conditions induced by cell injury, with certain viral or bacterial infections, and during malignant cell growth.[11,12] As noted by Jahn *et al.*,[1] there is as yet little information concerning the molecular mechanism involved in the extracellular fusion of cells, although some notable advances have been made in recent years. For example, the identification of genes essential for the formation of myotubes in *Drosophila,* such as *dumbfounded (duf)* and *rolling pebbles (rols),* and the determination of the roles of their protein products in cell fusion is proceeding (see, for example, Ruiz-Gomez *et al.*[13] and Rau *et al.*[14]). Recent work on the mechanisms involved in the formation of the syncytiotrophoblast has been recently reviewed.[15] In this system, translocation of phosphatidylserine from the inner to the outer plasmalemmal leaflet, an early step of the apoptosis cascade, and action of the fusogenic protein syncytin appear to be essential for fusion.[16–20]

Historical View

As observed by the early developers of cell culture techniques, cell fusion also occurs when animal cells are placed *in vitro,* even between cell types not normally observed to fuse in the intact animal. Such events may be induced by the artificial conditions of the *in vitro* environment; however, that they may be, at least in some cases, reflective of natural events in the animal cannot be excluded. As cited in Ringertz and Savage's classic 1976 review[11] of the literature of cell fusion, Lewis[21] described the occurrence of "spontaneous" cell fusion in 1927 as a mechanism for generating multinucleated cells from both tumor and normal tissue cells placed *in vitro.* The formation of hybrid cell lines resulting from such spontaneous fusion events was not proved until more than 30 years later, when Barski and colleagues[22,23] isolated such cells from mixed cultures of two sarcoma-forming mouse cell lines and showed that they possessed the karyotype and other marker properties expected of synkaryons (cells having chromosomes derived from both parents in a single nucleus). Cell fusion was soon confirmed using a variety of cell types. It is noteworthy that the first use of a genetic selection technique for isolating hybrid cells, Littlefield's[24] refinement and application of the hypoxanthine-aminopterin-thymidine (HAT) selection method of Szybalski *et al.*,[25] was used to isolate hybrid cells

Handbook of Stem Cells
Volume 2

formed "spontaneously" in mixed cultures of A9(HGPRT$^-$) and B82(TK$^-$) mouse cells. Davidson and Ephrussi[26] soon adapted this method to isolate hybrids formed spontaneously in mixed cultures of A9 cells and normal mouse cells. A9 parental cells died in the HAT medium. Normal mouse cells formed a monolayer of cells and soon stopped growing. Hybrids could survive in the HAT medium; in addition, they acquired from the A9 parent the property of vigorous growth in culture and lost the property of "contact inhibition" of growth exhibited by the normal cells.

These early studies illustrate some important concepts relevant to recent reports of spontaneous cell fusion in culture. First is the observation that hybrid cells, though burdened with a double complement of chromosomes, sometimes grow more rapidly than one or even both parental cell types because of the combination of traits they acquire. The term "hybrid vigor," borrowed from the jargon of plant and animal breeders, has been used to describe this trait (see Ringertz *et al.*[11]). Those experienced in tissue culture applications will appreciate that cells with even a slight growth advantage can, in a reasonably short amount of time, become a major component of a mixed cell culture. Second, the studies demonstrate that cell fusion is a relatively common event in mixed cell cultures, occurring with cells of many species and phenotypes. The comprehensive review of these early studies by Ringertz *et al.*[11] led to the conclusion that spontaneous fusion of cells in culture occurs with a frequency between 1 in 100 and 1 in 1 million cells depending on cell type and culture conditions. These authors also pointed out that "spontaneous" events in biology are "those for which a cause is not known," an important observation still relevant today. Spontaneous fusion of cocultured cells has been confirmed in more recent studies. For example, Wakeling *et al.*[27] determined the spontaneous rates of fusion for a variety of cell types and described one system, the fusion of melanocytes to melanoma cells, in which the rate of spontaneous fusion was higher than the rate observed with an added fusogen, such as polyethylene glycol. They also noted that fusion occurred at a higher frequency if the cells were treated with trypsin, indicating a role for cell surface changes that may facilitate fusion. Balakier *et al.*[28] have also shown that blastomeres spontaneously fuse to each other, forming polyploid and mosaic embryos, as a result of freezing and thawing during cryopreservation techniques.

The notion that spontaneous cell fusion could occur *in vivo* when cells are introduced into a host was repeatedly suggested by experiments in which tumor cells were introduced into an animal and cells with a higher chromosome number and altered properties were subsequently recovered (see, for example, Goldenberg *et al.*,[29] Hu and Pasztor[30] Kao and Hartz[31] Ber *et al.*,[32] and Lala *et al.*[33]). Since tumor cells often undergo such changes, a convincing demonstration of *in vivo* fusion required experiments in which cells of the host and the donor could be definitively identified by appropriate markers. Such a demonstration was of great interest to early tumor biologists, as it was hypothesized that tumor cells in an animal could acquire "useful" traits by fusion to normal host cells. For example, perhaps a solid tumor cell could acquire a metastatic property by fusion to a cell that is normally "nomadic" in the body, such as a lymphocyte.[34–36] Of the many studies demonstrating evidence for *in vivo* fusion, the 1983 report by Kerbel *et al.*[37] is noteworthy. Here, genetically marked, wheat germ agglutinin (WGA)-resistant, nonmetastatic tumor cells were introduced into a host mouse. Metastatic cells that had lost WGA resistance and had a higher chromosome number were isolated. Extensive genetic and molecular analyses, including cell surface antigen analysis, clearly showed that tumor cells had acquired some markers characteristic of recipient mouse strain cells by cell fusion. Results of experiments in which tumor cells were introduced into bone marrow radiation chimeras further showed that the normal parent cell in at least some fusion events was derived from bone marrow. It was concluded that tumor cells had fused to normal bone marrow cells, acquiring additional chromosomes and losing the recessive trait of WGA resistance. This study was unusual in that fusion appeared to occur at a relatively high frequency, thus facilitating its analysis. It was suggested that the marker used (WGA resistance) may have entailed cell surface changes that facilitated spontaneous fusion. Although fusion of normal and tumor cells *in vivo* likely plays little if any role in the origin and progression of malignancy, this and numerous other early studies showed that spontaneous fusion could occur within animals. Discussion at the time appears similar to current considerations of "genome plasticity." Although some made extravagant claims, others noted that the demonstration of low-frequency events required strict adherence to rigorous standards of scientific proof. Thus, as for spontaneous cell fusion *in vitro,* numerous early and now largely neglected studies provide precedent for our suggestion that recent examples of genome plasticity *in vivo* are at least partly the result of cell fusion despite the relatively low frequency of such events.

Cell Fusion versus Transdifferentiation

Cell fusion has been spotlighted recently as a potential mechanism to explain apparent occurrences of transdifferentiation. Adult stem cells have been generally considered organ specific; for example, hematopoietic stem cells can become only blood cells. Several studies, mainly published since 1997, have challenged this notion, proposing that adult stem cells have a much higher degree of plasticity than previously envisaged.[38–51] In a typical study of this kind, bone marrow cells from transgenic mice expressing green fluorescent protein (GFP) were transplanted into wild type mice; GFP$^+$ cells were found in unexpected organs such as brain or liver. Since such GFP$^+$ cells possessed traits characteristic of the organ in which they were found, it would be claimed that donor bone marrow cells had transdifferentiated into brain cells or liver cells. Such possibilities of transdifferentiation generated much interest and excitement for several reasons. First, they called into question traditional concepts of cell lineage and development, as mentioned previously. Second,

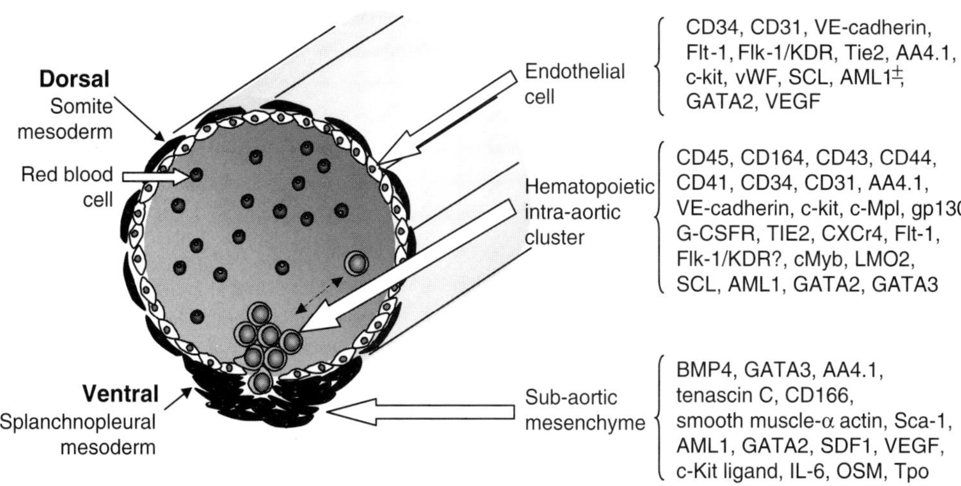

Figure 15–2. *Intra-aortic hematopoietic clusters formation in the floor of the dorsal aorta.* Based on data from E10.5 murine[71,72] and E27 human[19,20,69,70] studies. The dorsal endothelium of the aorta derive from angioblasts developing from somite mesoderm, whereas the ventral "hemogenic endothelium" or hemangioblast develops from splanchnopleural mesoderm.[68] The dorsal endothelium expresses markers associated with differentiated endothelium.[63] The hematopoietic intra-aortic cluster expresses surface antigens and cytoadhesion molecules found on hematopoietic stem and progenitor cells, hematopoiesis-related transcription factors, and receptors for hematopoietic and angiogenic growth factors.[92,99,100] The expression of Flk-1 on intra-aortic clusters is controversial.[11,32,101] The subaortic mesenchyme expresses cytokines, chemokines, and cytoadhesion molecules and has molecular features of vascular smooth muscle.[71,72,76,79,81,84,93]

E10.5 in the ventral floor of the dorsal aorta. They appear to be in direct contact with underlying mesenchyme where the endothelium is interrupted; however, ultrastructural studies in humans show that the endothelial basal lamina is intact where it interacts with the cells in the hematopoietic clusters and that the hematopoietic and endothelial cells are interconnected by tight junctions[71,72] (Fig. 15–2). VE-cadherin-expressing cells in the AGM have hematopoietic potential, and VE-cadherin is expressed on the luminal aspect of vascular endothelium but not in CD45^{+} aorta-associated hematopoietic clusters.[33,70,73,74] VE-cadherin is essential in stabilizing tight junctions between endothelial cells, suggesting the endothelial origin of hematopoiesis.[74] Similar populations of CD34^{+}CD45^{-ve} cells in the human para-aortic region label with the endothelial marker *Ulex Europus* and generate both von Willebrand (vW)$^{+}$ endothelium and hematopoietic cells.[70] This blood-forming "endothelium" is in the human embryo AGM region at 28 days, with a peak frequency at 31 days, and is absent by 44 days.[70] Culture of the P-Sp from 21- to 26-day human embryos on marrow stromal cells generated hematopoietic cells, demonstrating the hematogenic potential of P-Sp mesoderm that precedes the appearance of "hemogenic endothelium."[20] The pre-"endothelial" mesodermal precursors are CD34^{-ve}, CD45^{-ve},[20] and VEGFR2/KDR^{+}.[75]

Since cells in the human embryo AGM prior to 28 days lacked direct hematopoietic potential, it was postulated that they must receive some inductive signal from surrounding tissue to induce this potential. A discreet region of densely packed mesenchymal cells lies beneath the ventral floor of the dorsal aorta; it is 3–4 layers in the mouse and 5–7 layers in the human[19,71,72] (Fig. 15–2). These mesenchymal cells are interconnected by tight junctions, express smooth muscle α-actin (SMα-A), and may be precursor of vascular smooth muscle. BMP4 may play a crucial role in the induction of hematopoietic potential in the AGM region, much as it does in the YS.[25,76] BMP4 is polarized to the ventral wall of the dorsal aorta in the mesenchymal layer underlying the intra-aortic hematopoietic clusters, where it could induce P-Sp mesoderm to become hemangioblasts and HSCs[76] (Fig. 15–2). The mesenchyme probably also expresses the activated leukocyte cell adhesion molecule ALCAM/CD166 or its human equivalent, HSC antigen.[72] CD166 is expressed on embryonic (but not adult) aortic endothelium and has been implicated in capillary tube formation, hemangioblast differentiation, and homophilic adhesion of primitive CD166^{+} HSCs.[77,78] High levels of expression of the extracellular matrix glycoprotein tenascin-C have been observed in mesenchyme adjacent to the ventral half of the dorsal aorta in association with hematopoietic buds, and it is expressed on the basal surface of the hematopoietic cells budding into the lumen.[71,79] During development, tenascin influences cell shape and promotes motility of many cell types, possibly by interfering with cell-fibronectin interactions.[79] It may also function by immobilizing growth factors such as BMPs and TGFβ, favoring receptor binding. Stroma from tenascin-null mice have significantly reduced capacity to support hematopoiesis.[80]

The mesenchymal-inductive influence extends beyond the induction of multilineage hematopoietic precursors; it potentially includes the induction of development of B- and T-lineage–restricted progenitors (see the section "Cell Migration to Primary Lymphoid Organs") and of HSCs capable of long-term repopulation of adult mice. Medvinsky *et al.*[16] identified the mouse AGM region at E10.5 as a source of CFU-S, preceding their appearance in YS. CFU-S precursors were in both AGM and YS by E9 since cultures of either tissue at this stage generated CFU-S.[17] *In vivo* engraftment was obtained with cells from the E10.5 dorsal aorta and vitelline–umbilical artery.[81,82] Quantitation of long-term repopulating stem cell numbers by limiting dilution assay has shown that they first appear in the AGM at E10.5 and are present in equal numbers in AGM, YS, circulation, and early liver rudiment by E11[18] (Fig. 15–3). The colonization of the fetal liver by stem cells is initiated by a wave of migration from the AGM peaking at E11; this is followed by a second wave from the YS (Figs. 15–4 and 15–5). Cumano *et al.*[50] reported that cells capable of long-term lymphomyeloid engraftment could be generated in organ culture of P-Sp isolated prior to the onset of the circulation (E7.5–8), whereas cultured YS failed to generate such HSCs. However, Matsuoka *et al.*[21] were able to generate repopulating HSCs in coculture of equally early P-Sp and YS with a stromal line (AGM-S3) derived from the E10.5 AGM region. This line may have some unique properties since in a study of 100 stromal lines generated from AGM subregions, most were supportive of adult HSC expansion but none were able to induce development of engraftable HSCs when cocultured with CD34$^+$cKit$^+$ cells from E10 AGM or YS.[83] The AGM-S3 stromal line was VECAM-1$^+$, CD13$^+$, and Sca-1$^+$; it produced IL-6 and oncostatin M, cytokines that stimulate HSC proliferation using the gp130 signaling pathway.[84,85] Gp130-null mouse embryos have dramatically reduced numbers of hematopoietic progenitor cells in the AGM region and fetal liver.[86] The proliferative potential of hematopoietic cells

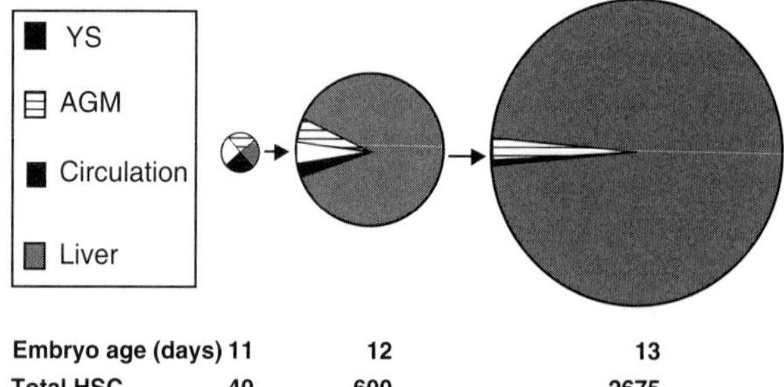

Figure 15–3. *Origin and distribution of definitive hematopoietic stem cells.* The numbers of CRUs are detected by limiting dilution, competitive, long-term repopulation assay in adult irradiated mice, adjusted for a calculated seeding efficiency of 10%. The figure shows absolute numbers in each tissue at daily intervals from E11 to E13 in the mouse embryo. Modified from Kumaravelu *et al.*[18]

in the gp130-null AGM could be restored by retroviral vector transduction of either wild-type gp130 or mutants capable of activating STAT3.

The various inductive influence of the subaortic mesenchyme could cause bipotential precursors located in the floor of the aorta to preferentially adopt a hematopoietic fate. Alternatively, endothelial cells may dedifferentiate and switch to a hematopoietic fate in response to local or transient signals. A third possibility is that hemangioblasts or their precursors may migrate secondarily into the aortic wall, either from the underlying mesenchyme or from the circulation, in response to a chemokine gradient. Endothelial cells,

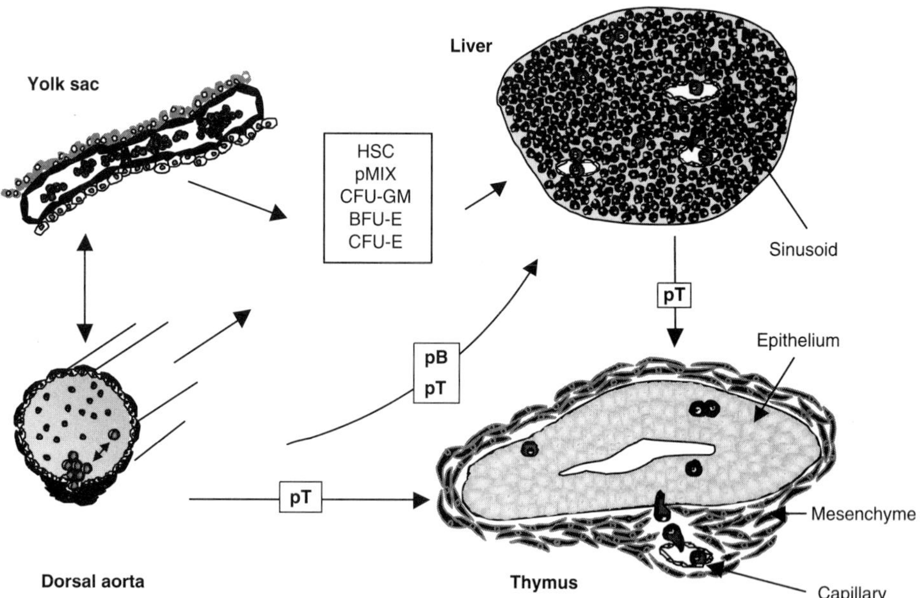

Figure 15–4. *Vascular migration streams of hematopoietic stem cells and myeloid (CFU-GM, BFU-E, CFU-E, pMix) and lymphoid (pT, pB) progenitor cells.* Migration between the dorsal aorta–AGM, the yolk sac blood islands, the embryonic liver, and the thymus occur between E10.5 and E11.5 in the mouse embryo. Immigrant cells (shown as basophilic blast cells), detach from the YS blood islands and from the aortic hematopoietic clusters, enter the circulation, egress from the microvessels within the hepatic rudiment or within the perithymic mesenchyme, and accumulate and proliferate within these developing organs.

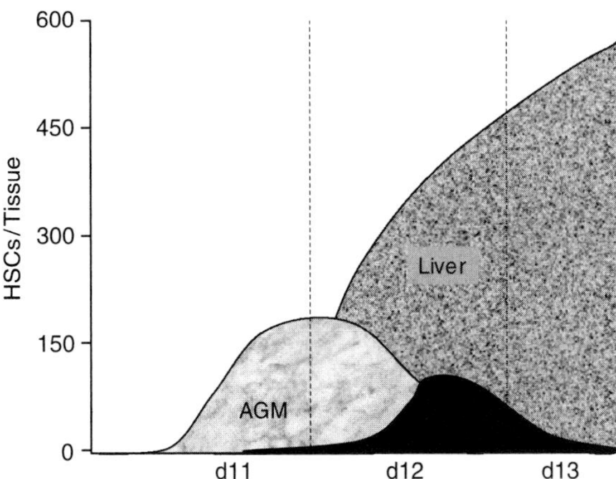

Figure 15-5. *Colonization of the embryonic liver of the mouse embryo with hematopoietic stem cells.* Determined by CRU assay in adult irradiated mice and adjusted for seeding efficiency. These numbers are based on the numbers that the AGM and YS are able to generate *in vitro*. *In vivo*, the high cumulative activity of the AGM region and the YS may provide the liver with a high proportion of definitive HSCs. The data suggests consecutive colonization of the embryonic liver with HSCs from the AGM region and the YS. Reproduced with permission from Kumaravelu *et al.*[18]

angioblasts, and HSCs express CXCR4, and mesenchyme adjacent to the dorsal aorta expresses high levels of its ligand SDF-1, indicating a role for this chemokine pathway in both vasculogenesis and migration of hemangioblastic precursors to the floor of the aorta.[87]

Studies using embryonic stem (ES) cells differentiating for 2.5–3.5 days have demonstrated the transient development of cells capable of forming blast cell colonies (BL-CFCs) in the presence of VEGF and the cKit ligand–stem cell factor (SCF), that precede the appearance of hematopoietic colony-forming cells.[37,88,89] Cells in the blast colony express several genes common to hematopoietic and endothelial lineages (CD34, SCL, and Flk1) and on replating generate endothelial progenitors and both definitive and primitive hematopoietic progenitors. The Tpo receptor cMpl was detected by day 3 of embryoid body formation when hemangioblasts first arise.[42] Tpo alone supported BL-CFC formation and nearly doubled the number of BL-CFCs when combined with VEGF and SCF. Since hematopoietic and endothelial development are not extinguished by targeted inactivation of *cMpl* or *Tpo* genes, there must be some redundancy of cytokine pathways acting on hemangioblasts. Other overlapping pathways active on hemangioblasts include VEGF/Flk1,[90] cKit/SCF,[37] BMP4,[25,91] and TGFβ.[29] The ES cell results support the concept of a hemangioblast as the precursor of both endothelium and hematopoiesis. Tpo and cMpl transcripts are present in the YS between E6.5–7.5 prior to appearance of the first blood islands[41]; from between E8.5–9.5, cMpl is expressed on embryonic blood vessels and aorta.[92] Other cytokines stimulating hemangioblasts are expressed in the AGM region, including VEGF, SCF, and BMP4.[72,76,93]

Most cells in the AGM region that express CD34, CD31, and Flk1 also express podocalyxin-like protein 1 (PCLP1), which has some sequence homology with CD34 and is a ligand for L-selectin.[94] This population differentiates into both endothelium and hematopoiesis, leading to the suggestion that PCLP1 may be a surface marker for hemangioblasts. The tunica interna endothelial cell kinase (TEK) that has a similar domain structure to Tie also appears to be a hemangioblast marker.[95] Mice lacking TEK die between E9.5–10.5 with defects in angiogenesis and vascular modeling, and cKit$^+$, CD34$^+$, and Sca-1$^-$ AGM cells that could generate both endothelium and hematopoiesis express TEK.[95]

The respective roles of hemangioblast and "hemogenic endothelium" for initiating hematopoiesis in the AGM or YS is debated.[33,37,65,70,72–74,84] Several studies identify endothelium as the source of hematopoiesis based upon isolation of cells expressing markers associated with endothelium (VE-cadherin, CD31/PECAM, Flk1 Flt1, Tie2, *Ulex Europus* binding, and Dil-Ac-LDL uptake). None of these markers are unique to endothelium and possibly could be expressed on hemangioblasts or prehematopoietic mesoderm; some are expressed on HSCs. Direct derivation of hematopoietic cells from mature, already differentiated endothelium has been reported in Dil-Ac-LDL labeling studies.[58,65,96] Following intra-cardiac injection of E10 mouse embryos with Dil-Ac-LDL, staining was found within 1 hour and was confined to CD31$^+$, CD34$^+$, and CD45^{-ve} endothelium along the entire vascular tree.[96] At 12 hours after injection, 1.4% of circulating cells were Dil-Ac-LDL, and of these, 43% expressed the erythroid marker Ter 119 and adult globin, characteristic of definitive erythropoiesis. The rest of the Dil-Ac-LDL cells are committed white blood cells, lineage-restricted and multipotent progenitors as revealed by colony formation, and HSCs. The remarkable feature of this observation is the rapidity with which the endothelium differentiates to multipotent HSCs and lineage-restricted erythroid progenitors (BFU-E) that in turn differentiate to the extent that they express globin genes—maturation steps that normally require at least 4 to 6 cell divisions. It is also likely that the transition from hemangioblast to endothelium or HSC is not abrupt but is a progressive process of increasing restriction, not unlike B- and T-cell commitment (see the section "Cell Migration to Primary Lymphoid Organs").

Ly-6A/Sca-1 is a stem cell marker. Using a transgenic approach with an *Sca-1-GFP* marker gene, it was shown that green fluorescent protein (GFP) was expressed in all functional HSCs in the midgestation aorta and was localized to cells residing in the endothelial layer lining the ventral wall of the dorsal aorta but not to the adjacent mesenchyme.[97] At E11, there were 1,600 Sca-1-GFP$^+$ (also cKit$^+$, CD31$^+$, CD34$^+$, and VE-cadherin$^+$) cells in the AGM, and they provided multilineage engraftment in adult mice. Note, however, that Sca-1 is probably not expressed on hemangioblasts or hemogenic endothelium in the AGM,[95] and its expression is not restricted to HSCs since it is expressed on AGM-derived stromal cell lines with hematopoietic support capacity.[84,98] Molecular analysis of single cKit$^+$CD34$^+$ cells from the E11 mouse AGM region, when populations of engraftable HSCs as well as lymphoid- and myeloid-committed progenitors are present, showed that most expressed hematopoietic-specific transcription factors AML1, GATA-2, PU-1, and LMO2.[99] The majority of cells also express the G-CSF receptor, and a minority express the erythropoietin receptor. The myeloid-specific gene *MPO* was expressed in 90% of cells, and the erythroid-specific β-globin was expressed in 50%, indicating that genes of mutually exclusive differentiation lineages may be expressed simultaneously in a single primitive cell prior to lineage commitment.

AML1 plays a critical role in the establishment of definitive hematopoiesis in the AGM. AML1 expression is initiated in mesenchymal cells at the distal tip of the allantois, in endothelial cells in the ventral portion of paired dorsal aorta at E8.5, in both endothelium and mesenchyme of the ventral AGM, and in the intra-aortic hematopoietic clusters between E9.5–11.5.[32] In AML1/LacZ mice, some 30% of the cells recovered from the AGM and the vitelline and umbilical arteries at E11.5 were AML1/LacZ$^+$; this population contained all HSCs capable of engrafting irradiated recipients.[32] These HSCs were initially CD45^{-ve} at E10.5, but by E11.5, HSC activity was present in both CD45$^+$ and CD45^{-ve} fractions. Most HSCs were CD41$^+$ and were found in both the positive and the negative fraction of AGM stained with CD31, Flk1, or VE-cadherin.[32,100] The expression of Flk1 on these HSC populations is controversial, with some studies showing expression of the receptor in the hematopoietic clusters,[101] others showing that it is barely detectable in hematopoietic clusters but is expressed on hemangioblastic precursors,[75] and still others providing data suggesting that some HSCs that lack Flk1 did engraft, indicating down-regulation of Flk1 on CD45$^+$ intra-aortic clusters.[32]

In AML1-deficient mice, HSCs and intra-aortic clusters were absent; in AML1 hemizygous mice, hematopoietic clusters were reduced in number and size and HSC numbers and distribution were altered, indicating a gene dosage effect.[32] Haploinsufficiency of AML1 results in an earlier appearance of engraftable HSCs in the YS, with E10 YS cells reconstituting the hematopoietic system of irradiated adult mice.[102] At the same time, there is premature termination of HSC activity in the AGM explants consistent with a change in the balance of HSC emergence, migration, maintenance, or a combination of these. With hemozygous levels of AML1, the YS may autonomously generate HSCs simultaneous to their generation in the AGM; the AGM may autonomously generate abundant HSCs that immediately and rapidly migrate to the YS, where they are detected in abundance; or AML1 insufficiency may block the emigration of HSCs from the YS, resulting in an accumulation there and a deficiency in the AGM.

Cell Migration to Later Sites of Hematopoiesis

ONTOGENY OF LIVER HEMATOPOIESIS

Lineage tracing studies support a derivation of the liver from ventral foregut endoderm induced by signals from pericardium and septum transversum mesenchyme to proliferate and adopt a hepatic state.[103] The fetal liver stroma consists of cells that express features of epithelium (cytokeratin-8), mesenchyme (vimentin and osteopontin), and vascular smooth muscle (SMα-A).[104] These cells are supportive of long-term HSC proliferation, and their presence in the liver coincides with the duration of hepatic hematopoiesis. At late gestation when hematopoiesis declines, these cells are replaced by epithelial cells resembling mature hepatocytes and by a minority of myofibroblasts. Oncostatin M, produced by hematopoietic cells within the liver, has been implicated in inducing hepatic maturation of the epithelial–mesenchymal stromal cells with loss of hematopoietic support capacity.[104]

Fetal liver isolated before the 28-somite stage (E9.5) and grafted beneath the kidney capsule of adult mice resulted in the survival of hepatic tissue, but no hematopoietic elements were present.[105] Administration of hematopoietic cells into the circulation of recipient mice resulted in multilineage hematopoietic engraftment of the implanted fetal liver. Grafts of liver isolated later than the 28-somite stage showed autonomous hematopoiesis, defining the time of initiation of HSC entry into the liver between E9.5–10. In humans, the number of BFU-E drops abruptly in the YS at 35 days; simultaneously, they appear in the liver, reflecting oriented migration.[106] The definitive BFU-E and CFU-E generated in the YS do not differentiate in that site; most likely, they seed the fetal liver and rapidly establish definitive erythropoiesis. This is supported by the observations that large numbers of CFU-E appear simultaneously with BFU-E at the onset of hepatic hematopoiesis and that embryonic blood contains significant numbers of definitive hematopoietic progenitors immediately prior to liver development.[47]

There is a daily logarithmic increase in CFU-GM and BFU-E in the liver between 10–13 days paralleled by an extensive expansion of CFU-S.[10,15] HSCs detected in long-term competitive repopulation assays were reported at E12 in the liver, increasing 38-fold to E16 and decreasing thereafter.[107] These investigators failed to find either short- or long-term repopulating HSCs in E11 liver. However, Kumaravelu *et al.*[18] used limiting dilution long-term repopulation assay to demonstrate at least one competitive repopulating unit (CRU) in the liver, circulation, AGM region, and YS at E11, with an increase in the liver to 53 CRU at E12 and 260 CRU at E13 (Fig. 15–3). The 24-hour seeding efficiency of murine fetal liver HSCs into adult marrow as measured by limiting dilution competitive repopulation assays is ~10%, essentially identical to seeding of adult marrow HSCs.[108] Thus ~10 HSCs initiate hematopoiesis by seeding the hepatic rudiment. These numbers could be explained by colonization from the AGM, but at E12, the YS makes a significant contribution; thus, these HSCs may not require processing in the AGM but may mature *in situ*.[18] Relative to adult bone marrow, fetal liver HSCs provide long-term lymphomyeloid repopulation of adult mice fivefold more efficiently than adult marrow,[109] explained by their sevenfold higher concentration and the observation that fetal HSC clones generated ~threefold more cells than marrow HSCs.[108]

In conclusion, the liver appears to be colonized by an early wave of committed and multipotent progenitors and macrophages that may be predominantly of YS origin and by two waves of HSCs. The initial HSC wave from the AGM appears to arrive at E10, reach a maximum at E11, and disappear by E13; on E12, a second wave arrives from the YS (Figs. 15–3 through 15–5). It is possible that angioblasts also migrate from the YS into the liver to initiate hepatic vasculogenesis. There is no evidence of hemangioblasts or hematogenic endothelium in fetal liver, and sorted hepatic endothelial cells isolated immediately prior to onset of human hepatic hematopoiesis (E27) were devoid of hematopoietic potential.[70]

ONTOGENY OF BONE MARROW

The primordium of the bone marrow cavity develops following penetration by perichondrial mesenchymal cells and blood vessels into the zone of calcified cartilage in the central region of the long bones.[3] Hypertrophic chondrocytes secrete VEGF that recruits vascular cells to penetrate the perichondrium and bring osteoblast precursors and circulating hematopoietic cells, including primitive macrophages.[110] Following resorption of the cartilaginous matrix, the developing marrow cavity appears as a network of connective tissue and a plexus of widely dilated veins. Marrow hematopoiesis is initiated by accumulation of large numbers of undifferentiated basophilic blast cells within the dilate marrow capillaries, beginning between E11–12 in the chick, at E17 in the mouse, and between E70–77 in the human.[10] Subsequently, separate and distinct areas of erythropoiesis and granulopoiesis develop. Avian parabiosis studies demonstrated that circulating stem cells colonize the developing marrow beginning between E11–12.[5] Following intravenous injection of tritiated thymidine-labeled embryonic YS or spleen cells into chick embryos, significant numbers of labeled blast cells localized in the marrow at E11.[10] Cells from these tissues also repopulated the marrow when injected into irradiated embryos.[6] In the mouse, CFU-GM/BFU-E, CFU-S and HSCs appear in the femoral marrow at E17; the populations double every 34 hours. The marrow progressively expands in the first 2 months of postnatal life, associated with a decline in hepatic hematopoiesis in the first week of life and a decline of splenic hematopoiesis after the third week.

Proof that fetal liver stem–progenitor cells were responsible for colonizing the marrow was provided in studies in which rats were injected *in utero* at E16 with a retroviral vector.[111] Clonal identification of viral integration sites showed that fetal liver–derived clones appeared in the marrow and circulated throughout the life of the animals. The role of SDF-1 produced by marrow stromal cells in the chemoattraction of CXCR4$^+$ HSCs is well established in the adult.[53] The failure of development of marrow hematopoiesis in mice with inactivation of the CXCR4/SDF-1 pathway[54] strongly suggests that the initial wave of HSC migration is also SDF-1 dependent.

ONTOGENY OF THE SPLEEN

The splenic primordium appears as a dense syncytial-like mesenchymal thickening in the dorsal mesogastrium. The mesenchymal condensation is interspersed with vascular spaces where circulating blood comes into direct contact with mesenchymal reticulum cells. At the earliest stage, corresponding to E8 in chick embryos and E13 in mouse, large immature cells characterized by intense cytoplasmic basophil and prominent nucleoli are observed both in the vascular spaces and in the perivascular mesenchyme of the spleen.[10] Within 24 hours, these basophilic cells appear scattered throughout the mesenchyme and frequently extend long tails of cytoplasm between the reticulum cells for some distance from the main body of the cells. By 72 hours, granulopoiesis is extensive with erythropoietic foci. Lymphopoiesis is initiated around birth, and myelopoietic activity progressively declines thereafter. Sex-chromosome marker studies in parabiosed and twin embryos demonstrated extensive chimerism in the splenic rudiment of the chick embryo as early as E12.[5] Cell-labeling studies confirmed that circulating cells colonized the avian splenic rudiment as early as E8 and, with embryonic hematopoietic cell reconstitution of irradiated embryos, indicated that splenic colonizing cells were in the YS and circulation at the initiation of splenic hematopoiesis.[10] Labeled thymic lymphocytes began to localize in the spleen with high efficiency by E17, coinciding with the initiation of lymphopoiesis.

The origin of cells initially colonizing the mammalian spleen rudiment is most likely the fetal liver, since the AGM and YS are no longer hematopoietic at this stage and the marrow has not yet developed. CFU-GM/BFU-E, CFU-S, and HSCs are detected by E15 in the splenic rudiment and increase in absolute numbers through the third week of postnatal life, then progressively decline as the spleen ceases to be a myelopoietic organ.

Cell Migration to Primary Lymphoid Organs

ONTOGENY OF THE THYMUS

The thymus is an example of interaction between mesenchymal (neural-crest–derived) and epithelial (endodermal) tissues. Notch signaling may play role in the induction of thymic epithelium. In the mouse embryo at E9.5, Notch receptors and the Notch ligand, Jagged1, are expressed in the third pharyngeal pouch at the initiation of thymic organogenesis.[112] The thymic anlage at E11 consists of stratified epithelium that over the following 24 hours changes to clustered epithelium and begins to express high levels of MHC class II antigen and of Delta1, the Notch ligand that plays a critical role in T-cell development.[112] Comparable development of the thymic rudiment is seen ~35 days in the human embryo and 7–8 days in the chick embryo. Chromosome marker studies in parabiotic chick embryos demonstrated very high levels of thymic lymphoid chimerism following the establishment of a YS vascular union between 6–7 days of incubation but not following a later-established chorioallantoic vascular anastomosis, indicating that circulating stem cells colonized the rudiment between 6–7 days.[8] Subsequent studies[113] showed the avian thymus is colonized in three waves during embryogenesis at E6, E12, and E18. Progenitors in the first wave came partly from para-aortic foci, with the second and subsequent waves coming from marrow and, to a minor extent, from spleen.

The role of the YS as a source of thymic immigrant cells was suggested by studies in which 7-day YS cells were injected into irradiated chick embryos and colonized the thymus.[6,13] However, sex-mismatched YS and embryo chimeras generated between 33–55 hours of incubation showed that the thymus as well as the bursa, spleen, and marrow were populated by cells of the sex of embryo and not by YS.[13] Studies in chick–quail chimeras also showed that the primary lymphoid organs were colonized by cells that originate in the para-aortic region.[11,12] It appears that in the avian system the YS is colonized at a very early stage by cells originating in the para-aortic region and, like the mammalian fetal liver, may serve as a site for expansion of lymphoid progenitors that secondarily migrate to the thymus and bursa of Fabricius. During initial thymic colonization (beginning E11 in the mouse and E7 in the chick), which precedes the onset of vascularization by 48 hours, blood-borne precursors must leave adjacent pharyngeal vessels then traverse perithymic mesenchyme and basement membrane surrounding the epithelial rudiment to enter the thymus (Fig. 15–4). Approximately 20 T-cell precursors enter the thymus between E11–12, 300 between E12–13, and 3,000 between E13–14.[114]

Evidence for thymic chemotactic factors have been provided in functional transfilter cell migration studies that have shown that alymphoid thymic lobes attract cells from fetal liver fragments.[115] MHC class II$^+$ epithelial cells are a source of a chemoattractant factors, and response is dependent on G-coupled receptors. Several chemokines and their receptors are expressed either on immigrant cells or epithelium; one example, TECK, is chemotactic for thymocytes.[115] Chemokine signaling can induce expression of metalloproteinases (MMP9) on immigrant cells that digest extracellular matrix and basement membrane material and aid penetration of the avascular epithelium. The failure of thymic development in the Nude mouse is caused by a loss of function mutation in the *Foxn1* transcription factor essential for thymic epithelial development and results in failure of lymphoid precursors to enter the epithelium from the perithymic mesenchyme.[116]

The lymphopoietic paths of intrathymic development occurs over 2 weeks with four phenotypically and genetically distinct phases.[117] The first stage (lineage double-negative stage 1) is CD4^{-ve}, CD8^{-ve}, CD25^{-ve}, and CD44^{hi}, and it generates T-cells, B-cells, dendritic cells (DCs) and NK cells. The second stage is CD4^{-ve}, CD8^{-ve}, CD25$^+$, and CD44^{hi} T-cells or DCs only. Stage 3 is CD4^{-ve}, CD8^{-ve}, CD25$^+$, and CD44^{lo} and is committed to T-cells. The final stage is pre-CD4$^+$, CD8$^+$, and CD25$^-$. A 4000-fold expansion occurs in the first three phases, and a 250-fold expansion takes place in the early pre-CD4$^+$ and CD8$^+$ double-positive stage.[117]

Origin and Commitment of Thymic-Colonizing Cells

The YS and AGM region and the early stage of fetal liver are all sources of lymphomyeloid stem cells (HSCs) at thymic colonization, yet extensive studies using *in vitro* thymic lobe cultures to identify thymic-colonizing cells suggest that they are not HSCs and are to some degree T-committed prior to entry into the thymus. Ohmura and Kawamoto and colleagues[73,118–123] report that lymphoid commitment coincides with the first appearance of hematopoietic clusters in the vascular endothelium of the AGM region between E9.5–10. At this stage, the CD45$^+$, cKit$^+$, and CD34$^+$ population contains multilineage progenitors as well as progenitors restricted to T (pT), T–NK plus macrophage (pTm), B (pB), or B plus macrophage (pBm) but not to pBT. A CLP identified in adult mouse marrow as a precursor of both B- and T-lineage can be distinguished from the HSC and CMP by expression of IL-7Rα, in addition to being Sca-1$^+$, cKit$^+$, and Lin^{-ve}.[4,124] It appears that in fetal development, a CLP stage comparable to the adult does not exist.[4,123,125] The fetal pT cells have T-cell receptor rearrangements and appear in the fetal blood and liver between E11–12, where they greatly outnumber pB.[125] This coincides with the period of initial thymic colonization, when pT in the liver initially increase then rapidly decline in number and pB, initially rare, rapidly increase in number (Fig. 15–4).

Cells isolated from the perithymic mesenchyme during initial colonization were IL-7Rα^+ and Lin^{-ve}.[126] Consistent with the paucity of Notch ligand in the fetal liver environment, expression of Notch target genes *Hes-1* and *pre-Tα* were not detectable in either fetal liver or perithymic IL-7Rα^+ and Lin^{-ve} populations, indicating that Notch signaling was not activated in these cells prior to thymic entry.[126] In contrast, Notch target genes were detected in precursors that had entered the epithelial environment where Jagged and Delta are readily detected. This suggests that a Notch influence on the T-lineage does not occur until cells enter the thymus. However, it is also possible that prethymic commitment to the T-lineage is induced by factors other than Notch but is only revealed as a result of Notch signaling in the thymus. The importance of Delta-Notch signaling in T-cell development has been shown by culturing fetal liver Sca-1^{hi}, cKit^{hi}, CD25^{lo}, and Lin^{-ve}cells on the OP9 marrow stromal cell line with IL-7 and c-Kit ligand.[127] Ectopic expression of Delta ligand inhibited B-lymphoid differentiation and induced a normal program of T-cell differentiation through to functionally mature CD4 and CD8 populations. The expression of IL-7Rα on the immigrant pT and the role of IL-7 on *in vitro* T-cell development contrasts with the reported lack of IL-7Rα on the earliest T-lineage progenitor within the thymus[128] and correlates with their loss of thymic homing capacity. Mouse IL-7Rα chain mutants show profound defects in thymopoiesis in the adult, but fetal thymopoiesis is relatively intact, suggesting alternate cytokine pathways can operate during ontogeny.[129] Further differences between adult and fetal thymopoiesis are revealed in *Ikaros*-null mutants that have defective fetal thymopoiesis even though the adult thymus is intact.[129]

To understand lymphoid-lineage specification from the HSC, it is best to think of it as a progressive bias along the T-, B-, or myeloid pathway without abrupt transition steps. The first cell to enter the thymus is predominantly T directed but retains some myeloid and B potential. The latter has been revealed by the ability of these cells to undergo delayed

B-cell development in culture and the appearance of B-cell development in the thymus of mice with null mutations of Delta.[130] The pB and the adult CLP are more biased toward B than toward T differentiation, and the former retain some myeloid potential. The expression of the Pax5 transcription factor has been correlated with B-cell differentiation and progressive down-regulation of myeloid and T-specific genes.[131] The existence of an embryonic precursor of both the T-biased and B-biased progenitors, with equal capacity to generate T or B, has been proposed.[132]

ONTOGENY OF B-LYMPHOCYTES

Avian Bursa of Fabricius

In the avian system, the bursa of Fabricius primordium appears by E5 as an epithelial thickening at the ventrocaudal contact of the cloaca with external ectodermal epithelium. As both bursal and thymic anlagen develop at sites of endodermal–ectodermal interaction, this origin may be of some fundamental importance in the early induction of primary lymphoid organs.[7,10] By E10–11, longitudinal folds of lining epithelium project into the lumen, and by E12–13, epithelial buds project into the underlying mesenchyme. Bursal lymphopoiesis begins by E14, and at this stage, many large basophilic cells are observed in the blood vessels of the mesenchyme adjacent to the epithelial buds. These cells pass through the epithelial basement membrane and localize within the epithelium follicle where they proliferate extensively, differentiating into typical bursal B-lymphocytes. Chromosome marker studies in parabiosed embryos and embryonic grafts of bursal rudiments demonstrated that the bursa was colonized by circulating lymphoid precursors that entered between E13–14.[6,7] Injection of embryos between E10–14 with tritiated thymidine-labeled embryonic YS, spleen marrow, and blood cells (but not thymocytes) showed rapid localization of labeled basophilic cells in the bursal epithelium with subsequent proliferation and lymphoid differentiation.[10] The "receptivity" of the bursal epithelium for labeled cells declined abruptly at E15. Parallel injection studies into E14 irradiated embryos using sex-chromosome marking confirmed that the preceding embryonic hematopoietic tissues, but not the thymus, contained bursal lymphoid precursors.[6] Using specific markers expressed on restricted B- and T-precursors, it was shown that cells on the E14 spleen or marrow that colonized the bursa upon injection were already B committed with VJ recombination and distinct from T-lineage precursors.[133] Since such B-restricted precursors appear to be in the circulation and in all hematopoietic organs at the time of bursal colonization, the precise site of B-lineage commitment is unclear. What is known, as a result of sex-mismatched and chick–quail YS–embryo chimeras, is that the B-precursors ultimately derive from the intraembryonic para-aortic region, possibly as early as E2[13,14]—although their subsequent expansion and B-commitment may occur within the YS and then the spleen.

Mammalian B-Cell Ontogeny

The fetal liver has long been considered the initial site of B-cell commitment beginning E14 in the mouse; from then on, the B-progenitors expand in a synchronous wave-like pattern, reaching a peak in the perinatal stage.[134] It was also generally accepted that early B-cell progenitors expressed CD45R/B220 prior to CD19 expression. However, it has become recognized that B-lineage gene expression (DJH rearrangements and Ig germ line transcripts) could be detected in P-Sp–AGM and liver before E12.5.[135] Furthermore, Rag-2, Rag-1, and *CD19* gene expression has been found at E9 in YS and P-Sp.[136,137] By functional and phenotypic analysis, AA4.1$^+$ and FcγR$^+$ or AA4.1$^+$, Sca-1$^+$, and B220^{-ve} cells with B-macrophage potential were detected in E12.5–13 fetal liver.[135,138,139] A novel population of cKit$^+$, AA4.1$^+$, CD34$^+$, Sca-1^{-ve}, CD45$^+$, and CD19$^+$ cells (70% expressing IL-7Rα but negative for CD45R/B220) were detected in E11 P-Sp–AGM and liver that differentiate exclusively into B-cells.[137] Numerically, at E11, these very early pro-B-progenitors comprised ~100 in the AGM region, ~500 in the liver, and smaller numbers in the blood and YS (Fig. 15–4).

Coculture on marrow stromal lines such as S17 or ST2, often with the addition of cytokines such as IL-7 and cKit ligand, has been used to assay for B-lymphoid potential.[118,140–142] Such studies have identified the emergence of B- or B-macrophage-restricted progenitors in the AGM region at E10, coinciding with the development of the aortic hematopoietic clusters.[121] The number of progenitors capable of generating B-cells in the AGM at E10 (30–35 somite pairs) was 10 and increased 400-fold by E12, when they were located in the fetal liver within the CD45$^+$, Kit$^+$, Sca-1^{lo}, and IL-7Rα^+ population.[121,123,125] The numbers and location of these B-progenitors correspond to the CD19$^+$ pro-B-cells described previously.[137]

There has been a long, and as yet unresolved, debate concerning the role of the YS in generating pB. Early studies with Ig allotype markers showed that YS cells transplanted into adult mice generated B-cells,[143] and *in utero* injection of E8–10 YS resulted in postnatal B and T chimerism.[144] Chromosome-marked E11 YS cells were shown to provide long-term lymphoid (T and B) and myeloid engraftment in mice.[15] In a series of studies, Auerbach *et al.*[141,142,145] showed that AA4.1$^+$ cells from YS as early as E8–E9, when cocultured on marrow stroma or YS endothelial lines, could generate cells with B and T potential as measured *in vitro* and when transferred *in vivo* into immunodeficient mice. Cumano *et al.*[146] initially reported that AA4$^+$, Sca-1$^-$ cells in both YS and embryo at E8.5 were able to generate both T- and B-cells in an S17 stromal coculture with IL-7 and cKit ligand. In a subsequent study, Cumano *et al.*[147] separately cultured mouse embryo and YS at the presomite, prevasculature E7.5–8 stage for 48 hours and observed B-cell differentiation only in the embryo. They only observed lymphoid potential in cultured YS after the circulation was established, favoring their view that the YS is colonized by P-Sp–derived lymphoid progenitors. The absence of definitive hematopoiesis (CFC-mix or BFU-E) in their cultured YS, despite the presence of these cells in the YS *in situ,* suggests that the culture conditions were deficient for maintenance of a normal pattern of lymphohematopoiesis, rendering a negative result inconclusive. Ogawa *et al.*[140] reported B-cell progenitors developing in cultures of E9.5 embryos but not of YS, although excessive production of mast cells in the latter cultures may have inhibited lymphoid differentiation. Nishikawa *et al.*[73] isolated VE-cadherin$^+$ and CD45^{-ve} "endothelial" cells from an E8.5–9.5 embryo and YS and showed B-cell differentiation on an OP9 stroma with IL-7. The variable and often conflicting data can be attributed partly to culture variables such as whole-tissue cultures versus dispersed cells, the use of different stromal lines, and particularly the use of supplemental cytokines such as IL-7 and cKit ligand. Certain of these conditions may provide an environment capable of supporting lymphoid differentiation from hemogenic endothelium or hemangioblasts, others may support differentiation from lymphomyeloid stem cells and pMix, and others can expand only those cells that have undergone B-cell commitment (pB or pBm). By restricting the criteria for a committed B-cell progenitor to cells expressing CD45, and probably CD19, IL-7Rα, and cKit, they first appear within the E10 AGM region where they may traffic to the YS as well as the early liver. It is unknown whether the more primitive cell populations in the YS that have B-lymphoid potential can migrate into the embryo and undergo pB commitment in the AGM region.

The myeloid suppressing transcription factor Pax5 plays a critical role in B-cell commitment, and Pax5-deficient mice display B-maturation arrest at the pro-B level.[131] The B–macrophage progenitors in the fetal liver and AGM expresses Pax5 but at a significantly lower level than the adult CLP.[139] This observation may account for the retention of macrophage potential in the fetal progenitor and the block of this pathway in the adult CLP. In the absence of Pax5, the pB, when transferred to RAG2-deficient mice, provide long-term reconstitution of the thymus and generate mature T-cells; *in vitro* with appropriate cytokines, they can produce T-cells, macrophages, osteoclasts, DCs, granulocytes, and NK cells.[131] Migration of B-progenitors from the AGM to the liver begins E10 with subsequent increase because of continued immigration and intrahepatic expansion (Fig. 15–4). Since HSCs are also colonizing the liver at this time, the possibility of intrahepatic generation of additional pB from these more primitive cells cannot be excluded.

The role of the chemokine SDF-1 in promoting the migration of pB from the AGM region to the liver is suggested by the demonstration that its receptor, CXCR4, is expressed on IL-7Rα^+ pB and that SDF-1 induces chemotaxis of these cells.[148] Mutant mice with targeted disruption of the *SDF-1* or *CXCR4* genes display defects in B-lymphocyte development in the fetal liver[54,149] that could be accounted for by defective colonization of the liver by pB as well as by impairment in B-cell proliferation, since SCF-1, acting in synergy with cKit and Flt-3 ligands, promotes proliferation of pB cells.[148]

REFERENCES

1. Danchakoff, V. (1916). Origin of blood cells: development of the hematopoietic organs and regeneration of blood cells from the standpoint of the monophyletic school. *Anat. Rec.* **10,** 397–413.
2. Maximow, A.A. (1924). Relation of blood cells to connective tissues and endothelium. *Physiol. Rev.* **1224,** 533–563.
3. Moore, M.A.S. (2003). *In vitro* and *in vivo* hematopoiesis. *In* "Atlas of Blood Cells: Function and Pathology" (D. Zucker-Franklin *et al.,* eds.), 3rd ed, Vol. 1, pp. 3–38. Edi Ermes, Milan, Italy.
4. Akashi, K., Traver, D., Kondo, M., and Weissman, I.L. (1999). Lymphoid development from hematopoietic stem cells. *Int. J. Hematol.* **69,** 217–226.
5. Moore, M.A.S., and Owen, J.J.T. (1965). Chromosome marker studies on the development of the hemopoietic system in the chick embryo. *Nature* **208,** 986–990.
6. Moore, M.A.S., and Owen, J.J.T. (1966). Chromosome marker studies in the irradiated chick embryo. *Nature* **215,** 1081–1082.
7. Moore, M.A.S., and Owen, J.J.T. (1966). Experimental studies on the development of the bursa of Fabricius. *Dev. Biol.* **14,** 40–51.
8. Moore, M.A.S., and Owen, J.J.T. (1967). Experimental studies on the development of the thymus. *J. Exp. Med.* **126,** 715–726.
9. Moore, M.A.S., and Owen, J.J.T. (1967). Stem cell migration in developing myeloid and lymphoid systems. *Lancet* **2,** 658–659.
10. Metcalf, D., and Moore, M.A.S. (1971). Hemopoietic Cells. *In* "Frontiers of Biology Series," pp. 1–550. North Holland Publishing Company, Amsterdam.
11. Dieterlen-Lievre, F. (1975). On the origin of hematopoietic cells in the avian embryo: an experimental approach. *J. Embryol. Exp. Morphol.* **33,** 607–619.
12. Dieterlen-Lievre, F., Godin, I., and Paranaud, L. (1997). Where do hematopoietic stem cells come from? *Int. Arch. Allergy. Immunol.* **112,** 3–8.
13. Lassila, O., Eskola, J., Toivanen, P., Martin, C., and Dieterlen-Lievre, F. (1978). The origin of lymphoid stem cells studied in chick yolk sac–embryo chimaeras. *Nature* **272,** 353–354.
14. Lassila, O., Martic, C., Dieterlen-Lievre, F., Gilmour, D.G., Eskola, J., and Toivanen, P. (1982). Migration of prebursal stem cells from early chick embryo to the yolk sac. *Scand. J. Immunol.* **16,** 265–268.
15. Moore, M.A.S., and Metcalf, D. (1970). Ontogeny of the hemopoietic system: yolk sac origin of *in vivo* and *in vitro* colony-forming cell in the developing mouse embryo. *Brit. J. Haematol.* **18,** 279–296.
16. Medvinsky, A.L., Samoylina, N.L., Muller, A.M., and Dzierzak, E.A. (1993). An early preliver intraembryonic source of CFU-S in the developing mouse. *Nature* **364,** 64–67.
17. Medvinsky, A., Dzierzak, E. (1996). Definitive hematopoiesis is autonomously initiated by the AGM region. *Cell* **86,** 897–906.
18. Kumaravelu, P., Hook, L., Morrison, A.M., Ure, J., Zhao, S., Zuyev, S., Ansell, J., and Medvinsky, A. (2002) Quantitative developmental anatomy of definitive hematopoietic stem cells–long-term repopulating units (HSCs–RUs): role of the aorta–gonad–mesonephros (AGM) region and the yolk sac in colonization of the mouse embryonic liver. *Development* **129,** 4891–4899.
19. Tavian, M., Hallais, M.F., and Peault, B. (1999). Emergence of intraembryonic hematopoietic precursors in the preliver human embryo. *Development* **126,** 793–803.
20. Tavian, M., Robin, C., Coulombel, L., and Peault, B. (2001). The human embryo, but not its yolk sac, generates lymphomyeloid stem cells: mapping multipotential hematopoietic cell fate in intraembryonic mesoderm. *Immunity* **15,** 487–495.
21. Matsuoka, S., Tsuji, K., Hisakawa, H., Xu, M.J., Ebihara, Y., Ishii, T., Sugiyama, D., Manabe, A., Tanaka, R., Ikeda, Y., Asano, S., and Nakahata, T. (2001). Generation of definitive hematopoietic stem cells from murine early yolk sac and para-aortic splanchnopleures by aorta–gonad–mesonephros region-derived stromal cells. *Blood* **98,** 9–12.

22. Yoder, M.C., and Hiatt, K. (1997). Engraftment of embryonic hematopoietic cells in conditioned newborn recipients. *Blood* **89,** 2176–2183.
23. Belaoussoff, M., Farrington, S.M., and Baron, M.H. (1998). Hematopoietic induction and respecification of A–P identity by visceral endodermal signaling in the mouse embryo. *Development* **125,** 5009–5018.
24. Baron, M. (2001). Induction of embryonic hematopoietic and endothelial stem–progenitor cells by Hedgehog-mediate signals. *Differentiation* **68,** 175–185.
25. Baron, M.H. (2001). Molecular regulation of embryonic hematopoiesis and vascular development: a novel pathway. *J. Hematother. Stem Cell Res.* **10,** 587–594.
26. Byrd, N., Becker, S., Maye, P., Narasimhaiah, R., St. Jacques, B., Zhang, X., McMahon, J., McMahon, A., and Grabel, L. (2002). Hedgehog is required for murine yolk sac angiogenesis. *Development* **129,** 361–372.
27. Liu, B., Sun, Y., Jiang, F., Zhang, S., Wu, Y., Lan, Y., Yang, X., and Mao, N. (2003). Disruption of *Smad5* gene leads to enhanced proliferation of high-proliferative potential precursors during embryonic hematopoiesis. *Blood* **101,** 124–133.
28. Cantor, A.B., and Orkin, S.H. (2002). Transcriptional regulation of erythropoiesis: An affair involving multiple partners. *Oncogene* **21,** 3368–3376.
29. Dickson, M.C., Martin, J.S., Cousins, F.M., Kulkarni, A.B., Karlsson, S., and Akhurst, R.J. (1995). Defective hematopoiesis and vasculogenesis in transforming growth factor-beta 1 knockout mice. *Development* **121,** 1845–1854.
30. Gering, M., Rodaway, A.R.F., Gottgens, B., Patient, R.K., and Green, A.R. (1998). The *SCL* gene specifies hemangioblast development from early mesoderm. *EMBO J.* **17,** 4029–4045.
31. Mikkola, H.K.A., Fujiwara, Y., Schlaeger, T.M., Traver, D., and Orkin, S.H. (2003). Expression of CD41 marks the initiation of definitive hematopoiesis in the mouse embryo. *Blood* 101, 508–516.
32. North, T.E., De Bruijn, M.F.T.R., Stacy, T., Talebian, L., Lind, E., Robin, C., Binder, M., Dzierzak, E., and Speck, N.A. (2002). Runx1 expression marks long-term repopulating hematopoietic stem cells in the midgestation mouse embryo. *Immunity* **16,** 661–672.
33. Mikkola, H.K.A., and Orkin, S.H. (2002). The search for the hemangioblast. *J. Hematother. Stem Cell Res.* **11,** 9–17.
34. Damert, A., Miquero, L., Gertsenstein, M., Risau1, W., and Nagy, A. (2002). Insufficient VEGFA activity in yolk sac endoderm compromises hematopoietic and endothelial differentiation. *Development* **129,** 1881–1892.
35. Kabrun, N., Buhring, H.J., Choi, K., Ullrich, A., Risau, W., and Keller, G. (1997). Flk-1 expression defines a population of early embryonic hematopoietic precursors. *Development* **124,** 2039–2048.
36. Nishikawa, S.I., Nishikawa, S., Hirashima, N., Matsuyoshi, N., and Kodama, H. (1997). Progressive lineage analysis by cell sorting and culture identifies FLK1+ VE-cadherin+ cells at a divergent point of endothelial and hematopoietic lineages. *Development* **125,** 1747–1757.
37. Choi, K. (2002). The hemangioblast: a common progenitor of hematopoietic and endothelial cells. *J. Hematother. Stem Cell Res.* **11,** 91–101.
38. Adelman, D., Maltepe, E., and Simon, M.C. (1999). Multilineage embryonic hematopoiesis requires hypoxic ARNT activity. *Genes Dev.* **19,** 2478–2483.
39. Oike, Y., Takakura, N., Hata, A., Kaname, T., Akizuki, M., Yamaguchi, Y., Yasue, H., Araki, K., Yamamura, K., and Suda, T. (1999). Mice homozygous for a truncated form of CREB-binding protein exhibit defects in hematopoiesis and vasculoangiogenesis. *Blood* **93,** 2771–2779.
40. Xu, M.J., Matsuoka, S., Yang, F.C., Ebihara, Y., Manabe, A., Tanaka, R., Eguchi, M., Asano, S., Nakahata, T., and Tsuji, K. (2001). Evidence for the presence of murine primitive megakaryocytopoiesis in the early yolk sac. *Blood* **97,** 2016–2022.
41. Xie, X., Chan, R.J., Johnson, S.A., Starr, M., McCarthy, J., Kapur, R., and Yoder, M.C. (2003). Thrombopoietin promotes mixed lineage and megakaryocytic colony-forming cell growth but inhibits primitive and definitive erythropoiesis in cells isolated from early murine yolk sacs. *Blood* **101,** 1329–1335.
42. Perlingeiro, C.R., Kyba, M., Bodie, S., and Daley, G.Q. (2003). A role for thrombopoietin in hemangioblast development. *Stem Cells* **21,** 272–280.
43. Palis, J., Chan, R.J., Koniski, A., Patel, R., Starr, M., and Yoder, M.C. (2001). Spatial and temporal emergence of high proliferative-potential hematopoietic precursors during murine embryogenesis. *Proc. Natl. Acad. Sci. U. S. A.* **98,** 4528–4533.
44. Yoder, M.C. (2001). Introduction: spatial origin of murine hematopoietic stem cells. *Blood* **98,** 3–5.
45. Yoder, M.C., and Hiatt, K. (1999). Murine yolk sac and bone marrow hematopoietic cells with high proliferative potential display different capacities for producing colony-forming cells *ex vivo. J. Hematother. Stem Cell Res.* **8,** 421–430.
46. Wong, P., Chung, S., Chui, D., and Eaves, C. (1986). Properties of the earliest clonogenic hematopoietic precursors to appear in the developing murine yolk sac. *Proc. Natl. Acad. Sci. U. S. A.* **83,** 3851–3854.
47. Johnson, G., and Barker, D. (1985). Erythroid progenitor cells and stimulating factors during murine embryonic and fetal development. *Exp. Hematol.* **13,** 200–203.
48. Huang, H., and Auerbach, R. (1993). Identification and characterization of hematopoietic stem cells from the yolk sac of the early mouse embryo. *Proc. Natl. Acad. Sci. U. S. A.* **90,** 10,110–10,114.
49. Cumano, A., Dieterlen-Lievre, F., and Godin, I. (2000). The splanchnopleura–AGM region is the prime site for generation of multipotent hematopoietic precursors in the mouse embryo. *Vaccine* **18,** 1621–1623.
50. Cumano, A., Ferraz, J.C., Klaine, M., Di Santo, J.P., and Godin, I. (2001). Intraembryonic, but not yolk sac hematopoietic precursors, isolated before circulation provide long-term multilineage reconstitution. *Immunity* **15,** 477–485.
51. Dagher, R.N., Hiatt, K., Traycoff, C., Srour, E.F., and Yoder, M.C. (1998). C-kit and CD38 are expressed by long-term reconstituting hematopoietic cells present in the murine yolk sac. *Biol. Blood Marrow Transp.* **4,** 69–74.
52. Potocnik, A.J., Brakebusch, C., and Fassler, R. (2000). Fetal and adult hematopoietic stem cells require beta1 integrin function for colonizing fetal liver, spleen, and marrow. *Immunity* **12,** 653–663.
53. Jo, D.Y., Rafii, S., Hamada, T., and Moore, M.A.S. (2000). Chemotaxis of primitive hematopoietic cells in response to stromal cell-derived factor-1. *J. Clin. Invest.* **105,** 101–111.
54. Nagasawa, T., Hirota, S., Tachibana, K., Takakura, N., Nishikawa, S., Kitamura, Y., Yoshida, N., Kikutani, H., and Kishimoto, T. (1996). Defects of B-cell lymphopoiesis and bone marrow myelopoiesis in mice lacking the CXC chemokine PBSF/SDF-1. *Nature* **382,** 635–638.
55. Kyba, M., Perlingeiro, R.C., and Daley, G.Q. (2002). HoxB4 confers definitive lymphoid–myeloid engraftment potential on embryonic stem cell and yolk sac hematopoietic progenitors. *Cell* **109,** 29–37.

56. Palis, J., Robertson, S., Kennedy, M., Wall, C., and Keller, G. (1999). Development of erythroid and myeloid progenitors in the yolk sac and embryo proper of the mouse. *Development* **126,** 5073–5084.
57. Cuadros, M.A., Coltey, P., Carmen Nieto, M., and Martin, C. (1992). Demonstration of a phagocytic cell system belonging to the hemopoietic lineage and originating from the yolk sac in the early avian embryo. *Development* **115,** 157–168.
58. Jaffredo, T., Gautier, R., Eichmann, A., and Dieterlen-Lievre, F. (1998). Intra-aortic hematopoietic cells are derived from endothelial cells during ontogeny. *Development* **125,** 4575–4583.
59. Kurz, H., and Christ B. (1998). Embryonic CNC macrophages and microglia do not stem from circulating but from extravascular precursors. *Glia* **22,** 98–102.
60. Alliot, F., Godin, I., and Pessac, B. (1999). Microglia derive from progenitors originating from the yolk sac and which proliferate in the brain. *Dev. Brain. Res.* **117,** 145–152.
61. Naito, M., Umeda, S., Yamamoto, T., Moriyama, H., Umezu, H., Hasegawa, G., Usuda, H., Shultz, L.D., and Takahashi, K. (1996). Development, differentiation, and phenotypic heterogeneity of murine tissue macrophages. *J. Leukoc. Biol.* **59,** 133–138.
62. Cline, M.J., and Moore, M.A.S. (1972). Embryonic origin of the mouse macrophage. *Blood* **36,** 842–849.
63. Drake, C.J., and Fleming, P.A. (2000). Vasculogenesis in the day 6.5 to 9.5 mouse embryo. *Blood* **95,** 1671–1679.
64. McGrath, K.E., Koniski, A.D., Malik, J., and Palis, J. (2003). Circulation is established in a stepwise pattern in the mammalian embryo. *Blood* **101,** 1669–1676.
65. Jaffredo, T., Gautier, R., Brajeul, V., and Dieterlen-Lievre, F. (2000). Tracing the progeny of the aortic hemangioblast in the avian embryo. *Dev. Biol.* **224,** 204–214.
66. Cormier, F., and Dieterlen-Lievre, F. (1988). The wall of the chick embryo aorta harbors M-CFC, G-CFC, GM-CFC, and BFU-E. *Development* **102,** 279–285.
67. Martin, C., Beaupain, D., and Dieterlen-Lievre, F. (1980). A study of the development of the hemopoietic system using quail–chick chimeras obtained by blastomere recombination. *Dev. Biol.* **75,** 303–314.
68. Pardanaud, L., and Dieterlen-Lievre, F. (1999). Manipulation of the angiopoietic–hemangioblastic commitment in the avian embryo. *Development* **126,** 617–627.
69. Tavian, M., Coulombel, L., Luton, D., Clemente, H.S., Dieterlen-Lievre, F., and Peault, B. (1996). Aorta-associated CD34+ hematopoietic cells in the early human embryo. *Blood* **87,** 67–72.
70. Oberlin, E., Tavian, M., Blazsek, I., and Peault, B. (2002). Blood-forming potential of vascular endothelium in the human embryo. *Development* **129,** 4147–4157.
71. Marshall, C.J., Moore, R.L., Thorogood, P., Brickell, P.M., Kinnon, C., and Thrasher, A.J. (1999). Detailed characterization of the human aorta–gonad–mesonephros region reveals morphological polarity resembling a hematopoietic stromal layer. *Dev. Dyn.* **215,** 139–147.
72. Marshall, C.J., and Thrasher, A.J. (2001). The embryonic origins of human hematopoiesis. *Br. J. Haematol.* **112,** 838–850.
73. Nishikawa, S.I., Nishikawa, S., Kawamoto, H., Yoshida, H., Kizumoto, M., Kataoka, H., and Katsura, Y. (1998). *In vitro* generation of lymphohematopoietic cells from endothelial cells purified from murine embryos. *Immunity* **8,** 761–769.
74. Fraser, S.T., Ogawa, M., Yu, R.T., Nishikawa, S., Yoder, M.C., and Nishikawa, S.I. (2002). Definitive hematopoietic commitment within the embryonic vascular endothelial-cadherin+ population. *Exp. Hematol.* **30,** 1070–1078.
75. Cortes, F., Debacker, C., Peault, B., and Labastie, M.C. (1999). Differential expression of KDR/VEGFR-2 and CD34 during mesoderm development of the early human embryo. *Mech. Dev.* **83,** 161–164.
76. Marshall, C.J., Kinnon, C., and Thrasher, A.J. (2000). Polarized expression of bone morphogenic protein-4 in the human aorta–gonad–mesonephros region. *Blood* **96,** 1591–1593.
77. Cortes, F., Deschaseaux, F., Uchida, N., Labastie, M.C., Friera, A.M., He, D., Charbord, P., and Peault, B. (1999). HCA, an immunoglobulin-like adhesion molecule present on the earliest human hematopoietic precursor cells, is also expressed by stromal cells in blood forming tissues. *Blood* **93,** 826–837.
78. Ohneda, O., Ohneda, K., Arai, F., Lee, J., Miyamoto, T., Fukushima, Y., Dowbenko, D., Lasky, L.A., and Suda, T. (2001). ALCAM (CD166): Its role in hematopoietic and endothelial development. *Blood* **98,** 2134–2142.
79. Anstrom, K.K., and Tucker, R.P. (1996). Tenascin-C lines the migratory pathways of avian primordial germ cells and hematopoietic progenitor cells. *Dev. Dyn.* **206,** 437–446.
80. Ohta, M., Sakai, T., Saga, Y., Aizawa, S., and Saito, M. (1998). Suppression of hematopoietic activity in tenascin-C-deficient mice. *Blood* **91,** 4074–4083.
81. De Bruijn, M.F., Speck, N.A., Peeters, M.C.E., and Dzierzak, E. (2000). Definitive hematopoietic stem cells first develop within the major arterial regions of the mouse. *EMBO J.* **19,** 2465–2474.
82. De Bruijn, M.F., Peeters, M.C., Luteijn, T., Visser, P., Speck, N.A., and Dzierzak, E. (2000). CFU-S11 activity does not localize solely with the aorta in the aorta–gonad–mesonephros region. *Blood* **96,** 2902–2904.
83. Oostendorp, R.A.J., Harvey, K.N., Kusadasi, N., de Bruijn, M.F., Saris, C., Ploemacher, R.E., Medvinsky, A.L., Dzierzak, E.A. (2002). Stromal lines from mouse aorta–gonads–mesonephros subregions are potent supporters of hematopoietic stem cell activity. *Blood* **99,** 1183–1189.
84. Xu, M.J., Tsuji, K., Ueda, T., Mukouyama, Y.S., Hara, T., Yang, F.C., Ebihara, Y., Matsuoka, S., Manabe A., Kikuchi, A., Ito, M., Miyajima, A., and Nakahata, T. (1998). Stimulation of mouse and human primitive hematopoiesis by murine embryonic aorta–gonad–mesonephros-derived stromal cell lines. *Blood* **92,** 2032–2040.
85. Mukouyama, Y.S., Hara, T., Xu, M.J. *et al.* (1998). *In vitro* expansion of murine multipotential hematopoietic progenitors from the embryonic aorta–gonad–mesonephros region. *Immunity* **8,** 105–114.
86. Takizawa, M., Nobuhisa, I., Igarashi, K., Ueno, M., Nakashima, K., Kitamura, T., and Taga, T. (2003). Requirement of gp130 signaling for the AGM hematopoiesis. *Exp. Hematol.* **31,** 283–289.
87. McGrath, K.E., Koniski, A.D., Maltby, K.M., McGann, J.K., and Palis, J. (1999). Embryonic expression and function of the chemokine and its receptor, CXCR4. *Dev. Biol.* **213,** 442–456.
88. Kennedy, M., Firpo, M., Choi, K., Wall, C., Robertson, S., Kabrun, N., and Keller, G. (1997). A common precursor for primitive erythropoiesis and definitive hematopoiesis. *Nature* **386,** 488–493.
89. Choi, K., Kennedy, M., Kazarov, A., Papadimitrious, J.C., and Keller, G. (1998). A common precursor for hematopoietic and endothelial cells. *Development* **125,** 725–732.
90. Shalaby, F., Rossant, J., Yamaguchi, T.P., Gertsenstein, M., Wu, X.F., Breitman, M.L., Schuh, A.C. (1995). Failure of blood island formation and vasculogenesis in Flk-1-deficient mice. *Nature* **376,** 62–66.
91. Johansson, B.M., and Wiles, M.V. (1995). Evidence for involvement of activin A and bone morphogenetic protein 4 in mammalian mesoderm and hematopoietic development. *Mol. Cell. Biol.* **15,** 141–151.
92. Ziegler, S., Burki, K., and Skoda, R.C. (2002). A 2-kb c-mpl promoter fragment is sufficient to direct expression to the

megakaryocyte lineage and sites of embryonic hematopoiesis in transgenic mice. *Blood* **100,** 1072–1074.

93. Teyssier-Le Discorde, M., Prost, S., Nandrot, S., Nandrot, E., and Kirszenbaum, M. (1999). Spatial and temporal mapping of c-Kit and its ligand, stem cell factor, expression during human embryonic hemopoiesis. *Br. J. Haematol.* **107,** 247–253.
94. Hara, T., Nakano, Y., Tanaka, M., Tamura, K., Sekiguchi, T., Minehata, K., Copeland, N.G., Jenkins, N.A., Okabe, M., Kogo, H., Mukouyama, Y., and Miyajima, A. (1999). Identification of podocalyxin-like protein 1 as a novel cell surface marker for hemangioblasts in the murine aorta–gonad–mesonephros region. *Immunity* **11,** 567–578.
95. Hamaguchi, I., Huang, X.L., Takakura, N., Tada, J., Yamaguchi, Y., Kodama, H., and Suda, T. (1999). *In vitro* hematopoietic and endothelial cell development from cells expressing TEK receptor in murine aorta–gonad–mesonephros region. *Blood* **93,** 1549–1556.
96. Sugiyama, D., Ogawa, M., Hirose, I., Jaffredo, T., Arai, K.I., and Tsuji, K. (2003). Erythropoiesis from acetyl LDL incorporating endothelial cells at the preliver stage. *Blood* **12,** 4733–4738.
97. De Bruijn, M.F., Ma, X., Robin, C., Ottersbach, K., Sanchez, M.J, and Dzierzak, E. (2002). Hematopoietic stem cells localize to the endothelial cell layer in the midgestation mouse aorta. *Immunity* **16,** 673–683.
98. Charbord, P., Oostendorp, R., Pang, W., Herault, O., Noel, F., Tsuji, T., Dzierzak, E., and Peault, B. (2002). Comparative study of stromal cell lines derived from embryonic, fetal, and postnatal mouse blood-forming tissues. *Exp. Hematol.* **30,** 1202–1210.
99. Delassus, S., Titley, I., and Enver, T. (1999). Functional and molecular analysis of hematopoietic progenitors derived from the aorta–gonad–mesonephros region of the mouse embryo. *Blood* **94,** 1495–1503.
100. Mitjavila-Gracia, M.T., Cailleret, M., Godin, I., Nogueira, M.M., Cohen-Solal, K., Schiavon, V., Lecluse, Y., Le Pesteur, F., Lagrue, A.H., and Vainchenker, W. (2002). Expression of CD41 on hematopoietic progenitors derived from embryonic hematopoietic cells. *Development* **129,** 2003–2013.
101. Labastie, M.C., Cortes, F., Romeo, P.H., Dulac, C., and Peault, B. (1998). Molecular identity of hematopoietic precursor cells emerging in the human embryo. *Blood* **92,** 3624–3635.
102. Cai, Z., de Bruijn, M., Ma, X., Dortland, B., Luteijn, T., Downing, J.R., and Dzierzak, E. (2000). Haploinsufficiency of AML1 affects the temporal and spatial generation of hematopoietic stem cells in the mouse embryo. *Immunity* **13,** 423–431.
103. Guladi, R., Bossard, P., Zheng, M., Hamada, Y., Coleman, J.R., and Zaret, K.S. (1996). Hepatic specification of the gut endoderm *in vitro:* cell signaling and transcriptional control. *Genes Dev.* **10,** 1670–1682.
104. Chagraoui, J., Lepage-Noll, A., Anjo, A., Uzan, G., and Charbord, P. (2003). Fetal liver stroma consists of cells in epithelial-to-mesenchymal transition. *Blood* **101,** 2973–2982.
105. Johnson, G.R., and Moore, M.A.S. (1975). Role of stem cell migration in initiation of mouse fetal liver hemopoiesis. *Nature* **258,** 726–728.
106. Peault, B. (1996). Hematopoietic stem cell emergence in embryonic life: developmental hematology revisited. *J. Hematother.* **5,** 369–378.
107. Ema, H., and Nakauchi, H. (2000). Expansion of hematopoietic stem cells in the developing liver of the mouse embryo. *Blood* **95,** 2284–2288.
108. Szilvassy, S.J., Meyerrose, T.E., Ragland, P.L., and Grimes, B. (2001). Differential homing and engraftment properties of hematopoietic progenitor cells from murine bone marrow, mobilized peripheral blood, and fetal liver. *Blood* **98,** 2108–2115.
109. Harrison, D., Zhong, R., Jordan, C., Lemischka, T., and Astle, C. (1997). Relative to adult marrow, fetal liver repopulates nearly five times more effectively long-term than short-term. *Exp. Hematol.* **25,** 293–297.
110. Blazsek, I., Chagraoui, J., and Peault, B. (2000). Ontogenic emergence of the hematon, a morphological stromal unit that supports multipotential hematopoietic progenitors in mouse bone marrow. *Blood* **96,** 3763–3771.
111. Clapp, D.W., Freie, B., Lee, W.H., and Zhang, Y.Y. (1995). Molecular evidence that *in situ*-transduced fetal liver hematopoietic stem–progenitor cells give rise to medullary hematopoiesis in adult rats. *Blood* **86,** 2113–2122.
112. Parreira, L., Neves, H., and Simoes, S. (2003). Notch and lymphopoiesis: a view from the microenvironment. *Semin. Immunol.* **15,** 81–89.
113. Cotley, M., Bucy, R.P., Chen, C.H., Cihak, J., Losch, U., Char, D., Le Douarin, N.M., and Cooper, M.D. (1989). Analysis of the first two waves of thymus homing stem cells and their T-cell progeny in chick–quail chimeras. *J. Exp. Med.* **170,** 543–557.
114. Douagi, I., Vieira, P., and Cumano, A. (2002). Lymphocyte commitment during embryonic development in the mouse. *Semin. Immunol.* **14,** 361–369.
115. Wilkinson, B., Owen, J.J.T., and Jenkinson, E.J. (1999). Factors regulating stem cell recruitment to the fetal thymus. *J. Immunol.* **162,** 3873–3881.
116. Nehls, M., Kyewski, B., Messerle, W., Waldschutz, R., Schuddekopf, K., Smith, A.J.H., and Boehm, T. (1996). Two genetically separable steps in the differentiation of thymic epithelium. *Science* **272,** 886–889.
117. Lind, E.F., Prockop, S.E., Porritt, H.E., and Petrie, H.T. (2001). Mapping precursor movement through the postnatal thymus reveals specific microenvironments supporting defined stages of early lymphoid development. *Science* **194,** 127–134.
118. Kawamoto, H., Ohmura, K., and Katsura, Y. (1997). Direct evidence for the commitment of hematopoietic stem cells to T-, B-, and myeloid lineages in murine fetal liver. *Int. Immunol.* **9,** 1011–1019.
119. Kawamoto, H., Ohmura, K., and Katsura, Y. (1998). Cutting edge: presence of progenitors restricted to T-, B-, or myeloid lineage, but absence of multipotent stem cells, in the murine fetal thymus. *J. Immunol.* **161,** 3799–3802.
120. Kawamoto, H., Ohmura, K., Fujimoto, S., and Katsura, Y. (1999), Emergence of T-cell progenitors without B-cell or myeloid differentiation potential at the earliest stage of hematopoiesis in the murine fetal liver. *J. Immunol.* **162,** 2725–2731.
121. Ohmura, K., Kawamoto, H., Fujimoto, S., Ozaki, S., Nakao, K., and Katsura, Y. (1999). Emergence of T-, B-, and myeloid lineage-committed as well as multipotent hematopoietic progenitors in the AGM region of the 10-day fetus of the mouse. *J. Immunol.* **163,** 4788–4795.
122. Itoi, M., Kawamoto, H., Katsura, Y., and Amagai, T. (2001). Two distinct steps of immigration of hematopoietic progenitors into the early thymus anlage. *Int. Immunol.* **9,** 1203–1211.
123. Kawamoto, H., Ikawa, T., Ohmura, K., Fujimoto, S., and Katsura, Y. (2000). T-cell progenitors emerge earlier than B-cell progenitors in the murine fetal liver. *Immunity* **12,** 441–450.
124. Kondo, M., Weissman, I.L., and Akashi, K. (1997). Identification of clonogenic common lymphoid progenitors by instructive actions of cytokines. *Cell* **91,** 661–672.
125. Ohmura, K., Kawamoto, H., Lu, M., Ikawa, T., Ozaki, S., Nakao, K., and Katsura, Y. (2001), Immature multipotent

hematopoietic progenitors lacking long-term bone marrow-reconstituting activity in the aorta–gonad–mesonephros region of murine day 10 fetuses. *J. Immunol.* **166,** 3290–3296.

126. Harman, B.C., Jenkinson, E.J., and Anderson, G. (2003). Microenvironmental regulation of Notch signaling in T-cell development. *Semin. Immunol.* **15,** 91–97.
127. Schmitt, T.M., and Zuniga-Pflucker, J.C. (2002). Induction of T-cell development from hematopoietic progenitor cells by Delta-like-1 *in vitro. Immunity* **17,** 749–756.
128. Allman, D., Sambandam, A., Kim, S., Miller, J.P., Pagan, A., Well, D., Meraz, A., and Bhandoola, A. (2003). Thympoiesis independent of common lymphoid progenitors. *Nat. Immunol.* **4,** 168–174.
129. Kincade, P.W., Owen, J.J.T., Igarishi, H., Kouro, T., Yokota, T., and Rossi, M.I. (2002). Nature or nurture? Steady-state lymphocyte formation in adults does not recapitulate ontogeny. *Immunol. Rev.* **187,** 116–125.
130. Radtke, F., Wilson, A., Stark, G., Bauer, M., van Meerwijk, J., MacDonald, H.R., and Aguet, M. (1999). Deficient T-cell fate specification in mice with induced inactivation of Notch1. *Immunity* **10,** 547–558.
131. Rolink, A., Nutt, S.L., Melchers, F., and Busslinger, M. (1999). Long-term *in vivo* reconstitution of T-cell development by Pax5-deficient B-cell progenitors. *Nature* **401,** 603–606.
132. Montecino-Rodriquez, E., and Dorshkind, K. (2003). To T or not to T: reassessing the common lymphoid progenitor. *Nat. Immunol.* **4,** 100–101.
133. Houssaint, E., Mansikka, A., and Vainio, O. (1991). Early separation of B- and T-lymphocyte precursors in chick embryo. *J. Exp. Med.* **174,** 397–406.
134. Strasser, A., Rolink, A., and Melchers, F. (1989). One synchronous wave of B-cell development in mouse fetal liver changes at day 16 of gestation from dependence to independence of a stromal cell environment. *J. Exp. Med.* **170,** 1973–1986.
135. Cumano, A., and Paige, C.J. (1992). Enrichment and characterization of uncommitted B-cell precursors from fetal liver at day 12 of gestation. *EMBO J.* **11,** 593–601.
136. Marcos, M.A.R., Morales-Alcelay, S., Godin, I.E., Dieterlen-Lievre, F., Copin, S.G., and Gaspar, M.L. (1997). Antigenic phenotype and gene expression pattern of lymphohematopoietic progenitors during early mouse ontogeny. *J. Immunol.* **158,** 2627–2637.
137. De Andres, B., Gonzalo, P., Minguet, S., Martinez-Marin, J.A., Soro, P.G., Marcos, M.A.R., and Gaspar, L. (2002). The first 3 days of B-cell development in the mouse embryo. *Blood* **100,** 4074–4081.
138. Lacaud, G., Carlsson, L., and Keller, G. (1998). Identification of a fetal hematopoietic precursor with B-cell, T-cell, and macrophage potential. *Immunity* **9,** 827–838.
139. Mebius, R.E., Miyamoto, T., Christensen, J. *et al.* (2001). The fetal liver counterpart of adult common lymphoid progenitors gives rise to all lymphoid lineages, CD45+CD4+ cells, as well as macrophages. *J. Immunol.* **166,** 6593–6601.
140. Ogawa, M., Nishikawa, S., Ikuta, F., Yamamura, F., Naito, M., Takahashi, K., and Nishikawa, S.I. (1988). B-cell ontogeny in murine embryo studied by a culture system with the monolayer of a stromal cell clone, ST2: B-cell progenitor develops first in the embryonal body rather than the yolk sac. *EMBO J.* **7,** 1337–1343.
141. Huang, H., Zettergren, L.D., and Auerbach, R. (1994). *In vitro* differentiation of B-cells and myeloid cells from the early mouse embryo and its extraembryonic yolk sac. *Exp. Hematol.* **22,** 19–25.
142. Lu, L.S., and Auerbach, R. (1998). Characterization and differentiation of an early murine yolk sac-derived IL-7 independent pre-pro-B-cell line. *J. Immunol.* **161,** 1284–1291.
143. Tyan, M.L., and Herzenberg, L.A. (1968). Studies on the ontogeny of the mouse immune system: II—Immunoglobulin-producing cells. *J. Immunol.* **101,** 446–450.
144. Weissman, I.L., Papaloannou, V., and Gardner, R. (1978). Fetal hematopoietic origins of the adult hematolymphoid system. *In* "Differentiation of Normal and Neoplastic Hematopoietic Cells" (B. Clarkson *et al.,* eds.), p. 33–47. Cold Spring Harbor Laboratory Symposium, Cold Spring Harbor, NY.
145. Lu, L.S., Wang, S.J., and Auerbach, R. (1996). *In vitro* and *in vivo* differentiation into B-cells, T-cells, and myeloid cells of primitive yolk sac hematopoietic precursor cells expanded >100-fold by coculture with a clonal yolk sac endothelial cell line. *Proc. Natl. Acad. Sci. U. S. A.* **93,** 14,782–14,787.
146. Cumano, A., Furlonger, C., and Paige, C.J. (1993). Differentiation and characterization of B-cell precursors detected in the yolk sac and embryo body of embryos beginning at the 10- to 12-somite stage. *Proc. Natl. Acad. Sci. U. S. A.* **90,** 6429–6433.
147. Cumano, A., Dieterlen-Lievre, F., and Godin, I. (1996). Lymphoid potential, probed before circulation in mouse, is restricted to caudal intraembryonic splanchnopleura. *Cell* **86,** 907–916.
148. Egawa, T., Kawabata, K., Kawamota, H., Kawabata, K., Kawamoto, H., Amada, K., Okamoto, R., Fujii, N., Kishimoto, T., Katsura, Y., and Nagasawa, T. (2001). The earliest stages of B-cell development require a chemokine stromal cell-derived factor–pre-B-cell growth stimulatory factor. *Immunity* **15,** 323–334.
149. Ma, Q., Jones, D., Borghesani, P.R., Segal, R.A., Nagasawa, T., Kishimoto, T., Bronson, R.T., and Springer, T.A. (1998). Impaired B-lymphopoiesis, myelopoiesis and derailed cerebellar migration in CXCR4- and SDF-1-deficient mice. *Proc. Natl. Acad. Sci. U. S. A.* **95,** 9448–9453.

16

Amniotic Fluid–Derived Pluripotential Cells

M. Minhaj Siddiqui and Anthony Atala

Introduction

Human amniotic fluid has been used in prenatal diagnosis for more than 70 years. It has proved to be a safe, reliable, and simple screening tool for a variety of developmental and genetic diseases.[1] However, there is now evidence that amniotic fluid may have more utility than as a diagnostic tool and may be a source of a powerful therapy for a multitude of congenital and adult disorders. A subset of cells in amniotic fluid has been isolated and found capable of maintaining prolonged undifferentiated proliferation as well as of differentiating into multiple tissue types encompassing the three germ layers. It is possible that we will soon see the development of therapies using progenitor cells isolated from amniotic fluid for the treatment of newborns with congenital malformations as well as therapies for adults using cryopreserved amniotic fluid.

In this chapter, we describe several experiments that have isolated and characterized pluripotent progenitor cells from amniotic fluid. We also provide various lineages that these cells have been differentiated into and directions in this area of research.

Amniotic Fluid and Amniocentesis

The first reported amniocentesis took place in 1930 when attempts were being made to correlate the cytologic examination of cell concentration, count, and phenotypes in the amniotic fluid to the sex and the health of the baby.[2,3] Since then, the development of techniques of karyotype and the discovery of reliable diagnostic markers such as α-fetoprotein, as well as the development of ultrasound-guided amniocentesis, have greatly increased the reliability of the procedure as a valid diagnostic tool as well as the safety of the procedure.[4]

One of the primary uses of amniocentesis is as a safe method of isolating cells from the fetus that can then be karyotyped and examined for chromosomal abnormalities. In general, the protocol consists of acquiring 10 to 20 ml of fluid using a transabdominal approach. Amniotic fluid samples are then centrifuged, and the cell supernatant is resuspended in culture medium. Approximately 10^4 cells are seeded on 22 × 22 mm cover slips. Cultures are grown to confluence for 3 to 4 weeks in 5% CO_2 at 37°C, and the chromosomes are characterized from mitotic phase cells.

Amniocentesis is performed typically around 16 weeks of gestation, although in some cases it may be performed as early as 14 weeks when the amnion fuses with the chorion and the risk of bursting the amniotic sac by needle puncture is minimized. Amniocentesis can be performed as late as term. The amniotic sac is usually noticed first by ultrasound around the 10-week gestational timepoint.[3,5]

Amniotic fluid cell culture consists of a heterogeneous cell population displaying a range of morphologies and behaviors. Studies on these cells have characterized them into many shapes and sizes varying from 6 μm to 50 μm in diameter and from round to squamous in shape.[3] Most cells in the fluid are terminally differentiated along epithelial lineages and have limited proliferative and differentiation capabilities.[6,7] Previous studies have noted an interesting composition of the fluid consisting of a heterogenous cell population expressing markers from all three germ layers.[8]

The source of these cells and of the fluid itself underwent a great deal of research. Current theories suggest that the fluid is largely derived from urine and peritoneal fluid from the fetus as well as from some ultrafiltrate from the plasma of the mother entering though the placenta. The cells in the fluid have been shown to be overwhelmingly from the fetus and are thought to be mostly cells sloughed off the epithelium and digestive and urinary tract of the fetus as well as off the amnion.[2]

Our laboratory investigated the possibility of isolating a progenitor cell population from amniotic fluid. The amniotic fluid was from normal fetuses obtained using a transabdominal approach from 14 to 21 weeks of gestation. Initially, male fetuses were used to preclude the possibility of maternal-derived cells.

Isolation and Characterization of Progenitor Cells

A pluripotential subpopulation of progenitor cells in the amniotic fluid can be isolated through positive selection for cells expressing the membrane receptor c-kit. This receptor binds to the ligand stem cell factor. Roughly 0.8 to 1.4% of cells in amniotic fluid have been shown to be c-kit^{pos} in analysis by fluorescence-activated cell sorting.

The progenitor cells maintain a round shape for 1 week after isolation when cultured in nontreated culture dishes. In this state, they demonstrate a very low proliferative capability.

Handbook of Stem Cells
Volume 2

After the first week, the cells begin to adhere to the plate and change their morphology, becoming more elongated and proliferating more rapidly to reach 80% confluence with a need for passage every 48–72 hours. No feeder layers are required for either maintenance or expansion. The progenitor cells derived from amniotic fluid show a high self-renewal capacity with >300 population doublings, far exceeding Hayflick's limit. The doubling time of the undifferentiated cells is noted to be 36 hours with little variation with passages.

These cells have been shown to maintain a normal karyotype at late passages and have normal G_1 and G_2 cell cycle checkpoints. They demonstrate telomere length conservation in the undifferentiated state as well as telomerase activity even in late passages.[9,10] Analysis of surface markers shows that progenitor cells from amniotic fluid expressed human embryonic stage-specific marker SSEA4 and the stem cell marker OCT4, but they did not express SSEA1, SSEA3, CD4, CD8, CD34, CD133, C-MET, ABCG2, NCAM, BMP4, TRA1-60, or TRA1-81, to name a few. This expression profile is of interest as it demonstrates expression by the amniotic fluid-derived progenitor cells of some key markers of embryonic stem cell phenotype but not the full complement of markers expressed by embryonic stem cells. This hints that the amniotic cells are not as primitive as embryonic cells yet maintain greater potential than most adult stem cells. Another behavior showing similarities and differences among these amniotic fluid–derived cells and blastocyst-derived cells are that although the amniotic fluid progenitor cells form embryoid bodies *in vitro* that stain positive for markers of all three germ layers, these cells do not form teratomas *in vivo* when implanted in immunodeficient mice.[11] Lastly, cells, when expanded from a single cell, maintained similar properties in growth and potential as the original mixed population of the progenitor cells.

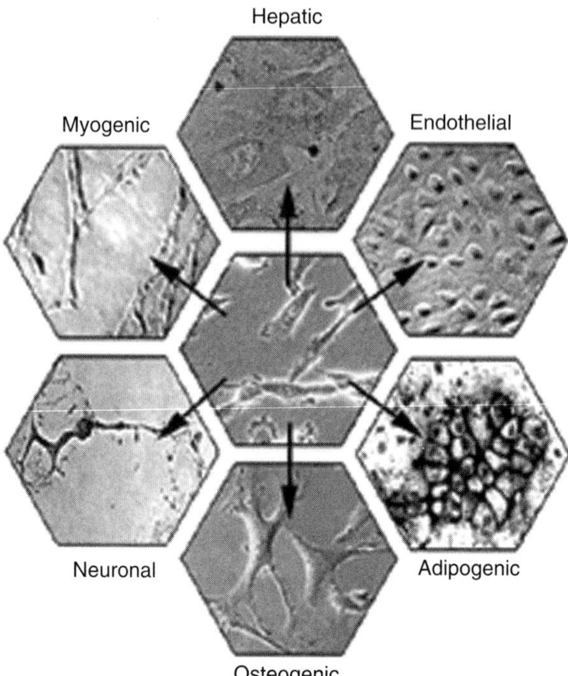

Figure 16–1. The isolated progenitor cells were capable of differentiation into multiple cell types, including muscle, liver, endothelial cells, adipocytes, osteoblasts, and neurons.

Differentiation Potential of Amniotic Progenitor Cells

The progenitor cells derived from human amniotic fluid are pluripotent and have been shown to differentiate into osteogenic, adipogenic, myogenic, neurogenic, endothelial, and hepatic phenotypes *in vitro*. Each differentiation has been performed through proof of phenotypic (Fig. 16–1) and biochemical (Fig. 16–2) changes consistent with the differentiated tissue type. We will describe each set of differentiations separately.

ADIPOCYTES

To promote adipogenic differentiation, the progenitor cells can be induced in dexamethasone, 3-isobutyl-1-methylxanthine, insulin, and indomethacin. The progenitor cells cultured with adipogenic supplements change their morphology from elongated to round within 8 days. This coincides with the accumulation of intracellular droplets. After 16 days in culture, more than 95% of the cells have their cytoplasm filled with lipid-rich vacuoles.

Adipogenic differentiation also demonstrates the expression of *peroxisome proliferation-activated receptor γ2 (pparγ2)*, a transcription factor that regulates adipogenesis, and of lipoprotein lipase through reverse transcription-polymerase chain reaction (RT-PCR) analysis.[12,13] Expression of these genes is noted in the progenitor cells under adipogenic conditions but not in undifferentiated cells.

ENDOTHELIAL CELLS

The amniotic fluid progenitor cells can be induced to form endothelial cells by culture in endothelial basal medium on gelatin-coated dishes. Full differentiation is affected with one month in culture; however, phenotypic changes are noticed within 1 week of initiation of the protocol. Human-specific endothelial cell surface marker (P1H12), factor VIII (FVIII), and kinase insert domain–containing receptor are specific for differentiated endothelial cells. The differentiated cells stain positively for FVIII, KDR, and P1H12. The progenitor cells do not stain for endothelial-specific markers. The amniotic fluid progenitor–derived endothelial cells, once differentiated, are able to grow in culture and form capillary-like structures *in vitro*. These cells also express *platelet endothelial cell adhesion molecule 1 (PECAM-1 or CD31)* and *vascular cell adhesion molecule (VCAM)*, which are not detected in the progenitor cells on RT-PCR analysis.

HEPATOCYTES

For hepatic differentiation, the progenitor cells are seeded on Matrigel- or collagen-coated dishes at different stages and cultured in the presence of hepatocyte growth factor, insulin,

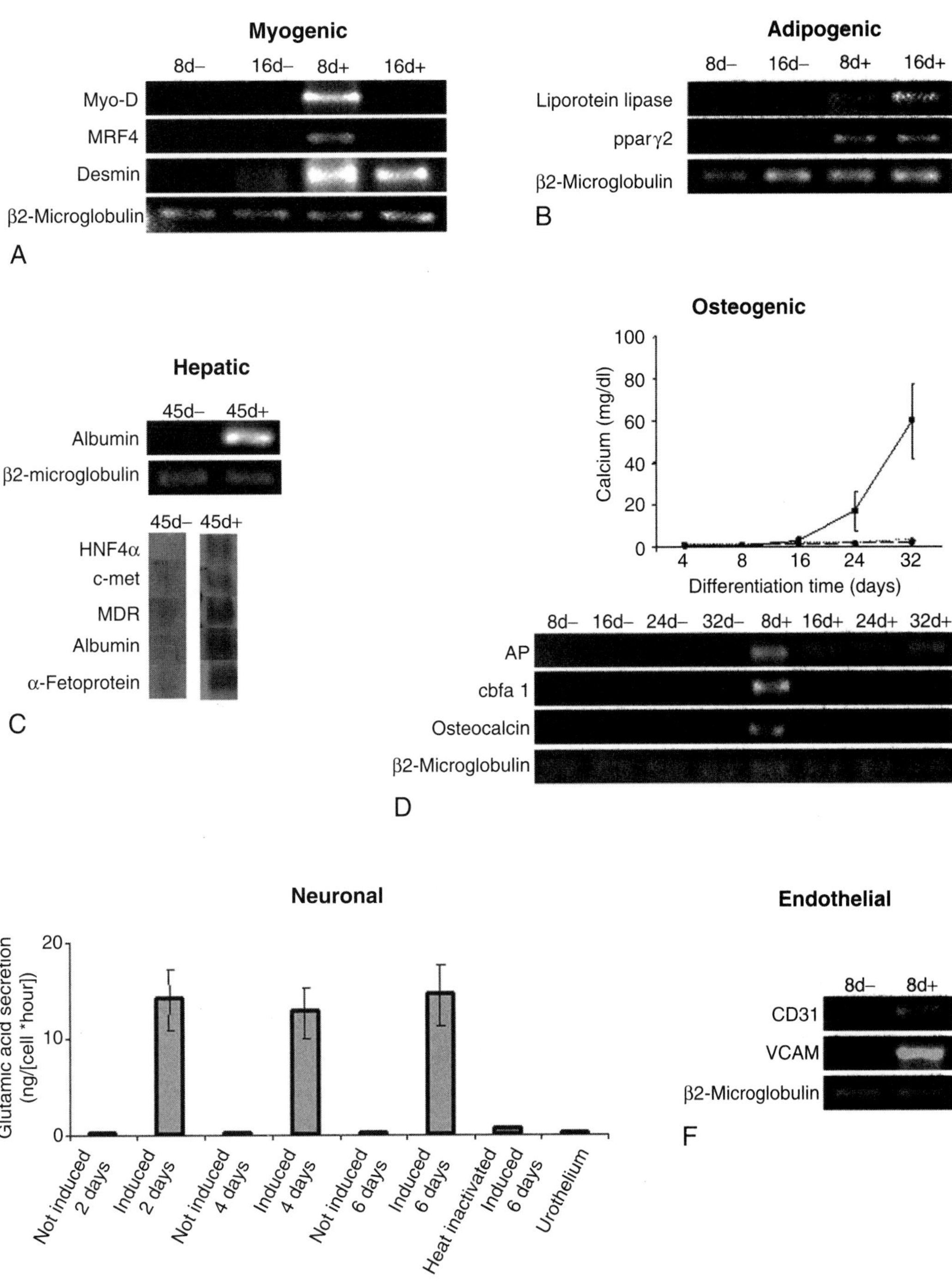

Figure 16–2. The differentiated cell types expressed functional and biochemical characteristics of the target tissue. (A) Myogenic-induced cells showed a strong expression of *desmin* expression at day 16 (lane 4). *MyoD* and *MRF4* were induced with myogenic treatment at day 8 (lane 3). Specific PCR-amplified DNA fragments of *MyoD, MRF4,* and *desmin* could not be detected in the control cells at days 8 and 16 (lanes 1 and 2). (B) Gene expression of *ppary2* and *lipoprotein lipase* in cells grown in adipogenic-inducing medium was noted at days 8 and 16 (lanes 3 and 4). (C) RT-PCR revealed an up-regulation of *albumin* gene expression. Western blot analyses of cell lysate showed the presence of the hepatic lineage-related proteins HNF-4α, c-met, MDR, albumin, and α-fetoprotein. Undifferentiated cells were used as negative control. (D) Osteogenic-induced progenitor cells showed a significant increase of calcium deposition starting at day 16 (solid line). No calcium deposition was detected in progenitor cells grown in control medium or the negative control cells grown in osteogenic conditions (dashed line). RT-PCR showed presence of *cbfa1* and *osteocalcin* at day 8 and confirmed the expression of *AP* in the osteogenic-induced cells. (E) Only the progenitor cells cultured under neurogenic conditions showed the secretion of glutamic acid in the collected medium. The secretion of glutamic acid could be induced (20 minutes in 50-mM KCl buffer). (F) RT-PCR of progenitor cells induced in endothelial medium (lane 2) showed the expression of *CD31* and *VCAM*.

oncostatin M, dexamethasone, fibroblast growth factor 4, and monothioglycerol for 45 days.[14,15] After 7 days of the differentiation process, cells exhibit morphological changes from an elongated to a cobblestone appearance. The cells show positive staining for albumin at day 45 after differentiation and also express the transcription factor HNF4α, the c-met receptor, the MDR membrane transporter, albumin, and α-fetoprotein. RT-PCR analysis further supports albumin production. The maximum rate of urea production for hepatic differentiation induced cells is up-regulated to 1.21×10^3 ng urea/hour/cell from 5.0×10^1 ng urea/hour/cell for the control progenitor cell populations.[16]

MYOCYTES

Myogenic differentiation is induced in the amniotic fluid–derived progenitor cells by culture in media containing horse serum and chick embryo extract on a thin gel coat of Matrigel.[17] To initiate differentiation, the presence of 5-azacytidine in the media for 24 hours is necessary. Phenotypically, the cells can be noted to organize themselves into bundles that fuse to form multinucleated cells. These cells express sarcomeric tropomyosin and desmin, both of which are not expressed in the original progenitor population.

The development profile of cells differentiating into myogenic lineages interestingly mirrors a characteristic pattern of gene expression seen with embryonic muscle development.[18,19] With this protocol, *Myf6* is expressed at 8 days and suppressed at 16 days. *MyoD* expression is detectable at 8 days and suppressed at 16 days in the progenitor cells. *Desmin* expression is induced at 8 days and increases by 16 days in the progenitor cells cultured in myogenic medium.[20,21]

NEURONAL CELLS

For neurogenic induction, the amniotic progenitor cells are induced in dimethyl sulfoxide, butylated hydroxyanisole, and neuronal growth factor.[22,23] The progenitor cells cultured in neurogenic conditions change their morphology within the first 24 hours. Two cell populations are apparent: morphologically large, flat cells and small, bipolar cells. The bipolar cell cytoplasm retracts toward the nucleus, forming contracted multipolar structures. Over the subsequent hours, the cells display primary and secondary branches and cone-like terminal expansions. The induced progenitor cells show a characteristic sequence of expression of neural-specific proteins. At an early stage, the intermediate filament protein nestin, specifically expressed in neuroepithelial stem cells, is highly expressed. The expressions of *βIII-tubulin* and *glial fibrillary acidic protein,* markers of neuron and glial differentiation, respectively, increased over time and seemed to reach a plateau around 6 days.[24] The progenitor cells cultured under neurogenic conditions showed the presence of the neurotransmitter glutamic acid in the collected medium. Glutamic acid is usually secreted in culture by a fully differentiated neuron.[25]

OSTEOCYTES

Osteogenic differentiation was induced in the progenitor cells with use of dexamethasone, β-glycerophosphate, and ascorbic acid-2-phosphate.[26] The progenitor cells maintained in this medium demonstrated phenotypic changes within 4 days with a loss of spindle-shape phenotype and a development of an osteoblast-like appearance with fingerlike excavations into the cytoplasm. At 16 days, the cells aggregated, showing typical lamellar bone–like structures. In terms of functionality, these differentiated cells demonstrate a major feature of osteoblasts, which is to precipitate calcium. Differentiated osteoblasts from the progenitor cells are able to produce alkaline phosphatase (AP) and to deposit calcium consistent with bone differentiation. The undifferentiated progenitor cells lacked this ability.

The progenitor cells in osteogenic medium express specific genes implicated in mammalian bone development *(AP, core-binding factor A1 [cbfa1],* and *osteocalcin)* in a pattern consistent with the physiological analogue. The progenitor cells grown in osteogenic medium show an activation of the *AP* gene at each time point. Expression of *cbfa1,* a transcription factor specifically expressed in osteoblasts and hypertrophic chondrocytes that regulates gene expression of structural proteins of the bone extracellular matrix, is highest in cells grown in osteogenic-inducing medium at day 8 and decreases slightly at days 16, 24, and 32. Osteocalcin is expressed only in the progenitor cells in osteogenic conditions at day 8.[27,28]

Future Directions

There is much interesting work that remains to be done with this cell population. *In vitro,* there remain a few cell types that have not been investigated but are of great interest scientifically and therapeutically. *In vivo* work to complement the *in vitro* differentiations demonstrating the functional capacity of these cells to supplement normal tissue will also be exciting, as it will highlight the true clinical potential of these cells. Of great interest may be cell types traditionally senescent in differentiated form, as these cells could be expanded in an undifferentiated form and differentiated into the cell type of interest in large numbers. For such reasons, the amniotic progenitor cells may also have practical use in tissue engineering of organs. Such cells that differentiate into a few relevant cell types in the tissue can be extremely powerful as these progenitor cells, if seeded on a scaffold, could be differentiated into the desired cell types. Such a mixture of correctly differentiated cells could process local cues to structure themselves into highly complex formations in the scaffold much as they do during development.

The ease of maintenance, proliferation, and differentiation of the amniotic progenitor cells also provides great promise as potential cells that could be used for other purposes such as investigation into development pathways or drug screening. Many experiments to probe the exact potential of these cells and fully characterize their source will be beneficial, as they will help to define realistic goals and applications for use of these cells.

Summary

The pluripotent progenitor cells isolated from amniotic fluid present an exciting possible contribution to the field of stem cell biology and regenerative medicine. These cells may be an excellent source for research and therapeutic applications. The embryonic and fetal progenitor cells have better potential for expansion than adult stem cells; for this reason, they could represent a better source for therapeutic applications in which large numbers of cells are needed. The ability to isolate the progenitor cells during gestation may also be advantageous for babies born with congenital malformations. Furthermore, the progenitor cells can be cryopreserved for future self-use. When compared with embryonic stem cells, the progenitor cells isolated from amniotic fluid have many similarities: They can differentiate into all three germ layers, they express common markers, and they preserve their telomere length. However, the progenitor cells isolated from amniotic fluid have, in our opinion, considerable advantages. They easily differentiate into specific cell lineages, they do not need feeder layers to grow, and they do not require the sacrifice of human embryos for their isolation, thus avoiding the current controversies associated with the use of human embryonic stem cells. The discovery of these cells has been recent, and a great deal of work remains to be done on the characterization and use of these cells. Initial results have been promising and are sure to lead to interesting developments.

REFERENCES

1. Fairweather, D.V.I., and Eskes, T.K.A.B. (eds.) (1978). "Amniotic Fluid: Research and Clinical Application." Excerpta Medica, New York.
2. Brace, R.A., Ross, M.G., and Robillard, J.E. (1989). "Fetal and Neonatal Body Fluids: The Scientific Basis for Clinical Practice." Perintology Press, New York.
3. Sandler, M. (1981). "Amniotic Fluid and Its Clinical Significance." Marcel Dekker, New York.
4. Brock, D.J.H. (1982). "Early Diagnosis of Fetal Defects." Churchill Livingston, New York.
5. Priest, J.H. (1991). Prenatal chromosomal diagnosis and cell culture. *In* "The ACT Cytogenetics Laboratory Manual," (M.J. Barch, ed.), Ed. 2, p. 149. Raven Press, New York.
6. Von Koskull, H., Virtanen, I., Lehto, V.P., Vartio, T., Dahl, D., and Aula, P. (1981). Glial and neuronal cells in amniotic fluid of anencephalic pregnancies. *Prenat. Diag.* **1,** 259–267.
7. Medina-Gomez, P., and Johnston, T.H. (1982). Cell morphology in long-term cultures of normal and abnormal amniotic fluids. *Hum. Genet.* **60,** 310–313.
8. Cremer, M., Schachner, M., Cremer, T., Schmidt, W., and Voigtlander, T. (1981). Demonstration of astrocytes in cultured amniotic fluid cells of three cases with neural-tube defect. *Hum. Genet.* **56,** 365–370.
9. Bryan, T.M., Englezou, A., Dunham, M.A., and Reddel, R.R. (1998). Telomere length dynamics in telomerase-positive immortal human cell populations. *Exp. Cell Res.* **239,** 370–378.
10. Bryan, T.M., Englezou, A., Gupta, J., Bacchetti, S., and Reddel, R.R. (1995). Telomere elongation in immortal human cells without detectable telomerase activity. *EMBO J.* **14,** 4240–4248.
11. Thomson, J.A., Itskovitz-Eldor, J., Shapiro, S.S., Waknitz, M.A., Swiergiel, J.J., Marshall, V.S., and Jones, J.M. (1998). Embryonic stem cell lines derived from human blastocysts. *Science* **282,** 1145–1147.
12. Kim, J.B., Wright, H.M., Wright, M., and Spiegelman, B.M. (1998). ADD1/SREBP1 activates PPAR-γ through the production of endogenous ligand. *Proc. Natl. Acad. Sci. U. S. A.* **95,** 4333–4337.
13. Rosen, E.D., Sarraf, P., Troy, A.E., Bradwin, G., Moore, K., Milstone, D.S., Spiegelman, B.M., and Mortensen, R.M. (1999). PPAR-γ is required for the differentiation of adipose tissue *in vivo* and *in vitro*. *Mol. Cell* **4,** 611–617.
14. Schwartz, R.E., Reyes, M., Koodie, L., Jiang, Y., Blackstad, M., Lund, T., Lenvik, T., Johnson, S., Hu, W.S., and Verfaillie, C.M. (2002). Multipotent adult progenitor cells from bone marrow differentiate into functional hepatocyte-like cells. *J. Clin. Invest.* **109,** 1291–1302.
15. Dunn, J.C., Yarmush, M.L., Koebe, H.G., and Tompkins, R.G. (1989). Hepatocyte function and extracellular matrix geometry: Long-term culture in a sandwich configuration. *FASEB J.* **3,** 174–177.
16. Hamazaki, T., Iiboshi, Y., Oka, M., Papst, P.J., Meacham, A.M., Zon, L.I., and Terada, N. (2001). Hepatic maturation in differentiating embryonic stem cells *in vitro*. *FEBS Lett.* **497,** 15–19.
17. Rosenblatt, J.D., Lunt, A.I., Parry, D.J., and Partridge, T.A. (1995). Culturing satellite cells from living single-muscle fiber explants. *In Vitro Cell Dev. Biol. Anim.* **31,** 773–779.
18. Rohwedel, J., Maltsev, V., Bober, E., Arnold, H.H., Hescheler, J., and Wobus, A.M. (1994). Muscle cell differentiation of embryonic stem cells reflects myogenesis *in vivo:* developmentally regulated expression of myogenic determination genes and functional expression of ionic currents. *Dev. Biol.* **164,** 87–101.
19. Bailey, P., Holowacz, T., and Lassar, A.B. (2001). The origin of skeletal muscle stem cells in the embryo and the adult. *Curr. Opin. Cell Biol.* **13,** 679–689.
20. Hinterberger, T.J., Sassoon, D.A., Rhodes, S.J., and Konieczny, S.F. (1991). Expression of the muscle regulatory factor MRF4 during somite and skeletal myofiber development. *Dev. Biol.* **147,** 144–156.
21. Patapoutian, A., Yoon, J.K., Miner, J.H., Wang, S., Stark, K., and Wold, B. (1995). Disruption of the mouse MRF4 gene identifies multiple waves of myogenesis in the myotome. *Development* **121,** 3347–3358.
22. Woodbury, D., Schwarz, E.J., Prockop, D.J., and Black, I.B. (2000). Adult rat and human bone marrow stromal cells differentiate into neurons. *J. Neurosci. Res.* **61,** 364–370.
23. Black, I.B., and Woodbury, D. (2001). Adult rat and human bone marrow stromal stem cells differentiate into neurons. *Blood Cells Mol. Dis.* **27,** 632–636.
24. Guan, K., Chang, H., Rolletschek, A., and Wobus, A.M. (2001). Embryonic stem cell-derived neurogenesis: retinoic acid induction and lineage selection of neuronal cells. *Cell Tissue Res.* **305,** 171–176.
25. Carpenter, M.K., Inokuma, M.S., Denham, J., Mujtaba, T., Chiu, C.P., and Rao, M.S. (2001). Enrichment of neurons and neural precursors from human embryonic stem cells. *Exp. Neurol.* **172,** 383–397.
26. Jaiswal, N., Haynesworth, S.E., Caplan, A.I., and Bruder, S.P. (1997). Osteogenic differentiation of purified, culture-expanded human mesenchymal stem cells *in vitro*. *J. Cell Biochem.* **64,** 295–312.
27. Karsenty, G. (2000). Role of Cbfa1 in osteoblast differentiation and function. *Semin. Cell Dev. Biol.* **11,** 343–346.
28. Komori, T., Yagi, H., Nomura, S., Yamaguchi, A., Sasaki, K., Deguchi, K., Shimizu, Y., Bronson, R.T., Gao, Y.H., Inada, M., Sato, M., Okamoto, R., Kitamura, Y., Yoshiki, S., and Kishimoto, T. (1997). Targeted disruption of Cbfa1 results in a complete lack of bone formation owing to maturational arrest of osteoblasts. *Cell* **89,** 755–764.

17

Stem and Progenitor Cells Isolated from Cord Blood

Hal E. Broxmeyer

Introduction

CORD BLOOD TRANSPLANTATION AND BANKING

Hematopoietic stem and progenitor cells from umbilical cord blood have been used to transplant more than 3000 recipients with various malignant or genetic disorders since the first transplant, performed in October 1988.[1] This cord blood transplant successfully cured the disordered and fatal hematological manifestations of Fanconi anemia; the male recipient of human lymphocyte antigen (HLA)-matched donor cord blood cells from a female sibling[1] is alive and well more than 15 years after the transplant. This and subsequent cord blood transplants using sibling cells[2–5] were the result of extensive laboratory-based studies and the first proof-of-principle cord blood bank, established in the author's laboratory, that suggested the feasibility of such transplants with cells[6–10] previously considered waste material except for some routine clinical testing needs. Since those initial clinical studies and banking efforts, numerous cord blood banks have been developed worldwide, allowing the extension of cord blood transplantation to situations using HLA-matched and partially HLA-matched cord blood cells from unrelated and related allogeneic donors.[5,11]

ADVANTAGES AND DISADVANTAGES OF CORD BLOOD FOR TRANSPLANTATION

Evidence suggests that cord blood transplantation can be used, especially in children, to treat a multiplicity of malignant and nonmalignant disorders currently treatable by bone marrow transplantation.[5,12] One obvious advantage of cord blood as a source of transplantable stem cells is the lower incidence of graft-vs-host disease compared to that of bone marrow, allowing the use of cord blood with a greater HLA-disparity than usually acceptable for bone marrow transplantation. However, engraftment of neutrophils and, even more so, of platelets is delayed after cord blood, compared with bone marrow, transplantation.[5,11,12] The limiting numbers of stem–progenitor cells in single collections of cord blood,[6–8] the immature nature of these rare repopulating cells,[5] the difficulty of cord blood progenitors to program themselves toward differentiation,[13] or all of these factors may be responsible for this relatively delayed blood cell engraftment. Although cord blood has been used successfully to transplant adults,[14–16] the limited number of collected cord blood cells has clearly limited the number of cord blood transplants performed in adults. The use of multiple, unrelated cord blood units is among a number of procedures being considered to alleviate the problem of limiting donor cord blood cell numbers, but enough information is not available to validate this concept yet. Several attempts to increase cord blood stem cell numbers through *ex vivo* expansion efforts and transplantation of "expanded cells" has not yet resulted in encouraging clinical results.[5,12,17,18] This chapter focuses on the functional characteristics of cord blood stem and progenitor cells for proliferation, self-renewal, and homing, three important functions for clinical transplantation. Current information on these functional activities of cord blood stem and progenitor cells helps to explain successes with cord blood transplantation. However, efforts to manipulate these cells for enhanced functional activity may prove efficacious in extending the clinical usefulness of cord blood transplantation, and new information in the field of hematopoiesis will be described that addresses this possibility.

Handbook of Stem Cells
Volume 2

Characteristics and Cryopreservation of Cord Blood Stem and Progenitor Cells

CYCLING STATUS AND RESPONSES TO GROWTH FACTORS

It was clear from initial laboratory studies that the frequency and proliferative capacity of hematopoietic progenitor cells in cord blood was enhanced compared to that found in bone marrow.[5–8,19–28] Although cord blood progenitors were in a slow (G_0/G_1) cell cycle state, they responded rapidly to the proliferation-inducing signals from growth factors.[29–31] These growth factors include the granulocyte–macrophage colony-stimulating factor (GM-CSF), macrophage (M)-CSF, granulocyte (G)-CSF, erythropoietin (Epo), thrombopoietin (TPO), the potent costimulating cytokines steel factor (SLF, also called stem cell factor), and Flt3-ligand (FL). SLF and FL activate their respective tyrosine kinase receptors c-kit and Flt3 and synergize with many other growth factors and themselves to enhance proliferation of cord blood progenitors.[19,32] SLF, with various CSFs, helped determine the enhanced frequency of immature subsets of progenitor cells in cord blood.[19] The combination of SLF and FL, alone and with other cytokines, helped elucidate the efficient recovery of high proliferative potential progenitor cells from cord blood stored frozen for 5 years,[19] 10 years,[33] and 15 years.[34] These proliferative characteristics, as well as *in vivo* studies in mice with the nonobese-diabetic severe-combined immunodeficiency (NOD–SCID) genotype, demonstrated the superiority of cord blood to bone marrow stem cells for engraftment.[35–45]

NUMBERS OF CORD BLOOD CELLS REQUIRED FOR DURABLE ENGRAFTMENT

Several parameters, including nucleated cellularity and progenitor cell content of cord blood collections, have been used to predict the engrafting capability of these cells.[5] One group provided evidence that the content of progenitor cells was a better predictor of speed of engraftment than the nucleated cellularity for cord blood transplantation,[46] but most clinicians still rely on nucleated cellularity as one of several parameters, including HLA-typing, when determining whether or not to use a specific collection of cord blood for transplantation. A collection in the range of $\geq 2 \times 10^7$ nucleated cord blood cells per kilogram of body weight is the cut-off many transplanters feel most comfortable using, although successful transplants have been reported with collections containing as few as 5×10^6 nucleated cells/kg.[5]

CRYOPRESERVATION OF CORD BLOOD

All cord blood transplants, except a few used in the context of gene transfer–gene therapy[5] and perhaps a few others, have used cord blood that was first frozen for cryopreservation and storage in the author's laboratory[1–3,9,10] or in a public or private cord blood bank.[11] Thus, it is clear that the success of cord blood transplantation has relied and will continue to rely heavily on the belief that cord blood stem and progenitor cells can be cryopreserved and recovered efficiently in terms of the quantity and quality of the stem and progenitor cells. That this is so was first reported by the author's group for short-term freezes[6] and then for longer term stored cells.[19,33,34] The ultimate test is to use the frozen cord blood collection in a clinical transplant setting. A cord blood has been stored and used successfully in a clinical setting probably no longer than in the 5–7 year range. The longest surviving recipient of a transplant with cord blood from a frozen and stored collection lived an additional 15 years. That was the recipient of the first cord blood transplant, performed in October 1988.[1] Three groups have reported the recovery of progenitors from cord blood stored frozen 12–15 years.[34,47,48] The most extensive study[34] demonstrated an average recovery (+/– 1SD) after 15 years storage of defrosted nucleated cells, granulocyte–macrophage (CFU-GM), erythroid (BFU-E), and multipotential (CFU-GEMM) progenitors respectively of 83 ± 12, 95 ± 16, 84 ± 25, and 85 ± 25. This was based on analysis of the same samples pre- and postfreeze, using the same culture conditions for progenitor cell analysis, and was comparable to the efficiency of recovery of these cells after 10 years of storage. The intact functional capabilities of these defrosted progenitors was highlighted by the extensive proliferative capacities of CFU-GM, BFU-E, and CFU-GEMM, which, respectively, generated colonies of up to 22,500, 182,500, and 292,500 cells after stimulation in a semisolid methylcellulose culture medium with Epo, GM-CSF, IL-3, and SLF. CFU-GEMM colonies could be replated in secondary dishes, with resultant CFU-GEMM colonies as large as those formed in the primary culture dishes. $CD34^+CD38^-$ cord blood cells isolated from the defrosts of the 15-year frozen cells demonstrated more than a 250-fold *ex vivo* expansion of progenitor cells. Perhaps of greater relevance to clinical transplantation, $CD34^+$ cells isolated from these defrosts were able to engraft NOD–SCID mice with a frequency equal to that of freshly isolated cord blood $CD34^+$ cells. Thus, it appears that cord blood can be stored frozen at least 15 years with the high likelihood that they will be able to engraft human recipients. A recent study suggested that measurement of progenitor cell recovery, as assessed by colony assays, is a more valid indicator than numbers of viable nucleated cells for cryopreserved cells.[49] This interpretation was based on the finding that research cord blood collections intentionally subjected to an overnight thaw and refreeze did not form colonies of progenitors, yet they demonstrated the viability of nucleated cells in the 68–98% range, as determined by Trypan Blue exclusion. Although cryopreservation efforts have been relatively successful,[34,47,48] studies continue to optimize methods for the cryopreservation of cord blood stem cells.[50]

Cord Blood Transplantation Problems and Possible Countermeasures

BACKGROUND TO PROBLEMS

Although cord blood has been successfully used for stem cell transplantation, most transplants have been done in children. Many clinicians feel that the limiting numbers found in single collections of cord blood preclude their routine use in adults. Moreover, even in children, cord blood transplantation is associated with delayed engraftment of neutrophils, and especially of platelets, increasing the hospitalization time of the transplanted recipients. Although one means of dealing with the issue of limiting numbers of stem cells in cord blood collection may be to use multiple cord blood units for transplantation into single recipients, efforts to enhance the clinical utility of cord blood for both children and adults will likely require a greater understanding than currently available of the self-renewal, proliferation, and homing characteristics of hematopoietic stem cells in general and of cord blood stem cells in particular. Information in these areas will clearly enhance prospects for successful *ex vivo* expansion of stem cells and for engrafting capabilities of these cells as well as of nonexpanded stem cells.

GENOMICS AND PROTEOMICS OF CORD BLOOD STEM–PROGENITOR CELLS

A comprehensive genomic and proteomic profile of cord blood, compared to that of adult bone marrow and mobilized peripheral blood, could shed light on the proliferative, self-renewal, and homing potentials of stem cells. Genomic profiling of stem cells has begun for cells from several sources,[51–53] including cord blood.[54] Additionally, first attempts at proteomic profiling are being reported.[55] However, these reports are limited to CD34+ cell populations, which contain hematopoietic progenitors as well as stem cells. A problem inherent in analysis of CD34+ cells is that they are not a pure population of stem cells; they contain progenitor cells, the stem cell content is likely a minor proportion of the total population, and this fraction is composed of more than stem and progenitor cells. Even the more highly purified population of human CD34+CD38− cells is not nearly pure in stem cell content. Unfortunately, the field of phenotypic characterization of human stem and progenitor cells is not at the level of that obtained for murine stem and progenitor cells,[56–60] and genomic and proteomic information on human stem cells will have to be interpreted cautiously with the understanding that what is detected may not be specific for or even present in the stem cell population. Until human stem cell populations are better characterized in terms of a phenotype that can consistently recapitulate detection of stem cell function, and until more in-depth analysis of cord blood stem cell genomics and proteomics is elucidated, we can rely on functional analysis of the responses of cord blood stem cells for self-renewal, proliferation, and homing.

EX VIVO EXPANSION

Current Knowledge

Although cord blood progenitor cell populations have been extensively expanded *ex vivo* by many different investigators,[5,19,21,22,61–68] it is not yet clear that stem cells have been expanded much, if at all. In fact, loss of stem cell function has been reported after *ex vivo* expansion procedures.[69,70] It may be of relevance in certain circumstances to use *ex vivo*-expanded hematopoietic progenitors in clinical settings[71]; however, use of *ex vivo*–expanded stem cells will likely require a greater understanding of the self-renewal process of stem cells. Recent studies suggest we may be closer to understanding cytokines and intracellular signaling events that influence the self-renewal process of stem cells.

Cytokines and Intracellular Molecules Implicated in Self-Renewal of Stem Cells

Numerous cytokines and chemokines, and their receptors, have been identified that act alone and together to modulate proliferation of myeloid progenitor cells.[72–75] Information on cell cycle regulation and cell cycle checkpoints is also accumulating for progenitor cells.[76]

A limited number of cytokines and intracellular signaling molecules have been implicated in proliferation, self-renewal, or both of hematopoietic stem cells. These include, but are not necessarily limited to, the following ligands and their receptors: SLF/c-kit,[77] FL,[77] Notch ligands–Notch,[78–96] and Wnt3a–Frizzled.[97–100] Intracellular molecules implicated include the following: p21cip1/waf1,[101,102] Hoxb4–Pbx1,[103–107] Bmi1,[108,109] and a stromal cell-derived membrane protein, mKirre.[110] Nanog,[111–113] Stat3,[114–116] and Hex[117] have been implicated in the growth and differentiation of embryonic stem cells. It is possible that intracellular molecules involved in the regulation of embryonic stem cells also play a role in the proliferation, self-renewal, or both of hematopoietic stem cells. Stat3 has been linked to *in vivo* regulation of hematopoiesis,[118] and serine phosphorylation of Stat3 has been linked to proliferation of progenitor cells in response to combined stimulation by SLF and GM-CSF or IL-3.[119] Overexpression of Hex is associated with enhanced proliferation of myeloid progenitor cells.[120] Stat5 is crucial for FL synergistic stimulation of myeloid progenitor.[121] Other cytokines that may influence stem cell proliferation, self-renewal, or both are TPO, Oncostatin M, and IL-20. TPO is an early acting cytokine,[122] has been implicated in hemangioblast development,[123] and is one of the ingredients, with SLF and FL, used by investigators to *ex vivo* expand hematopoietic stem and progenitor cells.[124,125] Oncostatin M is a T helper cell 1 produced cytokine that regulates progenitor cell homeostasis.[126] IL-20 is a new member of the interleukin family.[127,128] IL-20 is a candidate stem cell effector molecule that has selectivity for CFU-GEMM among myeloid progenitor cells. IL-20 enhances numbers of CFU-GEMM from human and mouse bone marrow and human cord blood in the presence of SLF and Epo *in vitro*. It has no effect *in vitro* on erythroid, granulocyte–macrophage, or megakaryocyte progenitors. IL-20 transgenic mice have increased numbers and cell cycling of CFU-GEMM but not of other myeloid progenitors, and the administration of IL-20 to normal mice significantly increases only CFU-GEMM numbers and cell cycling.[129] This is the first cytokine reported with such specificity. Because CFU-GEMM can be replated *in vitro* under appropriate cytokine conditions (SLF, −/+ cord blood plasma),[24,25,34] suggesting limited self-renewal capacity for CFU-GEMM, it is possible that IL-20 may also have proliferative- and/or self-renewal-enhancing effects on stem cells. IL-20 binds to both IL-20 receptor (R) types I and II.[130] IL-20R type 1 is composed of IL-20Rα and IL-20Rβ subunits; IL-20R type II is composed of the IL-20Rβ subunit and one subunit of the IL-22R. Interestingly, although both IL-19 and IL-24 bind the murine Baf3 cell lines engineered to express type I or type II IL-20Rs and stimulate proliferation of the appropriate receptor-containing cells, they did not demonstrate an effect on murine or human myeloid progenitor cells.[129] The IL-20R through which IL-20 is acting is not yet clear, nor is it clear how its mechanisms of action are mediated. Both IL-20RI and IL-20RII elicit intracellular signals using Stat3.[130] Stat3 plays an essential role in maintaining innate immunity.[118] It also is a signaling pathway involved in self-renewal signals induced by leukemia inhibitory factor in embryonic stem cells[114,115] and, with the JAK2 pathway, promotes self-renewal in drosophila germ line stem cell spermatogonia divisions.[116] When complemented by a second signal from either SLF/c-kit or FL/Flt3, Stat3 promotes self-renewal of primary multipotential hematopoietic cells.[131]

Cell Cycle Checkpoints, Asymmetry of Division, and Self-Renewal

Self-renewal of hematopoietic stem cells is a poorly understood event. Little is known of the mechanisms mediating stem cell self-renewal. Self-renewal requires cell division without loss of stemness and pluripotentiality in at least one of the daughter cells. This is sometimes referred to as asymmetric cell division.[132] Maintenance, expansion, or loss of stem cells will depend on the populations of stem cells produced or lost through symmetric or asymmetric divisions. The process by which cell fate determinants are segregated at cell division[133–135] depends on polarization and segregation across the mitotic spindle; daughters of cell division can inherit similar or very different cellular contents. Proper functioning of the mitotic spindle and its relative positioning is extremely important for regulation of self-renewal. Cell cycle checkpoints are necessary to maintain the progression of cell division events in a linear and ordered fashion.[136] Several cell cycle checkpoints have been described.[137] The mitotic spindle assembly checkpoint (MSAC) ensures that the cell cycle does not progress from metaphase to anaphase until all paired sister chromatids are arranged properly across the metaphase plate. This alignment establishes the plane of division. It also establishes the plane of polarity necessary for cell-fate determinant segregation (e.g., self-renewal or differentiation). The MSAC is probably critical for proper regulation of self-renewal and differentiation, and mitotic checkpoint proteins (such as mad and BUB gene products[138,139]) may be involved.

The cyclin-dependent kinase modulator, p21cip1/waf1, has been implicated in the SLF synergistic stimulation of the proliferation of progenitor cells[140,141] and in the functioning of stem cells.[101,102] Synergistic stimulation of cells by combinations of cytokines is likely important to the *in vivo* functioning of both progenitor and stem cells. Of the cytokines that influence stem cell proliferation, self-renewal, or both, they have all been shown to work only or more efficiently when used with other cytokines, such as SLF. p21cip1/waf1, because of its role in SLF synergy,[140,142] could be important for stem cell function.[101,102] Because p21cip1/waf1 has been linked to proper functioning of the MSAC,[76,143] it seems reasonable that the MSAC is involved in the proliferation, self-renewal, or both of stem cells. Moreover, because p21cip1/waf1 is linked to cytokine synergy and cytokine synergy likely influences stem cell function,[142] cytokines may act on stem cells through p21cip1/waf1 and the MSAC.

In addition to effects on growth, cytokines have been implicated in the survival–antiapoptosis of hematopoietic stem and progenitor cells. One such molecule is a CXC chemokine, stromal cell-derived factor-1 (Sdf1)/Cxcl12, which signals and induces its activities through the receptor Cxcr4.[144–146] It is possible that (Sdf1)/Cxcl12 can augment the *ex vivo* expansion of cord blood stem cells when used with one or more of the stem cell active growth factors.

Implications of Self-Renewal

Should any of the described growth factors, survival enhancing factors, or intracellular signaling molecules recently implicated in the regulation of hematopoietic, embryonic, or both types of stem cells prove useful in *ex vivo* expansion of hematopoietic stem cells, such activities may allow enhanced usefulness and broadness of applicability of cord blood transplantation.

Homing of Stem and Progenitor Cells

IMPORTANCE OF HOMING

A potential problem with *ex vivo*–expanded hematopoietic stem cells may be changes in the characteristics of the homing receptors, adhesion molecules, or both on these cells that could occur during their time in cell culture. Assessment of the engrafting capability of *ex vivo*–cultured stem cells may underestimate stem cell numbers and activity in a NOD–SCID or similar mouse model for human stem cells. Newer methods that use direct injection of the human cells into the marrow, rather than intravenous injection,[147–149] may allow the detection of stem cells that cannot accurately home to the marrow. Such intrafemoral transplantation of NOD–SCID mice revealed a short-term repopulating human cord blood cell with a unique phenotype.[149] Although this modification of the NOD–SCID human stem cell repopulating assay may allow a more accurate quantitation of the numbers of stem cells in the test inoculation, the lack of appropriate homing capacity in the NOD–SCID mice might indicate a potential problem with the homing capacity of these cells in human clinical transplantation. Thus, greater insight into the homing capacities and mechanisms involved would undoubtedly allow enhanced transplantation of donor cells in human recipients.

SDF1/CXCL12–CXCR4 AND CD26 IN HOMING OF STEM CELLS

It has been recently reported that stem cells home with absolute efficiency.[150] This, however, appears highly unlikely and is not consistent with the work of several other groups. It is possible to greatly increase the homing and engrafting capacity of long-term marrow competitive engrafting and self-renewing mouse bone marrow stem cells by decreasing the dipeptidylpeptidase IV (DPPIV) activity of CD26, or by eliminating CD26, on hematopoietic stem and progenitor cells.[151] DPPIV truncates Sdf1/Cxcl12 into an inactive form that does not have chemotactic activity but that can block the chemotactic activity of full-length Sdf1/Cxcl12.[152] The Sdf1/Cxcl12–Cxcr4 axis has been implicated in chemotaxis,[153–157] homing,[151,158–163] and mobilization.[154,164–166] Either inhibiting CD26 activity with a molecule such as Diprotin A[164] or functionally deleting CD26[165] results in greatly reduced G-CSF-induced mobilization of progenitor cells. It is believed that the mechanism of this latter effect is caused by the inactivation or elimination of CD26, which blocks the truncating effect of CD26 on Sdf1/Cxcl12, thus allowing stromal cell-produced Sdf1/Cxcl12 to maintain a greater "holding" action on Cxcr4-expressing stem and progenitor cells. Based on this belief, it was hypothesized that inactivation or elimination of CD26 on stem cells might enhance the homing capacity of exogenously infused stem cells.[151] Experimental evidence supported this hypothesis as Diprotin A-treated wild-type mouse marrow cells or marrow cells from $CD26^{-/-}$ mice demonstrated short-term homing and long-term marrow competitive repopulating capacities of these stem cells greater than the capacities of wild-type marrow cells treated with control medium or the capacities of untreated $CD26^{+/+}$

marrow cells.[151] It is possible that the enhanced marrow repopulating capability of stem cells in which CD26 is inactivated or eliminated may result partly from the enhanced stem cell survival activity of nontruncated–inactivated Sdf1/Cxcl12.[144–146] Treatments such as inactivation or loss of CD26 activity that have the capacity to enhance the homing–engrafting capability of hematopoietic stem cells may allow greater engrafting capability with limiting numbers of stem cells, such as found in cord blood, and may also enhance the homing–engrafting capability of *ex vivo*-expanded stem cells. Either possibility would likely enhance the effectiveness of cord blood transplantation, potentially resulting in more routine cord blood transplantation for adults and possibly in the use of single cord blood collections for multiple transplant recipients.

Summary

The enhanced frequency and quality of hematopoietic stem cells in cord blood at the birth of a baby has endowed cord blood with the capacity to cure a variety of malignant and genetic disorders. Cord blood transplantation works in both children and adults, but it has been used mainly in children because of the apparent limiting numbers of stem–progenitor cells in single cord blood collections. Being able to *ex vivo* expand and/or increase the homing efficiency of stem cells from cord blood would increase the usefulness and applicability of cord blood for transplantation. Although attempts at *ex vivo* expansion of stem cells for clinical cord blood transplantation have been disappointing thus far, new information regarding factors and intracellular signaling molecules involved in the regulation of hematopoietic stem cell activity and in the growth of embryonic stem cells (which may be translatable to hematopoietic stem cells), as well as advancements in understanding and manipulating the homing capacities of stem cells, offers hope that we may soon be ready to enhance stem cell transplantation in general and cord blood stem cell transplantation in particular.

REFERENCES

1. Gluckman, E., Broxmeyer, H.A., Auerbach, A.D., Friedman, H., Douglas, G.W., Devergie, A., Esperou, H., Thierry, D., Socie, G., Lehn, P., Cooper, S., English, D., Kurtzberg, J., Bard, J. and Boyse, E.A. (1989). Hematopoietic reconstitution in a patient with Fanconi anemia by means of umbilical-cord blood from an HLA-identical sibling. *N. Engl. J. Med.* **321,** 1174-1178.
2. Wagner, J.E., Broxmeyer, H.E., Byrd, R.L., Zehnbauer, B., Schmeckpeper, B., Shah, N., Griffin, C., Emanuel, P., Zuckerman, K., Cooper, S., Carow, C., Bias, W. and Santos, G.W. (1992). Transplantation of umbilical cord blood after myeloablative therapy: analysis of engraftment. *Blood* **79**, 1874-1881.
3. Kohli-Kumar, M., Shahidi, N.T., Broxmeyer, H.E., Masterson, M., Delaat, C., Sambrano, J., Morris, C., Auerbach, A.D., and Harris, R.E. (1993). Hemopoietic stem/progenitor cell transplant in Fanconi anemia using HLA-matched sibling umbilical cord blood cells. *Br. J. Haematol.* **85**, 419-422.
4. Wagner, J.E., Kernan, N.A., Steinbuch, M., Broxmeyer, H.E., and Gluckman, E. (1995). Allogeneic sibling umbilical-cord-blood transplantation in children with malignant and non-malignant disease. *Lancet* **346**, 214-219.
5. Broxmeyer, H.E., and Smith, F.O. (2004). Cord blood hematopoietic cell transplantation. *In* "Thomas' Hematopoietic Cell Transplantation, Third Edition" (Blum, Forman, Appelbaum, Ed.), pp. 550-564. Blackwell Sciences LTD, Malden, MA..
6. Broxmeyer, H.E., Douglas, G.W., Hangoc, G., Cooper, S., Bard, J., English, D., Arny, M., Thomas, L., and Boyse, E.A. (1989). Human umbilical cord blood as a potential source of transplantable hematopoietic stem/progenitor cells. *Proc. Natl. Acad. Sci. U. S. A.* **86**, 3828-3832.
7. Broxmeyer, H.E., Kurtzberg, J., Gluckman, E., Auerbach, A.D., Douglas, G., Cooper, S., Falkenburg, J.H.F., Bard, J. and Boyse, E.A. (1991). Umbilical cord blood hematopoietic stem and repopulating cells in human clinical transplantation. *Blood Cells* **17**, 313-329.
8. Broxmeyer, H.E., Gluckman, E., Auerbach, A., Douglas, G.W., Friedman, H., Cooper, S., Hangoc, G., Kurtzberg, J., Bard, J., and Boyse, E.A. (1990). Human umbilical cord blood: a clinically useful source of transplantable hematopoietic stem/progenitor cells. *Int J Cell Cloning* **8**, 76-91.
9. Broxmeyer, H.E. (1998). Introduction: the past, present, and future of cord blood transplantation. *In* "Cellular Characteristics of Cord Blood and Cord Blood Transplantation" (H.E. Broxmeyer, Ed.), pp. 1-9. Bethesda, MD: AABB Press.
10. Broxmeyer, H.E. (2000). Introduction. Cord blood transplantation: Looking back and to the future. *In* "Cord Blood Characteristics: Role in Stem Cell Transplantation" (S.B.A. Cohen, E. Gluckman, P. Rubinstein, and J.A. Madrigal, Eds.), pp. 1-12. London, U.K.: M. Dunitz.
11. Ballen, K., Broxmeyer, H.E., McCullough, J., Piaciabello, W., Rebulla, P., Verfaillie, C.M., and Wagner, J.E. (2001). Current status of cord blood banking and transplantation in the United States and Europe. *Biol. Blood Marrow Transplant.* **7**, 635-645.
12. Barker, J.N., and Wagner, J.E. (2003). Umbilical-cord blood transplantation for the treatment of cancer. *Nat. Rev.* **3**, 526-532.
13. Frassoni, F., Podesta, M., Maccario, R., Giorgiani, G., Rossi, G., Zecca, M., Bacigalupo, A., Piaggio, G., and Locatelli, F. (2003). Cord blood transplantation provides better reconstitution of hematopoietic reservoir compared with bone marrow transplantation. *Blood* **102**, 1138-1141.
14. Laughlin, M.J., Barker, J., Bambach, B., Koc, O.N., Rizzieri, D.A., Wagner, J.E., Lazarus, H.M., Cairo, M., Stevens, C.E., Rubinstein, P., and Kurtzberg, J. (2001). Hematopoietic engraftment and survival in adult recipients of umbilical-cord blood from unrelated donors. *N. Engl. J. Med.* **344**, 1815-1822.
15. Sierra, J., Storer, B., Hansen, J.A., Martin, P.J., Petersdorf, E.W., Woolfrey, A., Matthews, D., Sanders, J.E., Storb, R., Appelbaum, F.R., and Anasetti, C. (2000). Unrelated donor marrow transplantation for acute myeloid leukemia: an update of the Seattle experience. *Bone Marrow Transplant.* **26**, 397-404.
16. Barker, J.N., Davies, S.M., DeFor, T.E., Burns, L.J., McGlave, P.B., Miller, J.S., and Weisdorf, D.J. (2002). Determinants of survival after human leukocyte antigen matched unrelated donor bone marrow transplantation in adults. *Br. J. Haematol.* **118**, 101-107.
17. Shpall, E.J., Quinones, R., Giller, R., Zeng, C., Baron, A.E., Jones, R.B., Bearman, S.I., Nieto, Y., Freed, B., Madinger, N., Hogan, C.J., Slat-Vasquez, V., Russell, P., Blunk, B., Schissel, D., Hild, E., Malcolm, J., Ward, W., and McNiece, I.K. (2002).

Transplantation of ex vivo expanded cord blood. Biol. *Blood Marrow Transplant.* **8**, 368-376.
18. Jaroscak, J., Goltry, K., Smith, A., Waters-Pick, B., Martin, P.L., Driscoll, T.A., Howrey, R., Chao, N., Douville, J., Burhop, S., Fu, P., and Kurtzberg, J. (2003). Augmentation of umbilical cord blood (UCB) transplantation with ex vivo-expanded UCB cells: results of a phase 1 trail using the AastromReplicell System. *Blood* **101**, 5061-5067.
19. Broxmeyer, H.E., Hangoc, G., Cooper, S., Ribeiro, R.C., Graves, V., Yoder, M., Wagner, J., Vadhan-Raj, S., Rubinstein, P. and Broun, E.R. (1992). Growth characteristics and expansion of human umbilical cord blood and estimation of its potential for transplantation of adults. *Proc. Natl. Acad. Sci. USA* **89**, 4109-4113.
20. Lu, L., Xiao, M., Shen, R.N., Grigsby, S., and Broxmeyer, H.E. (1993). Enrichment, characterization and responsiveness of single primitive $CD34^{+++}$ human umbilical cord blood hematopoietic progenitor cells with high proliferative and replating potential. *Blood* **81**, 41-48.
21. Lansdorp, P.M., Dragowska, W., and Mayani, H. (1993). Ontogeny-related changes in proliferative potential of human hematopoietic cells. *J. Exp. Med.* **178**, 787-791.
22. Cardoso, A.A., Li, M.L. Batard, P., Hatzfeld, A., Brown, E.L., Levesque, J.P., Sookdeo, H., Panterne, B., Sansilvestri, P., Clark, S.C., and Hatzfeld, J. (1993). Release from quiescence of $CD34^+CD38^-$ human umbilical cord blood cells reveals their potentiality to engraft adults. *Proc Natl Acad Sci USA* **90**, 8707-8711.
23. Nakahata, T., and Ogawa, M. (1982). Hemopoietic colony-forming cells in umbilical cord blood with extensive capability to generate mono- and multi-potential hemopoietic progenitors. *J Clin Invest* **70**, 1324-1328.
24. Carow, C., Hangoc, G., Cooper, S., Williams, D.E. and Broxmeyer H.E. (1991). Mast cell growth factor (c-kit ligand) supports the growth of human multipotential (CFU-GEMM) progenitor cells with a high replating potential. *Blood* **78**, 2216-2221.
25. Carow, C.E., Hangoc, G., and Broxmeyer, H.E. (1993). Human multipotential progenitor cells (CFU-GEMM) have extensive replating capacity for secondary CFU-GEMM: An effect enhanced by cord blood plasma. *Blood* **81**, 942-949.
26. Hows, J.M., Bradley, B.A., Marsh, J.C., Luft, T., Coutinho, L., Testa, N.G., and Dexter, T.M. (1992). Growth of human umbilical-cord blood in long term hematopoietic cultures. *Lancet* **340**, 73-76.
27. Xiao, M., Broxmeyer, H.E., Horie, M., Grigsby, S., and Lu, L. (1994). Extensive proliferative capacity of single isolated $CD34^{+++}$ human cord blood cells in suspension culture. *Blood Cells* **20**, 455-467.
28. Smith, S., and Broxmeyer, H.E. (1986). The influence of oxygen tension on the long term growth in vitro of hematopoietic progenitor cells from human cord blood. *Br. J. Haematol.* **63**, 29-34.
29. Lu, L., Xiao, M., Grigsby, S., Wang, W.X., Wu, B., Shen, R-N, and Broxmeyer, H.E. (1993). Comparative effects of suppressive cytokines on isolated single $CD34^{+++}$ stem/progenitor cells from human bone marrow and umbilical cord blood plated with and without serum. *Exp. Hematol.* **21**, 1442-1446.
30. Traycoff, C.M., Abboud, M.R., and Laver, J., Clapp, D.W., and Srour, E.F. (1994). Rapid exit from G_0/G_1 phases of cell cycle in response to stem cell factor confers on umbilical cord blood $CD34^+$ cells an enhanced ex vivo expansion potential. *Exp. Hematol.* **22**, 1264-1272.
31. Leitner, A., Strobl, H., Fischmeister, G., Kurz, M., Romanakis, K., Haas, O.A., Printz, D., Buchinger, P., Bauer, S., Gadner, H., and Fritsch, G. (1996). Lack of DNA synthesis among $CD34^+$ cells in cord blood and in cytokine mobilized blood. *Br. J. Haematol.* **92**, 255-262.
32. Broxmeyer, H.E., Lu, L., Cooper, S., Ruggieri, L., Li, Z.H., and Lyman, S.D. (1995). Flt3 ligand stimulates/costimulates the growth of myeloid stem/progenitor cells. *Exp. Hematol.* **23**, 1121-1129.
33. Broxmeyer, H.E., and Cooper, S. (1997). High-efficiency recovery of immature haematopoietic progenitor cells with extensive proliferative capacity from human cord blood cryopreserved for 10 years. *Clin. Exp. Immunol.* **107** (Suppl 1) 45-53.
34. Broxmeyer, H.E., Srour, E.F., Hangoc, G., Cooper, S., Anderson, J.A., and Bodine, D. (2002). High efficiency recovery of hematopoietic progenitor cells with extensive proliferative and ex-vivo expansion activity and of hematopoietic stem cells with NOD/SCID mouse repopulation ability from human cord blood stored frozen for 15 years. *Proc. Natl. Acad. Sci. U. S. A.* **100**, 645-650.
35. Bodine, D.M. (1997). Animal models for the engraftment of human hematopoietic stem and progenitor cells. *In* "Cellular Characteristics of Cord Blood and Cord Blood Transplantation" (H.E. Broxmeyer, Ed.), pp 45-65. AABB, Bethesda, MD.
36. Vormoor, J., Lapidot, T., Pflumio, F., Risdon, G., Patterson, B., Broxmeyer, H.E., and Dick, J.E. (1994). Immature human cord blood progenitors engraft and proliferate to high levels in severe combined immunodeficient mice. *Blood* **83**, (9) 2489-2497.
37. Orazi, A., Braun, S.E., and Broxmeyer, H.E. (1994). Commentary: immunohistochemistry represents a useful tool to study human cell engraftment in SCID mice transplantation models. *Blood Cells* **20**, 323-330.
38. Bock, T.A., Orlic, D., Dunbar, C.E., Broxmeyer, H.E., Bodine, D.M. (1995). Improved engraftment of human hematopoietic cells in severe combined immunodeficient (SCID) mice carrying human cytokine transgenes. *J. Exp. Med.* **182**, 2037-2043.
39. Lowry, P.A., Shultz, L.D., Greiner, D.L., Hesselton, R.M., Kittler, E.L., Tiarks, C.Y., Rao, S.S., Reilly, J., Leif, J.H., Ramshaw, H., Stewart, F.M., and Quesenberry, P.J. (1996). Improved engraftment of human cord blood stem cells in NOD/LtSz- scid/scid mice after irradiation or multiple-day injections into unirradiated recipients. *Biol. Blood Marrow Transplant.* **2**, 15-23.
40. Larochelle, A., Vormoor, J., Hanenberg, H., Wang, J.C., Bhatia, M., Lapidot, T., Moritz, T., Murdoch, B., Xiao, X.L., Kato, I., Williams, D.A., and Dick, J.E. (1996). Identification of primitive human hematopoietic cells capable of repopulating NOD/SCID mouse bone marrow: implications for gene therapy. *Nat. Med.* **2**, 1329-1337.
41. Bhatia, M., Wang, J.C., Kapp, U., Bonnett, D., and Dick, J.E. (1997). Purification of primitive human hematopoietic cells capable of repopulating immune-deficient mice. *Proc. Natl. Acad. Sci. U. S. A.* **94**, 5320-5325.
42. Hogan, C.J., Shpall, E.J., McNulty, O., McNiece, I., Dick, J.E., Shultz, L.D., and Keller, G. (1997). Engraftment and development of human CD34(+)-enriched cells from umbilical cord blood in NOD/LtSz-scid/scid mice. *Blood* **90**, 85-96.
43. Wang, J.C., Doedens, M., and Dick, J.E. (1997). Primitive human hematopoietic cells are enriched in cord blood compared with adult bone marrow or mobilized peripheral blood as measured by the quantitative in vivo SCID-repopulating cell assay. *Blood* **89**, 3919-3924.
44. Tanavde, V.M., Malehorn, M.T., Lumkul, R., Gao, Z., Wingard, J., Garrett, E.S., and Civin, C.I. (2002). Human stem-progenitor

cells from neonatal cord blood have greater hematopoietic expansion capacity than those from mobilized adult blood. *Exp. Hematol.* **30**, 816-823.
45. Wilpshaar, J., Falkenburg, J.H.F., Tong, X., Noort, W.A., Breese, R., Heilman, D., Kanhai, H., Orschell-Traycoff, C.M., and Srour, E.F. (2000). Similar repopulating capacity of mitotically active and resting umbilical cord blood $CD34^+$ cells in NOD/SCID mice. *Blood* **96**, 2100-2107.
46. Migliaccio, A.R., Adamson, J.W., Stevens, C.E., Dobrila, N.L, Carrier, C.M., and Rubinstein, P. (2000). Cell dose and speed of engraftment in placental/umbilical cord blood transplantation: graft progenitor cell content is a better predictor than nucleated cell quantity. *Blood* **96**, 2717-2722.
47. Kobylka, P., Ivanyi, P., and Breur-Vriesendorf, B. (1998). Preservation of immunological and colony-forming capacities of long-term (15 years) cryopreserved cord blood cells. *Transplantation* **65**, 1275-1278.
48. Mugishima, H., Harada, K., Chin, M., Suzuki, T., Takagi, K., Hayakawa, S., Sato, K., Klein, J.P., Gale, R.P. (1999). Effects of long-term cryopreservation on hematopoietic progenitor cells in umbilical cord blood. *Bone Marrow Transplant.* **23**, 395-396.
49. Goodwin, H.S., Grunzinger, L.M., Regan, D.M., McCormick, K.A., Johnson, C.E., Oliver, D.A., Mueckl, K.A., Alonso, J.M. 3rd., and Wall, D.A. (2003). Long term cryostorage of UC blood units: ability of the integral segment to confirm both identity and hematopoietic potential. *Cytotherapy* **5**, 80-86.
50. Wood, E.J., Liu, J., Pollok, K., Hartwell, J., Smith, F.O., Williams, D.A., Yoder, M.C., and Critser, J.K. (2003). A theoretically optimized method for cord blood stem cell cryopreservation. *J. Hemat. Stem Cell Res.* **12**, 341-350.
51. Phillips, R.L., Ernst, R.E., Brunk, B., Ivanova, N., Mahan, M.A., Deanehan, J.K., Moore, K.A., Overton, G.C., and Lemischka, I.R. (2000). The genetic program of hematopoietic stem cells. *Science* **288**, 1635-1640.
52. Ramalho-Santos, M., Yoon, S., Matsuzaki, Y., Mulligan, R.C., and Melton, D.A. (2002). "Stemness": transcriptional profiling of embryonic and adult stem cells. *Science* **298**, 597-600.
53. Ivanova, N.B., Dimos, J.T., Schaniel, C., Hackney, J.A., Moore, K.A., and Lemischka, I.R. (2002). A stem cell molecular signature. *Science* **298**, 601-604.
54. Tao, W., Hangoc, G., Hawes, J.W., Si, Y., Cooper, S., and Broxmeyer, H.E. (2003). Profiling of differentially expressed apoptosis-related genes by cDNA arrays in human cord blood $CD34^+$ cells treated with VP-16 etoposide. *Exp. Hematol.* **31**, 251-260.
55. Tao, W., Wang, M., Decker, E.D., Cocklin, R.R., Cooper, S., and Broxmeyer, H.E. (2004). Comparative proteomic analysis of human $CD34^+$ stem/progenitor cells and mature $CD15^+$ myeloid cells. *Blood* **102** (Suppl 1), 823a.
56. Spangrude, G.J., Heimfeld, S., and Weissman, I.L. (1988). Purification and characterization of mouse hematopoietic stem cells [published erratum appears in Science 1989 Jun 2;244(4908): 1030]. *Science* **241**, 58-62.
57. Uchida, N., and Weissman, I.L. (1992). Searching for hematopoietic stem cells: evidence that Thy-1.1lo Lin- Sca-1+ cells are the only stem cells in C57BL/Ka-Thy-1.1 bone marrow. *J Exp Med* **175**, 175-184.
58. Morrison, S.J., Wandycz, A.M., Hemmati, H.D., Wrigt, D.E., and Weissman, I.L. (1997). Identification of a lineage of multipotent hematopoietic progenitors. *Development* **124**, 1929-1939.
59. Akashi, K., Traver, D., Miyamoto, T., and Weissman, I.L. (2000). A clonogenic common myeloid progenitor that gives rise to all myeloid lineages. *Nature* **404**, 193-197.
60. Kondo, M., Weissman, I.L., and Akashi, K. (1997). Identification of clonogenic common lymphoid progenitors in mouse bone marrow. *Cell* **91**, 661-672.
61. Sui, X., Tsuji, K., Tanaka, R., Tajima, S., Muraoka, K., Ebihara, Y., Ikebuchi, K., Yasukawa, K., Taga, T., Kishimoto, T., Nakahata, T. (1995). gp130 and c-kit signaling synergize for ex vivo expansion of human primitive progenitor cells. *Proc. Natl. Acad. Sci. U. S. A.* **92**, 2859-2863.
62. Piacibello, W., Sanavio, F., Garretto, L., Severino, A., Bergandi, D., Ferrario, J., Fagioli, F., Berger, M., and Aglietta, M. (1997). Extensive amplification and self-renewal of human primitive hematopoietic stem cells from cord blood. *Blood* **89**, 2644-2653.
63. Lu, L., Ge, Y., Li, Z.-H., Freie, B., Clapp, D.W., and Broxmeyer, H.E. (1995). $CD34^{+++}$ stem/progenitor cells purified from cryopreserved normal cord blood can be transduced with high efficiency by a retroviral vector and expanded ex vivo with stable integration and expression of Fanconi anemia complementation C gene. *Cell Transplant.* **4**, 493-503.
64. Gammaitoni, L., Bruno, S., Sanavio, F., Gunetti, M., Kollet, O., Cavalloni, G., Falda, M., Fagioli, F., Lapidot, T., Aglietta, M., and Piacibello, W. (2003). Ex vivo expansion of human adult stem cells capable of primary and secondary hemopoietic reconstitution. *Exp. Hematol.* **31**, 261-270.
65. Angelopoulou, M., Novelli, E., Grove, J.E., Rinder, H.M., Civin, C., Cheng, L., and Krause, D.S. (2003). Cotransplantation of human mesenchymal stem cells enhances human myelopoiesis and megakaryocytopoiesis in NOD/SCID mice. *Exp Hematol.* **31**, 413-420.
66. Kawano. Y., Kobune, M., Yamaguchi, M., Nakamura, K., Ito, Y., Sasaki, K., Takahashi, S., Nakamura, T., Chiba, H., Sato, T., Matsunaga, T., Azuma, H., Ikebuchi, K., Ikeda, H., Kato, J., Niitsu, Y., and Hamada, H. (2003). Ex vivo expansion of human umbilical cord hematopoietic progenitor cells using a coculture system with human telomerase catalytic subunit (hTERT)-transfected human stromal cells. *Blood* **101**, 532-540.
67. Kadereit, S., Deeds, L.S., Haynesworth, S.E., Koc, O.N., Kozik, M.M., Szekely, E., Daum-Woods, K., Goetchius, G.W., Fu, P., Welniak, L.A., Murphy, W.J., and Laughlin. M.J. (2002). Expansion of LTC-ICs and maintenance of p21 and BCL-2 expression in cord blood $CD34^+/CD38^-$ early progenitors cultured over human MSCs as a feeder layer. *Stem Cells* **20**, 573-582.
68. Li, Y., Ma, T., Kniss, D.A., Yang, S.T., and Lasky, L.C. (2001). Human cord cell hematopoiesis in three-dimensional nonwoven fibrous matrices: in vitro simulation of the marrow microenvironment. *J. Hemato. Stem Cell Res.* **10**, 355-368.
69. McNiece, I., Almeida-Porada, G., Shpall, E.J., and Zanjani, E. (2002). Ex vivo expanded cord blood cells provide rapid engraftment in fetal sheep but lack long-term engrafting potential. *Exp. Hematol.* **30**, 612-616.
70. Nitsche, A., Junghahn, I., Thulke, S., Aumann, J., Radonic, A., Fichtner, I., and Siegert, W. (2003). Interleukin-3 promotes proliferation and differentiation of human hematopoietic stem cells but reduces their repopulation potential in NOD/SCID mice. *Stem Cells* **21**, 236-244.
71. McNiece, I., and Briddell, R. (2001). Ex vivo expansion of hematopoietic progenitor cells and mature cells. *Exp. Hematol.* **29**, 3-11.
72. Shaheen, M., and Broxmeyer, H.E. (2003). The humoral regulation of hematopoiesis. *In* "Hematology: Basic Principles and Practice, 4th Edition" (R. Hoffman, E. Benz, S. Shattil, B. Furie, H. Cohen, L. Silberstein, and P. McGlave, Ed.), In Press.
73. Broxmeyer, H.E. (2001). Regulation of myelopoiesis as assessed by gene deletion and gene transduction. *In* "Hematopoiesis,

A Developmental Approach" (L.I. Zon, Ed.), Chapter 22:pp 247-257. Oxford University Press: NY.

74. Broxmeyer, H.E. (2001). Regulation of hematopoiesis by chemokine family members. *Int. J. Hematol.* **74**, 9-17.
75. Bagby, G.C. Jr., and Henrich, M. (1999). Growth factors, cytokines and the control of hematopoiesis. *In* "Hematology Basic Principles and Practice, 3rd Edition" (R. Hoffman, S. Shattil, B. Furie, H. Cohen, L. Silberstein, and P. McGlave, Ed.), pp. 154-201. Churchill Livingstone, Philadelphia.
76. Mantel, C.R., Gelfanov, V.M., Kim, Y.-J., McDaniel, A., Lee, Y.H., Boswell, H.S., and Broxmeyer, H.E. (2002). P21^{waf-1}-Chk1 pathway monitors G1-phase microtubule integrity and is crucial for restriction point transition. *Cell Cycle* **1**, 327-336.
77. Lyman, S.D., and Jacobsen, S.E.W. (1998). c-kit ligand and Flt3 ligand: stem/progenitor cell factors with overlapping yet distinct activities. *Blood* **91,** 1101-1134.
78. Milner, L.A., Kopan, R., Martin, D.I.K., and Bernstein, I.D. (1994). A human homologue of the drosophila developmental gene, notch, is expressed in CD34$^+$ hematopoietic precursors. *Blood* **83**, 2057-2062.
79. Milner, L.A., Bigas, A., Kopan, R., Brashem-Stein, C., Bernstein, I.D., and Martin, D.I. (1996). Inhibition of granulocytic - differentiation by mNotch1. *Proc. Natl. Acad. Sci. U. S. A.* **93**, 13014-13019.
80. Varnum-Finney, B., Purton, L.E., Yu, M., Brashem-Stein, C., Flowers, D., Staats, S., Moore, K.A., Le Roux, I., Mann, R., Gray, G., Artavanis-Tsakonas, S., and Bernstein, I.D. (1998). The notch ligand, jagged-1, influences the development of primitive hematopoietic precursor cells. *Blood* **91**, 4084-4091.
81. Bigas, A., Martin, D.I.K., and Milner, L.A. (1998). Notch1 and notch2 inhibit myeloid differentiation in response to different cytokines. *Mol. Cell. Biol.* **18**, 2324-2333.
82. Li, L., Milner, L.A., Deng, Y., Iwata, M., Banta, A., Graf, L., Marcovina, S., Friedman, C., Trask, B.J., Hood, L., and Torok-Storb. B. (1998). The human homolog of Rat Jagged1 expressed by marrow stroma inhibits differentiation of 32D cells through interaction with notch1. *Immunity* **8**, 43-55.
83. Milner, L.A., and Bigas, A. (1999). Notch as a mediator of cell fate determination in hematopoiesis: evidence and speculation. *Blood* **93**, 2431-2448.
84. Han, W., Ye, Q., and Moore, M.A. (2000). A soluble form of human Delta-like-1 inhibits differentiation of hematopoietic progenitor cells. *Blood* **95**, 1616-1625.
85. Karanu, F.N., Murdoch, B., Gallacher, L., Wu, D.M., Koremoto, M., Sakano, S., and Bhatia, M. (2000). The notch ligand Jagged-1 represents a novel growth factor of human hematopoietic stem cells. *J. Exp. Med.* **192**, 1365-1372.
86. Varnum-Finney, B., Xu, L., Brashem-Stein, C., Nourigat, C., Flowers, D., Bakkour, S., Pear, W.S., and Bernstein. I.D (2000). Pluripotent, cytokine-dependent, hematopoietic stem cells are immortalized by constitutive Notch1 signaling. *Nat. Med.* **6**, 1278-1281.
87. Varnum-Finney, B., Wu, L., Yu, M., Brashem-Stein, C., Staats, S., Flowers, D., Griffin, J.D., and Bernstein, I.D. (2000). Immobilization of Notch ligand, Delta-1, is required for induction of Notch signaling. *J. Cell Sci.* **113**, 4313-4318.
88. Karanu, F.N., Murdoch, B., Miyabayashi, T., Ohno, M., Koremoto, M., Gallacher, L., Wu, D., Itoh, A., Sakano, S., and Bhatia, M. (2001). Human homologues of Delta-1 and Delta-4 function as mitogenic regulators of primitive human hematopoietic cells. *Blood* **97**, 1960-1967.
89. Walker, L., Carlson, A., Tan-Pertel, H.T., Weinmaster, G., and Gasson, J. (2001). The Notch receptor and its ligands are selectively expressed during hematopoietic development in the mouse. *Stem Cells* **19**, 543-552.
90. Kojika, S., and Griffin, J.D. (2001). Notch receptors and hematopoiesis. *Exp. Hematol.* **29**, 1041-1052.
91. Ohishi, K., Varnum-Finney, B., and Bernstein, I.D. (2002). The Notch pathway: modulation of cell fate decisions in hematopoiesis. *Int. J. Hematol.* **75**, 449-459.
92. Stier, S., Cheng, T., Dombkowski, D., Carlesso, N., and Scadden, D.T. (2002). Notch1 activation increases hematopoietic stem cell self-renewal in vivo and favors lymphoid over myeloid lineage outcome. *Blood* **99**, 2369-2378.
93. Ohishi, K., Varnum-Finney, B., and Bernstein, I.D. (2002). Delta-1 enhances marrow and thymus repopulating ability of human CD34$^+$CD38$^-$ cord blood cells. *J. Clin. Invest.* **110**, 1165-1174.
94. Varnum-Finney, B., Brashem-Stein, C., and Bernstein, I.D. (2003). Combined effects of Notch signaling and cytokines induce a multiple log increase in precursors with lymphoid and myeloid reconstituting ability. *Blood* **101**, 1784-1789.
95. Maillard, I., He, Y., and Pear, W.S. (2003). From the yolk sac to the spleen: new roles for notch in regulating hematopoiesis. *Immunity* **18**, 587-589.
96. Kumano, K., Chiba, S., Kunisata, A., Sata, M., Saito, T., Nakagami-Yamaguchi, E., Yamaguchi, T., Masuda, S., Shimizu, K., Takahashi, T., Ogawa, S., Hamada, Y., and Hirai, H. (2003). Notch1 but not notch2 is essential for generating hematopoietic stem cells from endothelial cells. *Immunity* **18**, 699-711.
97. Austin, T.W., Solar, G.P., Ziegler, F.C., Liem, L., and Matthews, W. (1998). A role for Wnt gene family in hematopoiesis: expression of multilineage progenitor cells. *Blood* **89**, 3624-3635.
98. Van DerBerg, D.J., Sharma, A.K., Bruno, E., and Hoffman, R. (1998). Role of members of the Wnt gene family in human hematopoiesis. *Blood* **92**, 3189-3202.
99. Reya, T., Duncan, A.W., Ailles, L., Domen, J., Scherer, D.C., Willert, K., Hintz, L., Nusse, R., and Weissman, I.L. (2003). A role for Wnt signaling in self-renewal of hematopoietic stem cells. *Nature* **423**, 409-414.
100. Willert, K., Brown, J.D., Danenberg, E., Duncan, A.W., Weissman, I.L., Reya, T., Yates, J.R. 3rd., and Nusse, R. (2003). Wnt proteins are lipid-modified and can act as stem cell growth factors. *Nature* **423**, 448-452.
101. Cheng, T., Rodriques, N., Shen, H., Yang, Y., Dombkowski, D., Sykes, M., and Scadden, D.T. (2000). Hematopoietic stem cell quiescence maintained by p21$^{cip1/waf1}$. *Science* **287**, 1804-1808.
102. Stier, S., Cheng, T., Forkert, R., Lutz, C., Dombkowski, D.M., Zhang, J.L., and Scadden, D.T. (2003). Ex vivo targeting of p21$^{cip1/waf1}$ permits relative expansion of human hematopoietic stem cells. *Blood* **102**, 1260-1266.
103. Antonchuk, J., Sauvageau, G., and Humphries, R.K. (2001). HOXB4 overexpression mediates very rapid stem cell regulation and competitive hematopoietic repopulation. *Exp. Hematol.* **29**, 1125-1134.
104. Buske, C., Feuring-Buske, M., Abramovich, C., Spiekermann, K., Eaves, C.J., Coulombel, L., Sauvageau, G., Hogge, D.E., and Humphries, R.K. 2002. Deregulated expression of HOXB4 enhances the primitive growth activity of human hematopoietic cells. *Blood* **100**, 862-868.
105. Antonchuk, J., Sauvageau, G., and Humphries, R.K. (2002). HOXB4-induced expansion of adult hematopoietic stem cells ex vivo. *Cell* **109**, 39-45.
106. Kyba, M., Perlingeiro, R.C.R., and Daley, G.Q. (2002). HoxB4 confers definitive lymphoid-myeloid engraftment potential on

embryonic stem cell and yolk sac hematopoietic progenitors. *Cell* **109**, 29-37.

107. Krosl, J., Beslu, N., Mayotte, N., Humphries, R.K., and Sauvageau, G. (2003). The competitive nature of HOXB4-transduced HSC is limited by PBX1: the generation of ultra-competitive stem cells retaining full differentiation potential. *Immunity* **18**, 561-571.
108. Park, I.-K., Qian, D., Kiel, M., Becker, M.W., Pihalja, M., Weissman, I.L., Morrison, S.J., and Clarke, M.F. (2003). Bmi-1 is required for maintenance of adult self-renewing haematopoietic stem cells. *Nature* **423**, 302-305.
109. Lessard, J., and Sauvageau, G. (2003). Bmi-1 determines the proliferative capacity of normal and leukaemic stem cells. *Nat.* **423**, (6937) 255-260.
110. Ueno, H., Sakita-Ishikawa, M., Morikawa, Y., Nakano, T., Kitamura, T., and Saito, M. (2003). A stromal cell-derived membrane protein that supports hematopoietic stem cells. *Nat. Immunol.* **4**, 457-463.
111. Mitsui, K., Tokuzawa, Y., Itoh, H., Segawa, K., Murakami, M., Takahashi, K., Maruyama, M., Maeda, M., and Yamanaka, S. (2003). The homeoprotein Nanog is required for maintenance of pluripotency in mouse epiblast and ES cells. *Cell* **113**, 631-642.
112. Chambers, I., Colby, D., Robertson, M., Nichols, J., Lee, S., Tweedie, S., and Smith, A. (2003). Functional expression cloning of Nanog, a pluripotency sustaining factor in embryonic stem cells. *Cell* **113**, 643-655.
113. Cavaleri, F., and Scholer, H.R. (2003). Nanog: a new recruit to the embryonic stem cell orchestra. *Cell* **113**, 551-557.
114. Niwa, H., Burdon, T., Chambers, I., and Smith, A. (1998). Self renewal of pluripotent embryonic stem cells is mediated via activation of Stat3. *Genes Dev.* **12**, 2048-2060.
115. Raz, R., Lee, C.K., Cannizzaro, L.A., d'Eustachio, P., and Levy, D.E. (1999). Essential role of Stat3 for embryonic stem cell pluripotency. *Proc. Natl. Acad. Sci. U. S. A.* **96**, 2846-2851.
116. Kiger, A.A., Jones, D.L., Schulz, C., Rogers, M.B., and Fuller, M.T. (2001). Stem cell self-renewal specified by Jak-Stat activation in response to a support cell cue. *Science* **294**, 2542-2545.
117. Guo, Y., Chan, R., Ramsey, H., Li, W., Xie, X., Shelley, W.C., Martinez-Barbera, J.P., Bort, B., Zaret, K., Yoder, M., and Hromas, R. (2003). The homeoprotein Hex is required for hemangioblast differentiation. *Blood* **102**,2428-2435.
118. Welte, T., Zhang, S.S.M., Wang, T., Zhang, Z., Hesslein, D.G., Yin, Z., Kano, A., Iwamoto, Y., Li, E., Craft, J.E., Bothwell, A.L., Fikrig, E., Koni, P.A., Flavell, R.A., and Fu, X.Y. (2003). Stat3 deletion during hematopoiesis causes Crohn's disease-like pathogenesis and lethality: a critical role of Stat3 in innate immunity. *Proc. Natl. Acad. Sci. U. S. A.* **100**, 1879-1884.
119. Gotoh, A., Takahira, H., Mantel, C., and Broxmeyer, H.E. (1996). Steel factor induces serine phosphorylation of Stat3 in human growth factor-dependent myeloid cell lines. *Blood* **88**, 138-145.
120. Mack, D.L., Leibowitz, D.S., Cooper, S., Ramsey, H., Broxmeyer, H.E. and Hromas, R. (2002). Down-regulation of the myeloid homeobox protein Hex is essential for normal T-cell development. *Immunology* **107**, 444-451.
121. Zhang, S., Fukuda, S., Lee, Y.-H., Hangoc, G., Cooper, S., Spolski, R., Leonard, W.J. and Broxmeyer, H.E. (2000). Essential role of signal transducer and activator of transcription (Stat)5a but not Stat5B for Flt3-dependent signaling. *J. Exp. Med.* **192**, 719-728.
122. Carver-Moore, K., Broxmeyer, H.E., Luoh, S.-M., Cooper, S., Peng, J., Burstein, S., Moore, M.W., and de Sauvage, F.J. (1996). Low levels of erythroid and myeloid progenitors in TPO and c-mpl deficient mice. *Blood* **88**, 803-808.
123. Perlingeiro, R.C.R., Kyba, M., Bodie, S., and Daley, G.Q. (2003). A role for thrombopoietin in hemangioblast development. *Stem Cells* **21**, 272-280.
124. Piacibello, W., Sanavio, F., and Severino, A. (1999). Engraftment in nonobese diabetic severe combined immunodeficient mice of human CD34+ cord blood cells after ex-vivo expansion: evidence for the amplification and self-renewal of repopulating stem cells. *Blood* **93**, 3736-3749.
125. Lewis, I.D., Almeida-Porada, G., Du, J., Lemischka, I.R., Moore, K.A., Zanjani, E.D., and Verfaillie, C.M. (2001). Umbilical cord blood cells capable of engrafting in primary, secondary, and tertiary xenogeneic hosts are preserved after ex vivo culture in a noncontact system. *Blood* **97**, 3441-3449.
126. Broxmeyer, H.E., Bruns, H., Zhang, S., Cooper, S., Hangoc, G., McKenzie, A.N.J., Dent, A., Schindler, U., Naeger, L.K., Hoey, T., and Kaplan, M.K. (2002). Th1 cells regulate hematopoietic progenitor cell homeostasis by production of oncostatin M. *Immunity* **16**, 815-825.
127. Blumberg, H., Conklin, D., Xu, W., Grossmann, A., Brender, T., Carollo, S., Eagan, M., Foster, D., Haldeman, B.A., Hammond, A., Haugen, H., Jelinek, L., Kelly, J.D., Madden, K., Maurer, M.F., Parrish-Novak, J., Prunkard, D., Sexson, S., Sprecher, C., Waggie, K., West, J., Whitmore, T.E., Yao, L., Kuechle, M.K., Dale, B.A., and Chandrasekher, Y.A. (2001). Interleukin 20: Discovery, receptor identification, and role in epidermal function. *Cell* **104**, 9-19.
128. Rich, B.E, and Kupper, T.S. (2001). Cytokines: IL-20—a new effector in skin inflammation. *Curr. Biol.* **11**, 531-534.
129. Liu, L., Ding, C., Zeng, W., Heuer, J.G., Tetreault, J.W., Noblitt, T.W., Hangoc, G., Cooper, S., Brune, K.A., Sharma, G., Fox, N., Rowlinson, S.W., Rogers, D.P., Witcher, D.R., Lambooy, P.K., Wroblewski, V.J., Miller, J.R., and Broxmeyer, H.E., (2003). Selective enhancement of multipotential hematopoietic progenitors in vitro and in vivo by IL-20. *Blood* **102**, 3206-3209.
130. Dumoutier, L., Leemans, C., Lejeune, D., Kotenko, S.V., and Renauld, J.C. (2001). Cutting Edge: stat activation by IL-19, IL-20 and mda-7 through IL-20 receptor complexes of two types. *J. Immunol.* **167**, 3545-3549.
131. Zhao, S., Zoller, K., Masuko, M., Rojnuckarin, P., Yang, X.O., Parganas, E., Kaushansky, K., Ihle, J.N., Papayannopoulou, T., Willerford, D.M., Clackson, T., and Blau, C.A. (2002). Jak2, complemented by a second signal from c-kit or flt3, triggers extensive self-renewal of primary multipotential hematopoietic cells. *EMBO J.* **21**, 2159-2167.
132. Burns, C.E., and Zon, L.I. (2002). Portrait of a stem cell. *Dev. Cell* **3**, 612-613.
133. Morrison, S.J., Shah, N.M., and Anderson, D.J. (1997). Regulatory mechanisms in stem cell biology. *Cell* **88**, 287-298.
134. Jan, Y.N., and Jan, L.Y. (1998). Asymmetric cell division. *Nature* **392**, 775-779.
135. Brummendorf, T.H., Dragowska,W., Zijlmans, J.M., Thornbury, G., and Lansdorp, P.M. (1998). Asymmetric cell divisions sustain long-term hematopoiesis from single-sorted human fetal liver cells. *J. Exp. Med.* **188**, 1117-1124.
136. Hartwell, L., and Weinert, T. (1989). Checkpoints: controls that control the order of cell cycle events. *Science*. **246**, 629-634.
137. Murray, A. (1994). Cell cycle checkpoints. *Curr. Opin. Cell Biol.* **6**, 872-876.
138. Hoyt, M.A., Totis, L., and Roberts, B.T. (1991). *S. cerevisiae* genes required for cell cycle arrest in response to loss of microtuble function. *Cell* **66**, 507-517.
139. Li, R. and Murray, A.W. (1991). Feedback control of mitosis in budding yeast. *Cell* **66**, 519-531.

140. Mantel, C., Luo, Z., Canfield, J., Braun, S., Deng, C., and Broxmeyer, H.E. (1996). Involvement of $p21^{cip-1}$ and $p27^{kip-1}$ in the molecular mechanisms of steel factor induced proliferative synergy in vitro and of $p21^{cip-1}$ in the maintenance of stem/progenitor cells in vivo. *Blood* **88**, 3710-3719.
141. Braun, S.E., Mantel, C., Rosenthal, M., Hromas, R., Cooper, S., Robertson, K.A. and Broxmeyer, H.E. (1998). A positive effect of $p21^{cip1/waf1}$ in the proliferation of murine myeloid progenitor cells as assessed by retroviral mediated gene transfer. *Blood Cells Mol. Dis.* **24,** 138-148.
142. Mantel, C., Hendrie, P., and Broxmeyer, H.E., (2001). Steel factor regulates cell cycle asymmetry. *Stem Cells* **19**, 483-491.
143. Mantel, C., Braun, S.E., Reid, S., Henagarieu, O., Liu, L., Hangoc, G., and Broxmeyer, H.E. (1999). $P21^{waf-1/cip-1}$ deficiency causes deformed nuclear architecture, centriole overduplication, polyploidy, and relaxed microtubule damage checkpoints in human hematopoietic cells. *Blood* **93**, 1390-1398.
144. Broxmeyer, H.E., Kohli, L., Kim, C.H, Lee, Y., Mantel, C., Cooper, S., Hangoc, G., Shaheen, M., Li, X., and Clapp, D.W. (2003). Stromal Cell Derived Factor-1/CXCL12 Enhances Survival/Anti-Apoptosis of Hematopoietic Stem and Myeloid Progenitor Cells: Direct Effects Mediated Through CXCR4 and Gαi Proteins. *J. Leuk. Biol.* **73**, 630-638.
145. Broxmeyer, H.E., Cooper, S., Kohli, L., Hangoc, G., Lee, Y.H., Mantel, C., Clapp, D.W., and Kim, C.H. (2003). Transgenic expression of stromal cell derived factor-1/CXCL12 enhances myeloid progenitor cell survival/anti-apoptosis in vitro in response to growth factor withdrawal and enhances myelopoiesis in vivo. *J. Immunol.* **170**, 421-429.
146. Lee, Y., Gotoh, A., Kwon, H.-J., You, M., Kohli, L., Mantel, C., Cooper, S., Hangoc, G., Miyazawa, K., Ohyashiki, K., and Broxmeyer, H.E. (2002). Enhancement of intracellular signaling associated with hematopoietic progenitor cell survival in response to SDF-1/CXCL12 in synergy with other cytokines. *Blood* **99**, 4307-4317.
147. Yahata, T., Ando, K., Sato, T., Miyatake, H., Nakamura, Y., Muguruma, Y., Kato, S., and Hotta, T. (2003). A highly sensitive strategy for SCID-repopulating cell assay by direct injection of primitive human hematopoietic cells into NOD/SCID mice bone marrow. *Blood* **101**, 2905-2913.
148. Wang, J., Kimura, T., Asada, R., Harada, S., Yokota, S., Kawamoto, Y., Fujimura, Y., Tsuji, T., Ikehara, S., and Sonoda, Y. (2003). SCID-repopulating cell activity of human cord blood-derived CD34– cells assured by intra-bone marrow injection. *Blood* **101**, 2924-2931.
149. Mazurier, F., Doedens, M., Gan, O.I., and Dick, J.E. (2003). Rapid myeloerythroid repopulation after intrafemoral transplantation of NOD-SCID mice reveals a new class of human stem cells. *Nat. Med.* **9**, 959-963.
150. Benveniste, P., Cantin, C., Hyam, D., and Iscove, N.N. (2003). Hematopoietic stem cells engraft in mice with absolute efficiency. *Nat. Immunol.* **7**, 708-713.
151. Christopherson II, K.W., Hangoc, G., and Broxmeyer, H.E. (2003). Suppression or Deletion of CD26 (DPPIV) Activity on donor cells greatly enhances the efficiency of mouse hematopoietic stem & progenitor cell homing and engraftment in vivo. *Blood* **102** (Suppl 1), 38a.
152. Christopherson, K.W., Hangoc, G., and Broxmeyer, H.E. (2002). Cell surface peptidase CD26/DPPIV regulates CXCL12/SDF-1α mediated chemotaxis of human $CD34^+$ progenitor cells. *J. Immunol.* **169**, 7000-7008.
153. Aiuti, A., Webb, I.J., Bleul, C., Springer, T., and Gutierrez-Ramos, J.C. (1997). The chemokine SDF-1 is a chemoattractant for human $CD34^+$ progenitors to peripheral blood. *J. Exp. Med.* **185**, 111-120.
154. Kim, C.H., and Broxmeyer, H.E. (1998). In vitro behavior of hematopoietic progenitor cells under the influence of chemoattractants: stromal cell-derived Factor-1, steel factor and the bone marrow environment. *Blood* **91**, 100-110.
155. Kim, C.H., Qu, C.K., Hangoc, G., Cooper, S., Feng, G.S., and Broxmeyer, H.E. (1999). Abnormal chemokine-induced responses of immature and mature hematopoietic cells from motheaten mice implicates the protein tyrosine phosphatase SHP-1 in chemokine responses. *J. Exp. Med.* **190**, 681-690.
156. Kim, C.H., Hangoc, G., Cooper, S., Helgason, C.D., Yew, S., Humphries, R.K., Krystal, G., and Broxmeyer, H.E. (1999). Altered responsiveness to chemokines due to targeted disruption of SHIP. *J. Clin. Invest.* **104**, 1751-1759.
157. Wright, D.E., Bowman, E.P., Wagers, A.J., Butcher, E.C., and Weissman, I.L. (2002). Hematopoietic stem cells are uniquely selective in their migratory response to chemokines. *J. Exp. Med.* **195**, 1145-1154.
158. Peled, A., Petit, I., Kollet, O., Magid, M., Ponomaryov, T., Byk, T., Nagler, A., Ben-Hur, H., Many, A., Shultz, L., Lider, O., Alon, R., Zipori, D., and Lapidot, T. (1999). Dependence of human stem cell engraftment and repopulation of NOD/SCID mice on CXCR4. *Science* **283**, (5403) 845-848.
159. Kollet, O., Petit, I., Kahn, J., Samira, S., Dar, A., Peled, A., Deutsch, V., Gunetti, M., Piacibello, W., Nagle, A., and Lapidot, T. (2002). Human CD34(+)CXCR4(–) sorted cells harbor intracellular CXCR4, which can be functionally expressed and provide NOD/SCID repopulation. *Blood* **100**, (8) 2778-2786.
160. Lapidot, T., and Kollet, O. (2002). The essential roles of the chemokine SDF-1 and its receptor CXCR4 in human stem cell homing and repopulation of transplanted immune-deficient NOD/SCID and NOD/SCID/B2m(null) mice. *Leukemia* **16**, (10) 1992-2003.
161. Ara, T., Tokoyoda, K., Sugiyama, T., Egawa, T., Kawabata, K., and Nagasawa, T. (2003). Long-term hematopoietic stem cells require stromal cell-derived factor-1 or colonizing bone marrow during ontogeny. *Immunity* **19**, 257-267.
162. Liles, W.C., Broxmeyer, H.E., Rodger, E., Wood, B., Hubel, K., Cooper, S., Hangoc, G., Bridger, G.J., Henson, G.W., Calandra, G., and Dale, D.C. (2003). Mobilization of hematopoietic progenitor cells in healthy volunteers by AMD3100, a CXCR4 antagonist. *Blood* **102**, 2728-2730.
163. Broxmeyer, H.E., Hangoc, G., Cooper, S., Xiaxin, L., Bridger, G., and Clapp, D.W. (2002). AMD3100, An antagonist of CXCR4 and mobilizer of myeloid progenitor cells, is a potent mobilizer of competitive repopulating long term marrow self-renewing stem cells in mice. *Blood* **100** (Suppl 1), **609a** (abstract #2397).
164. Christopherson, K.W., II, Cooper, S., and Broxmeyer, H.E. (2003). Cell surface peptidase CD26/DPPIV mediates G-CSF mobilization of mouse progenitor cells. *Blood* **101**, 4680-4686.
165. Christopherson, K.W., Cooper, S., and Broxmeyer, H.E. (2003). CD26 is essential for normal G-CSF-induced progenitor cell mobilization as determined by CD26 –/– mice. *Exp. Hematol.* **31**, 1126-1134.
166. Petit, I., Szyper-Kravitz, M., Nagler, A., Lahav, M., Peled, A., Habler, L., Ponomaryov, T., Taichman, R.S., Arenzana-Seisdedos, F., Fujii, N., Sandbank, J., Zipori, D., and Lapidot, T. (2002). G-CSDF induces stem cell mobilization by decreasing bone marrow SDF-1 and up-regulating CXCR4. *Nat. Immunol* **3**, 687-694.

18

Neurogenesis in the Vertebrate Embryo

Chris Kintner and Naoko Koyano-Nakagawa

Introduction

A long-standing quest in the field of developmental biology is to determine how the diverse cell types that comprise the central nervous system (CNS) are generated during embryonic development. This issue has been difficult to address not only because the CNS is comprised of different cell types such as neurons and glia but also because the cellular composition of neural tissue varies enormously depending on its position along the body axis. Nonetheless, recent studies, mainly in the developing spinal cord, have revealed a rudimentary picture of the mechanisms that govern cell-type diversity in the vertebrate CNS. An important insight from these studies is that many of these mechanisms act in the early embryo when neural precursors first arise. In this chapter, we describe the early events that govern the formation of neural precursors and their differentiation into neurons in the developing vertebrate CNS. We first explain how the precursor cells for the CNS arise in the vertebrate embryo and how they differ from those for other developmental lineages. We next describe the role of the proneural genes as critical regulatory factors that promote the differentiation of neural precursors into neurons. Finally, we explain how the process of neural patterning may control the fate of neural precursors by regulating the activity of the proneural genes. The general model emphasized in this chapter is (1) that neural precursors in the CNS are already restricted in their fate when they form in the embryo as a consequence of the patterning processes that specify their position along the neuraxes and (2) that patterning genes trigger the proneural gene cascade at the proper time and place, thus determining patterns of neuronal differentiation. This model is likely to influence future studies of cell-type diversification in CNS development with the goal of manipulating embryonic and adult stem cells to restore damaged neural tissue in a therapeutic setting.

Embryonic Induction and the Establishment of Neural Tissue

The progenitor cells for the vertebrate CNS first appear in development with the formation of the neural plate from a portion of the ectoderm (also known as the epiblast) during gastrulation (Fig. 18–1). The neural plate subsequently forms a tube consisting of neuroepithelial cells (NECs) arranged around a central lumen that extends along the anterior–posterior axis (Fig. 18–2A, B). In addition to the neural plate, the ectoderm also forms the neural crest, a migrating population of precursors that move throughout the embryo, generating both neural and nonneural cell types. In addition, ectodermal cells produce placodal structures that contain neural precursors for sensory ganglia as well as neurons in the ear and nose. Finally, other regions of the ectoderm contain precursors for nonneural tissue, most prominently in ventral regions where they generate the skin. Thus, neural precursors arise in the vertebrate embryo at gastrulae stages when the ectoderm is subdivided into regions with different developmental fates, a process governed by inductive tissue interactions between the ectoderm and another region called the organizer.

In their classic experiment, Mangold and Spemann showed that the ventral ectoderm of a host embryo could be induced to form a complete nervous system when exposed to a transplanted piece of tissue called the organizer.[1] Subsequently, this process, called neural induction, has been described in chick[2] and mouse embryos,[3] suggesting that it is a key feature of neural tissue formation in all vertebrates, including, by extension, human embryos. Additional embryological experiments were subsequently instrumental in showing that neural tissue is specified during neural induction by two sets of signals.[1] One set neuralizes the ectodermal cells, thus causing them to form nerve cells rather than skin cells. A second set patterns the neuralized ectoderm, thus determining subregions that will form nerve cells of a brain type or spinal cord type, for example. As these two sets of signals have been identified and studied, it has become clear that neuralization and patterning are intimately linked. Indeed, the idea that a generic neural lineage exists is likely to be misleading because position plays such a prominent and early role in specifying cell fate in the CNS. To explain this, one needs to consider how neuralizing and patterning signals act during neural induction.

Neuralization of the Ectoderm

In amphibians, the ectoderm can be easily isolated from blastula-stage embryos and placed in culture, where it differentiates into skin but not into neural tissue. However, dissociating

Handbook of Stem Cells
Volume 2

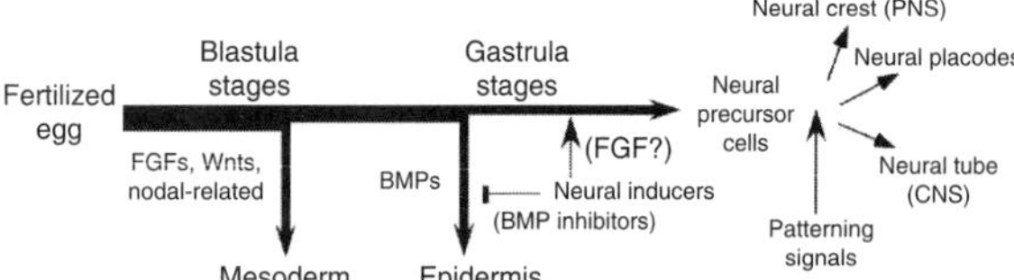

Figure 18–1. *Default model of neural induction.* Following fertilization, a region of the early embryo generates the ectoderm or epiblast, which responds to patterning signals as development progresses from left to right. At blastula stages, these signals include ones that induce mesodermal derivatives in posterior regions of the embryo using growth factors such as FGF, Wnts, and nodal-related families. At gastrulae stages, the ectoderm on the ventral side is induced to become epidermis by BMP signaling. However, a region of ectoderm avoids BMP signaling through inhibitors produced by the organizer, producing neural tissue. This neural tissue responds to a variety of patterning signals that divide it into different neural fates.

the isolated ectoderm into individual cells has been known since the experiments of Holtfreter to "induce" neural differentiation,[4] suggesting that ectodermal cells can generate neural precursors even in the absence of inductive signals from the organizer. A molecular understanding of this phenomenon was uncovered in *Xenopus* embryos during the study of signaling molecules that play prominent roles in axis determination.[5,6] One of these is the bone morphogenetic proteins (BMPs): members of the TGF-β superfamily of growth factors that play a key role in patterning the embryo along the dorsal–ventral axis.[7] Surprisingly, the inhibition of BMP signaling has been found to be the critical event required for converting ectoderm into neural tissue[8] (Fig. 18–1). When reagents that block the BMP signaling pathway are introduced into isolated ectoderm, they effectively convert it into neural tissue. Conversely, adding back BMPs as soluble ligands to dissociated ectodermal cells effectively blocks neural differentiation and promotes the formation of epidermal tissue. Finally, BMP inhibitors such as noggin, chordin, and follistatin have been identified that bind and antagonize BMP signaling extracellularly. These inhibitors are potent neural inducers, are expressed at quite high levels in organizer tissues, and underlie the molecular basis of organizer activity revealed in Mangold and Spemann's experiment.[9–11] These observations have led to the so-called default model for neural induction in which ectoderm is neuralized when inhibitors produced by the organizer block BMP signaling before and during gastrulation[12] (Fig. 18–1).

The default model also takes into account that growth factor signaling is required for the production of other embryonic cell lineages, such as those that generate mesodermal derivatives.[13] Induction of mesodermal derivatives occurs before gastrulation, mediated by different families of growth factors such as the Wnts, the fibroblast growth factors (FGFs), and the nodal-related members of the TGF-β superfamily[14,15] (Fig. 18–1). Significantly, ectoderm can be induced to produce mesodermal tissue if exposed to these factors at the appropriate stage. Thus, embryonic cells may only generate neural tissue if they avoid a series of signaling events that promote their differentiation along nonneural lineages (Fig. 18–1).

A major caveat to the default model is that other signaling pathways may act during neural induction to neuralize the ectoderm. For example, genetic experiments in mice show that some neural tissue forms even when neural induction has been disabled by mutations in the BMP inhibitors or by removal of the organizer.[16,17] This remaining neural tissue is an indication that additional pathways operate in embryos to specify neural tissue. Other results in chick experiments suggest that FGF is more effective than BMP inhibitors at inducing neural tissue in epiblast cells adjacent to the neural plate.[18–20] In *Xenopus* embryos, the ectoderm also forms neural tissue when exposed to FGF at the appropriate stage,[21,22] although whether or not FGF is normally required for neural induction remains controversial.[23,24] FGF action in this case may be mediated through Smad10, whose function is critical for the formation of neural precursors in *Xenopus* embryos.[25] In addition, FGF signaling is required for maintaining neural precursor cells in culture and for regulating their differentiation *in vivo*.[26,27] Together, these results point to a role for FGF signaling in the formation of neural precursors as a means of regulating their differentiation. The Wnt signaling pathway has also been implicated in the formation of neural precursors in early embryos. Reagents that block Wnt signaling in frog embryos antagonize neural tissue formation,[28] and blocking Wnt signaling in chick embryos allows the epiblast to respond to FGF and form neural tissue.[29] Inhibiting Wnt activity in ES cells also potentiates neural cell formation.[30] In summary, these results may indicate that the inhibition of BMP signaling is not sufficient for embryonic cells to form neural tissue. Nonetheless, they do not necessarily mean that the default model is incorrect. With further study, for example, these other pathways may contribute to neural induction in the same way as the BMP inhibitors: by preventing BMP activity[31] or the activity of other signals that promote a nonneural state.

Neural Patterning

The neuroectoderm of the neural plate produces the NECs of the neural tube, thus forming the neural progenitors that will generate the various neurons and glia that comprise the CNS. As the neural tube forms, the NECs are morphologically homogeneous, perhaps giving the mistaken impression that they are generic neural precursors at this stage. To the contrary, their homogenous appearance belies NECs status as an already diverse population of progenitor cells as a result of neural patterning. To illustrate this point, the following description will focus on the spinal cord, where perhaps the most is known about how patterning influences the formation and fate of neural precursors.

As NECs form the neural plate, they are exposed to a variety of signals that specify their position within the nervous system along two major cardinal axes. In the spinal cord, one of these axes, dorsal–ventral (D–V), depends largely on signals produced by two specialized midline structures, one at the ventral pole of neural tube (the floor plate)[32] and the other at the dorsal pole (the roof plate) (Fig. 18–2B). By acting as morphogens, the signals produced by these so-called organizing centers subdivide the NECs of the neural tube into domains with different developmental fates.[33] Specifically, the floor plate cells secrete a protein, called Sonic hedgehog (Shh, Fig. 18–2B), which induces or suppresses at different concentration thresholds the expression of genes, usually ones encoding homeodomain (HD) transcription factors, in NECs lying at different positions in the ventral spinal cord (Fig. 18–2C).[34] In this manner, the gradient of Shh activity subdivides the ventral NECs into at least five distinct areas by activating–suppressing the expression of different transcription factors, which then sharpen into nonoverlapping zones by cross-repression[35] (Fig. 18–2C). NECs in one of these zones (pMN, Fig. 18–2C) produce somatic motor neurons, and those in the other zones produce various classes of interneurons. These patterning events along the D–V axis take place in the context of a similarly complex patterning of the neural tube along a second orthogonal anterior–posterior (A–P) axis that also begins at neural plate stages.[36] Although the signals and target genes mediating this patterning are less understood, it is clear that they intersect with D–V patterning to generate a Cartesian coordinate system in which NECs express a unique code of transcription factors that determine cell fate at each point along the neuraxes. This code, for example, ensures that motor neurons form in response to Shh in a ventral domain along the entire spinal cord but that different motor neuron subtypes form at each A–P axial level.[37] In summary, neural patterning of the ventral spinal cord as well as other regions of the neural tube sets up a diverse pattern of gene expression within NECs that is already apparent when they form at neural plate stages. This pattern of gene expression is thought to be a major determinant of NEC fate, dictating when and where neurons and glia form.

Proneural Gene Cascade: A Downstream Target of Neural Patterning

How then does patterning of the NECs described previously dictate precise patterns of neuronal differentiation? The key finding addressing this question has come from the discovery of a class of basic helix–loop–helix (bHLH) proteins encoded by the so-called proneural genes. As transcriptional activators, the proneural proteins are thought to activate gene expression necessary both for the differentiation of precursors into neurons and for neuronal cell-type specification, thus acting as a molecular switch of differentiation (Table 18–1).

The vertebrate proneural bHLH genes fall into two families based on the homology to bHLH genes originally identified in *Drosophila* as mutations that block neural differentiation (Table 18–1).[38] One smaller family consists of those related to the *Drosophila* achaete–scute genes, such as *Mash1*. The second, larger family encodes proteins related to *Drosophila* atonal and can be subdivided structurally into three subfamilies: the neurogenin (Ngn)-like, the NeuroD-like, and the atonal-like. Expression of these different subfamilies occurs in precise spatial and temporal patterns both within the dividing NECs and within cells that have initiated neuronal differentiation. When eliminated by targeted mutation, loss of specific proneural bHLH genes results in deletion of specific populations of neurons.[39–41] However, the loss of neurons is likely to be much more severe when multiple members are simultaneously eliminated, indicating that the proneural genes have overlapping function as found in *Drosophila*.[42] Because of this genetic redundancy, it is difficult to test experimentally whether all neuronal differentiation is driven by proneural gene action. However, in gain-of-function experiments, proneural proteins are potent inducers of neuronal differentiation when ectopically expressed not only in neural precursors but also in some nonneural tissues.[43]

The proneural proteins function to initiate many of the physiological changes that occur when NECs undergo terminal neuronal differentiation (Table 18–1). One such function is to promote cell-cycle exit, an irreversible set of events incurred by all NECs as they form neurons.[44] NECs initiate cell-cycle exit when their nuclei move to the lateral edge of ventricular zone, where they enter the G_0 phase and eventually delaminate out of the neuroepithelium (Fig. 18–2D). Ectopic expression of the proneural proteins in NECs or in tissue culture models of NECS causes rapid cell-cycle arrest, although some subtypes of proneural proteins promote this transition better than others.[44,45] The mechanism by which the proneural proteins initiate irreversible cell-cycle exit appears to be quite complex and is an area of active research.[46,47] This mechanism may involve direct protein–protein interactions with cell-cycle machinery or alternatively transcriptional changes in expression of genes that encode cell-cycle regulators, such as cyclin-dependent kinase inhibitors p21, p16, and p27.[44]

Proneural proteins also function to activate the expression of genes associated with all subtypes of neurons, such as those that encode neuronal isoforms of the cytoskeletal proteins, channels involved in membrane excitability, and proteins involved in axon guidance. Significantly, genes encoding the proneural proteins are expressed in neural precursors and in committed neurons but often are transient in expression and lost as neurons mature.[38] Thus, proneural proteins may initiate expression of panneuronal genes directly then maintain expression indirectly by activating a downstream transcriptional network. This network may include not only transcriptional activators of the neuronal genes but also transcriptional repressors that relieve the repression of neuronal genes. For example, transcriptional enhancers for many of the panneuronal differentiation genes contain binding sites for a repressor, called REST/NRSF, which acts to extinguish the expression of these genes in nonneuronal cells as well as in neuronal precursors.[48] This repression is presumably blocked in neurons by a mechanism involving the proneural proteins.

Another function associated with the proneural proteins during neuronal differentiation is the inhibition of gene expression required for astroglia or oligodendrocytes differentiation.[38] Neural precursors first generate neurons then switch to produce both types of glia at later stages, suggesting that glial differentiation genes need to be repressed in neural precursors during neurogenesis. Studies using cultured neural stem cells indicate that the proneural proteins inhibit astroglia

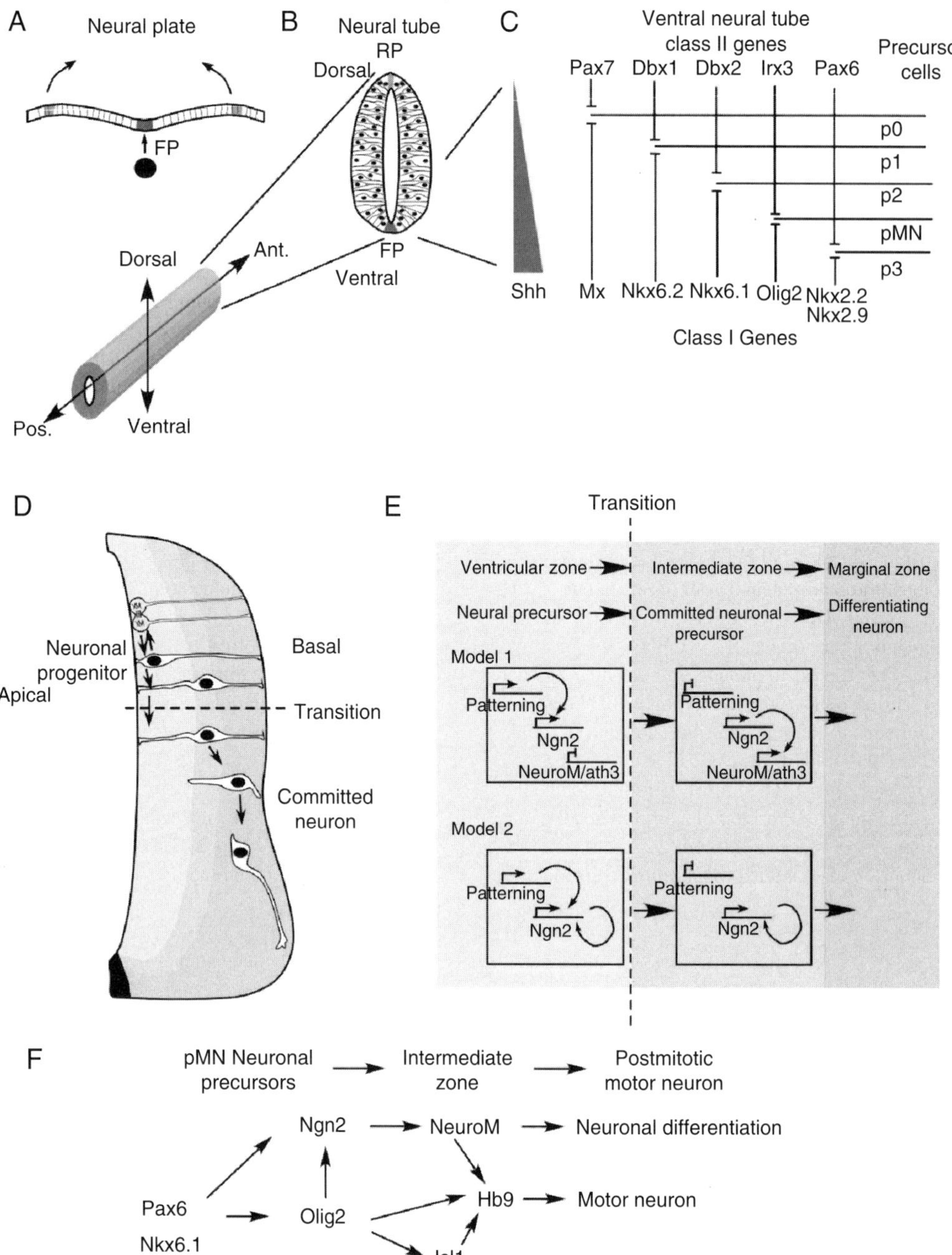

Figure 18–2. *Patterning and neurogenesis in the ventral spinal cord.* (A) The neural plate forms during gastrulation as a thickening of the ectoderm into a neuroepithelium, at which time patterning along the dorsal–ventral axis begins with the establishment of the floor plate (FP) and the roof plate (RP). (B) As the neural plate forms a neural tube, the NECs are patterned by signals emanating in part from the floor and roof plates. (C) In ventral spinal cord, this patterning consists of a gradient of Shh secreted by the floor plate, which activates–suppresses the expression of the class I and II homeodomain proteins (one exception is Olig2, a bHLH repressor) in a concentration dependent fashion. Mx is a hypothetical protein that has been proposed to contribute to ventral patterning by analogy with other class I proteins. (D) Neurogenesis within the neural tube is organized along a third developmental axis that corresponds to the apical–basal orientation of the neuroepithelium. Progenitor cells consist of NECs localized along the apical surface of the ventricular zone (no shading) within which their nucleus transverses during the cell cycle. During cell division, the two daughter cells separate at the apical surface, with recent studies suggesting that they maintain contact with the basal surface.[98] A precursor undergoes neuronal differentiation when its nucleus migrates laterally (light gray), exiting the cell cycle. Terminal neuronal differentiation is likely to be completed when a precursor delaminates from the neuroepithelium by detaching from ventricular surface, and migrating laterally into the marginal zone (dark gray shading). (E) Expression of proneural genes during the different phases of neurogenesis as shown by shading used in part D. Proneural genes such as the neurogenins are expressed in dividing precursors within the ventricular zone (no shading). Neuronal commitment occurs in the intermediate zone (light gray shading) when the levels of neurogenin are sufficiently high (in model 2) or when a downstream bHLH gene is activated (model 1). In either case, commitment causes the precursor to make the transition to a postmitotic

TABLE 18–1
Known Functions or Expression Patterns of bHLH Proteins in Neuronal Differentiation

Group	Subgroup	bHLH Name	Comments	References
Acheate–scute	Acheate–scute-like	Mash1	Required for autonomic neuronal differentiation	100, 101
			Autonomic and olfactory neuron differentiation	102
			Coordination of differentiation in ventral forebrain	103, 104
			Determination gene in olfactory sensory neurons	105, 106
			Promotes neuronal fate and inhibits astrocytic fate in cortical progenitors	59
			Negative indirect autoregulation of the promoter	107
			Retinal development	108, 109
		Xash1	*Xenopus* homolog of Mash1, expressed in anterior regions of the CNS	110
		Cash1	Chick homolog of Mash1 and Xash1; has similar expression pattern	111
		Xash3	Only in *Xenopus,* early neural plate expression	112–114
		Cash4	Only in chick, early proneural gene in posterior CNS	115
	Nscl-like	Nscl1, Nscl2	Expressed during "late" phases of neuronal commitment	116–120
Atonal	Neurogenin-like	Xngn1	Promotes neurogenesis in both neuroectoderm and ectoderm; overexpression in developing embryos induces various downstream targets such as Ath-3, Xcoe2, Delta, MyT1, NeuroD, Tubulin, Neurofilament, Hes6, XETOR, and NKL	58, 84, 86, 91, 121–123
		Ngn1/NeuroD3/Math4C	Sensory lineage	124, 125
			Required for proximal cranial sensory ganglia	126
			Neurogenesis in developing dorsal root ganglia	127
			Specification of dorsal interneurons by crossinhibition with Math1	128
			Differentiation in olfactory sensory neurons	105, 106
			Inhibits gliogenesis	49
		Ngn2/Math4A	Required for epibranchial placode-derived cranial sensory ganglia	129
			Promotes neuronal fate and inhibits astrocytic fate in cortical progenitors	59
			Induced by and cross-regulates with Pax6	42, 60
		Ngn3	Promotes gliogenesis in the spinal cord	130
	NeuroD-like	NeuroD/β2	Converts *Xenopus* ectoderm into neurons	43
			Cell fate, determination, differentiation, and survival in neural retina	93, 131–133
			Required for differentiation of the granule cells in cerebellum and hippocampus	134
			Survival of inner ear sensory neurons	135
			Neurite outgrowth	136
		NeuroD2/NDRF	Required for development and survival of CNS neurons	39

Continued

Figure 18–2. cont'd, neuron (light gray shading) that undergoes terminal neuronal differentiation (dark gray shading). (F) Integration of neuronal differentiation with neuronal subtype specification. In the ventral spinal cord, patterning leads to expression of both the proneural protein Ngn2 and HD transcription factors, which cooperate to activate the expression of the motor neuron determinate HB9. This cooperation integrates a program of neuronal differentiation promoted by Ngn2, and perhaps NeuroM, along with a program of motor neuron differentiation. (Part C is adapted from Shirasaki *et al.*[36]). (Please see CD-ROM for color version of this figure.)

TABLE 18–1
Known Functions or Expression Patterns of bHLH Proteins in Neuronal Differentiation—cont'd

Group	Subgroup	bHLH Name	Comments	References
		Math2/Nex1	Expressed in postmitotic cells of the brain	137
			Induces differentiation of PC12 cells and expression of *GAP-43* gene	138, 139
		Xath2	Expressed in postmitotic cells of stage 32+ *Xenopus* dorsal telencephalon	140
		Math3/NeuroD4/ NeuroM	Expressed in transition stage in neurogenesis	141
			Amacrine cell specification in the retina	142
			Cooperates with Lim-HD proteins to specify motor neurons	57
		Xath3	Converts ectoderm into a neural fate	143
			Promotes sensory neuron marker expression	144
	Atonal-like	Math1	Required for cerebellar granule neuron development	145
			Required for generation of inner ear hair cells	146
			Required for proprioceptor pathway development	147
			Specification of dorsal interneuron subpopulation	128
		Xath1	Expressed in hindbrain; induces neuronal differentiation in ectoderm	148
		Math5	Promotes retinal ganglion cell fate through brn-3b	41
			Retinogenesis, regulated by Pax6	149, 150
		Xath5	Retinal ganglion cell fate	47, 151
			Regulates neurogenesis in olfactory placode	152
		Math6	Promotes neuronal fate at the expense of glial fate	153
Olig	Olig-like	Olig1, Olig2	Specification of motor neurons and oligodendrocytes	61, 62, 154–157
			Motor neurons specification in combination with ngn2	57
		Olig3	Transiently expressed in different types of progenitors of embryonic CNS	158
E12	E12	E12/E47	Dimerization partner of various bHLH proteins	38

differentiation in neural precursors not by binding DNA but by competing for critical coactivators required to induce the expression of glial genes such as glial fibrillary acidic protein.[49] In addition, proneural proteins can interfere with growth factor induction of glial differentiation by binding to and inhibiting components of the CNTF signaling pathway. Ectopic expression of proneural proteins also suppresses the formation of oligodendrocyte precursors that normally arise within discrete regions of the neural tube after neurogenesis is largely complete.[50] Thus, one function of the proneural proteins is to prevent cells from expressing genes necessary for glial differentiation while activating those required for neuronal differentiation.

Finally, the proneural proteins are involved not only in promoting changes associated with generic neuronal differentiation but also in activating gene expression required for neuronal subtype specification.[38] Since proneural proteins fall into several subfamilies with distinct sequence differences, one possibility is that a given subfamily is specialized to promote the differentiation of a particular type of neuron. Indeed, in *Drosophila* there is strong evidence that the achaete–scute class of proneural proteins induces one type of external sense organ and the atonal class induces another.[51] Similar differences have been described for vertebrate proneural proteins, suggesting that they are designed partly to activate different downstream targets associated with neuronal cell-type specification.[52,53] The best-understood example of this occurs during the specification of motor neurons using the expression of an HD transcription factor called HB9 (Fig. 18–2F). Expression of HB9 is only activated where neural precursors in the ventral neural tube exit the cell cycle and produce motor neurons[54,55] (intermediate zone in Fig. 18–2D). Analysis of the enhancer required for this activation reveals an element with closely aligned binding sites for proneural proteins as well as for two HD proteins, Islet1 and Lhx2, know to be required for motor neuron differentiation.[56,57] Binding of these factors cooperatively activates expression of HB9, thus driving motor neuron differentiation. Significantly, although some proneural proteins can cooperate to activate HB9 expression, others cannot. Similar links have been made between the patterning of NECs and the expression of proneural proteins in the dorsal spinal cord.[52] In this case, neighboring domains of NECs produce different classes of interneurons by expressing distinct members of the proneural bHLH family. Thus, these observations strongly suggest that proneural proteins function to execute generic neuronal differentiation as well as to activate the downstream targets genes needed for neuronal cell-type specification.[38]

Potential Links Between Neural Patterning and Neurogenesis Control

Because the proneural proteins behave as a molecular "switch" that promotes neuronal differentiation, how their activity is regulated has important consequences for determining the fate of NECs. In some cases, the key element in this switch is a bHLH cascade in which the expression of one class of proneural protein in NECs can trigger neuronal differentiation by activating the expression of a downstream proneural gene (Fig. 18–2E, model 1). Alternatively, the key element may be in the form of a threshold in which only high levels of proneural gene expression in NECs are sufficient to trigger neuronal differentiation (Fig. 18–2E, model 2). In either case, sufficiently high activity of proneural proteins in NECs promotes exit from the cell cycle and terminal neuronal differentiation.[58] Conversely, if the activity or expression of proneural proteins is inhibited, NECs seem to revert to a ground state in which they have the option to divide and either become a neuron at a later time or serve as the source of progenitor cells for various glia at even later stages (Fig. 18–2D). Thus, proneural protein activity is not only a key factor in determining the onset and duration of neurogenesis but is also key in maintaining proper balance between the number of NECs that undergo terminal neuronal differentiation and the number that are retained in a progenitor mode, thus maintaining a progenitor cell pool for later-born neurons or for glia.[59] Not surprisingly, many of the factors that control the fate of NECs seem to converge on the expression or activity of the bHLH proteins, including the patterning genes described previously.

Analysis of the enhancer that drives expression of the proneural gene, *Ngn2,* in the spinal cord has revealed several discrete elements responsible for different spatial and temporal expression patterns in NECs.[42,60] These elements are likely to be driven by transcription factors whose expression is spatially restricted in NECs during neural patterning. For example, in the ventral spinal cord, the first neurons to be generated are motor neurons, and their generation in chick spinal cord is correlated with the early expression of Ngn2 within a narrow ventral domain of NECs. As already explained, this region of NECs is patterned by Shh signaling, which induces the expression of a key transcription factor, called Olig2, within the motor neuron–producing area of ventral NECs (Fig. 18–2C and F). When ectopically expressed in the embryonic spinal cord, Olig2 induces ectopic motor neuron differentiation and does so partly by inducing ectopic and precocious expression of Ngn2.[61,62] Significantly, motor neurons arise in response to ectopic Olig2 with kinetics similar to those they normally do in the ventral neural tube. Expressing high levels of Ngn2 along with Olig2 short-circuits this time course, resulting in rapid motor neuron differentiation. Thus, the interactions among the patterning gene, *Olig2,* and the proneural protein, *Ngn2,* seems to be key in promoting motor neuron differentiation. Since *Olig2* is a bHLH repressor,[61] its regulation of *Ngn2* expression seems to be indirect, perhaps through the regulation of inhibitors of proneural gene expression such as those described in later sections of this chapter.

Thus, the general emerging principle is that the fate of NECs during neurogenesis is established using interactions between patterning genes and proneural proteins. The remaining challenge is to determine how the bHLH cascade is engaged in a myriad of ways to produce the appropriate number and types of neurons that comprise each region of the CNS along the neuraxes. This challenge, although daunting in its complexity, is likely to revolve around the large number of factors that seem to regulate the expression or activity of the proneural proteins.

Regulation of Proneural Protein Expression and Activity

One striking feature of the bHLH proteins is their ability to feedback and autoactivate expression of themselves or to activate a downstream bHLH gene (Fig. 18–2E). As a result, direct or indirect changes in the strength of this positive feedback loop is one avenue that can be exploited during the process of patterning to control neuronal differentiation (Fig. 18–3). The following section reviews some of the prominent regulators of the bHLH cascade that have been described and are likely to be the focus of future research in this area.

Members of the Id family of bHLH proteins contain a dimerization domain but are unable to bind DNA.[63] Since the proneural proteins bind DNA as heterodimers with the ubiquitously expressed E proteins, they are inactivated when they instead form nonfunctional dimers with the Id proteins. Targeted mutations in Id1 and Id3 causes premature neuronal differentiation in mice, demonstrating these proteins negatively regulate the differentiation of neural precursors, most likely by inhibiting the activity of the proneural proteins.[64] The factors critical in regulating the expression of Id proteins are not known, but one potentially significant input is repression of these genes by the patterning genes that promote neurogenesis. In addition, expression of these genes are likely to be a target of the Notch signaling pathway, which plays a prominent role in regulating neurogenesis as described later in this chapter.

A well-established family of proteins that negatively regulate neurogenesis are the bHLH transcriptional repressors called Esr, Hes, Her, Hrt, and Hey, depending on their species of origin and the subfamily classification of their structure.[65]

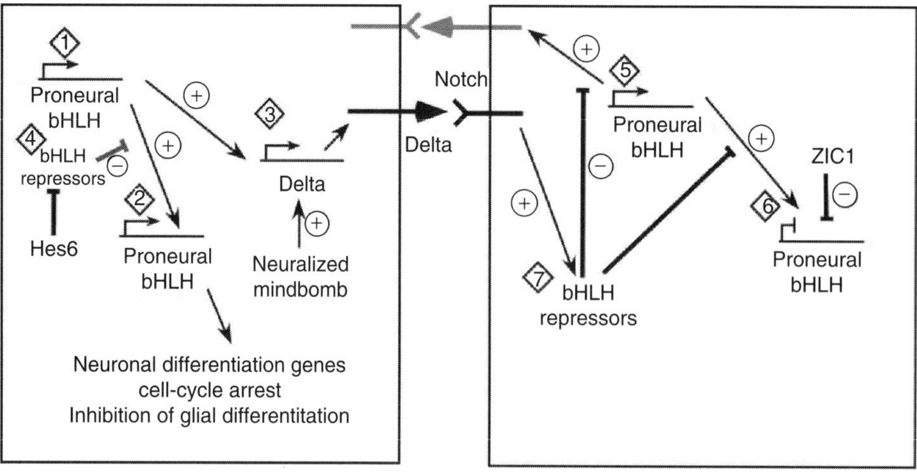

Figure 18-3. *Possible points of regulation of the bHLH cascade by patterning genes.* Differentiation of NECs depends on the bHLH cascade whose activity can be regulated in ways that promote neuronal differentiation, as shown on the left, or which keep the cell in a precursor state, as shown on the right. The bHLH proteins activate the expression of Delta (left panel), thus inhibiting neuronal differentiation noncell autonomously by activating the Notch receptor in neighboring cells (right panel). Products encoded by the patterning genes can potentially influence the activity of the proneural proteins in a variety of ways, as indicated by the numbers enclosed in diamonds. They can promote neuronal differentiation by promoting the expression of the neurogenins (1), the downstream bHLH (2), or the expression or activity of Delta (3), thereby enhancing lateral inhibition. Alternatively, neuronal differentiation can be enhanced by inhibiting the activity of proteins such as the bHLH repressors (4) that inhibit the activity of the bHLH proteins and thus neuronal differentiation. Patterning genes may prevent neuronal differentiation by inhibiting the activity of the neurogenins (5) or the downstream bHLHs (6), as shown for Zic1. Finally, patterning may inhibit neurogenesis by promoting the expression of the bHLH repressors (7).

Many of these genes were isolated and named based on homology to genes in *Drosophila,* called Hairy or Enhancer of Split, which play important roles in regulating proneural genes during fly neural development. Functional analysis of these bHLH repressors show that they potentially antagonize the activity of the proneural proteins by several mechanisms: interacting directly protein to protein,[66] competing with the proneural proteins for their binding sites (the E-box) in DNA,[67] or binding distinct DNA elements (the N-box or high-affinity repressor sites) in enhancers targeted by the proneural proteins.[68] An extremely large body of literature highlights the importance of bHLH repressors as potent regulators of the proneural proteins during neurogenesis. For example, targeted mutations of Hes1 or Hes5 in the mouse results in precocious and increased numbers of precursors undergoing neuronal differentiation,[69] and ectopic expression of these factors in *Xenopus* or zebra fish strongly inhibits neurogenesis in gain-of-function experiments.[70] In some cases, the bHLH repressors seem to regulate neurogenesis within relatively uniform domains of NECs.[71] In other cases, the expression of the repressor bHLH proteins is controlled by the Notch signaling pathway during a local patterning process, called lateral inhibition, which influences the ability of NECs to undergo differentiation.[72]

During lateral inhibition, the expression of the bHLH repressors are likely to be directly regulated by the Notch signal transduction pathway through binding sites for a DNA-binding protein referred to here as Suppressor of Hairless, or Su(H).[73] In the absence of Notch signaling, Su(H) acts as a transcriptional repressor thought to actively inhibit the expression of the bHLH repressors.[74] However, upon Notch receptor activation by ligand binding, the Notch intracellular domain (ICD) is released from the membrane, moves to the nucleus, and converts Su(H) from a repressor into an activator, thus rapidly inducing gene expression.[75] As a consequence, activating the Notch pathway induces the expression of repressor bHLH genes and thereby inhibits neurogenesis, and inhibiting the Notch pathway enhances the levels of neuronal differentiation within a pool of neural precursors.[76] Significantly, the proneural proteins are potent activators of a least one Notch ligand related to *Drosophila* Delta.[58,77] Thus, proneural proteins not only promote neuronal differentiation cell autonomously but also, by activating Delta, inhibit neuronal differentiation in their neighbors noncell autonomously (Fig. 18-3).

The interaction of the proneural proteins with the Notch pathway appears to be a critical factor in determining the number of neurons generated from NECs within a given region of the neural tube.[72] As a result, one can imagine a scenario where patterning genes act by targeting the activity of the Notch pathway, perhaps by targeting several proteins known to be Notch modulators. Activity of the Notch receptor, for example, is modulated by posttranslational modification mediated by glycosyltransferases encoded by the vertebrate homologs of the *Drosophila Fringe* gene.[78] The *Fringe* homologs are dynamically expressed within neural precursor populations, where they may influence the activity of the Notch pathway. Another Notch modulator expressed in neural precursors is a small ankyrin repeat protein, called NRARP, which promotes the turnover of Notch ICD.[79] Indeed, numerous mechanisms have been proposed to change the half-life of Notch ICD, thus altering the efficacy of Notch activity.[80,81] Finally, another potential mechanism of modulating Notch activity is by changing the activity, expression, or both of the ligands. In this respect, an important factor in ligand activity appears to be their removal from the cell surface following ubiquitination by specific E3 ligases.[82,83] In all, modulation of Notch activity is likely to be one way in which the output of the patterning genes could target the activity of the proneural proteins during neurogenesis.

In addition to negative regulators of proneural protein activity, the patterning genes could influence neurogenesis by regulating the expression of genes whose products promote the activity of proneural proteins. For example, proneural proteins induce the expression of a bHLH protein, called Hes6, distantly related to the repressor bHLH proteins described previously.[84,85] As a target of the proneural proteins, Hes6 is expressed ubiquitously in neural precursors in regions where neuronal differentiation occurs within neurogenic epithelium. However, in contrast to the other repressors bHLH protein, Hes6 promotes neurogenesis in ectopic expression experiments, and it seems to do so by antagonizing the activity of the repressor bHLH proteins. Thus targeting Hes6, a repressor of repressors, could conceivably be a means of regulating the efficacy of the bHLH cascade. A similar scenario applies to the HLH proteins called EBF/Olf-1/Coe, whose expression is activated in neural precursors by the proneural bHLH proteins and which can promote neurogenesis in some assays.[86,87] How these transcription factors modulate the activity of the proneural proteins is not known, but their expression is a potential target of regulation by patterning genes.

Another significant class of transcription factors that may link patterning and the bHLH cascade fall into a family of related Kruppel-like C2H2 zinc-finger proteins, including Gli1-3, Zic1-5, and Nkl. The *Gli* genes are the vertebrate homologs of *Drosophila Cubiutis Interruptus*, the downstream transcriptional mediators of Shh.[88] Given the importance of Shh signaling in regulating neurogenesis in the spinal cord as well as in other regions of the CNS, the Gli proteins are likely to have a role in regulating the bHLH cascade. Indeed both the Gli proteins as well as the closely related Zic and NKL proteins have been shown to have both positive and negative effects on neurogenesis when overexpressed in *Xenopus* embryos.[89–91] The mechanism by which these transcription factors regulate neurogenesis is mostly unknown. A major exception was revealed by the analysis of a proneural gene in chick and mouse called *Math1* and *Cath1*, respectively.[92] *Cath1/Math1* is expressed in NECs in the dorsal neural tube where it drives the differentiation of dorsal interneurons. The neuronal enhancer of *Math1* contains a site for autoregulation as well as a binding site for Zic1, which inhibits the activity of the autoregulatory site.[93] In this manner, Zic1 prevents *Math1* from activating its own promoter and inducing neuronal differentiation. How Zic1 is regulated in this case is not fully understood, but interestingly, the expression of other proneural genes does not appear to respond to Zic1 in the spinal cord. Thus, the Gli/Zic/Nkl family of proteins could contribute to the temporal and regional regulation of the proneural proteins as a downstream consequence of patterning.

The patterning of NECs may also result in changes in proneural protein activity by mechanisms involving posttranslational modifications. For example, bHLH proteins can be regulated by phosphorylation; a specific example of this regulation has been demonstrated for the proneural protein, NeuroD, in *Xenopus* embryos.[93] *Xenopus* NeuroD contains a consensus phosphorylation site for the regulatory kinase, GSK3β, that, when mutated, dramatically changes NeuroD's ability to promote neuronal differentiation. One possibility is that GSK3β regulates this using Wnt signaling, thereby changing the efficacy of proneural activity. Proneural activity might also be regulated by targeted protein turnover using degradation by the ubiquitin-proteasome pathway. Although this form of regulation has not been examined thoroughly in the context of neurogenesis, it is likely that proneural proteins, like other bHLH transcription factors, will be targeted by ubiquitin ligases for degradation in a regulated manner.[94,95] Finally, a relatively new and exciting level of regulation is likely to occur at the level of RNA. The recent identification of small, interfering microRNAs provides a compelling means of coordinated regulation of gene expression during differentiation. Finally, regulation of RNA activity during neurogenesis may occur through RNA-binding proteins, many of which are expressed in neural precursors in response to proneural gene activity.[96–98] Future work will undoubtedly uncover additional links with the patterning of neural precursors and the regulation of proneural activity at both the RNA and protein levels.

Summary

The development of the CNS can be represented as a series of fate choices progressively made by embryonic cells in response to both intrinsic and extrinsic cues. One of the first fate decisions is made in the ectoderm, where cells form the NECs of the neural plate rather than differentiating into nonneural tissues. This choice apparently can occur by default, suggesting that embryonic cells can form NECs in the absence of extrinsic instructions. However, a key process during neural induction is neural patterning during which a complex network of gene expression is established along the neuraxis, thereby specifying the position and subsequent fate of NECs. These complex genetic networks, many of which involve HD transcription factors, dictate patterns of neurogenesis by controlling when and where NECs undergo neuronal differentiation. Significantly, the patterning genes appear to regulate neurogenesis by converging on the activity of the proneural bHLH proteins, which function as molecular switches to initiate neuronal differentiation by promoting cell-cycle arrest, expression of neuronal differentiation genes, suppression of glial differentiation genes, and activation of neuronal subtype genes.

Thus, the neural precursors for the CNS initially choose their fate by default, but neural patterning is instrumental in instructing their subsequent neuronal fate by establishing a complex code of gene expression that drives the bHLH cascade at the proper time and place.

REFERENCES

1. Hamburger, V. (1988). "The Heritage of Experimental Embryology: Hans Spemann and the Organizer." Oxford University Press, Oxford.
2. Streit, A., and Stern, C.D. (1999). Neural induction. A bird's eye view. *Trends Genet.* **15,** 20–24.
3. Beddington, R.S. (1994). Induction of a second neural axis by the mouse node. *Development* **120,** 613–620.
4. Holtfreter, J. (1944). Neural differentiation of ectoderm through exposure to saline solution. *J. Exp. Zool.* **95,** 307–340.
5. Hemmati-Brivanlou, A., and Melton, D.A. (1994). Inhibition of activin receptor signaling promotes neuralization in *Xenopus. Cell* **77,** 273–281.
6. Hemmati-Brivanlou, A., Kelly, O.G., and Melton, D.A. (1994). Follistatin, an antagonist of activin, is expressed in the Spemann organizer and displays direct neuralizing activity. *Cell* **77,** 283–295.
7. Dale, L., and Wardle, F.C. (1999). A gradient of BMP activity specifies dorsal–ventral fates in early *Xenopus* embryos. *Semin. Cell Dev. Biol.* **10,** 319–326.
8. Harland, R. (2000). Neural induction. *Curr. Opin. Genet. Dev.* **10,** 357–362.
9. Sasal, Y., Lu, B., Steinbelsser, H., and De Robertis, E.M. (1995). Regulation of neural induction by the Chd and Bmp-4 antagonistic patterning signals in *Xenopus. Nature* **378,** 419.
10. Lamb, T.M., Knecht, A.K., Smith, W.C., Stachel, S.E., Economides, A.N., Stahl, N., Yancopolous, G.D., and Harland R.M. (1993). Neural induction by the secreted polypeptide noggin. *Science* **262,** 713–718.
11. Oelgeschlager, M., Kuroda, H., Reversade, B., and De Robertis, E.M. (2003). Chordin is required for the Spemann organizer transplantation phenomenon in *Xenopus* embryos. *Dev. Cell* **4,** 219–230.
12. Weinstein, D.C., Hemmati-Brivanlou, A. (1997). Neural induction in *Xenopus laevis:* evidence for the default model. *Curr. Opin. Neurobiol.* **7,** 7–12.
13. Smith, J.C. (1995). Mesoderm-inducing factors and mesodermal patterning. *Curr. Opin. Cell Biol.* **7,** 856–861.
14. Munoz-Sanjuan, I., and Hemmati Brivanlou, A. (2001). Early posterior–ventral fate specification in the vertebrate embryo. *Dev. Biol.* **237,** 1–17.
15. Schier, A.F., and Shen, M.M. (2000). Nodal signaling in vertebrate development. *Nature* **403,** 385–389.
16. Klingensmith, J., Ang, S.L., Bachiller, D., and Rossant, J. (1999). Neural induction and patterning in the mouse in the absence of the node and its derivatives. *Dev. Biol.* **216,** 535–549.
17. Bachiller, D., Klingensmith, J., Kemp, C., Belo, J.A., Anderson, R.M., May, S.R., McMahon, J.A., McMahon, A.P., Harland, R.M., Rossant, J., and De Robertis, E.M. (2000). The organizer factor Chordin and Noggin are required for mouse forebrain development. *Nature* **403,** 658–661.
18. Streit, A., Lee, K.J., Woo, I., Roberts, C., Jessell, T.M., and Stern, C.D. (1998). Chordin regulates primitive streak development and the stability of induced neural cells but is not sufficient for neural induction in the chick embryo. *Development* **125,** 507–519.
19. Streit, A., Berliner, A.J., Papanayotou, C., Sirulnik, A., and Stern, C.D. (2000). Initiation of neural induction by FGF signaling before gastrulation. *Nature* **406,** 74–78.
20. Wilson, S.I., Graziano, E., Harland, R., Jessell, T.M., and Edlund, T. (2000). An early requirement for FGF signaling in the acquisition of neural cell fate in the chick embryo. *Curr. Biol.* **10,** 421–429.
21. Lamb, T.M., and Harland, R.M. (1995). Fibroblast growth factor is a direct neural inducer, which combined with noggin generates anterior–posterior neural pattern. *Development* **121,** 3627–3636.
22. Kengaku, M., and Okamoto, H. (1993). Basic fibroblast growth factor induces differentiation of neural tube and neural crest lineages of cultured ectoderm cells from *Xenopus* gastrula. *Development* **119,** 1067–1078.
23. Kroll, K.L., and Amaya, E. (1996). Transgenic *Xenopus* embryos from sperm nuclear transplantations reveal FGF signaling requirements during gastrulation. *Development* **122,** 3173–3183.
24. Holowacz, T., and Sokol, S. (1999). FGF is required for posterior neural patterning but not for neural induction. *Dev. Biol.* **205,** 296–308.
25. LeSueur, J.A., Fortuno, E.S., 3rd, McKay, R.M., and Graff, J.M. (2002). Smad10 is required for formation of the frog nervous system. *Dev. Cell* **2,** 771–783.
26. Diez del Corral, R., Breitkreuz, D.N., and Storey, K.G. (2002). Onset of neuronal differentiation is regulated by paraxial mesoderm and requires attenuation of FGF signaling. *Development* **129,** 1681–1691.
27. Mathis, L., Kulesa, P.M., and Fraser, S.E. (2001). FGF receptor signaling is required to maintain neural progenitors during Hensen's node progression. *Nat. Cell Biol.* **3,** 559–566.
28. Baker, J.C., Beddington, R.S., and Harland, R.M. (1999). Wnt signaling in *Xenopus* embryos inhibits bmp4 expression and activates neural development. *Genes Dev.* **13,** 3149–3159.
29. Wilson, S.I., Rydstrom, A., Trimborn, T., Willert, K., Nusse, R., Jessell, T.M., and Edlund, T. (2001). The status of Wnt signaling regulates neural and epidermal fates in the chick embryo. *Nature* **411,** 325–330.
30. Willert, K., Brown, J.D., Danenberg, E., Duncan, A.W., Weissman, I.L., Reya, T., Yates, J.R., 3rd, and Nusse, R. (2003). Wnt proteins are lipid-modified and can act as stem cell growth factors. *Nature* **423,** 448–452.
31. Bainter J.J., Boos, A., and Kroll, K.L. (2001). Neural induction takes a transcriptional twist. *Dev. Dyn.* **222,** 315–327.
32. Yamada, T., Placzek, M., Tanaka, H., Dodd, J., and Jessell, T.M. (1991). Control of cell pattern in the developing nervous system: polarizing activity of the floor plate and notochord. *Cell* **64,** 635–647.
33. Jessell, T.M. (2000). Neuronal specification in the spinal cord: inductive signals and transcriptional codes. *Nat. Rev. Genet.* **1,** 20–29.
34. Briscoe, J., Pierani, A., Jessell, T.M., and Ericson, J. (2000). A homeodomain protein code specifies progenitor cell identity and neuronal fate in the ventral neural tube. *Cell* **101,** 435–445.
35. Muhr, J., Andersson, E., Persson, M., Jessell, T.M., and Ericson J. (2001). Groucho-mediated transcriptional repression establishes progenitor cell pattern and neuronal fate in the ventral neural tube. *Cell* **104,** 861–873.
36. Shirasaki, R., and Pfaff, S,L. (2002). Transcriptional codes and the control of neuronal identity. *Annu. Rev. Neurosci.* **25,** 251–281.

37. Ericson, J., Muhr, J., Jessell, T.M., and Edlund, T. (1995). Sonic hedgehog: a common signal for ventral patterning along the rostrocaudal axis of the neural tube. *Int. J. Dev. Biol.* **39,** 809–816.
38. Bertrand, N., Castro D.S., and Guillemot, F. (2002). Proneural genes and the specification of neural cell types. *Nat. Rev. Neurosci.* **3,** 517–530.
39. Olson, J.M., Asakura, A., Snider, L., Hawkes, R., Strand, A., Stoeck, J., Hallahan, A., Pritchard, J., and Tapscott, S.J. (2001). NeuroD2 is necessary for development and survival of central nervous system neurons. *Dev. Biol.* **234,** 174–187.
40. Schwab, M.H., Bartholomae, A., Heimrich, B., Feldmeyer, D., Druffel-Augustin, S., Goebbels, S., Naya, F.J., Zhao, S., Frotscher, M., Tsai, M.J., and Nave, K.A. (2000). Neuronal basic helix-loop-helix proteins (NEX and BETA2/Neuro D) regulate terminal granule cell differentiation in the hippocampus. *J. Neurosci.* **20,** 3714–3724.
41. Wang, S.W., Kim, B.S., Ding, K., Wang, H., Sun, D., Johnson, R.L., Klein, W.H., and Gan, L. (2001). Requirement for math5 in the development of retinal ganglion cells. *Genes Dev.* **15,** 24–29.
42. Scardigli, R., Schuurmans, C., Gradwohl, G., and Guillemot, F. (2001). Crossregulation between Neurogenin2 and pathways specifying neuronal identity in the spinal cord. *Neuron* **31,** 203–217.
43. Lee, J.E., Hollenberg, S.M., Snider, L., Turner, D.L., Lipnick, N., and Weintraub, H. (1995). Conversion of *Xenopus* ectoderm into neurons by NeuroD, a basic helix-loop-helix protein. *Science* **268,** 836–844.
44. Farah, M.H., Olson, J.M., Sucic, H.B., Hume, R.I., Tapscott, S.J., and Turner, D.L. (2000). Generation of neurons by transient expression of neural bHLH proteins in mammalian cells. *Development* **127,** 693–702.
45. Lo, L., Dormand, E., Greenwood, A., and Anderson, D.J. (2002). Comparison of the generic neuronal differentiation and neuron subtype specification functions of mammalian achaete–scute and atonal homologs in cultured neural progenitor cells. *Development* **129,** 1553–1567.
46. Souopgui, J., Solter, M., and Pieler, T. (2002). XPak3 promotes cell-cycle withdrawal during primary neurogenesis in *Xenopus laevis. EMBO J.* **21,** 6429–6439.
47. Ohnuma, S., Hopper, S., Wang, K.C., Philpott, A., and Harris, W.A. (2002). Coordinating retinal histogenesis: Early cell-cycle exit enhances early cell fate determination in the *Xenopus* retina. *Development* **129,** 2435–2446.
48. Jones, F.S., and Meech, R. (1999). Knockout of REST/NRSF shows that the protein is a potent repressor of neuronally expressed genes in nonneural tissues. *Bioessays* **21,** 372–376.
49. Sun, Y., Nadal-Vicens, M., Misono, S., Lin, M.Z., Zubiaga, A., Hua, X., Fan, G., and Greenberg, M.E. (2001). Neurogenin promotes neurogenesis and inhibits glial differentiation by independent mechanisms. *Cell* **104,** 365–376.
50. Ross, S.E., Greenberg, M.E., and Stiles, C.D. (2003). Basic helix–loop–helix factors in cortical development. *Neuron.* **39,** 13–25.
51. Jarman, A.P., Grau, Y., Jan, L.Y., and Jan, Y.N. (1993). *Atonal* is a proneural gene that directs chordotonal organ formation in the *Drosophila* peripheral nervous system. *Cell* **73,** 1307–1321.
52. Helms, A.W., and Johnson, J.E. (2003). Specification of dorsal spinal cord interneurons. *Curr. Opin. Neurobiol.* **13,** 42–49.
53. Parras, C.M., Schuurmans, C., Scardigli, R., Kim, J., Anderson, D.J., and Guillemot, F. (2002). Divergent functions of the proneural genes *Mash1* and *Ngn2* in the specification of neuronal subtype identity. *Genes Dev.* **16,** 324–338.
54. Tanabe, Y., William, C., and Jessell, T.M. (1998). Specification of motor neuron identity by the MNR2 homeodomain protein. *Cell* **95,** 67–80.
55. Arber, S., Han, B., Mendelsohn, M., Smith, M., Jessell, T.M., and Sockanathan, S. (1999). Requirement for the homeobox gene *Hb9* in the consolidation of motor neuron identity. *Neuron* **23,** 659–674.
56. Thaler, J.P., Lee, S.K., Jurata, L.W., Gill, G.N., and Pfaff, S.L. (2002). LIM factor Lhx3 contributes to the specification of motor neuron and interneuron identity through cell-type-specific protein–protein interactions. *Cell* **110,** 237–249.
57. Lee, S.K., and Pfaff, S.L. (2003). Synchronization of neurogenesis and motor neuron specification by direct coupling of bHLH and homeodomain transcription factors. *Neuron* **38,** 731–745.
58. Ma, Q., Kintner, C., and Anderson D.J. (1996). Identification of neurogenin, a vertebrate neuronal determination gene. *Cell* **87,** 43–52.
59. Nieto, M., Schuurmans, C., Britz, O., and Guillemot, F. (2001). Neural bHLH genes control the neuronal versus glial fate decision in cortical progenitors. *Neuron* **29,** 401–413.
60. Scardigli, R., Baumer, N., Gruss, P., Guillemot, F., and Le Roux, I. (2003). Direct and concentration-dependent regulation of the proneural gene *Neurogenin2* by Pax6. *Development* **130,** 3269–3281.
61. Novitch, B.G., Chen, A.I., and Jessell, T.M. (2001). Coordinate regulation of motor neuron subtype identity and panneuronal properties by the bHLH repressor Olig2. *Neuron* **31,** 773–789.
62. Mizuguchi, R., Sugimori, M., Takebayashi, H., Kosako, H., Nagao, M., Yoshida, S., Nabeshima, Y., Shimamura, K., and Nakafuku, M. (2001). Combinatorial roles of olig2 and neurogenin2 in the coordinated induction of panneuronal and subtype-specific properties of motoneurons. *Neuron* **31,** 757–771.
63. Yokota, Y. (2001). Id and development. *Oncogene* **20,** 8290–8298.
64. Lyden, D., Young, A.Z., Zagzag, D., Yan, W., Gerald, W., O'Reilly, R., Bader, B.L., Hynes, R.O., Zhuang, Y., Manova, K., and Benezra, R. (1999). Id1 and Id3 are required for neurogenesis, angiogenesis and vascularization of tumor xenografts. *Science* **401,** 670–677.
65. Davis, R.L., and Turner, D.L. (2001). Vertebrate hairy and enhancer of split-related proteins: transcriptional repressors regulating cellular differentiation and embryonic patterning. *Oncogene* **20,** 8342–8357.
66. Sasai, Y., Kageyama, R., Tagawa, Y., Shigemoto, R., and Nakanishi, S. (1992). Two mammalian helix-loop-helix factors structurally related to *Drosophila* hairy and enhancer of split. *Genes Dev.* **6,** 2620–2634.
67. Jennings, B.H., Tyler, D.M., and Bray, S.J. (1999). Target specificities of *Drosophila* enhancer of split basic helix-loop-helix proteins. *Mol. Cell Biol.* **19,** 4600–4610.
68. Giagtzoglou, N., Alifragis, P., Koumbanakis, K.A., and Delidakis, C. (2003). Two modes of recruitment of E(spl) repressors onto target genes. *Development* **130,** 259–270.
69. Ohtsuka, T., Ishibashi, M., Gradwohl, G., Nakanishi, S., Guillemot, F., and Kageyama, R. (1999). Hes1 and Hes5 as notch effectors in mammalian neuronal differentiation. *EMBO J.* **18,** 2196–2207.
70. Takke, C., Dornseifer, P., v. Weizsacker, E., and Campos-Ortega, J.A. (1999). *Her4,* a zebra fish homologue of the *Drosophila* neurogenic gene *E(spl),* is a target of Notch signaling. *Development* **126,** 1811–1821.
71. Geling, A., Itoh, M., Tallafuss, A., Chapouton, P., Tannhauser, B., Kuwada, J.Y., Chitnis, A.B., and Bally-Cuif, L. (2003). bHLH

transcription factor Her5 links patterning to regional inhibition of neurogenesis at the midbrain–hindbrain boundary. *Development* **130,** 1591–1604.

72. Lewis, J. (1998). Notch signaling and the control of cell fate choices in vertebrates. *Semin. Cell Dev. Biol.* **9,** 583–589.
73. Barolo, S., and Posakony, J.W. (2002). Three habits of highly effective signaling pathways: principles of transcriptional control by developmental cell signaling. *Genes Dev.* **16,** 1167–1181.
74. Kao, H.Y., Ordentlich, P., Koyano-Nakagawa, N., Tang, Z., Downes, M., Kintner, C.R., Evans, R.M., and Kadesch, T. (1998). A histone deacetylase corepressor complex regulates the Notch signal transduction pathway. *Genes Dev.* **12,** 2269–2277.
75. Weinmaster, G. (1997). The ins and outs of Notch signaling. *Mol. Cell Neurosci.* **9,** 91–102.
76. Chitnis, A., and Kintner, C. (1995). Neural induction and neurogenesis in amphibian embryos. *Perspect. Dev. Neurobiol.* **3,** 3–15.
77. Hans, S., and Campos-Ortega, J.A. (2002). On the organization of the regulatory region of the zebra fish *deltaD* gene. *Development* **129,** 4773–4784.
78. Hicks, C., Johnston, S.H., diSibio, G., Collazo, A., Vogt, T. F., and Weinmaster, G. (2000). Fringe differentially modulates Jagged1 and Delta1 signaling through Notch1 and Notch2. *Nat. Cell Biol.* **2,** 515–520.
79. Lamar, E., Deblandre, G., Wettstein, D., Gawantka, V., Pollet, N., Niehrs, C., and Kintner, C. (2001). Nrarp is a novel intracellular component of the Notch signaling pathway. *Genes Dev.* **15,** 1885–1899.
80. Fryer, C.J., Lamar, E., Turbachova, I., Kintner, C., and Jones, K.A. (2002). Mastermind mediates chromatin-specific transcription and turnover of the Notch enhancer complex. *Genes Dev.* **16,** 1397–1411.
81. Lai, E.C. (2002). Protein degradation: four E3s for the notch pathway. *Curr. Biol.* **12,** R74–78.
82. Deblandre, G.A., Lai, E.C., and Kintner, C. (2001). *Xenopus* neuralized is an ubiquitin ligase that interacts with XDelta1 and regulates Notch signaling. *Dev. Cell* **1,** 795–806.
83. Itoh, M., Kim, C.H., Palardy, G., Oda, T., Jiang, Y. J., Maust, D., Yeo, S.Y., Lorick, K., Wright, G.J., Ariza-McNaughton, L., Weissman, A.M., Lewis, J., Chandrasekharappa, S.C., and Chitnis, A.B. (2003). Mind bomb is a ubiquitin ligase that is essential for efficient activation of Notch signaling by Delta. *Dev. Cell* **4,** 67–82.
84. Koyano-Nakagawa, N., Kim, J., Anderson, D., and Kintner, C. (2000). Hes6 acts in a positive feedback loop with the neurogenins to promote neuronal differentiation. *Development* **127,** 4203–4216.
85. Bae, S., Bessho, Y., Hojo, M., and Kageyama, R. (2000). The bHLH gene *Hes6,* an inhibitor of Hes1, promotes neuronal differentiation. *Development* **127,** 2933–2943.
86. Dubois, L., Bally-Cuif, L., Crozatier, M., Moreau, J., Paquereau, L., and Vincent, A. (1998). XCoe2, a transcription factor of the Col/Olf-1/EBF family involved in the specification of primary neurons in *Xenopus. Curr. Biol.* **8,** 199–209.
87. Pozzoli, O., Bosetti, A., Croci, L., Consalez, G.G., and Vetter, M.L. (2001). Xebf3 is a regulator of neuronal differentiation during primary neurogenesis in *Xenopus. Dev. Biol.* **233,** 495–512.
88. Koebernick, K., and Pieler, T. (2002). Gli-type zinc finger proteins as bipotential transducers of Hedgehog signaling. *Differentiation* **70,** 69–76.
89. Brewster, R., Lee, J., and Ruiz i Altaba, A. (1998). Gli/Zic factors pattern the neural plate by defining domains of cell differentiation. *Nature* **393,** 579–583.
90. Mizuseki, K., Kishi, M., Matsui, M., Nakanishi, S., and Sasai, Y. (1998). *Xenopus* Zic-related-1 and Sox-2, two factors induced by chordin, have distinct activities in the initiation of neural induction. *Development* **125,** 579–587.
91. Lamar, E., Kintner, C., and Goulding, M. (2001). Identification of NKL, a novel Gli-Kruppel zinc-finger protein that promotes neuronal differentiation. *Development* **128,** 1335–1346.
92. Ebert, P.J., Timmer, J.R., Nakada, Y., Helms, A.W., Parab, P.B., Liu, Y., Hunsaker, T.L., and Johnson, J.E. (2003). Zic1 represses Math1 expression via interactions with the Math1 enhancer and modulation of Math1 autoregulation. *Development* **130,** 1949–1959.
93. Moore, K.B., Schneider, M.L., and Vetter, M.L. (2002). Posttranslational mechanisms control the timing of bHLH function and regulate retinal cell fate. *Neuron* **34,** 183–195.
94. Hirata, H., Yoshiura, S., Ohtsuka, T., Bessho, Y., Harada, T., Yoshikawa, K., and Kageyama, R. (2002). Oscillatory expression of the bHLH factor Hes1 regulated by a negative feedback loop. *Science* **298,** 840–843.
95. Sriuranpong, V., Borges, M.W., Strock, C.L., Nakakura, E.K., Watkins, D.N., Blaumueller, C.M., Nelkin, B.D., and Ball, D.W. (2002). Notch signaling induces rapid degradation of achaete–scute homolog 1. *Mol. Cell Biol.* **22,** 3129–3139.
96. Perron, M., Furrer, M.P., Wegnez, M., and Theodore, L. (1999). *Xenopus* elav-like genes are differentially expressed during neurogenesis. *Mech. Dev.* **84,** 139–142.
97. Park, H.C., Hong, S.K., Kim, H.S., Kim, S.H., Yoon, E.J., Kim, C.H., Miki, N., and Huh, T.L. (2000). Structural comparison of zebra fish Elav/Hu and their differential expressions during neurogenesis. *Neurosci. Lett.* **279,** 81–84.
98. Sakakibara, S., Nakamura, Y., Satoh, H., and Okano, H. (2001). RNA-binding protein Musashi2, developmentally regulated expression in neural precursor cells and subpopulations of neurons in mammalian CNS. *J. Neurosci.* **21,** 8091–8107.
99. Das, T., Payer, B., Cayouette, M., and Harris, W.A. (2003). *In vivo* time-lapse imaging of cell divisions during neurogenesis in the developing zebra fish retina. *Neuron* **37,** 597–609.
100. Sommer, L., Shah, N., Rao, M., and Anderson D.J. (1995). The cellular function of MASH1 in autonomic neurogenesis. *Neuron* **15,** 1245–1258.
101. Lo, L.C., Tiveron, M.C., and Anderson, D.J. (1998). MASH1 activates expression of the paired homeodomain transcription factor Phox2a and couples panneuronal and subtype-specific components of autonomic neuronal identity. *Development* **125,** 609–620.
102. Guillemot, F., Lo, L. C., Johnson, J.E., Auerbach, A., Anderson, D.J., and Joyner, A.L. (1993). Mammalian achaete–scute homolog 1 is required for the early development of olfactory and autonomic neurons. *Cell* **75,** 463–476.
103. Horton, S., Meredith, A., Richardson, J.A., and Johnson, J.E. (1999). Correct coordination of neuronal differentiation events in ventral forebrain requires the bHLH factor MASH1. *Mol. Cell Neurosci.* **14,** 355–369.
104. Casarosa, S., Fode, C., and Guillemot, F. (1999). Mash1 regulates neurogenesis in the ventral telencephalon. *Development* **126,** 525–534.
105. Cau, E., Casarosa, S., and Guillemot, F. (2002). Mash1 and Ngn1 control distinct steps of determination and differentiation in the olfactory sensory neuron lineage. *Development* **129,** 1871–1880.

106. Cau, E., Gradwohl, G., Fode, C., and Guillemot, F. (1997). Mash1 activates a cascade of bHLH regulators in olfactory neuron progenitors. *Development* **124,** 1611–1621.
107. Meredith, A., and Johnson, J.E. (2000). Negative autoregulation of Mash1 expression in CNS development. *Dev. Biol.* **222,** 336–346.
108. Tomita, K., Nakanishi, S., Guillemot, F., and Kageyama, R. (1996). Mash1 promotes neuronal differentiation in the retina. *Genes Cells* **1,** 765–774.
109. Ahmad, I., Dooley, C.M., and Afiat, S. (1998). Involvement of Mash1 in EGF-mediated regulation of differentiation in the vertebrate retina. *Dev. Biol.* **194,** 86–98.
110. Ferreiro, B., Skoglund, P., Bailey, A., Dorsky, R., and Harris, W.A. (1993). XASH1, a *Xenopus* homolog of achaete–scute: a proneural gene in anterior regions of the vertebrate CNS. *Mech. Dev.* **40,** 25–36.
111. Jasoni, C.L., Walker, M.B., Morris, M.D., and Reh, T.A. (1994). A chicken achaete-scute homolog (CASH-1) is expressed in a temporally and spatially discrete manner in the developing nervous system. *Development* **120,** 769–783.
112. Ferreiro, B., Kintner, C., Zimmerman, K., Anderson, D., and Harris, W.A. (1994). *XASH* genes promote neurogenesis in *Xenopus* embryos. *Development* **120,** 3649–3655.
113. Turner, D.L., and Weintraub, H. (1994). Expression of achaete–scute homolog 3 in *Xenopus* embryos converts ectodermal cells to a neural fate. *Genes Dev.* **8,** 1434–1447.
114. Zimmerman, K., Shih, J., Bars, J., Collazo, A., and Anderson D.J. (1993). XASH-3, a novel *Xenopus* achaete–scute homolog, provides an early marker of planar neural induction and position along the mediolateral axis of the neural plate. *Development* **119,** 221–232.
115. Henrique, D., Tyler, D., Kintner, C., Heath, J.K., Lewis, J.H., Ish-Horowicz, D., and Storey, K.G. (1997). Cash4, a novel achaete–scute homolog induced by Hensen's node during generation of the posterior nervous system. *Genes Dev.* **11,** 603–615.
116. Begley, C.G., Lipkowitz, S., Gobel, V., Mahon, K.A., Bertness, V., Green, A.R., Gough, N.M., and Kirsch, I.R. (1992). Molecular characterization of *NSCL,* a gene encoding a helix-loop-helix protein expressed in the developing nervous system. *Proc. Natl. Acad. Sci. U. S. A.* **89,** 38–42.
117. Duncan, M.K., Bordas, L., Dicicco-Bloom, E., and Chada, K.K. (1997). Expression of the helix-loop-helix genes *Id-1* and *NSCL-1* during cerebellar development. *Dev. Dyn.* **208,** 107–114.
118. Uittenbogaard, M., Peavy, D.R., and Chiaramello, A. (1999). Expression of the bHLH gene *NSCL-1* suggests a role in regulating cerebellar granule cell growth and differentiation. *J. Neurosci. Res.* **57,** 770–781.
119. Haire, M.F., and Chiaramello, A. (1996). Transient expression of the basic helix-loop-helix protein NSCL-2 in the mouse cerebellum during postnatal development. *Brain Res. Mol. Brain Res.* **36,** 174–178.
120. Kruger, M., and Braun, T. (2002). The neuronal basic helix-loop-helix transcription factor NSCL-1 is dispensable for normal neuronal development. *Mol. Cell Biol.* **22,** 792–800.
121. Bellefroid, E.J., Bourguignon, C., Hollemann, T., Ma, Q., Anderson, D.J., Kintner, C., and Pieler, T. (1996). X-MyT1, a *Xenopus* C2HC-type zinc finger protein with a regulatory function in neuronal differentiation. *Cell* **87,** 1191–1202.
122. Talikka, M., Perez, S.E., and Zimmerman, K. (2002). Distinct patterns of downstream target activation are specified by the helix-loop-helix domain of proneural basic helix-loop-helix transcription factors. *Dev. Biol.* **247,** 137–148.
123. Cao, Y., Zhao, H., and Grunz, H. (2002). XETOR regulates the size of the proneural domain during primary neurogenesis in *Xenopus laevis. Mech. Dev.* **119,** 35–44.
124. Perez, S.E., Rebelo, S., and Anderson, D.J. (1999). Early specification of sensory neuron fate revealed by expression and function of neurogenins in the chick embryo. *Development* **126,** 1715–1728.
125. Zirlinger, M., Lo, L.C., McMahon, J., McMahon, A.P., and Anderson D.J. (2002). Transient expression of the bHLH factor neurogenin-2 marks a subpopulation of neural crest cells biased for a sensory but not a neuronal fate. *Proc. Natl. Acad. Sci. U. S. A.* **99,** 8084–8089.
126. Ma, Q., Chen, Z., del Barco Barrantes, I., de la Pompa, J.L., and Anderson, D.J. (1998). Neurogenin1 is essential for the determination of neuronal precursors for proximal cranial sensory ganglia. *Neuron* **20,** 469–482.
127. Ma, Q., Fode, C., Guillemot, F., and Anderson, D.J. (1999). Neurogenin1 and neurogenin2 control two distinct waves of neurogenesis in developing dorsal root ganglia. *Genes Dev.* **13,** 1717–1728.
128. Gowan, K., Helms, A.W., Hunsaker, T.L., Collisson, T., Ebert, P.J., Odom, R., and Johnson, J.E. (2001). Crossinhibitory activities of Ngn1 and Math1 allow specification of distinct dorsal interneurons. *Neuron* **31,** 219–232.
129. Fode, C., Gradwohl, G., Morin, X., Dierich, A., LeMeur, M., Goridis, C., and Guillemot, F. (1998). The bHLH protein Neurogenin 2 is a determination factor for epibranchial placode-derived sensory neurons. *Neuron* **20,** 483–494.
130. Lee, J., Wu, Y.Y., Qi, Y.C., Xue, H.P., Liu, Y., Scheel, D., German, M., Qiu, M.S., Guillemot, F., and Rao, M. (2003). Neurogenin3 participates in gliogenesis in the developing vertebrate spinal cord. *Dev. Biol.* **253,** 84–98.
131. Morrow, E.M., Furukawa, T., Lee, J.E., and Cepko, C.L. (1999). NeuroD regulates multiple functions in the developing neural retina in rodent. *Development* **126,** 23–36.
132. Yan, R.T., and Wang, S.Z. (1998). NeuroD induces photoreceptor cell overproduction *in vivo* and *de novo* generation *in vitro. J. Neurobiol.* **36,** 485–496.
133. Ahmad, I., Acharya, H.R., Rogers, J.A., Shibata, A., Smithgall, T.E., and Dooley, C.M. (1998). The role of NeuroD as a differentiation factor in the mammalian retina. *J. Mol. Neurosci.* **11,** 165–178.
134. Miyata, T., Maeda, T., and Lee, J.E. (1999). NeuroD is required for differentiation of the granule cells in the cerebellum and hippocampus. *Genes Dev.* **13,** 1647–1652.
135. Kim, W.Y., Fritzsch, B., Serls, A., Bakel, L.A., Huang, E.J., Reichardt, L.F., Barth, D.S., and Lee, J.E. (2001). NeuroD-null mice are deaf due to a severe loss of the inner ear sensory neurons during development. *Development* **128,** 417–426.
136. Cho, J.H., Kwon, I.S., Kim, S., Ghil, S.H., Tsai, M.J., Kim, Y.S., Lee, Y.D., and Suh-Kim, H. (2001). Overexpression of BETA2/NeuroD induces neurite outgrowth in F11 neuroblastoma cells. *J. Neurochem.* **77,** 103–109.
137. Bartholoma, A., and Nave, K.A. (1994). NEX-1, a novel brain-specific helix-loop-helix protein with autoregulation and sustained expression in mature cortical neurons. *Mech. Dev.* **48,** 217–228.
138. Uittenbogaard, M., Martinka, D.L., and Chiaramello, A. (2003). The basic helix-loop-helix differentiation factor Nex1/MATH-2 functions as a key activator of the *GAP-43* gene. *J. Neurochem.* **84,** 678–688.
139. Uittenbogaard, M., and Chiaramello, A. (2002). Constitutive overexpression of the basic helix-loop-helix Nex1/MATH-2

transcription factor promotes neuronal differentiation of PC12 cells and neurite regeneration. *J. Neurosci. Res.* **67,** 235–245.

140. Taelman, V., Opdecamp, K., Avalosse, B., Ryan, K., and Bellefroid, E.J. (2001). *Xath2,* a bHLH gene expressed during a late transition stage of neurogenesis in the forebrain of *Xenopus* embryos. *Mech. Dev.* **101,** 199–202.
141. Roztocil, T., Matter-Sadzinski, L., Alliod, C., Ballivet, M., and Matter, J.M. (1997). NeuroM, a neural helix-loop-helix transcription factor, defines a new transition stage in neurogenesis. *Development* **124,** 3263–3272.
142. Inoue, T., Hojo, M., Bessho, Y., Tano, Y., Lee, J.E., and Kageyama, R. (2002). Math3 and NeuroD regulate amacrine cell fate specification in the retina. *Development* **129,** 831–842.
143. Takebayashi, K., Takahashi, S., Yokota, C., Tsuda, H., Nakanishi, S., Asashima, M., and Kageyama, R. (1997). Conversion of ectoderm into a neural fate by *ATH-3,* a vertebrate basic helix-loop-helix gene homologous to *Drosophila* proneural gene atonal. *EMBO J.* **16,** 384–395.
144. Perron, M., Opdecamp, K., Butler, K., Harris, W.A., and Bellefroid, E.J. (1999). X-ngnr-1 and Xath3 promote ectopic expression of sensory neuron markers in the neurula ectoderm and have distinct inducing properties in the retina. *Proc. Natl. Acad. Sci. U. S. A.* **96,** 14,996–15,001.
145. Ben-Arie, N., Bellen, H.J., Armstrong, D.L., McCall, A.E., Gordadze, P.R., Guo, Q., Matzuk, M.M., and Zoghbi, H.Y. (1997). Math1 is essential for genesis of cerebellar granule neurons. *Nature* **390,** 169–172.
146. Bermingham, N.A., Hassan, B.A., Price, S.D., Vollrath, M.A., Ben-Arie, N., Eatock, R.A., Bellen, H.J., Lysakowski, A., and Zoghbi, H.Y. (1999). *Math1,* an essential gene for the generation of inner ear hair cells. *Science* **284,** 1837–1841.
147. Bermingham, N.A., Hassan, B.A., Wang, V.Y., Fernandez, M., Banfi, S., Bellen, H.J., Fritzsch, B., and Zoghbi, H.Y. (2001). Proprioceptor pathway development is dependent on MATH1. *Neuron* **30,** 411–422.
148. Kim, P., Helms, A.W., Johnson, J.E., and Zimmerman, K. (1997). XATH-1, a vertebrate homolog of *Drosophila* atonal, induces a neuronal differentiation within ectodermal progenitors. *Dev. Biol.* **187,** 1–12.
149. Brown, N.L., Patel, S., Brzezinski, J., and Glaser, T. (2001). Math5 is required for retinal ganglion cell and optic nerve formation. *Development* **128,** 2497–2508.
150. Brown, N.L., Kanekar, S., Vetter, M.L., Tucker, P.K., Gemza, D.L., and Glaser, T. (1998). Math5 encodes a murine basic helix-loop-helix transcription factor expressed during early stages of retinal neurogenesis. *Development* **125,** 4821–4833.
151. Kanekar, S., Perron, M., Dorsky, R., Harris, W.A., Jan, L.Y., Jan, Y.N., and Vetter, M.L. (1997). Xath5 participates in a network of bHLH genes in the developing *Xenopus* retina. [Erratum appears in *Neuron* (1998). **21,** following 1221.] *Neuron* **19,** 981–994.
152. Burns, C.J., and Vetter, M.L. (2002). Xath5 regulates neurogenesis in the *Xenopus* olfactory placode. *Dev. Dyn.* **225,** 536–543.
153. Inoue, C., Bae, S.K., Takatsuka, K., Inoue, T., Bessho, Y., and Kageyama, R. (2001). *Math6,* a bHLH gene expressed in the developing nervous system, regulates neuronal versus glial differentiation. *Genes Cells* **6,** 977–986.
154. Zhou, Q., and Anderson, D.J. (2002). The bHLH transcription factors OLIG2 and OLIG1 couple neuronal and glial subtype specification. *Cell* **109,** 61–73.
155. Zhou, Q., Choi, G., and Anderson, D.J. (2001). The bHLH transcription factor Olig2 promotes oligodendrocyte differentiation in collaboration with Nkx2.2. *Neuron* **31,** 791–807.
156. Sun, T., Echelard, Y., Lu, R., Yuk, D., Kaing, S., Stiles, C.D., and Rowitch, D.H. (2001). Olig bHLH proteins interact with homeodomain proteins to regulate cell fate acquisition in progenitors of the ventral neural tube. *Curr. Biol.* **11,** 1413–1420.
157. Lu, Q.R., Sun, T., Zhu, Z.M., Ma, N., Garcia, M., Stiles, C.D., and Rowitch, D.H. (2002). Common developmental requirement for Olig function indicates a motor neuron–oligodendrocyte connection. *Cell* **109,** 75–86.
158. Takebayashi, H., Ohtsuki, T., Uchida, T., Kawamoto, S., Okubo, K., Ikenaka, K., Takeichi, M., Chisaka, O., and Nabeshima Y. (2002). Nonoverlapping expression of Olig3 and Olig2 in the embryonic neural tube. *Mech. Dev.* **113,** 169–174.

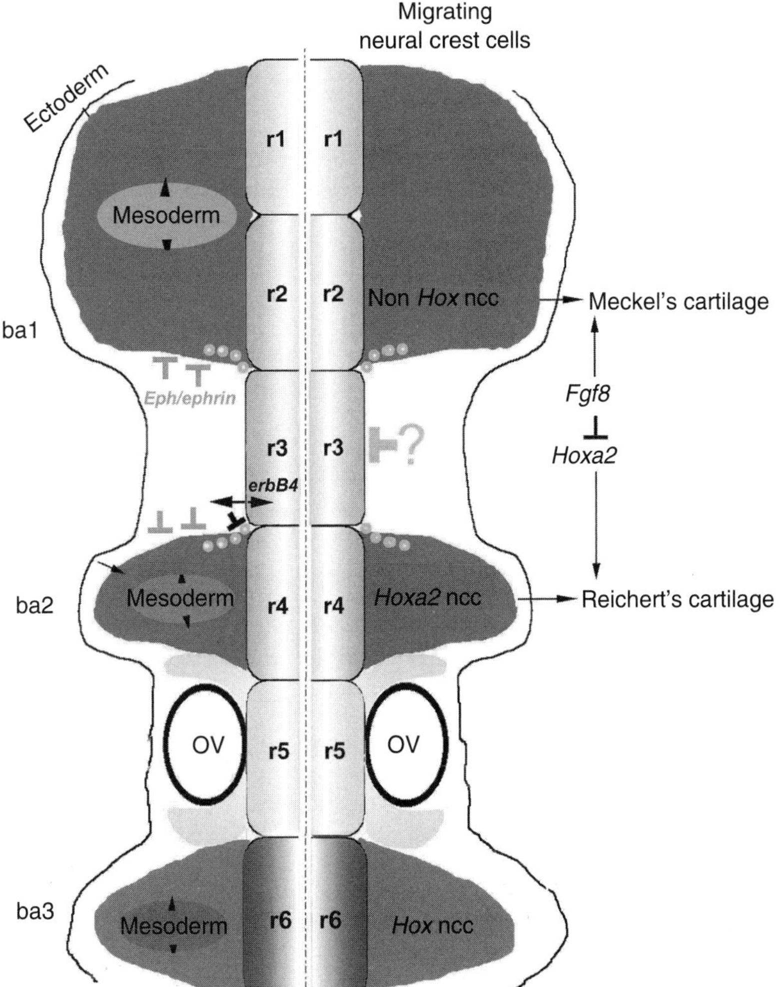

Figure 19–3. *Neural crest cell patterning.* Neural crest cells patterning is achieved through a combination of the information acquired in the neural tube during their formation and the influence of the environmental tissues they contact during their migration and differentiation. Interestingly, neural crest cells, mesoderm, ectoderm, and endoderm derived from the same axial level contribute to the formation of the same branchial arch (ba) in a conserved pattern. The mesoderm forms the myogenic cores of the branchial arches, which are enveloped by neural crest cells and are then surrounded by the surface ectoderm and endoderm. The cranial mesoderm is involved in maintaining the anterior–posterior character of migrating neural crest cells. The endoderm and ectoderm, respectively, influence neural crest cell differentiation into skeletogenic and tooth derivatives. It is important to note that *Hox* genes are not expressed in the first branchial arch, where Meckel's cartilage is one of the primary derivatives. In contrast, the second arch, which generates Reichert's cartilage, does express *Hox* genes; *Hoxa2* in particular is the primary determinant of second arch fate. In experiments in which *Hoxa2* is suppressed in the first arch either by null mutation or by ectopic sources of *FGf8*, such as the isthmus, the second arch identity is transformed into that of a first arch. Conversely, when *Hoxa2* is overexpressed in the first arch, its identity is transformed into that of a second arch. Therefore, it is crucial to keep *Hox*-expressing neural crest cells segregated from non–*Hox*-expressing neural crest cells. This is achieved through *ErbB4* signaling from the neural tube with Eph and ephrin signaling as well as yet unidentified signals, which restrict the lateral migration of neural crest cells from rhombomeres (r) 3 and 5. (See color plate 3 in volume 1.)

elements direct expression in the neural crest cells and hindbrain segments.[51] Further support for the independent specification of regional identity in neural crest cells and hindbrain segments comes from defects seen in *Hoxb1* and *Hoxa1* mutant mice. Mutation of *Hoxb1*, which is segmentally expressed in r4,[61] transforms r4 to an r2-like character, but neural crest elements in the second branchial arch are unaffected.[62–64] In *Hoxa1* mutants, minor hypoplasias in some neural crest–derived elements have been attributed to segmentation defects in the hindbrain that result in the loss of r5, a reduction of r4, and a misplaced otocyst, all of which could alter neural crest migration.[65–67] However the majority of the second arch crest-derived elements are not affected in *Hoxa1* mutants. Recent lineage-tracing studies have shown a dramatically reduced level of neural crest cell migration from r4 in *Hoxa1* mutants.[68] The reduced number of crest cells from r4 appears to be compensated for in later developmental stages, as the number of cells in the second arch and patterning of its elements are similar to wild-type animals later in gestation. This illustrates the regulative ability of neural crest cells and shows that a fixed number of early migrating cells are not essential to generate normally patterned structures.

In *Hoxb1* and *Hoxa1* double mutants, there is a complete loss of second arch neural crest–derived structures, even though these components were unaffected in the single mutants.[64,68–70] These defects could arise through effects on the neural crest itself or other tissues in which these genes are expressed (CNS, mesoderm, surface ectoderm, and endoderm). Compound mutants in which *Hoxb1* and *Hoxa1* were selectively eliminated together only in the CNS by targeted disruption of control regions demonstrated that the defects in second arch crest cells arise from a failure in neural crest formation.[68] In the absence of *Hoxb1* and *Hoxa1,* cells in r4 fail to adopt any regional character and are unable to respond to local signals that induce the formation of migratory neural crest. Cells from wild-type embryos grafted into these mutants are capable of generating neural crest cells, showing that the appropriate inductive signals are in the double mutants.[68] This is surprising because it is generally assumed that the events leading to the induction of crest from the midbrain to spinal cord regions (see "Induction of the Neural Crest") are not dependent upon the establishment of specific A–P characters. However, the genetic data in the mouse illustrates that there is a synergy between *Hoxa1* and *Hoxb1* in regional control of neural crest formation and implies that A–P patterning and induction of neural crest must be coupled in some manner. It will be important to determine whether this applies along the entire A–P axis. In the *Hoxa1–Hoxb1* double mutants, it is interesting that expression of markers for placodes (*Ngn2*), pharyngeal pouches (*Pax1*) and surface ectoderm signaling systems (*Fgf8, Fgf3, Shh,* and *Bmp7*) are properly activated in the absence of crest formation and migration into the second branchial arch.[68] Similar results are seen upon surgical ablation of crest cells in the chick embryo.[71] These results imply that interactions with and signals from the neural crest cells are not necessary to initiate localized expression of these components or to set up the A–P and proximal–distal regionalization of the branchial arches.

One of the most intriguing questions in neural crest cell biology relates to the timing and cell autonomy of the regulatory programs that govern the differentiation and patterning of this pluripotential population. In the trunk, the somites are the major segmental building blocks of bone and connective tissue. However, in the head, this role is taken over by the cranial neural crest cells, and there has been great interest in the nature of the patterning information that directs their morphogenesis during craniofacial development. Landmark transposition experiments in avian embryos by Noden[72] provided evidence that cranial neural crest cells might contain a prepattern before they emigrate from the neural tube. When neural crest primordia from the first branchial arch are grafted more posteriorly in place of those for the second or third branchial arches, crest cells are generated by the grafted tissue, and they migrate into the arch immediately adjacent to the graft.[72] Hence, they are not attracted back to their normal first arch environment. The surprising finding in such transpositions is that the neural crest cells derived from the grafted tissue differentiate into ectopic proximal first arch skeletal elements. The muscle cell types and attachments are also characteristic of those in the first arch. The generation of duplicated first-arch structures in an ectopic environment suggests a model in which neural crest cells possess a program that prepatterns their morphogenesis and sends spatial information to other cell types and tissues in the arch.

This research focused attention on the early patterning mechanisms established in the midbrain and hindbrain before emigration of neural crest cells. Based on the patterns of gene expression in hindbrain segments and on cranial neural crest[31,32,61] and craniofacial defects in targeted *Hox* mutants,[34,35,37,38] the *Hox* family of transcription factors appeared to be logical candidates for participating in any potential prepatterning mechanism for neural crest. However, analysis of *Hoxa2* neural crest expression demonstrated that this domain is generated by *cis* elements separate from those involved in modulating rhombomeric expression in the hindbrain.[51] Therefore, the expression domain of *Hoxa2* critical for patterning the second brachial arch is not established first in the hindbrain and then passively maintained in the neural crest cells during migration. New signals and inputs are required to activate *Hoxa2* in neural crest cells as they delaminate. One of these components is a member of the *AP2* transcription factor family.[51] *AP2* genes are globally expressed in migrating neural crest cells and play diverse functional roles in their development.[73–75] Therefore, other factors must restrict the activation of *Hoxa2* anterior to the second branchial arch and integrate environmental signals from the arches that modulate neural crest cell expression.[51,76,77]

Furthermore, an extensive series of transposition, ablation, and regeneration experiments in chick embryos have revealed context- and time-dependent influences on the ability to establish, maintain, and reprogram *Hox* expression in rhombomeres and cranial neural crest cells.[47,76,78–97] Some of these experiments are supportive of the prepatterning model and cell autonomy of *Hox* expression; other analyses; strongly argue for plasticity in crest patterning and *Hox* expression. Recent experiments aimed at resolving these conflicting points of view have begun to clarify this issue of autonomy versus plasticity. Transposing single or small numbers of rhombomeric cells from one segment into an ectopic segmental location in mouse[96] or zebra fish[91] embryos clearly demonstrates plasticity and reprogramming of *Hox* gene expression (reviewed by Trainor *et al.*[36,76]). This work shows that cells within the hindbrain are continually assessing their environment and that they maintain the ability to change their fate in response to signals in ectopic segmental locations.

Interestingly, this plasticity can be masked when larger groups of cells are transposed, indicating there are community effects or interactions between the host and grafted cells that modulate cell fate.[36,96] If sufficient numbers of cells are transposed to an ectopic location, they can reinforce each other and maintain their original A–P character. Such community effects would therefore explain data arguing for autonomy of *Hox* expression and prepatterning when entire rhombomeres or groups of segments were grafted.[36,76,83,86,88,94,97] Cell–cell interactions in the grafted tissue would maintain expression in ectopic locations, giving the impression of cell autonomy. This plasticity in rhombomeric and CNS cells means that critical A–P patterning programs are established at these stages but that these programs have the ability to be altered by environmental signals.

In the transpositions of small groups of cells, the patterns of *Hox* expression in migrating cranial neural crest cells derived from the graft were found to be completely plastic.[36,76,91,96] Neural crest cells failed to initiate expression appropriate to their axial level of origin, and when migratory neural crest cells from one arch were transposed to another, they rapidly down-regulated their *Hox* expression.[96] Therefore, in an ectopic arch environment, cranial neural crest cells are unable to initiate or maintain their proper A–P patterning program based on restricted *Hox* expression. However, when neural crest cells from the second branchial arch were grafted into the first arch environment in combination with second arch mesoderm, the neural crest cells maintained their original patterns of *Hox* expression.[96] This demonstrates that signals from the head mesoderm in the second arch helpr4-derived neural crest cells establish or maintain their proper genetic program of positional identity (see Fig. 19–3). The mesodermal signals appear to be permissive rather than instructive, as neural crest cells from other arches that interact with mesoderm from the second branchial arch do not change their fate.

There is an interesting difference in the plasticity of cranial neural crest cells and rhombomeric cells. When transposed along the A–P axis, rhombomeric cells will either maintain their original identity or adopt that of their new location depending upon the community effects.[91,96] However, transposed cranial neural crest cells in mice and zebrafish fail to activate their normal patterns of *Hox* expression; consequently, they are able to contribute to structures in the branchial arches, indicating they are not simply eliminated by cell death.[91] These results suggest that although cranial neural crest cell precursors may be programmed in the hindbrain before emigration, they are still competent to receive signals from mesoderm or other tissues (ectoderm and endoderm) in their prospective branchial arch. This enables them to adopt the proper regional identity.

The plasticity or lack of prepatterning for *Hox* expression in cranial neural crest cells raises the question of how ectopic first-arch structures can be generated in transposition experiments.[72] Community effects may play a role in preserving the original A–P character, as these experiments were done with large blocks of tissues. However, another contributing factor appears to be the influence of the organizing tissues such as the isthmus, which expresses *Fgf8*.[98] In transpositions of presumptive first-arch neural crest primordia, the rostral limit of the grafted tissue generally extends to the isthmus (midbrain–hindbrain junction). The isthmus acts as an organizing center and through *Fgf8* is able to induce regional midbrain identities in ectopic locations.[98–101] Recent experiments performing transpositions of first arch crest primordia with and without the isthmus have demonstrated that duplicated first-arch structures are only detected in grafts that contained the isthmus.[102] Isthmus grafts express *Fgf8* among many other factors, which in turn represses *Hoxa2* expression in neural crest cells, thereby generating a first arch fate.[36,102] Hence, in contrast to prepatterning, these results suggests a model in which ectopic first-arch structures arise because the grafts contain a regional signal that patterns crest and the crest cells are capable of responding to that signal. This again points to the critical role for environmental influences in elaborating the distinct programs of regional identity in cranial neural crest.[36,39,76,97,102] Therefore, neural crest cell patterning relies on a balance between signals acquired in the neuroepithelium during their formation and their competency to respond to environmental signals they receive from the tissues they contact during their migration and differentiation.

There is amazing morphological diversity in vertebrate craniofacial development, even though many common mechanisms underlie head patterning. What are the tissues and signals that contribute to this diversity? Recent experiments have illustrated that neural crest cells are an important source of information that can modulate interspecies variation in head derivatives.[103] As described previously, a program for specifying A–P patterning and regional identity is established in the hindbrain before crest cells emigrate, and this pathway is elaborated by appropriate signals in the surrounding arch environment. By exchanging the same presumptive neural crest primordia for an arch between ducks and quails, Schneider and Helms[103] have demonstrated through interspecies transplantations that differences in beak morphology correlate with species-specific neural crest cell programs. Hence, in these species, the donor neural crest primordia have established an autonomous program for a distinct morphology that will respond to evolutionary conserved signals in the host environment. This elegantly illustrates the importance of establishing fine-grained genetic programs in the CNS that can be modulated for evolutionary diversity.

Neural Crest and Stem Cells

Stem cells are defined as clonogenic self-renewing progenitor cells that can generate one or more specialized cell types.[104] Classically in vertebrates, there are two distinct groups of stem cells. The first group consists solely of embryonic stem (ES) cells, derived from the inner cell mass of the blastocyst. ES cells are totipotent and capable of generating all the differentiated cell types in the body. The second group consists of organ- or tissue-specific stem cells, which are derivatives of

ES cells. These stem cells are multipotent rather than totipotent and construct tissues and organs *de novo.* In adults, they maintain continuous cellular turnover and provide regenerative capacity in certain tissues. The phenotypic example of the second group is the hematopoietic stem cell, which generates all the cell types that make up the blood and immune systems.

A cardinal feature of stem cells is their ability to self-renew, that is, to divide so that each produces at least one daughter cell that maintains the multipotent character of its parent.[105] Probably the most important question in stem cell biology today is, What determines the self-renewing capacity? Studies of stem cell self-renewal require the identification of factors that promote stem cell division. It is possible that single growth factors promote cell division and maintain the stem cell state. However, not all factors that make stem cells divide are self-renewal factors. They could, for example, promote differentiation. Conversely, there could be factors that maintain the stem cell state but do not promote cell division.[104] One such example is Notch signaling, which can maintain neuroepithelial progenitors in a multipotent state without influencing proliferation (reviewed by Artavanis-Tsakonas *et al.*[106]). The maintenance of stem cell state or character therefore involves at least three distinct functions. First, there must be an inhibition of overt differentiation. Second, there has to be maintenance of proliferative capacity. Third, there needs to be maintenance of multipotency.

The other major issues being addressed in stem cell biology concern the differentiation of stem cells. For instance, how do stem cells choose their fates? To what degree do intrinsic cell autonomous programs versus extrinsic environmental signals influence lineage fate choices and specification? Are stem cells and their properties fixed and unchangeable, or are they plastic and adaptable? Stem cells *in vivo* are likely to encounter multiple simultaneous instructive signals. How do they interpret this information? Many of these issues have been tackled in great depth by the neural crest cell community during the past two decades, and interestingly, there are substantial similarities between neural crest cells and stem cells. Our knowledge of neural crest cell patterning therefore has a lot to offer toward understanding stem cell development and regulation, particularly in the area of cell-intrinsic versus cell-extrinsic regulation and specification of cell lineage and fate. Neural crest cell development is regulated by the interplay of intrinsic or autonomous signals received during their formation in the neural tube, balanced with the extrinsic environmental signals that they receive during their migration, which ultimately determines neural crest cell fate.

Neural crest cells are a multipotent embryonic migratory cell population, which give rise to a range of fates.[107] With a limited capacity for self-renewal, neural crest cells are regarded as stem cells or stem cell–like. The neural crest has been an attractive system for investigating the mechanisms underlying cell lineage specification, and one of the major issues in the field concerns how an apparently homogeneous population of nondifferentiated cells becomes channeled into distinct developmental pathways. As explained previously, neural crest cells exhibit an inherent plasticity or flexibility, which incidentally is one of the hallmarks of stems cells.

Multipotent, self-renewing neural crest stem cell progenitors of autonomic neurons and glia were first identified in the peripheral nervous system by *in vitro* subcloning experiments.[108] Neural crest stem cells do not generally generate sensory neurons and therefore contribute to only a subset of neural crest derivatives *in vivo.*[42,108] It's important to note the clear distinction in the differentiation ability of cranial versus trunk neural crest cells. *In vivo,* cranial neural crest cells generate cartilage, bone, and connective tissue, among many other cell types; trunk neural crest cells do not. Therefore, these neural crest stem cells are probably representative only of trunk and not of cranial neural crest stem cells. One would expect cranial neural crest stem cells to exhibit a wider differentiative capacity. Nonetheless, the differentiation of neural crest stem cells can be promoted by specific instructive extracellular signals. Neuregulin-1 promotes Schwann cell differentiation, BMP2/4 promotes autonomic neuronal and smooth muscle, and TGF-β promotes smooth muscle differentiation (Fig. 19–4).[109,110] In the peripheral nervous system, Notch signaling can restrict neural crest stem cell differentiation to nonneural fates while concomitantly promoting gliogenesis.[105] The inhibition of neuronal differentiation does not necessarily maintain multipotency, which is indicative of a requirement for other genes in this process.

Sox10 is one gene that could fulfill such a role. *Sox10* is expressed initially in early migrating neural crest cells and is maintained in satellite glia and Schwann cell precursors (Fig. 19–4). At the same time, it is down-regulated in neuronal derivatives.[111] Excess BMP2 or TGF-β down-regulates *Sox10* in neural crest stem cells, which is believed to mimic the normal process of lineage restriction during neural crest cell development. Conversely, the constitutive expression of *Sox10* in neural crest stem cells prevents BMP2 and TGF-β from extinguishing gliogenic potential.[112] *Sox10* therefore maintains the neurogenic potential of neural crest stem cells. Additionally, *Sox10* has been shown to inhibit proliferative arrest in neural crest stem cells, and it is critical for the induction of the transcriptional determinants of autonomic neurogenesis.[113] Given this combination of functions, the role of *Sox10* in neural crest stem cells therefore seems to be synonymous with maintenance of the stem cell state. This, however, raises the issue of whether other Sox proteins contribute to the maintenance of tissue-specific stem cell properties.

The *Sox* genes are a large family of transcriptional regulators that contain a conserved high mobility group, DNA-binding domain.[114] *Sox2* is particularly notable because it is expressed in the first stem cell populations within the early mouse embryo, namely, the inner cell mass cells of the blastocysts from which ES cells are derived. Interestingly, *Sox2* is also expressed in the uncommitted dividing stem cells and precursor cells of the developing fetal and adult CNSs, which suggests a potential role for *Sox2* in maintaining stem cell character.[115–117] Unlike *Sox10, Sox2* is not expressed in migrating neural crest cells, and although it may not be a neural crest stem cell marker, it could be a more general stem cell marker.

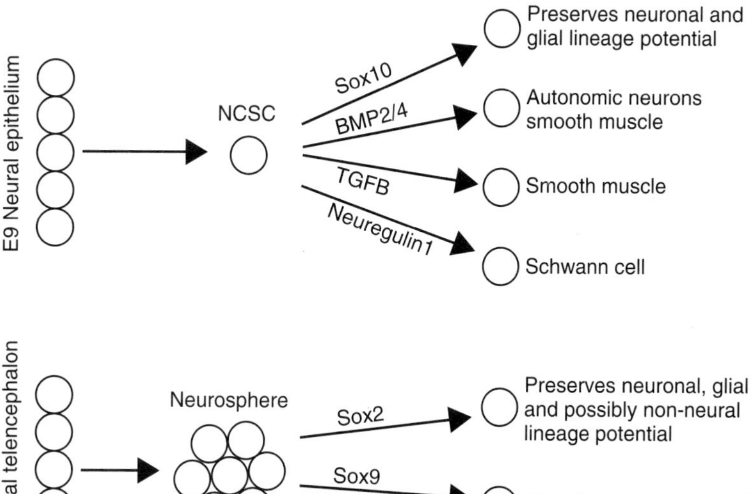

Figure 19–4. *Stem cells maintenance and dfifferentiation.* Neural crest stem cells (NCSC) can be isolated from embryonic day (E) 9 neural epithelium, and their subsequent differentiation can be regulated by several cell extrinsic factors *in vitro*. *Sox10* preserves neuronal and glial lineage potential in neural crest stem cells; BMP2/4 promotes autonomic neuron and smooth muscle differentiation. TGF-β also promotes smooth muscle differentiation, in contrast to Neuregulin, which regulates Schwann cell differentiation. Neurospheres can also be generated from E14 dorsal telencephalons, in which case, *Sox2* appears to be able to preserve neuronal glial and possibly non-neural lineage potential. High-level *Sox2*-expressing neurospheres maintain their undifferentiated state and exhibit a reduced capacity to generate neural crest cells when transplanted into the murine neural plates at the time of neural crest cell formation. In contrast, *Sox9* promotes the differentiation of neurospheres into migrating neural crest cells when low-level *Sox2*-expressing neurospheres are grafted into the neural plates of E8 mouse embryos. The *Sox* gene family may therefore regulate the transition of a stem cell from totipotent to multipotent.

In clonal density assays of cells isolated from the embryonic dorsal telencephalon either expressing or not expressing *Sox2,* only *Sox2*-expressing cells divided and generated secondary neurospheres. No secondary neurospheres were obtained from cells lacking *Sox2,* which is suggestive of *Sox2* playing a crucial role in the self-renewal capacity exhibited by neural stem cells. In differentiation assays, low-level *Sox2*-expressing neural stem cells primarily undergo gliogenesis. In contrast, neural stem cells selected for high levels of *Sox2* primarily produce neurons and radial glia, implying that high levels of *Sox2* are important for the self-renewal of stem cells and may define a stem cell type within the CNS. *Sox2* therefore may be crucial not only for the establishment but also for the maintenance of the undifferentiated neural stem cell state.[118]

Given the obvious similarities between stem cells and neural crest cells, an important issue to be addressed is whether neural stem cells can generate or regenerate migrating cranial neural crest cells *in vivo* by transplantation into the vertebrate embryonic neural plate. Neural stem cells are broadly classified as multipotent, self-renewing progenitor cells. In the CNS, these cells generate neurons, astrocytes, and oligodendrocytes. In the peripheral nervous system, they generate neurons, Schwann cells, and other derivatives, such as smooth muscle cells.[104] Cranial neural crest cells, however, produce a much broader range of cell fates than neural stem cells, including, cartilage, bone, connective tissue, and many of the sensory components of the peripheral nervous system.

Cranial neural crest cells migrate in discrete, segregated streams from the neural tube into the adjacent pharyngeal arches.[39–42] Cranial neural crest cell migration and patterning relies on a balance between the signals they acquire in the neural tube during their formation and their competency to respond to the signals they contact in the environment during their migration and differentiation[39,46,47,96] (see "Axial Patterning and Plasticity of Neural Crest Cells"). Of interest is whether neural stem cells would generate neural crest cells that migrate along the appropriate pathways, respecting the normally neural crest–free territories.[39,46] Therefore, to further characterize the multipotentiality and phenotypic plasticity of neural stem cells, recent experiments have challenged their potential to generate migrating neural crest cells. Both low- and high-level *Sox2* expressing neural stem cells were transplanted into r2 of neural plates in embryonic day 8.25 (5 somite stage) mouse embryos. During normal development, r2-derived neural crest cells migrate ventrolaterally into the first branchial arch. Neural stem cells expressing low or high levels of *Sox2* were both transplanted into r2 and readily incorporated into the neural plate as a cohort of cells with minimal intermingling with their immediate neighbors. Remarkably low *Sox2*-expressing neural stem cells exhibited a differentiative competency to generate migrating neural crest–cells as evidenced by DiI lineage tracing. Not only were these neural stem cells able to respond appropriately to neural crest–inducing signals, but they also migrated along the designated neural crest pathway and populated the full proximo–distal extent of the first arch.[119] This suggests that neural stem cells can correctly interpret local embryonic positional cues and generate neural crest cells that also follow appropriate migratory cues. In contrast, neural stem cells selected for high levels of *Sox2* expression, when transplanted into r2, generate very few migrating neural crest cells. These results are consistent with the role of *Sox2* as a stem cell maintenance signal, inhibitory to differentiation. It will be interesting to determine whether neural stem cells are competent to acquire appropriate A–P positional information (i.e., *Hox* code) following transplantation. Studies in progress in both avians and mammals are assessing the long-term differentiative fates of the neural stem cell–derived neural crest cells, as it remains to be seen whether neural stem cells derived from the CNS can produce nonneural derivatives. Based on the location of the transplanted cells after delamination from the neural tube and migration into the distal region of the branchial arches, with the clear role of the branchial arch environment in influencing neural crest cell differentiation, we would expect that these cells will be competent given the right conditions to differentiate into connective tissue as well as the hard tissues of the head, including cartilage, bone, and the odontoblasts of the teeth.

A recent study strongly supports this notion and highlights the influence of extrinsic environmental factors in stem cell differentiation. Mammalian ES cells as well as both fetal and adult neural stem cells can all generate cartilage, bone, and the odontoblasts of the teeth if they are recombined with embryonic oral epithelium and then cultured as explants under kidney capsules.[120]

In such experiments, which demonstrate that neural stem cells have the potential to produce non-neural derivatives, it is important to note that these cells are usually generated as "neurospheres," spheres of multipotent progenitors that grow out of mixed populations of CNS cells in bFGF-containing media.[121] Such neurospheres are thought of as CNS stem cells, but because the stem cells have only ever been studied in culture, it is not certain whether they have properties similar to normal CNS stem cells *in vivo*. For instance, neurosphere cells have been observed to generate blood cells upon transplantation into irradiated mice,[122] skeletal muscle upon coculture with a myogenic cell lines or upon transplantation into regenerating muscle *in vivo*,[123] or derivatives of all three germ layers upon injections into blastocysts or early chick embryos.[124] The implication is that CNS stem cells possibly retain a much broader developmental potential than is usually observed *in vivo*. One caveat, however, is that perhaps CNS progenitors lose patterning information and acquire a broader developmental potential as a result of being cultured in high concentrations of mitogens such as bFGF.[121] Such a dedifferentiation program has been previously observed in the demonstration that primordial germ cells become totipotent when cultured in growth factors such as bFGF and leukemia inhibitory factor (LIF). Primordial germ cells normally only produce germ cells; if transplanted into blastocysts, they do not detectably contribute to any somatic tissue. However, when primordial germ cells are first cultured in a bFGF- and LIF-containing medium and then transplanted into blastocysts, they can produce all somatic tissues as well as the germ line.[125,126] Similarly, additional evidence for dedifferentiation followed by redifferentiation has been provided by studies of neural crest–derived melanocytes, which lose their pigment and differentiate into glial cells upon clonal expansion in the presence of endothelin-3.[127,128] There is the possibility, however, that the *in vitro* cultivation necessary to isolate neural stem cells leads to their reprogramming.

These results challenge our notion of lineage restriction. The question remains as to whether pluripotent neural stem cells that generate neural derivatives *in situ*, do so only because they are located in the brain. Perhaps the only reason neural stem cells do not make blood or liver during normal development is that they are incapable of accessing the hematopoietic or hepatic microenvironments. These important questions will remain unanswered until CNS neural stem cells, purified from uncultured neural tissue, are tested for their ability to generate non-neuronal derivatives. Unfortunately, it may never be possible to truly address this question adequately. The nature of the stem cell niche is that the niche anchors and maintains the stem cell in place. The removal of the prospective stem cell from its niche environment could cause it to deregulate immediately and lose its spatial patterning information and regional identity. Hence, dissociation of the neuroepithelium necessary to isolate CNS neural stem cells might artificially expand the developmental capacities of these stem cells, even without the influence of expansion culture, and in doing so, it would facilitate the so-called dedifferentiation that has been observed in various transplantation assays. To date, therefore, it is not known whether neural stem cells correspond to normal CNS stem cells or whether their developmental potential has been broadened in culture. The implication, however, is that unexpectedly broad developmental potential may be a general phenomenon of progenitor cells given the right circumstances or conditions.

Significantly, an intriguing phenomenon may have been uncovered in which the developmental potential of cells can be reprogrammed under specific culture conditions or after transplantation without reflecting the normal developmental lineage relationships. It is critical both scientifically and clinically to understand this phenomenon, which poses the question as to whether differentiation is primarily environmentally regulated. This is one of the issues currently under intense investigation in the neural crest field, which makes neural crest cell development such a pertinent and analogous system for understanding stem cell patterning.

The possibility that any multipotential (or stem cell–like) cell population can respond to the appropriate positional cues to generate specific cell tissues and types, such as bone and the odontoblasts of teeth, has incredibly important implications in the possible treatment of craniofacial abnormalities. Craniofacial abnormalities constitute at least one third of all congenital abnormalities and are largely considered the consequence of defects in the formation, proliferation, migration, and differentiation of neural crest cells. The formation, migration, and early differentiation of neural crest cells *in vivo* occurs primarily between the third and eighth weeks of human gestation. There has been much talk about the potential use of stem cells not only in treating neurological disorders such as Alzheimer's and Parkinson's disease but also in possibly treating heart defects and congenital craniofacial abnormalities. The possibility of treating craniofacial abnormalities using stem cell therapy safely *in utero* during this critical period of gestation period remains an almost impossible dream. Not only are enormous advances in fetal surgery required but so are methods for detecting the early onset of craniofacial abnormalities. In the head, nearly all the cartilage, bone, and teeth are derived from neural crest cells, and it's intriguing that tooth and bone formation can be induced in stem cells without passing through a neural crest intermediate. Irrespective of the so-called dedifferentiation phenomenon, the remarkable demonstration that neural stem cells are competent under the right conditions to generate the hard tissues of the head opens the door for neural stem cell–derived tissue engineering as an alternative approach in the treatment of congenital craniofacial abnormalities.

ACKNOWLEDGMENTS

The authors wish to thank Morphoula Remboutsika, Robin Lovell-Badge, James Briscoe, and Paul Sharpe for contributing results to this manuscript prior to their publication. This work was supported by research funds from the Stowers Institute to Robb Krumlauf and Paul A. Trainor, by a Basil O'Connor Fellowship from the March of Dimes to Paul A. Trainor, and by an HFSP International Network Research Grant (RG0146/2000B) to Marianne Bronner-Fraser and Robb Krumlauf.

REFERENCES

1. Bronner-Fraser, M., and Fraser, S. (1988). Cell lineage analysis reveals multipotency of some avian neural crest cells. *Nature* **335,** 161–164.
2. Artinger, K.B., and Bronner-Fraser, M. (1993). Delayed formation of the floor plate after ablation of the avian notochord. *Neuron* **11,** 1147–1161.
3. Fraser, S.E., and Bronner-Fraser, M. (1991). Migrating neural crest cells in the trunk of the avian embryo are multipotent. *Development* **112,** 913–920.
4. Shah, N.M., and Anderson, D.J. (1997). Integration of multiple instructive cues by neural crest stem cells reveals cell-intrinsic biases in relative growth factor responsiveness. *Proc. Natl. Acad. Sci. USA* **94,** 11,369–11,374.
5. Ruffins, S., Artinger, K.B., and Bronner-Fraser, M. (1998). Early migrating neural crest cells can form ventral neural tube derivatives when challenged by transplantation. *Dev. Biol.* **203,** 295–304.
6. Sharma, K., Korade, Z., and Frank, E. (1995). Late-migrating neuroepithelial cells from the spinal cord differentiate into sensory ganglion cells and melanocytes. *Neuron* **14,** 143–152.
7. Korade, Z., and Frank, E. (1996). Restriction in cell fates of developing spinal cord cells transplanted to neural crest pathways. *J. Neurosci.* **16,** 7638–7648.
8. Nieto, M.A., Sargent, M.G., Wilkinson, D.G., and Cooke, J. (1994). Control of cell behavior during vertebrate development by slug, a zinc finger gene. *Science* **264,** 835–839.
9. Sasai, N., Mizuseki, K., and Sasai, Y. (2001). Requirement of Foxd3-class signaling for neural crest determination in Xenopus. *Development* **128,** 2525–2536.
10. Spokony, R.F., Aoki, Y., Saint-Germain, N., Magner-Fink, E., and Saint-Jeannet, J.P. (2002). The transcription factor Sox9 is required for cranial neural crest development in Xenopus. *Development* **129,** 421–432.
11. LaBonne, C., and Bronner-Fraser, M. (1998). Induction and patterning of the neural crest, a stem cell-like precursor population. *J. Neurobiol.* **36,** 175–189.
12. Gammill, L.S., and Bronner-Fraser, M. (2002). Genomic analysis of neural crest induction. *Development* **129,** 5731–5741.
13. Rollhäuser-ter-Horst, J. (1979). Artificial neural crest formation in amphibia. *Anat. Embryol. (Berl.)* **157,** 113–120.
14. Moury, J.D., and Jacobson, A.G. (1989). Neural fold formation at newly created boundaries between neural plate and epidermis in the axolotl. *Dev. Biol.* **133,** 44–57.
15. Selleck, M.A., and Bronner-Fraser, M. (1995). Origins of the avian neural crest: the role of neural plate-epidermal interactions. *Development* **121,** 525–538.
16. Basch, M.L., Selleck, M.A., and Bronner-Fraser, M. (2000). Timing and competence of neural crest formation. *Dev. Neurosci.* **22,** 217–227.
17. Dickinson, M.E., Selleck, M.A., McMahon, A.P., and Bronner-Fraser, M. (1995). Dorsalization of the neural tube by the non-neural ectoderm. *Development* **121,** 2099–2106.
18. Liem, K.F., Jr., Tremml, G., and Jessell, T.M. (1997). A role for the roof plate and its resident TGF-β-related proteins in neuronal patterning in the dorsal spinal cord. *Cell* **91,** 127–138.
19. Barembaum, M., Moreno, T.A., LaBonne, C., Sechrist, J., and Bronner-Fraser, M. (2000). Noelin-1 is a secreted glycoprotein involved in generation of the neural crest. *Nat. Cell Biol.* **2,** 219–225.
20. Basler, K., Edlund, T., Jessell, T.M., and Yamada, T. (1993). Control of cell pattern in the neural tube: regulation of cell differentiation by Dorsalin-1, a novel TGF beta family member. *Cell* **73,** 687–702.
21. Garcia-Castro, M.I., Marcelle, C., and Bronner-Fraser, M. (2002). Ectodermal Wnt function as a neural crest inducer. *Science* **13,** 13.
22. Watanabe, Y., and Le Douarin, N.M. (1996). A role for Bmp4 in the development of subcutaneous cartilage. *Mech. Dev.* **57,** 69–78.
23. Selleck, M.A., Garcia-Castro, M.I., Artinger, K.B., and Bronner-Fraser, M. (1998). Effects of Shh and Noggin on neural crest formation demonstrate that BMP is required in the neural tube but not ectoderm. *Development* **125,** 4919–4930.
24. Monsoro-Burq, A.H., Fletcher, R.B., and Harland, R.M. (2003). Neural crest induction by paraxial mesoderm in Xenopus embryos requires FGF signals. *Development* **130,** 3111–3124.

25. Mayor, R., Morgan, R., and Sargent, M.G. (1995). Induction of the prospective neural crest of Xenopus. *Development* **121,** 767–777.
26. Mayor, R., Guerrero, N., and Martinez, C. (1997). Role of FGF and noggin in neural crest induction. *Dev. Biol.* **189,** 1–12.
27. Godsave, S.F., and Durston, A.J. (1997). Neural induction and patterning in embryos deficient in FGF signaling. *Int. J. Dev. Biol.* **41,** 57–65.
28. Amaya, E., Musci, T.J., and Kirschner, M.W. (1991). Expression of a dominant negative mutant of the FGF receptor disrupts mesoderm formation in *Xenopus* embryos. *Cell* **66,** 257–270.
29. LaBonne, C., and Bronner-Fraser, M. (1998). Neural crest induction in *Xenopus:* evidence for a two-signal model. *Development* **125,** 2403–2414.
30. Saint-Jeannet, J.P., He, X., Varmus, H.E., and Dawid, I.B. (1997). Regulation of dorsal fate in the neuraxis by Wnt1 and Wnt3a. *Proc. Natl. Acad. Sci. USA* **94,** 13,713–13,718.
31. Hunt, P., Wilkinson, D., and Krumlauf, R. (1991). Patterning the vertebrate head: murine Hox 2 genes mark distinct subpopulations of premigratory and migrating neural crest. *Development* **112,** 43–51.
32. Hunt, P., Gulisano, M., Cook, M., Sham, M., Faiella, A., Wilkinson, D., Boncinelli, E., and Krumlauf, R. (1991). A distinct Hox code for the branchial region of the head. *Nature* **353,** 861–864.
33. McGinnis, W., and Krumlauf, R. (1992). Homeobox genes and axial patterning. *Cell* **68,** 283–302.
34. Krumlauf, R. (1994). Hox genes in vertebrate development. *Cell* **78,** 191–201.
35. Krumlauf, R. (1993). Hox genes and pattern formation in the branchial region of the vertebrate head. *Trends Genet.* **9,** 106–112.
36. Trainor, P.A., and Krumlauf, R. (2001). Hox genes, neural crest cells and branchial arch patterning. *Curr. Opin. Cell Biol.* **13,** 698–705.
37. Maconochie, M.K., Nonchev, S., Morrison, A., and Krumlauf, R. (1996). Paralogous Hox genes: Function and regulation. *Annu. Rev. Genet.* **30,** 529–556.
38. Lumsden, A., and Krumlauf, R. (1996). Patterning the vertebrate neuraxis. *Science* **274,** 1109–1115.
39. Trainor, P.A., Sobieszczuk, D., Wilkinson, D., and Krumlauf, R. (2002). Signaling between the hindbrain and paraxial tissues dictates neural crest migration pathways. *Development* **129,** 433–442.
40. Sechrist, J., Serbedzija, G.N., Scherson, T., Fraser, S.E., and Bronner-Fraser, M. (1993). Segmental migration of the hindbrain neural crest does not arise from its segmental generation. *Development* **118**(3), 691–703.
41. Köntges, G., and Lumsden, A. (1996). Rhombencephalic neural crest segmentation is preserved throughout craniofacial ontogeny. *Development* **122,** 3229–3242.
42. Le Douarin, N., and Kalcheim, C. (1999). "The Neural Crest," 2nd ed. Cambridge University Press, Cambridge.
43. Graham, A., Heyman, I., and Lumsden, A. (1993). Even-numbered rhombomeres control the apoptotic elimination of neural crest cells from odd-numbered rhombomeres in the chick hindbrain. *Development* **119,** 233–245.
44. Graham, A., Francis-West, P., Brickell, P., and Lumsden, A. (1994). The signaling molecule Bmp4 mediates apoptosis in the rhombencephalic neural crest. *Nature* **372,** 684–686.
45. Golding, J.P., Dixon, M., and Gassmann, M. (2002). Cues from neuroepithelium and surface ectoderm maintain neural crest-free regions within cranial mesenchyme of the developing chick. *Development* **129,** 1095–1105.
46. Farlie, P.G., Kerr, R., Thomas, P., Symes, T., Minichiello, J., Hearn, C.J., and Newgreen, D. (1999). A paraxial exclusion zone creates patterned cranial neural crest cell outgrowth adjacent to rhombomeres 3 and 5. *Dev. Biol.* **213,** 70–84.
47. Golding, J., Trainor, P., Krumlauf, R., and Gassman, M. (2000). Defects in pathfinding by cranial neural crest cells in mice lacking the neuregulin receptor Erbb4. *Nat. Cell Biol.* **2,** 103–109.
48. Ellies, D.L., Church, V., Francis-West, P., and Lumsden, A. (2000). The Wnt antagonist cSFRP2 modulates programmed cell death in the developing hindbrain. *Development* **127,** 5285–5295.
49. Ellies, D.L., Tucker, A.S., Lumsden, A. (2002). Apoptosis of premigratory neural crest cells in rhombomeres 3 and 5: consequences for patterning of the branchial region. *Dev. Biol.* **251,** 118–128.
50. Smith, A., Robinson, V., Patel, K., and Wilkinson, D.G. (1997). The EphA4 and EphB1 receptor tyrosine kinases and ephrin-B2 ligand regulate targeted migration of branchial neural crest cells. *Curr. Biol.* **7,** 561–570.
51. Maconochie, M., Krishnamurthy, R., Nonchev, S., Meier, P., Manzanares, M., Mitchell, P., and Krumlauf, R. (1999). Regulation of Hoxa2 in cranial neural crest cells involves members of the Ap2 family. *Development* **126,** 1483–1494.
52. Gendron-Maguire, M., Mallo, M., Zhang, M., and Gridley, T. (1993). Hoxa2 mutant mice exhibit homeotic transformation of skeletal elements derived from cranial neural crest. *Cell* **75,** 1317–1331.
53. Gavalas, A., Davenne, M., Lumsden, A., Chambon, P., and Rijli, F. (1997). Role of Hoxa2 in axon pathfinding and rostral hindbrain patterning. *Development* **124,** 3693–3702.
54. Rijli, F.M., Mark, M., Lakkaraju, S., Dierich, A., Dolle, P., and Chambon, P. (1993). A homeotic transformation is generated in the rostral branchial region of the head by disruption of Hoxa-2, which acts as a selector gene. *Cell* **75,** 1333–1349.
55. Hunter, M.P., and Prince, V.E. (2002). Zebra fish Hox paralogue group 2 genes function redundantly as selector genes to pattern the second pharyngeal arch. *Dev. Biol.* **247,** 367–389.
56. Pasqualetti, M., Ori, M., Nardi, I., and Rijli, F.M. (2000). Ectopic Hoxa2 induction after neural crest migration results in homeosis of jaw elements in *Xenopus. Development* **127,** 5367–5378.
57. Grammatopoulos, G.A., Bell, E., Toole, L., Lumsden, A., and Tucker, A.S. (2000). Homeotic transformation of branchial arch identity after Hoxa2 overexpression. *Development* **127,** 5355–5365.
58. Couly, G., Grapin-Botton, A., Coltey, P., Ruhin, B., and Le Douarin, N.M. (1998). Determination of the identity of the derivatives of the cephalic neural crest: incompatibility between Hox gene expression and lower jaw development. *Development* **128,** 3445–3459.
59. Rijli, F., Gavalas, A., and Chambon, P. (1998). Segmentation and specification in the branchial region of the head: the role of Hox selector genes. *Int. J. Dev. Biol.* **42,** 393–401.
60. Kessel, M., and Gruss, P. (1991). Homeotic transformations of murine prevertebrae and concomitant alteration of Hox codes induced by retinoic acid. *Cell* **67,** 89–104.
61. Wilkinson, D.G., Bhatt, S., Cook, M., Boncinelli, E., and Krumlauf, R. (1989). Segmental expression of Hox-2 homeobox-containing genes in the developing mouse hindbrain. *Nature* **341,** 405–409.
62. Goddard, J., Rossel, M., Manley, N., and Capecchi, M. (1996). Mice with targeted disruption of Hoxb1 fail to form the motor nucleus of the VIIth nerve. *Development* **122,** 3217–3228.
63. Studer, M., Lumsden, A., Ariza-McNaughton, L., Bradley, A., and Krumlauf, R. (1996). Altered segmental identity and

abnormal migration of motor neurons in mice lacking Hoxb1. *Nature* **384,** 630–635.

64. Studer, M., Gavalas, A., Marshall, H., Ariza-McNaughton, L., Rijli, F., Chambon, P., and Krumlauf, R. (1998). Genetic interaction between Hoxa1 and Hoxb1 reveal new roles in regulation of early hindbrain patterning. *Development* **125,** 1025–1036.
65. Chisaka, O., Musci, T., and Capecchi, M. (1992). Developmental defects of the ear, cranial nerves and hindbrain resulting from targeted disruption of the mouse homeobox gene Hox-1.6. *Nature* **355,** 516–520.
66. Lufkin, T., Dierich, A., LeMeur, M., Mark, M., and Chambon, P. (1991). Disruption of the Hox-1.6 homeobox gene results in defects in a region corresponding to its rostral domain of expression. *Cell* **66,** 1105–1119.
67. Mark, M., Lufkin, T., Vonesch, J.L., Ruberte, E., Olivo, J.C., Dollé, P., Gorry, P., Lumsden, A., and Chambon, P. (1993). Two rhombomeres are altered in Hoxa1 mutant mice. *Development* **119,** 319–338.
68. Gavalas, A., Trainor, P., Ariza-McNaughton, L., and Krumlauf, R. (2001). Synergy between Hoxa1 and Hoxb1: the relationship between arch patterning and the generation of cranial neural crest. *Development* **128,** 3017–3027.
69. Rossel, M., and Capecchi, M. (1999). Mice mutant for both Hoxa1 and Hoxb1 show extensive remodeling of the hindbrain and defects in craniofacial development. *Development* **126,** 5027–5040.
70. Gavalas, A., Studer, M., Lumsden, A., Rijli, F., Krumlauf, R., and Chambon, P. (1998). Hoxa1 and Hoxb1 synergize in patterning the hindbrain, cranial nerves and second pharyngeal arch. *Development* **125,** 1123–1136.
71. Veitch, E., Begbie, J., Schilling, T.F., Smith, M.M., and Graham, A. (1999). Pharyngeal arch patterning in the absence of neural crest. *Curr. Biol.* **9,** 1481–1484.
72. Noden, D. (1983). The role of the neural crest in patterning of avian cranial skeletal, connective, and muscle tissues. *Dev. Biol.* **96,** 144–165.
73. Zhang, J., Hagopian-Donaldson, S., Serbedzija, G., Elsemore, J., Plehn-Dujowich, D., McMahon, A.P., Flavell, R.A., and Williams, T. (1996). Neural tube, skeletal and body wall defects in mice lacking transcription factor Ap2. *Nature* **381,** 238–241.
74. Mitchell, P.J., Timmons, P.M., Hébert, J.M., Rigby, P.W.J., and Tjian, R. (1991). Transcription factor Ap2 is expressed in neural crest cell lineages during mouse embryogenesis. *Genes Dev.* **5,** 105–119.
75. Schorle, H., Meier, P., Buchert, M., Jaenisch, R., and Mitchell, P.J. (1996). Transcription factor AP-2 is essential for cranial closure and craniofacial development. *Nature* **381,** 235–238.
76. Trainor, P., and Krumlauf, R. (2000). Patterning the cranial neural crest: hindbrain segmentation and Hox gene plasticity. *Nat. Rev. Neurosci.* **1,** 116–124.
77. Tümpel, S., Maconochie, M., Wiedemann, L.M., and Krumlauf, R. (2002). Conservation and diversity in the *cis*-regulatory networks that integrate information controlling expression of Hoxa2 in hindbrain and cranial neural crest cells in vertebrates. *Dev. Biol.* **246,** 45–56.
78. Couly, G.F., Grapin-Bottom, A., Coltey, P., and Le Douarin, N.M. (1996). The regeneration of the cephalic neural crest, a problem revisited: the regenerating cells originate from the contralateral or from the anterior and posterior neural folds. *Development* **122,** 3393–3407.
79. Diaz, C., and Glover, J. (1996). Appropriate pattern formation following regulative regeneration in the hindbrain neural tube. *Development* **122,** 3095–3105.
80. Gould, A., Itasaki, N., and Krumlauf, R. (1998). Initiation of rhombomeric Hoxb4 expression requires induction by somites and a retinoid pathway. *Neuron* **21,** 39–51.
81. Grapin-Botton, A., Bonnin, M.A., Ariza-McNaughton, L., Krumlauf, R., and LeDouarin, N.M. (1995). Plasticity of transposed rhombomeres: hox gene induction is correlated with phenotypic modifications. *Development* **121,** 2707–2721.
82. Grapin-Botton, A., Bonnin, M.A., and Le Douarin, N. (1997). Hox gene induction in the neural tube depends on three parameters: competence, signal supply and paralogue group. *Development* **124,** 849–859.
83. Guthrie, S., Muchamore, I., Kuroiwa, A., Marshall, H., Krumlauf, R., and Lumsden, A. (1992). Neuroectodermal autonomy of Hox-2.9 expression revealed by rhombomere transpositions. *Nature* **356,** 157–159.
84. Hunt, P., Clarke, J.D.W., Buxton, P., Ferretti, P., and Thorogood, P. (1998). Stability and plasticity of neural crest patterning and branchial arch Hox code after extensive cephalic crest rotation. *Dev. Biol.* **198,** 82–104.
85. Hunt, P., Ferretti, P., Krumlauf, R., and Thorogood, P. (1995). Restoration of normal Hox code and branchial arch morphogenesis after extensive deletion of hindbrain neural crest. *Dev. Biol.* **168,** 584–597.
86. Itasaki, N., Sharpe, J., Morrison, A., and Krumlauf, R. (1996). Reprogramming Hox expression in the vertebrate hindbrain: influence of paraxial mesoderm and rhombomere transposition. *Neuron* **16,** 487–500.
87. Kulesa, P., Bronner-Fraser, M., and Fraser, S. (2000). *In ovo* time-lapse analysis after dorsal neural tube ablation shows rerouting of chick hindbrain neural crest. *Development* **127,** 2843–2852.
88. Kuratani, S.C., and Eichele, G. (1993). Rhombomere transposition repatterns the segmental organization of cranial nerves and reveals cell-autonomous expression of a homeodomain protein. *Development* **117,** 105–117.
89. Yntema, C., and Hammond, W. (1945). Depletions and abnormalities in the cervical sympathetic system of the chick following extirpation of the neural crest. *J. Exp. Zool.* **100,** 237–263.
90. Simon, H., Hornbruch, A., and Lumsden, A. (1995). Independent assignment of antero–posterior and dorso–ventral positional values in the developing chick hindbrain. *Curr. Biol.* **5,** 205–214.
91. Schilling, T. (2001). Plasticity of zebra fish Hox expression in the hindbrain and cranial neural crest hindbrain. *Dev. Biol.* **231,** 201–216.
92. Scherson, T., Serbedzija, G., Fraser, S., and Bronner-Fraser, M. (1993). Regulative capacity of the cranial neural tube and neural crest. *Development* **118,** 1049–1061.
93. Saldivar, J.R., Sechrist, J.W., Krull, C.E., Ruffin, S., and Bronner-Fraser, M. (1997). Dorsal hindbrain ablation results in the rerouting of neural crest migration and the changes in gene expression, but normal hyoid development. *Development* **124,** 2729–2739.
94. Saldivar, J., Krull, C., Krumlauf, R., Ariza-McNaughton, L., and Bronner-Fraser, M. (1996). Rhombomere of origin determines autonomous versus environmentally regulated expression of Hoxa3 in the avian embryo. *Development* **122,** 895–904.
95. McKee, G., and Ferguson, M. (1984). The effects of mesencephalic neural crest cell extirpation on the development of chicken embryos. *J. of Anat.* **139,** 491–512.
96. Trainor, P., and Krumlauf, R. (2000). Plasticity in mouse neural crest cells reveals a new patterning role for cranial mesoderm. *Nat. Cell Biol.* **2,** 96–102.
97. Prince, V., and Lumsden, A. (1994). Hoxa-2 expression in normal and transposed rhombomeres: independent regulation in the neural tube and neural crest. *Development* **120,** 911–923.

98. Crossley, P.H., Martinez, S., and Martin, G.R. (1996). Midbrain development induced by Fgf8 in the chick embryo. *Nature* **380,** 66–68.
99. Irving, C., and Mason, I. (1999). Regeneration of isthmic tissue is the result of a specific and direct interaction between rhombomere 1 and midbrain. *Development* **126,** 3981–3989.
100. Irving, C., and Mason, I. (2000). Signaling by Fgf8 from the isthmus patterns the anterior hindbrain and establishes the anterior limit of Hox gene expression. *Development* **127,** 177–186.
101. Martinez, S., Marin, F., Nieto, M.A., and Puelles, L. (1995). Induction of ectopic *engrailed* expression and fate change in avian rhombomeres: intersegmental boundaries as barriers. *Mech. of Dev.* **51,** 289–303.
102. Trainor, P.A., Ariza-McNaughton, L., and Krumlauf, R. (2002). Role of the isthmus and FGFs in resolving the paradox of neural crest plasticity and prepatterning. *Science* **295,** 1288–1291.
103. Schneider, R.A., and Helms, J.A. (2003). The cellular and molecular origins of beak morphology. *Science* **299,** 565–568.
104. Anderson, D.J. (2001). Stem cells and pattern formation in the nervous system: the possible versus the actual. *Neuron* **30,** 19–35.
105. Morrison, S.J., Shah, N.M., and Anderson, D.J. (1997). Regulatory mechanisms in stem cell biology. *Cell* **88,** 287–298.
106. Artavanis-Tsakonas, S., Rand, M.D., and Lake, R.J. (1999). Notch signaling: cell fate control and signal integration in development. *Science* **284,** 770–776.
107. Noden, D.M. (1982). Patterns and organization of craniofacial skeletogenic and myogenic mesenchyme: a perspective. *Prog. Clin. Biol. Res.* **101,** 167–203.
108. Stemple, D.L., and Anderson, D.J. (1992). Isolation of a stem cell for neurons and glia from the mammalian neural crest. *Cell* **71,** 973–985.
109. Shah, N.M., Groves, A.K., and Anderson, D.J. (1996). Alternative neural crest cell fates are instructively promoted by TGF-β superfamily members. *Cell* **85,** 331–343.
110. Shah, N.M., Marchionni, M.A., Isaacs, I., Stroobant, P., and Anderson, D.J. (1994). Glial growth factor restricts mammalian neural crest stem cells to a glial fate. *Cell* **77,** 349–360.
111. Pusch, C., Hustert, E., Pfeifer, D., Sudbeck, P., Kist, R., Roe, B., Wang, Z., Balling, R., Blin, N., and Scherer, G. (1998). The SOX10/Sox10 gene from human and mouse: sequence, expression, and transactivation by the encoded HMG domain transcription factor. *Hum. Genet.* **103,** 115–123.
112. Kim, J., Lo, L., Dormand, E., and Anderson, D.J. (2003). SOX10 maintains multipotency and inhibits neuronal differentiation of neural crest stem cells. *Neuron* **38,** 17–31.
113. Paratore, C., Eichenberger, C., Suter, U., and Sommer, L. (2002). Sox10 haploinsufficiency affects maintenance of progenitor cells in a mouse model of Hirschsprung disease. *Hum. Mol. Genet.* **11,** 3075–3085.
114. Wilson, M., and Koopman, P. (2002). Matching SOX: partner proteins and co-factors of the SOX family of transcriptional regulators. *Curr. Opin. Genet. Dev.* **12,** 441–446.
115. Zappone, M.V., Galli, R., Catena, R., Meani, N., De Biasi, S., Mattei, E., Tiveron, C., Vescovi, A.L., Lovell-Badge, R., Ottolenghi, S., and Nicolis, S.K. (2000). Sox2 regulatory sequences direct expression of a (beta)-geo transgene to telencephalic neural stem cells and precursors of the mouse embryo, revealing regionalization of gene expression in CNS stem cells. *Development* **127,** 2367–2382.
116. Rex, M., Orme, A., Uwanogho, D., Tointon, K., Wigmore, P.M., Sharpe, P.T., and Scotting, P.J. (1997). Dynamic expression of chicken Sox2 and Sox3 genes in ectoderm induced to form neural tissue. *Dev. Dyn.* **209,** 323–332.
117. Sasai, Y. (2001). Roles of Sox factors in neural determination: conserved signaling in evolution? *Int. J. Dev. Biol.* **45,** 321–326.
118. Remboutsika, M., and Lovell-Badge, R. (Personal communication).
119. Trainor, P.A., Remboutsika, M., and Lovell-Badge, R. (Personal communication).
120. Sharpe, P. (Personal communication).
121. Palmer, T.D., Markakis, E.A., Willhoite, A.R., Safar, F., and Gage, F.H. (1999). Fibroblast growth factor-2 activates a latent neurogenic program in neural stem cells from diverse regions of the adult CNS. *J. Neurosci.* **19,** 8487–8497.
122. Bjornson, C.R., Rietze, R.L., Reynolds, B.A., Magli, M.C., and Vescovi, A.L. (1999). Turning brain into blood: a hematopoietic fate adopted by adult neural stem cells *in vivo*. *Science* **283,** 534–537.
123. Galli, R., Borello, U., Gritti, A., Minasi, M.G., Bjornson, C., Coletta, M., Mora, M., De Angelis, M.G., Fiocco, R., Cossu, G., and Vescovi, A.L. (2000). Skeletal myogenic potential of human and mouse neural stem cells. *Nat. Neurosci.* **3,** 986–991.
124. Clarke, D.L., Johansson, C.B., Wilbertz, J., Veress, B., Nilsson, E., Karlstrom, H., Lendahl, U., and Frisen, J. (2000). Generalized potential of adult neural stem cells. *Science* **288,** 1660–1663.
125. Matsui, Y., Zsebo, K., and Hogan, B.L. (1992). Derivation of pluripotential embryonic stem cells from murine primordial germ cells in culture. *Cell* **70,** 841–847.
126. Donovan, P.J. (1994). Growth factor regulation of mouse primordial germ cell development. *Curr. Top. Dev. Biol.* **29,** 189–225.
127. Dupin, E., Real, C., Glavieux-Pardanaud, C., Vaigot, P., and Le Douarin, N.M. (2003). Reversal of developmental restrictions in neural crest lineages: transition from Schwann cells to glial-melanocytic precursors *in vitro*. *Proc. Natl. Acad. Sci. USA* **100,** 5229–5233.
128. Dupin, E., Glavieux, C., Vaigot, P., and Le Douarin, N.M. (2000). Endothelin 3 induces the reversion of melanocytes to glia through a neural crest-derived glial-melanocytic progenitor. *Proc. Natl. Acad. Sci. USA* **97,** 7882–7887.

20

Stem Cells in the Adult Brain

Christian Mirescu and Elizabeth Gould

Introduction

The adult mammalian brain has vastly reduced regenerative potential compared to the developing brain. Nevertheless, cell proliferation occurs in the adult brain, as does neurogenesis, and cells that generate neurons and glia *in vivo* and *in vitro* have been identified in the adult central nervous system (CNS). As our understanding of the factors that regulate stem cell proliferation and neurogenesis in the adult brain deepens, the development of methods directed at repairing the damaged brain through the transplantation of cultured cells or through the induction of endogenous neurogenesis in selected neuronal populations may lead to novel therapeutic strategies. This chapter reviews the evidence that neural stem cells exist in the adult brain and describes the factors that determine whether these cells divide and, if so, the fate of their progeny.

History of Stem Cells in the Adult CNS

Although studies dating to the 1960s have documented neurogenesis in the adult mammalian brain, the isolation of cells with stem cell properties, that is, multipotent and self-renewing, from adult neural tissue did not occur until much later. In the early 1990s, Reynolds and Weiss published a paper demonstrating that cultured cells from the adult rodent striatum produced both neurons and glia, effectively documenting multipotentiality.[1] This paper was followed by a similar report from Lois and Alvarez-Buylla, identifying proliferating cells as residents of the subventricular zone (SVZ),[2] which may have been included in the cultures used by Reynolds and Weiss. Since that time, numerous reports have identified cells from adult animals with the potential to produce neurons and glia when grown in culture or transplanted into other brain regions. These cells have been isolated from a variety of locations in the CNS, including the spinal cord, the hippocampus, the neocortex, and the striatum. The self-renewing capability of these cells was reported by McKay and colleagues in 1996, demonstrating conclusively that these cells had the characteristics of stem cells when grown *in vitro*.[3] Studies since that time have sought to identify stem cells *in vivo* with some success.

Handbook of Stem Cells
Volume 2

Glial Characteristics of Neural Stem Cells

Beginning with studies of neurogenesis in adult birds and extending to those in adult and developing mammals, several *in vivo* reports have suggested that stem cells have the characteristics of glia. These observations further expand the burgeoning list of functions attributed to glia and may lend insight into the production of neurons in the adult brain.[4]

RADIAL GLIA

In adult birds, the germinal zone of the lateral ventricles resembles that of the embryonic ventricular zone (VZ) of mammals. Adult-generated neurons appear to use radial glia processes as migratory guides to their final destination in the rostral forebrain. The spatial and temporal relationships of radial glia to new neurons were observations that led to the first suggestion that radial glia may serve as stem cells.[5] That is, radial glia may generate not only new glia but neurons as well.

Direct evidence that glia serve as neural stem cells in the avian VZ comes from retroviral lineage studies, which have shown that radial glia exhibit multipotent differentiation.[6–8] In the mammalian embryo, the VZ generates postmitotic cells that also take a rostral migratory route in forebrain development. Recent studies have shown that neuronal progenitors are radial glia in the embryonic mammalian forebrain.[9] During subsequent neonatal development, the radial glia of the VZ disappear and are replaced by multiciliated ependymal cells, which come to line the walls of the lateral ventricles. Coinciding with this, mitotically active cells begin to appear in the SVZ. These dividing cells show the ultrastructural characteristics of radial glia; furthermore, they express the radial glial marker RC-2.[8] That the postnatal SVZ progenitors share properties similar to the radial glia of the embryonic VZ suggests that the VZ may seed the mature SVZ with a self-replenishing population of adult neural stem cells. In adulthood, the fate of SVZ cells resembles the movement of cells born during development, as postmitotic cells appear to migrate toward anterior regions of the brain along the rostral migratory pathway. Similarities in the site of origin, migratory route, and ultimate position of adult-generated cells in avian species suggest that processes active in embryonic development are conserved in germinal regions of the adult brain.

Parallels across species and observations of structural similarities to embryonic VZ cells are indirect evidence that radial glia serve as primary neuronal precursors. Direct evidence supports this view; radial glia isolated by fluorescent-activated cell sorting have been observed to generate both neurons and astrocytes.[10] Furthermore, radial glia retrovirally tagged with green fluorescent protein in the developing rodent brain have been found to have mitotic activity and to subsequently generate neurons.[11,12] Such reports directly demonstrate that in mammals, radial glia also exhibit characteristics of neural stem cells.

Despite evidence that radial glia appear to serve as progenitors in the adult avian and reptilian brain as well as in the developing mammalian brain, it is less likely that new neurons arise from radial glia in the adult mammalian brain. The adult mammalian brain is mostly absent of radial glia; they are thought to differentiate into astrocytes following development. Thus, in adult mammalian germinal regions, there must exist a distinct type of progenitor, perhaps descended from embryonic radial glia, that retains the self-renewing and multilineage potentials of neural stem cells *in vivo.*

ASTROCYTES

Numerous recent studies suggest that progenitor cells in the adult mammalian brain share characteristics with astrocytes. Temporary destruction of neuroblasts and immature precursor cells in the adult brain by treatment with the antimitotic cytosine-beta-D-arabinofuranoside spares some astrocytes in the SVZ. Within hours after halting cell division, astrocytes begin to divide; several days later, migrating neuroblasts destined for the olfactory bulb, and possibly other regions, emerge. Finally, 10 days later, the orientation and organization of chains of migrating neuroblasts resemble those of normal adult mice.[13] Thus, astrocytes appear to function as neural progenitors both *in vitro* and *in vivo* and appear critical for the recovery of germinal activity within the SVZ.

In addition to the SVZ as an identified region of adult germinal activity, the subgranular zone (SGZ) of the hippocampal dentate gyrus appears to contain cells with stem cell-like characteristics in adulthood[14,15] (see Seaberg and van der Kooy[16]). The SGZ lies between the granule cell layer (GCL) and the hilus of the dentate gyrus. Astrocytes within the SGZ share ultrastructural features with SVZ astrocytes.[17] When dividing cells are labeled with the thymidine analog bromodeoxyuridine (BrdU) or with [^{3}H]-thymidine in adulthood, a large proportion of adult-generated cells in the dentate gyrus exhibit an astrocytic phenotype. The majority of BrdU-labeled Gfap$^+$ astrocytes disappear rapidly, coinciding with an increase in the number of BrdU-labeled Gfap$^-$ cells,[17] suggesting that SGZ astrocytes may undergo a transition from a glial to a nonglial phenotype. To examine whether this transition actually leads to the production of new neurons in adulthood, antimitotic treatment was used. Similar to the observed effects of such treatment in the SVZ, some astrocytes survived and began to divide soon after treatment. The administration of BrdU or [^{3}H]-thymidine 2 days after treatment, during SGZ astrocyte proliferation, yielded labeled granule neurons, astrocytes, and oligodendrocytes both 1 and 5 months later.[17] Thus, it appears that SGZ astrocytes share neural stem cell properties with SVZ astrocytes, namely the capacity for self-renewal and multilineage differentiation.

Adult Neurogenesis *In Vivo*

Numerous studies have conclusively demonstrated the production of new neurons in the brains of adult mammals. The case for the SGZ and the SVZ, brain regions discussed here, as germinal regions for new neurons in the adult brain is very strong. Collectively, this evidence supports the view that new neurons (i.e., cells with the morphological, ultrastructural, biochemical, and electrophysiological characteristics of neurons) are added to the dentate gyrus and olfactory bulb of adult mammals.[18] Evidence exists for adult neurogenesis in other brain regions, including the neocortex, striatum, olfactory tubercle, amygdala, and substantia nigra,[19–23] but these findings await further investigation. In light of *in vitro* studies demonstrating cells with stem cell-like characteristics in the parenchyma of regions other than the dentate gyrus and SVZ, adult neurogenesis in other brain structures would not be unexpected.

During development, neurogenesis is regulated by the complex interplay of peptide-signaling molecules and neurotransmitters.[24] Because neurogenesis persists in some regions after development is complete, it is possible that regulatory mechanisms of this process are preserved as well. The following sections will focus on the influence of various signaling molecules, such as growth factors, neurotransmitters, and hormones, on the production of new neurons in the adult brain.

NEUROTROPHINS

Brain-derived neurotrophic factor (BDNF) and neurotrophin-3 (NT-3) are members of a structurally related family of growth factors that function to prevent the death of embryonic neurons during development. Throughout the life span, neurotrophin expression varies dramatically. Embryonic expression of NT-3 appears highest in regions of the CNS where proliferation, migration, and differentiation are ongoing. Levels decrease with maturation. By contrast, BDNF expression is lowest in developing regions and increases with maturation.[25] Both BDNF and NT-3 expression, and their preferred receptors, TrkB and TrkC, have been demonstrated in cultures of cortical progenitor cells[26] and *in vivo* at the onset of cortical neurogenesis,[25,27] suggesting a possible direct action of these systems on neural progenitors. When regional BDNF expression is specifically enhanced by an adenoviral vector, a substantial increase in adult-generated neurons occurs in the mouse olfactory bulb, a known neurogenic region. Additionally, BDNF overexpression results in adult neuron production in the caudate putamen, normally a nonneurogenic site in adulthood.[28,29] By contrast, in hippocampal-derived stem cell clones, neurotrophins alone are only minimally effective in stimulating neurogenesis. However, in the presence of retinoic acid, both BDNF and NT-3 promote the acquisition of a neuronal fate by progenitors.[30] These results suggest that neurotrophins may have regionally distinct and synergistic effects on adult neural stem cells.

INSULIN-LIKE GROWTH FACTOR

Neurogenic effects of insulin-like growth factor (IGF) have been identified in cultures of embryonic neural stem cells as well as *in vivo* using transgenic models overexpressing or lacking specific IGF encoding genes. In proliferative cultures of embryonic precursors, insulin and IGFs promote the proliferation of neural stem cells[31,32] and the acquisition of neuronal phenotype.[33] In mice and humans, disruption of the IGF-I gene is associated with profound retardation of brain growth.[34–38] In contrast, overexpression of IGF-I results in larger brains marked by greater numbers of neurons.[39–42] Similar effects on proliferation and neuronal lineage appear conserved in adulthood, as peripheral IGF-I infusion (for 6 days) increases the number of proliferating cells and the fraction of new cells with neuronal characteristics in the hippocampus of the adult rat.[43]

FIBROBLAST GROWTH FACTOR

Extensive evidence suggests that basic fibroblast growth factor (bFGF) elicits neurogenic effects in culture[44–47] as well as in widespread regions of the prenatal brain, such as the cerebral cortex, the neonatal cerebellum, and the SVZ.[48,49] When administered during adulthood, bFGF also exerts a mitogenic effect in both the SVZ and the olfactory system.[48,49] However, no effect of bFGF was found in the adult hippocampus,[50] suggesting that the germinal effect of bFGF might be ubiquitous during development but regionally specific in adulthood. When bFGF is delivered to neonatal rats on P1, increases in hippocampal DNA content and enhanced production of BrdU-positive cells are observed beyond the early postnatal period.[51] Thus, bFGF seems to influence olfactory and SVZ neurogenesis throughout life, but it appears in the dentate gyrus only during development.

GLUTAMATE

The bulk of excitatory inputs throughout the mammalian brain uses glutamate as a neurotransmitter. Most inputs into the dentate gyrus GCL are glutamatergic afferents originating from the entorhinal cortex.[52] With regions of the hippocampus other than the dentate gyrus, granule neurons of the dentate gyrus express N-methyl-D-aspartate receptors (NMDAr). In development, NMDAr blockade results in profound changes in the dentate gyrus and the SVZ. Specifically, NMDAr antagonists increase cell proliferation in both germinal regions of rat pups.[53,54] Similarly, in adulthood, both lesions of the entorhinal cortex and injections of either a competitive or a noncompetitive NMDAr antagonist have been demonstrated to potentiate the birth and overall density of granule neurons. In contrast, injections of NMDA rapidly reduced the number of dividing cells in this region.[55] However, a direct influence of glutamatergic neurotransmission on proliferating cells in the adult dentate gyrus is not likely because granule cell progenitors do not express the NR1 NMDAr subunit, which is required for receptor function.[56]

SEROTONIN

Recent evidence suggests that serotonin (5-HT) exerts an influence on adult neurogenesis. Inhibition of 5-HT synthesis through parachlorophenylalanine administration and selective lesion of serotonergic neurons reduce numbers of adult-generated cells in the dentate gyrus and the SVZ.[57] Similarly, the selective blockade of 5-HT1A receptors potently decreases cell proliferation in the dentate gyrus, suggesting that the serotonergic influence on adult hippocampal cell production is mediated (at least partly) by this high-affinity 5-HT receptor.[58] Furthermore, treatment with a variety of antidepressants that work, at least partly, through 5-HT increases the production of new granule neurons in the dentate gyrus.[59]

ADRENAL STEROIDS

Numerous studies suggest that adrenal steroids influence cell proliferation in the dentate gyrus. A reduction in circulating adrenal steroids by adrenalectomy is associated with increased numbers of proliferating cells within the adult dentate gyrus.[60] In contrast, corticosterone administration reduces adult cell proliferation in the dentate gyrus of both neonatal and adult rats.[60] In agreement with such results, various naturalistic stressors induce suppressive effects on cell proliferation in both the neonatal and the adult mammalian dentate gyrus.[61–67] However, some evidence suggests that certain types of stressors may have lasting effects on adult neurogenesis independent of adrenal steroids.[67] Aging has also been associated with diminished adult cell production in adult rodents.[68,69] Adrenalectomy in aged rats appears capable of restoring proliferative activity to levels similar to those in young rats,[68] suggesting that adrenal hormones mediate age-associated effects on the dividing dentate gyrus.

OVARIAN STEROIDS

Ovarian hormones have also been found to influence the rate of cell proliferation in the dentate gyrus. In adult female rats, natural periods of high estradiol (proestrus) are associated with rapid increases in cell production.[70–72] In contrast, at longer survival times in both wild-reared and laboratory-reared meadow voles, cell proliferation and survival has been reported to be inversely related to the levels of circulating estradiol.[73,74] Thus, it appears that estradiol exerts a transient stimulatory effect and subsequent suppressive influence on dentate gyrus division. The estradiol-induced suppression appears mediated by adrenal steroids,[71] as corticosterone levels increase in response to elevated estradiol.[75]

Summary

Studies carried out over the past decade have identified cells with stem cell-like properties in the adult mammalian brain. The bulk of evidence suggests that these cells have the characteristics of glial cells, a finding that may elucidate basic mechanisms of neurogenesis and make isolating stem cells a more tractable problem. The production of new neurons in the adult brain has been shown to be regulated by growth factors, neurotransmitters, and hormones. An understanding of the potential interactions among these modulators of adult neurogenesis may enable the controlled manipulation of neuron production in the damaged brain.

Numerous neurological conditions are associated with the loss of neural cells, perhaps most notably Alzheimer's diseases and Parkinson's disease. The possibility that trauma and neurodegenerative disorders can be treated either by neural stem cell transplantation or by stimulating endogenous neurogenesis in existing populations of adult neural stem cells has theoretically powerful clinical potential. The key advantage of transplanting cell lines is that they can be genetically engineered, allowing customization depending on the disease. On the other hand, strategies designed to enhance endogenous neurogenesis (perhaps with regional specificity) would have the potential for clinical efficacy without requiring invasive techniques. Although it is unclear which manipulations will lead to specific types of clinical improvements, it is certain that the presence of neural stem cells in the adult CNS has opened a new frontier of scientific exploration.

REFERENCES

1. Reynolds, B.A., and Weiss, S. (1992). Generation of neurons and astrocytes from isolated cells of the adult mammalian central nervous system. *Science* **255,** 1707–1710.
2. Lois, C., and Alvarez-Buylla, A. (1993). Proliferating subventricular zone cells in the adult mammalian forebrain can differentiate into neurons and glia. *Proc. Natl. Acad. Sci. USA* **90,** 2074–2077.
3. Johe, K.K., Hazel, T.G., Muller, T., Dugich-Djordjevic, M.M., and McKay, R.D. (1996). Single factors direct the differentiation of stem cells from the fetal and adult central nervous system. *Genes Dev.* **10,** 3129–3140.
4. Barres, B. (2003). What is a glial cell? *Glia* **43,** 4–5.
5. Alvarez-Buylla, A., Theelen, M., and Nottebohm, F. (1990). Proliferation "hot spots" in adult avian ventricular zone reveal radial cell division. *Neuron* **5,** 101–109.
6. Goldman, J.E. (1995). Lineage, migration, and fate determination of postnatal subventricular zone cells in the mammalian CNS. *J. Neurooncol.* **24,** 61–64.
7. Levison, S.W., and Goldman, J.E. (1997). Multipotential and lineage restricted precursors coexist in the mammalian perinatal subventricular zone. *J. Neurosci. Res.* **48,** 83–94.
8. Tramontin, A.D., Garcia-Verdugo, J.M., Lim, D.A., and Alvarez-Buylla, A. (2003). Postnatal development of radial glia and the ventricular zone (VZ): a continuum of the neural stem cell compartment. *Cerebral Cortex* **13,** 580–587.
9. Kriegstein, A.R., and Gotz, M. (2003). Radial glia diversity: a matter of cell fate. *Glia* **43,** 37–43.
10. Malatesta, P., Hartfuss, E., and Gotz, M. (2000). Isolation of radial glial cells by fluorescent-activated cell sorting reveals a neuronal lineage. *Development* **127,** 5253–5263.
11. Miyata, T., Kawaguchi, A., Okano, H., and Ogawa, M. (2001). Asymmetric inheritance of radial glial fibers by cortical neurons. *Neuron* **31,** 727–741.
12. Noctor, S.C., Flint, A.C., Weissman, T.A., Dammerman, R.S., and Kriegstein, A.R. (2001). Neurons derived from radial glial cells establish radial units in neocortex. *Nature* **409,** 714–720.
13. Doetsch, F., García-Verdugo J.M., and Alvarez-Buylla, A. (1999). Regeneration of a germinal layer in the adult mammalian brain. *Proc. Natl. Acad. Sci. USA* **96,** 11,619–11,624.
14. Gage, F.H. (2000). Mammalian neural stem cells. *Science* **287,** 1433–1438.
15. Palmer, T.D., Takahashi, J., and Gage, F.H. (1997). The adult rat hippocampus contains primordial neural stem cells. *Mol. Cell. Neurosci.* **8,** 389–404.
16. Seaberg, R.M., and van der Kooy, D. (2002). Adult rodent neurogenic regions: The ventricular subependyma contains neural stem cells, but the dentate gyrus contains restricted progenitors. *J. Neurosci.* **22,** 1784–1793.
17. Seri, B., Garcia-Verdugo J.M., McEwen, B.S., and Alvarez-Buylla, A. (2001). Astrocytes give rise to new neurons in the adult mammalian hippocampus. *J. Neurosci.* **21,** 7153–7160.
18. Gould, E., and Gross, C.G. (2002). Neurogenesis in adult mammals: some progress and problems. *J. Neurosci.* **22,** 619–623.
19. Gould, E., Vail, N., Wagers, M., and Gross, C.G. (2001). Adult-generated hippocampal and neocortical neurons in macaques have a transient existence. *Proc. Nat. Acad. Sci. USA* **98,** 10,910–10,917.
20. Bernier, P.J., Bedard, A., Vinet, J., Leveseque, M., and Parent, A. (2002). Newly generated neurons in the amygdala and adjoining cortex of adult primates. *Proc. Natl. Acad. Sci. USA* **99,** 11,464–11,469.
21. Bedard, A., Cossette, M., Levesque, M., and Parent, A. (2002). Proliferating cells can differentiate into neurons in the striatum of normal adult monkey. *Neurosci. Lett.* **328,** 213–216.
22. Bedard, A., Levesque, M., Bernier, P.J., and Parent, A. (2002). The rostral migratory stream in adult squirrel monkeys: Contribution of new neurons to the olfactory tubercle and involvement of the antiapoptotic protein Bcl-2. *Eur. J. Neurosci.* **16,** 1917–1924.
23. Zhao, M., Momma, S., Delfani, K., Carlen, M., Cassidy, R.M., Johansson, C.B., Brismar, H., Shupliakov, O., Frisen, J., and Janson, A.M. (2003). Evidence for neurogenesis in the adult mammalian *substantia nigra*. *Proc. Natl. Acad. Sci. USA* **100,** 7925–7930.
24. Cameron, H.A., Hazel, T.G., and McKay, R.D.G. (1998). Regulation of neurogenesis by growth factors and neurotransmitters. *J. Neurobiol.* **36,** 287–306.
25. Maisonpierre, P.C., Belluscio, L., Squinto, S., Ip, N.Y., Furth, M.E., Lindsay, R.M., and Yancopoulos, G.D. (1990). Neurotrophin-3: a neurotrophic factor related to NGF and BDNF. *Science* **247,** 1446–1451.
26. Barnabe-Heider, F., and Miller F.D. (2003). Endogenously produced neurotrophins regulate survival and differentiation of cortical progenitors via distinct signaling pathways. *J. Neurosci.* **23,** 5149–5160.
27. Fukumitsu, H., Takase-Yoden, S., Furukawa, S., Nemoto, K., Ikeda, T., and Watanabe, R. (2002). Implantation of BDNF-producing packaging cells into brain. *Cell Transplant.* **11,** 459–464.
28. Benraiss, A., Chmielnicki, E., Lerner, K., Roh, D., and Goldman, S.A. (2001). Adenoviral brain-derived neurotrophic factor induces both neostriatal and olfactory neuronal recruitment from endogenous progenitor cells in the adult forebrain. *J. Neurosci.* **21,** 6718–6731.
29. Pencea, V., Bingaman, K.D., Wiegand, S.J., and Luskin, M.B. (2001). Infusion of brain-derived neurotrophic factor into the lateral ventricle of the adult rat leads to new neurons in the parenchyma of the striatum, septum, thalamus, and hypothalamus. *J. Neurosci.* **21,** 6706–6717.
30. Takahashi, J., Palmer, T.D., and Gage, F.H. (1999). Retinoic acid and neurotrophins collaborate to regulate neurogenesis in adult-derived neural stem cell cultures. *J. Neurobiol.* **38,** 65–81.
31. DiCicco-Bloom, E., and Black, I.B. (1988). Insulin growth factors regulate the mitotic cycle in cultured rat sympathetic neuroblasts. *Proc. Natl. Acad. Sci. USA* **85,** 4066–4070.

of both the adult and young adult VNSE, but, over time, labeled cells were located within the VNO neuron compartment.[52–54] BrdU studies in adult rat and opossum have indicated two populations of dividing cells located either at the margins (as seen with [^{3}H]thymidine labeling) or in the basal compartment of the VNSE.[49,55,56]

SELF-RENEWAL OF OLFACTORY CELLS *IN VITRO*

The capacity for stem cell self-renewal in the nervous system has largely relied upon observing stem cells in culture. For example, neural stem cells in the subventricular zone of the CNS proliferate continuously in the presence of EGF to generate relatively undifferentiated clusters of precursors called "neurospheres."[53,55] These multipotent neurospheres can give rise to all cell types of the CNS. When a primary neurosphere is dissociated and single cells are individually replated, new secondary neurospheres form, further illustrating the capacity for self-renewal.[53,55]

Although it has not yet been completely analyzed, the capacity for olfactory stem cell self-renewal has also been addressed by observing olfactory progenitors analyzed in culture. Specifically, olfactory progenitors were purified from explant cultures of embryonic MOE and co-cultured with cells from the stroma underlying the MOE.[57] Although most cells immediately differentiated into neurons within 2 days, a small percentage formed proliferating colonies that retained both proliferating cells and the ability to give rise to NCAM$^+$ neurons for over 7 days.[57] These results might suggest that neuronal colony-forming cells of the olfactory system have the capacity for self-renewal and give rise to differentiated cells, two key features of stem cells.[57] Unfortunately, neither the identification of the NCAM$^+$ neurons as olfactory neurons nor the identity of the neuronal colony-forming cells in culture was determined. Furthermore, without *in vivo* demonstration of self-renewal it is difficult to make conclusions about the nature of these cells.

OLFACTORY ENSHEATHING CELLS

Severed neurons in the CNS are unable to regrow. However, newly generated olfactory and vomeronasal neurons exhibit the unique ability to extend axons into the CNS to the olfactory bulb throughout life. This property is thought to rely on a specialized glial cell called the olfactory ensheathing cell (OEC) that surrounds bundles of olfactory axons or vomeronasal axons from the underlying lamina propria all the way to the olfactory bulb.[58–60] *In vitro* experiments have demonstrated that OECs can both stimulate axon growth of ORNs, hippocampal and cortical neurons, and retinal ganglion cells and remyelinate spinal cord axons.[61–65] In addition, transplantation of rat OECs has been shown to stimulate axon growth across lesions in the brain, spinal cord, and spinal dorsal root.[62,66–72] Interestingly, transplantation of OECs has been shown not only to aid in axon growth but also to aid in the functional recovery of breathing and locomotor activity in the rat following various types of spinal cord injuries.[72–74] Clearly, the clinical implications of OECs for repair of lesions in the human spinal cord and brain are extremely exciting. In fact, it was recently proven that human OECs can be isolated and are able to enhance axon growth in rodents.[75–77] For a comprehensive review of OECs, the reader is referred to Boyd *et al.*[78]

Identification of Olfactory Stem Cells

Several different experimental approaches have been taken to identify olfactory progenitors: detection of cells that proliferate in response to injury, retroviral lineage analysis, and *in vitro* assays to test neurogenic capability of enriched basal subpopulations.

PROLIFERATION IN RESPONSE TO INJURY

To identify potential populations of olfactory progenitors, researchers sought olfactory cells that increased proliferation following experimental degeneration of the MOE. Under several MOE regeneration paradigms including olfactory bulbectomy, neurectomy, and inhalation with MeBr gas, rapid proliferation was consistently induced in the population of GBCs.[11,17,79,80] This suggested that the GBC population might indeed contain an olfactory precursor. Furthermore, a selective increase in basal cell mitoses was detected in the VNO suggesting that vemeronasal precursors may also reside in the basal compartment.[49]

To further characterize the basal cell populations in the intact MOE, the dynamics of basal cell division were analyzed using ^{3}[H]thymidine autoradiography.[81] Specifically, the MOEs of mice were examined 7 to 90 days following a single injection with [^{3}H]thymidine. By counting the silver grain density over each nucleus, the number of labeled cells, and the distance of the nucleus from the basal lamina at various time points, the relative rates of division of basal cells were estimated. This experiment documented two groups of mitotically active basal cells with different rates of division: cells presumed to be GBCs divide rapidly (1 division/day), whereas cells presumed to be HBCs divide much more slowly (1 division/60 days). Intriguingly, tissues capable of continuous regeneration often contain both a slowly dividing stem cell population and a rapidly dividing committed intermediate precursor population called transit amplifying cells.[82–85] In fact, slow division is a feature commonly associated with stem cells in adult hematopoietic, epidermal, intestinal, and neural systems and is thought to play a critical role in reducing DNA replication-related errors and preserving the cell's proliferative potential.[86] The proliferation kinetics of cells in the basal MOE might suggest that HBCs act as olfactory stem cells and give rise to transit-amplifying GBCs that can differentiate into ORNs.

Interestingly, HBCs had largely been discounted as potential MOE stem cells because they do not proliferate in response to olfactory nerve transection or bulbectomy.[11,80,81,87] However, in the last decade, this interpretation has become quite controversial. Some stem cells may not be induced to proliferate unless damage to the tissue is severe. This is seen in the liver where a large percentage of hepatocyte precursors must be destroyed before liver stem cell proliferation is upregulated.[88] Likewise, HBC proliferation has been demonstrated in response to MeBr inhalation, which elicits widespread loss of olfactory neurons, supporting cells, and basal cells.[33,89] In contrast, the destruction of mature olfactory neurons seen in bulbectomy and neurectomy may not be sufficient to invoke proliferation of an olfactory stem cell.

RETROVIRAL LINEAGE ANALYSIS

To address the question of lineage more directly, retroviral lineage analysis was performed by several groups in rats with both normal and injured MOE. Using a replication incompetent retrovirus expressing an alkaline phosphatase reporter gene, Caggiono and colleagues were able to label dividing cells and their progeny. Two types of infected cell clusters were found: GBC/ORN clusters and HBC clusters.[80] This suggested that GBCs give rise to neurons, whereas HBCs do not. Olfactory nerve transection did not affect the composition of these clusters. In fact, of 530 clusters analyzed, none contained HBCs and GBCs and/or neurons again suggesting that HBCs are not lineally related to GBCs and neurons.

In contrast, another group found clusters containing supporting cells, GBCs, neurons, and HBCs following MeBr inhalation.[89,90] This indicates a common lineage among all olfactory cell types. This contradiction to the Caggiono study might be explained by important experimental differences like survival times and method of injury. First, Caggiono *et al.* analyzed the MOE for only 40 days postinfection, whereas Huard *et al.* waited for 60 days. Because the average cycle of a HBC has been estimated to be approximately 60 days, the time course of the Caggiono experiment may have been too short to detect a second HBC division. In fact, the size of the clusters containing HBCs did not increase over the 40-day analysis period. Second, another source of difference may be the type of MOE injury. Olfactory neurectomy only produces loss of mature olfactory neurons, whereas MeBr gas inhalation produces widespread loss of both immature and mature neurons, supporting cells, and basal cells. An olfactory progenitor might exist that could give rise to many different cell types depending on the extent of injury (i.e., ORNs following neurectomy or HBCs, neurons, and supporting cells following MeBr exposure).

NEUROGENIC POTENTIAL OF PUTATIVE OLFACTORY PROGENITORS *IN VITRO*

Another method of identifying olfactory progenitors has relied on reproducing olfactory neurogenesis *in vitro*. This approach allows an investigator to directly observe the ability of a specific olfactory cell population, selected on the basis of immunohistochemistry or purification, to generate neurons.

To directly assay the neurogenic potential of HBCs, two separate groups monitored neuronal production in cultures of purified HBCs. In one study, adult rat MOE was dissociated and cultivated in a serum-free medium.[91,92] In an attempt to enrich HBCs, which along with supporting cells are the only cell types in the MOE to express EGFR, epidermal growth factor (EGF) was added to the media.[9,10] After 5 days in culture, immunohistochemistry revealed that only HBCs and supporting cells remained. The culture was then mechanically stressed, and new bipolar cells expressing olfactory neuron markers such as NCAM and OMP appeared suggesting that neurons can be generated from HBCs in culture. To prove that these neurons were generated *in vitro* and were not neurons from the primary culture, BrdU was administered right before passage and 20% of the bipolar neurons were indeed labeled. The possibility that the supporting cells and not the HBCs might give rise to neurons was not addressed but perhaps should have been in light of the recent work showing that neurons arise from astrocytes in the adult subventricular zone.[82]

In another study, a CK14-positive cell line was derived from embryonic mouse MOE.[93] Expression of the olfactory neuronal marker NCAM was induced in this cell line with the administration of transforming growth factor (TGF)β-1 and TGFβ-2. Although one might conclude from this experiment that HBCs can give rise to neurons under certain conditions, the purity of the cultures was not established. The cultures could have contained a few CK14-negative cells that may have acted as the real olfactory precursors. In addition, the authors admit that, although all the cells of the HBC cell line expressed CK14, 5% of the cells also expressed NCAM. Serious questions arise about the validity of these culture conditions because these CK14/NCAM-positive cells *in vitro* have no demonstrated counterpart *in vivo*.

MASH1

The first real information about the genetic control of olfactory neurogenesis came in 1993 with disruption of the Mash1 gene (Fig. 22–2A).[94] Mash1 is a member of the basic helix-loop-helix family of transcription factors that have been shown to regulate neurogenesis in the developing CNS. Analysis of the $MASH^{-/-}$ mutant reveals a severe reduction in autonomic, enteric, and ORNs. In the early embryonic MOE, Mash1 is expressed by a population of rapidly dividing apical precursor cells that then translocate to form a basal pool of dividing Mash-1 progenitors.[95–98] In the adult MOE, Mash1 expression is restricted to a subpopulation of GBCs.[99] Following unilateral bulbectomy, there is an eight-fold increase in Mash1-expressing cells and three-fold increase in Mash1/ [^{3}H]thymidine double-labeled cells.[99]

The basal expression pattern of Mash1, the phenotype of the Mash1 mutant, and the response of Mash1 cells to injury have led to the conclusion that Mash1 marks a population of olfactory precursors. This theory was evaluated with explant cultures of embryonic mouse MOE.[13,99–101] At this stage, three distinguishable cell types were detected *in vitro*: CK14-positive nonmigrating HBCs, NCAM-positive postmitotic neurons, and migrating non-neurite bearing cells that did not express NCAM or CK14 and gave rise to the neurite-bearing cells after one to two rounds of division. This last cell type was postulated to contain the immediate neuronal precursors (INPs) for olfactory neurons. Interestingly, a subpopulation of the migrating neuron-producing cells in culture also expressed Mash1.[99] After 2 days in culture, the Mash1-positive cells disappeared, which might reflect either differentiation into neurons or cell death. Because no increase in TUNEL staining

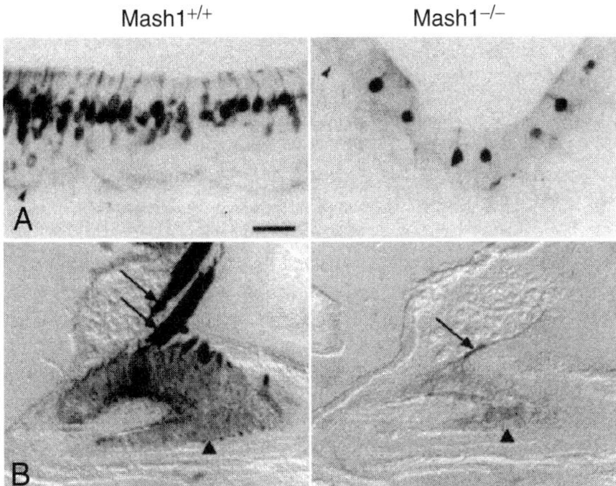

Figure 22-2. Altered olfactory neurogenesis in the Mash1 knockout mutant. (A) Coronal sections of +/+ and −/− main olfactory epithelium (MOE) from newborn mice. Immunohistochemical analysis of olfactory marker protein reveals a near complete deficit in mature olfactory neurons. (B) Sagittal sections of +/+ and −/− E18.5 vomeronasal organ (VNO). To visualize defects in the Mash mutant more readily, the Mash mutant was crossed to a reporter mouse line in which the cell bodies and axons of central and peripheral neurons express LacZ. X-gal staining indicates a reduction in both the number of sensory neurons and the size of the vomeronasal nerve. There is also a striking decrease in the size of the VNO.(A from Guillemot, F., Lo, L.-C., Johnson, J.E., Auerbach, A., Anderson, D.J., and Joyner, A. (1993). Mammalian achaete-scute homolog 1 is required for the early development of olfactory and autonomic neurons. *Cell* **75,** 463–476, with permission; B, from Murray, R.C., Navi, D., Fesenko, J., Lander, A.D., and Calof, A.L. (2003). Widespread defects in the primary olfactory pathway caused by loss of Mash1 function. *J. Neurosci.* **23,** 1769–1780, with permission.)

was noted, it was concluded that Mash1 cells ultimately give rise to neurons after a limited number of divisions. Moreover, $Mash1^+$ cells disappeared faster than $Mash1^-$ INPs hinting that Mash1 cells may give rise to the $Mash1^-$ INPs, which in turn generate ORNs.

Recently, analysis of the Mash mutant has revealed a potential population of VNO precursors as well (Fig. 22–2B). The VNOs of $Mash^{-/-}$ animals were analyzed for neuronal number and expression of normal vomeronasal markers. Interestingly, there were no major deficits at early time points (E12.5); however, by E18.5 there was a profound decrease in neuronal number and expression of neuronal markers, as observed in the MOE.[98,102] Furthermore, the expression of Mash1 at E14.5 was observed primarily in the basal VNO, a region that contains dividing cells.[102] From this data, it has been preliminarily postulated that $Mash1^+$ cells may indeed act as vomeronasal precursors.

Intrinsic Regulation of Olfactory Neurogenesis

BHLH GENE FAMILY

Recent studies indicate that neurogenesis is largely controlled by multiple basic helix-loop-helix transcription factors. The bHLH genes can be divided into two broad categories: those that promote neurogenesis (Mash1, Hes6, NGN1) and those that negatively regulate neurogenesis by antagonizing the former (Hes1). Several bHLH genes have been identified in the MOE, including Mash1, NGN1, NeuroD, Hes1, and Hes5.[96–98,103] At E12.5, a stage when dividing cells are located throughout the epithelium, Mash1 and NGN1 appear to label distinct subpopulations of olfactory precursors: Mash1 labeling is seen throughout the epithelium, whereas expression of NGN1 is restricted to the basal MOE.[98] Analysis of $Mash1^{-/-}$ animal exhibits a severe reduction in NGN1 expression, whereas Mash1 expression is largely unaffected in the NGN1 mutant. These data suggest that Mash1 is likely upstream of NGN1 and is corroborated by double *in situs* indicating the presence of Mash1-positive, NGN1-positive, and double-labeled Mash1/NGN1 cells. In contrast, expression of NeuroD, another transcription factor expressed in dividing cells in the basal MOE, is nearly absent in both the $Mash^{-/-}$ and $NGN^{-/-}$ mutant suggesting the following regulatory cascade: Mash1>NGN1>NeuroD.[96,98]

The bHLH repressors of neurogenesis Hes1 and Hes5 have also been analyzed in the MOE. At E12.5, Hes1 expression in restricted to the apical MOE, whereas Hes5 is expressed basally.[97] The expression of both Hes1 and Hes5 is lost in the Mash1 mutant suggesting that Hes1/5 expression is Mash1-dependent. Loss of Hes1 function results in ectopic Mash1 expression and increased neuron production indicating that Hes1 may initially regulate Mash1 expression.[97] Disruption of the Hes 5 gene does not have any apparent phenotype; however, a double Hes1/Hes5 mutant demonstrates dramatically increased neurogenesis and upregulation of NGN1.[97] This is consistent with studies of the developing CNS, which prove that Hes1 and Hes5 can negatively regulate neurogenesis in the developing CNS.

NOTCH SIGNALING

The Notch signaling pathway also seems to play a major role in neurogenesis. The Notch family includes four Notch receptors and multiple ligands encoded by the Delta and Serrate gene families. Retroviral misexpression of Notch1 promotes glial formation in the murine forebrain and retina.[104,105] Similarly, mutations in Notch pathway members promote the premature expression of early neuronal markers. Recent data suggest that Notch1 may act through Hes1 and Hes5 to regulate neurogenesis.[106] Notch signaling has also been implicated in maintaining stem cell identity in the hematopoietic, auditory, neural, and epidermal systems.[107–110]

Although the molecular characterization of the MOE is preliminary, it has become likely that Notch signaling may be involved in olfactory neurogenesis. Notch 1 is expressed throughout development in basal cells of the MOE.[111] The expression patterns of various Notch ligands have been evaluated in the embryonic MOE: Dll3 is expressed in the basal MOE, Ser1 is restricted mostly to apical cells, and Ser2 is found throughout the epithelium.[98] Analysis of the Mash mutant reveals a loss of Notch1, Dll3, Ser1, and Ser2 revealing that expression of these genes is dependent on Mash.[98,111] Clearly, more data is needed to truly understand the function of Notch signaling in the MOE.

TRANSCRIPTIONAL PROFILE OF NEURONAL PROGENITORS

Most recently, olfactory neurogenesis was analyzed at the single-cell level by comparing the transcriptional profiles of mature ORNs and embryonic Mash1-positive olfactory progenitor cells (OPCs).[103] This study provided a snapshot of the different regulatory networks concurring or competing within a single cell at a specific developmental stage to control cell proliferation and olfactory specification.

ORNs were characterized by the robust expression of OMP and olfactory receptor together with the lack of Mash1. In turn, progenitor cells were identified by the robust expression of Mash1, by the cell division markers cdc2 and Ki67, and by the absence of OMP and OR.[112,113] This analysis identified 23 OPC-enriched genes, 19 of which were found in the precursor cells of the E15 MOE and the basal layer of the mature MOE (Fig. 22–3A). An additional four transcripts were detected in precursor cells of the E15 MOE but not in the mature MOE. This observation suggests that, although there are some differences between OPCs originating from E15 and from mature MOE, the transcriptional profile of the two progenitors is mostly similar.

OPC-specific transcripts displayed distinct types of expression patterns in the E15 MOE. A subset of transcripts, including Hes6, Tis21, Enx1, ETF, and Eed, were found predominantly or exclusively in basal neuronal progenitors,

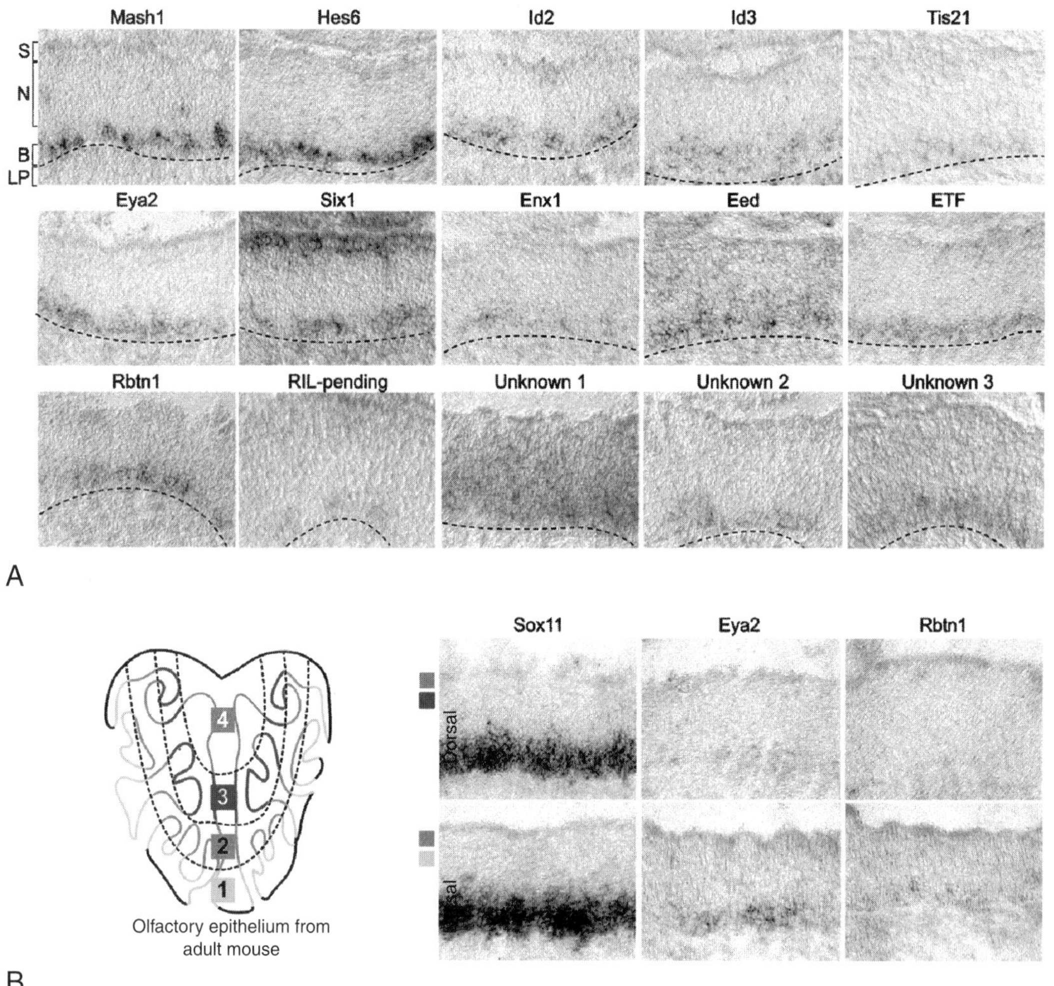

Figure 22–3. Gene expression in olfactory progenitor cells (OPCs) and OPC-enriched transcription factors in olfactory-receptor zones. (A) RNA ***in situ*** hybridization of coronal sections of p21 main olfactory epithelium (MOE). By comparing the transcriptional profiles of single olfactory sensory neurons and Mash1[+] OPCs, 23 OPC-enriched genes were identified. Included in this pool are genes in the Notch signaling pathway (RBP, Hes6), genes involved in cell cycle regulation (Id1-3 and Tis21), and genes involved in patterning (Enx1, Eed, Etf, Rbtn1, Eya1, Pax6, Six1). (B) RNA ***in situ*** hybridization patterns on coronal sections of p21 MOE. Sox11 is strongly expressed throughout the MOE. In contrast, Eya2 and Rbtn1 are preferentially expressed in ventral zones. A schematic of the four zones in adult MOE is shown at left. B, basal cell layer; LP, lamina propria; N, neuronal layer; S, supporting cell layer. (B from Tietjen, I., Rihel, J.M., Cao, Y., Koentges, G., Zakhary, L., and Dulac, C. Single-cell transcriptional analysis of neuronal progenitors. ***Neuron* 38**, 161–175, with permission.) (Please see CD-ROM for color version of this figure.)

whereas others, notably Pax6, Id2, Eya2, and Six1, were equally expressed by both apical and basal progenitors. This result is in agreement with the existence of distinct pools of basal and apical Mash1-positive progenitors and further indicates that the transcriptional programs of basal and apical progenitors have already significantly diverged. Moreover, the presence of transcripts with exclusive basal expression in all OPCs enabled the precise identification of the Mash1-positive cells as basal neuronal progenitors.

Among the OPC-specific transcripts, members of the Notch pathway were identified. RBP, a member of the transcriptional complex controlled by Notch signaling, and Hes6, which inhibits Hes1 transcription, both appear upregulated in Mash1-positive cells.[114,115] In contrast, none of the OPCs were found to express Hes1, shown to be present in apical Mash1-positive precursors.[98] The expression of other members of the Notch pathway could not be investigated through the Affymetrix Murine11K probe arrays.

OPCs also express multiple factors involved in both the positive and negative regulation of cell proliferation, suggesting that this cell type is in a highly dynamic state. Three members of the Id protein family, Id1, Id2, and Id3, had strong and specific expression in OPCs, hinting at a potential role in preventing neuroblasts from exiting the cell cycle and differentiating into neurons.[116] However, the simultaneous detection of the antiproliferative gene Tis21 indicates that OPCs also receive signals to leave the cell cycle. Indeed, Tis21 expression has been shown in neuroepithelial cells, which, at their last division, will generate postmitotic neurons.[117]

Interestingly, the vast majority of differentially expressed transcripts appear exclusively expressed in basal neuronal progenitors, consistent with the idea that the process of neurogenesis and patterning is initiated in these cells. Two interacting Polycomb-group genes, Enx1 and Eed, were identified, suggesting a role for chromatin remodeling in olfactory specification.[118,119] In addition, an embryonic TEA domain-containing transcription factor (ETF) and a LIM domain-containing nuclear protein expressed in specific areas of the developing brain, Rhombotin1 (Rbtn1), were detected.[120–122] ETF appears transiently expressed by Mash1-positive precursors of the basal embryonic epithelium, whereas Rbtn1, although clearly excluded from apical precursors, is more widely expressed in basal precursors and in immature olfactory neurons, suggesting a role throughout olfactory differentiation.

Finally, three genes, Eya2, Six1, and Pax6, belonging to a regulatory network involved in eye development, were identified. Eya2 and Six1 are homologs of Drosophila eyes absent (eya) and sine occulis (so), respectively. Eya and so interact physically, synergize to induce ectopic eyes, and function within a transcriptional network that also includes eyeless/Pax6 to control cell proliferation, patterning, and neuronal specification within the developing eye.[123,124] The expression of three members of the same genetic network in the developing MOE may indicate that the function of the complex is conserved in olfactory neurogenesis.

Interestingly, partial epistasis analysis on olfactory epithelia from the Mash1 mutant mouse line revealed that, although the expression of genes related to cell proliferation and Notch signaling such as Hes5, Hes 6, Notch1, and Tis21 and the transcription factors Rbtn1 and Lhx2 was abolished or strongly reduced in the absence of Mash1 function, other transcriptional regulators such as Enx1, Eed, ETF, Sox11, and the three members of the retinal development signaling network (Six1, Eya2 and Pax 6) were consistently detected in the mutant epithelium.[103] This result indicates that although the ultimate survival of neuronal precursors relies on Mash1 function, some aspects of neurogenesis and neuronal specification might be readily initiated in the absence of Mash1 expression.

OLFACTORY PATTERNING AND RECEPTOR CHOICE

The expression of olfactory receptor (OR) genes is segregated along a dorsoventral axis such that all neurons expressing a given OR reside within one of four distinct zones of the olfactory epithelium. This raises the interesting issue of whether olfactory stem cells are already committed to the expression of a restricted subset of olfactory receptor genes. Recent studies in a variety of nonolfactory embryonic cells have revealed the replication asynchrony of the maternal and paternal alleles of olfactory genes, a phenomenon that has been associated with allelic exclusion of olfactory gene expression.[125,126] This suggests that some steps linked to OR choice occur very early during development. Accordingly, systematic *in situ* hybridization performed on serial sections of the MOE with RNA probes corresponding to ORs and to OPC-specific transcription factors revealed that a subset of the genes identified with the single-cell profiling study displayed a dramatic restriction of their expression to a subset of the MOE zones both in adult and in the embryo (Fig. 22–3B). Indeed, although Sox 11, Hes6, and Mash1, as well as Six1 and Lhx2, are widely expressed along the whole epithelium, Eya2, Rbtn1, Id2, and Id3 are present in progenitors of one or two ventral zones exclusively. Thus, it appears that restricted expression of transcriptional regulators in distinct zones of the MOE can be detected in early progenitors that have yet to express a given OR. These genes in turn represent good candidates to participate in the combinatorial coding of a dorsoventral MOE patterning axis, a process that ultimately results in the zonal organization of OR expression.

Extrinsic Regulation of Olfactory Neurogenesis

Olfactory neurogenesis is under tight homeostatic control. An example of this is seen following transection of the olfactory nerves. There is an initial increase in neuronal cell death but the missing ORNs are quickly replaced by an increase in basal cell mitoses. Similarly, neuronal colony formation is inhibited when olfactory progenitors are cultured with a large number of differentiated neurons.[57] Strategies to evaluate the regulation of olfactory neurogenesis have largely fallen into three broad categories: (1) analysis of the MOE for expression of various growth factors and their receptors, (2) assessment of neuron production in primary MOE cultures following growth factor administration, and (3) transgenics to perturb normal growth factor pathways. Although the experiments addressing the affects of growth factors on the MOE are somewhat incomplete and at times inconsistent (because of the lack of cellular markers and differences in culturing conditions), several key players including EGF, TGF, and fibroblast growth factor (FGF), have emerged (Fig. 22–1). For a comprehensive review, see Mackay-Sim and Chuah.[127]

GROWTH FACTORS INVOLVED IN THE PROLIFERATION OF BASAL CELLS

Both TGFα and EGF induced proliferation of CK14-positive HBCs in dissociated and semidissociated embryonic and newborn MOE cultures.[128–130] These factors act through the EGF receptor, which is strongly expressed in HBCs and more weakly in the supporting cells.[9,10] In accordance with the *in vitro* data, overexpression of TGFα in CK14-positive HBCs stimulated a selective increase in the proliferation of the HBCs.[131] TGFα is presumed to be the endogenous ligand with expression in basal cells, supporting cells, the glands of the MOE, and the lamina propria underlying the MOE.[130] In contrast, the expression of EGF in the MOE and surrounding regions has not been observed.[130]

Administration of FGF2 to cultures of either embryonic or adult mouse MOE induced the proliferation of neuronal precursors presumed by their morphology and behavior in culture to be GBCs.[101,132] In addition, FGF2 induced an increase in cells expressing GBC-1, a marker of globose basal cells, in a cell line derived from adult rat MOE.[133] Using reverse transcriptase polymerase chain reaction (RT-PCR) of MOE extracts, FGF receptors including FGFR-1 and FGFr-2 have been identified.[101,134] One in particular, FGFR-1, is present on basal cells and ORNs, which nicely corresponds to the FGF2-responsive cells *in vitro*. Determining which cells express FGF2 has been far more difficult as several groups have reported different results; however, there is agreement that FGF2 is found in the neurons and the supporting cells of the MOE.[101,134]

GROWTH FACTORS INVOLVED IN NEURONAL DIFFERENTIATION AND SURVIVAL

The TGFβ superfamily of growth factors is composed of more than 25 different molecules, several of which have been studied in the MOE. Administration of TGFβ-1 and TGFβ-2 to both mouse explant and newborn rat cultures enhanced the differentiation of olfactory progenitors into neurons.[93,128,132] The same effect was observed in an olfactory-derived cell line.[93] Because *in situ* hybridization demonstrates only the expression of TGFβ-2 in the MOE, TGFβ-2 is likely to be the relevant ligand *in vivo*. Determining which cells TGFβ-2 might be acting on (either HBCs or GBCs) has been confounded by the lack of expression patterns of TGFβ receptors and TGFβ-1/2.

In contrast, other members of the TGFβ superfamily, namely BMP 2, BMP4, and BMP 7, strongly inhibit neurogenesis in embryonic mouse explant cultures.[135,136] BMP2, BMP4, and BMP7 seem to target the MASH1 protein in olfactory progenitors for degradation resulting in a premature end to neurogenesis.[135] This effect appears to be concentration-dependent; at low concentrations, BMP4 actually seems to induce neurogenesis by promoting neuron survival.[136] *In vivo* analysis of the embryonic and adult MOE reveals the expression of BMP4 throughout the neuronal layers and BMP7 in basal cells. All three factors were present in the underlying mesenchyme, and BMP receptors have been observed in the embryonic olfactory epithelium.[136,137]

Like TGFβ-1 and TGFβ-2, dopamine (DA) seems to induce neuronal differentiation as well. In fact, administration of DA to both mouse and human olfactory explants and an olfactory-derived cell line stimulates neuronal differentiation.[138–140] This is most likely not the result of increasing progenitor proliferation because DA was shown to either have no effect or, when administered to human olfactory explants, to reduce basal cell mitoses.[138–140] Although the exact source of DA in the MOE has not yet been identified, it is present in the olfactory mucus.[141] Expression of the D2 receptor is restricted to the basal cells, ORNs, and underlying lamina propria.[139,142,143] Interestingly, an increase in apoptosis has also been observed following administration of DA, suggesting that DA may negatively regulate neuronal survival. In contrast, platelet-derived growth factor (PDGF-AB) promotes neuronal survival when administered to freshly dissociated neurons or to those that have been induced to differentiate with TGFβ-2 *in vitro*.[132]

Conclusion

Two features of the olfactory system particularly stand out: (1) the MOE and VNO maintain neuronal production throughout life and replenish both neuronal and non-neuronal cells following experimental injury and (2) OECs can stimulate axon growth in the CNS. In most mammalian nervous tissues, the vast majority of cells are born during the embryonic and neonatal period with the exception of the hippocampus, the subventricular zone that generates olfactory bulb interneurons, the MOE, and the VNO. That three of the four sites supporting adult neurogenesis are dedicated to olfaction is particularly intriguing from both a scientific and evolutionary standpoint. Many questions remain. What is the molecular identity of the olfactory and vomeronasal stem cells? How is proliferation of these stem cells regulated? Is neuronal cell fate/receptor choice specified in the stem cell, or is it defined after withdrawal from the cell cycle? Despite these apparent gaps, the reparative properties of the OECs and a readily accessible source of new neurons from the MOE offer enormous potential in the context of brain and spinal cord repair. Hopefully, as we gain more insight into olfactory neurogenesis, these possibilities will become reality.

REFERENCES

1. Parmentier, M., et al. (1992). Expression of members of the putative olfactory receptor gene family in mammalian germ cells. *Nature* **355,** 453–455.

2. Buck, L., and Axel, R. (1991). A novel multigene family may encode odorant receptors: a molecular basis for odor recognition. *Cell* **65,** 175–187.
3. Ngai, J., et al. (1993). Coding of olfactory information: Topography of odorant receptor expression in the catfish olfactory epithelium. *Cell* **72,** 667–680.
4. Ressler, K.J., Sullivan, S.L., and Buck, L.B. (1993). A zonal organization of odorant receptor gene expression in the olfactory epithelium. *Cell* **73,** 597–609.
5. Vassar, R., et al. (1994). Topographic organization of sensory projections to the olfactory bulb. *Cell* **79,** 981–991.
6. Ressler, K.J., Sullivan, S.L., and Buck, L.B. (1994). Information coding in the olfactory system: evidence for a stereotyped and highly organized epitope map in the olfactory bulb. *Cell* **79,** 1245–1255.
7. Mombaerts, P., et al. (!996). Visualizing an olfactory sensory map. *Cell* **87,** 675–686.
8. Graziadei, P.P., and Graziadei, G.A. (1979). Neurogenesis and neuron regeneration in the olfactory system of mammals. I. Morphological aspects of differentiation and structural organization of the olfactory sensory neurons. *J. Neurocytol.* **8,** 1–18.
9. Holbrook, E.H., Szumowski, K.E., and Schwob, J.E. (1995). An immunochemical, ultrastructural, and developmental characterization of the horizontal basal cells of rat olfactory epithelium. *J. Comp. Neurol.* **363,** 129–146.
10. Krishna, N.S., Little, S.S., and Getchell, T.V. (1996). Epidermal growth factor receptor mRNA and protein are expressed in progenitor cells of the olfactory epithelium. *J. Comp. Neurol.* **373,** 297–307.
11. Schwartz Levey, M., Chikaraishi, D.M., and Kauer, J.S. (1991). Characterization of potential precursor populations in the mouse olfactory epithelium using immunocytochemistry and autoradiography. *J. Neurosci.* **11,** 3556–3564.
12. Huard, J.M., and Schwob, J.E. (1995). Cell cycle of globose basal cells in rat olfactory epithelium. *Dev. Dyn.* **203,** 17–26.
13. Calof, A.L., and Chikaraishi, D.M. (1989). Analysis of neurogenesis in a mammalian neuroepithelium: proliferation and differentiation of an olfactory neuron precursor in vitro. *Neuron* **3,** 115–127.
14. Verhaagen, J., et al. (1989). The expression of the growth associated protein B50/GAP43 in the olfactory system of neonatal and adult rats. *J. Neurosci.* **9,** 683–691.
15. Farbman, A.I., and Margolis, F.L. (1980). Olfactory marker protein during ontogeny: immunohistochemical localization. *Dev. Biol.* **74,** 205–215.
16. Weiler, E., and Farbman, A.I. (1998). Supporting cell proliferation in the olfactory epithelium decreases postnatally. *Glia* **22,** 315–328.
17. Suzuki, Y., Takeda, M., and Farbman, A.I. (1996). Supporting cells as phagocytes in the olfactory epithelium after bulbectomy. *J. Comp. Neurol.* **376,** 509–517.
18. Getchell, T.V., Margolis, F.L., and Getchell, M.L. (1984). Perireceptor and receptor events in vertebrate olfaction. *Prog. Neurobiol.* **23,** 317–345.
19. Berghard, A., Buck, L.B., and Liman, E.R. (1996). Evidence for distinct signaling mechanisms in two mammalian olfactory sense organs. *Proc. Natl. Acad. Sci. USA* **93,** 2365–2369.
20. Johnson, E.W., Eller, P.M., and Jafek, B.W. (1993). An immunoelectron microscopic comparison of olfactory marker protein localization in the supranuclear regions of the rat olfactory epithelium and vomeronasal organ neuroepithelium. *Acta Otolaryngol.* **113,** 766–771.
21. Graziadei, G.A., Stanley, R.S., and Graziadei, P.P. (1980). The olfactory marker protein in the olfactory system of the mouse during development. *Neuroscience* **5,** 1239–1252.
22. Krishna, N.S., Getchell, M.L., and Getchell, T.V. (1992). Differential distribution of gamma-glutamyl cycle molecules in the vomeronasal organ of rats. *Neuroreport* **3,** 551–554.
23. Takami, S., Getchell, M.L., and Getchell, T.V. (1994). Lectin histochemical localization of galactose, N-acetylgalactosamine, and N-acetylglucosamine in glycoconjugates of the rat vomeronasal organ, with comparison to the olfactory and septal mucosae. *Cell Tissue Res.* **277,** 211–230.
24. Takami, S., Getchell, M.L., and Getchell, T.V. (1995). Resolution of sensory and mucoid glycoconjugates with terminal alpha-galactose residues in the mucomicrovillar complex of the vomeronasal sensory epithelium by dual confocal laser scanning microscopy. *Cell Tissue Res.* **280,** 211–216.
25. Takami, S., et al. (1995). Enhanced extrinsic innervation of nasal and oral chemosensory mucosae in keratin 14-NGF transgenic mice. *Cell Tissue Res.* **282,** 481–491.
26. Schultz, E., and Gebhardt, L. (1937). Zinc sulfate prophylaxis in poliomyelitis. *JAMA.* 2182–2184.
27. Schultz, E. (1960). Repair of the olfactory mucosa. *Am. J. Path.* **37,** 1–19.
28. Alberts, J.R., Galef B.G., Jr. (1971). Acute anosmia in the rat: a behavioral test of a peripherally-induced olfactory deficit. *Physiol. Behav.* **6,** 619–621.
29. Mulvaney, B.D., and Heist, H.E. (1971). Regeneration of rabbit olfactory epithelium. *Am. J. Anat.* **131,** 241–251.
30. Matulionis, D.H. (1975). Ultrastructural study of mouse olfactory epithelium following destruction by ZnSO4 and its subsequent regeneration. *Am. J. Anat.* **142,** 67–89.
31. Matulionis, D.H. (1976). Light and electron microscopic study of the degeneration and early regeneration of olfactory epithelium in the mouse. *Am. J. Anat.* **145,** 79–99.
32. Burd, G.D. (1993). Morphological study of the effects of intranasal zinc sulfate irrigation on the mouse olfactory epithelium and olfactory bulb. *Microsc. Res. Tech.* **24,** 195–213.
33. Schwob, J.E., Youngentob, S.L., and Mezza, R.C. (1995). Reconstitution of the rat olfactory epithelium after methyl bromide-induced lesion. *J. Comp. Neurol.* **359,** 15–37.
34. Hinds, J.W., Hinds, P.L., and McNelly, N.A. (1984). An autoradiographic study of the mouse olfactory epithelium: evidence for long-lived receptors. *Anat. Rec.* **210,** 375–383.
35. Graziadei, P.P. (1973). Cell dynamics in the olfactory mucosa. *Tissue Cell* **5,** 113–131.
36. Graziadei, P.P., and DeHan, R.S. (1973). Neuronal regeneration in frog olfactory system. *J. Cell Biol.* **59,** 525–530.
37. Harding, J., et al. (1977). Denervation in the primary olfactory pathway of mice. IV. Biochemical and morphological evidence for neuronal replacement following nerve section. *Brain Res.* **132,** 11–28.
38. Graziadei, G.A., and Graziadei, P.P. (1979). Neurogenesis and neuron regeneration in the olfactory system of mammals. II. Degeneration and reconstitution of the olfactory sensory neurons after axotomy. *J. Neurocytol.* **8,** 197–213.
39. Simmons, P.A., Rafols, J.A., and Getchell, T.V. (1981). Ultrastructural changes in olfactory receptor neurons following olfactory nerve section. *J. Comp. Neurol.* **197,** 237–257.
40. Costanzo, R.M. (1984). Comparison of neurogenesis and cell replacement in the hamster olfactory system with and without a target (olfactory bulb). *Brain Res.* **307,** 295–301.
41. Nagahara, Y. (1940). Experimentelle studien uber die histologischen veranderungen das geruchorgans nach der

Olfactoriusdurchschneidung beitrage zur kenntnis des geineren Baus der Geruchsorgans. *JPS. J. Med. Sci. Pathol.* **5,** 165–199.

42. Costanzo, R.M., and Graziadei, P.P. (1983). A quantitative analysis of changes in the olfactory epithelium following bulbectomy in hamster. *J. Comp. Neurol.* **215,** 370–381.
43. Verhaagen, J., et al. (1990). Neuroplasticity in the olfactory system: differential effects of central and peripheral lesions of the primary olfactory pathway on the expression of B-50/GAP43 and the olfactory marker protein. *J. Neurosci. Res.* **26,** 31–44.
44. Schwob, J.E., Szumowski, K.E., and Stasky, A.A. (1992). Olfactory sensory neurons are trophically dependent on the olfactory bulb for their prolonged survival. *J. Neurosci.* **12,** 3896–3919.
45. Carr, V.M., and Farbman, A.I. (1992). Ablation of the olfactory bulb up-regulates the rate of neurogenesis and induces precocious cell death in olfactory epithelium. *Exp. Neurol.* **115,** 55–59.
46. Holcomb, J.D., Mumm, J.S., and Calof, A.L. (1995). Apoptosis in the neuronal lineage of the mouse olfactory epithelium: regulation in vivo and in vitro. *Dev. Biol.* **172,** 307–323.
47. Barber, P.C., and Raisman, G. (1978). Replacement of receptor neurones after section of the vomeronasal nerves in the adult mouse. *Brain Res.* **147,** 297–313.
48. Ichikawa, M., Osada, T., and Costanzo, R.M. (1998). Replacement of receptor cells in the hamster vomeronasal epithelium after nerve transection. *Chem. Senses* **23,** 171–179.
49. Jia, C., and Halpern, M. (1998). Neurogenesis and migration of receptor neurons in the vomeronasal sensory epithelium in the opossum, Monodelphis domestica. *J. Comp. Neurol.* **400,** 287–297.
50. Yoshida-Matsuoka, J., et al. (2000). Morphological and histochemical changes in the regenerating vomeronasal epithelium. *J. Vet. Med. Sci.* **62,** 1253–1261.
51. Graziadei, P.P., and Metcalf, J.F. (1971). Autoradiographic and ultrastructural observations on the frog's olfactory mucosa. *Z. Zellforsch. Mikrosk. Anat.* **116,** 305–318.
52. Moulton, D., Celebi, G., and Fink, R.P. (1970). Olfaction in mammals-two aspects: proliferation of cells in the olfactory epithelium and sensitivity to odours. *In* "Ciba Foundation Symposium on Taste and Smell in Vertebrates" (J. Knight, Ed.), pp. 227–250. Churchill, London.
53. Barber, P.C., and Raisman, G. (1978). Cell division in the vomeronasal organ of the adult mouse. *Brain Res.* **141,** 57–66.
54. Graziadei, P.P. (1977). Functional anatomy of the mammalian chemoreceptor system. *In* "Chemical Signals in Vertebrates" (M. Mozell, Ed.), pp. 435–454. Plenum Press, New York.
55. Weiler, E., McCulloch, M.A., and Farbman, A.I. (1999). Proliferation in the vomeronasal organ of the rat during postnatal development. *Eur. J. Neurosci.* **11,** 700–711.
56. Inamura, K., et al. (2000). Cluster of proliferating cells in rat vomeronasal sensory epithelium. *Neuroreport* **11,** 477–479.
57. Mumm, J.S., Shou, J., and Calof, A.L. (1996). Colony-forming progenitors from mouse olfactory epithelium: evidence for feedback regulation of neuron production. *Proc. Natl. Acad. Sci. USA* **93,** 11167–11172.
58. Ramon-Cueto, A., and Valverde, F. (1995). Olfactory bulb ensheathing glia: a unique cell type with axonal growth-promoting properties. *Glia* **14,** 163–173.
59. Raisman, G. (1985). Specialized neuroglial arrangement may explain the capacity of vomeronasal axons to reinnervate central neurons. *Neuroscience* **14,** 237–254.
60. Doucette, J.R. (1984). The glial cells in the nerve fiber layer of the rat olfactory bulb. *Anat. Rec.* **210,** 385–391.
61. Franklin, R.J., et al. (1996). Schwann cell-like myelination following transplantation of an olfactory bulb-ensheathing cell line into areas of demyelination in the adult CNS. *Glia* **17,** 217–224.
62. Imaizumi, T., et al. (1998). Transplanted olfactory ensheathing cells remyelinate and enhance axonal conduction in the demyelinated dorsal columns of the rat spinal cord. *J. Neurosci.* **18,** 6176–6785.
63. Kafitz, K.W., and Greer, C.A. (1998). The influence of ensheathing cells on olfactory receptor cell neurite outgrowth in vitro. *Ann. NY Acad. Sci.* **855,** 266–269.
64. Kafitz, K.W., and Greer, C.A. (1999). Olfactory ensheathing cells promote neurite extension from embryonic olfactory receptor cells in vitro. *Glia* **25,** 99–110.
65. Sonigra, R.J., et al. (1999). Adult rat olfactory nerve ensheathing cells are effective promoters of adult central nervous system neurite outgrowth in coculture. *Glia* **25,** 256–269.
66. Smale, K.A., Doucette, R., and Kawaja, M.D. (1996). Implantation of olfactory ensheathing cells in the adult rat brain following fimbria-fornix transection. *Exp. Neurol.* **137,** 225–233.
67. Guntinas-Lichius, O., et al. (2001). Transplantation of olfactory ensheathing cells stimulates the collateral sprouting from axotomized adult rat facial motoneurons. *Exp. Neurol.* **172,** 70–80.
68. Imaizumi, T., Lankford, K.L., and Kocsis, J.D. (2000). Transplantation of olfactory ensheathing cells or Schwann cells restores rapid and secure conduction across the transected spinal cord. *Brain Res.* **854,** 70–78.
69. Li, Y., Field, P.M., and Raisman, G. (1997). Repair of adult rat corticospinal tract by transplants of olfactory ensheathing cells. *Science* **277,** 2000–2002.
70. Li, Y., Field, P.M., and Raisman, G. (1998). Regeneration of adult rat corticospinal axons induced by transplanted olfactory ensheathing cells. *J. Neurosci.* **18,** 10514–10524.
71. Ramon-Cueto, A., and Nieto-Sampedro, M. (1994). Regeneration into the spinal cord of transected dorsal root axons is promoted by ensheathing glia transplants. *Exp. Neurol.* **127,** 232–244.
72. Ramon-Cueto, A., et al. (2000). Functional recovery of paraplegic rats and motor axon regeneration in their spinal cords by olfactory ensheathing glia. *Neuron* **25,** 425–435.
73. Lu, J., et al. (2002). Olfactory ensheathing cells promote locomotor recovery after delayed transplantation into transected spinal cord. *Brain* **125,** 14–21.
74. Li, Y., Decherchi, P., and Raisman, G. (2003). Transplantation of olfactory ensheathing cells into spinal cord lesions restores breathing and climbing. *J. Neurosci.* **23,** 727–731.
75. Barnett, S.C., et al. (2000). Identification of a human olfactory ensheathing cell that can effect transplant-mediated remyelination of demyelinated CNS axons. *Brain* **123,** 1581–1588.
76. Kato, T., et al. (2000). Transplantation of human olfactory ensheathing cells elicits remyelination of demyelinated rat spinal cord. *Glia* **30,** 209–218.
77. Roisen, F.J., et al. (2001). Adult human olfactory stem cells. *Brain Res.* **890,** 11–22.
78. Boyd, J.G., et al. (2003). Olfactory ensheathing cells: historical perspective and therapeutic potential. *Anat. Rec.* **271B** (1), 49–60.
79. Goldstein, B.J., and Schwob, J.E. (1996). Analysis of the globose basal cell compartment in rat olfactory epithelium using GBC-1, a new monoclonal antibody against globose basal cells. *J. Neurosci.* **16,** 4005–4016.
80. Caggiano, M., Kauer, J.S., and Hunter, D.D. (1994). Globose basal cells are neuronal progenitors in the olfactory epithelium: a lineage analysis using a replication-incompetent retrovirus. *Neuron* **13,** 339–352.

Given the importance of extracellular matrix adhesion in regulating epidermal differentiation, it was obvious to examine the role of intercellular adhesion. A dominant negative E-cadherin construct was found to stimulate terminal differentiation, but surprisingly this occurred when both transduced and control cells were in suspension and unable to form cell–cell contacts.[82] It turns out that the E-cadherin cytoplasmic domain acts by sequestering β-catenin, which is not only a component of adherens junctions but also a key signaling component in the wnt pathway.[53] A dominant negative β-catenin mutant increases the proportion of abortive clones of cultured human keratinocytes (from 33% in control cultures to 53%), whereas a constitutively active form increases the proportion of putative stem clones (to 89%) and also increases cell surface integrin levels[53] (Fig. 23–5, A). It is important to note that the effect of activating β-catenin is on clonal type not on the size of individual clones (Fig. 23–5, B) and also that expansion of the stem cell compartment does not lead to inhibition of terminal differentiation.[53] This emphasizes the pitfalls of relying on growth curves to analyze epidermal stem cells, because the overall growth rate of a population of keratinocytes will reflect a variety of variables, such as cell cycle time, ratio of stem to transit amplifying cells, and proportion of cells undergoing terminal differentiation.

In cultured human epidermis the level of β-catenin signaling controls the ratio of stem to transit amplifying cells; however, *in vivo* it appears to be primarily a lineage regulator, with high levels favoring *de novo* hair follicle formation[83] and low levels promoting IFE and sebocyte differentiation.[84–86] It is interesting to speculate that the reason for the discrepancy between the *in vitro* and *in vivo* effects may be that the culture conditions are not conducive to hair follicle lineage differentiation, causing cells to back up in the stem cell compartment.

p63 is another important regulator of the epidermal stem cell compartment. Mice lacking p63 have a number of major defects, including a striking absence of epidermis.[87,88] p63 is mutated in Hay-Wells syndrome,[89] a rare autosomal dominant disorder characterized by congenital ectodermal dysplasia, including alopecia and dystrophic nails, and in a number of other dominant human syndromes with epidermal phenotypes.[90] The p63 gene encodes six splice variants and the predominant form expressed by human IFE keratinocytes serves as a transcriptional repressor that binds to the 14-3-3σ promoter.[91] The protein 14-3-3σ in turn promotes exit from the stem cell compartment *in vitro.*[92]

Terminal differentiation of keratinocytes involves irreversible growth arrest; however, the relationship between growth arrest and differentiation is not straightforward. Inhibition of proliferation is not sufficient to induce terminal differentiation, and cultured human keratinocytes do not undergo terminal differentiation from G_0; instead, they can initiate differentiation at any phase of the cell cycle.[72,93] In addition, it is possible to alter the proportion of stem cell colonies in culture without altering the size of those colonies.[53] These observations suggest that there may be distinct regulators of proliferation and terminal differentiation. Some of the factors that control withdrawal from the cell cycle have now been identified. These include Shh, which promotes proliferation of primary human keratinocytes and may oppose stimuli for cell cycle arrest.[94] NF-κB proteins also play an important role in the switch from proliferation to growth arrest and differentiation.[95,96] Functional blockade of NF-κB stimulates proliferation, whereas overexpression of active p50 and p65 NF-κB subunits results in growth inhibition both *in vivo* and in cultured human keratinocytes.[95] NF-κB profoundly inhibits the cell cycle and causes irreversible growth arrest in association with selective induction of the cyclin-dependent kinase inhibitor p21CiP1.[96]

NON-CELL AUTONOMOUS REGULATION

There is evidence that stem cell number and distribution may be influenced by signals from neighboring keratinocytes. Confluent sheets of cultured human keratinocytes contain a relatively constant number of cells with high β1 integrin expression, putative stem cells, independent of the absolute number or proportion of high β1 integrin expressing cells in the starting population.[43] One of the signaling pathways that appears to be involved in non-cell autonomous control of stem cell number is via Notch, which controls cell fate decisions through local intercellular interactions in a variety of embryonic and adult tissues. In human epidermis, clusters of cells that correspond to high β1 integrin expressing cells express higher levels of the Notch ligand Delta1 than neighboring cells in the basal layer. In cultured keratinocytes Delta1 mRNA is about two-fold more abundant in adhesion selected stem cells than transit amplifying cells.[54]

When keratinocytes are transduced with full-length Delta1 or a truncated form that acts as a dominant negative inhibitor of Notch activation, there is no effect on clonal growth (Fig. 23–2, A–C). However, when Delta is expressed in the feeder layer of the cultures keratinocyte colony formation is inhibited (Fig. 23–2, D–F). The effects of Delta have been examined by *in vitro* lineage marking[50,54] in which the test keratinocytes are labeled with green fluorescent protein (GFP) and seeded at low density into confluent sheets of unlabeled cells (Fig. 23–6). Delta expression in the unlabeled cells promotes wild-type GFP labeled cells to become transit amplifying cells and form abortive clones of terminally differentiating cells (Fig. 23–6, A and B). However, when Delta is expressed in both labeled and unlabeled cells or when the GFP cells express dominant negative Delta the proportion of clones attributable to stem cells is the same as in wild-type cultures.

The *in vitro* experiments have led to the model that high Delta1 expression by epidermal stem cells has three effects: a protective effect on stem cells by blocking Notch signaling, enhanced cohesiveness of stem cell clusters, and signaling to cells at the edges of clusters to become transit amplifying cells.[54,55] Adult mouse epidermis does not express Delta1, but keratinocyte-specific deletion of Notch1 supports the conclusion that in mouse epidermis, as in keratinocyte cultures, Notch signaling triggers the onset of differentiation.[97] The Notch intracellular domain binds to RBP-J to transactivate transcription of target genes. Epidermal disruption of the mouse

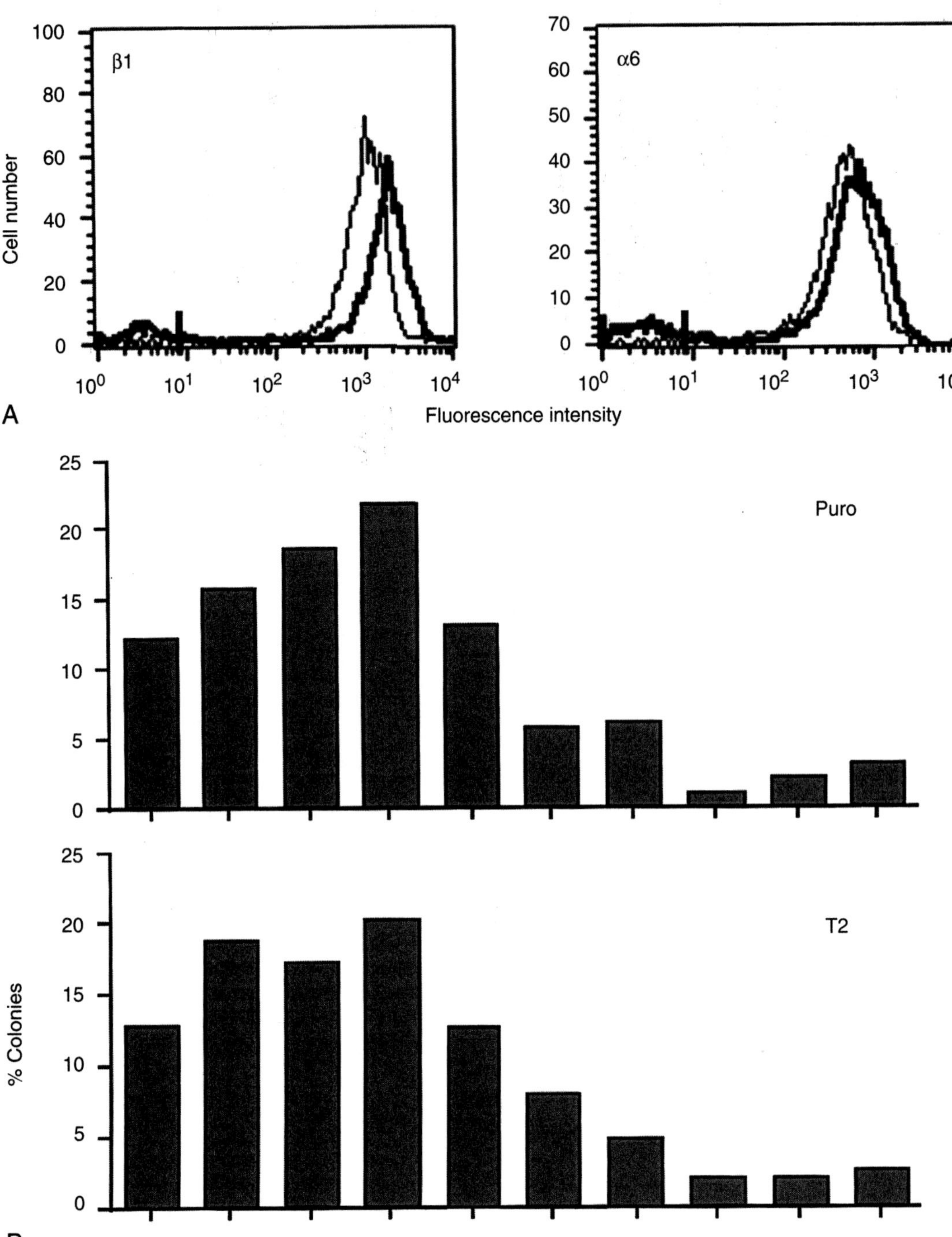

Figure 23-5. Effects of altered β-catenin signaling on keratinocyte integrin levels and colony size. (A) Surface levels of β1 or α6β4 integrins in keratinocytes transduced with dominant negative (grey lines) or stabilized (T2 construct; black lines) forms of β-catenin. (B) Size of individual stem cell colonies founded by keratinocytes expressing T2 or empty retroviral vector (Puro). The colonies are grouped according to size. The first (left hand) column contains colonies with an area of 51–75 units; the next, colonies of 76–100 units, and so on until the last column (right hand side) contains all colonies with an area of greater than 276 units. One hundred units corresponds to a colony area of 2.4 mm^2. Although T2 greatly increases the proportion of putative stem cells it has no effect on the number of cells per clone. (Reproduced from Zhu, A.J., and Watt, F.M. (1999). β-Catenin signalling modulates proliferative potential of human epidermal keratinocytes independently of intercellular adhesion. *Development* **126,** 2285–2298. Reprinted with permission from the Company of Biologists, Ltd.)

24

Epithelial Skin Stem Cells

Tudorita Tumbar and Elaine Fuchs

Skin is a complex tissue made of a structured combination of cell types. It has an enormous regenerative capacity and contains several different kinds of stem cells (SCs). Fundamental differences likely exist between embryonic skin stem cells and adult skin stem cells. In this chapter we focus on epithelial skin stem cells (ESSCs) in postnatal mouse skin. Nonhuman studies allow for high flexibility and increased depth of study and are less restricted by ethical issues. ESSC are thought to reside in a specialized area of the hair follicle called "the bulge." Cells in this compartment possess the ability to differentiate, at least under stress conditions, into different cell lineages to regenerate not only the hair follicle but also the sebaceous gland (SG) and the epidermis. In adult skin, stem cells are thought to be the slow cycling cells that retain bromo-deoxy-uridine (BrdU) DNA label over long periods of time. How these cells maintain their properties of self-renewal and differentiation remains largely unknown. Whether these cells are fundamentally different from their progeny, or whether it is simply their location, the so-called niche that instructs them to behave as stem cells remains an open question. Recent work has begun to elucidate signaling mechanisms that control the fate of these cells in mouse skin. The challenge to isolate slowly cyling cells and to identify markers of ESSC, which may specify unique characteristics of these cells, is now overcome, opening new and exciting avenues for future insight into understanding what maintains these cells in a dormant but potent state.

A Brief Introduction to Mouse Skin Organization

The complex process of constructing the protective cover of the body[1] starts around day 9 of mouse embryonic life (E9). Through a succession of signal exchanges between the ectoderm and mesoderm, a very structured tissue emerges designed to seal and protect the body of the animal against a diverse range of environmental assaults.[2] The barrier function, or the sealing of the body from the external environment, is essential for the survival of the animal and is fully completed at E18, the day before the mouse is born.[3] Hair follicle morphogenesis starts around E13 and takes place in waves until just after birth. The hair follicles are specified embryologically, and, consequently, the maximum number of hair follicles that an animal will have for the rest of its life is determined before birth.[2]

Mature skin is composed of two main tissues: the *epidermis* and its appendages, largely composed of specialized epithelial cells (keratinocytes) and the *dermis,* largely composed of mesenchymal cells. Epidermis consists of an innermost basal layer (BL) of mitotically active keratinocytes that express diagnostic keratins K5 and K14.[4] As these cells withdraw from the cell cycle and commit to a program of terminal differentiation, they remain transcriptionally active and move upward toward the skin surface. As they enter the spinous layers, they first protect themselves by switching from expression of K5 and K14 to K1 and K10, which form keratin filaments that bundle and provide a robust inner strength to the cells.[5] As they complete this process, they next go about producing the barrier by synthesizing and depositing proteins, such as involucrin, loricrin, SPRR, and others beneath the plasma membrane.[6–10] In addition, as the cells enter the granular layer, they begin to produce and package lipids into lamellar granules,[11] and they produce filaggrin, which bundles the keratin filaments even further to form cables.[12,13] As the cells complete these tasks, an influx of calcium activates transglutaminases, which cross-link involucrin and its associates into a cornified envelope that serves as a scaffold for organization of the extruded lipids into external bilayers. Metabolically inert, these cells undergo an apoptotic-like loss of their nuclei and organelles, resulting in flattened, dead squames. These highly keratinized cells provide a seal to the body surface from which they are eventually sloughed, replaced by differentiating cells that are continuously moving outward.[3] Epidermis regenerates itself every few weeks and has a remarkable ability to heal, expand, or retract in response to environmental cues.

Epidermal appendages, including the hair follicle and the sebaceous gland (SG) (Fig. 24–1), are inserted deep into the dermis. The hair follicle is a complex structure made of at least eight different cell types. The hair shaft is located in the middle of the follicle and grows upward, "breaking" the surface of the skin. Concentric layers of cells surrounding the shaft form the outer root sheaths (ORS) and inner root sheaths (IRS) (Fig. 24–1). The basal layer of the epidermis is contiguous with the ORS of the epidermis, which the IRS degenerates in the upper portion of the follicle, liberating the hair shaft.

Handbook of Stem Cells
Volume 2

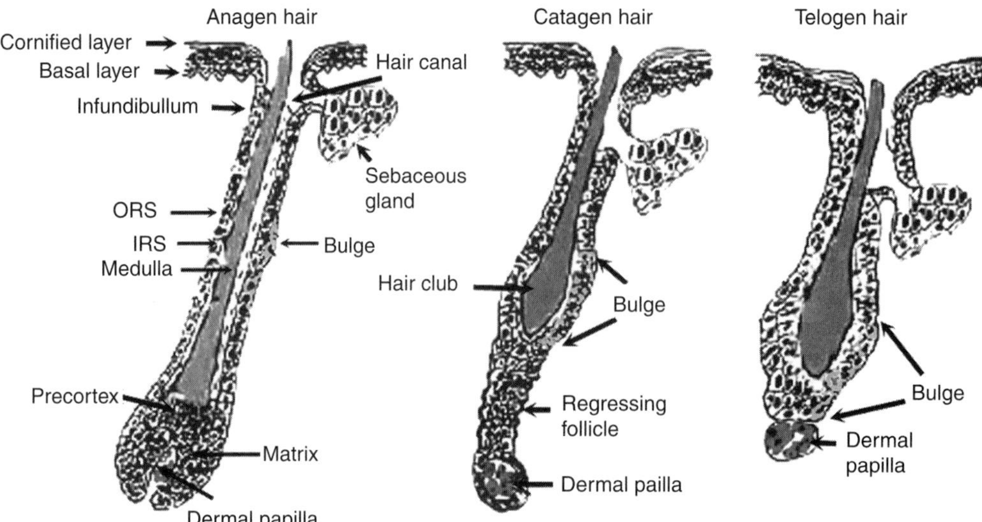

Figure 24–1. The hair follicle cycle in adult mouse skin. (Please see CD-ROM for color version of this figure.)

The basal epidermal layer and the ORS share a number of common biochemical markers, including K5, K14, and $\alpha 6\beta 4$ integrins and they represent potent proliferative compartments of the follicle. The highest proliferation, however, is seen in the matrix cells at the bulb of the follicle, which generate the IRS and the hair cells. Matrix cells surround a pocket of specialized mesenchymal cells, the dermal papilla (DP), with potential hair growth inductive properties.[14–19] Matrix cells express a number of transcription factors (e.g., Lef1 and Msx-2) implicated in hair follicle differentiation.[20–23] To some extent, IRS cells resemble epidermal granular cells, but their granules are uniquely composed of trichohyalin.[24] In contrast, hair cells are more similar to stratum corneum because they are metabolically inert as they complete differentiation; however, they express a unique set of hair-specific keratins.[25] Finally, the SG is located in the upper portion of the hair follicle, just above the arrector pili muscle and is made of fat-containing cells that will release their lipid content into the hair canal.[26] The mitotically active cells of the SG express K5 and K14.

At birth, the morphogenesis of the hair follicle is almost complete. Certainly by day 4 of postnatal life all hair follicles in a mouse skin have reached maturity and hair shafts start to appear at the skin surface. In postnatal life, the ORS of maturing follicles widens a bit on one side, creating a bulge. Located below the SG, and near or at the juncture of the arrector pili muscle, this specialized region is thought to be the compartment where epithelial stem cells reside.[27]

Stem cells in postnatal skin are required for self-renewal of the epithelial tissues. Like epidermis, cells of the postnatal hair follicles are in a state of flux, undergoing perpetual cycles of growth, regression, and rest.[2] In relative synchrony at least for the early hair cycles, mouse hairs continue to grow and complete anagen, the growth phase of the hair cycle. Around 17 days of postnatal development, anagen ceases and massive cell death occurs in the bulb of the hair follicle, the catagen phase. Follicle cells below the bulge area are destroyed, except for the DP, which moves upward by virtue of its attachment to a shrinking basement membrane that separates the epithelial and mesenchymal compartments. The DP comes to rest just beneath the bulge. At this stage, hair follicles enter their rest, or telogen phase. The new anagen is re-initiated around 21 days of life, and hair follicles start again performing this precise choreography of changes.[28,29] Yet unidentified signals from the surrounding environment and from the DP are thought to be necessary to reactivate stem cells to restart the process of follicle morphogenesis.

Adult mouse skin contains epithelial stem cells located in at least two different compartments: epidermis and hair follicle. This review focuses primarily on the hair follicle stem cells located in the bulge area of the hair follicle. Despite their location in the hair follicle ORS, cells within this compartment have been shown to give rise to all the different hair cell lineages, the SG, and the epidermis.[5,30–34]

The Bulge as a Residence of Epithelial Skin Stem Cells

It has been postulated that stem cells should have evolved special mechanisms of protecting their DNA against accumulation of replication errors, which may otherwise result in a high rate of tissue cancer.[35] These mechanisms may involve either slow or rare cell cycling and/or asymmetrically segregating the newly synthesized DNA into the non–stem cell progeny (the immortal DNA strand hypothesis).[36,37] To date, the validity of these hypotheses remains uncertain. In the hair follicle, the cell cycle times of ESSCs relative to transit amplifying (TA) (progeny) cells have been difficult to measure with precision.[38]

However, the concept of SCs as rarely dividing cells is in good agreement with the low mitotic activity detected in the bulge.[27,39,40] Second, in a similar epithelial system, there are some suggestions that intestinal epithelial stem cells might be segregating their newly synthesized DNA strands asymmetrically[38] such that adult stem cells always inherit the original strand of DNA. In the future, it will be important to assess whether asymmetrical divisions might also occur in the bulge. However, the lack of markers for SC and the apparent scarcity of SC divisions in postnatal skin have made this issue technically difficult to address.

What is certain is that a population of slow cycling and/or asymmetrically dividing cells, likely to be the stem cells, is detected in the skin epithelium. When mouse pups are administered tritiated thymidine or BrdU from 3 to 6 days of postnatal life, the label is incorporated into the newly replicated DNA and is found abundantly distributed in the BL and ORS.[41–48] When labeling is subsequently followed by 4 to 8 weeks of chase, transient amplifying cells quickly divide and dilute the label, as they move up into the differentiated layers of hair follicle and epidermis, eventually being eliminated from the tissue. In contrast, the slow cycling cells retain the label and are kept within the tissue. Using this approach, label-retaining cells (LRCs) have been localized predominantly to the bulge area of the murine hair follicle, with fewer scattered cells in the basal layer of the epidermis or elsewhere in the epidermis or hair follicle.[27,34,40,49] If the LRCs in the skin epithelium are stem cells, then the bulge represents a major stem cell compartment of postnatal skin epithelium. Recently, a novel strategy was developed to fluorescently tag and isolate infrequently cycling stem cells in tissues.[50] The method was based upon driving expression of a green fluorescent protein (GFP) fused to histone H2B in a cell type-specific and tetracycline-regulatable fashion. When expression is shut off, all dividing and differentiating cells dilute out the label and/or are sloughed from the tissue, leaving only the infrequently cycling cells brightly labeled. The system was successfully used in skin to monitor the label-retaining cells (LRCs) in the bulge and to isolate and characterize these cells.[50]

With BrdU as a means of labeling the bulge cells, LRCs have been shown to contribute to the formation of both lower hair follicle and the upper region of the hair follicle ORS, called the infundibulum.[40] This is based on the observation that LRCs can be found exclusively in the bulge area during the telogen phase of the hair cycle, but, on initiation of a new anagen, cells containing less BrdU signal, presumably derived from division of bulge cells, were also found in the lower and upper ORS, matrix, and even medulla (in the hair shaft). The correlation with the bulge was indirect with a single-label experiment. Using a double-label technique that marked the upper ORS cells based on distinct division time, Lavker and colleagues were able to show a flux of the infundibular (upper follicle above the bulge) cells into the basal layer of the epidermis in neonates and in wounded adult skin.[40]

Using the tetracycline-regulatable H2B-GFP pulse and chase system, LRCs were both efficiently and sufficiently brightly labeled such that progeny could be tracked for eight divisions.[50] At the start of the new hair cycle (early anagen), transiently amplifying progeny of bulge LRCs could be found in the matrix in the follicle bulb. Remarkably, even the terminally differentiating hair and inner root sheath cells could be assigned on the basis of fluorescence as being cellular derivatives of the bulge.[50] Moreover, in response to a wounding stimulus, these H2B-GFP LRCs appeared to exit the bulge and migrate toward the wound site. In transit to replenish the damaged epidermis, these cells also appeared to proliferate, deposit a fresh basement membrane, and change some biochemical properties.[50]

The bulge area of the rat vibrissae has been shown to contain multipotent cells that have tissue morphogenesis ability.[39] Although clonal analyses will be required to establish multipotency of individual bulge cells, microdissected rat vibrissae bulge tissue transplanted onto the back of athymic mice yielded entire hair follicles, SG, and epidermis further demonstrated by latter studies.[51] Bulge cells also exhibited the highest colony-forming ability when cells were placed in tissue culture, and this was true irrespective of hair follicle cycle stage. In other follicle regions, efficient, colony-forming cells were not found except for the bulb of the rat vibrissae, where such cells were detected only in early anagen. Although the mouse vibrissae and pelage follicle bulge did not function in these assays, this seemed to be due to technical difficulties arising from the size of the follicles, because human follicles displayed a distribution of clonal cells that was similar to that of rat vibrissae.[39,52]

The rationale for attributing clone-forming ability to stem cells, at least in the hair follicle, is based on the assumption that the high tissue regenerative potential of stem cells will be manifested as an ability of these cells to give rise to large colonies of cells in tissue culture. Consistent with this notion is the fact that cultured skin keratinocytes are capable of long-term skin engraftment and regeneration of injured skin.[53]

There is a paradox between the slow cycling-features of bulge stem cells in skin and the ability of cultured cells isolated from the bulge region to form large colonies over a 2-week period. *A priori* it is possible that stem cells in culture divide more rapidly either through the trauma of the isolation process or through their exposure to culture medium. Alternatively, the large colony may arise not from expansion of stem cells per se but instead from a rare asymmetrical division of the original stem cells to produce a heterogeneous mixture of stem cells and TA cells. The authors' data suggest that a concentrated population of isolated stem cells may be necessary to achieve efficient colony formation *in vitro* or successful grafting *in vivo*.[39]

It is not yet clear precisely what is the relation between LRCs identified in the bulge and the cells dissected from the bulge that give rise to cloned colonies or grafted follicles. There is some indication, however, that LRCs are the cells that form colonies in culture.[54] In a recent commentary, Potten and Booth[38] cautioned about the use of *in vitro* approaches for stem cell studies. The study of stem cells outside of their tissue has been called "the biologic version of the Heisenberg principle."

In other words, properties attributed to stem cells, (i.e., colony forming or grafting), cannot be studied "without altering the tissue and in so doing altering the stem cell state of the tissue."

Label-retention ability seems to be a good marker for characterizing a slow cycling and/or asymmetric dividing population of cells that are likely to be stem cells. However, it may be possible that in the tissue there are stem cells that do not possess LRC properties. Thus, although intriguing as a potential stem cell marker, label retention is circumstantial and clearly dependent on the label-chase scheme used. Thus, it is possible that researchers may be overlooking the existence of stem cells that are not label retaining but that are nevertheless critical in tissue regeneration. Future studies will be necessary to evaluate this possibility.

Recent studies using retroviral transduction of keratinocytes have revisited the concept that the bulge contains a population of stem cells that is the normal source of tissue regeneration.[55,56] In one study, Ghazizadeh and Taichman[56] dermabraded mouse skin and transduced it with a retrovirus encoding the β-galactosidase reporter gene, followed by a 36-week chase with five cycles of depilation-induced hair follicle cycles.[55] If the entire skin epithelium is generated from multipotent, long-lived stem cells within the bulge, then the distribution of β-Gal positive cells might be expected to be uniform across the different cell lineages in the hair follicle and epidermis. The result was puzzling because, even after the long chase and repeated stimulation of stem cells, only 30% of the hair follicles were uniformly blue. The rest of the follicles were positive in the ORS, IRS, or SG but not in all three locations. Moreover, there were defined units of blue in the epidermis far away from the hair follicle.[55] Similar results were obtained when the skin of mosaic mice obtained by aggregation of two stem cell types of different genetic background was analyzed.[56] These results suggest that there may be multiple classes of stem cells that are long lived, each with restricted potency that may not even reside in a single niche (the bulge).[32,57–61]

Although these data are difficult to reconcile solely on the basis of the multipotent bulge hypothesis, it does not necessarily rule out the hypothesis. It could be that the special slow cycling properties of multipotent stem cells render them exceptionally difficult to infect. Those follicles with mosaic patterns of β-Gal expression may arise either from perhaps more easily infectible cells that have left the niche and are already committed to a particular lineages. It is well established that mosaicism can arise from a chromatin inactivation mechanism, referred to as position effect variegation that often operates to spontaneously silence retroviral or transgene promoter activity. This mechanism may operate differently in stem cells and their committed progeny, leading to a nonrandom silencing pattern of gene expression of the reporter, in which the transduced retroviral DNA is silenced with higher efficiency in stem cells. This said, an equally plausible hypothesis is that lineage-specific and multipotent stem cells exist in the skin. Irrespective of resolving the issue of stem cell variability, it should be noted that again there is the underlying caveat that different kinds of injury (i.e., dermabrasion, depilation, cell grafting) have been used as representative models for the normal tissue homeostasis. Resolution of these various issues will require clonal analyses with single stem cells and/or their descendants.

Despite the controversy, the evidence is compelling that (1) the bulge contains a large pool of LRCs that participate in the regeneration of the hair follicle and of the wounded skin; (2) bulge cells form large colonies in culture; and (3) bulge cells regenerate the entire hair follicle, SG, and epidermis after grafting. These cells have many of the characteristics expected of epithelial skin stem cells. Keeping the "principle of uncertainty" in mind, we consider in the next sections the different models of stem cell activation and stem cell function in the skin epithelium.[30]

Models of Epithelial Stem Cell Activation

Early data on hair follicle growth and stem cell function suggested that the bulb of the hair follicle, containing matrix cells, is the residence of stem cells (see reference 27 and references therein). This hypothesis was hard to explain because of the cycling nature of the bulb, which undergoes extensive apoptosis in catagen, leaving only a small strand of epithelial cells connecting the DP and the bulge. In addition, the hair follicle can completely regenerate even after the bulb is surgically removed.[62,63]

Evidence that the bulge contains a large pool of LRCs, together with the appealing location of the bulge as a "niche" at the base of the permanent portion of the hair follicle, suggested a novel model for hair follicle growth, the "bulge activation hypothesis" (Fig. 24–2C).[27] In this model, stem cells are activated by yet unidentified signals transmitted through direct contact with the DP. Such contact occurs at the end of each hair cycle, as the surrounding dermal sheath shrinks during the apoptotic phase, and drags the DP upward until it comes into contact with the bulge. Although this contact does not appear to be the sole source of stimulation, it seems to be a necessary stimulus to activate one or more bulge cells to divide, resulting in TA cells with decreasing levels of stemness.[27,40]

At least in neonate and wounded adult skin, stem cell activation may be accompanied by a flux of upper ORS cells to the epidermis. When cells exit the bulge and migrate upward, they take on the fate of a TA epidermal or SG cell. When they migrate downward during early anagen, they give rise to a population of TA ORS and matrix cells that in turn further specialize to form the IRS, cortex, and medulla.[27,40] When matrix TA cells cease dividing, perhaps through exhaustion of their proliferative capacity, the bulb of the hair follicle undergoes apoptosis (catagen phase). Mutations in a number of genes, including those encoding the transcription factors hairless and RXRα, result in a failure of the DP to be dragged upward at the end of the first postnatal hair cycle.[64–66] The consequence is a block in bulge activation and a loss of all subsequent hair cycles.

The bulge activation hypothesis on its own does not explain why bulge cells and DP can sometimes sit adjacent to each other for extended periods of time, without stem cell

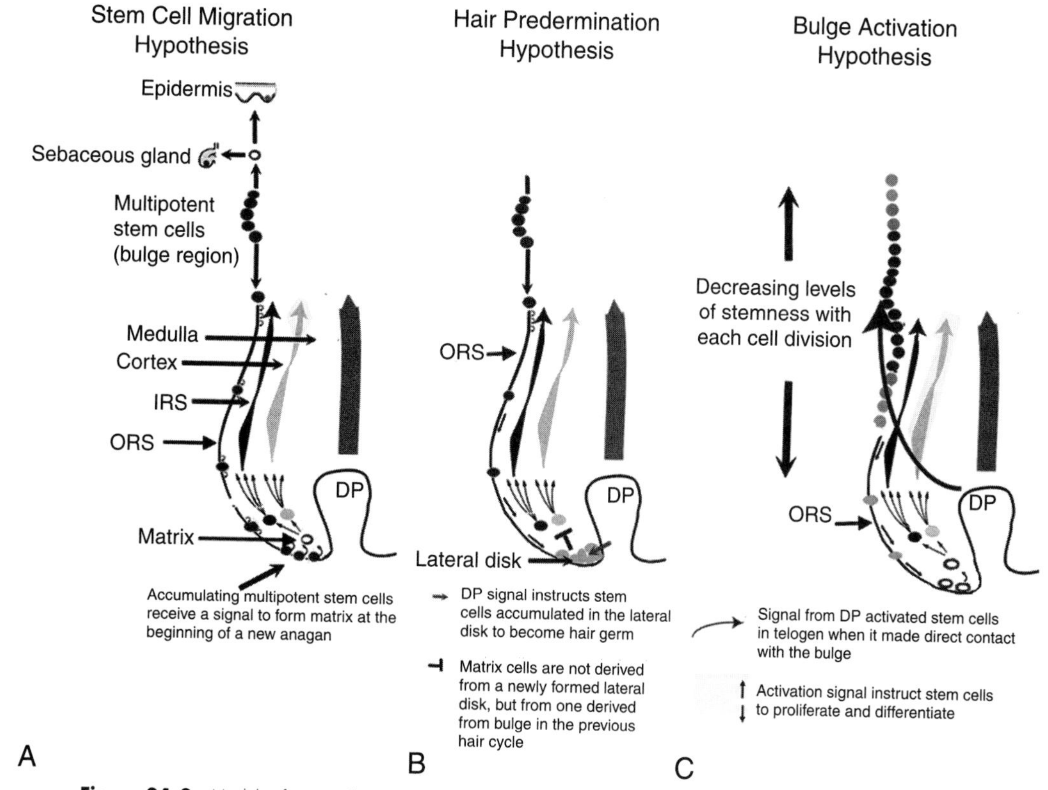

Figure 24–2. Models of stem cell activation in the hair follicle. (Please see CD-ROM for color version of this figure.)

activation, but further experiments may bring more evidence in support of this model. Although a number of possibilities could be envisioned to account for this lag period, one model is that stem cells in the bulge may need to replenish themselves during telogen to reach a critical threshold density.

A second model for stem cell activation is the "cell migration or the traffic light hypothesis."[39] This model is based on the observation that clonogenic and morphogenic cells in the rat vibrissae are found in the bulge at any hair follicle stage, but they are found at the base of the bulb in late catagen and early anagen. The telogen phase is short if not absent from vibrissae, and a new vibrissae cycle is initiated before the DP has moved upward completely to come into contact with the bulge. In investigating this process, Oshima *et al.*[39] discovered that stem cells or their more or less committed progeny appeared to migrate along the ORS to come in contact with the DP, which then seemed to signal their pathway to differentiate. During catagen and early anagen, these bulge cell derivatives accumulated at the base of the hair follicle in a relative undifferentiated state. Later in anagen, this "traffic stop" appeared to be removed, and cells at the base of the bulb seemed to progress to become matrix and then differentiate into IRS and hair shaft cells. While in transit along the basement membrane surrounding the ORS, these cells were not able to form colonies or engraft successfully, perhaps because of their low concentration. In this model, stem cells or their immediate progeny leave the niche and with an estimated speed of ~100 μm/day, they migrate with minimal division along 2 mm of ORS to reach the bulb (Fig. 24–2A).

A third model has come from an integrative reassessment of the literature, with a novel interpretation of the accumulated data. Known as "hair follicle predetermination," this model is based on multiple studies of hair follicle growth[32], and although speculative, it offers an alternative explanation for conflicting results.[48,67] In this model, during mid and late anagen, SCs are stimulated to leave the bulge niche and migrate away to form the ORS but not the matrix or the rest of the hair. It is postulated that these SC progeny then accumulate at the base of the follicle, adjacent to the DP, where they are modified to form a "lateral disc" in the bulb (Fig. 24–2B). During telogen, the lateral disc maintains contact with the DP, and, upon the next anagen, it proliferates (upward) and forms the new matrix and the inner layers of the hair follicle. During this phase newly activated bulge cells give rise to the ORS and replenish the lateral disc.[32] Therefore, the new hair follicle is formed from lateral disc cells that are predetermined for this role during the previous hair cycle. Based on the recent H2B-GFP LRC study, it would seem that a modification of the predetermination model is now warranted to explain how, possibly as a secondary step following the initial "lateral disk" activation, the H2B-GFP LRCs are stimulated to exit the bulge area, proliferate, and participate in the formation of the matrix, all within a single anagen.[50] Finally, some models postulate the presence of multiple populations of non-bulge skin epithelial stem cells that are long-lived and either unipotent or of interchangeable potential (hair cells can make epidermis and/or SG and vice versa).[55–57,68] These models are discussed in more details in Volume 2, Chapter 23. These epidermal cells must divide more frequently than bulge LRCs to account for why they were much less brightly labeled with H2B-GFP in the pulse and chase experiments outlined above.[50]

Molecular Fingerprint of the Bulge-Putative Stem Cell Markers

One of the major problems in the advancement of the stem cell field has been the lack of specific biochemical markers characteristic for stem cells despite extensive searches.[34,59,69] This has raised the possibility that stem cells may have few if any unique features, but instead it is their niche that instructs stem cells to behave differently than their offspring.[70] Recently, infrequently cycling bulge cells have been isolated based on their H2B-GFP retention, and their transcriptional profile has been compared with progeny in the basal layer of the epidermis and ORS of the hair follicle.[50] Probing a third of the mouse genome, 154 mRNAs scored as being upregulated by greater than two-fold in the bulge LRCs relative to the BL/ORS. Similar studies using a K15-GFP transgenic mouse to purify bulge cells have recently corroborated many of these results.[50a] Although a detailed analyses of all these newly identified factors will take time to complete, immunofluorescence microscopy has already indicated that a number of the proteins encoded by these bulge-upregulated mRNAs are expressed within the bulge, but are not necessarily specific for the brightest LRCs within the bulge. Additionally, based upon the comparison made, these mRNAs cannot be considered as exclusive markers for the bulge, and indeed some are expressed in other cell types within the skin. This said, some appear to be specific for the bulge, and a few appear to be better markers for the bulge than previously identified factors.[50]

Traditionally, some of the best characterized markers relating to stem cell function are integrins.[71] β1 and α6 integrins are increased in keratinocytes in culture with high proliferative capacity, and they also appear to be enhanced in the bulge area, relative to the lower and upper segments of the anagen phase follicle.[72,73] Interestingly, both β1 and α6 integrin mRNAs are among the 200 mRNAs identified in three different populations of stem cells when compared with their TA progeny, suggesting that the correlation between integrin levels and "stemness" may extend to stem cells beyond those of the skin.[74,75]

The relation between integrin levels and stem cells is intriguing, because it suggests the possibility that stem cells may be kept tight within the niche by adherence to each other and to the basement membrane.[59,71] The need for stem cell progeny to migrate along the basement membrane surrounding the epidermis and its appendages may be fulfilled by a reduction in cell-substratum anchorage through downregulation of integrins. Alternatively, however, it could be that, because cell proliferation is dependent on integrins, cells with high proliferative capacity by nature have elevated integrin levels.[76,77] The extent to which regulation of integrins in the bulge is a reflection of hair growth mechanisms versus stem cell characteristics per se is an important issue, and one that has not yet been unequivocally resolved. Interestingly, up-regulation of cell migration associated integrin β6 in the ORS during anagen, when bulge and ORS cells migrate downward to make the new hair follicle, seems to suggest the second possibility.[50]

What are the cellular mechanisms that regulate differences in integrin levels? Are there specific stem cell cues that prompt these changes in integrin levels in TA cells to allow them to exit the niche and migrate? These questions remain to be addressed. In the meantime, integrins are thought to play a major role in the skin, in general, irrespective of stem cells in regulating epidermal adhesion, growth, and differentiation.[71,76–79]

Other studies reported proteins expressed differentially in the bulge. They include keratins K15[80–82] and K19,[83,84] both also present in a large fraction of basal layer cells; CD71 low[73]; S100 proteins[85]; E-cad low[69]; p63[86]; and CD34.[87] Of these, CD34, S100A6, and S100A4 were all upregulated at the level of mRNA expression in the bulge.[50,50a]

Although it is found throughout the mitotically active cells of the skin and hence is not restricted to the bulge, a p53 homologue protein called p63 may play a role in stem cell function. P63 null mice exhibit defects in epidermal proliferation, leading to the possibility that p63 might function in repressing epidermal growth factor (EGF) receptor and other cell cycle–regulated genes[88-91] Interestingly, a naturally occurring dominant negative isoform of p63 is induced in the stratified epithelial layers, where it appears to promote cell cycle withdrawal and commitment to terminal differentiation.[92]

Another putative regulator of stem cell function is c-myc. Transgenic mice with elevated c-myc levels in the basal layer and ORS, which encompass both stem and TA skin cells, show epidermal hyperproliferation, severely impaired wound healing, and loss of hair.[93,94] The recent microarray profiling of bulge LRCs adds new candidates that may be involved in regulating the transition between infrequently cycling skin stem cells and their transit-amplifying progeny.[50] As these candidates are systematically tested, new inroads into our understanding of stem cell activation are likely to emerge.

Cell Signaling in Multipotent Epithelial Skin Stem Cells

What coaxes stem cells to become hair follicles rather than epidermis is one of the most fascinating questions in the skin stem cell field. Many of the answers are still not in, but hints have begun to emerge in the past 5 years. It has long been known that in embryonic development, as in postnatal hair cycling, this decision to coax cells toward the hair pathway involves critical cross-talk between the epithelial and mesenchymal cells.[2] What is interesting is that similar signals seem to be used in specification of not only hair but also nail, mammary glands, and teeth.[23,30,95,96]

In embryonic development of skin and its appendages, wnt and bone morphogenic pathway (bmp) signaling have surfaced as two major players that are critical for normal morphogenesis.[97,98] Gene targeting of Lef1,[95,99] β-catenin[100] sonic hedgehog,[101,102] and the noggin inhibitor of the bmp pathway[103,104] results in reduction, loss, or developmental impairment of hair follicles.

The wnt signaling acts through a large family of soluble wnt morphogens that recognize a specific receptor family known as frizzles to stimulate β-catenin, a dual protein that acts at the crossroads between cell adhesion and cell signaling.[105] A wnt signal results in an inhibition of β-catenin degradation, leading to an accumulation of the protein above and beyond what is required for adherens junctions. β-catenin can then complex with members of the Lef/Tcf family of HMG DNA binding proteins and affect expression of transcription of downstream target genes.[106,107] A truncated, constitutively active form of β-catenin expressed at high levels in the ORS of basal layer results in excess skin and *de novo* initiation of hair follicle buds in postnatal skin, a characteristic normally specific to the embryonic skin.[96] Taken together, these data suggest that wnt signaling may induce adult stem cells into a state more specific for their embryonic relatives or that the wnt signaling has a major role in specifying hair follicle fate to relatively undifferentiated cells.[96]

In the adult hair follicle, two members of the Tcf/Lef1 family are expressed in strategic places. Lef1 is in the matrix, precortex, and DP,[23,95] whereas Tcf3 is in the bulge and the ORS of skin epithelium.[108] mRNA profiling revealed that Tcf3 mRNA is also preferentially upregulated in bulge LRCs, suggesting that this regulation is at the level of gene expression.[50] The localization of Tcf3 in the bulge is intriguing because a related protein Tcf4 is found in the intestinal stem cell compartment, or crypt, where it appears to play a role in intestine stem cell maintenance.[109] *In vitro,* Tcf3 acts as a repressor in the absence of wnt signaling, and, in its presence, it can be converted to an activator.[110] *In vivo,* transgenic expression of the repressor forms of Tcf3 both in stem cells and TA cells of the skin results in a lethal phenotype, in which epidermal basal cells are conferred ORS characteristics.[110] Taken together, these findings suggest that Tcf3 in the bulge acts as a repressor. Although target genes for Tcf3 have not yet been identified in the skin, one candidate is c-Myc, an established Tcf/Lef1 target gene, which induces hyperproliferation and appears to deplete the stem cell compartment of the skin when c-Myc is overexpressed in transgenic mice.[93,94]

In contrast to Tcf3, Lef1 is expressed in the matrix but accumulates more strongly in the nuclei of precortical cells. The progenitor cells of the hair shaft precortex expresses a bank of hair-specific keratin genes that possess Lef1 binding sites in their promoters.[23] Precortex also shows nuclear β-catenin, and it expresses a wnt-responsive reporter gene TOPGAL.[108,110] These cells are thus likely to receive a wnt signal, and wnt expression is seen in this region of the anagen hair follicle.[111–113] Interestingly, when expressed in hair precursor cells in transgenic mice, dominant negative forms of Lef1 result in the production of SG cells[110] while loss of β-catenin results in production of epidermal cells at the expense of hair differentiation[114] (Fig. 24–3).

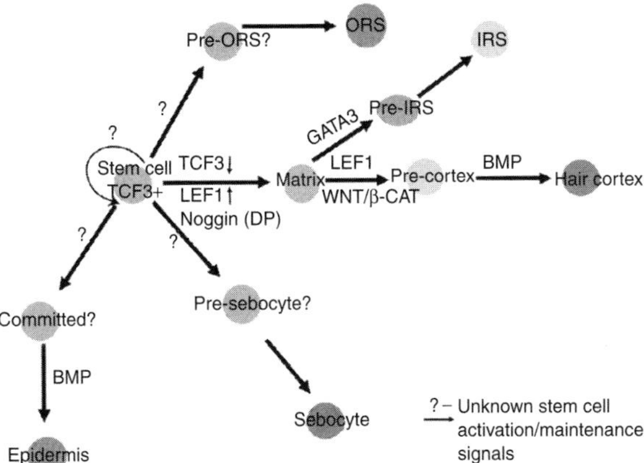

Figure 24–3. Schematics of signaling pathways in stem cell activation and fate choice. (Please see CD-ROM for color version of this figure.)

In contrast, the transcription factor GATA3 was recently demonstrated to be indispensable for inner root sheath differentiation.[115] Curiously, Lef1 and GATA3 have both been implicated in hematopoietic stem cell lineage determination.

Although wnts are clearly necessary for β-catenin stabilization, to obtain a wnt response, a cell must express Tcf/Lef factors. Recently, Jamora *et al.*[97] showed that noggin, a bmp inhibitor, can induce Lef1 expression in keratinocytes *in vitro,* a feature corroborated in keratinocytes and skin epithelium null for the Bmp receptor-1a.[116–116c] When these cells are also treated with Wnt3a, they affect the transcription of wnt-responsive reporter genes. In most cases, this combination leads to transactivation, but curiously, the E-cadherin promoter seems to be downregulated by these factors.[97] *In vivo,* downregulation of the E-cadherin promoter accompanies induction of hair placodes in embryogenesis and secondary hair germs in cycling hair follicles, and transgenic elevation of E-cadherin blocks follicle morphogenesis. Taken together, these findings suggest a model whereby activation of wnt signaling and inhibition of bmp signaling work together to maintain wnt responsiveness in skin epithelial cells and that, through downregulation of E-cadherin, the cells are able to undergo epithelial cell–cell remodeling, necessary for follicle morphogenesis. Moreover, the findings further suggest that adult and embryonic stem cells may use similar signals to control their differentiation.

An intriguing feature of the wnt signaling pathway is that when constitutively activated, it leads to elevated levels of tissue progenitor cells in skin,[96] brain,[117] and intestine.[118] Additionally, purified Wnts stimulate isolated hematopoietic stem cells to proliferate in culture,[119,120] and, following skeletal muscle injury, Wnts appear to mobilize resident stem cells during the regeneration process.[121] Taken together, these findings implicate the wnt signaling pathway in the self-renewal of stem cells and/or their transit-amplifying progeny. Consistent with these observations is the recent finding that the growth-restricted environment of the bulge is associated with an upregulation of mRNAs more typically affiliated with wnt-inhibition.[50] Future studies will be required to assess whether this tantalizing correlation is functionally significant.

Commentary and Future Directions

Probing more deeply into the molecular mechanisms of stem cell maintenance and lineage determination in the skin is now possible using newly identified factors that distinguish putative bulge stem cells from their progeny.[50,50a] Interestingly, a large fraction of these factors are either secreted or transmembrane factors likely involved in interactions with the environment. Some of these have been previously associated with stimulation of different cell types that coincidentally surround the bulge area, while others are likely involved in extracellular matrix and basement membrane organization. Still others are candidates for creating a local gradient of signaling molecules that could maintain stem cells within the bulge area in a growth and differentiation inhibited environment. These findings are in agreement with the bulge being an entity with tissue morphogenesis activity upon grafting,[39] and begin to unravel the molecular mechanisms and the identity of the cells within the bulge that perform this activity. If future tests of these candidates support these predictions, then the concept of preformed niches, in which stem cells find their "home," may have to be reconsidered. In this regard, somatic stem cells may be even more potent than initially surmised, and may be actively involved in building and maintaining their own niches through adult life.[50]

For skin stem cells in particular, many of the most interesting questions still remain unaddressed. Are there multipotent stem cells, or does the bulge contain a heterogenous mixture of unipotent stem cells? What specific genes are responsible for stem cell maintenance? How will their expression change during the hair cycle? How will their patterns change as stem cells either exit from their niche and migrate *in vivo* or are removed from their niche and cultured *in vitro?* How does wounding influence the status of stem cells, and what particular signals penetrate the bulge to instruct cells to exit and help replenish the epidermis? How strong is the correlation between slow-cycling cells and stem cells? Are there long-term and short-term stem cells, and, if so, what makes them different? Do stem cells of the skin undergo asymmetrical or symmetrical divisions?

Once we begin to learn more about the stem cells of the skin, and their spectacular self-renewing properties, it should be possible to begin to identify the niche cues that these cells respond to and the specific environmental cues that coax stem cells along specific lineages. As we gain further insights into these issues, we will begin to explore the relation between adult and embryonic skin stem cells and the parallels between skin stem cells and other stem cells of the body, including pluripotent embryonic stem cells. It is the ultimate goal of the stem cell field to understand enough about the various unipotent, multipotent, and pluripotent cells of the body to make major inroads in the interface between stem cell biology and human medicine.

REFERENCES

1. Fuchs, E. (1990). Epidermal differentiation. *Curr. Opin. Cell. Biol.* **2,** 1028–1035.
2. Hardy, M.H. (1992). The secret life of the hair follicle. *Trends Genet.* **8** (2), 55–61.
3. Fuchs, E., and Raghavan, S. (2002). Getting under the skin of epidermal morphogenesis. *Nat. Rev. Genet.* **3,** 199–209.
4. Fuchs, E., Green, H. (1980). Changes in keratin gene expression during terminal differentiation of the keratinocyte. *Cell* **19,** 1033–1042.
5. Fuchs, E. (1998). Beauty is skin deep: the fascinating biology of the epidermis and its appendages. *Harvey Lect.* **94,** 47–77.
6. Rice, R.H., and Green, H. (1979). Presence in human epidermal cells of a soluble protein precursor of the cross-linked envelope: activation of the cross-linking by calcium ions. *Cell* **18,** 681–694.
7. Watt, F.M., and Green, H. (1982). Stratification and terminal differentiation of cultured epidermal cells. *Nature* **295,** 434–436.
8. Steven, A.C., and Steinert, P.M. (1994). Protein composition of cornified cell envelopes of epidermal keratinocytes. *J. Cell Sci.* **107,** 693–700.
9. Mehrel, T., Hohl, D., Rothnagel, J.A., Longley, M.A., Bundman, D., Cheng, C., Lichti, U., Bisher, M.E., Steven, A.C., Steinert, P.M., *et al.* (1990). Identification of a major keratinocyte cell envelope protein, loricrin. *Cell* **61,** 1103–1112.
10. Marshall, D., Hardman, M.J., Nield, K.M., and Byrne, C. (2001). Differentially expressed late constituents of the epidermal cornified envelope. *Proc. Natl. Acad. Sci. U. S. A.* **98,** 13031–13036.
11. Wertz, P.W. (2000). Lipids and barrier function of the skin. *Acta Derm. Venereol. Suppl. (Stockh.).* **208,** 7–11.
12. Kuechle, M.K., Thulin, C.D., Presland, R.B., and Dale, B.A. (1999). Profilaggrin requires both linker and filaggrin peptide sequences to form granules: implications for profilaggrin processing *in vivo. J. Invest. Dermatol.* **112,** 843–852.
13. Dale, B.A., Lonsdale-Eccles, J.D., and Holbrook, K.A. (1980). Stratum corneum basic protein: an interfilamentous matrix protein of epidermal keratin. *Curr. Probl. Dermatol.* **10,** 311–325.
14. Reynolds, A.J., and Jahoda, C.A. (1992). Cultured dermal papilla cells induce follicle formation and hair growth by transdifferentiation of an adult epidermis. *Development* **115,** 587–593.
15. Lichti, U., Weinberg, W.C., Goodman, L., Ledbetter, S., Dooley, T., Morgan, D., and Yuspa, S.H. (1993). *In vivo* regulation of murine hair growth: insights from grafting defined cell populations onto nude mice. *J. Invest. Dermatol.* **101** (1 Suppl), 124S–129S.
16. Kishimoto, J., Burgeson, R.E., and Morgan, B.A. (2000). Wnt signaling maintains the hair-inducing activity of the dermal papilla. *Genes Dev.* **14,** 1181–1185.
17. Jahoda, C.A., Horne, K.A., and Oliver, R.F. (1984). Induction of hair growth by implantation of cultured dermal papilla cells. *Nature* **311,** 560–562.
18. Jahoda, C.A., and Oliver, R.F. (1984). Vibrissa dermal papilla cell aggregative behaviour *in vivo* and *in vitro. J. Embryol. Exp. Morphol.* **79,** 211–224.
19. Oliver, R.F. (1969). The vibrissa dermal papilla and its influence on epidermal tissues. *Br. J. Dermatol.* **81** (Suppl 3), 55+.

20. Hamrick, M.W. (2001). Development and evolution of the mammalian limb: adaptive diversification of nails, hooves, and claws. *Evol. Dev.* **3,** 355–363.
21. Jiang, T.X., Liu, Y.H., Widelitz, R.B., Kundu, R.K., Maxson, R.E., and Chuong, C.M. (1999). Epidermal dysplasia and abnormal hair follicles in transgenic mice overexpressing homeobox gene MSX-2. *J. Invest. Dermatol.* **113,** 230–237.
22. Noveen, A., Jiang, T.X., Ting-Berreth, S.A., and Chuong, C.M. (1995). Homeobox genes Msx-1 and Msx-2 are associated with induction and growth of skin appendages. *J. Invest. Dermatol.* **104,** 711–719.
23. Zhou, P., Jacobs, J., Byrne, C., and Fuchs, E. Lymphoid enhancer factor (LEF-1) plays a major role in hair follicle morphogenesis and gene expression. *Genes Dev.* **9,** 700–713.
24. Fietz, M.J., Presland, R.B., and Rogers, G.E. (1990). The cDNA-deduced amino acid sequence for trichohyalin, a differentiation marker in the hair follicle, contains a 23 amino acid repeat. *J. Cell Biol.* **110,** 427–436.
25. Lynch, M.H., O'Guin, W.M., Hardy, C., Mak, L., and Sun, T.T. (1986). Acidic and basic hair/nail ("hard") keratins: their colocalization in upper cortical and cuticle cells of the human hair follicle and their relationship to "soft" keratins. *J. Cell Biol.* **103** (6 Pt 2), 2593–2606.
26. Stewart, M.E., Downing, D.T., Cook, J.S., Hansen, J.R., and Strauss, J.S. (1992). Sebaceous gland activity and serum dehydroepiandrosterone sulfate levels in boys and girls. *Arch. Dermatol.* **128,** 1345–1348.
27. Cotsarelis, G., Sun, T.T., and Lavker, R.M. (1990). Label-retaining cells reside in the bulge area of pilosebaceous unit: implications for follicular stem cells, hair cycle, and skin carcinogenesis. *Cell* **61,** 1329–1337.
28. Muller-Rover, S., Handjiski, B., van der Veen, C., Eichmuller, S., Foitzik, K., McKay, I.A., Stenn, K.S., and Paus, R. (2001). A comprehensive guide for the accurate classification of murine hair follicles in distinct hair cycle stages. *J. Invest. Dermatol.* **117,** 3–15.
29. Paus, R., Muller-Rover, S., Van Der Veen, C., Maurer, M., Eichmuller, S., Ling, G., Hofmann, U., Foitzik, K., Mecklenburg, L., and Handjiski, B. (1999). A comprehensive guide for the recognition and classification of distinct stages of hair follicle morphogenesis. *J. Invest. Dermatol.* **113,** 523–532.
30. Fuchs, E., Merrill, B.J., Jamora, C., and DasGupta, R. (2001). At the roots of a never-ending cycle. *Dev. Cell* **1,** 13–25.
31. Potten, C.S., and Morris, R.J. (1988). Epithelial stem cells in vivo. *J. Cell Sci. Suppl.* **10,** 45–62.
32. Panteleyev, A.A., Jahoda, C.A., and Christiano, A.M. (2001). Hair follicle predetermination. *J. Cell Sci.* **114,** 3419–3431.
33. Reynolds, A.J., and Jahoda, C.A. (1994). Hair follicle stem cells: characteristics and possible significance. *Skin Pharmacol.* **7** (1–2), 16–19.
34. Lavker, R.M., Miller, S., Wilson, C., Costarelis, G., Wei, Z.G., Yang, J.S., and Sun, T.T. (1993). Hair follicle stem cells: their location, role in hair cycle, and involvement in skin tumor formation. *J. Invest. Dermatol.* **101** (1 Suppl), 16S–26S.
35. Ruff, M.R., and Pert, C.B. (1984). Small cell carcinoma of the lung: macrophage-specific antigens suggest hemopoietic stem cell origin. *Science* **225,** 1034–1036.
36. Potten, C.S., Hume, W.J., Reid, P., and Cairns, J. (1978). The segregation of DNA in epithelial stem cells. *Cell* **15,** 899–906.
37. Cairns, J. (2002). Somatic stem cells and the kinetics of mutagenesis and carcinogenesis. *Proc. Natl. Acad. Sci. U. S. A.* **99,** 10567–10570.
38. Potten, C.S., and Booth, C. (2002). Keratinocyte stem cells: a commentary. *J. Invest. Dermatol.* **119,** 888–899.
39. Oshima, H., Rochat, A., Kedzia, C., Kobayashi, K., and Barrandon, Y. (2001). Morphogenesis and renewal of hair follicles from adult multipotent stem cells. *Cell* **104,** 233–245.
40. Taylor, G., Lehrer, M.S., Jensen, P.J., Sun, T.T., and Lavker, R.M. (2000). Involvement of follicular stem cells in forming not only the follicle but also the epidermis. *Cell* **102,** 451–461.
41. Dunnwald, M., Tomanek-Chalkley, A., Alexandrunas, D., Fishbaugh, J., and Bickenbach, J.R. (2001). Isolating a pure population of epidermal stem cells for use in tissue engineering. *Exp. Dermatol.* **10,** 45–54.
42. Bickenbach, J.R., and Chism, E. (1998). Selection and extended growth of murine epidermal stem cells in culture. *Exp. Cell Res.* **244,** 184–195.
43. Bickenbach, J.R., and Holbrook, K.A. (1987). Label-retaining cells in human embryonic and fetal epidermis. *J. Invest. Dermatol.* **88,** 42–46.
44. Bickenbach, J.R., McCutecheon, J., and Mackenzie, I.C. (1986). Rate of loss of tritiated thymidine label in basal cells in mouse epithelial tissues. *Cell Tissue Kinet.* **19,** 325–333.
45. Mackenzie, I.C., and Bickenbach, J.R. (1985). Label-retaining keratinocytes and Langerhans cells in mouse epithelia. *Cell Tissue Res.* **242,** 551–556.
46. Bickenbach, J.R., and Mackenzie, I.C. (1984). Identification and localization of label-retaining cells in hamster epithelia. *J. Invest. Dermatol.* **82,** 618–622.
47. Bickenbach, J.R. (1981). Identification and behavior of label-retaining cells in oral mucosa and skin. *J. Dent. Res.* **60** (Spec No C), 1611–1620.
48. Morris, R.J., and Potten, C.S. (1999). Highly persistent label-retaining cells in the hair follicles of mice and their fate following induction of anagen. *J. Invest. Dermatol.* **112,** 470–475.
49. Cotsarelis, G., Cheng, S.Z., Dong, G., Sun, T.T., and Lavker, R.M. (1989). Existence of slow-cycling limbal epithelial basal cells that can be preferentially stimulated to proliferate: implications on epithelial stem cells. *Cell* **57,** 201–209.
50. Tumbar, T., Guasch, G., Greco, V., Blanpain, C., Lowry, W.E., Rendl, M., and Fuchs, E. (2004). Defining the epithelial stem cell niche in skin. *Science* **303**(5656), 359–363.
50a. Morris, R.J., Liu, Y., Marles, L., Yang, Z., Trempus, C., Li, S., Lin, J.S., Sawicki, J.A., Cotsarelis, G. (2004). Capturing and profiling adult hair follicle stem cells *Nat. Biotechnol.* **22,** 411–417.
51. Panteleyev, A.A., Rosenbach, T., Paus, R., and Christiano, A.M. (2000). The bulge is the source of cellular renewal in the sebaceous gland of mouse skin. *Arch. Dermatol. Res.* **292,** 573–576.
52. Rochat, A., Kobayashi, K., and Barrandon, Y. (1994). Location of stem cells of human hair follicles by clonal analysis. *Cell* **76,** 1063–1073.
53. Green, H. (1991). Cultured cells for the treatment of disease. *Sci. Am.* **265** (5), 96–102.
54. Morris, R.J., and Potten, C.S. (1994). Slowly cycling (label-retaining) epidermal cells behave like clonogenic stem cells *in vitro. Cell Prolif.* **27** (5), 279–289.
55. Kopan, R., Lee, J., Lin, M.H., Syder, A.J., Kesterson, J., Crutchfield, N., Li, C.R., Wu, W., Books, J., and Gordon, J.I. (2002). Genetic mosaic analysis indicates that the bulb region of coat hair follicles contains a resident population of several active multipotent epithelial lineage progenitors. *Dev. Biol.* **242,** 44–57.
56. Ghazizadeh, S., and Taichman, L.B. (2001). Multiple classes of stem cells in cutaneous epithelium: a lineage analysis of adult mouse skin. *EMBO. J.* **20,** 1215–1222.

57. Watt, F.M. (2002). The stem cell compartment in human interfollicular epidermis. J. *Dermatol. Sci.* **28** (3), 173–180.
58. Watt, F.M. (2000). Epidermal stem cells as targets for gene transfer. *Hum. Gene Ther.* **11,** 2261–2266.
59. Watt, F.M. (1998). Epidermal stem cells: markers, patterning and the control of stem cell fate. *Philos. Trans. R. Soc. Lond. B Biol. Sci.* **353,** 831–837.
60. Jones, P.H., Harper, S., and Watt, F.M. (1995). Stem cell patterning and fate in human epidermis. *Cell* **80,** 83–93.
61. O'Shaughnessy, R.F., and Christiano, A.M. (2001). Stem cells in the epidermis. *Skin Pharmacol. Appl. Skin Physiol.* **14,** 350–357.
62. Oliver, R.F. (1967). The experimental induction of whisker growth in the hooded rat by implantation of dermal papillae. *J. Embryol. Exp. Morphol.* **18,** 43–51.
63. Oliver, R.F. (1966). Whisker growth after removal of the dermal papilla and lengths of follicle in the hooded rat. *J. Embryol. Exp. Morphol.* **15,** 331–347.
64. Li, M., Indra, A.K., Warot, X., Brocard, J., Messaddeq, N., Kato, S., Metzger, D., and Chambon, P. (2000). Skin abnormalities generated by temporally controlled RXRalpha mutations in mouse epidermis. *Nature* **407,** 633–636.
65. Li, M., Chiba, H., Warot, X., Messaddeq, N., Gerard, C., Chambon, P., and Metzger, D. (2001). RXR-alpha ablation in skin keratinocytes results in alopecia and epidermal alterations. *Development* **128,** 675–688.
66. Ahmad, W., Faiyaz ul Haque, M., Brancolini, V., Tsou, H.C., ul Haque, S., Lam, H., Aita, V.M., Owen, J., deBlaquiere, M., Frank, J., Cserhalmi-Friedman, P.B., Leask, A., McGrath, J.A., Peacocke, M., Ahmad, M., Ott, J., and Christiano, A.M. (1998). Alopecia universalis associated with a mutation in the human hairless gene. *Science* **279,** 720–724.
67. Silver, A.F., Chase, H.B.A., and Arsenault, C.T. (1969). Early anagen initiated by plucking compared with early spontaneous anagen. *Adv. Biol. Skin* **9,** 265–286.
68. Watt, F.M., and Hogan, B.L. (2000). Out of Eden: stem cells and their niches. *Science* **287,** 1427–1430.
69. Akiyama, M., Smith, L.T., and Shimizu, H. (2000). Changing patterns of localization of putative stem cells in developing human hair follicles. *J. Invest. Dermatol.* **114,** 321–327.
70. Spradling, A., Drummond-Barbosa, D., and Kai, T. (2001). Stem cells find their niche. *Nature* **414,** 98–104.
71. Watt, F.M. (2002). Role of integrins in regulating epidermal adhesion, growth and differentiation. *EMBO J.* **21,** 3919–3926.
72. Jones, P.H., and Watt, F.M. (1993). Separation of human epidermal stem cells from transit amplifying cells on the basis of differences in integrin function and expression. *Cell* **73,** 713–724.
73. Tani, H., Morris, R.J., and Kaur, P. (2000). Enrichment for murine keratinocyte stem cells based on cell surface phenotype. *Proc. Natl. Acad. Sci. U. S. A.* **97,** 10960–10965.
74. Ivanova, N.B., et al. (2002). A stem cell molecular signature. *Science* **298,** 601–604.
75. Ramalho-Santos, M., et al. (2002). "Stemness": transcriptional profiling of embryonic and adult stem cells. *Science* **298,** 597–600.
76. Brakebusch, C., et al. (2000). Skin and hair follicle integrity is crucially dependent on beta 1 integrin expression on keratinocytes. *EMBO J.* **19,** 3990–4003.
77. Raghavan, S., et al. (2000). Conditional ablation of beta1 integrin in skin: severe defects in epidermal proliferation, basement membrane formation, and hair follicle invagination. *J. Cell Biol.* **150,** 1149–1160.
78. Dowling, J., Yu, Q.C., and Fuchs, E. (1996). Beta4 integrin is required for hemidesmosome formation, cell adhesion and cell survival. *J. Cell Biol.* **134,** 559–572.
79. De Arcangelis, A., and Georges-Labouesse, E. (2000). Integrin and ECM functions: roles in vertebrate development. *Trends Genet.* **16,** 389–395.
80. Lyle, S., et al. (1999). Human hair follicle bulge cells are biochemically distinct and possess an epithelial stem cell phenotype. *J. Invest. Dermatol. Symp. Proc.* **4,** 296–301.
81. Kanitakis, J., Bourchany, D., Faure, M., and Claudy, A. (1999). Expression of the hair stem cell-specific keratin 15 in pilar tumors of the skin. *Eur. J. Dermatol.* **9,** 363–365.
82. Jih, D.M., Lyle, S., Elenitsas, R., and Elder, D.E., and Costarelis, G. (1999). Cytokeratin 15 expression in trichoepitheliomas and a subset of basal cell carcinomas suggests they originate from hair follicle stem cells. *J. Cutan. Pathol.* **26** (3), 113–118.
83. Commo, S., Gaillard, O., and Bernard, B.A. (2000). The human hair follicle contains two distinct K19 positive compartments in the outer root sheath: a unifying hypothesis for stem cell reservoir? *Differentiation* **66** (4–5), 157–164.
84. Michel, M., et al. (1996). Keratin 19 as a biochemical marker of skin stem cells *in vivo* and *in vitro*: keratin 19 expressing cells are differentially localized in function of anatomic sites, and their number varies with donor age and culture stage. *J. Cell Sci.* **109,** 1017–1028.
85. Ito, M., and Kizawa, K. (2001). Expression of calcium-binding S100 proteins A4 and A6 in regions of the epithelial sac associated with the onset of hair follicle regeneration. *J. Invest. Dermatol.* **116,** 956–963.
86. Pellegrini, G., et al. (2001). p63 identifies keratinocyte stem cells. *Proc. Natl. Acad. Sci. U. S. A.* **98,** 3156–3161.
87. Trempus, C.S., et al. (2003). Enrichment for living murine keratinocytes from the hair follicle bulge with the cell surface marker CD34. *J. Invest. Dermatol.* **120,** 501–511.
88. Nishi, H., et al. (2001). p53 Homologue p63 represses epidermal growth factor receptor expression. *J. Biol. Chem.* **276,** 41,717–41,724.
89. Nishi, H., et al. (1999). Mutation and transcription analyses of the p63 gene in cervical carcinoma. *Int. J. Oncol.* **15,** 1149–1153.
90. Mills, A.A., Qi, Y., and Bradley, A. (2002). Conditional inactivation of p63 by Cre-mediated excision. *Genesis* **32** (2), 138–141.
91. Mills, A.A., et al. (1999). p63 is a p53 homologue required for limb and epidermal morphogenesis. *Nature* **398,** 708–713.
92. Koster, M.I., Kim, S., Mills, A.A., DeMayo, F.J., and Roop, D.R. (2004). p63 is the molecular switch for initiation of an epithelial stratification program. *Genes Dev.* **18**(2), 126–131.
93. Arnold, I., and Watt, F.M. (2001). c-Myc activation in transgenic mouse epidermis results in mobilization of stem cells and differentiation of their progeny. *Curr. Biol.* **11,** 558–568.
94. Waikel, R.L., Kawachi, Y., Waikel, P.A., Wang, X.J., and Roop, D.R. (2001). Deregulated expression of c-Myc depletes epidermal stem cells. *Nat. Genet.* **28,** 165–168.
95. van Genderen, C., Okamura, R.M., Farinas, I., Quo, R.G., Parslow, T.G., Bruhn, L., and Grosschedl, R. (1994). Development of several organs that require inductive epithelial-mesenchymal interactions is impaired in LEF-1-deficient mice. *Genes Dev.* **8,** 2691–2703.
96. Gat, U., DasGupta, R., Degenstein, L., and Fuchs, E. (1998). *De novo* hair follicle morphogenesis and hair tumors in mice expressing a truncated beta-catenin in skin. *Cell* **95,** 605–614.
97. Jamora, C., DasGupta, R., Kocieniewski, P., and Fuchs, E. (2003). Links between signal transduction transcription and

adhesion in epithelial bud development. *Nature* **422**(6929), 317–322.

98. Botchkarev, V.A. (2003). Bone morphogenetic proteins and their antagonists in skin and hair follicle biology. *J. Invest. Dermatol.* **120,** 36–47.
99. Kratochwil, K., et al. (1996). Lef1 expression is activated by BMP-4 and regulates inductive tissue interactions in tooth and hair development. *Genes Dev.* **10,** 1382–1394.
100. Behrens, J., von Kries, J.P., Kuhl, M., Bruhn, L., Wedlich, D., Grosschedl, R., and Birchmeier, W. (1996). Functional interaction of beta-catenin with the transcription factor LEF-1. *Nature* **382,** 638–642.
101. Oro, A.E., Higgins, K.M., Hu, Z., Bonifas, J.M., Epstein, E.H., Jr., and Scott, M.P. (1997). Basal cell carcinomas in mice overexpressing sonic hedgehog. *Science* **276,** 817–821.
102. Oro, A.E., and Higgins, K. (2003). Hair cycle regulation of Hedgehog signal reception. *Dev. Biol.* **255,** 238–248.
103. Botchkarev, V.A., Botchkareva, N.V., Roth, W., Nakamura, M., Chen, L.H., Herzog, W., Lindner, G., McMahon, J.A., Peters, C., Lauster, R., McMahon, A.P., and Paus, R. (1999). Noggin is a mesenchymally derived stimulator of hair-follicle induction. *Nat. Cell Biol.* **1,** 158–164.
104. Botchkarev, V.A., Botchkareva, N.V., Nakamura, M., Huber, O., Funa, K., Lauster, R., Paus, R., and Gilchrest, B.A. (2001). Noggin is required for induction of the hair follicle growth phase in postnatal skin. *FASEB J.* **15,** 2205–2214.
105. Nusse, R. (1999). WNT targets: repression and activation. *Trends Genet.* **15,** 1–3.
106. Cavallo, R.A., et al. (1998). Drosophila Tcf and Groucho interact to repress Wingless signalling activity. *Nature* **395,** 604–608.
107. Brantjes, H., et al. (2002). TCF: Lady Justice casting the final verdict on the outcome of Wnt signalling. *Biol. Chem.* **383,** 255–261.
108. DasGupta, R., and Fuchs, E. (1999). Multiple roles for activated LEF/TCF transcription complexes during hair follicle development and differentiation. *Development* **126,** 4557–4568.
109. Korinek, V., et al. (1998). Depletion of epithelial stem-cell compartments in the small intestine of mice lacking Tcf-4. *Nat. Genet.* **19,** 379–383.
110. Merrill, B.J., et al. (2001). Tcf3 and Lef1 regulate lineage differentiation of multipotent stem cells in skin. *Genes Dev.* **15,** 1688–1705.
111. Millar, S.E. (2003). WNTs: Multiple genes, multiple functions. *J. Invest. Dermatol.* **120,** 7–8.
112. Andl, T., Reddy, S.T., Gaddapara, T., and Millar, S.E. (2002). WNT signals are required for the initiation of hair follicle development. *Dev. Cell* **2,** 643–653.
113. Millar, S.E., Willert, K., Salinas, P.C., Roelink, H., Nusse, R., Sussman, D.J., and Barsh, G.S. (1999). WNT signaling in the control of hair growth and structure. *Dev. Biol.* **207,** 133–149.
114. Huelsken, J., Vogel, R., Erdmann, B., Costarelis, G., and Birchmeier, W. (2001). Beta-catenin controls hair follicle morphogenesis and stem cell differentiation in the skin. *Cell* **105**(4), 533–545.
115. Kaufman, C.K., Zhou, P., Pasolli, H.A., Rendl, M., Bolotin, D., Lim, K.C., Dai, X., Alegre, M.L., and Fuchs, E. (2003). GATA-3: an unexpected regulator of cell lineage determination in skin. *Genes Dev.* **17**(17), 2108–2122.
116. Kobielak, K., Pasolli, H.A., Alonso, L., Polak, L., and Fuchs, E. (2003). Defining BMP function s in the hair follicle by conditional ablation of BMP receptor IA. *J. Cell Biol.* **163**(3), 609–623.

116a. Ming Kwan, K., Li, A.G., Wang, X.J., Wurst, W., and Behringer, R.R. (2004). Essential roles of BMPR-IA signaling in differentiation and growth of hair follicles and in skin tumorigenesis. *Genesis* **39,** 10–25.

116b. Andl, T., Ahn, K., Kairo, A., Chu, E.Y., Wine-Lee, L., Reddy, S.T., Croft, N.J., Cebra-Thomas, J.A., Metzger, D., Chambon, P., Lyons, K.M., Mishina, Y., Seykora, J.T., Crenshaw EB 3rd, Millar SE (2004). Epithelial Bmpr1a regulates differentiation and proliferation in postnatal hair follicles and is essential for tooth development. *Development* **131,** 2257–2268.

116c. Yuhki, M., Yamada, M., Kawano, M., Iwasato, T., Itohara, S., Yoshida, H., Ogawa, M., and Mishina, Y. (2004). BMPR1A signaling is necessary for hair follicle cycling and hair shaft diffrentiation in mice. *Development* **131,** 1825–1833.

117. Chenn, A., and Walsh, C.A. (2002). Regulation of cerebral cortical size by control of cell cycle exit in neural precursors. *Science* **297**(5580), 365–369.
118. Korinek, V., Barker, N., Willert, K., Molenaar, M., Roose, J., Wagenaar, G., Markman, M., Lamers, W., Destree, O., and Clevers, H. Two members of the Tcf family implicated in Wnt/beta-catenin signaling during embryogenesis in the mouse. *Mol. Cell Biol.* **18**(3), 1248–1256.
119. Willert, K., Brown, J.D., Danenberg, E., Duncan, A.W., Weissman, I.L., Reya, T., Yates, J.R., 3rd, and Nusse, R. (2003). Wnt proteins are lipid-modified and can act as stem cell growth factors. *Nature* **423**(6938), 448–452.
120. Reya, T., Duncan, A.W., Ailles, L., Domen, J., Scherer, D.C., Willert, K., Hintz, L., Nusse, R., and Weissman, I.L. (2003). A role for Wnt signaling in self-renewal of haematopoietic stem cells. *Nature* **423**(6938), 409–414.
121. Polesskaya, A., Seale, P., and Rudnicki, M.A. (2003). Wnt signaling induces the myogenic specification of resident CD45+ adult stem cells during muscle regeneration. *Cell* **113**(7), 841–852.

25

Stem Cells in Mammary Epithelium

Gilbert H. Smith and Corinne A. Boulanger

Introduction

The human mammary gland has at times been considered a relatively dispensable organ relative to survival, regarded as necessary, if at all, only during a period of lactation. Despite this, a long history of scientific interest is associated with this organ because of its seminal role in infant nutrition and well-being and because it is often afflicted by cancer development. In fact, before the beginning of the 20th century, there were already more than 10,000 scientific references to published articles relating to mammary biology.[1] It was an interest in cancer and cancer development in the breast that brought about the first series of experiments that led to our current concept of tissue-specific mammary epithelial stem cells. The occurrence of what appeared to be premalignant lesions of the glandular epithelium led DeOme *et al.*[2] to develop a biologic system to recognize, characterize. and study hyperplastic nodules (HANs) in the mammary glands of mouse mammary tumor virus (MMTV)-infected mice. These investigators developed a surgical method for removing the endogenous mammary epithelium from the number 4 mammary fat pad. Subsequently, the "cleared" pad was used as a site of implantation where suspected premalignant lesions could be placed and their subsequent growth and development could be observed. Using this approach, they were able to show that both premalignant and normal mammary implants could grow and fill the empty fat pad within several weeks. During this growth period the premalignant implants recapitulated their hyperplastic phenotype, whereas normal implants produced normal branching mammary ducts. Serial transplantation of normal and premalignant outgrowths demonstrated that, although normal implants invariably showed growth senescence after several generations, hyperplastic outgrowths did not. It soon became apparent that any portion of the normal mammary parenchyma could regenerate a complete mammary tree over several transplant generations, suggesting the existence of cells capable of reproducing new mammary epithelium through several rounds of self-renewal. However, it was some time later before this property was recognized as representative of the presence of mammary epithelial stem cells.[3]

Handbook of Stem Cells
Volume 2

Aging and Reproductive Senescence

The discovery that all portions of the mouse mammary gland appeared competent to regenerate an entire new gland on transplantation triggered a series of articles relating to the reproductive lifetime of mammary cells.[4–7] It was determined that no difference existed in the regenerative ability of mammary tissue taken from very old mice versus that taken from very young mice during serial transplantation. In addition, neither reproductive history nor developmental state had a significant impact on the reproductive longevity of mammary tissue implants. The ability of grafts from old donors to proliferate equivalently to those from young in young hosts suggested to these authors that the life span of mammary cells is primarily affected by the number of mitotic divisions rather than by the passage of chronologic or metabolic time. The authors in a series of experiments tested this (i.e., where mammary implants were serially transplanted). In one series, fragments were taken from the periphery of the outgrowth for subsequent transplantation; in the other the fragments for transplant were removed from the center. The supposition was that the cells at the periphery had undergone more mitotic events than those in the center, and, therefore, peripheral tissue would show growth senescence more quickly than tissue near the center. Outgrowths from fragments taken from the periphery repeatedly showed senescent growth in earlier passages when compared with those generated from implants from the centers of outgrowths.[5] The authors concluded that growth senescence in transplanted mammary epithelium was related primarily to the number of cell divisions. In contrast, mouse mammary epithelial cells could be transformed to unlimited division potential either spontaneously, by MMTV infection, or by treatment with carcinogens.[4,8] At the time this observation was taken to signify that "immortalization" (i.e., attainment of unlimited division potential) was an important early step in malignant transformation. More recently, Medina *et al.*[9] showed that mammary epithelium from $p53^{-/-}$ mice also exhibits an immortal phenotype on serial transplantation. This is a striking discovery because of the essential role that p53 signaling plays in the maintenance and genomic stability of the stem cells within the crypts of the small intestine. For example, radiation sensitivity is absent in the intestinal crypt stem cells in p53 null mice.[10]

With respect to transplantation of mammary fragments to epithelium-free fat, extensive studies indicate that rat mammary epithelium shows similar clonogenic activity to that of the mouse. In fact, rat mammary implants grow extensively to complete glandular structures within "cleared" mouse mammary fat pads.[11] In addition, there is a similar indication that all parts of the rat gland have regenerative capacities. Little is known regarding the regenerative ability of human breast on transplantation. Human mammary fragments were maintained and could be stimulated to functional differentiation in mouse mammary fat pads but did not grow extensively.[12] Xenografts of human breast in immunocompromised Nu/Nu mice have been shown to exhibit a mitogenic response on exposure to increased levels of estrogen and progesterone.[13] Because of the lack of a functional transplantation assay for human breast epithelium, virtually nothing is known about its growth longevity or capacity to self-renew.

In Vitro Studies

Dispersed mouse mammary epithelial cells have been shown to be able to recombine and grow to form a new gland within the epithelium-free mammary fat pad.[14–17] In these experiments, both normal and transformed mammary outgrowths were developed, indicating that both normal and abnormal mammary cells could exist within any given apparently normal glandular population. More recently, irradiated feeder cells have been employed to propagate primary cultures of mouse mammary epithelium. Under these conditions, the cells were maintained for nine passages and produced normal mammary outgrowths on introduction into cleared mammary fat pads.[18] The number of dispersed mammary cells required to produce a positive take (i.e., form a glandular structure within the fat pad) increased with increasing passage number. This observation applies to all mouse mammary epithelial cell lines that have been developed *in vitro* and maintained through serial passages. Eventually with passage, as with the fragment implants, either no growth is attained or neoplastic development is achieved when the cells are placed into cleared fat pads.[19] Some mouse mammary cell lines that were grown for various periods in culture demonstrated an extended reproductive life span when reintroduced into cleared mammary fat pads and transplanted serially. The resulting outgrowths appeared in every way to be normal and did not exhibit hyperplastic or tumorigenic growth.[20] The authors concluded that the immortalization phenotype could be dissociated from the preneoplastic phenotype and suggested that these mammary cell lines may represent an early stage, perhaps the earliest, in progression to mammary tumorigenesis. Human breast epithelium in culture endures at least two growth senescent periods before progressing to an immortalized population. The molecular events accompanying these conversions have been studied very extensively (reviewed in reference 21). Nothing from these *in vitro* studies has shed any light on either the biology or characterization of human mammary epithelial stem cells.

During the last decade, a number of authors have investigated the endpoint of the clonogenic capacity of dispersed rodent mammary epithelial cells in limiting dilution transplantation experiments.[22–25] Both in the mouse and in the rat, 1000 to 2000 mammary epithelial cells represent the smallest number required for the establishment of an epithelial growth in a fat pad. Earlier it was shown that genes could be introduced into primary mammary epithelial cell cultures with retroviral vectors. Subsequently, the genetically modified epithelial cells were reintroduced into cleared mammary fat pads for evaluation *in vivo*.[26] Although stable transduction of gene expression could be achieved in a high percentage of mammary cells in culture, recovery of these retroviral-marked cells in regenerated glandular structures was only possible when virtually 100% of the implanted cells were stably modified. It was determined that this resulted from the fact that only a very small proportion of the primary epithelial cells inoculated were capable of contributing to tissue renewal *in vivo*. This was the first indication that only a subset of the mammary epithelial population possessed the capacity to regenerate mammary tissue on transplantation. From this followed the possibility that this cellular subset represented the mammary epithelial stem cell compartment.

For two entirely different purposes, dispersed rat and mouse mammary cells were tested for their ability to form epithelial structures in empty fat pads at limiting dilution. This author investigated the possibility that lobule and ductal-lineage limited cells existed among the mouse mammary epithelial population based on the common observation that lobular development could be suppressed in transgenic mouse models when ductal branching morphogenesis was unaffected. The results of this study provided evidence for distinct lobule-limited and ductal-limited progenitors in the mouse mammary gland.[22] Figure 25–1 depicts a growing implant in an impregnated host both ductal branching morphogenesis and lobulogenesis occur simultaneously under these circumstances. In Figure 25–1A, an arrowhead indicates the growing terminal end bud of a duct, and the small arrows point out developing secretory acini on the subtending duct. Figure 25–1B represents our current understanding of the location and type of mammary epithelial progenitors in cartoon form. In an effort to establish the total number of clonogenic cells in the rat mammary gland as a measure of radiogenic susceptibility to cancer induction, Kamiya *et al.*[23,25] conducted similar experiments. These authors found that like the mouse, rat mammary glands possessed distinct lobule-committed and duct-committed progenitors. In the mouse, it was shown in clonal-dominant mammary populations that both of these progenitors arose from a common antecedent (i.e., a primary mammary epithelial stem cell).[24]

As described previously, efforts to propagate mammary epithelial cells in continuous culture and subsequently demonstrate their ability to reconstitute the mammary gland *in vivo* have met with limited success. A different approach to understanding mammary epithelial cell lineage was applied by using cell surface markers to distinguish basal (myoepithelial) from luminal (secretory) epithelial cells. With fluorescence-activated cell sorting (FACS), human mammary epithelial cells were separated into myoepithelial (CALLA-positive) and luminal (MUC-positive) populations and evaluated for their respective capacity to produce mixed colonies in cloning assays.[27,28] These authors reported that individual

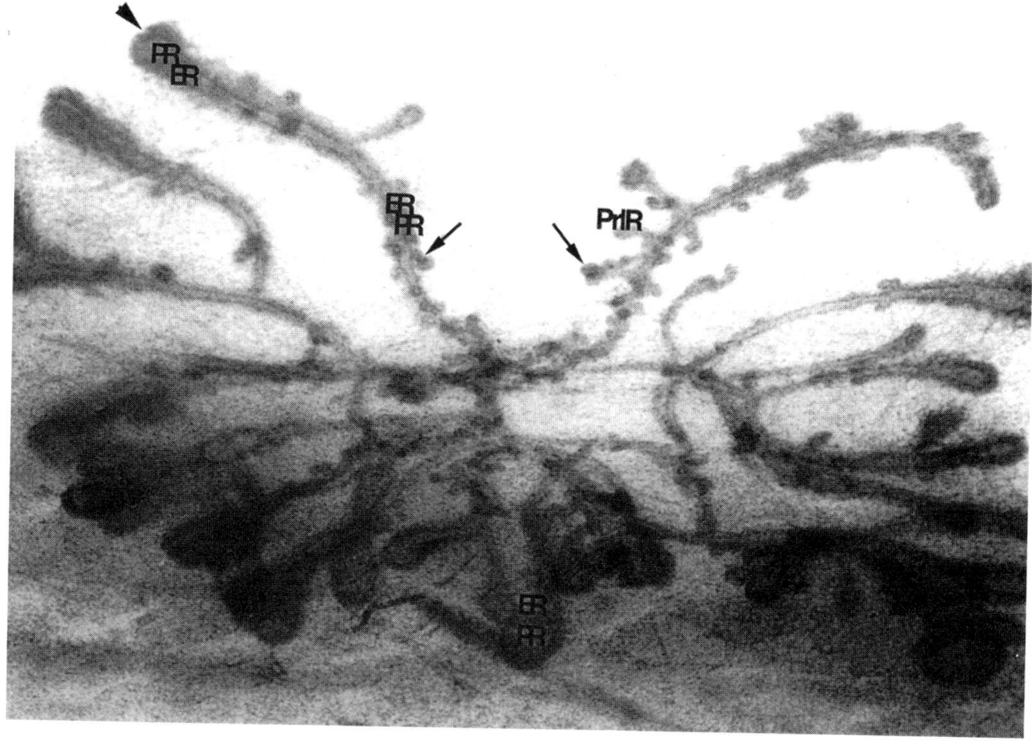

A

Mammary Stem Cells and Progeny

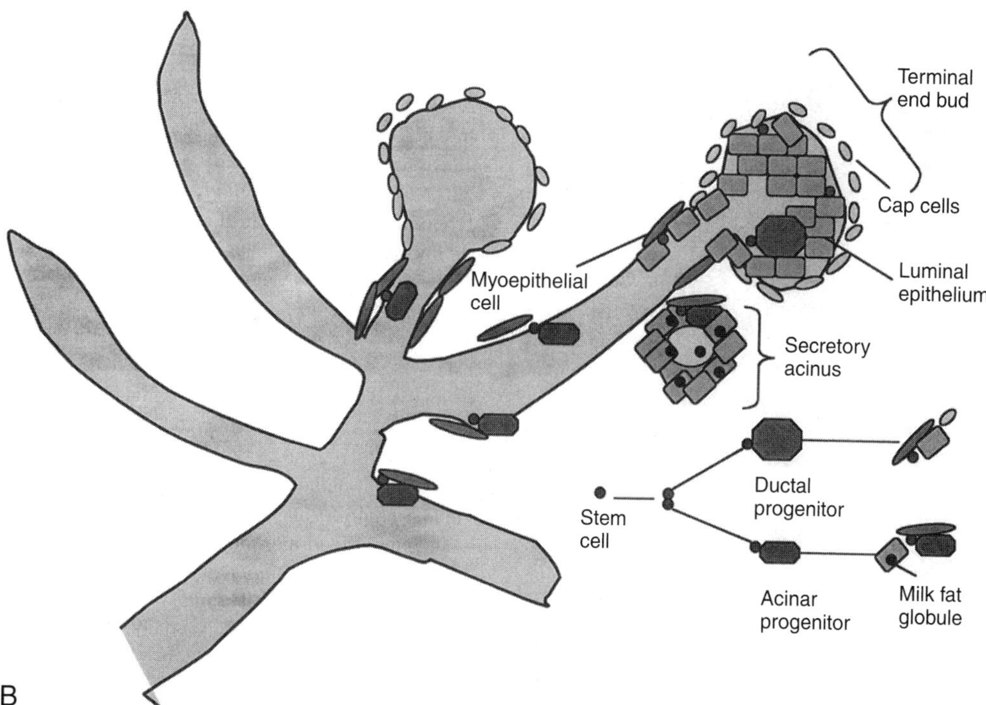

Figure 25–1. (A, B) A growing mammary implant is shown in panel A. The outgrowth is 11 days old and is in the cleared mammary fat pad of a 4-day pregnant host. Active ductal growth and elongation is present with the extension of ducts occurring radially from the implant. Terminal end buds (arrowhead) are enlarged and actively growing, and along the subtending ducts small secretory acini (arrows) are developing. Estrogen, progesterone, and prolactin signaling through their cognate receptors (ER, PR, and PrlR) are essential in this activity. A cartoon in panel B indicates the type and location of pluripotent mammary epithelial cells and their respective progeny.

epithelial cells bearing luminal markers alone or both luminal and myoepithelial surface markers could give rise to colonies with a mixed lineage phenotype. Cells bearing only the CALLA marker (basal/myoepithelial) were only able to produce like epithelial progeny. Using a similar approach, another group[29] demonstrated that CALLA-positive (myoepithelial) and MUC-1 positive (luminal) mammary epithelial cells could be purified to essentially homogeneous populations and maintained as such under certain specific culture conditions *in vitro.* Expression of distinctive keratin gene patterns and other genetic markers also characterized these disparate cellular populations. It was further demonstrated that only the luminal epithelial cell population was able to produce both luminal and myoepithelial cell progeny *in vitro,* providing further evidence that the multipotent cellular subset in mammary epithelial resided among the luminal rather than the myoepithelial lineage. More recently, this same group has shown that unlike myoepithelial cells from normal glands, tumor-derived myoepithelial cells were unable to support three-dimensional growth when combined with normal luminal cells *in vitro.*[30] This deficiency was shown to be the inability of the tumor myoepithelial cells to express a specific laminin gene (LAM1) product.

Mouse mammary epithelial cells have been FACS separated according to their luminal or myoepithelial surface markers. Subsequent study of these different populations *in vitro* gave results that agree with those reported for human cells. The cells capable of giving rise to mixed colonies in cloning studies were only found among the cells bearing luminal epithelial cell markers.[31]

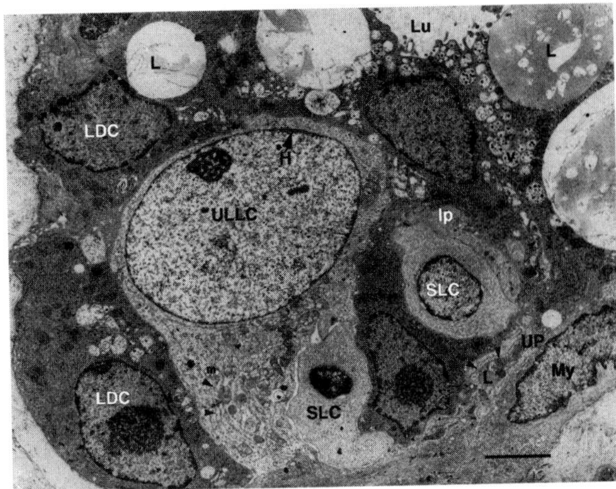

Figure 25–2. In a secretory acinus from a lactating rat mammary gland, a small light cell (SLC) and an undifferentiated large light cell (ULLC) appear juxtaposed suggesting they result from a single mitotic event. To the right, a second pair is present in which only the SLC is completely within the plane of section. Portions of its undifferentiated neighbor (lp) and (UP) are seen beside it. Differentiated secretory mammary epithelial cells (LDC) lie on either side an in an adjacent acinus. Milk fat globules (L) and casein micelles in secretory vesicles (v) are present within the LDC and in the lumen (Lu). A portion of a myoepithelial cell cytoplasm (My) also appears near the SLC. The bar equals 4.0 μm.

Mammary Stem Cell Markers

Several recent studies have demonstrated that the multipotent cells in mammary epithelium reside within the luminal cell population in human and mouse.[29,31] However, no specific molecular signature for mammary epithelial stem cells was revealed. Smith and Medina[3] presented an earlier marker that held promise for identifying mammary stem cells in the ultrastructural description of mitotic cells in mammary epithelial explants. These investigators noticed that mouse mammary explants, like mammary epithelium *in situ,* contained pale or light-staining cells and that it was only these cells that entered mitosis when mammary explants were cultured.

Chepko and Smith[32] analyzed light cells in the electron microscope using their ultrastructural features to distinguish them from other mammary epithelial cells. The following basic features expected of stem cells were applied in the ultrastructural evaluation: division-competence (presence of mitotic chromosomes) and an undifferentiated cytology (Fig. 25–2). Figure 25–1 shows the side-by-side appearance of an undifferentiated large light cell (ULLC) and a small undifferentiated light cell (SLC) in a secretory acinus of a lactating rat mammary gland. The pale-staining (stem) cells are of distinctive morphology; therefore, their appearance in side-by-side pairs or in one-above-the-other pairs (relative to the basement membrane) was interpreted as the result of a recent symmetric mitosis. In addition to pairs, other informative images would be of juxtaposed cells that were morphologically intermediate between a primitive and differentiated morphology based on the number, type, and development of cytoplasmic organelles. Cells were evaluated for cytologic differentiation with respect to their organelle content and distribution (e.g., cells differentiated toward a secretory function might contain specific secretory products, such as milk protein granules or micelles, which have been ultrastructurally and immunologically defined).[33] In addition the presence and number of intracellular lipid droplets, the extent and distribution of Golgi vesicles and rough endoplasmic reticulum (RER) attest to the degree of functional secretory differentiation of a mammary epithelial cell. These features are characteristically well developed in the luminal cells of active lactating mammary gland. Myoepithelial cells are flattened, elongated cells located at the basal surface of the epithelium, and their prominent cytoplasmic feature is the presence of many myofibrils and the absence of RER or lipid droplets.

In a retrospective analysis of light and electron micrographs, a careful and detailed scrutiny of mammary tissue was performed to determine the range of morphologic features among the cell types that had previously been reported. The samples evaluated included mouse mammary explants; pregnant and lactating mouse mammary glands; and rat mammary gland from 17 stages of development beginning with nulliparous through pregnancy, lactation, and involution.[32,34–36] From this analysis, we were able to expand the number of cell types in the epithelium from two: secretory (or luminal) and myoepithelial cells to five distinguishable structural phenotypes or morphotypes. Our observations strengthened the conclusion that the undifferentiated (light) cells are the only cell type to enter mitosis. The undifferentiated cells were found in two easily recognized forms: small (~8 microns) and large (15 to 20 microns). Mitotic chromosomes were never found within the differentiated cells, namely secretory and myoepithelial cells, suggesting that they were terminally differentiated and out of the cell cycle. Using all of the preceding features we were able to develop a more detailed description of the epithelial subtypes that make up the mammary epithelium.

The characteristics used to develop a standardized description of five mammary epithelial cellular morphotypes were staining of nuclear and cytoplasmic matrix, cell size, cell shape, nuclear morphology, amount and size of cytoplasmic organelles, location within the epithelium, cell number, and grouping relative to each other and to other morphotypes. These characteristics were used to perform differential cell counts and morphometric analysis of the cell populations in rat mammary epithelium.[32] Figure 25–3 presents an illustration of each mammary cell type and can be used on both the light and electron levels to help form a search image for recognizing them *in situ.* The five morphotypes we recognize in rodent mammary epithelium are a primitive SLC, ULLC, a very differentiated large light cell (DLLC), the classic cytologically

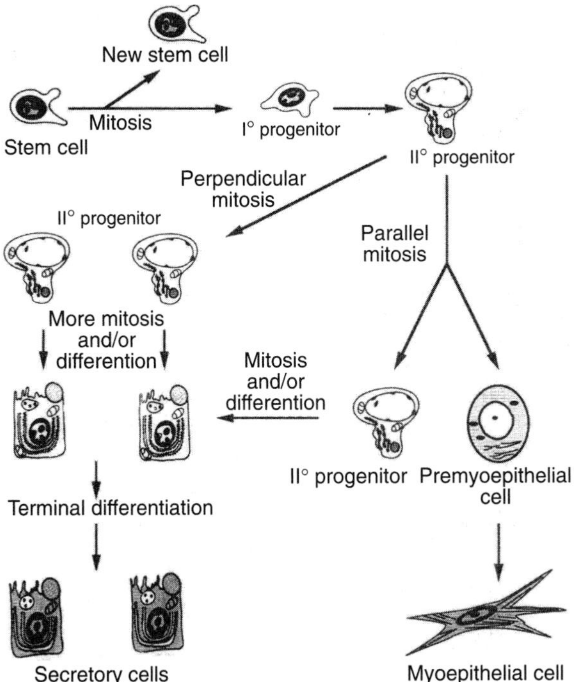

Figure 25–3. This illustration portrays the various morphologic forms that make up the fully differentiated murine mammary epithelium. It is not drawn to scale, instead it indicates our interpretation of the lineal relationships between the mammary stem cell at the top left, the lineage-limited progenitors I° and II° progenitors, and the fully differentiated secretory and myoepithelial cells.

differentiated luminal cell (LDC), and the myoepithelial cell. We described three sets of division-competent cells in rodent mammary epithelium, and demonstrated that mammary epithelial stem cells and their downstream progenitors are morphologically much less differentiated than either the secretory or the myoepithelial cells. We counted a total of 3552 cells through 17 stages of rat mammary gland development and calculated the percent of each morphotype. This analysis showed that the population density (number of cells/mm^2) of SLCs among mammary epithelium did not change from puberty through postlactation involution. The proportion of SLCs remained at 3%. This means that although the number of mammary epithelial cells increased by 27-fold during pregnancy in the mouse,[24,37] the percent of SLCs in the population does not change. Therefore, SLC increase and decrease in absolute number at the same relative rate as the differentiating epithelial cells.

If these undifferentiated epithelial cells represent structures essential for self-renewal and stem cell function, they would be rare or absent in growth and regeneration senescent populations. In support of this conclusion, neither SLCs nor ULLCs were observed in an extensive study of growth senescent mouse mammary transplants. Examination of growth competent implants in the same host reveals easily detectable SLCs and ULLCs.[38] Furthermore, immortal premalignant mammary outgrowths, which never show a growth senescent phenotype on serial transplantation, persistently contain both SLCs and ULLCs. These observations lend additional support to the conclusion that both SLCs and ULLCs represent important components in the mechanism for mammary epithelial stem cell maintenance and self-renewal *in situ.*

Gudjonnson *et al.*[39] predicted that if human mammary epithelium contained cells similar to the SLCs and ULLCs described in rodents that these cells would be low or negative for the luminal surface marker, sialomucin (MUC-1), because they do not commonly contact the luminal surface. Coincidentally, such cells would be positive for epithelial specific antigen (ESA) but negative for the basal myoepithelial cell marker, smooth muscle actin (SMA). Using this approach, they isolated two luminal epithelial cell populations. One, the major population, co-expressed MUC-1 and ESA. The other, a minor population, was found in a suprabasal location *in vivo* and expressed ESA but not MUC-1 or SMA. These latter cells were multipotent and formed elaborate branching structures, composed of both luminal and myoepithelial lineages, both *in vitro* and *in vivo.* The outgrowths that were produced resembled terminal duct lobular units both by morphology and marker expression. These data provide strong evidence for the presence of mammary epithelial stem cells in the human breast with characteristics similar, if not identical, to those described previously for rodent mammary gland.

At present there are no specific cellular markers that identify the "stemness" of any particular mammary epithelial cell. Several features known to define stem cells in other organs have been applied to the mammary gland. For example, the property of retaining DNA synthesis incorporated label over a long chase following labeling (i.e., long label-retaining cells in 3H-thymidine or 5-bromo-2′-deoxyuridine [5BrdU] pulsed mammary tissue). Mammary cells in the mouse with this property have been identified and were found scattered along the mammary ducts. Estrogen receptor (ER) immunostaining suggests that these cells are often ER positive.[40] These authors made no further characterization of these cells.

In a recent attempt to further characterize label-retaining cells (LRCs) in the mouse mammary gland, specific cellular markers were applied to mammary cells pulsed for 14 days *in vivo* with BrdU and chased for 9 weeks.[41] Two characteristics, efficient efflux of Hoechst dye (SP) and the presence of stem cell antigen-1 (Sca-1) known to associate with stem cells in other organ systems were used to enrich for putative mammary epithelial stem cells by FACS. Isolation of mammary cells with these properties revealed the following. LRCs isolated from primary cultures were enriched for Sca-1 expression and SP dye-effluxing properties. *In situ,* LRCs represent 3 to 5% of the population after 9 weeks, in good agreement with the number of SLCs.[32] In addition, the SP mammary cells, which showed increased clonogenic activity *in vivo,* possessed a frequency and size distribution that was very similar to SLCs. The Sca-1 positive mammary cells showed a greater regenerative potential in cleared fat pads than similar numbers of Sca-1 negative cells. This study represents a first important step toward prospectively isolating mammary epithelial progenitors and may permit the identification of additional markers useful in determining the biologic potential of mammary stem cells. Side population (SP) cells have been detected by FACS in human breast epithelium, but further characterization is lacking.

In the small intestine, the interfollicular integument and in hair follicles, evidence has accumulated that strongly supports the existence of an " immortal strand" in somatic stem cells (i.e., during asymmetric division the stem cell retains its template DNA in a conservative manner). This feature protects the stem cell from genetic errors arising from DNA replication. Direct evidence demonstrates that this phenomenon occurs in the ultimate stem cells of the crypts in the small intestine[42] and in tissue culture lines modified to undergo asymmetric divisions under specified culture conditions.[10] Whether this template strand conservation occurs in mammary stem cells has not been determined. Nevertheless, the stability of the pattern of proviral insertions in serial transplants of retroviral-infected, clonal-dominant mammary epithelial outgrowths argues that this may be the case. New proviral insertions occur during DNA synthesis in the cell cycle of chronically infected cells. Therefore, in cells replicating exponentially as opposed to asymmetrically, new proviral insertions would be common in the renewing population and they are not.[43] Evidence for active MMTV replication in these mammary populations is provided by the demonstration of easily detectable unintegrated proviral DNA by Southern analysis.[24]

Mammary Stem Cells in Carcinogenesis

Contiguous portions of the human mammary gland possess the identical pattern of X-chromosome inactivation. Thus, local portions of the gland are derived from a single antecedent.[44] In a further study of human mammary tissue this same group[45] showed that mammary cancer *in situ* and the apparently normal tissue surrounding the lesion shared similar genetic alterations. This was interpreted to indicate that mammary lesions arise as a result of the clonal expansion of previously affected epithelium subsequent to further genetic change. The results imply that local genetically damaged mammary stem cells may give rise to premalignant lesions, which may progress to frank malignancy. Studies by several other laboratories[46–48] have confirmed and extended these observations, supporting the concept of clonal progression in the development of breast cancer in humans. Therefore, it is conceivable that mammary hyperplasia and tumors develop locally from damaged clonogenic epithelial progenitors (stem cells). Using an immunologic rather than a genetic approach, Boecker *et al.*[49] reported a bipotent progenitor cell in normal breast tissue capable of giving rise to glandular and myoepithelial cell lineages, characterized by its expression of cytokeratin 5/6 (CK5/6). Subsequent analysis of benign usual ductal hyperplasia, atypical hyperplasia, and ductal cell carcinoma *in situ* by these authors led them to speculate that there was no obligate biologic continuum in the development of these three types of intraductal lesions of the breast. Instead they suggested that all three could arise independently and directly from the progeny of a committed stem (progenitor) mammary cell.

Experimental evidence from MMTV-induced mouse mammary hyperplasia and tumorigenesis (reviewed in reference 50) provides strong genetic support for the concept of clonal progression from normal through premalignant to malignant epithelium in the rodent mammary gland. In an effort to provide a proof of principle (i.e., mammary stem cells may contribute to mammary tumor development), mice exhibiting a mammary growth senescent phenotype in transplant experiments were challenged with the oncogenic retrovirus MMTV.[51] Only one tumor was induced by MMTV in these mice. On the other hand, more than half of their MMTV-infected wild-type female littermates developed mammary tumors. The result indicates that premature regenerative senescence in mammary epithelial stem cells can reduce the subsequent risk for mammary tumorigenesis in MMTV-challenged mice.

Previous experimentation with retrovirus-marked (MMTV) clonal-dominant mammary populations demonstrated that an entire functional mammary glandular outgrowth might comprise the progeny of a single antecedent.[24] These populations have been serially transplanted to study the properties of aging, self-renewing, mammary clonogens derived from the original progenitor. Premalignant, malignant, and metastatic clones arose from these transplants during passage. All of these bore a lineal relationship with the original antecedent because all of the original proviral insertions were represented in each of these lesions.[43] Although this does not prove that mammary stem cell may directly give rise to cancerous lesions within the mammary gland, it demonstrates that normal, premalignant, and malignant progeny are all within the repertoire of an individual mammary cell.

Pregnancy and Breast Cancer Risk

In mice, rats, and humans a single early pregnancy provides a significant lifelong reduction in mammary cancer risk. In rats and mice, the protective effect of pregnancy can be mimicked through hormonal application in the absence of pregnancy. This refractoriness to chemical induction of mammary tumorigenesis has recently been linked to the absence of a proliferative response in the parous epithelium when confronted with the carcinogen as compared with the nulliparous gland.[52,53] Concomitant with the reduction in proliferative response is the appearance of stable activation of p53 in epithelial cell nuclei. This suggests that in response to the hormonal stimulation of pregnancy that a new cellular population is created with an altered response to carcinogen exposure. A new parity-induced mammary epithelial cell population was discovered[54] using a conditionally activated Cre/lox recombinase/ LacZ system to identify mammary cells *in situ,* which had differentiated during pregnancy and survived post lactation involution. Transplantation studies indicate that the surviving, LacZ-positive, parity-specific epithelial cells have the capacity for self-renewal and contribute extensively to regeneration of mammary glands in cleared fat pads. This population accumulates in parous females on successive pregnancies. *In situ,* these cells are committed to secretory cell fate and proliferate extensively during the formation of secretory lobule development on successive pregnancies. In this process both secretory and myoepithelial cell lineages arise from the LacZ positive survivors (Fig. 25–4) and ER-positive and progesterone receptor (PR) positive epithelial progeny (manuscript in progress). Transplantation of dispersed cells indicates that this population is preferentially included in growth competent mammary cell reassembly and has an individual capacity to undergo at least eight cell doublings. Studies are in progress to isolate and characterize these cells and to determine their contribution to the refractoriness of parous mammary tissue to cancer development.

Future Prospects

The existence of epithelial stem cells in the mammary glands of rodents and humans has been established. Much remains to be learned about the mechanism(s) involved in the maintenance of these cells *in situ* and the signals that govern their behavior. A number of candidate genes, which may play a role in mammary stem cell biology, have appeared during the study of mammary gland growth and development in

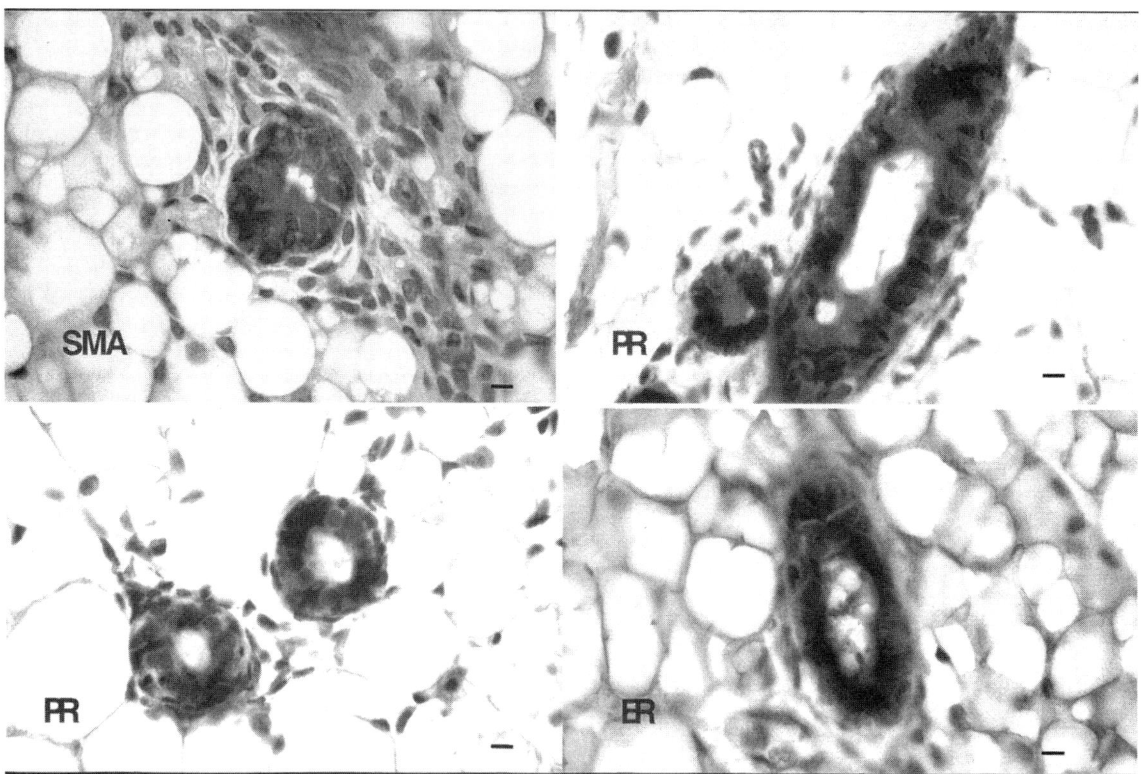

Figure 25–4. All panels contain mammary epithelium from an 8-day pregnant primiparous mouse mammary gland after detection of β-galactosidase by the X-gal reaction (blue). The presence of β-galactosidase expression indicates that that cell arose from a mother whose β-gal gene was conditionally activated during the first pregnancy. Immunologic staining for smooth muscle actin (SMA), a myoepithelial cell marker; progesterone receptor (PR); and estrogen receptor (ER) demonstrate that parity-specific, WAP-Cre-activated mammary epithelial cells may give rise to of various mammary cell lineages.

transgenic and gene deletion models. However, none of these genes has been fully assessed under conditions where mammary stem cell function is required, namely during regeneration of the glandular epithelium. The MMTV-induced Notch4/Int3 mutation results in the unregulated constitutive signaling of the Notch intracellular domain in the affected epithelium, invariably leading to the development of mammary cancer. The presence of this mutation in mammary epithelium prevents the development of the secretory cell fate.[55] Transplantation of mammary epithelium containing MMTV-Notch4/Int3 into cleared fat pads routinely fails to result in growth. Hormonal stimulation with estrogen and progesterone rescues ductal growth and development in these implants but not secretory cell fate. These results imply that Notch signaling is essential in regulating mammary stem cell function. Expression of a Notch4/Int3 transgene lacking the CBF-1 (mammalian homologue of Suppressor of Hairless) binding domain and the ability to affect the cascade of genes effected by Hairy Enhancer of Split (HES), in mammary gland does not block secretory development or ductal growth in transplants (R. Callahan, personal communication). This result implicates Notch signaling through HES in mammary cell fate decisions.

The vast array of genetic models and manipulations developed in the mouse has yet to be fully used in the dissection of stem cell biology in the mammary gland or for that matter in a number of other organ systems. This will change with the increased awareness of multipotent cells in adult organs and mounting evidence for the importance of somatic cell signaling on stem cell behavior in tissue-specific stem cell niches.[56] The application of conditional gene deletion or expression in stem cell populations in the epidermis provides an excellent example of this approach.[57] Here conditional activation of myc, even transiently, in epidermal stem cells commits them to the production of sebaceous epithelial progeny at the expense hair follicle progeny. In the mammary gland, only indirect evidence supports the possible role of somatic cell control of stem cell behavior for mammary tumor induction by MMTV.[51] Modulation of stem cell behavior holds exceptional promise of a new prophylactic approach for controlling mammary cancer risk. An important step toward the achievement of this control will be the characterization of the stem cell niche in the rodent mammary gland and ultimately in humans.

REFERENCES

1. Lyons, W.R. (1958). Hormonal synergism in mammary growth. *Proc. Royal Soc. Lond.* **149,** 303–325.
2. DeOme, K.B., Fauklin, L.J., Bern, H.A., and Blair, P.B. (1959). Development of mammary tumors from hyperplastic alveolar nodules transplanted into gland-free mammary fat pads of female C3H mice. *J. Natl. Cancer Inst.* **78,** 751–757.
3. Smith, G.H., and Medina, D. (1988). A morphologically distinct candidate for an epithelial stem cell in mouse mammary gland. *J. Cell Sci.* **90,** 173–183.
4. Daniel, C., DeOme, K., Young, L., Blair, P., and Faulkin, L. (1968). The in vivo life span of normal and preneoplastic mouse mammary glands: a serial transplantation study. *Proc. Natl. Acad. Sci. U. S. A.* **61,** 53–60.
5. Daniel, C.W., and Young, L.J. (1971). Influence of cell division on an aging process. Life span of mouse mammary epithelium during serial propagation in vivo. *Exp. Cell Res.* **65,** 27–32.
6. Daniel, C.W., Young, L.J., Medina, D., and DeOme, K.B. (1971). The influence of mammogenic hormones on serially transplanted mouse mammary gland. *Exp. Gerontol.* **6,** 95–101.
7. Young, L.J., Medina, D., DeOme, K.B., and Daniel, C.W. (1971). The influence of host and tissue age on life span and growth rate of serially transplanted mouse mammary gland. *Exp. Gerontol.* **6,** 49–56.
8. Daniel, C.W., Aidells, B.D., Medina, D., and Faulkin, L.J., Jr. (1975). Unlimited division potential of precancerous mouse mammary cells after spontaneous or carcinogen-induced transformation. *Fed. Proc.* **34,** 64–67.
9. Medina, D., Kittrell, F.S., Shepard, A., Stephens, L.C., Jiang, C., Lu, J., Allred, D.C., McCarthy, M., and Ullrich, R.L. (2002). Biological and genetic properties of the p53 null preneoplastic mammary epithelium. *FASEB. J.* **16,** 881–883.
10. Merok, J.R., Lansita, J.A., Tunstead, J.R., and Sherley, J.L. (2002). Cosegregation of chromosomes containing immortal DNA strands in cells that cycle with asymmetric stem cell kinetics. *Cancer Res.* **62,** 6791–6795.
11. Welsch, C.W., O'Connor, D.H., Aylsworth, C.F., and Sheffield, L.G. (1987). Normal but not carcinomatous primary rat mammary epithelium: readily transplanted to and maintained in the athymic nude mouse. *J. Natl. Cancer Inst.* **78,** 557–565.
12. Sheffield, L.G., and Welsch, C.W. (1988). Transplantation of human breast epithelia to mammary-gland-free fat- pads of athymic nude mice: influence of mammotrophic hormones on growth of breast epithelia. *Int. J. Cancer* **41,** 713–719.
13. Anderson, E., Clarke, R.B., and Howell, A. (1998). Estrogen responsiveness and control of normal breast proliferation. *J. Mammary Gland Biol. Neoplasia* **3,** 23–35.
14. Daniel, C.W., and DeOme, K.B. (1965). Growth of mouse mammary gland in vivo after monolayer culture. *Science* **149,** 634–636.
15. DeOme, K.B., Miyamoto, M.J., Osborn, R.C., Guzman, R.C., and Lum, K. (1978). Effect of parity on recovery of inapparent nodule-transformed mammary gland cells in vivo. *Cancer Res.* **38,** 4050–4053.
16. DeOme, K.B., Miyamoto, M.J., Osborn, R.C., Guzman, R.C., and Lum, K. (1978). Detection of inapparent nodule-transformed cells in the mammary gland tissues of virgin female BALB/cfC3H mice. *Cancer Res.* **38,** 2103–2111.
17. Medina, D., Oborn, C.J., Kittrell, F.S., and Ullrich, R.L. (1986). Properties of mouse mammary epithelial cell lines characterized by in vivo transplantation and in vitro immunocytochemical methods. *J. Natl. Cancer Inst.* **76,** 1143–1156.
18. Ehmann, U.K., Guzman, R.C., Osborn, R.C., Young, J.T., Cardiff, R.D., and Nandi, S. (1987). Cultured mouse mammary epithelial cells: normal phenotype after implantation. *J. Natl. Cancer Inst.* **78,** 751–757.
19. Kittrell, F.S., Oborn, C.J., and Medina, D. (1992). Development of mammary preneoplasias in vivo from mouse mammary epithelial cell lines in vitro. *Cancer Res.* **52,** 1924–1932.
20. Medina, D., and Kittrell, F.S. (1993). Immortalization phenotype dissociated from the preneoplastic phenotype in mouse mammary epithelial outgrowths in vivo. *Carcinogenesis* **14,** 25–28.

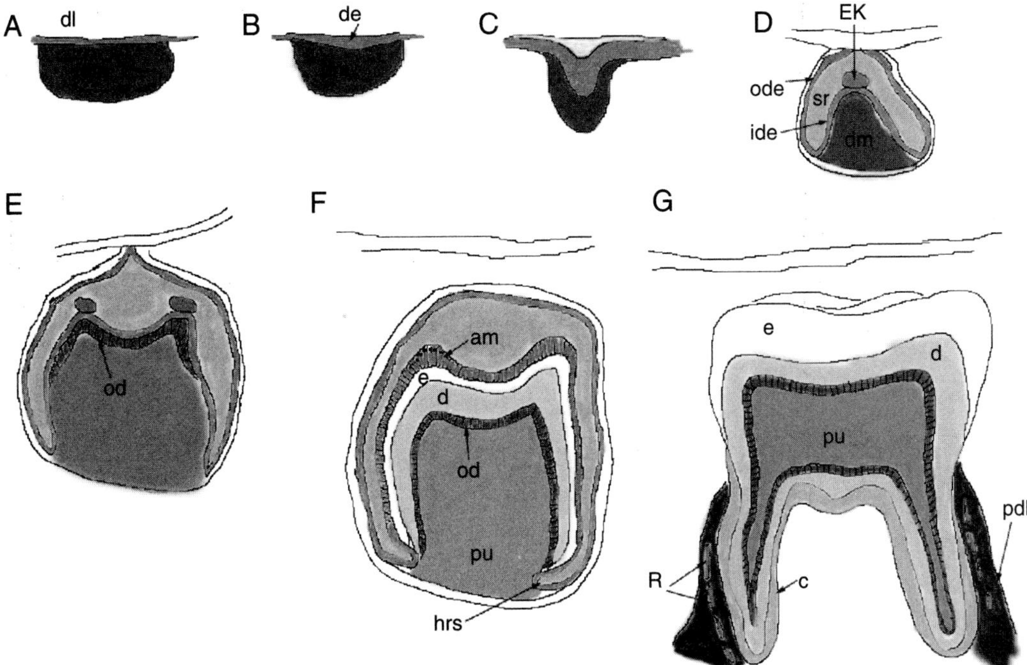

Figure 26–2. *Morphologic stages of tooth development.* (A) Oral epithelium and mesenchyme. (B) Dental epithelial thickening. (C) Bud stage, dental invagination into dental mesenchyme (D) cap stage, dental proliferation, dental mesenchyme condensation and formation of enamel knot. (E) Bell stage tooth, exhibiting cytodifferentiation of odontoblasts. (F) Late bell stage tooth, exhibiting cytodifferentiation of both odontoblasts and ameloblasts. (G) Unerupted molar tooth. am, ameloblasts; c, cementum; cl, cervical loop; de, dental epithelium; dl, dental lamina; dm, dental mesenchyme; EK, enamel knot; hrs, Hertwig's root sheath; od, odontoblasts; oe, oral epithelium; pdl, periodontal ligament; pu, pulp; R, rests of Malassez; sr, stellate reticulum.

condensing mesenchyme, forming the cervical loop structures (Fig. 26–2 E and F). In molar teeth, secondary enamel knots form at positions of future molar tooth cusps, expressing many, but not all, of the genes expressed in primary enamel knots.[29,30]

In bell stage teeth, so named for their characteristic bell-shaped appearance, distinct dental epithelial and mesenchymal cell populations become evident as cells of the enamel organ and pulp organ differentiate (Fig. 26–2 E and F). Stellate reticulum, consisting of epithelial cells with distinctive star-shaped morphology, is now recognizable between the outer dental epithelium (ODE) and inner dental epithelium (IDE) and the stratum intermedium is morphologically recognizable as a cell layer directly effacing IDE (Fig. 26–2 E). At the forming tooth crown, mesenchymally derived dental papilla cells directly underlying the IDE layer are induced to form odontoblasts, which differentiate and begin to synthesize dentin (Fig. 26–2 E and F). By late bell stage, odontoblasts induce ameloblast formation in the adjacent inner enamel epithelium, and the ameloblasts differentiate and begin to synthesize enamel (Fig. 26–2 F). Enamel synthesis is dependent on the prior synthesis of dentin, reflecting inductive interactions between differentiated odontoblasts and ameloblasts. Also at the bell stage, the dental lamina connecting the tooth germ to the oral epithelium disappears, isolating the tooth from the oral cavity.

Following crown formation, root formation begins at the apical end of the tooth, where inner epithelial cells of the Hertwig's epithelial root sheath (hrs) induce the formation of odontoblasts, which secrete the dentin of the root (Fig. 26–2 F). Odontoblast differentiation proceeds from the root toward the crown as root dentin forms. The root sheath becomes stretched as the tooth root grows, eventually fragmenting into clusters of epithelial cells termed the rests of Malassez, which persist in human adult teeth within the periodontal ligament. Cementum is synthesized by cementoblasts present in mesenchymal tissue adjacent to the root dentin and embeds forming periodontal ligament fibers. Root formation signals tooth eruption, as the tooth becomes fully functional.

The molecular signals regulating tooth development have been revealed by analysis of gene expression patterns in the dental epithelium and mesenchyme of developing teeth.[21,22,28,31,32] Furthermore, analyses of tooth development in transgenic mice with targeted deletions of individual genes including growth factor family members, their receptors, and downstream transcription factors have revealed functional gene requirements at distinct stages of tooth development.[21] Despite these advances, a number of significant questions remain about the manner in which teeth develop including the following: How are gene expression patterns regulated to direct the formation of teeth of particular size and shape? How are individual tooth types patterned and coordinated such that maxillary and mandibular teeth accurately occlude? What tissues contribute to developing teeth and when are tooth fated tissues committed to tooth fates? Why are humans limited to only two sets of teeth? What adult tissues can be used to regenerate teeth?

Early Tooth Regeneration Efforts

Efforts to regenerate teeth have been ongoing for more than a century.[33,34] Early experiments analyzed the growth of early tooth germs in *in vitro* organ cultures,[35–37] in subcutaneous transplants *in vivo,*[10,38] in intraocular sites,[39,40] using chick chorioallantois explants,[41–43] and using combinations of these techniques. Experiments implanting immature tooth buds into the abdomens of dogs demonstrated that when both dental epithelial and mesenchymal cells were transplanted, mature tooth structures formed.[44] Dental tissue explant recombination studies performed *in vitro* using the Trowell method[45] among others were used to reveal the inductive potential of developing dental epithelial and mesenchymal tissues.[23,40,46–48] The importance of the dental epithelium in initiating tooth development and of the dental papilla in instructing tooth shape was demonstrated in recombination experiments of enzymatically separated dental epithelium and dental papilla.[49] Although these efforts allowed for the continuous monitoring of developing tooth structures, most *in vitro* cultured teeth failed to calcify, with only a few investigators successfully generating mineralized dentin and enamel tissues *in vitro.*[50]

Tooth "replantation," the replacement of an avulsed tooth back into the same location from which it was lost, and "intentional replantation," the removal of a tooth from one location and replantation at another location, have successfully been performed in a variety of animal model systems, and in humans. These studies demonstrated the importance of tooth root structures for tooth survival, by revealing that teeth with partially formed roots could be replanted immediately, whereas those lacking root structures must first undergo root canal treatment before reinsertion.[51–53] Although useful on occasion, this method does not result in a net gain in tooth number, and heterotypic tooth replacements, from one individual to another, do not exhibit widespread utility because of donor–host incompatibility and immune rejection.

Characterizing Dental Stem Cell (DSC) Populations

An ideal replacement tooth therapy would use DSCs isolated from an individual to generate his or her replacement teeth as needed. DSCs are an elusive population of self-renewing cells with potential utility in generating biologic replacement teeth in humans. Because tooth development is dependent on epithelial–mesenchymal cell interactions, DSCs necessarily consist of two types: epithelial stem cells, which contribute to dental epithelial structures including outer and inner dental epithelial cell layers, stellate reticulum, stratum intermedium, ameloblasts and enamel; and dental mesenchymal cells, which contribute to mesenchymally derived tooth structures including the dental papilla, dental sac, odontoblasts, predentin, dentin, cementum, periodontal ligament, and alveolar bone.[8]

As for any type of stem cell, DSCs are defined as slowly dividing populations of cells that give rise to additional DSCs and to daughter cell populations that give rise to "transit" cells that are not self-maintaining but that differentiate into mature tooth structures.[54] Other features thought to be shared by stem cells include location deep in tissues out of the general cell flow; slow cell cycling times, including long G_0 cycle; small size and scarcity of organelles; the ability to function in tissue regeneration after injury; and their maintenance in the body throughout life.[55] Adult stem cells are located in an exclusive environment, termed a "stem cell niche,"[56–58] which "allows the stem cells to function: it houses the stem cells, allows for self-renewal of the stem cells, and is instructive in the generation of the differentiated progeny."[59]

For over a century, animal model systems have been used to study tooth development and to reveal properties of DSCs including the location of their niche, their characteristics, and their behaviors. Rodents, including mice and rats, exhibit continuous incisor development, whereas others, including the vole, guinea pig, and rabbit, exhibit continuous incisor and molar development. The variety of animal models and experimental techniques used to study tooth development have resulted in a significant body of knowledge of DSCs. The availability of diverse tooth developmental model systems provides the opportunity to examine natural variations in tooth development, which may be exploited in human tooth regeneration efforts. The characteristics of DSCs are currently being explored using both traditional and new animal models including the zebrafish, *Danio rerio,* and using state-of-the-art tooth tissue engineering methods. An overview of past and present characterizations of dental applications are presented in the following sections.

Characterization of Epithelial DSC Populations

CONTINUOUSLY GROWING RODENT TOOTH MODELS

Rodent models have proven to be informative sources for studies of tooth development. Although mice and rats form only one set of teeth, the paired maxillary and mandibular incisors are hypselodont, or continuously growing, providing an opportunity to study the DSC populations contributing to continuously forming tooth structures. Developmental analyses of the rodent incisor have established that the dental epithelial stem cell niche is located at the apical end of the tooth, in the stellate reticulum, and that epithelial DSC progeny give rise to ameloblasts, which integrate, differentiate, and migrate in an apical to incisal direction as they produce enamel matrix proteins to form enamel (Fig. 26–3). Supporting evidence for this model has been growing since the time it was first proposed that the inner enamel epithelium (IEE) was derived from the outer enamel epithelium (OEE), in a model described as an "endless conveyor belt" around the cervical loop.[60] This model integrated cell proliferation in

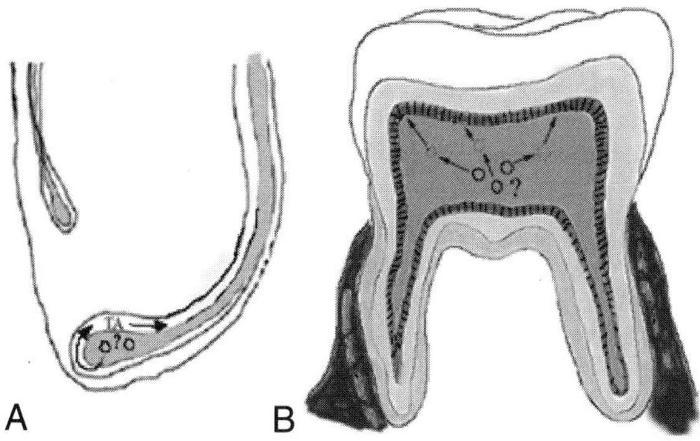

Figure 26–3. *Dental stem cells.* (A) Dental epithelial stem cell niche (black circles in gray stellate reticulum cell layer). (B) Dental mesenchymal stem cell niche (black solid circles in dental pulp, and TA cells, dotted circles). TA, transit amplifying cells.

the OEE layer with continuous cell migration toward the tooth cervical region of the tooth cusp in the IEE cell layer (Fig. 26–3).

In the rabbit, autoradiographic analyses concluded that the life cycle of cells at the apex of the cervical loop clearly distinguished them from ODE cells.[61] Similar interpretations were reached a number of decades later by scientists concluding that a "blast cell" population at the base of the ameloblast column preserved the physical position of the cells and served as the source of ameloblast progenitor cells proliferating at the base of the cervical loop and migrating in a coronal direction.[62–64] Additional study of rat incisors concluded that two discrete, slowly dividing cell populations present in the ODE and in the stellate reticulum likely represented discrete stem cell populations contributing to the IDE and to the stratum intermedium, respectively.[65]

Collectively, these studies concluded that the cervical loop area and in particular the stellate reticulum tissue located opposite the distal tip of the tooth is the likely site of the epithelial stem cell niche of the hypselodont rodent incisor.[66] Epithelial stem cells migrating from the stellate reticulum to the IDE contribute to a population of proliferating, transit amplifying (TA) cells of the ameloblast lineage, which continuously form and move toward the distal tip of the incisor as they differentiate and deposit enamel matrix proteins to replace enamel that has been worn away. The expression of fibroblast growth factor 10 (Fgf10) in the dental mesenchyme, together with Notch signaling in the adjacent dental epithelium, is thought to support the epithelial stem cell niche.[67]

CONTINUOUSLY GROWING GUINEA PIG MOLARS

The continuously growing molars of the guinea pig have effectively been used to identify progenitor cells contributing to molar tooth tissues. Cell migration analyses in the early 1960s concluded that epithelial cell migration proceeded from the stratum intermedium toward the lateral and superior borders of the stellate reticulum and that these cells ceased to divide once they became morphologically distinguishable as stellate reticulum.[68] More recently, tritiated thymidine incorporation into developing guinea pig second molars at 3 days of age was used to examine DSC populations revealing that (1) stem cells derived from the ODE near the cervical loop area differentiate into IDE cells or presecretory ameloblasts (also known as dividing transit cells), which subsequently differentiate into secretory ameloblasts or simple transit cells, and (2) ODE stem cells near the tooth crown differentiate into stratum intermedium cells (transit dividing cells), which in turn produce nondividing stratum intermedium and stellate reticulum cells (simple transit cells).[69]

CONTINUOUSLY ERUPTING INCISORS AND MOLARS OF THE VOLE

A recent report characterizing tooth development in the sibling vole *(Microtus rossiaemeridionalis)* compares and contrasts DSC populations contributing to continuously forming molars versus incisors and of the continuously forming vole molar to the terminally differentiated mouse molar.[59] Because tooth morphogenesis and gene expression patterns are virtually identical in the mouse and vole,[29] accurate comparison of stem cell populations contributing to the mouse molar, which stops growing, and the vole molar, which exhibits continuous growth, can be made.[59] These studies concluded that molar DSCs can adopt one of two fates: (1) they can remain as a self-renewing stem cell niche supporting continuous tooth crown formation as observed in the vole or (2) they can adopt a terminally differentiated tooth root fate, resulting in the irreversible elimination of the stem cell niche, and subsequent loss of ability to regenerate DSCs and/or dental tissues as is observed in the mouse molar tooth. The cells regulating either the continuous formation of crown structures, or the adoption of a tooth root fate, are located in the cervical loop region and, in particular, in stem cells present within the stellate reticulum and stratum intermedium.[59] Another noteworthy feature of the vole molar is the presence of three small restricted regions along the apex of the tooth, which lack both ameloblast and odontoblast cells. These structures, termed "root analogues," closely resemble structures present on the lingual side of the rat incisor, which similarly lack classical root structures but express cementum markers[70] and serve to anchor the tooth in place, as do classical root structures. Significantly, root analogues demonstrate that the adoption of a tooth root or crown fate can be determined locally within a single tooth.[59]

Gene expression studies of the continuously erupting vole molar suggest that mesenchymally expressed Fgf10 and Bmp4 and epithelially expressed Notch signaling are important in maintaining the dental epithelial stem cell niche, as previously demonstrated for the continuously growing mouse incisor.[66,67] The absence of Fgf10, Bmp4, and Notch expression in the hypsodont mouse molar, which exhibits arrested crown growth and the formation of roots, provides further support for this model. In conclusion, comparison of continuously forming vole molars to terminally differentiated mouse molars allows for the following model to be proposed. In mouse molars and in all human teeth, none of which exhibit continuous growth, the stellate reticulum containing the epithelial stem cell niche is lost after crown formation, and the remaining outer and inner enamel epithelial layers of tooth sheath epithelium, now devoid of epithelial stem cells, direct the formation of terminally differentiated tooth root structures.[59]

Characterization of Dental Mesenchymal Stem Cell Populations

In contrast to dental epithelial tissues, which are not capable of self-repair or renewal in human adult teeth, dental mesenchymal tissues do exhibit properties of self-renewal. Odontoblasts and cementoblasts are present in postnatal and adult teeth (whereas ameloblasts are not), and the formation of dentin by odontoblasts and of cementum by cementoblasts can occur in response to tooth injury or disease. The reasons why mesenchymal stem cell populations persist in adult teeth, while epithelial stem cell populations do not, are not understood at the present time.

POSTNATAL DENTAL PULP STEM CELLS (DPSCs)

The ability for dentin to self-repair after injury or disease has been studied extensively, and efforts to facilitate dentin repair are a major focus of tooth tissue bioengineering efforts (see later discussion). Almost 40 years ago, it was observed that [^{3}H] thymidine labeling of undifferentiated rat incisor pulp cells in contact with odontoblasts decreased as odontoblast labeling increased, suggesting that basal pulp cells were continuously incorporated into the odontoblast layer.[71] Later studies concluded that postmitotic odontoblasts formed reactionary dentin and that multipotential pulp cells differentiate into preodontoblasts to form reparative dentin as needed.[72–80]

Although the exact location of mesenchymal stem cell populations within the tooth pulp remains elusive, two sources of replacement odontoblasts have been suggested. The first is that a predetermined population of G_2 cell cycle–arrested odontoblast replacement cells exists,[81–83] and the second is that replacement odontoblasts are generated from undifferentiated pulp cells, likely the coronal pulp, which first dedifferentiate and then differentiate into odontoblasts.[78,80,84,85] The first theory is supported by studies demonstrating the lack of [^{3}H] thymidine incorporation into replacement odontoblasts after destruction of existing odontoblasts by tooth grinding,[71,86] interpreted to mean that predetermined, nondividing cells were able to form replacement odontoblasts likely from the cell-rich zone of the pulp.[87,88] The second theory is supported by the fact that replacement odontoblasts have been demonstrated to replicate and incorporate label.[80,85,89] A more recent study using radiolabeling techniques to monitor replacement odontoblast formation in primate teeth after pulp exposure concluded that the source of the replacement odontoblast cells was the pulp proper, deep to the wound site.[90] The fact that the number of labeled replacement odontoblasts increased over time suggested the existence of a continuous source of replacement odontoblasts, and the shift of labeled cell populations was consistent with an influx of cells from deep in the pulp to the periphery. The recently characterized transgenic mouse line exhibiting green fluorescent protein (GFP) expression directed by the collagen type I promoter in dental mesenchymal tissues, including odontoblasts, will likely facilitate identification of the odontoblast stem cell niche within the tooth pulp.[91]

It has been reported that dental pulp stem cells (DPSCs) isolated from postnatal tooth pulp tissue are capable of forming dentin.[92] Comparison of DPSCs to bone marrow stromal cells (BMSCs), known precursors of osteoblasts, demonstrated that, in tissue culture, DPSCs produced only sporadic calcified nodules and did not form adipocytes, whereas BMSCs formed uniform mineralized tissues and clustered adipocytes.[92] When transplanted subcutaneously in nude mice, DPSCs formed what appeared to be dentin lined with odontoblasts surrounding a pulp center, whereas BMSCs formed lamellar bone containing osteocytes and surface osteoblasts surrounding a narrow tissue consisting of fibrous vascular tissue exhibiting active hematopoiesis and adipocytes. Analysis of gene expression profiles by cDNA microarray techniques[93] demonstrated common expression levels for more than 4000 known human genes and distinct expression patterns for certain genes, which can be used to distinguish and further characterize these two discrete cell populations. Analysis of clonally derived DPSC lines suggests that these clones represent cells at different committed states of differentiation.[94]

PERIODONTAL STEM CELL POPULATIONS

Dental mesenchymal cell derived periodontal tissues include cementum, periodontal ligament (PDL), gingiva, and alveolar bone. For the past decade, periodontal tissue repair research has focused on (1) identification of the stem cells that contribute to the repair of periodontal tissues, (2) characterization of these cells undergoing active repair, and (3) ways in which the repair process can be manipulated by exogenous growth factor administration.[95] The ability for periodontal tissues, in particular the PDL, to exhibit regenerative properties has long been appreciated. The extremely short half-life of collagens in the PDL allows for rapid turnover and remodeling in this highly dynamic tissue.[96] Normally functioning periodontal tissues regenerate at a rate of 0.5 to 2%, a relatively rapid rate when compared with other soft tissues.[97] In response to wounding, the PDL increases its proliferation rate by fivefold, primarily from paravascular tissues located deep in the ligament.[98,99] The periodontal fibroblast lineage has been characterized as a steady-state system, similar to other renewal systems in which the generation of new cells is balanced by the number of cells lost to apoptosis and/or migration.[97,100] It has been determined that the PDL stem cell niche resides close to blood vessels and exhibits typical characteristics of stem cells including small size and slow cycling times.[97,99,101] Slowly dividing cell populations, located close to blood vessels (consistent with the presence of stem cells in paravascular zones), were identified in the PDL using [^{3}H] thymidine labeling.[101]

PDL progenitor cells are multipotential, exhibiting the ability to generate fibroblastic, osteogenic, or cementogenic cells, while maintaining the width of the PDL and the integrity of the periodontal space. Current thought is that periodontal tissue progenitor cells are either derived from a small population of multipotential stem cells, or from a number of populations of committed progenitor cells, that either are present at local sites or are derived systemically in response to the wound-healing process. Molecular and cellular analyses revealed that periodontal tissue regeneration closely mimics *de novo* periodontal tissue formation and identified a population of periodontal stem cells located close to the bone that are thought to generate osteoblasts, whereas tissue close to the cementum is thought to produce cementoblasts.[111] PDL regeneration studies suggest that a heterogeneous population of undifferentiated stem cells persists in the PDL space throughout life and is available to function in the coordinated repair of cementum, PDL, and alveolar bone regeneration in response to damage of disease, while maintaining the integrity and function of periodontal space.[102]

Although cementum appears morphologically similar to bone, culturing, expansion, and comparison of human cementum-derived cells (HCDCs) and human BMSCs demonstrates that each type of cell differentiates into morphologically distinct mineralized tissue types and exhibits distinct gene expression profiles.[103] Clusters of cells on the root surface, called rests of Malassez,[104,105] are responsible for primary cementogenesis and are thought to protect against root resorption. These cells initially disappear during hyalinization of the PDL[106] and later reappear in areas of root repair.[107] Cementum repair closely resembles early cementogenesis in developing teeth, suggesting that similar mechanisms are involved in both primary and repair processes.[108,109] Although it is generally agreed that fibroblast-like cementoblast cells actually repair the root, it remains unclear where these reparative cells reside in periods of inactivity. Analyses of cementum repair and regeneration in orthodontic root resorption lacunae, monitored using light, scanning, and transmission electron microscopic analyses,[110–112] demonstrate that the repair process is initiated by the attachment of connective tissue to exposed dentinal and cemental collagen, as mediated by the deposition of small amounts of fibrillar cementum. Two types of cells are present in resorption lacunae: multinucleated odontoclast-like cells with ruffled borders and clear zones indicating active resorption and mononucleated cementoblast/fibroblast-like cells rich in endoplasmic reticulum and dense bodies, indicating synthesis of collagen fibrillar material.[112] The presence of both odontoclast and cementoblast cells at the site was interpreted as indicating a transition from a process of active root resorption to one of repair.

Gingival fibroblasts consist of two cell populations: one of which exhibits limited proliferative potential and the other with extensive self-renewing capacity.[113] A comparison of cultured gingival and periodontal ligament tissues demonstrated significantly higher protein and collagen production in periodontal ligament cells as compared with gingival fibroblasts.[114]

TOOTH REGENERATION IN THE ZEBRA FISH

The small vertebrate zebra fish *Danio rerio,* which continuously regenerates teeth throughout its life, offers unique characteristics including molecular genetic studies of replacement tooth development that may facilitate human tooth tissue engineering efforts. Although zebra fish teeth are pharyngeal and do not form in the dentary, morphologic analyses of zebra fish tooth development demonstrate distinct similarities to mammalian tooth development.[115–117] Zebra fish teeth develop rapidly; primary tooth buds are present in 2-day-old embryos, and, by 5 days, three functional teeth are present on each of two bilateral supporting ceratobranchial 5 (cb5) arch cartilages (Fig. 26–4 A).[118,119] By 1 month a full complement of 11 teeth plus continuously forming replacement teeth are present on each bilateral cb5 arch, consisting of five ventral, four mediodorsal, and two dorsal teeth (Fig. 26–4 A and B). Each tooth exhibits distinct dorsoventral, mediolateral, mesial/buccal patterning and distinct size and shape, as do teeth of higher vertebrates, and zebra fish teeth are cusped, suggesting the presence of enamel knot signaling centers.[22,120] Although zebra fish teeth are smaller in size and fewer in number than those of higher vertebrates, similar embryologic patterning events govern the formation of teeth in both species.[117]

Similar to human secondary tooth development, zebra fish replacement teeth form as an epithelial thickening and invagination off of the outer enamel epithelium of a predecessor tooth that is destined to be shed (Fig. 26–4 C and D). The forming replacement tooth bud undergoes distinct bud, cap, bell, and differentiation stages, similar to mammalian tooth development. Once a replacement tooth has formed, the older tooth is shed and the replacement tooth becomes functional by attaching to the cb5 arch.[121] Preliminary gene expression studies suggest that similar molecular cues, including Bmp, Fgf, Wnt, and Shh family members, regulate both mammalian and zebra fish tooth development. To date, Bmp ligands, receptors, and downstream signaling partners have been implicated in zebra fish tooth development.[116,117]

The ability to use forward genetic approaches to identify genes regulating tooth development is a distinct advantage of the zebra fish model. Chemical and insertional mutagenesis screens have been successfully used in zebra fish to reveal gene requirements for a variety of early developmental processes.[122–124] Forward genetic mutagenesis screens for primary and replacement tooth formation, currently being performed, will undoubtedly produce zebra fish tooth mutants that will advance our understanding of functional roles for tooth expressed genes and, in particular, gene cascades regulating replacement tooth formation.

Therapeutic Strategies for Dental Tissue Regeneration

Decades of research on tooth development leaves us poised to use the accumulated body of knowledge to implement therapeutic strategies to extend the lives and functions of natural teeth. Already, therapies to facilitate the repair of dentin and periodontal tissues including cementum, PDL, and alveolar bone have been demonstrated.[12] Recent advances in the characterization of epithelial DSCs are also likely to facilitate effective repair therapies for enamel tissue, which normally

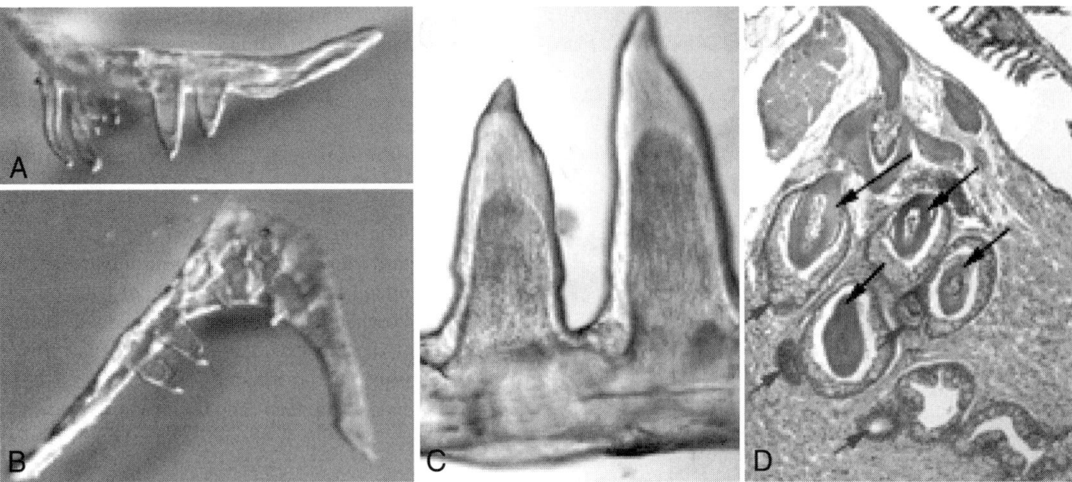

Figure 26–4. *Continuous tooth regeneration in adult zebra fish.* (A) Adult pharyngeal teeth and cb5 arch, lateral view, and buccal view (B). (C) Lateral view of two adult ventral teeth. (D) Transverse section demonstrates adult teeth (large arrows) and replacement tooth buds (small arrows).

exhibits no reparative capacity.[125] Current therapeutic techniques for direct gene delivery of growth factor proteins and for tissue-mediated gene product delivery offer potential utility in dental tissue engineering efforts.[86,126–132] In addition, state-of-the-art tissue engineering techniques[133] to expand autologous dental tissue grafts *in vitro,* to use the cells to seed three-dimensional biodegradable scaffolds, and then to implant the cell-seeded scaffolds back into individuals are under intense investigation. Recent success in whole-tooth tissue engineering efforts suggest that, in the foreseeable future, tissue engineered biologic replacement tooth therapies will be available to replace teeth that were not salvageable by more conventional methods, and to provide teeth for those individuals born without.[125]

REPARATIVE DENTIN

Dentin repair therapies are rapidly advancing. The ability for cultured gingival and dental pulp cells (seeded onto scaffolds and implanted subcutaneously in nude mice) to differentiate and express extracellular matrix proteins demonstrates promise for this method in dental tissue regeneration therapies.[134]

PERIODONTAL TISSUE REGENERATION

The inability to unequivocally identify periodontal tissue stem cells or to determine whether they originate from a common precursor or from individual progenitors have thwarted efforts to achieve consistent and predictable therapeutic regeneration results.[135] The wide prevalence of periodontal disease, the limited regenerative activity exhibited by the PDL, and the critical role of the PDL in maintaining tooth health and function has made PDL tissue engineering an extremely active area of research.[136,137] Periodontal tissues exhibit a remarkable ability to maintain discrete cellular compartments such as the width of the PDL, and in particular, the preservation of the hard and soft tissue boundaries of the periodontal space, while exhibiting rapid remodeling abilities.[138] The failure to maintain homeostasis of periodontal tissues results in tooth ankylosis in which the tooth root fuses with the surrounding alveolar bone, resulting in tooth damage and eventual root resorption.

Periodontal therapies seek to restore the fibrous attachments of the tooth and lost alveolar bone. The promising use of exogenous growth factors and biomolecules to facilitate the regenerative process and the use of guided tissue regeneration (GTR) methods, based on the principle of selective repopulation of debrided root surfaces by cells exhibiting the potential to reform original tissue architecture,[139] are likely to result in reproducible therapies that exhibit predictable outcomes. Guided tissue methods have been successfully used to regenerate periodontal tissues, using Millipore filters to prevent gingival epithelial and connective tissue growth into the periodontal space,[137] among other methods.[140–143] More recently, the demonstration that pulpal and gingival fibroblasts can survive, proliferate, and synthesize and secrete extracellular matrix proteins when seeded onto biodegradable scaffolds first grown *in vitro* and then transplanted into dermal pouches for 3 weeks, is a promising step toward therapeutic delivery of restorative tissues.[134] The use of polypeptide growth factors to facilitate periodontal tissue regeneration has produced promising results. Periodontal regeneration in response to application of platelet-derived growth factor (PDGF) and insulin-like growth factor (IGF) in beagles[126] and in monkeys[144,145] has been reported. Studies in human periodontal tissue regeneration using osteogenin (Bmp3) demonstrated enhanced regeneration,[146] whereas both Bmp2 and osteogenin enhanced periodontal regeneration in beagles and in baboons.[147,148]

The demonstrated ability for gingival and pulp fibroblasts to respond to Bmp administration by forming distinct tissues, bone and reparative dentin, respectively, demonstrates that these cells exhibit distinct therapeutic applications.[134] Efforts to identify growth factors that stimulate PDL growth and differentiation suggest that Bmps, in particular, have demonstrated utility in periodontal ligament regeneration efforts. Animal studies show that a single dose of recombinant human Bmp2 or Bmp7 can increase the rate of bone formation and enhance cementum formation during periodontal wound healing.[149,150] Research efforts have also clarified criteria to consider when assessing the efficacy of growth factor therapies in periodontal regeneration efforts including: the condition of the root and size of the periodontal defect; the balance of oral bacteria in the individual; the manner in which applied pressure to the tooth affects the repair therapy; and the delivery method, concentrations, and dosage regiments used to administer the growth factors.

As PDL regeneration research nears clinical trials, the following areas appear particularly promising. The utility of Bmp2 in cementum regeneration is supported by the successful use of recombinant human Bmp2 in submerged periodontal wound healing in dogs and rodents,[149] and rhBmp7 has exhibited promise in healing nonsubmerged periodontal defects in dogs and baboons.[132,147,148,151] A potential complication of Bmp therapies for root repair is the obliteration of the PDL space and subsequent ankylosis of the tooth,[112] although many reports find no correlation between Bmp therapies and ankylosis.[132,147,148,152–154] The role of masticatory function and PDL/cementum repair remains unclear, although a number of reports suggest that masticatory function stimulates the repair process and helps to resolve transient ankylosis.[155]

ALVEOLAR BONE REPAIR

Although the empty socket left after tooth extraction becomes rapidly filled with bone producing PDL fibroblasts,[156] over time a common effect of tooth loss is a reduction in both the height and width of the supporting alveolar bone. A 25% alveolar bone loss during the first year and a 40 to 60% reduction in alveolar bone width within the first 3 years has been reported.[157] Reduced alveolar bone provides inadequate support for prosthetic tooth implants and contributes to a high implant failure rate. Rebuilding alveolar bone using techniques such as bone allografts and alloplasts,[158] the use of osteoconducting and osteoinductive bioactive glasses,[159] and combination therapeutic approaches to preserve the edentulous ridge have exhibited only limited success.

A promising alternative approach to alveolar bone tissue engineering is provided by the recent report documenting the successful tissue engineering of mandibular bone using the Yucatan minipig model and methods using minimally invasive techniques that eliminate the necessity of donor bone grafts and accompanying morbidity at the primary graft donor site.[160] Needle-aspirated BMSCs were used to seed biodegradable polymer scaffolds, which were then grown in a rotational oxygen-permeable bioreactor system (ROBS). Histologic analyses demonstrated the generation of a uniform 0.3-mm bone layer on the surface of polylactate glycolic acid (PLGA) scaffolds, consisting of an outer osteoid layer and inner deep layer, containing osteocytes in lacunae surrounded by bone matrix similar to naturally forming bone.

WHOLE-TOOTH TISSUE ENGINEERING

A recent achievement promises to revolutionize human tooth replacement therapies. Combined cell biology and bioengineering approaches were used to generate accurately formed, biologic tooth structures containing both dental epithelial and mesenchymal derived tooth structures.[125] Using a tissue engineering approach previously used to regenerate neonatal intestine,[161] small, accurately formed tooth crowns containing both dentin and enamel were produced. The technique used dissociated, immature tooth bud cells to seed biodegradable polymer scaffolds, which were then implanted in the omenta of host animals. Analysis of excised implants at 20, 25, and 30 weeks demonstrated the sequential formation of dentin and enamel tissues in accurately formed small tooth crowns, whose morphology closely resembled that of normally developing teeth. In addition, less mature developing tooth structures were also present, suggesting that continuous, *de novo* tooth development was occurring in the implants. The continuous formation of developing bioengineered tooth structures suggests the self-renewal of both epithelial and mesenchymal DSC populations using this approach.[125] These results demonstrate for the first time the successful application of tissue engineering techniques to whole-tooth regeneration and suggest that biologic whole-tooth replacement therapies may soon be possible for both orthodontic and restorative dentistry purposes.

The ability to bioengineer whole teeth suggests additional important therapeutic strategies. For example, a potential therapeutic approach for treatment of edentulism and accompanying alveolar bone loss would be to combine whole-tooth tissue engineering approaches with that of the above-mentioned mandibular tissue engineering.[160] The combined use of these methods would result in the generation of mandible and tooth segments, to provide teeth and supporting alveolar bone and jaw structures for individuals born without, or to replace structures lost to disease or injury. Again, the widespread availability of such combined therapeutic treatments would dramatically alter the current landscape of treatments for a variety of craniofacial anomalies.

Conclusions

Tissue engineering methodologies combined with an increased understanding of stem cell biology provide powerful tools for dental tissue therapeutic strategies. The demonstrated enhancement of regenerative capabilities of mesenchymal dental tissues is very promising. In addition, the ability to bioengineer both mesenchymal and epithelial derived dental tissues in accurately formed tooth crown structures suggests the feasibility of whole-tissue engineering approaches. The rapid advances in tissue engineering methods, including material science fabrication and design combined with gene delivery techniques, is likely to spur significant advances. We have entered an exciting era, which shows great promise in applying dental therapeutics to meet the needs of a variety of craniofacial and dental deficits. We anticipate that the next decade will bring great advances in dental and craniofacial stem cell and tissue engineering therapies.

ACKNOWLEDGMENTS

We would like to thank Drs. Mina Mina and Conan S. Young for critical reading and comments, Megan Mack for expert secretarial assistance, and Dan McCloskey and Susan Orlando for library science expertise.

REFERENCES

1. Cole, A. S., and Eastoe, J. (1988). "Biochemistry and Oral Biology," 2nd ed., pp. 460–474, Butterworth & Co. LTD, London.
2. Snead, M.L., Zeichner-David, M., Chandra, T., Robson, K.J., Woo, S.L., and Slavkin, H.C. (1983). Construction and identification of mouse amelogenin cDNA clones. *Proc. Natl. Acad. Sci. U. S. A.* **80,** 7254–7258.
3. Krebsbach, P.H., Lee, S.K., Matsuki, Y., Kozak, C.A., Yamada, K.M., and Yamada, Y. (1996). Full-length sequence, localization, and chromosomal mapping of ameloblastin. A novel tooth-specific gene. *J. Biol. Chem.* **271,** 4431–4435.
4. Uchida, T., Murakami, C., Dohi, N., Wakida, K., Satoda, T., and Takahashi, O. (1997). Synthesis, secretion, degradation, and fate of ameloblastin during the matrix formation stage of the rat incisor as shown by immunocytochemistry and immunochemistry using region-specific antibodies. *J. Histochem. Cytochem.* **45,** 1329–1340.
5. Robey, P.G. (1996). Vertebrate mineralized matrix proteins: Structure and function. *Connect. Tissue Res.* **35** (1–4), 131–136.
6. Begue-Kirn, C., Ruch, J.V., Ridall, A.L., and Butler, W.T. (1998). Comparative analysis of mouse DSP and DPP expression in odontoblasts, preameloblasts, and experimentally induced odontoblast-like cells. *Eur. J. Oral. Sci.* **106** (Suppl 1), 254–259.
7. Butler, W.T., Brunn, J.C., Qinm C., and McKee, M.D. (2002). Extracellular matrix proteins and the dynamics of dentin formation. *Connect. Tissue Res.* **43** (2–3), 301–307.
8. Ten Cate, A.R. (1994). "Oral Histology, Development, Structure, and Function," 4th ed. Mosby. St. Louis, MO.
9. Beertsen, W., McCulloch, C.A., and Sodek, J. (1997). The periodontal ligament: a unique, multifunctional connective tissue. *Periodontology. 2000* **13,** 20–40.
10. Ten Cate, A.R., Mills, C., and Solomon, G. (1971). The development of the periodontium: a transplantation and autoradiographic study. *Anat. Rec.* **170,** 365–379.
11. Somerman, M.J., Ouyang, H.J., Berry, J.E., Saygin, N.E., Strayhorn, C.L., D'Errico, J.A., Hullinger, T., and Giannobile, W.V. (1999). Evolution of periodontal regeneration: From the roots' point of view. *J. Periodontal. Res.* **34,** 420–424.
12. Krebsbach, P.H., and Robey, P.G. (2002). Dental and skeletal stem cells: potential cellular therapeutics for craniofacial regeneration. *J. Dent. Educ.* **66,** 766–773.
13. Cho, M.I., and Garante, P. R. (1989). Radioautographic study of [3H] mannose utilization during cementoblast differentiation, formation of acellular cementum and development of periodontal ligament principle fibers. *Anat. Rec.* **223,** 209–222.
14. Davidovitch, Z. (1991). Tooth movement. *Crit. Rev. Oral Biol. Med.* **2,** 411–450
15. Takano-Yamamoto, T., Takemura, T., Kitamura, Y., and Nomura, S. (1994). Site-specific expression of mRNAs for osteonectin, osteocalcin, and osteopontin revealed by in situ hybridization in rat periodontal ligament during physiological tooth movement. *J. Histochem. Cytochem.* **42,** 885–896.
16. Sodek, J., Brunette, D.M., Feng, J., Heersche, J.N., Limeback, H.F., Melcher, A.H., and Ng, B. (1977). Collagen synthesis is a major component of protein synthesis in the periodontal ligament in various species. *Arch. Oral Biol.* **22,** 647–653.
17. Thesleff, I., and Sharpe, P. (1997). Signaling networks regulating dental development. *Mech. Dev.* **67,** 111–123.
18. Lumsden, A. (1988). Spatial organization of the epithelium and the role of neural crest cells in the initiation of the mammalian tooth. *Development* **103,** 55–169.
19. Hall, B.K. (2000). The neural crest as a fourth germ layer and vertebrates as quadroblastic not triploblastic. *Evol. Dev.* **2** (1), 3–5.
20. Chai, Y., Jiang, X., Ito, Y., Bringas P., Jr., Han, J., Rowitch, D.H., Soriano, Ph., McMahon, A.P., and Sucov, H.M. (2000). Fate of mammalian cranial neural crest during tooth and mandibular morphogenesis. *Development* **127,** 1671–1679.
21. Thesleff, I. (1998). The genetic basis of normal and abnormal craniofacial development. *Acta Odontol. Scand.* **56,** 321–325.
22. Thesleff, I., Keranen, S., and Jernvall, J. (2001). Enamel knots as signaling centers linking tooth morphogenesis and odontoblast differentiation. *Adv. Dent. Res.* **15,** 14–18.
23. Mina, M., and Kollar, E.J. (1987). The induction of odontogenesis in nondental mesenchyme combined with early murine mandibular arch epithelium. *Arch. Oral Biol.* **2,** 123–127.
24. Jernvall, J., Kettunen, P., Karavanova, I., Martin, L.B., and Thesleff, I. (1994). Evidence for the role of the enamel knot as a control center in mammalian tooth cusp formation: non-dividing cells express growth stimulating Fgf-4 gene. *Int. J. Dev. Biol.* **38,** 463–469.
25. Koling, A., and Rask-Anderson, H. (1983). Membrane junctions in the subodontoblastic region. *Acta Odontol. Scand.* **41,** 99–109.
26. Thesleff, I., and Nieminen, P. (2000). Tooth induction. *In* "Nature Encyclopedia of Life Sciences." pp. 1–8. Nature Publishing Group, London. www.els.net.
27. Jernvall, J., and Thesleff, I. (2000). Reiterative signaling and patterning during mammalian tooth morphogenesis. *Mech. Dev.* **92,** 19–29.
28. Bei, M., Kratochwil, K., and Maas, R.L. (2000). BMP4 rescues a non-cell autonomous function of Msx2 in tooth development. *Development* **127,** 4711–4718.
29. Keranen, S.V., Aberg, T., Kettunen, P., Thesleff, I., and Jernvall, J. (1998). Association of developmental regulatory genes with the development of different molar tooth shapes in two species of rodents. *Dev. Genes Evol.* **208,** 477–486.
30. Kettunen, P., and Thesleff, I. (1998). Expression and function of FGFs-4, -8, and -9 suggest functional redundancy and repetitive use as epithelial signals during tooth morphogenesis. *Dev. Dyn.* **211,** 256–268.
31. Bei, M., and Maas, R. (1998). FGFs and BMP4 induce both Msx1-independent and Msx1-dependent signaling pathways in early tooth development. *Development* **125,** 4325–4333.
32. Peters, H., and Balling, R. (1999). Teeth. Where and how to make them. *Trends Genet.* **15** (2), 59–65.
33. Guerini, V. (1909). "A History of Dentistry in the Most Ancient Times Until the End of the Eighteenth Century," pp. 280–336. Philadelphia, Lea & Febiger.
34. Chai, Yang, and Slavkin, H.C. (2003). Prospects for tooth regeneration in the 21st century: a perspective. *Microsc. Res. Tech.* 60, 469–479.
35. Glasstone, S. (1938). A comparative study of the development *in vivo* and *in vitro* of rat and rabbit molars. *Proc. R. Soc. B* **126,** 315–330.

36. Hay, M.F. (1961). The development *in vivo* and *in vitro* of the lower incisor and molars of the mouse. *Arch. Oral Biol.* **3,** 86–109.
37. Creslin, E.S., Koch, W.E. (1965). Development of mouse pubic joint *in vivo* following initial differentiation in vitro. *Anat. Rec.* **153**(2), 161–171.
38. Ten Cate, A.R., and Mills, C. (1972). The development of the periodontium: The origin of alveolar bone. *Anat. Rec.* **173,** 69–77.
39. Yoshikawa, D.K., and Kollar, E.J. (1981). Recombination experiments on the odontogenic roles of mouse dental papilla and dental sac tissues in ocular grafts. *Arch. Oral Biol.* **26,** 303–307.
40. Mina, M., Upholt, W.B., and Kollar, E.J. (1991). Stage-related chondrogenic potential of avian mandibular ectomesenchymal cells. *Differentiation* **48,** 9–16.
41. Slavkin, H.C., and Bavetta, L.A. (1968). Odontogenesis in vivo and in xenografts on chick chorio-allantois. I. Collagen and hexosamine biosynthesis. *Arch. Oral Biol.* **13,** 145–154.
42. Yamada, M., Bringas, P., Jr., Grodin, M., MacDougall, M., and Slavkin, H.C. (1980). Developmental comparisons of murine secretory amelogenesis in vivo, as xenografts on the chick chorioallantoic membrane, and in vitro. *Calcif. Tissue Int.* **31,** 161–171.
43. Langille, R.M., and Hall, B.K. (1988). The organ culture and grafting of lamprey cartilage and teeth. *In Vitro Cell Dev. Biol.* **24** (1), 1–8.
44. Huggins, C.B., McCarroll, H.R., and Blockson, B.H. (1936). Experiments on the theory of osteogenesis. *Arch. Surg.* **32,** 915–931.
45. Trowell, O.A. (1959). The culture of mature organs in a synthetic medium. *Exp. Cell Res.* **16,** 118–147.
46. Kollar, E.J., and Mina, M. (1991). Role of the early epithelium in the patterning of the teeth and Meckel's cartilage. *J. Craniofac. Genet. Dev. Biol.* **11,** 223–228.
47. Thesleff, I., and Sahlberg, C. (1999). Organ culture in the analysis of tissue interactions. *Methods Mol. Biol.* **97,** 23–31.
48. Sahlberg, C., Mustonen, T., and Thesleff, I. (2002). Explant cultures of embryonic epithelium: analysis of mesenchymal signals. *Methods Mol. Biol.* **188,** 373–382.
49. Kollar, E.J., and Baird, G.R. (1969). The influence of the dental papilla on the development of tooth shape in embryonic mouse tooth germs. *J. Embryol. Exp. Morphol.* **21,** 131–148.
50. Wigglesworth, D.J. (1967). Formation and mineralization of enamel and dentine by rat tooth germs in vitro. *Exp. Cell Res.* **49,** 211–215.
51. Miller, H.M. (1956). Transplantation and reimplantation of teeth, *Oral Surg.* **9,** 84–95.
52. Costich, E.R., Haley, E., and Hoek, R. (1963). Plantation of teeth, a review of the literature *N. Y. State Dent. J.* **29,** 3–13.
53. Nasjleti, C.E., Castelli, W.A., and Keller, B.E. (1977). Effects of amalgam restoration on the periodontal membrane in monkeys, *J. Dent. Res.* **56,** 1127–1131, 1978.
54. Potten, C.S. (1986). Cell cycles in cell hierarchies. *Int. J. Radiat. Biol. Relat. Stud. Phys. Chem. Med.* **49,** 257–278.
55. Hume, W.J., and Potten, C.S. (1979). Advances in epithelial kinetics-an oral view. *J. Oral Pathol.* **8,** 3–22.
56. Watt, F.M., and Hogan, B.L. (2000). Out of Eden: stem cells and their niches. *Science* **287,** 1427–1430.
57. Spradling, A., Drummond-Barbosa, D., and Kai, T. (2001). Stem cells find their niche. *Nature* **414,** 98–104.
58. Nishimura, E.K., Jordan, S.A., Oshima, H., Yoshida, H., Osawa, M., Moriyama, M., Jackson, I.J., Barrandon, Y., Miyachi, Y., and Nishikawa, S. (2002). Dominant role of the niche in melanocyte stem-cell fate determination. *Nature* **416,** 854–860.
59. Tummers, M., and Thesleff, I. (2003). Root or crown: a developmental choice orchestrated by the differential regulation of the epithelial stem cell niche in the tooth of two rodent species. *Development* **130,** 1049–1057.
60. Baume, L.J., Beck, M.S., and Evans, H.M. (1954). Hormonal control of tooth eruption: I. The effect of thyroidectomy on the upper rat incisor and the response to growth hormone, thyroxin or the combination of both. *J. Dent. Res.* **22,** 80–90.
61. Starkey, W.E. (1963). The migration and renewal of tritium labeled cells in the developing enamel organ of rabbits. *Br. Dent. J.* **115,** 143–153.
62. Zajicek, G., and Bar-Lev, M. (1971). Kinetics of the inner enamel epithelium in the adult rat incisor: I. Experimental results. *Cell Tissue Kinet.* **4,** 155–162.
63. Zajicek, G., and Bar-Lev, M. (1971). Kinetics of the inner enamel epithelium in the adult rat incisor. II. Computer model. *Cell Tissue Kinet.* **4,** 163–170.
64. Lehmann, R., and Slavkin, H.C. (1984). Identification of inner and outer cell proliferation centers during fetal tooth morphogenesis. *J. Craniofac. Genet. Dev. Biol.* **4,** 47–57.
65. Smith, C.E. (1980). Cell turnover in the odontogenic organ of the rat incisor as visualized by graphic reconstructions following a single injection of 3H-thymidine. *Am. J. Anat.* **158,** 321–343.
66. Harada, H., Toyono, T., Toyoshima, K., Yamasaki, M., Itoh, N., Kato, S., Sekine, K., and Ohuchi, H. (2002). FGF10 maintains stem cell compartment in developing mouse incisors. *Development* **129,** 1533–1541.
67. Harada, H., Kettunen, P., Jung, H.S., Mustonen, T., Wang, Y.A., and Thesleff, I. (1999). Localization of putative stem cells in dental epithelium and their association with Notch and FGF signaling. *J. Cell Biol.* **147,** 105–120.
68. Hunt, A.M., and Paynter, K.J. (1963). The role of the cells of the stratum intermedium in the development of the guinea pig molar. *Arch. Oral Biol.* **8,** 65–78.
69. Nataatmadja, M.I., Orans, H.J., and Reade, P.C. (1991). The type, origin and function of the odontogenic cells of continuously growing guinea-pig molars. *Cell Prolif.* **24,** 543–555.
70. D'Errico, J.A., MacNeil, R.L., Takata, T., Berry J., Strayhorn, C., and Somerman, M.J. (1997). Expression of bone associated markers by tooth root lining cells, in situ and in vitro. *Bone* **20,** 117–126.
71. Cotton, W.R. (1968). *In* "Biology of the Dental Pulp Organ" (S.B. Finn, ed.), Part I, pp. 69–90. University of Alabama Press, Birmingham.
72. Stene, T., and Koppang, H.S. (1980). Autoradiographic investigation of proliferative responses in rat incisor pulp after vincristine administration. *Scand. J. Dent. Res.* **88,** 96–103.
73. Stene, T., and Koppang, H.S. (1980). Autoradiographic investigation of dentin production in rat incisors after vincristine administration. *Scand. J. Dent. Res.* 88, 104–112.
74. Dahl, J.E. (1984). Effects of methylmercury chloride on rat incisor odontoblasts and dentinogenesis. *Acta Odontol. Scand.* **42,** 251–255.
75. Ten Cate, A.R. (1989). The fibroblast and its products. *In* "Oral Histology, Development, Structure and Function," 3rd ed. (A.R. Ten Cate, ed..), pp. 90–105. Mosby, St. Louis.
76. Nakashima, M. (1994). Induction of dentine in amputated pulp of dogs by recombinant human bone morphogenetic proteins-2 and -4 with collagen matrix. *Arch. Oral Biol.* **39,** 1085–1089.
77. Pashley, D.H. (1996). Dynamics of the pulpo-dentin complex. *Crit. Rev. Oral Biol. Med.* **7,** 104–133.

78. Tziafas, D. (1995). Basic mechanisms of cytodifferentiation and dentinogenesis during dental pulp repair. *Int. J. Dev. Biol.* **39,** 281–290.
79. Tziafas, D., and Kolokuris, I. (1990). Inductive influences of demineralized dentin and bone matrix on pulp cells: an approach of secondary dentinogenesis *J. Dent. Res.* 69, 75–81.
80. Yamamura, T. (1985). Differentiation of pulpal cells and inductive influences of various matrices with reference to pulpal wound healing. *J. Dent. Res.* **64** (Spec. Issue) 530–540.
81. Stanley, H.R. (1962). The cells of the dental pulp. *Oral Surg.* **15,** 849–585.
82. Takuma, S., and Nagai, N. (1971). Ultrastructure of rat odontoblasts in various stages of their development and maturation. *Arch. Oral Biol.* **16,** 993–1011.
83. Slavkin, H.C. (1974). Tooth formation: a tool in developmental biology. *Oral Sci. Rev.* **4,** 7–136.
84. Fitzgerald, M. (1979). Cellular mechanics of dentinal bridge repair using ^{3}H-thymidine. *J. Dent. Res.* **58,** 2198–2206.
85. Yamamura, T., Shimono, M., Koike, H., Terao, M., Tanaka, Y., Sakai, Y., Inoue, T., Yoshiki, S., Tachikawa, T., Kawahara, H., and Watanabe, O. (1980). Differentiation and induction of undifferentiated mesenchymal cells in tooth and periodontal tissue during wound healing and regeneration. *Bull. Tokyo Dent. Coll.* **21,** 181–222.
86. Torneck, C.D., and Wagner, D. (1980). The effect of a calcium hydroxide cavity liner on early cell division in the pulp subsequent to cavity preparation and restoration. *J. Endocr.* **6,** 719–723.
87. Ruch, J.V. (1984). *In* "Dentin and Dentinogenesis," vol. 1 (A. Linde, ed.), pp. 47–79. CRC Press, Boca Raton, FL.
88. Veis, A., Tsay, T.-G., and Kanwar, Y. (1984). An immunological study of the location of dentin phosphoporyns in the tooth. *INSERM.* **125,** 223–232.
89. Feit, J., Metelova, M., and Sindelka, Z. (1970). Incorporation of 3H thymidine into damaged pulp of rat incisors. *J. Dent. Res.* **49,** 783–786.
90. Fitzgerald, M., Chiego, Fr., D.J., and Heys, D.R. (1990). Autoradiographic analysis of odontoblast replacement following pulp exposure in primate teeth. *Arch. Oral Biol.* **35,** 707–715.
91. Braut, A., Kalajzic, I., Kalajzic, Z., Rowe, D.W., Kollar, E.J., and Mina, M. (2002). Col1a1-GFP transgene expression in developing incisors. *Connect. Tissue Res.* **43** (2–3), 216–219.
92. Gronthos, S., Mankani, M., Brahim, J., Robey, P.C., and Shi, S. (2000). Postnatal human dental pulp stem cells (DPSCs in vitro and in vivo. *Proc Natl. Acad, Sci. U. S. A.* **97,** 13625–13630.
93. Shi, S., Robey, P.G., and Gronthos, S. (2001). Comparison of human dental pulp and bone marrow stromal stem cells by cDNA microarray analysis. *Bone* **29,** 532–539.
94. Gronthos, S., Brahim, J., Li, W., Fisher, L.W., Cherman, N., Boyde, A., DenBesten, P., Robey, P.G., and Shi, S. (2002). Stem cell properties of human dental pulp stem cells. *J. Dent. Res.* **81,** 531–535.
95. Amar S., and Chung, K.M. (1994). Clinical implications of cellular biologic advances in periodontal regeneration. *Curr. Opin. Periodontol.* **2,** 128–140.
96. Sodek, J., and Limeback, H.F. (1979). Comparison of the rates of synthesis, conversion, and maturation of type I and type III collagens in rat periodontal tissues. *J. Biol. Chem.* **254,** 10,496–10,502.
97. McCulloch, C.A., and Melcher, A.H. (1983). Cell density and cell generation in the periodontal ligament of mice. *Am. J. Anat.* **167,** 43–58.
98. Roberts, W.E. (1975). Cell population dynamics of periodontal ligament stimulated with parathyroid extract. *Am. J. Anat.* **143,** 363–370.
99. Gould, T.R., Melcher, A.H., and Brunette, D.M. (1980). Migration and division of progenitor cell populations in periodontal ligament after wounding. *J. Periodont. Res.* **15,** 20–42.
100. McCulloch, C.A., Barghava, U., and Melcher, A.H. (1989). Cell death and the regulation of populations of cells in the periodontal ligament. *Cell Tissue Res.* **255,** 129–138.
101. McCulloch, C.A. (1985). Progenitor cell populations in the periodontal ligament of mice. *Anat. Rec.* **211,** 258–262.
102. McCulloch, C.A.C. (1995). Origins and functions of cells essential for periodontal repair: the role of fibroblasts in tissue homeostasis. *Oral Dis.* **1,** 271–278.
103. Grzesik, W.J., Cheng, H., Oh, J.S., Kuznetsov, S.A., Mankani, M.H., Uzawa, K., Robey, P.G., and Yamauchi, M. (2000). Cementum-forming cells are phenotypically distinct from bone-forming cells. *J. Bone Miner. Res.* **15,** 52–59.
104. Valderhaug, J. P., and Nylen, M.U. (1966). Function of epithelial rests as suggested by their ultrastructure. *J. Periodont. Res.* **1,** 69–78.
105. Furseth, R. (1970). A microradiographic, light microscopic and electron microscopic study of the cementum from deciduous teeth of pigs. *Acta Odontol. Scand.* **28,** 811–831.
106. Reitan, K. (1961). Behavior of Malassez' epithelial rests during orthodontic tooth movement. *Acta Odontol. Scandinavica* 19:443–468.
107. Brice, G.L., Sampson, W.J., and Sims, M.R. (1991). An ultrastructural evaluation of the relationship between epithelial rests of Malassez and orthodontic root resorption and repair in man. *Aust. Orthod. J.* **12,** 90–94.
108. Selvig, K. (1964). An ultrastructural study of cementum formation. *Acta Odontol. Scand.* **22,** 105–120.
109. Grevstad H. J., and Selvig, K.A. (1985). Location and ultrastructure of the first cementum formed in rabbit incisors. *Scand. J. Dent. Res.* **93,** 289–330.
110. Reitan, K. (1974). Initial tissue behavior during apical root resorption. *Angle Orthodontist* **44,** 68–82.
111. Rygh, P. (1977). Orthodontic root resorption studies by electron microscopy. *Adult Orthodontist* 47, 1–16.
112. Brudvik, P., and Rygh, P. (1995). Transition and determinants of orthodontic root resorption–repair sequence. *Eur. J. Orthod.* **7,** 177–188.
113. McCulloch, C.A., and Knowles, G. (1991). Discrimination of two fibroblast progenitor populations in early explant cultures of hamster gingiva. *Cell Tissue Res.* **264,** 87–94.
114. Somerman, M.J., Archer, S.Y., Imm, G.R., and Foster, R.A. (1988). A comparative study of human periodontal liga-ment cells and gingival fibroblasts in vitro. *J. Dent. Res.* **67,** 66–70.
115. Huysseune, A., Van der heyden, C., and Sire, J.Y. (1998). Early development of the zebrafish *(Danio rerio)* pharyngeal dentition (Teleostei, Cyprinidae). *Anat. Embryol. (Berl.).* **198,** 289–305.
116. Payne, T.L., Skobe, Z., and Yelick, P.C. (2001). Regulation of tooth development by the novel type I TGFbeta family member receptor Alk8. *J. Dent. Res.* **80,** 1968–1973.
117. Yelick, P.C., and Schilling, T.F. (2002). Molecular dissection of craniofacial development using zebrafish. *Crit. Rev. Oral Biol. Med.* **13,** 308–322.
118. Piotrowski, T., Schilling, T.F., Brand, M., Jiang, Y.J., Heisenberg, C.P., Beuchle, D., Grandel, H., van Eeden, F.J., Furutani-Seiki, M., Granato, M., Haffter, P., Hammerschmidt, M., Kane, D.A., Kelsh, R.N., Mullins, M.C., Odenthal, J., Warga, R.M., and Nusslein-Volhard, C. (1996). Jaw and branchial arch mutants in zebra fish: II. Anterior arches and cartilage differentiation. *Development* **123,** 345–356.

In yet another *in vivo* study,[19] we evaluated the effect of human MAPCs in a rat stroke model. Cortical brain ischemia was produced in male rats by permanently ligating the right-middle cerebral artery farthest from the striatal branch. Animals were placed on cyclosporine-A, and 2 weeks later, 2×10^5 human MAPCs were injected around the infarct zone. As controls, animals received normal saline or MAPC-conditioned medium. Limb placement test and tactile stimulation test were blindly assessed 1 week before brain ischemia, 1 day before transplantation, and at 2 and 6 weeks after grafting. The limb placement test included eight subtests described by Johansson and coworkers.[20] In a tactile stimulation test,[21] a small piece of adhesive tape was rapidly applied to the radial aspect of each forepaw. The rats were then returned to their home cages, and the order of the tape removal (i.e., left versus right) was recorded. Three to five trials were conducted on each test day. Each trail was terminated when the tapes were removed from both forepaws or after 3 minutes. Animals were subsequently sacrificed to determine the fate of the human cells injected in the brain. After 2 and 6 weeks, animals that received human MAPCs scored statistically better in the limb placement test as well as the tactile stimulation test than animals that received only chondrogenic stimulating activity or were injected with normal saline or MAPC-conditioned medium. The level of recuperation of motor and sensory function was 80% of animals without stroke. When the brain was examined for the presence and differentiation of human MAPCs to neuroectodermal cells, we found that human MAPCs were present but remained immature. Therefore, we cannot attribute the motor and sensory improvement to region-specific differentiation to neuronal cells and integration of neurons derived from MAPCs in the host brain. Rather, the improvement must be caused by trophic effects emanated by the human MAPCs to improve vascularization of the ischemic area, to support survival of the remaining endogenous neurons, or to recruit neuronal progenitors from the host brain. These possibilities are being evaluated.

Possible Mechanisms Underlying the Phenomenon of MAPCs

We do not fully understand the mechanism or mechanisms underlying the culture selection of MAPCs. We have definitive data to demonstrate that the pluripotency of MAPCs is not caused by coculture of several stem cells. First, using retroviral marking studies, we have definitive proof that a single cell can differentiate *in vitro* to cells of mesoderm, both mesenchymal and nonmesenchymal; neuroectoderm; and hepatocyte-like cells for human,[1,6] mouse, and rat MAPCs.[2,6] Second, we have shown that a single mouse MAPC is sufficient for generation of chimeric animals.[2] Indeed, we published information that 1/3 animals born from blastocysts in which a single MAPC was injected were chimeric with chimerism degrees varying between 1 and 45%. This rules out that the pluripotent nature of these cells is the result of coexistence in culture of multiple somatic stem cells.

A second possibility for the greater degree of differentiation potential would be that cells undergo fusion and acquire through this mechanism greater pluripotency. Fusion has been shown to be responsible for apparent ES characteristics of marrow and NSCs[22,23] cocultured with ES cells *in vitro* and more recently for the apparent lineage switch of bone marrow cells to hepatocytes when hematopoietic cells were infused in animals with hereditary tyrosinemia because of a lack of the fumarylacetoacetate hydroxylase *(FAH)* gene.[24,25] In the former two studies, most genes expressed in the marrow or neural cell that fused with ES cells were silenced, and most genes expressed in the ES cell were persistently expressed. Likewise, for the bone marrow-hepatocyte fusion, most genes expressed normally in hematopoietic cells (except the *FAH* gene) were silenced, whereas genes expressing hepatocytes predominated. Finally, the cells generated were in general tetraploid or aneuploid. We do not believe that this phenomenon underlies the observation that MAPCs are pluripotent. Cultivation and differentiation *in vitro* (except for the final differentiation step for neuroectoderm) does not require that MAPCs are cocultured with other cells, making the likelihood very low that MAPCs are the result of fusion. Smith *et al.* suggested in a recent commentary that MAPCs could be caused by fusion of multiple cell types early in culture, leading to reprogramming of the genetic information and pluripotency [REF].[26] Studies are ongoing to rule this out.

The *in vivo* studies were not set up to fully be capable of ruling out this possibility. However, several findings suggest that fusion may not be the cause of the engraftment seen postnatally or of the chimerism in the blastocyst injection experiment. The frequency of the fusion event described for the ES–bone marrow, ES–NSC, and HSC–hepatocyte fusion was in general very low (i.e., 1/100,000 cells). Expansion of such fused cells could only be detected when drug selection was applied in the *in vitro* systems and withdrawal of NTBC (2-(2-nitro-4-trifluoro-methylbenzoyl)-1,3-cyclohexane-dione) in the *FAH* mouse model was used to select for cells expressing the *FAH* gene. The percent of engraftment seen in our postnatal transplant models was 1–9%. The chimerism seen in blastocyst injection studies ranged between 33% and 80% when 1, and 10–12 MAPCs were injected, respectively. These frequencies are significantly higher than what has been described for the fusion events *in vitro* with ES cells and *in vivo* in the HSC–hepatocyte studies. Furthermore, in contrast to papers indicating that fusion may be responsible for apparent plasticity, all *in vivo* studies with MAPCs were done without selectable pressure, mainly in uninjured animals. Finally, tertaploid ES cells do not commonly contribute to chimerism. Therefore, it is less likely that the pluripotent behavior of MAPCs *in vivo* is because of fusion between the MAPCs and the tissues where they engraft or that they contribute to. Specific studies are being designed to formally rule this out.

We do not have proof that MAPCs exist as such *in vivo.* Until we have positive selectable markers for MAPCs, this proof will be difficult to provide. If the cell exists *in vivo,* we might hypothesize that it is derived, for instance, from primordial germ cells that migrated aberrantly to tissues outside the gonads during development. It is also possible that the removal of certain (stem) cells from their *in vivo* environment "reprograms" the cells to acquire greater pluripotency. The studies on human MAPCs suggest that such a cell that might undergo a degree of reprogramming is likely a protected (stem) cell *in vivo,* as the telomere length of MAPCs from younger and older donors is similar and is significantly longer than what is found in hematopoietic cells from the same donor. That MAPCs can be isolated from multiple tissues might argue that stem cells from each tissue might be able to be reprogrammed. However, as was indicated previously, the studies in which different organs were used as the initiating cell population for the generation of MAPCs did not purify tissue-specific cells or stem cells. Therefore, an alternative explanation is that the same cells isolated from bone marrow that can generate MAPCs in culture might circulate and be collected from other organs. However, we have been unsuccessful in isolating MAPCs from blood or from umbilical cord blood, arguing against this phenomenon. Finally, cells selected from the different organs could be the same cells in multiple organs, such as MSCs present in different locations or cells associated with tissues present in all organs—for instance, blood vessels. Studies are ongoing to determine which of these many possibilities is correct.

We believe that MAPCs would have clinical relevance whether they exist *in vivo* or are created *in vitro.* However, understanding the nature of the cell will affect how we would approach their clinical use. If they exist *in vivo,* it will be important to learn where they are located and to determine whether their migration, expansion, and differentiation in a tissue-specific manner can be induced and controlled *in vivo.* If they are a culture creation, understanding the mechanism underlying the reprogramming event will be important, as that might allow this phenomenon to happen on a more routine and controlled basis.

REFERENCES

1. Reyes, M., Lund, T., Lenvik, T., Aguiar, D., Koodie, L., and Verfaillie, C.M. (2001). Purification and *ex vivo* expansion of postnatal human marrow mesodermal progenitor cells. *Blood* **98,** 2615–2625.
2. Jiang, Y., Jahagirdar, B., Reyes, M., Reinhardt, R.L., Schwartz, R.E., Chang, H.C., Lenvik, T., Lund, T., Blackstad, M., Du, J., Aldrich, S., Lisberg, A., Kaushal, S., Largaespada, D.L., and Verfaillie, C.M. (2002). Pluripotent nature of adult marrow-derived mesenchymal stem cells. *Nature* **418,** 41–49.
3. Niwa, H., Miyazaki, J., Smith, A.G. Quantitative expression of Oct-3/4 defines differentiation, dedifferentiation, or self-renewal of ES cells. *Nat. Genet.* (2000). **24,** 372–376.
4. Jiang, Y., Vaessen, B., Lenvik, T., Blackstad, M., Reyes, M., and Verfaillie, C.M. (2002). Multipotent progenitor cells can be isolated from postnatal murine bone marrow, muscle, and brain. *Exp. Hematol.* **30,** 896–904.
5. Reyes, M., Dudek, A., Jahagirdar, B., Koodie, K., Marker, P.H., and Verfaillie, C.M. (2002). Origin of endothelial progenitors in human postnatal bone marrow. *J. Clin. Invest.* **109,** 337–346.
6. Schwartz, R.E., Reyes, M., Koodie, L., Jiang, Y., Blackstad, M., Johnson, S., Lund, T., Lenvik, T., Hu, W.S., and Verfaillie, C.M. (2002). Multipotent adult progenitor cells from bone marrow differentiate into functional hepatocyte-like cells. *J. Clin. Invest.* **96,** 1291–1302.
7. Jiang, Y., Henderson, D., Blackstad, M., Chen, A., Miller, F.F., and Verfaillie, C.M. (2003). Neuroectodermal differentiation from mouse multipotent adult progenitor cells. *Proc. Natl. Acad. Sci. U. S. A.* **100** (Suppl. 1), 11,854–11,860.
8. Ling, Z., Potter, E., Lipton, J., and Carvey, P. (1998). Differentiation of mesencephalic progenitor cells into dopaminergic neurons by cytokines. *Exp. Neurol.* **149,** 411–423.
9. Lee, S.H., Lumelsky, N., Studer, L., Auerbach, J.M., and McKay, R.D. (2000). Efficient generation of midbrain and hindbrain neurons from mouse embryonic stem cells. *Nat. Biotechnol.* **18,** 675–679.
10. Wagner, J., Akerud, P., Castro, D.S., Holm, P.C., Canals, J.M., Snyder, E.Y., Perlmann, T., and Arenas, E. (1999). Induction of a midbrain dopaminergic phenotype in Nurr1-overexpressing neural stem cells by type 1 astrocytes. *Nat. Biotechnol.* **17,** 653–659.
11. Song, H., Stevens, C.F., and Gage, F.H. (2002). Astroglia induce neurogenesis from adult neural stem cells. *Nature* **417,** 39–44.
12. Tanaka, M., Chen, Z., Bartunkova, S., Yamasaki, N., and Izumo, S. (1999). The cardiac homeobox gene *Csx/Nkx2.5* lies genetically upstream of multiple genes essential for heart development. *Development* **126,** 1269–1280.
13. Laverriere, A.C., MacNeill, C., Mueller, C., Poelmann, R.E., Burch, J.B., and Evans, T. (1994). GATA-4/5/6, a subfamily of three transcription factors transcribed in developing heart and gut. *J. Biol. Chem.* **269,** 23,177–23,184.
14. Klug, M.G., Soonpaa, M.H., Koh, G.Y., and Field, L.J. (1996). Genetically selected cardiomyocytes from differentiating embryonic stem cells form stable intracardiac grafts. *J. Clin. Invest.* **98,** 216–224.
15. Qi, H., Aguiar, D.J., Williams, S.M., La Pean, A., Pan, W., and Verfaillie, C.M. (2003). Identification of genes responsible for osteoblast differentiation from human mesodermal progenitor cells. *Proc. Natl. Acad. Sci. U. S. A.* **100,** 3305–3310.
16. Keene, C.D., Ortiz-Gonzalez, X.R., Jiang, Y., Largaespada, D.A., Verfaillie, C.M., and Low, W.C. (2003). Neural differentiation and incorporation of bone marrow-derived multipotent adult progenitor cells after single-cell transplantation into blastocyst stage mouse embryos. *Cell Transplant.* **12,** 201–213.
17. Wang, Z.Q., Kiefer, F., Urbanek, P., and Wagner, E.F. (1997). Generation of completely embryonic stem cell-derived mutant mice using tetraploid blastocyst injection. *Mech. Dev.* **62,** 137–145.
18. (Unpublished observations).
19. Zhao, L.R., Duan, W.M., Reyes, M., Keene, C.D., Verfaillie, C.M., and Low, W.C. (2002). Human bone marrow stem cells exhibit neural phenotypes and ameliorate neurological deficits after grafting into the ischemic brain of rats. *Exp. Neurol.* **174,** 11–20.
20. Ohlsson, A.L., and Johansson, B.B. (1995). Environment influences functional outcome of cerebral infarction in rats. *Stroke* **4,** 644–649.
21. Netto, C.A., Hodges, J.D., Sinden, J.D., LePeillet, E., Kershaw, T., Schallert, T., and Whishaw, I.Q. (1984). Bilateral cutaneous stimulation of the somatosensory system in hemidecorticate rats. *Behav. Neurosci.* **98,** 518–540.
22. Ying, Q.Y., Nichols, J., Evans, E.P., and Smith, A.G. (2002). Changing potency by spontaneous fusion. *Nature* **416,** 545–548.
23. Terada, N., Hamazaki, T., Oka, M., Hoki, M., Mastalerz, D.M., Nakano, Y., Meyer, E.M., Morel, L., Petersen, B.E., and Scott, E.W.

(2002). Bone marrow cells adopt the phenotype of other cells by spontaneous cell fusion. *Nature* **416,** 542–545.
24. Lagasse, E., Connors, H., Al-Dhalimy, M., Reitsma, M., Dohse, M., Osborne, L., Wang, X., Finegold, M., Weissman, I.L., and Grompe, M. (2000). Purified hematopoietic stem cells can differentiate into hepatocytes *in vivo. Nat. Med.* **6,** 1229–1234.
25. Wang *et al.* (2003). *Nature*Wang X, Willenbring H, Akkari Y, Torimaru Y, Foster M, Al-Dhalimy M, Lagasse E, Finegold M, Olson S, Grompe M. Cell fusion is the principal source of bone-marrow-derived hepatocytes. *Nature* 422:897-901.
26. Medvinsky A, Smith A. (2003) Stem cells: fusion brings down barriers. *Nature* 422:823-5.

normally provide suitable numbers of progenitors themselves, we must provide these progenitors from exogenous sources. Concomitantly, we must attempt to mimic selected principles of embryonic development and recapitulate these events in adults.[63,92,93] The most important aspect of embryonic mesogenesis is that the progenitor cell to matrix ratio is very high just prior to lineage pathway entrance and that the exact limits or *edges* of the neotissue are defined. Moreover, we now recognize that each site and each tissue have a unique sequence of inductive events and boundary conditions. Below, I briefly describe the use of MSCs for specific tissue regeneration, taking this embryonic recapitulation logic into account. Fig. 28–3 emphasizes that many millions of MSCs can be generated in culture, stored frozen, or used directly for regenerative tissue repair.[71]

BONE REPAIR

The first and most obvious use of MSCs is in the area of bone regeneration in sites where the body cannot organize this activity, such as in nonunions. Critical size defects in nonunion models have clearly shown that culture-expanded marrow MSCs in a porous, calcium phosphate, ceramic delivery vehicle are capable of regenerating structurally sound bone, where whole marrow or the vehicle alone cannot satisfactorily accomplish this repair.[77,86,94–97] Importantly, these preclinical models include the use of human MSCs in a femoral nonunion model in an athymic rat.[86]

Proliferation and osteogenic potential of MSCs

Cell preparation	Number of MSCs	Fold expansion	Osteogenic in vitro
Initial preparation	2,200	0	N/A
Primary culture	16×10^6	7.3×10^3	N/A
1st Passage	53×10^6	24×10^3	Yes
2nd Passage	176×10^6	81×10^3	Yes
3rd Passage	586×10^6	270×10^3	Yes
4th Passage	1.9×10^9	901×10^3	Yes
5th Passage	6.5×10^9	3×10^6	Yes
6th Passage	22×10^9	10×10^6	Yes
7th Passage	72×10^9	33×10^6	Yes
8th Passage	241×10^9	110×10^6	Yes
9th Passage	803×10^9	370×10^6	Yes
10th Passage	2.7×10^{12}	1.2×10^6	Yes

Figure 28–3. Cell numbers were carefully tallied following each of 10 passages to document that from 2200 initial colony-forming cells, a 1 billion-fold expansion could be observed. At each passage, the "stem cell" quality of the cells was separately assessed.

CARTILAGE REPAIR

Cartilage is an avascular tissue incapable of regeneration–repair of even small defects in adults. Although chondrocytes have been used to attempt to repair large cartilage defects,[98] it is difficult to integrate the neotissue with that of the host. In this case, we have pioneered the use of hyaluronan (HA) scaffolds because of the high content of HA in the embryonic mesenchyme of precartilaginous tissues.[93,99–103] These HA-based scaffolds are in human clinical trials in Europe using autologous chondrocytes.[104] These scaffolds provide an inductive microenvironment for MSCs to enter the chondrogenic lineage,[105,106] and HA-scaffold breakdown products (oligomers) appear to facilitate the integration of neotissue with that of the host.[93]

MARROW REGENERATION

Injected MSCs make it back to the bone marrow to refabricate injured marrow stroma. This observation is the basis for a multifocus clinical trial to add back autologous MSCs to chemotherapy–radiation patients receiving bone marrow (phoresised progenitors) transplants.[51,88,89,107]

MUSCLE REGENERATION

We were the first to document that congenic (i.e., normal) MSCs could be injected into a specific muscle of the muscular dystrophy *(mdx)* mouse to cure it by providing newly synthesized dystrophin to the affected myotubes.[108] In this case, the donor MSCs differentiated into skeletal myoblasts, fused with the host myotubes, and caused the synthesis and distribution of dystrophin. Moreover, labeled MSCs injected into injured (infarct model) rat or pig heart appear to differentiate into cardiac myocytes.[109,110]

FAT

MSCs have been induced into the adipocyte pathway and can massively accumulate fat droplets.[54,55,62,63] Although not used in tissue engineering models, we propose that bags of autologous fat are more appropriate for some plastic surgeries than bags of saline or silicone (Fig. 28–4).

TENDON REPAIR

Studies initiated in my laboratory and later completed at OTI and the University of Cincinnati[85,111] clearly establish the use of autologous MSCs for repair of tendons. The innovative design of an MSC-contracted collagen gel around a resorbable suture held in tension allows tendon defects to be spanned by these composite constructs under normal loads (Fig. 28–5). In this case, the same MSC able to differentiate into cartilage or bone develops into appropriate tendon tissue at Achilles or patellar tendon sites.

GENE THERAPY

The studies with the *mdx* mouse cited previously establish the capacity of allo-MSCs to cure genetic defects.[108] This principle has been translated to the clinical use of allogeneic bone marrow transplantation with or without additional culture-expanded MSCs to attempt to cure polysaccharide storage

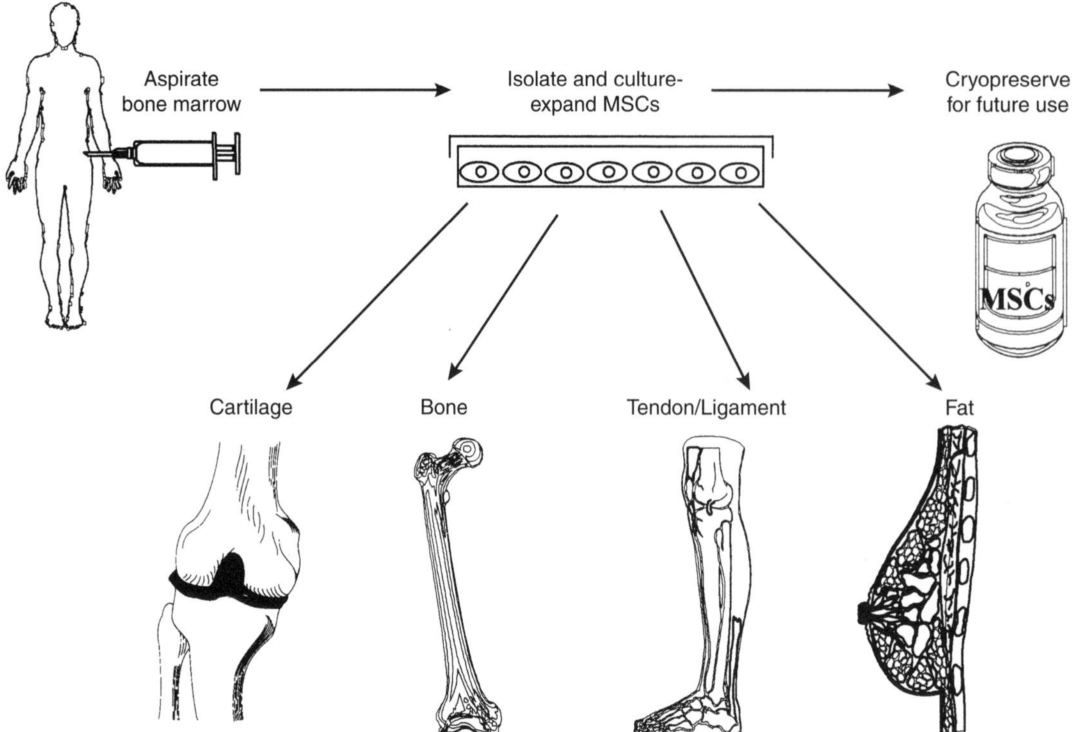

Figure 28–4. From an iliac bone marrow aspirate, MSCs could be used for tissue-engineered repair of cartilage, bone, or tendon or for plastic-surgical implant of fat from fresh or frozen–stored cells.

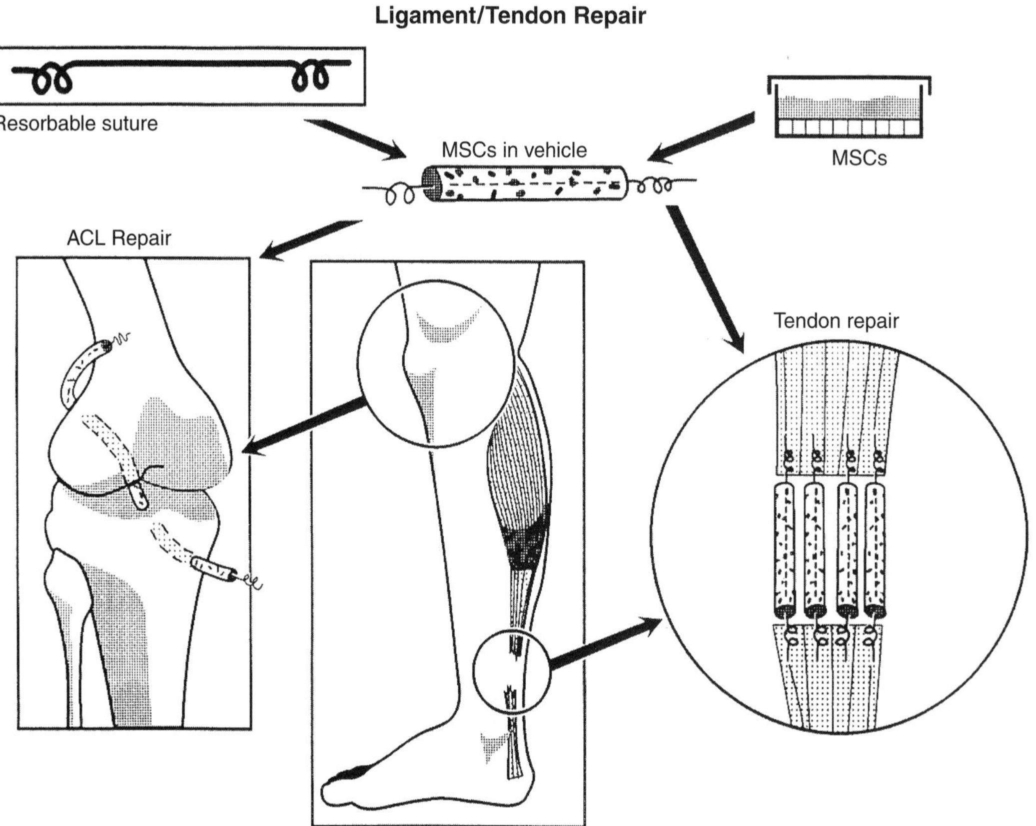

Figure 28–5. Construction of struts of a composite formed from a resorbable suture held under tension around which a collagen gel with MSCs condenses and contracts. These struts are then sutured into an Achilles tendon defect to form neotendon tissue.

diseases or osteogenesis imperfecta with some substantial success.[112–114] In addition, we long ago showed that human MSCs could be transfected with a retroviral construct without affecting their differentiation capacity.[115] Molecules coded for by these gene inserts could be shown to be present many months after introduction into the *in vivo* model. Thus, MSCs hold the potential for a variety of gene therapy applications.

VASCULAR SUPPORT

Not well studied is the relationship between vascular endothelial cells and MSCs. It is clear that multipotent mesenchymal progenitor cells are present with blood vessels (pericytes[59]). More important are the details of the interaction between these vascular support cells and angiogenesis–vasculogenesis.[116] Certainly in embryonic angiogenesis, MSCs play a strong role.[117] In adults, for example, it is now clear that vascular endothelial cells in bone make skeletal inductive molecules, such as BMPs.[118] In addition, MSCs make vascular endothelial growth factor.[119] Based on these and other observations, we predict that although nearly all tissues contain blood vessels, each tissue has specifically differentiated endothelial cells and perhaps even unique MSC-derived vascular support cells.

NEURAL ENVIRONMENTS

Although there are reports that MSCs can differentiate into neural cell types,[120–122] the use of MSCs in neural environments as growth factor pumps that facilitate axonal reconnection and NSC growth, migration, and differentiation may be clinically more relevant.[123,124] Again, I emphasize the principle that the secretion of cytokines–growth factors by MSCs that recreates an embryonic-like or formative microenvironment could be of substantial clinical relevance.

Summary

Adult bone marrow contains mesenchymal progenitor cells that I refer to as MSCs. Whether these preparations are composed of a pure population of stem cells or a spectrum of cells ranging from pluripotent stem cells to lineage-committed progenitors, it seems clear that these culture-expanded cells have the impressive potential to be used in tissue engineered regeneration and repair of a variety of tissues. In some cases, like bone nonunions, these cells are capable of differentiating directly into osteogenic cells. In the case of neural systems, these cells appear to provide instructive and inductive microenvironments for facilitated repair of critical lesions. That mesenchymal cells appear to be unusually plastic in their developmental capabilities opens the door for their use in several cell-based therapies.

ACKNOWLEDGMENTS

My thanks to my colleagues and collaborators at Case Western Reserve University and elsewhere for their assistance and encouragement. The National Institutes of Health generously supported much of the experimentation reviewed here.

REFERENCES

1. Caplan, A.I., Zwilling, E., and Kaplan, N.O. (1968). 3-Acetylpyridine: effects *in vitro* related to teratogenic activity in chick embryos. *Science* **160,** 1009–1010.
2. Caplan, A.I. (1970). Effects of the nicotinamide-sensitive teratogen 3-acetylpyridine on chick limb cells in culture. *Exp. Cell Res.* **62,** 341–355.
3. Caplan, A.I. (1972). Effects of a nicotinamide-sensitive teratogen 6-aminonicotinamide on chick limb cells in culture. *Exp. Cell Res.* **70,** 185–195.
4. Caplan, A.I. (1972). The effects of the nicotinamide-sensitive teratogen 3-acetylpyridine on chick limb mesodermal cells in culture: biochemical parameters. *J. Exp. Zool.* **180,** 351–362.
5. Caplan, A.I., and Koutroupas, S. (1973). The control of muscle and cartilage development in the chick limb: the role of differential vascularization. *J. Embryol. Exp. Morph.* **29,** 571–583.
6. Caplan, A.I., and Stoolmiller, A.C. (1973). Control of chondrogenic expression in mesodermal cells of embryonic chick limb. *Proc. Natl. Acad. Sci. U. S. A.* **70,** 1712–1717.
7. Caplan, A.I. (1981). The molecular control of muscle and cartilage development. *In* "39th Annual Symposium of the Society for Developmental Biology," (S. Subtelney *et al.,* eds.), pp. 37–68. Alan R. Liss, New York.
8. Caplan, A.I. (1984). Cartilage. *Sci. Am.* **251,** 84–94.
9. Hascall, V.C., Oegema, T.R., Brown, M., and Caplan, A.I. (1976). Isolation and characterization of proteoglycans from avian embryonic limb bud chondrocytes grown *in vitro. J. Biol. Chem.* **251,** 3511–3519.
10. DeLuca, S., Heinegard, D., Hascall, V.C., Kimura, J.H., and Caplan, A.I. (1977). Chemical and physical changes in proteoglycans during development of chick limb bud chondrocytes grown *in vitro. J. Biol. Chem.* **252,** 6600–6608.
11. DeLuca, S., Caplan, A.I., and Hascall, V.C. (1978). Biosynthesis of proteoglycans by chick limb bud chondrocytes. *J. Biol. Chem.* **253,** 4713–4720.
12. Caplan, A.I., and Hascall, V.C. (1980). Structure and development changes in proteoglycans. *In* "Dilatation of the Uterine Cervix," (F. Naftolin *et al.,* eds.), pp. 79–98. Raven Press, New York.
13. Caplan, A.I., Fiszman, M.Y., and Eppenberger, H.M. (1983). Molecular and cell isoforms during development. *Science* **221,** 921–927.
14. Melching, L.I., Cs-Szabo, G., and Roughley, P.J. (1997). Analysis of proteoglycan messages in human articular cartilage by a competitive PCR technique. *Matrix Biol.* **16,** 1–11.
15. Urist, M.R. (1965). Bone: Formation by autoinduction. *Science* **150,** 839–899.
16. Urist, M.R., Lietze, A., Mizutani, H., Takagi, K., Tiffitt, J.T., Amstutz, J., DeLange, R., Termine, J., and Finerman, G.A.M. (1982). A bovine low-molecular-weight bone morphogenetic protein (BMP) fraction. *Clin. Orthop.* **162,** 219–232.
17. Van de Putte, K.A., and Urist, M.R. (1996). Osteogenesis in the interior of intramuscular implants of decalcified bone matrix. *Clin. Ortho. Rel. Res.* **43,** 257–270.
18. Urist, M.R., Kovacs, S., and Yates, K.A. (1986). Regeneration of an enchondroma defect under the influence of an implant of human bone morphogenetic protein. *J. Hand Surg.* **11,** A, 417–419.
19. Urist, M.R. (1994). The search for and discovery of bone morphogenetic protein (BMP). *In* "Bone Grafts Derivatives and Substitutes," (M.R. Urist *et al.,* eds.), pp. 315–362. Butterworth Heinemann, London.

20. Syftestad, G.T., and Caplan, A.I. (1984). A fraction from extracts from demineralized bone stimulates the conversion of mesenchymal cells into chondrocytes. *Dev. Biol.* **104,** 348–356.
21. Syftestad, G.T., and Caplan, A.I. (1984). Effects of osteoinductive bone matrix extracts on the transition of mesenchymal cells into chondrocytes. *Calc. Tiss. Intl.* **36,** 625–627.
22. Syftestad, G.T., Lucas, P.A., and Caplan, A.I. (1985). The *in vitro* chondrogenic response of limb bud mesenchyme to a water-soluble fraction prepared from demineralized bone matrix. *Differentiation* **29,** 230–237.
23. Caplan, A.I., and Syftestad, G.T. (1986). Bone protein purification process. Patent No. 4,608,199.
24. Caplan, A.I., and Syftestad, G.T. (1986). Process of adapting soluble bone protein for use in stimulating osteoinduction. Patent No. 4,620,327.
25. Wozney, J.M., Rosen, V., Celest, A.J., Mitsock, L.M., Whitters, J.J., Kriz, R.W., Hewick, R.M., and Wang, E.A. (1988). Novel regulators of bone formation: molecular clones and activities. *Science* **242,** 1528–1534.
26. Wozney, J.M. (1992). The bone morphogenetic protein family and osteogenesis. *Mol. Repro. Dev.* **32,** 160–167.
27. Caplan, A.I. (1991). Mesenchymal stem cells. *J. Ortho. Res.* **9,** 641–650.
28. Marshall, C.J., and Adrian, J.T. (2001). The embryonic origins of human hematopoiesis. *Br. J. Heamatol.* **112,** 838–850.
29. Wagers, A.J., Sherwood, R.I., Christensen, J.L., and Weissman, I.L. (2002). Little evidence for developmental plasticity of adult hematopoietic stem cells. *Science* **297,** 2256–2259
30. Owen, M. (1988). Marrow stromal stem cells. *J. Cell. Sci. Suppl.* **10,** 63–76.
31. Friedenstein, A.J. (1976). Precursor cells of mechanocytes. *Int. Rev. Cytol.* **47,** 327–355.
32. Friedenstein, A.J., Chailakhyan, R.K., and Gerasimov, U.V. (1987). Bone marrow osteogenic stem cells: *in vitro* cultivation and transplantation in diffusion chambers. *Cell Tiss. Kinet.* **20,** 263–272.
33. Caplan, A.I. (1994). The mesengenic process. *Clin. Plas. Surg.* **21,** 429–435.
34. Pechak, D.G., Kujawa, M.J., and Caplan, A.I. (1986). Morphological and histological events during first bone formation in embryonic chick limbs. *Bone* **7,** 441–458.
35. Pechak, D.G., Kujawa, M.J., and Caplan, A.I. (1986). Morphology of bone development and bone remodeling in embryonic chick limbs. *Bone* **7,** 459–472.
36. Caplan, A.I., and Pechak, D.G. (1987). The cellular and molecular embryology of bone formation. *In* "Bone and Mineral Research," (W.A. Peck, ed.), Vol. 5, pp. 117–184. Elsevier, New York.
37. Caplan, A.I. (1988). Bone development. *In* "Cell and Molecular Biology of Vertebrate Hard Tissues," (CIBA Foundation Symposium 136), pp. 3–21. Wiley, Chichester.
38. Osdoby, P., and Caplan, A.I. (1979). Osteogenesis in cultures of limb mesenchymal cells. *Dev. Biol.* **73,** 84–102.
39. Osdoby, P., and Caplan, A.I. (1980). Scanning electron microscopy of *in vitro* osteogenesis. *Calcif. Tiss. Intl.* **30,** 43–50.
40. Osdoby, P., and Caplan, A.I. (1981). First bone formation in embryonic chick limbs. *Dev. Biol.* **86,** 147–156.
41. Osdoby, P., and Caplan, A.I. (1981). Characterization of a bone-specific alkaline phosphatase in cultures of chick limb mesenchymal cells. *Dev. Biol.* **86,** 136–146.
42. Syftestad, G.T., Weitzhandler, M., and Caplan, A.I. (1985). Isolation and characterization of osteogenic cells derived from first bone of the embryonic tibia. *Dev. Biol.* **110,** 275–283.
43. Bruder, S.P., and Caplan, A.I. (1989). First bone formation and the dissection of an osteogenic lineage in the embryonic chick tibia is revealed by monoclonal antibodies against osteoblasts. *Bone* **10,** 359–375.
44. Bruder, S.P., and Caplan, A.I. (1989). Cellular and molecular events during embryonic bone development. *Conn. Tiss. Res.* **20,** 65–71.
45. Bruder, S.P., and Caplan, A.I. (1989). Discrete stages within the osteogenic lineage are revealed by alterations in the cell surface architecture of embryonic bone cells. *In* "The Chemistry and Biology of Mineralized Tissue," (M.J. Glimcher *et al.,* eds.), pp. 73–79. Gordon and Breach, New York.
46. Bruder, S.P., and Caplan, A.I. (1989). Cellular and molecular events during embryonic bone development. *In* "The Chemistry and Biology of Mineralized Tissue," (M.J. Glimcher *et al.,* eds.), pp. 65–71. Gordon and Breach, New York.
47. Stockdate, F.E., Miller, J.B., Fedman, J.L., Lamson, G., and Hager, J. (1989). Myogenic cell lineages: Commitment and modulation during differentiation of avian muscle. *In* "Cell. Mol. Biol. Muscle Dev.," pp. 3–13. Alan R. Liss, Inc., New York.
48. Stockdale, F.E. (1997). Mechanisms of formation of muscle fiber types. *Cell Struct. Funct.* **22,** 37–43.
49. Dexter, T.M. (1982). Stromal cell-associated hemopoiesis. *J. Cell. Physiol.* **Suppl. 1,** 87–94.
50. Dexter, T.M., Allen, T.D., and Lajtha, L.G. (1977). Conditions controlling the proliferation of hemopoietic stems cells *in vitro. J. Cell. Physiol.* **91,** 335–344.
51. Lazarus, H.M., Thiede, M.A., Haynesworth, S.E., Gerson, S.L., and Caplan, A.I. (1998). Human bone marrow-derived mesenchymal progenitor cells (MPCs) cannot be recovered from peripheral blood progenitor cell collections. *J. Hematother.* **6,** 447–455.
52. Haynesworth, S.E., Goshima, J., Goldberg, V.M., and Caplan, A.I. (1992). Characterization of cells with osteogenic potential from human marrow. *Bone* **13,** 81–88.
53. Deasy, B.M., Qu-Peterson, Z., Greenberger, J.S., and Huard, J. (2002). Mechanisms of muscle stem cell expansion with cytokines. *Stem Cells* **20,** 50–60.
54. Gimble, J.M., Robinson, C.E., Wu, X., and Kelly, K.A. (1996). The function of adipocytes in the bone marrow stroma: an update. *Bone* **19,** 421–428.
55. Zuk, P.A., Zhu, M., Mizuno, H., Huang, J., Futrell, J.W., Katz, A.J., Benhaim, P., Lorenz, H.P., and Hedrick, M.H. (2001). Multilineage cells from human adipose tissue: implications for cell-based therapies. *Tiss. Eng.* **7,** 211–228.
56. Mizuno, S., and Glowacki, J. (1996). Chondroinduction of human dermal fibroblasts by demineralized bone in three-dimensional culture. *Exp. Cell Res.* **227,** 89–97.
57. Tallheden, T., Dennis, J.E., Lennon, D.P., Sjögren-Jansson, E., Caplan, A.I., and Lindahl, A. (2003). Phenotypic plasticity of human articular chondrocytes. *J. Bone Joint Surg.* **85-A Suppl 2,** 93–100.
58. Nutall, M.E., Patton, A.J., Olivera, D.L., Nadeau, D.P., and Gowen, M. (1998). Human trabecular bone cells are able to express both osteoblastic and adipocytic phenotypes: implications for osteogenic disorders. *J. Bone Miner. Res.* **13,** 371–382.
59. Schor, A.M., and Canfield, A.E. (1998). Osteogenic potential of vascular pericytes. *In* "Marrow Stromal Cell Culture," (J.N. Beresford *et al.,* eds.), pp.128–148. Cambridge University Press, Cambridge.
60. Wakitani, S., Saito, T., and Caplan, A.I. (1995). Myogenic cells derived from rat bone marrow mesenchymal stem cells exposed to 5-azacytidine. *Muscle Nerve* **18,** 1417–1426.

61. Jaiswal, N., Haynesworth, S.E., Caplan, A.I., and Bruder, S.P. (1997). Osteogenic differentiation of purified, culture-expanded human mesenchymal stem cells *in vitro*. *J. Cell Biochem.* **64,** 295–312.
62. Dennis, J.E., and Caplan, A.I. (1996). Differentiation potential of conditionally immortalized mesenchymal progenitor cells from adult marrow of an H-2K^b-tsA58 transgenic mouse. *J. Cell. Physiol.* **167,** 523–538.
63. Dennis, J.E., Merriam, A., Awadallah, A., Yoo, J.U., Johnstone, B., and Caplan, A.I. (1999). A quadripotential mesenchymal progenitor cell isolated from the marrow of an adult mouse. *J. Bone Miner Res.* **14,** 700–709.
64. Haynesworth, S.E., Baber, M.A., and Caplan, A.I. (1992). Cell surface antigens on human marrow-derived mesenchymal cells are detected by monoclonal antibodies. *Bone* **13,** 69–80.
65. Dennis, J.E., Carbillet, J.P., Caplan, A.I., and Charbord, P. (2002). The STRO-1+ marrow cell population is multipotential. *Cells Tis. Organs* **170,** 73–82.
66. Dennis, J.E., and Charbord, P. (2002). Origin and differentiation of human and murine stroma. *Stem Cells* **20,** 205–214.
67. Dennis, J.E. (1995). Mesenchymal progenitor cells in adult marrow. *Biology,* 203. Case Western Reserve University, Cleveland.
68. Jat, P.S., Nobel, M.D., Ataloitis, P., Tanaka, Y., Yannoutsos, N., Larsen, L., and Kioussis, K. (1991). Direct derivation of conditionally immortal cell lines from an *H-2K^b-tsA58* transgenic mouse. *Proc. Natl. Acad. Sci. U. S. A.* **88,** 5096–5100.
69. Haynesworth, S.E., Goldberg, V.M., and Caplan, A.I. (1994). Diminution of the number of mesenchymal stem cells as a cause for skeletal aging. *In* "Musculoskeletal Soft-Tissue Aging: Impact on Mobility," (J.A. Buckwalter *et al.,* eds.), pp. 79–87. American Academy of Orthopaedic Surgeons, Rosemont, IL.
70. Muschler, G.F., and Midura, R.J. (2002). Connective tissue progenitors: practical concepts for clinical applications. *Clin. Ortho. Rel. Res.* **395,** 66–80.
71. Lennon, D.P., Haynesworth, S.E., Bruder, S.P., Jaiswall, N., and Caplan, A.I. (1996). Human and animal mesenchymal progenitor cells from bone marrow: identification of serum for optimal selection and proliferation. *In Vitro Cell Develop. Bio.* **32,** 602–611.
72. Connolly, J., Guise, R., Lippiello, L., and Dehne, R. (1989). Development of an osteogenic bone-marrow preparation. *J. Bone Joint Surg.* **71,** 684–91.
73. Connolly, J.F. (1998). Clinical use of marrow osteoprogenitor cells to stimulate osteogenesis. *Clin. Ortho. Rel. Res.* **355S,** S257–S266.
74. Muschler, G.F., Nitto, H., Matsukura, Y., Boehm, C., Valdevit, A., Kambic, H., Davros, W., Powell, K., and Easley, K. (2003). Spine fusion using cell matrix composites enriched in bone marrow-derived cells. *Clin. Ortho. Rel. Res.* **407,** 102–118.
75. Bruder, S. Osteobiologics, DePuy. (Personal communication).
76. Caplan, A.I., and Goldberg, V.M. (1999). The principles of tissue engineered regeneration of skeletal tissues. *Clin. Orthop. Rel. Res.* **367S,** S12–S16.
77. Caplan, A.I., and Bruder, S.P. (1996). Cell and molecular engineering of bone regeneration. *In* "Principles of Tissue Engineering," (R.P. Lanza *et al.,* eds.), pp. 599–618. R.G. Landes, Springer, NY.
78. Caplan, A.I. (1999). Tissue engineering strategies for mesenchymal or skeletal tissues. *In* "Tissue Engineering for Therapeutic Use 4: Proceedings of the Fourth International Symposium on Tissue Engineering," (Y. Ikada *et al.,* eds.), pp 67–72. Elsevier Science/BV: Kyoto, Japan.
79. Pittenger, M., Mackay, A., Beck, S., Jaiswal, R., Douglas, R., Mosca, J., Moorman, M., Simonetti, D., Craig, S., and Marshak, D. (1999). Multiple potential of adult human mesenchymal stem cells. *Science* **284,** 143–147.
80. Lennon, D.P., Haynesworth, S.E., Arm, D.M., Baber, M., and Caplan, A.I. (2000). Dilution of human mesenchymal stem cells with dermal fibroblasts and the effects on *in vitro* and *in vivo* osteogenesis. *Dev. Dyn.* **219,** 50–62.
81. Caplan, A.I., and Haynesworth, S.E., (1993). Method for enhancing the implantation and differentiation of marrow-derived mesenchymal cells. Patent No. 5,197,985.
82. Caplan, A.I., and Haynesworth, S.E., (1993). Method for treating connective tissue disorders. Patent No. 5,226,914.
83. Caplan, A.I., and Haynesworth, S.E. (1996). Human mesenchymal stem cells. Patent No. 5,486,359.
84. Caplan, A.I., Gerson, S.L., and Haynesworth, S.E., (1997). Transduced mesenchymal stem cells. Patent No. 5,591,625.
85. Young, R.G., Butler, D.L., Weber, W., Gordon, S.L., Fink, D.J., and Caplan, A.I. (1998). The use of mesenchymal stem cells in Achilles tendon repair. *J. Orthop. Res.* **16,** 406–413.
86. Bruder, S.P., Kurth, A.A., Shea, M., Hayes, W.C., Jaiswal, N., and Kadiyala, S. (1998). Bone regeneration by implantation of purified, culture-expanded human mesenchymal stem cells. *J. Ortho. Res.* **16,** 155–162.
87. Jaiswal, R.K., Jaiswal, N., Bruder, S.P., Mbalaviele, G., Marshak, D.R., and Pittenger, M.F. (2000). Adult human mesenchymal stem cell differentiation to the osteogenic or adipogenic lineage is regulated by mitogen-activated protein kinase. *J. Biol Chem.* **275,** 9645–9652.
88. Lazarus, H.M., Haynesworth, S.E., Gerson, S.L., Rosenthal, N., and Caplan, A.I. (1995). *Ex vivo* expansion and subsequent infusion of human bone marrow-derived stromal progenitor cells (mesenchymal progenitor cells) (MPCs): implications for therapeutic use. *Bone Marrow Trans.* **16,** 557–564.
89. Koç, O.N. (2000). Rapid hematopoietic recovery after coinfusion of autologous-blood stem cells and cultured-expanded marrow mesenchymal stem cells in advanced breast cancer patients receiving high-dose chemotherapy. *J. Clin. Oncol.* **18,** 307–316.
90. Osdoby, P., Martini, M.C., and Caplan, A.I. (1982). Isolated osteoclasts and their presumed progenitor cells, the monocyte, in culture. *J. Exp. Biol.* **224,** 331–344.
91. Collin-Osdoby P., and Osdoby, P. (1996). The role of nitric oxide in regulating bone remodeling. *In* "Biological Mechanisms of Tooth Movement and Craniofacial Adaptation," (Z. Davidovitch *et al.,* eds.), pp. 69–82. Harvard Society for the Advancement of Orthodontics, Boston.
92. Caplan, A.I. (2003). Embryonic development and the principles of tissue engineering. *In* "Novartis Foundation: Tissue Engineering of Cartilage and Bone," John Wiley & Sons, London.
93. Caplan, A.I. (2000). Tissue engineering designs for the future: new logics, old molecules. *Tiss. Eng.* **6,** 1–8.
94. Bruder, S.P., Fink, D.J., and Caplan, A.I. (1994). Mesenchymal stem cells in bone development, bone repair, and skeletal regeneration. *J. Cell Biochem.* **56,** 283–294.
95. Bruder, S.P., and Caplan, A.I. (2000). Bone Regeneration through cellular engineering. *In* "Principles in Tissue Engineering," (R. Lanza *et al.,* eds.), 2nd ed., pp. 683–696, Springer, NY.
96. Ohgushi, H., and Caplan, A.I. (1999). Stem cell technology and bioceramics: from cell to gene engineering. *J. Biomed. Mater Res.* **48,** 913–927.

97. Bruder, S.P., Kraus, K.H., Goldberg, V.M., and Kadiyala, S. (1998). The effect of implants loaded with autologous mesenchymal stem cells on the healing of canine segmental bone defects. *J. Bone Joint Surg. Am.* **80-A,** 985–996.
98. Wakitani, S. (1989). Repair of rabbit articular cartilage surfaces with allograft chondrocytes embedded in collagen gel. *J. Bone Joint Surg. Br.* **71,** 74–80.
99. Caplan, A.I., Elyaderani, M., Mochizuki, Y., Wakitani, S., and Goldberg, V.M. (1997). The principles of cartilage repair/regeneration. *Clin. Orth. Rel. Res.* **342,** 254–269.
100. Solchaga, L.A., Dennis, J.E., Goldberg, V.M., and Caplan, A.I. (1999). Hyaluronic acid-based polymers as cell carriers for tissue engineered repair of bone and cartilage. *J. Orthop. Res.* **17,** 205–213.
101. Solchaga, L.A., Yoo, J.U., Lundberg, M., Dennis, J.E., Huibregtse, B.A., Goldberg, V.M., and Caplan, A.I. (2000). Hyaluronic acid-based polymers in the treatment of osteochondral defects. *J. Orthop Res.* **18,** 773–780.
102. Solchaga, L.A., Goldberg, V.M., and Caplan, A.I. (2000). Hyaluronic acid-based biomaterials in tissue engineered cartilage repair. *In* "New Frontiers in Medical Sciences: Redefining Hyaluronan," (G. Abatangelo *et al.,* eds.), pp. 233–246. Elsevier Science, Amsterdam.
103. Solchaga, L.A., Goldberg, V.M., and Caplan, A.I. (2001). Cartilage regeneration using principles of tissue engineering. *Clin. Orthop. Suppl.* **391,** S161–S170.
104. Pavesio, A., Abatangelo, G., Borrione, A., Brocchetta, D., Hollander, A.P., Kon, E., Torasso, F., Zanasi, S., and Marcacci, M. (2003). Hyaluronan-based scaffolds (Hyalograft C) in the treatment of knee cartilage defects: Preliminary clinical findings. *In* "Tissue Engineering of Cartilage and Bone," pp. 203–217, Novartis Foundation Symposium 249, Wiley, Chichester.
105. Kujawa, M.J., and Caplan, A.I. (1986). Hyaluronic acid bonded to cell culture surfaces stimulates chondrogenesis in stage 24 limb mesenchyme cell cultures. *Dev. Biol.* **114,** 504–518.
106. Kujawa, M.J., Carrino, D.A., and Caplan, A.I. (1986). Substrate-bonded hyaluronic acid exhibits a size-dependent stimulation of chondrogenic differentiation of stage 24 limb mesenchymal cells in culture. *Dev. Biol.* **114,** 519–528.
107. Koc, O.N., Peters, C., Aubourg, P., Raghavan, S., Dyhouse, S., DeGasperi, R., H. Kolodny, E.H., Yoseph, Y.B., Gerson, S.L., Lazarus, H.M., and Caplan, A.I. (1999). bone marrow-derived mesenchymal stem cells remain host-derived despite successful hematopoietic engraftment after allogeneic transplantation in patients with lysosomal and peroxisomal storage diseases. *Exp. Hemtaol.* **27,** 1675–1681.
108. Saito, T., Dennis, J.E., Lennon, D.P., Young, R.G., and Caplan, A.I. (1996). Myogenic expression of mesenchymal stem cells within myotubes of *mdx* mice *in vitro* and *in vivo. Tiss. Eng.* **1,** 327–344.
109. Shake, J.G., Gruber, P.J., Baumgartner, W.A., Senechal, G., Meyers, J., Redmond, J.M., Pittenger, M.F., and Martin, F.J. (2002). *In vivo* mesenchymal stem cell grafting in a swine myocardial infarct model: molecular and physiologic consequences. *Ann. Thorac. Surg.* **73,** 1919–1926.
110. Toma, C., Pittenger, M.F., Cahill, K.S., Byrne, B.J., and Kessler, P.D. (2002). Human mesenchymal stem cells differentiate to a cardiomyocyte phenotype in the adult murine heart. *Circulation* **105,** 93–98.
111. Awad, H., Butler, D.L., Malaviag, P., Boivin, G.P., Smith, F.N., Huibregste, B., and Caplan, A.I. (1999). Autologous mesenchymal stem cell-mediated repair of tendon. *Tiss. Eng.* **5** (3), 267–277.
112. Caplan, A.I. (1995). Osteogenesis imperfecta, rehabilitation medicine, and fundamental research. *Conn. Tiss. Res.* **31,** S9–S14.
113. Horwitz, E., Prockop, D., Fitzpatrick, L., Koo, W., Gordon, P., Neel, M., Sussman, M., Orchard, P., Marx, J., Pyeritz, R., and Brenner, M. (1999). Transplantability and therapeutic effects of bone marrow-derived mesenchymal cells in children with osteogenesis imperfecta. *Nat. Med.* **5,** 309–313.
114. Horwitz, E.M., Gordon, P.L., Koo, W.K.K., Arx, J.C., Neel, M.D., McNall, R.Y., Muul, L., and Hofmann, T. (2002). Isolated allogeneic bone marrow-derived mesenchymal cells engraft and stimulate growth in children with osteogenesis imperfecta: implications for cell therapy of bone. *Proc. Natl. Acad. Sci. U. S. A.* **99,** 8932–8937.
115. Allay, J.A., Dennis, J.E., Haynesworth, S.E., Majumdar, M., Wade Clapp, D., Caplan, A.I., and Gerson, S.L. (1997). LacZ and IL-3 expression *in vivo* after retroviral transduction of marrow-derived human osteogenic mesenchymal progenitors. *Hum. Gene Ther.* **8,** 1417–1427.
116. Shimada, T., Kitamura, H., Nakamura, M. (1992). Three-dimensional architecture of pericytes with special reference to their topographical relationship to microvascular beds. *Arch. Histol. Cytol.* **55 (Suppl.),** 77–85.
117. Folkman, J., and D'Amore, P.A. (1996). Blood vessel formation: what is its molecular basis? *Cell* **87,** 1153–1155.
118. Peng, H., and Wright, V. (2002). Synergistic enhancement of bone formation and healing by stem cell-expressed VEGF and bone morphogenetic protein-4. *J. Clin. Invest.* **110,** 751–759.
119. Thomas, T.N., and Haynesworth, S.E. (In preparation). Human mesenchymal stem cells and vascular endothelial cells reciprocally induce growth and migration. *Biology,* Case Western Reserve University.
120. Eglitis, M.A., and Mezey, E. (1997). Hematopoietic cells differentiate into both microglia and microglia in the brains of adult mice. *Proc. Natl. Acad. Sci. U. S. A.* **94,** 4080–4085.
121. Braxelton, T.R., Rossi, F.M.V., Keshet, G.I., and Blau, H.M. (2000). From marrow to brain: expression of neuronal phenotypes in adult mice. *Science* **290,** 1775–1779.
122. Black, I.B., and Woodbury, D. (2001). Adult rat and human bone marrow stromal stem cells differentiate into neurons. *Blood Cells Mol. Dis.* **27,** 632–636.
123. Mezey, E., Chandross, K.J., Harta, G., Maki, R.A., and McKercher, S.R. (2000). Turning blood into brain: cells bearing neuronal antigens generated *in vivo* from bone marrow. *Science* **290,** 1779–1782.
124. Dezawa, M., Takahashi, I., Esaki, M., Takano, M., and Sawada, H. (2001). Sciatic nerve regeneration in rats induced by transplantation of *in vitro* differentiated bone-marrow stromal cells. *Eur. J. Neuro.* **14,** 1771–1776.

29

Transcriptional Regulation of Hematopoietic Stem Cells

Berthold Göttgens and Anthony Richard Green

Introduction

One of the fundamental issues facing current biology concerns the molecular mechanisms whereby multipotent stem cells are formed and subsequently undergo tightly regulated differentiation to form multiple, distinct progeny. Hematopoiesis has served as a model process for studying stem cell biology, and a close developmental link between the formation of embryonic blood and the formation of endothelial cells has long been recognized. However, the transcriptional networks that control the formation and function of hematopoietic stem cells (HSCs) are still poorly understood. HSCs are the targets for transformation in many forms of leukemia,[1–4] and the importance of transcriptional networks in both normal and leukemic stem cell biology is underlined by the large number of transcription factor genes that are disrupted as part of the pathogenesis of hematological malignancies.[5,6]

Here, we illustrate how an understanding of transcriptional regulation within HSCs is helping to answer two critical questions: What are the mechanisms that specify HSC formation, and how do transcriptional networks influence subsequent HSC behavior?

Formation of HSCs

BIOLOGY OF MAMMALIAN HSC FORMATION

Hematopoietic cells are generated early during mammalian development in close association with the development of the vascular system. Mesodermal cells migrate through the primitive streak to the region destined to form the yolk sac. Here, individual cells (hemangioblasts) are thought to differentiate into endothelial cells and primitive erythroblasts and thus to generate the yolk sac blood islands (Fig. 29–1). This first wave of hematopoiesis is predominantly unilineage and declines by day 11.5 (E11.5) of mouse embryonic development. A second wave of definitive hematopoiesis is initiated in the fetal liver around E10, when the liver rudiment is seeded by incoming HSCs. These are thought to be generated primarily through budding of cells from so-called hematogenic endothelial cells lining the ventral floor of the dorsal aorta,[7–10] with an additional possible source being the yolk sac.[11] Fetal liver hematopoiesis is multilineage and generates most cell types found in the adult. Later in fetal development, hematopoiesis shifts to the bone marrow, the site of adult blood cell formation. *In vitro* differentiation of embryonic stem (ES) cells has provided a powerful approach for the study of early events in blood cell specification.[12] As in the embryo, two consecutive waves of hematopoiesis occur, and clonal analysis has identified cells with hemangioblast and hematogenic endothelial phenotypes.[13,14]

It is unclear whether *de novo* formation of HSCs is a regular feature of adult hematopoiesis. Several studies are consistent with the presence of bipotent hemangioblast cells in adult bone marrow.[15–17] Moreover, multipotent adult progenitor cells have been described recently.[18] After prolonged *in vitro* culture, these cells can generate most somatic cell types *in vitro* or *in vivo,* including blood and endothelium. Furthermore, it has been suggested that tissue-specific adult stem cells may exhibit plasticity, with, for example, HSCs being generated by stem cells from other tissues.[19–22] However, these processes remain poorly defined,[23] and there is little evidence so far that they contribute to the physiological formation of adult HSCs.

TRANSCRIPTION FACTORS AND HSC FORMATION

Normal HSC formation is dependent on several transcription factor genes, many of which were originally identified because of their involvement in chromosomal abnormalities associated with various types of leukemia. Interestingly, one class of genes is required for the formation of both primitive and definitive hematopoietic cells, and a second category contains genes essential only for the generation of the definitive lineage. The former class contains the basic helix–loop–helix (bHLH) transcription factor *SCL* (also known as *Tal-1*) and the Lim domain transcriptional cofactor *LMO-2.* Mice lacking either of these genes die during embryogenesis because they fail to generate any hematopoietic cells.[24–29] Moreover, although endothelial cells are formed initially, these later fail to remodel into larger blood vessels.[30,31] Together with ES cell studies,[32,33] these data suggest that *SCL* and *LMO-2* are required for hemangioblasts to produce hematopoietic progeny. A third transcription factor important for the formation of both primitive and definitive hematopoietic cells is the

Handbook of Stem Cells
Volume 2

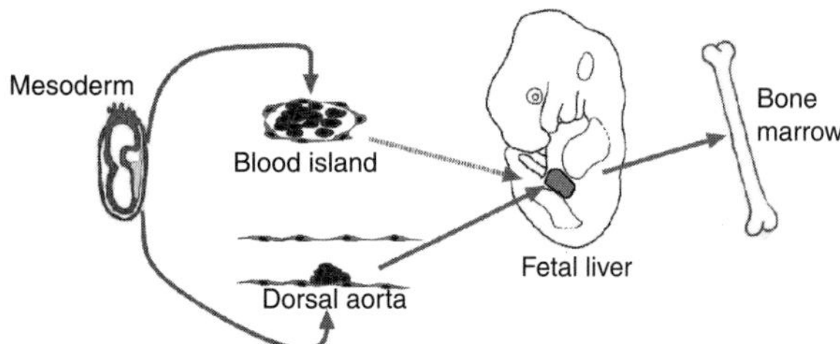

Figure 29–1. *Blood formation during mouse embryonic development.* Mesodermal cells destined to form blood migrate through the primitive streak to the extraembryonic region, generating the yolk sac. Here, individual cells (hemangioblasts) are thought to differentiate into endothelial cells and primitive erythroblasts, thus forming the yolk sac blood islands. This first wave of hematopoiesis is predominantly unilineage and rapidly declines by E11.5. A second wave of definitive hematopoiesis is initiated in the fetal liver around E10, when the liver rudiment is seeded by incoming HSCs. These are thought to be generated primarily through budding of cells from so-called hematogenic endothelial cells lining the ventral floor of the dorsal aorta. Later in fetal development, hematopoiesis shifts to the bone marrow, the site of adult blood cell formation.

zinc-finger gene *GATA-2*. *GATA-2* knockout mice also die during embryogenesis as a consequence of deficient hematopoiesis.[34] Moreover, both *in vitro* differentiation and chimera analysis using *GATA-2*$^{-/-}$ ES cells demonstrated a significant reduction in hematopoietic progenitors as well as a proliferation defect in the progenitors formed.[35]

The second class of transcription factor genes includes the *Runx1* (also known as *AML1*) and *CBF*β genes. Knockout mice for both are embryonically lethal with an absence of definitive hematopoietic cells yet apparently normal primitive hematopoietic development, thus indicating that *Runx1* and *CBF*β are required for hematogenic endothelium to acquire the potential to produce HSCs.[8,36,37] The differences between the two classes of transcription factor genes described above may be more apparent than real since much of our understanding is derived from knockout experiments, which only reveal nonredundant requirements for a given gene. For example, *Runx1* belongs to a multigene family[38]; hence, other family members may compensate during primitive hematopoiesis for loss of *Runx1*. Nonetheless, the division into the two categories is consistent with the observation that members within each category are functionally linked. The knockout phenotypes for *Runx1* and *CBF*β are similar, consistent with the fact that their protein products participate in the formation of a multiprotein complex proposed to be essential for formation of HSCs from hemogenic endothelium.[8] Inactivation of two further transcription factor genes (*c-myb* and the Ets family transcription factor *tel*) also appeared to target definitive hematopoiesis,[39,40] but the initial formation of HSCs may not be perturbed. In *c-myb*$^{-/-}$ embryos, definitive progenitors were generated yet failed to expand and differentiate.[41] *Tel*$^{-/-}$ fetal liver contains HSCs, which fail to either home to or survive in the bone marrow.[39]

Within the other group of genes, *SCL*, *LMO-2*, and *GATA-2* are also functionally linked. Their protein products form a multiprotein complex,[42] and experiments in lower vertebrates suggest that SCL/LMO/GATA protein complexes are capable of specifying developing embryonic mesoderm to form hematopoietic cells.[43] Such an early requirement for *SCL* would be consistent with the recent demonstration that formation of definitive hematopoietic cells during differentiation of *SCL*$^{-/-}$ ES cells requires expression of exogenous *SCL* prior to the formation of endothelial cells.[33]

SCL GENE ENCODES A KEY REGULATOR OF HSC FORMATION

The *SCL* gene (also known as *Tal-1*) encodes a bHLH protein and is normally expressed in hematopoietic cells, in endothelium, and in specific regions of the central nervous system, a pattern of expression conserved across vertebrate species from mammals to teleost fish (reviewed by Begley *et al.*[44]). Within the blood and endothelial system, *SCL* is expressed in hemangioblasts, HSCs, a subset of hematopoietic lineages, and at lower levels in angioblasts and mature endothelial cells.[32,45–54]

Targeted mutation of the *SCL* gene has shown that it is essential for the formation of HSCs during development[26,27] and for the remodeling of primary yolk sac vascular networks but not for the formation of endothelial cells.[31,32] Ectopic expression of *SCL* during zebra fish development or ES cell differentiation results in excessive formation of hemangioblasts and blood cells at the expense of other mesodermal lineages.[48,55] Studies of conditional *SCL* knockout mice showed that *SCL* may not be required for adult HSC function[56] but have demonstrated that continued *SCL* expression is essential for the normal formation of megakaryocytic and erythroid cells.[56,57] Together, current evidence therefore suggests that *SCL* transcription is initiated in hemangioblasts or their precursors and that *SCL* is required for lineage commitment to HSC formation as well as for normal function of adult progenitors and HSCs.

TRANSCRIPTIONAL REGULATION OF THE *SCL* GENE

The observation that *SCL* expression is required for HSC formation focuses attention on the mechanisms whereby transcription of *SCL* is initiated and maintained. We therefore elected several years ago to investigate the molecular mechanisms controlling *SCL* expression. Both human and murine *SCL* are transcribed from two lineage-specific promoters upstream of exons 1a and 1b, the activity of which depended on *GATA* and *Ets* motifs, respectively.[58–62] Neither *SCL* promoter was sufficient to direct expression to hematopoietic cells *in vivo*.

A comprehensive analysis of the entire *SCL* locus was therefore undertaken employing a variety of approaches. A survey of the chromatin structure surrounding the murine *SCL* gene revealed a panel of DNase I hypersensitive sites associated with enhancer or silencer activity in transfection assays.[63] Comparative genomic sequence analysis using five vertebrate *SCL* loci demonstrated that all regions of open chromatin within the mouse *SCL* locus coincided with peaks of human–mouse sequence similarity and allowed prioritization of additional peaks for subsequent functional analysis based on homology to nonmammalian *SCL* loci.[64–66] The likely genomic domain required for appropriate *SCL* expression was functionally defined by crossing transgenic mice carrying a 130-kb transgene encompassing the human *SCL* locus into the *SCL* background, which rescued the lethal *SCL* phenotype.[67] Finally, transgenic reporter assays identified five independent enhancers, each of which targets expression to a specific subdomain of the normal *SCL* expression pattern[54,63–66,68,69] (Fig. 29–2).

SCL STEM CELL ENHANCER

A 3′ enhancer contained within a 5.5-kb fragment displayed particularly striking properties. It was active in the region of E7.5 extraembryonic mesoderm that produces the yolk sac, and it subsequently directed reporter gene expression to endothelial and blood cells within yolk sac blood islands of E8 embryos.[68] Within the embryo proper, the enhancer was active in endothelial cells and in hematopoietic progenitors at multiple sites and times, including E8 para-aortic splanchnopleura, E11 aorta–gonad–mesonephros (AGM) region, and E11 fetal liver.[68] In adult mice, the 3′ enhancer was active in most bone marrow HSCs and progenitors[70] as well as in most endothelial cells. Molecular analysis of the *SCL* 3′ enhancer defined a 641-bp conserved core element responsible for targeting expression to blood progenitors and endothelium in transgenic mice.[71] Activity of the core enhancer critically depends on three motifs, which bind the GATA and Ets family proteins GATA-2, Fli-1, and Elf-1. These three transcription factors are components of a complex, the formation of which appears to be essential for *SCL* enhancer function.[71]

The expression patterns and functions of GATA-2, Fli-1, and Elf-1, where known, are consistent with a role for all three proteins in the regulation of *SCL* expression during blood and endothelial development.[46,72–74] Yet, the absence of primitive and definitive hematopoiesis that typifies the *SCL* phenotype is not reproduced by targeted mutation of GATA-2, Fli-1, or Elf-1.[34,35,75–77] This could reflect the existence of additional *SCL* regulatory elements that can substitute for the +19 enhancer or could indicate that altered levels of related transcription factors can compensate to varying degrees for absence of GATA-2, Fli-1, or Elf-1. In all, the functional dissection of the *SCL* +19 enhancer strongly suggests that GATA-2, Fli-1, and Elf-1 are key components of an enhanceosome responsible for directing expression to hemangioblasts and their endothelial and hematopoietic progeny, including

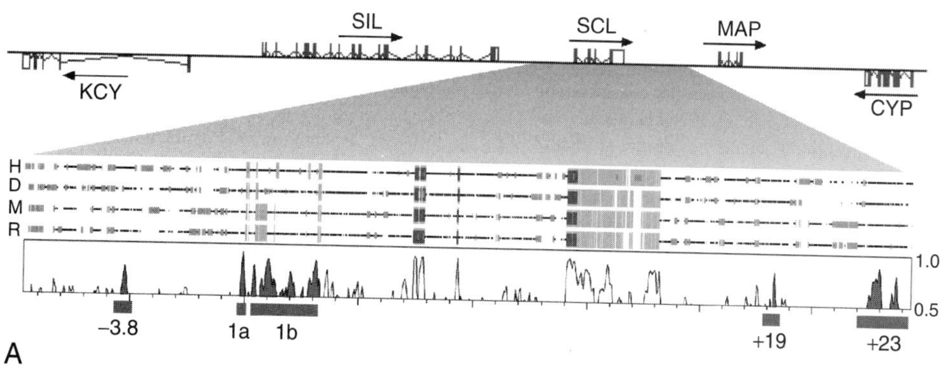

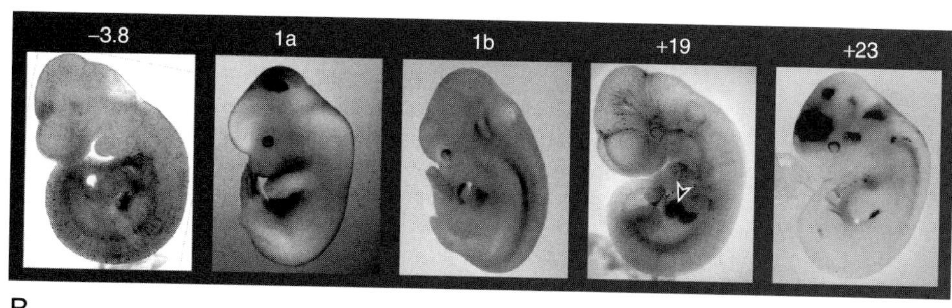

Figure 29–2. *Transcriptional regulation of the SCL gene.* (A) Depiction of the human *SCL* locus with exon–intron structures for *SCL* and its 5′ and 3′ flanking genes above a homology profile of an alignment of the human (H), dog (D), mouse (M), and rat (R) *SCL* genomic sequences. Lines above the homology profile represent the four mammalian gene loci and indicate the positions of gaps inserted in the individual sequences to permit optimal alignment. Small boxes represent repetitive DNA, gray boxes represent noncoding exons, and dark gray boxes represent coding exons. Fragments used for functional analysis are indicated by horizontal bars and shaded within the homology profile. (B) Mouse *SCL* enhancers are active in subdomains of the expression pattern of the endogenous *SCL* gene. Shown are representative E11.5 mouse embryos carrying *lacZ* reporter transgenes linked to the –3.8, 1a, 1b, +19, and +23 regulatory elements. Staining indicates enhancer activity. Note the fetal liver staining of the +19 embryo (arrowhead). (Please see CD-ROM for color version of this figure.)

HSCs (Fig. 29–3). With the evidence that *SCL* is crucial for hemangioblast and HSC formation,[26,27,32,48,51] these data suggest that the *SCL* enhanceosome functions as a node for the integration of signals responsible for establishing the transcriptional program for blood cell development.

Although expression profiling can identify all transcription factor genes expressed in HSCs[78–80] and thus define the *possible* components of an HSC transcriptional network, determining the *actual* transcriptional interactions requires functional analysis of HSC gene regulatory cassettes. The integration of transcriptional networks with genome sequences is now recognized as key to a full understanding of developmental processes such as HSC formation and will require molecular analysis of the transcriptional control regions of all members of a given gene regulatory network.[81,82]

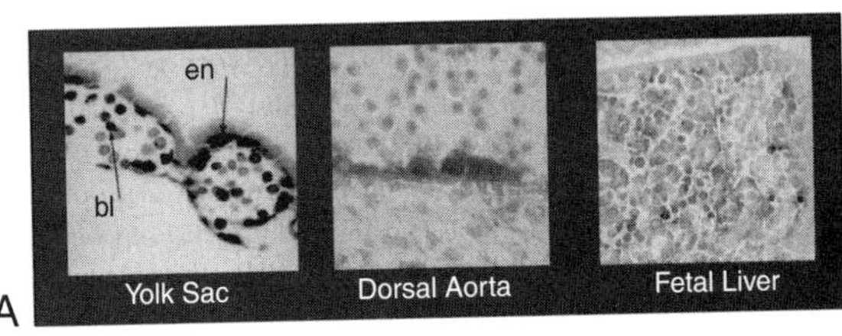

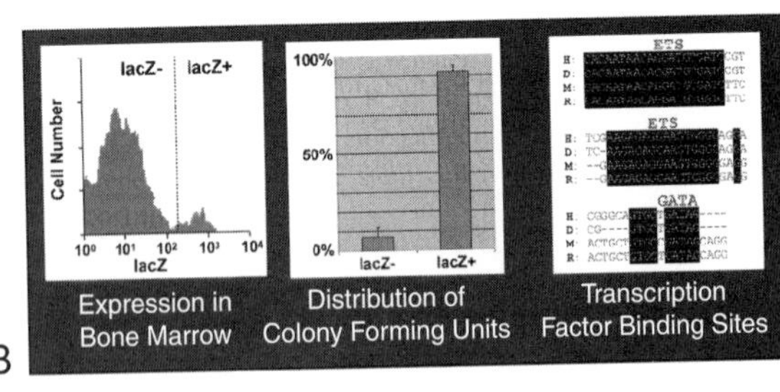

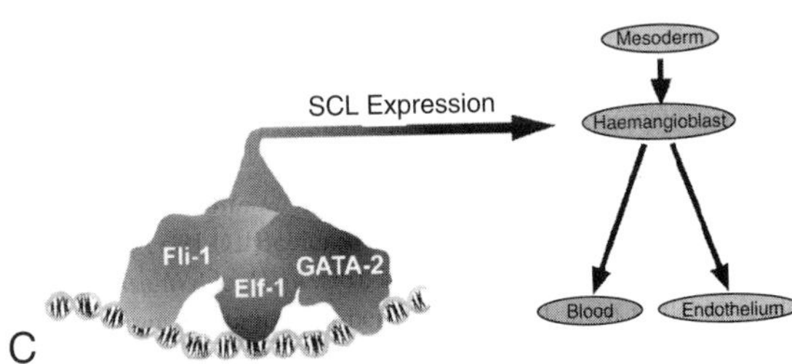

Figure 29–3. *SCL stem cell enhancer.* (A) The *SCL* +19 stem cell enhancer targets embryonic hematopoietic and endothelial cells. Shown are histological sections of E8.5 yolk sac and E11.5 dorsal aorta and fetal liver from transgenic mice carrying a lacZ reporter construct. (B) The +19 *SCL* stem cell enhancer targets hematopoietic progenitors in transgenic mice and contains three critical binding sites. From left to right: A FACS plot indicating the percentage of lacZ-expressing cells in adult bone marrow; distribution of hematopoietic colony-forming activity between nonexpressing and expressing cells in bone marrow; and a human– dog–mouse–rat sequence alignment of the +19 core enhancer, indicating two conserved Ets sites and one conserved GATA site. (C) A model for the role of the +19 enhanceosome in the development of HSCs and blood. It is anticipated that different GATA and Ets family members may participate in distinct cell types or in response to specific signals. *SCL* expression is essential for lineage commitment to blood but not to endothelium (bl, blood; en, endothelium; H, human; D dog, M, mouse; and R, rat). (Please see CD-ROM for color version of this figure.)

Our analysis of *SCL* regulation has shown that a single enhancer is employed to direct expression to endothelium, HSCs, and multipotent progenitors, suggesting that the close developmental and phenotypic relationship between blood progenitors and endothelium is reflected at a molecular level by the existence of individual bifunctional regulatory elements. This leads us to speculate that analogous enhancers may control other genes exhibiting dual hematopoietic and endothelial expression. Consistent with this concept, colocalization of hematopoietic and endothelial activity to the same genomic region may be a recurrent theme, as illustrated by recent transgenic analysis of c-mpl and LY6 regulatory cassettes.[9,83,84] Dual hematopoietic–endothelial enhancers may mark genes expressed in hemangioblasts and hematogenic endothelium as well as in their respective progeny. This arrangement may be an economic strategy for regulating the transcriptional programming necessary for transitions among hemangioblasts, endothelium, and hematopoietic progenitors.

Behavior of HSCs

HSC FATE CHOICES

Adult mammalian tissues exist in a dynamic state of homeostasis. Differentiated cells lost because of either physiological turnover or injury are constantly replenished through regeneration mediated by somatic stem cells. Adult somatic stem cells are therefore defined functionally as regeneration units capable of both extensive self-renewal and multilineage differentiation. Most adult HSCs are thought to be quiescent, and cells from the small, active stem cell pool face three fates: self-renewal, differentiation, or cell death. The control mechanisms governing these cell fate decisions in HSCs are largely unknown. Studies of other stem cell systems suggest that the environment surrounding HSCs, the so-called stem cell niche, is likely to provide cell–cell and cell–extracellular matrix interactions important for stem cell self-renewal.[85,86]

Two main concepts have been put forward to explain how HSCs undergo lineage commitment: First, there are instructive models in which HSCs respond to external stimuli such as cytokines, cell–cell, and cell–extracellular matrix interactions. Although the primary role of cytokines within the hematopoietic system was thought to reflect selective rather than instructive mechanisms,[87,88] it has more recently been suggested that cytokines can convert common lymphoid progenitors (CLPs) to a myeloid fate in an instructive manner.[89] Second, there are selective models in which lineage choice would be mostly random with the appropriate number of mature cells being controlled by external stimuli acting selectively on HSC progeny.[90] Lineage commitment at the level of HSCs may thus reflect the stochastic nature of gene expression described in other model systems.[91,92] Whatever the mechanisms responsible for lineage commitment of HSCs, it is clear that transcription factors play a central role in regulating their self-renewal and differentiation.

Differentiation of HSCs into the various mature blood lineages is thought to proceed via a hierarchy of progenitors. Studies over the last decade have lead to the development of protocols that allow the prospective isolation of HSCs and the various progenitor cells.[93–98] Lineage commitment is likely to involve a gradual loss of potential eventually resulting in unipotent progenitors. Interestingly, two recent studies using primary cells[89,99] support the concept of plasticity of hematopoietic progenitors previously described in transformed multipotent avian hematopoietic progenitor cells.[100,101] These studies suggest that alterations in the level of individual transcription factors can cause a lineage switch, although the physiological relevance of progenitor plasticity remains unclear.

TRANSCRIPTIONAL REGULATION OF HSC SELF-RENEWAL

The molecular mechanisms of HSC self-renewal are largely unknown. Recent evidence suggests that Wnt and fibroblast growth factor signaling molecules can promote HSC self-renewal[102–104] and that the Polycomb-family transcription factor Bmi-1 is a positive regulator of self-renewal.[105,106] More tractable stem cell systems such as mouse ES cells and *Drosophila* germ line stem cells identified a role for STAT transcription factors in promoting self-renewal.[107,108] STAT transcription factors are the effectors of the JAK–STAT signaling pathway, suggesting that instructive mechanisms can be important for the regulation of self-renewal. Roles for STAT transcription factors in the regulation of HSC activity were suggested in two recent studies. First, HSCs in STAT5a$^{-/-}$/STAT5b$^{-/-}$ double-knockout mice displayed a cell-intrinsic defect in long-term repopulating activity.[109,110] Second, mice deficient in STAT1 and STAT3 signaling because of a carboxy terminal deletion of the gp130 receptor subunit have increased numbers of immature multipotent progenitor cells.[111]

In addition to the emerging crucial role of cytokines in regulating self-renewal, it was demonstrated recently that direct manipulation of transcription factors provides a powerful strategy for amplification of HSCs. The most promising results so far were obtained after overexpressing the homeobox transcription factor HoxB4 in HSCs. Endogenous HoxB4 is expressed in a variety of developing embryonic and adult tissues including a highly enriched hematopoietic progenitor–stem cell population.[112] Retroviral overexpression of HoxB4 in mouse HSCs resulted in a 50-fold amplification of HSCs, initially without identifiable anomalies in the peripheral blood of HoxB4-transduced mice.[113] Moreover, HoxB4-mediated expansion of HSCs could be accomplished *ex vivo*,[114] and expression of HoxB4 was able to confer adult-type HSC engraftment potential to hematopoietic progenitors generated from mouse ES cells.[115] Although promising, translation of these results into novel therapeutic approaches will require circumventing the genetic manipulation required to overexpress HoxB4 and an understanding of why, in some systems, HoxB4 expression compromises lymphoid or multilineage differentiation.[116,117]

Cell–cell interactions are a key component of the concept of the stem cell niche, which has been developed for several stem cell types other than HSCs.[118,119] A direct link between cell–cell interactions and transcriptional regulation is provided by members of the *Notch* gene family.[120] Both Notch and its ligands delta and serrate–jagged are evolutionarily highly conserved integral membrane proteins, and all influence numerous cell fate decisions in both vertebrates and invertebrates. Activation of Notch through ligand binding results in proteolytic cleavage of the intracellular domain of Notch, which subsequently transfers to the nucleus where it acts as a transcriptional regulator. *Notch* genes mediate binary cell-fate decisions, and evidence emerging from a range of model systems suggests that activation of Notch proteins inhibits differentiation and promotes self-renewal of progenitor cells.[121–123]

HSCs express *Notch* genes, and bone marrow stromal cells express the *serrate* homologue *Jagged-1*. Exposure of HSCs to *Jagged-1* in culture causes an increase in the number of multipotent progenitors.[124–126] Moreover, *in vitro* incubation with a soluble form of *Jagged-1* causes expansion of pluripotent human HSCs assayed by transplantation into immunodeficient mice.[127] Similar results were obtained when equivalent experiments were carried out using soluble forms of the Notch ligands Delta-1 and Delta-4.[128] The recently reported expansion of HSCs from human cord blood in defined serum-free culture media with an immobilized variant of Delta-1 suggests that manipulation of the Notch pathway may be incorporated into clinical protocols.[129] Further scope for *in vitro* amplification of HSCs was indicated through the demonstration that the combination of delta proteins with a cocktail of cytokines supporting early hematopoietic cells provides culture conditions that allow a multiple log increase in the numbers of lymphoid and myeloid reconstituting cells.[130] Finally, two further observations emphasize the potential role of Notch in stem cell maintenance. First, constitutive Notch signaling in hematopoietic cells generates immortalized multipotent cell lines with both lymphoid and myeloid differentiation potential.[131] Second, expression in HSCs of the bHLH transcription factor HES-1, a direct target of Notch1, preserves long-term repopulating stem cells *ex vivo*, and increases the numbers of immature progenitor cells after transplantation.[132]

MULTILINEAGE PRIMING AND LINEAGE COMMITMENT

Much work has been carried out to investigate the transcriptional control of lineage specification. Analysis of single, multipotent myeloid progenitor cells demonstrated low-level expression of multiple genes previously regarded as restricted to individual lineages.[133–136] Analysis of CLPs proved consistent with this concept, as CLPs were found to coexpress low levels of both T- and B-lymphoid genes.[137] By extrapolation, it was postulated that all hematopoietic lineage programs may be primed at low levels in HSCs in contrast to nonhematopoietic lineage programs. Lineage specification would thus be initiated when a single hematopoietic lineage program exceeds a set threshold.[90] Further molecular evidence for this concept has come from studies showing that the chromatin structure of myeloid genes was not closed in progenitors.[138,139] Instead, genes appear to be primed with a subset of regulatory regions accessible. However, those regions do not seem to be bound by the same set of factors in progenitors and mature cells, indicating that distinct mechanisms are responsible for initiating low-level expression in multipotent progenitors and for subsequent high-level expression in mature cells. The concept of multilineage priming is being extended to other stem cell types such as mesenchymal stem cells[140] and may emerge as an important feature of stemness.

However, recent transcriptome analyzes of HSCs suggests that the multilineage priming model of HSCs needs to be modified in two ways. First, although HSCs coexpressed marker genes for several myeloid lineages, most lymphoid marker genes were not expressed.[137] These observations were subsequently confirmed and extended using microarray analysis covering more than 150 lymphoid genes.[45] Thus, although multilineage priming provides an attractive mechanism underlying specification of myeloid cells from HSCs, it is possible that a lymphoid gene expression program may need to be actively "switched on" whenever HSCs differentiate into CLPs. Since myeloid cells preceded the appearance of lymphoid cells during evolution[141] and myeloid cells are generated prior to the formation of lymphoid cells during mammalian embryonic development,[142] it is possible that myeloid differentiation is an ancient default fate for HSCs. A second modification to the concept of multilineage priming may come from the observation that the most immature HSC fraction analyzed expressed marker genes associated with nonhematopoietic lineages.[45] Interestingly, these genes were not expressed by multipotent progenitors, and the authors suggested that their observation may warrant an extension of the original concept by suggesting that this promiscuous expression profile of HSCs may be related to the recently discovered phenomenon of adult stem cell plasticity.

One implication of the concept of multilineage priming is that initiation of a given lineage differentiation program can be triggered when key transcription factors exceed a threshold level within the multiply primed multipotent progenitors. However, assessing the functional consequences of enforced expression of transcription factors in HSCs is challenging for several reasons. First, HSCs are extremely rare, and to permit subsequent biochemical analysis, most transcription factors have been tested in multipotent progenitors. Much of our view of transcriptional control of HSC differentiation is thus extrapolated from analysis of multipotent progenitors. Reassuringly though, when overexpression data in HSCs are available (see, for example, results[143] for Pax5), they often confirm the function extrapolated from studies in progenitors. Second, several different thresholds for a single transcription factor may trigger alternative differentiation programs, some of which would not be recognized following simple overexpression approaches. For example, low-level expression of GATA-1 in chicken myeloblasts resulted in the formation of eosinophils, whereas levels only fourfold higher favored development into erythroid and thromboblast cells.[101] Third, high-level overexpression of factors already expressed in HSCs may trigger nonphysiological consequences such as the sequestration of cofactors. Future research strategies may therefore place more emphasis on inhibiting the levels of endogenous factors through conditional knockout or siRNA approaches.

It is also important to note that HSCs may not be the target cells in which a lineage specification factor normally exerts its prime function. This point is illustrated by a recent study of GATA-3. Overexpression of GATA-3 in HSCs inhibited expansion of stem cells and selectively induced megakaryocytic and erythroid differentiation.[144] Given that GATA-3 is a key regulator of T-lymphoid development, promoting T-helper-cell type 2 development from CD4(+) T-cells but inhibiting the maturation of CD8(+) cells,[145–149] this last result was unexpected. However, a related protein, GATA-1, was known to promote megakaryocyte and erythroid differentiation when overexpressed in multipotent progenitors.[150,151] Since GATA-3 can functionally replace GATA-1,[152,153] it is likely that the observed differentiation effect seen after overexpressing GATA-3 in HSCs is caused by GATA-3 acting on *GATA-1* target genes. Importantly, *GATA-1* itself is a *GATA-1* target gene,[154,155] so the initial expression of GATA-3 in HSCs may "lock" these cells into the megakaryocyte–erythroid differentiation program.[156] It is also tempting to speculate that the preferential effect of GATA-3 on myeloid over lymphoid gene expression programs could be related to HSCs possibly being primed for myeloid but not for lymphoid differentiation (see the previous section).

POSITIVE FEEDBACK AND RECIPROCAL REPRESSION DRIVE DIFFERENTIATION

With HSCs and multipotent progenitors being characterized by a state of transcriptional promiscuity, the question arises as to what mechanisms reinforce and stabilize commitment to specific lineages from multiply primed precursors. Recent studies suggest that expression of certain "lineage specifying" transcription factors above a threshold level results in two lineage-determining effects. First, lineage-specific genes including the transcription factor are up-regulated, thus specifying a given lineage and reinforcing this specification through a positive feedback loop. Second, alternative lineage choices are inhibited through down-regulation of alternative transcription factor programs, either at the transcriptional or the protein level (Fig. 29–4).

Many genes encoding critical hematopoietic transcription factors have been shown to undergo transcriptional autoregulation (i.e., *GATA-1*,[154,155] *C/EBPβ*,[157] *C/EBPα*,[158] and *PU.1*[159]), thus providing a link between initiation and maintenance of a given lineage expression program. For example, when GATA-1 protein levels exceed a set threshold in multipotent progenitor cells through either an instructive or stochastic mechanism, differentiation toward the erythroid lineage would be initiated, and this lineage choice would be maintained and reinforced through autoregulation of GATA-1.

A further means to "lock in" differentiation states within the hematopoietic system is reciprocal repression of key transcription factors. For example, within the myeloid differentiation pathway, expression of GATA-1 specifies the development of erythroid and megakaryocytic cells,[101] whereas PU.1 specifies the development of monocytes.[100]

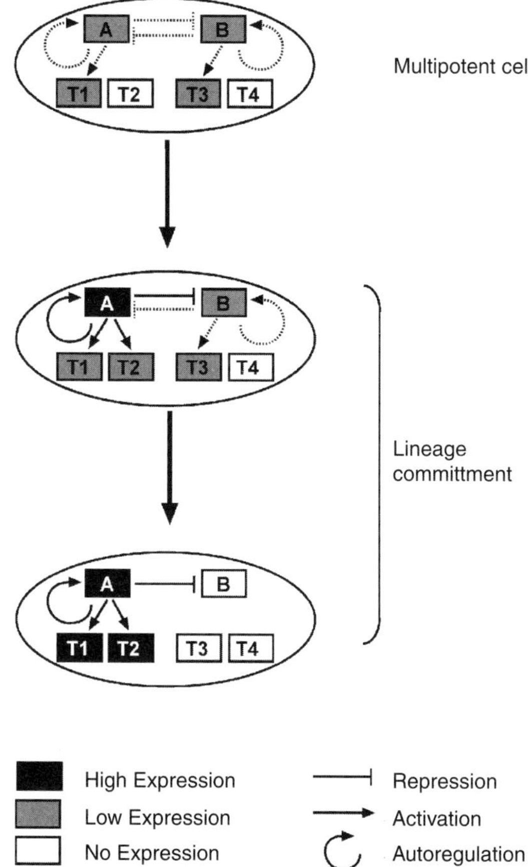

Figure 29–4. *Model for lineage commitment.* Multilineage priming, autoregulation, and reciprocal repression combine in a model for lineage commitment of HSCs. The multipotent cell at the top expresses low levels of two lineage-affiliated transcription factors, A and B, and a subset of their respective target genes, *T1* and *T3*, associated with the corresponding differentiation programs. Up-regulation of factor A by instructive or selective means results in lineage commitment by enhanced autoregulation and simultaneous repression of factor B, eventually leading to a cell that only expresses genes affiliated with lineage A.

Moreover, GATA-1 actively inhibits monocyte differentiation,[160] whereas PU.1 inhibits erythroid differentiation.[161,162] An elegant explanation for this functional cross-antagonism was provided by several recent studies demonstrating direct physical interaction of GATA-1 and PU.1 proteins.[160,161,163] PU.1 binding to GATA-1 prevents GATA-1 from binding to DNA. By contrast, GATA-1/PU.1 protein complexes can bind to PU.1-binding sites. However, GATA-1 binding to PU.1 displaces the transcriptional coactivator c-jun, resulting in a transcriptionally inactive protein complex.[161]

Several additional examples of reciprocal repression have been discovered. First, MafB induces monocyte differentiation[164] yet inhibits erythroid differentiation by repressing Ets-1–mediated transactivation of erythroid-specific genes.[165] Second, C/EBPβ cross-antagonizes FOG-1 during eosinophil development.[166] Third, C/EBPα promotes granulocytic development and inhibits monocyte differentiation.[167] It was subsequently shown that this inhibition of monocyte development is likely to be because C/EBPα can bind to PU.1, displacing its coactivator c-jun.[168] Finally, reciprocal repression is emerging as a key property of the Pax5 transcription factor, a key regulator of B-cell development.[169] Although $Pax5^{-/-}$ pro-B-cells are unable to differentiate farther down the B-lymphoid lineage, they have acquired the potential to develop into multiple other hematopoietic lineages.[170] Restoration of Pax5 expression in these cells promotes B-lymphoid differentiation and suppresses multilineage potential, implying that Pax5 normally represses these alternative lineage choices. Recent data suggest that this suppression is direct. Pax5 appears to inhibit T-cell development by directly repressing transcription of the T-lymphoid specification gene *Notch1*.[171] Moreover, Pax5 may inhibit myeloid differentiation by down-regulating expression of the GM-CSF receptor α-chain.[172]

The construction of regulatory gene networks is emerging as an important way of integrating expression, regulatory, and developmental information with the underlying genome sequence, which contains the code controlling development. Interestingly, a combination of autoregulation and reciprocal repression appears to provide gene regulatory networks with one of their key features, an inherent forward momentum driving progression through consecutive transcriptional regulatory states.[82]

LEUKEMOGENESIS AND TRANSCRIPTIONAL REGULATION

HSCs are the targets for transformation in many hematological malignancies, including acute myeloid leukemia (AML), chronic myeloid leukemia, the myelodysplastic syndromes, and the myeloproliferative disorders.[1–4] Originally, involvement of HSCs was inferred from the discovery that X-linked markers such as glucose-6-phosphate-dehydrogenase displayed skewed X-inactivation patterns in multiple hematopoietic lineages in individual patients.[173–175] Further evidence for a stem cell origin was provided by the observation that the Philadelphia chromosome associated with chronic myeloid leukemia is present in multiple hematopoietic lineages,[176–178] suggesting that the leukemogenic chromosome rearrangement occurred in a multipotent HSC. This concept was subsequently extended to acute leukemias in studies involving transplantation of leukemic cells to engraft the hematopoietic system of nonobese diabetic severe-combined immunodeficiency mice. Subfractionation of bone marrow cells prior to transplantation revealed that AML and acute lymphoblastic leukemia (ALL) stem cells copurify with normal HSCs.[2,179,180] These results lead to the theory that many malignancies including non-hematopoietic tumors may be maintained by a small number of cancer stem cells (for review, see Reya *et al.*[181]), a concept receiving much interest as illustrated by the recent characterization of breast cancer stem cells.[182]

The association between the incidence of cancer and age led Armitage and Doll to develop the multistage model of cancer 50 years ago.[183] The requirement for multiple mutations to accumulate may explain why stem cells are frequently targets for tumorigenic alterations—mutations occurring in a

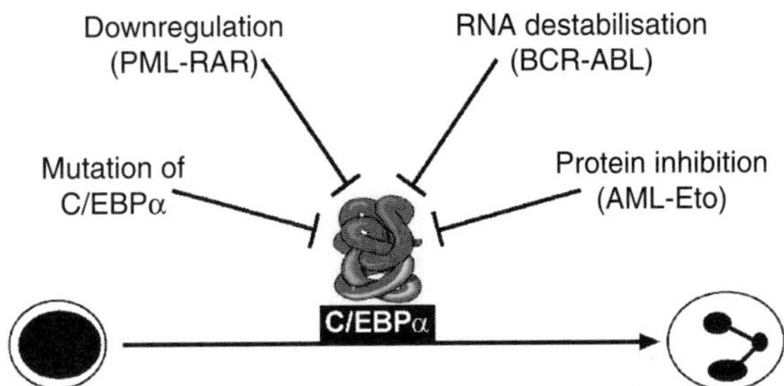

Figure 29–5. *Different leukemogenic mutations converge on a common transcriptional target.* C/EBPα is a critical regulator of normal myeloid differentiation and is inactivated through mutations in a subset of patients with acute myeloid leukemia (AML). In other subsets of AML, C/EBPα activity is repressed by down-regulation of its expression (e.g., PML-RARα), by inhibition of its translation (e.g., BCR-ABL) or by direct protein–protein interaction (e.g., AML-Eto).

cell that has lost the ability to self-renew are likely to be lost as that cell and its progeny differentiate and die. The development of an overt malignancy seems to require cooperation among different classes of mutations. In the context of acute leukemia, several lines of evidence suggest that in some cases transcription factor mutations, which block differentiation, may need to synergize with mutations that dysregulate growth factor-signaling pathways.[184] By contrast, perturbation of signaling pathways appears to be sufficient to generate the initial phase of chronic malignancies such as chronic myeloid leukemia, in which differentiation still occurs.

Transcription factor genes seem to be particularly common targets for leukemogenic mutations in acute leukemias. The reason for this is not clear, but it may relate to the fact that changes to a transcription factor directly influence target genes and hence the transcriptional program of a cell, whereas the effect of mutations within a signaling pathway may be attenuated by multiple levels of compensatory feedback mechanisms. A description of the numerous transcription factor alterations identified in various types of leukemia is beyond the scope of this chapter, and you are referred to several recent excellent reviews.[5,185,186] However, it is worth noting two emerging themes.

First, mutations to several genes may converge on a common transcriptional target, frequently a transcription factor essential for normal differentiation of a particular lineage. For example C/EBPα, a critical regulator of normal myeloid differentiation, is inactivated through mutations in a subset of patients with AML.[187] However as shown in Fig. 29–5, in other subsets of AML, C/EBPα activity is repressed by down-regulation of its expression (e.g., PML-RARα[188]), by inhibition of its translation (e.g., BCR-ABL[189]) or by direct protein–protein interaction (e.g., AML-Eto[190]). Similarly, several transcription factors ectopically expressed in T-cell ALL are thought to sequester members of the E2A family essential for normal T-cell differentiation.[191–193]

A second theme is the realization that leukemias are sustained by relatively rare leukemic stem cells, which are phenotypically and functionally similar to HSCs.[2] This concept is consistent with the finding that targeted mutation of the *Bmi-1* gene, a member of the Polycomb family of transcription factors, impairs the self-renewal of both normal and leukemic stem cells.[105,106] It also is unlikely to be a coincidence that, of six transcription factors (SCL, LMO-2, Runx1, tel, MLL, and GATA-2) with critical roles in HSC formation or behavior, the first five were identified by their alteration in leukemia. Studies of leukemia are likely to continue to illuminate normal HSC biology, and vice versa.

REFERENCES

1. Bench, A.J., Nacheva, E.P., Champion, K.M., and Green, A.R. (1998). Molecular genetics and cytogenetics of myeloproliferative disorders. *Baillieres Clin. Haematol.* **11,** 819–848.
2. Bonnet, D., and Dick, J.E. (1997). Human acute myeloid leukemia is organized as a hierarchy that originates from a primitive hematopoietic cell. *Nat. Med.* **3,** 730–737.
3. Deininger, M.W., Goldman, J.M., and Melo, J.V. (2000). The molecular biology of chronic myeloid leukemia. *Blood* **96,** 3343–3356.
4. Faderl, S., Talpaz, M., Estrov, Z., O'Brien, S., Kurzrock, R., and Kantarjian, H.M. (1999). The biology of chronic myeloid leukemia. *N. Engl. J. Med.* **341,** 164–172.
5. Dash, A., and Gilliland, D.G. (2001). Molecular genetics of acute myeloid leukemia. *Best Pract. Res. Clin. Haematol.* **14,** 49–64.
6. Alcalay, M., Orleth, A., Sebastiani, C., Meani, N., Chiaradonna, F., Casciari, C., Sciurpi, M.T., Gelmetti, V., Riganelli, D., Minucci, S., Fagioli, M., and Pelicci, P.G. (2001). Common themes in the pathogenesis of acute myeloid leukemia. *Oncogene* **20,** 5680–5694.
7. Garcia-Porrero, J.A., Godin, I.E., and Dieterlen-Lievre, F. (1995). Potential intraembryonic hemogenic sites at preliver stages in the mouse. *Anat. Embryol. (Berl.)* **192,** 425–435.
8. North, T., Gu, T.L., Stacy, T., Wang, Q., Howard, L., Binder, M., Marin-Padilla, M., and Speck, N.A. (1999). Cbfa2 is required for the formation of intra-aortic hematopoietic clusters. *Development* **126,** 2563–2575.
9. De Bruijn, M.F., Ma, X., Robin, C., Ottersbach, K., Sanchez, M.J., and Dzierzak, E. (2002). Hematopoietic stem cells localize to the endothelial cell layer in the midgestation mouse aorta. Immunity 16, 673–683.
10. Tavian, M., Coulombel, L., Luton, D., Clemente, H.S., Dieterlen-Lievre, F., and Peault, B. (1996). Aorta-associated CD34+ hematopoietic cells in the early human embryo. *Blood* **87,** 67–72.
11. Yoder, M.C., Hiatt, K., Dutt, P., Mukherjee, P., Bodine, D.M., and Orlic, D. (1997). Characterization of definitive lymphohematopoietic stem cells in the day 9 murine yolk sac. *Immunity* **7,** 335–344.
12. Kennedy, M., Firpo, M., Choi, K., Wall, C., Robertson, S., Kabrun, N., and Keller, G. (1997). A common precursor for primitive erythropoiesis and definitive hematopoiesis. *Nature* **386,** 488–493.
13. Lacaud, G., Robertson, S., Palis, J., Kennedy, M., and Keller, G. (2001). Regulation of hemangioblast development. *Ann. NY Acad. Sci.* **938,** 96–107; discussion 108.
14. Hirai, H., Ogawa, M., Suzuki, N., Yamamoto, M., Breier, G., Mazda, O., Imanishi, J., and Nishikawa, S. (2003). Hemogenic and nonhemogenic endothelium can be distinguished by the activity of fetal liver kinase (Flk)-1 promoter–enhancer during mouse embryogenesis. *Blood* **101,** 886–893.

15. Grant, M.B., May, W.S., Caballero, S., Brown, G.A., Guthrie, S.M., Mames, R.N., Byrne, B.J., Vaught, T., Spoerri, P.E., Peck, A.B., and Scott, E.W. (2002). Adult hematopoietic stem cells provide functional hemangioblast activity during retinal neovascularization. *Nat. Med.* **8,** 607–612.
16. Pelosi, E., Valtieri, M., Coppola, S., Botta, R., Gabbianelli, M., Lulli, V., Marziali, G., Masella, B., Muller, R., Sgadari, C., Testa, U., Bonanno, G., and Peschle, C. (2002). Identification of the hemangioblast in postnatal life. *Blood* **100,** 3203–3208.
17. Oberlin, E., Tavian, M., Blazsek, I., and Peault, B. (2002). Blood-forming potential of vascular endothelium in the human embryo. *Development* **129,** 4147–4157.
18. Jiang, Y., Jahagirdar, B.N., Reinhardt, R.L., Schwartz, R.E., Keene, C.D., Ortiz-Gonzalez, X.R., Reyes, M., Lenvik, T., Lund, T., Blackstad, M., Du, J., Aldrich, S., Lisberg, A., Low, W.C., Largaespada, D.A., and Verfaillie, C.M. (2002). Pluripotency of mesenchymal stem cells derived from adult marrow. *Nature* **418,** 41–49.
19. Bjornson, C.R., Rietze, R.L., Reynolds, B.A., Magli, M.C., and Vescovi, A.L. (1999). Turning brain into blood: a hematopoietic fate adopted by adult neural stem cells *in vivo*. *Science* **283,** 534–537.
20. Zhao, L.R., Duan, W.M., Reyes, M., Keene, C.D., Verfaillie, C.M., and Low, W.C. (2002). Human bone marrow stem cells exhibit neural phenotypes and ameliorate neurological deficits after grafting into the ischemic brain of rats. *Exp. Neurol.* **174,** 11–20.
21. LaBarge, M.A., and Blau, H.M. (2002). Biological progression from adult bone marrow to mononucleate muscle stem cell to multinucleate muscle fiber in response to injury. *Cell* **111,** 589–601.
22. Krause, D.S., Theise, N.D., Collector, M.I., Henegariu, O., Hwang, S., Gardner, R., Neutzel, S., and Sharkis, S.J. (2001). Multiorgan, multilineage engraftment by a single bone marrow-derived stem cell. *Cell* **105,** 369–377.
23. Morshead, C.M., Benveniste, P., Iscove, N.N., and van der Kooy, D. (2002). Hematopoietic competence is a rare property of neural stem cells that may depend on genetic and epigenetic alterations. *Nat. Med.* **8,** 268–273.
24. Yamada, Y., Warren, A.J., Dobson, C., Forster, A., Pannell, R., and Rabbitts, T.H. (1998). The T-cell leukemia LIM protein Lmo2 is necessary for adult mouse hematopoiesis. *Proc. Natl. Acad. Sci. U. S. A.* **95,** 3890–3895.
25. Robb, L., Lyons, I., Li, R., Hartley, L., Kontgen, F., Harvey, R.P., Metcalf, D., and Begley, C.G. (1995). Absence of yolk sac hematopoiesis from mice with a targeted disruption of the *scl* gene. *Proc. Natl. Acad. Sci. U. S. A.* **92,** 7075–7079.
26. Robb, L., Elwood, N.J., Elefanty, A.G., Kontgen, F., Li, R., Barnett, L.D., and Begley, C.G. (1996). The *scl* gene product is required for the generation of all hematopoietic lineages in the adult mouse. *EMBO J.* **15,** 4123–4129.
27. Porcher, C., Swat, W., Rockwell, K., Fujiwara, Y., Alt, F.W., and Orkin, S.H. (1996). The T-cell leukemia oncoprotein SCL/tal-1 is essential for development of all hematopoietic lineages. *Cell* **86,** 47–57.
28. Shivdasani, R.A., Mayer, E.L., and Orkin, S.H. (1995). Absence of blood formation in mice lacking the T-cell leukemia oncoprotein tal-1/SCL. *Nature* **373,** 432–434.
29. Warren, A.J., Colledge, W.H., Carlton, M.B., Evans, M.J., Smith, A.J., and Rabbitts, T.H. (1994). The oncogenic cysteine-rich LIM domain protein rbtn2 is essential for erythroid development. *Cell* **78,** 45–57.
30. Yamada, Y., Pannell, R., Forster, A., and Rabbitts, T.H. (2000). The oncogenic LIM-only transcription factor Lmo2 regulates angiogenesis but not vasculogenesis in mice. *Proc. Natl. Acad. Sci. U. S. A.* **97,** 320–324.
31. Visvader, J.E., Fujiwara, Y., and Orkin, S.H. (1998). Unsuspected role for the T-cell leukemia protein SCL/tal-1 in vascular development. *Genes Dev.* **12,** 473–479.
32. Robertson, S.M., Kennedy, M., Shannon, J.M., and Keller, G. (2000). A transitional stage in the commitment of mesoderm to hematopoiesis requiring the transcription factor SCL/tal-1. *Development* **127,** 2447–2459.
33. Endoh, M., Ogawa, M., Orkin, S., and Nishikawa, S. (2002). SCL/tal-1-dependent process determines a competence to select the definitive hematopoietic lineage prior to endothelial differentiation. *EMBO J.* **21,** 6700–6708.
34. Tsai, F.Y., Keller, G., Kuo, F.C., Weiss, M., Chen, J., Rosenblatt, M., Alt, F.W., and Orkin, S.H. (1994). An early hematopoietic defect in mice lacking the transcription factor GATA-2. *Nature* **371,** 221–226.
35. Tsai, F.Y., and Orkin, S.H. (1997). Transcription factor GATA-2 is required for proliferation–survival of early hematopoietic cells and mast cell formation but not for erythroid and myeloid terminal differentiation. *Blood* **89,** 3636–3643.
36. Wang, Q., Stacy, T., Miller, J.D., Lewis, A.F., Gu, T.L., Huang, X., Bushweller, J.H., Bories, J.C., Alt, F.W., Ryan, G., Liu, P.P., Wynshaw-Boris, A., Binder, M., Marin-Padilla, M., Sharpe, A.H., and Speck, N.A. (1996). The CBFβ subunit is essential for CBF-α2 (AML1) function *in vivo*. *Cell* **87,** 697–708.
37. Sasaki, K., Yagi, H., Bronson, R.T., Tominaga, K., Matsunashi, T., Deguchi, K., Tani, Y., Kishimoto, T., and Komori, T. (1996). Absence of fetal liver hematopoiesis in mice deficient in transcriptional coactivator core-binding factor beta. *Proc. Natl. Acad. Sci. U. S. A.* **93,** 12,359–12,363.
38. Lund, A.H., and van Lohuizen, M. (2002). *RUNX:* a trilogy of cancer genes. *Cancer Cell* **1,** 213–215.
39. Wang, L.C., Swat, W., Fujiwara, Y., Davidson, L., Visvader, J., Kuo, F., Alt, F.W., Gilliland, D.G., Golub, T.R., and Orkin, S.H. (1998). The *TEL/ETV6* gene is required specifically for hematopoiesis in the bone marrow. *Genes Dev.* **12,** 2392–2402.
40. Mucenski, M.L., McLain, K., Kier, A.B., Swerdlow, S.H., Schreiner, C.M., Miller, T.A., Pietryga, D.W., Scott, W.J., Jr., and Potter, S.S. (1991). A functional *c-myb* gene is required for normal murine fetal hepatic hematopoiesis. *Cell* **65,** 677–689.
41. Sumner, R., Crawford, A., Mucenski, M., and Frampton, J. (2000). Initiation of adult myelopoiesis can occur in the absence of c-Myb, whereas subsequent development is strictly dependent on the transcription factor. *Oncogene* **19,** 3335–3342.
42. Wadman, I.A., Osada, H., Grutz, G.G., Agulnick, A.D., Westphal, H., Forster, A., and Rabbitts, T.H. (1997). The LIM-only protein Lmo2 is a bridging molecule assembling an erythroid, DNA-binding complex, which includes the TAL1, E47, GATA-1, and Ldb1/NLI proteins. *EMBO J.* **16,** 3145–3157.
43. Mead, P.E., Deconinck, A.E., Huber, T.L., Orkin, S.H., and Zon, L.I. (2001). Primitive erythropoiesis in the *Xenopus* embryo: the synergistic role of LMO-2, SCL, and GATA-binding proteins. *Development* **128,** 2301–2308.
44. Begley, C.G., and Green, A.R. (1999). The *SCL* gene: from case report to critical hematopoietic regulator. *Blood* **93,** 2760–2770.
45. Akashi, K., He, X., Chen, J., Iwasaki, H., Niu, C., Steenhard, B., Zhang, J., Haug, J., and Li, L. (2003). Transcriptional accessibility for genes of multiple tissues and hematopoietic lineages is hierarchically controlled during early hematopoiesis. *Blood* **101,** 383–389.
46. Ciau-Uitz, A., Walmsley, M., and Patient, R. (2000). Distinct origins of adult and embryonic blood in *Xenopus*. *Cell* **102,** 787–796.

47. Drake, C.J., Brandt, S.J., Trusk, T.C., and Little, C.D. (1997). TAL1/SCL is expressed in endothelial progenitor cells–angioblasts and defines a dorsal-to-ventral gradient of vasculogenesis. *Dev. Biol.* **192,** 17–30.
48. Gering, M., Rodaway, A.R., Gottgens, B., Patient, R.K., and Green, A.R. (1998). The *SCL* gene specifies hemangioblast development from early mesoderm. *EMBO J.* **17,** 4029–4045.
49. Green, A.R., Lints, T., Visvader, J., Harvey, R., and Begley, C.G. (1992). SCL is coexpressed with GATA-1 in hemopoietic cells but is also expressed in developing brain. *Oncogene* **7,** 653–660.
50. Kallianpur, A.R., Jordan, J.E., and Brandt, S.J. (1994). The *SCL/TAL-1* gene is expressed in progenitors of both the hematopoietic and vascular systems during embryogenesis. *Blood* **83,** 1200–1208.
51. Liao, E.C., Paw, B.H., Oates, A.C., Pratt, S.J., Postlethwait, J.H., and Zon, L.I. (1998). SCL/Tal-1 transcription factor acts downstream of cloche to specify hematopoietic and vascular progenitors in zebra fish. *Genes Dev.* **12,** 621–626.
52. Mead, P.E., and Zon, L.I. (1998). Molecular insights into early hematopoiesis. *Curr. Opin. Hematol.* **5,** 156–160.
53. Mouthon, M.A., Bernard, O., Mitjavila, M.T., Romeo, P.H., Vainchenker, W., and Mathieu-Mahul, D. (1993). Expression of tal-1 and GATA-binding proteins during human hematopoiesis. *Blood* **81,** 647–655.
54. Sinclair, A.M., Göttgens, B., Barton, L.M., Stanley, M.L., Pardanaud, L., Klaine, M., Gering, M., Bahn, S., Sanchez, M., Bench, A.J., Fordham, J.L., Bockamp, E., and Green, A.R. (1999). Distinct 5′ SCL enhancers direct transcription to developing brain, spinal cord, and endothelium: neural expression is mediated by GATA factor-binding sites. *Dev. Biol.* **209,** 128–142.
55. Ema, M., Faloon, P., Zhang, W.J., Hirashima, M., Reid, T., Stanford, W.L., Orkin, S., Choi, K., and Rossant, J. (2003). Combinatorial effects of Flk1 and Tal1 on vascular and hematopoietic development in the mouse. *Genes Dev.* **17,** 380–393.
56. Mikkola, H.K., Klintman, J., Yang, H., Hock, H., Schlaeger, T.M., Fujiwara, Y., and Orkin, S.H. (2003). Hematopoietic stem cells retain long-term repopulating activity and multipotency in the absence of stem cell leukemia *SCL/tal-1* gene. *Nature* **421,** 547–551.
57. Hall, M.A., Curtis, D.J., Metcalf, D., Elefanty, A.G., Sourris, K., Robb, L., Gothert, J.R., Jane, S.M., and Begley, C.G. (2003). The critical regulator of embryonic hematopoiesis, SCL, is vital in the adult for megakaryopoiesis, erythropoiesis, and lineage choice in CFU-S12. *Proc. Natl. Acad. Sci. U. S. A.* **100,** 992–997.
58. Aplan, P.D., Nakahara, K., Orkin, S.H., and Kirsch, I.R. (1992). The *SCL* gene product: a positive regulator of erythroid differentiation. *EMBO J.* **11,** 4073–4081.
59. Bockamp, E.O., McLaughlin, F., Murrell, A.M., Göttgens, B., Robb, L., Begley, C.G., and Green, A.R. (1995). Lineage-restricted regulation of the murine SCL/TAL-1 promoter. *Blood* **86,** 1502–1514.
60. Bockamp, E.O., McLaughlin, F., Göttgens, B., Murrell, A.M., Elefanty, A.G., and Green, A.R. (1997). Distinct mechanisms direct SCL/tal-1 expression in erythroid cells and CD34+ primitive myeloid cells. *J. Biol. Chem.* **272,** 8781–8790.
61. Bockamp, E.O., Fordham, J.L., Gottgens, B., Murrell, A.M., Sanchez, M.J., and Green, A.R. (1998). Transcriptional regulation of the stem cell leukemia gene by PU.1 and Elf-1. *J. Biol. Chem.* **273,** 29,032–29,042.
62. Lecointe, N., Bernard, O., Naert, K., Joulin, V., Larsen, C.J., Romeo, P.H., and Mathieu-Mahul, D. (1994). GATA-and SP1-binding sites are required for the full activity of the tissue-specific promoter of the *tal-1* gene. *Oncogene* **9,** 2623–2632.
63. Göttgens, B., McLaughlin, F., Bockamp, E.O., Fordham, J.L., Begley, C.G., Kosmopoulos, K., Elefanty, A.G., and Green, A.R. (1997). Transcription of the *SCL* gene in erythroid and CD34+ primitive myeloid cells is controlled by a complex network of lineage-restricted chromatin-dependent and chromatin-independent regulatory elements. *Oncogene* **15,** 2419–2428.
64. Göttgens, B., Barton, L.M., Gilbert, J.G., Bench, A.J., Sanchez, M.J., Bahn, S., Mistry, S., Grafham, D., McMurray, A., Vaudin, M., Amaya, E., Bentley, D.R., Green, A.R., and Sinclair, A.M. (2000). Analysis of vertebrate SCL loci identifies conserved enhancers. *Nat. Biotechnol.* **18,** 181–186.
65. Göttgens, B., Gilbert, J.G., Barton, L.M., Grafham, D., Rogers, J., Bentley, D.R., and Green, A.R. (2001). Long-range comparison of human and mouse SCL loci: localized regions of sensitivity to restriction endonucleases correspond precisely with peaks of conserved noncoding sequences. *Genome Res.* **11,** 87–97.
66. Göttgens, B., Barton, L.M., Chapman, M.A., Sinclair, A.M., Knudsen, B., Grafham, D., Gilbert, J.G., Rogers, J., Bentley, D.R., and Green, A.R. (2002). Transcriptional regulation of the stem cell leukemia gene *(SCL)*—Comparative analysis of five vertebrate *SCL* loci. *Genome Res.* **12,** 749–759.
67. Sinclair, A.M., Bench, A.J., Bloor, A.J., Li, J., Göttgens, B., Stanley, M.L., Miller, J., Piltz, S., Hunter, S., Nacheva, E.P., Sanchez, M.J., and Green, A.R. (2002). Rescue of the lethal $scl^{-/-}$ phenotype by the human SCL locus. *Blood* **99,** 3931–3938.
68. Sanchez, M., Göttgens, B., Sinclair, A.M., Stanley, M., Begley, C.G., Hunter, S., and Green, A.R. (1999). An SCL 3′ enhancer targets developing endothelium together with embryonic and adult hematopoietic progenitors. *Development* **126,** 3891–3904.
69. Fordham, J.L., Göttgens, B., McLaughlin, F., and Green, A.R. (1999). Chromatin structure and transcriptional regulation of the stem cell leukemia *(SCL)* gene in mast cells. *Leukemia* **13,** 750–759.
70. Sanchez, M.J., Bockamp, E.O., Miller, J., Gambardella, L., and Green, A.R. (2001). Selective rescue of early hematopoietic progenitors in $Scl^{-/-}$ mice by expressing Scl under the control of a stem cell enhancer. *Development* **128,** 4815–4827.
71. Göttgens, B., Nastos, A., Kinston, S., Piltz, S., Delabesse, E.C., Stanley, M., Sanchez, M.J., Ciau-Uitz, A., Patient, R., and Green, A.R. (2002). Establishing the transcriptional program for blood: the SCL stem cell enhancer is regulated by a multiprotein complex containing Ets and GATA factors. *EMBO J.* **21,** 3039–3050.
72. Minegishi, N., Ohta, J., Yamagiwa, H., Suzuki, N., Kawauchi, S., Zhou, Y., Takahashi, S., Hayashi, N., Engel, J.D., and Yamamoto, M. (1999). The mouse *GATA-2* gene is expressed in the para-aortic splanchnopleura and aorta–gonads and mesonephros region. *Blood* **93,** 4196–4207.
73. Vlaeminck-Guillem, V., Carrere, S., Dewitte, F., Stehelin, D., Desbiens, X., and Duterque-Coquillaud, M. (2000). The Ets family member *Erg* gene is expressed in mesodermal tissues and neural crests at fundamental steps during mouse embryogenesis. *Mech. Dev.* **91,** 331–335.
74. Dube, A., Thai, S., Gaspar, J., Rudders, S., Libermann, T.A., Iruela-Arispe, L., and Oettgen, P. (2001). Elf-1 is a transcriptional regulator of the *Tie2* gene during vascular development. *Circ. Res.* **88,** 237–244.
75. Spyropoulos, D.D., Pharr, P.N., Lavenburg, K.R., Jackers, P., Papas, T.S., Ogawa, M., and Watson, D.K. (2000). Hemorrhage, impaired hematopoiesis, and lethality in mouse embryos carrying a targeted disruption of the Fli1 transcription factor. *Mol. Cell Biol.* **20,** 5643–5652.

76. Hart, A., Melet, F., Grossfeld, P., Chien, K., Jones, C., Tunnacliffe, A., Favier, R., and Bernstein, A. (2000). Fli-1 is required for murine vascular and megakaryocytic development and is hemizygously deleted in patients with thrombocytopenia. *Immunity* **13,** 167–177.
77. Garrett-Sinha, L.A., Dahl, R., Rao, S., Barton, K.P., and Simon, M.C. (2001). PU.1 exhibits partial functional redundancy with Spi-B but not with Ets-1 or Elf-1. *Blood* **97,** 2908–2912.
78. Ivanova, N.B., Dimos, J.T., Schaniel, C., Hackney, J.A., Moore, K.A., and Lemischka, I.R. (2002). A stem cell molecular signature. *Science* **298,** 601–604.
79. Phillips, R.L., Ernst, R.E., Brunk, B., Ivanova, N., Mahan, M.A., Deanehan, J.K., Moore, K.A., Overton, G.C., and Lemischka, I.R. (2000). The genetic program of hematopoietic stem cells. *Science* **288,** 1635–1640.
80. Ramalho-Santos, M., Yoon, S., Matsuzaki, Y., Mulligan, R.C., and Melton, D.A. (2002). "Stemness": transcriptional profiling of embryonic and adult stem cells. *Science* **298,** 597–600.
81. Arnone, M.I., and Davidson, E.H. (1997). The hardwiring of development: organization and function of genomic regulatory systems. *Development* **124,** 1851–1864.
82. Davidson, E.H., Rast, J.P., Oliveri, P., Ransick, A., Calestani, C., Yuh, C.H., Minokawa, T., Amore, G., Hinman, V., Arenas-Mena, C., Otim, O., Brown, C.T., Livi, C.B., Lee, P.Y., Revilla, R., Rust, A.G., Pan, Z., Schilstra, M.J., Clarke, P.J., Arnone, M.I., Rowen, L., Cameron, R.A., McClay, D.R., Hood, L., and Bolouri, H. (2002). A genomic regulatory network for development. *Science* **295,** 1669–1678.
83. Ziegler, S., Burki, K., and Skoda, R.C. (2002). A 2-kb c-mpl promoter fragment is sufficient to direct expression to the megakaryocytic lineage and sites of embryonic hematopoiesis in transgenic mice. *Blood* **100,** 1072–1074.
84. Ma, X., Robin, C., Ottersbach, K., and Dzierzak, E. (2002). The *Ly-6A (Sca-1)* GFP transgene is expressed in all adult mouse hematopoietic stem cells. *Stem Cells* **20,** 514–521.
85. Watt, F.M. (2002). Role of integrins in regulating epidermal adhesion, growth, and differentiation. *EMBO J.* **21,** 3919–3926.
86. Batlle, E., Henderson, J.T., Beghtel, H., van den Born, M.M., Sancho, E., Huls, G., Meeldijk, J., Robertson, J., van de Wetering, M., Pawson, T., and Clevers, H. (2002). β-catenin and TCF mediate cell positioning in the intestinal epithelium by controlling the expression of EphB/ephrinB. *Cell* **111,** 251–263.
87. Fairbairn, L.J., Cowling, G.J., Reipert, B.M., and Dexter, T.M. (1993). Suppression of apoptosis allows differentiation and development of a multipotent hemopoietic cell line in the absence of added growth factors. *Cell* **74,** 823–832.
88. Ogawa, M. (1993). Differentiation and proliferation of hematopoietic stem cells. *Blood* **81,** 2844–2853.
89. Kondo, M., Scherer, D.C., Miyamoto, T., King, A.G., Akashi, K., Sugamura, K., and Weissman, I.L. (2000). Cell fate conversion of lymphoid-committed progenitors by instructive actions of cytokines. *Nature* **407,** 383–386.
90. Enver, T., and Greaves, M. (1998). Loops, lineage, and leukemia. *Cell* **94,** 9–12.
91. McAdams, H.H., and Arkin, A. (1997). Stochastic mechanisms in gene expression. *Proc. Natl. Acad. Sci. U. S. A.* **94,** 814–819.
92. Blake, W.J., M, K.A., Cantor, C.R., and Collins, J.J. (2003). Noise in eukaryotic gene expression. *Nature* **422,** 633–637.
93. Akashi, K., Traver, D., Miyamoto, T., and Weissman, I.L. (2000). A clonogenic common myeloid progenitor that gives rise to all myeloid lineages. *Nature* **404,** 193–197.
94. Manz, M.G., Miyamoto, T., Akashi, K., and Weissman, I.L. (2002). Prospective isolation of human clonogenic common myeloid progenitors. *Proc. Natl. Acad. Sci. U. S. A.* **99,** 11, 872–11, 877.
95. Mebius, R.E., Miyamoto, T., Christensen, J., Domen, J., Cupedo, T., Weissman, I.L., and Akashi, K. (2001). The fetal liver counterpart of adult common lymphoid progenitors gives rise to all lymphoid lineages, CD45+CD4+CD3− cells, as well as macrophages. *J. Immunol.* **166,** 6593–6601.
96. Kondo, M., Weissman, I.L., and Akashi, K. (1997). Identification of clonogenic common lymphoid progenitors in mouse bone marrow. *Cell* **91,** 661–672.
97. Akashi, K., Traver, D., Kondo, M., and Weissman, I.L. (1999). Lymphoid development from hematopoietic stem cells. *Int. J. Hematol.* **69,** 217–226.
98. Nakorn, T.N., Miyamoto, T., and Weissman, I.L. (2003). Characterization of mouse clonogenic megakaryocyte progenitors. *Proc. Natl. Acad. Sci. U. S. A.* **100,** 205–210.
99. Heyworth, C., Pearson, S., May, G., and Enver, T. (2002). Transcription factor-mediated lineage switching reveals plasticity in primary committed progenitor cells. *EMBO J.* **21,** 3770–3781.
100. Nerlov, C., and Graf, T. (1998). PU.1 induces myeloid lineage commitment in multipotent hematopoietic progenitors. *Genes Dev.* **12,** 2403–2412.
101. Kulessa, H., Frampton, J., and Graf, T. (1995). GATA-1 reprograms avian myelomonocytic cell lines into eosinophils, thromboblasts, and erythroblasts. *Genes Dev.* **9,** 1250–1262.
102. Willert, K., Brown, J.D., Danenberg, E., Duncan, A.W., Weissman, I.L., Reya, T., Yates, J.R., and Nusse, R. (2003). Wnt proteins are lipid-modified and can act as stem cell growth factors. *Nature* **423,** 448–452.
103. Reya, T., Duncan, A.W., Ailles, L., Domen, J., Scherer, D.C., Willert, K., Hintz, L., Nusse, R., and Weissman, I.L. (2003). A role for Wnt signaling in self-renewal of hematopoietic stem cells. *Nature* **423,** 409–414.
104. De Haan, G., Weersing, E., Dontje, B., van Os, R., Bystrykh, L.V., Vellenga, E., and Miller, G. (2003). *In vitro* generation of long-term repopulating hematopoietic stem cells by fibroblast growth factor-1. *Dev. Cell* **4,** 241–251.
105. Park, I.K., Qian, D., Kiel, M., Becker, M.W., Pihalja, M., Weissman, I.L., Morrison, S.J., and Clarke, M.F. (2003). Bmi-1 is required for maintenance of adult self-renewing hematopoietic stem cells. *Nature* **423,** 302–305.
106. Lessard, J., and Sauvageau, G. (2003). Bmi-1 determines the proliferative capacity of normal and leukemic stem cells. *Nature* **423,** 255–260.
107. Matsuda, T., Nakamura, T., Nakao, K., Arai, T., Katsuki, M., Heike, T., and Yokota, T. (1999). STAT3 activation is sufficient to maintain an undifferentiated state of mouse embryonic stem cells. *EMBO J.* **18,** 4261–4269.
108. Tulina, N., and Matunis, E. (2001). Control of stem cell self-renewal in *Drosophila* spermatogenesis by JAK–STAT signaling. *Science* **294,** 2546–2549.
109. Bunting, K.D., Bradley, H.L., Hawley, T.S., Moriggl, R., Sorrentino, B.P., and Ihle, J.N. (2002). Reduced lymphomyeloid repopulating activity from adult bone marrow and fetal liver of mice lacking expression of STAT5. *Blood* **99,** 479–487.
110. Bradley, H.L., Hawley, T.S., and Bunting, K.D. (2002). Cell intrinsic defects in cytokine responsiveness of STAT5-deficient hematopoietic stem cells. *Blood* **100,** 3983–3989.
111. Jenkins, B.J., Quilici, C., Roberts, A.W., Grail, D., Dunn, A.R., and Ernst, M. (2002). Hematopoietic abnormalities in mice

deficient in gp130-mediated STAT signaling. *Exp. Hematol.* **30,** 1248–1256.

112. Sauvageau, G., Lansdorp, P.M., Eaves, C.J., Hogge, D.E., Dragowska, W.H., Reid, D.S., Largman, C., Lawrence, H.J., and Humphries, R.K. (1994). Differential expression of homeobox genes in functionally distinct CD34+ subpopulations of human bone marrow cells. *Proc. Natl. Acad. Sci. U. S. A.* **91,** 12,223–12,227.
113. Sauvageau, G., Thorsteinsdottir, U., Eaves, C.J., Lawrence, H.J., Largman, C., Lansdorp, P.M., and Humphries, R.K. (1995). Overexpression of HOXB4 in hematopoietic cells causes the selective expansion of more primitive populations *in vitro* and *in vivo*. *Genes Dev.* **9,** 1753–1765.
114. Antonchuk, J., Sauvageau, G., and Humphries, R.K. (2002). HOXB4-induced expansion of adult hematopoietic stem cells *ex vivo*. *Cell* **109,** 39–45.
115. Kyba, M., Perlingeiro, R.C., and Daley, G.Q. (2002). HoxB4 confers definitive lymphoid–myeloid engraftment potential on embryonic stem cell and yolk sac hematopoietic progenitors. *Cell* **109,** 29–37.
116. Rideout, W.M., 3rd, Hochedlinger, K., Kyba, M., Daley, G.Q., and Jaenisch, R. (2002). Correction of a genetic defect by nuclear transplantation and combined cell and gene therapy. *Cell* **109,** 17–27.
117. Schiedlmeier, B., Klump, H., Will, E., Arman-Kalcek, G., Li, Z., Wang, Z., Rimek, A., Friel, J., Baum, C., and Ostertag, W. (2003). High-level ectopic HOXB4 expression confers a profound *in vivo* competitive growth advantage on human cord blood CD34+ cells but impairs lymphomyeloid differentiation. *Blood* **101,** 1759–1768.
118. Lin, H. (2002). The stem cell niche theory: lessons from flies. *Nat. Rev. Genet.* **3,** 931–940.
119. Spradling, A., Drummond-Barbosa, D., and Kai, T. (2001). Stem cells find their niche. *Nature* **414,** 98–104.
120. Lewis, J. (1998). Notch signaling and the control of cell fate choices in vertebrates. *Semin. Cell Dev. Biol.* **9,** 583–589.
121. Hitoshi, S., Alexson, T., Tropepe, V., Donoviel, D., Elia, A.J., Nye, J.S., Conlon, R.A., Mak, T.W., Bernstein, A., and van der Kooy, D. (2002). Notch pathway molecules are essential for the maintenance, but not the generation, of mammalian neural stem cells. *Genes Dev.* **16,** 846–858.
122. Kopan, R., Nye, J.S., and Weintraub, H. (1994). The intracellular domain of mouse Notch: a constitutively activated repressor of myogenesis directed at the basic helix–loop–helix region of MyoD. *Development* **120,** 2385–2396.
123. Delfini, M., Hirsinger, E., Pourquie, O., and Duprez, D. (2000). Delta-1-activated notch inhibits muscle differentiation without affecting Myf5 and Pax3 expression in chick limb myogenesis. *Development* **127,** 5213–5224.
124. Varnum-Finney, B., Purton, L.E., Yu, M., Brashem-Stein, C., Flowers, D., Staats, S., Moore, K.A., Le Roux, I., Mann, R., Gray, G., Artavanis-Tsakonas, S., and Bernstein, I.D. (1998). The Notch ligand, Jagged-1, influences the development of primitive hematopoietic precursor cells. *Blood* **91,** 4084–4091.
125. Jones, P., May, G., Healy, L., Brown, J., Hoyne, G., Delassus, S., and Enver, T. (1998). Stromal expression of Jagged-1 promotes colony formation by fetal hematopoietic progenitor cells. *Blood* **92,** 1505–1511.
126. Li, L., Milner, L.A., Deng, Y., Iwata, M., Banta, A., Graf, L., Marcovina, S., Friedman, C., Trask, B.J., Hood, L., and Torok-Storb, B. (1998). The human homolog of rat Jagged-1 expressed by marrow stroma inhibits differentiation of 32D cells through interaction with Notch-1. *Immunity* **8,** 43–55.
127. Karanu, F.N., Murdoch, B., Gallacher, L., Wu, D.M., Koremoto, M., Sakano, S., and Bhatia, M. (2000). The Notch ligand Jagged-1 represents a novel growth factor of human hematopoietic stem cells. *J. Exp. Med.* **192,** 1365–1372.
128. Karanu, F.N., Murdoch, B., Miyabayashi, T., Ohno, M., Koremoto, M., Gallacher, L., Wu, D., Itoh, A., Sakano, S., and Bhatia, M. (2001). Human homologues of Delta-1 and Delta-4 function as mitogenic regulators of primitive human hematopoietic cells. *Blood* **97,** 1960–1967.
129. Ohishi, K., Varnum-Finney, B., and Bernstein, I.D. (2002). Delta-1 enhances marrow and thymus repopulating ability of human CD34+CD38− cord blood cells. *J. Clin. Invest.* **110,** 1165–1174.
130. Varnum-Finney, B., Brashem-Stein, C., and Bernstein, I.D. (2003). Combined effects of Notch signaling and cytokines induce a multiple log increase in precursors with lymphoid and myeloid reconstituting ability. *Blood* **101,** 1784–1789.
131. Varnum-Finney, B., Xu, L., Brashem-Stein, C., Nourigat, C., Flowers, D., Bakkour, S., Pear, W.S., and Bernstein, I.D. (2000). Pluripotent, cytokine-dependent, hematopoietic stem cells are immortalized by constitutive Notch1 signaling. *Nat. Med.* **6,** 1278–1281.
132. Kunisato, A., Chiba, S., Nakagami-Yamaguchi, E., Kumano, K., Saito, T., Masuda, S., Yamaguchi, T., Osawa, M., Kageyama, R., Nakauchi, H., Nishikawa, M., and Hirai, H. (2003). HES-1 preserves purified hematopoietic stem cells *ex vivo* and accumulates side population cells *in vivo*. *Blood* **101,** 1777–1783.
133. Brady, G., Billia, F., Knox, J., Hoang, T., Kirsch, I.R., Voura, E.B., Hawley, R.G., Cumming, R., Buchwald, M., and Siminovitch, K. (1995). Analysis of gene expression in a complex differentiation hierarchy by global amplification of cDNA from single cells. *Curr. Biol.* **5,** 909–922.
134. Cheng, T., Shen, H., Giokas, D., Gere, J., Tenen, D.G., and Scadden, D.T. (1996). Temporal mapping of gene expression levels during the differentiation of individual primary hematopoietic cells. *Proc. Natl. Acad. Sci. U. S. A.* **93,** 13,158–13,163.
135. Cross, M.A., and Enver, T. (1997). The lineage commitment of hemopoietic progenitor cells. *Curr. Opin. Genet. Dev.* **7,** 609–613.
136. Hu, M., Krause, D., Greaves, M., Sharkis, S., Dexter, M., Heyworth, C., and Enver, T. (1997). Multilineage gene expression precedes commitment in the hemopoietic system. *Genes Dev.* **11,** 774–785.
137. Miyamoto, T., Iwasaki, H., Reizis, B., Ye, M., Graf, T., Weissman, I.L., and Akashi, K. (2002). Myeloid or lymphoid promiscuity as a critical step in hematopoietic lineage commitment. *Dev. Cell* **3,** 137–147.
138. Tagoh, H., Himes, R., Clarke, D., Leenen, P.J., Riggs, A.D., Hume, D., and Bonifer, C. (2002). Transcription factor complex formation and chromatin fine structure alterations at the murine c-fms (CSF-1 receptor) locus during maturation of myeloid precursor cells. *Genes Dev.* **16,** 1721–1737.
139. Kontaraki, J., Chen, H.H., Riggs, A., and Bonifer, C. (2000). Chromatin fine structure profiles for a developmentally regulated gene: reorganization of the lysozyme locus before trans-activator binding and gene expression. *Genes Dev.* **14,** 2106–2122.
140. Dennis, J.E., and Charbord, P. (2002). Origin and differentiation of human and murine stroma. *Stem Cells* **20,** 205–214.
141. Hansen, J.D., and Zapata, A.G. (1998). Lymphocyte development in fish and amphibians. *Immunol. Rev.* **166,** 199–220.

142. Cumano, A., and Godin, I. (2001). Pluripotent hematopoietic stem cell development during embryogenesis. *Curr. Opin. Immunol.* **13,** 166–171.
143. Cotta, C.V., Zhang, Z., Kim, H.G., and Klug, C.A. (2003). Pax5 determines B-versus T-cell fate and does not block early myeloid-lineage development. *Blood* **101,** 4342–4346.
144. Chen, D., and Zhang, G. (2001). Enforced expression of the GATA-3 transcription factor affects cell fate decisions in hematopoiesis. *Exp. Hematol.* **29,** 971–980.
145. Farrar, J.D., Ouyang, W., Lohning, M., Assenmacher, M., Radbruch, A., Kanagawa, O., and Murphy, K.M. (2001). An instructive component in T-helper-cell type 2 (Th2) development mediated by GATA-3. *J. Exp. Med.* **193,** 643–650.
146. Ho, I.C., Vorhees, P., Marin, N., Oakley, B.K., Tsai, S.F., Orkin, S.H., and Leiden, J.M. (1991). Human GATA-3: A lineage-restricted transcription factor that regulates the expression of the T-cell receptor alpha gene. *EMBO J.* **10,** 1187–1192.
147. Oosterwegel, M., Timmerman, J., Leiden, J., and Clevers, H. (1992). Expression of GATA-3 during lymphocyte differentiation and mouse embryogenesis. *Dev. Immunol.* **3,** 1–11.
148. Ting, C.N., Olson, M.C., Barton, K.P., and Leiden, J.M. (1996). Transcription factor GATA-3 is required for development of the T-cell lineage. *Nature* **384,** 474–478.
149. Nawijn, M.C., Ferreira, R., Dingjan, G.M., Kahre, O., Drabek, D., Karis, A., Grosveld, F., and Hendriks, R.W. (2001). Enforced expression of GATA-3 during T-cell development inhibits maturation of CD8 single-positive cells and induces thymic lymphoma in transgenic mice. *J. Immunol.* **167,** 715–723.
150. Seshasayee, D., Gaines, P., and Wojchowski, D.M. (1998). GATA-1 dominantly activates a program of erythroid gene expression in factor-dependent myeloid FDCW2 cells. *Mol. Cell Biol.* **18,** 3278–3288.
151. Visvader, J.E., Elefanty, A.G., Strasser, A., and Adams, J.M. (1992). GATA-1 but not SCL induces megakaryocytic differentiation in an early myeloid line. *EMBO J.* **11,** 4557–4564.
152. Takahashi, S., Shimizu, R., Suwabe, N., Kuroha, T., Yoh, K., Ohta, J., Nishimura, S., Lim, K.C., Engel, J.D., and Yamamoto, M. (2000). *GATA* factor transgenes under *GATA-1* locus control rescue germ line *GATA-1* mutant deficiencies. *Blood* **96,** 910–916.
153. Blobel, G.A., Simon, M.C., and Orkin, S.H. (1995). Rescue of GATA-1-deficient embryonic stem cells by heterologous GATA-binding proteins. *Mol. Cell Biol.* **15,** 626–633.
154. Vyas, P., McDevitt, M.A., Cantor, A.B., Katz, S.G., Fujiwara, Y., and Orkin, S.H. (1999). Different sequence requirements for expression in erythroid and megakaryocytic cells within a regulatory element upstream of the *GATA-1* gene. *Development* **126,** 2799–2811.
155. Tsai, S.F., Strauss, E., and Orkin, S.H. (1991). Functional analysis and *in vivo* footprinting implicate the erythroid transcription factor GATA-1 as a positive regulator of its own promoter. *Genes Dev.* **5,** 919–931.
156. Visvader, J., and Adams, J.M. (1993). Megakaryocytic differentiation induced in 416B myeloid cells by *GATA-2* and *GATA-3* transgenes or 5-azacytidine is tightly coupled to *GATA-1* expression. *Blood* **82,** 1493–1501.
157. Niehof, M., Kubicka, S., Zender, L., Manns, M.P., and Trautwein, C. (2001). Autoregulation enables different pathways to control CCAAT/enhancer-binding protein beta (C/EBP-β) transcription. *J. Mol. Biol.* **309,** 855–868.
158. Legraverend, C., Antonson, P., Flodby, P., and Xanthopoulos, K.G. (1993). High-level activity of the mouse CCAAT/enhancer-binding protein (C/EBP-α) gene promoter involves autoregulation and several ubiquitous transcription factors. *Nucleic Acids Res.* **21,** 1735–1742.
159. Chen, H., Ray-Gallet, D., Zhang, P., Hetherington, C.J., Gonzalez, D.A., Zhang, D.E., Moreau-Gachelin, F., and Tenen, D.G. (1995). PU.1 (Spi-1) autoregulates its expression in myeloid cells. *Oncogene* **11,** 1549–1560.
160. Nerlov, C., Querfurth, E., Kulessa, H., and Graf, T. (2000). GATA-1 interacts with the myeloid PU.1 transcription factor and represses PU.1-dependent transcription. *Blood* **95,** 2543–2551.
161. Zhang, P., Zhang, X., Iwama, A., Yu, C., Smith, K.A., Mueller, B.U., Narravula, S., Torbett, B.E., Orkin, S.H., and Tenen, D.G. (2000). PU.1 inhibits GATA-1 function and erythroid differentiation by blocking GATA-1 DNA binding. *Blood* **96,** 2641–2648.
162. Yamada, T., Kondoh, N., Matsumoto, M., Yoshida, M., Maekawa, A., and Oikawa, T. (1997). Overexpression of PU.1 induces growth and differentiation inhibition and apoptotic cell death in murine erythroleukemia cells. *Blood* **89,** 1383–1393.
163. Rekhtman, N., Radparvar, F., Evans, T., and Skoultchi, A.I. (1999). Direct interaction of hematopoietic transcription factors PU.1 and GATA-1: functional antagonism in erythroid cells. *Genes Dev.* **13,** 1398–1411.
164. Kelly, L.M., Englmeier, U., Lafon, I., Sieweke, M.H., and Graf, T. (2000). MafB is an inducer of monocytic differentiation. *EMBO J.* **19,** 1987–1997.
165. Sieweke, M.H., Tekotte, H., Frampton, J., and Graf, T. (1996). MafB is an interaction partner and repressor of Ets-1 that inhibits erythroid differentiation. *Cell* **85,** 49–60.
166. Querfurth, E., Schuster, M., Kulessa, H., Crispino, J.D., Doderlein, G., Orkin, S.H., Graf, T., and Nerlov, C. (2000). Antagonism between C/EBP-β and FOG in eosinophil lineage commitment of multipotent hematopoietic progenitors. *Genes Dev.* **14,** 2515–2525.
167. Radomska, H.S., Huettner, C.S., Zhang, P., Cheng, T., Scadden, D.T., and Tenen, D.G. (1998). CCAAT/enhancer-binding protein alpha is a regulatory switch sufficient for induction of granulocytic development from bipotential myeloid progenitors. *Mol. Cell Biol.* **18,** 4301–4314.
168. Reddy, V.A., Iwama, A., Iotzova, G., Schulz, M., Elsasser, A., Vangala, R.K., Tenen, D.G., Hiddemann, W., and Behre, G. (2002). Granulocyte inducer C/EBP-α inactivates the myeloid master regulator PU.1: possible role in lineage commitment decisions. *Blood* **100,** 483–490.
169. Urbanek, P., Wang, Z.Q., Fetka, I., Wagner, E.F., and Busslinger, M. (1994). Complete block of early B-cell differentiation and altered patterning of the posterior midbrain in mice lacking Pax5/BSAP. *Cell* **79,** 901–912.
170. Nutt, S.L., Heavey, B., Rolink, A.G., and Busslinger, M. (1999). Commitment to the B-lymphoid lineage depends on the transcription factor Pax5. *Nature* **401,** 556–562.
171. Souabni, A., Cobaleda, C., Schebesta, M., and Busslinger, M. (2002). Pax5 promotes B-lymphopoiesis and blocks T-cell development by repressing Notch1. *Immunity* **17,** 781–793.
172. Chiang, M.Y., and Monroe, J.G. (2001). Role for transcription Pax5A factor in maintaining commitment to the B-cell lineage by selective inhibition of granulocyte–macrophage colony-stimulating factor receptor expression. *J. Immunol.* **166,** 6091–6098.
173. Fialkow, P.J., Jacobson, R.J., and Papayannopoulou, T. (1977). Chronic myelocytic leukemia: clonal origin in a stem cell common to the granulocyte, erythrocyte, platelet, and monocyte–macrophage. *Am. J. Med.* **63,** 125–130.

174. Fialkow, P.J., Faguet, G.B., Jacobson, R.J., Vaidya, K., and Murphy, S. (1981). Evidence that essential thrombocythemia is a clonal disorder with origin in a multipotent stem cell. *Blood* **58,** 916–919.
175. Adamson, J.W., Fialkow, P.J., Murphy, S., Prchal, J.F., and Steinmann, L. (1976). Polycythemia vera: Stem cell and probable clonal origin of the disease. *N. Engl. J. Med.* **295,** 913–916s.
176. Aye, M.T., Till, J.E., and McCulloch, E.A. (1973). Cytological studies of granulopoietic colonies from two patients with chronic myelogenous leukemia. *Exp. Hematol.* **1,** 115–118.
177. Golde, D.W., Burgaleta, C., Sparkes, R.S., and Cline, M.J. (1977). The Philadelphia chromosome in human macrophages. *Blood* **49,** 367–370.
178. Fauser, A.A., Kanz, L., Bross, K.J., and Lohr, G.W. (1985). T-cells and probably B-cells arise from the malignant clone in chronic myelogenous leukemia. *J. Clin. Invest.* **75,** 1080–1082.
179. Cobaleda, C., Gutierrez-Cianca, N., Perez-Losada, J., Flores, T., Garcia-Sanz, R., Gonzalez, M., and Sanchez-Garcia, I. (2000). A primitive hematopoietic cell is the target for the leukemic transformation in human Philadelphia-positive acute lymphoblastic leukemia. *Blood* **95,** 1007–1013.
180. Verstegen, M.M., Cornelissen, J.J., Terpstra, W., Wagemaker, G., and Wognum, A.W. (1999). Multilineage outgrowth of both malignant and normal hemopoietic progenitor cells from individual chronic myeloid leukemia patients in immunodeficient mice. *Leukemia* **13,** 618–628.
181. Reya, T., Morrison, S.J., Clarke, M.F., and Weissman, I.L. (2001). Stem cells, cancer, and cancer stem cells. *Nature* **414,** 105–111.
182. Al-Hajj, M., Wicha, M.S., Benito-Hernandez, A., Morrison, S.J., and Clarke, M.F. (2003). Prospective identification of tumorigenic breast cancer cells. *Proc. Natl. Acad. Sci. U. S. A.* **100,** 3983–3988.
183. Armitage, P., and Doll, R. (1954). The age distribution of cancer and a multistage theory of carcinogenesis. *Br. J. Cancer* **8,** 1.
184. Gilliland, D.G. (2002). Molecular genetics of human leukemias: new insights into therapy. *Semin. Hematol.* **39,** 6–11.
185. Tenen, D.G. (2003). Disruption of differentiation in human cancer: AML shows the way. *Nat. Rev. Cancer* **3,** 89–101.
186. Scandura, J.M., Boccuni, P., Cammenga, J., and Nimer, S.D. (2002). Transcription factor fusions in acute leukemia: variations on a theme. *Oncogene* **21,** 3422–3444.
187. Pabst, T., Mueller, B.U., Zhang, P., Radomska, H.S., Narravula, S., Schnittger, S., Behre, G., Hiddemann, W., and Tenen, D.G. (2001). Dominant-negative mutations of CEBPA, encoding CCAAT/enhancer binding protein-alpha (C/EBP-α), in acute myeloid leukemia. *Nat. Genet.* **27,** 263–270.
188. Truong, B.T., Lee, Y.J., Lodie, T.A., Park, D.J., Perrotti, D., Watanabe, N., Koeffler, H.P., Nakajima, H., Tenen, D.G., and Kogan, S.C. (2003). CCAAT/enhancer-binding proteins repress the leukemic phenotype of acute myeloid leukemia. *Blood* **101,** 1141–1148.
189. Perrotti, D., Cesi, V., Trotta, R., Guerzoni, C., Santilli, G., Campbell, K., Iervolino, A., Condorelli, F., Gambacorti-Passerini, C., Caligiuri, M.A., and Calabretta, B. (2002). BCR-ABL suppresses C/EBP-α expression through inhibitory action of hnRNP E2. *Nat. Genet.* **30,** 48–58.
190. Pabst, T., Mueller, B.U., Harakawa, N., Schoch, C., Haferlach, T., Behre, G., Hiddemann, W., Zhang, D.E., and Tenen, D.G. (2001). AML1-ETO down-regulates the granulocytic differentiation factor C/EBP-α in t(8;21) myeloid leukemia. *Nat. Med.* **7,** 444–451.
191. Blom, B., Heemskerk, M.H., Verschuren, M.C., van Dongen, J.J., Stegmann, A.P., Bakker, A.Q., Couwenberg, F., Res, P.C., and Spits, H. (1999). Disruption of alpha–beta but not of gamma–delta T-cell development by overexpression of the helix–loop–helix protein Id3 in committed T-cell progenitors. *EMBO J.* **18,** 2793–2802.
192. Yan, W., Young, A.Z., Soares, V.C., Kelley, R., Benezra, R., and Zhuang, Y. (1997). High incidence of T-cell tumors in E2A-null mice and E2A/Id1 double-knockout mice. *Mol. Cell Biol.* **17,** 7317–7327.
193. Barndt, R.J., Dai, M., and Zhuang, Y. (2000). Functions of E2A-HEB heterodimers in T-cell development revealed by a dominant negative mutation of HEB. *Mol. Cell Biol.* **20,** 6677–6685.

30

Phenotype of Mouse Hematopoietic Stem Cells

Hideo Ema, Yohei Morita, and Hiromitsu Nakauchi

Great progress has been made in the purification of hematopoietic stem cells (HSCs) using multicolor flow cytometry over the last two decades. As a result, representative HSCs have been phenotypically defined. They are lineage marker-negative (lineage marker$^-$), c-Kit–positive (c-Kit$^+$), Sca-1$^+$, Thy-1-low (Thy-1^{low}), CD34$^{-/low}$, Rhodamine^{low}, and Hoechst^{low}. Highly purified stem cells now serve as a basic tool for the characterization of HSCs at the cellular and the molecular levels.

Introduction

There exist a great variety of blood cells in the bone marrow, the active site for adult hematopoiesis. Mature blood cells of more than eight lineages and their precursor cells at various developmental stages are scattered in its tissue. HSCs are rare among these cells. In the adult mouse bone marrow, the frequency of HSCs is estimated to be 1 in 10^4~10^5 cells. It is thus necessary to isolate HSCs from the other cells for their characterization. HSCs are functionally defined by their capabilities of self-renewal and multilineage differentiation. Long-term multilineage repopulation cells only measurable by experimental transplantation are considered to represent HSCs. Because of this, it has been difficult to identify human HSCs. The mouse system has served as an excellent model in the study of HSCs. Adult mouse HSCs have been successfully purified from bone marrow cells by using flow cytometry. It has recently been shown that more than 30% of such purified cells show long-term repopulating activity. This high degree of purification has enabled us to analyze HSCs at the clonal level.[1–3] Accordingly, the functional heterogeneity in a stem cell population has begun to emerge. On the other hand, transcriptional profiling of purified cells has become available.[4,5] Molecular analysis for stem cell function will be a focus of attention in the coming years.

In this review, we focus on surface markers as well as dye efflux properties that have been implicated as specific for mouse HSCs. The number of HSCs in bone marrow is known to vary among strains of mice.[6] Sca-1 (Ly-6A/E) antigen, one of the most reliable stem cell markers, is expressed at a high level in HSCs of the C56BL/6 (B6) mouse. Congenic mice have been available for this strain. The B6 mouse has been preferentially used for studies of HSCs. Findings described here are based on data of the B6 mouse.

Surface Makers

CD34 antigen was initially characterized as a glycoprotein expressed on human hematopoietic progenitor and vascular endothelial cells.[7] Most *in vitro* colony-forming cells can be enriched in the CD34$^+$ fraction of the adult bone marrow, peripheral blood, and cord blood in human. It remains controversial as to whether all long-term repopulating cells express this antigen.[8] It has been reported that recipients of purified CD34$^+$ cells, in an allogeneic bone marrow transplantation setting, have so far shown engraftment for seven years.[9] This study clearly demonstrates that a population of CD34$^+$ cells contains repopulating stem cells that sustain hematopoiesis for 7 years, but there remains the question of whether 7 years is considered "long term" for human HSCs.

By contrast, in the mouse, long-term repopulating activity is present in the CD34$^{-/low}$ fraction but not in the CD34$^+$ fraction of adult bone marrow cells.[3] HSCs in the aorta–gonads–mesonephros region and fetal liver are, however, known to express CD34 antigen.[10,11] Therefore, the expression of CD34 antigen on HSCs is developmentally regulated. A transition from CD34$^+$ HSCs to CD34$^-$ HSCs in the bone marrow has been observed between birth and 8 months.[12,13] The sorting gates for CD34$^-$ and CD34$^+$ cells have arbitrarily been set in these studies. More attention should be paid to the gate setting for CD34, because depending on whether CD34^{low} cells are included in either the CD34$^-$ or the CD34$^+$ fraction, different conclusions can be drawn. It is recommended to use a standard gate, such as the one used for the separation of c-Kit$^+$, Sca-1$^+$, lineage marker$^-$ cells in adult bone marrow cells,[3] for all experiments.

Null mutations for CD34 and its related molecules, such as podocalyxin-like protein 1, have shown no remarkable abnormality in hematopoietic and vascular development.[14,15] Functional redundancy in members of the sialomucin family has been suggested. Roles of these proteins in HSC function are not known.

It has generally been accepted that HSCs do not express lineage-specific markers such as granulocyte–macrophage, erythrocyte, B-, and T-cell surface antigens.[16] A combination of anti-Gr-1, Mac-1, Ter119, B220, CD3, CD4, CD5, and CD8 antibodies and others have been used to exclude

Handbook of Stem Cells
Volume 2

lineage-committed cells from bone marrow cells in a process of HSC purification.

Stem cell activity is certainly present in a population of CD34$^{-/low}$, c-Kit^{+}, Sca-1^{+}, and lineage marker^{-} (CD34$^{-/low}$ KSL) cells, but not all stem cell activity in the bone marrow belongs to this population, suggesting that the remaining HSCs exist in the other fractions of bone marrow. CD34$^{-/low}$ KSL cells are mostly devoid of the expression of Mac and CD4 antigens as represented in Fig. 30–1. It has recently been claimed that a significant part of HSCs is also in the CD34^{+} fraction expressing Mac-1 and CD4 in the adult life.[17] The presence of CD4^{+} HSCs has previously been recognized.[18,19] Our preliminary data have recently showed that Mac-1^{dull}CD34$^{-/low}$ KSL fraction of bone marrow has a low level of stem cell activity.[20] Nevertheless, most stem cell activity in the adult bone marrow is likely presented by CD34$^{-/low}$ KSL cells. Fetal liver HSCs uniformly express Mac-1 antigen at a low level,[21] whereas these cells are negative for CD4. Similarly to CD34 antigen, it is likely that the expression level for Mac-1 antigen on HSCs is associated with the sites where they reside and with the age of the mice. Mac-1 belongs to the integrin family. This molecule may mediate adhesion to stromal cells, which support hematopoiesis. Its role in HSCs is, however, not clear yet.

c-Kit (CD117) is a receptor tyrosine kinase. Long-term repopulating activity has consistently been detected in c-Kit^{+} fraction of adult bone marrow and fetal liver cells. When cultured *in vitro,* these cells are dependent on its ligand, stem cell factor, for their survival and proliferation. c-Kit^{-} HSCs have also been described.[22] These cells took a longer period of time to reconstitute the hematopoietic system than did c-Kit^{+} HSCs after transplanted into lethally irradiated mice. c-Kit^{+} hematopoietic cells were produced *in vivo* by c-Kit^{-} HSCs, suggesting that c-Kit^{-} HSCs are more immature than c-Kit^{+} ones. On the other hand, multipotent adult progenitor cells (MAPCs) have been described.[23] These cells can be generated by a long-term culture of adult bone marrow. Surprisingly, MAPCs have shown not only a high degree of repopulating activity but also a differentiation capacity to various cell types, including vascular endothelial cells, nerve cells, and visceral epithelium cells. Recently, it was reported that a long-term bone marrow culture with FGF-1 alone can lead to *in vitro* generation of HSCs.[24] Cells capable of initiating MAPCs and HSCs in culture have not been identified. These lines of evidence, however, suggest the presence of embryonic stem cell-like cells, perhaps negative for c-Kit expression, in the adult bone marrow. Purification and identification of such cells are of great importance to address this issue. Nonetheless, long-term culture may be a key for this type of stem cell to obtain the differentiation potential or even plasticity, presumably through epigenetic changes.

Flt-3/Flk-2 (CD135) is another receptor tyrosine kinase originally cloned from a stem cell population of fetal liver cells.[25,26] Recent studies have demonstrated that this receptor is not expressed in HSCs but rather is expressed in lymphoid precursor cells in the adult bone marrow.[27,28] Fig. 30–2 shows the expression of CD34 antigen and Flt-3/Flk-2 receptor on KSL cells. The expression of Flt-3/Flk-2 receptor is detectable in a significant portion of CD34^{+} KSL cells but almost undetectable in CD34$^{-/low}$ KSL cells, consistent with the previous observation.[27]

Dye Efflux Property

HSCs show low-staining with a mitochondrial fluorescent dye, Rhodamine 123.[29] This is because of the multidrug-resistance 1a/b *(MDR1a/b)* gene expressed in HSCs. *MDR1a/b* encodes P-glycoprotein, a transmembrane pump

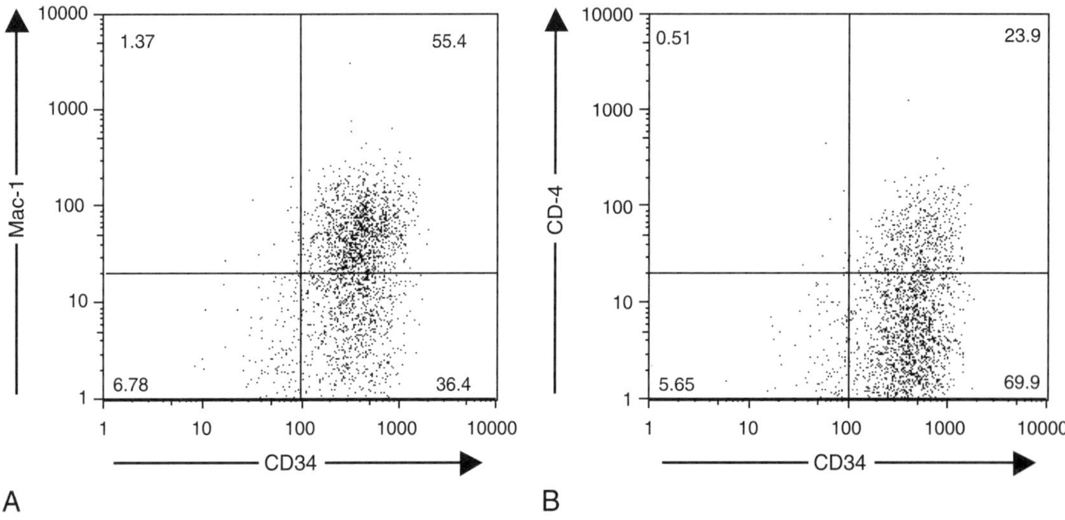

Figure 30–1. *Mac-1 and CD4 expression on KSL cells in the adult mouse bone marrow.* Bone marrow cells were obtained from a 9-week-old mouse. Only c-Kit^{+}Sca-1+Lin^{-} cells are gated on and shown here. Anti-Mac-1 or CD4 antibody was excluded from a mixture of lineage makers and independently used for staining. More than 80% of the CD34$^{-/low}$ KSL cells are negative for Mac-1 or CD4 antigen. There is some variation in Mac-1 expression level among individual mice.

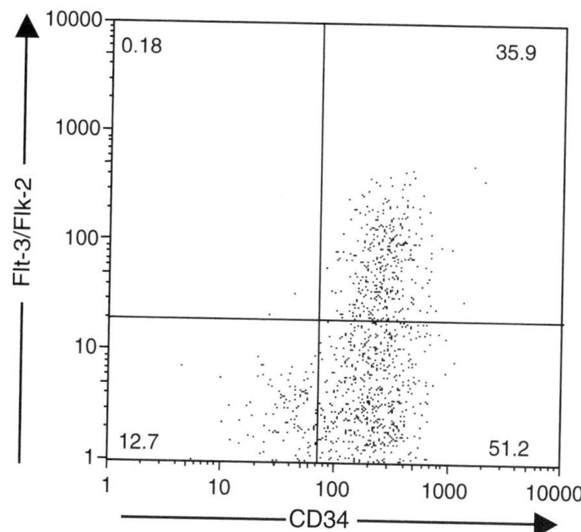

Figure 30–2. *Flt-3/Flk-2 expression on KSL cells.* KSL cells are displayed for their expression of CD34 and Flt-3/Flk-2. Few CD34$^{-/low}$ KSL cells express Flt-3/Flk-2. About 40% of the CD34^{+} KSL cells are positive for Flt-3/Flk-2.

that can efflux this dye.[30] A fluorescent DNA-binding dye, Hoechst 33342, is also actively excluded from HSCs.[31] An ATP-binding cassette transporter gene, *Bcrp-1,* has appeared responsible for this function.[32] It is still unclear whether these dye efflux properties of HSCs are directly linked to the function of "stemness."[33] It is recommended to follow a rigid protocol to reproduce the same staining pattern with Hoechst 33342 in every experiment, because it can be varied by subtle changes in staining conditions such as temperature, cell density, and lot quality of this dye.

Stem Cell Phenotype

Adult bone marrow HSCs are highly enriched in relevant populations: CD34$^{-/low}$ KSL cells, c-Kit^{+}Thy-1.1^{low}lineage$^{-/low}$ Sca-1^{+} cells, and Rhodamine^{low} and Hoechst^{low} or side population (SP) cells.[34] These populations overlap. On average, more than 30% and 90% of the CD34$^{-/low}$ KSL cells are detectable as long-term repopulating stem cells and *in vitro* colony-forming cells, respectively.[35] Single CD34$^{-/low}$ KSL cells show a variety of reconstitution levels in myeloid, B-cell and T-cell lineages, suggesting heterogeneity in repopulating capacities of HSCs. CD34$^{-/low}$ KSL cells can be further divided into SP and main population (MP) when costained with Hoechst dye, as shown in Fig. 30–3. More enrichment of HSCs in CD34$^{-/low}$ KSL SP cells was expected. However, long-term repopulating activity has been detected in both SP and MP fractions.[36] This indicates that all of the HSCs do not have the SP phenotype. It has recently been reported that HSCs can be ultimately enriched in cells with the strongest dye efflux activity (Tip-SP cells) among CD34^{-}KSL cells.[37] More than 90% of such cells were detected as long-term repopulating cells. Thus, a particular subset of HSCs is highly capable of the dye efflux. Of interest is whether there is a functional difference between Tip-SP HSCs and MP HSCs.

As previously described, an HSC population expresses CD27,[38] CD43,[39] and CD44 antigens. These antigens do not subdivide CD34$^{-/low}$ KSL cells. We are seeking a marker that can be used for purification of HSCs or subdivision of HSCs with different degrees of repopulating activity.

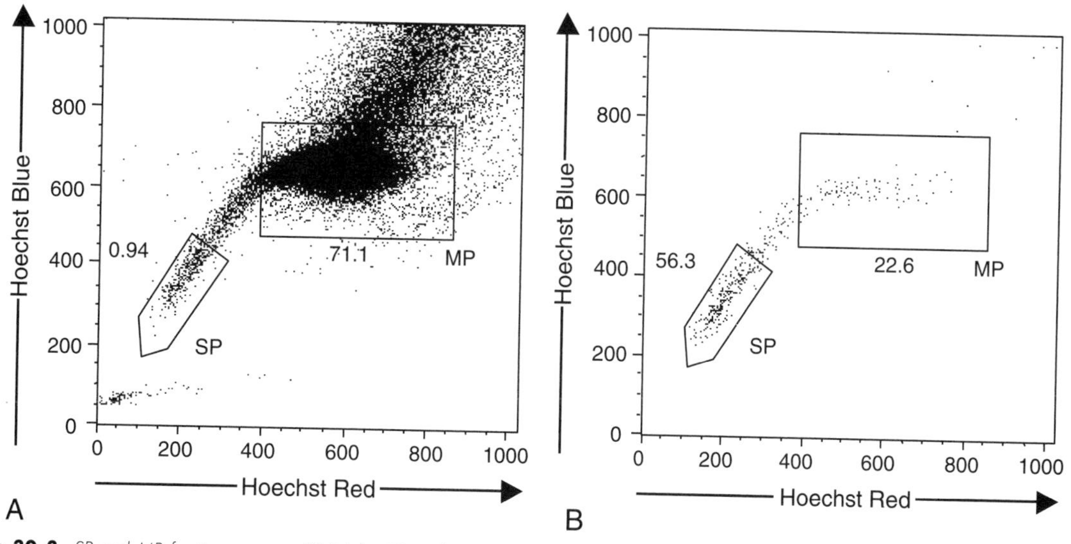

Figure 30–3. *SP and MP fractions among CD34$^{-/low}$ KSL cells.* Bone marrow cells were incubated with Hoechst 33342 followed by staining with a combination of antibodies. (A) Lin^{-} cells and (B) CD34$^{-/low}$ KSL cells are displayed. About half of the CD34$^{-/low}$ KSL cells belong to the SP fraction in this case. The percentages of SP cells among CD34$^{-/low}$ KSL cells varied depending on the lot of Hoechst dye used.

REFERENCES

1. Smith, L.G., Weissman, I.L., and Heimfeld, S. (1991). Clonal analysis of hematopoietic stem cell differentiation *in vivo*. *Proc. Natl. Acad. Sci. U. S. A.* **88,** 2788–2792.
2. Spangrude, G.J., Brooks, D.M., and Tumas, D.B. (1995). Long-term repopulation of irradiated mice with limiting numbers of purified hematopoietic stem cells: *in vivo* expansion of stem cell phenotype but not function. *Blood* **85,** 1006–1016.
3. Osawa, M., Hanada, K., Hamada, H., and Nakauchi, H. (1996). Long-term lymphohematopoietic reconstitution by a single $CD34^{-/neg}$ hematopoietic stem cell. *Science* **273,** 242–245.
4. Ivanova, N.B., Dimos, J.T., Schaniel, C., Hackney, J.A., Moore, K.A., and Lemischka, I.R. (2002). A stem cell molecular signature. *Science* **298,** 601–604.
5. Ramalho-Santos, M., Yoon, S., Matsuzaki, Y., Mulligan, R.C., and Melton, D.A. (2002). "Stemness": transcriptional profiling of embryonic and adult stem cells. *Science* **298,** 597–600.
6. De Haan, G., Nijhof, W., and Van Zant, G. (1997). Mouse strain-dependent changes in frequency and proliferation of hematopoietic stem cells during aging: correlation between lifespan and cycling activity. *Blood* **89,** 1543–1550.
7. Krause, D.S., Fackler, M.J., Civin, C.I., and May, W.S. (1996). CD34: Structure, biology, and clinical utility. *Blood* **87,** 1–13.
8. Nakauchi, H. (1998). Hematopoietic stem cells: are they CD34-positive or CD34-negative? *Nat. Med.* **4,** 1009–1010.
9. Kato, S., Ando, K., Nakamura, Y., Muguruma, Y., Sato, T., Yabe, H., Yabe, M., Hattori, K., Yasuda, Y., and Hotta, T. (2001). Absence of a $CD34^-$ hematopoietic precursor population in recipients of $CD34^+$ stem cell transplantation. *Bone Marrow Transplant.* **28,** 587–595.
10. Sanchez, M.J., Holmes, A., Miles, C., and Dzierzak, E. (1996). Characterization of the first definitive hematopoietic stem cells in the AGM and liver of the mouse embryo. *Immunity* **5,** 513–525.
11. Yoder, M.C., Hiatt, K., Dutt, P., Mukherjee, P., Bodine, D.M., and Orlic, D. (1997). Characterization of definitive lymphohematopoietic stem cells in the day 9 murine yolk sac. *Immunity* **7,** 335–344.
12. Ito, T., Tajima, F., and Ogawa, M. (2000). Developmental changes of CD34 expression by murine hematopoietic stem cells. *Exp. Hematol.* **28,** 1269–1273.
13. Matsuoka, S., Ebihara, Y., Xu, M., Ishii, T., Sugiyama, D., Yoshino, H., Ueda, T., Manabe, A., Tanaka, R., Ikeda, Y., Nakahata, T., and Tsuji, K. (2001). CD34 expression on long-term repopulating hematopoietic stem cells changes during developmental stages. *Blood* **97,** 419–425.
14. Cheng, J., Baumhueter, S., Cacalano, G., Carver-Moore, K., Thibodeaux, H., Thomas, R., Broxmeyer, H.E., Cooper, S., Hague, N., Moore, M., and Lasky, L.A. (1996). Hematopoietic defects in mice lacking the sialomucin CD34. *Blood* **87,** 479–490.
15. Doyonnas, R., Kershaw, D.B., Duhme, C., Merkens, H., Chelliah, S., Graf, T., and McNagny, K.M. (2001). Anuria, omphalocele, and perinatal lethality in mice lacking the CD34-related protein podocalyxin. *J. Exp. Med.* **194,** 13–27.
16. Morrison, S.J., Wandycz, A.M., Hemmati, H.D., Wright, D.E., and Weissman, I.L. (1997). Identification of a lineage of multipotent hematopoietic progenitors. *Development* **124,** 1929–1939.
17. Ishida, A., Zeng, H., and Ogawa, M. (2002). Expression of lineage markers by $CD34^+$ hematopoietic stem cells of adult mice. *Exp. Hematol.* **30,** 361–365.
18. Wineman, J.P., Gilmore, G.L., Gritzmacher, C., Torbett, B.E., and Muller-Sieburg, C.E. (1992). CD4 is expressed on murine pluripotent hematopoietic stem cells. *Blood* **80,** 1717–1724.
19. Onishi, M., Nagayoshi, K., Kitamura, K., Hirai, H., Takaku, F., and Nakauchi, H. (1993). $CD4^{dull/+}$ hematopoietic progenitor cells in murine bone marrow. *Blood* **81,** 3217–3225.
20. Morita, Y., and Nakauchi, H. (Unpublished data).
21. Rebel, V.I., Miller, C.L., Thornbury, G.R., Dragowska, W.H., Eaves, C.J., and Lansdorp, P.M. (1996). A comparison of long-term repopulating hematopoietic stem cells in fetal liver and adult bone marrow from the mouse. *Exp. Hematol.* **24,** 638–648.
22. Ortiz, M., Wine, J.W., Lohrey, N., Ruscetti, F.W., Spence, S.E., and Keller, J.R. (1999). Functional characterization of a novel hematopoietic stem cell and its place in the c-Kit maturation pathway in bone marrow cell development. *Immunity* **10,** 173–182.
23. Jiang, Y., Jahagirdar, B.N., Reinhardt, R.L., Schwartz, R.E., Keene, C.D., Ortiz-Gonzalez, X.R., Reyes, M., Lenvik, T., Lund, T., Blackstad, M., Du, J., Aldrich, S., Lisberg, A., Low, W.C., Largaespada, D.A., and Verfaillie, C.M. (2002). Pluripotency of mesenchymal stem cells derived from adult marrow. *Nature* **418,** 41–49.
24. de Haan, G., Weersing, E., Dontje, B., van Os, R., Bystrykh, L.V., Vellenga, E., and Miller, G. (2003). *In vitro* generation of long-term repopulating hematopoietic stem cells by fibroblast growth factor-1. *Dev. Cell* **4,** 241–251.
25. Matthews, W., Jordan, C.T., Wiegand, G.W., Pardoll, D., and Lemischka, I.R. (1991). A receptor tyrosine kinase specific to hematopoietic stem and progenitor cell-enriched populations. *Cell* **65,** 1143–1152.
26. Rosnet, O., Marchetto, S., de Lapeyriere, O., and Birnbaum, D. (1991). Murine *Flt3,* a gene encoding a novel tyrosine kinase receptor of the PDGFR/CSF1R family. *Oncogene* **6,** 1641–1650.
27. Adolfsson, J., Borge, O.J., Bryder, D., Theilgaard-Monch, K., Astrand-Grundstrom, I., Sitnicka, E., Sasaki, Y., and Jacobsen, S.E. (2001). Up-regulation of Flt3 expression within the bone marrow $Lin^-Sca1^+c\text{-}kit+$ stem cell compartment is accompanied by loss of self-renewal capacity. *Immunity* **15,** 659–669.
28. Christensen, J.L., and Weissman, I.L. (2001). Flk-2 is a marker in hematopoietic stem cell differentiation: a simple method to isolate long-term stem cells. *Proc. Natl. Acad. Sci. U. S. A.* **98,** 14,541–14,546.
29. Spangrude, G.J., and Johnson, G.R. (1990). Resting and activated subsets of mouse multipotent hematopoietic stem cells. *Proc. Natl. Acad. Sci. U. S. A.* **87,** 7433–7437.
30. Chaudhary, P.M., and Roninson, I.B. (1991). Expression and activity of P-glycoprotein, a multidrug efflux pump, in human hematopoietic stem cells. *Cell* **66,** 85–94.
31. Wolf, N.S., Kone, A., Priestley, G.V., and Bartelmez, S.H. (1993). *In vivo* and *in vitro* characterization of long-term repopulating primitive hematopoietic cells isolated by sequential Hoechst 33342–Rhodamine 123 FACS selection. *Exp. Hematol.* **21,** 614–622.
32. Zhou, S., Schuetz, J.D., Bunting, K.D., Colapietro, A.M., Sampath, J., Morris, J.J., Lagutina, I., Grosveld, G.C., Osawa, M., Nakauchi, H., and Sorrentino, B.P. (2001). The ABC transporter Bcrp1/ ABCG2 is expressed in a wide variety of stem cells and is a molecular determinant of the side population phenotype. *Nat. Med.* **7,** 1028–1034.
33. Zhou, S., Morris, J.J., Barnes, Y., Lan, L., Schuetz, J.D., and Sorrentino, B.P. (2002). *Bcrp1* gene expression is required for normal numbers of side population stem cells in mice and confers relative protection to mitoxantrone in hematopoietic cells *in vivo*. *Proc. Natl. Acad. Sci. U. S. A.* **99,** 12,339–12,344.
34. Goodell, M.A., Brose, K., Paradis, G., Conner, A.S., and Mulligan, R.C. (1996). Isolation and functional properties of murine hematopoietic stem cells that are replicating *in vivo*. *J. Exp. Med.* **183,** 1797–1806.

35. Takano, H., Ema, H., Sudo, K., and Nakauchi, N. (2004). Asymmetric division and lineage commitment at the level of hematopoietic stem cells. *J. Exp. Med.* **199,** 295–302.
36. Morita, Y., and Nakauchi, N. (Unpublished data).
37. Matsuzaki, Y., Kinjo, K., Mulligan, R.C., and Okano, H. (2004). Unexpectedly efficient homing capacity of purified murine hematopoietic stem cells. *Immunity* **20,** 87–93.
38. Wiesmann, A., Phillips, R.L., Mojica, M., Pierce, L.J., Searles, A.E., Spangrude, G.J., and Lemischka, I. (2000). Expression of CD27 on murine hematopoietic stem and progenitor cells. *Immunity* **12,** 193–199.
39. Moore, T., Huang, S., Terstappen, L.W., Bennett, M., and Kumar, V. (1994). Expression of CD43 on murine and human pluripotent hematopoietic stem cells. *J. Immunol.* **153,** 4978–4987.

31

Side Population Phenotype

Fernando D. Camargo, Carlos Almeida Ramos, and Margaret A. Goodell

The most exciting phrase to hear in science, the one that heralds new discoveries, is not "Eureka!" but "That's funny..."

Isaac Asimov (1920–1992)

Introduction

One critical issue in the study of adult stem cells is the development of technologies to define and isolate stem cells. Most methods involve purification on the basis of cell surface markers specifically associated with the population of interest. However, the availability of such markers is lacking for many tissue sources, and any single marker is never exclusive to stem cells. Also, it has been repeatedly shown that the functionality of a stem cell population does not always correlate with its cell surface phenotype. In this chapter, we review a general method for the isolation of stem–progenitor cells that relies upon a physiological property of these cells: the active efflux of the Hoechst 33342 dye, resulting in the so-called side population (SP). We focus on murine bone marrow SP cells, commenting on the mechanisms of Hoechst staining, the phenotype and the engraftment behavior of SP cells, the SP phenomenon in other tissues and species, and the applicability of Hoechst staining as a universal stem cell marker.

Hoechst 33342

In the late 1960s, during a screen for antiparasitic agents, it was observed that several base-substituted bisbenzimidazole derivatives had high filaricidal activity. These compounds were known to be fluorescent, and microscopic analysis of blood smears of animals infected with filariae and injected with one of the compounds, Hoechst preparation 33258, showed fluorescent staining of the parasites' nuclei as well as persistent staining of the nuclei in all host tissues. The exclusive nuclear staining suggested that the dye bound DNA in some form.[1]

Further studies of the Hoechst dyes showed that they bind the minor groove of double-stranded DNA, preferentially in adenine-thymidine-rich regions, in a stoichometric fashion.[2–5] Binding of the dye to DNA causes a small spectral shift and enhancement of its fluorescence, which enables its detection above background. The amount of dye fluorescence should be proportional to the cellular DNA content, enabling determination of ploidy and cell cycle stage (i.e., $G_{0/1}$, S, or G_2/M). The combination of Hoechst dye staining with flow cytometry allowed the characterization of the ploidy of complex mixtures of cells.[6] Contrary to Hoechst 33258, Hoechst 33342 (Ho) is more lipophilic (or more easily transported across cytoplasmic membranes) and can be used as a vital dye (Fig. 31–1A).

Traditionally, cell cycle studies performed with Ho detect fluorescence emission at a single, short wavelength (blue). This strategy was applied during the 1980s to bone marrow suspensions to investigate the relationship between cell cycle and stem cell potential. By using Ho staining singly or with forward and side scatter analysis, two groups were able to identify hematopoietic fractions enriched ~20- to 500-fold for stem cell activity.[7,8] Curiously, these subsets of cells exhibited lower levels of Ho fluorescence when compared to the rest of the bone marrow. Since no cell should have less than a diploid DNA content, it was suggested that stem cells were less permeable to Ho, that the dye had less accessibility to the DNA because of chromatin structure, or that other cellular components with affinity to the dye were less abundant in these cells.[7]

The fortuitous discovery that distinct subpopulations could be resolved in Hoechst-stained whole bone marrow by simultaneous display of fluorescence emission at two wavelengths led to a renewed interest in using this dye to fractionate bone marrow[9] (Fig. 31–1B). In particular, it was observed that a small proportion (0.03–0.07%) of bone marrow cells that appeared less fluorescent than the rest of the bone marrow stood out as a distinct tail, which became known as the SP.[9]

Complex Pattern of Hoechst Staining

Dual-wavelength analysis of Ho-stained murine bone marrow reveals two striking aspects: the presence of more than one $G_1/S/G_2$-M population of cells and the definition of a small understained tail of cells (Fig. 31–1B). In theory, since we are looking at the fluorescence emission of a single fluorophore, the intensity of the emission for any wavelength (e,g., red) should be proportional to that for the peak wavelength (blue). Yet if this was the case, all the cells should align in a straight profile. Since this does not happen, it indicates that bone marrow cells shift the emission spectrum of Ho and that this shift is variable among bone marrow fractions.

Handbook of Stem Cells
Volume 2

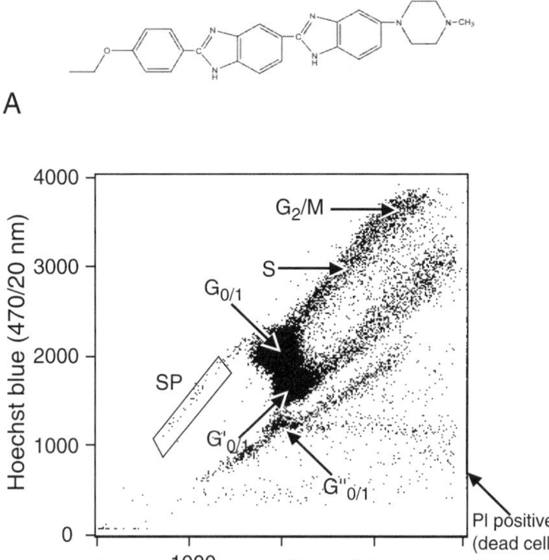

Figure 31–1. *Side population.* (A) The Hoechst 33342 molecule, also called bisbenzimidazole. (B) The cytometry profile obtained after staining whole mouse bone marrow with 5 μg/ml of Hoechst 33342. The SP stands out as a distinct tail, as boxed. You can also distinguish three main $G_{0/1}$ populations (G, G′, and G″) with the corresponding G_2/M sets and the intervening S-phase cells. PI uptake by dead cells is also visualized along the Hoechst red axis.

Multiple Ho-staining populations have been noted previously. In the early 1980s, it was reported that using low Ho concentrations, Ho fluorescence no longer appeared strictly proportional to DNA content: Resting diploid T- or B-lymphocytes from the spleen were resolved as distinct peaks in a single wavelength (blue) histogram.[10] Also, when chicken thymocytes were stained with Ho and measured at violet and green wavelengths, three populations could be resolved.[11] Furthermore, there was a strong influence of the dye concentration and staining time on the appearance of these subpopulations. The authors proposed that two binding sites, or types of binding, exist for Ho in DNA and that these possessed different binding energies and, therefore, distinct emission properties.

These results were consistent with *in vitro* studies that suggested at least two modes of binding of Hoechst 33258 (a close relative of Ho 33342) to chromatin, with higher dye–phosphate ratios resulting in the red-shifting of the emission spectrum and lower fluorescence quantum yield and in the eventual precipitation of the dye–DNA complex.[12] The relative amount of each type of binding was different in distinct cell types[13] and differed between supercoiled and relaxed plasmid DNA.[14] Thus, it appeared that these dissimilarities were a function of chromatin structure, and it was proposed that differences in chromatin structure might be detected by the spectral characteristics of Hoechst 33258 fluorescence at higher concentrations.[13]

If different bone marrow cell types possess distinct chromatin conformations, we would expect to find different subpopulations with Ho staining, provided that the dye concentration is adequate. In fact, the main $G_{0/1}$-S–G_2/M populations defined by the Ho protocol are stained differentially by some lineage antibodies: For instance, antibodies against the granulocytic lineage, such as Gr-1, recognize predominantly the upper population (G), and those against the B-cell lineage, such as B220, stain mainly the population immediately below (G′).[15]

Although some of the studies mentioned looked at a nonstandard wavelength (green) apart from the conventional one (blue),[11] none detected the emission of red light. It is unusual for a fluorochrome to display significant fluorescence more than 200 nm from its peak (approximately 450 nm in this case), but this does not appear to be a separate emission peak. Rather, Ho staining is so bright that it can still be detected at the opposite side of the visible spectrum, though dimmer than for the peak wavelength. Of note, the red emission is not caused by propidium iodide (PI) staining. When this dye is used in conjunction with the Ho, PI^{pos} dead cells are extremely bright in the red channel and line up against the far right of the profile (Fig. 31–1B). Apart from this, however, if PI is not used, the emission pattern looks similar.

In summary, Ho is a vital dye that appears to be able to bind chromatin in more than one mode, which results in different spectral properties. These properties explain the emergence of more than one population in Ho-stained bone marrow analyzed on two wavelengths (and the presence of multiple peaks on a conventional Ho histogram). Within each population, emission is still proportional to DNA content; thus, it is possible to define subsets in different phases of the cell cycle.

Side Population

In contrast to the other populations that appear in Ho-stained marrow, the SP contains cells whose staining is not proportional to their DNA content. Attempts at explaining this finding showed that if bone marrow cells were concomitantly incubated with Ho and multidrug-resistance (MDR) protein inhibitors (such as verapamil), the SP vanished.[9] This led to the idea that ATP-binding cassette (ABC) transporters, a family of proteins that include MDR1 and that were known to be in hematopoietic cells,[16] could be responsible for extruding the dye from cells that make up the SP, causing them to appear less stained. Although the nature of the transporter involved in the generation of the SP phenomenon is not definitely known (as explained later in this chapter), the critical influence that staining time, dye concentration, and cell dilution have in the whole procedure offers a little more insight into the mechanisms involved.

The Ho 33342 molecule penetrates into cells at a limited rate, beginning as soon as the whole bone marrow sample is placed in Ho-containing medium. Whether the molecules enter cells by simple or facilitated diffusion is not known. That the cells appear unstained after 2 hours when left at 4°C[15] and that the molecular weight of Ho is relatively large (greater than that of glucose, for instance, which enters cells by facilitated diffusion) suggests that a carrier mediated process may be involved.

During incubation at 37°C in Ho-containing medium, the amount of dye bound to DNA inside each nucleus increases with time and the concentration of free dye in the medium decreases until equilibrium is reached between diffusion into the cells and diffusion or transport out of the cells. If you look at a bone marrow preparation during the Ho-staining procedure, you will see that the cells are initially understained and localize where the SP will be resolved (Fig. 31–2). This will progress to brighter staining of most of the cells and the appearance of several main populations of cells as described previously. Notably, after 90 minutes under standard staining conditions, the concentration of free dye drops approximately 20%, as can be assessed by spectrophotometrically measuring the concentration of Ho in the supernatant.[15] Obviously, the point at which the equilibrium between transport into and transport out of cells is established is affected by the concentration of both dye and nucleated cells: Lowering the dye concentration or increasing the cell concentration in the medium reduces proportionally the number of Ho molecules available to incorporate in each nucleus and can potentially prevent the visualization of the SP cells.

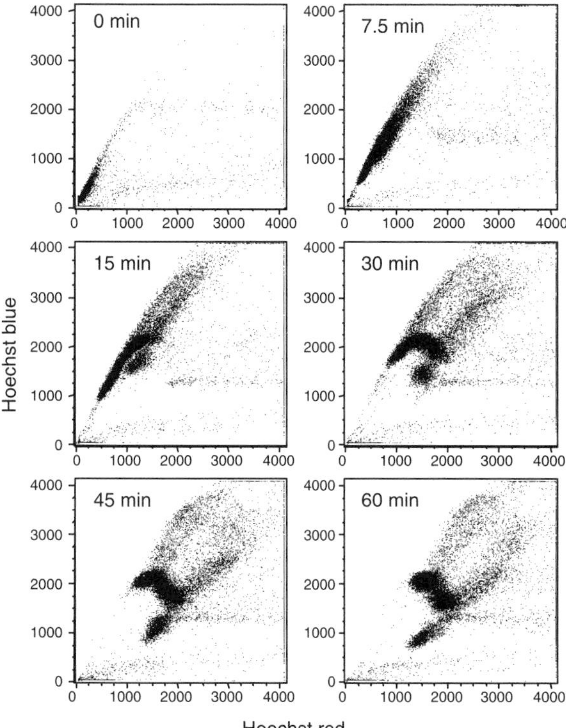

Figure 31–2. *Progression of bone marrow staining during incubation with hoechst dye.* At early time points, most of the cells have not acquired the dye and the population is markedly understained. Note that the first stained cells appear in the position that will be occupied by the SP cells. Later, the complex Hoechst-staining pattern of bone marrow emerges with definition of different populations.

As the dye diffuses into the cells and its concentration drops in the medium, some of it is being actively pumped out of the cells by transmembrane proteins with MDR-like activity. Probably, most cells will have some members of the ABC transporter family in their membranes, but stem cells may possess different members or greater amounts or activity of those components. When the speed of efflux of the dye is greater than that of diffusion into cells, the SP cells stand out as a discrete population. In other words, the SP is able to extrude the dye against a concentration gradient, unlike the rest of the bone marrow cells. When bone marrow cells are incubated with ABC inhibitors, the speed of dye extrusion is decreased and the SP disappears because the cells are unable to pump against the gradient established. Likewise, increasing the concentration of Ho or decreasing the concentration of cells enhances the dye gradient and can preclude detection of the SP.

Hoechst Transporter

As already alluded to, there are substantial data supporting the hypothesis that ABC transporters are involved in generating the SP profile obtained with Ho staining.[9] The ABC transporter family comprises transmembrane proteins able to translocate a variety of substrates across cell membranes.[17] They are grouped into seven subfamilies (ABCA through ABCG) based on phylogenetic analysis. Structurally, each member possesses two nucleotide-binding folds, responsible for ATP binding and hydrolysis, and two transmembrane domains, which confer substrate specificity. The only exception to this rule is subfamily ABCG, whose elements possess only half the domains and require dimerization to exert their function. Many of the ABC transporters are involved in the translocation of various physiologic substrates, such as iron, cholesterol, and peptides, but several of them were initially described in the context of chemotherapeutic drug resistance and were shown to be able to extrude several anticancer agents.

The first reference to expression and activity of the product of the *ABCB1* gene (formerly known as *MDR1*), P-glycoprotein, in human bone marrow stem cells appeared a little more than a decade ago.[16] MDR-mediated efflux offered an explanation for low Ho staining associated with stem cell-enriched fractions. It also explained the low accumulation of Rhodamine 123 (Rh123) in hematopoietic stem cells (HSCs), which had been previously ascribed to their low metabolic activity, since Rh123 behaves as a mitochondrial probe.[18]

Further work has shown that retroviral-mediated overexpression of the *ABCB1* gene expands the SP compartment with maintenance of its stem cell potential after transplantation.[19,20] That some transplanted animals develop a myeloproliferative disease originating in the transduced cells suggested that enforced expression appeared to prevent appropriate differentiation. However, mice in which the *ABCB1* homologs are ablated have normal numbers and normal function of SP cells in the bone marrow.[21] SP cells in these mice are unable to extrude Rh123, a known substrate for P-glycoprotein, but are still able to export Ho. This meant that other transporters were likely to be involved in the generation of the SP phenomenon, and attention was turned to *ABCG2.*

ABCG2 was shown to be in hematopoietic cells from wild-type and *Abcb1*-null mice, mainly in the SP, even though other types of cells, such as erythrocytic and natural killer precursors, have detectable expression of this gene product.[21,22] Additionally, SPs isolated from other tissues express *ABCG2.* As with *ABCB1,* retroviral-mediated overexpression of *ABCG2* expanded the size of the SP, conferred an SP phenotype on other cells, and impaired hematopoietic differentiation of transduced cells.[21] However, in this case, deletion of the transporter gene resulted in the near disappearance of the SP.[23] Moreover, the few remaining SP cells seemed to possess much less repopulating activity than wild-type stem cells. This would seem to indicate that *ABCG2* was the only transporter responsible for the SP phenomenon. Nevertheless, bone marrow from *ABCG2*-null animals displays normal steady-state hematopoiesis and competes adequately with wild-type bone marrow in transplants, indicating that the HSCs in these animals function normally.[23]

How can we reconcile the normal function of ABCG2-null HSCs with the absence of a SP phenotype? One word of caution is necessary: SP phenotype (as assessed only by Ho extrusion ability) cannot always be equated with stem cell function. Under normal circumstances, cells that can be identified by Ho extrusion are the ones that behave as stem cells. On the other hand, it is unlikely (though not impossible) that an energy-spending process such as transport by ABC proteins would play no physiologic role in these cells. Yet, we do not know what the physiologic substrate is, and chances are that this substrate is able to be transported by multiple ABC proteins. There is good evidence that other ABC transporters are in SP cells[21,22] and overexpression of some may functionally compensate for the absence of others, even if Ho efflux ability is not restored. Interesting questions to be addressed are what happens to other ABC family members in single knockouts for Abcb1 or Abcg2 and what occurs in double-knockouts for both these genes.

Side Population Cells as Hematopoietic Stem Cells

HSCs are undoubtedly the most highly characterized mammalian adult stem cell population. In the murine system, HSCs can easily be assayed *in vivo* by testing their ability to reconstitute the hematopoietic system of lethally irradiated recipient mice. Using this assay, cell populations purified on the basis of the presence or absence of specific cell surface antigens have been identified and catalogued as putative HSCs. The bone marrow population expressing both the tyrosine kinase receptor c-Kit and the antigen Sca-1, and expressing negative or low levels of lineage differentiation markers (c-Kit^{pos}Sca-1^{pos}Lin$^{neg/low}$, also known as KSL) has been repeatedly shown to contain the cells responsible for hematopoietic reconstitution.[24,25] Two groups have further defined more enriched HSC populations that express low levels of the Thy-1 antigen (KTLS)[24] or that express negative or low levels of the CD34 glycoprotein (KSL CD34$^{neg/low}$).[26]

Our initial report on the isolation of murine bone marrow SP cells described a cell population highly enriched for the stem–progenitor-enriched Lin^{neg}Sca-1^{pos} phenotype, thus suggesting that SP cells were putative HSCs.[9] This was confirmed by transplantation assays in which SP cells were used to reconstitute the hematopoietic system of lethally irradiated recipient mice.[9] Remarkably, these cells were shown to be at least 1000-fold enriched in hematopoietic activity when compared to whole bone marrow. Furthermore, SP cells were shown to contribute to both myeloid and lymphoid blood lineages *in vivo,* and at low cell doses, they were able to rescue transplanted hosts from lethal irradiation. In addition, numerous experiments demonstrated that the entire hematopoietic activity in murine bone marrow resided exclusively within the SP subset.[9] Thus, SP cells seemed to be a unique population that harbored cells with the functional and phenotypic characteristics of true HSCs.

Given the data from these initial experiments, an obvious question is as follows: What is the relationship of SP cells with the other HSC populations isolated by previous groups (i.e., KSL, KTLS, and KSL CD34$^{neg/low}$)? Are SP cells a subset of these cell fractions, or vice versa? Do SP cells represent a more primitive stem cell than the previously described HSCs? To address these important issues, we carried out more detailed cell surface and functional analyses of the SP population. Our group[27] and others have demonstrated that, phenotypically, SP cells are a homogenous population. Most SP cells (>85%) are positive for all the known long-term HSC markers and negative for antigens expressed in committed short-term hematopoietic progenitors[27] (Fig. 31–3A). Thus, in general, SP cells have the KTLS and KSL CD34$^{neg/low}$ phenotypes of previously described marrow-derived stem cell populations, indicating that the cells within the SP region are phenotypically defined HSCs. Interestingly, not all KTLS or KSL cells fall within the SP gate; approximately only 50% and 25% of the KTLS and KSL populations, respectively, show an SP phenotype (Fig. 31–3B). When KSL cells are fractionated based upon their SP phenotype and transplanted into mice, the long-term hematopoietic activity cosegregates with the cells actively effluxing Hoechst.[28] KSL non-SP cells, on the other hand, only contribute short term to blood production.[28] Thus, it appears that SP cells are the most primitive subset of the KSL population and that all functional long-term stem cells have an efflux phenotype.

When the homogeneity and potency of the SP cells was analyzed by transplanting a limited number of cells into irradiated hosts, up to 25% of mice receiving a single, physically isolated SP cell showed evidence of multilineage long-term hematopoietic engraftment, and transplants with 10 and 20 SP cells resulted in near 100% reconstitution efficiencies.[28] These results are comparable to engraftment using small numbers of KSL CD34$^{neg/low}$ HSCs,[26] indicating that SP cells are bona fide HSCs functionally comparable to those isolated exclusively on cell surface characteristics.

32

Hematopoietic Stem Cells and Aging

Amiela Globerson

Age-related changes have been noted in the hematopoietic stem cell (HSC) compartment as well as in the individual stem cell and its descendants. This distinction is crucial for a comprehensive understanding the dynamics and the developmental potential of the stem cell pool in the aged. In addition, the issue of stem cell aging, particularly replicative senescence, deserves special attention in relation to transplantation and the *in vitro* approaches for expansion of the cells for clinical purposes, including gene therapy. Expansion of long-term functioning stem cells is therefore one arm of stem cell aging biology, in addition to the status of hematopoiesis in the aged. Finally, the findings on the plasticity of adult stem cells are of interest in view of the potential applications of autologous HSCs in the aged: promoting tissue repair *in situ* and transplanting *in vitro*–generated tissues. This chapter reviews the state of knowledge about these aspects and points to unresolved questions.

Introduction

HSCs are characterized by their ability to produce diverse types of blood cells and by their capacity for self-renewal. Blood cell turnover continues throughout the life span of the individual, leading to the notion that the stem cells retain their properties and potential continuously with no manifestation of aging. However, experimental evidence, as well as clinical data, indicates age-related changes in the stem cell compartment and in the biology of the individual stem cell and its progeny, as recently reviewed in several publications.[1–5]

Sequential age-related changes in the HSC compartment were identified from the early stage of embryonic development to the ultimate residence of the cells in the adult bone marrow.[6] In addition to stem cells sites, changes were noted in the relevant properties of the cell population.[7] Continuous changes in the stem cell compartment from birth to old age thus could be predicted, yet this issue has been controversial. Controversy arose because the original studies were carried out on the intact bone marrow cell population, when techniques for the isolation of the relevant cells were not yet known.[2,8,9] Conclusions regarding the stem cell properties were thus based on extrapolation from observations on the intact bone marrow. The basic information derived from those studies is valid despite the methodological limitations. The data pointed to the need to distinguish hematopoiesis under normal conditions in the aged from the possibly limited potential of the cells for self-renewal under the experimental conditions.[10,11] The establishment of tools to identify and isolate stem cells by distinct membrane markers has enabled critical experimental approaches and led to major progress in this area. Furthermore, procedures that enable the mobilization of the cells from the bone marrow to the peripheral blood have made the isolated stem cells accessible for research and clinical applications. Extensive expansion of the cells is an additional important tool for these purposes.

Stem cell senescence can thus be approached in terms of the potential for generating the diverse blood cell types as well as the capacity for continuous self-renewal. Furthermore, recent studies pointing to the plasticity of cells, beyond the repertoire of hematopoiesis,[12–14] have opened potential clinical applications of adult HSCs[15–17] and possibly the use of autologous HSCs for tissue repair and replacement in the elderly. The question of whether stem cell plasticity for transdifferentiation is affected by aging is thus important.

This chapter reviews current knowledge on the status of HSCs in the aged and data showing aging effects on the potential of isolated cells, as reflected from clinical situations and experimental models. The progress in research on stem cell biology indicates properties and biological behavior that are of interest in relation to aging, but there are still many gaps in knowledge in that respect. This chapter calls attention to the open questions.

HSCs in the Aged

BASAL HEMATOPOIESIS AND COPING WITH HEMATOLOGICAL STRESS

Basal hematopoiesis normally continues into old age, as shown in studies of aged humans,[2,15,18–20] including special insight to centenarians.[18,19] Similar observations were reported on experimental animals.[21–23] Anemia observed in elderly subjects is usually associated with underlying disease or clinical problems.[24,25] Anemia in aging was also causally related to the status of inflammatory cytokines, particularly increased IL6 levels.[26] However, aged humans as well as various animals seem to fail to cope with major hematological stress. Hence, the manifestation of anemia is recorded in elderly patients receiving chemotherapy treatment.[27,28] It appears that the stem cell compartment is capable of maintaining the normal level of blood cell turnover but becomes inefficient under conditions requiring extensive hematopoietic function.

Handbook of Stem Cells
Volume 2

Decline in the ability to cope with hematological stress and to up-regulate hematopoiesis under such conditions is based on complex mechanisms that have not been fully elucidated. Various age-related changes may lead to these manifestations, e.g., decreased capacity for sequential cell replications, altered production of relevant growth factors, and the eventual profile of the different cytokines. Evidence from relevant clinical situations and experimental models supports these possibilities; it is reviewed in the following sections.

BONE MARROW STEM CELL COMPARTMENT IN AGING

The classical studies were based on the transplantation of cells into hematologically compromised recipients.[8–11] Competitive transplantation of stem cell populations was found to be a powerful tool for measuring the functional potential of stem cell populations.[29] Cells from aged donors were thus found to be inferior to those of the young in reconstituting the bone marrow of young, hematologically compromised recipients.

Competitive transplantation of equal doses of bone marrow cells from young and old homozygous Ly5 congenic mice (Ly5.1 and Ly5.2, respectively) into heterozygous, young, irradiated recipients revealed age-related differences in the resulting donor-type blood cells.[30] Cells of the old gave rise to higher levels of white blood cells, particularly in the myeloid lineage. Because the cells from different age-group donors developed competitively within the same recipient, the observations could not be attributed to the recipient; rather, they were caused by intrinsic properties of the bone marrow cells.

Although hematopoietic sites in the bone marrow of the aged are accommodated by adipocytes, the HSC compartment seems to support normal hematopoiesis under steady-state conditions. To establish the decreased efficiency of that compartment under hematological stress, it was necessary to use proper experimental models. Transplantation to hematologically compromised, young recipients was used as an experimental model. It was thus shown that bone marrow cells from aged mice could reconstitute young, irradiated recipients, as could cells from young donors.[31]

Harrison *et al.* noted an increased proportion of the more primitive cell types in aged mice.[32] Studies by Morrison *et al.* using isolated murine HSCs[30] showed a fivefold increase in the proportion of cells bearing the stem cell phenotype Thy1.1^{low}Sca-1^{+}Lin^{-} and a decrease in the multipotent progenitor subpopulations (Mac-1^{low}CD4^{-}c-kit^{+}, Mac-1^{low}CD4^{-}, and Mac-1^{low}CD4^{low}).

Subsequent studies showed that isolated populations of HSCs originating in old mice could reconstitute irradiated mice to the same extent as those in the young. This was the case as long as a large cell dose was used (>10^{5}). Transplantation under limit-dilution conditions disclosed a higher frequency (a fivefold increase) of the cells in the bone marrow of old mice than in that of the young, but they were only 25% as efficient in engrafting the bone marrow of irradiated recipients.[30] Although the total size of the HSC pool is sufficient for normal blood cell turnover, the profile of cells in the bone marrow compartment changes with age. A variety of parameters were recorded as indicators of such changes, including an increase in the more primitive stem cells in the bone marrow of aged mice.[32] The detailed properties of the nonfunctional cells are not yet elucidated.

REPLICATION OF HSCs IN THE AGED

Aging mice have elevated values of stem cells in cycle, as shown from a variety of experimental data. Studies on bone marrow cells cultured on supportive mesenchymal stroma cell monolayers,[33] as well as on seeding onto fetal thymus explants,[34,35] suggested that cells of the aged were a priori in cycle and that they replicated upon culture without the lag periods observed in case of the young. Indeed, direct monitoring of Sca-1^{+} cells from the bone marrow of aged mice disclosed a relatively high proportion in cycle (G2/M); in the young, these cells are mostly quiescent.[30]

Being in cycle may be visualized as an advantage mechanism for compensation of the reduced frequency of functional cells, because this enables immediate cell replication. On the other hand, cells in cycle are at an increased risk of genetic instability, particularly under conditions of decreased capacity for DNA repair in aging.[36,37] Observations by Ben Yehuda *et al.* on a significantly increased rate of microsatellite instability in the DNA mismatch repair (MMR) system of elderly individuals[38] is in line with that concept.

Although the bulk of transplantation studies led to the conclusion that stem cells in the aged can replenish the bone marrow of irradiated recipients, reconstitution of the various blood cell types is differential and limited. This is concluded from evaluation of the T-cell compartment 6 months or more after irradiation.[39,40] Reduced T-cell values under these conditions could not be related solely to thymic involution, because bone marrow cells from young donors provided long-term reconstitution of T-cells in the irradiated recipients under the same conditions. Similarly, bone marrow CD34^{+} cells generated fewer T-cells *in vitro* as a function of advanced age.[28] These observations are consistent with the notion that self-renewal of HSC in the aged may become limited as a result of replicative senescence under enforced replication.[41,42] The outcome of limited development of T-lymphocytes is thus causally related to the nature of the transplanted bone marrow cells. It could be determined by the intrinsic properties of HSCs in the aged donors or by distinct cells associated in the donor bone marrow samples. Identifiable thymus progenitor cells in the bone marrow are of interest in that respect. The data leading to this conclusion showed that adult mouse bone marrow depleted of cells that express any of a panel of lineage-specific markers, stem cell Ag-1^{+}, and not expressing the Thy1.1 antigen repopulated the thymus 9 days faster than HSC.[43]

It would thus appear that this cell-type population is particularly sensitive to aging effects and subject to replicative senescence.

HSC MIGRATION AND HOMING

Migration and homing of HSCs need to be considered along two avenues. First, cells migrate from the bone marrow to the circulation system, under normal physiological conditions and in the course of arbitrarily induced mobilization. Second, cell migration and homing to the bone marrow is an integral component of HSC transplantation. In addition, cells exiting the bone marrow migrate to different tissues (e.g., the spleen and thymus) and settle there. The mechanisms underlying these processes have attracted considerable attention.

Migration and homing of HSCs are mediated by adhesion molecules receptors, such as the very late antigen-4 (VLA-4), VLA-5, L-selectin, leukocyte function-associated antigen 1 (LFA-1), CD44, and the stromal cell-derived factor 1 (Sdf1) receptor Cxcr4. Altered expression of these receptors may determine the efficiency of HSC homing.[44] The chemokine Sdf1 and its Cxcr4 receptor were found critical for the engraftment of human stem cells in the bone marrow of severe-combined immunodeficiency (SCID) mice.[45,46] Accordingly, migration to Sdf1 is associated with the localization of stem cells in the bone marrow, and differentiating cells with reduced migration levels are prone to exit to the blood circulation system. The effects of aging on expression of the Cxcr4 receptor and its Sdf1 ligand in the bone marrow are as yet unknown. The possibility that aged cells are unable to down-regulate Cxcr4 expression in the bone marrow needs to be considered.

The pattern of expression of these receptors is cytokine dependent.[44] Changes in integrin expression were associated with altered homing patterns of murine HSCs following the mobilization by the cyclophosphamide–granulocyte colony-stimulating factor (CSF).[47] Changes in integrin expression by blood-borne HSCs correlated with a 50% decrease in their ability to home to the bone marrow in short-term assays and with previously observed defects in competitive engraftment by these HSCs. Similar reductions in bone marrow homing were observed for HSCs treated with alpha 4 integrin function blocking mAb prior to injection.[47] Modulation of integrin expression induced by mobilization was not associated with cell-cycle progression. Hence, changes in integrin expression and function are associated with HSC mobilization and affect the engraftment potential of HSCs. Altered HSC migration and homing may thus be causally tied to the age-related changes in the cytokine profile[48–51] and the production in response to stimulation.[48,49]

High levels of CD44$^+$ expression in the bone marrow and thymus of aged mice[52,53] suggested that down-regulation of CD44 expression is less efficient in aging. It may thus be assumed that the cells remain adherent to stroma elements and fail to proceed through the subsequent steps of differentiation.

CIRCULATING HSCs UNDER NORMAL CONDITIONS AND INDUCED MOBILIZATION

A decrease in circulating HSCs in the blood was observed in old age.[18,54] Studies on centenarians showed the presence of CD34$^+$ cells in the circulation, although at a lower frequency than in the young.[18] However, in terms of hematopoietic function, the cells were capable of differentiation *in vitro* to colony-forming units (CFUs).

Although the cytokine network undergoes remodeling as a function of age,[48–51,55] HSCs of the old respond to hemopoietic growth factors.[18] This raises the question of whether arbitrary mobilization is feasible in old age to the same extent as in the young. From a clinical standpoint, the mobilization of cells to the peripheral blood in elderly subjects would be a routine procedure to obtain autologous cells for tissue repair. Currently, data in that respect indicate several problems.[56–59] The mobilization of cells for transplantation revealed that the yields of circulating stem cells under conditions of allogeneic donors were higher than the yields from autologous transplantation.[58] This was explained by the possibility that the candidates for transplants had a priori a different status of cytokine profile, because of their clinical status, superimposed on aging effects; therefore, their baseline for mobilized cells was different than the baseline in the healthy allogeneic donors.[60]

Analysis of CD34$^+$ cells disclosed distinct differences between the cells in the bone marrow and those in the circulation. Interestingly, HSCs in the bone marrow of old mice share several properties with the case of cytokine-mobilized mice.[61] The increased number of HSCs in cycle is just one of the shared properties.

Gene expression profiling led to the identification of significant differences between the molecular phenotypes of bone marrow-derived and circulating human CD34 HSCs.[62] The gene profiling data seem to explain the finding that CD34 cells residing in the bone marrow cycle more rapidly, whereas circulating CD34 cells consist of a higher number of quiescent stem and progenitor cells. The relevance of the cell cycle to HSC engraftment ability was further elucidated by experiments in which HSC cycling was inhibited.[63]

Together, the normally circulating HSCs under steady-state conditions and the mobilized cells represent potentially active candidates for clinical applications.

Aging of the Stem Cells

IN VIVO EXPERIMENTAL MODELS AND CLINICAL DATA

Indications that HSCs are subject to aging processes were derived from a variety of experimental models as well as from clinical data. These studies pointed to manifestations of aging in HSCs.

Sequential transplantation of limited numbers of bone marrow cells to a series of irradiated mice was used as a tool for evaluating the self-renewal capacity of HSCs. Bone marrow cells harvested from the recipients following transplantation were examined for their capacity to generate spleen colonies (CFUs-S). Such studies of HSCs from young donors revealed a gradual reduction in the number of CFUs-S that developed from the bone marrow of the recipients after 4 to 5 serial transplantations, and eventually there were no detectable CFUs-S.[1,8,9] More recent studies on serial transplantation of HSCs lent support to the original conclusion on the limited capacity for serial transplantation and pointed to telomere shortening as underlying mechanism.[61] Whereas these studies suggested that HSCs are limited in their capacity for self-renewal in the bone marrow, arbitrary hematological depletion within the individual mouse did not lead to a decline in subsequent HSC function.[10,11]

The studies on the *in vivo* experimental models have indicated the need to distinguish between the processes of hematopoiesis *in situ,* manifesting an overall capacity to cope with a certain degree of hematological loss, and the biological potential of the individual stem cell and its progeny, as revealed from conditions of enforced extensive stress.

IN VITRO EXPERIMENTAL MODELS

Studies on isolated HSCs *in vitro* were conducted on several experimental models. Methods enabling a quantitative expansion of HSCs have been a goal for both basic research and clinical purposes. To that end, various stroma cell lines have been developed to support stem cell proliferation. Studies by Sharp *et al.*[33] represent that particular focus on HSCs in aging. Sharp and colleagues examined murine bone marrow cultured on mesenchymal stroma cells (14F1.1) that selectively support long-term stem cell maintenance and expansion. The cells from aged mice showed initially higher proliferation rates than those from the young.[3,33] In addition, they generated increased levels of myeloid cells (CFU-culture and CFU-S), in line with the observations on elderly human subjects.[64]

More advanced methods were established for the maintenance of HSCs without stroma cell support using a combination of relevant growth factors, particularly, the stem cell factor (SCF; c-kit ligand), Flt3 ligand, the megakaryocyte growth and development factor (MGDF), and IL-6.[65] The *in vitro* propagated cells showed maintenance of hematopoietic function, manifested in the reconstitution of nonobese diabetic SCID mice. The studies showed expansion of the CD34$^+$ cells for at least 10 generations under such conditions.[53,65] However, experiments by Sharp *et al.* pointed to a limit in the capacity for T-cell differentiation of the expanded cells, although the cells did generate myeloid colonies in CFU assays (unpublished) in line with the data on HSCs expanded on supportive stroma cell monolayers.[33]

It thus appears that HSCs from young donors can replicate under proper conditions, yet they eventually undergo replicative senescence. Accordingly, the *in vitro* propagated cells may manifest aging patterns that reflect *in vivo* processes of enforced sequential replications.

HSC SELF-RENEWAL AND REPLICATIVE SENESCENCE

It could be predicted that the replicative potential of stem cells is indefinite, ensuring long-term fidelity of self-renewal. Whether stem cell replication is associated with a decrease in telomere length has thus been a question of major interest. As an example, Vaziri *et al.* found that CD34$^+$CD38^{low} cells purified from human bone marrow have shorter telomeres than similar cell types from the fetal liver or cord blood.[66] A decrease in telomere length *in vivo* was detected following bone marrow transplantation in humans.[67,68] Telomeres in the donor-derived peripheral blood cells of the recipients were shorter than those in the respective donors.

These observations have led to the conclusion that under conditions of enforced extensive replication, the transplanted cells undergo telomere shortening. Relevance of telomerase to these processes is indicated from a variety of studies.

Telomerase activity is present at basal levels in primitive cycle-quiescent stem cells and is up-regulated by cytokines.[69] This point is important for long-term maintenance of functional stem cells *in vitro* in the presence of cytokines. Because telomerase expression is induced by cytokines, it could be expected that under *in vitro* conditions, in which cytokines are present continuously, telomerase expression would be constantly high. Noteworthy that an analogous situation triggering T-cell replication indicated that antigen challenge resulted in reduction, rather than increase, in telomerase expression and function in CD8 T-cells.[70] By analogy, Effros and Globerson have proposed that telomerase expression may decrease in spite of the continuous exposure of the cells to cytokines.[42]

Differences in levels of telomerase expression were also recorded in relation to age. Sakabe *et al.* demonstrated that human cord blood–derived CD34$^+$CD38$^-$, as well as CD34$^+$c-kit$^-$ cells characterized as primitive progenitors, have low telomerase activity.[71,72] Low levels of telomerase in primitive hematopoietic cells (CD34$^+$CD71^{low}CD45RA^{low}) and higher levels in the early progenitor cells (CD34$^+$CD71$^+$) were also shown by Chiu *et al.*[73] Nonexpanding CD34$^+$ cells had low or undetectable telomerase levels. Accordingly, there is a distinction between primitive and more advanced stem cells in terms of telomerase function.

Weismann *et al.* investigated the relevance of telomerase function in relation to telomere size in HSC self-renewal.[74,75] They showed that telomerase-deficient mice had a reduced capacity for sequential reconstitution of irradiated mice compared to wild-type mice (two serial transplantations compared to four). It should be noted that telomerase function might reduce, but not prevent, telomere shortening during cell replication.[76]

Together, replicative senescence evolving to telomere shortening is at least one of the underlying mechanisms in HSCs potential problems under *in vivo* conditions of transplantation.

AGING EFFECTS ON HSC DIFFERENTIATION INTO DIVERSE BLOOD CELL TYPES

Studies designed to examine the developmental potential of the HSC pool in aging or to examine the capacity for *in vitro* differentiation to CFUs were based on the transplantation of bone marrow cells to hematologically compromised mice (irradiated or genetically anemic mice). In general, hematological reconstitution was recorded; however, several studies indicated qualitative differences in the pattern of reconstitution by cells from old and young donors (reviewed by Globerson[2]). Efficient hematological reconstitution was exhibited by long-term erythropoiesis[77] and granulopoiesis.[3,30] In contrast, T-lymphocyte values eventually decreased in such hematologically reconstituted mice,[39,40] suggesting a selective decline in the capacity to generate T-lymphocytes.

The question of whether aging of HSCs may manifest in patterns of differentiation into blood cells is of interest, particularly because the T-lymphocyte axis is subject to pronounced aging effects. To focus on the aging of the bone marrow as separate from the issue of thymus involution in that respect, Eren *et al.* seeded bone marrow cells from young and old mice onto fetal thymic organ cultures (FTOC) under conditions favoring T-cell development.[78,79] Identification of T-cells originating from each donor was feasible by using congenic mice that express different Thy1 allotypes (Thy1.1 and Thy1.2). A difference between old and young bone marrow–derived cells was apparent under competitive reconstitution, when identifiable cells of the young and the old donors were seeded onto the same individual thymic lobe. The relevance of competitive colonization to normal regeneration and continuous developmental processes was inferred from the observation that donor-type bone marrow cells competed with intrinsic thymic cells following exposure to low doses of irradiation.[80] Inferiority of the old to the young donor–derived bone marrow cells was also observed under conditions of competition with the thymic resident cells. Interestingly, although the frequency of the bone marrow cells that colonized the thymic lobes was reduced with donor age, it initially had no effect on the total cell number; the low yield of old bone marrow donor–derived thymocytes became apparent after longer culture periods. This was because the bone marrow cells of old donors replicated upon seeding in the thymus, and the cells of the young started replication 24 hours later.[34,35] The decreased capacity for subsequent sequential cell replications led to the ultimate lower yield of thymocytes under these conditions.

In vitro studies based on the FTOC experimental model were carried out on isolated human CD34 cells. The results showed that bone marrow CD34 cells from old donors generated fewer T-cells than those of the young.[28]

In conclusion, then, HSCs of the old are characterized by a large proportion being in cycle yet are limited in the capacity for extensive sequential replications.

The trend for increased myelopoiesis by HSCs from old donors was revealed from a variety of experimental conditions[3] in line with the clinical observations on elderly human subjects.[64] This was indicated from *in vitro* studies of bone marrow cells in the FTOC experimental model[3] as well as from HSC transplantation in irradiated mice.[30] Hence, isolated HSCs from the aged mice led to a similar tendency for increased myelopoiesis in the recipients.

Age-related changes in the bone marrow cells were also detected from analyses of membrane markers. Increased levels of cells expressing the stem cell marker c-kit[3] and the adhesion molecule CD44[52,53] suggested a limit in the capacity for down-regulation of these membrane markers. In addition, whereas bone marrow cells from young donors seemed to down-regulate membrane markers in the thymic stroma upon settling in the thymus, cells derived from old donor bone marrow failed to do so.[81] Accordingly, various age-related effects are manifested in the bone marrow cells at an early phase of interaction with the thymic stroma.

The question of whether the cells settling in the thymus are multipotential HSCs, or whether they represent a more advanced, committed cell or a distinct population, deserves attention. Recent observations on a distinct thymocyte progenitor type within the bone marrow[43] are of interest. Whatever the nature of cells settling in the thymus, the data indicate that they manifest aging effects in line with the observations on HSCs described previously.

A critical examination is still needed to determine whether chronically expanded HSCs can remain functional indefinitely, or whether they eventually age. Furthermore, the question of whether the expanded stem cells have the full developmental potential of freshly drawn stem cells from young donors is open.

Does replicative senescence narrow the range of developmental potential in the cells? When HSCs from aged mice were expanded on the stroma cell monolayer for several weeks, they could reconstitute FTOC and generate T-cells *in vitro.* However, aging became apparent when a competitive colonization assay was used. The competitive FTOC assay was based on the assumption that if stem cells of the old are not different from those of the young, then transplanting them in a mixture into the same individual FTOC will result in progeny blood cells derived from both donors at the same proportions as in the transplanted inoculum.[3,33] After 1 week of HSC culture on the stroma cell line, both young and old donor-derived cells failed to compete with fresh bone marrow cells in reconstituting FTOC, although they could develop under these conditions in the absence of competition. Stem cells of the young thus seemed to have aged *in vitro,* in the sense that they were inferior in competition to fresh bone marrow cells, as were cells from old donors.

The molecular mechanisms underlying the lineage-specific events in HSCs and aging effects on these mechanisms have not yet been fully elucidated. One avenue of interest in that respect is the Notch1 receptor, a known modulator of lineage-specific events in hematopoiesis.[82,83] Studies on Rag1 ($^{-/-}$) mouse stems cells showed increased stem cell numbers, related to decreased differentiation and enhanced stem cell self-renewal induced by Notch1.[84] Unexpectedly, preferential lymphoid-over-myeloid lineage commitment was noted when differentiation occurred. It was thus proposed that Notch1 affects two decision points in stem cell regulation, favoring self-renewal over differentiation and a lymphoid over a myeloid lineage outcome.[84,85] It is thus possible to speculate that the decrease in both self-renewal and lymphoid development, and the increase in myeloid differentiation, are causally related to the status and pattern of Notch1 function in aging. Research in that area is needed.

HSC PLASTICITY

The concept of HSC plasticity developed in the past 4 years from observations that stem cells deriving from adult tissues can differentiate outside their tissue of origin into a range of types. Hence, it was found that bone marrow–derived HSCs can generate cells other than blood cells, including cardiac muscle, liver cells, neuronal and nonneuronal cell types of the brain, endothelial cells, and osteoblasts.[17,86–89] These observations challenged the classical view of the biology of stem cells in the adult, which regarded them as committed to producing cell types that characterize the site in which they normally lodge. The notion that the cells have the potential for transdifferentiation raised the question of whether circulating HSCs play a role in tissue repair. This leads to the need to establish whether plasticity is subject to aging effects.

As it stands, there are certain discrepancies regarding the transdifferentiation events. Although this issue is beyond the scope of this chapter, it deserves attention in relation to the issue of aging. The bone marrow contains many cell types in addition to HSCs, including stroma, vascular cells, adipocytes, osteoblasts, osteoclasts, and mesenchymal stem cells. This has raised the need for caution in interpretations of data on HSC plasticity, because it could be related to diversity within the HSC population.[90,91] Jackson *et al.* outlined the possible source of discrepancies in relation to the various kinds of methodologies used in different studies, including analyses of cell surface marker expression, such as Sca-1, c-kit, CD34, and lineage markers as well as the ability to efflux the vital dye Hoecsht 33342.[92] The current data point to approaches required to understand the possible relevance of the effects of aging on HSC plasticity and the potential contribution to tissue repair. It is therefore relevant to HSC aging as well as to the nature of stem cells in the aged.

Dynamics of the HSC Compartment in Aging

The distinction between aging of stem cells and stem cells in the aged indicates the complexity of processes that characterize the HSC compartment. The bone marrow in the aged includes HSCs that have undergone replicative senescence and a significant level of functional cells. Several processes and mechanisms that operate *in vivo* deserve attention, including the altered cytokine and hormonal status and the nature of interaction with neighboring cells.

An age-related shift in the cytokine network may have a profound effect on hematopoiesis in the bone marrow and possibly on the mobilization of the cells. Age-related changes in cytokine levels were noted in the bone marrow in aging[48] and were similar to observations on the spleen.[49,50] Furthermore, Buchanan *et al.* demonstrated that light-density leukocytes from aged subjects released less CSF than cells from the young, and granulocyte–macrophage CSF (GM-CSF) accounted for 72–100% of colony stimulating activity of the young and only 0–42% of the old. This idea was substantiated by the findings on the expression of mRNA for GM-CSF. A sequential order of cytokine function was important for activation and proliferation of CD34 cells,[93] pointing to the need for the availability of an optimal cytokine profile in the HSC compartment.

The level of hematopoietic tissue in the bone marrow of aged mice was shown to be subject to growth hormone effect. Treatment with growth hormone was shown to increase the size of hematopoietic tissue in the bone marrow of aged mice,[94] suggesting augmented proliferation rates. *In vivo* treatment with growth hormone was also found effective in increasing thymic size in aged mice, and it was causally related to mobilization of HSCs from the bone marrow to the thymus.[95]

Interaction with neighboring cells[96] is noteworthy. First, the bone marrow stroma components[96–98] need to be considered because they are subject to aging effects, as revealed from studies on the replication of the cells in aged mice.[1,97] In addition, the levels of both B- and T-lymphocytes are increased in the bone marrow of aged mice.[99] This may result in an altered cytokine profile within the bone marrow.[53] The neuro–endocrine axis is of interest in view of the neurohormones and catecholamines constituting functional components of the bone marrow microenvironment[100] and the effects of substance P on the dynamics of bone marrow stroma and hematopoietic cell interactions.[101]

Together, the status of HSCs in aging is a combination of their intrinsic properties, their interaction with neighboring cells, and the microenvironmental effects of cytokine profiles and hormonal function. A mathematical model for the dynamics of stem cell interaction with thymic stromal cell elements[102] may be applicable to the bone marrow. Age-related remodeling of all of these components under steady-state conditions is balanced to ensure continuously normal levels of hematopoiesis. However, hematological stress leads to enforced replicative senescence of HSCs and, eventually, to distortion of that balance.

Summary

Recent advances in our understanding of stem cell biology points to a range of cell properties and processes that may change with age. The data suggest multifactorial mechanisms that may vary in their manifestation and dimensions in individuals. In addition, sequential replications of HSCs may result in changes in the developmental potential of the descendent cells.

The following conclusions can be drawn from the data gained so far:

- A comprehensive consideration of stem cells in aging requires critical evaluation of their intrinsic properties and developmental potential as well as of microenvironmental conditions, including the profile of cytokines, chemoattractants, growth factors, and hormones.
- Mechanisms that may compensate for aging effects at the tissue or cell population level have been indicated. Understanding the basis of compensatory mechanisms is key in designing strategies to prevent or minimize the potential risks of aging effects.
- Although what cells can do under experimental conditions does not necessarily reflect phenomena that normally occur *in vivo,* processes considered unconventional in the young adult might become dominant in the aged.
- Enforced sequential replications (e.g., *in vitro* or in transplantation) may result in the manifestation of HSC aging. The outcome of HSC expansion *in vitro* for

transplantation and gene therapy therefore needs to be carefully evaluated.

- Distinguishing between age-related changes in the stem cell compartment within the individual and manifestations of aging in the HSC and its progeny has extended the scope of understanding of HSCs and aging and offers goals for research and development toward understanding of basic mechanisms of stem cells aging as well as for future clinical applications.

REFERENCES

1. Globerson, A. (1997). Thymocytopoiesis in aging: the bone marrow–thymus axis. (Review). *Arch. Gerontol Geriat.* **24,** 141–155.
2. Globerson, A. (1999). Hematopoietic stem cells and aging. *Exp. Gerontol.* **34,** 137–146.
3. Globerson, A. (2001). Hematopoietic stem cell aging. *In* "A Research Agenda on Aging for the 21st Century," *Wiley, Chichester Novartis Found. Symp.* **235,** 85–100.
4. Van Zant, G., Manning, E.L., and Geiger, H. (2002). Hematopoietic stem cells and aging. *In* "Advances Cell Aging Gerontology — Stem Cells: A Cellular Fountain of Youth," (M.P. Mattson *et al.,* eds.) Vol. 9, pp. 19–42. Elsevier, New York.
5. Allsopp, R.C., and Weissman, I.L. (2002). Replicative senescence of hematopoietic stem cells during serial transplantation: does telomere shortening play a role? (Review). *Oncogene* **21,** 3270–3273.
6. Medvinsky, A.L., and Dzierzak, E.A. (1998). Development of the definitive hematopoietic hierarchy in the mouse. (Review). *Dev. Comp. Immunol.* **22,** 289–301.
7. Auerbach, R., and Huang, H. (1996). Hematopoietic stem cells in the mouse embryonic yolk sac. *Stem Cells* **14,** 269–280.
8. Ogden, D.A., and Micklem, H.S. (1976). The rate of serially transplanted bone marrow cell population from young and old donors. *Transplantation* **22,** 237–293.
9. Harrison, D.E., and Astle, C.M. (1982). Loss of stem cell repopulating ability upon transplantation. *J. Exp. Med.* **156,** 1767–1779.
10. Harrison, D.E., Astle, C.M., and Delaittre, J.A. (1978). Loss of proliferative capacity in immunohematopoietic stem cells caused by serial transplantation rather than aging. *J. Exp. Med.* **147,** 1526–1531.
11. Ross, E.A.M., Anderson, N., and Micklem, H.S. (1982). Serial depletion and regeneration of the murine hematopoietic system: implications for hematopoietic regeneration and the study of cellular aging. *J. Exp. Med.* **155,** 432–444.
12. Jackson, K.A., Majka, S.M., Wang, H., Pocius, J., Hartley, C.J., Majesky, M.W., Entman, M.L., Michael, L.H., Hirschi, K.K., and Goodell, M.A. (2001). Regeneration of ischemic cardiac muscle and vascular endothelium by adult stem cells. *J. Clin. Invest.* **107,** 1395–1402.
13. Chandross, K.J., and Mezey, E. (2002). Plasticity of adult bone marrow stem cells. *In* "Advances Cell Aging Gerontology — Stem Cells: A Cellular Fountain of Youth," (M.P. Mattson *et al.,* eds.), Vol. 9, pp. 73–95. Elsevier, New York.
14. Horwitz, E.M. (2003). Stem cell plasticity: a new image of the bone marrow stem cell. *Curr. Opin. Pediatr.* **15,** 1–2.
15. Malaguarnea, M., Di Fazio, I., Vinci, E., Bentivegna, P., Mangione, G., and Romano, M. (1999). Hematologic pattern in healthy elderly subjects. *Panminerva Med.* **41,** 227–231.
16. Kuehnle, I., and Goodell, M.A. (2002). The therapeutic potential of stem cells from adults. *BMJ* **325,** 372–376.
17. Majka, S.M., Jackson, K.A., Kienstra, K.A., Majesky, M.W., Goodell, M.A., and Hirschi, K.K. (2003). Distinct progenitor populations in skeletal muscle are bone marrow derived and exhibit different cell fates during vascular regeneration. *J. Clin. Invest.* **111,** 71–79.
18. Bagnara, G.P., Bonsi, L., Strippoli, P., Bonifazi, F., Tonelli, R., D'Addato, S., Paganelli, R., Scala, E., Fagiolo, U., Monti, D., Cossarizza, A., Bonafe, M., and Franceschi, C. (2000). Hemopoiesis in healthy old people and centenarians: well-maintained responsiveness of CD34+ cells to hemopoietic growth and remodeling of cytokine network. *J. Gerontol. A. Biol. Sci. Med. Sci.* **55(2),** B61–B66.
19. Globerson, A. (2000). *Commentary on* Hematopoiesis in healthy old people and centenarians: well-maintained responsiveness of CD34+ cells to hemopoietic growth factors and remodeling of cytokine network. *J. Gerontol. A. Biol. Sci. Med. Sci.* **55(2),** B69–B70.
20. Carmel, R. (2001). Anemia and aging: an overview of clinical, diagnostic, and biological issues. *Blood Rev.* **15,** 9–18.
21. Hayari, Y., Kukulansky, T., and Globerson, A. (1984). Effects of *in vivo* indomethacin treatment in aging mice. *Prostaglandins Leukotrienes Med.* **15,** 69–78.
22. Williams, L.H., Kodetthoor, B.U., and Lipschitz, D.A. (1986). Evaluation of the effect of age on hematopoiesis in the C57BL/6 mouse. *Exp. Hematol.* **14,** 827–832.
23. Zaucha, J.M., Yu, C., Mathioudakis, G., Seidel, K., Georges, G., Sale, G., Little, M.T., Torok-Storb, B., and Storb, R. (2001). Hematopoietic responses to stress conditions in young dogs compared with elderly dogs. *Blood* **98,** 322–327.
24. Timiras, M.L., and Brownstein, H. (1987). Prevalence of anemia and correlation of hemoglobin with age in a geriatric screening clinic population. *J. Am. Geriatr. Soc.* **35,** 639–643.
25. Rothstein, G. (2003). Disordered hematopoiesis and myelodysplasia in the elderly. *J. Am. Geriatr. Soc.* **51(3 Suppl.),** S22– S26.
26. Ershler, W.B. (2003). Biological interactions of aging and anemia: A focus on cytokines. *J. Am. Geriatr. Soc.* **51(3 Suppl.),** S18–S21.
27. Chatta, G.S., and Dale, D.C. (1996). Aging and hematopoiesis: implication for treatment with hematopoietic growth factors. *Drugs Aging* **9,** 37–47.
28. Offner, F., Kerre, T., Smedt, M., and Plum, J. (1999). Bone marrow CD34 cells generate fewer T-cells *in vitro* with increasing age and following chemotherapy. *Br. J. Haematol.* **104,** 801–808.
29. Harrison, D.E. (1980). Competitive repopulation: a new assay for long-term cell functional capacity. *Blood* **55,** 77–81.
30. Morrison, S.J., Wandycz, A.M., Akashi, K., Globerson, A., and Weissman, I.L. (1996). The aging of hematopoietic stem cells. *Nature Med.* **2,** 1011–1016.
31. Harrison, D.E., Astle, C.M., and Stone, M. (1989). Numbers and functions of transplantable primitive immunohematopoietic stem cells: Effects of age. *J. Immunol.* **142,** 3833–3841.
32. Harrison, D.E., Jordan, C.T., Zhong, R.K., and Astle, C.M. (1993). Primitive hemopoietic stem cells: direct assay of most productive populations by competitive repopulation with simple binomial, correlation and covariance calculations. *Exp. Hematol.* **21,** 206–219.
33. Sharp, A., Zipori, D., Toledo, J., Tal, S., Resnitzky, P., and Globerson, A. (1989). Age-related changes in hemopoietic capacity of bone marrow cells. *Mech. Ageing Dev.* **48,** 91–99.
34. Sharp, A., Kukulansky, T., and Globerson, A. (1990). *In vitro* analysis of age-related changes in the developmental potential of bone marrow thymocyte progenitors. *Eur. J. Immunol.* **20,** 2541–2546.

35. Sharp, A., Brill, S., Kukulansky, T., and Globerson, A. (1991). Developmental changes in the bone marrow thymocyte progenitors and Thy1+ cells in aging. *In* "Physiological senescence and its postponement: theoretical approaches and rational interventions." Second Stromboli Conference on Aging and Cancer. *Ann. NY Acad. Sci.* **621,** 229–238.
36. Vijg, J., and Knook, D.L. (1987). DNA repair in relation to the aging process. *J. Am. Geriatr. Soc.* **35,** 532–541.
37. Van Zant, G. (2003). Genetic control of stem cells: implications for aging. *Int. J. Hematol.* **77,** 29–36.
38. Ben Yehuda, A., Globerson, A., Krichevsky, S., Bar On, H., Kidron, M., Friedlander, Y., Friedman, G., and Ben Yehuda, D. (2000). Ageing and the mismatch repair system. *Mech. Ageing Dev.* **121,** 173–179.
39. Gozes, Y., Umiel, T., and Trainin, N. (1982). Selective decline in differentiating capacity of immunohemopoietic stem cells with aging. *Mech. Ageing Dev.* **18,** 251–259.
40. Globerson, A. (1986). Immunoregulatory cells in aging. *In* "Topics in Ageing Research in Europe," (A. Facchini *et al.,* eds.), Vol. 9, pp. 9–15. EURAGE, Rijswijk, The Netherlands.
41. Traycoff, C.M., Orazi, A., Ladd, A.C., Rice, S., McMahel, J., and Srour, E.F. (1998). Proliferation-induced decline of primitive hematopoietic progenitor cell activity is coupled with an increase in apoptosis of *ex vivo* expanded CD34+ cells. *Exp. Hematol.* **26,** 53–62.
42. Effros, R.B., and Globerson, A. (2002). Hematopoietic cells and replicative senescence. *Exp. Gerontol.* **37,** 191–196.
43. Perry, S.S., Pierce, L.J., Slayton, W.B., and Spangrude, G.J. (2003). Characterization of thymic progenitors in adult mouse bone marrow. *J. Immunol.* **170,** 1877–1886.
44. Denning-Kendall, P., Singha, S., Bradley, B., and Hows, J. (2003). Cytokine expansion culture of cord blood CD34(+) cells induces marked and sustained changes in adhesion receptor and Cxcr4 expressions. *Stem Cells* **21,** 61–70.
45. Peled, A., Petit, I., Kollet, O., Magid, M., Pnomaryov, T., Byk, T., Nagler, A., Ben-Hur, H., Many, A., Shultz, L., Lider, O., Alon, R., Zipori, D., and Lapidot, T. (1999). Dependence of human stem cell engraftment and repopulation of NOD–SCID mice on Cxcr4. *Science* **283,** 845–848.
46. Peled, A., Kollet, O., Ponomoyov, T., Petit, I., Franitza, S., Grabovsky, V., Slav, M.M., Nagler, A., Lider, O., Alon, R., Zipori, D., and Lapidot, T. (2000). The chemokine Sdf1 activates the integrins LFA-1, VLA-4, and VLA-5 on immature human CD34(+) cells: role in transendothelial–stromal migration and engraftment of NOD–SCID mice. *Blood* **95,** 3289–3296.
47. Wagers, A.J., Allsopp, R.C., and Weissman, I.L. (2002). Changes in integrin expression are associated with altered homing properties of Lin(−/lo)Thy1.1(lo)Sca-1(+)c-kit(+) hematopoietic stem cells following mobilization by cyclophosphamide–granulocyte colony-stimulating factor. *Exp. Hematol.* **30,** 176–185.
48. Buchanan, J.P., Peters, C.A., Rasmussen, C.J., and Rothstein, G. (1996). Impaired expression of hematopoietic growth factors: a candidate mechanism for hematopoietic defect of aging. *Exp. Gerontol.* **31,** 135–144.
49. Segal, R., Dayan, M., Globerson, A., Habot, B., Shearer, G., and Mozes, E. (1997). Effect of aging on cytokine production in normal and experimental systemic lupus erythematosus afflicted mice. *Mech. Ageing Dev.* **96,** 47–58.
50. Dayan, M., Segal, R., Globerson, A., Habut, B., Shearer, G.M., and Mozes, E. (2000). Effect of aging on cytokine production in normal and experimental systemic lupus erythematosus-afflicted mice. *Exp. Gerontol.* **35,** 225–236.
51. Bruunsgaard, H., and Pedersen, B.K. (2003). Age-related inflammatory cytokines and disease. *Immunol. Allergy Clin. North Am.* **23,** 15–39.
52. Yu, S., Abel, L., and Globerson, A. (1997). Thymocyte progenitors and T-cell development in aging. *Mech. Ageing Dev.* **94,** 103–111.
53. Globerson, A. (Unpublished data).
54. Egusa, Y., Fujiwara, Y., Syahruddin, E., Isobe, T., and Yamakido, M. (1998). Effect of age on human peripheral blood stem cells. *Oncol. Rep.* **5,** 397–400.
55. Balducci, L., Hardy, C.L., and Lyman, G.H. (2001). Hematopoietic growth factors in the older cancer patient. *Curr. Opin. Hematol.* **8,** 170–187.
56. Kessinger, A., and Sharp, J.G. (1998). Mobilization of blood stem cells. *Stem Cells* **16 (Suppl. 1),** 139–143.
57. Siegel, D.S., Desikan, K.R., Mehta, J., Singhal, S., Fassas, A., Munshi, N., Anaissie, E., Naucke, S., Ayers, D., Spoon, D., Vesole, D., Tricot, G., and Barlogie, B. (1999). Age is not a prognostic variable with autotransplants for multiple myeloma. *Blood* **93,** 51–54.
58. McGuire, T.R., Kessinger, A., Hock, L., and Sharp, J.G. (2001). Elevated transforming growth factor beta levels in the plasma of cytokine-treated cancer patients and normal allogeneic stem cell donors. *Cytotherapy* **3,** 361–364.
59. Kessinger, A., and Sharp, J.G. (2003). The whys and hows of hematopoietic progenitor and stem cell mobilization. *Bone Marrow Transplant.* **31,** 319–329.
60. Balducci, L., Hardy, C.L., and Lyman, G.H. (2000). Hemopoietic reserve in the older cancer patient: clinical and economic considerations. *Cancer Control* **7,** 539–547.
61. Allsopp, R.C., Cheshier, S., and Weissman, I.L. (2001). Telomere shortening accompanies increased cell cycle activity during serial transplantation of hematopoietic stem cells. *J. Exp. Med.* **193,** 917–924.
62. Steidl, U., Kronenwett, R., Rohr, U.P., Fenk, R., Kliszewski, S., Maercker, C., Neubert, P., Aivado, M., Koch, J., Modlich, O., Bojar, H., Gattermann, N., and Haas, R. (2002). Gene expression profiling identifies significant differences between the molecular phenotypes of bone marrow-derived and circulating human CD34 hematopoietic stem cells. *Blood* **99,** 2037–2044.
63. Cashman, J., Dykstra, B., Clark-Lewis, I., Eaves, A., and Eaves, C. (2002). Changes in the proliferative activity of human hematopoietic stem cells in NOD–SCID mice and enhancement of their transplantability after *in vivo* treatment with cell cycle inhibitors. *J. Exp. Med.* **196,** 1141–1149.
64. Resnitzky, P., Segal, M., Barak, Y., and Dassa, C. (1987). Granulopoiesis in aged people: Inverse correlation between bone marrow cellularity and myeloid progenitor cell numbers. *Gerontology* **33,** 109–114.
65. Piacibello, W., Sanavio, F., Severino, A., Dane, A., Gammaitoni, L., Fagioli, F., Perissinotto, E., Cavalloni, G., Kollet, O., Lapidot, T., and Aglietta, M. (1999). Engraftment in nonobese diabetic severe combined immunodeficient mice of human CD34+ cord blood cells after *ex vivo* expansion: evidence for the amplification and self-renewal of repopulating stem cells. *Blood* **93,** 3736–3749.
66. Vaziri, H., Dragowska, W., Allsopp, R.C., Thomas, T.E., Harley, C.B., and Lansdorp, P.M. (1994). Evidence for a mitotic clock in human hematopoietic cells: loss of telomeric DNA with age. *Proc. Nat. Acad. Sci. USA* **91,** 9857–9860.

67. Notaro, R., Cimmino, A., Tabarini, D., Rotoli, B., and Luzzatto, L. (1997). *In vivo* telomere dynamics of human hematopoietic stem cells. *Proc. Nat. Acad. Sci. USA* **94,** 13,782–13,785.
68. Wynn, R.F., Cross, M.A., Hatton, C., Will, A.M., Lashford, L.S., Dexter, T.M., and Testa, N.G. (1998). Accelerated telomere shortening in young recipients of allogeneic bone-marrow transplants. *Lancet* **351,** 178–181.
69. Szyper-Kravitz, M., Uziel, O., Shapiro, H., Radnay, J., Katz, T., Rowe, J.M., Lishner, M., and Lahav, M. (2003). Granulocyte colony-stimulating factor administration upregulates telomerase activity in CD34+ hematopoietic cells and may prevent telomere attrition after chemotherapy. *Br. J. Haematol.* **120,** 329–336.
70. Valenzuela, H.F., and Effros, R.B. (2002). Divergent telomerase and CD28 expression patterns in human CD4 and CD8 T-cells following repeated encounters with the same antigenic stimulus. *Clin. Immunol.* **105,** 117–125.
71. Sakabe, H., Ohmizono, Y., Tanimukai, S., Kimura, T., Mori, K.J., Abe, T., and Sonoda, Y. (1997). Functional differences between subpopulations of mobilized peripheral blood-derived CD34+ cells expressing different levels of HLA-DR, CD33, CD38, and c-kit antigens. *Stem Cells* **15,** 73–81.
72. Sakabe, H., Yahata, N., Kimura, T., Zeng, Z.Z., Minamiguchi, H., Kaneko, H., Mori, K.J., Ohyashiki, K., Ohyashiki, J.H., Toyama, K., Abe, T., and Sonoda, Y. (1998). Human cord blood-derived primitive progenitors are enriched in CD34+c-kit– cells: correlation between long-term culture-initiating cells and telomerase expression. *Leukemia* **12,** 728–734.
73. Chiu, C.P., Draowska, W., Kim, N.W., Vaziri, H., Yui, J., Thomas, T.E., Harley, C.B., and Lansdorp, P.M. (1996). Differential expression of telomerase activity in hematopoietic progenitors from adult human bone marrow. *Stem Cells* **14,** 239–248.
74. Allsopp, R.C., Cheshier, S., and Weissman, I.L. (2002). Telomerase activation and rejuvenation of telomere length in stimulated T-cells derived from serially transplanted hematopoietic stem cells. *J. Exp. Med.* **196,** 1427–1433.
75. Allsopp, R.C., Morin, G.B., DePinho, R., Harley, C.B., and Weissman, I.L. (2003). Telomerase is required to slow telomere shortening and extend replicative life span of HSC during serial transplantation. *Blood* **102,** 517–520.
76. Engelhardt, M., Kumar, R., Albanell, J., Pettengell, R., Han, W., and Moore, M.A. (1997). Telomerase regulation, cell cycle, and telomere stability in primitive hematopoietic cells. *Blood* **90,** 182–193.
77. Harrison, D.E. (1983). Long-term erythropoietic repopulating ability of old, young, and fetal stem cells. *J. Exp. Med.* **157,** 1496–1504.
78. Eren, R., Zharhary, D., Abel, L., and Globerson, A. (1988). Age-related changes in the capacity of bone marrow cells to differentiate in thymic organ cultures. *Cell Immunol.* **112,** 449–455.
79. Eren, R., Globerson, A., Abel, L., and Zharhary, D. (1990). Quantitative analysis of bone marrow thymic progenitors in young and aged mice. *Cell Immunol.* **127,** 238–246.
80. Fridkis-Hareli, M., Abel, L., and Globerson, A. (1992). Patterns of dual lymphocyte development in cocultures of fetal thymus and lymphohemopoietic cells from young and old mice. *Immunology* **77,** 185–188.
81. Francz, P.I., Fridkis-Hareli, M., Abel, L., Bayreuther, K., and Globerson, A. (1992). Differential expression of membrane polypeptides on fetal thymic stroma cocultured with bone marrow cells from young and old mice. *Mech. Ageing Dev.* **64,** 99–109.
82. Ohishi, K., Varnum-Finney, B., and Bernstein, I.D. (2002). The notch pathway: modulation of cell fate decisions in hematopoiesis. *Int. J. Hematol.* **75,** 449–459.
83. Ohishi, K., Katayama, N., Shiku, H., Varnum-Finney, B., and Bernstein, I.D. (2003). Notch signaling in hematopoiesis. *Semin. Cell Dev. Biol.* **14,** 143–150.
84. Stier, S., Cheng, T., Dombkowski, D., Carlesso, N., and Scadden, D.T. (2002). Notch1 activation increases hematopoietic stem cell self-renewal *in vivo* and favors lymphoid over myeloid lineage outcome. *Blood* **99,** 2369–2378.
85. Varnum-Finney, B., Brashem-Stein, C., and Bernstein, I.D. (2003). Combined effects of Notch signaling and cytokines induce a multiple log increase in precursors with lymphoid and myeloid reconstituting ability. *Blood* **101,** 1784–1789.
86. Goodell, M.A., Jackson, K.A., Majka, S.M., Mi, T., Wang, H., Pocius, J., Hartley, C.J., Majesky, M.W., Entman, M.L., Michael, L.H., and Hirschi, K.K. (2001). Stem cell plasticity in muscle and bone marrow. *Ann. NY Acad. Sci.* **938,** 208–218; discussion, 218–220.
87. McKinney-Freeman, S.L., Jackson, K.A., Camargo, F.D., Ferrari, G., Mavilio, F., and Goodell, M.A. (2002). Muscle-derived hematopoietic stem cells are hematopoietic in origin. *Proc. Nat. Acad. Sci. USA* **99,** 1341–1346.
88. Hirschi, K.K., Goodell, M.A. (2002). Hematopoietic, vascular, and cardiac fates of bone marrow-derived stem cells. *Gene Ther.* **9,** 648–652.
89. Wulf, G.G., Luo, K.L., Jackson, K.A., Brenner, M.K., and Goodell, M.A. (2003). Cells of the hepatic side population contribute to liver regeneration and can be replenished with bone marrow stem cells. *Haematologica* **88,** 368–378.
90. Orkin, S.H., and Zon, L.I. (2002). Hematopoiesis and stem cells: plasticity versus developmental heterogeneity. *Nat. Immunol.* **3,** 323–328.
91. Goodell, M.A. (2003). Stem-cell "plasticity": befuddled by the muddle. *Curr. Opin. Hematol.* **10,** 208–213.
92. Jackson, K.A., Majka, S.M., Wulf, G.G., and Goodell, M.A. (2002). Stem cells: a minireview. *J. Cell Biochem. Suppl.* **38,** 1–6.
93. Ladd, A.C., Pyatt, R., Gothot, A., Rice, S., McMahel, J., Traycoff, C.M., Srour, F.F. (1997). Orderly process of sequential cytokine stimulation required for activation and maximal proliferation of primitive human bone marrow CD34+ hematopoietic progenitor cells residing in G0. *Blood* **90,** 658–668.
94. French, R.A., Broussard, S.R., Meier, W.A., Minshall, C., Arkins, S., Zachary, J.F., Dantzer, R., and Kelley, K.W. (2002). Age-associated loss of bone marrow hematopoietic cells is reversed by GH and accompanies thymic reconstitution. *Endocrinology* **143,** 690–699.
95. Knyszynski, A., Adler-Kunin, S., and Globerson, A. (1992). Effects of growth hormone on thymocyte development from progenitor cells in the bone marrow. *Brain Behav. Immun.* **6,** 327–340.
96. Adams, G.B., Chabner, K.T., Foxall, R.B., Weibrecht, K.W., Rodrigues, N.P., Dombkowski, D., Fallon, R., Poznansky, M.C., and Scadden, D.T. (2003). Heterologous cells cooperate to augment stem cell migration, homing, and engraftment. *Blood* **101,** 45–51.
97. Jiang, D., Fei, R.G., Pendergrass, W.R., and Wolf, N.S. (1992). An age-related reduction in the replicative capacity of two murine hematopoietic stroma cell types. *Exp. Hematol.* **20,** 1216–1222.

98. Gimble, J.M., Robinson, C.E., Wu, X., and Kelly, K.A. (1996). The function of adipocytes in the bone marrow stroma: an update. *Bone* **19,** 421–428.
99. Sharp, A., Kukulansky, T., Malkinson, Y. and Globerson, A. (1990). The bone marrow as an effector T-cell organ in aging. *Mech. Ageing Dev.* **52,** 219–233.
100. Maestroni, G.J. (2000). Neurohormones and catecholamines as functional components of the bone marrow microenvironment. *Ann. NY Acad. Sci.* **917,** 29–37.
101. Rameshwar, P., Zhu, G., Donnelly, R.J., Qian, J., Ge, H., Goldstein, K.R., Denny, T.N., and Gascon, P. (2001). The dynamics of bone marrow stromal cells in the proliferation of multipotent hematopoietic progenitors by substance P: an understanding of the effects of a neurotransmitter on the differentiating hematopoietic stem cell. *J. Neuroimmunol.* **121,** 22–31.
102. Mehr, R., Fridkis-Hareli, M., Abel, L., Segel, L., and Globerson, A. (1995). Lymphocyte development in irradiated thymuses: dynamics of colonization by progenitor cells and regeneration of resident cells. *J. Theor. Biol.* **177,** 181–192.

33

Common Lymphoid Progenitors

Gay M. Crooks

Introduction

For several decades, our understanding of hematopoiesis has been built on a hierarchical paradigm in which all the pathways of differentiation lead from a pluripotent hematopoietic stem cell (HSC) and progress through discrete progenitor stages that mark each branch point of lineage commitment.[1] This model assumes that pathways are always divergent and nonoverlapping, representing mutually exclusive stages of lineage potential. The first branch point of this lineage tree has long been assumed to be the point at which the lymphoid lineages and "myeloid" (i.e., myeloid, erythroid, and megakaryocytic) lineages diverge. Thus, in this model, all lymphoid cells (i.e., T-, B-, and NK-cells) are generated from the same progenitor, the common lymphoid progenitor (CLP); all myeloid, erythroid, and megakaryocytic cells are generated from the common myeloid progenitor (CMP).

The concept of the lymphoid–myeloid dichotomy initially came from numerous but circumstantial pieces of evidence. B-, T-, and NK-cells are associated anatomically (e.g., in lymph nodes, the spleen, and the thymus), and B- and T-cells are linked through functional interdependence. The molecular mechanisms of T-cell receptor rearrangements and B-cell immunoglobulin gene rearrangements are closely related. Several mechanisms for the regulation of early lymphopoiesis are shared by the T-, B-, and NK-lineages. For example, murine studies of *Ikaros* gene mutations are frequently cited as evidence of the existence of the CLP, as *Ikaros* knockout mice were initially thought to have an exclusive and profound deficiency in lymphoid cells.[2,3] However, since these original reports, it has been realized that not only lymphoid but also myeloid and stem cell defects are found in the *Ikaros*$^{-/-}$ mice.[4,5] In further support of the contention that Ikaros expression is not lymphoid specific, it has been shown that certain *Ikaros* isoforms are expressed in stem cells and myeloid cells, as well as in lymphoid lineages, in mice[6,7] and humans.[7,8]

More convincing molecular evidence for a developmental link among the lymphoid lineages is presented by severe-combined immunodeficiency (SCID) syndrome, a group of diseases caused by different genetic mutations that result in clinical abnormalities in one or more of the T-, B-, or NK-lymphoid lineages with normal myelopoiesis.[9] Similar genetic mutations in mice result in exclusively lymphoid defects, although the murine phenotypes are not always identical to the human diseases.[9]

Although gene expression data provide evidence of a probable developmental link among cells of the lymphoid lineages, definitive proof of the existence of a lymphoid differentiation pathway that diverges from the myeloid and erythroid lineages requires the identification of a discrete progenitor stage, the CLP, that marks such a pathway. By definition, proof of the existence of the CLP requires the prospective identification of single, clonogenic cells able to generate all lymphoid lineages (B, T, and NK), but unable to generate any myelo–erythroid lineages. Although the existence of the CLP has been assumed for years, the clonal CLP had not been identified in mice or humans until recently. This is mainly because clonal assays for lymphoid lineage cells, particularly assays able to measure human lymphoid potential, have only recently become available.

Clonal assays for progenitors with myeloid potential have existed for more than 30 years[10,11] and can be used to prove the presence of a common progenitor with at least trilineage potential (called a colony-forming unit [CFU] granulocyte–erythroid–monocyte–megakaryocyte or CFU-mix). However, the inability to simultaneously read out lymphoid potential in these assays meant that, initially, these progenitors could not be distinguished from HSCs and thus could not be identified as myeloid-restricted progenitors (i.e., as common myeloid progenitors [CMPs]). Thus, functional clonal assays that can demonstrate both myeloid and lymphoid potential are essential to prove a progenitor stage that has the potential to form certain lineages and the inability to form others.

Another reason for the relatively few reports describing the CLP in either mice or humans is the technical difficulty of isolating rare, functionally uniform populations. Cell sorting of rare populations requires scrupulous care to avoid contaminating cells. The presence of clonogenic cells with a lineage potential different from that of the target population will skew the functional readout and cause great problems in proving that a particular immunophenotypically defined population has functional relevance. This is a problem especially when trying to identify populations such as CLPs that are lineage restricted. In this case, the common problem in cell sorting is contamination by highly clonogenic and proliferative pluripotent HSCs. Cell enrichment before flow cytometry and double-cell sorting techniques are essential to increase

Handbook of Stem Cells
Volume 2

the frequency of target cells and minimize the chance of contaminating cells. Inadequate attention to this mundane but critical technical issue is often the cause of misleading conclusions based on the functional and gene expression data of mixed cell populations.

Murine Studies

FUNCTIONAL EVIDENCE FOR THE MURINE CLP

The existence of the murine CLP was first clearly demonstrated at a clonal level by Kondo *et al.*[12] A primitive bone marrow population that expressed the receptor that binds to interleukin 7 (IL7r-α) was found to satisfy the criteria of the CLP using *in vitro* and *in vivo* models. The IL7r+ cells rapidly reconstituted B- and T-lymphopoiesis after transplantation into lethally irradiated Ly5.1 mice using a competitive repopulation assay. Similarly, when IL7r+ cells were transplanted alone into sublethally irradiated syngeneic Rag2-deficient mice, T-, B-, and NK-progeny could be detected. In both models, myelopoiesis was restored from HSC populations but not from IL7r+ populations. Engraftment with IL7r+ cells was relatively short-lived, with peak B-cell levels at 4 weeks and peak T-cell levels between 4 and 6 weeks, suggesting a limited proliferative potential relative to HSCs.

Clonal evidence that CLPs were contained within the IL7r+ population was provided by plating cells in a semisolid medium (methylcellulose assay) under myeloid and lymphoid conditions.[12] No myeloid progeny were generated from CLPs. However, 20% formed colonies in methylcellulose in the presence of IL7, Kl, and Fl. All colonies so formed contained pro-B–pre-B-cells. When colonies obtained from single IL7r+ cells were injected intrathymically into sublethally irradiated congenic mice, 7 out of 20 colonies generated T-cells. Clonal analysis of NK cell potential was not reported. However, the finding that individual clonogenic IL7r+ cells were able to generate both T- and B-cells but lacked myeloid potential satisfied the key criteria for the CLP and established the standard for immunophenotyping the murine CLP based on IL7r expression. Later studies with the IL7r+ CLP in murine bone marrow demonstrated that dendritic cell potential also exists in this progenitor population.[13]

Mebius *et al.* reported that the immunophenotypic counterpart of the murine bone marrow CLP could also be detected in murine fetal liver.[14] The IL7r+ population in fetal liver generated B-, T-, NK-, and dendritic-cells. However, in contrast to the CLP bone marrow studies, macrophages were also generated *in vitro* from fetal liver IL7r+ cells. The significance of the generation of macrophages in this study is unclear, as no granulocyte, erythroid, or megakaryocytic potential was demonstrated. In addition, no clonal analysis was performed so that the presence of two separate types of progenitors, one with lymphoid and the other with macrophage potential, could not be excluded.

MURINE CLP IMMUNOPHENOTYPE

Similar to HSCs, IL7r+ CLPs do not express antigens found on mature hematopoietic cells; that is, they are lineage negative (Lin^{neg}). However, other immunophenotypic features distinguish CLPs from HSCs. Whereas murine HSCs express high levels of c-kit and Sca-1 and low levels of Thy1, murine CLPs express low levels of c-kit and Sca-1 and do not express Thy1. Thus, the murine CLP has been defined as Lin^{neg}IL7r+Thy-1^{neg}Sca-1^{lo}c-kit^{lo} in contrast to murine HSC, which are Lin^{neg}IL7r^{neg}Thy-1^{lo}Sca-1^{hi}c-kit^{hi} (Table 33–1). Murine CLPs also express lower levels of CD43 and CD44 than HSCs.[12] Approximately 0.02% of total murine bone marrow cells have the IL7r+ CLP immunophenotype.[12]

GENE EXPRESSION IN MURINE CLP

Certain genes expressed in HSCs, such as *Gata3* and *PU.1*, are also expressed in IL7r+ CLPs.[12] However, in contrast to HSCs, murine IL7r+ CLPs from adult bone marrow were

TABLE 33-1
Immunophenotypes of Multilymphoid Progenitors in Mice and Humans

Species	Source	Immunophenotype	Lineage Potential	Reference
Murine	BM (Adult)	Lin^{neg}IL7r-α+Thy1 ^{neg} Sca-1 ^{lo} c-kit^{lo}	B, T, NK (DC)	Kondo *et al.*, 1997.[12] Manz *et al.*, 2001.[13]
Murine	BM (Fetal)	Lin^{neg}IL7r-α+Thy1 ^{neg} Sca-1 ^{lo} c-kit^{lo}	B, T, NK, MQ[1]	Mebius *et al.*, 2001.[14]
Murine	Thymus	DN1 (CD44+CD25^{neg}) c-kit^{hi}IL7r-$\alpha^{neg/lo}$ Sca-1+	B,T, NK, My[2]	Allman *et al.*, 2003.[48]
Human	BM (Adult)	CD34+Lin^{neg} CD10+ (IL7r-α unknown, CD38+ Thy-1 ^{neg}c-kit^{lo})	B, T, NK, DC	Galy *et al.*, 1995.[34]
Human	CB	CD34+CD38−CD7+ (IL7r-α^{neg}Thy-1 ^{neg} c-kit^{lo})	B, NK, DC (T)	Hao *et al.*, 2001.[36] Crooks *et al.*, (Unpublished data).[37]

MQ[1]= macrophage
My[2] = myeloid

found to express RNA transcripts for terminal deoxynucleotide transferase (Tdt) and Pax5.[12] Tdt is a lymphoid-specific molecule that functions in immunoglobulin and T-cell receptor gene rearrangement. Pax5 is required for B-lymphoid differentiation and, as such, is expressed in B-cell progenitors but not in T-cell progenitors.[15] It is unknown whether all IL7r+ CLPs or only a subset of the CLPs express Tdt and Pax5. Despite the expression of Tdt, no rearrangement of immunoglobulin heavy chains or T-cell receptor-β were detected in the IL7r+ CLPs.[12] Interestingly, murine IL7r+ CLPs from fetal liver expressed significantly lower levels of Pax5 than did their adult counterparts.[14]

Using oligonucleotide microarray analysis, Akashi *et al.* demonstrated that certain T- and B-cell-specific genes, although not expressed in HSCs, were expressed at the CLP level.[16] This study, however, was performed on bulk cell populations and could not address the question of heterogeneity of gene expression within the population nor whether such lineage-specific genes were coexpressed in single cells. This question was answered by Miyamoto *et al.*,[17] who showed by a reverse transcription-polymerase chain reaction of single murine progenitor and precursor cells that some multipotent progenitors (CMPs and CLPs) express low levels of transcription factors and cytokine receptors normally associated with more mature, lineage-restricted progeny. For example, 31% of a single immunophenotypic murine CLP demonstrated a pro-B-cell, 15% a pro-T-cell, and 21% both a pro-T and pro-B gene expression profile. Murine HSCs, however, did not express lymphoid-specific genes (with the exception of the T-cell-associated transcription factor *Gata3*). Progenitors at later commitment steps (pro-B- and pro-T-cells) expressed only B- and T-cell-specific genes, respectively. Thus it was concluded that, at the multipotent progenitor level represented by the CLP, promiscuous gene expression precedes lineage commitment. It should be noted that in these studies, 33% of the CLP expressed none of the lineage-specific genes, exhibiting a primitive HSC gene profile. In addition, in those CLP that did express lineage-specific genes, the levels of expression were 10-fold less than those in the mature B- and T-cell progeny. At this point, it is not known whether the low levels of gene expression in the CLP are sufficient to induce lineage commitment. Although no myeloid-specific genes are expressed in the CLP, another study using transgene expression of IL2r or GMCSFR revealed a "latent" myeloid differentiation profile, suggesting that myeloid genes are not irreversibly silenced in the CLP.[18]

Human Studies

FUNCTIONAL ASSAYS FOR HUMAN LYMPHOPOIESIS

The understanding of early human lymphopoiesis has lagged behind that of the murine system because of the inadequacy, until recently, of assays to measure primitive human lymphoid progenitors. In contrast to murine cells, lymphoid differentiation from human progenitors cannot be detected in semisolid assays. *In vitro* assays for human lymphoid potential became available when it was observed that selected murine stromal cell lines were capable of supporting lymphoid differentiation from primitive human progenitors.[19–22] Each of these assays to a greater or lesser extent support B-, NK-, and dendritic-cell differentiation from primitive human progenitor cells. Modifications to the assays have allowed identification of individual human cells with both myeloid and lymphoid potential, criteria necessary to prove the presence of pluripotent HSCs.[19,20,23,24] T-lineage potential can now be assessed *in vitro* by introducing human cells into murine or human fetal thymuses devoid of T-cells (fetal thymic organ cultures, or FTOC),[25,26] or by culturing cells on human[27] or rhesus macaque[28,29] thymic stromal cells.

Xenograft transplant models can also be used to assess the lineage potential of human progenitor populations *in vivo*.[30,31] Most xenogeneic models rely on immune-deficient mice as hosts. However, each model has different skewing in terms of lineage readout and engraftment efficiency. In addition, the common origin of multiple lineages in xenografts can only be shown if transplanted cells have been retrovirally tagged,[32] or if clones are expanded *in vitro* prior to transplantation—a technically difficult feat, particularly when studying cells of limited proliferative potential. Thus, although *in vivo* models are essential for questions of homing and engraftment, *in vitro* models are most often used to assess the differentiation potential of stem and progenitor cells at a clonal level.

FUNCTIONAL LINEAGE ANALYSIS

Human Bone Marrow CLP

Galy *et al.* found that the Lin− cells from the adult human bone marrow that coexpress the progenitor antigen CD34 and the "RA" isoform of the panleukocyte marker CD45 (CD45RA) are devoid of erythroid potential but possess lymphoid and myeloid potential.[33] Further studies revealed that a subpopulation of the CD34+Lin−CD45RA+ cells express the neutral endopeptidase CD10.[34] Careful FACS isolation and functional analysis of the CD34+Lin−CD10+ cells showed the presence of full lymphoid (B-cell, T-cell, NK, and dendritic) potential but an almost complete absence of myeloid and erythroid potential in this population. Limiting dilution analysis showed that approximately 21% of clonogenic CD10+ cells had detectable B-, NK,- and dendritic-cell potential. T-cell potential within the whole population was shown by injecting as few as 500 CD34+Lin−CD10+ cells into fetal thymic fragments placed under the kidney capsule of SCID mice. As with murine studies using the IL7r+ bone marrow CLP, thymopoiesis from human CD10+ lymphoid progenitors was short lived, declining between weeks 8 and 11. An immunophenotypically and functionally similar population was found in human fetal bone marrow, although these cells were not examined by clonal analysis.[34]

Although the CD10+ population as a whole was shown to possess full lymphoid potential and single CD10+ cells were shown to possess B-, NK-, and dendritic-potential, clonal analysis was not extended to the T-cell lineage. Despite the lack of definitive clonal proof of all lymphoid lineages, it seems very likely that the human CLP exist in the CD10+ population of bone marrow.

In another study of human bone marrow, Ryan *et al.* reported enrichment of B-lymphoid potential in human CD34+CD19$^-$ cells that express IL7r-α.[35] These IL7r-α+ cells were CD38+CD45RA+ HLA-DR+ and expressed both Tdt and Pax5. The authors proposed that Tdt expression occurs before IL7r-α and Pax5 expression and that CD19 expression occurs after IL7r-α and Pax5 expression. Myeloid and erythroid potential was depleted but not absent in the CD34+Lin– IL7r-α population. As NK and T-cell potential was not evaluated, it was unclear exactly where the CD34+Lin–IL7r-α population lies in the pathway of lymphoid differentiation and whether this immunophenotype encompasses more than one progenitor type.

Human Cord Blood CLP

Hao *et al.* provided the first clonal evidence for the existence of multilymphoid progenitors in human umbilical cord blood.[36] In this study, it was found that the CD7+ subpopulation of CD34+CD38– cord blood cells lacked myeloid and erythroid potential but possessed B-, NK-, and dendritic-cell potential both in bulk cultures and single cell clonal cultures. Although T-cell production was not evaluated in this report, follow-up studies using FTOC have revealed the T-cell potential of the CD34+CD38–CD7+ population.[37]

Interestingly, almost all of the CD34+CD38–CD7+ population coexpresses CD10 (although most CD10+ cells do not express CD7). Thus, the CD7+ CLP is a subpopulation of the CD34+CD38–CD10+ population in cord blood. Similar to the murine and human CLPs, the CD7+ CLPs express HLA-DR and CD45RA and do not express c-kit and Thy1.[36]

At least two other reports have described lymphoid progenitors in cord blood that express the surface molecule CD7. Canque *et al.* described a CD34+CD7+CD45RA+ population with NK and dendritic cell potential.[38] Clonal analysis demonstrated bipotent NK–dendritic cell progenitors. B-, T-, and myeloid potential were not reported in this study. In contrast to the study by Hao *et al.*, the CD34+CD7+CD45RA+ population reported by Canque *et al.* expressed CD38.

Storms *et al.* also described a lymphoid progenitor population in cord blood that expressed CD7 but did not express CD38.[39] Unlike other reports in the field, this progenitor did not express CD34 but was identified within the so-called side population (SP), revealed on the basis of Hoechst 33342 dye efflux.[40] The CD7+CD34–Lin– cells coexpressed CD11b (an antigen found on myeloid and NK cells) but did not express a variety of other lineage-specific markers. When cocultivated on a murine stromal cell line in multiple cytokines, the CD7+CD34–Lin– population differentiated predominantly, if not entirely, into NK cells. No clonogenic myeloid progenitors were detected in this population and B-, T-, and dendritic-cell potential were not reported. It thus appears most likely that the CD7+CD34–Lin– SP cells represent early progenitors with NK-restricted potential.

IMMUNOPHENOTYPIC ANALYSIS OF HUMAN CLP

Many immunophenotypic similarities exist between the bone marrow CD10+ CLP identified by Galy *et al.*[34] and the cord blood CD7+ CLP described by Hao *et al.*[36] (see Table 33–1). Both populations express the progenitor antigens CD34, HLA-DR, and CD45RA, and both have absent to low expression of c-kit and Thy1. With the exception of CD34, this combination of markers is also found on the murine IL7r+ CLP. In addition, CD25 (IL2r-α) is not expressed on either the human bone marrow CD10+ CLP or the cord blood CD7+ CLP.[34,36] Importantly, and unlike the murine bone marrow CLP, IL7r-α• is not expressed on cord blood CD34+CD38– CD7+ cells. IL7r-α• expression on the human bone marrow CD10+ CLP was not reported.

CD10+ cells are 5.9 ± 3.7% of the CD34+Lin– cells (0.09% of total mononuclear cells) of adult human bone marrow.[34] All CD34+Lin–CD10+ cells in bone marrow express the antigen CD38. Most, but not all, CD34+Lin–CD7+ cells in cord blood express CD38. Unlike bone marrow, as mentioned previously, CD7+ cells are also found in the CD34+CD38– fraction of cord blood; 8.2 ± 1.6% of the CD34+CD38– cells (approximately 0.1% of total mononuclear cells) of human cord blood express CD7. It is the small fraction of CD34+CD38– cells that coexpress CD7 that have been reported to exhibit the CLP-functional phenotype in cord blood.[36]

Interestingly, Galy *et al.* reported that 12% of the CD34+Lin–CD10+ CLP in human bone marrow also express CD7.[34] More recent studies with human bone marrow have reported that the subpopulation of CD34+Lin–CD10+ cells that do not express CD7 (the CD10+CD7– cells) represent a primitive B-cell progenitor population with little NK potential,[41] whereas the inverse population (CD7+CD10–) possesses predominantly NK potential. Hao *et al.* reported that most of the CD34+CD38–CD7+ CLP population of the cord blood coexpressed CD10.[36] A small population of CD34+Lin– cells that coexpress CD7 and CD10 exists in human bone marrow; limiting dilution studies demonstrate that the CD34+Lin–CD7+CD10+ cells possess both B- and NK potential and thus probably represent the CLP.[42]

Based on these studies in human hemato–lymphopoiesis, the onset of CD10 expression on CD34+Lin– cells appears to correlate with the divergence of the lymphoid and myeloid pathways. Coexpression of CD10 and CD7 is associated with multilymphoid (B-, NK, and dendritic ± T-cell) potential. Exclusive CD10 or CD7 expression appears to herald the divergence of the B- or NK cell lineages, respectively.

GENE EXPRESSION IN HUMAN CLP

Almost all data on gene expression in the human CLP has been generated from cord blood, and thus any comparisons with murine bone marrow data have the added variable of analyzing different stages of ontogeny. With this caveat, some notable differences can be seen in the gene expression profile of the human CD34+CD38–CD7+ cord blood CLP and the murine IL7r+ bone marrow CLP. Three key genes associated with lymphoid commitment—Tdt, Pax5, and IL7r-α—are at extremely low or undetectable levels in the human CD34+CD38–CD7+ cord blood CLP but are readily detected in the murine bone marrow CLP.[36] The absence of Tdt and

34

Common Myeloid Progenitors

David Traver and Koichi Akashi

Hematopoiesis is initiated by rare hematopoietic stem cells (HSCs) that maintain production of blood cells for life. The hallmarks of HSCs are self-renewal and multipotent differentiation to all lineages of the hematolymphoid system. Over the past decade, the biology of HSCs has received considerable attention because of the ability to prospectively isolate HSCs to purity by cell surface phenotype. In humans, HSCs generate more than 1 trillion mature blood cells per day. This astounding production is the result of mitotic amplification of the lineage-committed progenitor cells that are the daughters of HSCs. Although the existence of lineage-restricted hematopoietic progenitors has been postulated for many years, the ability to prospective isolate HSCs paved the way for the phenotypic discovery of lineage-restricted progenitors downstream of HSCs, such as common lymphoid progenitors (CLPs) and common myeloid progenitors (CMPs), which can be similarly isolated by cell surface characteristics. These progenitor subsets, along with granulocyte–monocyte-restricted progenitors (GMPs) and megakaryocyte–erythrocyte-restricted progenitors (MEPs), appear to represent the points at which hematopoietic fate decisions occur. Prospective isolation of each subset has identified the lineal relationships among all blood cell types and has allowed their gene expression profiles to be assayed. Transcriptional profiling of the major hematopoietic branch points can be used to address the molecular mechanisms of cell fate decisions and may also elucidate potential mechanisms of lineage promiscuity and plasticity, which can be tested directly by ectopic activation of specific signaling pathways in purified progenitor populations. In this chapter, we present a brief history of hematopoietic stem and progenitor cell biology, emphasizing commitment to the myeloerythroid fates. We describe the cell surface profiles of recently identified stem and progenitor cell subsets in both mice and humans, and we explain potential therapeutic applications of committed progenitor cells.

Introduction

HSCs are clonogenic, self-renewing multipotent progenitors that generate all blood cell types for the life of the host. The initial events in HSC differentiation include the transition of highly self-renewing long-term (LT) HSCs into short-term (ST) HSCs and multipotent progenitors (MPPs) that possess increasingly limited self-renewal activity.[1–4] Downstream of MPPs, multipotency is believed to be lost as commitment to the various effector cell lineages occurs.[1,5–7] Direct evidence for such lineage transitions was unavailable until recently.

Because both B- and T-lymphocytes display similar mechanisms for antigen receptor rearrangement and selection, it was postulated that both lineages arise from common progenitors that have lost myeloid differentiation potential. Support for the existence of lymphoid-restricted progenitors came from studies using chromosomally marked HSCs,[8] from the results of cultured bone marrow cells transplanted into immunodeficient mice,[9] and from the loss of both T- and B-cell subsets in patients with severe-combined immunodeficiency (SCID).[10,11] More recently, a rare population within whole mouse bone marrow was shown to generate all lymphoid subsets but lack myeloerythroid differentiation potential. These were termed CLPs.[12] Subsequently, CLP counterparts, myeloerythroid-restricted progenitors (CMPs), and their lineal descendents, GMPs and MEPs, were similarly identified by cell surface phenotype.[13] Continuing studies support the concept that the lymphoid and myeloerythroid pathways diverge at mutually exclusive branch points downstream of HSCs within the bone marrow of adult mice.[14,15] Using these prospectively isolatable populations, it is now possible to precisely examine the relationships among all blood cell lineages, the molecular mechanisms of cell fate determination, and the hematopoietic defects resulting from induced mutations at each of the major hematopoietic branch points.

Hematopoietic Stem Cells as the Root of the Hematopoietic Tree

The concept of the HSC was born following the close of World War II, when it was observed that many civilians surviving the initial blasts of the atomic bombs dropped over Hiroshima and Nagasaki later died from complications related to severely decreased blood counts. Using mouse models, pioneering studies in the 1960s showed that lethally irradiated mice could be rescued by the shielding of hematopoietic tissues, and that intravenous transplantation of bone marrow from an unirradiated donor could rescue irradiated animals.[16,17] Bone marrow transplants into irradiated hosts generated donor-derived cells for the life of the recipients, as evidenced by chromosomal differences. Subsequent experiments demonstrated the ability of rare cells within whole mouse bone marrow to

Handbook of Stem Cells
Volume 2

form clonal splenic colonies,[18] a fraction of which contained cells able to repopulate multilineage hematopoiesis in transplanted hosts.[19,20] Many subsequent retrospective transplantation experiments suggested that rare populations of HSCs existed within total bone marrow.[21,22] The modern era of HSC biology began with the first rigorous, prospective isolation of murine HSCs by cell surface phenotype.[23–25] Investigators showed that long-term, multilineage reconstitution activity was present only within a population of $Lin^{-/lo}Thy1.1^{lo}Sca\text{-}1^{+}$ bone marrow cells. A subset of these cells displayed long-term self-renewing potential[26] that, at the single-cell level, could generate both myeloid and lymphoid outcomes.[27] Subsequent studies, however, showed that the $Lin^{-/lo}$ $Thy1.1^{lo}Sca\text{-}1^{+}$ bone marrow fraction was heterogeneous in terms of self-renewal activity; HSCs with long-term self-renewal activity could be further fractionated by isolating cells expressing c-Kit, a receptor for steel factor.[1] It was later shown that within the $Lin^{-}Sca\text{-}1^{+}c\text{-}Kit^{+}$ population, only $CD34^{-/lo}$ cells are LT-HSCs; the remaining $CD34^{+}$ cells generate only short-term, multilineage reconstitution.[3] Both $Thy1.1^{lo}Lin^{-}Sca\text{-}1^{+}c\text{-}Kit^{+}$ and $CD34^{-/lo}Lin^{-}Sca\text{-}1^{+}c\text{-}Kit^{+}$ populations constitute ~0.01% of total bone marrow cells, and we have confirmed that >60% of these populations phenotypically overlap. Multilineage, long-term reconstitution from single cells was observed in ~20% and ~35% of $Thy1.1^{lo}Lin^{-}$ $Sca\text{-}1^{+}c\text{-}Kit^{+}$ and $CD34^{-/lo}Lin^{-}Sca\text{-}1^{+}c\text{-}Kit^{+}$ populations, respectively, after competitive reconstitution assays.[3,28] Recently, the $Thy1.1^{lo}Lin^{-}Sca\text{-}1^{+}c\text{-}Kit^{+}$ population was further subdivided by expression of the Fms-like tyrosine kinase-3 (Flt3 or Flk-2).[2,4] Around 60% of $Thy1.1^{lo}Lin^{-}Sca\text{-}1^{+}c\text{-}Kit^{+}$ cells express Flk-2, and LT-HSC activity was found only within the $Flk\text{-}2^{-}Thy1.1^{lo}Lin^{-}Sca\text{-}1^{+}c\text{-}Kit^{+}$ fraction, enabling the further enrichment of LT-HSCs. Another marker for HSCs, as well as for stem cell subsets in other tissues,[29–32] is the differential efflux of the intracellular dye Hoechst 33342. $Hoechst^{low}$ cells, termed the side population, are highly enriched for the LT-HSC subset.[30] Purified side population cells were $Lin^{-}Sca\text{-}1^{+}c\text{-}Kit^{+}$, and contained >30% $CD34^{-/lo}$ cells.[33] A recent report by Matsuzaki *et al.* demonstrated that $Lin^{-}Sca\text{-}1^{+}c\text{-}Kit^{+}CD34^{-}$ SP cells can reconstitute long-term multilineage hematopoiesis in 96% of animals receiving only one cell.[34] Isolation of LT-HSCs by the preceding phenotypes has likely reached purity.

Commitment of HSCs to Lineage-Restricted Progenitors

Perhaps the most important questions in stem cell biology are how stem cells self-renew and how multipotent cells choose one cell fate. The mechanisms of HSC self-renewal remain obscure, likely because of multigenic and redundant requirements that are not apparent from single-gene knockout studies. The commitment and subsequent differentiation of HSCs likely occurs because of the selective activation and silencing of particular gene expression programs. Changes in chromatin structure permitting or denying access to transcriptional machinery is likely critical for this process.[35,36]

A basic understanding of the relationships among the myeloerythroid lineages came from the development of *in vitro* clonogenic assays. Early work in this area retrospectively defined subsets of myeloerythroid progenitors that appeared to have restricted differentiation capacities.[37,38] Unfractionated bone marrow was found to contain oligopotent colony-forming units (CFU) for all myeloerythroid lineages (CFU-GEMMeg or CFU-Mix),[39,40] for granulocytes and macrophages (CFU-GM), and for megakaryocytes and erythrocytes (CFU-MegE). Monopotent CFU for granulocytes (CFU-G), macrophages (CFU-M), erythrocytes (CFU-E), or megakaryocytes (CFU-Meg) were also observed. The combinations of cell types within these colonies supported the notion of clonal progenitor subsets with progressive loss of lineage potentials, and suggested close relationships among cells within each of the GM and MegE branches of the hematopoietic tree. If multipotent HSCs indeed generate progenitors with progressive lineage restriction *in vitro,* it is logical to place these progenitors in a hierarchical order in the hematopoietic lineage map[41] (Fig. 34–1), and myeloerythroid differentiation might initiate from clonogenic progenitors of all mature cell types, such as CFU-GEMMeg.

All *in vitro* experiments, however, have the critical caveat that retrospective lineage outcomes may not reflect the full commitment potential of each assayed cell type. This is because no single *in vitro* assay system exists that is permissive for each blood cell lineage. Although retrospective identification of a CFU-GEMM colony is often attributed to an early myeloerythroid progenitor, this colony could have equally resulted from a plated HSC that could not produce lymphocytes because of culture limitations. If *in vitro* colony conditions are fully permissive for all myeloerythroid fates, it may be logically assumed that HSCs should always produce CFU-GEMMeg. It is known, however, that single $Thy1.1^{lo}$ $Lin^{-}Sca\text{-}1^{+}c\text{-}Kit^{+}$ HSCs produce many different colony types, including burst-forming unit erythroid (BFU-E), CFU-E, CFU-GM, CFU-Meg, and multilineage CFU-GEMMeg colonies at high frequencies.[13,33,42] Thus, it is still unclear whether highly purified HSCs commit randomly to the various myeloerythroid fates or whether these phenomena simply represent the imperfect conditions of *in vitro* assay systems.

Lineage commitment models have been established mainly on the *in vitro* behaviors of stem and progenitor cells to generate myeloerythroid but not lymphoid cell types. This is largely because lymphoid culture systems are inefficient compared to myeloerythroid assays. Conversely, unlike most evanescent myeloerythroid cells, mature lymphoid cells can autonomously proliferate *in vivo,* which has facilitated the search for lymphoid-restricted progenitors in mouse bone marrow.

The Common Lymphoid Progenitor as the Earliest Defined Step in Lymphoid Commitment

Unlike the random, biochemical approach that led to HSC isolation, lymphoid-committed progenitors were sought through

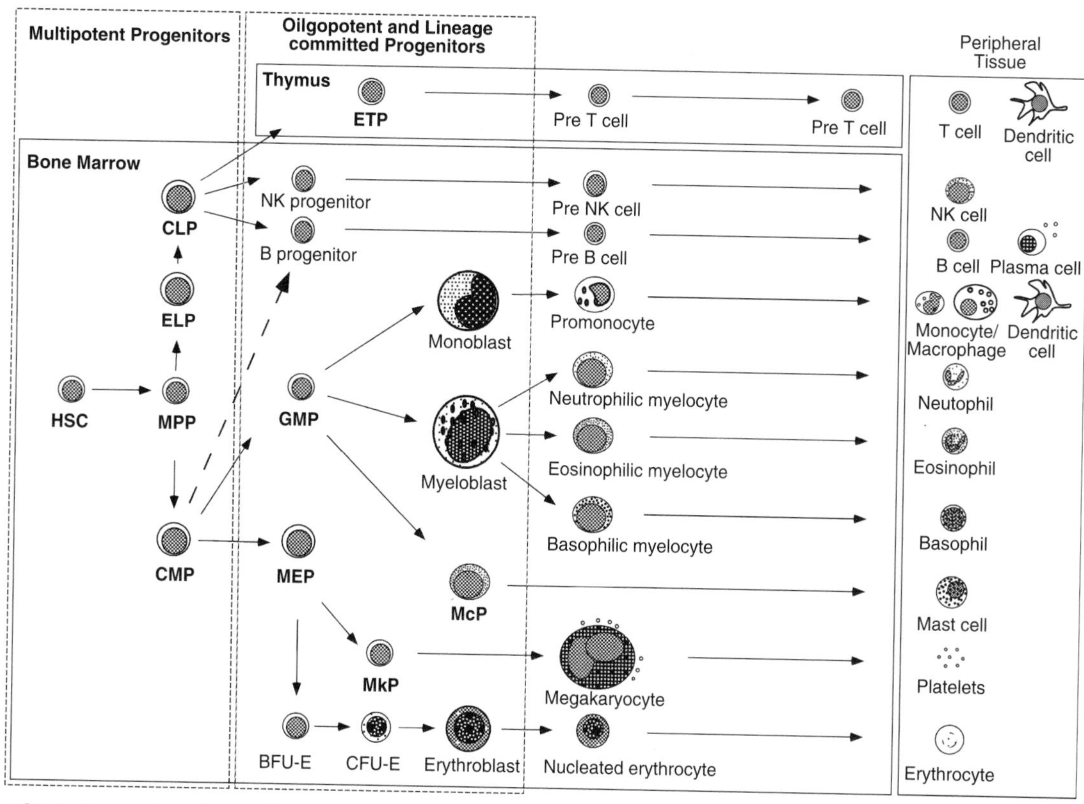

Figure 34–1. *Lineage relationships and hematopoietic hierarchies based on prospective isolation of lineage-restricted progenitors.* HSC, hematopoietic stem cell; MPP, multipotent progenitor; ELP, early lymphocyte progenitor; CLP, common lymphoid progenitor; ETP, early thymocyte progenitor; CMP, common myeloid progenitor; GMP, granulocyte–monocyte progenitor; MEP, megakaryocyte–erythrocyte progenitor; MCP, mast cell progenitor; MKP, megakaryocyte progenitor.

a candidate approach based on lymphoid-specific cell surface markers. Both Thy1 and Sca-1, critical markers for HSC isolation, are expressed on most mature T-cells. Based on targeted gene disruptions, Thy1 does not play a critical role in myeloid or lymphoid development,[43] and Sca-1 functions in HSC self-renewal and granulocyte development but is not required for lymphoid development.[44] Mice genetically deficient for IL7 or the IL7 receptor (IL7r), however, lack both T- and B-cells,[45,46] and administration of neutralizing anti-IL7 antibodies resulted in severe inhibition of T- and B-lymphopoiesis but not of myelopoiesis.[47] Accordingly, IL7r is expressed in early pro-T- and pro-B-cells.[48] In T-cell development, signaling through IL7r was found to be critical in maintaining the survival of developing α–β•-T-cells through the up-regulation of the anti-apoptotic protein, Bcl2.[49] In B-cell development, signaling through IL7r is necessary for the rearrangement of immunoglobulin heavy chain V segments through activation of the Pax5 gene.[50] Taken together, these data suggested that IL7rα expression is one of the most reliable functional markers for lymphoid commitment, and the IL7rα$^+$ fraction of mouse bone marrow was thus assayed for the presence of lymphoid-restricted progenitor subsets.

It was first demonstrated by Kondo *et al.* that IL7rα$^+$ cells were devoid of myeloerythroid potential both *in vitro* and *in vivo.*[12] Within the IL7rα$^+$ bone marrow fraction, robust differentiation potential to the T-, B-, and NK cell lineages was further enriched within the Lin$^-$Sca-1^{lo}c-Kit^{lo} population *in vivo* (Fig. 34–2). Transplantation using this fraction showed that donor-derived T- and B-cells began to decline after 4–6 weeks, indicating that this population has no significant self-renewal activity. Importantly, in a two-step clonogenic assay, approximately 20% of single IL7rα$^+$Lin$^-$Sca-1^{lo}c-Kit^{lo} cells could generate both T- and B-cells. Thus, IL7rα$^+$Lin$^-$Sca-1^{lo} c-Kit^{lo} cells contain clonogenic T- and B-cell progenitors and completely lack myeloerythroid differentiation potential. In a subsequent study, more than 40% of single IL7rα$^+$Lin$^-$Sca-1^{lo}c-Kit^{lo} cells could differentiate to NK cells. Cells within this population were therefore termed CLPs.[12] The clonogenic T–B bipotentiality of CLPs has recently been confirmed by another group[51] using a modified fetal thymic organ culture (FTOC) system.[52] Interestingly, most CLPs express Flk-2, suggesting that this marker can also be used to prospectively isolate CLPs.[53]

The isolation of additional lymphoid-restricted progenitors has been documented using mice in which reporter constructs have been homologously recombined into either the lymphoid-specific Rag1[54,55] or the T-cell-specific pre-T-α receptor (pTα) locus.[56,57] Rag1^{eGFP} mice were assayed for early lymphoid

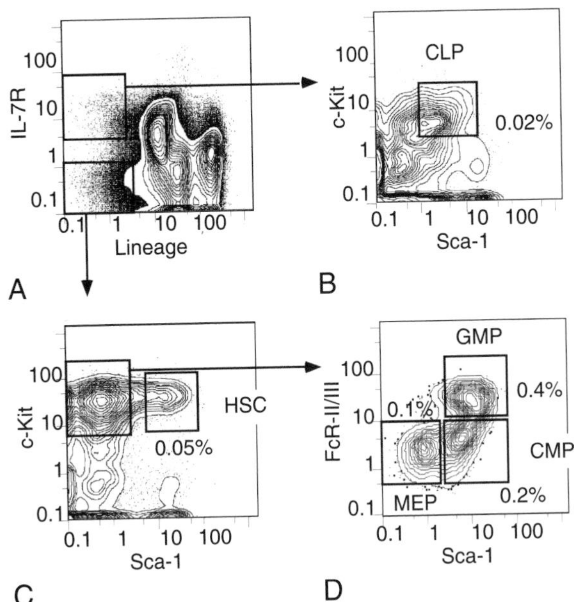

Figure 34–2. *Cell surface marker profiles of hematopoietic stem and progenitor cells in mouse bone marrow.* (A) Cells negative for lineage (Lin) markers including B220, CD4, CD8, CD3, Gr-1, Mac-1 and TER119 were subdivided into IL7rα positive and negative fractions. (B) Sca-1–c-Kit profiles of Lin⁻IL7rα⁺ cells. Lin⁻IL7rα⁺Sca-1^lo^c-Kit^lo^ cells are CLPs. (C) Sca-1–c-Kit profiles of Lin⁻IL7rα⁻ cells. Lin⁻IL7rα⁻Sca-1^hi^c-Kit^hi^ subset includes HSCs, whereas the LinIL7rα–Sca-1⁻c-Kit^hi^ subset contains all myeloid progenitor populations. (D) Myeloid progenitor subsets are separated according to their FcγRII/III and CD34 profiles as noted.

progenitor activity.[14] Over 90% of IL7rα$^+$Lin$^-$Sca-1^{lo}c-Kit^{lo} CLPs expressed green fluorescent protein (GFP) in these animals. Interestingly, Rag1 expression was also observed in ~5% of the Lin$^-$Sca-1$^+$c-Kit$^+$ HSC fraction. Like CLPs,[53] GFP$^+$Lin$^-$Sca-1$^+$c-Kit$^+$ cells also expressed Flk-2, indicating that they are not LT-HSCs[2,4] but likely are committed progenitors within the (Flk-2$^+$)Thy1.1$^-$Lin$^-$Sca-1$^+$c-Kit$^+$ population.[4,58] GFP$^+$Lin$^-$Sca-1$^+$c-Kit$^+$ cells in knockin animals also expressed CD27,[59] a member of the tumor necrosis factor receptor family previously shown to play a role in lymphoid proliferation, differentiation and apoptosis. Rag1^{GFP+}Lin$^-$Sca-1$^+$c-Kit$^+$CD27$^+$ cells exhibited potent T-, B-, and NK differentiation potential after transplantation into congenic hosts. The timing of thymic T-cell reconstitution by this donor population preceded that of the CLP population by ~7 days, suggesting that these cells are more immature than IL7rα$^+$Lin$^-$Sca-1^{lo}c-Kit^{lo} CLPs. Accordingly, a fraction of Rag1^{GFP+}Lin$^-$Sca-1$^+$c-Kit$^+$CD27$^+$ cells formed CFU-GM *in vitro*, indicating that this population is not entirely committed to the lymphoid fates. Although this population, termed early lymphocyte progenitors (ELPs), may be upstream of CLPs, this study did not demonstrate clonal T- and B-cell progeny from single Rag1^{GFP+}Lin$^-$Sca-1$^+$c-Kit$^+$CD27$^+$ cells. The homogeneity of this population therefore remains to be determined.

Since pTα is used for pre-T-cell receptor (TCR) formation after TCR-β gene rearrangement, pTα transcription should be a relatively late marker for lymphoid development as compared to Rag1 transcription. A transgene containing a 9kb fragment spanning all characterized pTα promoter and enhancer sequences was used to drive expression of a human CD25 minigene.[56,57] In pTα^{hCD25} transgenic mice, the expression of hCD25 was highly correlated with that of the endogenous pTα receptor as quantified by real-time reverse transcription-polymerase chain reaction (RT-PCR) analyses.[15] In the bone marrow, 6% of Lin$^-$ cells were hCD25$^+$, all of which displayed the IL7rα$^+$Sca-1^{lo}-c-Kit^{lo} CLP phenotype, whereas only 7% of CLPs were positive for hCD25 expression.[57] This result indicates that CLPs are the earliest population to initiate pTα transcription but that most CLPs have not initiated pTα transcription. Conventional CLPs are thus likely upstream of pTα$^+$ cells.

The Common Myeloid Progenitor as the Earliest Defined Step in Myeloerythroid Commitment

The preceding studies demonstrate that IL7r is currently the most reliable and efficient marker of lymphoid commitment from multipotent progenitors. Because IL7rα expression marks lymphoid-committed cells that lack myeloerythroid potential, we began the search for a complementary CMP in the IL7rα$^-$ fraction of mouse bone marrow. By plating various phenotypic IL7rα$^-$ fractions into methylcellulose cultures, myeloid colony-forming cells were found almost exclusively within the c-Kit$^+$ fraction; ~80% of single Lin$^-$IL7rα$^-$c-Kit$^+$ cells formed various myeloid colonies in methylcellulose containing steel factor, Flt3 ligand, IL3, IL11, GM-CSF, thrombopoietin (Tpo), and erythropoietin (Epo), whereas <0.1% of Lin$^-$IL7rα$^-$c-Kit$^-$ cells could form myeloid colonies. Accordingly, we estimated that the c-Kit$^+$ fraction contains ~99% of the myeloid colony-forming activity within the Lin$^-$ IL7rα$^-$ population of mouse bone marrow.

The Lin$^-$IL7rα$^-$Sca-1$^-$c-Kit$^+$ fraction was further divided into three functionally distinct myeloid progenitor populations based on the additional CD34 and FcγRII/III cell surface markers: FcγRII/III^{lo}CD34$^+$ CMPs, FcγRII/III^{lo}CD34$^-$ MEPs, and FcγRII/III^{hi}CD34$^+$ GMPs (Fig. 34–2 and Table 34–1). CMPs generated all myeloerythroid colony types *in vitro* including CFU-Mix, GMPs generated only GM-affiliated colonies (CFU-G, CFU-M, and CFU-GM), and MEPs generated only MegE-affiliated colonies (BFU-E, CFU-Meg, and CFU-MegE). Lineage studies demonstrated that CMPs differentiated into phenotypic GMPs and MEPs; both daughter populations were replated and generated only GM- or MegE-restricted progeny, respectively. Most single CMPs generated both GM- and MegE-related progeny in two-step culture assays.[13] Upon *in vivo* transfer, these populations displayed short-term production of lineages corresponding to their *in vitro* activities, indicating that they do not appreciably self-renew.[60] These three myeloid progenitor subsets likely represent the major pathways for myeloerythoid cell differentiation, because little colony-forming activity exists outside of the

IL7rα^-Lin$^-$Sca-1$^-$c-Kit$^+$ fraction in steady-state bone marrow. These data also indicate that the commitment of CMPs toward the megakaryocyte–erythrocyte or the granulocyte–macrophage lineages are mutually exclusive events, because highly purified MEPs and GMPs never produced colony types outside of their noted potentials.

How do each of the prospectively isolatable stem and progenitor subsets correspond to classical, retrospective, functional definitions? As noted previously, the cell types responsible for the formation of *in vitro* colonies such as CFU-GEMMeg include CMPs or any upstream cell type. Similarly, a clonogenic GM colony can be formed by any of the prospectively isolatable cell types along the LT-HSC → ST-HSC → MPP → CMP → GMP myeloid differentiation hierarchy.[13] Because the development of all myelomonocytic cells likely occurs through the GMP stage, this cell type can be considered the phenotypic equivalent of the classical CFU-GM definition. Likewise, the MEP represents the CFU-MegE and the CMP represents the CFU-GEMMeg, as it is the most mature cell type to possess full myeloerythroid differentiation potential. The ability of each stem and progenitor cell subset to form spleen colonies in lethally irradiated recipients (CFU-S) has also been examined. Early work showed that colonies arising early after transplantation (days 8–9) were largely composed of erythroid precursors,[61,62] whereas later colonies (days 10–12) contained erythroid and myeloid elements.[1,63–65] The latter colony types, upon retransplantation, were also shown to occasionally contain cells capable of multilineage reconstitution.[64] Together, these studies led to the notion that early spleen colonies were formed by committed progenitors and late colonies by more primitive, multilineage stem or progenitor cells. Using highly purified stem and progenitor cell subsets, day 8 CFU-S potential was highest within MEPs with a frequency of 1/15 cells (Table 34–2). In contrast, HSC subsets had no detectable day 8 activity. Day 12 colony-forming potential was most highly enriched within ST-HSCs. GMPs had no detectable CFU-S activity either day. Together, these data support the previous findings that CFU-S from days 8–9 are largely erythroid and show that GM-committed progenitors do not contribute to this classical assay. For day 12 CFU-S formation, about half of the observed colony frequency resided within lineage-committed progenitors, and about half were within the more primitive HSC–MPP populations (Table 34–2). The day 12 activity observed within the MEP population may be explained by previous studies suggesting that some day 12 colonies derive from surviving day 8 colonies.[65] CLPs do not possess either day 8 or day 12 CFU-S activity.[12] Thus, these studies demonstrate directly that the classical day 8 CFU-S assay is largely a measure of MEP activity.

TABLE 34–1
Phenotypic and Functional Characteristics of Stem and Primitive Hematopoietic Progenitors

	Location	Sca-1–c-Kit–Thy1	CD34–FcγII/IIIR	Flt3	Additional markers	Radio-protective	Lineage potential as a population	Clonal studies
HSC	BM	Sca-1$^+$c-Kit$^+$Thy1^{lo}	CD34$^-$ FcγII/IIIR^{lo}	–	Rhodamine^{lo} Hoescht^{lo}	?	All lineage	Yes
ST-HSC	BM	Sca-1$^+$c-Kit$^+$Thy1^{lo}	CD34$^+$ FcγII/IIIR^{lo}	+	Mac-1^{lo}	Yes	All lineages	Yes
MPP	BM	Sca-1$^+$c-Kit$^+$Thy1$^-$	CD34$^+$ FcγII/IIIR^{lo}	+	Mac-1^{lo}			
					CD4^{lo}	Yes	All lineages	ND
ELP	BM	Sca-1$^+$c-Kit$^+$Thy1$^-$	CD34$^+$	++	CD27$^+$			
					Rag1^{eGFP}	ND	T, B, NK, GM*	ND
CLP	BM	Sca-1^{lo}c-Kit^{lo}Thy1$^-$	CD34$^+$	++	IL7rα^+	NO	T, B, NK, DC	Yes
PTα^+B220$^+$	BM	Sca-1$^-$c-Kit$^-$Thy1$^-$	N.D	ND	IL7rα^+	ND	T, B (NK?)	Yes
ETP	Thymus	Sca-1$^+$c-Kit$^+$Thy1^{lo}	N.D	+	–	ND	T, B, NK GM*	ND
CMP	BM	Sca-1$^-$c-Kit$^+$Thy1$^-$	CD34$^+$ FcγII/IIIR^{lo}	–	–	Yes	G, M, E,	Yes
GMP	BM	Sca-1$^-$c-Kit$^+$Thy1$^-$	CD34$^+$ FcγII/IIIR$^+$	–	M-CSFR$^+$		Meg, DC	Yes
					βc^+	NO	G, M, DC	Yes
MEP	BM	Sca-1$^-$c-Kit$^+$Thy1$^-$	CD34$^-$ FcγII/IIIR^{lo}	–	–	Yes	E, Meg	Yes
MKP	BM	Sca-1$^-$c-Kit$^+$Thy1$^-$	CD34$^-$ FcγII/IIIR^{lo}	ND	CD9$^+$	ND	Meg	Yes
					CD41$^+$	ND	Meg	Yes
MCP	BM	Sca-1$^-$c-Kit$^+$Thy1^{lo}	CD34$^+$ FcγII/IIIR$^+$	ND	FcϵRI$^+$	ND	Mast cells	Yes

HSC: hematopoietic stem cell; ST-HSC: short-term HSC; ELP: early lymphocyte progenitor;[14] CLP: common lymphoid progenitor;[12] ETP: early T lineage progenitor.[212] *: the GM potential in ELPs and ETPs were found in 3 and 1%, respectively by methylcellulose assays. CMP, common myeloid progenitor; GMP, granulocyte–monocyte progenitor; MEP, megakaryocyte–erythrocyte progenitors;[13] MKP, Megakaryocyte progenitor; MCP, Mast cell progenitor.

TABLE 34–2
CFU-S Activity of Hematopoietic Stem and Progenitor Cells Populations

LT-HSC	ST-HSC	CMP	MEP	GMP
Day 12				
Bone marrow CFU-S frequency:				
1/61	1/14	1/200	1/53	<1/500
Number of CFU-S/10^6 bone marrow cells:				
2	29	10	19	<1
Day 8				
Bone marrow CFU-S frequency:				
<1/100	<1/100	1/67	1/15	<1/500
Number of CFU-S/10^6 bone marrow cells:				
<1	<1	30	67	<1
Fetal liver CFU-S frequency:				
1/38	ND	<1/1000	<1/1000	<1/1000

CFU-S frequencies presented represent the number of spleen colonies formed per total number of cells injected from each population. Numbers of CFU-S/10^6 bone marrow cells are calculated by using frequencies of LT-HSC, ST-HSC–MPP, CMP, MEP and GMP = 0.01%, 0.04%, 0.2%, 0.1% and 0.4% of nucleated bone marrow cells, respectively.

From the differentiation model in Fig. 34–1, it is logical to assume that GMPs and MEPs generate monopotent precursors. Recent data suggests that this is indeed the case for at least megakaryocyte and mast cell development. Megakaryocyte-restricted progenitors (MKPs) were recently identified within the IL7rα$^-$Lin$^-$Sca-1$^-$c-Kit$^+$Thy1.1$^-$ marrow fraction using an additional CD9 surface marker.[66] MKPs were found to generate only megakaryocytes *in vitro* and could produce platelets for approximately 3 weeks when transplanted into mice. MKPs could be phenotypically isolated following culture of both CMPs and MEPs, suggesting that they are downstream of both progenitor subsets. Mast cell progenitors (MCPs)[67] and eosinophil progenitors[68] were similarly identified downstream of GMPs. One potential caveat to these studies is that, by five-color FACS, only certain combinations of surface markers can be simultaneously analyzed. It will therefore be of interest to expand these studies to nine-color FACS, for example, to simultaneously visualize MKP and MCP cell surface profiles with the markers used to isolate the CMP, MEP, and GMP subsets. Similar approaches will likely yield monopotent progenitors for erythrocytes, monocytes, and all granulocyte subsets.

Lineage-Restricted Progenitors Clarify Dendritic Cell Ontogeny

Dendritic cells (DCs) are one of the most important cell types in the immune system because of their unique ability to orchestrate an acquired immune response.[69,70] DCs are instrumental in priming both cell-mediated and humoral immunity[70] and are also believed to prevent autoimmunity through the deletion of potentially autoreactive T-cell clones.[71] The ability of DCs to act as either immune catalysts or tolerizing agents makes them highly suitable for clinical manipulation aimed at either engineering improved vaccines or tolerizing patients receiving allogeneic organ transplants. The varied and often apparently contradictory functions of DCs have been suggested to result from the actions of different subsets of DCs.[72,73]

Recently, many populations of DCs have been described based on anatomic localization[73] and cell surface phenotype.[74,75] Although all DCs express CD11c and major histocompatibility class II (MHCII) proteins on their surfaces,[74] purification of DC subsets based on expression differences among CD11b, CD8α, and DEC205 has been performed by flow cytometry.[75] Assays using these purified populations have shown that different DC subsets often display differing functions. DCs bearing the CD11c$^+$MHCII$^+$Mac-1$^+$CD8α$^-$ cell surface phenotype have been shown to derive from myeloid precursors in both mice[76] and humans[70] and are potent stimulators of naive T-lymphocytes and the allogeneic mixed leukocyte reaction.[72] Myeloid DCs are found in tissues throughout the body. Alternatively, DCs bearing the CD11c$^+$MHCII$^+$Mac-1$^-$CD8α$^+$ cell surface phenotype have been shown to arise at low frequencies from T-cell-committed progenitors, pro-T-cells and pre-T-cells within the murine thymus, and have been termed lymphoid DCs.[77] Lymphoid DCs are found in the thymus, spleen, and lymph nodes; in the thymus, they are thought to direct negative selection of developing thymocytes.[71] Together, these results suggest that the ontogeny of DCs underlie these largely nonoverlapping functions, with myeloid DCs directing specific immune responses and lymphoid DCs eliminating self-reactive lymphocytes in both primary and secondary lymphoid organs. This hypothesis would predict that transplantation experiments using progenitors committed to either the myeloid or the lymphoid lineages would yield their respective DC subsets in appropriate tissues.

Interestingly, CMPs could generate both CD8α⁺ and CD8α⁻ DCs.[78] Both CD8α⁺ and CD8α⁻ DCs were produced from CLPs and CMPs with similar efficiency per cell.[79,80] Thus, expression of CD8α is not indicative of a lymphoid origin, and CD8α expression on DC subsets is likely to reflect maturation status rather than ontogeny. The precursor–progeny relationship between CD8α⁺ and CD8α⁻ DCs, however, is controversial. Splenic CD8α⁻CD11c⁺ DCs were reportedly able to generate CD8α⁺CD11c⁺ DCs,[81] but this finding was not supported by a recent report.[82] It has also been suggested that the acquisition of CD8α expression is likely to initiate in splenic DC precursors that are CD11c⁻, because CD8α⁺ CD11c⁻ spleen cells produce mature CD8α⁺CD11c⁺ DCs.[83] On the other hand, both CD8α⁺ and CD8α⁻ DCs are reported to originate from CD11c⁺MHCII⁻ DC progenitors that were devoid of other myeloid or lymphoid differentiation potential.[84] This population was also shown to generate interferon-γ-producing plasmacytoid DCs (PDCs, as described later).[84] These data suggest that the CD11c⁺MHCII⁻ DC progenitors may represent a DC stage independent of DC pathways from CLPs or CMPs. It is more likely, however, that CLPs, CMPs, or both generate CD11c⁺MHCII⁻ DC precursors upstream of mature CD8α⁺ and CD8α⁻ DCs.

Interestingly, DC potential is maintained downstream of CLPs in pro-T-cells and downstream of CMPs in GMPs, whereas DC potential is lost once B-cell or megakaryocyte–erythrocyte commitment occurs.[79] Although murine DCs and their precursors are usually isolated from lymphoid organs or bone marrow, human DCs are usually isolated from peripheral blood (reviewed by Shortman and Liu[85]). Human DCs can be derived from CD34⁺ progenitors, lymphoid-restricted progenitors, and peripheral blood monocytes, suggesting that human DCs similarly derive from both myeloid and lymphoid pathways.[86–91] In both mice and humans, there appears to be no functional difference between lymphoid- and myeloid-derived DCs as evaluated by mixed leukocyte reactions, immunophenotyping, and cytokine production.[78,79]

A precursor population that immediately generates DCs capable of producing interferon-γ was identified in humans[92–96] and subsequently in mice.[97–99] In addition to the conventional DC markers such as CD11c and MHCII, these cells express CD45RA. This population has been termed PDC or DC2.[100] In humans, DCs of this phenotype were reportedly generated from at least myeloid progenitors that express macrophage colony-stimulating factor receptor (M-CSFR).[101] On the other hand, human CD34⁺ cells with enforced Id2 or Id3 expression reportedly differentiated into conventional DCs but not into T-cells, B-cells, or PDCs,[102–104] suggesting that PDCs may have a lymphoid origin. Accordingly, PDCs express genes usually found in the lymphoid lineage such as pTα, 14.1, and Spi-B.[104,105] In our hands, murine PDC equivalents could be induced from both CLPs and CMPs.[106] Thus, it is likely that PDCs as well as conventional DCs originate from both lymphoid and myeloid pathways.

CLPs and pro-T-cells, but not pre-T- or pro-B-cells, can differentiate into DCs.[78,79,107] It is interesting to note that DC potential is within the same lymphoid precursor subsets that can be converted to myeloid fates by ectopic cytokine signals[108] (as explained later in this chapter). This correlation may suggest that "lymphoid" DC potential within CLPs and pro-T-cells is a residual function of latent myeloid potential. Conversely, DC derivation from bona fide lymphoid and myeloid pathways may have important functional differences that remain to be identified.

Transcriptional Profiling Supports the Lineage-Priming Model of Hematopoietic Commitment

The ability to prospectively isolate lineage-restricted progenitor subsets representing the major hematopoietic branch points enables analysis of the molecular mechanisms of lineage commitment. For specific genetic programs to be activated, local chromatin must be accessible to transcription machinery.[35,36] The activation of chromatin remodeling can occur prior to significant expression of genes in the region of interest.[109,110] These results led to the hypothesis that open chromatin structure is maintained in early hematopoietic progenitors, enabling multilineage differentiation programs to be readily accessible.[111] This "priming" of genes affiliated with multiple lineages would allow flexibility in cell fate decisions and allow multipotent precursors to rapidly respond to environmental cues.[112] If many genes are primed at multi- or oligopotent progenitor stages, these progenitors should then "promiscuously" express genes of multiple lineages at the single-cell level. This issue was recently addressed in purified progenitor populations at the population and single-cell levels by oligonucleotide microarrays and RT-PCR, respectively.

Global Profiling of Gene Expression Within Early Hematopoietic Stem and Progenitor Cells

A global view of gene expression, including hematopoietic and nonhematopoietic genes, was assayed in purified HSC subsets, CLPs, and CMPs to address the issues of self-renewal and lineage commitment within these early hematopoietic populations.[113] Using Affymetrix 20,000 gene chips, we found that HSCs expressed a variety of myeloid (GM- and MegE-affiliated) genes but not lymphoid genes. CMPs coexpressed many GM- and MegE-affiliated genes, and CLPs coexpressed many T-, B-, and NK lymphoid-related genes. This genomewide gene profiling thus revealed that HSCs predominantly exhibit myeloid promiscuity and that CLPs and CMPs exclusively possess lymphoid and myeloid priming programs, respectively. In ST-HSCs (or MPPs), both lymphoid and myeloid genes were primed. However, myeloid and lymphoid gene coexpression was not assayed at the single-cell level in these cell types. Therefore, these findings in "ST-HSCs" could be caused by a combination of heterogeneous expression profiles. Nonetheless, this study strongly suggests that lineage-promiscuous priming might be a common transcriptional feature in uncommitted stem and progenitor cells and that primed genes may represent the full and immediate differentiation potential of each assayed subset.[57]

Perhaps the most surprising finding of these studies is that CD45$^+$ HSCs, a hematopoietic cell-specific marker, express approximately 70% of all nonhematopoietic genes, including genes characteristic of neuronal, endothelial, pancreatic, kidney, liver, heart, hair, epithelial, and muscle cell types.[113] These nonhematopoietic genes were detectable by nested RT-PCR in CD45$^+$ HSCs at the single- to 10-cell level. This broad transcriptional usage, however, is lost as HSCs generate CMPs and CLPs; these cell types displayed only myeloid and lymphoid expression profiles, respectively. These data demonstrate that HSCs possess transcriptional accessibility for nonhematopoietic genes associated with multiple organ systems. Recent reports demonstrate that murine bone marrow contains cells capable of differentiation into multiple organs, including endothelial cells, skeletal and cardiac muscle,[114,115] neurons and glia,[116] parenchymal liver cells,[117] epithelial cells,[118] and hematopoietic cells. Although these reports suggest that the bone marrow may be special in harboring precursors of nonhematopoietic fates, the notion of HSC "plasticity" was challenged by a study in which mice reconstituted with single, GFP$^+$ HSCs were extensively analyzed for GFP expression in nonhematopoietic tissues.[28] These clonal experiments demonstrated that HSCs rarely contributed to nonhematopoietic fates, suggesting that "transdifferentiation" of HSCs is unlikely.[28] It was also reported that cell fusion can occur during coculture of embryonic stem cells with HSCs or neural stem cells. Although cell fusion was observed at an extremely rare incidence (10^{-4} to 10^{-5}), "conversion" from neural stem cells (or HSCs) to other cell types could be obtained through spontaneous generation of hybrid cells rather than epigenetic reprogramming of somatic stem cells.[119,120] Thus, it is likely that transdifferentiation is a rare event under physiological conditions.[121,122] Transdifferentiation in the settings of increased tissue renewal or tissue damage remains to be precisely addressed using prospectively isolated HSCs. Based on the findings that HSCs normally express many nonhematopoietic genes, it will be interesting to search among these genes for candidate molecules that may instruct nonhematopoietic fate outcomes from bona fide HSCs.

Lymphoid and Myeloid Priming Demonstrated by Single-Cell Analyses

Because CMPs possess both myeloid and erythroid differentiation potentials and generate MEPs and GMPs with restricted, mutually exclusive potentials, highly purified single progenitors were analyzed for gene expression profiles.[57] Virtually all single GMPs expressed GM-related genes, such as myeloperoxidase (Mpo) and granulocyte colony-stimulating factor receptor (G-CSFR), but did not express MegE-related genes, such as β-globin or erythropoietin receptor (Epor) (Fig. 34–3). Conversely, all single MEPs expressed β-globin, Epor, or both but not Mpo or G-CSFR (Fig. 34–3). In this way, the genetic "fingerprints" of committed GMPs and MEPs were identified. In marked contrast, ~60% of single CMPs coexpressed all of these GM- and MegE-affiliated genes. Analysis of additional myeloerythroid transcription factors at the single-cell level displayed a similar pattern:[57] More than 50% of single CMPs expressed both PU.1, a master gene for GM- and B-cell development,[123,124] and NF-E2, a critical gene for erythroid–megakaryocyte differentiation, survival, or both.[125,126] These data demonstrate directly that priming of many myeloerythroid genes occurs in CMPs and that quenching of gene expression inappropriate for GM- and MegE-related programs occurs in downstream MEPs and GMPs, respectively (Figs. 34–3 and 34–4).

Reporter gene experiments have been used to determine whether the priming of lineage-affiliated genes always marks commitment to the lineage of interest. Mice harboring an eGFP reporter construct in the murine lysozyme M (LysM) locus[127] were used to obtain progenitors with active expression of this myelomonocytic-related gene. Approximately 60% of CMPs expressed significant levels of LysM^{eGFP}. Both LysM^{eGFP+} and LysM^{eGFP-} CMPs expressed erythroid β-globin, demonstrating coexpression of myeloid and erythroid genes, and displayed MegE differentiation potential at equal efficiencies.[57] LysM transcripts, therefore, do not impair cellular viability, and they do not necessarily mark commitment to myelomonocytic fates. This evidence indicates that promiscuous gene expression likely plays a key role in maintaining flexibility in oligopotent precursors.

Priming and Competition of Lineage-Specific Gene Programs

Commitment from stem or multipotent progenitor cells exhibiting promiscuous gene expression likely involves the collaboration or competition of several "master regulator" genes. For example, transcription factor activity can be potentiated,[128] or suppressed,[129,130] by interaction with other transcription factors. Changes in key transcription-factor expression levels[131,132] could also be critical for specific lineage outcomes. Using multipotent cell lines, it has been reported that overexpression of transcription factors, including PU.1, Gata1, and C–EBP, results in the preference of one cell fate.[131–135] Recent studies suggest that the mechanism of "lineage instruction" by transcription factors should also include "lineage exclusion," whereby the suppression of specific differentiation programs may be as important as "lineage specification."[136]

PU.1 and Gata1 in Myeloerythroid Fate Decisions

One of the most important molecular examples of fate instruction investigated to date is the interaction between PU.1 and Gata1. PU.1 is expressed in myeloid cells, B-cells, and NK

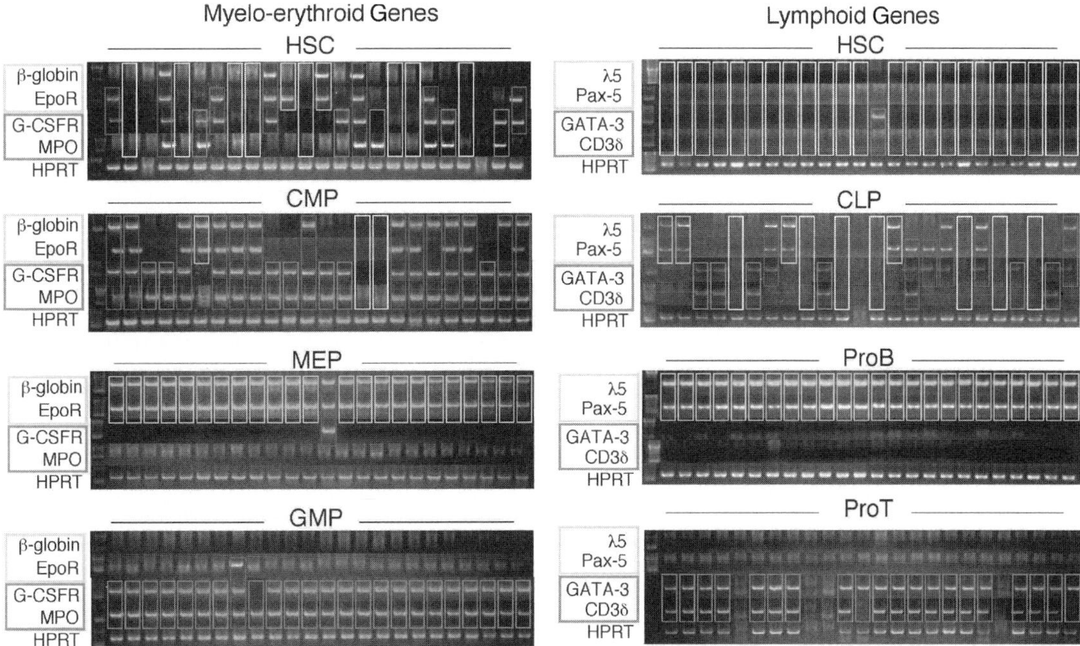

Figure 34–3. *Transcriptional priming stages in single hematopoietic progenitors.* Single cell mutiplex-RT-PCR assays for myeloid-related (β-globin and Epor for erythroid, G-CSFR and Mpo for myelomonocytic) and for lymphoid-related genes (λ5 and Pax-5 for B-lymphoid, Gata3 and CD3δ for T-lymphoid). Gray boxes indicate lineage promiscuous expression and white boxes no expression. More than 50% of single common myeloid progenitors (CMPs) co-express both erythroid and myelomonocytic genes, and ~20% of single common lymphoid progenitors (CLPs) co-express both B- and T-lymphoid-related genes. These data strongly suggest that expression of lineage-related genes precedes commitment, that relevant genes are upregulated upon commitment, and that downregulation of irrelevant genes is likewise important in fate decisions from oligopotent progenitors. (Please see CD-ROM for color version of this figure.)

cells but not in erythrocytes or T-cells. PU.1 is expressed in HSCs at a low level, and its expression increases in CMPs and GMPs, but it is absent in MEPs.[13,57] In the lymphoid pathway, PU.1 is expressed in CLPs and pro-B-cells but not in pro-T-cells.[57] PU.1 binds to many myeloid gene promoters, including the G-CSFR, GM-CSFR, M-CSFR, CD11b, and Mpo genes to regulate their expression (reviewed by Tenen *et al.*[137]). A recent study reported that PU.1 also regulates expression of IL7r,[131] which is necessary for T- and B-cell development.[45,49,138] PU.1 knockout mice display variable anemia and lack all leukocytes, including monocytes, neutrophils, and B-cells.[123] Mice reconstituted with PU.1$^{-/-}$ fetal liver cells exhibit a reduced number of NK cells in addition to loss of T- and B-cells.[139] These findings suggest that PU.1 may play a critical role in the differentiation of HSCs into CLPs and of CMPs into GMPs. Gata1 is an essential transcription factor for maturation of both megakaryocytic and erythroid precursors. Gata1 knockout studies suggest that Gata1 is necessary for terminal differentiation of erythrocytes and platelets.[140,141] Gata1 is expressed in HSCs at a low level,[13,57] and its expression increases in CMPs and MEPs. GMPs and CLPs do not express Gata1. In chickens, forced expression of Gata1 reprograms Myb–Ets-transformed progenitors into the erythroid, eosinophilic, and megakaryocytic pathways (reviewed by Graf[142]).

Along the hematopoietic hierarchy, PU.1 expression increases as stem cells commit to the myeloid lineage, and PU.1 expression declines with erythroid differentiation as Gata1 expression increases. Do the low expression levels of PU.1 and Gata1 in HSCs represent an early stage in commitment? When Gata1 is introduced into HSCs at an expression level comparable to that in MEPs, HSCs immediately lose their self-renewal activity and commit into the MegE lineage.[143] It is thus highly likely that at the low expression levels normally observed in HSCs, these transcription factors do not exert lineage decisive effects. This in turn suggests that changes in expression levels of each transcription factor may be critical for lineage commitment. In cell line studies, PU.1 suppresses Gata1 activity to block erythroid differentiation.[134] Conversely, Gata1 inhibits binding of PU.1 to c-Jun, a critical coactivator of PU.1 transactivation of myeloid promoters.[130,144,145] This mutually antagonizing effect of PU.1 and Gata1 may play an important role in GMP vs MEP commitment at the CMP stage. Expression levels of PU.1 and Gata1 may be critical for cell fate decisions at hematopoietic branch points. For example, in a bipotent cell line, high expression levels of PU.1 instructed macrophage differentiation, whereas B-cell differentiation occurred at low levels.[132] In addition, once up-regulated, Gata1 and PU.1 can stabilize their own expression by positive autoregulation.[144,146]

In T-cell development, a "lineage exclusive" effect was recently demonstrated for PU.1.[147] Fetal liver cells were retrovirally transduced with PU.1 and cultured in FTOC systems.[147] PU.1 overexpression severely inhibited T-cell development

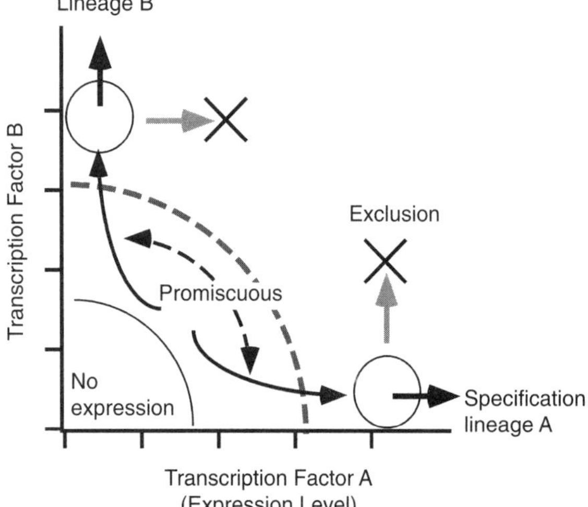

Figure 34–4. *Schematic representation of promiscuous gene priming and lineage commitment.* In this model, commitment occurs if cells express more than threshold levels (dashed line) of either of transcription factors. Transcription factors A and B are simultaneously expressed at low levels at bipotent stages (lineage promiscuity), and their expression levels may fluctuate. Once commitment occurs, irrelevant transcritptional programs are downregulated, and threshold levels of deterministic transcription factors may be stabilized by gene autoregulation. The upregulation of either TF might also exclude unrelated developmental programs to stabilize cell fate choice.

with a block at the $CD25^+CD4^-CD8^-$ stage. B-cell development was also inhibited, but macrophage development proceeded normally. The reason PU.1 inhibited B-cell development may be related to the finding that high PU.1 expression directs macrophage commitment at the expense of B-cells.[132] This lineage exclusion effect has also been reported for Gata1, where ectopic expression in pro-B-cells or GMPs blocked the normal differentiation of each.[143] Rather than differentiating to mature B- or GM cells as usual, Gata1 overexpression caused each precursor subset to immediately undergo apoptotic cell death *in vitro*[143] that could not be rescued by Bcl2. Likewise, enforced expression of human granulocyte–macrophage colony-stimulating factor receptor (hGM-CSFR) signaling in $Gata1^+$ GMPs could not restore normal GM differentiation.[143] Thus, Gata1 appears to directly inhibit lymphoid and GM differentiation rather than inhibit "permissive" survival signals. Mechanisms of differentiation arrest and apoptosis induction remain to be elucidated. Competition of lineage programs could be similarly involved at many hematopoietic branch points.

Lineage Conversion in Purified Progenitors by Ectopic Signals

As described previously, promiscuous gene expression in stem and oligopotent progenitor cells may exist to maintain differentiation flexibility in response to environmental cues.[113] For commitment to a particular fate, it is conceivable that both the up-regulation of genes related to the selected lineage and the down-regulation of genes irrelevant to the selected lineage are required. This might suggest that dysregulation of gene expression—for example, by oncogenic events—could lead to lineage conversion. Recent evidence suggests that this phenomenon can occur.[142]

Lineage conversion was originally reported in murine B-cell lines: Pre-B-cell lines transformed by the Abelson virus differentiated into macrophages following treatment with a DNA demethylating agent, 5-azacytidine,[148] and B-cell lines immortalized with Eμ-Myc transgenes differentiated into macrophages upon overexpression of v-Raf.[149] Thus, committed B-cell precursors harbor latent myelomonocytic potential that can be activated by specific genetic alterations. Conversely, granulocytic conversion was reported in a pre-B-lymphoma line.[150] These findings have postulated a "close" relationship between the B and GM lineages, but it is unclear whether the latent GM potential in B-cell lines represents residual oligopotentiality maintained from upstream progenitors or whether B and GM lineages use similar genetic programs. In a fraction of human acute myelogenous leukemias, leukemic blasts possess lymphoid markers including monoclonal rearrangement of TCR or Ig genes.[151] Conversely, acute lymphoblastic leukemias or even myeloma cells occasionally express myeloid markers.[152,153] Conversions between lymphoid and myeloid leukemias have also been seen.[154,155] These "mixed" leukemias have been ascribed to nonphysiological differentiation induced by oncogenic events (lineage infidelity).[156,157] Recent studies demonstrate that lineage conversion can be induced in committed progenitors simply by enforcing or eliminating single differentiation-related genes such as cytokine receptors and transcription factors.

Lymphoid-Committed Progenitors Can Be Instructed to Myeloid Fates

Mice with targeted disruptions in myeloid cytokine or cytokine receptor genes have not shown a complete loss of specific lineages,[158–161] suggesting that cytokine signaling is not instructive for myeloid fate determination. Myeloerythroid progenitors expressing transgenic receptors for myeloid cytokines such as hGM-CSF,[162] human granulocyte colony-stimulating factor (hG-CSF),[163,164] and murine interleukin 5 (IL5)[165] also did not affect their physiological fate outcomes. Constitutive expression of the activated form of Epor in bone marrow cells supports GM differentiation,[166] and transgenic animals with chimeric extracellular G-CSFR–cytoplasmic-Epor show normal granulocyte development.[167] Therefore, signals from myeloerythroid cytokine receptors may be largely redundant or may simply enhance survival. Thus, the lineage-specific actions of these myeloid cytokines may require the lineage-specific expression of their cognate receptors.

In CLPs, however, signals from myeloid-related cytokines can instruct myelomonocytic differentiation. GM conversion by ectopic IL2 or GM-CSF signaling was observed in purified CLPs and pro-T-cells with rearranged T-cell receptor-β genes but not in downstream pre-T-cells or B-cell progenitors.[168,169]

In another study using hGM-CSFR-βc double transgenic mice, >50% of transgenic CLPs and >20% of transgenic pro-T-cells generated granulocytes, monocytes, DCs, or all of these but not MegE-lineage cells in the presence of hGM-CSF.[108] These data suggest that conversion to GM fates by ectopic GM-CSF signals can occur in CLPs and their downstream lymphoid progeny but that this potential progressively disappears as cells mature. During the conversion of CLPs into the myelomonocytic lineage, several GM-related cytokine receptors (i.e., G-CSFR and M-CSFR) and transcription factors (i.e., C–EBP-α and PU.1) were reactivated, whereas MegE-related genes such as Epor and Gata1 were not.[108] Thus, GM-CSF signals can activate GM but not MegE differentiation programs, demonstrating an instructive role in lineage commitment. This effect was specifically found with GM-CSFR, since similar experiments using G-CSFR or M-CSFR could not induce GM conversion from CLPs.

Lymphoid-Committed Progenitors Can Be Instructed to Erythroid and Megakaryocytic Fates

The nearly mutually exclusive differentiation potential of CMPs and CLPs suggest that loss of lymphoid or myeloid potential occurs as multipotent HSCs generate each respective subset. If the inducible GM potential in CLPs reflects residual multipotentiality from an upstream progenitor, it is reasonable to expect that MegE conversion could similarly be induced in CLPs or their lymphoid progeny.

Perhaps the best candidate molecule to instruct MegE conversion is Gata1, a transcription factor critical for both megakaryocyte and erythrocyte development. A lineage instructive effect for Gata1 was first demonstrated in a multipotential chicken cell line transformed by the Myb–Ets-encoding E26 leukemia virus.[131] This cell line differentiates to the GM lineages following enforced expression of PU.1, whereas enforced expression of Gata1 caused erythroid or eosinophilic differentiation.[131] Within the myelomonocytic lineages, overexpression of GATA transcription factors can induce MegE phenotypes (reviewed by Graf[142]). Introduction of Gata1 into myeloid cell lines induces megakaryocyte differentiation[170] with up-regulation of MegE-affiliated genes such as the Epor and α-globin.[171,172] Furthermore, both GM-restricted colony-forming cells, which are selectively generated in culture, and purified GMPs can generate erythroblasts, megakaryocytes, and eosinophils by Gata1 transduction.[173] These studies suggest that Gata1 is sufficient to reactivate MegE, eosinophil, or both differentiation programs in immature myelomonocytic cells.

In a recent report, Gata1 was retrovirally introduced into CLPs.[143] Strikingly, Gata1 converted CLPs into the MegE lineages, inducing differentiation of hemoglobinized erythroblasts and mature megakaryocytes even in the absence of Tpo or Epo. Gata1-transduced CLPs could not differentiate into T- or B-cells *in vivo,* indicating that ectopic Gata1 inhibited normal lymphoid differentiation. Gata1 altered the expression profiles of lineage-affiliated genes in CLPs into those observed in MegE-committed MEPs, inducing the up-regulation of genes essential for MegE development such as FOG-1, and concomitantly down-regulated genes related to the GM and lymphoid lineages, including PU.1, Pax5, and IL7rα. The reactivation of Gata1 appears to be sufficient, and a minimum requirement, MegE conversion from CLPs.[143]

Interestingly, transduction of Gata2 into purified stem and progenitor cells shows a different effect. Gata2 does not instruct MegE conversion from CMPs or CLPs, nor does overexpression prevent GM or lymphoid differentiation. Enforced expression in GMPs, however, led to the exclusive production of pure eosinophil colonies.[174] Thus, Gata2 appears to be instructive specifically for eosinophil development, as previously reported.[175] In normal hematopoiesis, the eosinophil pathway diverges from that of neutrophils and monocytes at the GMP stage.[174] These data collectively suggest that Gata1 but not Gata2 is the master regulator for MegE commitment; Gata2 likely plays a central role in the generation of eosinophils from GMPs. It is of interest to similarly test the function of Gata3 in MegE and eosinophil development at each hematopoietic stage, because enforced expression of Gata3 in HSCs was shown to induce their preferential differentiation into MegE cells.[176]

Fetal Hematopoietic Progenitors Show Incomplete Lineage Restriction

During development, definitive multilineage hematopoiesis first occurs in the fetal liver (FL). At this stage, the effector cell types produced are similar to those in the adult bone marrow, but important phenotypic and functional differences exist.[177–180] For example, fetal liver HSCs can generate $V\gamma 3^+$ and $V\gamma 4^+$ T-cells[181] and B-1a lymphocytes;[182] whereas adult HSCs cannot. Analysis of the surface markers used to isolate adult hematopoietic progenitors has yielded similar fetal counterparts that are prospectively isolatable. These include fetal CLPs ($Lin^-IL7r\alpha^+B220^{-/lo}Sca\text{-}1^{lo}c\text{-}Kit^{lo}$),[183] CMPs ($Lin^-IL7r\alpha^-Sca\text{-}1^-c\text{-}Kit^+AA4.1^-Fc\gamma RII/III^{lo}CD34^+$), GMPs ($Lin^-IL7r\alpha^-Sca\text{-}1^-c\text{-}Kit^+AA4.1^-Fc\gamma RII/III^{hi}CD34^+$), and MEPs ($Lin^-IL7r\alpha^-Sca\text{-}1^-c\text{-}Kit^+AA4.1^-$ $Fc\gamma RII/III^{lo}CD34^-$).[184] Each fetal population displays similar differentiation potential but shows incomplete lineage restriction when compared to their adult counterparts.

Previous studies showed that clonogenic progenitors for T-cells, B-cells, and macrophages were contained within the $AA4.1^+Fc\gamma RII/III^+$ fraction in mouse fetal liver.[185] Similar studies showed that clonogenic B-cell and macrophage progenitors could be found within FL $AA4.1^+B220^-Mac\text{-}1^-$ $Sca\text{-}1^+$ cells, although T-cell differentiation potential was not tested.[186] $IL7r\alpha\bullet^+B220^+c\text{-}Kit^+$ FL cells efficiently produced T-cells, B-cells, and macrophages.[187] Interestingly, unlike the adult BM fraction, IL7rα expression does not preclude cells with macrophage potential in the FL. A fetal counterpart of adult CLPs, $IL7r\alpha^+B220^{-/lo}Sca\text{-}1^{lo}c\text{-}Kit^{lo}$ cells, comprises ~0.5 to 1.2 % of embryonic day (E) 12.5–14.5 fetal liver cells. These cells are positive for AA4.1 but negative for FcγRII/III, indicating that there is no overlap with the population reported by Lacaud *et al.*[185] By phenotype, FL CLPs should be included within the populations reported by Cumano *et al.*[186] and Sagara *et al.*[187] Clonal cultures of FL CLPs on S17 stromal layers showed that ~5% of single cells differentiated into both macrophages and B-cells.[183] Macrophages were the only myeloerythroid cell type produced from this population, although the burst sizes of macrophage colonies were minimal.[183] Accordingly, injection of fetal CLPs into the liver.[188] of sublethally irradiated newborn mice showed T-, B-, and NK cell-restricted differentiation without detectable macrophage progeny.[183] Together, these findings suggest that low-level macrophage potential is maintained following commitment to the fetal lymphoid fates.

Incomplete restriction to the myeloerythroid fates from the FL CMP was also observed. FL CMPs, which form all myeloerythroid colony types, show a relatively high propensity to differentiate into B-cells.[184] In limiting dilution assays, B-cell frequency was ~0.8% from fetal CMPs. The B-cell potential in fetal CMPs has not been tested at the single-cell level and therefore could result from minor contamination of the phenotypic CMP fraction with B-cell precursors. T-cell developmental potential, however, was absent; no donor-derived progeny was found following intrathymic injection of 10,000 fetal CMPs. Thus, fetal CMPs and CLPs appear to maintain minor potentials for B-cell and macrophage development, respectively.[183,184] Perhaps transcriptional profiling will reveal the molecular bases for these differences between fetal and adult progenitor populations.

Functional differences also exist among adult and fetal stem and progenitor cells. For example, most day 8 CFU-S potential within the FL is possessed by HSCs (Table 34–2). As explained previously, this is in stark contrast to adult bone marrow, where most day 8 CFUs-S are produced by MEPs (Table 34–2, see Na Nakorn *et al.*[60]). Adult HSCs have little day 8 CFU-S activity; instead, HSCs have been shown to generate colonies appearing 12 days after transplantation. This delay, when compared to FL HSCs, may be caused by increased relative quiescence of adult HSCs, as previously reported. Previous experiments showed that short-term, reconstituting HSCs from adult bone marrow, which are actively in the cell cycle, contain fourfold more day 12 CFU-S activity than the quiescent long-term, reconstituting HSC subset (Table 34–2, see Morrison and Weissman[1]). Even the more rapidly cycling adult subset, however, fails to produce significant numbers of day 8 colonies, suggesting intrinsic differences exist in FL HSCs. Interestingly, FL MEP and FL CMP populations had no detectable CFU-S activity (Table 34–2). This was not attributable to inefficient homing of FL progenitors to adult spleens because donor-derived progeny from both populations could be detected in recipient spleens by FACS at similar times. Failure of FL MEPs to generate spleen colonies may be explained by the relatively small burst sizes of colonies, as detected in methylcellulose assays.[184] Although the plating efficiency of single FL MEPs in these assays was roughly equivalent to that described from adult MEPs, the numbers of cells arising in each colony was dramatically reduced. Because FL CMPs generated robust, multilineage colonies under identical conditions, these findings suggest that FL MEPs are limited in proliferative capacity when compared to adult MEPs. This is paradoxical, however, because approximately 80% of FL cells at E14 are erythroid. Although we cannot rule out the possibility that additional pathways of erythroid production exist in FL, FL CMPs generate robust BFU-E colonies (not shown) and FL MEPs generate small, evanescent CFU-E colonies, which may suggest that the FL CMP is largely responsible for the production of erythrocytes. Accordingly, a comparison of differential counts of colony types derived from single fetal and adult CMPs showed an approximately twofold increase in MegE production from the FL CMP, suggesting that FL CMPs are predisposed to differentiate along the erythroid pathway. Supporting a critical role of FL CMPs in the generation of erythroid progeny are the findings in Pbx1-deficient mice.

Use of Myeloid Progenitor Subsets to Precisely Characterize Hematopoietic Mutants

The ability to quantitate and isolate lineage-restricted progenitors in the fetus permits a thorough investigation of the hematopoietic system in mice that die *in utero* because of targeted gene disruptions. Analyses of midgestation fetal liver cells in mice with targeted disruptions in the *Pbx1, PU.1,* or *C/EBP*α genes have demonstrated important hematopoietic defects at the stem and progenitor cell level. Pbx1 is a cofactor for transcriptional activation by Hox complexes, is expressed in the aorta–gonad–mesonephros region of the developing embryonic immune system, and is expressed in FL stem and progenitor cell subsets.[189] Pbx1-deficient mice show several defects, the most important of which is embryonic death resulting from profound anemia by day 16 of development.[189] Phenotypic analyses of stem and progenitor cells in E14 FL showed approximately twofold decreases in the total numbers of HSCs, MEPs, and GMPs. Strikingly, the FL CMP population showed a five- to tenfold decrease. Analysis of clonal colony distributions showed that FL-CMPs preferentially differentiated to GM lineages and showed approximately a threefold decrease in erythroid-containing colonies.[189] Together, these data demonstrated a role for Pbx1 in the maintenance of definitive hematopoiesis and suggested that the fatal anemia in Pbx1$^{-/-}$ embryos is the collective result of defects in all hematopoietic progenitors normally possessing erythroid differentiation capacity. Additionally, the results in both wild-type and Pbx1$^{-/-}$ mice suggest that the FL-CMP stage in hematopoietic differentiation is critical for the generation of erythrocyte numbers sufficient to oxygenate the rapidly expanding tissues of the mid- to late-gestation embryo.

As described previously, PU.1 is expressed in HSCs, CMPs, GMPs, and CLPs but is absent in MEPs.[13,57] Expression is found in downstream myeloid cells, B-cells, and NK cells but not in erythrocytes or T-cells. PU.1 knockout mice display variable anemia and lack all leukocytes, including monocytes, neutrophils, and B-cells.[123] Mice reconstituted with $PU.1^{-/-}$ fetal liver cells exhibit a reduced number of NK cells in addition to loss of T- and B-cells.[139] These findings suggest that PU.1 may play a critical role in the differentiation of HSCs into CLPs and of CMPs into GMPs. Accordingly, examination of hematopoietic stem and progenitor cell subsets in $PU.1^{-/-}$ E14.5 FL showed that the HSC and MEP subsets were intact, but phenotypic CLP, CMP, and GMP populations could not be detected.[190]

C/EBPα deficient mice cannot store hepatic glycogen and die shortly after birth because of severe hypoglycemia.[191] Analysis of fetal animals showed a specific and cell-autonomous defect in granulocyte differentiation.[128] More recent investigations have shown that $C/EBP\alpha^{-/-}$ mice possess normal numbers of stem and progenitor subsets—with the exception of FL GMPs, which were phenotypically absent.[192] Adult mice conditionally deleted with $C/EBP\alpha^{-/-}$ do not have GMPs, mature granulocytes, or mature monocytes, although they display an increased number of myeloblasts in blood and bone marrow and meet the criteria of acute myelogenous leukemia in humans. Accordingly, C/EBPα deficiency likely causes differentiation inhibition from the CMP to the GMP stage, resulting in an accumulation of early GM precursors. Conditional $C/EBP\alpha^{-/-}$ mice, however, do not die because of invasive proliferation of myeloblasts and have MEPs with normal numbers of erythrocytes and platelets, indicating that an accumulation of myeloblasts alone does not represent acute leukemic transformation.[192] These data strongly suggest that an additional mutation or mutations, which lead to acquisition of self-renewal or abnormal proliferation activity, might be required for leukemia development. Thus, the ability to isolate myeloid progenitors at different hematopoietic stages is useful not only in understanding the stages at which transcription factors play critical roles in lineage commitment or development but also in analyzing the pathogenesis of malignant hematopoiesis.

Counterpart Populations in Human Bone Marrow

Over the past decade, the work of several investigators has shown that human HSCs can be prospectively purified by cell surface phenotype. Early work by Civin *et al.*[193] using an antibody raised against a human myeloid cell line termed My-10 (now known as CD34) showed it to specifically mark immature bone marrow cells. Mouse LT-HSCs in steady-state bone marrow do not express significant levels of mCD34 (see Osawa *et al.*[3]), which raised the important question of whether $hCD34^+$ cells contain self-renewing human LT-HSCs. Thus, it is important to evaluate whether the expression of hCD34 mimics that of mCD34 in the hematopoietic system. Mouse lines harboring human genomic P1 artificial chromosome clones containing the entire hCD34 gene, including all exons, introns, and more than 18 kb of flanking 5′ and 3′ genomic sequences, were established.[194] In all transgenic mouse strains, most phenotypic and functional HSC populations, including $mCD34^{-/lo}$, expressed the hCD34 transgene. In progenitor populations, the hCD34 transgene was expressed in most CLPs, CMPs, and GMPs and in ~30% of MEPs.[194] These data strongly support the notion that $hCD34^+$ human bone marrow cells contain LT-HSCs that can maintain hematopoiesis throughout life, as well as primitive myeloid and lymphoid progenitors.

Terstappen and colleagues showed that stem and progenitor cell activity within this $CD34^+$ fraction could be functionally separated by the CD38 molecule.[195] More than 99% of the $CD34^+$ fraction expresses CD38, and the expression of mature lineage markers, such as the lymphoid-related CD10 and myeloid-related CD33 molecules, was detectable only within the $CD38^+$ fraction. Isolation of the $CD34^+CD38^-$ fraction showed morphologically immature cell types, and functional testing showed it to contain most primitive colony-forming activity *in vitro*. Parallel studies showed that HSC activity could be enriched within $CD34^+$ marrow cells by negative staining for lineage markers and by positive staining for the additional Thy1 marker.[196] More recent studies have demonstrated that human $Lin^-CD34^+CD38^-$ cells can clonally generate B-lymphocytes and -granulocytes;[197] B-lymphocytes and myeloid CFU;[198] and B-lymphocytes, NK cells, DCs, and myeloid cells,[199] suggesting that this population is highly enriched at least for multipotent HSCs.

Similar prospective isolation strategies showed that lymphoid-restricted progenitors could be found within the $Lin^-CD34^+CD38^+CD45RA^+CD10^+$ subset of human bone marrow cells.[200] Lymphoid potential was determined by reconstitution of human bone and thymus fragments implanted into SCID mice as well as by *in vitro* culture systems. Limiting dilution assays suggested that this population contains clonal progenitors of B-, NK, and DC lineages.[200] Similar to mouse CLPs, this population expresses IL7rα. Another clonal study showed that CD7 is an important marker of CLP activity within the $CD34^+CD38^-CD45RA^+$ fraction of human cord blood.[89]

Subfractionation of $CD34^+$ bone marrow cells also yielded substantial enrichments of myeloid-restricted progenitors. Based on CD45 isoforms, immature erythroid-forming elements were most highly enriched within a $CD34^+CD45RO^+$ fraction, whereas most GM-forming precursors were localized to a $CD34^+CD45RO^-$ fraction.[201] A similar study showed that immature myeloerythroid CFU were largely within $CD34^+CD45RA^-$ cells, and CFU-GM were within $CD34^+CD45RA^+$ cells.[202] The CD64,[203] Flk-2,[204] and CCR1[205] receptors have also been suggested to mark GM commitment within the $CD34^+$ fraction. Based on IL3rα expression, a receptor that supports proliferation and differentiation of primitive progenitors,[206] three subsets could be resolved within $CD34^+$ cells, marker expression profiles and *in vitro* behaviors suggestive of each containing different classes of stem and progenitor cells.[207] $CD34^+IL3r\alpha^{hi}$ cells were enriched for GM and B-lymphoid precursors, $CD34^+IL3r\alpha^{lo}$ cells for primitive myeloerythroid precursors, and $CD34^+IL3r\alpha^-$ cells for erythroid precursors.[207] Based on these findings, more recent studies have shown that clonogenic human CMPs, GMPs, and MEPs can be isolated from human bone marrow and cord blood cells.[208]

As these studies suggested, all three hCMP, hGMP, and hMEP subsets are within the CD34$^+$CD38$^+$ fraction, and all are negative for multiple mature lineage markers, including the early lymphoid markers CD10, CD7, and IL7rα. The CD34$^+$CD38$^+$ fraction was further subdivided by CD45RA and IL3rα expression. CD45RA$^-$IL3rα^{lo} (hCMPs), CD45RA$^+$IL3rα^{lo} (hGMPs), and CD45RA$^-$IL3rα$^-$ (hMEPs) efficiently formed distinct myeloerythroid colony types according to their definitions, in agreement with the earlier studies by Huang *et al.*[207] None of these populations exhibited significant lymphoid or LTC-IC activity. hCMPs generate hMEPs and hGMPs *in vitro,* and a significant proportion of CMPs were demonstrated to possess clonal granulocyte–macrophage and megakaryocyte–erythrocyte potentials.[208] Thus, the hierarchical progenitor relationships demonstrated in the mouse also exist in human hematopoiesis, and each subset can now be isolated prospectively. Phenotypic comparisons between mouse and human subsets show that CD34, a marker of only murine CMPs and GMPs, is uniformly expressed on all three human subsets and that the FcγRII/III (CD16–CD32), marking murine CMPs and GMPs, was not detectable on human myeloid progenitor populations (Figs. 34–2 and 34–5).

Clinical Relevance

Prospective isolation of myeloerythroid-committed progenitors has shown that the major lineage relationships in the hematopoietic hierarchy are in agreement with those postulated from early, retrospective colony assays. That we can now isolate distinct cell types with discrete lymphoid, myeloerythroid, GM, or MegE differentiation potentials suggests that each may have clinical utility. Several complications are associated with clinical bone marrow transplantation (BMT). BMT into myeloablated individuals often gives rise to graft versus host disease when using total bone marrow or mobilized peripheral blood cells. This is because of the transfer of allogeneic lymphocytes within the transplanted cells. It has been shown that transplantation of CD34$^+$-enriched HSCs alleviates most cases of graft vs host disease, presumably because newly arising donor-derived lymphocytes can be educated in host tissues to prevent alloreactivity.[209] Pure HSC transplants, however, are relatively slow to generate sufficient numbers of mature cell types. Using a mouse progenitor transplantation model, it was recently shown that high-dose transplantation of either CMPs or MEPs—in the absence of HSCs—was sufficient for radioprotection over a 1-month interval.[60] After this time, rare, surviving host HSCs recovered to produce all blood cell subsets.[60] Another important complication following BMT is infection. Myeloablative irradiation, cytoreductive drugs, or both cause the rapid disappearance of myelomonocytes as well as of lymphocytes. This leaves a window following transplantation for opportunistic pathogens such as *Aspergillus fumigatus* or *Pseudomonas aeruginosa* to flourish. Using another mouse model, it was shown that transplantation of CMPs, GMPs, or both in conjunction with HSC

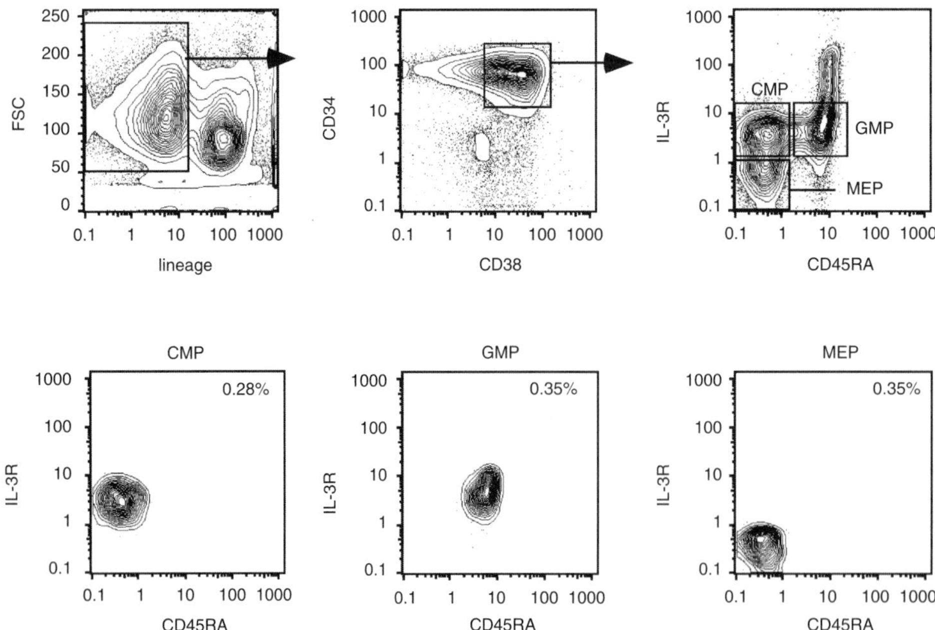

Figure 34–5. *Prospective isolation of myeloid progenitors in adult human bone marrow. Lin$^-$CD34$^+$CD38$^+$ fraction was subdivided according to IL3rα and CD45RA expression (upper panels). Reanalysis of the sorted human CMPs, GMPs, and MEPs (bottom panels). Percentages relative to mononuclear bone marrow cells are shown.*

transplants could protect against otherwise lethal challenges of either pathogen because of increased numbers of myelomonocytic cells.[210] Viral complications, such as cytomegalovirus infection, are also associated with BMT. Similar cotransplantation experiments using CLPs and HSCs showed significant protection against murine cytomegalovirus infection when compared to HSC transplants alone.[211] Together, these transplant experiments show that distinct lineages of hematopoietic cells are sufficient for radioprotection and immunity. Rapid production of erythrocytes, platelets, or both is required for radioprotection, whereas GMP transplants had no effect on host survival. Conversely, early production of myelomonocytes appeared critical in protecting against common fungal and bacterial infection. The use of lymphoid-committed progenitors was similarly useful in protecting against cytomegalovirus infection, and because incipient T-lymphocytes are educated in the host thymus, CLP infusions should not result in allogeneic responses, even if their progeny survive for long periods in the host. Based on these preclinical findings, it may be of clinical interest to purify human counterpart populations to augment purified HSC transplants.

Summary

The ability to prospectively isolate lineage-committed progenitors to purity represents an important step in the precise definition of the lineal relationships among all hematolymphoid cells. This has allowed the ontogenies of cells with controversial origins, such as DCs and mast cells, to be elucidated. Prospective isolation of each of the major hematopoietic branch points, in conjunction with HSC isolation, also permits the study of the transcriptional control of hematopoiesis. Transcriptional profiling at the population level has shown that the "master regulator" genes identified from mouse knockout studies are expressed in the progenitor subsets upstream of the noted defective lineages. Single-cell profiling has supported the hypothesis of "priming stages," whereby promiscuous, low-level expression of many genes appears to maintain flexibility in cell fate choices. Interestingly, enforced expression of single, inappropriate genes within lineage-restricted progenitors can reprogram normal fate outcomes. This demonstrates that the nucleus maintains developmental flexibility and that the progressive loss of fate potential upon differentiation is likely controlled initially by strict regulation of growth factor receptor expression. Description of embryonic progenitors can be used to accurately phenotype mice that die during fetal development from the targeted deletion of genes critical in hematopoiesis. The ability to purify the progenitors of all major hematopoietic lineages in the embryo and adult now allows for a more complete assessment of the normal function of deleted genes.

Preliminary studies using lineage-restricted progenitors in clinically relevant settings may eventually be useful in creating additional reagents to augment HSC transplantation. Defined progenitor subsets may also be used to determine the points at which leukemogenic transformation occurs along normal hematopoietic differentiation pathways. Although the mutations underlying leukemogenesis are commonly thought to accumulate only in HSCs, it is plausible that mutations in downstream progenitors underlie transformation. Myeloid leukemias might thus be malignancies of defined normal subsets of myeloerythroid progenitors that have acquired the fundamental properties of HSCs—the ability to self-renew and proliferate without apparent limit. Work with both normal and neoplastic stem and progenitor populations may thus elucidate how stem cells and leukemic clones choose between self-renewal and differentiation.

REFERENCES

1. Morrison, S.J., and Weissman, I.L. (1994). The long-term repopulating subset of hematopoietic stem cells is deterministic and isolatable by phenotype. *Immunity* **1,** 661–673.
2. Adolfsson, J., Borge, O.J., Bryder, D., Theilgaard-Monch, K., Astrand-Grundstrom, I., Sitnicka, E., Sasaki, Y., and Jacobsen, S.E. (2001). Up-regulation of Flt3 expression within the bone marrow Lin(−)Sca1(+)c-Kit(+) stem cell compartment is accompanied by loss of self-renewal capacity. *Immunity* **15,** 659–669.
3. Osawa, M., Hanada, K., Hamada, H., and Nakauchi, H. (1996). Long-term lymphohematopoietic reconstitution by a single CD34-low–negative hematopoietic stem cell. *Science* **273,** 242–245.
4. Christensen, J.L., and Weissman, I.L. (2001). Flk-2 is a marker in hematopoietic stem cell differentiation: a simple method to isolate long-term stem cells. *Proc. Natl. Acad. Sci. U. S. A.* **98,** 14,541–14,546.
5. Lemischka, I.R., Raulet, D.H., and Mulligan, R.C. (1986). Developmental potential and dynamic behavior of hematopoietic stem cells. *Cell* **45,** 917–927.
6. Dexter, T.M. (1990). Introduction to the hemopoietic system. *Cancer Surv.* **9,** 1–5.
7. Akashi, K., Kondo, M., M., Schlageter, A.M., and Weissman, I.L. (1998). T-cell development from hematopoietic stem cells. *In* "Molecular Biology of B-cell and T-cell Development," (J.G. Monroe *et al.,* Eds.), pp. 305–336. Humana Press, Totowa.
8. Abramson, S., Miller, R.G., and Phillips, R.A. (1977). The identification in adult bone marrow of pluripotent and restricted stem cells of the myeloid and lymphoid systems. *J. Exp. Med.* **145,** 1567–1579.
9. Fulop, G.M., and Phillips, R.A. (1989). Use of SCID mice to identify and quantitate lymphoid-restricted stem cells in long-term bone marrow cultures. *Blood* **74,** 1537–1544.
10. Fischer, A. (1992). Severe combined immunodeficiencies. *Immunodefic. Rev.* **3,** 83–100.
11. Hirschhorn, R. (1990). Adenosine deaminase deficiency. *Immunodefic. Rev.* **2,** 175–198.
12. Kondo, M., Weissman, I.L., and Akashi, K. (1997). Identification of clonogenic common lymphoid progenitors in mouse bone marrow. *Cell* **91,** 661–672.
13. Akashi, K., Traver, D., Miyamoto, T., and Weissman, I.L. (2000). A clonogenic common myeloid progenitor that gives rise to all myeloid lineages. *Nature* **404,** 193–197.
14. Igarashi, H., Gregory, S.C., Yokota, T., Sakaguchi, N., and Kincade, P.W. (2002). Transcription from the Rag1 locus marks the earliest lymphocyte progenitors in bone marrow. *Immunity* **17,** 117–130.
15. Gounari, F., Aifantis, I., Martin, C., Fehling, H.J., Hoeflinger, S., Leder, P., von Boehmer, H., and Reizis, B. (2002). Tracing

lymphopoiesis with the aid of a pTα-controlled reporter gene. *Nat. Immunol.* **3,** 489–496.
16. McCulloch, E.A., and Till, J.E. (1960). The radiation sensitivity of normal mouse bone marrow cells, determined by quantitative marrow transplantation into irradiated mice. *Radiat. Res.* **13,** 115–125.
17 Jacobsen, L.D., Simmons, E.L., Markes, E.K., Gasten, E.O., Robson, M.J., and Eldridge, J.H. (1951). Further studies on recovery from radiation injury. *J. Lab. Clin. Med.* **37,** 683–697.
18. Becker, A., McCulloch, E., and Till, J. (1963). Cytological demonstration of the clonal nature of spleen colonies derived from transplanted mouse marrow cells. *Nature* **197,** 452–454.
19. Till, J.E., and McCulloch, E.A. (1961). A direct measure of the radiation sensitivity of normal mouse bone marrow cells. *Radiat. Res.* **14,** 213–222.
20. Wu, A., Till, J., Siminovitch, L., and McCulloch, E. (1968). Cytological evidence for a relationship between normal hematopoietic colony-forming cells and cells of the lymphoid system. *J. Exp. Med.* **127,** 455–467.
21. Visser, J.W., Bauman, J.G., Mulder, A.H., Eliason, J.F., and de Leeuw, A.W. (1984). Isolation of murine pluripotent hemopoietic stem cells. *J. Exp. Med.* **59,** 1576–1590.
22. Mulder, A.H., and Visser, J.W.M. (1987). Separation and functional analysis of bone marrow cells separated by rhodamine-123 fluorescence. *Exp. Hematol.* **15,** 99–104.
23. Spangrude, G.J., Aihara, Y., Weissman, I.L., and Klein, J. (1988). The stem cell antigens Sca-1 and Sca-2 subdivide thymic and peripheral T-lymphocytes into unique subsets. *J. Immunol.* **141,** 3697–3707.
24. Uchida, N., and Weissman, I. (1992). Searching for hematopoietic stem cells: evidence that Thy1.1^{lo}Lin$^-$Sca-1$^+$ cells are the only stem cells in C57BL–Ka-Thy1.1 bone marrow. *J. Exp. Med.* **175,** 175–184.
25. Uchida, N., Aguila, H.L., Fleming, W.H., Jerabek, L., and Weissman, I.L. (1994). Rapid and sustained hematopoietic recovery in lethally irradiated mice transplanted with purified Thy1.1^{lo}Lin$^-$Sca-1+ hematopoietic stem cells. *Blood* **83,** 3758–3779.
26. Spangrude, G.J., Smith, L., Uchida, N., Ikuta, K., Heimfeld, S., Friedman, J., and Weissman, I.L. (1991). Mouse hematopoietic stem cells. *Blood* **78,** 1395–1402.
27. Smith, L.G., Weissman, I.L., and Heimfeld, S. (1991). Clonal analysis of hematopoietic stem cell differentiation *in vivo. Proc. Natl. Acad. Sci. U. S. A.* **88,** 2788–2792.
28. Wagers, A.J., Sherwood, R.I., Christensen, J.L., and Weissman, I.L. (2002). Little evidence for developmental plasticity of adult hematopoietic stem cells. *Science* **297,** 2256–2259.
29. Goodell, M.A., Jackson, K.A., Majka, S.M., Mi, T., Wang, H., Pocius, J., Hartley, C.J., Majesky, M.W., Entman, M.L., Michael, L.H., and Hirschi, K.K. (2001). Stem cell plasticity in muscle and bone marrow. *Ann. NY Acad. Sci.* **938,** 208–218; discussion 218–220.
30. Goodell, M.A., Rosenzweig, M., Kim, H., Marks, D.F., DeMaria, M., Paradis, G., Grupp, S.A., Sieff, C.A., Mulligan, R.C., and Johnson, R.P.. (1997). Dye efflux studies suggest that hematopoietic stem cells expressing low or undetectable levels of CD34 antigen exist in multiple species. *Nat. Med.* **3,** 1337–1345.
31. Jackson, K.A., Majka, S.M., Wang, H., Pocius, J., Hartley, C.J., Majesky, M.W., Entman, M.L., Michael, L.H., Hirschi, K.K., and Goodell, M.A. (2001). Regeneration of ischemic cardiac muscle and vascular endothelium by adult stem cells. *J. Clin. Invest.* **107,** 1395–1402.
32. Storms, R.W., Goodell, M.A., Fisher, A., Mulligan, R.C., and Smith, C. (2000). Hoechst dye efflux reveals a novel CD7(+) CD34(−) lymphoid progenitor in human umbilical cord blood. *Blood* **96,** 2125–2133.
33. Okuno, Y., Iwasaki, H., Huettner, C.S., Radomska, H.S., Gonzalez, D.A., Tenen, D.G., and Akashi, K. (2002). Differential regulation of the human and murine CD34 genes in hematopoietic stem cells. *Proc. Natl. Acad. Sci. U. S. A.* **99,** 6246–6251.
34. Matsuzaki, Y., Kinjo, K., Mulligan, R.C., and Okano, H. (2004). Unexpectedly efficient homing capacity of purified murine hematopoietic stem cells. *Immunity* **20,** 87–93.
35. Felsenfeld, G., Boyes, J., Chung, J., Clark, D., and Studitsky, V. (1996). Chromatin structure and gene expression. *Proc. Natl. Acad. Sci. U. S. A.* **93,** 9384–9388.
36. Berger, S.L., and Felsenfeld, G.. (2001). Chromatin goes global. *Mol. Cell* **8,** 263–268.
37. Bradley, T.R., and Metcalf, D. (1966). The growth of mouse bone marrow cells *in vitro. Aust. J. Exp. Biol. Med. Sci.* **44,** 287–299.
38. Pluznik, D.H., and Sachs, L. (1965). The cloning of normal "mast" cells in tissue culture. *J. Cell Physiol.* **66,** 319–324.
39. Johnson, G.R., and Metcalf, D. (1977). Pure and mixed erythroid colony formation *in vitro* stimulated by spleen conditioned medium with no detectable erythropoietin. *Proc. Natl. Acad. Sci. U. S. A.* **74,** 3879–3882.
40. Metcalf, D., Johnson, G.R., and Mandel, T.E. (1979). Colony formation in agar by multipotential hemopoietic cells. *J. Cell Physiol.* **98,** 401–420.
41. Dexter, T.M., and Testa, N.G. (1980). *In vitro* methods in hemopoiesis and lymphopoiesis. *J. Immunol. Methods* **38,** 177–190.
42. Heimfeld, S., Hudak, S., Weissman, I., and Rennick, D. (1991). The *in vitro* response of phenotypically defined mouse stem cells and myeloerythroid progenitors to single or multiple growth factors. *Proc. Natl. Acad. Sci. U. S. A.* **88,** 9902–9906.
43. Nosten-Bertrand, M., Errington, M.L., Murphy, K.P., Tokugawa, Y., Barboni, E., Kozlova, E., Michalovich, D., Morris, R.G., Silver, J., Stewart, C.L., Bliss, T.V., and Morris, R.J. (1996). Normal spatial learning despite regional inhibition of LTP in mice lacking Thy1. *Nature* **379,** 826–829.
44. Ito, C.Y., Li, C.Y., Bernstein, A., Dick, J.E., and Stanford, W.L. (2003). Hematopoietic stem cell and progenitor defects in Sca-1–Ly-6A-null mice. *Blood* **101,** 517–523.
45. Peschon, J.J., Morrissey, P.J., Grabstein, K.H., Ramsdell, F.J., Maraskovsky, E., Gliniak, B.C., Park, L.S., Ziegler, S.F., Williams, D.E., and Ware, C.B.. (1994). Early lymphocyte expansion is severely impaired in interleukin 7 receptor-deficient mice. *J. Exp. Med.* **180,** 1955–1960.
46. von Freeden-Jeffry, U., Vieira, P., Lucian, L.A., McNeil, T., Burdach, S.E., and Murray, R. (1995). Lymphopenia in interleukin (IL) 7 gene-deleted mice identifies IL7 as a nonredundant cytokine. *J. Exp. Med.* **181,** 1519–1526.
47. Bhatia, S.K., Tygrett, L.T., Grabstein, K.H., and Waldschmidt, T.J. (1995). The effect of *in vivo* IL7 deprivation on T-cell maturation. *J. Exp. Med.* **181,** 1399–1409.
48. Akashi, K., Kondo, M., and Weissman, I.L. (1998). Role of interleukin 7 in T-cell development from hematopoietic stem cells. *Immunol. Rev.* **165,** 13–28.
49. Akashi, K., Kondo, M., von Freeden-Jeffry, U., Murray, R., and Weissman, I.L. (1997). Bcl2 rescues T-lymphopoiesis in interleukin 7 receptor-deficient mice. *Cell* **89,** 1033–1041.
50. Corcoran, A.E., Riddell, A., Krooshoop, D., and Venkitaraman, A.R. (1998). Impaired immunoglobulin gene rearrangement in mice lacking the IL7 receptor. *Nature* **391,** 904–907.
51. Izon, D., Rudd, K., DeMuth, W., Pear, W.S., Clendenin, C., Lindsley, R.C., and Allman, D. (2001). A common pathway for

dendritic cell and early B-cell development. *J. Immunol.* **167,** 1387–1392.

52. Kawamoto, H., Ohmura, K., and Katsura, Y. (1997). Direct evidence for the commitment of hematopoietic stem cells to T-, B-, and myeloid lineages in murine fetal liver. *Int. Immunol.* **9,** 1011–1019.
53. Sitnicka, E., Bryder, D., Theilgaard-Monch, K., Buza-Vidas, N., Adolfsson, J., and Jacobsen, S.E. (2002). Key role of Flt3 ligand in regulation of the common lymphoid progenitor but not in maintenance of the hematopoietic stem cell pool. *Immunity* **17,** 463–472.
54. Kuwata, N., Igarashi, H., Ohmura, T., Aizawa, S., and Sakaguchi, N. (1999). Cutting edge: absence of expression of Rag1 in peritoneal B-1 cells detected by knocking into Rag1 locus with green fluorescent protein gene. *J. Immunol.* **163,** 6355–6359.
55. Igarashi, H., Kuwata, N., Kiyota, K., Sumita, K., Suda, T., Ono, S., Bauer, S.R., and Sakaguchi, N. (2001). Localization of recombination activating gene 1–green fluorescent protein (Rag1–GFP) expression in secondary lymphoid organs after immunization with T-dependent antigens in Rag1–GFP knockin mice. *Blood* **97,** 2680–2687.
56. Reizis, B., and Leder, P. (2001). The upstream enhancer is necessary and sufficient for the expression of the pre-T-cell receptor alpha gene in immature T-lymphocytes. *J. Exp. Med.* **194,** 979–990.
57. Miyamoto, T., Iwasaki, H., Reizis, B., Ye, M., Graf, T., Weissman, I.L., and Akashi, K. (2002). Myeloid or lymphoid promiscuity as a critical step in hematopoietic lineage commitment. *Dev. Cell* **3,** 137–147.
58. Searles, A.E., Pohlmann, S.J., Pierce, L.J., Perry, S.S., Slayton, W.B., Mojica, M.P., and Spangrude, G.J. (2000). Rapid, B-lymphoid-restricted engraftment mediated by a primitive bone marrow subpopulation. *J. Immunol.* **165,** 67–74.
59. Wiesmann, A., Phillips, R.L., Mojica, M., Pierce, L.J., Searles, A.E., Spangrude, G.J., and Lemischka, I. (2000). Expression of CD27 on murine hematopoietic stem and progenitor cells. *Immunity* **12,** 193–199.
60. Na Nakorn, T., Traver, D., Weissman, I.L., and Akashi, K. (2002). Myeloerythroid-restricted progenitors are sufficient to confer radioprotection and provide the majority of day 8 CFU-S. *J. Clin. Invest.* **109,** 1579–1585.
61. Humphries, R.K., Eaves, A.C., and Eaves, C.J. (1979). Characterization of a primitive erythropoietic progenitor found in mouse marrow before and after several weeks in culture. *Blood* **53,** 746–763.
62. Magli, M.C., Iscove, N.N., and Odartchenko, N. (1982). Transient nature of early hematopoietic spleen colonies. *Nature* **295,** 527–529.
63. Siminovitch, L., McCulloch, E., and Till, J. (1963). The distribution of colony-forming cells among spleen colonies. *J. Cell. Comp. Physiol.* **62,** 327–336.
64. Wu, A., Till, J., Siminovitch, L., and McCulloch E. (1967). A cytological study of the capacity for differentiation of normal hemopoietic colony-forming cells. *J. Cell. Physiol.* **69,** 177–184.
65. Lepault, F., Ezine, S., and Gagnerault, M.C. (1993). T- and B-lymphocyte differentiation potentials of spleen colony-forming cells. *Blood* **81,** 950–955.
66. Nakorn, T.N., Miyamoto, T., and Weissman, I.L. (2003). Characterization of mouse clonogenic megakaryocyte progenitors. *Proc. Natl. Acad. Sci. U. S. A.* **100,** 205–210.
67. Iwasaki, H., and Akashi, K. (2001). Mast cells originate from granulocyte–macrophage-committed progenitors. *Blood* **98,** 275a.
68. Iwasaki, H., Mizuno, S., Takatsu, K., and Akashi, K. (2003). GATA-2 but not GATA-1 is the major instructive regulator for eosinophil development from granulocyte/monocyte progenitors. *Blood* **102,** 197a.
69. Banchereau, J., and Steinman, R.M. (1998). Dendritic cells and the control of immunity. *Nature* **392,** 245–252.
70. Hart, D.N. (1997). Dendritic cells: unique leukocyte popul-ations which control the primary immune response. *Blood* **90,** 3245–3287.
71. Brocker, T., Riedinger, M., and Karjalainen K. (1997). Targeted expression of major histocompatibility complex (MHC) class II molecules demonstrates that dendritic cells can induce negative but not positive selection of thymocytes *in vivo*. *J. Exp. Med.* **185,** 541–550.
72. Shortman, K., and Caux, C. (1997). Dendritic cell development: multiple pathways to nature's adjuvants. *Stem Cells* **15,** 409–419.
73. Steinman, R.M., and Inaba, K. (1999). Myeloid dendritic cells. *J. Leukoc. Biol.* **66,** 205–208.
74. Steinman, R.M., Pack, M., and Inaba, K. (1997). Dendritic cells in the T-cell areas of lymphoid organs. *Immunol. Rev.* **156,** 25–37.
75. Vremec, D., and Shortman, K. (1997). Dendritic cell subtypes in mouse lymphoid organs: cross-correlation of surface markers, changes with incubation, and differences among thymus, spleen, and lymph nodes. *J. Immunol.* **159,** 565–573.
76. Inaba, K., Inaba, M., Deguchi, M., Hagi, K., Yasumizu, R., Ikehara, S., Muramatsu, S., and Steinman, R.M. (1993). Granulocytes, macrophages, and dendritic cells arise from a common major histocompatibility complex class II-negative progenitor in mouse bone marrow. *Proc. Natl. Acad. Sci. U. S. A.* **90,** 3038–3042.
77. Ardavin, C. (1997). Thymic dendritic cells. *Immunol. Today* **18,** 350–361.
78. Traver, D., Akashi, K., Manz, M., Merad, M., Miyamoto, T., Engleman, E.G., and Weissman, I.L. (2000). Development of CD8α+ dendritic cells from a common myeloid progenitor. *Science* **290,** 2152–2154.
79. Manz, M.G., Traver, D., Miyamoto, T., Weissman, I.L., and Akashi, K. (2001). Dendritic cell potentials of early lymphoid and myeloid progenitors. *Blood* **97,** 3333–3341.
80. Wu, L., D'Amico, A., Hochrein, H., O'Keeffe, M., Shortman, K., and Lucas, K. (2001). Development of thymic and splenic dendritic cell populations from different hemopoietic precursors. *Blood* **98,** 3376–3382.
81. Martinez del Hoyo, G., Martin, P., Arias, C.F., Marin, A.R., and Ardavin, C. (2002). CD8α+ dendritic cells originate from the CD8α− dendritic cell subset by a maturation process involving CD8α, DEC-205, and CD24 up-regulation. *Blood* **99,** 999–1004.
82. Naik, S., Vremec, D., Wu, L., O'Keeffe, M., and Shortman, K. (2003). CD8α+ mouse spleen dendritic cells do not originate from the CD8α dendritic cell subset. *Blood* **102,** 601–604.
83. Wang, Y., Zhang, Y., Yoneyama, H., Onai, N., Sato, T., and Matsushima, K. (2002). Identification of CD8α+CD11c− lineage phenotype-negative cells in the spleen as committed precursor of CD8α+ dendritic cells. *Blood* **100,** 569–577.
84. del Hoyo, G.M., Martin, P., Vargas, H.H., Ruiz, S., Arias, C.F., and Ardavin, C. (2002). Characterization of a common precursor population for dendritic cells. *Nature* **415,** 1043–1047.
85. Shortman, K., and Liu, Y.J. (2002). Mouse and human dendritic cell subtypes. *Nat. Rev. Immunol.* **2,** 151–161.
86. Caux, C., Vanbervliet, B., Massacrier, C., Dezutter-Dambuyant, C., de Saint-Vis, B., Jacquet, C., Yoneda, K., Imamura, S., Schmitt, D., and Banchereau, J. (1996). CD34+ hematopoietic progenitors from human cord blood differentiate along two independent dendritic cell pathways in response to GM–CSF+TNF-α. *J. Exp. Med.* **184,** 695–706.

87. Young, J.W., Szabolcs, P., and Moore, M.A. (1995). Identification of dendritic cell colony-forming units among normal human CD34+ bone marrow progenitors that are expanded by c-Kit-ligand and yield pure dendritic cell colonies in the presence of granulocyte–macrophage colony-stimulating factor and tumor necrosis factor alpha. *J. Exp. Med.* **182,** 1111–1119.
88. Hao, Q.L., Zhu, J., Price, M.A., Payne, K.J., Barsky, L.W., and Crooks, G.M. (2001). Identification of a novel, human multilymphoid progenitor in cord blood. *Blood* **97,** 3683–3690.
89. Sallusto, F., and Lanzavecchia, A. (1994). Efficient presentation of soluble antigen by cultured human dendritic cells is maintained by granulocyte–macrophage colony-stimulating factor plus interleukin 4 and down-regulated by tumor necrosis factor alpha. *J. Exp. Med.* **179,** 1109–1118.
90. Randolph, G.J., Beaulieu, S., Lebecque, S., Steinman, R.M., and Muller, W.A. (1998). Differentiation of monocytes into dendritic cells in a model of transendothelial trafficking. *Science* **282,** 480–483.
91. Romani, N., Gruner, S., Brang, D., Kampgen, E., Lenz, A., Trockenbacher, B., Konwalinka, G., Fritsch, P.O., Steinman, R.M., and Schuler, G. (1994). Proliferating dendritic cell progenitors in human blood. *J. Exp. Med.* **180,** 83–93.
92. Grouard, G., Rissoan, M.C., Filgueira, L., Durand, I., Banchereau, J., and Liu, Y.J. (1997). The enigmatic plasmacytoid T-cells develop into dendritic cells with interleukin (IL) 3 and CD40-ligand. *J. Exp. Med.* **185,** 1101–1111.
93. Cella, M., Jarrossay, D., Facchetti, F., Alebardi, O., Nakajima, H., Lanzavecchia, A., and Colonna, M. (1999). Plasmacytoid monocytes migrate to inflamed lymph nodes and produce large amounts of type I interferon. *Nat. Med.* **5,** 919–923.
94. Kadowaki, N., Antonenko, S., Lau, J.Y., and Liu, Y.J. (2000). Natural interferon α–β-producing cells link innate and adaptive immunity. *J. Exp. Med.* **192,** 219–226.
95. Kadowaki, N., Ho, S., Antonenko, S., Malefyt, R.W., Kastelein, R.A., Bazan, F., and Liu, Y.J. (2001). Subsets of human dendritic cell precursors express different toll-like receptors and respond to different microbial antigens. *J. Exp. Med.* **194,** 863–869.
96. Jarrossay, D., Napolitani, G., Colonna, M., Sallusto, F., and Lanzavecchia, A. (2001). Specialization and complementarity in microbial molecule recognition by human myeloid and plasmacytoid dendritic cells. *Eur. J. Immunol.* **31,** 3388–3393.
97. Nakano, H., Yanagita, M., and Gunn, M.D. (2001). CD11c(+)B220(+)Gr-1(+) cells in mouse lymph nodes and spleen display characteristics of plasmacytoid dendritic cells. *J. Exp. Med.* **194,** 1171–1178.
98. Asselin-Paturel, C., Boonstra, A., Dalod, M., Durand, I., Yessaad, N., Dezutter-Dambuyant, C., Vicari, A., O'Garra, A., Biron, C., Briere, F., and Trinchieri, G.. (2001). Mouse type I IFN-producing cells are immature APCs with plasmacytoid morphology. *Nat. Immunol.* **2,** 1144–1150.
99. Bjorck, P. (2001). Isolation and characterization of plasmacytoid dendritic cells from Flt3 ligand and granulocyte–macrophage colony-stimulating factor-treated mice. *Blood* **98,** 3520–3526.
100. Liu, Y.J. (2001). Dendritic cell subsets and lineages, and their functions in innate and adaptive immunity. *Cell* **106,** 259–262.
101. Olweus, J., Thompson, P.A., and Lund-Johansen, F. (1996). Granulocytic and monocytic differentiation of $CD34^{hi}$ cells is associated with distinct changes in the expression of the PU.1-regulated molecules, CD64, and macrophage colony-stimulating factor receptor. *Blood* **88,** 3741–3754.
102. Jaleco, A.C., Stegmann, A.P., Heemskerk, M.H., Couwenberg, F., Bakker, A.Q., Weijer, K., and Spits, H. (1999). Genetic modification of human B-cell development: B-cell development is inhibited by the dominant negative helix–loop–helix factor Id3. *Blood* **94,** 2637–2646.
103. Heemskerk, M.H., Blom, B., Nolan, G., Stegmann, A.P., Bakker, A.Q., Weijer, K., Res, P.C., and Spits, H. (1997). Inhibition of T-cell and promotion of natural killer cell development by the dominant negative helix–loop–helix factor Id3. *J. Exp. Med.* **186,** 1597–1602.
104. Spits, H., Couwenberg, F., Bakker, A.Q., Weijer, K., and Uittenbogaart, C.H. (2000). Id2 and Id3 inhibit development of CD34(+) stem cells into predendritic cell (pre-DC) 2 but not into pre-DC1: Evidence for a lymphoid origin of pre-DC2. *J. Exp. Med.* **192,** 1775–1784.
105. Bendriss-Vermare, N., Barthelemy, C., Durand, I., Bruand, C., Dezutter-Dambuyant, C., Moulian, N., Berrih-Aknin, S., Caux, C., Trinchieri, G., and Briere, F. (2001). Human thymus contains IFN-α-producing CD11c(−), myeloid CD11c(+), and mature interdigitating dendritic cells. *J. Clin. Invest.* **107,** 835–844.
106. Traver, D., and Akashi, K. (Unpublished data).
107. Wu, L., Li, C.L., and Shortman, K. (1996). Thymic dendritic cell precursors: relationship to the T-lymphocyte lineage and phenotype of the dendritic cell progeny. *J. Exp. Med.* **184,** 903–911.
108. Iwasaki-Arai, J., Iwasaki, H., Miyamoto, T., Watanabe, S., and Akashi, K. (2003). Enforced GM-CSF signals do not support lymphopoiesis but instruct lymphoid to myelomonocytic lineage conversion. *J Exp Med.* (In press).
109. Weintraub, H. (1985). Assembly and propagation of repressed and depressed chromosomal states. *Cell* **42,** 705–711.
110. Kontaraki, J., Chen, H.H., Riggs, A., and Bonifer, C. (2000). Chromatin fine structure profiles for a developmentally regulated gene: reorganization of the lysozyme locus before trans-activator binding and gene expression. *Genes Dev.* **14,** 2106–2122.
111. Cross, M.A., and Enver, T. (1997). The lineage commitment of hemopoietic progenitor cells. *Curr. Opin. Genet. Dev.* **7,** 609–613.
112. Hu, M., Krause, D., Greaves, M., Sharkis, S., Dexter, M., Heyworth, C., and Enver, T. (1997). Multilineage gene expression precedes commitment in the hemopoietic system. *Genes Dev.* **11,** 774–785.
113. Akashi, K., He, X., Chen, J., Iwasaki, H., Niu, C., Steenhard, B., Zhang, J., Haug, J., and Li, L. (2003). Transcriptional accessibility for genes of multiple tissues and hematopoietic lineages is hierarchically controlled during early hematopoiesis. *Blood* **101,** 383–389.
114. Orlic, D., Kajstura, J., Chimenti, S., Jakoniuk, I., Anderson, S.M., Li, B., Pickel, J., McKay, R., Nadal-Ginard, B., Bodine, D.M., Leri, A., and Anversa, P. (2001). Bone marrow cells regenerate infarcted myocardium. *Nature* **410,** 701–705.
115. LaBarge, M.A., and Blau, H.M. (2002). Biological progression from adult bone marrow to mononucleate muscle stem cell to multinucleate muscle fiber in response to injury. *Cell* **111,** 589–601.
116. Priller, J., Flugel, A., Wehner, T., Boentert, M., Haas, C.A., Prinz, M., Fernandez-Klett, F., Prass, K., Bechmann, I., de Boer, B.A., Frotscher, M., Kreutzberg, G.W., Persons, D.A.,

and Dirnagl, U. (2001). Targeting gene-modified hematopoietic cells to the central nervous system: Use of green fluorescent protein uncovers microglial engraftment. *Nat. Med.* **7,** 1356–1361.

117. Lagasse, E., Connors, H., Al-Dhalimy, M., Reitsma, M., Dohse, M., Osborne, L., Wang, X., Finegold, M., Weissman, I.L., and Grompe, M. (2000). Purified hematopoietic stem cells can differentiate into hepatocytes *in vivo*. *Nat. Med.* **6,** 1229–1234.
118. Krause, D.S., Theise, N.D., Collector, M.I., Henegariu, O., Hwang, S., Gardner, R., Neutzel, S., and Sharkis, S.J. (2001). Multiorgan, multilineage engraftment by a single bone marrow-derived stem cell. *Cell* **105,** 369–377.
119. Terada, N., Hamazaki, T., Oka, M., Hoki, M., Mastalerz, D.M., Nakano, Y., Meyer, E.M., Morel, L., Petersen, B.E., and Scott, E.W. (2002). Bone marrow cells adopt the phenotype of other cells by spontaneous cell fusion. *Nature* **416,** 542–545.
120. Ying, Q.L., Nichols, J., Evans, E.P., and Smith, A.G. (2002). Changing potency by spontaneous fusion. *Nature* **416,** 545–548.
121. Lemischka, I. (2002). Rethinking somatic stem cell plasticity. *Nat. Biotechnol.* **20,** 425.
122. McKay, R. (2002). A more astonishing hypothesis. *Nat. Biotechnol.* **20,** 426–427.
123. Scott, E.W., Simon, M.C., Anastasi, J., and Singh, H. (1994). Requirement of transcription factor PU.1 in the development of multiple hematopoietic lineages. *Science* **265,** 1573–1577.
124. McKercher, S.R., Torbett, B.E., Anderson, K.L., Henkel, G.W., Vestal, D.J., Baribault. H., Klemsz, M., Feeney, A.J., Wu, G.E., Paige, C.J., and Maki, R.A. (1996). Targeted disruption of the PU.1 gene results in multiple hematopoietic abnormalities. *EMBO J.* **15,** 5647–5658.
125. Romeo, P.H., Prandini, M.H., Joulin, V., Mignotte, V., Prenant, M., Vainchenker, W., Marguerie, G., and Uzan, G. (1990). Megakaryocytic and erythrocytic lineages share specific transcription factors. *Nature* **344,** 447–449.
126. Shivdasani, R.A., Rosenblatt, M.F., Zucker-Franklin, D., Jackson, C.W., Hunt, P., Saris, C.J., and Orkin, S.H. (1995). Transcription factor NF-E2 is required for platelet formation independent of the actions of thrombopoietin–MGDF in megakaryocyte development. *Cell* **81,** 695–704.
127. Faust, N., Varas, F., Kelly, L.M., Heck, S., and Graf, T. (2000). Insertion of enhanced green fluorescent protein into the lysozyme gene creates mice with green fluorescent granulocytes and macrophages. *Blood* **96,** 719–726.
128. Zhang, D.E., Zhang, P., Wang, N.D., Hetherington, C.J., Darlington, G.J., and Tenen, D.G. (1997). Absence of granulocyte colony-stimulating factor signaling and neutrophil development in CCAAT enhancer binding protein-α– deficient mice. *Proc. Natl. Acad. Sci. U. S. A.* **94,** 569–574.
129. Sieweke, M.H., Tekotte, H., Frampton, J., and Graf, T. (1996). MafB is an interaction partner and repressor of Ets-1 that inhibits erythroid differentiation. *Cell* **85,** 49–60.
130. Zhang, P., Zhang, X., Iwama, A., Yu, C., Smith, K.A., Mueller, B.U., Narravula, S., Torbett, B.E., Orkin, S.H., and Tenen, D.G.. (2000). PU.1 inhibits Gata1 function and erythroid differentiation by blocking Gata1 DNA binding. *Blood* **96,** 2641–2648.
131. Kulessa, H., Frampton, J., and Graf, T. (1995). Gata1 reprograms avian myelomonocytic cell lines into eosinophils, thromboblasts, and erythroblasts. *Genes Dev.* **9,** 1250–1262.
132. DeKoter, R.P., and Singh, H. (2000). Regulation of B-lymphocyte and -macrophage development by graded expression of PU.1. *Science* **288,** 1439–1441.
133. Scott, E.W., Fisher, R.C., Olson, M.C., Kehrli, E.W., Simon, M.C., and Singh, H. (1997). PU.1 functions in a cell-autonomous manner to control the differentiation of multipotential lymphoid–myeloid progenitors. *Immunity* **6,** 437–447.
134. Nerlov, C., and Graf, T. (1998). PU.1 induces myeloid lineage commitment in multipotent hematopoietic progenitors. *Genes Dev.* **12,** 2403–2412.
135. Nerlov, C., McNagny, K.M., Doderlein, G., Kowenz-Leutz, E., and Graf, T. (1998). Distinct C–EBP functions are required for eosinophil lineage commitment and maturation. *Genes Dev.* **12,** 2413–2423.
136. Rothenberg, E.V., and Dionne, C.J. (2002). Lineage plasticity and commitment in T-cell development. *Immunol. Rev.* **187,** 96–115.
137. Tenen, D.G., Hromas, R., Licht, J.D., and Zhang, D.E. (1997). Transcription factors, normal myeloid development, and leukemia. *Blood* **90,** 489–519.
138. von Freeden-Jeffry, U., Solvason, N., Howard, M., and Murray, R. (1997). The earliest T-lineage-committed cells depend on IL7 for Bcl2 expression and normal cell cycle progression. *Immunity* **7,** 147–154.
139. Colucci, F., Samson, S.I., DeKoter, R.P., Lantz, O., Singh, H., and Di Santo, J.P. (2001). Differential requirement for the transcription factor PU.1 in the generation of natural killer cells versus B- and T-cells. *Blood* **97,** 2625–2632.
140. Fujiwara, Y., Browne, C.P., Cunniff, K., Goff, S.C., and Orkin, S.H. (1996). Arrested development of embryonic red cell precursors in mouse embryos lacking transcription factor Gata1. *Proc. Natl. Acad. Sci. U. S. A.* **93,** 12,355–12,358.
141. Shivdasani, R.A., Fujiwara, Y., McDevitt, M.A., and Orkin, S.H. (1997). A lineage-selective knockout establishes the critical role of transcription factor Gata1 in megakaryocyte growth and platelet development. *EMBO J.* **16,** 3965–3973.
142. Graf, T. (2002). Differentiation plasticity of hematopoietic cells. *Blood* **99,** 3089–3101.
143. Iwasaki, H., Mizuno, S., and Akashi, K. (2002). Gata1 converts lymphoid and myelomonocytic progenitors into the megakaryocyte–erythroid lineages. *Blood* **100,** 258a.
144. Zhang, P., Behre, G., Pan, J., Iwama, A., Wara-Aswapati, N., Radomska, H.S., Auron, P.E., Tenen, D.G., and Sun, Z. (1999). Negative cross-talk between hematopoietic regulators: Gata proteins repress PU.1. *Proc. Natl. Acad. Sci. U. S. A.* **96,** 8705–8710.
145. Nerlov, C., Querfurth, E., Kulessa, H., and Graf, T. (2000). Gata1 interacts with the myeloid PU.1 transcription factor and represses PU.1-dependent transcription. *Blood* **95,** 2543–2551.
146. Chen, H., Ray-Gallet, D., Zhang, P., Hetherington, C.J., Gonzalez, D.A., Zhang, D.E., Moreau-Gachelin, F., and Tenen, D.G. (1995). PU.1 (Spi-1) autoregulates its expression in myeloid cells. *Oncogene* **11,** 1549–1560.
147. Anderson, M.K., Weiss, A.H., Hernandez-Hoyos, G., Dionne, C.J., and Rothenberg, E.V. (2002). Constitutive expression of PU.1 in fetal hematopoietic progenitors blocks T-cell development at the pro-T-cell stage. *Immunity* **16,** 285–296.
148. Boyd, A.W., and Schrader, J.W. (1982). Derivation of macrophage-like lines from the pre-B-lymphoma ABLS 8.1 using 5-azacytidine. *Nature* **297,** 691–693.
149. Klinken, S.P., Alexander, W.S., and Adams, J.M. (1988). Hemopoietic lineage switch: v-Raf oncogene converts Emu–Myc transgenic B-cells into macrophages. *Cell* **53,** 857–867.

150. Lindeman, G.J., Adams, J.M., Cory, S., and Harris, A.W. (1994). B-lymphoid to granulocytic switch during hematopoiesis in a transgenic mouse strain. *Immunity* **1,** 517–527.
151. Cheng, G.Y., Minden, M.D., Toyonaga, B., Mak, T.W., and McCulloch, E.A. (1986). T-cell receptor and immunoglobulin gene rearrangements in acute myeloblastic leukemia. *J. Exp. Med.* **163,** 414–424.
152. Grogan, T.M., Durie, B.G., Spier, C.M., Richter, L., and Vela, E. (1989). Myelomonocytic antigen positive multiple myeloma. *Blood* **73,** 763–769.
153. Akashi, K., Harada, M., Shibuya, T., Fukagawa, K., Kimura, N., Sagawa, K., Yoshikai, Y., Teshima, T., Kikuchi, M., and Niho, Y. (1991). Simultaneous occurrence of myelomonocytic leukemia and multiple myeloma: involvement of common leukemic progenitors and their developmental abnormality of "lineage infidelity." *J. Cell Physiol.* **148,** 446–456.
154. Stass, S., Mirro, J., Melvin, S., Pui, C.H., Murphy, S.B., and Williams, D. (1984). Lineage switch in acute leukemia. *Blood* **64,** 701–706.
155. Murphy, S.B., Stass, S., Kalwinsky, D., and Rivera, G. (1983). Phenotypic conversion of acute leukemia from T-lymphoblastic to -myeloblastic induced by therapy with 2′-deoxycoformycin. *Br. J. Haematol.* **55,** 285–293.
156. Smith, L.J., Curtis, J.E., Messner, H.A., Senn, J.S., Furthmayr, H., and McCulloch, E.A. (1983). Lineage infidelity in acute leukemia. *Blood* **61,** 1138–1145.
157. McCulloch, E.A. (1987). Lineage infidelity or lineage promiscuity? *Leukemia* **1,** 235.
158. Lieschke, G.J., Grail, D., Hodgson, G., Metcalf, D., Stanley, E., Cheers, C., Fowler, K.J., Basu, S., Zhan, Y.F., and Dunn, A.R. (1994). Mice lacking granulocyte colony-stimulating factor have chronic neutropenia, granulocyte and macrophage progenitor cell deficiency, and impaired neutrophil mobilization. *Blood* **84,** 1737–1746.
159. Stanley, E., Lieschke, G.J., Grail, D., Metcalf, D., Hodgson, G., Gall, J.A., Maher, D.W., Cebon, J., Sinickas, V., and Dunn, A.R. (1994). Granulocyte–macrophage colony-stimulating factor-deficient mice show no major perturbation of hematopoiesis but develop a characteristic pulmonary pathology. *Proc. Natl. Acad. Sci. U. S. A.* **91,** 5592–5596.
160. Gillessen, S., Mach, N., Small, C., Mihm, M., and Dranoff, G. (2001). Overlapping roles for granulocyte–macrophage colony-stimulating factor and interleukin 3 in eosinophil homeostasis and contact hypersensitivity. *Blood* **97,** 922–928.
161. Wu, H., Liu, X., Jaenisch, R., and Lodish, H.F. (1995). Generation of committed erythroid BFU-E and CFU-E progenitors does not require erythropoietin or the erythropoietin receptor. *Cell* **83,** 59–67.
162. Nishijima, I., Nakahata, T., Hirabayashi, Y., Inoue, T., Kurata, H., Miyajima, A., Hayashi, N., Iwakura, Y., Arai, K., and Yokota, T. (1995). A human GM-CSF receptor expressed in transgenic mice stimulates proliferation and differentiation of hemopoietic progenitors to all lineages in response to human GM-CSF. *Mol. Biol. Cell* **6,** 497–508.
163. Yang, F.C., Watanabe, S., Tsuji, K., Xu, M.J., Kaneko, A., Ebihara, Y., and Nakahata, T. (1998). Human granulocyte colony-stimulating factor (G-CSF) stimulates the *in vitro* and *in vivo* development but not commitment of primitive multipotential progenitors from transgenic mice expressing the human G-CSF receptor. *Blood* **92,** 4632–4640.
164. Yang, F.C., Tsuji, K., Oda, A., Ebihara, Y., Xu, M.J., Kaneko, A., Hanada, S., Mitsui, T., Kikuchi, A., Manabe, A., Watanabe, S., Ikeda, Y., and Nakahata, T. (1999). Differential effects of human granulocyte colony-stimulating factor (hG-CSF) and thrombopoietin on megakaryopoiesis and platelet function in hG-CSF receptor-transgenic mice. *Blood* **94,** 950–958.
165. Takagi, M., Hara, T., Ichihara, M., Takatsu, K., and Miyajima, A. (1995). Multicolony-stimulating activity of interleukin 5 (IL5) on hematopoietic progenitors from transgenic mice that express IL5 receptor alpha subunit constitutively. *J. Exp. Med.* **181,** 889–899.
166. Pharr, P.N., Hankins, D., Hofbauer, A., Lodish, H.F., and Longmore, G.D. (1993). Expression of a constitutively active erythropoietin receptor in primary hematopoietic progenitors abrogates erythropoietin dependence and enhances erythroid colony-forming unit, erythroid burst-forming unit, and granulocyte–macrophage progenitor growth. *Proc. Natl. Acad. Sci. U. S. A.* **90,** 938–942.
167. Semerad, C.L., Poursine-Laurent, J., Liu, F., and Link, D.C. (1999). A role for G-CSF receptor signaling in the regulation of hematopoietic cell function but not lineage commitment or differentiation. *Immunity* **11,** 153–161.
168. King, A.G., Kondo, M., Scherer, D.C., and Weissman, I.L. (2002). Lineage infidelity in myeloid cells with TCR gene rearrangement: a latent developmental potential of pro-T-cells revealed by ectopic cytokine receptor signaling. *Proc. Natl. Acad. Sci. U. S. A.* **99,** 4508–4513.
169. Kondo, M., Scherer, D.C., Miyamoto, T., King, A.G., Akashi, K., Sugamura, K., and Weissman, I.L. (2000). Cell fate conversion of lymphoid-committed progenitors by instructive actions of cytokines. *Nature* **407,** 383–386.
170. Visvader, J.E., Elefanty, A.G., Strasser, A., and Adams, J.M. (1992). Gata1 but not SCL induces megakaryocytic differentiation in an early myeloid line. *EMBO J.* **11,** 4557–4564.
171. Seshasayee, D., Gaines, P., and Wojchowski, D.M. (1998). Gata1 dominantly activates a program of erythroid gene expression in factor-dependent myeloid FDCW2 cells. *Mol. Cell Biol.* **18,** 3278–3288.
172. Yamaguchi, Y., Zon, L.I., Ackerman, S.J., Yamamoto, M., and Suda, T. (1998). Forced Gata1 expression in the murine myeloid cell line M1: induction of c-Mpl expression and megakaryocytic–erythroid differentiation. *Blood* **91,** 450–457.
173. Heyworth, C., Pearson, S., May, G., and Enver, T. (2002). Transcription factor-mediated lineage switching reveals plasticity in primary committed progenitor cells. *EMBO J.* **21,** 3770–3781.
174. Iwasaki, H., and Akashi, K. (Unpublished results).
175. Hirasawa, R., Shimizu, R., Takahashi, S., Osawa, M., Takayanagi, S., Kato, Y., Onodera, M., Minegishi, N., Yamamoto, M., Fukao, K., Taniguchi, H., Nakauchi, H., and Iwama, A. (2002). Essential and instructive roles of Gata factors in eosinophil development. *J. Exp. Med.* **195,** 1379–1386.
176. Chen, D., and Zhang, G. (2001). Enforced expression of the Gata3 transcription factor affects cell fate decisions in hematopoiesis. *Exp. Hematol.* **29,** 971–980.
177. Holyoake, T.L., Nicolini, F.E., and Eaves, C.J. (1999). Functional differences between transplantable human hematopoietic stem cells from fetal liver, cord blood, and adult marrow. *Exp. Hematol.* **27,** 1418–1427.
178. Jordan, C.T., Astle, C.M., Zawadzki, J., Mackarehtschian, K., Lemischka, I.R., and Harrison, D.E. (1995). Long-term repopulating abilities of enriched fetal liver stem cells measured by competitive repopulation. *Exp. Hematol.* **23,** 1011–1015.

179. Pawliuk, R., Eaves, C., and Humphries, R.K. (1996). Evidence of both ontogeny and transplant dose-regulated expansion of hematopoietic stem cells *in vivo*. *Blood* **88,** 2852–2858.
180. Morrison, S.J., Hemmati, H.D., Wandycz, A.M., and Weissman, I.L. (1995). The purification and characterization of fetal liver hematopoietic cells. *Proc. Natl. Acad. Sci. U. S. A.* **92,** 10,302–10,306.
181. Ikuta, K., Kina, T., MacNeil, I., Uchida, N., Peault, B., Chien, Y.H., and Weissman, I.L. (1990). A developmental switch in thymic lymphocyte maturation potential occurs at the level of hematopoietic stem cells. *Cell* **62,** 863–874.
182. Hayakawa, K., and Hardy, R.R. (2000). Development and function of B-1 cells. *Curr. Opin. Immunol.* **12,** 346–353.
183. Mebius, R.E., Miyamoto, T., Christensen, J., Domen, J., Cupedo, T., Weissman, I.L., and Akashi, K. (2001). The fetal liver counterpart of adult common lymphoid progenitors gives rise to all lymphoid lineages, CD45+CD4+CD3– cells, as well as macrophages. *J. Immunol.* **166,** 6593–6601.
184. Traver, D., Miyamoto, T., Christensen, J., Iwasaki-Arai, J., Akashi, K., and Weissman, I.L. (2001). Fetal liver myelopoiesis occurs through distinct, prospectively isolatable progenitor subsets. *Blood* **98,** 627–635.
185. Lacaud, G., Carlsson, L., and Keller, G. (1998). Identification of a fetal hematopoietic precursor with B-cell, T-cell, and macrophage potential. *Immunity* **9,** 827–838.
186. Cumano, A., Paige, C.J., Iscove, N.N., and Brady, G. (1992). Bipotential precursors of B-cells and -macrophages in murine fetal liver. *Nature* **356,** 612–615.
187. Sagara, S., Sugaya, K., Tokoro, Y., Tanaka, S., Takano, H., Kodama, H., Nakauchi, H., and Takahama, Y. (1997). B220 expression by T-lymphoid progenitor cells in mouse fetal liver. *J. Immunol.* **158,** 666–676.
188. Domen, J., Gandy, K.L., and Weissman, I.L. (1998). Systemic overexpression of Bcl2 in the hematopoietic system protects transgenic mice from the consequences of lethal irradiation. *Blood* **91,** 2272–2282.
189. DiMartino, J.F., Selleri, L., Traver, D., Firpo, M.T., Rhee, J., Warnke, R., O'Gorman, S., Weissman, I.L., and Cleary, M.L. (2001). The Hox cofactor and proto-oncogene Pbx1 is required for maintenance of definitive hematopoiesis in the fetal liver. *Blood* **98,** 618–626.
190. Iwasaki-Arai, J., Pu, Z., Huettner, C.S., Fenyus, M., Lekstrom-Himes, J., Tenen, D.G., and Akashi, K. (2002). C/EBPα deficiency in hematopoiesis induces accumulation of non-malignant myeloblasts mimicking acute myelogenous leukemia. *Blood* **100,** 218a.
191. Wang, N.D., Finegold, M.J., Bradley, A., Ou, C.N., Abdelsayed, S.V., Wilde, M.D., Taylor, L.R., Wilson, D.R., and Darlington, G.J. (1995). Impaired energy homeostasis in C–EBP-α knockout mice. *Science* **269,** 1108–1112.
192. Iwasaki-Arai, J., and Akashi, K. (Unpublished results).
193. Civin, C.I., Strauss, L.C., Brovall, C., Fackler, M.J., Schwartz, J.F., and Shaper, J.H. (1984). Antigenic analysis of hematopoiesis — III: A hematopoietic progenitor cell surface antigen defined by a monoclonal antibody raised against KG-1a cells. *J. Immunol.* **133,** 157–165.
194. Okuno, Y., Huettner, C.S., Radomska, H.S., Petkova, V., Iwasaki, H., Akashi, K., and Tenen, D.G. (2002). Distal elements are critical for human CD34 expression *in vivo*. *Blood* **22,** 22.
195. Terstappen, L.W., Huang, S., Safford, M., Lansdorp, P.M., and Loken, M.R. (1991). Sequential generations of hematopoietic colonies derived from single nonlineage-committed CD34+ CD38– progenitor cells. *Blood* **77,** 1218–1227.
196. Baum, C.M., Weissman, I.L., Tsukamoto, A.S., Buckle, A.M., and Peault, B. (1992). Isolation of a candidate human hematopoietic stem cell population. *Proc. Natl. Acad. Sci. U. S. A.* **89,** 2804–2808.
197. Berardi, A.C., Meffre, E., Pflumio, F., Katz, A., Vainchenker, W., Schiff, C., and Coulombel, L. (1997). Individual CD34+ CD38lowCD19–CD10– progenitor cells from human cord blood generate B-lymphocytes and -granulocytes. *Blood* **89,** 3554–3564.
198. Hao, Q.L., Smogorzewska, E.M., Barsky, L.W., and Crooks, G.M. (1998). *In vitro* identification of single CD34+CD38– cells with both lymphoid and myeloid potential. *Blood* **91,** 4145–4151.
199. Miller, J.S., McCullar, V., Punzel, M., Lemischka, I.R., and Moore, K.A. (1999). Single adult human CD34(+)/Lin–/CD38(–) progenitors give rise to natural killer cells, B-lineage cells, dendritic cells, and myeloid cells. *Blood* **93,** 96–106.
200. Galy, A., Travis, M., Cen, D., and Chen, B. (1995). Human T-, B-, natural killer, and dendritic cells arise from a common bone marrow progenitor cell subset. *Immunity* **3,** 459–473.
201. Lansdorp, P.M., Sutherland, H.J., and Eaves, C.J. (1990). Selective expression of CD45 isoforms on functional subpopulations of CD34+ hemopoietic cells from human bone marrow. *J. Exp. Med.* **172,** 363–366.
202. Fritsch, G., Buchinger, P., Printz, D., Fink, F.M., Mann, G., Peters, C., Wagner, T., Adler, A., and Gadner, H. (1993). Rapid discrimination of early CD34+ myeloid progenitors using CD45RA analysis. *Blood* **81,** 2301–2309.
203. Olweus, J., Lund-Johansen, F., and Terstappen, L.W.. (1995). CD64–Fc gamma RI is a granulo–monocytic lineage marker on CD34+ hematopoietic progenitor cells. *Blood* **85,** 2402–2413.
204. Rappold, I., Ziegler, B.L., Kohler, I., Marchetto, S., Rosnet, O., Birnbaum, D., Simmons, P.J., Zannettino, A.C., Hill, B., Neu, S., Knapp, W., Alitalo, R., Alitalo, K., Ullrich, A., Kanz, L., and Buhring, H.J. (1997). Functional and phenotypic characterization of cord blood and bone marrow subsets expressing Flt3 (CD135) receptor tyrosine kinase. *Blood* **90,** 111–125.
205. de Wynter, E.A., Heyworth, C.M., Mukaida, N., Jaworska, Weffort-Santos, A., Matushima, K., and Testa, N.G. (2001). CCR1 chemokine receptor expression isolates erythroid from granulocyte–macrophage progenitors. *J. Leukoc. Biol.* **70,** 455–460.
206. Kimura, T., Sakabe, H., Tanimukai, S., Abe, T., Urata, Y., Yasukawa, K., Okano, A., Taga, T., Sugiyama, H., Kishimoto, T., and Sonoda, Y. (1997). Simultaneous activation of signals through gp130, c-Kit, and interleukin 3 receptor promotes a trilineage blood cell production in the absence of terminally acting lineage-specific factors. *Blood* **90,** 4767–4778.
207. Huang, S., Chen, Z., Yu, J.F., Young, D., Bashey, A., Ho, A.D., and Law, P. (1999). Correlation between IL3 receptor expression and growth potential of human CD34+ hematopoietic cells from different tissues. *Stem Cells* **17,** 265–272.
208. Manz, M.G., Miyamoto, T., Akashi, K., and Weissman, I.L. (2002). Prospective isolation of human clonogenic common myeloid progenitors. *Proc. Natl. Acad. Sci. U. S. A.* **99,** 11,872–11,877.
209. Link, H., Arseniev, L., Bahre, O., Kadar, J.G., Diedrich, H., and Poliwoda, H. (1996). Transplantation of allogeneic CD34+ blood cells. *Blood* **87,** 4903–4909.
210. BitMansour, A., Burns, S.M., Traver, D., Akashi, K., Contag, C.H., Weissman, I.L., and Brown, J.M. (2002). Myeloid

progenitors protect against invasive aspergillosis and *Pseudomonas aeruginosa* infection following hematopoietic stem cell transplantation. *Blood* **100,** 4660–4660.

211. Arber, C., BitMansour, A., Sparer, T.E., Higgins, J.P., Mocarski, E.S., Weissman, I.L., Shizuru, J.A., and Brown, J.M. (2003). Common lymphoid progenitors rapidly engraft and protect against lethal murine cytomegalovirus infection after hematopoietic stem cell transplantation. *Blood* **102,** 421–428.

212. Allman, D., Sambandam, A., Kim, S., Miller, J..P., Pagan, A., Well, D., Meraz, A., and Bhandoola, A. (2003). Thymopoiesis independent of common lymphoid progenitors. *Nat. Immunol.* **4,** 168–174.

35

Molecular and Cellular Pathways Involved in the Recruitment of Proangiogenic Stem Cells from Bone Marrow Microenvironments

Shahin Rafii, Scott T. Avecilla, Rafael Tejada, David K. Jin, and Sergey V. Shmelkov

Self-renewal and differentiation of stem cells is regulated through interaction with cytokines and microenvironmental cues. Although much is known about the cytokines that modulate survival and lineage-specific differentiation of stem cells, the identities of the factors within the bone marrow microenvironments that modulate stem cell regeneration and differentiation remain unknown. Several lines of evidence suggest that most stem cells reside in the endosteal niche, where they are maintained in a quiescent state. Physiological stress including marrow suppression or activation of the angiogenic switch results in the plasma elevation of certain chemokines and angiogenic factors leading to the recruitment of stem cells. Angiogenic factors, such as placental growth factor (PlGF) and vascular endothelial growth factor A (VEGF-A), through interaction with their tyrosine kinase receptor, VEGFR1, induce expression of active matrix metalloproteinase-9 (MMP-9) in the marrow, mediating the release of stem cell active cytokines, such as soluble Kit-ligand. This increases motility of stem and progenitor cells by physically translocating them to the vascular niche. Localization of stem cells to the vascular niche favors differentiation, mobilization, and acceleration in the reconstitution of hematopoiesis. Identification of the cellular and molecular factors differentially expressed in the endosteal and vascular niche will increase our understanding of the mechanism or mechanisms involved in regulated proliferation and differentiation of stem cells.

Introduction

The signaling pathways involved in stem cell regeneration and lineage-specific differentiation have eluded scientists for decades. Stem cell proliferation and differentiation may be regulated either by the expression of certain stem cell-specific genes and/or molecular cues or by cellular instructions provided by a unique niche in which the stem cells are temporally localized. Accumulating evidence suggests that the factors released by the stem cells and the signaling cues conferred by the stem cell niches are essential in orchestrating stem cell survival, self-renewal, and accelerated differentiation during physiological stress.

Gene profiling studies have shown that the intrinsic molecular programming of hematopoietic stem cells (HSCs)[1,2] may play a critical role in stem cell self-regeneration and differentiation. Using differential gene display technology, clusters of genes selectively expressed on organ-specific stem cells have been identified. Nonetheless, expression and function of these stem cell-specific genes may be influenced by the microenvironment (niche) in which they reside.[3–5]

The concept of an HSC niche was introduced by Schofield,[6] who hypothesized that HSCs are fixed within a specific microenvironment, providing conditions conducive to the survival and differentiation of HSCs. Subsequently, it was demonstrated that the HSC niche may be physically localized primarily in the endosteal region of the bone marrow.[7] Repopulating HSCs, as represented by colony-forming unit–spleen (CFU-S), were shown to reside in high concentration near the endosteal region.[8,9] Subsequently, it was demonstrated that transplanted HSCs home to the endosteal region of the bone marrow;[10,11] where expression of hyaluronic acid may play a role in directing their localization to this region.[12] Based on these studies, it has become apparent that bone marrow may be functionally compartmentalized into defined niches. Expression of chemokines, tethered cytokines, or of yet unrecognized factors may provide "road maps" for the localization of stem cells within their respective marrow microenvironments.

The interest in studying the cellular and molecular mechanisms involved in the recruitment of stem cells from their niches has recently been ignited by reports that the marrow microenvironments provide a rich reservoir for organ-specific stem cells, including neuronal, cardiac, hepatic, and vascular progenitors. Mobilization of organ-specific stem cells has been shown to play a critical role in the regulation of various postnatal processes, including wound healing, organ regeneration,[13] and tumor growth.[14]

Clues to the cellular mediators involved in the recruitment of HSCs and endothelial progenitors emerged from studies

Handbook of Stem Cells
Volume 2

that demonstrated mobilization of HSCs and endothelial progenitors is critical for neoangiogenesis, as it may occur during tumor growth or wound healing. Angiogenic factors induce mobilization of HSCs and endothelial progenitors partly by activation of proteases. However, the precise mechanism whereby activation of certain proteases induces mobilization of stem cells has yet to be determined. In this regard, the interaction between angiogenic factors and the various cell types within the marrow has provided an instructive model for identifying molecular mediators that help to recruit stem cells from distinct marrow niches. In this chapter, we describe the mechanism by which angiogenic factors influence the localization of HSCs to various marrow niches, thereby facilitating their proliferation, differentiation, and recruitment to various tissues.

Roles of Bone Marrow-Derived Hematopoietic and Endothelial Stem and Progenitor Cells in the Regulation of Postnatal Neoangiogenesis

Bone marrow-derived, circulating endothelial progenitor cells have been shown to be recruited from the marrow to functionally contribute to neoangiogenesis during wound healing,[15–18] vascularization after myocardial ischemia[19–22] and limb ischemia,[23–25] endothelialization of vascular grafts,[26,27] atherosclerosis,[28] and retinal neovascularization.[29,30] The growth of certain tumors depends on the corecruitment of marrow-derived endothelial progenitor cells as well as subsets of hematopoietic cells to the tumor vasculature. The release of angiogenic factors by tumor cells is essential to induce timely mobilization of endothelial progenitors and hematopoietic cells stimulating tumor angiogenesis and growth.[16,31–36] Inhibition of the mobilization of the endothelial progenitors and hematopoietic cells results in growth retardation of certain tumors, underscoring the significance of marrow-derived cells in supporting tumor angiogenesis.

These data suggest that the release of angiogenic factors by tumor cells or injured tissue induces comobilization of marrow-derived endothelial and hematopoietic cells, promoting wound healing and tumor growth.[31] Therefore, these studies raise the intriguing possibility that angiogenic factors may convey signals for the reconstitution of postnatal hematopoiesis by recruiting, quiescent noncycling pluripotent HSCs from the various marrow microenvironments (Fig. 35–1). In addition, studying angiogenic factors, in particular VEGF, provides for a novel means of identifying the molecular and cellular pathways involved in the recruitment of hematopoietic and endothelial stem and progenitor cells.

VEGF Family of Angiogenic Factors

Within the VEGF family of cytokines, VEGF-A is the most potent mediator of the angiogenic switch.[37,38] VEGF-A exerts its effect through interaction with two tyrosine kinase receptors, VEGF receptor 1 (VEGFR1 or Flt1) and VEGF receptor 2 (VEGFR2, Flk-1, or Kdr) (Fig. 35–2). PlGF and VEGF-B, the other members of the VEGF family, function as angiogenic amplifiers by signaling through VEGFR1.[39] Although VEGFR1 and VEGFR2 convey signals that regulate angiogenesis, their role in the regulation of hematopoietic reconstitution *in vivo* is not well characterized. VEGFR2 has been shown to be expressed on a primitive population of murine embryonic hematopoietic precursors.[40] Mice deficient in VEGFR2 display profound defects in vasculogenesis and hematopoiesis.[41,42] Because of early embryonic lethality, it has been difficult to assess whether VEGFR2 expression is absolutely essential in HSC proliferation, survival, or migration in adult mice. Similarly, as VEGFR1$^{-/-}$ mice die from vascular disorganization during early embryogenesis, the role of VEGFR1 in the regulation of hematopoiesis during late embryonic development has been difficult to evaluate.[43,44] In contrast, mice deficient in VEGFR1 intracellular kinase domain have no apparent hematopoietic defects, suggesting that VEGFR1 does not convey signals that regulate hematopoiesis.[45] However, few studies have evaluated the hematopoietic reconstitution in adult mice during myelosuppression or other physiological stresses. Because recent evidence suggests that VEGFR1 kinase-deficient mice have angiogenic defects,[46,47] it remains to be determined whether VEGFR1 kinase deficiency also results in defective hematopoietic reconstitution after myelosuppression.

Although the functional roles of VEGFR1 and VEGFR2 on the regulation of embryonic hematopoiesis remain unclear, several studies have shown that these VEGF receptors are likely expressed on postnatally derived hematopoietic cells. VEGFR2 has been shown to be expressed on human CD34$^+$ repopulating cells in nonobese-diabetic severe-combined immunodeficiency (NOD-SCID) mice.[48] However, murine marrow-derived VEGFR2$^+$ cells do not readily repopulate in lethally irradiated recipients.[49] In this regard, the functional role of VEGFR2 expression on murine HSCs in the regulation of postnatal hematological processes is as yet unknown.

Role of VEGFR1 Signaling in Recruitment of HSCs from Marrow Endosteal Niche

Several lines of evidence suggest that VEGFR1 may play an essential role in regulating specific aspects of adult hematopoiesis. Recently, functional VEGFR1 has been shown to be expressed on the mature lineage-committed myelomonocytic cells, conveying signals that support their migration *in vitro*[50–52] and *in vivo* studies.[39] Plasma elevation of VEGF-A stimulates hematopoiesis, under steady-state conditions, by mobilizing marrow repopulating cells.[53] In *Drosophila*, VEGF supports the motility of hemocytes,[54] cells that are ancestral homologues of murine and human hematopoietic cells. These data suggest that expression of VEGF receptors, in particular VEGFR1, may regulate hematopoiesis by increasing motility, thereby altering their localization to the various niches.

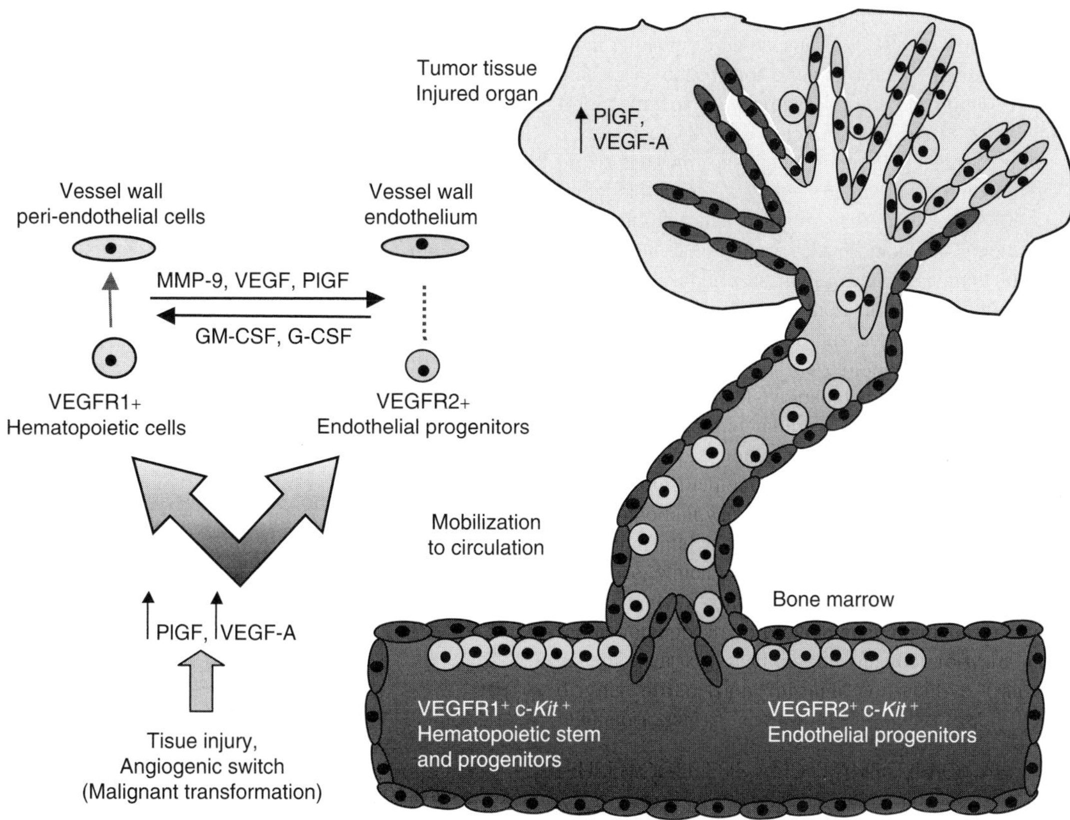

Figure 35–1. *Angiogenic switch and tissue injury promote mobilization of VEGFR1⁺ hematopoietic stem cells and VEGFR2⁺ endothelial progenitor cells.* Angiogenic switch turned on by malignant transformation, tissue injury, wound healing, organ regeneration, or other physiological processes results in the plasma elevation of angiogenic factors, including vascular endothelial growth factor (VEGF-A) and placental growth factor (PlGF). VEGF-A and PlGF, through activation of VEGFR1 expressed on c-kit⁺ HSCs and VEGFR2 expressed on c-kit⁺ endothelial progenitors, induce mobilization to the peripheral circulation where they incorporate into tumor tissue or regenerating organs. Cellular collaboration between hematopoietic and endothelial progenitors results in the functional incorporation of endothelial cells into the vessel wall. (Please see CD-ROM for color version of this figure.)

Activation of VEGFR1 Is Essential for Marrow Reconstitution and Hematopoietic Recovery

We have recently shown that functional VEGFR1 (Flt1) is expressed on a subpopulation of human CD34⁺ and murine Lin⁻Sca-1⁺c-kit⁺ marrow-repopulating stem cells, conveying signals for recruitment of HSCs and reconstitution of hematopoiesis.[55] Inhibition of VEGFR1, but not of VEGFR2, blocked the recruitment of HSCs from their resting microenvironment, thereby retarding hematopoietic reconstitution after myelosuppression (Figs. 35–3 and 35–4). Mice treated with 5-Fluorouracil (5FU) and neutralizing monoclonal antibody (mab) to VEGFR1 showed impaired trilineage cell recovery with prolonged pancytopenia, which resulted in the demise of 70% of treated mice kept under germ-free conditions. In myelosuppressed mice treated with mab to VEGFR1, most repopulating hematopoietic cells were found to be physically arrested in the endosteal region (Fig. 35–4). Therefore, plasma elevation of angiogenic factors, including PlGF and VEGF-A, after myelosuppression results in the activation of VEGFR1, leading to restoration of hematopoiesis.

How Do Angiogenic Factors Recruit VEGFR1⁺ HSCs from Bone Marrow Niches?

HSCs and endothelial progenitors reside in a marrow microenvironment where they can readily sense and respond to the stress-induced demands for supporting hematopoiesis and angiogenesis. To meet such high demands, rapid availability of cytokines is essential for the recruitment of quiescent HSCs and endothelial progenitors to a permissive niche, where they can proliferate, differentiate, and replenish the exhausted progenitor and precursor pool. It is conceivable that the release of cytokines or chemokines will recruit stem cells from their quiescent niche, such as the endosteal zone. An increase in the

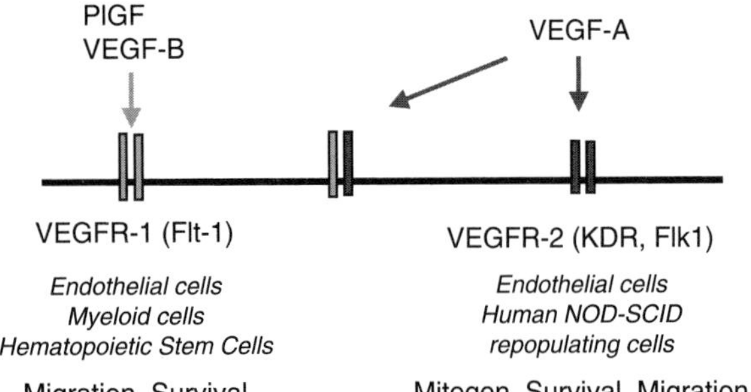

Figure 35–2. *Regulation of hematopoiesis and angiogenesis by VEGF receptors.* Expression of VEGFR2 is limited to endothelial cells conveying signals that support survival, motility, and proliferation. VEGFR2 may also be expressed on subsets of human NOD-SCID repopulating cells. VEGFR1 is expressed on both murine and human endothelial cells as well as on HSCs and mature hematopoietic cells, including monocytic cells. PlGF and VEGF promote the motility of HSCs through VEGFR1 activation. The function of VEGFR1 on endothelial cells is less well defined, but it may provide signals for the remodeling of developing vasculature. (Please see CD-ROM for color version of this figure.)

cell cycling and motility of HSCs and endothelial progenitors results in expression of adhesion molecules and other factors that facilitate their translocation to other permissive niches, which support their proliferation, differentiation, and mobilization to the peripheral circulation. Most evidence suggests that the localization of cycling stem and progenitor cells to the vascular-enriched microenvironment within the marrow supports their survival, differentiation, and mobilization. However, the precise mechanism whereby physiological stress modulates the translocation of stem cells among various niches remains unknown, and it is plausible that this may be mediated partly through the activation of angiogenic factors.

Angiogenic Factors Recruit HSCs Through Matrix Metalloprotinase Activation

Increased MMP-9 has been demonstrated in the serum of IL8-treated monkeys and was linked to the mobilization of progenitor cells by Pruijt *et al.*[56] These authors hypothesized

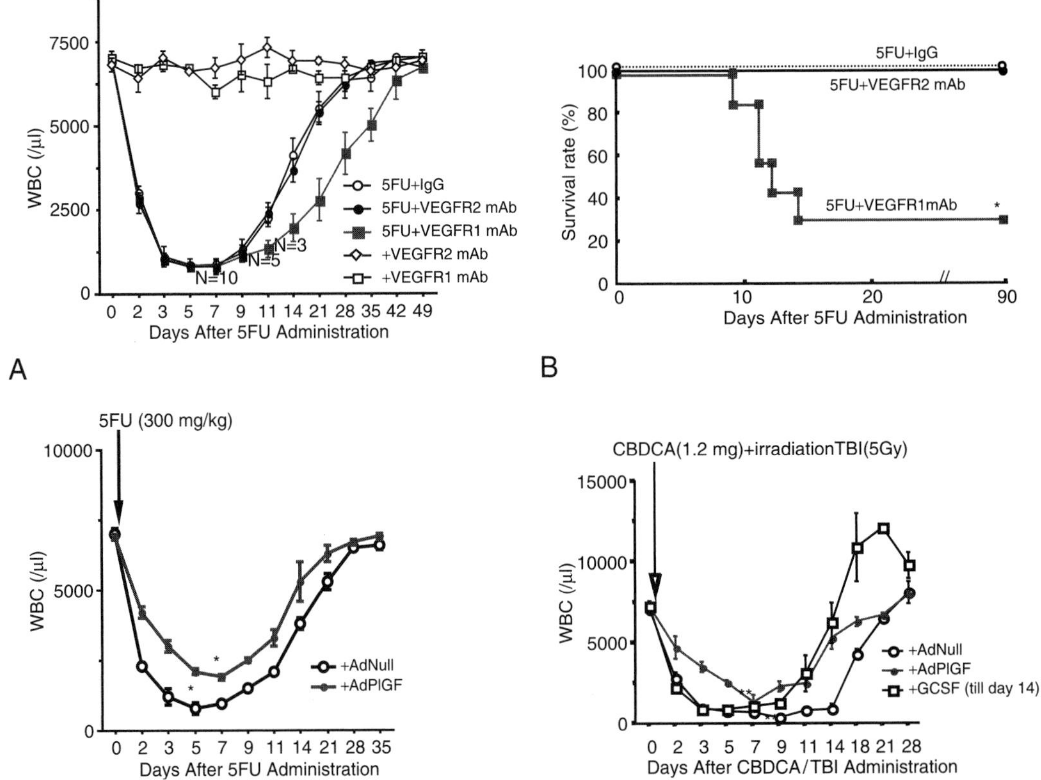

Figure 35–3. *Inhibition of VEGFR1, but not VEGFR2, after myelosuppression delays hematopoietic recovery and increases mortality of treated mice.* Myelosuppression was induced by a single dose of 5FU. Twelve 5FU-treated BALB/c mice in each group were injected intraperitoneally (i.p.) with neutralizing doses of mab to VEGFR1, VEGFR2, or IgG control (O) in two-day intervals starting from day 0. Groups of animals were treated with mab to VEGFR1 (□) and VEGFR2 (♦) alone. (a) White blood cells (WBCs) were quantified. (b) The survival rate was monitored daily. The survival rate was significantly lower in the VEGFR1-treated group than in the IgG-treated control group ($*P < 0.001$). Hematopoietic recovery following (c) a single dose of 5FU (n = 6) or (d) total body irradiation (TBI) plus carboplatin (n = 6) was followed by a single dose of adenovirus expressing either PlGF (AdPlGF, •) or no transgene (AdNull, O) on day 0. (d) Recombinant G-CSF (injected subcutaneously day 0–14, □) promotes rapid hematopoietic reconstitution. Extent and duration of WBCs < 2000/ml was significantly shorter in the AdPlGF-treated group than in the AdNull-treated 5FU- and carboplatin–irradiation-treated groups (c: $*P < 0.001$, and d: $*P < 0.005$). (Please see CD-ROM for color version of this figure.)

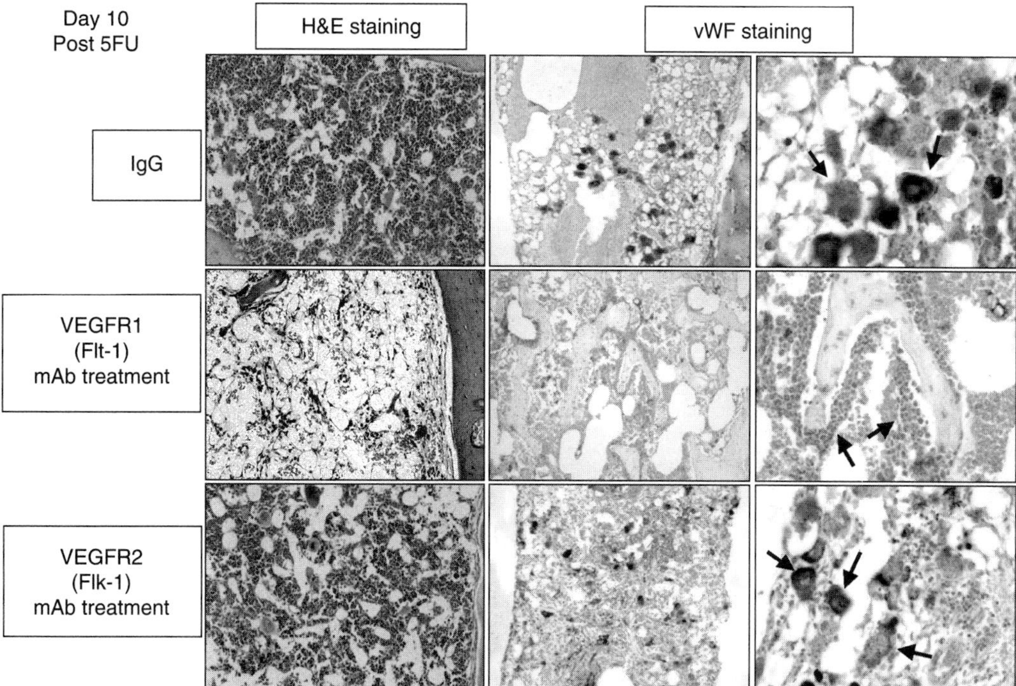

Figure 35–4. *Inhibition of VEGFR1 impairs recruitment of hematopoietic cells from the bone marrow endosteal region.* Treatment of wild-type mice depletes hematopoietic progenitors, resulting in the activation of signaling pathways that promote the recruitment of HSCs from the endosteal region of the bone marrow. Increased motility of regenerating HSCs or other hematopoietic cells reconstitutes hematopoiesis. Inhibition of VEGFR1 signaling, which partly blocks the motility of HSCs and progenitors, impairs the recruitment of HSCs from the endosteal niche. However, inhibition of VEGFR2 alone had a minimal effect on the reconstitution of hematopoiesis. (Please see CD-ROM for color version of this figure.)

that the IL8-induced activation of neutrophils generates high levels of MMP-9. In another report, intravenous injection of recombinant MMP-9 into rabbits produced a rapid and transient neutropenia followed by a profound neutrophilia and the appearance of immature myeloid cells, including myeloblasts.[57] Endothelial-active chemo–cytokines, including VEGF, and SDF-1 also induce mobilization of marrow-repopulating cells.[53,58] As mobilization of HSCs with repopulating potential was markedly impaired in mice treated with metalloproteinase inhibitor or in Mmp9$^{-/-}$ mice, we speculated that MMP-9 activation may contribute to angiogenic factor-mediated mobilization of HSCs.

In addition to remodeling the extracellular matrix, MMP-9 has been shown to cleave several cytokines, their receptors, or both, processes that can either activate or inactivate the cytokines.[59] A precedent for such a process is the MMP-9-induced VEGF-A release from the tethered pool within the microenvironment of developing bone[60] or within tumors of pancreatic islets.[61]

Clues to the mechanism MMP-9 uses to modulate recruitment of HSCs from the endosteal region originated from studies that demonstrated the levels of soluble Kit-ligand (sKitL) were decreased in Mmp9$^{-/-}$ mice—even after marrow suppression, when there is usually a rebound increase in sKitL levels.[62] Most sKitL is believed to be the product of the membrane-bound Kit-ligand (mKitL) expressed on the surface of various stromal cells within the bone marrow. Previous studies have shown that mKitL is a glycoprotein of 248 amino acids that is rapidly cleaved from the cell to release an active soluble protein, sKitL, of 164 amino acids. In contrast, a glycoprotein of 220 amino acids, which lacks the proteolytic cleavage site encoded by differentially spliced exon six sequences, remains predominantly membrane associated.[63] The only enzyme reported to date to cleave mKitL is a mast cell chymase.[64] The extracellular domain of mKitL has two potential consensus sequences that can be hydrolyzed by MMP-9.[65] The rapid increase in plasma sKitL levels in Mmp9$^{+/+}$ mice, and the relative deficiency of sKitL at baseline or after myelosuppression in Mmp9$^{-/-}$mice, strongly suggests that MMP-9 plays a physiological role in releasing sKitL, setting the stage for hematopoietic reconstitution. PlGF and VEGF promote the release of sKitL, an essential factor in the recruitment of HSCs from the endosteal region, through the activation of MMP-9.[62]

Angiogenic Factors Recruit HSCs and Endothelial Progenitors Through MMP-9-Mediated Cleavage of mKitL

To elucidate the mechanism angiogenic factors may reconstitute hematopoiesis, we took advantage of marrow reconstitution

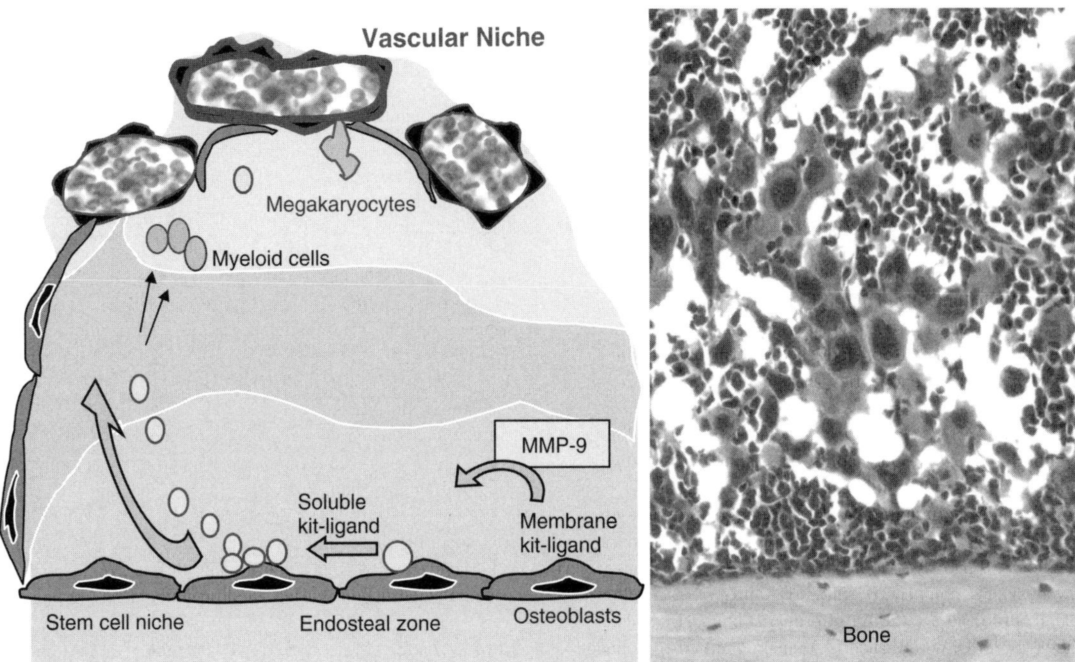

Figure 35–5. *Angiogenic factors promote hematopoiesis through the MMP-9-mediated release of sKitL.* Plasma elevation of angiogenic factors induced by angiogenic switch or bone marrow suppression results is up-regulation or activation of MMP-9. Mmp9 promotes the release of soluble Kit-ligand (sKitL), thereby inducing cycling of quiescent HSCs. An increase in the cell cycling of HSCs increases their motility, translocating them to a permissive vascular zone conducive to proliferation, differentiation, and mobilization to the peripheral circulation. (Please see CD-ROM for color version of this figure.)

after 5FU-induced marrow suppression. In this model, injection of 5FU results in the depletion of cycling hematopoietic cells followed by the release of specific chemokines and cytokines that promote recruitment of hibernating HSCs from the endosteal region. Because VEGFR1 is expressed on the hematopoietic cells, we examined the role of angiogenic factors that selectively bind to VEGFR1, specifically PlGF, in the recruitment of HSCs from the marrow's endosteal zone (Fig. 35–2). We demonstrated that PlGF augments early phases of hematopoietic recovery by promoting recruitment, chemotaxis, and mobilization of VEGFR1$^+$ HSCs and progenitors; during later phases of marrow recovery, PlGF-mediated up-regulation of MMP-9 facilitates the release of sKitL. These data suggest that PlGF activates nonangiogenic pathways and thus serves functions other than regulating angiogenesis.

PlGF reconstitutes hematopoiesis in a biphasic manner (Figs. 35–3 and 35–4). Chemotaxis of VEGFR1$^+$ HSCs and progenitors accounts for the increase in circulatory leukocytes in the early phase of PlGF-induced mobilization. PlGF mobilized CFU–cultures (CFU-Cs) and CFU-Ss in Mmp9$^{+/+}$ mice but to a lesser extent in Mmp9$^{-/-}$ mice. In later phases, PlGF-induced cell mobilization was impaired in Mmp9$^{-/-}$ mice, suggesting that PlGF recruits HSCs and progenitors by a different mechanism. Treatment of the myelosuppressed mice with neutralizing mab to VEGFR1 localized most hematopoietic cells to the endosteal region, with the paucity of cells in the more vascular-enriched zone of the marrow. PlGF through MMP-9 activation induces the release of sKitL, which through interaction with its receptor c-kit, increases mobilization by promoting cell cycle transition.[66,67] Activation of this pathway accounts for the hematopoietic reconstitution during later phases of marrow recovery. Neutralizing mab to VEGFR1 greatly diminished plasma elevation of sKitL in myelosuppressed mice during marrow recovery, and introducing sKitL into myelosuppressed mice treated with mab to VEGFR1 completely restored hematopoiesis. These data suggest that prototypic angiogenic factors, such as PlGF, through interaction of VEGFR1 induce the release of sKitL. This leads to an increase in the cycling of HSCs, facilitating their physical delivery to the marrow vascular zone, which is conducive to proliferation and differentiation of cycling HSCs (Fig. 35–5).

The increase in cell cycling and proliferation of VEGFR1$^+$Sca-1$^+$ cells after marrow suppression is most likely not a direct effect of PlGF, as the activation of VEGFR1 did not change HSC survival or colony formation *in vitro*. These data support other reports in which it was demonstrated that VEGF-A or PlGF had no major effect on the proliferation or survival of HSCs or progenitors.[68–70] However, it does not rule out the possibility that VEGF–VEGF-receptor internal autocrine signaling pathways may synergize with other cytokines to convey survival signals for repopulating cells. In fact, it has been recently demonstrated that intracine activity conferred by VEGFR1, VEGFR2, or both may play a critical role in the regulation of HSC survival and repopulating capacity.[71]

In humans, rapid marrow recovery after repetitive treatment with chemotherapeutic agents is essential to avoid morbidity and mortality secondary to prolonged marrow suppression. Life-threatening infections and bleeding are direct effects of prolonged chemotherapy-related neutropenia and thrombocytopenia. It is conceivable that chronic use of certain chemotherapeutic agents may alter MMP-9 secretion and activation; therefore, they may induce long-term marrow suppression or disrupt trafficking of HSCs, contributing to marrow failure. On the other hand, the inhibition of MMP-9 may provide a novel mechanism to regulate hematopoiesis in myeloproliferative disorders.

Summary

Adult bone marrow is functionally compartmentalized into several defined microenvironments or niches. The physical localization of HSCs and progenitors within each niche may dictate the proliferation and differentiation status of HSCs. During steady-state conditions, instruction for the localization of the HSCs to the various niches is most likely conferred by the distinct expression of chemokines and cytokines. Several lines of evidence suggest that the marrow's endosteal zone is permissive for the maintenance of HSCs. Physiological stress, such as marrow suppression or tumor growth, results in the release of angiogenic factors that support the recruitment of HSCs from the endosteal zone to the vascular-enriched zone (Fig. 35–5). Localization of the HSCs and their progenies to the marrow's vascular zone supports survival and differentiation.

Stem cell-active angiogenic factors, including the VEGF and PlGF released during marrow suppression or tumor growth, promote the recruitment of HSCs and progenitors from an endosteal marrow niche. VEGF and PlGF communicate with the VEGFR1$^+$ hematopoietic cells through the activation of MMP-9. The release of MMP-9 promotes the release of sKitL, which induces cycling and increased motility of HSCs, translocating them to a permissive vascular zone where they undergo proliferation and differentiation (Fig. 35–5).

Several antiangiogenic factors that may block VEGFR1 are being evaluated in both preclinical and clinical settings. Based on these data, the clinical use of neutralizing mab to VEGFR1 and, to a lesser degree, VEGFR2 delivered with myelosuppressive agents may result in prolonged marrow suppression. In this respect, suppression of hematopoiesis through VEGFR1 inhibition has two ramifications. On one hand, blocking VEGFR1 may inhibit tumor angiogenesis and growth; on the other hand, it may introduce untoward marrow toxicity. Nonetheless, because toxicity associated with VEGFR1 blockade is dose dependent, concurrent delivery of sKitL and lower-dose VEGFR1 inhibitors may reduce the marrow toxicity profile and therefore rescue patients from infection or hemorrhage. On the other hand, therapeutic strategies to up-regulate VEGFR1, PlGF, and MMP-9 may provide an effective means of restoring the motogenic potential of HSCs and endothelial progenitors and may help to replenish the stem cell pool after marrow–stem cell transplantation. Furthermore, PlGF and VEGF may be effective in restoring hematopoiesis after myelosuppression.

There is no doubt that many other stem cell-active cytokines, chemokines, and proteases may contribute to stem cell recruitment during steady state as well as during marrow recovery. Further studies are in progress to identify and study the functional roles of these stem cell-specific cytokines–chemokines in the context of their respective marrow microenvironments that support long-term proliferation and differentiation of HSCs and progenitor cells.

REFERENCES

1. Ivanova, N.B., Dimos, J.T., Schaniel, C., Hackney, J.A., Moore, K.A., and Lemischka, I.R. (2002). A stem cell molecular signature. *Science* **298,** 601–604.
2. Phillips, R.L., Ernst, R.E., Brunk, B., Ivanova, N., Mahan, M.A., Deanehan, J.K., Moore, K.A., Overton, G.C., and Lemischka, I.R. (2000). The genetic program of hematopoietic stem cells. *Science* **288,** 1635–1640.
3. Hackney, J.A., Charbord, P., Brunk, B.P., Stoeckert, C.J., Lemischka, I.R., and Moore, K.A. (2002). A molecular profile of a hematopoietic stem cell niche. *Proc. Natl. Acad. Sci. USA* **99,** 13,061–13,066.
4. Lin, H. (2002). The stem cell niche theory: lessons from flies. *Nat. Rev. Genet.* **3,** 931–940.
5. Spradling, A., Drummond-Barbosa, D., and Kai, T. Stem cells find their niche. (2001). *Nature* **414,** 98–104.
6. Schofield, R. (1978). The relationship between the spleen colony-forming cell and the haemopoietic stem cell. *Blood Cells* **4,** 7–25.
7. Gong, J.K. (1978). Endosteal marrow: a rich source of hematopoietic stem cells. *Science* **199,** 1443–1445.
8. Lord, B.I., Testa, N.G., and Hendry, J.H. (1975). The relative spatial distributions of CFU-S and CFU-C in the normal mouse femur. *Blood* **46,** 65–72.
9. Mason, T.M., Lord, B.I., and Hendry, J.H. (1989). The development of spatial distributions of CFU-S and *in vitro* CFC in femora of mice of different ages. *Br. J. Haematol.* **73,** 455–461.
10. Nilsson, S.K., Johnston, H.M., and Coverdale, J.A. (2001). Spatial localization of transplanted hemopoietic stem cells: inferences for the localization of stem cell niches. *Blood* **97,** 2293–2299.
11. Askenasy, N., Zorina, T., Farkas, D.L., and Shalit, I. (2002). Transplanted hematopoietic cells seed in clusters in recipient bone marrow *in vivo*. *Stem Cells* **20,** 301–310.
12. Nilsson, S.K., Haylock, D.N., Johnston, H.M., Occhiodoro, T., Brown, T.J., and Simmons, P.J. (2003). Hyaluronan is synthesized by primitive hemopoietic cells, participates in their lodgment at the endosteum following transplantation, and is involved in the regulation of their proliferation and differentiation *in vitro*. *Blood* **101,** 856–862.
13. Rafii, S., and Lyden, D. (2003). Therapeutic stem and progenitor cell transplantation for organ vascularization and regeneration. *Nat. Med.* **9,** 702–712.
14. Rafii, S., Lyden, D., Benezra, R., Hattori, K., and Heissig, B. (2002). Vascular and hematopoietic stem cells: novel targets for antiangiogenesis therapy? *Nat. Rev. Cancer* **2,** 826–835.
15. Asahara, T., Murohara, T., Sullivan, A., Silver, M., van der Zee, R., Li, T., Witzenbichler, B., Schatteman, G., and Isner, J.M. (1997).

Isolation of putative progenitor endothelial cells for angiogenesis. *Science* **275,** 964–967.

16. Asahara, T., Masuda, H., Takahashi, T., Kalka, C., Pastore, C., Silver, M., Kearne, M., Magner, M., and Isner, J.M. (1999). Bone marrow origin of endothelial progenitor cells responsible for postnatal vasculogenesis in physiological and pathological neovascularization. *Circ. Res.* **85,** 221–228.
17. Asahara, T., Takahashi, T., Masuda, H., Kalka, C., Chen, D., Iwaguro, H., Inai, Y., Silver, M., Isner, J.M. (1999). VEGF contributes to postnatal neovascularization by mobilizing bone marrow-derived endothelial progenitor cells. *EMBO J.* **18,** 3964–3972.
18. Crisa, L., Cirulli, V., Smith, K.A., Ellisman, M.H., Torbett, B.E., and Salomon, D.R. (1999). Human cord blood progenitors sustain thymic T-cell development and a novel form of angiogenesis. *Blood* **94,** 3928–3940.
19. Orlic, D., Kajstura, J., Chimenti, S., Jakoniuk, I., Anderson, S.M., Li, B., Pickel, J., McKay, R., Nadal-Ginard, B., Bodine, D.M., Leri, A., and Anversa, P. (2001). Bone marrow cells regenerate infarcted myocardium. *Nature* **410,** 701–705.
20. Orlic, D., Kajstura, J., Chimenti, S., Limana, F., Jakoniuk, I., Quaini, F., Nadal-Ginard, B., Bodine, D.M., Leri, A., and Anversa, P. (2001). Mobilized bone marrow cells repair the infarcted heart, improving function and survival. *Proc. Natl. Acad. Sci. USA* **98,** 10,344–10,349.
21. Orlic, D., Kajstura, J., Chimenti, S., Bodine, D.M., Leri, A., and Anversa, P. (2001). Transplanted adult bone marrow cells repair myocardial infarcts in mice. *Ann. NY Acad. Sci.* **938,** 221–229; discussion 229–230.
22. Kocher, A.A., Schuster, M.D., Szabolcs, M.J., Takuma, S., Burkhoff, D., Wang, J., Homma, S., Edwards, N.M., and Itescu, S. (2001). Neovascularization of ischemic myocardium by human bone marrow-derived angioblasts prevents cardiomyocyte apoptosis, reduces remodeling, and improves cardiac function. *Nat. Med.* **7,** 430–436.
23. Iwaguro, H., Yamaguchi, J., Kalka, C., Murasawa, S., Masuda, H., Hayashi, S., Silver, M., Li, T., Isner, J.M., and Asahara, T. (2002). Endothelial progenitor cell vascular endothelial growth factor gene transfer for vascular regeneration. *Circulation* **105,** 732–738.
24. Kalka, C., Masuda, H., Takahashi, T., Kalka-Moll, W.M., Silver, M., Kearney, M., Li, T., Isner, J.M., and Asahara, T. (2000). Transplantation of *ex vivo*-expanded endothelial progenitor cells for therapeutic neovascularization. *Proc. Natl. Acad. Sci. USA* **97,** 3422–3427.
25. Schatteman, G.C., Hanlon, H.D., Jiao, C., Dodds, S.G., and Christy, B.A. (2000). Blood-derived angioblasts accelerate blood-flow restoration in diabetic mice. *J. Clin. Invest.* **106,** 571–578.
26. Shi, Q., Rafii, S., Wu, M.H., Wijelath, E.S., Yu, C., Ishida, A., Fujita, Y., Kothari, S., Mohle, R., Sauvage, L.R., Moore, M.A., Storb, R.F., and Hammond, W.P. (1998). Evidence for circulating bone marrow-derived endothelial cells. *Blood* **92,** 362–367.
27. Bhattacharya, V., McSweeney, P.A., Shi, Q., Bruno, B., Ishida, A., Nash, R., Storb, R.F., Sauvage, L.R., Hammond, W.P., and Wu, M.H. (2000). Enhanced endothelialization and microvessel formation in polyester grafts seeded with CD34(+) bone marrow cells. *Blood* **95,** 581–585.
28. Sata, M., Saiura, A., Kunisato, A., Tojo, A., Okada, S., Tokuhisa, T., Hirai, H., Makuuchi, M., Hirata, Y., and Nagai, R. (2002). Hematopoietic stem cells differentiate into vascular cells that participate in the pathogenesis of atherosclerosis. *Nat. Med.* **8,** 403–409.
29. Otani, A., Kinder, K., Ewalt, K., Otero, F.J., Schimmel, P., and Friedlander, M. (2002). Bone marrow-derived stem cells target retinal astrocytes and can promote or inhibit retinal angiogenesis. *Nat. Med.* **29,** 29.
30. Grant, M.B., May, W.S., Caballero, S., Brown, G.A., Guthrie, S.M., Mames, R.N., Byrne, B.J., Vaught, T., Spoerri, P.E., Peck, A.B., and Scott, E.W. (2002). Adult hematopoietic stem cells provide functional hemangioblast activity during retinal neovascularization. *Nat. Med.* **8,** 607–612.
31. Lyden, D., Hattori, K., Dias, S., Costa, C., Blaikie, P., Butros, L., Chadburn, A., Heissig, B., Marks, W., Witte, L., Wu, Y., Hicklin, D., Zhu, Z., Hackett, N.R., Crystal, R.G., Moore, M.A., Hajjar, K.A., Manova, K., Benezra, R., and Rafii, S. (2001). Impaired recruitment of bone marrow-derived endothelial and hematopoietic precursor cells blocks tumor angiogenesis and growth. *Nat. Med.* **7,** 1194–1201.
32. Reyes, M., Dudek, A., Jahagirdar, B., Koodie, L., Marker, P.H., and Verfaillie, C.M. (2002). Origin of endothelial progenitors in human postnatal bone marrow. *J. Clin. Invest.* **109,** 337–346.
33. Moore, M.A. (2002). Putting the neo into neoangiogenesis. *J. Clin. Invest.* **109,** 313–315.
34. Gehling, U.M., Ergun, S., Schumacher, U., Wagener, C., Pantel, K., Otte, M., Schuch, G., Schafhausen, P., Mende, T., Kilic, N., Kluge, K., Schafer, B., Hossfeld, D.K., and Fiedler, W. (2000). *In vitro* differentiation of endothelial cells from AC133-positive progenitor cells. *Blood* **95,** 3106–3112.
35. Marchetti, S., Gimond, C., Iljin, K., Bourcier, C., Alitalo, K., Pouyssegur, J., and Pages, G. (2002). Endothelial cells genetically selected from differentiating mouse embryonic stem cells incorporate at sites of neovascularization *in vivo*. *J. Cell Sci.* **115,** 2075–2085.
36. Davidoff, A.M., Ng, C.Y., Brown, P., Leary, M.A., Spurbeck, W.W., Zhou, J., Horwitz, E., Vanin, E.F., and Nienhuis, A.W. (2001). Bone marrow-derived cells contribute to tumor neovasculature and, when modified to express an angiogenesis inhibitor, can restrict tumor growth in mice. *Clin. Cancer Res.* **7,** 2870–2879.
37. Carmeliet, P., and Jain, R.K. (2000). Angiogenesis in cancer and other diseases. *Nature* **407,** 249–257.
38. Hanahan, D., and Folkman, J. (1996). Patterns and emerging mechanisms of the angiogenic switch during tumorigenesis. *Cell* **86,** 353–364.
39. Carmeliet, P., Moons, L., Luttun, A., Vincenti, V., Compernolle, V., De Mol, M., Wu, Y., Bono, F., Devy, L., Beck, H., Scholz, D., Acker, T., DiPalma, T., Dewerchin, M., Noel, A., Stalmans, I., Barra, A., Blacher, S., Vandendriessche, T., Ponten, A., Eriksson, U., Plate, K.H., Foidart, J.M., Schaper, W., Charnock-Jones, D.S., Hicklin, D.J., Herbert, J.M., Collen, D., and Persico, M.G. (2001). Synergism between vascular endothelial growth factor and placental growth factor contributes to angiogenesis and plasma extravasation in pathological conditions. *Nat. Med.* **7,** 575–583.
40. Kabrun, N., Buhring, H.J., Choi, K., Ullrich, A., Risau, W., and Keller, G. (1997). Flk-1 expression defines a population of early embryonic hematopoietic precursors. *Development* **124,** 2039–2048.
41. Shalaby, F., Rossant, J., Yamaguchi, T.P., Gertsenstein, M., Wu, X.F., Breitman, M.L., and Schuh, A.C. (1995). Failure of blood-island formation and vasculogenesis in Flk-1-deficient mice. *Nature* **376,** 62–66.
42. Shalaby, F., Ho, J., Stanford, W.L., Fischer, K.D., Schuh, A.C., Schwartz, L., Bernstein, A., and Rossant, J. (1997). A requirement for Flk-1 in primitive and definitive hematopoiesis and vasculogenesis. *Cell* **89,** 981–990.

43. Fong, G.H., Rossant, J., Gertsenstein, M., and Breitman, M.L. (1995). Role of the Flt1 receptor tyrosine kinase in regulating the assembly of vascular endothelium. *Nature* **376,** 66–70.
44. Fong, G.H., Zhang, L., Bryce, D.M., and Peng, J. (1999). Increased hemangioblast commitment, not vascular disorganization, is the primary defect in Flt1 knockout mice. *Development* **126,** 3015–3025.
45. Hiratsuka, S., Minowa, O., Kuno, J., Noda, T., and Shibuya, M. (1998). Flt1 lacking the tyrosine kinase domain is sufficient for normal development and angiogenesis in mice. *Proc. Natl. Acad. Sci. USA* **95,** 9349–9354.
46. Hiratsuka, S., Maru, Y., Okada, A., Seiki, M., Noda, T., and Shibuya, M. (2001). Involvement of Flt1 tyrosine kinase (vascular endothelial growth factor receptor 1) in pathological angiogenesis. *Cancer Res.* **61,** 1207–1213.
47. Hiratsuka, S.S.M. (2002). The tyrosine kinase domain of Flt1 (vascular endothelial growth factor receptor 1) is required for a tumor angiogenesis and its progression. *Proceedings of the American Association for Cancer Research,* 43.
48. Ziegler, B.L., Valtieri, M., Porada, G.A., De Maria, R., Muller, R., Masella, B., Gabbianelli, M., Casella, I., Pelosi, E., Bock, T., Zanjani, E.D., and Peschle, C. (1999). Kdr receptor: a key marker defining hematopoietic stem cells. *Science* **285,** 1553–1558.
49. Haruta, H., Nagata, Y., and Todokoro, K. (2001). Role of Flk-1 in mouse hematopoietic stem cells. *FEBS Lett.* **507,** 45–48.
50. Sawano, A., Iwai, S., Sakurai, Y., Ito, M., Shitara, K., Nakahata, T., and Shibuya, M. (2001). Flt1, vascular endothelial growth factor receptor 1, is a novel cell surface marker for the lineage of monocyte macrophages in humans. *Blood* **97,** 785–791.
51. Clauss, M., Weich, H., Breier, G., Knies, U., Rockl, W., Waltenberger, J., and Risau, W. (1996). The vascular endothelial growth factor receptor Flt1 mediates biological activities: implications for a functional role of placenta growth factor in monocyte activation and chemotaxis. *J. Biol. Chem.* **271,** 17,629–17,634.
52. Barleon, B., Sozzani, S., Zhou, D., Weich, H.A., Mantovani, A., and Marme, D. (1996). Migration of human monocytes in response to vascular endothelial growth factor (VEGF) is mediated via the VEGF receptor Flt1. *Blood* **87,** 3336–3343.
53. Hattori, K., Dias, S., Heissig, B., Hackett, N.R., Lyden, D., Tateno, M., Hicklin, D.J., Zhu, Z., Witte, L., Crystal, R.G., Moore, M.A., and Rafii, S. (2001). Vascular endothelial growth factor and angiopoietin-1 stimulate postnatal hematopoiesis by recruitment of vasculogenic and hematopoietic stem cells. *J. Exp. Med.* **193,** 1005–1014.
54. Cho, N.K., Keyes, L., Johnson, E., Heller, J., Ryner, L., Karim, F., and Krasnow, M.A. (2002). Developmental control of blood cell migration by the *Drosophila* VEGF pathway. *Cell* **108,** 865–876.
55. Hattori, K., Heissig, B., Wu, Y., Dias, S., Tejada, R., Ferris, B., Hicklin, D.J., Zhu, Z., Bohlen, P., Witte, L., Hendrikx, J., Hackett, N.R., Crystal, R.G., Moore, M.A., Werb, Z., Lyden, D., and Rafii, S. (2002). Placental growth factor reconstitutes hematopoiesis by recruiting VEGFR1(+) stem cells from bone marrow microenvironment. *Nat. Med.* **8,** 841–849.
56. Pruijt, J.F., Fibbe, W.E., Laterveer, L., Pieters, R.A., Lindley, I.J., Paemen, L., Masure, S., Willemze, R., and Opdenakker, G. (1999). Prevention of interleukin 8-induced mobilization of hematopoietic progenitor cells in rhesus monkeys by inhibitory antibodies against the metalloproteinase gelatinase-B (MMP-9). *Proc. Natl. Acad. Sci. USA* **96,** 10,863–10,868.
57. Masure, S., Paemen, L., Van Aelst, I., Fiten, P., Proost, P., Billiau, A., Van Damme, J., and Opdenakker, G. (1997). Production and characterization of recombinant active mouse gelatinase-B from eukaryotic cells and *in vivo* effects after intravenous administration. *Eur. J. Biochem.* **244,** 21–30.
58. Hattori, K., Heissig, B., Tashiro, K., Honjo, T., Tateno, M., Shieh, J.H., Hackett, N.R., Quitoriano, M.S., Crystal, R.G., Rafii, S., and Moore, M.A. (2001). Plasma elevation of stromal cell-derived factor 1 induces mobilization of mature and immature hematopoietic progenitor and stem cells. *Blood* **97,** 3354–3360.
59. Vu, T.H., and Werb, Z. (2000). Matrix metalloproteinases: Effectors of development and normal physiology. *Genes Dev.* **14,** 2123–2133.
60. Engsig, M.T., Chen, Q.J., Vu, T.H., Pedersen, A.C., Therkidsen, B., Lund, L.R., Henriksen, K., Lenhard, T., Foged, N.T., Werb, Z., and Delaisse, J.M. (2000). Matrix metalloproteinase 9 and vascular endothelial growth factor are essential for osteoclast recruitment into developing long bones. *J. Cell Biol.* **151,** 879–890.
61. Bergers, G., Brekken, R., McMahon, G., Vu, T.H., Itoh, T., Tamaki, K., Tanzawa, K., Thorpe, P., Itohara, S., Werb, Z., Hanahan, D. (2000). Matrix metalloproteinase 9 triggers the angiogenic switch during carcinogenesis. *Nat. Cell Biol.* **2,** 737–744.
62. Heissig, B., Hattori, K., Dias, S., Friedrich, M., Ferris, B., Hackett, N.R., Crystal, R.G., Besmer, P., Lyden, D., Moore, M.A., Werb, Z., and Rafii, S. (2002). Recruitment of stem and progenitor cells from the bone marrow niche requires MMP-9 mediated release of Kit-ligand. *Cell* **109,** 625–637.
63. Huang, E.J., Nocka, K.H., Buck, J., and Besmer, P. (1992). Differential expression and processing of two cell-associated forms of the Kit-ligand: KL-1 and KL-2. *Mol. Biol. Cell* **3,** 349–362.
64. Longley, B.J., Tyrrell, L., Ma, Y., Williams, D.A., Halaban, R., Langley, K., Lu, H.S., and Schechter, N.M. (1997). Chymase cleavage of stem cell factor yields a bioactive, soluble product. *Proc. Natl. Acad. Sci. USA* **94,** 9017–9021.
65. Kridel, S.J., Chen, E., Kotra, L.P., Howard, E.W., Mobashery, S., and Smith, J.W (2001). Substrate hydrolysis by matrix metalloproteinase-9. *J. Biol. Chem.* **276,** 20,572–20,578.
66. Morrison, S.J., Wandycz, A.M., Hemmati, H.D., Wright, D.E., and Weissman, I.L. (1997). Identification of a lineage of multipotent hematopoietic progenitors. *Development* **124,** 1929–1939.
67. Morrison, S.J., Wright, D.E., and Weissman, I.L. (1997). Cyclophosphamide–granulocyte colony-stimulating factor induces hematopoietic stem cells to proliferate prior to mobilization. *Proc. Natl. Acad. Sci. USA* **94,** 1908–1913.
68. Huang, X.L., Takakura, N., and Suda, T. (1999). *In vitro* effects of angiopoietins and VEGF on hematopoietic and endothelial cells. *Biochem. Biophys. Res. Commun.* **264,** 133–138.
69. Broxmeyer, H.E., Cooper, S., Li, Z.H., Lu, L., Song, H.Y., Kwon, B.S., Warren, R.E., and Donner, D.B. (1995). Myeloid progenitor cell regulatory effects of vascular endothelial cell growth factor. *Int. J. Hematol.* **62,** 203–215.
70. Ratajczak, M.Z., Ratajczak, J., Machalinski, B., Majka, M., Marlicz, W., Carter, A., Pietrzkowski, Z., and Gewirtz, A.M. (1998). Role of vascular endothelial growth factor (VEGF) and placenta-derived growth factor (PlGF) in regulating human haemopoietic cell growth. *Br. J. Haematol.* **103,** 969–979.
71. Gerber, H.P., Malik, A.K., Solar, G.P., Sherman, D., Liang, X.H., Meng, G., Hong, K., Marsters, J.C., and Ferrara, N. (2002). VEGF regulates hematopoietic stem cell survival by an internal autocrine loop mechanism. *Nature* **417,** 954–958.

36

Genes That Specify Hemangioblasts

Kyunghee Choi, Iva Afrikanova, Yun Shin Chung, and Wen Jie Zhang

During mouse embryogenesis, blood cells develop in close association with endothelial cells. In the yolk sac, primitive erythrocytes differentiate with endothelial cells within blood islands. In the intraembryonic para-aortic splanchnopleure (PAS)/aorta–gonad–mesonephros (AGM), clumps of blood cells can be found on the ventral wall of the dorsal aorta. The close temporal and spatial association between hematopoietic and endothelial cells has led to the hypothesis that they share a common progenitor, the hemangioblast. Emerging studies support the existence of such cells. Specifically, gene targeting studies and *in vitro* differentiation models of embryonic stem (ES) cells have been instrumental in identifying genes critical for hematopoietic and endothelial cell lineage differentiation.

Hemangioblasts

The first mature blood cells, known as primitive erythrocytes, are produced from the extraembryonic tissue, the yolk sac. Mesodermal cells that have migrated from the primitive streak colonize the presumptive yolk sac at approximately embryonic day (E) 7 and aggregate to form blood islands. During the next 12 hours, central cells within the aggregates produce embryonic blood cells, and peripheral cells differentiate into endothelial cells. Each blood island subsequently fuses to form the first extraembryonic vascular network (the primary plexus). The close developmental association of the hematopoietic and endothelial cells within yolk sac blood islands has led to the hypothesis that they arise from a common precursor, the hemangioblast.[1–3] Similarly, blood cells of the embryo proper develop in close association with the endothelium of the dorsal aorta.[4–7] Major arteries such as the vitelline and umbilical arteries of embryos have also been reported to associate with emerging blood cells.[4,8] In contrast to the common progenitor concept in the yolk sac, blood cells in the embryo proper are believed to differentiate from the endothelium. For example, at the base of the dorsal aorta of the chicken or quail,[9] intra-aortic $CD45^{+}VEGFR\text{-}2^{-}$ (Flk-1^{-}) hematopoietic cells appear to develop from VEGFR-2^{+} (Flk-1^{+}) cells that take up DiI-conjugated acetylated low-density lipoprotein (DiI-Ac-LDL). In mice, VE-cadherin^{+}, $CD45^{-}$, and $Ter119^{-}$ cells (potentially endothelial cells) from the E9.5 mouse yolk sac and embryos could generate hematopoietic cells including lymphocytes.[10] Therefore, the term hemogenic endothelium is often used in describing the hematopoietic potential of presumably aortic endothelial cells. However, the precise relationship between the hemangioblast and the hemogenic endothelial cells is not known.

IDENTIFICATION OF BL-CFCS FROM *IN VITRO* DIFFERENTIATED ES CELLS

Even though there has been a great interest in identifying the hemangioblast in the developing embryo, the use of embryo-derived cells has proved to be difficult since the developmental sequence occurs rapidly, the tissues are difficult to access, and only a small number of cells can be obtained. An alternative source of embryonic cells for the studies of early embryonic events is the *in vitro*–differentiated progeny of ES cells. ES cells differentiate efficiently *in vitro* and produce a three-dimensional, differentiated cell mass called an embryoid body (EB, reviewed by Keller[11]). ES cells can also be differentiated on top of stromal cells or type IV collagen two dimensionally without intermediate formation of the EB structure.[12,13]

Many lineages have been reported to develop within EBs, including neuronal, muscle, endothelial, and hematopoietic lineages.[12–21] Of these, the hematopoietic lineage has been the most extensively characterized. The development of hematopoietic and endothelial cells within EBs mimics *in vivo* events such that yolk sac blood island–like structures with vascular channels containing hematopoietic cells can be found within cystic EBs.[22] As in the developing embryo, the primitive erythroid cells develop prior to any definitive hematopoietic populations.[15,23] The developmental kinetics of various hematopoietic lineage precursors within EBs and molecular and cellular studies of these cells have indicated that the sequence of events leading to the onset of hematopoiesis within EBs is similar to that found within the normal mouse embryo (Fig. 36–1). Most importantly, ES cells differentiated for 2.5–3.5 days contain a unique cell population, the blast colony–forming cell (BL-CFC). BL-CFCs are transient and develop prior to the primitive erythroid population[24,25] (Fig. 36–2). BL-CFCs form blast colonies in response to vascular endothelial growth factor (VEGF), a ligand for the receptor tyrosine kinase Flk-1,[26,27] in semisolid media such as methylcellulose cultures. Gene expression analysis indicated that cells within the blast colonies (blast cells) expressed several genes common to both hematopoietic and endothelial lineages, including *Scl, CD34,* and the VEGF receptor *Flk1.*[24]

Handbook of Stem Cells
Volume 2

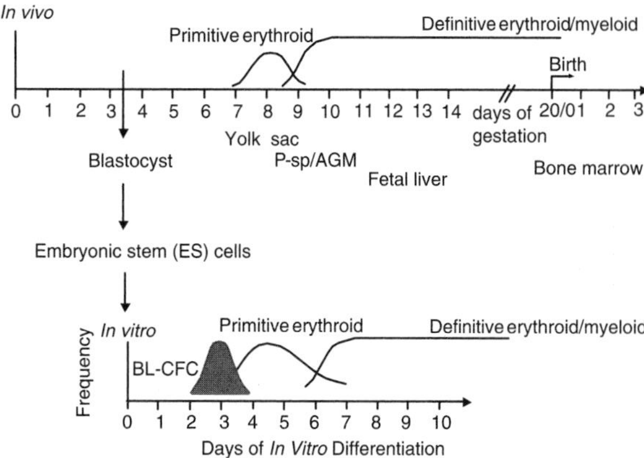

Figure 36–1. *In vitro hematopoietic differentiation.* Hematopoietic development within EBs is compared to *in vivo* hematopoietic differentiation. Note that the BL-CFCs develop first followed by primitive erythroids. As shown, both BL-CFCs and primitive erythroids are transient cell populations. Definitive erythroid and myeloid lineages develop shortly after, and they persist throughout EB differentiation. Only the developmental kinetics, not the actual numbers, of each hematopoietic cell population is given. (Please see CD-ROM for color version of this figure.)

In addition, blast cells are clonal, and produce primitive, definitive hematopoietic, and endothelial cells when replated in a medium with both hematopoietic and endothelial cell growth factors.[24,25] Based on these studies, ES-derived BL-CFCs are thought to represent the hemangioblast.

FLK-1 AND *SCL*

Gene targeting studies indicate that *Flk-1,* a receptor tyrosine kinase, and *Scl,* a transcription factor, function at the earliest steps in the establishment of hematopoietic and endothelial cell lineages. In the mouse embryo, *Flk-1* expression can be detected in the presumptive mesodermal yolk-sac blood-island progenitors as early as E7.0.[28,29] Mice deficient in *Flk-1* do not develop blood vessels or yolk sac blood islands, and die between E8.5 and 9.5.[30] *Flk-1*$^{-/-}$ ES cells fail to participate in vessel formation and fail to contribute to primitive or definitive hematopoiesis in chimeras generated with wild-type embryos.[31] Our earlier studies that BL-CFCs form blast colonies in response to VEGF and that blast cells express the *Flk1* gene argue that *Flk-1* is a hemangioblast/BL-CFC marker.[25] Indeed, blast colonies develop from a sorted Flk-1^{+} but not *Flk-1*$^{-}$ cell population from day 2.75–3 EBs.[32] Consistently, *VEGFR2*$^{+}$ *(Flk-1*$^{+}$*)* cells from the mesoderm of chicken embryos generate both hematopoietic and endothelial cells.[33] In this system, the differentiation of hematopoietic cells from the *VEGFR2*$^{+}$ cells occurred in the absence of VEGF, and endothelial cell generation required VEGF.

There are many studies supporting the view that *Scl* is critical for hemangioblast development. *Scl* is a basic helix–loop–helix transcription factor (see Barton *et al.*[34] and Orkin[35] for a review of transcription factors in hematopoietic lineage development). Mice carrying homozygous mutations at the *Scl* locus die around E10.5 because of defective

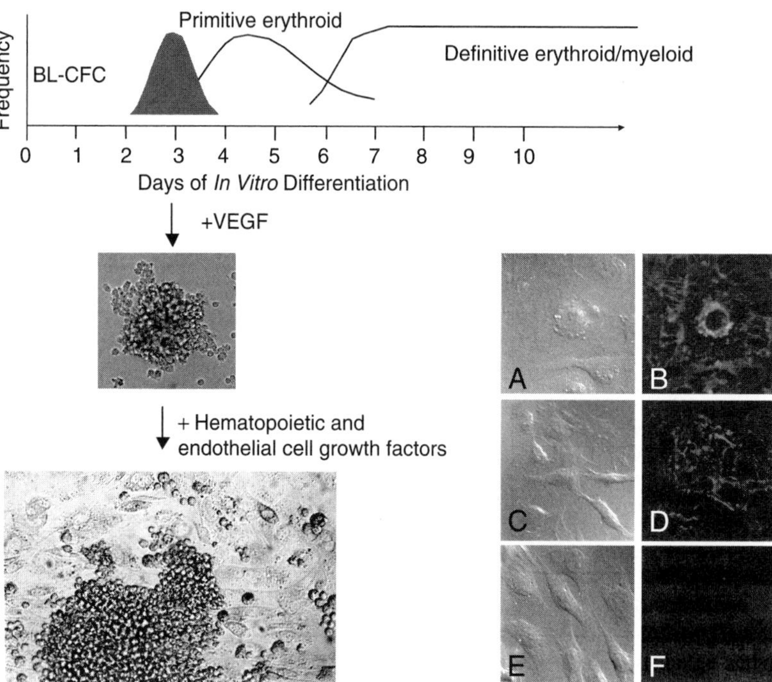

Figure 36–2. *ES-derived BL-CFCs contain hemangioblast activity.* BL-CFCs produce blast colonies in response to VEGF. Upon transfer to media containing both hematopoietic and endothelial cell growth factors, blast cells differentiate to blood and adherent cells. (A–F) Cell staining of the adherent cells. (A, B) D4T endothelial cells, (C, D) adherent cells derived from blast cells, and (E–F) NIH3T3 cells. (A, C, and E) Phase contrast image of cells; (B, D, and F) cell staining for CD31 and DiI-Ac-LDL uptake. (Please see CD-ROM for color version of this figure.)

embryonic hematopoiesis.[36,37] Scl is also required for adult hematopoietic stem cell development, as $Scl^{-/-}$ ES cells fail to contribute to definitive hematopoiesis in chimeric mice generated with wild-type embryos.[38] Subsequent studies showed that Scl is also required for endothelial cell development, as $Scl^{-/-}$ ES cells failed to contribute to the remodeling of the primary vascular plexus in the yolk sac.[38] When examined *in vitro,* $Scl^{-/-}$ ES cells still produced *Flk-1*-expressing cells,[32] but they failed to generate blast colonies.[39] These observations suggest that Scl is required for hemangioblast development and that the hemangioblast constitutes a subpopulation of *Flk-1*$^{+}$ cells.

In studies delineating hematopoietic and endothelial cell lineage differentiation, we recently showed that *Flk-1*–expressing cells developed first and that a subpopulation of *Flk-1* cells went on to express *Scl* to generate Flk-1^{+}Scl^{+} cells.[40] The initially arising Flk-1^{+}Scl^{+} cells from day 2.75 EBs were enriched for BL-CFCs, suggesting that the hemangioblast can be identified as an Flk-1^{+}Scl^{+} cell population. The expression of *Scl, Gata-1, Gata-2,* and *Lmo-2* genes, known to be critical for early hematopoietic progenitor development was higher in Flk-1^{+}hCD4^{+} cells than in Flk-1^{+}Scl^{-} cells. Drake and Fleming[41] have examined early mouse embryos for *Flk-1* and *Scl* expression. At E6.5, *Flk-1*$^{+}$*Scl*$^{+}$ cells were already present, albeit dispersed, in the extraembryonic yolk sac. Primary vascular networks became evident in the regions where *Flk-1*$^{+}$*Scl*$^{+}$ cells were detected. Even though the nature of these *Flk-1*$^{+}$*Scl*$^{+}$ cells needs to be characterized, it is possible that the initial *Flk-1*$^{+}$*Scl*$^{+}$ cells represent hemangioblasts. Ema *et al.* recently knocked *Scl* into *Flk-1* locus to further understand the function of *Scl* in hematopoietic and endothelial cell differentiation.[42] *Scl* expression could not rescue the lethal embryonic phenotype of *Flk-1*$^{-/-}$ embryos, perhaps still because of the migratory defects of *Flk-1*-deficient cells.[43] However, the ectopic expression of *Scl* within *Flk-1*-expressing cells enhanced the frequency of BL-CFCs generated *in vitro.* The subsequent generation of hematopoietic and endothelial cells also increased. These studies suggest that combined signaling of Flk-1 and Scl is critical for proper blood and blood vessel differentiation.

In zebra fish, *Scl* is expressed in the lateral mesoderm, which generates hematopoietic, endothelial, and pronephric lineages.[44] The zebra fish *cloche (clo)* mutation affects both hematopoietic and endothelial differentiation.[45] *Scl* expression is greatly reduced in *clo* mutants.[45] More importantly, ectopically expressed *Scl* can rescue, although incompletely, the hematopoietic and endothelial cell defects in these mutants.[45] Cells expressing both *Flk-1* and *Scl* appear to produce *Scl*$^{+}$*Flk-1*$^{-}$ hematopoietic and *Scl*$^{-}$*Flk-1*$^{+}$ endothelial cells.[44] These observations predict that cells expressing both *Scl* and *Flk-1* represent hemangioblasts. Indeed, cells expressing both *Scl* and *Flk-1* increase dramatically when *Scl* is overexpressed in zebra fish embryos.[44] As a result, both hematopoietic and endothelial cells also increase. In this study, the expansion of *Scl*$^{+}$*Flk-1*$^{+}$ cells occurs at the expense of somitic and pronephric duct tissues.[44] Collectively, these studies suggest that hemangioblast specification from Flk-1^{+} cells is acomplished by the acquisition of Scl expression.

Runx1

Initially produced hematopoietic cells in the yolk sac are primitive erythrocytes, which are nucleated and express embryonic globin genes. As hematopoiesis is shifted to the PAS/AGM, fetal liver, and bone marrow, the blood cells generated represent a spectrum of cell types, including lymphoid and myeloid lineages. While the yolk sac stage of hematopoiesis are referred to as primitive hematopoiesis, PAS/AGM, fetal liver, and adult hematopoiesis are referred to as definitive hematopoiesis. Gene targeting studies show that primitive vs definitive hematopoiesis is regulated differently. For example, Runx1-deficient mice display defects in definitive hematopoiesis, but primitive hematopoiesis occurs normally.[46,47] Runx1 belongs to the core binding factor (CBF) transcription factors.[48] The CBFs consist of three DNA-binding CBFα subunits (Runx1, Runx2, and Runx3) and a common non–DNA-binding CBFβ subunit. The Runx1 and CBFβ transcription factor are the most frequent targets of chromosomal rearrangements in human leukemia. Mice lacking Runx1 or CBFβ die between E11.5–13.5 and display similar phenotypes.[46,47] The cause of embryonic lethality in these mice appears to be hemorrhages in the central nervous system. Both Runx1- and CBFβ-deficient embryos show normal primitive erythropoiesis but lack definitive hematopoietic development.

Runx1 is initially expressed in E7.5 endoderm and some extraembryonic mesodermal cells. Shortly after, Runx1 is expressed in the E8.0 yolk sac including all primitive erythrocytes. Runx1 expression in primitive erythrocytes declines with time and is not detectable by E10.5. At E8.5, Runx1 expression is maintained within the yolk sac endoderm, endothelial cells in yolk sac capillaries, and hematopoietic cells closely associated with the yolk sac endothelium. Runx1 expression in the embryo proper is detectable within endothelial cells of the vitelline artery and within the ventral region of the paired dorsal aorta. By E10.5, Runx1 expression can be detected in vitelline and umbilical arteries, the fetal liver, and the AGM region. Within the AGM region, Runx1 is expressed in the ventral wall, from which clusters of hematopoietic cells emerge. Most importantly, the emerging clusters of blood cells start expressing Runx1, and these clusters of blood cells are missing in Runx1-deficient embryos. Runx1 expression in the endothelium is also missing in these mice, suggesting that Runx1 is required for generating the clusters of definitive hematopoietic cells.[46,47,49]

Lacaud *et al.*[50] recently demonstrated that primitive erythroid progenitors developed in *Runx1*$^{-/-}$ ES cells. However, the number of blast colonies generated dramatically decreased in the absence of Runx1. Runx1-deficient blast cells could differentiate into primitive erythrocytes as judged by βH1 expression. Based on these findings, the authors suggested that there were two types of hemangioblasts, primitive and definitive. Primitive hemangioblasts would produce primitive erythroid and endothelial cells, and definitive hemangioblasts would produce definitive hematopoietic and endothelial cells.

BMP-4, VEGF, and TGF-β1

Despite recent advances in cellular and molecular understandings of how hematopoietic and endothelial cells form in the developing embryo, very little knowledge exists regarding factors controlling hematopoietic and endothelial cell lineage specification. Such information should be valuable for further understanding molecular pathways leading to the onset of hematopoietic and endothelial cell differentiation and for expanding and manipulating primitive hematopoietic and endothelial cell progenitors. Previous studies implicate that endoderm derived factors and mesoderm-inducing factors could play a role in hematopoietic and endothelial cell differentiation. For example, in Xenopus, the formation of erythroid cells from the animal cap is induced by BMP-4 and basic fibroblast growth factor (bFGF) or by BMP-4 and Activin A, and the generation of erythroid cells by exogenously expressed GATA-1 can be potentiated by bFGF.[51] Studies of quail-chick chimeras have shown that the endoderm can induce the formation of hematopoietic cells from the somatopleural mesoderm, which normally does not have such potential.[52] In addition, the formation of blood islands from quail epiblasts is dependent on bFGF.[53] In this system, bFGF-mediated blood island formation correlates with the induction of the *Flk-1* gene,[54] suggesting that bFGF is critical for the emergence of the hemangioblast, the common progenitor of hematopoietic and endothelial cells.[1–3] Furthermore, in quail embryos, the combination of bFGF, vascular endothelial growth factor (VEGF), and transforming growth factor (TGF)-β1 can induce hematopoietic differentiation from the somatopleural mesoderm.[52] Similarly in mice, the primitive endoderm can induce hematopoietic differentiation from the anterior epiblast, a tissue that cannot generate hematopoietic cells.[55] Specifically, both Activin A and BMP-4 can induce hematopoietic differentiation from the anterior headfold region,[56] and an Indian hedgehog can promote hematopoietic differentiation from the anterior epiblast.[57]

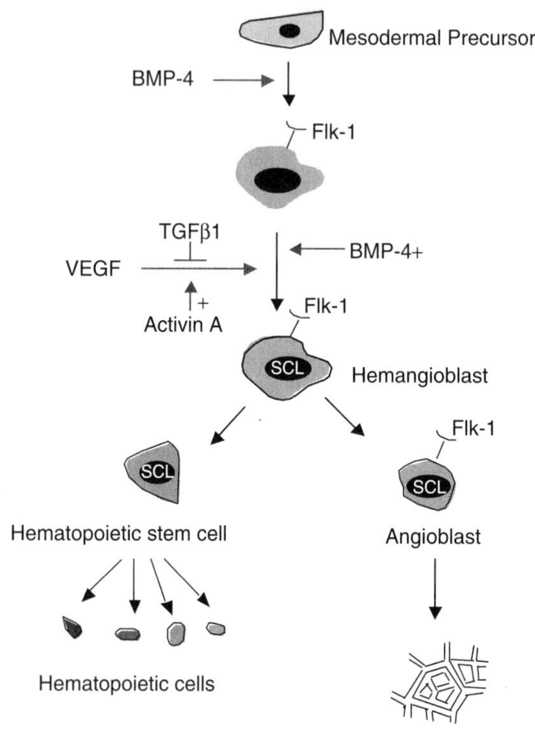

Figure 36–3. *Factors involved in hematopoietic and endothelial cell lineage differentiation within EBs. (Please see CD-ROM for color version of this figure.)*

Gene targeting studies largely support the notion that TGF-β growth factor family–mediated signals are important for hematopoietic and vascular development. For example, *BMP-4* deficient mice die between E7.5 and E9.5 with defects in mesoderm formation and patterning. Those that survive up to E9.5 show severe defects in blood island formation.[58] In addition, mice lacking the type I BMP receptor (*Alk-3*) fail to complete gastrulation and die by E9.5.[59] Mice with targeted mutations of TGF-β1 and TGF-β receptor II display abnormal yolk sac hematopoietic and endothelial cell development.[60,61] The initial vasculogenesis occurs in these mice, but subsequent angiogenesis and capillary formation are defective. As for the hematopoiesis, Larsson et al. (2001) have shown that the number of erythroid progenitors was largely increased in TGF-β receptor I deficient yolk sac compared to wild-type yolk sac, while CFU-GM and CFU-Mix appeared to be similar. Mice deficient in *Smad1* or *Smad5*, TGF-β family downstream signaling molecules, display varying degrees of defects in hematopoietic and vascular development, perhaps due to the overlapping function between Smad1, 5 and 8.[62] For instance, *Smad1* deficient mice display defects in chorioallantoic fusion and die between E9.5 and E10.5.[62,63] Although overall hematopoietic and vascular development appears to be normal, some *Smad1*-deficient embryos display defects in yolk sac angiogenesis.[63] *Smad5* deficient mice also show early embryonic lethality. The primitive plexus can be found in mutant embryos, but they fail to form organized vessels. There seem to be more primitive blood cells in E8.5 mutant yolk sacs, although E9.5 mutant yolk sacs contained almost none.[64] Furthermore, *Smad5*-deficient yolk sacs contained a higher frequency of high-proliferative potential colony forming cells (HPP-CFCs), and *Smad5*-deficient ES cells gave rise to an increased number of hematopoietic progenitors including blast colonies in vitro.[65]

While these studies support the notion that TGF-β family members and bFGF are important regulators of hematopoietic and endothelial cell differentiation, they do not provide mechanistic information. As Flk-1 and Scl functions are required initially in the establishment of hematopoietic and endothelial cell development, we used ES-derived Flk-1$^+$ and Scl$^+$ cells as a means to further understand the developmental stages at which these factors function.[66] Our studies indicate that BMP-4 is required sequentially from ES cells to the mesoderm, from the mesoderm to Flk-1$^+$ cells and from Flk-1$^+$ to Scl$^+$ cells. VEGF then acts through Flk-1 to expand Scl$^+$ cells. The activation of the Smad and map kinase pathways by BMP-4 and VEGF, respectively, is critical in this process. TGF-β1 and Activin A function to further modulate the expansion and differentiation of hematopoietic and endothelial cells by BMP-4 and VEGF (Fig. 36–3). Future studies will be required if additional factors are involved in this hierarchy in regulating hematopoietic and endothelial cell development. Also, future *in vivo* studies are required to verify the observations made in the ES/EB system.

Summary

During ES differentiation, Flk-1–expressing cells initially arise from the mesoderm forming a subset of Flk-1–expressing mesoderm. Flk-1$^+$ cells represent a precursor of cells forming the circulation system, which include blood, blood vessel, smooth muscle cells, cardiomyocytes, and skeletal muscle. Scl expression will specify Flk-1$^+$ cells to become hemangioblast. Flk-1$^+$Scl$^+$ cells will continuously expand up to day 5–6 of EB differentiation. At this stage, Flk-1+Scl+ cells are committed to either blood or blood vessel cells. Additional markers should be helpful to distinguish Flk-1+Scl$^+$ hemangioblasts present in day 2.75 EBs and Flk-1$^+$Scl$^+$ angioblast present in day 5–6 EBs. Pending issues concerning hemangioblasts are as follows. First, ES-derived BL-CFCs fit the description of *in vitro* equivalent hemangioblasts of the yolk sac, blood islands. Nevertheless, there is no definite proof that such a cell exists in the developing embryo, yolk sac, and AGM. Clearly, cell-marking experiments will be necessary in determining the existence of a common progenitor. Second, the existence of the hemangioblast in adults needs to be addressed. Although it is conceptually accepted that hemangioblasts develop during embryogenesis and produce hematopoietic and endothelial cells of the adults, recent studies suggest that hemangioblasts exist in adult stages as well. For example, human AC133$^+$ cells from granulocyte colony-stimulating factor mobilized peripheral blood can differentiate into both hematopoietic and endothelial cells in cultures. These AC133$^+$ cells can form new blood vessels *in vivo*.[67] In addition, Pelosi *et al.*[68] showed that single CD34$^+$Flk-1$^+$ cells from human bone marrow or cord blood can generate both, hematopoietic and endothelial cells. These potential postnatal hemangioblasts exhibited long-term proliferative potential in culture. Furthermore, a population of cells enriched for hematopoietic stem cells, such as Sca-1$^+$c-Kit$^+$Lin$^-$ cells, could also contribute to new blood vessel formation at the single-cell level as shown by retinal neovascularization.[69,70] Third, the full developmental potential of the hemangioblast should be determined. BL-CFCs can generate both, hematopoietic and endothelial cells. However, its full potential has not been carefully examined. Recent studies suggest that smooth muscle cells can also differentiate from BL-CFCs.[42] In this study, Ema and colleagues showed that blast cells generated smooth muscle cells in the absence of VEGF. Flk-1–expressing cells from *Scl*$^{-/-}$ ES cells could not differentiate into endothelial cells, but readily generated smooth muscle cells *in vitro*. Flk-1–expressing cells from *Flk-1*$^{+/Scl}$ produced predominantly hematopoietic and endothelial cells in culture. Collectively, these studies suggest that *Scl* expression is critical for hemangioblast development. Identification of additional transcriptional factors specifying Flk-1$^+$ cells to other cell lineages should be critical for further understanding how the circulation system is established during embryonic development.

ACKNOWLEDGMENTS

We would like to thank the lab members for their dedication to ES cell research. This work was supported by grants from the National Institutes of Health, NHLBI, R01 HL55337 and R01 HL63736 (to K.C.).

REFERENCES

1. Sabin, F.R. (1920). Studies on the origin of blood vessels and of red corpuscles as seen in the living blastoderm of the chick during the second day of incubation. *Contrib. Embryol.* **9,** 213–262.
2. Murray, P.D.F. (1932). The development in vitro of the blood of the early chick embryo. *Proc. Roy. Soc. London* **11,** 497–521.
3. Wagner, R.C. (1980). Endothelial cell embryology and growth. *Adv. Microcirc.* **9,** 45–75.
4. Garcia-Porrero, J.A., Godin, I.E., and Dieterlen-Lievre, F. (1995). Potential intraembryonic hemogenic sites at pre-liver stages in the mouse. *Anat. Embryol. (Berl).* **192,** 425–435.
5. Dieterlen-Lievre, F. (1997). Intraembryonic hematopoietic stem cells. *Aplastic Anemia Stem cell Biol.* **11,** 1149–1171.
6. Tavian, M., Coulombel, L., Luton, D., Clemente, H. S., Dieterlen-Lievre, F., and Peault, B. (1996). Aorta-associated CD34+ hematopoietic cells in the early human embryo. *Blood* **87,** 67–72.
7. Tavian, M, Hallais, M.F., and Peault, B. (1999). Emergence of intraembryonic hematopoietic precursors in the pre-liver human embryo. *Development* **126,** 793–803.
8. de Bruijn, M.F., Speck, N.A., Peeters, M.C., and Dzierzak, E. (2000). Definitive hematopoietic stem cells first develop within the major arterial regions of the mouse embryo. *EMBO J.* **19,** 2465–2474.
9. Jaffredo, T., Gautier, R., Eichmann, A., and Dieterlen-Lievre, F. (1998). Intraaortic hemopoietic cells are derived from endothelial cells during ontogeny. *Development* **125,** 4575–4583.
10. Nishikawa, S.I., Nishikawa, S., Kawamoto, H., Yoshida, H., Kizumoto, M., Kataoka, H., and Katsura, Y. (1998). In vitro generation of lymphohematopoietic cells from endothelial cells purified from murine embryos. *Immunity* **8,** 761–769.
11. Keller, G. M. (1995). In vitro differentiation of embryonic stem cells. *Curr. Opin. Cell Biol.* **7,** 862–869.
12. Nishikawa, S.I., Nishikawa, S., Hirashima, M., Matsuyoshi, N., and Kodama, H. (1998). Progressive lineage analysis by cell sorting and culture identifies FLK1+VE-cadherin+ cells at a diverging point of endothelial and hemopoietic lineages. *Development* **125,** 1747–1757.
13. Nakano, T., Kodama, H., and Honjo, T. (1994). Generation of lymphohematopoietic cells from embryonic stem cells in culture. *Science* **265,** 1098–1101.
14. Bain, G., Kitchens, D., Yao, M., Huettner, J. E., and Gottlieb, D. I. (1995). Embryonic stem cells express neuronal properties in vitro. *Dev. Biol.* **168,** 342–357.

15. Keller, G., Kennedy, M., Papayannopoulou, T., and Wiles, M.V. (1993). Hematopoietic commitment during embryonic stem cell differentiation in culture. *Mol. Cell. Biol.* **13,** 473–486.
16. Muthuchamy, M., Pajak, L., Howles, P., Doetschman, T., and Wieczorek, D. F. (1993). Developmental analysis of tropomyosin gene expression in embryonic stem cells and mouse embryos. *Mol. Cell. Biol.* **13,** 3311–3323.
17. Potocnik, A.J., Nielsen, P.J., and Eichmann, K. (1994). *In vitro* generation of lymphoid precursors from embryonic stem cells. *EMBO J.* **13,** 5274–5283.
18. Risau, W., Sariola, H., Zerwes, H.G., Sasse, J., Ekblom, P., Kemler, R., and Doetschman, T. (1988). Vasculogenesis and angiogenesis in embryonic-stem-cell-derived embryoid bodies. *Development* **102,** 471–478.
19. Vittet, D., Prandini, M.H., Berthier, R., Schweitzer, A., Martin-Sisteron, H., Uzan, G., and Dejana, E. (1996). Embryonic stem cells differentiate *in vitro* to endothelial cells through successive maturation steps. *Blood* **88,** 3424–3431.
20. Wang, R., Clark, R., and Bautch, V.L. (1992). Embryonic stem cell-derived cystic embryoid bodies form vascular channels: an *in vitro* model of blood vessel development. *Development* **114,** 303–316.
21. Wiles, M.V., and Keller, G. (1991). Multiple hematopoietic lineages develop from embryonic stem (ES) cells in culture. *Development* **111,** 259–267.
22. Doetschman, T.C., Eistetter, H., Katz, M., Schmidt, W., and Kemler, R. (1985). The *in vitro* development of blastocyst-derived embryonic stem cell lines: formation of visceral yolk sac, blood islands and myocardium. *J. Embryol. Exp. Morphol.* **87,** 27–45.
23. Palis, J., Robertson, S., Kennedy, M., Wall, C., and Keller, G. (1999). Development of erythroid and myeloid progenitors in the yolk sac and embryo proper of the mouse. *Development* **126,** 5073–5084.
24. Kennedy, M., Firpo, M., Choi, K., Wall, C., Robertson, S., Kabrun, N., and Keller, G. (1997). A common precursor for primitive erythropoiesis and definitive haematopoiesis. *Nature* **386,** 488–493.
25. Choi, K., Kennedy, M., Kazarov, A., Papadimitriou, J.C., and Keller, G. (1998). A common precursor for hematopoietic and endothelial cells. *Development* **125,** 725–732.
26. Matthews, W., Jordan, C.T., Gavin, M., Jenkins, N.A., Copeland, N.G., and Lemischka, I.R. (1991). A receptor tyrosine kinase cDNA isolated from a population of enriched primitive hematopoietic cells and exhibiting close genetic linkage to c- kit. *Proc. Natl. Acad. Sci. U. S. A.* **88,** 9026–9030.
27. Millauer, B., Wizigmann-Voos, S., Schnurch, H., Martinez, R., Moller, N.P., Risau, W., and Ullrich, A. (1993). High affinity VEGF binding and developmental expression suggest Flk-1 as a major regulator of vasculogenesis and angiogenesis. *Cell* **72,** 835–846.
28. Dumont, D.J., Fong, G.H., Puri, M.C., Gradwohl, G., Alitalo, K., and Breitman, M.L. (1995). Vascularization of the mouse embryo: a study of flk-1, tek, tie, and vascular endothelial growth factor expression during development. *Dev. Dyn.* **203,** 80–92.
29. Yamaguchi, T.P., Dumont, D.J., Conlon, R.A., Breitman, M.L., and Rossant, J. (1993). flk-1, an flt-related receptor tyrosine kinase is an early marker for endothelial cell precursors. *Development* **118,** 489–498.
30. Shalaby, F., Rossant, J., Yamaguchi, T.P., Gertsenstein, M., Wu, X.F., Breitman M.L., and Schuh, A.C. (1995). Failure of blood-island formation and vasculogenesis in Flk-1-deficient mice. *Nature* **376,** 62–66.
31. Shalaby, F., Ho, J., Stanford, W.L., Fischer, K.D., Schuh, A.C., Schwartz, L., Bernstein, A., and Rossant, J. F. (1997). A requirement for Flk1 in primitive and definitive hematopoiesis and vasculogenesis. *Cell* **89,** 981– 990.
32. Faloon, P., Arentson, E., Kazarov, A., Deng, C.X., Porcher, C., Orkin, S., and Choi, K. (2000). Basic fibroblast growth factor positively regulates hematopoietic development. *Development* **127,** 1931–1941.
33. Eichmann, A., Corbel, C., Nataf, V., Vaigot, P., Breant, C., and Le Douarin, N.M. (1997). Ligand-dependent development of the endothelial and hemopoietic lineages from embryonic mesodermal cells expressing vascular endothelial growth factor receptor 2. *Proc. Natl. Acad. Sci. U. S. A.* **94,** 5141–5146.
34. Barton, L.M., Gottgens, B., and Green, A. R. (1999). The stem cell leukaemia (SCL) gene: a critical regulator of haemopoietic and vascular development. *Int. J. Biochem. Cell Biol.* **31,** 1193–1207.
35. Orkin, S.H. (1996). Development of the hematopoietic system. *Curr. Opin. Genet. Dev.* **6,** 597–602.
36. Shivdasani, R.A., Mayer, E.L., and Orkin, S.H. (1995). Absence of blood formation in mice lacking the T-cell leukaemia oncoprotein tal-1/SCL. *Nature* **373,** 432–434.
37. Robb, L., Lyons, I., Li, R., Hartley, L., Kontgen, F., Harvey, R.P., Metcalf, D., and Begley, C. G. (1995). Absence of yolk sac hematopoiesis from mice with a targeted disruption of the scl gene. *Proc. Natl. Acad. Sci. U. S. A.* **92,** 7075–7079.
38. Visvader, J.E., Fujiwara, Y., and Orkin, S.H. (1998). Unsuspected role for the T-cell leukemia protein SCL/tal-1 in vascular development. *Genes Dev* **12,** 473–479.
39. Robertson, S.M., Kennedy, M., Shannon, J.M., and Keller, G. (2000). A transitional stage in the commitment of mesoderm to hematopoiesis requiring the transcription factor SCL/tal-1. *Development* **127,** 2447–2459.
40. Chung, Y.S., Zhang, W.J., Arentson, E., Kingsley, P.D., Palis, J., and Choi, K. (2002). Lineage analysis of the hemangioblast as defined by Flk-1 and SCL expression. *Development* **129,** 5511–5520.
41. Drake, C.J., and Fleming, P.A. (2000). Vasculogenesis in the day 6.5 to 9.5 mouse embryo. *Blood* **95,** 1671–1679.
42. Ema, M., Faloon, P., Zhang, W.J., Hirashima, M., Redi, T., Stanford, W., Choi, K., and Rossant, J. (2003). Combinatorial effects of Flk-1 and Tal1 (SCL) on vascular and hematopoietic development in the mouse. *Genes Dev.* **17,** 380–393.
43. Schuh, A.C., Faloon, P., Hu, Q.L., Bhimani, M., and Choi, K. (1999). *In vitro* hematopoietic and endothelial potential of flk-1 (–/–) embryonic stem cells and embryos. *Proc. Natl. Acad. Sci. U. S. A.* **96,** 2159–2164.
44. Gering, M., Rodaway, A.R.F., Gottgens, B., Patient, R.K., and Green, A.R. (1998). The SCL gene specifies haemangioblast development from early mesoderm. *EMBO J.* **17,** 4029–4045.
45. Liao, E.C., Paw, B.H., Oates, A.C., Pratt, S.J., Postlethwait, J.H., and Zon, L.I. (1998). SCL/Tal-1 transcription factor acts downstream of cloche to specify hematopoietic and vascular progenitors in zebrafish. *Genes Dev.* **12,** 621–626.
46. Okuda, T., van Deursen, J., Hiebert, S.W., Grosveld, G., and Downing, J.R. (1996). AML1, the target of multiple chromosomal translocations in human leukemia, is essential for normal fetal liver hematopoiesis. *Cell* **84,** 321–330.
47. Wang, Q., Stacy, T., Binder, M., Marin-Padilla, M., Sharpe, A., and Speck, N. (1996). Disruption of the Cbfa2 gene causes necrosis and hemorrhaging in the central nervous system and blocks definitive hematopoiesis. *Proc. Natl. Acad. Sci. U. S. A.* **93,** 3444–3449.
48. Speck, N.A., and Gilliland, D.G. (2002). Core-binding factors in haematopoiesis and leukaemia. *Nat. Rev. Cancer* **2,** 502–513.

49. North, T., Gu, T.L., Stacy, T., Wang, Q., Howard, L., Binder, M., Marin-Padilla, M., and Speck, N.A. (1999). Cbfa2 is required for the formation of intra-aortic hematopoietic clusters. *Development* **126,** 2563–2575.
50. Lacaud, G., Gore, L., Kennedy, M., Kouskoff, V., Kingsley, P., Hogan, C., Carlsson, L., Speck, N., Palis, J., and Keller, G. (2002) Runx1 is essential for hematopoietic commitment at the hemangioblast stage of development in vitro. *Blood* **100,** 458–466.
51. Huber, T.L., Zhou, Y., Mead, P.E., and Zon, L.I. (1998). Cooperative effects of growth factors involved in the induction of hematopoietic mesoderm. *Blood* **92,** 4128–4137.
52. Pardanaud, L., Luton, D., Prigent, M., Bourcheix, L.M., Catala, M., and Dieterlen-Lievre, F. (1996). Two distinct endothelial lineages in ontogeny, one of them related to hemopoiesis. *Development* **122,** 1363–1371.
53. Flamme, I., and Risau, W. (1992). Induction of vasculogenesis and hematopoiesis *in vitro. Development* **116,** 435–439.
54. Flamme, I., Breier, G., and Risau, W. (1995). Vascular endothelial growth factor (VEGF) and VEGF receptor 2 (flk-1) are expressed during vasculogenesis and vascular differentiation in the quail embryo. *Dev. Biol.* **169,** 699–712.
55. Belaoussoff, M., Farrington, S.M., and Baron, M.H. (1998). Hematopoietic induction and respecification of A-P identity by visceral endoderm signaling in the mouse embryo. *Development* **125,** 5009–5018.
56. Kanatsu, M., and Nishikawa, S.I. (1996). In vitro analysis of epiblast tissue potency for hematopoietic cell differentiation. *Development* **122,** 823–830.
57. Dyer, M.A., Farrington, S.M., Mohn, D., Munday, J.R., and Baron, M.H. (2001). Indian hedgehog activates hematopoiesis and vasculogenesis and can respecify prospective neurectodermal cell fate in the mouse embryo. *Development* **128,** 1717–1730.
58. Winnier, G., Blessing, M., Labosky, P.A., and Hogan, B.L. (1995). Bone morphogenetic protein-4 is required for mesoderm formation and patterning in the mouse. *Genes Dev.* **9,** 2105–2116.
59. Mishina, Y., Suzuki A., Ueno N., and Behringer, R.R. (1995). Bmpr encodes a type I bone morphogenetic protein receptor that is essential for gastrulation during mouse embryogenesis. *Genes Dev.* **9,** 3027–3037.
60. Dickson, M.C., Martin, J.S., Cousins, F.M., Kulkarni, A.B., Karlsson, S., and Akhurst, R. J. (1995). Defective haematopoiesis and vasculogenesis in transforming growth factor-beta 1 knock out mice. *Development* **121,** 1845–1854.
61. Oshima, M., Oshima, H., and Taketo, M.M. (1996). TGF-beta receptor type II deficiency results in defects of yolk sac hematopoiesis and vasculogenesis. *Dev. Biol.* **179,** 297–302.
62. Tremblay, K.D., Dunn, N.R., and Robertson, E.J. (2001). Mouse embryos lacking Smad1 signals display defects in extra-embryonic tissues and germ cell formation. *Development* **128,** 3609–3621.
63. Lechleider, R.J., Ryan, J.L., Garrett, L., Eng, C., Deng, C., Wynshaw-Boris, A., and Roberts, A. B. (2001). Targeted mutagenesis of Smad1 reveals an essential role in chorioallantoic fusion. *Dev. Biol.* **240,** 157–167.
64. Chang, H., Huylebroeck, D., Verschueren, K., Guo, Q., Matzuk, M., and Zwijsen, A. (1999). Smad5 knockout mice die at mid-gestation due to multiple embryonic and extraembryonic defects. *Development* **126,** 1631–1642.
65. Liu, B., Sun, Y., Jiang, F., Zhang, S., Wu, Y., Lan, Y., Yang, X., and Mao, N. (2003). Disruption of Smad5 gene leads to enhanced proliferation of high-proliferative potential precursors during embryonic hematopoiesis. *Blood* **101,** 124–133.
66. Park, C., Afrikanov, I., Chung, Y.S., Zhang, W.J., Arentson, E., Fong Gh, G., Rosendahl, A., and Choi, K. (2004). A hierarchical order of factors in the generation of Flk1- and Scl-expressing hematopoietic and endothelial progenitors from embryonic stem cells. *Development* **131,** 2749–2762.
67. Gehling, U.M., Ergun, S., Schumacher, U., Wagener, C., Pantel, K., Otte, M., Schuch, G., Schafhausen, P., Mende, T., Kilic, N., Kluge, K., Schafer, B., Hossfeld, D. K., and Fiedler, W. (2000). *In vitro* differentiation of endothelial cells from AC133-positive progenitor cells. *Blood* **95,** 3106–3112.
68. Pelosi, E., Valtieri, M., Coppola, S., Botta, R., Gabbianelli, M., Lulli, V., Marziali, G., Masella, B., Muller, R., Sgadari, C., Testa, U., Bonanno, G., and Peschle, C. (2002). Identification of the hemangioblast in postnatal life. *Blood* **100,** 3203–3208.
69. Grant, M.B., May, W.S., Caballero, S., Brown, G.A., Guthrie, S.M., Mames, R.N., Byrne, B.J., Vaught, T., Spoerri, P.E., Peck, A.B., and Scott, E.W. (2002). Adult hematopoietic stem cells provide functional hemangioblast activity during retinal neovascularization. *Nat. Med.* **8,** 607–612.
70. Bailey, A.S., Jiang, S., Afentoulis, M., Baumann, C.I., Schroeder, D.A., Olson, S.B., Wong, M.H., and Fleming, W.H. (2004). Transplanted adult hematopoietic stem cells differentiate into functional endothelial cells. *Blood,* **103,** 13–19.

37

Skeletal Muscle Stem Cells

Mark A. LaBarge and Helen M. Blau

Introduction

This chapter considers the fundamental unit of muscle regeneration, the muscle stem cell (MuSC). In recent years, study in this field has been revitalized because of several provocative reports of potential plasticity of function within the heterogeneous MuSC population that can participate in processes ranging widely from hematopoiesis to osteogenesis, adipogenesis, and myogenesis. Moreover, there are also reports suggesting that cells from the circulation and from the vasculature give rise to MuSCs and ultimately to skeletal muscle fibers. Here we discuss the identification and function of MuSCs in adult animals, their elusive and complex biochemical and functional heterogeneity, and their essential role in muscle regeneration throughout an organism's life span. We also review the plethora of recent unorthodox reports suggesting that cells responsible for muscle regeneration may originate from tissues other than skeletal muscle in adult animals, such as the bone marrow. Finally, we hypothesize, based on studies of muscular dystrophy and aging, how the MuSC niche could recruit and alter the fate of cells that enter that niche.

Tissue-specific stem cells in adult animals have been described most widely in tissues with high turnover, such as blood, skin, or in tissues with a diverse cellular composition, such as the central nervous system (CNS). These tissues have a need for either frequent replenishment or for frequent remodeling; both are processes that lend themselves to the activity of a proliferative subpopulation of cells with the capacity to replace any cell type within that tissue. The classical characteristics used to define a cell as a stem cell derive from the best studied system, hematopoiesis. Accordingly, stem cells must be self-renewing, highly proliferative, and capable of differentiating into at least one other cell type.[1,2] Unlike blood, skin, and CNS tissues, skeletal muscle fibers, the essence of muscle tissue, do not have an apparently rapid turnover. Because muscle tissue possesses a highly specialized cellular architecture and is prone to being damaged by physiologic use throughout life, its persistence and function necessitates the ability to regenerate.[3]

Handbook of Stem Cells
Volume 2

Skeletal muscles are composed of bundles of muscle fibers (myofibers) that are large, terminally differentiated, multinucleate cells formed by the fusion of mononucleate MuSCs. Myofibers can generally be grouped into two different types based on function, fast or slow contracting, a distinction that depends largely on the composition of myosin heavy chain (MyHC) isoforms they express. As shown by interspecies grafting techniques or lineage tracing experiments during embryogenesis, MyHC-expressing mononucleate cells that produce muscle fibers in the limbs originate from the mesodermal somites.[4–6] By contrast, the muscles of the craniofacial region originate from the sometomeres.[7] To form the muscles of the limb, mononucleate myocytes migrate from the somites into the limb buds in two waves. In mouse, primary muscle fibers are formed at embryonic day 13 (E13) and are followed by the formation of secondary muscle fibers at E16, which surround and align themselves in parallel with the primary fibers. In the limb, these two phases of myogenesis are accompanied by changes in fiber type: primary fibers are relatively large in diameter and they express slow MyHCs, whereas secondary fibers are smaller and express fast MyHCs when they are first formed.[8–11] Eventually, the primary or secondary origin of the fibers cannot be distinguished, because at birth muscle consists of a mosaic of both fast and slow fibers of similar size. Even the MyHC composition within an individual fiber can differ, because myosins are encoded by distinct nuclei and maintained in nuclear domains.[12,13] Myoblasts isolated from mice and cloned express all MyHCs irrespective of their muscle of origin, suggesting that regulation is imposed *in vivo*.[14] The myogenic process is regulated by a well-known cascade of basic helix-loop-helix transcription factors, known as muscle regulatory factors (MRFs), expressed sequentially during myogenic development. Myf-5 and MyoD are expressed during the monocyte stage and then decline during differentiation and are followed by the expression of myogenin and MRF4.[15] Once formed, myofibers express myosins, actins, and other proteins that comprise the contractile apparatus and the complex cell surface array of dystroglycans, integrins, and dystrophin. The constant threat of damage in adult animals to these structurally complex, postmitotic cells resulting from exercise, chemical agents, or genetic deficiencies suggests that the need for a regenerative pool of cells within the muscle is profound. This need is particularly apparent when a muscle's pool of regenerative cells is exhausted or becomes nonfunctional, as happens in muscular dystrophies such as Duchenne's,[16] the aging process,[17] or following high doses of γ-irradiation.[18,19] When MuSCs are inadequate in number or function, the result is progressive muscle degeneration and atrophy.

The Original Muscle Stem Cell: The Satellite Cell

The canonical MuSC in adult animals, designated "satellite cell," was anatomically defined in 1961 by transmission electron microscopy (TEM) studies of the peripheral region of muscle fibers in the tibialis anticus muscle of the frog.[20] The discovery of the satellite cell heralded the birth of the field of muscle regeneration. Satellite cells have a high ratio of nucleus to cytoplasm and are intimately juxtaposed to muscle fibers and resident in their own membrane-enclosed compartment, between the sarcolemma of the myofiber and the surrounding basal laminal membrane. So intimately are the satellite cells associated with the myofiber that they are impossible to discern from myonuclei within the fiber by conventional light microscopy. As a result, definitive identification requires laser scanning confocal microscopy or TEM. By grafting quail somites into chicken embryos, organisms with similar developmental time courses, but distinct nuclear morphology, it was shown that these cells in the adult muscle are descended from the cells of the somites.[21] Before the discovery of the satellite cell it was unclear whether there existed a mononucleate cell with the sole purpose of repairing damaged muscle fibers or if the nuclei of damaged fibers underwent a process whereby they replicated and ensheathed themselves in their own membrane, thereby proceeding to participate in their own repair.[22,23] The former model is widely accepted, but it has yet to be demonstrated conclusively. Thus far, it has proven impossible to observe the same satellite cell in its characteristic anatomic position divide asymmetrically, renew itself, and then differentiate and give rise to a myonucleus in a myofiber. However, as described later, there are several lines of evidence strongly suggesting that the satellite cell is a MuSC that does just that.

The first evidence that satellite cells are derived from MuSC were electron microscopy (EM) studies, which showed that after a single injection of [^{3}H] thymidine, only a small number of satellite cells, not myonuclei, had incorporated the radioactive label. These findings suggested that satellite cells were quiescent most of the time and were the only muscle-associated cells that could proliferate.[24] A subsequent study showed that after transplantation of a[H^3]+thymidine labeled EDL into the muscle bed of another animal, the myonuclei of the myofibers of the host animal had [^{3}H] thymidine labeled myonuclei.[25] Apparently, the damage inflicted to the muscle during the transplantation procedure caused the satellite cells of the donor EDL to proliferate and differentiate, contributing donor myonuclei to the host myofibers. Taken together, these data suggest that satellite cells were stimulated to multiply and contribute to muscle in response to tissue damage.

The second line of evidence that satellite cells are MuSC derived from experiments that showed that, like other populations of proliferative cells, satellite cells are sensitive to γ-irradiation, which renders them unable to meet the demands imposed by increased weight or exercise.[18,19,26,27] When part of the tibialis anterior (TA) muscle is surgically removed, the demands on the neighboring EDL muscle are increased. In response to the additional weight and exercise, the EDL increases in mass because of a hypertrophic adaptive response. Both the gram weight and the average myofiber diameter of the overloaded EDL increased substantially when compared with the EDL of the contralateral leg in which the TA was not resected. Moreover, if one limb was treated with a high dose of γ-irradiation (25 Gy) before TA resection, the EDL could not adapt as well and was both reduced in mass and had significantly smaller myofiber diameters than nonirradiated controls.[26,27] These results provided evidence that the proliferative activity of satellite cells was integral to the hypertrophic response, an observation confirmed by others.[28,29]

A third line of investigation that implicated satellite cells as the primary regenerative cell of skeletal muscle derived from the characterization of animal models with muscular dystrophy. One of the most commonly used mouse models of Duchenne's muscular dystrophy (DMD) is the mdx mutant, which carries a point mutation in the dystrophin gene that creates a translational block leading to a truncated protein. As described previously, dystrophin is a key protein in the membrane-bound dystrophin glycoprotein complex (DGC), which is thought to fortify the plasma membrane of the muscle against the intense shearing forces that are generated during daily exercise.[30] The muscles of mdx mice have spontaneously revertant muscle fibers that express dystrophin resulting from a compensatory point mutation that corrects the translational block. Thus, as the mdx mice age, revertant fibers are found in clusters, in which each constituent myofiber harbors the same compensatory mutation.[31] Interestingly, the compensatory mutations found in different bundles are unique to each bundle suggesting that they are derived from the progeny of a single cell. This interpretation is supported by experiments in which limiting dilutions of β-galactosidase (β-gal) encoding retroviruses were used to demonstrate that a satellite cell infected with a single retrovirus has the ability to proliferate and migrate laterally. As a result, it can participate in regeneration of not only its own fiber but also of nearby fibers, leading to bundles of fibers regenerated by the progeny of the same satellite cell.[32] Taken together, these data suggest that the bundles of revertant fibers in the mdx mouse are the result of fusion and differentiation of progeny derived from a single satellite cell or clone.

The fourth line of evidence that satellite cells are MuSC derives from a mouse model used to study pathogenesis in dystroglycan-based muscular dystrophies, another constituent of the DGC. In these experiments satellite cells are labeled as they fuse with muscle fibers.[33] A mouse was engineered with a transgene, in which Cre-recombinase was under control of the muscle creatine kinase promoter, which is only active in differentiated myofibers. This mouse was mated with transgenic mice, in which the gene encoding dystroglycan was flanked by LOX sites. The satellite cells expressed normal levels of dystroglycan until they fused with the

14. Cho, M., Webster, S.G., and Blau, H.M. (1993). Evidence for myoblast-extrinsic regulation of slow myosin heavy chain expression during muscle fiber formation in embryonic development. *J. Cell Biol.* **121,** 795–810.
15. Buckingham, M., Bajard, L., Chang, T., Daubas, P., Hadchouel, J., Meilhac, S., Montarras, D., Rocancourt, D., and Relaix, F. (2003). The formation of skeletal muscle: from somite to limb. *J. Anat.* **202,** 59–68.
16. Blau, H.M., Webster, C., and Pavlath, G.K. (1983). Defective myoblasts identified in Duchenne muscular dystrophy. *Proc. Natl. Acad. Sci. U. S. A.* **80,** 4856–4860.
17. Snow, M.H. (1977). The effects of aging on satellite cells in skeletal muscles of mice and rats. *Cell Tiss. Res.* **185,** 399–408.
18. Mastaglia, F.L., Dawkins, R.L., and Papadimitriou, J.M. (1975). Morphological changes in skeletal muscle after transplantation. A light and electron-microscopic study of the initial phases of degeneration and regeneration. *J. Neurol. Sci.* **25,** 227–247.
19. Heslop, L., Morgan, J.E., and Partridge, T.A. (2000). Evidence for a myogenic stem cell that is exhausted in dystrophic muscle. *J. Cell Sci.* **113,** 2299–2308.
20. Mauro, A. (1961). Satellite cell of skeletal muscle fibers. *J. Biophys. Biochem.* **9,** 493–495.
21. Armand, O., Boutineau, A.M., Mauger, A., Pautou, M.P., and Kieny, M. (1983). Origin of satellite cells in avian skeletal muscles. *Arch. Anat. Microsc. Morphol. Exp.* **72,** 163–181.
22. Sloper, J.C., and Partridge, T.A. (1980). Skeletal muscle: regeneration and transplantation studies. *Br. Med. Bull.* **36,** 153–158.
23. Grounds, M.D., White, J.D., Rosenthal, N., and Bogoyevitch, M.A. (2002). The role of stem cells in skeletal and cardiac muscle repair. *J. Histochem. Cytochem.* **50,** 589–610.
24. Moss, F.P., and Leblond, C.P. (1971). Satellite cells as the source of nuclei of muscles in growing rats. *Anat. Rec.* **170,** 421–435.
25. Snow, M.H. (1978). An autoradiographic study of satellite cell differentiation into regenerating myotubes following transplantation of muscles in young rats. *Cell Tiss. Res.* **186,** 535–540.
26. Rosenblatt, J.D., and Parry, D.J. (1992). Gamma irradiation prevents compensatory hypertrophy of overloaded mouse extensor digitorum longus muscle. *J. Appl. Physiol.* **73,** 2538–2543.
27. Rosenblatt, J.D., and Parry, D.J. (1993). Adaptation of rat extensor digitorum longus muscle to gamma irradiation and overload. *Pflugers Arch. Eur. J. Physiol.* **423,** 255–264.
28. Barton-Davis, E.R., Shoturma, D.I., and Sweeney, H.L. (1999). Contribution of satellite cells to IGF-I induced hypertrophy of skeletal muscle. *Acta Physiol. Scand.* **167,** 301–305.
29. Adams, G.R., Caiozzo, V.J., Haddad, F., and Baldwin, K.M. (2002). Cellular and molecular responses to increased skeletal muscle loading after irradiation. *Am. J. Physiol. Cell. Physiol.* **283,** C1182–1195.
30. Winder, S.J. (1997). The membrane-cytoskeleton interface: the role of dystrophin and utrophin. *J. Muscle Res. Cell Motil.* **18,** 617–629.
31. Lu, Q.L., Morris, G.E., Wilton, S.D., Ly, T., Artem'yeva, O.V., Strong, P., and Partridge, T.A. (2000). Massive idiosyncratic exon skipping corrects the nonsense mutation in dystrophic mouse muscle and produces functional revertant fibers by clonal expansion. *J. Cell Biol.* **148,** 985–996.
32. Hughes, S.M., and Blau, H.M. (1990). Migration of myoblasts across basal lamina during skeletal muscle development. *Nature* **345,** 350–353.
33. Cohn, R.D., Henry, M.D., Michele, D.E., Barresi, R., Saito, F., Moore, S.A., Flanagan, J.D., Skwarchuk, M.W., Robbins, M.E., Mendell, J.R., Williamson, R.A., and Campbell, K.P. (2002). Disruption of DAG1 in differentiated skeletal muscle reveals a role for dystroglycan in muscle regeneration. *Cell* **110,** 639–648.
34. Konigsberg, I. (1963). Clonal analysis of myogenesis. *Science* **140,** 1273–1284.
35. Bischoff, R. (1974). Enzymatic liberation of myogenic cells from adult rat muscle. *Anat. Rec.* **180,** 645–661.
36. Webster, C., Filippi, G., Rinaldi, A., Mastropaolo, C., Tondi, M., Siniscalco, M., and Blau, H.M. (1986). The myoblast defect identified in Duchenne muscular dystrophy is not a primary expression of the DMD mutation. Clonal analysis of myoblasts from five double heterozygotes for two X-linked loci: DMD and G6PD. *Hum. Genet.* **74,** 74–80.
37. Yablonka-Reuveni, Z., Quinn, L.S., and Nameroff, M. (1987). Isolation and clonal analysis of satellite cells from chicken pectoralis muscle. *Dev. Biol.* **119,** 252–259.
38. Rando, T.A., and Blau, H.M. (1994). Primary mouse myoblast purification, characterization, and transplantation for cell-mediated gene therapy. *J. Cell Biol.* **125,** 1275–1287.
39. Bischoff, R. (1975). Regeneration of single skeletal muscle fibers in vitro. *Anat. Rec.* **182,** 215–235.
40. Rosenblatt, J.D., Lunt, A.I., Parry, D.J., and Partridge, T.A. (1995). Culturing satellite cells from living single muscle fiber explants. *In Vitro Cell Dev. Biol. Anim.* **31,** 773–779.
41. Bischoff, R. (1986). Proliferation of muscle satellite cells on intact myofibers in culture. *Dev. Biol.* **115,** 129–139.
42. Allen, D.L., Monke, S.R., Talmadge, R.J., Roy, R.R., and Edgerton, V.R. (1995). Plasticity of myonuclear number in hypertrophied and atrophied mammalian skeletal muscle fibers. *J. Appl. Physiol.* **78,** 1969–1976.
43. Allen, D.L., Linderman, J.K., Roy, R.R., Grindeland, R.E., Mukku, V., and Edgerton, V.R. (1997). Growth hormone/IGF-I and/or resistive exercise maintains myonuclear number in hindlimb unweighted muscles. *J. Appl. Physiol.* **83,** 1857–1861.
44. Tamaki, T., Akatsuka, A., Tokunaga, M., Ishige, K., Uchiyama, S., and Shiraishi, T. (1997). Morphological and biochemical evidence of muscle hyperplasia following weight-lifting exercise in rats. *Am. J. Physiol.* **273,** C246–256.
45. Grounds, M.D. (1998). Age-associated changes in the response of skeletal muscle cells to exercise and regeneration. *Ann. N. Y. Acad. Sci.* **854,** 78–91.
46. Kadi, F., and Thornell, L.E. (2000). Concomitant increases in myonuclear and satellite cell content in female trapezius muscle following strength training. *Histochem. Cell Biol.* **113(2),** 99–103.
47. Blaveri, K., Heslop, L., Yu, D.S., Rosenblatt, J.D., Gross, J.G., Partridge, T.A., and Morgan, J.E. (1999). Patterns of repair of dystrophic mouse muscle: Studies on isolated fibers. *Dev. Dyn.* **216,** 244–256.
48. Rosenblatt, J.D., Parry, D.J., and Partridge, T.A. (1996). Phenotype of adult mouse muscle myoblasts reflects their fiber type of origin. *Differentiation* **60,** 39–45.
49. Pavlath, G.K., Thaloor, D., Rando, T.A., Cheong, M., English, A.W., and Zheng, B. (1998). Heterogeneity among muscle precursor cells in adult skeletal muscles with differing regenerative capacities. *Dev. Dyn.* **212,** 495–508.
50. Rantanen, J., Hurme, T., Lukka, R., Heino, J., and Kalimo, H.. (1995). Satellite cell proliferation and the expression of myogenin and desmin in regenerating skeletal muscle: evidence for two different populations of satellite cells. *Lab. Invest.* **72,** 341–347.
51. Schultz, E. (1996). Satellite cell proliferative compartments in growing skeletal muscles. *Dev. Biol.* **175,** 84–94.

52. Baroffio, A., Hamann, M., Bernheim, L., Bochaton-Piallat, M.L., Gabbiani, G., and Bader, C.R. (1996). Identification of self-renewing myoblasts in the progeny of single human muscle satellite cells. *Differentiation* **60,** 47–57.
53. Yoshida, N., Yoshida, S., Koishi, K., Masuda, K., and Nabeshima, Y. (1998). Cell heterogeneity upon myogenic differentiation: down-regulation of MyoD and Myf-5 generates 'reserve cells'. *J. Cell Sci.* **111,** 769–779.
54. Cornelison, D.D., and Wold, B.J. (1997). Single-cell analysis of regulatory gene expression in quiescent and activated mouse skeletal muscle satellite cells. *Dev. Biol.* **191,** 270–283.
55. Beauchamp, J.R., Heslop, L., Yu, D.S., Tajbakhsh, Kelly, R.G., Wernig, A., Buckingham, M.E., Partridge, T.A., and Zammit, P.S. (2000). Expression of CD34 and Myf5 defines the majority of quiescent adult skeletal muscle satellite cells. *J. Cell Biol.* **151,** 1221–1234.
56. Seale, P., Sabourin, L.A., Girgis-Gabardo, A., Mansouri, A., Gruss, P., and Rudnicki, M.A. (2000). Pax7 is required for the specification of myogenic satellite cells. *Cell* **102,** 777–786.
57. Ferrari, G., Cusella-De Angelis, G., Coletta, M., Paolucci, E., Stornaiuolo, A., Cossu, G., and Mavilio, F. (1998). Muscle regeneration by bone marrow-derived myogenic progenitors. *Science* **279,** 1528–1530.
58. Ferrari, G., Stornaiuolo, A., and Mavilio, F. (2001). Failure to correct murine muscular dystrophy. *Nature* **411,** 1014–1015.
59. Goodell, M.A., Jackson, K.A., Majka, S.M., Mi, T., Wang, H., Pocius, J., Hartley, C.J., Majesky, M.W., Entman, M.L., Michael, L.H., and Hirschi, K.K. (2001). Stem cell plasticity in muscle and bone marrow. *Ann. N. Y. Acad. Sci.* **938,** 208–218.
60. Gussoni, E., Soneoka, Y., Strickland, C.D., Buzney, E.A., Khan, M.K., Flint, A.F., Kunkel, L.M., and Mulligan, R.C. (1999). Dystrophin expression in the mdx mouse restored by stem cell transplantation. *Nature* **401,** 390–394.
61. Gussoni, E., Bennett, R.R., Muskiewicz, K.R., Meyerrose, T., Nolta, J.A., Gilgoff, I., Stein, J., Chan, Y.M., Lidov, H.G., Bèonnemann, C.G., Von Moers, A., Morris, G.E., Den Dunnen, J.T., Chamberlain, J.S. (2002). Long-term persistence of donor nuclei in a Duchenne muscular dystrophy patient receiving bone marrow transplantation. *J. Clin. Invest.* **110,** 807–814.
62. Bittner, R.E., Schèofer, C., Weipoltshammer, K., Ivanova, S., Streubel, B., Hauser, E., Freilinger, M., Hèoger, H., Elbe-Bèurger, A., and Wachtler, F. (1999). Recruitment of bone-marrow-derived cells by skeletal and cardiac muscle in adult dystrophic mdx mice. *Anat. Embryol.* **199,** 391–396.
63. Brazelton, T.R., Rossi, F.M., Keshet, G.I., and Blau, H.M. (2000). From marrow to brain: expression of neuronal phenotypes in adult mice. *Science* **290,** 1775–1779.
64. Fukada, S., Miyagoe-Suzuki, Y., Tsukihara, H., Yuasa, K., Higuchi, S., Ono, S., Tsujikiwara, K., Takeda, S., and Yamamoto, H. (2002). Muscle regeneration by reconstitution with bone marrow or fetal liver cells from green fluorescent protein-gene transgenic mice. *J. Cell Sci.* **115,** 1285–1293.
65. Jackson, K.A., Mi, T., and Goodell, M.A. (1999). Hematopoietic potential of stem cells isolated from murine skeletal muscle. *Proc. Natl. Acad. Sci. U. S. A.* **96,** 14482–14486.
66. Krause, D.S., Theise, N.D., Collector, M.I., Henegariu, O., Hwang, S., Gardner, R., Neutzel, S., and Sharkis, S.J. (2001). Multi-organ, multi-lineage engraftment by a single bone marrow-derived stem cell. *Cell* **105,** 369–377.
67. LaBarge, M.A., and Blau, H.M. (2002). Biological progression from adult bone marrow to mononucleate muscle stem cell to multinucleate muscle fiber in response to injury. *Cell* **111,** 589–601.
68. Lagasse, E., Connors, H., Al-Dahlimy, M., Reitsma, M., Dohse, M., Osborne, L., Wang, X., Finegold, M., Weissman, I.L., and Grompe, M. (2000). Purified hematopoietic stem cells can differentiate into hepatocytes in vivo. *Nat. Med.* **6,** 1229–1234.
69. Mezey, E., Chandross, K.J., Harta, G., Maki, R.A., and McKercher, S.R. (2000). Turning blood into brain: cells bearing neuronal antigens generated in vivo from bone marrow. *Science* **290,** 1779–1782.
70. Orlic, D., Kajstura, J., Chimenti, S., Jakoniuk, I., Anderson, S.M., Li, B., Pickel, J., McKay, R., Nadal-Ginard, B., Bodine, D.M., Leri, A., and Anversa, P. (2001). Bone marrow cells regenerate infarcted myocardium. *Nature* **410,** 701–705.
71. Bateson, R.G., Woodrow, D.F., and Sloper, J.C. (1967). Circulating cell as a source of myoblasts in regenerating injured mammalian skeletal muscle. *Nature* **213,** 1035–1036.
72. Grounds, M.D. (1983). Skeletal muscle precursors do not arise from bone marrow cells. *Cell Tissue Res.* **234,** 713–722.
73. Irintchev, A., and Wernig, A. (1987). Muscle damage and repair in voluntarily running mice: strain and muscle differences. *Cell Tissue Res.* **249,** 509–521.
74. Wernig, A., Irintchev, A., and Weisshaupt, P. (1990). Muscle injury, cross-sectional area and fibre type distribution in mouse soleus after intermittent wheel-running. *J. Physiol.* **428,** 639–652.
75. Corti, S., Strazzer, S., Del Bo, R., Salani, S., Bossolasco, P., Fortunato, F., Locatelli, F., Soligo, D., Moggio, M., Ciscato, P., Prelle, A., Borsotti, C., Bresolin, N., Scarlato, G., and Comi, G.P. (2002). A subpopulation of murine bone marrow cells fully differentiates along the myogenic pathway and participates in muscle repair in the mdx dystrophic mouse. *Exp. Cell Res.* **277,** 74–85.
76. Corbel, S.Y., Lee, A., Yi, L., Duenas, J., Brazelton, T.R., Blau, H.M., and Rossi, F.M. (2003). Contribution of hematopoietic stem cells to skeletal muscle. *Nat. Med.* **9(12),** 1528–1532.
77. Asakura, A., Komaki, M., and Rudnicki, M. (2001). Muscle satellite cells are multipotential stem cells that exhibit myogenic, osteogenic, and adipogenic differentiation. *Differentiation* **68 (4–5),** 245–253.
78. McKinney-Freeman, S.L., Jackson, K.A., Camargo, F.D., Ferrari, G., Mavilio, F., and Goodell, M.A. (2002). Muscle-derived hematopoietic stem cells are hematopoietic in origin. *Proc. Natl. Acad. Sci. U. S. A.* **99,** 1341–1346.
79. Asakura, A., Seale, P., Girgis-Gabardo, A., and Rudnicki, M.A. (2002). Myogenic specification of side population cells in skeletal muscle. *J. Cell Biol.* **159,** 123–134.
80. De Angelis, L., Berghella, L., Coletta, M., Lattanzi, L., Zanchi, M., Cusella-De Angelis, M.G., Ponzetto, C., and Cossu, G. (1999). Skeletal myogenic progenitors originating from embryonic dorsal aorta coexpress endothelial and myogenic markers and contribute to postnatal muscle growth and regeneration. *J. Cell Biol.* **147,** 869–878.
81. Schofield, R. (1978). The relationship between the spleen colony forming cell ant the haematopoietic stem cell. *Blood Cells* **4,** 7–25.
82. Watt, F.M., and Hogan, B.L. (2000). Out of Eden: stem cells and their niches. *Science* **287,** 1427–1430.
83. Spradling, A., Drummond-Barbosa, D., and Kai, T. (2001). Stem cells find their niche. *Nature* **414,** 98–104.
84. Kiger, A.A., Jones, D.L., Schulz, C., Rogers, M.B., and Fuller, M.T. (2001). Stem cell self-renewal specified by JAK-STAT activation in response to a support cell cue. *Science* **294,** 2542–2545.
85. Schultz, E., and Lipton, B.H. (1982). Skeletal muscle satellite cells: changes in proliferation potential as a function of age. *Mech. Ageing Dev.* **20,** 377–383.

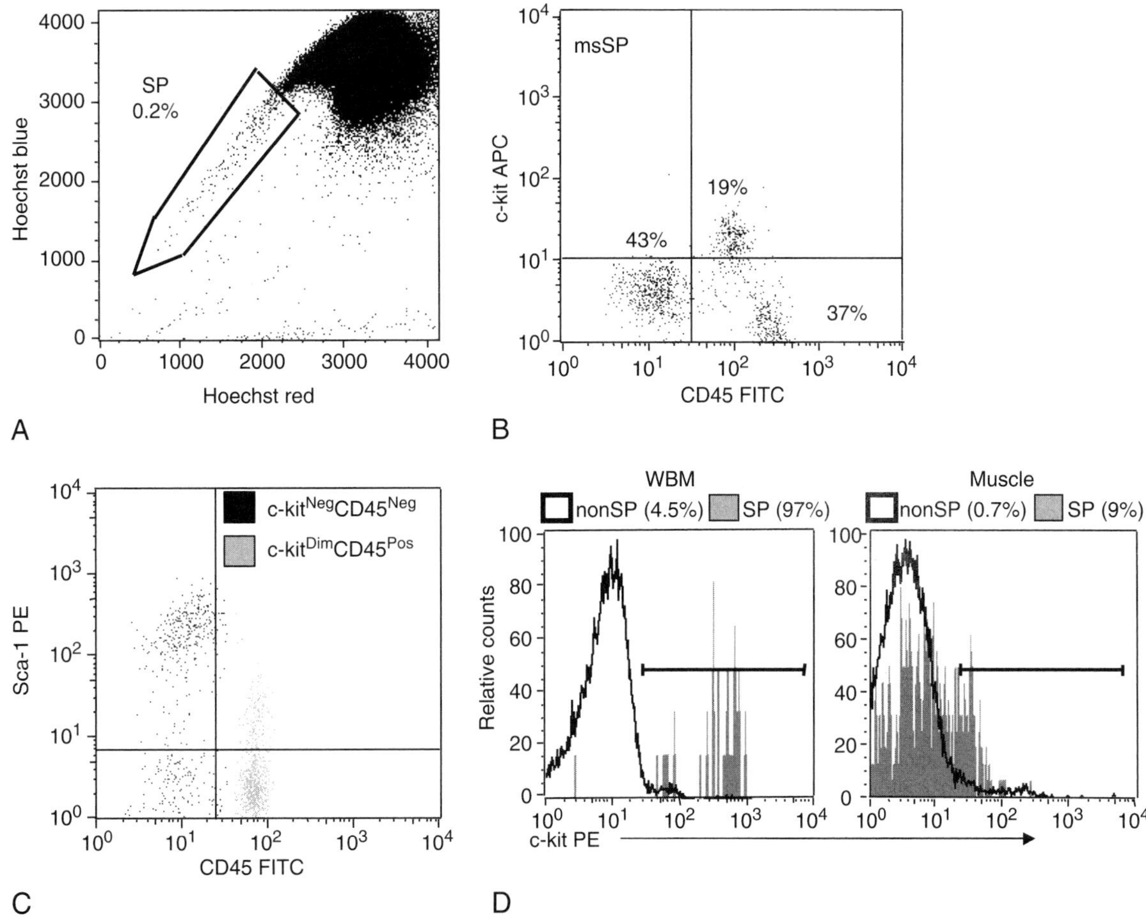

Figure 38-2. *Phenotype of skeletal muscle-derived hematopoietic stem cells (ms-HSCs).* (**A**) Representation of the Hoechst staining distribution in skeletal muscle: skeletal muscle–derived cells are stained with Hoechst 33342 and analyzed by flow cytometry. Gate designates the side population (SP) compartment. (**B**) Flow cytometry analysis of the distribution of c-kit and CD45 on skeletal muscle–side population (ms-SP) cells, which reveals the distinct c-kit^{dim}CD45^{+} population of ms-SP cells containing all ms-HSCs. (**C**) Distribution of Sca-1 and CD45 in ms-SP cells. Note, all Sca-1^{bright} cells in ms-SP cells are CD45^{-} and only the Sca-1^{intermediate} population expresses CD45. (**D**) The ms-HSCs express lower levels of c-kit then whole bone marrow (WBM) HSCs: distribution of c-kit on cell surface of WBM and muscle SP and non-SP cells assessed by flow cytometry.

By 6 months post-transplant, most CD45^{+} ms-SP cells also expressed β-galactosidase, indicating that they originated with the transplanted HSCs. Thus, ms-HSCs are ultimately derived from bone marrow HSCs.

Ms-HSCs Are in Flux with the WBM HSC Compartment

The data suggest that muscle and bone marrow HSCs are the same stem cell population in two different environments. Because the myogenic and hematopoietic systems are both derived from mesoderm during development, it is feasible that all ms-HSCs are seeded during development and that WBM HSCs do not actively seed skeletal muscle in adult animals. Transplantation experiments that reveal a hematopoietic origin for ms-HSCs cannot address whether HSCs are actively exchanged between the bone marrow and muscle, because the conditions used in these experiments do not reflect the steady state—the hematopoietic system of recipients has been ablated and cells that may not circulate under normal conditions have been injected into the PB.

Bone marrow HSCs travel through the peripheral circulation at low levels under steady-state conditions and can be induced to circulate at high levels when exposed to growth factors that promote mobilization out of the WBM and into the periphery. Experiments using parabiotic mice (mice joined surgically such that they share a common circulatory system [Fig. 38–4]) revealed that a mouse could be rescued from lethal irradiation by parabiosis to a nonirradiated partner animal.[17] Clearly, HSCs from the nonirradiated partner were able to migrate through the circulation to mediate the rescue of the irradiated partner.

Because irradiation could have induced the production of cytokines that may have mediated mobilization of HSCs from the nonirradiated partner, this study does not reflect HSCs moving through the circulation of steady-state animals. However, it was also shown that mice could also be rescued

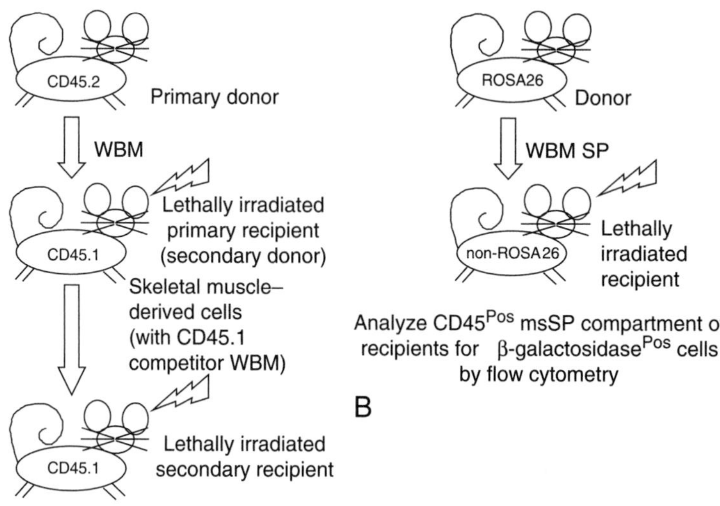

Figure 38–3. *Skeletal muscle-derived hematopoietic stem cell (ms-HSC) oigin experiments.* (**A**) Schematic of serial transplantation experiments performed by Kawada *et al.* evaluating whether ms-HSCs are derived from whole bone marrow (WBM). (**B**) Schematic of experiments performed by Jackson *et al.* evaluating whether ms-HSCs are derived from WBM hematopoietic stem cells (purified by side population [SP] fractionation). Rosa26 animals express lacZ ubiquitously, allowing analysis of multiple cell types for donor engraftment.

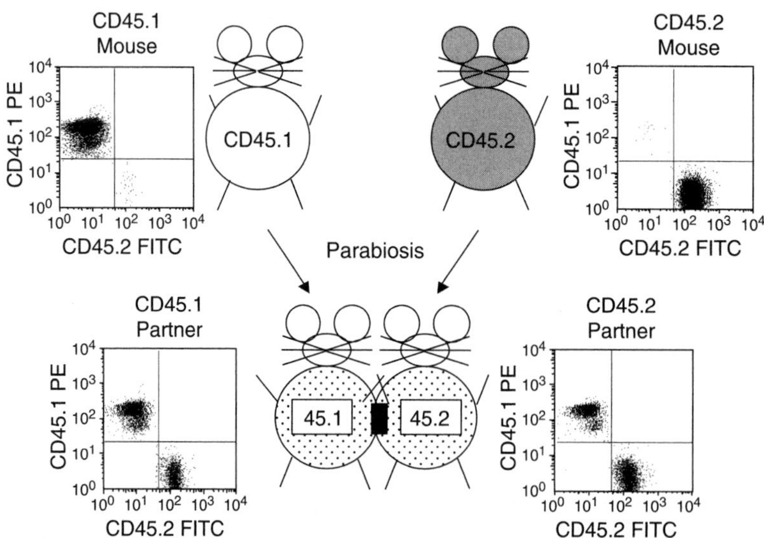

Figure 38–4. *Parabiotic mouse model.* Example of cross circulation in a parabiotic mouse pair: a CD45.1 and CD45.2 animal are joined surgically and then peripheral blood (PB) aliquots from each surgical partner are analyzed by flow cytometry using monoclonal antibodies to CD45.1 and CD45.2. These antibodies allow one to monitor the appearance of cells from one surgical partner in the circulation of the opposite surgical partner (lower flow cytometry plots), that is, there are now CD45.2$^+$ cells present in the PB of the CD45.1 partner.

from lethal irradiation by transplantation with 36 to 75 million PB leukocytes (about 200 times fewer WBM cells will rescue a mouse from lethal irradiation)[18] and that HSCs can be exchanged between nonirradiated parabiotic partners.[19] Because the donor animals were not subject to irradiation or chemical mobilization, these results clearly indicate that HSCs are present in the circulation of steady-state animals, although at a very low frequency because large numbers of PB cells were required to mediate rescue. Spleen colony assays, which test for hematopoietic progenitors, also suggest that PB-derived HSCs may be functionally less potent than bone marrow-derived HSCs.[20] Thus, the HSCs moving through the circulation may not be functionally analogous to HSCs resident in WBM.

Parabiotic mice have recently been used to address whether HSCs actively migrate from bone marrow to skeletal muscle in normal, steady-state adult mice that have not been subjected to a bone marrow transplant. By parabiosing mice congenic at the CD45 locus, stem cells moving through the circulation of one partner can be detected both functionally and phenotypically in the opposite partner and vice versa. To assess whether HSCs actively traffic between the bone marrow and skeletal muscle, muscle-derived cells were isolated from parabiotic partners and transplanted with competitor WBM into the appropriate recipients such that partner-derived HSCs within the muscle could be functionally observed (Fig. 38–5). Using this approach, it was found that HSCs from one parabiotic partner can migrate through the circulation and into the skeletal muscle of the opposite partner (Fig. 38–5; McKinney-Freeman unpublished data). Thus, ms-HSCs are ultimately and actively derived from circulating bone marrow HSCs.

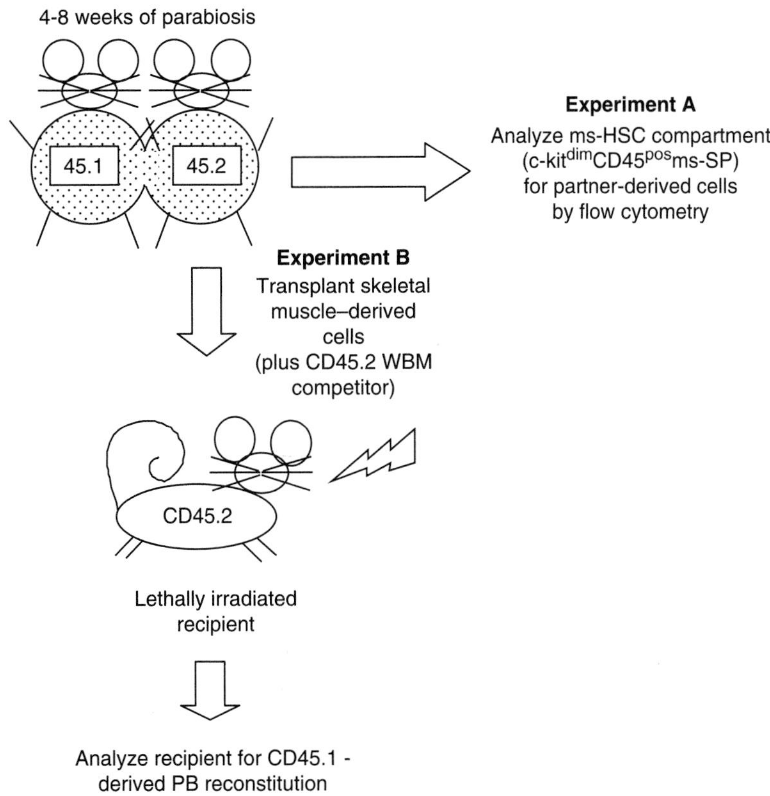

Figure 38–5. *Parabiotic experiment to observe circulating hematopoietic stem cells (HSCs) in skeletal muscle.* Schematic of experiment using parabiotic mice to evaluate whether skeletal muscle–derived hematopoietic stem cells (ms-HSCs) are seeded by circulating HSCs. Experiment A: Phenotypic evaluation of circulating HSCs in skeletal muscle: evaluate the ms-HSCs (c-kit^{dim}CD45^{+} ms-SP) compartment of parabiotic partners 4 weeks post-parabiosis with flow cytometry for the presence of partner-derived cells. Experiment B: Transplant muscle–derived cells from a parabiotic partner 4 weeks post-parabiosis into the appropriate recipients such that partner-derived reconstitution of the recipient animals can be detected by flow cytometry. For example, muscle-derived cells from a CD45.2 partner are transplanted into CD45.2 recipients along with CD45.2 competitive whole bone marrow (WBM). The peripheral blood (PB) of the recipient is then analyzed for the presence of CD45.1 cells, which would only be present if CD45.1 HSC had trafficked into the skeletal muscle of the donor CD45.2 parabiotic partner.

Recently, hematopoietic progenitors were detected by *in vitro* assays in many tissues, including smooth muscle, liver, lung, kidney, brain, heart, and small intestine in mice.[21] The most primitive hematopoietic progenitors, however, were only detected in hematopoietic tissues (spleen and bone marrow) and skeletal muscle. Also, cells with HSC activity have reportedly been purified from the brain and assayed *in vivo* via transplantation,[22] although this finding has been refuted in the literature.[23] Nevertheless, these data suggest that circulating hematopoietic progenitors/stem cells may seed many tissues in adult mice, most likely via the circulation.[21,22]

WBM HSC and ms-HSC Are Functionally and Phenotypically Distinct

Although the data strongly support the assertion that ms-HSCs are derived from bone marrow HSCs, there are clear differences between these two cell populations both phenotypically and functionally. For example, bone marrow HSCs in both mice and humans express high levels of the tyrosine kinase receptor c-kit, whereas ms-HSCs express only dim levels of this molecule (Fig. 38–2, d). Cell surface expression of c-kit is reportedly down-regulated on circulating and actively cycling HSCs.[24–26] Thus, the down-regulation of c-kit by ms-HSCs supports the conclusion that they are derived from circulating HSCs that have established a reservoir in skeletal muscle. Because c-kit has been shown to be required for hematopoietic engraftment of HSCs *in vivo*,[27–29] ms-HSCs may up-regulate c-kit after transplantation into lethally irradiated mice. *In vitro* culture experiments reveal that these cells are capable of up-regulating c-kit when subjected to cytokines that induce hematopoiesis (McKinney-Freeman, unpublished data).

Purified ms-HSCs were found to be not nearly as potent in their hematopoietic repopulating activity as bone marrow HSCs.[9] The ms-HSC cells are only, on average, 46 times enriched for HSC activity relative to WBM, whereas WBM HSCs are 1000-fold enriched relative to WBM.[30] The ms-HSCs also have about 20 times less HSC activity than bone marrow HSCs on a per-cell basis. Thus, although ms-HSCs are derived from bone marrow HSCs, they are functionally distinct. If ms-HSCs do need to up-regulate c-kit *in vivo* to mediate hematopoietic engraftment, this may result in a delayed engraftment of ms-HSCs, which could potentially contribute to their apparent diminished HSC activity relative to WBM HSCs. Furthermore, it is possible that a regulatory mechanism may be in play either in the PB or the skeletal muscle to actively suppress circulating HSCs to reduce the likelihood of extramedullary hematopoiesis, although there is no direct evidence for this theory.

Skeletal Muscle-derived Hematopoietic Stem Cells in Primates and Humans

Muscle-derived hematopoietic activity from humans and nonhuman primates has also been reported. Cultured human skeletal muscle–derived cells, reportedly largely negative for CD45, were able to repopulate the hematopoietic system of sublethally irradiated NOD/SCID animals,[31] although the reported engraftment was on average less than 1% of the PB of transplanted animals, was not well characterized for multipotency, and was only assessed 6 to 8 weeks post-transplant. It has also been reported that cultured muscle-derived cells from nonhuman primates can produce hematopoietic colonies *in vitro*.[32] However, because these cultures were not examined for the expression of CD45, it is likely that the observed colony activity was derived from contaminating hematopoietic cells, as is the case in mice.[9] In accordance with this speculation, the majority of both cultured human and nonhuman primate muscle-derived cells in this study expressed CD34, a marker of human HSCs. In conclusion, it remains to be seen whether findings in mice regarding the phenotype and function of ms-HSCs will be reflected in humans and nonhuman primates.

A Relationship Between the Skeletal Muscle-derived Hematopoietic Stem Cells and Satellite Cells?

As discussed previously, ms-HSC activity was first assumed to be the product of transdifferentiating satellite cells. It is now generally accepted that ms-HSCs and satellite cells represent two distinct stem cell compartments in skeletal muscle. However, it is still possible that a biologic relationship may exist between these two cell populations. Several lines of evidence have been interpreted to suggest that ms-HSCs may act as precursors of satellite cells within skeletal muscle.

For example, obliteration of Pax7 expression leads to a 10-fold increase in hematopoietic progenitor activity by muscle-derived cells. This finding has been interpreted to suggest that if ms-HSCs are in fact satellite cell precursors, Pax7 might be regulating their decision to undergo hematopoietic or myogenic specification, perhaps by muffling hematopoietic differentiation cues in favor of myogenic.[13] Because the ms-SP compartment is not expanded in Pax7-deficient animals, if this hypothesis is in fact correct, Pax7 would likely be regulating hematopoietic activity on a per-cell basis rather than simply blocking the ability of ms-HSCs to differentiate into satellite cells, which might result in an expansion in the ms-HSC compartment. Also, ms-SP cells and WBM cells reportedly contribute to the satellite cell compartment when injected into preinjured muscle or transplanted peripherally into irradiated recipients.[8,33] Although these findings need to be verified by independent groups, they support the proposal that ms-HSCs may be satellite cell precursors because the ms-SP compartment contains ms-HSCs and ms-HSCs are derived from WBM. Furthermore, $CD45^+$ muscle-derived cells can participate in limited myogenic activity *in vivo* and both $CD45^+$ ms-SP cells and $CD45^-$ ms-SP cells display myogenic activity *in vitro* when co-cultured with myoblasts or C2C12 cells.[8,9] Thus, in addition to potentially contributing directly to the satellite cell compartment, ms-HSCs may participate in myogenesis under certain conditions. Finally, both $CD45^+$ and

39

Skeletal Stem Cells

Paolo Bianco and Pamela Gehron Robey

Introduction

Most bones develop from mesenchymal condensations giving rise to cartilaginous rudiments via a prechondrogenic blastema. The outermost portion of the chondrogenic blastema later evolves into a perichondrium and further into a primitive periosteum at the time when cartilage cores mature to hypertrophy and the primary centers of ossification are established. Chondroprogenitors and osteoprogenitors within the perichondrium and periosteum allow the growth of cartilage and bone. Once a bony collar has been established around the midshaft of the rudiments, blood vessels and cells derived from the primitive periosteum invade the developing marrow cavity and establish a bone marrow stroma therein during fetal life (reviewed in reference 1). Cartilaginous epiphyses of developing bones are in turn invaded by ingrowing blood vessels (vascular canals). These structures, and a specialized structure called Ranvier's notch at the physis of the growing bone, replenish the epiphyses with progenitor cells derived from the perichondrium. Once epiphyses have ossified, it is these cells that establish and maintain postnatal growth plates, in which typical stem cell–dependent kinetics fuel longitudinal growth of bone at the physes for 15 years in humans, until the process is abated by a hormonal crisis (puberty). Within the epiphyseal end of the growth plates, resting chondrocytes divide asymmetrically, each generating one resting chondrocyte and one proliferating (transit amplifying) chondrocyte. The progeny of proliferating chondrocytes undergo hypertrophy and apoptosis, and the matrix around them is replaced by bone. Growth of bone and of the bone marrow tissues are allowed by cell divisions occurring in osteogenic cells at the opposite (metaphyseal) end of the physes. These divisions (asymmetrically) generate bone-forming osteoblasts and non–bone-forming stromal cells. Once bone growth has ceased, multipotent progenitors capable of giving rise to cartilage, bone, and bone marrow stroma remain in the bone marrow, their ultimate destination. Throughout development and growth, human skeletal stem cells generate 15 kg of bone. After the end of skeletal growth, the entire skeleton is made anew another three to five times through remodeling, without any significant consumption of its progenitor/stem cells in the bone marrow.[2] Furthermore, 30–300 kg of bone and cartilage can be generated with the cells contained in 0.5 g of adult rabbit bone marrow.[3]

Handbook of Stem Cells
Volume 2

Heterotopic Bone Organs

A single cell retained in the postnatal bone marrow at the end of skeletal growth can give rise to four differentiated cell types/tissues that are found in the skeleton (cartilage, bone, hematopoiesis-supporting reticular stromal cells, and marrow adipocytes) and generate, following *ex vivo* culture, large quantities of differentiated skeletal tissues.[4,5] This well-established notion evolved from the classical observation (in fact going back to the 19th century) that the bone marrow is endowed with a remarkable osteogenic potential. Ectopic transplantation of marrow fragments results in the formation of a complete bone organ.[6] The distinct osteogenic potential of marrow as a tissue is ascribed to the nonhematopoietic, stromal component, which provides the hematopoietic microenvironment *in vivo*. Stromal cell strains derived in culture from explanted adherent, clonogenic, fibroblast-like cells, generate bone and cartilage when transplanted in diffusion chambers and generate a complete heterotopic bone organ upon *in vivo* transplantation in open systems (i.e., they not only establish ectopic bone tissue but also transfer the hematopoietic microenvironment to the ectopic bone).[7–13] In these systems, bone-forming cells and the stromal components of the bone marrow (reticular cells and adipocytes) are derived from the donor cell population, whereas hematopoietic cells filling the marrow space originate from host hematopoietic stem cells (HSCs).[14–16] Importantly, not only are the tissues comprised in a normal postnatal bone present together in heterotopic bone organs ("ossicles") but the ontogenesis of bone and bone marrow is recapitulated in these systems. Bone and bone marrow eventually become organized in a fashion directly replicating their natural structural layout *in vivo* (cortical bone, marrow cavity with trabecular bone and hematopoiesis; Fig. 39–1), emphasizing the inherent property of self-organization of the transplanted cell population. Interestingly, the establishment of marrow tissue follows temporally the establishment of bone, and of a stromal tissue in the prospective marrow space, and it is never observed in heterotopic transplants in which bone is not generated. This recapitulates the sequence of events leading to the establishment of the bone marrow during organogenesis of bone *in vivo*.[1]

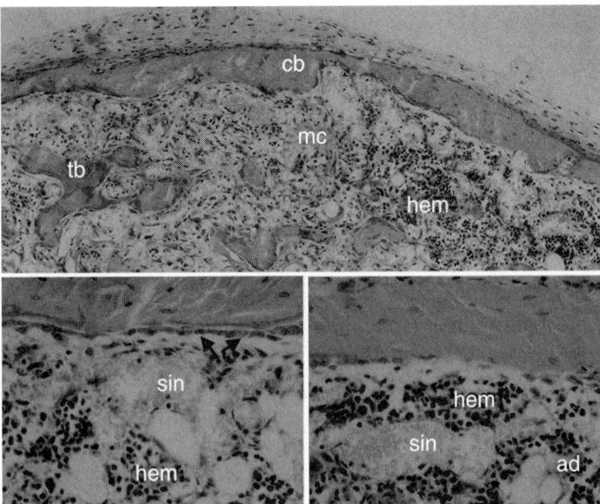

Figure 39–1. Establishment of heterotopic bone and marrow by marrow stromal cells. Heterotopic ossicle formed in the subcutaneous tissue of a SCID mouse upon transplantation of 10^6 stromal cells obtained from the *ex vivo* expansion of multiple colony forming units-fibroblastic (CFU-F). Six weeks post-transplants, cortical bone (ct), a marrow cavity (mc), and trabecular bone (tb) have formed. Osteogenesis (arrows, osteoblasts) and adipogenesis (ad) are underway. Patent marrow sinusoids (sin) are obvious, and hematopoiesis (hem) is being established in the extravascular space of the marrow. (Please see CD-ROM for color version of this figure.)

Skeletal Stem Cells in the Postnatal Bone Marrow

Stromal cell strains are established *in vitro* through the clonal growth of single clonogenic cells (colony-forming units-fibroblastic [CFU-F]) contained in single-cell suspensions of bone marrow cells at a frequency of ~10 in 10^5 mononuclear cells. Expansion of a single CFU-F *in vitro,* followed by transplantation *in vivo,* demonstrates that complete heterotopic bone organs, including a bone marrow stroma, can be generated by a single cell.[8,13,16,17] The generation of a bone marrow stroma from a single stromal cell, capable of making bone as well, implies the restoration of the tissue compartment from which the *in vitro* expanding progenitors were originally derived. Hence, it implies the self-renewal of the progenitor compartment. Heterotopic bone organs generated in this way remain viable for the life span of the recipient animal, and stromal cells that develop therein can be used for serial retransplantation resulting in the establishment anew of heterotopic bones at each time.[18]

Evidence for the existence in the postnatal bone marrow of a self-maintaining, common progenitor of multiple skeletal tissues is thus obtained through a sequence of *ex vivo* culture and *in vivo* transplantation experiments. The entire cycle from a single bone marrow stromal cell contained in the donor bone organ to a single bone marrow stromal cell contained into a newly generated heterotopic bone organ is completed over the entire *ex vivo–in vivo* sequence, and definitive proof of self-maintenance of a stromal stem cell is only obtained by serial retransplantation (Fig. 39–2).

ASSAYS OF SKELETAL STEM CELLS

No proof of "stemness" is provided by *in vitro* assays alone or by *in vivo* assays relying on nonclonal transplantation. Likewise, *in vitro* assays of the differentiation potential of stromal cells have empirical but limited value. The *in vivo* potential for tissue generation of stromal cells is not predicted by the detection of tissue-specific phenotypic markers (mRNA or protein) *in vitro* or by the observation of *in vitro* surrogates of *in vivo* differentiated features, such as the deposition of alcianophilic matrix (cartilage), mineralization nodules (bone), or intracellular lipid accumulation (adipocytes). One noted exception is represented by the development of true cartilage *in vitro* upon micromass culture of stromal cells.[19,20] Here, expression of cartilage-specific genes translates into histology and electron microscopy-proven reproduction of structure. Furthermore, coordinated chondrogenesis and osteogenesis can be obtained in these systems, along with a precise *in vitro* reproduction not only of the structural layout of an embryonic bone rudiment but also of the molecular events that mark the onset of osteogenesis in endochondrally formed bones *in vivo.*[21] Hence, both embryonic and adult bone structures can be generated by the same strain of stromal cells upon micromass culture *in vitro* or *in vivo* transplantation, respectively.

STEM CELLS, CLONOGENIC CELLS, AND THEIR PROGENY

CFU-F derived from a single marrow sample differ markedly in their capacity to generate heterotopic ossicles. Five to 8% of murine[3,13] and ~20% of human[17] CFU-F generate a complete ossicle on *in vivo* transplantation. A higher fraction (>30% in the mouse, ~25% in humans) generates bone but fails to establish a hematopoietic microenvironment, whereas the remainder of the clones either generate fibrous tissues or

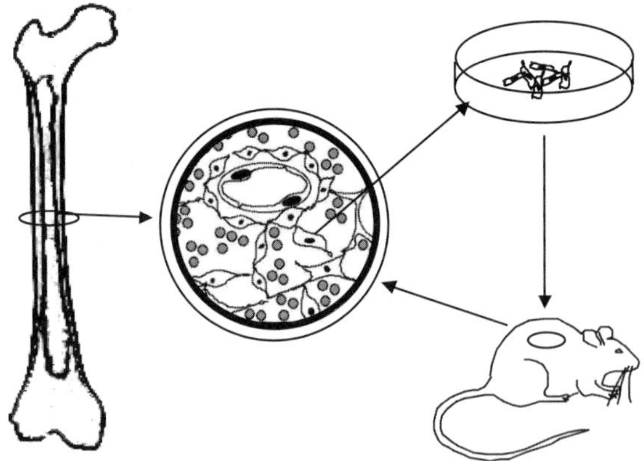

Figure 39–2. The *in vitro–in vivo* sequence showing self-renewal of skeletal stem cells. A single stromal cell generates a single colony *in vitro.* Expansion of the colony generates enough cells to be transplanted at an ectopic site. Here, bone and bone marrow stroma develop. Establishment of the bone marrow stroma equates the restoration of the physical compartment from which the clonogenic progenitor was derived. The bone marrow stroma can be serially retransplanted.

fail to generate any tissue. Based on these observations, it was hypothesized that a hierarchy of progenitors with variably restricted differentiation potential would be found along with a multipotent skeletal stem cell in the clonogenic population of stromal cells.[4,5] In this view, cells capable of reestablishing bone *and* bone marrow stroma would be the skeletal stem cells, whereas cells capable of establishing bone only would be committed (restricted) osteogenic progenitors.

CFU-F are noncycling *in vivo,* and enter S-phase several hours to several days after exposure to serum *in vitro.* Their *in vitro* progeny are endowed with remarkable growth potential. Multicolony-derived strains established in the same individual dish through clonal growth of multiple CFU-F can expand for ~40 population doublings,[22] while retaining the capacity (as a whole) to generate a complete heterotopic bone. Clones, however, derived from a single CFU-F and expanded in isolation appear more restricted in growth potential (possibly indicating an internal feeder effect in nonclonal culture), but at least a fraction of them can be expanded for more than 20 PD (population doublings).[23] Conditions for *in vitro* expansion of single clones may be different from those permissive for initiation of clonal growth and initial expansion. Consistent with the observed, relative expression of the cognate receptors,[24] PDGF-BB (platelet-derived growth factor BB) and epidermal growth factor (EGF) appear to improve cell growth in a proportion of single-cell–derived stromal clones under serum-free conditions.[25] Basic FGF (fibroblast growth factor) has also been proposed as a critical ingredient for supporting the expansion of single clones,[26,27] which, however, remains limited to 20 to 25 PD.[23,27]

STEM CELL KINETICS IN STROMAL CELLS *IN VITRO*

Bone marrow stromal cell populations *in vitro* are density sensitive, adopt asymmetrical cell kinetics, and undergo senescence. In establishing stromal cultures, density sensitivity of the population selects the fraction of cells retaining the capacity to initiate clonal growth at low density. Combined with selection for adhesion to plastic, this undoubtedly poses an experimental bias to the *in vitro* assay of skeletal stem cells and their actual frequency *in vivo.*

Asymmetrical cell kinetics is the defining characteristic of stem cells *in vivo* (reviewed in reference 28). Self-renewal of a stem cell is permitted by asymmetrical cell *division* (reviewed in reference 29). The replicative kinetics of the two daughter cells is divergent (asymmetrical cell *kinetics*). One daughter cell remains a stem cell, whereas the other initiates clonal expansion through a series of symmetrical cell divisions, each generating two identical proliferative progenitors (transit amplifying) ultimately capable of differentiation. This predicts that if all divisions entered by a stem cell are asymmetrical, the absolute number of stem cells in the population will not change over time, whereas the size of the population will increase, as will the number of differentiating progeny. Asymmetrical cell kinetics, which is possibly p53-dependent,[30,31] is the standard behavior of normal diploid growth-controlled (nonimmortalized) fibroblasts in culture.[32] The observed senescence of fibroblast cultures over time is predicted based on asymmetrical cell kinetics. In this respect, the observed replicative senescence of stromal cell populations *in vitro*[33] fits the general paradigm of asymmetrical cell kinetics.

The total number of clonogenic cells is greatly expanded during *in vitro* growth of stromal cell strains. However, the frequency of clonogenic cells declines at the same time. The expansion of the total clonogenic population does not imply expansion of the stem cell subset, because restricted progenitors downstream of the stem cell are clonogenic in their own right, as indicated by the heterogeneous potential of different CFU-F upon transplantation *in vivo.* On the other hand, the steady decline in frequency of clonogenic cells over time in culture is again predicted by asymmetrical cell kinetics.

Current culture conditions used to grow the progeny of primary clonogenic cells explanted from the bone marrow do permit expansion of the total cell population and of the total clonogenic population, including amplifying and committed progenitors. They do not necessarily permit expansion of the stem cells per se. Continuous growth, cell-autonomous expansion *in vitro,* and unlimited life span are not inherent or defining properties of stem cells. In fact, self-renewal (asymmetrical cell kinetics) and expansion of stem cells (symmetrical replication of nondifferentiating progenitors) are opposite to one another. As long as asymmetrical cell kinetics is maintained, a stem cell cannot expand in number regardless of the number of cell divisions made. Stochastic fluctuation between asymmetrical and symmetrical kinetics (see e.g., references 34 and 35), however, may allow for some expansion of stem cells in culture. The magnitude of this event in stromal cell cultures, however, cannot be predicted from considerations of kinetics or from analysis of population kinetics. Because of the lack of specific markers of the true stem cell subset, the extent to which skeletal stem cells are self-renewed and expanded *in vitro* can only be probed by direct transplantation assays *in vivo.* Relative to the growth kinetics of the entire population, expansion of stem cells is obviously suppressed in currently used stromal cell cultures, in which asymmetry of cell kinetics must predominate, or else senescence would not be observed. In this context, the lack of telomerase expression in cultures of marrow stromal cells reported by several groups[36,37] remains fully consistent with characteristic asymmetrical cell kinetics. Although telomerase is sometimes considered an inherent requirement (and perhaps defining characteristic) of stem cells, it must be noted that telomerase can be induced or suppressed (and may in fact be suppressed once stromal cells are established in culture[23]), is expressed in rapidly dividing progenitors in many systems,[38] and relates more to the frequency of division than to the ability of a stem cell to self-renew. The number of cell divisions that a stem cell (and also a transit amplifying progenitor) can engage *in vivo* may be very high or very limited, depending on the overall rate of turnover of the dependent system. However, even in rapidly renewing systems, stem cells are thought to divide very rarely,[29] which would not predict a stringent need for telomerase in stem cells. In fact, purified HSCs from telomerase-deficient mice can reconstitute hematopoiesis over two rounds of serial transplantation.[39]

THE PHENOTYPE OF SKELETAL STEM CELLS

The heterogeneity of growth and differentiation potential among different CFU-F has elicited multiple attempts to identify the true skeletal stem cells through the characterization of a surface phenotype defined by molecular markers that would enable subsequent purification through cell sorting (e.g., references 23, 40–44). However, the outcome of sorting based on surface markers has been the isolation of a cell population that is homogeneous in terms of phenotype but not necessarily in terms of biologic properties. With respect to the ability *of single cells* to self-renew and generate the complete range of relevant skeletal tissues *in vivo,* skeletal stem cells have never been purified. However, the total *clonogenic* population can be enriched to near purity. Pivotal for the task has been the identification of a single, trypsin-resistant epitope, defined by the monoclonal antibody Stro-1.[45] The Stro-1^{bright} fraction (~10 per 10^5) of marrow mononuclear cells includes virtually all of the adherent clonogenic cells.[43] Other markers reported to be effective for enriching stromal clonogenic cells include HOP-26/CD63,[46,47] CD166 (ALCAM[48,49]), and CD49a (α_1 integrin subunit[50,51]). Refined approaches may envision the combined use of Stro-1 in combination with one or more of these additional markers. Clonogenic stromal cells are negative for hematopoietic markers, express variable levels of alkaline phosphatase (ALP)[41] and synthesize a host of extracellular matrix proteins that are found in bone (osteonectin, osteopontin, type I collagen) and normally expressed in preosteogenic cells *in vivo.* In addition, they express variable levels of markers considered characteristic of adipocytes (e.g., lipoprotein lipase [LPL]) (reviewed in references 52 and 53).

Most endothelial markers (factor VIII related antigen, VE-cadherin, CD31) are not expressed on stromal cells. Nonetheless, they do express a range of markers otherwise noted on endothelial cells or progenitors thereof, such as CD146 (Muc18, Mel-CAM), VCAM-1, (vascular cell adhesion molecule-1) and endoglin.[23,54] α-Smooth muscle actin, which is restricted to arterial capillary pericytes in the bone marrow microenvironment *in vivo,* is expressed in a high proportion of stromal cells in culture (reviewed in reference 53).

Skeletal Stem Cells in the Bone Marrow Vasculature

The bone marrow can be seen as an extraordinarily rich vascular network, noted for a prominent sinusoidal (venous) compartment. Other than hematopoietic cells, there is very little else in the extravascular space of bone marrow. Anatomically, all the nonhematopoietic, nonendothelial, stromal cells that we are able to identify in the postnatal bone marrow *in situ* can be seen as specific varieties of pericytes (subendothelial cells with variable properties and phenotype, sharing a basement membrane with endothelial cells[55]). Across different tissues and histologic compartments thereof, pericytes are heterogeneous in phenotype[56] and may be heterogeneous in origin (reviewed in reference 53). Interestingly, pericytes from nonskeletal sites can also be induced to form bone and cartilage *in vitro* and *in vivo.*[57,58] In the bone marrow, pericytes of arterial capillaries and venous sinusoids are different in phenotype (Fig. 39–3), and likely in developmental origin. Although arterial pericytes likely arise from resident cells of vascular walls (either endothelial cells or subendothelial cells) during growth-related angiogenesis, venous pericytes (including reticular cells and adipocytes) may also be recruited from local osteogenic cells during bone organogenesis and growth.[53,59,60] Hence, it is reasonable to speculate that the two compartments of cells *in vivo* may be endowed with distinct differentiation potential. *In vitro,* stromal cells express markers that are either expressed in, or highly restricted to, pericytes in the bone marrow *in vivo,* such as alkaline phosphatase (ALP), α-SM-actin, or MUC18 (CD146), a marker of circulating endothelial progenitors expressed in pericytes and smooth muscle cells, but not in steady-state endothelial cells.[61] CD146 is highly restricted to pericytes of arterial capillaries in the bone marrow *in vivo* and is expressed in 70% of stromal cells in culture, and about 80% of all clonogenic cells are recovered in the CD146-sorted fraction of stromal cells. CD146 is co-expressed in Stro-1^{bright} cells, and CD146-sorted stromal cells do form bone in an *in vivo* transplantation assay.[62] A rare subset of $CD146^+$ stromal cells also express Flk-1 (fetal liver kinase-1, vascular endothelial growth factor receptor [VEGF] receptor-2), a marker of early endothelial progenitors. Likely, this subset corresponds to the rare population of Flk-1^+ postnatal endothelial progenitors that co-purify with marrow stromal stem cells and retain the differentiation potential thereof.[63] Hence, a rare common progenitor for endothelial and skeletal cells may be found in the postnatal bone marrow stroma.

Flk-1 positive (and Flk-1 negative) progenitors for skeletal and other mesodermal tissues, which give rise to fully differentiated cartilage, bone, and muscle cells upon transplantation,[64,65] are found in the wall of the embryonic dorsal aorta in the aorta–gonad–mesonephron (AGM) region, where definitive HSCs are thought to emerge from the ventral floor of the

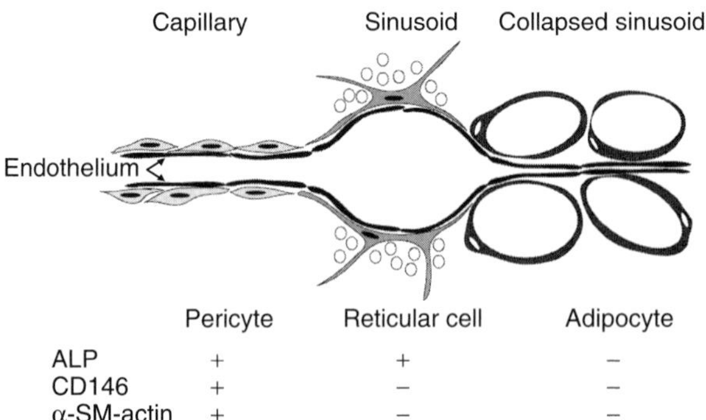

Figure 39–3. Perivascular location of stromal cells in the bone marrow. Distinct phenotypes are associated with distinct sections of the microvascular bed of the bone marrow.

aorta.[66,67] In this region, a spatial specification of the mesoderm generates an abluminal (outer) layer of cells, which is interpreted as a most primitive hematopoietic stroma.[68,69] Stromal cell lines derived from the AGM region efficiently support hematopoiesis *in vitro,*[70] as do postnatal stromal cells. The association of stromal stem cells with the bone marrow vasculature in the postnatal organism may thus be rooted in development.

CIRCULATING SKELETAL STEM CELLS

Circulating cells with assayable *in vivo* osteogenic potential have been identified in a variety of species, including humans.[71] These cells establish complete heterotopic ossicles on *in vivo* transplantation and display an *in vitro* phenotype partially similar to their marrow stromal counterparts. The origin and physiologic significance of these cells remains to be elucidated. The view that skeletal progenitors may be associated with microvessel walls and be generated and recruited during angiogenesis[72] would accommodate the hypothesis that skeletal (mesodermal) progenitors may be released from the wall of growing blood vessels and enter the circulation. However, whether the circulation is indeed a route negotiated by skeletal progenitor cells for any physiologic purpose is unclear. Recent and less recent data on the origin of bone marrow stromal cells in recipients of bone marrow transplants have mostly indicated that the bone marrow stroma is not transplantable at the dosages and per the routes involved in systemic infusion of hematopoietic stem and progenitor cells (reviewed in reference 52). No doubt the circulation is a natural route for the systemic integration of hematopoietic function in the body, rooted into the ability of the HSCs to circulate, negotiate marrow sinusoidal walls, and home to the bone marrow microenvironment. In contrast, and regardless of the apparent physiologic occurrence of rare circulating skeletal stem cells, progenitor cells relevant to skeletal morphogenesis and growth exploit noncirculatory pathways of cell migration.

Skeletal Stem Cells and Skeletal Diseases

The notion of a stem cell in the skeleton and of a lineage emanating from it affects skeletal diseases in many different ways.[73] The one most immediately perceived involves the attempts to generate strategies for tissue engineering and reconstruction of bone segments (reviewed in reference 74). More daring approaches to therapy would involve the correction of genetic defects via cell therapy or gene therapy strategies.[75] Four considerations are important in this respect. First of all, correction of a genetic defect using skeletal stem cells will imply a more accurate notion of the phenotypic identity of the single cells endowed with complete differentiation potential and self-renewal capacities and of culture conditions suited to preserve or expand the stem cell subset in a population of stromal cells. Although transplanting an expanded population of progenitors may suffice to restore a physical defect in a bone, restoring normal bone formation during growth and adult turnover of the skeleton implies the necessary ability to restore a stem cell compartment. Second, a suitable protocol of systemic administration must be devised. This involves obtaining convincing proof in animal models of successful homing and engraftment under the test conditions (reviewed in reference 52) and exploration of route and dosage to be used. Third, effective ways for stable transduction of the stromal cells must be identified and tested, as preliminary to any attempt of genetic correction. Fourth, the inherent biologic dynamics of the skeleton and its rate of turnover must be taken into account. Hematopoietic reconstitution is rapidly achieved on bone marrow transplantation because of the rapid time of renewal of hematopoietic cells. In contrast, the slow turnover rate of the skeleton would imply a longer time for correction and the design of strategies for manipulating skeletal turnover as well.

As much as stem cells are the units of development and growth in the skeleton, they are also the units of disease. Hence, the notion of a stem cell and a lineage in the skeletal tissues can be additionally bent to better understand mechanisms of disease and how they alter the properties and the kinetics of the lineages. The transplantation assays designed to understand skeletal stem cell biology are amenable to fruitful application in the understanding of skeletal stem cell disease.[76–79] Miniature models of disease can be obtained, as well as identification of the specific cell-autonomous effects of gene defects,[80] by transplanting stromal cell strains carrying natural or target mutations. In addition, transplantation studies can be used to investigate how the internal composition of the CFU-F population is altered in disease and how this translates into clinical effects.

Determination, Commitment, and Induction

The multiple phenotypes that arise from a single progenitor stromal cell (cartilage, bone, hematopoiesis supporting stroma) are all found in individual skeletal segments at the same or different developmental stage(s). A stromal stem cell is naturally competent to generate multiple phenotypes of skeletal tissues upon *in vivo* transplantation. This does not require induction, nor does it require transplantation into an osteogenic site or environment ("determined" osteogenic progenitors[18]). The multiple differentiation events occur within the limits of a common general transcriptional control, established by the master gene of osteogenesis, Cbfa1 (reviewed in reference 52). Although Cbfa1 may not be expressed in freshly isolated Stro-1^{bright} cells,[23] it appears to be consistently expressed in cultures of stromal cells and in derivative clones and cell lines.[81] Consistent with the requirement for additional transcription factors acting downstream of Cbfa1 (e.g., osterix[82]) for a complete osteogenic commitment, expression of Cbfa1 does not dictate an obligatory osteogenic differentiation in stromal cells nor does it exclude nonosteogenic differentiation,[81] in a way highlighting a multistep, flexible mechanism for transcriptional control of osteogenesis (and the distinction between determination to skeletogenesis and commitment to a specific skeletal lineage).

Differentiation of stromal cell populations to extraskeletal phenotypes, in contrast, involves induction. Skeletal myogenic differentiation of stromal cells in culture,[83] for example, involves the use of a demethylating agent and significant alteration of the native chromatin structure. Induction of a cardiomyogenic fate *in vitro* has only been convincingly observed in spontaneously immortalized murine stromal cell lines, in turn exposed to the effects of 5′ azacytidine.[84] Exposure of stromal cells to tissue-specific differentiative cues may in principle provide induction of unorthodox differentiation. This can be mimicked *in vitro* by co-culture systems and may underlie some instances of the non-orthodox differentiation reported to occur upon *in vivo* transplantation of stromal cells into specific sites (e.g., reference 85). Although the skeletogenic potential of skeletal stem cells unfolds upon transplantation at nonspecific, nonskeletal sites (e.g., subcutaneously, or under the renal capsule) without the influence of a cue conveyed by a preexisting skeletal environment, the reported ability of stromal cells strains to differentiate into nonskeletal phenotypes involves exposure to specific tissue environments.

The existence of skeletal progenitors in nonskeletal tissues, which can generate heterotopic bone but only upon specific induction mediated by bone morphogenetic proteins (BMPs), is well established. Dramatic illustration of such inducible progenitors is found not only in a number of classical experiments in animal models[18,86] but also in a human disease. Patients with fibrodysplasia ossificans progressiva develop massive quantities of ectopic bone in their muscle, possibly as a result of ectopic expression of BMPs in circulating blood cells.[87] Many of the sporadic observations of inducible extraskeletal (e.g., myogenic) differentiation of cells that are conversely found in the bone/bone marrow environment (marrow stromal cells) may be inscribed in the same perspective. Cells inducible to multiple differentiation fates, at least within the range of mesoderm-derived tissues, could be found in a variety (possibly all) of postnatal mesodermal tissues. In fact, recent reports suggest the possible existence of inducible progenitors in articular soft tissues and subcutaneous fat.[88–91]

Whether the same set of cells in the bone marrow are both the determined progenitors for skeletal tissues and the inducible progenitors for other tissues, or if there are instead two distinct subsets of determined and inducible progenitors, remains to be resolved. Likewise, it remains to be established whether the cells capable of adopting inducible fates are in fact stem cells and whether the induced nonorthodox, differentiated phenotypes are stable, self-maintaining, and functional. A general hypothesis, currently being tested, would ascribe a repertoire of multipotent inducible mesodermal progenitors to the microvascular bed of all tissues.[72] These would be the postnatal correlate of the mesoangioblasts of the embryonic dorsal aorta, capable of concurrent myogenic and skeletogenic potential.[65] The inducible nature of these cells is reflected in their ability to adopt different fates (e.g., muscle or bone) upon their inclusion into different growing tissues (e.g., muscle or bone) during growth. The phenotypic heterogeneity of stromal cells associated with the bone marrow microvasculature suggests the testable hypothesis that determined (i.e., spontaneously skeletogenic, Cbfa1-expressing) and inducible (i.e., myogenic) progenitors may reside within distinct compartments of the bone marrow stroma.

Plasticity and the Skeleton

Obvious considerations apply when scrutinizing properties observed in cells kept in culture for extraordinary numbers of population doublings, brought to a state of relative immortalization, and/or exposed to empirically defined doses of empirically selected growth factors. The observation of unexpected differentiation in this context is not surprising. Epigenetic states are reversible, even in fully differentiated cells.[92] Nuclear reprogramming is, of course, to be kept distinct from lineage tracing and also from proof of "stemness." Generating a neuron from a marrow fibroblast hardly proves that fibroblasts are *progenitors* of neurons. However, learning how to do it in a reproducible and controlled manner can teach important lessons as to how to reprogram a cell.

The multiple skeletal lineages emanating from the common postnatal progenitor (osteoblastic, chondrocytic, adipocytic, and reticular/fibroblastic) are interconnected by a remarkable degree of plasticity, which extends beyond the putative undifferentiated stem cell. Differentiated cells in the skeleton can change phenotype *in vitro* and *in vivo*. Clonal cultures of marrow adipogenic cells can be induced to form bone on *in vivo* transplantation.[93] Reticular cells in the bone marrow *in vivo* convert to adipocytes directly.[59] Prenatal chondrocytes dedifferentiate, redifferentiate, and further differentiate into osteoblast-like cells in culture,[94] and chondrocytes turn on osteoblastic phenotypic traits at specific sites.[95]

The remarkable plasticity of a single differentiated cell in the skeleton corresponds to a high need for tissue plasticity, which becomes apparent during growth and adaptive responses. A number of examples from natural pathophysiologic circumstances in humans illustrate how in the skeleton one tissue turn into another (red marrow into yellow marrow, bone into red marrow, bone into yellow marrow, etc.), at least in terms of volume shifts.[96] One single animal model, in which the ability of connective tissue cells to degrade collagenous matrices is abolished,[80] reveals the occurrence of extensive remodeling *across* different connective tissues (remodeling of tendon into bone, cartilage into bone, ligament into bone, etc.) during growth. These remodeling events take place at sites of transition between different tissues and at sites of postnatal morphogenesis, such as the development of calvarial bones or Meckel's cartilage derivatives. At such sites, the occurrence in mammals of events representing a true correlate of metamorphosis of lower vertebrates were revealed by the MT1-MMP deficient mouse.[97] Shifts between one tissue-specific phenotype and another occur in the context of this type of remodeling. Disruption of this type of remodeling is incompatible with growth of the organism, maintenance of skeletal integrity, and ultimately life.

Concluding Remarks

The two magic words around which interest in stem cells revolves, regeneration and plasticity, point to two ancestral functions with which lower vertebrates (frogs, newts) cope with catastrophes. A newt can regenerate a severed limb[98]; a frog can adapt to the dramatic change in diet and habitat imposed by transition from life in water to land-dwelling, by plastically changing entire organs at metamorphosis. For humans, both types of catastrophes proceed to tragedy. We cannot regenerate a limb and cannot survive a ship wreck by adapting to ocean life. However, regeneration and plasticity have been selectively conserved in different tissues of higher vertebrate to cope with tissue-specific needs for constant cell renewal or plastic adaptation. The epidermis survives the limited life span of its cells by maintaining cells able to defeat Hayflick's limit. The skeleton (the hardest of all organs, except teeth) survives through the plasticity of its tissues and of its cells. A stem cell does not know the exact definition of a stem cells. From its own point of view, the whole problem is just survival. For humans, it is our own survival. Different stem cells teach us different strategies, and the skeleton, with its changing and self-renewing differentiated cells, teaches us their varied repertoire.

ACKNOWLEDGMENTS

The support of Telethon Fondazione Onlus Grant E1029 (to P.B.) is gratefully acknowledged.

REFERENCES

1. Bianco, P., Riminucci, M., Kuznetsov, S., and Robey, P.G. (1999). Multipotential cells in the bone marrow stroma: regulation in the context of organ physiology. *Crit. Rev. Eukaryot. Gene Expr.* **9,** 159–173.
2. Stenderup, K., Justesen, J., Eriksen, E.F., Rattan, S.I., and Kassem, M. (2001). Number and proliferative capacity of osteogenic stem cells are maintained during aging and in patients with osteoporosis. *J. Bone Mine. Res.* **16,** 1120–1129.
3. Friedenstein, A.J., Chailakhyan, R.K., and Gerasimov, U.V. (1987). Bone marrow osteogenic stem cells: *in vitro* cultivation and transplantation in diffusion chambers. *Cell Tissue Kinet.* **20,** 263–72.
4. Owen, M., and Friedenstein, A.J. (1988). Stromal stem cells: marrow-derived osteogenic precursors. *Ciba Found. Symp.* **136,** 42–60.
5. Owen, M. (1988). Marrow stromal stem cells. *J. Cell Sci.* (Suppl). **10,** 63–76.
6. Tavassoli, M., and Crosby, W.H. (1968). Transplantation of marrow to extramedullary sites. *Science* **161,** 54–56.
7. Friedenstein, A.J., Piatetzky, S., II, and Petrakova, K.V. (1966). Osteogenesis in transplants of bone marrow cells. *J. Embryol. Exp. Morphol.* **16,** 381–390.
8. Friedenstein, A.J., Petrakova, K.V., Kurolesova, A.I., and Frolova, G.P. (1968). Heterotopic of bone marrow: analysis of precursor cells for osteogenic and hematopoietic tissues. *Transplantation* **6,** 230–247.
9. Friedenstein, A.J., Chailakhjan, R.K., and Lalykina, K.S. (1970). The development of fibroblast colonies in monolayer cultures of guinea-pig bone marrow and spleen cells. *Cell Tissue Kinet.* **3,** 393–403.
10. Friedenstein, A.J., Deriglasova, U.F., Kulagina, N.N., Panasuk, A.F., Rudakowa, S.F., Luria, E.A., and Ruadkow, I.A. (1974). Precursors for fibroblasts in different populations of hematopoietic cells as detected by the *in vitro* colony assay method. *Exp. Hematol.* **2,** 83–92.
11. Friedenstein, A.J., Gorskaja, J.F., and Kulagina, N.N. (1976). Fibroblast precursors in normal and irradiated mouse hematopoietic organs. *Exp. Hematol.* **4,** 267–274.
12. Friedenstein, A.J., Chailakhyan, R.K., Latsinik, N.V., Panasyuk, A.F., and Keiliss-Borok, I.V. (1974). Stromal cells responsible for transferring the microenvironment of the hemopoietic tissues: cloning *in vitro* and retransplantation *in vivo*. *Transplantation* **17,** 331–340.
13. Friedenstein, A.J., Latzinik, N.W., Grosheva, A.G., and Gorskaya, U.F. (1982). Marrow microenvironment transfer by heterotopic transplantation of freshly isolated and cultured cells in porous sponges. *Exp. Hematol.* **10,** 217–227.
14. Friedenstein, A.J., Kuralesova, A.J. (1971). Osteogenic precursor cells of bone marrow in radiation chimeras. *Transplantation* **12,** 99–108.
15. Friedenstein, A.J., Ivanov-Smolenski, A.A., Chajlakjan, R.K., Gorskaya, U.F., Kuralesova, A.I., Latzinik, N.W., and Gerasimow, U.W. (1978). Origin of bone marrow stromal mechanocytes in radiochimeras and heterotopic transplants. *Exp. Hematol.* **6,** 440–444.
16. Friedenstein, A.J. (1980). Stromal mechanisms of bone marrow: cloning *in vitro* and retransplantation *in vivo*. *Haematol. Blood Transfus.* **25,** 19–29.
17. Kuznetsov, S.A., Krebsbach, P.H., Satomura, K., Kerr, J., Riminucci, M., Benayahu, D., and Robey, P.G. (1997). Single-colony derived strains of human marrow stromal fibroblasts form bone after transplantation *in vivo*. *J. Bone Miner. Res.* **12,** 1335–1347.
18. Friedenstein, A.J. (1990). Osteogenic stem cells in the bone marrow. *In* "Bone and Mineral Research"; Heersche, J.N.M., Kanis, J.A., Eds., pp. 243–272. Elsevier, San Diego.
19. Johnstone, B., Hering, T.M., Caplan, A.I., Goldberg, V.M., and Yoo, J.U. (1998). *in vitro* chondrogenesis of bone marrow-derived mesenchymal progenitor cells. *Exp. Cell Res.* **238,** 265–272.
20. Sekiya, I., Vuoristo, J.T., Larson, B.L., and Prockop, D.J. (2002). *in vitro* cartilage formation by human adult stem cells from bone marrow stroma defines the sequence of cellular and molecular events during chondrogenesis. *Proc. Natl. Acad. Sci. U. S. A.* **99,** 4397–402.
21. Muraglia, A., Corsi, A., Riminucci, M., Mastrogiacomo, M., Cancedda, R., Bianco, P., and Quarto, R. (2003). Formation of a chondro-osseous rudiment in micromass cultures of human bone-marrow stromal cells. *J. Cell Sci.* **116,** 2949–2955.
22. Bruder, S.P., Jaiswal, N., and Haynesworth, S.E. (1997). Growth kinetics, self-renewal, and the osteogenic potential of purified human mesenchymal stem cells during extensive subcultivation and following cryopreservation. *J. Cell Biochem.* **64,** 278–294.
23. Gronthos, S., Zannettino, A.C., Hay, S.J., Shi, S., Graves, S.E., Kortesidis, A., and Simmons, P.J. (2003). Molecular and cellular characterisation of highly purified stromal stem cells derived from human bone marrow. *J. Cell Sci.* **116,** 1827–1835.
24. Satomura, K., Derubeis, A.R., Fedarko, N.S., Ibaraki-O'Connor, K., Kuznetsov, S.A., Rowe, D.W., Young, M.F., and Gehron

Robey, P. (1998). Receptor tyrosine kinase expression in human bone marrow stromal cells. *J. Cell Physiol.* **177,** 426–438.
25. Gronthos, S., and Simmons, P.J. (1995). The growth factor requirements of STRO-1-positive human bone marrow stromal precursors under serum-deprived conditions *in vitro. Blood* **85,** 929–940.
26. Martin, I., Muraglia, A., Campanile, G., Cancedda, R., and Quarto, R. (1997). Fibroblast growth factor-2 supports ex vivo expansion and maintenance of osteogenic precursors from human bone marrow. *Endocrinology* **138,** 4456–4462.
27. Muraglia, A., Cancedda, R., and Quarto, R. (2000). Clonal mesenchymal progenitors from human bone marrow differentiate *in vitro* according to a hierarchical model. *J. Cell Sci.* **113,** 1161–1166.
28. Sherley, J.L. (2002). Asymmetric cell kinetics genes: the key to expansion of adult stem cells in culture. *Stem Cells* **20,** 561–572.
29. Watt, F.M., and Hogan, B.L.M. (2000). Out of Eden: stem cells and their niches. *Science* **287,** 1427–1430.
30. Sherley, J.L., Stadler, P.B., and Johnson, D.R. (1995). Expression of the wild-type p53 antioncogene induces guanine nucleotide-dependent stem cell division kinetics. *Proc. Natl. Acad. Sci U. S. A.* **92,** 136–140.
31. Sherley, J.L. (1991). Guanine nucleotide biosynthesis is regulated by the cellular p53 concentration. *J. Biol. Chem.* **266,** 24815–28.
32. Rambhatla, L., Bohn, S.A., Stadler, P.B., Boyd, J.T., Coss, R.A., and Sherley, J.L. (2001). Cellular Senescence: ex vivo p53-dependent asymmetric cell kinetics. *J. Biomed. Biotechnol.* **1,** 28–37.
33. Banfi, A., Bianchi, G., Notaro, R., Luzzatto, L., Cancedda, R., and Quarto, R. (2002). Replicative aging and gene expression in long-term cultures of human bone marrow stromal cells. *Tissue Eng.* **8,** 901–910.
34. Yatabe, Y., Tavare, S., and Shibata, D. (2001). Investigating stem cells in the human colon by using methylation patterns. *Proc. Natl. Acad. Sci U. S. A.* **981,** 10839–10844.
35. Loeffler, M., and Potten, C.S. (1997). Stem cells and cellular pedigrees: a conceptual introduction. *In* Stem cells; Potte, S., Ed., pp. 1–28. Harcourt Brace & Co., San Diego, CA.
36. Bianchi, G., Banfi, A., Mastrogiacomo, M., Notaro, R., Luzzatto, L., Cancedda, R., and Quarto, R. (2003). Ex vivo enrichment of mesenchymal cell progenitors by fibroblast growth factor 2. *Exp. Cell. Res.* **287,** 98–105.
37. Zimmermann, S., Voss, M., Kaiser, S., Kapp, U., Waller, C.F., and Martens, U.M. (2003). Lack of telomerase activity in human mesenchymal stem cells. *Leukemia* **17,** 1146–1149.
38. Allsopp, R.C., Cheshier, S., and Weissman, I.L. (2002). Telomerase activation and rejuvenation of telomere length in stimulated T cells derived from serially transplanted hematopoietic stem cells. *J. Exp. Med.* **196,** 1427–1433.
39. Allsopp, R.C., Morin, G.B., DePinho, R., Harley, C.B., and Weissman, I.L. (2003). Telomerase is required to slow telomere shortening and extend replicative lifespan of HSCs during serial transplantation. *Blood* **102,** 517–520.
40. Pittenger, M.F., Mackay, A.M., Beck, S.C., Jaiswal, R.K., Douglas, R., Mosca, J.D., Moorman, M.A., Simonetti, D.W., Craig, S., and Marshak, D.R. (1999). Multilineage potential of adult human mesenchymal stem cells. *Science* **284,** 143–147.
41. Walsh, S., Jefferiss, C., Stewart, K., Jordan, G.R., Screen, J., and Beresford, J.N. (2000). Expression of the developmental markers STRO-1 and alkaline phosphatase in cultures of human marrow stromal cells: regulation by fibroblast growth factor (FGF)-2 and relationship to the expression of FGF receptors 1-4. *Bone* **27,** 185–195.
42. Stewart, K., Walsh, S., Screen, J., Jefferiss, C.M., Chainey, J., Jordan, G.R., and Beresford, J.N. (1999). Further characterization of cells expressing STRO-1 in cultures of adult human bone marrow stromal cells. *J. Bone Miner. Res.* **14,** 1345–1356.
43. Gronthos, S., Graves, S.E., Ohta, S., and Simmons, P.J. (1994). The STRO-1+ fraction of adult human bone marrow contains the osteogenic precursors. *Blood* **84,** 4164–4173.
44. Gronthos, S., Zannettino, A.C., Graves, S.E., Ohta, S., Hay, S. J., and Simmons, P.J. (1999). Differential cell surface expression of the STRO-1 and alkaline phosphatase antigens on discrete developmental stages in primary cultures of human bone cells. *J. Bone Miner. Res.* **14,** 47–56.
45. Simmons, P.J., and Torok-Storb, B. (1991). Identification of stromal cell precursors in human bone marrow by a novel monoclonal antibody, STRO-1. *Blood* **78,** 55–62.
46. Joyner, C.J., Bennett, A., and Triffitt, J.T. (1997). Identification and enrichment of human osteoprogenitor cells by using differentiation stage-specific monoclonal antibodies. *Bone* **21,** 1–6.
47. Zannettino, A.C., Harrison, K., Joyner, C.J., Triffitt, J.T., and Simmons, P.J. (2003). Molecular cloning of the cell surface antigen identified by the osteoprogenitor-specific monoclonal antibody, HOP-26. *J. Cell Biochem.* **89,** 56–66.
48. Bruder, S.P., Horowitz, M.C., Mosca, J.D., and Haynesworth, S.E. (1997). Monoclonal antibodies reactive with human osteogenic cell surface antigens. *Bone* **21,** 225–235.
49. Bruder, S.P., Ricalton, N.S., Boynton, R.E., Connolly, T.J., Jaiswal, N., Zaia, J., and Barry, F.P. (1998). Mesenchymal stem cell surface antigen SB-10 corresponds to activated leukocyte cell adhesion molecule and is involved in osteogenic differentiation. *J. Bone Miner. Res.* **13,** 655–663.
50. Deschaseaux, F., and Charbord, P. (2000). Human marrow stromal precursors are alpha 1 integrin subunit-positive. *J. Cell Physiol.* **184,** 319–325.
51. Stewart, K., Monk, P., Walsh, S., Jefferiss, C.M., Letchford, J., and Beresford, J.N. (2003). STRO-1, HOP-26 (CD63), CD49a and SB-10 (CD166) as markers of primitive human marrow stromal cells and their more differentiated progeny: a comparative investigation *in vitro. Cell Tissue Res.* **313,** 281–290.
52. Bianco, P., and Gehron Robey, P. (2000). Marrow stromal stem cells. *J. Clin. Invest.* **105,** 1663–8.
53. Bianco, P., Riminucci, M., Gronthos, S., and Robey, P. G. (2001). Bone marrow stromal stem cells: nature, biology, and potential applications. *Stem Cells* **19,** 180–92.
54. Simmons, P.J., Masinovsky, B., Longenecker, B.M., Berenson, R., Torok-Storb, B., and Gallatin, W.M. (1992). Vascular cell adhesion molecule-1 expressed by bone marrow stromal cells mediates the binding of hematopoietic progenitor cells. *Blood* **80,** 388–395.
55. Hirschi, K.K., and D'Amore, P.A. (1996). Pericytes in the microvasculature. *Cardiovasc. Res.* **32,** 687–698.
56. Nehls, V., and Drenckhahn, D. (1993). The versatility of microvascular pericytes: from mesenchyme to smooth muscle? *Histochemistry* **99,** 1–12.
57. Doherty, M., Boot-Handford, R.P., Grant, M.E., and Canfield, A.E. (1998). Identification of genes expressed during the osteogenic differentiation of vascular pericytes *in vitro. Biochem. Soc. Trans.* **26,** S4.
58. Doherty, M.J., Ashton, B.A., Walsh, S., Beresford, J.N., Grant, M.E., and Canfield, A.E. (1998). Vascular pericytes express osteogenic potential *in vitro* and in vivo. *J. Bone Miner. Res.* **13,** 828–838.
59. Bianco, P., Costantini, M., Dearden, L.C., and Bonucci, E. (1988). Alkaline phosphatase positive precursors of adipocytes in the human bone marrow. *Br. J. Haematol.* **68,** 401–403.

60. Bianco, P., and Boyde, A. (1993). Confocal images of marrow stromal (Westen-Bainton) cells. *Histochemistry* **100,** 93–99.
61. Filshie, R.J., Zannettino, A.C., Makrynikola, V., Gronthos, S., Henniker, A.J., Bendall, L.J., Gottlieb, D.J., Simmons, P.J., and Bradstock, K.F. (1998). MUC18, a member of the immunoglobulin superfamily, is expressed on bone marrow fibroblasts and a subset of hematological malignancies. *Leukemia* **12,** 414–421.
62. Shi, S., and Gronthos, S. (2003). Perivascular niche of postnatal mesenchymal stem cells in human bone marrow and dental pulp. *J. Bone Miner. Res.* **18,** 696–704.
63. Reyes, M., Dudek, A., Jahagirdar, B., Koodie, L., Marker, P.H., and Verfaillie, C.M. (2002). Origin of endothelial progenitors in human postnatal bone marrow. *J. Clin. Invest.* **109,** 337–346.
64. Minasi, M.G., Riminucci, M., De Angelis, L., Borello, U., Berarducci, B., Innocenzi, A., Caprioli, A., Sirabella, D., Baiocchi, M., De Maria, R., Boratto, R., Jaffredo, T., Broccoli, V., Bianco, P., and Cossu, G. (2002). The meso-angioblast: a multipotent, self-renewing cell that originates from the dorsal aorta and differentiates into most mesodermal tissues. *Development* **129,** 2773–2783.
65. Cossu, G., and Bianco, P. (2003). Mesoangioblasts: vascular progenitors for extravascular mesodermal tissues. *Curr. Op. Genet. Dev* **13,** 537–542.
66. Medvinsky, A., and Dzierzak, E. (1996). Definitive hematopoiesis is autonomously initiated by the AGM region. *Cell* **86,** 897–906.
67. Dzierzak, E. (2003). Ontogenic emergence of definitive hematopoietic stem cells. *Curr. Opin. Hematol.* **10,** 229–34.
68. Marshall, C.J., Moore, R.L., Thorogood, P., Brickell, P.M., Kinnon, C., and Thrasher, A.J. (1999). Detailed characterization of the human aorta-gonad-mesonephros region reveals morphological polarity resembling a hematopoietic stromal layer. *Dev. Dyn.* **215,** 139–147.
69. Marshall, C.J., Kinnon, C., and Thrasher, A.J. (2000). Polarized expression of bone morphogenetic protein-4 in the human aorta-gonad-mesonephros region. *Blood* **96,** 1591–1593.
70. Oostendorp, R.A., Harvey, K.N., Kusadasi, N., de Bruijn, M.F., Saris, C., Ploemacher, R.E., Medvinsky, A.L., and Dzierzak, E.A. (2002). Stromal cell lines from mouse aorta-gonads-mesonephros subregions are potent supporters of hematopoietic stem cell activity. *Blood* **99,** 1183–1189.
71. Kuznetsov, S.A., Mankani, M.H., Gronthos, S., Satomura, K., Bianco, P., and Robey, P.G. (2001). Circulating skeletal stem cells. *J. Cell Biol.* **153,** 1133–1140.
72. Bianco, P., and Cossu, G. (1999). Uno, nessuno e centomila: searching for the identity of mesodermal progenitors. *Exp. Cell Res.* **251,** 257–263.
73. Bianco, P., and Robey, P. (1999). Diseases of bone and the stromal cell lineage. *J. Bone Miner. Res.* **14,** 336–341.
74. Bianco, P., and Robey, P.G. (2001). Stem cells in tissue engineering. *Nature* **414,** 118–121.
75. Horwitz, E.M., Prockop, D.J., Fitzpatrick, L.A., Koo, W.W., Gordon, P.L., Neel, M., Sussman, M., Orchard, P., Marx, J.C., Pyeritz, R.E., and Brenner, M.K. (1999). Transplantability and therapeutic effects of bone marrow-derived mesenchymal cells in children with osteogenesis imperfecta. *Nat. Med.* **5,** 309–313.
76. Bianco, P., Kuznetsov, S.A., Riminucci, M., Fisher, L.W., Spiegel, A.M., and Robey, P.G. (1998). Reproduction of human fibrous dysplasia of bone in immunocompromised mice by transplanted mosaics of normal and Gsalpha-mutated skeletal progenitor cells. *J. Clin. Invest.* **101,** 1737–1744.
77. Bianco, P., and Robey, P.G. (1999). An animal model of fibrous dysplasia. *Mol. Med. Today* **5,** 322–323.
78. Bianco, P., Riminucci, M., Majolagbe, A., Kuznetsov, S.A., Collins, M.T., Mankani, M.H., Corsi, A., Bone, H.G., Wientroub, S., Spiegel, A.M., Fisher, L.W., and Robey, P.G. (2000). Mutations of the GNAS1 gene, stromal cell dysfunction, and osteomalacic changes in non-McCune-Albright fibrous dysplasia of bone. *J. Bone Miner. Res.* **15,** 120–128.
79. Riminucci, M., Collins, M.T., Corsi, A., Boyde, A., Murphey, M.D., Wientroub, S., Kuznetsov, S.A., Cherman, N., Robey, P.G., and Bianco, P. (2001). Gnathodiaphyseal dysplasia: a syndrome of fibro-osseous lesions of jawbones, bone fragility, and long bone bowing. *J. Bone Miner. Res.* **16,** 1710–1718.
80. Holmbeck, K., Bianco, P., Caterina, J., Yamada, S., Kromer, M., Kuznetsov, S.A., Mankani, M., Robey, P.G., Poole, A.R., Pidoux, I., Ward, J.M., and Birkedal-Hansen, H. (1999). MT1-MMP-deficient mice develop dwarfism, osteopenia, arthritis, and connective tissue disease due to inadequate collagen turnover. *Cell* **99,** 81–92.
81. Satomura, K., Krebsbach, P., Bianco, P., and Gehron Robey, P. (2000). Osteogenic imprinting upstream of marrow stromal cell differentiation. *J. Cell Biochem.* **78,** 391–403.
82. Nakashima, K., Zhou, X., Kunkel, G., Zhang, Z., Deng, J.M., Behringer, R.R., and de Crombrugghe, B. (2002). The novel zinc finger-containing transcription factor osterix is required for osteoblast differentiation and bone formation. *Cell* **108,** 17–29.
83. Wakitani, S., Saito, T., and Caplan, A.I. (1995). Myogenic cells derived from rat bone marrow mesenchymal stem cells exposed to 5-azacytidine. *Muscle Nerve* **18,** 1417–1426.
84. Makino, S., Fukuda, K., Miyoshi, S., Konishi, F., Kodama, H., Pan, J., Sano, M., Takahashi, T., Hori, S., Abe, H., Hata, J., Umezawa, A., and Ogawa, S. (1999). Cardiomyocytes can be generated from marrow stromal cells *in vitro*. *J. Clin. Invest.* **103,** 697–705.
85. Kopen, G.C., Prockop, D.J., and Phinney, D.G. (1999). Marrow stromal cells migrate throughout forebrain and cerebellum, and they differentiate into astrocytes after injection into neonatal mouse brains. *Proc. Natl. Acad. Sci. U. S. A.* **96,** 10711–10716.
86. Friedenstein, A.J. (1962). Humoral nature of osteogenic activity of transitional epithelium. *Nature* **194,** 698–699.
87. Shafritz, A.B., Shore, E.M., Gannon, F.H., Zasloff, M.A., Taub, R., Muenke, M., and Kaplan, F.S. (1996). Overexpression of an osteogenic morphogen in fibrodysplasia ossificans progressiva. *N. Engl. J. Med.* **335,** 555–561.
88. Halvorsen, Y.C., Wilkison, W.O., and Gimble, J.M. (2000). Adipose-derived stromal cells–their utility and potential in bone formation. *Int. J. Obes. Relat. Metab. Disord.* **24** (Suppl 4), S41–S44.
89. Wickham, M.Q., Erickson, G.R., Gimble, J.M., Vail, T.P., and Guilak, F. (2003). Multipotent stromal cells derived from the infrapatellar fat pad of the knee. *Clin. Orthop.* **412,** 196–212.
90. De Bari, C., Dell'Accio, F., Tylzanowski, P., and Luyten, F.P. (2001). Multipotent mesenchymal stem cells from adult human synovial membrane. *Arthritis Rheum.* **44,** 1928–1942.
91. De Bari, C., Dell'Accio, F., Vandenabeele, F., Vermeesch, J.R., Raymackers, J.M., and Luyten, F.P. (2003). Skeletal muscle repair by adult human mesenchymal stem cells from synovial membrane. *J. Cell Biol.* **160,** 909–918.
92. Surani, M.A. (2001). Reprogramming of genome function through epigenetic inheritance. *Nature* **414,** 122–128.
93. Bennett, J.H., Joyner, C.J., Triffitt, J.T., and Owen, M.E. (1991). Adipocytic cells cultured from marrow have osteogenic potential. *J. Cell Sci.* **99,** 131–139.
94. Gentili, C., Bianco, P., Neri, M., Malpeli, M., Campanile, G., Castagnola, P., Cancedda, R., and Cancedda, F.D. (1993).

Cell proliferation, extracellular matrix mineralization, and ovotransferrin transient expression during *in vitro* differentiation of chick hypertrophic chondrocytes into osteoblast-like cells. *J. Cell Biol.* **122,** 703–712.

95. Riminucci, M., Bradbeer, J.N., Corsi, A., Gentili, C., Descalzi, F., Cancedda, R., and Bianco, P. (1998). Vis-a-vis cells and the priming of bone formation. *J. Bone Miner. Res.* **13,** 1852–1861.

96. Bianco, P., and Riminucci, M. (1998). The bone marrow stroma in vivo: ontogeny, structure, cellular composition and changes in disease. *In* Marrow stromal cell culture; Beresford, J.N., Owen, M.E., Eds., pp. 10–25. Cambridge University Press, Cambridge, U.K.

97. Holmbeck, K., Bianco, P., Chrysovergis, K., Yamada, S., and Birkedal-Hansen, H. (2003). MT1-MMP-dependent, apoptotic remodeling of unmineralized cartilage: a critical process in skeletal growth. *J. Cell Biol.* **163,** 661–671.

98. Brockes, J.P., and Kumar, A. (2002). Plasticity and reprogramming of differentiated cells in amphibian regeneration. *Nat. Rev. Mol. Cell Biol.* **3,** 566–574.

40

Stem Cells from Adipose Tissue

Patricia A. Zuk, Prosper Benhaim, and Marc H. Hedrick

Much of the work conducted on adult stem cells has concentrated on mesenchymal stem cells (MSCs) found within the bone marrow stroma. However, isolation of bone marrow is frequently painful and often yields low doses of MSCs that require extensive *in vitro* cultivation. Adipose tissue, like bone marrow, is derived from the embryonic mesoderm and contains a stroma that is easily isolated in larger quantities compared with bone marrow. As such, adipose tissue may represent an attractive source for adult stem cells. In the original work by Zuk *et al.*,[1] these stem cells, termed processed lipoaspirate (PLA) cells, can be isolated from cosmetic liposuctions in large numbers and grow easily under standard tissue culture conditions. With appropriate exogenous stimulation, PLA cells differentiate toward the osteogenic, adipogenic, myogenic, and chondrogenic lineages *in vitro,* expressing multiple lineage-specific genes and proteins. This multipotential mesodermal capacity is also observed in single PLA cell-derived clones, confirming the stem cell phenotype. To date, several groups have confirmed the multipotency of these stem cells, in addition to demonstrating their *in vivo* differentiative capacity, suggesting that these cells may be useful for mesodermal tissue engineering strategies. However, PLA cells may not be restricted to just the mesodermal lineage because they have recently been shown to differentiate into putative neurogenic cells, exhibiting a neuronal-like morphology and expressing several proteins consistent with the neuronal phenotype. This plasticity has been demonstrated in other adult stem cell populations and suggests that adult stem cells in general may have broader lineage capabilities than their tissue of origin.

Introduction

Historically, the adipose compartment has been considered primarily a metabolic reservoir—effectively packaging, storing, and releasing high-energy substrates in the form of triglycerides and cholesterol and lipid soluble vitamins. However, it is now known that excess adipose stores are also associated with a variety of serious disorders such as heart disease, diabetes, and stroke. Clearly, the study of the adipose compartment will have important implications for our collective health. However, in contrast to the complex metabolic pathways mediating lipid storage, relatively little is known about the ontogeny, cellular composition, and turnover of adipose tissue and its broader roles beyond its importance in metabolism. Recent findings suggest that the adipose compartment may possess another function–that of progenitor cell reservoir. The purpose of this chapter is to describe the cellular composition and biology of the stem cell component of the adipose compartment as it is currently understood.

Handbook of Stem Cells
Volume 2

Background

The identification of pluripotent MSCs in the bone marrow stroma more than 25 years ago[2] has led researchers to a variety of exciting research avenues. Capable of differentiating to multiple mesodermal lineages, including bone and cartilage, bone marrow MSCs have become a standard in the field of adult stem cell biology.[3–10] However, difficulties in the isolation and culturing of MSCs have prompted researchers to look for analogous stem cell populations elsewhere.

Like the bone marrow, adipose tissue is mesodermally derived and contains an extensive cellular stroma. In 1964, Rodbell, using a combination of proteolytic digestion and differential centrifugation, successfully separated mature adipocytes from a more dense, cellular fraction that he termed the stromo-vascular fraction (SVF).[11] Characterization of this SVF fraction revealed the presence of fibroblastic connective tissue cells, mast cells, and macrophages. Using a similar protocol, Van *et al.* and Poznanski *et al.* established cultures from the SVF.[12,13] Together with Green and Meuth[14] they found that these SVF cells differentiate into the lipid-filled cells characteristic of mature adipocytes. As such, these connective tissue cells within the SVF were considered to be preadipocytes. In 1987, Deslex and colleagues confirmed the adipocytic conversion of these preadipocytes in a chemically defined, serum-free medium containing insulin, transferrin, and triiodothryonine.[15] Further work, by Hauner in 1989, expanded the knowledge that the preadipocytes within the SVF represented a progenitor population, although apparently limited to the adipocytic lineage.[16] However, in 2001, Zuk *et al.* showed that a population of adipose derived cells similar to the SVF fraction contained cells with multilineage potential.[1] In their work, cells isolated from human lipoaspirates, termed PLA cells, underwent adipogenesis, osteogenesis, chondrogenesis, and myogenesis *in vitro,* suggesting that the SVF fraction of adipose tissue may be composed not just of lineage-limited preadipocytes but of multipotent stem cells.

ADIPOSE TISSUE AS A STEM CELL SOURCE

Currently, multiple sources for the isolation of adult stem cells have been identified. Pluripotent cells similar to MSCs have been identified and isolated from multiple connective tissue sources in both animals and humans. Stem cells isolated from heart tissue differentiate into several mesodermal lineages.[17] Umbilical cord blood stem cells show similar differentiation capacities.[18,19] Muscle-derived satellite cells and/or stem cells express cellular markers of the myogenic, osteogenic, endothelial, and neuronal lineages.[20–24] Multipotent adult stem cells can be isolated from the dermis of skin.[25] Furthermore, a significant body of literature exists that describes the multipotent capacity of bone marrow MSCs. Adipose tissue may be a source of similar stem cells. The removal of fat through suction-assisted lipectomy or liposuction is the most commonly performed cosmetic surgical procedure. Performed often under local anesthesia and as an outpatient procedure, liposuction represents a safe source of unprecedented volumes of autologous tissue. Together with the multipotentiality of PLA cells, these characteristics may make adipose tissue a clinically relevant source of cells similar to MSCs found in bone marrow.

The PLA Cell Population: Composition and Characterization

In 2001, Zuk *et al.* characterized the multilineage differentiation potential of SVF-like cells, obtained from human lipoaspirates, and termed this stem cell population PLA cells.[1] As outlined in several studies, PLA cells are isolated from lipoaspirates through a short-term collagenase digestion, followed by centrifugation. Although PLA cells are isolated using a similar protocol as described for the SVF fraction, Zuk and co-workers chose the term PLA cells to represent a heterogenous stem cell population derived from lipoaspirates rather than cells derived from intact fat. Therefore, the term PLA cells is used in this chapter to represent a multipotent stem cell population derived specifically from liposuctioned adipose tissue rather than intact fat and is comparable in many ways to SVF cell populations.

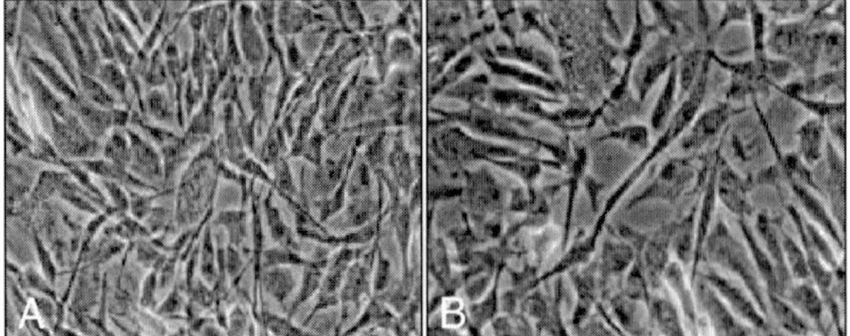

Figure 40–1. *Processed lipoaspirate (PLA) cells and mesenchymal stem cells (MSCs) have similar morphologies in culture.* The morphology of PLA cells (A) and bone marrow-derived MSCs (B), maintained under standard tissue culture conditions (Dulbeccos modified essential medium [DMEM], 10% fetal bovine serum [FBS]) is shown.

Morphologically, freshly isolated PLA fractions are heterogenous containing, in addition to fibroblastic cells, endothelial cells, macrophages, and smooth muscle cells. Using conventional flow cytometry, contaminating cells (i.e., endothelial cells and smooth muscle cells) are found to typically make up 5 to 20% of the PLA population. However, these cell populations diminish over subsequent culture passages, leaving a homogenous fibroblastic PLA cell population similar in appearance to cultured MSCs (Fig. 40–1). The remaining 80% of the PLA population is confirmed as mesenchymal in origin based on expression of vimentin and the fibroblastic marker AS02.[1] PLA cells differentiate readily *in vitro* to the adipogenic, osteogenic, chondrogenic, myogenic, and neurogenic lineages on treatment with lineage-specific factors (Table 40–1). These differentiation capacities are highly reproducible, with most patients exhibiting all lineages. PLA cells,

TABLE 40–1
Lineage-specific Differentiation of Processed Lipoaspirate (PLA) Cells Induced by Media Supplementation

Medium	Media	Serum	Supplementation
Control	DMEM	10% FBS	1% antibiotic/antimycotic
Adipogenic (AM)	DMEM	10% FBS	0.5 mM isobutyl-methylxanthine (IBMX), 1 μM dexamethasone, 10 μM insulin, 200 μM indomethacin, 1% antibiotic/antimycotic
Osteogenic (OM/VD)	DMEM	10% FBS	0.01 μM 1,25-dihydroxyvitamin D3*, 50 μM ascorbate-2-phosphate, 10 mM β-glycerophosphate, 1% antibiotic/antimycotic
Chondrogenic (CM)	DMEM	1% FBS	6.25 μg/ml insulin, 10 ng/ml TGFβ1, 50 nm ascorbate-2-phosphate, 1% antibiotic/antimycotic
Myogenic (MM)	DMEM	10% FBS, 5% HS	50 μM hydrocortisone, 1% antibiotic/antimycotic
Neurogenic (NM)	DMEM	none	5–10 mM β-mercaptoethanol

*0.1 μM dexamethasone can be used in replacement of 0.01 μM vitamin D.

AM, Adinogenic medium; CM, chondrogenic medium; DMEM, dulbeccos modified essential medium; FBS, fetal bovine serum; HS, horse serum; MM, myogenic medium; NM, neurogenic medium; OM, osteogenic medium; TGFβ1, transforming growth factor beta 1; VD, vitamin D.

obtained from multiple donors, exhibit an average population doubling time of 60 to 80 hours under standard tissue culture conditions (Dulbeccos modified essential medium [DMEM], 10% fetal bovine serum [FBS]) with senescence levels at early passages well below 5% of the total population cell number.[1,26] This doubling rate was not significantly different from that measured in bone marrow MSCs (30 to 86 hours).[26–28] Moreover, PLA growth kinetics and differentiation capacities are not significantly altered by long-term culture (Fig. 40–2).

The heterogeneity of freshly isolated PLA populations represents a significant problem for confirming the presence of a stem cell population. Specifically, the apparent multidifferentiative capacity of PLA cells may be due to the presence of a contaminating cell population that possesses multipotentiality. As an example, the liposuction procedure and the unavoidable vascular damage that results may be an avenue for the introduction of pericytes, a cell type known to possess multilineage mesodermal capacity.[29–31] However, analysis of cultured PLA populations using indirect immunofluorescence reveals negligible levels of a pericyte-specific glycoprotein 3G5,[32] indicating low levels of pericyte contamination with the PLA cell population. Furthermore, vascular damage may introduce circulating MSCs from the peripheral blood. However, the presence of significant numbers of MSCs within peripheral blood is controversial and does not adequately explain the significant numbers of stem cells isolated from adipose tissue.[33,34] Therefore, it is likely that the multilineage differentiation of PLA cells observed by Zuk *et al.* is due to the presence of a bona fide stem cell from the adipose tissue itself.

Characterization of PLA cell surface markers by flow cytometry and indirect immunofluorescence has identified several cell surface markers common to bone marrow MSCs. Both MSCs and PLA cells express STRO-1, a marker protein originally used to isolate osteogenic progenitors from bone marrow[35] in addition to SH3, a cell surface antigen found on human MSCs.[36] Furthermore, both PLA and MSC populations express similar CD antigen profiles. Consistent with their characterization as mesodermal stem cells, both MSC and PLA cell populations do not express hematopoietic markers, such as CD31 and CD45 (Fig. 40–3A). Although expression of CD34 is measured in freshly isolated cells, this marker decreases significantly on *in vitro* culture. In addition, PLA cells and MSCs express multiple CD antigens in common, including CD44/Pgp-1, CD90/Thy-1, CD9, CD10, CD11b/integrin-α_M, CD13, CD29/integrin-β_1, CD54/ICAM-1, CD55, CD91, CD105/endoglin, CD71/TfR, CD146/Muc-18, and CD166/ALCAM.[37,38,38a] Two of these markers, CD105 and CD166, have been used to define bone marrow MSCs that are capable of differentiating into multiple mesodermal lineages.[6,39,40] Specifically, CD105/ endoglin–the transforming growth factor beta (TGFβ) receptor type III—has been shown to play a putative role in TGFβ-induced chondrogenic differentiation by MSCs.[41] It is likely that these CD antigens play a similar role in PLA cells. Furthermore, antibodies to CD9, CD29 and CD44 have been shown to interfere with the differentiation of hematopoietic stem cells (HSCs) suggesting that stem cells expressing these proteins may be capable of hematopoietic support.

Based on the similarity in CD marker expression profile it is possible that PLA cells and MSCs are variants of the same cell type, with the adipose compartment becoming "seeded" with circulating MSCs. However, important distinctions in

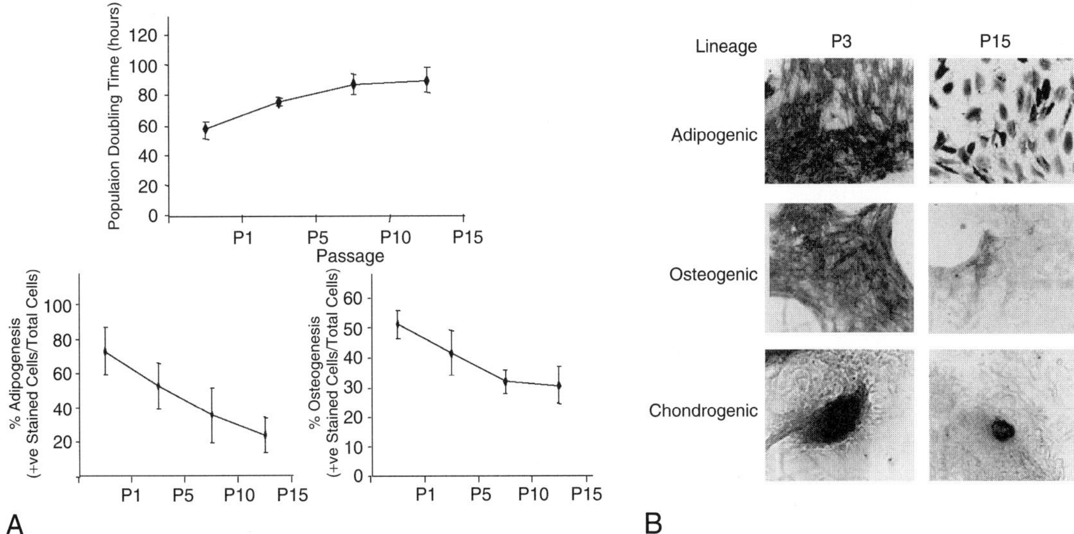

Figure 40–2. *Processed lipoaspirate (PLA) cells retain their multipotentiality over long-term culture.* (A) Top: Growth kinetics of PLA cells was measured over long-term culture conditions. Cells were cultured under standard culture conditions and population doubling determined at passages 1, 5, 10, and 15 (P1, P5, P10, P15). Bottom: Cultures at these passages were differentiated toward the adipogenic and osteogenic lineages and differentiation levels expressed as the percentage of differentiated cells per total cell number. (B) Histologic confirmation of PLA adipogenesis (oil red O staining), osteogenesis (alkaline phosphatase activity), and chondrogenesis (alcian blue staining) at passage 3 (P3: approximately 21 days) and passage 15 (P15; approximately 195 days). (Please see CD-ROM for color version of this figure.)

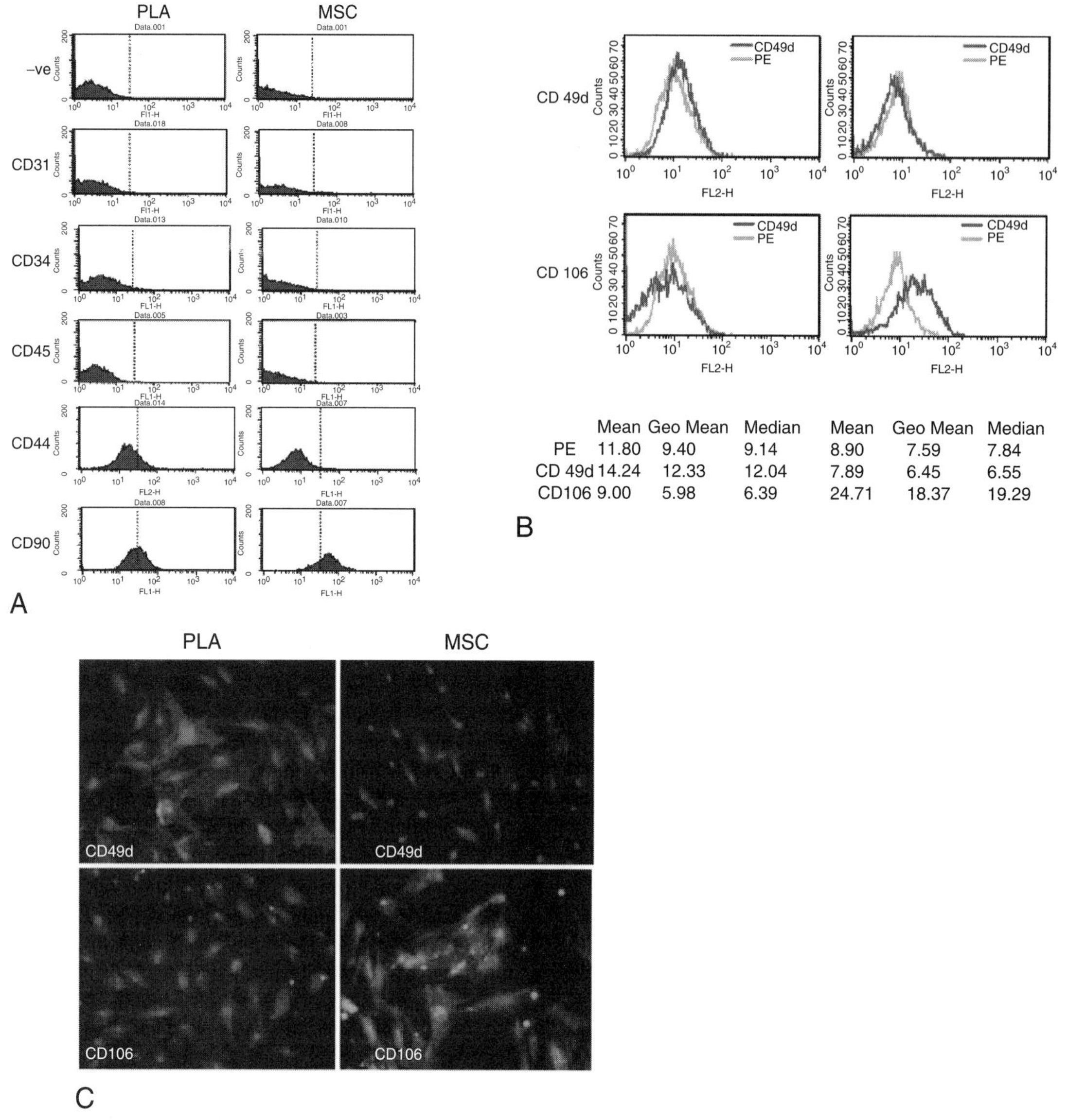

Figure 40–3. *Processed lipoaspirate (PLA) cells exhibit distinctions in CD antigen expression from bone marrow MSCs.* (A) PLA cells and bone marrow mesenchymal stem cells (MSCs) were analyzed by flow cytometry for the indicated CD antigens. Cells stained with a fluorochrome-conjugated nonspecific IgG were examined as a negative control (-ve). (B) Flow cytometric analysis of PLA cells and MSCs for the expression of CD49d and CD106 was performed. Cells stained with a fluorochrome-conjugated nonspecific IgG were examined as a control (PE). The geometric mean and median values for CD49d and CD106 are shown and significant differences are indicated in bold. (C) PLA cells and MSCs were analyzed by immunofluorescence for the expression of CD49d and CD106. Cells were co-stained with DAPI to visualize nuclei and the fluorescent images were combined. (Reproduced with permission from *Mol. Biol. Cell* 13:4279. 2002.) (Please see CD-ROM for color version of this figure.)

CD antigen expression can be discerned between the two populations, suggesting that they are more likely distinct stem cell populations. Gronthos *et al.* measure significant levels of CD34–a marker protein expressed on hematopoietic precursors and endothelial cells–on the surface of cultured MCSs by flow cytometry.[38] In contrast, Zuk and co-workers measure negligible levels of this CD antigen on cultured PLA cells, although detectable expression of this antigen is observed in freshly isolated cells (Fig. 40–3A). Furthermore, several groups have reported the expression of CD140–a platelet-derived growth factor (PDGF) receptor–on the MSC surface. Like CD34, this antigen is not detected on PLA cells.[42] Most significantly, Zuk *et al.* detect expression of CD49d/integrin-α_4 on PLA cells using both immunofluorescence and flow cytometry.[37] CD49d, an adhesion protein that dimerizes with CD29/integrin-β_1 to form the very late antigen/VLA-4, is a ligand for CD106/VCAM-1 and expression of these markers on MSCs is supportive of their role in hematopoiesis.[6,43,44] However, Zuk *et al.* fail to detect CD49d expression in MSCs using both immunofluorescence and flow cytometry (Fig. 40–3B and C), a finding that is supported by others.[40,45] Moreover, in contrast to MSCs, cultured PLA cells do not express the CD49d receptor, VCAM-1. The absence of VCAM-1 in PLA populations may be due to several reasons ranging from a response to *in vitro* adhesion conditions, to the proliferative stage of the cells, to the absence of factors required for VCAM-1 induction. Whatever the reason, the differential expression of CD antigens like CD49d and CD106 between MSCs and PLA stem cells may represent a useful tool for identifying progenitors in the PLA population as unique and for their subsequent isolation.

PLA Multipotentiality

ADIPOGENESIS

In Vitro Adipogenesis

Preadipocytes treated with cAMP agonists (i.e., IBMX), anti-inflammatories (i.e., indomethacin and dexamethasone), and hormones (i.e., insulin) develop lipid-containing intracellular vacuoles, a hallmark of the mature adipocyte phenotype.[14–16,46–48] The adipogenic differentiation of these cells is not surprising, and there are extensive studies that confirm this phenomenon. However, because the recent finding that PLA cells may contain a multipotential population, it is necessary to readjust our thinking.

Consistent with this, PLA cells cultured in the presence of IBMX, insulin, indomethacin, and dexamethasone reproducibly develop intracellular vacuoles that accumulate the lipid dye oil red O as early as 2 weeks.[1] This differentiation capacity appears to be influenced by the composition of the induction medium as decreases in adipogenic differentiation capacity is observed on removal of dexamethasone (21% decrease) or indomethacin (28% decrease) from the adipogenic medium (Fig. 40–4). These decreases were specific to these agents because no significant difference in adipogenesis is measured on removal of IBMX or insulin. Interestingly, removal of both insulin and IBMX results in a slight enhancement of differentiation (18% increase) versus complete adipogenic medium.

Consistent with adipogenesis, induced PLA cells express several genes and proteins unique to the adipogenic lineage (Fig. 40–5A), including expression of (1) lipoprotein lipase (LPL)–a lipid exchange enzyme upregulated during adipogenesis,[49] (2) aP2 or P442–a protein associated with lipid accumulation in mature adipocytes,[50,51] and (3) the specific expression of the fat-specific transcription factor Peroxisome proliferator activated receptorγ2 (PPARγ2) to adipo-induced PLA cells and MSCs.[37] PPARγ2 is expressed by differentiating preadipocytes only[52,53] and appears early in the PLA differentiation program, thus indicating the adipogenic capacity of these stem cells. In addition, indirect immunofluorescence of both differentiating PLA cells and MSCs also confirms the expression of leptin and GLUT4, two proteins upregulated in differentiating adipocytes.[54,55] Expression of these proteins is specific to adipo-induced PLA cells because no expression is observed in noninduced cell cultures. Moreover, the expression of these proteins appear to be restricted to the mature, lipid-filled stem cells, consistent with their role in adipogenesis. Like MSCs, the expression of many of these adipogenic genes is also observed in noninduced PLA cells and indicates that stem cell populations constitutively express many adipogenic lineage genes. However, Zuk and colleagues measure a significant increase in LPL expression within 1 week after induction, followed by decreases in expression at 3 and 4 weeks, suggesting that LPL plays a relatively early role in adipogenesis.[37] Finally, biochemical quantitation of glycerol-3-phosphate dehydrogenase (GPDH)—a lipogenic enzyme–confirms a time-dependent increase in activity that is similar to induced 3T3-L1 preadipocytes.[37]

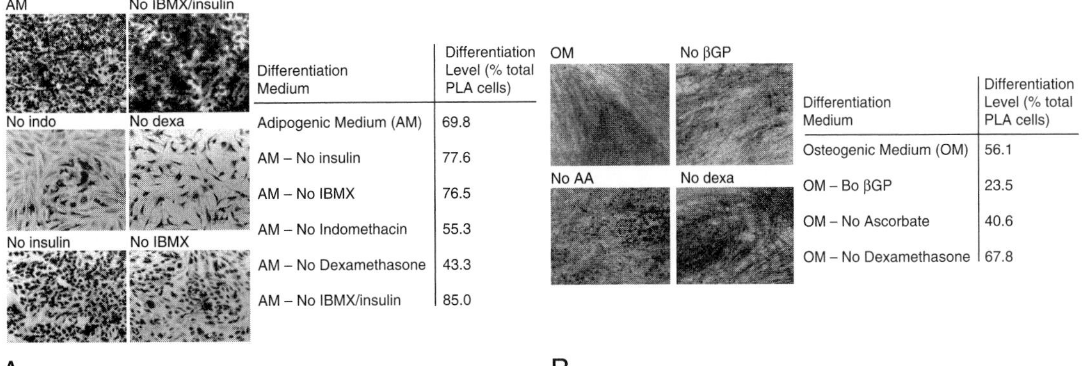

Differentiation Medium	Differentiation Level (% total PLA cells)
Adipogenic Medium (AM)	69.8
AM – No insulin	77.6
AM – No IBMX	76.5
AM – No Indomethacin	55.3
AM – No Dexamethasone	43.3
AM – No IBMX/insulin	85.0

Differentiation Medium	Differentiation Level (% total PLA cells)
Osteogenic Medium (OM)	56.1
OM – Bo βGP	23.5
OM – No Ascorbate	40.6
OM – No Dexamethasone	67.8

Figure 40–4. *Induction conditions can affect processed lipoaspirate (PLA) differentiation capacity.* (A) PLA cells were induced for 14 days in standard adipogenic medium (AM) and in AM lacking (1) Indomethacin (No Indo), (2) dexamethasone (No Dexa), (3) insulin (No insulin), (4) IBMX (No IBMX), or (5) insulin and IBMX (No IBMX/insulin). Differentiated cells were stained with oil red O and the number of positive cells quantitated. Oil red O staining/differentiation level was expressed as a percentage of the total number of PLA cells. A representative sample is shown. (B) PLA cells were induced for 21 days in standard osteogenic medium (OM) and in OM lacking: (1) β-glycerophosphate (No βGP), (2) ascorbic acid (No AA), or (3) lacking dexamethasone (No Dexa). Differentiated cells were stained for alkaline phosphatase (AP) activity and quantitated. AP staining/differentiation level was expressed as a percentage of the total surface area (% total PLA cells). A representative sample is shown. (Please see CD-ROM for color version of this figure.)

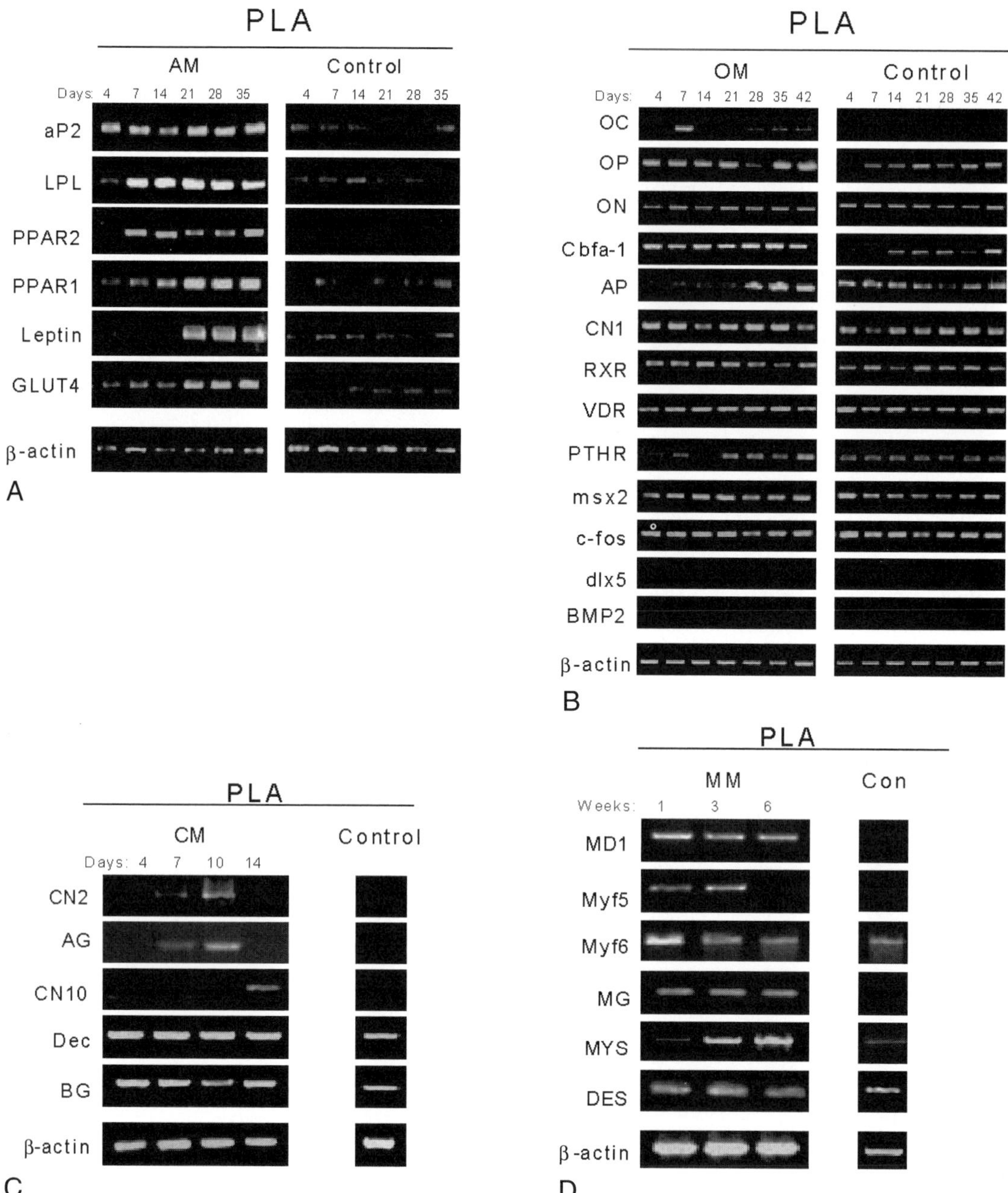

Figure 40–5. *Processed lipoaspirate (PLA) cells express multiple mesodermal lineage-specific markers.* PLA cells were induced toward the following mesodermal lineages *in vitro:* (A) adipogenic, (B) osteogenic, (C) chondrogenic, and (D) skeletal myogenic. Induced cells were examined for the expression of established lineage-specific genes using reverse transcriptase polymerase chain reaction (RT-PCR). (Reproduced with permission from Mol. Biol. Cell 13:4279–4295. 2002.)

Taken together, these results confirm the adipogenic capacity of PLA derived stem cells and are consistent with previous work on SVF cells isolated from intact fat. Interestingly, the kinetics of the PLA stem cell differentiation program appear to be temporally distinct from that of lineage committed progenitors. For example, although the expression of several adipogenic genes can be observed in both stem cells and the preadipocyte cell line 3T3-L1, the timing of their differentiation differs. Induction of the adipogenic differentiation program is primarily initiated in preadipocytes by the PPAR genes, with gene such as aP2 and LPL playing a later role in the maturing adipocyte. Indeed, PPARγ induction in non-adipogenic, Swiss 3T3 fibroblasts promotes the accumulation of lipid droplets and the induction of adipose characteristic genes including aP2 and GLUT4.[56] Introduction of PPARγ2 is also capable of upregulating aP2 expression in hematopoietic cell lines.[57] However, aP2 and LPL are expressed relatively early on in the PLA adipogenic program, coexpressing with PPARγ2.[37] This altered sequence of adipose gene expression may by due to a distinct developmental program characteristic of stem cells and has also been observed in bone marrow MSCs undergoing osteogenesis.[58,59]

In Vivo Adipogenesis

Soft tissue, composed of adipose tissue, maintains contours and also serves as a cushion for muscles, tendons, and ligaments. Therefore, augmentation or reconstruction of soft tissues is often a goal of surgeons and tissue engineers. Adipose tissue transplantation is frequently used in the replacement of soft tissues lost to congenital defects and oncologic resection, in the treatment of depressed regions or scars in the breast and facial areas, and as a general bulking agent for the treatment of urinary incontinence. However, autografting is often unsuccessful because of necrosis and progressive absorption.[60,61] The development of adipose tissue *de novo* following transplantation of stem cells into damaged regions may represent a viable option. Early work involving the subcutaneous injection of adipocyte precursors results in the formation of a well-defined fat pad after 6 weeks.[62] Furthermore, enhanced *in vivo* adipogenesis is observed on injection of preadipocyte cell lines in combination with the basement membrane extract Matrigel and growth factors like basic fibroblast growth factor (bFGF).[63] However, the use of Matrigel in humans is problematic because this basement membrane extract is derived from tumor cell lines. Borrowing from tissue engineering concepts used in *in vivo* osteogenesis, von Heimberg and colleagues successfully induce adipogenesis *in vitro* in hyaluronan and collagen sponges seeded with either rat or human preadipocytes and duplicate this differentiation on implantation into mice.[64,65] In addition to these earlier studies, several other groups have since confirmed *in vivo* adipogenesis using a variety of scaffolds, including poly L-lactic-coglycolic/PLGA,[66] alginate gels,[67] hyaluronan gels,[68] and PTF scaffolds.[69] Most recently, Lee and colleagues[224] generate adipose-like tissue in rats using polyglycolic acid (PGA) scaffolds seeded with autologous adipose-derived stem cells differentiated toward the adipogenic lineage. Histologic examination of these scaffolds reveals the presence of cells containing lipid-filled vacuoles that accumulate oil red O. However, it appears that effective fat formation requires the predifferentiation of these stem cells before seeding because no adipogenesis is observed in scaffolds seeded with noninduced PLA cells. Similarly, subcutaneous implantation of PLA cells, seeded into fibrin glue constructs, into athymic mice is followed by formation of well-defined fat pads that contain mature adipocytes and are surrounded by new blood vessels (Fig. 40–6).[70] Taken together, the *in vivo* data on preadipocytes and adipose-derived stem cells indicates that the engineering of soft tissues may be possible. However, the optimal scaffold for this engineering remains elusive as rigid supports (i.e., PGA, PGLA) do not provide the flexibility required for soft tissue replacement and the more malleable materials (hyaluronan gels) may degrade too rapidly for sufficient tissue formation. An alternative approach may involve injection of PGA/PEG microspheres loaded with pro-adipogenic factors (bFGF, insulin-like growth factor-1 [IGF-1], and insulin). Such biodegradable microspheres differentiate precursor cells into mature adipocytes.[71] The engineering of clinically useful adipose tissue will likely combine emerging advances in polymer technology with ongoing research into the genetic programs that dictate PLA conversion into mature adipocytes.

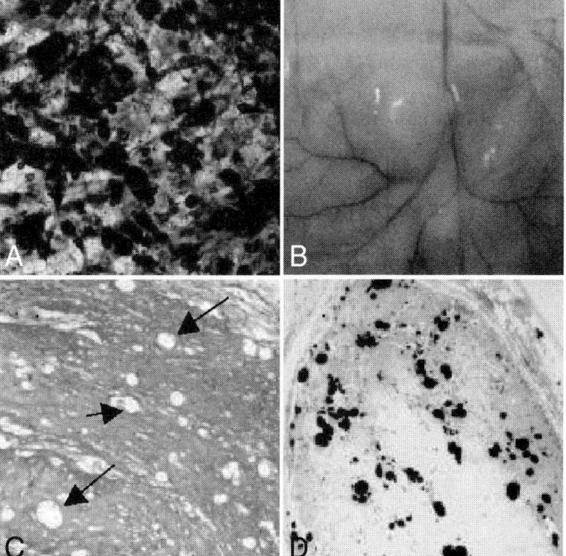

Figure 40–6. *Adipogenesis by processed lipoaspirate (PLA) cells in vivo.* PLA cells were predifferentiated in adipogenic medium (AM) for 1 week, followed by implantation into fibrin glue carriers. PLA constructs were implanted subcutaneously into athymic mice and harvested at 4 weeks. (A) Histologic confirmation (oil red O staining) of PLA cell adipogenic capacity following 2 weeks induction in AM. (B) Gross morphologic appearance of PLA construct before harvest. (C) Hematoxylin and eosin analysis of harvested fat pads showing putative lipid-contained adipocytes (arrows). (D) Osmium tetraoxide staining of harvested fat pads to confirm presence of lipid-containing cells (black). (Please see CD-ROM for color version of this figure.)

OSTEOGENESIS

In Vitro Osteogenesis

The differentiation of osteoprogenitor cells and MSCs is characterized by several well-defined stages: (1) proliferation, characterized by cell multiplication and the synthesis and deposition of an osteogenic matrix containing predominantly collagen type I fibers; (2) matrix maturation, associated with the increased expression of several osteogenic genes, such as alkaline phosphatase (AP); and (3) matrix calcification, occurring with the deposition of calcium phosphate crystals and the expression of additional late osteogenic markers, such as bone sialoprotein and osteocalcin.[58]

Differentiation of human and rodent osteoprogenitor cells and MSCs into osteoblasts can be induced *in vitro* by treating cells with low concentrations of ascorbic acid, β-glycerophosphate (βGP), and dexamethasone or vitamin D analogs.[6,7,40,72,73] Consistent with this, human MSCs treated with these agents exhibit AP activity as early as 4 days[73] and undergo matrix deposition and mineralization as early as 8 days.[74] Like MSCs and osteoprogenitor cells, adipose-derived PLA stem cells, cultured in dexamethasone, ascorbic acid, and βGP form an extensive network of dense, multilayered nodules that stain positively for AP activity and calcium phosphate using Alizarin Red and von Kossa histochemical stains.[1,75] Quantitation of AP activity and calcium phosphate levels using biochemical assays shows time-dependent increases that are specific to osteogenic induction conditions.[37] However, like adipogenesis, differentiation levels appear to be influenced by medium composition, with removal of ascorbic acid or βGP decreasing AP activity (Fig. 40–4B). Consistent with this, the presence of ascorbate and βGP is critical to enhanced AP activity and the mineralization of the extracellular matrix by pre-osteoblasts.[76]

In addition to histochemical and biochemical confirmation of calcium phosphate production, Fourier transform infrared (FTIR) imaging of osteo-induced fat-derived stem cells by Halvorsen and colleagues detects a mineral and matrix protein distribution typical of bone–specifically, a predominantly collagenous extracellular matrix with a spectra characteristic of apatite.[75] Confirmation of this matrix composition is obtained through time-resolved (lifetime) laser-induced fluorescence spectroscopy (TR-LIFS), a novel spectroscopic approach[77,78] (Fig. 40–7). In this work, noninvasive analysis

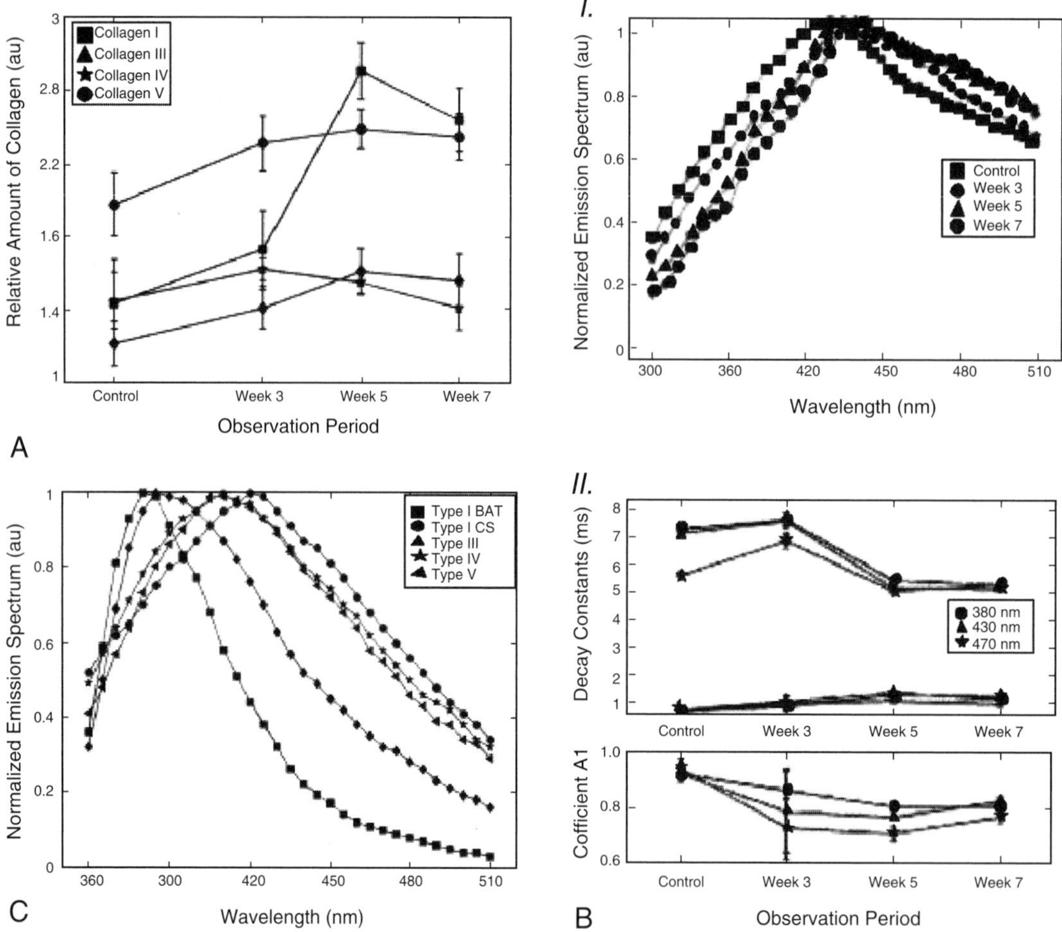

Figure 40–7. *Time-resolved laser-induced fluorescence spectroscopy analysis of processed lipoaspirate (PLA) cells.* PLA cells were induced toward the osteogenic lineage for 3, 5, and 7 weeks. The extracellular matrix, synthesized by noninduced control PLA cells and osteo-induced samples, was analyzed using laser-induced fluorescence spectroscopy (TR-LIFS). (A) Relative amount of collagens synthesized by non-induced PLA cells (control) and osteo-induced samples (weeks 3, 5, 7) as measured by Western blotting. (B) TR-LIFS analysis of osteo-induced PLA matrices. Panel I: The mean values for the fluorescence emission spectra were measured in control and induced PLA cells ($n = 3$). A peak wavelength of 430 nm was measured in all samples. Panel II: Time-resolved decay constant changes (Decay constants [ms]) were measured in the PLA matrix at three emission wavelengths (380 nm: blue-shifter range; 430 nm: peak emission range; 470 nm: red-shifted range) and plotted as a function differentiation time. Top graph: fast-decay time constant (filled symbols [top]), slow-decay time constants (open symbols [bottom]). Bottom graph: Fractional contribution of the fast-decay time component A1 (Coefficient A1). Values are mean ± SE for the three patients. (C) Commercial samples of collagen type I from bovine Achilles tendon (CNI-BAT) and calf skin (CNI-CS), and placental collagens type III, IV, and V were analyzed by TR-LIFS as described for PLA samples. Peak fluorescence of collagen type I was measured at 430 nm. (Reproduced with permission from Tissue Engineering (Ashjian et al. 2004. Tiss. Eng. 10, 411–420).

of the PLA osteogenic matrix using TR-LIFS identifies significant similarities between the fluorescent emission spectra of the osteogenic PLA matrix and collagen type I samples.[79] A peak emission spectrum of 430 nm is measured in PLA osteogenic matrices—a spectrum that is also measured in commercial collagen I. Moreover, TR-LIFS also detects significant increases in the level of this collagen type over differentiation time, increases that can be confirmed using conventional molecular approaches. In summary, the work of the these two groups indicates the synthesis of a collagen type I-rich extracellular matrix by PLA cells *in vitro* is similar to that found native bone tissue.

Osteogenic differentiation of MSCs results in the increased expression of several osteogenic lineage genes and proteins (Fig. 40–5B), including collagen type I, osteonectin, osteopontin,[80] osteocalcin, and AP.[59] Furthermore, quantitative real-time polymerase chain reaction (PCR) confirms enhanced expression of bone morphogenic protein-2 (BMP2), bone sialoprotein, osteopontin, and CBFA-1 on osteogenic induction of human MSCs.[81] Consistent with this, osteogenic induction of PLA cells results in the expression of CBFA-1 and collagen type I mRNA, in addition to osteonectin, osteopontin, and AP at both the gene and protein level. Moreover, real-time quantitation of CBFA-1 and AP gene expression during differentiation reveals a significant time-dependent increase in their expression.[37] Although increased expression of genes like CBFA-1 and AP are indicative of osteogenic capacity, it is not absolute proof. For this, one requires osteogenic-specific genes, such as bone sialoprotein and osteocalcin.[58] Increased expression of bone sialoprotein is observed in mineralizing osteoblasts,[82] embryonic stem (ES) cells,[83] and osteo-induced MSCs,[81] consistent with its role in mediating attachment of terminally differentiated osteoblasts to the extracellular matrix.[84] Although bone sialoprotein expression is absent in noninduced PLA cells, it is expressed at significant levels in PLA cells treated with osteogenic factors in combination with BMP-2.[85] Like bone sialoprotein, osteocalcin is a late marker of differentiation in osteoblasts; however, it is expressed specifically during the early stages of MSC osteogenesis.[59] Like MSCs, PLA cells also express osteocalcin during both the early and later stages of osteogenesis.[37] However, distinctions in osteocalcin expression kinetics appear to differ between PLA and MSCs. First, researchers have reported constitutive expression of osteocalcin in MSCs.[86] No such basal level can be observed in PLA cells. Second, osteocalcin expression appears to be more sensitive to induction conditions in PLA cells versus MSCs. Although 1,25-dihydroxyvitamin D_3 treatment induces *osteocalcin* expression in both stem cell populations, dexamethasone-induced MSCs express lower levels[37,73,87,88] and complete inhibition of this gene is seen in similarly induced PLA cells.

The kinetics of osteocalcin expression by PLA cells and MSCs suggests that the osteogenic differentiation program of PLA cells and MSCs may be subtly different. Indeed, like the differential expression of CD antigens, there appear to be distinctions in gene expression profile during PLA and MSC osteogenesis. For example, osteogenic induction of PLA cells does not induce expression of BMP-2, a member of the TGF-β superfamily known to participate in osteogenesis,[89] whereas basal expression and osteo-induced expression of this gene is noted in MSC cultures.[37] Furthermore, PLA cells and MSCs differ in their expression of the homeobox gene distal-less 5 (dlx5), with again only MSCs showing basal and induced expression. Finally, microarray analysis identifies additional distinctions, including increased expression of osteocalcin and osteopontin and specific expression of proline/arginine-rich end leucine-rich repeat protein (PRELP) in osteo-induced MSCs.[86] These distinctions in CD antigen and gene expression profiles between MSCs and PLA cells may represent something as simple as culturing artifacts or may be due to an alternate osteogenic differentiation program for PLA cells, possibly the result of their tissue of origin.

In Vivo Osteogenesis

Although the expression of osteogenic genes by osteo-induced PLA cells is strongly suggestive of osteogenic capacity, differentiation of these cells *in vivo* is required for confirmation of bone-forming capacity. Several groups have since confirmed the *in vivo* osteogenic capacity of both animal and human MSCs on various materials, such as hydroxyapatite,[90] calcium alginate,[91] and hyaluronan-gelatin sponges.[92] However, these studies are often characterized by poor bone formation and researchers are now opting to "boost" the osteogenic capacity of stem cells with pro-osteogenic agents, such as BMP-2.[93] Addition of recombinant BMP-2 protein potentiates the *in vivo* osteogenic capacity of both MSC/hydroxyapatite composites[94] and MSC/demineralized bone matrix complexes.[95] Enhanced *in vivo* bone formation is observed in MSCs infected with an adenovirus encoding human BMP-2.[95–99] Similar to these studies, induction of PLA cells infected with this recombinant BMP-2 virus (Ad-BMP-2) or treated with recombinant BMP-2 protein (rh-BMP-2), results in increased activities of AP enzyme; enhanced matrix calcification (Fig. 40–8A); and expression of osteogenic genes, including osteonectin, osteopontin, and bone sialoprotein.[85] More importantly, Ad-BMP-2-infected human PLA cells, seeded into standard collagen type I sponges and implanted intramuscularly into SCID mice adjacent to the femur, undergo differentiation *in vivo* to form tissue that is histologically analogous to bone.[85] Like MSCs, overexpression of BMP-2 appears to be critical for sufficient bone formation, as no bony tissue was observed in collagen sponges seeded with noninfected PLA cells alone. Recent results using BMP-2-expressing PLA cells implanted into critical-sized femoral defects confirm this preliminary study.[100] As in the study by Dragoo and colleagues, overexpression of BMP-2 by PLA cells enhances *in vivo* bone formation, with 11 of the 12 collagen ceramic carriers seeded with BMP-2-expressing PLA cells forming morphologic bone. In addition, bone formation is also observed in carriers impregnated with rh-BMP-2 and seeded with non-infected PLA cells. As shown in Fig. 40–8B, both carrier models form tissue that is histologically similar to bone. Moreover, bone formed by both the Ad-BMP-2 and rh-BMP-2 is also functionally similar to native bone tissue

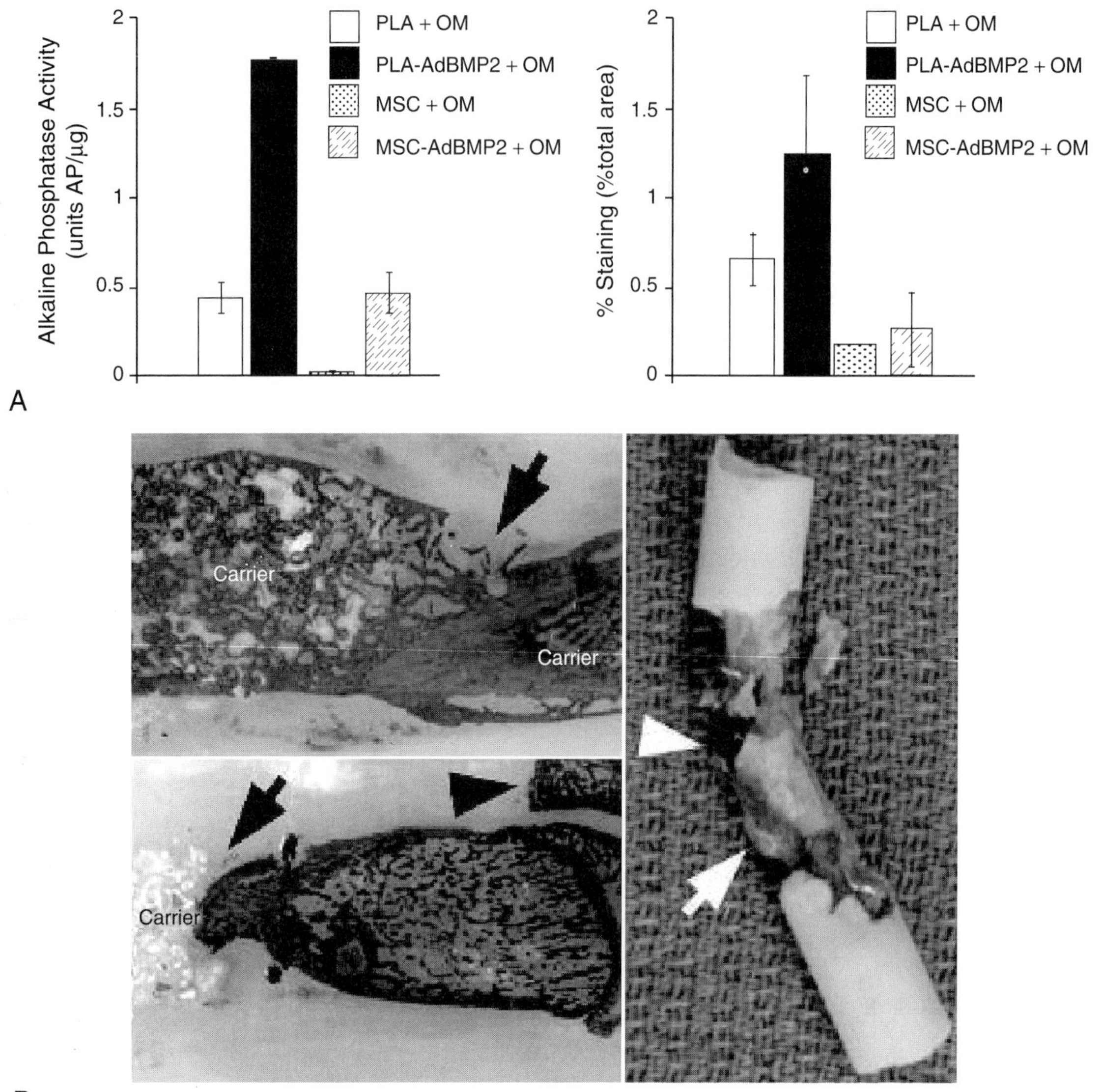

Figure 40–8. *Processed lipoaspirate (PLA) cells undergo osteogenesis* in vivo. (A) PLA cells and mesenchymal stem cells (MSCs), infected with a BMP2 recombinant adenovirus, were induced *in vitro* in osteogenic medium for 4 weeks (PLA-Ad-BMP2 + OM, MSC-Ad-BMP2 + OM, respectively) and osteogenesis confirmed using (1) alkaline phosphatase spectroscopy assay (top graph) and (2) von Kossa staining (bottom graph). Differentiation levels were compared with uninfected cells (PLA + OM, MSC + OM). (B): AdBMP2-infected human PLA cells were seeded into ceramic collagen carriers and implanted into critical-sized femoral defects in athymic rats. The carrier and surrounding defect region were analyzed for the expression of bone collagens by toluidine blue staining (upper left panel A; arrow–new bone growth). Carriers containing no PLA cells were implanted into defects and analyzed as above (lower left panel B; arrow–implantation site). Healed femur from BMP2-expressing PLA cells following biomechanical testing. Arrow indicates healed defect region. Arrowhead indicates sight of failure (right panel). Implanted PLA-seeded carriers are indicated (carrier). (Please see CD-ROM for color version of this figure.)

with no significant differences in torsional stiffness, energy to failure, and torque to failure observed between PLA-based bony tissue and native bone.[101]

CHONDROGENESIS

In Vitro Chondrogenesis

Cell condensation precedes chondrogenesis *in vivo* and is a critical step in cartilage formation.[102] To mimic this precartilage condensation event *in vitro*, high-density culture systems, such as micromass culture, are frequently employed using both lineage-committed prechondrocytes and MSCs.[9,40,103–106] Recently, several groups have shown that adipose-derived stem cells (i.e., PLA cells) cultured under this system undergo chondrogenic differentiation.[1,37,83,107] In addition, chondrogenesis can also be observed *in vitro* using alginate bead cultures,[108] a system that promotes chondrogenesis of MSCs and chondrocytes *in vitro*[109,110] and *in vivo*.[111,112] Similar studies with MSCs and other chondrocytic precursors,[113] PLA

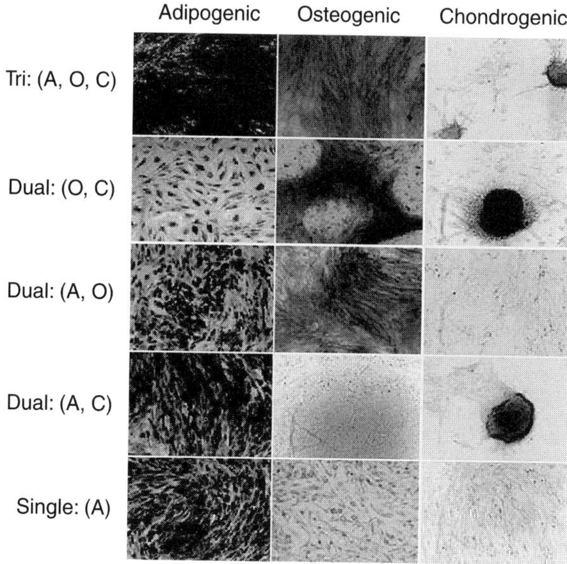

Figure 40–12. *Processed lipoaspirate (PLA) clones (adipose-derived stem cells [ADSCs]) exhibit multilineage capacity.* PLA cells were plated at extremely low confluency to result in isolated single cells. Cultures were maintained in noninductive medium until proliferation of single PLA cells resulted in the formation of well-defined colonies. The colonies were harvested using sterile cloning rings and 0.25% trypsin/EDTA, subcloned and amplified in cloning medium (15% fetal bovine serum [FBS], 1% antibiotic/antimycotic in F12/Dulbeccos modified essential medium [DMEM] [1:1]). The isolated PLA clones were differentiated in osteogenic medium (OM), adipogenic medium (AM), and chondrogenic medium (ChM) and multilineage capacity assessed by histology and immunohistochemistry using the following assays: alkaline phosphatase (osteogenesis, O), oil red O (adipogenesis, A) and Alcian blue (chondrogenesis, C). Trilineage, single PLA cell-derived clones (O, A, C) were termed ADSCs.(Reproduced with permission from Zuk, P.A., Zhu, M., Ashjian, P., De Ugarte, D.A., Huang, J.I., Mizuno, H., Alfonso, Z.C., Fraser, J.K., Benhaim, P., and Hedrick, M.H. (2002). Human adipose tissue is a source of multipotent stem cells. *Mol. Biol. Cell.* 13, 4279–4295.) (Please see CD-ROM for color version of this figure.)

isolation of osteogenic/chondrogenic PLA clones supports this model, the presence of both adipogenic/osteogenic and adipogenic/chondrogenic isolates (not previously reported in MSC populations) suggests that the differentiation of adipo-derived stem cells is complex.

POTENTIAL ALTERNATIVE USES FOR PROCESSED LIPOASPIRATE CELLS

Gene Therapy Vehicles

The ideal cellular vehicle for many gene therapy applications is autologous, easily expandable in culture, and capable of long-term transgene expression. Human MSCs and HSCs have recently been used as gene therapy vehicles, capable of introducing coagulation factors, hormones, and growth factors.[215–227] In a direct comparison between human MSCs and PLA cells, both adult stem cell populations are found to be amenable for gene therapy applications. PLA cell populations can be efficiently effected with lentivirus, adenovirus, and retrovirus constructs and express the transgene (GFP) before and after mesodermal differentiation.[26] The ease of infection with a variety of viral constructs and the resulting stable expression of the transgene makes PLA cells an attractive option for gene therapy applications.

Support of Hematopoiesis

Preadipocytes/PLA cells have been shown to express markers of the monocyte-macrophage lineage, suggesting that these cells may possess hematopoietic potential.[228] In addition, preadipocytes secrete hematopoietic factors, suggesting that these cells may be able to support hematopoiesis to some degree.[229] In support of this, SVF cells isolated from murine adipose depots, give rise to hematopoietic colonies *in vitro* and rescue lethally irradiated hosts.[228] Mice receiving SVF injections show reconstitution myeloid and lymphoid lineage cells, in addition to migration and engraftment of PLA cells to the major hematopoietic organs.

Control of Diabetes

In lipoatrophic diabetes, diminished fat stores are associated with insulin resistance and hyperglycemia. Transplantation of subcutaneous fat into white adipose-deficient transgenic mice (A-ZIP/F-1) dramatically increases insulin sensitivity and reverses all diabetic aspects of these mice. However, reversal requires transplantation of near physiologic levels of fat.[230] It is possible that transplantation of purified populations of PLA cells may have a similar effect and may allow for reversal of disease using significantly smaller amounts of material.

Summary

The data presented in this chapter provide proof that adipose-derived stem cells or PLA cells represent a multipotent stem cell population and appear to be similar to bone marrow MSCs. Like MSCs, PLA cells differentiate to the osteogenic, adipogenic, chondrogenic, and myogenic lineages *in vitro* and appear to form bone, fat, and cartilage *in vivo*. However, analysis of CD marker expression indicates that PLA cells may be a distinct stem cell population from MSCs. Like other adult stem cell populations, adipose-derived stem cells appear to possess plasticity that may extend beyond the mesoderm. Induction toward the neurogenic lineage results in expression of several attributes consistent with neurogenesis. These stem cells also appear to constitutively express markers of the endodermal germline, in addition to two, well-established totipotent stem cell markers, Oct4 and Rex1. Although this expression profile is not proof of totipotency—a *de facto* characteristic of ES cells—it does suggest that adult stem cells, like PLA cells, may be more broadly pluripotent than thought.

Although a relatively new addition to the growing list of adult stem cells sources, adipose tissue and its resident stem cell populations may be attractive options to both the researcher and clinician. Obtained through cosmetic procedures, such as liposuction, PLA cells can be harvested in large quantities, with minimal pain and morbidity incurred by the patient. This simple fact may make substantial quantities of adult stem cells available for either clinical or tissue engineering applications or for molecular characterization.

ACKNOWLEDGMENTS

The authors wish to acknowledge the generous input from the following: John Fraser, Ph.D., Min Zhu, M.D., Peter Ashjian, M.D., Dan De Ugarte, M.D., Jason Dragoo, M.D., Grace Carlson, M.D., Hiroshi Mizuno, M.D., Zeni Alfonso, Ph.D., Silvia Kurtovic, B.S., Brian Strem, B.S., Brian Edmonds, Ph.D., Peter Lorenz, M.D., Amir Elbarbary, M.D., Neil Jones, M.D., Jerry Huang, M.D., Laura Marcu, Ph.D., Warren Grundfest, Ph.D., Ben Wu, Ph.D., Brett Peterson, M.D., Jay Lieberman, M.D., Joon Choi, M.D., Jeffery Zhang, M.D., Irvin Chen, M.D., Peter Fodor, M.D., George Rudkin, M.D., Andrew Da Lio, M.D., Tim Miller, M.D., Mack Holmes, M.D., Fernando Almeida, M.D., and Larissa Rodriguez, M.D., Jan Notta Ph.D., Todd Meyerose, B.S., and William, Shaw, M.D. In addition, we would like to thank the following for their generous financial support: Severin Wunderman and the Wunderman Family Foundation; the American Society for Aesthetic Plastic Surgery; the Plastic Surgery Educational Foundation; the Los Angeles Orthopaedic Hospital Foundation; the American College of Surgeons; and the National Institute of Arthritis, Musculoskeletal and Skin Diseases at the NIH.

REFERENCES

1. Zuk, P.A., Zhu, M., Mizuno, H., Huang, J.I., Futrell, W.J, Katz, A.J., Benhaim, P., Lorenz, H.P., and Hedrick, M.H. (2001). Multilineage cells from human adipose tissue: Implications for cell-based therapies. *Tissue Eng.* **7,** 211–226.
2. Friedenstein, A.J., Petrakova, K.V., Kurolesova, A.I., and Frolova, G.P. (1968). Heterotopic of bone marrow. Analysis of precursor cells for osteogenic and hematopoietic tissues. *Transplantation* **6,** 230–247.
3. Grigoradis, A., Heersche, J.N.M., and Aubin, J. (1988). Differentiation of muscle fat, cartilage and bone from progenitor cells present in a bone-derived clonal cell population: effect of dexamethasone. *J. Cell Biol.* **106,** 2139–2151.
4. Beresford, J.N., Bennett, J.H., Devlin, C., Leboy, P.S., and Owen, M.E. (1992). Evidence for an inverse relationship between the differentiation of adipocytic and osteogenic cells in rat marrow stromal cell cultures. *J. Cell Sci.* **102,** 341–351.
5. Berry, L., Grant, M.E., McClure, J., and Rooney, P. (1992). Bone-marrow-derived chondrogenesis in vitro. *J. Cell Sci.* **101,** 333–342.
6. Haynesworth, S.E., Goshima, J., Goldberg, V.M., and Caplan, A.I. (1992). Characterization of cells with osteogenic potential from human marrow. *Bone* **13,** 81–88.
7. Cheng, S.-L., Yang, J.W., Rifas, L., Zhang, S-F., and Avioli, L.V. (1994). Differentiation of human bone marrow osteogenic stromal cells in vitro: induction of the osteoblast phenotype by dexamethasone. *Endocrinology* **134,** 277–286.
8. Wakitani, S., Saito, T., and Caplan, A.I. (1995). Myogenic cells derived from rat bone marrow mesenchymal stem cells exposed to 5-azacytidine. *Muscle Nerve* **18,** 1417–1426.
9. Johnstone, B., Hering, T.M., Caplan, A.I., Goldberg, V.M., and Yoo, J.U. (1998). In vitro chondrogenesis of bone marrow-derived mesenchymal progenitor cells. *Exp. Cell Res.* **238,** 265–272.
10. Yoo, J.U., Barthel, T.S., Nishimura, K., Solchaga, L., Caplan, A.I., Goldberg, V.M., and Johnstone, B. (1998). The chondrogenic potential of human bone-marrow-derived mesenchymal progenitor cells. *J. Bone Joint Surg. Am.* **80,** 1745–1757.
11. Rodbell, M. (1964). Metabolism of isolated fat cells. *J. Biol. Chem.* **239,** 375–380.
12. Pozanski, W.J., Waheed, I., and Van, R. (1973). Human fat cell precursors: Morphologic and metabolic differentiation in culture. *Lab. Invest.* **29,** 570–576.
13. Van, R.L., Bayliss, C.E., and Roncari, D.A. (1976). Cytological and enzymological characterization of adult human adipocyte precursors in culture. *J. Clin. Invest.* **58,** 699–704.
14. Green, H., and Meuth, M. (1974). An established pre-adipose cell line and its differentiation in culture. *Cell* **3,** 127–133.
15. Deslex, S., Negrel, R., Vannier, C., Etienne, J., and Ailhaud, G. (1987). Differentiation of human adipocyte precursors in a chemically defined serum-free medium. *Int. J. Obesity* **11,** 19–27.
16. Hauner, H., Schmid, P., and Pfeiffer, E.F. (1987). Glucocorticoids and insulin promote the differentiation of human adipocyte precursor cells into fat cells. *J. Clin. Endocrinol. Metabol.* **64,** 832–835.
17. Warejcka, D.J., Harvey, R., Taylor, B.J., Young, H.E., and Lucas, P.A. (1996). A population of cells isolated from rat heart capable of differentiating into several mesodermal phenotypes. *J. Surg. Res.* **62,** 233–242.
18. Campagnoli, C., Roberts, I.A., Kumar, S., Bennett, P.R., Bellantuono, I., and Fisk, N.M. (2001). Identification of mesenchymal stem/progenitor cells in human first-trimester fetal blood, liver, and bone marrow. *Blood* **98,** 2396–2402.
19. Romanov, Y.A., Svintsitskaya, V.A., and Smirnov, V.N. (2003). Searching for alternative sources of postnatal human mesenchymal stem cells: candidate MSC-like cells from umbilical cord. *Stem Cells* **21,** 105–110.
20. Asakura, A., Komaki, M., and Rudnicki, M. (2001). Muscle satellite cells are multipotential stem cells that exhibit myogenic, osteogenic, and adipogenic differentiation. *Artif. Organs* **25,** 187–193.
21. Lucas, P.A., Calcutt, A.F., Mulvaney, D.J., Young, H.E., and Southerland, S.S. (1992). Isolation of putative mesenchymal stem cells from rat embryonic and adult skeletal muscle. *In Vitro Cell Biol.* **28,** 154A.
22. Qu-Petersen, Z., Deasy, B., Jankowski, R., Ikezawa, M., Cummins, J., Pruchnic, R., Mytinger, J., Cao, B., Gates, C., Wernig, A., and Huard, J. (2002). Identification of a novel population of muscle stem cells in mice: potential for muscle regeneration. *J. Cell Biol.* **157,** 851–864.
23. Noth, U., Tuli, R., Osyczka, A.M., Danielson, K.G., and Tuan, R.S. (2002). In vitro engineered cartilage constructs produced by press-coating biodegradable polymer with human mesenchymal stem cells. *Tissue Eng.* **8,** 131–144.
24. Wada, M.R., Inagawa-Ogashiwa, M., Shimizu, S., Yasumoto, S., and Hashimoto, N. (2002). Generation of different fates from multipotent muscle stem cells. *Development* **129,** 2987–2995.
25. Toma, J. G., Akhavan, M., Fernandes, K.J., Barnabe-Heider, F., Sadikot, A., Kaplan, D.R., and Miller, F.D. (2001). Isolation of multipotent adult stem cells from the dermis of mammalian skin. *Nat. Cell Biol.* **3,** 778–784.
26. De Ugarte, D.A., Morizono, K., Elbarbary, A., Alfonso, Z.C., Zuk, P.A., Zhu, M., Dragoo, J.L., Ashjian, P.H., Thomas, B., Benhaim, P., Chen, I., Fraser, J.K., and Hedrick, M.H. (2003). Comparison of multi-lineage cells from human adipose tissue and bone marrow. *Cells Tissues Organs* **174,** 101–109.

27. Kadiyala, S., Young, R.G., Thiede, M.A., and Bruder, S.P. (1997). Culture expanded canine mesenchymal stem cells possess osteochondrogenic potential in vivo and in vitro. *Cell Transplant.* **6,** 125–134.
28. Guo, Z., Yang, J., Liu, X., Li, X., Hou, C., Tang, P.H., and Mao, N. (2001). Biological features of mesenchymal stem cells from human bone marrow. *Chin. Med. J. (Engl.)* **114,** 950–953.
29. Shor, A.M., Allen, T.D., Canfield, A.E., Sloan , P., and Schor, S.L. (1990). Perictye derived from the retinal microvasculature undergo calcification in vitro. *J. Cell Sci.* **97,** 449–461.
30. Doherty, M.J., Ashton, B.A., Walsh, S., Beresford, J.N., Grant, M.E., and Canfield, A.E. (1998). Vascular pericytes express osteogenic potential in vitro and in vivo. *J. Bone Miner. Res.* **13,** 828–838.
31. Diefenderfer, D.L., and Brighton, C.T. (2000). Microvascular pericytes express aggrecan message which is regulated by BMP2. *Biochem. Biophys. Res. Commun.* **269,** 172–178.
32. Zuk, P.A., *et al.* (Unpublished results).
33. Huss, R. (2000). Isolation of primary and immortalized CD34-hematopoietic and mesenchymal stem cells from various sources. *Stem Cells* **18,** 1–9.
34. Lazaras, H.M., Haynesworth, S.E., Gerson, S.L., and Caplan, A.I. (1997). Human bone marrow-derived mesenchymal (stromal) progenitor cells (MPCs) cannot be recovered from peripheral blood progenitor cell collections. *J. Hematother.* **6,** 447–455.
35. Gronthos, S., Graves, S.E., Ohta, S., and Simmons, P.J. (1994). The STRO-1+ fraction of adult human bone marrow contains osteogenic precursors. *Blood* **84,** 4164–4173.
36. Haynesworth, S.E., Baber, M.A., and Caplan, A.I. (1992). Cell surface antigens on human marrow-derived mesenchymal cells are detected by monoclonal antibodies. *Bone* **13,** 69–80.
37. Zuk, P.A., Zhu, M., Ashjian, P., De Ugarte, D.A., Huang, J.I., Mizuno, H., Alfonso, Z.C., Fraser, J.K., Benhaim, P., and Hedrick, M.H. (2002). Human adipose tissue is a source of multipotent stem cells. *Mol. Biol. Cell.* **13,** 4279–4295.
38. Gronthos, S., Zannettino, A.C., Hay, S.J., Shi, S., Graves, S.E., Kortesidis, A., and Simmons, P.J. (2003). Molecular and cellular characterisation of highly purified stromal stem cells derived from human bone marrow. *J. Cell Sci.* **116,** 1827–1835.
38a. Zuk *et al.,* unpublished data.
39. Cortes, F., Deschaseaux, F., Uchida, N., Labastie, M.C., Friera, A.M., He, D., Charbord, P., and Peault, B. (1999). HCA, an immunoglobulin-like adhesion molecule present on the earliest human hematopoietic precursor cells, is also expressed by stromal cells in blood-forming tissues. *Blood* **93,** 826–837.
40. Pittenger, M.F., Mackay, A.M., Beck, S.C., Jaiswal, R.K., Douglas, R., Mosca, J.D., Moorman, M.A., Simonetti, D.W., Craig, S., and Marshak, D.R. (1999). Multilineage potential of adult human mesenchymal stem cells. *Science* **284,** 143–147.
41. Barry, F.P., Boynton, R.E., Haynesworth, S., Murphy, J.M., and Zaia, J. (1999). The monoclonal antibody SH-2, raised against human mesenchymal stem cells, recognizes an epitope on endoglin (CD105). *Biochem. Biophys. Res. Commun.* **265,** 134–139.
42. Zuk, P.A., *et al.* (Unpublished results).
43. Thomas, P.S., Pietrangeli, C.E., Hayashi, S., Schachner, M., Goridis, C., Low, M., and Kincade, P.W. (1988). Demonstration of neural cell adhesion molecules on stromal cells that support lymphopoiesis. *Leukemia* **2,** 171–175.
44. Gimble, J.M., Pietrangeli, C., Henley, A., Dorheim, M.A., Silver, J., Namen, A., Takeichi, M., Goridis, C., and Kincade, P.W. (1989). Characterization of murine bone marrow and spleen-derived stromal cells: analysis of leukocyte marker and growth factor mRNA transcript levels. *Blood* **74,** 303–311.
45. Conget, P.A., and Minguell, J.J. (1999). Phenotypical and functional properties of human bone marrow mesenchymal progenitor cells. *J. Cell Physiol.* **181,** 67–73.
46. Rubin, C.S., Hirsch, A., Fung, C., and Rosen, O.M. (1978). Development of hormone receptors and hormonal responsiveness *in vitro.* Insulin receptors and insulin sensitivity in the preadipocyte and adipocyte forms of 3T3-L1 cells. *J. Biol. Chem.* **253,** 7570–7578.
47. Pettersson, P., Van, R.L., Lonnroth, P., Bjoerntorp, P., and Smith, U. (1985). Insulin binding in differentiating rat preadipocytes in culture. *J. Lipid Res.* **26,** 1187–1195.
48. Loffler, G., and Hauner, H. (1987). Adipose tissue development: The role of precursor cells and adipogenic factors. Part II: The regulation of the adipogenic conversion by hormones and serum factors. *Klin. Wochenschr.* **65,** 812–817.
49. Ailhaud, G., Grimaldi, P., and Negrel, R. (1992). Cellular and molecular aspects of adipose tissue development. *Annu. Rev. Nutr.* **12,** 207–233.
50. Bernlohr, D.A., Angus, C.W., Lane, M.D., Bolanowski, M.A., and Kelly, T. (1984). Expression of specific mRNAs during adipose differentiation, identification of an mRNA encoding a homologue of myelin P2 protein. *Proc. Natl. Acad. Sci. U. S. A.* **81,** 468–472.
51. Bernlohr, D.A., Doering, T.L., Kelly, T.J., and Lane, M.D. (1985). Tissue specific expression of p422 protein, a putative lipid carrier in mouse adipocytes. *Biochem. Biophys. Res. Commun.* **132,** 850–855.
52. Tontonoz, P., Hu, E., Graves, R.A., Budavari, A.I., and Spiegelman, B.M. (1994). mPPAR gamma 2: tissue-specific regulator of an adipocyte enhancer. *Genes Dev.* **8,** 1224–1234.
53. Auwerx, J., Martin, G., Guerre-Millo, M., and Staels, B. (1996). Transcription, adipocyte differentiation, and obesity. *J. Mol. Med.* **74,** 347–352.
54. Chen, X., Hausman, D.B., Dean, R.G., and Hausman, G.J. (1997). Differentiation-dependent expression of obese (ob) gene by preadipocytes and adipocytes in primary cultures of porcine stromal-vascular cells. *Biochim. Biophys. Acta* **1359,** 136–142.
55. Tanner, J.W., Leingang, K.A., Mueckler, M.M., and Glenn, K.C. (1992). Cell mechanism of the insulin-like effect of growth hormone in adipocytes. Rapid translocation of the HepG2 type and adipocyte/muscle glucose transporters. *Biochem. J.* **182,** 99–106.
56. Hamm, J.K., el Jack, A.K., Pilch, P.F., and Farmer, S.R. (1999). Role of PPAR gamma in regulating adipocyte differentiation and insulin-responsive glucose uptake. *Ann. NY Acad. Sci.* **892,** 134–145.
57. Pelton, P.D., Zhou, L., Demarest, K.T., and Burris, T.P. (1999). PPARgamma activation induces the expression of the adipocyte fatty acid binding protein gene in human monocytes. *Biochem. Biophys. Res. Commun.* **261,** 456–458.
58. Owen, T.A., Aronow, M., Shalhoub, V., Barone, L.M., Wilming, L., Tassinari, M.S., Kennedy, M.B., Pockwinse, S., Lian, J.B., and Stein, G.S. (1990). Progressive development of the rat osteoblast phenotype in vitro: reciprocal relationships in expression of genes associated with osteoblast proliferation and differentiation during formation of the bone extracellular matrix. *J. Cell Physiol.* **143,** 420–430.
59. Malaval, L., Madrowski, D., Gupta, A.K., and Aubin, J.E. (1994). Cellular expression of bone-related proteins during in vitro osteogenesis in rat bone marrow stromal cell cultures. *J. Cell. Physiol.* **158,** 555–572.
60. Smahel, J. (1989). Experimental implantation of adipose tissue fragments. *Br. J. Plast. Surg.* **42,** 207–211.

61. Kononas, T.C., Bucky, L.P., Hurley, C., and May, J.W., Jr. (1193). The fate of suctioned and surgically removed fat after reimplantation for soft-tissue augmentation: a volumetric and histologic study in the rabbit. *Plast. Reconstr. Surg.* **91,** 763–768.
62. Green, H., and Kehinde, O. (1979). Formation of normally differentiated subcutaneous fat pads by an established preadipose cell line. *J. Cell Physiol.* **101,** 169–171.
63. Kawaguchi, N., Toriyama, K., Nicodemou-Lena, E., Inou, K., Torii, S., and Kitagawa, Y. (1998). De novo adipogenesis in mice at the site of injection of basement membrane and basic fibroblast growth factor. *Proc. Natl. Acad. Sci. U. S. A.* **95,** 1062–1066.
64. von Heimburg, D., Zachariah, S., Heschel, I., Kuhling, H., Schoof, H., Hafemann, B., and Pallua, N. (2001). Human preadipocytes seeded on freeze-dried collagen scaffolds investigated *in vitro* and *in vivo*. *Biomaterials* **22,** 429–438.
65. von Heimburg, D., Zachariah, S., Low, A., and Pallua, N. (2001). Influence of different biodegradable carriers on the in vivo behavior of human adipose precursor cells. *Plast. Reconstr. Surg.* **108,** 411–420.
66. Patrick, C.W.J., Zheng, B., Johnston, C., and Reece, G.P. (2002). Long-term implantation of preadipocyte-seeded PLGA scaffolds. *Tissue Eng.* **8,** 283–293.
67. Marler, J.J., Guha, A., Rowley, J., Koka, R., Mooney, D., Upton, J., Vacanti, J.P. (2000). Soft-tissue augmentation with injectable alginate and syngeneic fibroblasts. *Plast. Reconstr. Surg.* **105,** 2049–2058.
68. Duranti, F., Salti, G., Bovani, B., Calandra, M., and Rosati, M.L. (1998). Injectable hyaluronic acid gel for soft tissue augmentation. A clinical and histological study. *Dermatol. Surg.* **24,** 1317–1325.
69. Kral, J.G., and Crandall, D.L. (1999). Development of a human adipocyte synthetic polymer scaffold. *Plast. Reconstr. Surg.* **104,** 1732–1738.
70. Zhu, *et al.* (Unpublished results).
71. Yuksel, E., Weinfeld, A.B., Cleek, R., Waugh, J.M., Jensen, J., Boutros, S., Shenaq, S.M., and Spira, M. (2000). De novo adipose tissue generation through long-term, local delivery of insulin and insulin-like growth factor-1 by PLGA/PEG microspheres in an in vivo rat model: a novel concept and capability. *Plast. Reconstr. Surg.* **105,** 1721–1729.
72. Lennon, D.P., Haynesworth, S.E., Young, R.G., Dennis, J.E., and Caplan, A.I. (1995). A chemically defined medium supports in vitro proliferation and maintains the osteochondral potential of rat marrow-derived mesenchymal stem cells. *Exp. Cell Res.* **219,** 211–222.
73. Jaiswal, N., Haynesworth, S.E., Caplan, A.I., and Bruder, S.P. (1997). Osteogenic differentiation of purified, culture-expanded human mesenchymal stem cells in vitro. *J. Cell Biochem.* **64,** 295–312.
74. Bruder, S.P., Jaiswal, N., and Haynesworth, S.E. (1997). Growth kinetics, self-renewal, and the osteogenic potential of purified human mesenchymal stem cells during extensive subcultivation and following cryopreservation. *J Cell Biochem.* **64,** 278–294.
75. Halvorsen, Y.D., Franklin, D., Bond, A.L., Hitt, D.C., Auchter, C., Boskey, A.L., Paschalis, E.P., Wilkison, W.O., and Gimble, J.M. (2001). Extracellular matrix mineralization and osteoblast gene expression by human adipose tissue-derived stromal cells. *Tissue Eng.* **7,** 729–741.
76. Choong, P.F.M., Martin, T.J., and Ng, K.W. (1993). Effects of ascorbic acid, calcitrol and retinoic acid on the differentiation of preostoblasts. *J. Orthop. Res.* **11,** 638–647.
77. Marcu, L., Grundfest, W.S., and Maarek, J.M. (1999). Photobleaching of arterial fluorescent compounds: characterization of elastin, collagen and cholesterol time-resolved spectra during prolonged ultraviolet irradiation. *Photochem. Photobiol.* **69,** 713–721.
78. Maarek, J.M., Marcu, L., Fishbein, M.C., and Grundfest, W.S. (2000). Time-resolved fluorescence of human aortic wall: use for improved identification of atherosclerotic lesions. *Lasers Surg. Med.* **27,** 241–254.
79. Ashjian, P.H., Elbarbary, A., Zuk, P.A., De Ugarte, D.A., Benhaim, P., Marcu, L., and Hedrick, M.H. (2003). Non-invasive *in-situ* evaluation of osteogenic differentiation by time-resolved laser induced spectroscopy. *Tissue Eng.* In press.
80. Yao, K.L., Todescan, R., Jr., and Sodek, J. (1994). Temporal changes in matrix protein synthesis and mRNA expression during mineralized tissue formation by adult rat bone marrow cells in culture. *J. Bone Miner. Res.* **9,** 231–240.
81. Frank, O., Heim, M., Jakob, M., Barbero, A., Schafer, D., Bendik, I., Dick, W., Heberer, M., and Martin, I. (2002). Real-time quantitative RT-PCR analysis of human bone marrow stromal cells during osteogenic differentiation in vitro. *J. Cell Biochem.* **85,** 737–746.
82. Chen, J., Shapiro, H.S., and Sodek, J. (1992). Development expression of bone sialoprotein mRNA in rat mineralized connective tissues. *J. Bone Miner. Res.* **7,** 987–997.
83. Zur Nieden, N.I., Kempka, G., and Ahr, H.J. (2003). In vitro differentiation of embryonic stem cells into mineralized osteoblasts. *Differentiation* **71,** 18–27.
84. Harris, N.L., Rattray, K.R., Tye, C.E., Underhill, T.M., Somerman, M.J., D'Errico, J.A., Chambers, A.F., Hunter, G.K., and Goldberg, H.A. (2000). Functional analysis of bone sialoprotein: identification of the hydroxyapatite-nucleating and cell-binding domains by recombinant peptide expression and site-directed mutagenesis. *Bone* **27,** 795–802.
85. Dragoo, J.L., Samimi, B., Zhu, M., Hame, S.L., Thomas, B.J., Lieberman, J.R., Hedrick, M.H., and Benhaim, P. (2003). Tissue-engineered cartilage and bone using stem cells from human infrapatellar fat pads. *J. Bone Joint Surg. Br.* **85,** 740–747.
86. Winter, A., Breit, S., Parsch, D., Benz, K., Steck, E., Hauner, H., Weber, R.M., Ewerbeck, V., and Richter, W. (2003). Cartilage-like gene expression in differentiated human stem cell spheroids: a comparison of bone marrow-derived and adipose tissue-derived stromal cells. *Arthritis Rheum.* **48,** 418–429.
87. Beresford, J.N., Gallagher, J.A., and Russel, R.G.G. (1986). 1,25-Dihydroxyvitamin D3 and human bone-derived cells in vitro: effects on alkaline phosphatase, type I collagen and proliferation. *Endocrinology* **119,** 1776–1785.
88. Leboy, P.S., Beresford, J.N., Devlin, C., and Owen, M.E. (1991). Dexamethasone induction of osteoblast mRNAs in rat marrow stromal cell cultures. *J. Cell Physiol.* **146,** 370–378.
89. Benson, M.D., Bargeon, J.L., Xiao, G., Thomas, P.E., Kim, A., Cui, Y., and Franceschi, R.T. (2000). Identification of a homeodomain binding element in the bone sialoprotein gene promoter that is required for its osteoblast-selective expression. *J. Biol. Chem.* **275,** 13907–13917.
90. Ohgushi, H., Dohi, Y., Tamai, S., and Tabata, S. (1993). Osteogenic differentiation of marrow stromal stem cells in porous hydroxyapatite ceramics. *J. Biomed. Mater. Res.* **27,** 1401–1407.
91. Shang, Q., Wang, Z., Liu, W., Shi, Y., Cui, L., and Cao, Y. (2001). Tissue-engineered bone repair of sheep cranial defects with autologous bone marrow stromal cells. *J. Craniofac. Surg.* **12,** 586–593.

92. Angele, P., Kujat, R., Nerlich, M., Yoo, J., Goldberg, V., and Johnstone, B. (1999). Engineering of osteochondral tissue with bone marrow mesenchymal progenitor cells in a derivatized hyaluronan-gelatin composite sponge [In Process Citation]. *Tissue Eng.* **5,** 545–554.
93. Hanada, K., Dennis, J.E., and Caplan, A.I. (1997). Stimulatory effects of basic fibroblast growth factor and bone morphogenetic protein-2 on osteogenic differentiation of rat bone marrow-derived mesenchymal stem cells. *J. Bone Miner. Res.* **12,** 1606–1614.
94. Noshi, T., Yoshikawa, T., Dohi, Y., Ikeuchi, M., Horiuchi, K., Ichijima, K., Sugimura, M., Yonemasu, K., and Ohgushi, H. (2001). Recombinant human bone morphogenetic protein-2 potentiates the in vivo osteogenic ability of marrow/hydroxyapatite composites. *Artif. Organs* **25,** 201–208.
95. Lieberman, J.R., Daluiski, A., Stevenson, S., Wu, L., McAllister, P., Lee, Y.P., Kabo, J.M., Finerman, G.A., Berk, A.J., and Witte, O.N. (1999). The effect of regional gene therapy with bone morphogenetic protein-2-producing bone-marrow cells on the repair of segmental femoral defects in rats. *J. Bone Joint Surg. Am.* **81,** 905–917.
96. Lieberman, J.R., Le, L.Q., Wu, L., Finerman, G.A., Berk, A., Witte, O.N., and Stevenson, S. (1998). Regional gene therapy with a BMP-2-producing murine stromal cell line induces heterotopic and orthotopic bone formation in rodents. *J. Orthop. Res.* **16,** 330–339.
97. Laurencin, C.T., Attawia, M.A., Lu, L.Q., Borden, M.D., Lu, H.H., Gorum, W.J., and Lieberman, J.R. (2001). Poly(lactide-co-glycolide)/hydroxyapatite delivery of BMP-2-producing cells: a regional gene therapy approach to bone regeneration. *Biomaterials* **22,** 1271–1277.
98. Olmsted-Davis, E.A., Gugala, Z., Gannon, F.H., Yotnda, P., McAlhany, R.E., Lindsey, R.W., and Davis, A.R. (2002). Use of a chimeric adenovirus vector enhances BMP2 production and bone formation. *Hum. Gene Ther.* **20,** 1337–1347.
99. Sugiyama, O., Orimo, H., Suzuki, S., Yamashita, K., Ito, H., and Shimada, T. (2003). Bone formation following transplantation of genetically modified primary bone marrow stromal cells. *J. Orthop. Res.* **21,** 630–637.
100. Peterson, *et al.* (Unpublished results).
101. Peterson, *et al.* (Unpublished results).
102. Tacchetti, C., Tavella, S., Dozin, B., Quarto, R., Robino, G., and Cancedda, R. (1992). Cell condensation in chondrogenic differentiation. *Exp. Cell Res.* **200,** 26–33.
103. Ahrens, P.B., Solursh, M., and Reiter, R.S. (1977). Stage-related capacity for limb chondrogenesis in cell culture. *Dev. Biol.* **60,** 69–82.
104. Reddi, A.H. (1982). Regulation of local differentiation of cartilage and bone by extracellular matrix: a cascade type mechanism. *Prog. Clin. Biol. Res.* **110,** 261–268.
105. Denker, A.E., Nicoll, S.B., and Tuan, R.S. (1995). Formation of cartilage-like spheroids by micromass cultures of murine C3H10T1/2 cells upon treatment with transforming growth factor beta1. *Differentiation* **59,** 25–34.
106. Yoo, J.U., and Johnstone, B. (1998). The role of osteochondral progenitor cells in fracture repair. *Clin. Orthop.* **355 Suppl,** S73–81.
107. Ahrens, P.B., Solursh, M., and Reiters, R. (1977). Stage-related capacity for limb chondrogenesis in cell culture. *Dev. Biol.* **60,** 69–82.
108. Erickson, G.R., Gimble, J.M., Franklin, D.M., Rice, H.E., Awad, H., and Guilak, F. (2002). Chondrogenic potential of adipose tissue-derived stromal cells in vitro and in vivo. *Biochem. Biophys. Res. Commun.* **290,** 763–769.
109. Lindenhayn, K., Perka, C., Spitzer, R., Heilmann, H., Pommerening, K., Mennicke, J., and Sittinger, M. (1999). Retention of hyaluronic acid in alginate beads: aspects for in vitro cartilage engineering. *J. Biomed. Mater. Res.* **44,** 149–155.
110. Ma, H.L., Hung, S.C., Lin, S.Y., Chen, Y.L., and Lo, W.H. (2003). Chondrogenesis of human mesenchymal stem cells encapsulated in alginate beads. *J. Biomed. Mater. Res.* **64A,** 273–281.
111. Hauselmann, H.J., Fernandes, R.J., Mok, S.S., Schmid, T.M., Block, J.A., Aydelotte, M.B., Kuettner, K.E., and Thonar, E.J. (1994). Phenotypic stability of bovine articular chondrocytes after long-term culture in alginate beads. *J. Cell Sci.* **107,** 17–27.
112. Hauselmann, H.J., Masuda, K., Hunziker, E.B., Neidhart, M., Mok, S.S., Michel, B.A., and Thonar, E.J. (1996). Adult human chondrocytes cultured in alginate form a matrix similar to native human articular cartilage. *Am. J. Physiol.* **271,** C742–C752.
113. Goetinck, P.F., Kiss, I.A., Deak, F., and Stirpe, N.S. (1990). Macromolecular organization of the extracellular matrix of cartilage. *Ann. NY Acad. Sci.* **599,** 29–38.
114. Rodgers, B.J., Kulyk, W.M., and Kosher, R.A. (1989). Stimulation of limb cartilage differentiation by cyclic AMP is dependent on cell density. *Cell Differ. Dev.* **28,** 179–187.
115. Tsonis, P.A., and Goetinck, P.F. (1990). Cell density dependent effect of a tumor promoter on proliferation and chondrogenesis of limb bud mesenchymal cells. *Exp. Cell Res.* **190,** 247–253.
116. Huang, L., Solursh, M., and Sandra, A. (1996). The role of transforming growth factor alpha in rat craniofacial development and chondrogenesis. *J. Anat.* **189,** 73–86.
117. Huang, J.I., Zuk, P.A., Jones, N.F., Zhu, M., Lorenz, H.P., Hedrick, M.H., and Benhaim, P. (2003). Chondrogenic potential of multipotential cells from human adipose tissue. *Plast. Reconstr. Surg.* **113,** 585–594.
118. Yoon, K., Rutledge, S.J.C., Buenaga, R.F., and Rodan, G.A. (1988). Characterization of the rat osteocalcin gene: Stimulation of promoter activity by 1,25-dihydroxyvitamin D3. *Biochemistry* **27,** 8521–8526.
119. Mackay, A.M., Beck, S.C., Murphy, J.M., Barry, F.P., Chichester, C.O., and Pittenger, M.F. (1998). Chondrogenic differentiation of cultured human mesenchymal stem cells from marrow. *Tissue Eng.* **4,** 415–428.
120. Kosher, R.A., Gay, S.W., Kamanitz, J.R., Kulyk, W.M., Rodgers, B.J., Sai, S., Tanaka, T., and Tanzer, M.L. (1986). Cartilage proteoglycan core protein gene expression during limb cartilage differentiation. *Dev. Biol.* **118,** 112–117.
121. Castagnola, P., Moro, G., Descalzi-Cancedda, F., and Cancedda, R. (1986). Type X collagen synthesis during in vitro development of chick embryo tibial chondrocytes. *J. Cell Biol.* **102,** 2310–2317.
122. Kosher, R.A., Kulyk, W.M., and Gay, S.W. (1986). Collagen gene expression during limb cartilage differentiation. *J. Cell Biol.* **102,** 1151–1156.
123. Linsenmayer, T.F., Eavey, R.D., and Schmid, T.M. (1988). Type X collagen: a hypertrophic cartilage-specific molecule. *Pathol. Immunopathol Res.* **7,** 14–19.
124. Sandell, L.J., and Adler, P. (1999). Developmental patterns of cartilage. *Front. Biosci.* **4,** D731–D742.
125. Zenmyo, M., Komiya, S., Kawabata, R., Sasaguri, Y., Inoue, A., and Morimatsue, M. (1996). Morphological and biochemical evidence for apoptosis in the terminal hypertrophic chondrocytes of the growth plate. *J. Pathol.* **180,** 430–433.

126. Sun, Y., and Kandel, R. (1999). Deep zone articular chondrocytes in vitro express genes that show specific changes with mineralization. *J. Bone Miner. Res.* **14,** 1916–1925.
127. Moskalewski, S., and Malejczyk, J. (1989). Bone formation following intrarenal transplantation of isolated murine chondrocytes: chondrocyte-bone cell trandifferentiation? *Development* **107,** 473–480.
128. Ishizeki, K., Hiraki, Y., Kubo, M., and Nawa, T. (1997). Sequential synthesis of cartilage and bone marker proteins during transdifferentiation of mouse Meckel's cartilage chondrocytes in vitro. *Int. J. Dev. Biol.* **41,** 83–89.
129. Bianco, P., Cancedda, F.D., Riminucci, M., and Cancedda, R. (1998). Bone formation via cartilage models: The "borderline" chondrocyte. *Matrix Biol.* **17,** 185–192.
130. Gerstenfeld, L.C., Cruceta, J., Shea, C.M., Sampath, K., Barnes, G.L., and Einhorn, T.A. (2002). Chondrocytes provide morphogenic signals that selectively induce osteogenic differentiation of mesenchymal stem cells. *J. Bone Miner. Res.* **17,** 221–230.
131. Bianco, P., Fisher, L.W., Young, M.F., Termine, J.D., and Robey, P.G. (1991). Expression of bone sialoprotein (BSP) in developing human tissues. *Calcif. Tissue Int.* **49,** 421–426.
132. Descalzi Cancedda, F., Gentili, C., Manduca, P., and Cancedda, R. (1992.). Hypertrophic chondrocytes undergo further differentiation in culture. *J. Cell Biol.* **117,** 427–435.
133. Gerstenfeld, L.C., and Shapiro, F.D. (1996). Expression of bone-specific genes by hypertrophic chondrocytes: implication of the complex functions of the hypertrophic chondrocyte during endochondral. *J. Cell Biochem.* **62,** 1–9.
134. Kergosien, N., Sautier, J., and Forest, N. (1998). Gene and protein expression during differentiation and matrix mineralization in a chondrocyte cell culture system. *Calcif. Tissue Int.* **62,** 114–121.
135. Tuckermann, J.P., Pittois, K., Partridge, N.C., Merregaert, J., and Angel, P. (2000). Collagenase-3 (MMP-13) and integral membrane protein 2a (Itm2a) are marker genes of chondrogenic/osteoblastic cells in bone formation: sequential temporal, and spatial expression of Itm2a, alkaline phosphatase, MMP-13, and osteocalcin in the mouse. *J. Bone Miner. Res.* **15,** 1257–1265.
136. de Crombrugghe, B., Lefebvre, V., and Nakashima, K. (2001). Regulatory mechanisms in the pathways of cartilage and bone formation. *Curr. Opin. Cell Biol.* **13,** 721–727.
137. Pullig, O., Weseloh, G., Ronneberger, D., Kakonen, S., and Swoboda, B. (2002). Chondrocyte differentiation in human osteoarthritis: expression of osteocalcin in normal and osteoarthritic cartilage and bone. *Calcif. Tissue Int.* **67,** 230–240.
138. Hegert, C., Kramer, J., Hargus, G., Muller, J., Guan, K., Wobus, A.M., Muller, P.K., and Rohwedel, J. (2002). Differentiation plasticity of chondrocytes derived from mouse embryonic stem cells. *J. Cell Sci.* **115,** 4617–4628.
139. Zuk, P.A., *et al.* (Unpublished results).
140. Brittberg, M., Lindahl, A., Nilsson, A., Ohlsson, C., Isaksson, O., and Peterson, L. (1994). Treatment of deep cartilage defects in the knee with autologous chondrocyte transplantation. *N. Engl. J. Med.* **331,** 889–895.
141. Wakitani, S., Goto, T., Pineda, S.J., Young, R.G., Mansour, J.M., Caplan, A.I., and Goldberg, V.M. (1994). Mesenchymal cell-based repair of large, full-thickness defects of articular cartilage. *J. Bone Joint Surg. Am.* **76,** 579–592.
142. Chen, F.S., Frenkel, S.R., and Di Cesare, P.E. (1997). Chondrocyte transplantation and experimental treatment options for articular cartilage defects. *Am. J. Orthop.* **26,** 396–406.
143. Freed, L.E., Hollander, A.P., Martin, I., Barry, J.R., Langer, R., and Vunjak-Novakovic, G. (1998). Chondrogenesis in a cell-polymer-bioreactor system. *Exp. Cell Res.* **240,** 58–65.
144. Rahfoth, B., Weissner, J., and Sternkopf, F. (1998). Transplantation of allograft chondrocytes embedded in agarose gel into cartilage defects of rabbit. *Osteoarthritis Cartil.* **6,** 50–65.
145. Brittberg, M. (1999). Autologous chondrocyte transplantation. *Clin. Orthop.* **367,** S147–155.
146. Bruder, S.P., Fink, D.J., and Caplan, A.I. (1994). Mesenchymal stem cells in bone development, bone repair, and skeletal regeneration therapy. *J. Cell Biochem.* **56,** 283–294.
147. Butnariu-Ephrat, M., Robinson, D., Mendes, D.G., Halperin, N., and Nevo, Z. (1996). Resurfacing of goat articular cartilage by chondrocytes derived from bone marrow. *Clin. Orthop.* **330,** 234–243.
148. Oreffo, R.O., and Triffitt, J.T. (1999). Future potentials for using osteogenic stem cells and biomaterials in orthopedics. *Bone* **25,** 5S–9S.
149. Quintavalla, J., Uziel-Fusi, S., Yin, J., Boehnlein, E., Pastor, G., Blancuzzi, V., Singh, H.N., Kraus, K.H., O'Byrne, E., and Pellas, T.C. (2002). Fluorescently labeled mesenchymal stem cells (MSCs) maintain multilineage potential and can be detected following implantation into articular cartilage defects. *Biomaterials* **23,** 109–119.
150. Noel, D., Djouad, F., and Jorgense, C. (2002). Regenerative medicine through mesenchymal stem cells for bone and cartilage repair. *Curr. Opin. Invest. Drugs* **3,** 1000–1004.
151. Carlson, *et al.* (Unpublished results).
152. Wickham, M.Q., Erickson, G.R., Gimble, J.M., Vail, T.P., and Guilak, F. (2003). Multipotent stromal cells derived from the infrapatellar fat pad of the knee. *Clin. Orthop.* **412,** 196–212.
153. Campion, D.R. (1984). The muscle satellite cell: a review. *Int. Rev. Cytol.* **87,** 225–251.
154. Alameddine, H.S., Dehaupas, M., and Fardeau, M. (1989). Regeneration of skeletal muscle fibers from autologous satellite cells multiplied in vitro. An experimental model for testing cultured cell myogenicity. *Muscle Nerve* **12,** 544–555.
155. Seale, P., and Rudnicki, M.A. (2000). A new look at the origin, function, and "stem-cell" status of muscle satellite cells. *Dev. Biol.* **218,** 115–124.
156. Boheler, K.R., Czyz, J., Tweedie, D., Yang, H.T., Anisimov, S.V., and Wobus, A.M. (2002). Differentiation of pluripotent embryonic stem cells into cardiomyocytes. *Circ. Res.* **91,** 189–201.
157. Maltsev, V.A., Rohwedel, J., Hescheler, J., and Wobus, A.M. (1993). Embryonic stem cells differentiate in vitro into cardiomyocytes representing sinus nodal, atrial and ventricular cell types. *Mech. Dev.* **441,** 41–50.
158. Baker, R.K., and Lyons, G.E. (1996). Embryonic stem cells and in vitro muscle development. *Curr. Top. Dev. Biol.* **33,** 263–279.
159. Ferrari, G., Cusella-De Angelis, G., Coletta, M., Paolucci, E., Stornaiuolo, A., Cossu, G., and Mavilio, F. (1998). Muscle regeneration by bone marrow-derived myogenic progenitors [see comments] [published erratum appears in *Science* (1998) **281,** 923]. *Science* 279, 1528–1530.
160. Grounds, M.D., Garrett, K.L., Lai, M.C., Wright, W.E., and Beilharz, M.W. (1992). Identification of skeletal muscle precursor cells in vivo by use of MyoD1 and myogenin probes. *Cell Tiss. Res.* **267,** 99–104.
161. Sassoon, D.A. (1993). Myogenic regulation factors: dissecting their role and regulation during vertebrate embryogenesis. *Dev. Biol.* **156,** 11–23.

162. Weintraub, H., Davis, R., and Tapscott, S. (1991). The myoD gene family: nodal point during specification of the muscle cell lineage. *Science* **251,** 761–763.
163. Atchley, W.R., Fitch, W.M., and Bronner-Fraser, M. (1994). Molecular evolution of the MyoD family of transcription factors. *Proc. Natl. Acad. Sci. U. S. A.* **91,** 11522–11526.
164. Lassar, A., and Munsterberg, A. (1994). Wiring diagrams: regulatory circuits and the control of skeletal myogenesis. *Curr. Opin. Cell Biol.* **6,** 432–442.
165. Megeney, L.A., Kablar, B., Garrett, K., Anderson, J.E., and Rudnicki, M.A. (1996). MyoD is required for myogenic stem cell function in adult skeletal muscle. *Genes Dev.* **10,** 1173–1183.
166. Periasamy, M., Gregory, P., Martin, B.J., and Stirewalt, W.S. (1989). Regulation of myosin heavy-chain gene expression during skeletal-muscle hypertrophy. *Biochem. J.* **257,** 691–698.
167. Butler-Browne, G.S., Barbet, J.P., and Thornell, L.E. (1990). Myosin heavy and light chain expression during human skeletal muscle development and precocious muscle maturation induced by thyroid hormone. *Anat. Embryol.* **181,** 513–522.
168. Mizuno, H., Zuk, P.A., Zhu, M., Lorenz, H.P., Benhaim, P., and Hedrick, M.H. (2001). Myogenic differentiation of human processed lipoaspirate cells. *Plast. Reconstr. Surg.* **109,** 199–209.
169. Makino, S., Fukuda, K., Miyoshi, S., Konishi, F., Kodama, H., Pan, J., Sano, M., Takahashi, T., Hori, S., Abe, H., Hata, J., Umezawa, A., and Ogawa, S. (1999). Cardiomyocytes can be generated from marrow stromal cells in vitro. *J. Clin. Invest.* **103,** 697–705.
170. Fukuda, J., Kaneko, T., Egashira, M., and Oshimi, K. (1998). Direct measurement of CD34+ blood stem cell absolute counts by flow cytometry. *Stem Cells* **16,** 294–300.
171. Fukuda, K. (2001). Development of regenerative cardiomyocytes from mesenchymal stem cells for cardiovascular tissue engineering. *Artif. Organs* **25,** 187–193.
172. Rangappa, S., Fen, C., Lee, E.H., Bongso, A., and Wei, E.S. (2003). Transformation of adult mesenchymal stem cells isolated from the fatty tissue into cardiomyocytes. *Ann. Thorac. Surg.* **75,** 775–779.
173. Schultz, E., and Lipton, B.H. (1982). Skeletal muscle satellite cells: changes in proliferation potential as a function of age. *Mech. Aging Dev.* **20,** 377–383.
174. Yoo, J.J., Park, H.J., and Atala, A. (2000). Tissue-engineering applications for phallic reconstruction [In Process Citation]. *World J. Urol.* **18,** 62–66.
175. Hutcheson, K.A., Atkins, B.Z., Hueman, M.T., Hopkins, M.B., Glower, D.D., and Taylor, D.A. (2000). Comparison of benefits on myocardial performance of cellular cardiomyoplasty with skeletal myoblasts and fibroblasts. *Cell Transplant.* **9,** 359–368.
176. Anversa, P., and Nadal-Ginard, B. (2002). Myocyte renewal and ventricular remodelling. *Nature* **415,** 240–243.
177. Liechty, K.W., MacKenzie, T.C., Shaaban, A.F., Radu, A., Moseley, A.M., Deans, R., Marshak, D.R., and Flake, A.W. (2000). Human mesenchymal stem cells engraft and demonstrate site-specific differentiation after in utero transplantation in sheep. *Nat. Med.* **6,** 1282–1286.
178. Ferrari, G., and Mavilio, F. (2002). Myogenic stem cells from the bone marrow: a therapeutic alternative for muscular dystrophy? *Neuromusc. Disord.* **12,** S7–S10.
179. Tomita, S., Li, R.K., Weisel, R.D., Mickle, D.A., Kim, E.J., Sakai, T., and Jia, Z.Q. (1999). Autologous transplantation of bone marrow cells improves damaged heart function. *Circulation* **100** (Suppl), 11247–11256.
180. Gojo, S., Gojo, N., Takeda, Y., Mori, T., Abe, H., Kyo, S., Hata, J., and Umezawa, A. (2003). In vivo cardiovasculogenesis by direct injection of isolated adult mesenchymal stem cells. *Exp. Cell Res.* **288,** 51–59.
181. Shake, J.G., Gruber, P.J., Baumgartner, W.A., Senechal, G., Meyers, J., Redmond, J.M., Pittenger, M.F., and Martin, B.J. (2002). Mesenchymal stem cell implantation in a swine myocardial infarct model: Engraftment and functional effects. *Ann. Thorac. Surg.* **73,** 1919–1925.
182. Saito, T., Kuang, J.Q., Lin, C.C., and Chiu, R.C. (2003). Transcoronary implantation of bone marrow stromal cells ameliorates cardiac function after myocardial infarction. *Thorac. Cardiovasc. Surg.* **126,** 114–123.
183. Terada, N., Hamazaki, T., Oka, M., Hoki, M., Mastalerz, D.M., Nakano, Y., Meyer, E.M., Morel, L., Petersen, B.E., and Scott, E.W. (2002). Bone marrow cells adopt the phenotype of other cells by spontaneous cell fusion. *Nature* **416,** 542–545.
184. Ying, Q.L., Nichols, J., Evans, E.P., and Smith, A.G. (2002). Changing potency by spontaneous fusion. *Nature* **416,** 545–548.
185. Austin, T.W., and Lagasse, E. (2003). Hepatic regeneration from hematopoietic stem cells. *Mech. Dev.* **120,** 131–135.
186. Fiegel, H.C., Lioznov, M.V., Cortes-Dericks, L., Lange, C., Kluth, D., Fehse, B., and Zander, A.R. (2003). Liver-specific gene expression in cultured human hematopoietic stem cells. *Stem Cells* 21, 98–104.
187. Hao, H.N., Zhao, J., Thomas, R.L., Parker, G.C., and Lyman, W.D. (2003). Fetal human hematopoietic stem cells can differentiate sequentially into neural stem cells and then astrocytes in vitro. *J. Hematother. Stem Cell Res.* **12,** 23–32.
188. Eglitis, M.A., and Mezey, E. (1997). Hematopoietic cells differentiate into both microglia and macroglia in the brains of adult mice. *Proc. Natl. Acad. Sci. U. S. A.* **94,** 4080–4085.
189. Mezey, E., Chandross, K.J., Harta, G., Maki, R.A., and McKercher, S.R. (2000). Turning blood into brain: cells bearing neuronal antigens generated in vivo from bone marrow. *Science* **290,** 1779–1782.
190. Bonilla, S., Alarcon, P., Villaverde, R., Aparicio, P., Silva, A., and Martinez, S. (2002). Haematopoietic progenitor cells from adult bone marrow differentiate into cells that express oligodendroglial antigens in the neonatal mouse brain. *Eur. J. Neurosci.* **15,** 575–582.
191. Jackson, K.A., Majka, S.M., Wang, H., Pocius, J., Hartley, C.J., Majesky, M.W., Entman, M.L., Michael, L.H., Hirschi, K.K., and Goodell, M.A. (2001). Regeneration of ischemic cardiac muscle and vascular endothelium by adult stem cells. *Clin. Invest.* **107,** 1395–1402.
192. Malouf, N.N., Coleman, W.B., Grisham, J.W., Lininger, R.A., Madden, V.J., Sproul, M., and Anderson, P.A. (2001). Adult-derived stem cells from the liver become myocytes in the heart in vivo. *Am. J. Pathol.* **158,** 1929–1935.
193. Deng, J., Steindler, D.A., Laywell, E.D., and Petersen, B.E. (2003). Neural trans-differentiation potential of hepatic oval cells in the neonatal mouse brain. *Exp. Neurol.* **182,** 373–382.
194. Ishikawa, F., Drake, C.J., Yang, S., Fleming, P., Minamiguchi, H., Visconti, R.P., Crosby, C.V., Argraves, W.S., Harada, M., Key, L.L., Jr., Livingston, A.G., Wingard, J.R., and Ogawa, M. (2003). Transplanted human cord blood cells give rise to hepatocytes in engrafted mice. *Ann. NY Acad. Sci.* **996,** 174–185.
195. Newsome, P.N., Johannessen, I., Boyle, S., Dalakas, E., McAulay, K.A., Samuel, K., Rae, F., Forrester, L., Turner, M.L., Hayes, P.C., Harrison, D.J., Bickmore, W.A., and Plevris, J.N.

(2003). Human cord blood-derived cells can differentiate into hepatocytes in the mouse liver with no evidence of cellular fusion. *Gastroenterology* **124,** 1891–1900.

196. Goodell, M.A., Rosenzweig, M., Kim, H., Marks, D.F., DeMaria, M., Paradis, G., Grupp, S.A., Sieff, C.A., Mulligan, R.C., and Johnson, R.P. (1997). Dye efflux studies suggest that hematopoietic stem cells expressing low or undetectable levels of CD34 antigen exist in multiple species. *Nat. Med.* **3,** 1337–1345.
197. Bosch, P., Musgrave, D.S., Lee, J.Y., Cummins, J., Shuler, T., Ghivizzani, T.C., Evans, T., Robbins, T.D., and Huard, J. (2000). Osteoprogenitor cells within skeletal muscle. *J. Orthop. Res.* **18,** 933–944.
198. Lin, J., Arnold, H.B., Della-Fera, M.A., Azain, M.J., Hartzell, D.L., and Baile, C.A. (2002). Myostatin knockout in mice increases myogenesis and decreases adipogenesis. *Biochem. Biophys. Res. Commun.* **291,** 701–706.
199. Sordella, R., Jiang, W., Chen, G.C., Curto, M., and Settleman. J. (2003). Modulation of Rho GTPase signaling regulates a switch between adipogenesis and myogenesis. *Cell* **113,** 147–158.
200. Woodbury, D., Schwarz, E.J., Prockop, D.J., and Black, I.B. (2000). Adult rat and human bone marrow stromal cells differentiate into neurons. *J. Neurosci. Res.* **61,** 364–370.
201. Weiss, S., Dunne, C., Hewson, J., Wohl, C., Wheatley, M., Peterson, A.C., and Reynolds, B.A. (1996). Multipotent CNS stem cells are present in the adult mammalian spinal cord and ventricular neuroaxis. *J. Neurosci.* **16,** 7599–7609.
202. Temple, S. (1999). CNS development: The obscure origins of adult stem cells. *Curr. Biol.* **9,** R397–R399.
203. Deng, W., Obrocka, M., Fischer, I., and Prockop, D.J. (2001). *In vitro* differentiation of human marrow stromal cells into early progenitors of neural cells by conditions that increase intracellular cyclic cAMP. *Biochem. Biophys. Res. Commun.* **282,** 148–152.
204. Sanchez-Ramos, J., Song, S., Cardozo-Palaez, Hazzi, C., Stedeford, T., Willing, A., Freeman, T.B., Saporta, S., Janssen, W., Patel, N., Cooper, D.R., and Sanberg, P.R. (2000). Adult bone marrow stromal cells differentiate into neural cells *in vitro*. *Exp. Neurol.* **164,** 247–256.
205. Lendahl, U., Zimmerman, L.B., and McKay, R.D.G. (1990). CNS stem cells express a new class of intermediate filament protein. *Cell* **60,** 585–595.
206. Ashjian, P.H., Elbarbary, A.S., Edmonds, B., De Ugarte, D.A., Kong, W., Zhu, M., Zuk, P.A., Lorenz, H.P., Benhaim, P., and Hedrick, M.H. 2003. *In vitro* differentiation of human processed lipoaspirate cells into early neural progenitors. *Plast. and Reconstr. Surg.* **116,** 1922–1931.
207. Safford, K.M., Hicok, K.C., Safford, S.D., Halvorsen, Y.D., Wilkison, W.O., Gimble, J.M., and Rice, H.E. (2002). Neurogenic differentiation of murine and human adipose-derived stromal cells. *Biochem. Biophys. Res. Commun.* **294,** 371–379.
208. Kohyama, J., Abe, H., Shimazaki, T., Koizumi, A., Nakashima, K., Gojo, S., Taga, T., Okano, H., Hata, J., and Umezawa, A. (2001). Brain from bone: Efficient "meta-differentiation" of marrow stroma-derived mature osteoblasts to neurons with Noggin or a demethylating agent. *Differentiation* **68,** 235–244.
209. Woodbury, D., Reynolds, K., and Black, I.B. (2002). Adult bone marrow stromal stem cells express germline, ectodermal, endodermal, and mesodermal genes prior to neurogenesis. *J. Neurosci. Res.* **69,** 908–917.
210. Zuk, P.A. (Unpublished results).
211. Rathjen, J., Lake, J.A., Bettess, M.D., Washington, J.M., Chapman, G., and Rathjen, P.D. (1999). Formation of a primitive ectoderm like cell population, EPL cells, from ES cells in response to biologically derived factors. *J. Cell Sci.* **112,** 601–612.

211a. Nolta, unpublished results.

212. Dennis, J.E., Merriam, A., Awadallah, A., Yoo, J.U., Johnstone, B., and Caplan, A.I. (1999). A quadripotential mesenchymal progenitor cell isolated from the marrow of an adult mouse. *J. Bone Miner. Res.* **14,** 700–709.
213. Muraglia, A., Cancedda, R., and Quarto, R. (2000). Clonal mesenchymal progenitors from human bone marrow differentiate in vitro according to a hierarchical model. *J. Cell Sci.* **113,** 1161–1166.
214. Friedenstein, A.J. (1990). Osteogenic stem cells in the bone marrow. *In* "Bone and Mineral Research," vol. 7. (J.N.M. Heersche, and Kanis, J.A., Eds.), pp. 243–272. Elsevier Science, San Diego, CA.
215. Bartholomew, A., Patil, S., Mackay, A., Nelson, M., Buyaner, D., Hardy, W., Mosca, J., Sturgeon, C., Siatskas, M., Mahmud, N., Ferrer, K., Deans, R., Moseley, A., Hoffman, R., and Devine, S.M. (2001). Baboon mesenchymal stem cells can be genetically modified to secrete human erythropoietin in vivo. *Hum. Gene Ther.* **10,** 1527–1541.

215a. Caplan, A.I. (2000). Mesenchymal stem cells and gene therapy. *Clin. Orthop.* **379,** S67–S70.

216. Lendahl, U., Zimmerman, L.B., and McKay, R.D.G. (1990). CNS stem cells express a new class of intermediate filament protein. *Cell* **60,** 585–595.
217. Case, S.S., Price, M.A., Jordan, C.T., Yu, X.J., Wang, L., Bauer, G., Haas, D.L., Xu, D., Stripecke, R., Naldini, L., Kohn, D.B., and Crooks, G.M. (1999). Stable transduction of quiescent CD34(+)CD38(-) human hematopoietic cells by HIV-1-based lentiviral vectors. *Proc. Natl. Acad. Sci. U. S. A.* **96,** 2988–2993.
218. Cherington, V., Chiang, G.G., McGrath, C.A., Gaffney, A., Galanopoulos, T., Merrill, W., Bizinkauskas, C.B., Hansen, M., Sobolewski, J., Levine, P.H., Greenberger, J.S., and Hurwitz, D.R. (1998). Retroviral vector-modified bone marrow stromal cells secrete biologically active factor IX in vitro and transiently deliver therapeutic levels of human factor IX to the plasma of dogs after reinfusion. *Hum. Gene Ther.* **9,** 1397–1407.
219. Cherry, S.R., Biniszkiewicz, D., van Parijs, L., Baltimore, D., and Jaenisch, R. (2000). Retroviral expression in embryonic stem cells and hematopoietic stem cells. *Mol. Cell Biol.* **20,** 7419–7426.
220. Gordon, E.M., Skotzko, M., Kundu, R.K., Han, B., Andrades, J., Nimni, M., Anderson, W.F., and Hall, F.L. (1997). Capture and expansion of bone marrow-derived mesenchymal progenitor cells with a transforming growth factor-beta1-von Willebrand's factor fusion protein for retrovirus-mediated delivery of coagulation factor IX. *Hum. Gene Ther.* **8,** 1385–1394.
221. Hurwitz, D.R., Kirchgesser, M., Merrill,, W., Galanopoulos T., McGrath, C.A., Emami, S., Hansen, M., Cherington, V., Appel, J.M., Bizinkauskas, C.B., Brackmann, H.H., Levine, P.H., and Greenberger, J.S. (1997). Systemic delivery of human growth hormone or human factor IX in dogs by reintroduced genetically modified autologous bone marrow stromal cells. *Hum. Gene Ther.* **20,** 137–156.
222. Marx, J.C., Allay, J.A., Persons, D.A., Nooner, S.A., Hargrove, P.W., Kelly, P.F., Vanin, E.F., and Horwitz, E.M. (1999). High-efficiency transduction and long-term gene expression with a murine stem cell retroviral vector encoding the green fluorescent protein in human marrow stromal cells. *Hum. Gene Ther.* **10,** 1163–1173.

223. Mosca, J.D., Hendricks, J.K., Buyaner, D., Davis-Sproul, J., Chuang, L.C., Majumdar, M.K., Chopra, R., Barry, F., Murphy, M., Thiede, M.A., Junker, U., Rigg, R.J., Forestell, S.P., Bohnlein, E., Storb, R., and Sandmaier, B.M. (2000). Mesenchymal stem cells as vehicles for gene delivery. *Clin. Orthop.* **379,** S71–S90.

224. Lee, K., Majumdar, M.K., Buyaner, D., Hendricks, J.K., Pittenger, M.F., and Mosca, J.D. (2001). Human mesenchymal stem cells maintain transgene expression during expansion and differentiation. *Mol. Ther.* **3,** 857–866.

225. Cai, S., Ma, Q., Yu, X., Dang, G., and Ma, D. (2002). Expression of human VEGF(121) cDNA in mouse bone marrow stromal cells. *Chin. Med. J. (Engl).* **115,** 914–918.

226. Guo, X., Du, J., Zheng, Q., Yang, S., Liu, Y., Duan, D., and Yi, C. (2002). Expression of transforming growth factor beta 1 in mesenchymal stem cells: Potential utility in molecular tissue engineering for osteochondral repair. *J. Huazhong Univ. Sci. Technolog. Med. Sci.* **22,** 112–115.

227. Eliopoulos, N., Al-Khaldi, A., Crosato, M., Lachapelle, K., and Galipeau, J. (2003). A neovascularized organoid derived from retrovirally engineered bone marrow stroma leads to prolonged in vivo systemic delivery of erythropoietin in nonmyeloablated, immunocompetent mice. *Gene Ther.* **10,** 478–489.

228. Cousin, B., Andre, M., Arnaud, E., Penicaud, L., and Casteilla, L. (2003). Reconstitution of lethally irradiated mice by cells isolated from adipose tissue. *Biochem. Biophys. Res. Commun.* **21,** 1016–1022.

229. Gimble, J.M., Robinson, C.E., Wu, X., and Kelly, K.A. (1996). The function of adipocytes in the bone marrow stroma: an update. *Bone* **19,** 421–428.

230. Gavrilova, O., Marcus-Samuels, B., Graham, D., Kim, J.K., Schulman, G.I., Castle, A.L., Vinson, C., Eckhaus, M., and Reitman, M.L. (2000). Surgical implantation of adipose tissue reverses diabetes in lipoatrophic mice. *J. Clin. Invest.* **105,** 271–278.

41

Stem Cells and the Regenerating Heart

Nadia Rosenthal and Maria Paola Santini

Introduction

Against a backdrop of seemingly limitless possibilities for endogenous or supplementary stem cells to restore aging or damaged tissues, the restricted regenerative capacity of the mammalian heart remains a perplexing exception. The regenerative response launched by other injured organs involves local populations of self-renewing precursor cells or recruitment of circulating stem cells to replace or repair the injured areas. In response to functional stress, the heart can increase its muscle mass through cellular hypertrophy, but the damaged heart needs a rapid response to repair damage to the muscle wall and maintain adequate blood flow to the rest of the body. Paradoxically, this most critical organ cannot restore the muscle loss that accompanies myocardial infarction and ischemia-reperfusion injury. Instead, interruption of the coronary blood supply results in apoptosis and fibrotic scar formation at the cost of functional muscle. As a result, the remaining cardiomyocytes undergo cellular hypertrophy, leading to decompensated function and congestive heart failure, an increasingly prevalent disease in the industrialized world.

What underlies the inability of the mammalian heart to rebuild itself in response to injury? Where are the stem cells of this vital organ, and, if there are none, how does it maintain its structural and functional integrity for decades? The impediment to adult mammalian cardiac regeneration has been attributed to its distinct embryonic history. The heart is the first fully differentiated structure to form and function during vertebrate development. The primitive heart tube, composed of contracting cardiomyocytes lined by a layer of endocardial cells, ensures the establishment of a circulatory system that is critical to support rapid rates of embryonic growth. The astonishing capacity of the embryonic heart to perform at such an early stage depends on its rapid assembly from the multipotent mesoderm, a cumulative process that depends on a series of sequential inductive interactions. The progressive acquisition of the cardiac phenotype by precursor cells starts early in the primitive streak stage, so that by the time a cardiac crescent is fully formed, coordinated contractions in the primitive heart tube. In contrast to fetal skeletal myocytes, which no longer proliferate once a functioning contractile apparatus has been elaborated, actively contracting fetal cardiomyocytes must continue to divide to provide for further growth of the embryonic heart. This phase of cardiomyocyte division ends soon after birth, when increase in myocardial mass is achieved largely through cellular hypertrophy, at which point the heart is considered fully formed.

The unusual capacity of embryonic and fetal cardiomyocytes to re-enter the cell cycle appears to be largely lost once the heart is developed. In contrast to mammalian skeletal muscle, which regenerates injured tissue through activation of quiescent myogenic precursor or multipotent adult stem cell populations, the heart does not appear to retain equivalent reserve cell populations to promote myofiber repair. The relative paucity of progenitor cells residing within the heart may impose severe limits on replacement of damaged myocardium. Thus, the prevailing assumption has been that the heart cannot regenerate as well as other organs because it does not maintain a sufficiently robust progenitor cell population.

Recruiting Circulating Stem Cell Reserves

The relative scarcity of progenitor cells residing in the adult myocardium has prompted a search for a renewable source of circulating somatic progenitor cells that might home to the heart in response to damage. The existence of such cell populations has gained credibility from observations of sex mismatched cardiac human transplants in which a female heart is transplanted into a male host. In these patients, the presence of the Y chromosome[1] marks host-derived cells in the transplanted heart. Various numbers of Y chromosome-positive myocytes and coronary vessels in transplanted heart's male cells could be found.[2–4] Cell fusion of host cells with donor cardiac cells, as has been proven for other regenerating tissues,[5] was ruled out in by the presence of a single X chromosome.[4] The presence of differentiated host cells in the transplanted tissues proves the existence of migratory precursor cells that are induced to differentiate by the cardiac milieu. Although this phenomenon could be a response to organ transplantation, it may also reflect a normal homeostatic process for the maintenance of cardiac muscle and coronary vasculature.

The lack of information regarding the precise origin of donor cells in these human transplants has prompted animal experiments in which stem cells isolated from bone marrow were enriched for various surface markers. A stem cell-enriched

Handbook of Stem Cells
Volume 2

side population[6] (SP) can be isolated by the relative efflux of Hoechst dye 33342 through MDR1, a P-glycoprotein capable of extruding dyes, toxic substances, and drugs.[7,8] The movement of bone marrow SP cells can be traced if they are isolated from donor mice expressing a genetic marker such as lacZ and used to reconstitute the bone marrow of lethally irradiated recipient mice. In such experiments, very few marked cells can normally be found in extrahematopoietic tissues of the reconstituted animals.[9] However, in reconstituted mice that were subsequently subjected to coronary artery occlusion, lacZ marked cells could be found in vascular endothelium and cardiomyocytes of the border zone adjacent to the infarct.[10] In other studies, cell populations expressing c-kit, the receptor for stem cell factor,[11,12] were isolated from bone marrow and injected directly into the border zone of an experimentally induced infarct where they migrated into the damaged region, differentiated into cardiomyocytes and vascular cells and partially replaced necrotic myocardium.[13] To what extent these different subsets of marked bone marrow cells represent the same cell population as migratory Y chromosome-containing donor cells in the human transplant studies remains to be determined.

Other bone marrow-derived candidates for cardiac regeneration include mesenchymal stem cells, distinct from hematopoietic stem cells, that have multilineage potential, normally generating multiple mesenchymal tissue types.[14] When mesenchymal stem cells isolated from human donors were injected into the ventricular cavity of uninjured mice, they were subsequently found at low levels in the muscle wall, having acquired cardiomyocyte characteristics.[15] Higher levels of mesenchymal stem cell engraftment into the myocardium were achieved by direct injection into the porcine ventricular wall after acute ischemic damage[16] underscoring the importance of injury in the homing process. Numerous cell types have since shown promise in improving cardiac regeneration after acute myocardial infarction in patients, including bone marrow cells,[17,18] endothelial progenitor cells, or skeletal myoblasts.[19] Whatever their source, the newly formed cardiomyocytes must integrate precisely into the existing myocardial muscle to avoid life-threatening arrhythmia, a frequently cited complication of the therapeutic use of cells from noncardiac tissue when treating acute postinfarct ischemia.

Insufficient revascularization represents another major impediment to the reconstitution of ischemic myocardial tissue and the prevention of further scar tissue formation. Although angiogenesis within the infarcted area is an integral component of the remodeling process, the capillary network is normally unable to support the greater demands of the hypertrophied myocardium. Fortunately, adult bone marrow contains endothelial precursors that resemble embryonic angioblasts that, if sufficiently mobilized, could participate in revascularization of the ischemic tissue. In an exciting proof of concept,[20] endothelial progenitor cells, isolated from human adult bone marrow on the basis of CD34 and c-kit expression, were injected intravenously into athymic rats in which myocardial infarction had been recently induced. The human endothelial precursors selectively migrated to ischemic myocardium, where they mediated new blood vessel formation in the infarct bed (vasculogenesis) and proliferation of vasculature (angiogenesis) from pre-existing mature host endothelium in the border zone. The treated animals displayed decreased apoptosis of hypertrophied myocytes in the peri-infarct region, long-term salvage and survival of viable myocardium, reduction in collagen deposition, and sustained improvement in cardiac function. A recent human trial[21] has confirmed that intracoronary infusion of endothelial progenitor cells in patients with acute myocardial infarction (AMI) significantly improves postinfarction left ventricular (LV) remodeling processes, regional contractile function of the infarcted segment, and coronary blood flow reserve in the infarct artery.

Although cardiomyocyte survival in these studies was undoubtedly enhanced by the revascularization of injured myocardium, it is also possible that endothelial precursors contribute directly to regenerating myocardial tissue. Indeed, human umbilical vein endothelial cells, or clonal cultures of endothelial cells isolated from embryonic mouse dorsal aorta, can be induced to express sarcomeric proteins after only 5 days of co-culture with neonatal rat cardiomyocytes.[22] Additional evidence supporting this possibility comes from the conversion of adult human endothelial progenitor cells, derived from peripheral blood mononuclear cells, or $CD34^+$ hematopoietic progenitor cells into cardiomyocytes on co-culture with rat cardiomyocytes.[23] In both studies, cell–cell contact or an extracellular matrix-associated signaling appeared to be critical, because conditioned media from cardiocyte cultures was not sufficient for conversion to a cardiomyocyte phenotype.

Whatever the provenance and potential of cardiac progenitors, it is clear that, at least in mammals, the relatively poor recruitment of circulating stem cells to the site of myocardial injury limits the body's ability to aid in the repair process. Numerous chemotactic signals associated with inflammation, including cytokines and adhesion molecules, are preferentially expressed by the infarct border zone,[24] and may improve stem cell homing as well. Indeed, increasing evidence[24a] supports the notion that chemokines play a central role in directing angioblasts from the bone marrow to ischemic myocardium. Angioblast population of injured cardiac tissue can be experimentally increased either by inhibiting interactions between the bone marrow-derived CXC chemokine SDF-1 and its receptor CXCR4 on angioblasts or by increasing expression of SDF-1 in the ischemic rat heart. The resulting sustained improvement in cardiac involves both protection against apoptosis and induction of proliferation of endogenous cardiomyocytes, suggesting new therapeutic avenues in which enhancement of stem cell trafficking could be harnessed to amplify the endogenous homing process.

The Illusive Cardiac Stem Cell

The adult mammalian heart has long been considered a post-mitotic organ without an endogenous population of stem cells, which instead contains a relatively constant number of myocytes that cease to divide shortly after birth and remain constant into senescence. A long-standing view is that the inability of differentiated cardiac myocytes to re-enter the cell cycle may present the ultimate impediment to the heart's regenerative capacity. The terminal differentiation of cardiomyocytes is likely to be under the control of tumor suppressors, such as Rb, and cyclin-dependent kinase inhibitors.[25,26] Because mice in which individual components of these cell cycle checkpoints have been systemically disrupted by gene knockout do not show dramatic increase myocyte cell numbers,[27] multiple mechanisms must exist to prevent adult myocytes from further proliferation.

The assumption that the myocardium is a terminally differentiated tissue has been subjected to intense scrutiny and considerable debate. The irreversible withdrawal of cardiomyocytes from the cell cycle soon after birth[28] has been held responsible for the drastic effects of acute and chronic myocyte death in the surviving myocardium after infarction and for the failure to derive replicating mammalian myocyte cell cultures from the adult mammalian heart. The fact that cardiac myocytes are multinucleated and polyploid in many mammalian species[29] has complicated interpretation of any observed DNA synthesis that might represent myocyte proliferation.[25] Nevertheless, it has been argued that, in the face of massive cardiomyocyte apoptosis and necrosis, the diseased heart could not continue to function in the absence of new myocyte formation.[30] Increases in myocyte number do not provide information about the origin of these new cells, however. Although most of the controversy surrounding mammalian heart regeneration has focused on the evidence for or against the replication of existing myocytes, cells capable of differentiating into a myocyte in the adult heart[2,4] could originate through the commitment of precursor cells to the myocyte lineage, through replication of preexisting myocytes, or by a combination of these two mechanisms.

Decades of frustrated searching for a resident cardiac stem cell population have recently yielded more encouraging results through the application of methods used to study stem cells in the adult hematopoietic compartment. SPs of cells resembling those isolated from the bone marrow[31] have been found in adult rodent myocardium[32,33] expressing the corresponding transport proteins.[34] Cell surface proteins that mark stem cell populations in other tissues are also found on a subpopulation of undifferentiated precursor cells in the adult heart. These primitive cells can be detected by Sca-1, which is involved in cell signaling and cell adhesion.[35,36] Sca-1 is not specific for stem cells because it is found on the surface of hematopoietic stem cells and other cell types.[37,38] In certain instances[39] cells isolated from adult heart by virtue of their stem cell markers not only express appropriate markers but behave like cardiac progenitor cells *in vitro,* giving rise to clones that express biochemical markers of myocytes, smooth muscle, and endothelial cells.

Another hallmark of progenitor cells is the maintenance of chromosomal telomere integrity through the action of telomerase. In the heart, telomerase levels decrease after birth when most myocardial cells withdraw from the cell cycle. Although telomere shortening has been shown in a small percentage of adult rat cardiomyocytes,[35,40] forced expression of telomerase prolongs cardiac myocyte cycling *in vivo*[41] and confers protection from stress-induced telomere shortening and apoptosis in the adult heart.[42] Notably, telomerase activity in the adult myocardium is restricted to small interstitial cells that express Sca-1 but lack other markers of hematopoietic stem cells (c-kit, CD45, CD34) or endothelial progenitor cells (CD45, CD34, Flk-1, Flt-1).[42] Purified cardiac Sca-1^+ cells home specifically to infarcted myocardium and activate the cardiogenic program, with a significant proportion fusing to existing cardiocytes. These studies suggest that, in the heart, telomere integrity is a key factor in maintaining a Sca-1^+ progenitor cell pool.

It remains to be seen how these cells relate to a population of rare small cycling cardiomyocytes that retain the capacity to proliferate in response to damage and are continuously renewed by the differentiation of stem-like cells as a normal function of cardiac homeostasis.[2,4,39,43,44] The origins of cycling myocardial cells may be attributed to recently characterized Lin^-/c-kit^+ cells isolated from the adult rat heart that retain stem cell characteristics.[45] These cells are self-renewing, clonogenic, and multipotent *in vitro* and *in vivo* and give rise to myocytes and smooth muscle and endothelial vascular cells. When injected into an ischemic rat heart, a population of these cells or their clonal progeny reconstitute up to 70% of the injured myocardial wall. The regenerated myocardium contains small myocytes that present the anatomical, biochemical, and functional properties of young myocytes. These data support the notion that myocyte renewal in the adult mammalian heart occurs constantly, albeit at a very low rate. The possibility that endogenous cardiac stem cells can be mobilized to migrate from their niche within the healthy heart to support regeneration of diseased myocardium has exciting implications for therapeutic intervention.

Evolving Concepts of Regeneration

The limited restorative capacity of the adult mammalian heart has been attributed to the loss of cardiomyocyte versatility soon after birth. The emerging concept of regeneration as an evolutionary variable[46] is dramatically illustrated by the relatively robust proliferative capacity of the injured heart in other vertebrate species. The dramatic regeneration of urodele amphibian limb and lens extends to their efficient repair of injured myocardium.[47–49] Newts repair their hearts in response to cardiac damage, leaving none of the dysfunctional scar tissue typical of the postinfarct mammalian myocardium. Unlike their mammalian counterparts, adult newt cardiomyocytes can readily proliferate after injury and contribute to the functional regeneration of the damaged heart. The recognition that cardiac tissue in certain vertebrates can undergo extensive repair has prompted the proposal that regeneration may be a primordial attribute that has been lost during mammalian evolution.[46]

Recent studies of newt limb regeneration provide a mechanism whereby the rebuilding of damaged tissue could couple acute response to injury with local activation of plasticity in surrounding tissues and/or activation of stem cell pools. A transient activity generated by thrombin, a critical component of the clotting cascade that ensures hemostasis and triggers other events of wound healing, has been linked to cell cycle re-entry in multinucleate myotubes during urodele limb regeneration. Selective activation of thrombin protease action in response to injury provides a feasible connection between damage control and initiation of regenerative growth.[49] It remains to be seen if such a linkage can be established in the regenerating myocardium.

The capacity of the newt heart to regenerate may not be a common attribute shared by all cardiomyocytes. Although longitudinal analyses of single cultured newt cardiomyocytes revealed that many cells enter into S phase in response to serum-activated pathways dependent on the phosphorylation of the Rb protein, the majority of these cells stablely arrest at either entry to mitosis or during cytokinesis. Nevertheless, a significant cell subset progresses through mitosis and participates in successive cell divisions, providing a tractable model system to investigate the mechanisms underlying the ability of newt cardiomyocytes maintain their remarkable proliferative potential.

Regeneration of the zebrafish heart offers a more genetically accessible model for dissecting the molecular basis of cardiac repair. After surgical removal of the ventricular apex and rapid clotting at the site of amputation, proliferating cardiac myofibers replace the clot and regenerate missing tissue, with minimal scarring.[50] The requirement for cell cycle re-entry in this model is supported by the decreased regeneration and increased fibrosis in a temperature-sensitive mutant of a mitotic checkpoint kinase, mps1.[51]

It is still formally possible that the activation of cardiac progenitor cells is largely responsible for the extraordinary capacity of the adult zebrafish to restore extensive portions of the heart. Regeneration has been traditionally assumed to involve the recapitulation of genetic pathways used during embryonic development. This scenario has been challenged by a recent study demonstrating that markers, such as Nkx2-5 or Tbx-5, which play a critical role in heart development, were not detected in regenerating zebrafish myocardium.[52] Rather, an increase in cycling cells expressing myocardial markers was accompanied by activation of genes such as Msx transcription factors and Notch pathway components that are expressed during heart development. The novel profile of genes activated during zebrafish cardiac regeneration, distinct from that associated with cardiogenesis, is consistent with the emerging concept that differentiated myocytes can re-enter the cell cycle and proliferate in response to heart injury.[52] This would provide evidence for true epimorphic regeneration in the vertebrate heart and argues for a clear distinction between mechanisms at work during regeneration versus development. If cardiac progenitor cells are indeed involved in this process, they may play a more instructive role in reforming damaged heart tissue.

The possibility that a process of limited cardiomyocyte proliferation may not be formally excluded in mammalian species is supported by the "healer" phenotype of the MRL mouse strain, a well-characterized model of autoimmunity. Significant myocyte re-entry to S phase and myocardial replacement without scarring has been observed after cryogenic injury of MRL mouse heart tissue.[53] The enhanced and heritable capacity of the MRL mouse to heal surgical wounds is a complex trait that maps to at least 20 genetic loci.[54,55] Although the potential role of autoimmunity remains to be determined, MRL wound repair is potentially mediated by differences in the activity of matrix metalloproteinases and their inhibitors.[56] The similarity of the MRL healer phenotype to newt regenerative processes has suggested a general mechanism whereby a regeneration blastema forms by local dedifferentiation of cells underlying the wound, followed by growth and then reversal to the differentiated cell type.[53,56] Further study of the MRL mouse will be necessary to define molecular commonalities with the more regenerative vertebrates and to determine the potential role of cardiac stem cells in the healing capacity of this tantalizing mouse model.

The regenerative potential of the mammalian heart is a rapidly evolving concept. In the near future, cardiac repair is likely to be augmented through a number of avenues (Fig. 41–1). The dramatic improvements that exogenously administered progenitor cells can effect in both animal and human myocardial repair underscore their therapeutic potential. Although resident cardiac progenitor cell populations have now been identified, the insufficiencies of endogenous stem cells to alleviate acute and chronic damage to mammalian cardiac tissue remain to be overcome. Recent advances in our understanding have uncovered an unexpected dynamism in cardiac homeostasis and highlight the heterogeneous proliferative potential of resident cardiomyocytes. Enhancing the functional regeneration of this most obdurate of organs raises

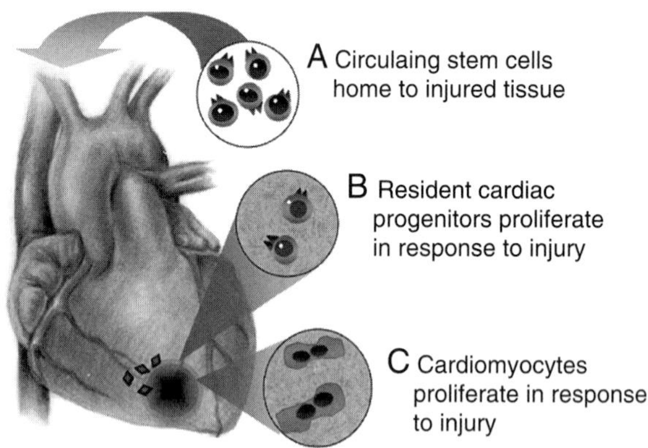

Figure 41–1. Several modes of cardiac regeneration supported by recent studies. (A) Circulating stem cells home to the infarcted area, guided by chemoattractive mechanisms, and participate in multiple functions including neoangiogenesis and myocyte renewal.[24] (B) Injury stimulates the proliferation of resident cardiac progenitors, which resemble tissue stem cells in their phenotype and ability to participate in cardiac renewal.[45] (C) A subset of competent cardiomyocytes re-enter the cell cycle to replace and rebuild missing tissue.[43,44] Although these endogenous regenerative modes are not mutually exclusive, they provide different possibilities for therapeutic intervention. (Please see CD-ROM for color version of this figure.)

the exciting prospect that regenerative processes in other tissues of the adult mammalian soma might be similarly harnessed to fend off the ravages of aging and disease in a new paradigm of self-renewal.

REFERENCES

1. Grounds, M.D. (2000). Muscle regeneration: molecular aspects and therapeutic implications. *Curr. Opin. Neurol.* **12,** 535–543.
2. Quaini, F., Urbanek, K., Beltrami, A.P., Finato, N., Beltrami, C.A., Nadal-Ginard, B., Kajstura, J., Leri, A., and Anversa, P. (2002). Chimerism of the transplanted heart. *N. Engl. J. Med.* **346,** 5–15.
3. Muller, A., Homey, B., Soto, H., Ge, N., Catron, D., Buchanan, M.E., McClanahan, T., Murphy, E., Yuan, W., Wagner, S.N., Barrera, J.L., Mohar, A., Verastegui, E., Zlotnik, A. (2001). Involvement of chemokine receptors in breast cancer metastasis. *Nature* **410,** 50–56.
4. Muller, P., Pfeiffer, P., Koglin, J., Schafers, H.J., Seeland, U., Janzen, I., Urbschat, S., and Bohm, M. (2002). Cardiomyocytes of noncardiac origin in myocardial biopsies of human transplanted hearts. *Circulation* **106,** 31–35.
5. Wang, X., Willenbring, H., Akkari, Y., Torimaru, Y., Foster, M., Al-Dhalimy, M., Lagasse, E., Finegold, M., Olson, S., and Grompe, M. (2003). Cell fusion is the principal source of bone-marrow-derived hepatocytes. *Nature* **422,** 897–901.
6. Goodell, M.A., Rosenzweig, M., Kim, H., Marks, D.F., DeMaria, M., Paradis, G., Grupp, S.A., Sieff, C.A., Mulligan, R.C., and Johnson, R.P. (1997). Dye efflux studies suggest that hematopoietic stem cells expressing low or undetectable levels of CD34 antigen exist in multiple species. *Nat. Med.* **3,** 1337–1345.
7. Bakos, E., Evers, R., Calenda, G., Tusnady, G.E., Szakacs, G., Varadi, A., and Sarkadi, B. (2000). Characterization of the amino-terminal regions in the human multidrug resistance protein (MRP1). *J. Cell Sci.* **113,** 4451–4461.
8. Bunting, K.D., Zhou, S., Lu, T., and Sorrentino, B.P. (2000). Enforced P-glycoprotein pump function in murine bone marrow cells results in expansion of side population stem cells in vitro and repopulating cells in vivo. *Blood* **96,** 902–909.
9. Wagers, A.J., Sherwood, R.I., Christensen, J.L., and Weissman, I.L. (2002). Little evidence for developmental plasticity of adult hematopoietic stem cells. *Science* **297,** 2256–2259.
10. Jackson, K.A., Majka, S.M., Wang, H., Pocius, J., Hartley, C.J., Majesky, M.W., Entman, M.L., Michael, L.H., Hirschi, K.K., and Goodell, M.A. (2001). Regeneration of ischemic cardiac muscle and vascular endothelium by adult stem cells. *J. Clin. Invest.* **107,** 1395–1402.
11. Jiang, X., Gurel, O., Mendiaz, E.A., Stearns, G.W., Clogston, C.L., Lu, H.S., Osslund, T.D., Syed, R.S., Langley, K.E., and Hendrickson, W.A. (2000). Structure of the active core of human stem cell factor and analysis of binding to its receptor kit. *EMBO. J.* **19,** 3192–3203.
12. Lyman, S.D., and Jacobsen, S.E. (1998). c-kit ligand and Flt3 ligand: stem/progenitor cell factors with overlapping yet distinct activities. *Blood* **91,** 1101–1134.
13. Orlic, D., Kajstura, J., Chimenti, S., Limana, F., Jakoniuk, I., Quaini, F., Nadal-Ginard, B., Bodine, D.M., Leri, A., and Anversa, P. (2001). Mobilized bone marrow cells repair the infarcted heart, improving function and survival. *Proc. Natl. Acad. Sci. USA* **98,** 10344–10349.
14. Pittenger, M.F., Mosca, J.D., and McIntosh, K.R. (2000). Human mesenchymal stem cells: Progenitor cells for cartilage, bone, fat and stroma. *Curr. Top. Microbiol. Immunol.* **251,** 3–11.
15. Toma, C., Pittenger, M.F., Cahill, K.S., Byrne, B.J., and Kessler, P.D. (2002). Human mesenchymal stem cells differentiate to a cardiomyocyte phenotype in the adult murine heart. *Circulation* **105,** 93–98.
16. Shake, J.G., Gruber, P.J., Baumgartner, W.A., Senechal, G., Meyers, J., Redmond, J.M., Pittenger, M.F., and Martin, B.J. (2002). Mesenchymal stem cell implantation in a swine myocardial infarct model: engraftment and functional effects. *Ann. Thorac. Surg.* **73,** 1919–1925; discussion 1926.
17. Stamm, C., Westphal, B., Kleine, H.D., Petzsch, M., Kittner, C., Klinge, H., Schumichen, C., Nienaber, C.A., Freund, M., and Steinhoff, G. (2003). Autologous bone-marrow stem-cell transplantation for myocardial regeneration. *Lancet* **361,** 45–46.
18. Strauer, B.E., Brehm, M., Zeus, T., Kostering, M., Hernandez, A., Sorg, R.V., Kogler, G., and Wernet, P. (2002). Repair of infarcted myocardium by autologous intracoronary mononuclear bone marrow cell transplantation in humans. *Circulation* **106,** 1913–1918.
19. Menasche, P., Hagege, A.A., Vilquin, J.T., Desnos, M., Abergel, E., Pouzet, B., Bel, A., Sarateanu, S., Scorsin, M., Schwartz, K., Bruneval, P., Benbunan, M., Marolleau, J.P., Duboc, D. (2003). Autologous skeletal myoblast transplantation for severe postinfarction left ventricular dysfunction. *J. Am. Coll. Cardiol.* **41,** 1078–1083.
20. Itescu, S., Kocher, A.A., and Schuster, M.D. (2003). Myocardial neovascularization by adult bone marrow-derived angioblasts: strategies for improvement of cardiomyocyte function. *Heart Fail. Rev.* **8,** 253–258.
21. Assmus, B., Schachinger, V., Teupe, C., Britten, M., Lehmann, R., Dobert, N., Grunwald, F., Aicher, A., Urbich, C., Martin, H., Hoelzer, D., Dimmeler, S., Zeiher, A.M. (2002). Transplantation of progenitor cells and regeneration enhancement in acute myocardial infarction (TOPCARE-AMI). *Circulation* **106,** 3009–3017.
22. Condorelli, G., Borello, U., De Angelis, L., Latronico, M., Sirabella, D., Coletta, M., Galli, R., Balconi, G., Follenzi, A., Frati, G., Cussella De Angelis, M.G., Gioglio, L., Amuchastegui, S., Adorini, L., Naldini, L., Vescovi, A., Dejana, E., Cossu, G. (2001). Cardiomyocytes induce endothelial cells to trans-differentiate into cardiac muscle: Implications for myocardium regeneration. *Proc. Natl. Acad. Sci. USA* 98, 10733–10738.
23. Badorff, C., Brandes, R.P., Popp, R., Rupp, S., Urbich, C., Aicher, A., Fleming, I., Busse, R., Zeiher, A.M., and Dimmeler, S. (2003). Transdifferentiation of blood-derived human adult endothelial progenitor cells into functionally active cardiomyocytes. *Circulation* **107,** 1024–1032.
24. Dewald, O., Frangogiannis, N.G., Zoerlein, M., Duerr, G.D., Klemm, C., Knuefermann, P., Taffet, G., Michael, L.H., Crapo, J.D., Welz, A., Entman, M.L. (2003). Development of murine ischemic cardiomyopathy is associated with a transient inflammatory reaction and depends on reactive oxygen species. *Proc. Natl. Acad. Sci. USA* **100,** 2700–2705.

24a. Itescu, S. personal communication.

25. Pasumarthi, K.B., and Field, L.J. (2002). Cardiomyocyte cell cycle regulation. *Circ. Res.* **90,** 1044–1054.
26. MacLellan, W.R., and Schneider, M.D. (2000). Genetic dissection of cardiac growth control pathways. *Annu. Rev. Physiol.* **62,** 289–319.

27. Poolman, R.A., Li, J.M., Durand, B., and Brooks, G. (1999). Altered expression of cell cycle proteins and prolonged duration of cardiac myocyte hyperplasia in p27KIP1 knockout mice. *Circ. Res.* **85,** 117–127.
28. Chien, K.R., and Olson, E.N. (2002). Converging pathways and principles in heart development and disease: CV@CSH. *Cell* **110,** 153–162.
29. Anversa, P., and Kajstura, J. (1998). Ventricular myocytes are not terminally differentiated in the adult mammalian heart. *Circ. Res.* **83,** 1–14.
30. Nadal-Ginard, B., Kajstura, J., Leri, A., and Anversa, P. (2003). Myocyte death, growth, and regeneration in cardiac hypertrophy and failure. *Circ. Res.* **92,** 139–150.
31. Goodell, M.A., Brose, K., Paradis, G., Conner, A.S., and Mulligan, R.C. (1996). Isolation and functional properties of murine hematopoietic stem cells that are replicating in vivo. *J. Exp. Med.* **183,** 1797–1806.
32. Asakura, A., Seale, P., Girgis-Gabardo, A., and Rudnicki, M.A. (2002). Myogenic specification of side population cells in skeletal muscle. *J. Cell Biol.* **159,** 123–134.
33. Hierlihy, A.M., Seale, P., Lobe, C.G., Rudnicki, M.A., and Megeney, L.A. (2002). The post-natal heart contains a myocardial stem cell population. *FEBS. Lett.* **530,** 239–243.
34. Martin, C.M., Meeson, A.P., Robertson, S., Richardson, J., Bates, S., Gallardo, T., and Garry, D.J. (2004). Persistent expression of the ATP-cassette transporter, Abcg2, identifies cardiac stem cells in the adult heart. *Dev. Biol.* **265,** 262–275.
35. Anversa, P., and Nadal-Ginard, B. (2002). Myocyte renewal and ventricular remodelling. *Nature* **415,** 240–243.
36. van de Rijn, M., Heimfeld, S., Spangrude, G.J., and Weissman, I.L. (1989). Mouse hematopoietic stem-cell antigen Sca-1 is a member of the Ly-6 antigen family. *Proc. Natl. Acad. Sci. USA* **86,** 4634–4638.
37. English, A., Kosoy, R., Pawlinski, R., and Bamezai, A. (2000). A monoclonal antibody against the 66-kDa protein expressed in mouse spleen and thymus inhibits Ly-6A.2-dependent cell-cell adhesion. *J. Immunol.* **165,** 3763–3771.
38. Kissel, H., Timokhina, I., Hardy, M.P., Rothschild, G., Tajima, Y., Soares, V., Angeles, M., Whitlow, S.R., Manova, K., and Besmer, P. (2000). Point mutation in kit receptor tyrosine kinase reveals essential roles for kit signaling in spermatogenesis and oogenesis without affecting other kit responses. *EMBO. J.* **19,** 1312–1326.
39. Beltrami, A.P., Chimenti, S., Limana, F., Barlucci, L., Quaini, F., Kajstura, J., Nadal-Ginard, B., Anversa, P., and Leri, A. (2001). Cardiac c-kit positive cells proliferate in vitro and generate new myocardium in vivo. *Circulation* **104** (Suppl II), 324 (abstract).
40. Kajstura, J., Pertoldi, B., Leri, A., Beltrami, C.A., Deptala, A., Darzynkiewicz, Z., and Anversa, P. (2000). Telomere shortening is an in vivo marker of myocyte replication and aging. *Am. J. Pathol.* **156,** 813–819.
41. Oh, H., Taffet, G.E., Youker, K.A., Entman, M.L., Overbeek, P.A., Michael, L.H., and Schneider, M.D. (2001). Telomerase reverse transcriptase promotes cardiac muscle cell proliferation, hypertrophy, and survival. *Proc. Natl. Acad. Sci. USA* **98,** 10308–10313.
42. Oh, H., Wang, S.C., Prahash, A., Sano, M., Moravec, C.S., Taffet, G.E., Michael, L.H., Youker, K.A., Entman, M.L., and Schneider, M.D. (2003). Telomere attrition and Chk2 activation in human heart failure. *Proc. Natl. Acad. Sci. USA* **100,** 5378–5383.
43. Kajstura, J., Leri, A., Finato, N., Di Loreto, C., Beltrami, C.A., and Anversa, P. 1998. Myocyte proliferation in end-stage cardiac failure in humans. *Proc. Natl. Acad. Sci. USA* 95:8801–8805.
44. Beltrami, A.P., Urbanek, K., Kajstura, J., Yan, S.M., Finato, N., Bussani, R., Nadal-Ginard, B., Silvestri, F., Leri, A., Beltrami, C.A., Anversa, P. (2001). Evidence that human cardiac myocytes divide after myocardial infarction. *N. Engl. J. Med.* **344,** 1750–1757.
45. Beltrami, A.P., Barlucchi, L., Torella, D., Baker, M., Limana, F., Chimenti, S., Kasahara, H., Rota, M., Musso, E., Urbanek, K., Leri, A., Kajstura, J., Nadal-Ginard, B., Anversa, P. (2003). Adult cardiac stem cells are multipotent and support myocardial regeneration. *Cell* **114,** 763–776.
46. Brockes, J.P., Kumar, A., and Velloso, C.P. (2001). Regeneration as an evolutionary variable. *J. Anat.* **199,** 3–11.
47. McDonnell, T.J., and Oberpriller, J.O. (1984). The response of the atrium to direct mechanical wounding in the adult heart of the newt, *Notophthalmus viridescens.* An electron-microscopic and autoradiographic study. *Cell Tissue Res.* **235,** 583–592.
48. Brockes, J.P., and Kumar, A. (2002). Plasticity and reprogramming of differentiated cells in amphibian regeneration. *Nat. Rev. Mol. Cell Biol.* **3,** 566–574.
49. Imokawa, Y., and Brockes, J.P. (2003). Selective activation of thrombin is a critical determinant for vertebrate lens regeneration. *Curr. Biol.* **13,** 877–881.
50. Poss, K.D., Wilson, L.G., and Keating, M.T. (2002). Heart regeneration in zebrafish. *Science* **298,** 2188–2190.
51. Poss, K.D., Nechiporuk, A., Hillam, A.M., Johnson, S.L., and Keating, M.T. (2002). Mps1 defines a proximal blastemal proliferative compartment essential for zebrafish fin regeneration. *Development* **129,** 5141–5149.
52. Raya, A., Koth, C.M., Buscher, D., Kawakami, Y., Itoh, T., Raya, R.M., Sternik, G., Tsai, H.J., Rodriguez-Esteban, C., and Izpisua-Belmonte, J.C. (2003). Activation of Notch signaling pathway precedes heart regeneration in zebrafish. *Proc. Natl. Acad. Sci. USA* **100 Suppl 1,** 11889–11895.
53. Leferovich, J.M., Bedelbaeva, K., Samulewicz, S., Zhang, X.M., Zwas, D., Lankford, E.B., and Heber-Katz, E. (2001). Heart regeneration in adult MRL mice. *Proc. Natl. Acad. Sci. USA* **98,** 9830–9835.
54. Blankenhorn, E.P., Troutman, S., Clark, L.D., Zhang, X.M., Chen, P., and Heber-Katz, E. (2003). Sexually dimorphic genes regulate healing and regeneration in MRL mice. *Mamm. Genome* **14,** 250–260.
55. McBrearty, B.A., Clark, L.D., Zhang, X.M., Blankenhorn, E.P., and Heber-Katz, E. (1998). Genetic analysis of a mammalian wound-healing trait. *Proc. Natl. Acad. Sci. USA* **95,** 11792–11797.
56. Gourevitch, D., Clark, L., Chen, P., Seitz, A., Samulewicz, S.J., and Heber-Katz, E. 2003. Matrix metalloproteinase activity correlates with blastema formation in the regenerating MRL mouse ear hole model. *Dev. Dyn.* **226,** 377–387.

42

Formation of Blood and Lymphatic Vessels: Role of Progenitors

Aernout Luttun,* Marc Tjwa,* and Peter Carmeliet

Introduction

Nearly all tissues in higher vertebrates are supplied by and dependent on two largely separated but functionally complementary vascular circuits, one carrying blood cells for oxygen and nutrient delivery (e.g., the blood circulation) and the other recirculating immune cells and extravasated tissue fluid or *lymph* (e.g., the lymphatic circulation). Both systems connect at a single level—that is, at the base of the neck (the jugulo-subclavian junction) where the lymphatic ducts anastomose with the venous part of the blood vasculature. Not surprisingly, developmental defects in either of these important systems are usually incompatible with life or cause severe morbidity. In addition, the dysfunction or lack of blood or lymphatic vessels in later life underlies numerous life-threatening diseases, such as ischemic disorders and lymphedema. Therefore, unraveling the cellular and molecular players in the formation of both vascular systems is invaluable for designing therapeutic interventions to correct blood or lymphatic vessel defects. This chapter overviews how functional blood and lymphatic vessels form in the embryo and the adult from vascular stem/progenitor cells and how this knowledge has contributed to the emergence of several stem/progenitor cell-based approaches to stimulate vessel growth in preclinical and clinical settings.

Blood Vascular System

CELLULAR MECHANISMS OF BLOOD VESSEL FORMATION IN THE EMBRYO

Endothelial Progenitors, Vasculogenesis, and Angiogenesis

Since all embryonic tissues rely on the transportation of oxygen and nutrients for their growth and development, the blood vascular system is one of the first organs to arise, starting around embryonic day (E) 7.5 in the mouse. Blood vessels in the embryo emerge at distinct locations from separate mesodermal precursors. In the yolk sac, bipotential precursors (e.g., hemangioblasts) aggregate to form blood islands. Although cells from the outer rim of these islands differentiate into endothelial cells (ECs), the inner cells differentiate into erythrocytes, the first primitive blood cells, indicating that blood and blood vessels form in close association. Within the embryo, blood vessels arise from various precursors in different areas of the mesoderm. Quail–chick chimera experiments suggest that precursors in the splanchnic mesoderm are bipotential, differentiating to ECs and hematopoietic cells, and that the somatic mesoderm harbors monopotential endothelial precursors (angioblasts).[1] Hematopoiesis in the embryo also occurs in close association with vessels, as clusters of hematopoietic cells have been observed to bud from the endothelial and subendothelial layers of the major embryonic blood vessels (e.g., the dorsal aorta).[2,3]

Following differentiation and—for some endothelial precursors—migration, these cells coalesce to form a primitive vascular plexus, a process called vasculogenesis. Although the dorsal aortae and trunk veins in the embryo are formed by vasculogenesis from the splanchnic mesoderm, other vessels such as the intersomitic arteries are formed by sprouting from these initial vessels—a process termed angiogenesis.[4] The decision to become artery or vein (arteriovenous specification) is one of the important steps, which seems to depend on the expression of certain "signature molecules" even before blood flow is established in the primitive vascular network[4] (see later sections of this chapter). In addition to sprouting, vessels can develop by nonsprouting mechanisms such as intussusception and bridging, together resulting in distinct vessel patterns (so-called angiotypes), which may be strikingly different in various tissues.[5] Besides vessel growth, regression of vascular beds is an intrinsic property of vascular development. For instance, some of the pharyngeal arch arteries need to regress to establish the network of the great thoracic arteries.[6] The aortic arch and its branches, which develop from the pharyngeal arch arteries, are a common site for aberrant vessel patterning (see later sections of this chapter). A diagram is presented in Fig. 42–1.

Smooth Muscle Progenitors and Arteriogenesis

To be functional, the endothelium-lined vessels need to mature by acquiring a basement membrane and a peri-EC layer consisting of smooth muscle cells (SMCs) in large vessels and pericytes in small vessels—a process termed arteriogenesis.[7] This process of "muscularization" is codetermined by blood flow. For instance, in coronary arteries, the pressure increase and blood flow alteration after connection to the

*These authors contributed equally to this chapter.

Handbook of Stem Cells
Volume 2

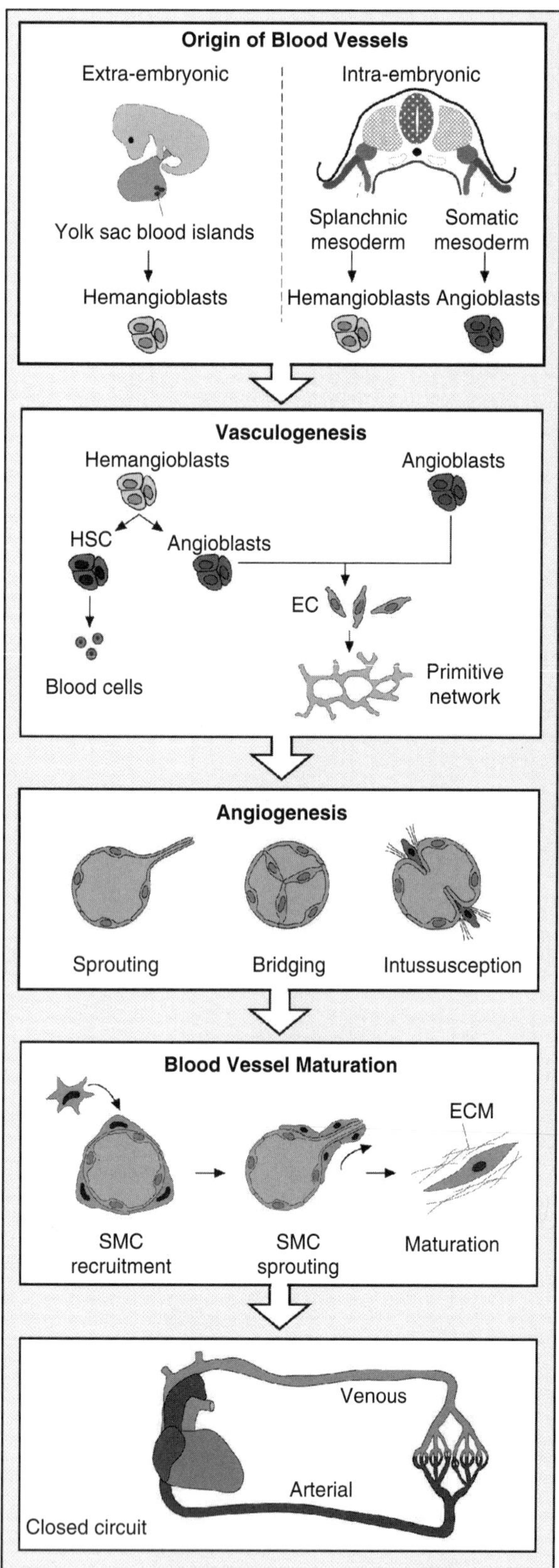

Figure 42–1. *Origin and formation of blood vessels.* Outside the embryo, the first blood vessels originate from bipotential hemangioblasts in the blood islands, which generate primitive hematopoietic cells and endothelial cells (ECs). Inside the embryo, depending on the location, endothelium forms from either monopotential endothelial precursors (angioblasts) or bipotential hemangioblasts. The latter produce hematopoietic stem cells (HSCs) and ECs. The latter coalesce into a primitive network (vasculogenesis), which subsequently expands by angiogenesis (thereby involving different mechanisms, both sprouting and nonsprouting) and matures by acquisition of a smooth muscle cell (SMC) coat (arteriogenesis) and an extracellular matrix (ECM). As a result, a closed circuit of functional blood vessels is generated, bringing blood from (arterial system) and to (venous system) the heart. (Please see CD-ROM for color version of this figure.)

aorta are triggers for SMC differentiation; differentiation is delayed in the low-pressure environment in coronary veins.[8] SMCs have a complex origin, depending on their location in the embryo[9] (Fig. 42–2). The first SMCs in the dorsal aorta transdifferentiate from the endothelium,[9] and the SMC-like myofibroblasts in the prospective cardiac valves are also derived from ECs.[10] Cardiac neural crest cells are the source of the SMCs in the great thoracic blood vessels and the proximal coronary arteries.[9,11] Mural cells of the distal coronary arteries are derived from epicardium-derived cells,[9] and coronary vein SMCs are derived from the atrial myocardium.[12] Although the *in vivo* existence of such a precursor needs to be established, SMCs and ECs may also derive from a common vascular precursor in the embryo, which has been identified in embryonic stem (ES) cell culture systems[13–15] (Fig. 42–2).

Vascular cells in different organs acquire specialized characteristics, which permit these cells to optimally perform specific functions in each organ.[16] For instance, ECs in the brain are tightly linked to each other and are surrounded by numerous peri-ECs, which constitute a barrier that protects brain cells from potentially toxic blood-derived molecules. In contrast, vessels in endocrine glands are leaky and their ECs have fenestrations, allowing hormone trafficking. Pericytes in the brain or liver (the latter are known as Ito cells) also acquire specialized functions.[17] Besides vascular cell heterogeneity in distinct organs, ECs and SMCs within the same organ can be heterogeneous. In the heart, for instance, ECs in distinct locations of the coronary vascular tree differ in their expression of the endothelial constitutive nitric oxide synthase isoform,[18] brain-derived neurotrophic factor,[19] or adhesion molecules.[20,21] Coronary SMCs also seem to be heterogeneous since culture studies revealed that neural crest-derived SMCs behave differently from mesoderm-derived cells in their response to transforming growth factor beta (TGF-β).[9]

MOLECULAR BASIS OF BLOOD VESSEL FORMATION IN THE EMBRYO

Identifying the molecular signals responsible for proper blood vessel formation has been a major interest during the past decade. Studies in the chick, zebra fish, and gene-deficient mice have significantly contributed to our understanding of molecular signaling during vessel development. Several vasculo–angiogenic families have emerged, such as the

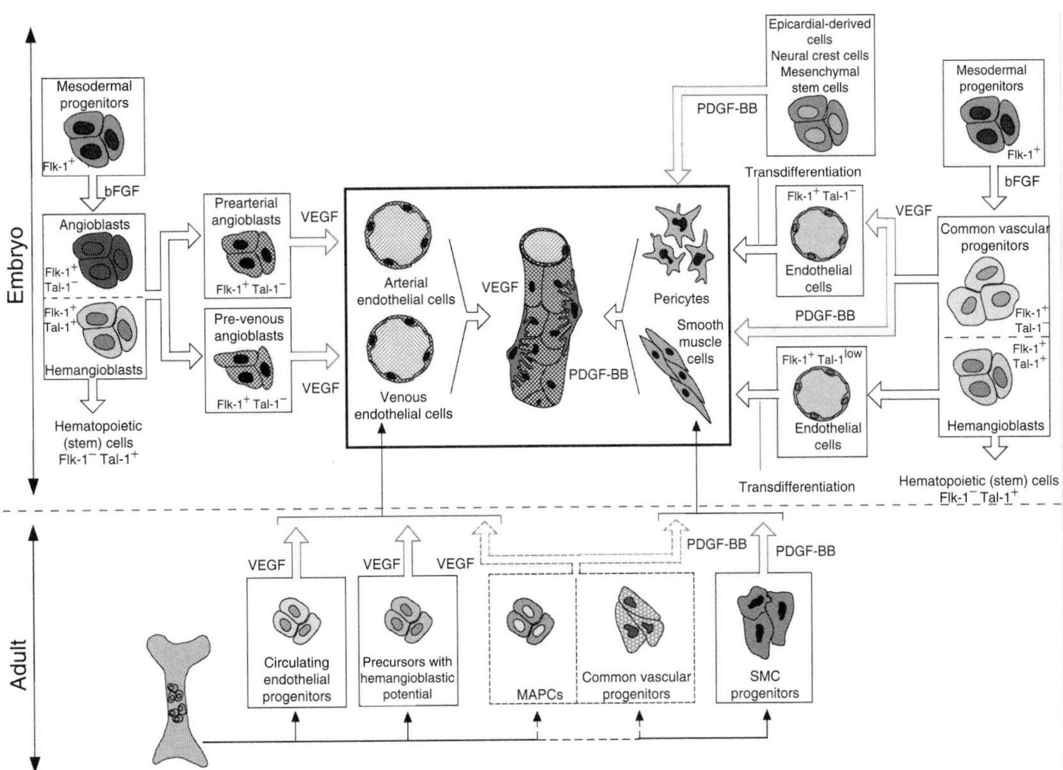

Figure 42–2. *Complex origin for the two types of blood vessel cell.* Endothelial cells (ECs) and smooth muscle cells (SMCs) arise from different types of precursors. Embryonic ECs arise from mesodermal progenitors expressing fetal liver kinase-1 (Flk-1), which, in turn, are induced to form angioblasts or hemangioblasts under the influence of basic fibroblast growth factor (bFGF). Angioblasts produce arterial and venous lineages. SMCs and pericytes have a complex origin and, depending on their location, derive from distinct progenitors (including Flk-1+ mesodermal progenitors, neural crest cells, mesenchymal stem cells, and epicardial-derived cells). In addition, the two types of blood vessel cell can develop from common progenitors. First, a new bipotential vascular progenitor cell that generates both ECs (when stimulated with vascular endothelial growth factor, or VEGF) and SMCs (when stimulated by platelet-derived growth factor-BB, or PDGF-BB) has been recently described in the embryo. Second, depending on the expression levels of Tal-1, hemangioblasts may also produce ECs and SMCs, the latter following transdifferentiation from hemangioblast-derived ECs. In the adult, ECs and SMCs were shown to arise from bone marrow-derived circulating precursors. Whether bipotential or multipotential (multipotent adult progenitor cells, or MAPCs) progenitors exist *in vivo* in the adult and whether they contribute to both blood cell vessel types remains to be determined (indicated with dotted lines). (Please see CD-ROM for color version of this figure.)

members of the vascular endothelial growth factor (VEGF), angiopoietin (Ang), platelet-derived growth factor (PDGF), and ephrin families, as well as many others. For a detailed overview, see other recent reviews.[7,22–24] In the following sections, we primarily highlight some of the recent findings of the role of the angiogenic growth factor VEGF or VEGF-A (hereafter referred to as VEGF) and its receptors.

Induction of the Vascular Cell Lineage

As mentioned previously, the ontogeny of blood vessels from the mesoderm occurs in close association with the formation of blood cells, most strikingly illustrated by the common origin of ECs and primitive blood cells from hemangioblasts in the extraembryonic blood islands. Thus, one of the first critical steps in blood vessel development is the complex decision to become blood or blood vessel. The molecular identity of the hemangioblast is still under investigation, but phenotypic analysis in gene-targeted mice and zebra fish mutants and expression pattern analysis have indicated VEGFR-2 (also fetal liver kinase-1, or Flk-1) and the helix–loop–helix (HLH) transcription factor Tal-1 (or Scl) as potential markers.[25–28] In addition, differentiation studies with mouse ES cells have identified the *in vitro* equivalent of the hemangioblast, the so-called blast colony-forming cell.[14,29,30] VEGFR-2 is a receptor for VEGF, and mice deficient in this receptor feature an arrest in hemangioblast differentiation into ECs and blood cells.[28] Although VEGF promotes hemangioblast differentiation into endothelium, it is not a prerequisite, since ECs develop in VEGF-deficient embryos.[31,32] This finding implies that other VEGFR-2 ligands or additional VEGFR-2-dependent factors are involved in EC specification. Deficiency of VEGFR-1 (also fms-like tyrosine kinase-1, or Flt-1), another VEGF receptor, impairs hemangioblast commitment into ECs.[33,34] Recent findings document, however, that a defect in EC division rather than in hemangioblast commitment might underlie the vascular abnormalities in VEGFR-1-deficient embryos.[35] In addition to a physical association, the hematopoietic and vascular systems may be functionally linked, as evidenced by the observation that hematopoietic stem cells (HSCs) can stimulate EC growth by releasing Ang-1.[36]

The role of Tal-1 in the ontogeny of blood and blood vessels was recently revisited in a study by Ema *et al.*, in which they expressed Tal-1 under the control of the *VEGFR-2* promoter.[14] Previous studies in mice and zebra fish suggested different levels of involvement of this transcription factor in blood vessel development. Studies in *Tal-1*$^{-/-}$ mice revealed the presence of ECs but abnormal remodeling of the yolk sac capillary network into branching vitelline vessels, suggesting a role for Tal-1 downstream of hemangioblast formation and differentiation into ECs.[37,38] In contrast, overexpression of Tal-1 in the zebra fish mutant *cloche* was able to partially rescue both hematopoietic and vascular defects, suggesting a much closer relationship between Tal-1 function and the hemangioblast.[27] Based on their recent *in vitro* findings, Ema *et al.*[14] propose an integrative model in which Tal-1, with VEGFR-2, determines hemangioblast formation and differentiation. First, Tal-1 expression in VEGFR-2$^+$ mesodermal precursors would favor proliferation of VEGFR-2$^+$Tal-1$^+$ hemangioblasts at the expense of VEGFR-2$^+$Tal-1$^-$ angioblasts, the latter lacking hematopoietic potential. Second, the expression level of Tal-1 in the VEGFR-2$^+$ precursors would determine subsequent hemangioblast differentiation, with the lowest levels of Tal-1 promoting SMC rather than EC differentiation (see Fig. 42–2). This model is compatible with previous quail–chick experiments suggesting that the endothelium derives from either hemangioblasts or angioblasts depending on the location within the embryo[1] (see Fig. 42–1). Angioblast induction from the mesoderm requires additional signals from the endodermal layer, such as basic fibroblast growth factor (bFGF) and Indian hedgehog (Ihh).[4,39] This theory was recently challenged by a study in *Xenopus* that showed angioblast specification proceeds in endoderm-depleted embryos, suggesting that this process may arise within the mesoderm proper. Rather, endoderm was necessary for tube formation.[40]

Endothelial Cell Fate: Artery or Vein

The next step in the decision process is to differentiate into an arterial or a venous EC. Although it was previously considered that hemodynamic forces determined arterial versus venous EC specification, recent genetic evidence in mice and fish indicates that ECs acquire such identity even before the onset of flow. Whether ECs in arteries and veins derive from common or separate angioblasts remains to be identified. Arteriovenous specification likely involves several classes of molecules, but Notch signals seem to be critical. Using lateral inhibition, Notch represses the default differentiation of angioblasts into venous ECs.[41] Sonic hedgehog (Shh)—released from the notochord—induces the somite to release VEGF, which then acts upon angioblasts in the lateral mesoderm and, through the release of Notch, induces angioblasts to differentiate into arterial ECs.[42] Possible downstream candidates of Notch include the basic HLH transcriptional repressor gridlock A.[43] Other molecules specifically expressed in either venous or arterial ECs—involved in the formation, patterning, or maintenance of arteries or veins, or both—include the ephrins and their Eph receptors, bone marrow tyrosine kinase and the TGF-β receptor activin receptor-like kinase-1 (reviewed by Roman and Weinstein and Luttun *et al.*[44]). Quail–chick transplantation experiments have indicated that in addition to these "signature molecules," local cues may determine EC identity.[45] Recent findings from our laboratory suggest a role for *VEGF* isoforms and neuropilin-1 (Nrp-1) in the diversification between arteries and veins in the mouse retina.[46] Although mice singly expressing the $VEGF_{164}$ isoform (*VEGF*$^{164/164}$) had normal retinal vessel outgrowth and patterning, there were fewer and smaller venules and arterioles in *VEGF*$^{120/120}$ mice with venules reaching over 80% of the retinal vascular bed and arterioles over only 50%. Arteriolar defects were even more pronounced in *VEGF*$^{188/188}$ mice (outgrowth over only 18%) with no obvious abnormalities in the venules. Thus, the matrix-binding $VEGF_{188}$ isoform is crucial for arterial development, but the underlying mechanisms remain to be studied. Interestingly, Nrp-1 (a $VEGF_{164}$-specific receptor and a neurorepellant receptor) was predominantly expressed in retinal arterioles, which might explain the more severe arteriolar defects in mice lacking $VEGF_{164}$. Instead, expression of Nrp-2, another neurorepellant receptor, is restricted to venous and lymphatic ECs.[47] These data suggest that nerves and vessels may use similar molecular cues for fate determination.

Smooth Muscle Cell Fate

To confer functionality and stability of the nascent vessel, blood vessels acquire an outer layer of SMCs or pericytes embedded in extracellular matrix. The origin of SMCs is complex, involving EC transdifferentiation, differentiation from neural crest or epicardial-derived cells, and recruitment of specialized mesenchymal SMC precursors from organ-specific primordia or possibly bipotential EC–SMC precursors.[48] EC transdifferentiation into SMC-like myofibroblasts seems to require signaling by TGF-β3 in the prospective cardiac valves.[10] TGF-β1, another family member, has been implicated in the differentiation of a mesenchymal stem cell to a progenitor, which expresses PDGFR-β.[49,50] By releasing PDGF-BB, ECs stimulate growth and differentiation of this precursor. Differentiation of coronary SMCs from proepicardial cells involves serum response factor, a member of the MADS box family of DNA-binding proteins.[51] Using ES cell differentiation methods, Yamashita *et al.* discovered a VEGFR-2$^+$ common vascular progenitor, which differentiates into both ECs and SMCs. The SMCs arising from these progenitors were not simply transdifferentiated ECs expressing the atypical smooth muscle α-actin marker. Instead, they expressed an entire set of SMC markers and were capable of covering endothelial channels *in vivo*. The vascular progenitors differentiated into ECs in response to VEGF and into SMCs in response to PDGF-BB.[13] The model proposed by Ema *et al.*[14] confirms the existence of such a bipotential precursor and integrates several of the pathways described previously that can generate SMCs. According to this model, SMCs are formed when Tal-1 expression in hemangioblasts and angioblasts drops below a threshold level. Thus, SMCs could differentiate directly from VEGFR-2$^+$Tal-1$^-$ angioblasts or could transdifferentiate from angioblast-derived VEGFR-2$^+$ Tal-1$^-$ ECs and hemangioblast-derived VEGFR-2$^+$ ECs[14] (Fig. 42–2).

Blood Vessel Patterning and Boundary Formation

The building of functional blood vessels requires not only the induction of ECs and SMCs but also their correct assembly and patterning to establish a unidirectional flow from and back to the heart. Blood vessel patterning in development is highly stereotyped. For example, there are fixed branching sites from the aorta for arteries supplying the head, internal organs, and legs. However, vessel formation in the embryo is extremely dynamic, with vessel tracts appearing and disappearing and links between vessels severing and then reconnecting in entirely new patterns until they have found their target.[52] Much still needs to be unraveled about the molecular guidance and patterning cues of blood vessels, but some insights have been obtained about how the large blood vessels form in the early embryo. Following their induction, angioblasts such as the ones that form the endocardium or the dorsal aorta migrate before assembly into a primitive plexus.[22] The endoderm is proposed to be a source of guidance cues for migrating angioblasts. Studies in *Xenopus* have shown that the endoderm-derived hypochord expresses high levels of the diffusible VEGF$_{122}$ isoform, which could create a gradient responsible for patterning the dorsal aorta.[53] The extent to which this isoform is involved in dorsal aortic patterning in vertebrates that lack a hypochord remains to be determined. Knockin studies in mice have provided insights into how VEGF, through localization of heparin-binding isoforms in the extracellular matrix, provides short-range-acting matrix-associated VEGF$_{188}$ guidance cues as well as long-range-acting soluble VEGF$_{120}$ cues, laid as a gradient from the target to the EC growth cones at the leading tip (see later sections of this chapter and Stalmans *et al.*[46,54]). In zebra fish, the *sonic you* mutant (involving the *Shh* gene) shows disorganization of endothelial precursors and patterning defects in the dorsal aorta, suggesting that this factor might also be involved in orchestrating angioblast migration.[55] Whether this is a direct effect on angioblasts requires further investigation. In the adult, *Shh* seems to exert indirect effects on vessels by up-regulating VEGF and angiopoietins.[56] The ephrinB2/B3-expressing somites constitute repulsive corridors for the EphB3/4-expressing intersegmental vessels; thus, loss of ephrinB2/B3 in mice or disruption of EphB4/ephrinB2 in *Xenopus* causes these vessels to deviate from their normal path and penetrate the somites.[57,58] Repulsive Nrp-1 signals also appear to guide intersegmental vessels, as their trajectories are abnormal in Nrp-1-deficient mice.[59] Correct patterning likely involves additional signals, and in some cases, their function has become especially evident in particular vascular beds: R-cadherin in the retina,[60] connexin 43 in coronary arteries,[61] and β8 integrin in brain capillary patterning.[62]

The organization of the vascular system also requires mechanisms that maintain physical segregation of distinct cell populations. A typical example of boundary formation in the vasculature is that between arterial and venous ECs. Like neural cells, vascular cells use Eph/ephrin signals to establish these boundaries.[63,64] The prevailing dogma was that capillaries have neither arterial nor venous identity. However, LacZ knockin studies showed that expression of ephrinB2 extends into capillaries about midway between terminal arterioles and postcapillary veins, whereas EphB4 has an equivalent expression pattern at the venous side. These nonoverlapping expression patterns may not only prevent intermixing of both cell types and permit spatial segregation of arterial and venous vessels, they may also ensure that arterial capillaries connect appropriately to the venous system, thereby precluding abnormal fusion into cavernous vessel lakes.[57,65–67]

The outlet of the heart (e.g., the aortic arch and its branches, which develop from the pharyngeal arch arteries) is a common site of abnormal vessel patterning, leading to—often life-threatening—congenital malformations. Such defects of pharyngeal arch artery patterning can exist in isolation (e.g., type-B aortic arch interruption and arteria lusoria[68]), but they often occur with craniofacial, thymic, and parathyroid birth defects as part of the DiGeorge–velo-cardio-facial syndrome, affecting 1 in 4000 live births.[69,70] Most patients have a hemizygous chromosomal deletion of 22q11(del22q11). Mouse genetic studies have identified the transcription factor gene *Tbx1,* expressed in the pharyngeal arches, as a disease-causing candidate of this disorder. However, unlike the hemizygous character of the deletion in humans, both *Tbx1* alleles need to be absent in mice for a DiGeorge-like spectrum of abnormalities to develop.[71] In addition, remarkable phenotypic variability exists among DiGeorge patients. Therefore, it appears that other genes, either within or outside the 22q11 region, might modulate the *Tbx1* genetic pathway. Using a multispecies genetic approach, we have recently shown that *VEGF* is a candidate modifier of the cardiovascular syndrome phenotype.[54] Although *VEGF* isoforms were redundant for initial formation of the arch arteries, absence of the *VEGF*$_{164}$ isoform generated birth defects similar to what is reported in del22q11 patients, suggesting a role for this isoform in pharyngeal arch patterning. *VEGF* interacted with *Tbx1,* since the expression of the latter was reduced in these mice and knockdown of *VEGF* in zebra fish aggravated the pharyngeal arch artery defects induced by *Tbx1* knockdown. Moreover, a *VEGF* promoter haplotype was associated with an increased risk for cardiovascular birth defects in del22q11 patients. A role for *VEGF* was further suggested by its temporospatial expression at all DiGeorge-predilection sites. Nrp-1 likely is involved, since it was coordinately expressed with *VEGF*. The underlying mechanism remains to be determined. Although the organs affected in DiGeorge syndrome are all derived from the neural crest, obvious cell-intrinsic neural crest cell defects were not detected in *VEGF*-isoform mice[72] nor in *Tbx1*-deficient mice.[70,71,73,74] Vascular dysgenesis in *VEGF*$^{120/120}$ and *VEGF*$^{180/180}$ mice might contribute to the patterning defects, since the severity of the defects correlated with the degree of vascular impairment—a hypothesis that should be tested.

BLOOD VESSEL FORMATION IN THE ADULT: ROLE AND THERAPEUTIC POTENTIAL OF VASCULAR PROGENITORS

In contrast to the active vessel growth in the embryo and the newborn, the adult endothelium remains in a quiescent state—in other words, the angiogenic switch is off. Maintenance of adult blood vessels requires some threshold level of angiogenic growth factors adequately balanced by angiogenic inhibitors. When insufficient vascular survival signals are available, vessel dysfunction, regression, or both may develop. A growing list of disorders is increasingly recognized to be attributable to or complicated by such vessel regression (reviewed by Carmeliet[75]). For instance, when the placenta of preeclamptic mothers produces increased levels of soluble Flt-1, a VEGF and placental growth factor (PlGF) scavenger, VEGF plasma levels drop below a critical maintenance level, resulting in generalized vascular dysfunction with secondary organ failure.[76,77] Adult blood vessels retain, however, a remarkable plasticity and can be induced to grow rapidly and aggressively when provoked by stress or pathologic conditions (e.g., myocardial, brain, or limb ischemia)—that is, angiogenesis is switched on. Blood vascular expansion may encompass three mechanisms, possibly driven by distinct signals—that is, through the sprouting of mature ECs from preexisting vessels (angiogenesis), through the *in situ* enlargement of collateral vessels from preexisting arteriolar anastomoses (collateral growth or "adaptive arteriogenesis"), and through endothelial progenitor cells (EPCs), which circulate postnatally in the peripheral blood and may be recruited from the bone marrow (BM) and incorporated into sites of active neovascularization—a process termed postnatal vasculogenesis.[78]

Switching on angiogenesis requires sufficient amounts of angiogenic signals as well as ECs that can respond to these signals. Unfortunately, in ischemic patients in need of new blood vessels, the capacity to lift the angiogenic switch is often limited by associated clinical conditions (e.g., senescence, diabetes, or hypercholesterolemia), which reduce the expression of angiogenic factors, impair the responsiveness of ECs to these factors, or both. Although BM-derived endothelial precursors may overcome such a lack of responsive ECs in ischemic tissues,[79] these precursors may be dysfunctional or reduced in number.[80–83] Therefore, therapeutic stimulation of vessel growth in ischemic disease may be achieved by delivering angiogenic factors or their corresponding genes (therapeutic angiogenesis), by supplying vascular progenitor cells for vascular regeneration therapy, or by mobilizing endogenous vascular progenitors. These approaches may be combined, as stem cell transplantation may complement therapeutic angiogenesis for patients in whom endogenous endothelial (precursor) cells fail to sufficiently respond to growth factor treatment. The following overview elaborates how and to what extent vascular progenitors contribute to the formation of vessels in the adult and how this can be therapeutically exploited. For overviews on the mechanisms and therapeutic stimulation of angiogenesis and collateral growth, see other reviews.[7,75,84–86]

Adult Endothelial Progenitor Cells

EPCs were first identified in 1997 in peripheral blood by Asahara *et al.* and were shown to express CD34, VEGFR-2, and vascular endothelial cadherin.[79] Subsequently, other phenotypic markers were added to this expression pattern, most importantly AC133, an orphan receptor specifically expressed on EPCs but not on mature ECs.[87] A high proliferation potential and late outgrowth *ex vivo* distinguishes EPCs from poorly proliferating mature ECs, which grow early after plating.[88] The contribution of EPCs to neovascularization in the adult has been documented in animals in several experimental settings, such as ischemia, tumor growth, and wound healing. We showed that the restoration of VEGF-induced angiogenesis in Matrigel was partly dependent on BM-derived cells (including EPCs) in mice lacking PlGF, a mouse model of impaired pathological angiogenesis.[89] Reports on the numeric contribution of EPCs to vessel growth are variable, ranging from very low (less than 0.1%) to high (50%) and likely dependent on the type of angiogenesis model used.[90,91] In some cases, neovascularization seemed to be almost exclusively dependent on the contribution of BM-derived precursor cells. Lyden *et al.* showed that tumor vascularization and growth in tumor-resistant inhibitor of differentiation (ID) mutant mice required mobilization of BM-derived EPCs.[92] In patients, ischemic conditions increase the circulating levels of EPCs up to 1000-fold,[78,93] and these levels may be used as a prognostic marker for determination of cardiovascular risk.[83,94,95] EPC recruitment to sites of neoangiogenesis is likely triggered by the increased bioavailability of angiogenic growth factors or chemokines such as VEGF, angiopoietin and stromal cell-derived factor-1-alpha (SDF1α)[96–99] (see later sections of this chapter). Once arrived at the site of neovascularization, EPCs may recruit additional EPCs by secreting growth factors.[100,101] Thus, EPCs might contribute in two ways to vessel growth: by differentiating to mature ECs, which become incorporated as building blocks in nascent vessels, and by creating a proangiogenic microenvironment through the release of cytokines and growth factors.

Adult Smooth Muscle Progenitor Cells

Nascent vessels are stabilized by the formation of a SMC coat. Although SMCs may be derived from the division of preexisting SMCs, recent findings suggested an additional source of SMCs: circulating BM-derived SMC progenitors. After heterotypic cardiac[102,103] or aortic[103] transplantation in mice, most of the neointimal α-actin positive SMCs in the donor coronary arteries or aortas were from host origin, suggesting that these SMCs may be at least partly derived from BM-derived SMC progenitors. In support of this concept, transplantation of β-galactosidase-expressing BM into irradiated aortic allograft recipient mice revealed that part of the neointimal SMC-like population consisted of BM-derived cells.[104] In humans, SMC progenitors were recently shown to be present in the mononuclear fraction of the peripheral blood.[105] Although their existence is accepted, their numeric contribution to vessel growth or remodeling is debated. In some animal studies, BM-derived SMCs (and ECs) contributed importantly (10–50%) to neointima formation and reendothelialization in the context of transplant atherosclerosis, balloon injury, and primary atherosclerosis.[106–108] Orlic *et al.* revealed that after implantation of cKit$^+$Lin$^-$ BM cells into the ischemic myocardium, up to 44% of the newly formed SMCs were BM derived.[91] However, other reports demonstrated a more modest (1–10%) contribution of BM-derived cells during these events.[109,110] Possibly, SMCs may be derived from bipotential vascular progenitors similar to SMC development from ES cells,[13] although this needs to be further demonstrated. In addition, circulating EPCs and mature ECs were shown to be able to transdifferentiate to SMCs.[105,111] Little is known about the mechanisms that trigger SMC progenitor recruitment. Consequently, therapeutic stimulation of SMC progenitor recruitment remains an important challenge.

Adult Hematopoietic Stem and Progenitor Cells: Link to Vessel Formation

In the embryo, vessels develop in close association with blood cells. The shared expression of CD34, VEGFR-2, and AC133 on EPCs and HSCs raised the question of whether, like in the embryo, EPCs and HSCs in the adult might be derived from a common precursor—the adult equivalent of the hemangioblast. An increasing number of reports suggest the existence of such a bipotential precursor. Grant *et al.* demonstrated that individual Sca1$^+$cKit$^+$Lin$^-$ murine BM cells, enriched for HSCs, differentiated into both hematopoietic cells and ECs *in vivo.*[112] Subsequently, Pelosi *et al.* reported that a small subset of CD34$^+$VEGFR-2$^+$ cells from human BM or cord blood had the same capacity to differentiate to hematopoietic cells and ECs *in vitro.*[113] Furthermore, multipotent adult progenitor cells (MAPCs) generated both ECs and hematopoietic cells *in vivo,* although *in vitro* differentiation into hematopoietic cells has not been observed yet.[114,115] Additional evidence will help to conclusively establish the identity and molecular signals influencing the putative adult hemangioblast.

As in the embryo, it becomes increasingly evident that adult vascular and hematopoietic lineages cross talk using common receptors and ligands—blood vessels and angiogenic factors regulate HSC homeostasis—and that HSCs and mature leukocytes affect vessel growth by secreting angiogenic factors. How do angiogenic factors affect HSCs? In humans, VEGFR-1 and VEGFR-2 are expressed on NOD-SCID-repopulating HSCs.[116–118] In the mouse, VEGFR-1 expression on HSCs is 40-fold higher than VEGFR-2, and VEGFR-1$^+$ but not VEGFR-2$^+$ HSCs repopulate BM-depleted mice.[116–118] VEGF and PlGF, locally produced in the BM microenvironment,[75,119,120] can induce the recruitment of HSCs, whereas a VEGFR-1-inhibitor impairs HSC mobilization, proliferation, and survival *in vivo.*[98,118,121] Loss of VEGF in HSCs reduced their survival, whereas overexpression of VEGF and PlGF in HSCs increased their proliferation and survival *in vitro.*[122] Thus, angiogenic factors regulate HSC homeostasis and mobilization.

Conversely, HSCs may orchestrate new blood vessel formation. Mice deficient in hematopoietic transcription factors—for example, acute myeloid leukemia-1, SH2 domain-containing leukocyte protein–molecular mass 76 (SLP-76), or spleen tyrosine kinase (Syk)—feature angiogenic defects, which can be rescued by transplantation of wild-type BM or growth factor administration.[36,123] In the adult, corecruitment of VEGFR-1$^+$ BM-derived hematopoietic (stem) cells and VEGFR-2$^+$ EPCs was shown to contribute to tumor growth and vascularization, suggesting that comobilization of VEGFR-1$^+$ HSCs is essential for the incorporation of EPCs into newly formed vessels.[92] In agreement with the involvement of VEGFR-1$^+$ stem cells in angiogenesis, we demonstrated that blocking VEGFR-1 reduced angiogenesis in ischemic retinopathy, tumor growth, and rheumatoid arthritis.[121] How HSCs stimulate blood vessel growth largely remains to be determined. Possibly, undifferentiated HSCs or their mature blood cell descendants secrete growth factors such as VEGF or PlGF, which affect the incorporation of EPCs, the growth of ECs *in situ,* or both.[124] The critical role of monocytes in collateral growth has been well documented,[75,85] and selective neutrophil neutralization decreased angiogenesis during wound[125] and myocardial healing.[126] T-lymphocytes have been implicated in angiogenesis during tumor growth and atherosclerosis, as they secrete angiogenic factors like VEGF and bFGF.[127–129] Whether HSCs directly contribute by incorporating into the vessel wall is an unknown but plausible mechanism. Interestingly, Moldovan *et al.* documented the formation of macrophage-containing tunnels in the hearts of mice overexpressing MCP-1.[130] Alternatively, hematopoietic cells may serve as precursors for EPCs or ECs after transdifferentiation.[100,131]

Mechanisms of Progenitor Cell Mobilization

Which signals regulate the proliferation, differentiation, and mobilization of these progenitors from the BM to the peripheral blood? In baseline conditions, stem cells reside in specific niches within the BM microenvironment, where they are sequestered by adhesion molecules and maintained in an undifferentiated and quiescent state. Pathological stress, such as ischemia, or cytokine administration alters this equilibrium, resulting in stem cell mobilization to the blood circulation.[132] The mobilization of stem cells from the BM is a dynamic process, regulated by shear stress imparted by blood flow, and the activation of metalloproteinases, which induce the release of "Kit ligand," facilitating egress from the marrow to the circulation. Matrix metalloproteinase-9 (MMP-9), induced in BM cells by SDF1α, releases soluble Kit-ligand (sKitL), which then permits the transfer of c-Kit$^+$ stem–progenitors from the quiescent to the proliferative niche in the BM. Release of sKitL by MMP-9 enables BM-repopulating cells to translocate to a permissive vascular niche favoring differentiation and reconstitution of the stem–progenitor cell pool.[118,133] By inducing BM neutrophils to release neutrophil elastase, which proteolytically inactivates SDF1α in the BM compartment, granulocyte colony-stimulating factor (G-CSF) controls the navigation of progenitors between the BM and the blood.[134] In addition to cytokines and proteinases, physical factors, such as shear stress fluctuations in the BM vasculature, may influence stem cell trafficking from and to the BM,[135] possibly by altering the expression in BM ECs of adhesion receptors and mobilization cues (e.g., VEGF, PlGF, and SDF1α).[136] Cytokines such as VEGF, PlGF, and SDF1α stimulate the proliferation, differentiation, and survival of EPCs, hematopoietic progenitors, or both.[96–98,118]

Exogenous Stem Cell Delivery for Vascular Regeneration in Preclinical Models

As mentioned previously, patients with ischemic heart or limb disease may have fewer and dysfunctional endothelial progenitors, which could limit the therapeutic potential to mobilize endogenous stem cells for blood vessel formation. An exogenous supply of EPCs (vascular regeneration) may overcome this limitation. An important issue in vascular regenerative therapy is therefore to identify the most suitable stem cell source. The use of unfractionated BM or mononuclear cell populations, enriched in vascular progenitors, provided proof of principle that such cells could be successfully applied for vascular regeneration of the ischemic heart and limbs in pigs, dogs, and rodents.[137–142] Importantly, these BM cells were capable of improving revascularization in conditions of impaired angiogenesis and EC dysfunction (e.g., diabetes mellitus and aging).[80,143]

Other studies attempted to isolate more purified BM cell fractions. Therapeutic vasculogenesis with purified EPCs was initially hampered by the absence of specific markers, which precluded their easy purification and characterization. Selective expansion *ex vivo* of mononuclear cells from the BM (BM-MNCs) or peripheral blood (PB-MNCs) permitted researchers to obtain EPC-enriched populations (Table 42–1). Administration of such *ex vivo*-expanded cell preparations improved postischemic revascularization and function, even though only 2% of neovessels showed incorporation of EPCs.[144–147] Homing of EPCs into the ischemic site was increased when the cells were administered locally in the ischemic tissue to avoid sequestration into the spleen.[148] The sorting of freshly isolated cells recovered more enriched cell populations for vascular regeneration (Table 42–1). For instance, the delivery of freshly isolated CD34$^+$ PB-MNCs increased the contribution of vascular progenitors into newly formed capillaries.[79]

Since obtaining sufficient numbers of pure EPCs for clinical use may be problematic,[83,95,97] many strategies have been designed to improve their yield or function. Gene transfer methods and hypoxia have been used to prolong the life span of circulating EPCs and to increase their proliferation or homing using modulation of EPC adhesion molecules[97,149,150]; statins have also been used for this purpose.[151] Isolation based on their expression of multiple phenotypic markers such as AC133, CD34, and VEGFR-2 resulted in a purer stem cell population with better expansion capacity *ex vivo*.[87,152] In addition, stimulation with cytokines, such as G-CSF or the use of cord blood, has been applied to increase EPC yield. Compared to CD34$^+$ PB-MNCs, administration of cord blood CD34$^+$ PB-MNCs accelerated EPC functions and increased incorporation into newly formed vessels twofold even after systemic delivery[153,154] (Table 42–1).

The growth of new vessels may relieve ischemia, rescue viable myocardium, and accelerate the postinfarction healing process. However, necrotic myocardium will be replaced by collagenous scar tissue, instead of by contractile cardiomyocytes, with progressive ventricular dysfunction. Although EPCs are able to transdifferentiate into cardiomyocytes *in vitro*,[155] multipotent stem cells may offer the opportunity to stimulate not only angiogenesis but also cardiomyogenesis. Mainly, two types of multipotent stem cells exist: those derived from the embryo (ES cells) and those derived from adult sources. Murine or human ES cells are capable of differentiating into different vascular cell types (including ECs, SMCs, and pericytes) and cardiomyocytes *in vitro*,[13,156–159] and following differentiation, these cells have been shown to contribute to vessels and cardiac muscle.[15,157,160,161] A concern with ES cell transplantation is the possible contamination of the differentiated cells with undifferentiated ES cells, since the latter may induce tumors.[159] As for EPCs, genetic manipulation of the ES cells may help in obtaining a pure differentiated population or may increase their function. Cardiac-specific expression of enhanced green fluorescent protein or antibiotic resistance genes has been used to obtain pure cardiomyocyte cultures from ES cells.[158–160] Overexpression of VEGF in early differentiated ES cells further improved the recovery of postischemic cardiac function.[161]

Because of ethical considerations, the use of adult stem cell sources for vascular regenerative therapy has been explored. Orlic *et al.* injected labeled cKit$^+$Lin$^-$ BM cells directly into the myocardial infarct region of mice.[91] These transplanted cells differentiated into ECs, pericytes, and cardiomyocytes at a high efficiency (44%), resulting in improved postischemic cardiac function (Table 42–1). Jackson *et al.* used another BM fraction, the CD34^{low}cKit$^+$Sca1$^+$ cells or the so-called side population (SP), which regenerated endothelium and cardiac muscle, albeit at a rather modest engraftment rate (only 0.02% for cardiomyocytes and 3.3% for ECs).[162] However, in cardiotoxin-injured mouse muscles, the same SP cells isolated from muscle contributed to endothelial (4% engraftment) but not to pericyte or skeletal muscle regeneration[163] (Table 42–1). Interestingly, coadministration of another population enriched for mesenchymal progenitors (the non-SP) contributed to pericytes. Thus, vascular regenerative therapy may be improved by administering combinations of defined cell populations, each capable of regenerating specific cell types. Recently, Jiang and colleagues identified a new population of stem cells, the MAPCs, from adult species including mice, rats, and humans.[115] MAPCs can be expanded *in vitro* for more than 100 population doublings and are able to differentiate into cell types of all three germ layers *in vitro* and *in vivo*. MAPCs differentiate to ECs and SMCs *in vitro*. Undifferentiated MAPCs contributed significantly (12%) to endothelial regeneration *in vivo*, and their incorporation *in vivo* was increased threefold when the cells were differentiated to endothelium with VEGF.[114] Whether MAPCs are useful for cardiomyogenesis and vascular regenerative therapy in ischemia remains to be determined.

TABLE 42–1
Exogenous Delivery of Stem Cells for Vascular Regeneration in Animal Models

Cell type	Function	Cell number	Delivery	Model	Vascularity	Perfusion	Function	Ref.
BM[a] cells								
— Unfractionated	ND	5×10^6 (6x)	Direct intramyocardial	Rat acute MI	Improved	ND	ND	137
— MNC	Improved	ND (12x)	Transendocardial	Pig chronic MI	NS	Improved	Improved	138
— MNC	Improved	4×10^6 (25x)	Direct intramyocardial	Pig acute MI	Improved	Improved	Improved	139
— MNC	Improved	2×10^7 (2x)	Direct intramyocardial	Dog chronic MI	Improved	ND	Improved	140
— MNC	Improved	2.5×10^7 (20x)	Transendocardial	Pig chronic MI	Improved	Improved	Improved	141
— MNC	ND	6×10^7 (6x)	Intramuscular	Diabetes, rat limb ischemia	Improved	Improved	ND	143
EPCs								
— PB-MNC, 4d culture	ND	5×10^5 (1x)	Intracardiac	Mouse limb ischemia	Improved	Improved	ND	144
— PB-MNC, 7d culture	Improved	1×10^6 (1x)	Intravenous	Rat acute MI	Improved	ND	Improved	145
— BM-MNC, 7d culture	ND	1×10^6 (6x)	Intramuscular	Rabbit limb ischemia	Improved	Improved	ND	146
— PB-MNC, CD31$^+$, 1d culture	Improved	1×10^7 (1x)	Transendocardial	Pig chronic MI	Improved	ND	Improved	147
— PB-MNC, CD34$^+$	ND	1×10^5 (1x)	Intravenous	Mouse limb ischemia	Improved	ND	ND	79
— CB-MNC, CD34$^+$, 7d culture	ND	3×10^5 (1x)	Intramuscular	Rat limb ischemia	Improved	Improved	ND	153
— PB-MNC, CD34$^+$, mobilized	Improved	2×10^6 (1x)	Intravenous	Rat acute MI	Improved	ND	Improved	154
HSCs								
— BM cKit$^+$Lin$^-$	Improved	1×10^5 (2x)	Direct intramyocardial	Mouse acute MI	Improved	ND	Improved	91
— Muscle SP	ND	2×10^3 (1x)	Intramuscular	Mouse muscle injury	Improved	ND	ND	163

[a]BM: bone marrow, MNC: mononuclear cells, PB-MNC: peripheral blood MNC, BM-MNC: bone marrow MNC, CB-MNC: cord blood MNC, SP: side population, MI: myocardial ischemia, ND: not determined, and NS: not significantly improved.

TABLE 42–2
Clinical Experience in Vascular Regeneration[a]

Cell population	N	Placebo, double blind	Experimental setup	Follow-up	Perfusion	Function	Ref.
BM-MNC (1d culture)	10	No, no	Acute myocardial infarction Autologous cell transplantation Combined with angioplasty Intracoronary infusion of 4×10^6 BM-MNC (7x)	3 months	Reduced infarct region (LV cineventriculography)	NS	164
BM-MNC (direct), or PB-MNC (3d culture) (TOPCARE-AMI)	19	No, no	Acute myocardial infarction Autologous cell transplantation Combined with angioplasty Intracoronary infusion of 7×10^7 cells (3x)	4 months	ND	Improved EF (LV cineventriculography)	165
BM-MNC (direct)	14	No, no	Severe ischemic heart failure Autologous cell transplantation Monotherapy Transendocardial injection of 2×10^6 BM-MNC (15x)	2 months	Improved (stress SPECT)	Improved EF (echo)	166
BM-MNC (direct) (TACT)	20	No, yes	Peripheral artery disease Autologous cell transplantation Monotherapy Intramuscular injection of 2.8×10^9 BM-MNC	6 months	Improved (ankle-brachial index)	Improved exercise (pain-free walking time)	168

[a]Comparative analysis of experimental parameters between treatment groups and control groups. (BM-MNC: bone marrow mononuclear cells, PB-MNC: peripheral blood mononuclear cells, LV: left ventricle, SPECT: single-photon emission computed tomography, EF: ejection fraction, and NS: not significantly improved).

Clinical Results of Vascular Regeneration and Future Perspectives

Soon after obtaining proof of principle in preclinical models, vascular regeneration was assessed in patients using autologous cell populations. The results so far obtained are described in the following paragraphs and summarized in Table 42–2. At first, vascular regeneration was used as adjuvant therapy in patients undergoing angioplasty through the intracoronary infusion of expanded BM-MNCs[164] or cultured EPCs.[165] Comparative analysis with a control group showed reduced infarct size and improved global cardiac function. Importantly, EPC administration resulted in increased coronary blood flow reserve and myocardial viability. BM-MNCs improved blood flow with efficiency comparable to EPCs. These findings were extended in a trial, using vascular regeneration as monotherapy in *no-option* patients (i.e., not eligible for standard revascularization procedures) with chronic ischemia in heart or limb. When compared to a control group, transendocardial injection of BM-MNCs into viable but ischemic myocardium reduced angina score and improved cardiac perfusion, function, and exercise capacity.[166,167] In addition, when BM-MNCs were injected in ischemic skeletal muscle, patients had fewer symptoms and ischemia-related morbidity and had increased perfusion and exercise capacity, which salvaged the extremity during a 2-year follow-up.[168] Thus, these data support (vascular) regeneration of ischemic heart and limb in patients, when BM-MNCs, EPCs, or both are administered as monotherapy or as adjuvant treatment.

To evaluate the therapeutic benefit of more defined cell populations, Stamm *et al.* performed direct intramyocardial injection of autologous AC133$^+$ BM-MNCs into six patients undergoing coronary bypass surgery for acute myocardial infarction.[169] Administration of 1×10^6 cells in the infarcted area improved cardiac perfusion, function, and exercise capacity after 3 months. Noticeably, however, previously akinetic myocardium remained akinetic, although local perfusion was improved, suggesting that the administration of AC133$^+$ cells facilitated mainly angiogenesis in the infarct zone. Thus, administration of directly isolated autologous AC133$^+$ BM-MNCs may be an attractive alternative cell population to *ex vivo*-expanded blood-derived EPCs for clinical vascular regeneration.

Together, the initial clinical experiences with vascular regeneration are promising. The delivery strategies applied so far appear to be safe with no cell therapy-related mortality.[169] Nonetheless, additional investigations are required to address several unanswered issues: (1) the choice of the optimal cell population, with definition of the plasticity spectrum; (2) a detailed analysis of the numerical and functional contribution of administered cells to angiogenesis, myogenesis, or cardiomyogenesis; (3) the optimal delivery method; and (4) the evaluation of therapeutic efficacy and safety in large-scale, randomized, double-blind, placebo-controlled trials, because the placebo effect may be substantial.[170] In addition, one particular limitation of using autologous adult stem cells is the delay between harvesting and readministrating the cells, which may significantly compromise their use in acute ischemic patients. Therefore, identification of defined subpopulations and characterization of senescence and expansion capacity of adult stem cells may further improve the therapeutic concept and significantly increase the number of patients that could benefit from this approach.

Lymphatic Vascular System

ORIGIN OF LYMPHATIC VESSELS IN THE EMBRYO

Lymphatic vessels start developing after the blood vascular system (at E9.5 in the mouse), an argument in favor of a blood vessel origin of lymphatics. In 1902, long before specific lymphatic EC markers became available, Sabin launched her theory that the first lymphatic ECs (which organize into lymph sacs) develop by budding from a certain region in the cardinal veins[171] (Fig. 42–3). Almost a century later, further evidence supporting this theory was found in mouse studies with the *Prox-1* homeobox gene, a specific lymphatic marker proposed to determine the lymphatic fate of a subpopulation of ECs in the cardinal veins and to induce budding from these cells.[172] The rest of the lymphatic network would result from sprouting from these initial lymph vessels (lymphangiogenesis). However, an alternative theory, developed by Huntington and McClure in 1910, states that lymphatics develop independently of veins from separate mesenchymal precursors (lymphangioblasts)[173] (Fig. 42–3), suggesting that the formation of

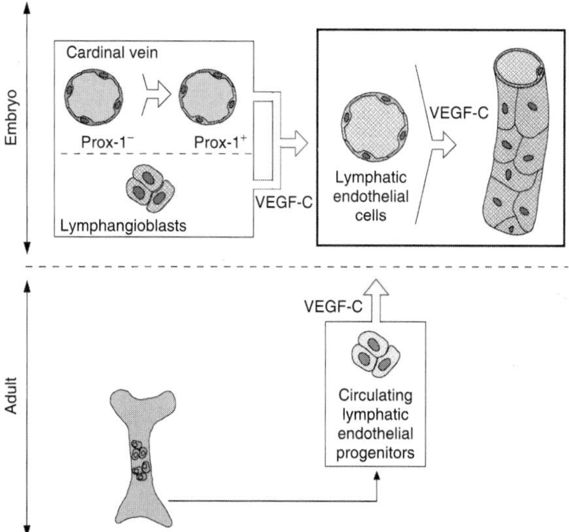

Figure 42–3. *Origin of lymphatic vessel cells.* In the embryo, lymphatic endothelial cells (ECs) derive from cardinal vein ECs induced to express Prox-1. A second possible origin in the embryo (at least in avians) is lymphangioblasts derived from the mesoderm. Vascular endothelial growth factor-C (VEGF-C) is a potent mitogen for lymphatic ECs. The origin of lymphatic smooth muscle cells around larger vessels and the signals responsible for their growth remain elusive. In the adult, the existence of circulating bone marrow-derived lymphatic endothelial precursors was recently established. (Please see CD-ROM for color version of this figure.)

the first lymphatics is the result of coalescence of lymphatic precursors, a process which could be called *lymphvasculogenesis* in analogy with blood vessel ontogeny.[174] Quail–chick chimera experiments have proven the existence of separate mesenchymal lymphatic precursors, at least in the avian embryo, at the level of the paraxial and splanchnic mesoderm.[175–177] Although the existence of lymphangioblasts in mammalian tissues needs to be demonstrated, mechanisms proposed by both theories may act together to form the lymphatic vasculature.

Like blood vessels, some lymphatic vessels (i.e., the larger collecting lymphatics) are enveloped by SMCs, particularly around the luminal valves.[178,179] In mammals and birds, contractility of the collecting lymphatics is of great functional importance.[180] Indeed, the autocontractile smooth muscle coat, the presence of intraluminal valves, and external factors such as skeletal muscle contraction and arterial pulsation promote unidirectional fluid transport in the lymphatic vasculature. The origin of lymphatic SMCs remains to be investigated.

Unlike the blood vasculature, which is a closed circuit (Fig. 42–1), lymphatics form an open-ended system. It is unclear whether the mechanisms determining lymphatic vessel patterning are similar to those for blood vessels. Nevertheless, lymphatic vessels are, like blood vessels, organized in a hierarchic network. First, the lymphatic capillaries (or initial lymphatics) begin as closed saccules and form a network even more extensive than the network of blood capillaries.[178,181] These capillaries drain into small precollector lymphatics and large collecting lymphatics. The collecting vessels coalesce into larger vessels that run along the veins and drain into lymph nodes. The efferent lymphatics emanating from the nodes coalesce into larger collecting ducts (which may be interconnected by collateral lymphatic vessels) and finally empty into the thoracic duct (on the left) or the right lymphatic duct.[178,181] The thoracic duct empties at the level of the aortic arch in the left jugulosubclavian vein junction, and the right lymphatic duct connects to the right jugulosubclavian vein junction. Just as variations in the patterning in the aortic arch and its branches occur frequently, considerable anatomic variations have been described in the connections of the lymphatic vessels to the venous system.[178] However, unlike blood vessel patterning abnormalities (see previous sections), these anatomic variations do not seem to cause life-threatening complications.

It has been shown that receptor expression varies among subsets of lymphatic vessels,[174,182–184] indicating that—like blood ECs—lymphatic ECs are heterogeneous. This heterogeneity may be partly determined by origin—that is, sprouting from veins or stemming from separate lymphatic precursors. Furthermore, the extent of the lymphatic network differs among organs. Although lymphatic capillaries occur frequently in cardiac muscle, they are infrequent in skeletal muscle and might even be absent in the central nervous system, BM, parenchyma of the thymus and the spleen, periocular system, and placenta.[180,185]

MOLECULAR BASIS OF LYMPHANGIOGENESIS IN THE EMBRYO

The ontogeny of lymphatic vessels has remained largely descriptive until recently, when lymphatic markers and growth factors were discovered. Two theories have emerged to explain the formation of the lymphatic system. The most widely accepted view is that lymphatics derive from veins. The precise signals that induce venous ECs to become lymphatic ECs remain elusive. Subsequent budding of lymphatic ECs from veins occurs in Prox-1-deficient mice at E10.5 but becomes aberrant at E11.5, indicating that Prox-1 is necessary to sustain budding.[172] In wild-type mice, but not in Prox-1-deficient mice, classical EC markers (e.g., CD34) and laminin are down-regulated in the budding cells, indicating that these cells are already committed to a lymphatic fate and supporting a role for Prox-1 in determining the lymphatic fate of the budding cells.[186] The expression pattern of the lymphatic endothelial hyaluronan receptor LYVE-1 largely overlaps with that of Prox-1; however, its precise role in lymphatic development is unclear. VEGFR-3 is first expressed on veins, but its expression becomes largely restricted to lymphatic ECs later. Since VEGFR-3 deficient mice die at midgestation because of blood vascular defects before the emergence of the lymphatic vessels, study of the role of VEGFR-3 in embryonic lymph vessel development will need to be addressed in conditional knockout studies.[187] Mice with a hemizygous inactivating *VEGFR-3* missense mutation (Chy mice) survive until birth, but 10% of these mice die within 3 weeks because of severe leakage of lymph fluid.[184] Interestingly, deficiency of Nrp-2, which has been suggested to function as a coreceptor for VEGFR-3,[184] resulted in defects of the distal lymphatic vessels.[48] VEGF-C is coordinately expressed with its receptor VEGFR-3, and its pattern of expression parallels that of the development of lymphatic vessels.[188] Although the lymphangiogenic effect of VEGF-D, the other VEGFR-3 ligand, in adult or pathological context has been documented,[189–191] its role in lymphatic development remains to be defined. Mice deficient of the Ets DNA-binding domain for the transcription factor Net or the integrin subunit $\alpha 9$ succumb shortly after birth because of insufficient lymph drainage, suggesting a role for these factors in proper lymph vessel formation.[192,193] Recently, Ang-2 was shown to play a role in the maturation and patterning of the newly formed lymph vessels, thereby functioning as an agonist for the Tie-2 receptor expressed on lymphatic ECs.[194]

In avians, at least part of the lymphatic system finds its origin in the mesenchyme (e.g., from lymphangioblasts).[175–177] The existence of lymphangioblasts in mammalians needs to be further investigated. Isolated mesenchymal precursors producing lymphatics were first Prox-1^- but soon became Prox-1^+, suggesting that Prox-1 may be a lymphangioblast marker.[177] *VEGFR-3* expression is not observed in isolated mesenchymal precursors but becomes restricted to lymphatic ECs in later stages, suggesting that this receptor is not a marker for embryonic lymphangioblasts, at least not in chicks.[177] In contrast, a recent study has suggested that in human adults the

VEGFR-3$^+$ fraction of BM-derived CD34$^+$ cells may mark a population of lymphatic progenitors[195] (Fig. 42–3).

MOLECULAR BASIS OF LYMPHANGIOGENESIS IN THE ADULT: THERAPEUTIC LYMPHANGIOGENESIS

Lymphatic vessels do not actively grow in steady-state conditions in the adult. Like blood vessels, a constitutive expression of lymphangiogenic factors, balanced by inhibitors, may be required for vascular maintenance. This may be of particular importance for lymphatic capillaries that are not stabilized by a continuous basement membrane or pericytes. Lymphangiogenesis only appears to occur in a limited number of physiological situations, such as wound healing,[196] and is mostly associated with pathological situations, including lymphangiomata, Crohn's disease, or Kaposi's sarcoma.[197] Conversely, a lack of lymphatic vessels causes lymphedema, a condition characterized by disfiguring and disabling swelling of the extremities and eventually fibrofatty changes in the skin.[198] Lymphedema can be primary (i.e., because of mutations in the *VEGFR-3* or *FOXC2* gene) or secondary (e.g., because of surgical removal of lymph nodes in the context of cancer).[174] Therapeutic correction of lymphedema could follow several strategies. One would involve the administration of lymphangiogenic growth factors (therapeutic lymphangiogenesis), such as VEGF-C or VEGF-D, which was shown to be effective in animal models.[184,199,200] Moreover, analogous to EPCs, lymphatic EPCs were recently identified as VEGFR-3$^+$AC133$^+$ CD34$^+$ in human fetal liver, cord, and peripheral blood.[195] Therefore, lymphatic EPCs could be administered, although proof of principle still needs to be established in animal models.

WHICH SIGNALS KEEP BLOOD AND LYMPHATIC VESSELS SEPARATE?

It is of great functional importance that the blood and lymphatic vascular systems do not communicate with each other (except at the level of the jugulosubclavian junction). The occurrence of arteriovenous–lymphatic shunts would compromise a blood supply to vital organs, since blood would be drawn to lymphatic vessels, thereby bypassing the blood capillaries where exchange of oxygen and nutrients takes place. How, then, are the systems kept separate? A recent study in mice has identified in BM-derived hematopoietic cells a signaling pathway involving SLP-76 and Syk, which segregate both vascular circuits.[123] Loss of either factor fused lymphatic and blood vessels as well as arteries and veins, and blood appeared in all large lymphatics. Aberrant communication was established early in development (at E11.5) when the lymph sacs are formed. How these hematopoietic cells regulate the separation of lymph and blood vessels requires further study. In addition, since the transplantation of wild-type BM rescued the vascular defects, the involvement of (lymphatic) EPCs cannot be excluded.

Summary

The formation of blood and lymphatic vessels in development and in the adult involves a complex plethora of interactions among stem cells, lineage-specific differentiated cells, cytokines, and environmental cues. Although many of the pathways have been revealed by the use of genetic and expression studies in multiple species, there are as many unknowns that invoke further detailed research. Nevertheless, because of the knowledge acquired, several therapeutic avenues involving vascular stem/progenitor cells to treat vascular disorders have been designed and tested in animals, some of which have already progressed into phase I clinical trials. The first outlook on these trials is a promising one and should stimulate vascular and stem cell biologists and clinicians to join efforts in finding new and even more effective treatments for those many patients with inherited or acquired vascular or lymph vascular disorders.

REFERENCES

1. Pardanaud, L., Luton, D., Prigent, M., Bourcheix, L.M., Catala, M., and Dieterlen-Lievre, F. (1996). Two distinct endothelial lineages in ontogeny, one of them related to hemopoiesis. *Development* **122,** 1363–1371.
2. de Bruijn, M.F., Speck, N.A., Peeters, M.C., and Dzierzak, E. (2000). Definitive hematopoietic stem cells first develop within the major arterial regions of the mouse embryo. *EMBO J.* **19,** 2465–2474.
3. de Bruijn, M.F., Ma, X., Robin, C., Ottersbach, K., Sanchez, M.J., and Dzierzak, E. (2002). Hematopoietic stem cells localize to the endothelial cell layer in the midgestation mouse aorta. *Immunity* **16,** 673–683.
4. Poole, T.J., Finkelstein, E.B., and Cox, C.M. (2001). The role of FGF and VEGF in angioblast induction and migration during vascular development. *Dev. Dyn.* **220,** 1–17.
5. Hansen-Smith, F.M. (2000). Capillary network patterning during angiogenesis. *Clin. Exp. Pharmacol. Physiol.* **27,** 830–835.
6. Sadler, T.W. (2000). Cardiovascular system. *In* "Langman's Medical Embryology," pp. 208–259. Williams & Wilkins, Baltimore.
7. Carmeliet, P. (2000). Mechanisms of angiogenesis and arteriogenesis. *Nat. Med.* **6,** 389–395.
8. Vrancken Peeters, M.P., Gittenberger-de Groot, A.C., Mentink, M.M., Hungerford, J.E., Little, C.D., and Poelmann, R.E. (1997). Differences in development of coronary arteries and veins. *Cardiovasc. Res.* **36,** 101–110.
9. Gittenberger-de Groot, A.C., DeRuiter, M.C., Bergwerff, M., and Poelmann, R.E. (1999). Smooth muscle cell origin and its relation to heterogeneity in development and disease. *Arterioscler. Thromb. Vasc. Biol.* **19,** 1589–1594.
10. Nakajima, Y., Mironov, V., Yamagishi, T., Nakamura, H., and Markwald, R.R. (1997). Expression of smooth muscle alpha-actin in mesenchymal cells during formation of avian endocardial cushion tissue: A role for transforming growth factor beta3. *Dev. Dyn.* **209,** 296–309.
11. Creazzo, T.L., Godt, R.E., Leatherbury, L., Conway, S.J., and Kirby, M.L. (1998). Role of cardiac neural crest cells in cardiovascular development. *Annu. Rev. Physiol.* **60,** 267–286.
12. Dettman, R.W., Denetclaw, W. Jr., Ordahl, C.P., and Birstow, J. (1998). Common epicardial origin of coronary vascular smooth muscle, perivascular fibroblasts, and intermyocardial fibroblasts in the avian heart. *Dev. Biol.* **193,** 169–181.
13. Yamashita, J., Itoh, H., Hirashama, M., Ogawa, M., Nishikawa, S., Yurugi, T., Naito, M., and Nakao, K. (2000). Flk1-positive cells derived from embryonic stem cells serve as vascular progenitors. *Nature* **408,** 92–96.

14. Ema, M., Faloon, P., Zhang, W.J., Hirashima, M., Reid, T., Stanford, W.L., Orkin, S., Choi, K., and Rossant, J. (2003). Combinatorial effects of Flk1 and Tal1 on vascular and hematopoietic development in the mouse. *Genes Dev.* **17,** 380–393.
15. Yurugi-Kobayashi, T., Itoh, H., Yamashita, J., Yamahara, K., Hirai, H., Kobayashi, T., Ogawa, M., Nishikawa, S., and Nakao, K. (2003). Effective contribution of transplanted vascular progenitor cells derived from embryonic stem cells to adult neovascularization in proper differentiation stage. *Blood* **101,** 2675–2678.
16. Ruoslahti, E., and Rajotte, D. (2000). An address system in the vasculature of normal tissues and tumors. *Annu. Rev. Immunol.* **18,** 813–827.
17. Sims, D.E. (2000). Diversity within pericytes. *Clin. Exp. Pharmacol. Physiol.* **27,** 842–846.
18. Andries, L.J., Brutsaert, D.L., and Sys, S.U. (1998). Nonuniformity of endothelial constitutive nitric oxide synthase distribution in cardiac endothelium. *Circ. Res.* **82,** 195–203.
19. Donovan, M.J., Lin, M.I., Wiegn, P., Ringstedt, T., Kraemer, R., Hahn, R., Wang, S., Ibanez, C.F., Rafii, S., and Hempstead, B.L. (2000). Brain-derived neurotrophic factor is an endothelial cell survival factor required for intramyocardial vessel stabilization. *Development* **127,** 4531–4540.
20. Derhaag, J.G., Duijvestijn, A.M., Emeis, J.J., Engels, W., and van Breda Vriesman, P.J. (1996). Production and characterization of spontaneous rat heart endothelial cell lines. *Lab. Invest.* **74,** 437–451.
21. Derhaag, J.G., Duijvestijn, A.M., and Van Breda Vriesman, P.J. (1997). Heart EC respond heterogeneous on cytokine stimulation in ICAM-1 and VCAM-1 but not in MHC expression: A study with three rat heart endothelial cell (RHEC) lines. *Endothelium* **5,** 307–319.
22. Roman, B.L., and Weinstein, B.M. (2000). Building the vertebrate vasculature: Research is going swimmingly. *Bioessays* **22,** 882–893.
23. Oettgen, P. (2001). Transcriptional regulation of vascular development. *Circ. Res.* **89,** 380–388.
24. Hirschi, K.K., Skalak, T.C., Peirce, S.M., and Little, C.D. (2002). Vascular assembly in natural and engineered tissues. *Ann. NY Acad. Sci.* **961,** 223–242.
25. Drake, C.J., and Fleming, P.A. (2000). Vasculogenesis in the day 6.5 to 9.5 mouse embryo. *Blood* **95,** 1671–1679.
26. Gering, M., Rodaway, A.R., Gottgens, B., Patient, R.K., and Green, A.R. (1998). The *SCL* gene specifies hemangioblast development from early mesoderm. *Embo. J.* **17,** 4029–4045.
27. Liao, E.C., Paw, B.H., Oates, A.C., Pratt, S.J., Postlethwait, J.H., Zon, L.I. (1998). SCL/Tal-1 transcription factor acts downstream of cloche to specify hematopoietic and vascular progenitors in zebra fish. *Genes Dev.* **12,** 621–626.
28. Shalaby, F., Rossant, J., Yamaguchi, T.P., Gertsenstein, M., Wu, X.F., Breitman, M.L., and Schuh, A.C. (1995). Failure of blood island formation and vasculogenesis in Flk-1-deficient mice. *Nature* **376,** 62–66.
29. Nishikawa, S.I., Nishikawa, S., Hirashima, M., Matsuyoshi, N., and Kodamma, H. (1998). Progressive lineage analysis by cell sorting and culture identifies FLK1^{+}VE-cadherin^{+} cells at a diverging point of endothelial and hemopoietic lineages. *Development* **125,** 1747–1757.
30. Chung, Y.S., Zhang, W.J., Arentson, E., Kingsley, P.D., Palis, J., and Choi, K.. (2002). Lineage analysis of the hemangioblast as defined by FLK1 and SCL expression. *Development* **129,** 5511–5520.
31. Carmeliet, P., Ferreira, V., Breier, G., Pollefeyt, S., Kieckens, L., Gertsenstein, M., Fahrig, M., Vandenhoeck, A., Harpal, K., Eberhart, C., Declercq, C., Pawling, J., Moons, L., Collen, D., Risau, W., and Nagy, A. (1996). Abnormal blood vessel development and lethality in embryos lacking a single VEGF allele. *Nature* **380,** 435–439.
32. Ferrara, N., Carver-Moore, K., Chen, H., Dowd, M., Lu, L., O Shea, K.S., Powell-Braxton, L., Hillan, K.J., and Moore, M.W. (1996). Heterozygous embryonic lethality induced by targeted inactivation of the *VEGF* gene. *Nature* **380,** 439–442.
33. Fong, G.H., Rossant, J., Gertsenstein, M., and Breitman, M.L. (1995). Role of the Flt-1 receptor tyrosine kinase in regulating the assembly of vascular endothelium. *Nature* **376,** 66–70.
34. Fong, G.H., Zhang, L., Bryce, D.M., and Peng, J. (1999). Increased hemangioblast commitment, not vascular disorganization, is the primary defect in flt-1 knockout mice. *Development* **126,** 3015–3025.
35. Kearney, J.B., Ambler, C.A., Monaco, K.A., Johnson, N., Rapoport, R.G., and Bautch, V.L. (2002). Vascular endothelial growth factor receptor Flt-1 negatively regulates developmental blood vessel formation by modulating endothelial cell division. *Blood* **99,** 2397–2407.
36. Takakura, N., Watanabe, T., Suenobu, S., Yamada, Y., Noda, T., Ito, Y., Satake, M., and Suda, T. (2000). A role for hematopoietic stem cells in promoting angiogenesis. *Cell* **102,** 199–209.
37. Visvader, J.E., Fujiwara, Y., and Orkin, S.H. (1998). Unsuspected role for the T-cell leukemia protein SCL/tal-1 in vascular development. *Genes Dev.* **12,** 473–479.
38. Robb, L., Drinkwater, C.C., Metcalf, E., Li, R., Kontgen, F., Nicola, N.A., and Begley, C.G. (1995). Absence of yolk sac hematopoiesis from mice with a targeted disruption of the *scl* gene. *Proc. Nat. Acad. Sci. USA* **92,** 7075–7079.
39. Dyer, M.A., Farrington, S.M., Mohn, D., Munday, J.R., and Bron, M.H. (2001). Indian hedgehog activates hematopoiesis and vasculogenesis and can respecify prospective neurectodermal cell fate in the mouse embryo. *Development* **128,** 1717–1730.
40. Vokes, S.A., and Krieg, P.A. (2002). Endoderm is required for vascular endothelial tube formation but not for angioblast specification. *Development* **129,** 775–785.
41. Lawson, N.D., Scheer, N., Pham, V.N., Kim, C.H., Chitnis, A.B., Campos-Ortega, J.A., and Weinstein, B.M. (2001). Notch signaling is required for arterial–venous differentiation during embryonic vascular development. *Development* **128,** 3675–3683.
42. Lawson, N.D., Vogel, A.M., and Weinstein, B.M. (2002). Sonic hedgehog and vascular endothelial growth factor act upstream of the Notch pathway during arterial endothelial differentiation. *Dev. Cell* **3,** 127–136.
43. Zhong, T.P., Rosenberg, M., Mohideen, M.A., Weinstein, B., and Fishman, M.C. (2000). *Gridlock,* an HLH gene required for assembly of the aorta in zebra fish. *Science* **287,** 1820–1824.
44. Luttun, A., Carmeliet, G., and Carmeliet, P. (2002). Vascular progenitors: From biology to treatment. *Trends Cardiovasc. Med.* **12,** 88–96.
45. Othman-Hassan, K., Patel, K., Papoutsi, M., Rodreguez-Niedenfuhr, M., Christ, B., and Wilting, J. (2001). Arterial identity of endothelial cells is controlled by local cues. *Dev. Biol.* **237,** 398–409.
46. Stalmans, I., Ng, Y.S., Rohan, R., Fruttiger, M., Bouche, A., Yuce, A., Fujisawa, H., Hermans, B., Shani, M., Jansen, S., Hicklin, D., Anderson, D.J., Gardiner, T., Hammes, H.P., Moons, L., Dewerchin, M., Collen, D., Carmeliet, P., and D Amore, P.A. (2002). Arteriolar and venular patterning in retinas of mice selectively expressing VEGF isoforms. *J. Clin. Invest.* **109,** 327–336.

47. Yuan, L., Yuan, L., Moyon, D., Pardanaud, L., Breant, C., Karkainen, M.J., Alitalo, K., and Eichmann, A. (2002). Abnormal lymphatic vessel development in neuropilin-2-mutant mice. *Development* **129,** 4797–4806.
48. Jain, R.K. (2003). Molecular regulation of vessel maturation. *Nat. Med.* **9,** 685–693.
49. Hellstrom, M., Kalen, M., Lindahl, P., Abramsson, A., and Betsholtz, C. (1999). Role of PDGF-B and PDGFR-β in recruitment of vascular smooth muscle cells and pericytes during embryonic blood vessel formation in the mouse. *Development* **126,** 3047–3055.
50. Hirschi, K.K., Rohovsky, S.A., and D'Amore, P.A. (1998). PDGF, TGF-β, and heterotypic cell–cell interactions mediate endothelial cell-induced recruitment of 10T1/2 cells and their differentiation to a smooth muscle fate. *J. Cell Biol.* **141,** 805–814.
51. Landerholm, T.E., Dong, X.R., Lu, J., Belaguli, N.S., Schwartz, R.J., and Majesky, M.W. (1999). A role for serum response factor in coronary smooth muscle differentiation from proepicardial cells. *Development* **126,** 2053–2062.
52. Isogai, S., Horiguchi, M., and Weinstein, B.M. (2001). The vascular anatomy of the developing zebra fish: An atlas of embryonic and early larval development. *Dev. Biol.* **230,** 278–301.
53. Cleaver, O., and Krieg, P.A. (1998). VEGF mediates angioblast migration during development of the dorsal aorta in *Xenopus. Development* **125,** 3905–3914.
54. Stalmans, I., Lambrechts, D., De Smet, F., et al. (2003) VEGF: A modifier of the del22q11 (DiGeorge) syndrome? *Nat. Med.* **9,** 173–182.
55. Brown, L.A., Rodaway, A.R., Schilling, T.F., Jowett, T., Ingham, P.W., Patient, R.K., and Sharrocks, A.D. (2000). Insights into early vasculogenesis revealed by expression of the ETS-domain transcription factor Fli-1 in wild-type and mutant zebra fish embryos. *Mech. Dev.* **90,** 237–252.
56. Pola, R., Ling, L.E., Silver, M., Corbley, M.J., Kearney, M., Blake Pepinsky, R., Shapiro, R., Taylor, F.R., Baker D.P., Asahara, T., and Isner, J.M. (2001). The morphogen Sonic hedgehog is an indirect angiogenic agent up-regulating two families of angiogenic growth factors. *Nat. Med.* **7,** 706–711.
57. Adams, R.H., Wilkinson, G.A., Weiss, C., Diella, F., Gale, N.W., Deutsch, U., Risau, W., and Klein, R. (1999). Roles of ephrinB ligands and EphB receptors in cardiovascular development: Demarcation of arterial–venous domains, vascular morphogenesis, and sprouting angiogenesis. *Genes Dev.* **13,** 295–306.
58. Helbling, P.M., Saulnier, D.M., and Brandli, A.W. (2000). The receptor tyrosine kinase EphB4 and ephrin-B ligands restrict angiogenic growth of embryonic veins in *Xenopus laevis. Development* **127,** 269–278.
59. Ruhrberg, C., Gerhardt, H., Golding, M., Watson, R., Ioannidou, S., Fujisawa, H., Betsholtz, C., and Shima, D.T. (2002). Spatially restricted patterning cues provided by heparin-binding VEGF-A control blood vessel branching morphogenesis. *Genes Dev.* **16,** 2684–2698.
60. Dorrell, M.I., Aguilar, E., and Friedlander, M. (2002). Retinal vascular development is mediated by endothelial filopodia, a preexisting astrocytic template and specific R-cadherin adhesion. *Invest. Ophthalmol. Vis. Sci.* **43,** 3500– 3510.
61. Li, W.E., Waldo, K., Linask, K.L., Chen, T., Wessels, A., Parmacek, M.S., Kirby, M.L., and Lo, C.W. (2002). An essential role for connexin43 gap junctions in mouse coronary artery development. *Development* **129,** 2031–2042.
62. Zhu, J., Motejlek, D., Wang, D., Zang, K., Schmidt, A., and Reichardt, L.F. (2002). β8-integrins are required for vascular morphogenesis in mouse embryos. *Development* **129,** 2891–2903.
63. Adams, R.H., and Klein, R. (2000). Eph receptors and ephrin ligands: Essential mediators of vascular development. *Trends Cardiovasc. Med.* **10,** 183–188.
64. Cheng, N., Brantley, D.M., and Chen, J. (2002). The ephrins and Eph receptors in angiogenesis. *Cytokine Growth Factor Rev.* **13,** 75–85.
65. Gale, N.W., Baluk, P., Pan, L., Kwan, M., Holash, J., DecChiara, T.M., McDonald, D.M., Yancopoulos, G.D. (2001). Ephrin-B2 selectively marks arterial vessels and neovascularization sites in the adult, with expression in both endothelial and smooth muscle cells. *Dev. Biol.* **230,** 151–160.
66. Shin, D., Garcia-Cardena, G., Hayashi, S., Gerety, S., Asahara, T., Stavrakis, G., Isner, J., Folkman, J., Gimbrone, M.A., Jr. and Anderson, D.J. (2001). Expression of ephrinB2 identifies a stable genetic difference between arterial and venous vascular smooth muscle as well as endothelial cells and marks subsets of microvessels at sites of adult neovascularization. *Dev. Biol.* **230,** 139–150.
67. Wang, H.U., Chen, Z.F., and Anderson, D.J. (1998). Molecular distinction and angiogenic interaction between embryonic arteries and veins revealed by ephrin-B2 and its receptor Eph-B4. *Cell* **93,** 741–753.
68. Bergwerff, M., DeRuiter, M.C., Hall, S., Poelmann, R.E., and Gittenberger-de Groot, A.C. (1999). Unique vascular morphology of the fourth aortic arches: Possible implications for pathogenesis of type-B aortic arch interruption and anomalous right subclavian artery. *Cardiovasc. Res.* **44,** 185–196.
69. Emanuel, B.S., McDonald-McGinn, D., Saitta, S.C., and Zackai, E.H. (2001). The 22q11.2 deletion syndrome. *Adv. Pediatr.* **48,** 39–73.
70. Lindsay, E.A. (2001). Chromosomal microdeletions: Dissecting del22q11 syndrome. *Nat. Rev. Genet.* **2,** 858–868.
71. Vitelli, F., Morishima, M., Taddei, I., Lindsay, E.A., Baldini, A. (2002). Tbx1 mutation causes multiple cardiovascular defects and disrupts neural crest and cranial nerve migratory pathways. *Hum. Mol. Genet.* **11,** 915–922.
72. (Unpublished observations).
73. Jerome, L.A., and Papaioannou, V.E. (2001). DiGeorge syndrome phenotype in mice mutant for the T-box gene, *Tbx1. Nat. Genet.* **27,** 286–291.
74. Merscher, S., Funke, B., Epstein, J.A., et al. (2001). TBX1 is responsible for cardiovascular defects in velo-cardio-facial–DiGeorge syndrome. *Cell* **104,** 619–629.
75. Carmeliet, P. (2003). Angiogenesis in health and disease. *Nat. Med.* **9,** 653–660.
76. Maynard, S.E., Min, J.Y., Merchan, J., Lim, K.H., Li, J., Mondal, S., Libermann, T.A., Morgan, J.P., Sellke, F.W., Stillman, I.E., Epstein, F.H., Sukhatme, V.P., and Karumanchi, S.A. (2003). Excess placental soluble fms-like tyrosine kinase 1 (sFlt1) may contribute to endothelial dysfunction, hypertension, and proteinuria in preeclampsia. *J. Clin. Invest.* **111,** 649–658.
77. Luttun, A., and Carmeliet, P. (2003). Soluble VEGF receptor Flt1: The elusive preeclampsia factor discovered? *J. Clin. Invest.* **111,** 600–602.
78. Takahashi, T., Kalka, C., Masuda, H., Chen, D., Silver, M., Kearney, M., Magner, M., Isner, J.M., and Asahara, T. (1999). Ischemia- and cytokine-induced mobilization of bone marrow-derived endothelial progenitor cells for neovascularization. *Nat. Med.* **5,** 434–438.
79. Asahara, T., Murohara, T., Sullivan, A., Silver, M., Van der Zee, R., Li, T., Witzenbichler, B., Schatteman, G., and Isner, J.M. (1997). Isolation of putative progenitor endothelial cells for angiogenesis. *Science* **275,** 964–967.
80. Edelberg, J.M., Tang, L., Hattori, K., Lyden, D., and Rafii, S. (2002). Young adult bone marrow-derived endothelial precursor

cells restore aging-impaired cardiac angiogenic function. *Circ. Res.* **90,** E89–E93.

81. Tepper, O.M., Galiano, R.D., Capla, J.M., Kalka, C., Gagne, P.J., Jocobowitz, G.R., Levine, J.P., and Gurtner, G.C. (2002). Human endothelial progenitor cells from type II diabetics exhibit impaired proliferation, adhesion, and incorporation into vascular structures. *Circulation* **106,** 2781–2786.
82. Schatteman, G.C., Hanlon, H.D., Jiao, C., Dodds, S.G., and Christy, B.A. (2000). Blood-derived angioblasts accelerate blood flow restoration in diabetic mice. *J. Clin. Invest.* **106,** 571–578.
83. Vasa, M., Fichtlscherer, S., Aicher, A., Adler, K., Urbich, C., Martin, H., Zeiher, A.M., and Dimmeler, S. (2001). Number and migratory activity of circulating endothelial progenitor cells inversely correlate with risk factors for coronary artery disease. *Circ. Res.* **89,** E1–E7.
84. Ferrara, N., Gerber, H.P., and LeCouter, J. (2003). The biology of VEGF and its receptors. *Nat. Med.* **9,** 669–676.
85. Van Royen, N., Piek, J.J., Bushmann, I., Hoefer, I., Voskuil, M., and Schaper, W. (2001). Stimulation of arteriogenesis: A new concept for the treatment of arterial occlusive disease. *Cardiovasc. Res.* **49,** 543–553.
86. Yancopoulos, G.D., Davis, S., Gale, N.W., Rudge, J.S., Wiegand, S.J., and Holash, J. (2000). Vascular-specific growth factors and blood vessel formation. *Nature* **407,** 242–248.
87. Peichev, M., Naiyer, A.J., Pereira, D., Zhu, Z., Lane, W.J., Williams, M., Oz, M.C., Hicklin, D.J., Witte, L., Moore, M.A., and Rafii, S. (2000). Expression of VEGFR-2 and AC133 by circulating human $CD34^+$ cells identifies a population of functional endothelial precursors. *Blood* **95,** 952–958.
88. Lin, Y., Weisdorf, D.J., Solovey, A., and Hebbel, R.P. (2000). Origins of circulating endothelial cells and endothelial outgrowth from blood. *J. Clin. Invest.* **105,** 71–77.
89. Carmeliet, P., Moons, L., Luttun A. et al. (2001). Synergism between vascular endothelial growth factor and placental growth factor contributes to angiogenesis and plasma extravasation in pathological conditions. *Nat. Med.* **7,** 575–583.
90. De Palma, M., Venneri, M.A., Roca, C., and Naldini, L. (2003). Targeting exogenous genes to tumor angiogenesis by transplantation of genetically modified hematopoietic stem cells. *Nat. Med.* **9,** 789–795.
91. Orlic, D., Kajstura, J., Chimenti, S., Jakoniuk, I., Anderson, S.M., Li, B., Pickel, J., McKay, R., Nadal-Ginard, B., Bodine, D.M., Leri, A., and Anversa, P. (2001). Bone marrow cells regenerate infarcted myocardium. *Nature* **410,** 701–705.
92. Lyden, D., Hattori, K., Dias, S., Costa, C., Balikie, P., Butros, L, Chadburn, A., Heissig, B., Marks, W., Witte, L., Wu, Y., Hicklin, D., Zhu, Z., Hackett, N.R., Crystal, R.G., Moore, M.A., Hajjar, K.A., Manova, K., Benezra, R., and Rafii, S. (2001). Impaired recruitment of bone marrow-derived endothelial and hematopoietic precursor cells blocks tumor angiogenesis and growth. *Nat. Med.* **7,** 1194–1201.
93. Gill, M., Dias, S., Hattori, K., Rivera, M.L., Hicklin, D., Witte, L., Girardi, L., Yurt, R., Himel, H., and Rafii, S. (2001). Vascular trauma induces rapid but transient mobilization of $VEGFR2^+AC133^+$ endothelial precursor cells. *Circ. Res.* **88,** 167–174.
94. Shintani, S., Murohara, T., Ikeda, H., Ueno, T., Honma, T., Katoh, A., Sasaki, K., Shimada, T., Oike, Y., and Imaizumi, T. (2001). Mobilization of endothelial progenitor cells in patients with acute myocardial infarction. *Circulation* **103,** 2776–2779.
95. Hill, J.M., Zalos, G., Halcox, J.P., Schenke, W.H., Waclawiw, M.A., Quyyumi, A.A., and Finkel, T. (2003). Circulating endothelial progenitor cells, vascular function, and cardiovascular risk. *N. Engl. J. Med.* **348,** 593–600.
96. Yamaguchi, J. Kusano, K., and Masuo, O. (2003). Stromal cell-derived factor-1 effects on *ex vivo* expanded endothelial progenitor cell recruitment for ischemic neovascularization. *Circulation* **107,** 1316–1322.
97. Iwaguro, H., Yamaguchi, J., Kalka, C., Murasawa, S., Masuda, H., Hayashi, S., Silver, M., Li, T., Isner, J.M., and Asahara, T. (2002). Endothelial progenitor cell vascular endothelial growth factor gene transfer for vascular regeneration. *Circulation* **105,** 732–738.
98. Hattori, K. Dias, S., Heissig, B., Hackett, N.R., Lyden, D., Tateno, M., Hicklin, D.J., Zhu, Z., Witte, L., Crystal R.G., Moore, M.A., and Rafii, S. (2001). Vascular endothelial growth factor and angiopoietin-1 stimulate postnatal hematopoiesis by recruitment of vasculogenic and hematopoietic stem cells. *J. Exp. Med.* **193,** 1005–1014.
99. Asahara, T., Takahashi, T., Masuda, H., Kalka, C., Chen, D., Iwaguro, H., Inai, Y., Silver, M., and Isner, J.M. (1999). VEGF contributes to postnatal neovascularization by mobilizing bone marrow-derived endothelial progenitor cells. *Embo. J.* **18,** 3964–3972.
100. Rehman, J., Li, J., Orschell, C.M., and March, K.L. (2003). Peripheral blood "endothelial progenitor cells" are derived from monocyte–macrophages and secrete angiogenic growth factors. *Circulation* **107,** 1164–1169.
101. Carmeliet, P., and Luttun, A. (2001). The emerging role of the bone marrow-derived stem cells in (therapeutic) angiogenesis. *Thromb. Haemost.* **86,** 289–297.
102. Saiura, A., Sata, M., Hirata, Y., Nagai, R., and Makuuchi, M. (2001). Circulating smooth muscle progenitor cells contribute to atherosclerosis. *Nat. Med.* **7,** 382–383.
103. Hillebrands, J.L., Klatter, F.A., van den Hurk, B.M., Popa, E.R., Nieuwenhuis, P., and Rozing, J. (2001). Origin of neointimal endothelium and alpha-actin-positive smooth muscle cells in transplant arteriosclerosis. *J. Clin. Invest.* **107,** 1411–1422.
104. Shimizu, K., Sugiyama, S., Aikawa, M., Fukumoto, Y., Rabkin, E., Libby, P., and Mitchell, R.N. (2001). Host bone marrow cells are a source of donor intimal smooth muscle-like cells in murine aortic transplant arteriopathy. *Nat. Med.* **7,** 738–741.
105. Simper, D., Stalboerger, P.G., Panetta, C.J., Wang, S., and Caplice, N.M. (2002). Smooth muscle progenitor cells in human blood. *Circulation* **106,** 1199–1204.
106. Caplice, N.M., Bunch, T.J., Stalboerger, P.G., Wang, S., Simper, D., Miller, D.V., Russell, S.J., Litzow, M.R., and Edwards, W.D. (2003). Smooth muscle cells in human coronary atherosclerosis can originate from cells administered at marrow transplantation. *Proc. Nat. Acad. Sci. USA* **100,** 4754–4759.
107. Religa, P., Bojakowski, K., Maksymowicz, M., Bojakowska, M., Sirsjo, A., Gaciong, Z., Olszewski, W., Hedin, U., and Thyberg, J. (2002). Smooth muscle progenitor cells of bone marrow origin contribute to the development of neointimal thickenings in rat aortic allografts and injured rat carotid arteries. *Transplantation* **74,** 1310–1315.
108. Sata, M., Saiura, A., Kunisato, A., Tojo, A., Okada, S., Tokuhisa, T., Hirai, H., Makuuchi, M., Hirata, Y., and Nagai, R. (2002). Hematopoietic stem cells differentiate into vascular cells that participate in the pathogenesis of atherosclerosis. *Nat. Med.* **8,** 403–409.
109. Hillebrands, J.L., Klatter, F.A., van Dijk, W.D., and Rozing, J. (2002). Bone marrow does not contribute substantially to endothelial cell replacement in transplant arteriosclerosis. *Nat. Med.* **8,** 194–195.

110. Li, J., Han, X., Jiang, J., Zhong, R., Williams, G.M., Pickering, J.G., and Chow, L.H. (2001). Vascular smooth muscle cells of recipient origin mediate intimal expansion after aortic allotransplantation in mice. *Am. J. Pathol.* **158,** 1943–1947.
111. Frid, M.G., Kale, V.A., and Stenmark, K.R. (2002). Mature vascular endothelium can give rise to smooth muscle cells via endothelial–mesenchymal transdifferentiation: *In vitro* analysis. *Circ. Res.* **90,** 1189–1196.
112. Grant, M.B., May, W.S., Caballero, S., Brown, G.A., Guthrie, S.M., Mames, R.N., Byrne, B.J., Vaught, T., Spoerri, P.E., Peck, A.B., and Scott, E.W. (2002). Adult hematopoietic stem cells provide functional hemangioblast activity during retinal neovascularization. *Nat. Med.* **8,** 607–612.
113. Pelosi, E., Valtieri, M., Coppola, S., Botta, R., Gabbianelli, M., Lulli, V., Marziali, G., Masella, B., Muller, R., Sgadari, C., Testa, U., Bonanno, G., and Peschle, C. (2002). Identification of the hemangioblast in postnatal life. *Blood* **100,** 3203–3208.
114. Reyes, M., Dudek, A., Jahagirdar, B., Koodie, L., Marker, P.H., and Verfaillie, C.M. (2002). Origin of endothelial progenitors in human postnatal bone marrow. *J. Clin. Invest.* **109,** 337–346.
115. Jiang, Y., Jahagirdar, B.N., Reinhardt, R.L., Schwarz, R.E., Keene, C.D., Ortiz-Gonzalez, X.R., Reyes, M., Levnik, T., Lund, T., Blackstad, M., Du, J., Aldrich, S., Lisberg A., Low, W.C., Largaespada, D.A., and Verfaillie, C.A. (2002). Pluripotency of mesenchymal stem cells derived from adult marrow. *Nature* **418,** 41–49.
116. Ziegler, B.L., Valtieri, M., Porada, G.A,, De Maria, R., Muller, R., Masella, B., Gabbiznelli, M., Casella, I., Pelosi, E., Bock, T., Zanjani, E.D., and Peschle, C. (1999). KDR receptor: A key marker defining hematopoietic stem cells. *Science* **285,** 1553–1558.
117. Haruta, H., Nagata, Y., and Todokoro, K. (2001). Role of Flk-1 in mouse hematopoietic stem cells. *FEBS Lett.* **507,** 45–48.
118. Hattori, K., Heissig, B., Wu, Y., Dias, S., Tejada, R., Ferris, B., Hicklin, D.J., Zhu, Z., Bohlen, P., Witte, L., Hendrikx, J., Hackett, N.R., Crystal, R.G., Moore, M.A., Werb, Z., Lyden, D., and Rafii, S. (2002). Placental growth factor reconstitutes hematopoiesis by recruiting VEGFR1$^+$ stem cells from bone marrow microenvironment. *Nat. Med.* **8,** 841–849.
119. Hackney, J.A., Charbord, P., Brunk, B.P., Stoeckert, C.J., Lemishka, I.R., and Moore, K.A. (2002). A molecular profile of a hematopoietic stem cell niche. *Proc. Nat. Acad. Sci. USA* **99,** 13,061–13,066.
120. Tordjman, R., Delaire, S., Plouet, J., Ting, S., Gaulard, P., Fichelson, S., Romeo, P.H., and Lemarchandel, V. (2001). Erythroblasts are a source of angiogenic factors. *Blood* **97,** 1968–1974.
121. Luttun, A., Tjwa, M., Moons, L., Wu, Y., Angelillo-Scherrer, A., Liao, F., Nagy, J.A., Hooper, A., Priller, J., De Klerck, B., Compernolle, V., Daci, E., Bohlen, P., Dewerchin, M., Herbert, J.M., Fava, R., Matthys, P., Carmeliet, G., Collen, D., Dvorak, H.F., Hicklin, D.J., and Carmeliet, P. (2002). Revascularization of ischemic tissues by PlGF treatment, and inhibition of tumor angiogenesis, arthritis, and atherosclerosis by anti-Flt1. *Nat. Med.* **8,** 831–840.
122. Gerber, H.P., Malik, A.K., Solar, G.P., Sherman, D., Liang, X.H., Meng, G., Hong, K., Marsters, J.C., and Ferrara, N. (2002). VEGF regulates hematopoietic stem cell survival by an internal autocrine loop mechanism. *Nature* **417,** 954–958.
123. Abtahian, F., Guerriero, A., Sebza, E., Lu, M.M., Zhou, R., Mocsai, A., Myers, E.E., Huan, B., Jackson, D.G., Ferrari, V.A., Tybulewicz, V., Lowell, C.A., Lepore, J.J., Koretzky, G.A., and Kahn, M.L. (2003). Regulation of blood and lymphatic vascular separation by signaling proteins SLP-76 and Syk. *Science* **299,** 247–251.
124. Bautz, F., Rafii, S., Kanz, L., and Mohle, R. (2000). Expression and secretion of vascular endothelial growth factor-A by cytokine-stimulated hematopoietic progenitor cells: Possible role in the hematopoietic microenvironment. *Exp. Hematol.* **28,** 700–706.
125. Simpson, D.M., and Ross, R. (1972). The neutrophilic leukocyte in wound repair a study with antineutrophil serum. *J. Clin. Invest.* **51,** 2009–2023.
126. Heymans, S., Luttun, A., Nuyens, D., et al. (1999). Inhibition of plasminogen activators or matrix metalloproteinases prevents cardiac rupture but impairs therapeutic angiogenesis and causes cardiac failure. *Nat. Med.* **5,** 1135–1142.
127. Blotnick; S., Peoples, G.E., Freeman, M.R., Eberlein, T.J., and Klagsbrun, M. (1994). T-lymphocytes synthesize and export heparin-binding epidermal growth factor-like growth factor and basic fibroblast growth factor, mitogens for vascular cells and fibroblasts: Differential production and release by CD4$^+$ and CD8$^+$ T-cells. *Proc. Nat. Acad. Sci. USA* **91,** 2890–2894.
128. Freeman, M.R., Schneck, F.X., Gagnon, M.L., Corless, C., Soker, S., Niknejad, K., Poples, G.E., and Klagsbrun, M. (1995). Peripheral blood T-lymphocytes and lymphocytes infiltrating human cancers express vascular endothelial growth factor: A potential role for T-cells in angiogenesis. *Cancer Res.* **55,** 4140–4145.
129. Peoples, G.E., Blotnick, S., Takahashi, K., Freeman, M.R., Klagsbrun, M., and Eberlein, T.J. (1995). T-lymphocytes that infiltrate tumors and atherosclerotic plaques produce heparin-binding epidermal growth factor-like growth factor and basic fibroblast growth factor: A potential pathologic role. *Proc. Nat. Acad. Sci. USA* **92,** 6547–6551.
130. Moldovan, N.I., Goldschmidt-Clermont, P.J., Parker-Thornburg, J., Shapiro, S.D., and Kolattukudy, P.E. (2000). Contribution of monocytes– macrophages to compensatory neovascularization: The drilling of metalloelastase-positive tunnels in ischemic myocardium. *Circ. Res.* **87,** 378–384.
131. Schmeisser, A., and Strasser, R.H. (2002). Phenotypic overlap between hematopoietic cells with suggested angioblastic potential and vascular endothelial cells. *J. Hematother. Stem Cell Res.* **11,** 69–79.
132. Moore, M.A. (2002). Cytokine and chemokine networks influencing stem cell proliferation, differentiation, and marrow homing. *J. Cell Biochem. Suppl.* **38,** 29–38.
133. Heissig, B., Hattori, K., Dias, S., Friedrich, M., Ferris, B., Hackett, N.R., Crystal, R.G., Besmer, P., Lyden, D., Moore, M.A., Werb, Z., and Rafii, S. (2002). Recruitment of stem and progenitor cells from the bone marrow niche requires MMP-9 mediated release of kit-ligand. *Cell* **1095,** 625–637.
134. Petit, I., Szyper-Kravitz, M., Nagler, A., Lahav, M., Peled, A., Habler, L., Ponomaryov, T., Taichman, R.S., Arenzana- Seisdedos, F., Fujii, N., Sandbank, J., Zipori, D., and Lapidot, T. (2002). G-CSF induces stem cell mobilization by decreasing bone marrow SDF-1 and up-regulating CXCR4. *Nat. Immunol.* **3,** 687–694.
135. Greenberg, A.W., Kerr, W.G., and Hammer, D.A. (2000). Relationship between selectin-mediated rolling of hematopoietic stem and progenitor cells and progression in hematopoietic development. *Blood* **95,** 478–486.
136. Rabbany, S.Y., Heissig, B., Hattori, K., and Rafii, S. (2003). Molecular pathways regulating mobilization of marrow-derived stem cells for tissue revascularization. *Trends Mol. Med.* **9,** 109–117.
137. Kobayashi, T., Hamano, K., Li, T.S., Katoh, T., Kobayashi, S., Matsuzaki, M., Esato, K. (2000). Enhancement of angiogenesis

by the implantation of self bone marrow cells in a rat ischemic heart model. *J. Surg. Res.* **89,** 189–195.
138. Fuchs, S., Baffour, R., Zhou, Y.F., Shou, M., Pierre, A., Tio, F.O., Weissman, N.J., Leon, M.B., Epstien, S.E., and Kornowski, R. (2001). Transendocardial delivery of autologous bone marrow enhances collateral perfusion and regional function in pigs with chronic experimental myocardial ischemia. *J. Am. Coll. Cardiol.* **37,** 1726–1732.
139. Kamihata, H., Matsubara, H., Nishiue, T., Fujiyama, S., Tsutsumi, Y., Ozono, R., Masaki, H., Mori, Y., Iba, O., Tateishi, E., Kosaki, A., Shintani, S., Murohara, T., Imaizumi, T., and Iwasaka, T. (2001). Implantation of bone marrow mononuclear cells into ischemic myocardium enhances collateral perfusion and regional function via side supply of angioblasts, angiogenic ligands, and cytokines. *Circulation* **104,** 1046–1052.
140. Hamano, K., Li, T.S., Kobayashi, T., Hirata, K., Yano, M., Kohno, M., and Matsuzaki, M. (2002). Therapeutic angiogenesis induced by local autologous bone marrow cell implantation. *Annu. Thorac. Surg.* **73,** 1210–1215.
141. Kamihata, H., Matsubara, H., Nishiue, T., Fujiyama, S., Amano, K., Iba, O., Imada, T., and Iwasaka, T. (2002). Improvement of collateral perfusion and regional function by implantation of peripheral blood mononuclear cells into ischemic hibernating myocardium. *Arterioscler. Thromb. Vasc. Biol.* **22,** 1804–1810.
142. Hamano, K., Li, T.S., Kobayashi, T., Kobayashi, S., Matsuzaki, M., and Esato, K. (2000). Angiogenesis induced by the implantation of self-bone marrow cells: A new material for therapeutic angiogenesis. *Cell Transplant.* **9,** 439–443.
143. Hirata, K., Li, T.S., Nishida, M., Ito, H., Matsuzaki, M., Kasaoka, S., and Hamano, K. (2003). Autologous bone marrow cell implantation as therapeutic angiogenesis for ischemic hind limb in diabetic rat model. *Am. J. Physiol. Heart Circ. Physiol.* **284,** H66–H70.
144. Kalka, C., Masuda, H., TAkahashi, T., Kalka-Moll, W.M., Silver, M., Kearney, M., Li, T., Isner, J.M., and Asahara, T. (2000). Transplantation of *ex vivo*-expanded endothelial progenitor cells for therapeutic neovascularization. *Proc. Nat. Acad. Sci. USA* **97,** 3422–3427.
145. Kawamoto, A., Gwon, H.C., Iwaguro, H., Yamaguchi, J.I., Uchida, S., Masuda, H., Silver, M., Ma, H., Kearney, M., Isner, J.M., and Asahara, T. (2001). Therapeutic potential of *ex vivo*-expanded endothelial progenitor cells for myocardial ischemia. *Circulation* **103,** 634–637.
146. Shintani, S., Murohara, T., Ikeda, H., Ueno, T., Sasaki, K., Duan, J., and Imaizumi, T. (2001). Augmentation of postnatal neovascularization with autologous bone marrow transplantation. *Circulation* **103,** 897–903.
147. Kawamoto, A. Tkebuchava, T., Yamaguchi, J., Nishimura, H., Yoon, Y.S., Milliken, C., Uchida, S., Masao, O., Iwaguro, H., Ma, H., Hanley, A., Silver, M., Kearney, M., Losordo, D.W., Isner, J.M., and Asahara, T. (2003). Intramyocardial transplantation of autologous endothelial progenitor cells for therapeutic neovascularization of myocardial ischemia. *Circulation* **107,** 461–468.
148. Aicher, A., Brenner, W., Zuhayra, M., Badorff, C., Massoudi, S., Assmus, B., Eckey, T., Henze, E., Zeiher, A.M., and Dimmeler, S. (2003). Assessment of the tissue distribution of transplanted human endothelial progenitor cells by radioactive labeling. *Circulation* **107,** 2134–2139.
149. Akita, T., Murohara, T., Ikeda, H., Sasaki, K., Shimada, T., Egami, K., and Imaizumi, T. (2003). Hypoxic preconditioning augments efficacy of human endothelial progenitor cells for therapeutic neovascularization. *Lab. Invest.* **83,** 65–73.
150. Murasawa, S., Llevadot, J., Silver, M., Isner, J.M., Losordo, D.W., and Asahara, T. (2002). Constitutive human telomerase reverse transcriptase expression enhances regenerative properties of endothelial progenitor cells. *Circulation* **106,** 1133–1139.
151. Walter, D.H., Rittig, K., Bahlmann, F.H., Kirchmair, R., Silver, M., Murayama, T., Nishimura, H., Losordo, D.W., Asahara, T., and Isner, J.M. (2002). Statin therapy accelerates reendothelialization: A novel effect involving mobilization and incorporation of bone marrow-derived endothelial progenitor cells. *Circulation* **105,** 3017–3024.
152. Quirici, N., Soligo, D., Caneva, L., Servida, F., Bossolasco, P., and Deliliers, G.L. (2001). Differentiation and expansion of endothelial cells from human bone marrow $CD133^+$ cells. *Br. J. Haematol.* **115,** 186–194.
153. Murohara, T., Ikeda, H., Duan, J., Shintani, S., Sasaki, K., Eguchi, H., Onitsuka, I., Matsui, K., and Imaizumi, T. (2000). Transplanted cord blood-derived endothelial precursor cells augment postnatal neovascularization. *J. Clin. Invest.* **105,** 1527–1536.
154. Kocher, A.A., Schister, M.D., Szabolcs, M.J., Takuma, S., Burkhoff, D., Wang, J., Homma, S., Edwards, N.M., and Itescu, S. (2001). Neovascularization of ischemic myocardium by human bone marrow-derived angioblasts prevents cardiomyocyte apoptosis, reduces remodeling, and improves cardiac function. *Nat. Med.* **7,** 430–436.
155. Badorff, C., Brandes, R.P., Popp, R., Rupp, S., Urbich, C., Aicher, A., Fleming, I., Busse, R., Zeiher, A.M., and Dimmeler, S. (2003). Transdifferentiation of blood-derived human adult endothelial progenitor cells into functionally active cardiomyocytes. *Circulation* **107,** 1024–1032.
156. Levenberg, S., Golub, J.S., Amit, M., Itskovitz-Eldor, J., and Langer, R. (2002). Endothelial cells derived from human embryonic stem cells. *Proc. Nat. Acad. Sci. USA* **99,** 4391–4396.
157. Marchetti, S., Gimond, C., Iljin, K., Bourcier, C., Alitalo, K., Pouyssegur, J., and Pages, G. (2002). Endothelial cells genetically selected from differentiating mouse embryonic stem cells incorporate at sites of neovascularization *in vivo. J. Cell Sci.* **115(Pt. 10),** 2075–2085.
158. Sachinidis, A., Fleishmann, B.K., Kolossov, E., Wartenberg, M., Sauer, H., and Hescheler, J. (2003). Cardiac-specific differentiation of mouse embryonic stem cells. *Cardiovasc. Res.* **58,** 278–291.
159. Boheler, K.R., Czyz, J., Tweedie, D., Yang, H.T., Anisimov, S.V., and Wobus, A.M. (2002). Differentiation of pluripotent embryonic stem cells into cardiomyocytes. *Circ. Res.* **91,** 189–201.
160. Klug, M.G., Soonpaa, M.H., Koh, G.Y., and Field, L.J. (1996). Genetically selected cardiomyocytes from differentiating embryonic stem cells form stable intracardiac grafts. *J. Clin. Invest.* **98,** 216–224.
161. Yang, Y., Min, J.Y., Rana, J.S., Ke, Q., Cai, J., Chen, Y., Morgan, J.P., and Xiao, Y.F. (2002). VEGF enhances functional improvement of postinfarcted hearts by transplantation of ESC-differentiated cells. *J. Appl. Physiol.* **93,** 1140–1151.
162. Jackson, K.A., Majka, S.M., Wang, H., Pocius, J., Hartley, C.J., Majesky, M.W., Entman, M.L., Michael, L.H., Hirschi, K.K., and Goodell, M.A. (2001). Regeneration of ischemic cardiac muscle and vascular endothelium by adult stem cells. *J. Clin. Invest.* **107,** 1395–1402.
163. Majka, S.M., Jackson, K.A., Kienstra, K.A., Majesky, M.W., Goodell, M.A., and Hirschi, K.K. (2003). Distinct progenitor

populations in skeletal muscle are bone marrow-derived and exhibit different cell fates during vascular regeneration. *J. Clin. Invest.* **111,** 71–79.

164. Strauer, B.E., Brehm, M., Zeus, T., Kostering, M., Hernandez, A., Sorg, R.V., Kogler, G., and Wernet, P. (2002). Repair of infarcted myocardium by autologous intracoronary mononuclear bone marrow cell transplantation in humans. *Circulation* **106,** 1913–1918.
165. Assmus, B., Schachinger, V., Teupe, C., Britten, M., Lehmann, R., Dobert, N., Grunwald, F., Aicher, A., Urbich, C., Martin, H., Hoelzer, D., Dimmeler, S., and Zeiher, A.M. (2002). Transplantation of progenitor cells and regeneration enhancement in acute myocardial infarction (TOPCARE-AMI). *Circulation* **106,** 3009–3017.
166. Perin, E.C., Dohmann, H.F., Borojevic, R., Silva, S.A., Sousa, A.L., Mesquita, C.T., Rossi, M.I., Carvalho, A.C., Dutra, H.S., Dohmann, H.J., Silva, G.V., Belem, L., Vivacqua, R., Rangel, F.O., Esporcatte, R., Gent, Y.J., Vaughn, W.K., Assad, J.A., Mesquita, E.T., and Willerson, J.T. (2003). Transendocardial, autologous bone marrow cell transplantation for severe, chronic ischemic heart failure. *Circulation* **107,** 2294–2302.
167. Tse, H.F., Kwong, Y.L., Chan, J.K., Lo, G., Ho, C.L., and Lau, C.P. (2003). Angiogenesis in ischemic myocardium by intramyocardial autologous bone marrow mononuclear cell implantation. *Lancet* **361,** 47–49.
168. Tateishi-Yuyama, E., Matsubara, H., Murohara, T., Ikeda, U., Shintani, S., Masaki, H., Amano, K., Kishimoto, Y., Yoshimoto, K., Asaki, H., Shimada, K., Iwasaka, T., and Imaizumi, T. (2002). Therapeutic angiogenesis for patients with limb ischemia by autologous transplantation of bone marrow cells: A pilot study and a randomized controlled trial. *Lancet* **360,** 427–435.
169. Stamm, C., Westphal, B., Kleine, H.D., Petzsch, M., Kittner, C., Klinge, H., Schumichen, C., Nienaber, C.A., Freund, M., and Steinhoff, G. (2003). Autologous bone marrow stem cell transplantation for myocardial regeneration. *Lancet* **361,** 45–46.
170. Simons, M., Bonow, R.O., Chronos, N.A., Cohen, D.J., Giordano, F.J., Hammond, H.K., Laham, R.J., Li, W., Pike, M., Sellke, F.W., Stegmann, T.J., Udelson, J.E., and Rosengart, T.K. (2000). Clinical trials in coronary angiogenesis: Issues, problems, consensus—An expert panel summary. *Circulation* **102,** E73–E86.
171. Sabin, F.R. (1902). On the origin of the lymphatic system from the veins and the development of the lymph hearts and thoracic duct in the pig. *Am. J. Anat.* **1,** 367–391.
172. Wigle, J.T., and Oliver, G. (1999). Prox1 function is required for the development of the murine lymphatic system. *Cell* **98,** 769–778.
173. Huntington, G.S., and McClure, C.F.W. (1910). The anatomy and development of the jugular lymph sac in the domestic rat *(Felis domestica). Am. J. Anat.* **10,** 177–311.
174. Saaristo, A., Karkkainen, M.J., and Alitalo, K. (2002). Insights into the molecular pathogenesis and targeted treatment of lymphedema. *Ann. NY Acad. Sci.* **979,** 94–110.
175. Wilting, J., Papoutsi, M., Schneider, M., and Christ, B. (2000). The lymphatic endothelium of the avian wing is of somitic origin. *Dev. Dyn.* **217,** 271–278.
176. Schneider, M., Othmari-Hassan, K., Christ, B., and Wilting, J. (1999). Lymphangioblasts in the avian wing bud. *Dev. Dyn.* **216,** 311–319.
177. Papoutsi, M., Tomarev, S.I., Eichmann, A., Prols, F., Christ, B., and Wilting, J. (2001). Endogenous origin of the lymphatics in the avian chorioallantoic membrane. *Dev. Dyn.* **222,** 238–251.
178. Foster, R.S., Jr. (1996). General anatomy of the lymphatic system. *Surg. Oncol. Clin. N. Am.* **5,** 1–13.
179. Berens von Rautenfeld, D., and Drenckhahn, D. (1994). Bau der Lymphgefäße. "Anatomie: Makroskopische Anatomie, Embryologie und Histologie des Menschen," (D. Drenckhahn *et al.,* eds.), pp. 756–761. Urban & Schwarzenberg, Munich.
180. Wilting, J., Neeff, H., and Christ, B. (1999). Embryonic lymphangiogenesis. *Cell Tissue Res.* **297,** 1–11.
181. Casley-Smith, J.R. (1980). The fine structure and functioning of tissue channels and lymphatics. *Lymphology* **13,** 177–183.
182. Nibbs, R.J., Kriehuber, E., Ponath, P.D., Parent, D., Qin, S., Campbell, J.D., Henderson, A., Kerjaschki, D., Maurer, D., Graham, G.J., and Rot, A. (2001). The beta-chemokine receptor D6 is expressed by lymphatic endothelium and a subset of vascular tumors. *Am. J. Pathol.* **158,** 867–877.
183. Makinen, T., Veikkola, T., Mustjoki, S., Karpanen, T., Catimel, B., Nice, E.C., Wise, L., Mercer, A., Kowalski, H., Kerjaschki, D., Stacker, S.A., Achen, M.G., and Alitalo, K. (2001). Isolated lymphatic endothelial cells transduce growth, survival, and migratory signals via the VEGF-C/D receptor VEGFR-3. *Embo. J.* **20,** 4762–4773.
184. Karkkainen, M.J., Saaristo, A., Jussila, L., Karila, K.A., Lawrence, E.C., Pajusola, K., Bueler, H., Eichmann, A., Kauppinen, R., Kettumen, M.I., Yla-Herttuala, S., Finegold, D.N., Ferrell, R.E., and Alitalo, K. (2001). A model for gene therapy of human hereditary lymphedema. *Proc. Nat. Acad. Sci. USA* **98,** 12,677–12,682.
185. Shimada, T., Noguchi, T., Takita, K., Kitamura, H., and Nakamura, M. (1989). Morphology of lymphatics of the mammalian heart with special reference to the architecture and distribution of the subepicardial lymphatic system. *Acta. Anat. (Basel)* **136,** 16–20.
186. Oliver, G., and Harvey, N. (2002). A stepwise model of the development of lymphatic vasculature. *Ann. NY Acad. Sci.* **979,** 159–165; discussion 188–196.
187. Dumont, D.J., Jussila, L., Taipale, J., Lymboussaki, A., Mustonen, T., Pajusola, K., Breitman, M., and Alitalo, K. (1998). Cardiovascular failure in mouse embryos deficient in VEGF receptor-3. *Science* **282,** 946–949.
188. Kukk, E., Lymboussaki, A., Taira, S., Kaipainen, A., Jeltsch, M., Joukov, V., and Alitalo, K. (1996). VEGF-C receptor binding and pattern of expression with VEGFR-3 suggests a role in lymphatic vascular development. *Development* **122,** 3829–3837.
189. Byzova, T.V., Goldman, C.K., Jankau, J., Chen, J., Cabrera, G., Achen, M.G., Stacker, S.A., Carnevale, K.A., Siemionow, M., Deitcher, S.R., and DiCorleto, P.E. (2002). Adenovirus encoding vascular endothelial growth factor-D induces tissue-specific vascular patterns *in vivo. Blood* **99,** 4434–4442.
190. Marconcini, L., Marchio, S., Morbidelli, L., Cartocci, E., Albini, A., Ziche, M., Bussolino, F., and Oliviero, S. (1999). C-fos-induced growth factor–vascular endothelial growth factor D induces angiogenesis *in vivo* and *in vitro. Proc. Nat. Acad. Sci. USA* **96,** 9671–9676.
191. Veikkola, T., Jussila, L., Makinen, T., Karpanen, T., Jeltsch, M., Petrova, T.V., Kubo, H., Thurston, G., McDonald, D.M., Achen, M.G., Stacker, S.A., and Alitalo, K. (2001). Signaling via vascular endothelial growth factor receptor-3 is sufficient for lymphangiogenesis in transgenic mice. *Embo. J.* **20,** 1223–1231.
192. Huang, X., Wu, J.F., Ferrando, R., Lee, J.H., Wang, Y.L., Farese, R.V. Jr., and Sheppard, D. (2000). Fatal bilateral chylothorax in mice lacking integrin alpha9betal. *Moll. Cell Biol.* **20,** 1223–1231.

193. Ayadi, A., Zheng, H., Sobieszczuk, Buchwalter, G., Moerman, P., Alitalo, K., and Wasylyk, B. (2001). Net-targeted mutant mice develop a vascular phenotype and up-regulate egr-1. *Embo. J.* **20,** 5139–5152.
194. Gale, N.W., Thurston, G., Hackett, S.F., Renard, R., Wang, Q., McC.ain, J., Martin, C., Witte, C., Witte, M.H., Jackson, D., Suri, C., Campochiaro, P.A., Wiegand, S.J., and Yancopoulos, G.D. (2002). Angiopoietin-2 is required for postnatal angiogenesis and lymphatic patterning, and only the latter role is rescued by Angiopoietin-1. *Dev. Cell* **3,** 411–423.
195. Salven, P., Mustjoki, S., Alitalo, R., Alitalo, K., and Rafii, S. (2003). VEGFR-3 and CD133 identify a population of $CD34^+$ lymphatic–vascular endothelial precursor cells. *Blood* **101,** 168–172.
196. Daniels, C.B., Lewis, B.C., Tsopelas, C., Munns, S.L., Orgeig, S., Baldwin, M.E., Stacker, S.A., Achen, M.G., Chatterton, B.E., and Cooter, R.D. (2003). Regenerating lizard tails: A new model for investigating lymphangiogenesis. *FASEB J.* **17,** 479–481.
197. Alitalo, K., and Carmeliet, P. (2002). Molecular mechanisms of lymphangiogenesis in health and disease. *Cancer Cell* **1,** 219–227.
198. Browse, N.L. (1986). The diagnosis and management of primary lymphedema. *J. Vasc. Surg.* **3,** 181–184.
199. Yoon, Y.S., Murayama, T., Gravereaux, E., Tkebuchava, T., Silver, M., Curry, C., Wecker, A., Kirchmair, R., Hu, C.S., Kearney, M., Ashare, A., Jackson, D.G., Kubo, H., Isner, J.M., and Losordo, D.W. (2003). *VEGF-C* gene therapy augments postnatal lymphangiogenesis and ameliorates secondary lymphedema. *J. Clin. Invest.* **111,** 717–725.
200. Rissanen, T.T., Markkanen, J.E., Gruchala, M., Heikura, T., Puranen, A., Kettunen, M.I., Kholova, I., Kauppinen, R.A., Achen, M.G., Stacker, S.A., Alitalo, K., and Yla-Herttuala, S. (2003). VEGF-D is the strongest angiogenic and lymphangiogenic effector among VEGFs delivered into skeletal muscle via adenoviruses. *Circ. Res.* **92,** 1098–1106.

44

Adult Liver Stem Cells

Markus Grompe

In mammals, the adult liver contains many cell types of various embryological origins. Nevertheless, the terms *liver stem cell* and *hepatic stem cell* are used only for precursors of the two epithelial liver cell types, the hepatocytes and the bile duct epithelial cells. Therefore, only hepatocyte and bile duct stem cells are described here.

Organization and Functions of Adult Mammalian Liver

To provide background for this chapter on liver stem cell biology, the normal anatomy and function of adult liver is briefly described.

The liver consists of several separate lobes and represents about 2% of human and 5% of mouse body weight.[1] It is the only organ with two afferent blood supplies. The portal vein brings venous blood rich in nutrients and hormones from the splanchnic bed (intestines and pancreas), and the hepatic artery provides oxygenated blood. Venous drainage is into the vena cava. The bile secreted by hepatocytes is collected in a branched collecting system, the biliary tree, which drains into the duodenum. The hepatic artery, portal vein, and common bile duct enter the liver in the same location, the porta hepatis.

The main cell types resident in the liver are hepatocytes, bile duct epithelium, stellate cells (formerly called Ito cells), Kupffer cells, vascular endothelium, fibroblasts, and leukocytes.[1] An adult mouse liver contains about 5×10^7 hepatocytes, and an adult human contains 80×10^9 hepatocytes. The microscopic structure of the liver is essential to the understanding of hepatic stem cell biology. The hepatic lobule (Fig. 44–1) is the functional unit of the liver.[2] The portal triad consisting of a small portal vein, a hepatic artery branch, and a bile duct is located on the perimeter. Arterial and portal venous blood enter here, mix, and flow past the hepatocytes toward the central vein in the middle of the lobule. Liver sinusoids are the vasculature connecting the portal triad vessels and the central vein. Contrary to other capillary beds, sinusoidal vessels have a fenestrated endothelium, thus permitting direct contact between the blood and the hepatocyte cell surface.[3] In two-dimensional images, rows of hepatocytes oriented from portal to central form a hepatic plate. A channel formed by adjacent hepatocytes forms a bile canaliculus, which drains secreted bile toward the bile duct in the portal triad. Bile secreted by the hepatocytes is collected in bile ducts, lined by duct epithelial cells. The canal of Hering is the connection between the bile canaliculi (the interhepatocyte space into which bile is secreted) and the bile ducts at the interface between the lobule and the portal triad. Stellate cells represent about 5–10% of all hepatic cells. In addition to storing vitamin A, they are essential for the synthesis of extracellular matrix proteins and produce many hepatic growth factors that play a vital role in the biology of liver regeneration.[4] Kupffer cells also represent about 5% of all liver cells and are tissue macrophages.

The liver is responsible for the intermediary metabolism of amino acids, lipids, and carbohydrates; the detoxification of xenobiotics; and the synthesis of serum proteins. In addition, the liver produces bile, important for the intestinal absorption of nutrients as well as the elimination of cholesterol and copper. All of these functions are primarily executed by hepatocytes. The biochemical properties and pattern of gene expression is not uniform among all hepatocytes. The term metabolic zonation has been coined to indicate the different properties of periportal (adjacent to the portal triad) and pericentral (adjacent to the central vein) hepatocytes.[5,6] For example, only pericentral hepatocytes express glutamine synthase and use ammonia to generate glutamine.[7,8] In contrast, periportal hepatocytes express urea cycle enzymes and convert ammonia to urea.[9,10]

Liver Stem Cells

The liver is known to have a very high capacity for regeneration. Mammals (including humans) can survive surgical removal of up to 75% of the total liver mass. The original number of cells is restored within 1 week, and the original tissue mass is returned within 2–3 weeks.[11,12] Importantly, liver size is also controlled by prevention of organ overgrowth. Hepatic overgrowth can be induced by a variety of compounds, such as hepatocyte growth factor (HGF) or peroxisome proliferators, but the liver size rapidly returns to normal after removal of the growth-inducing signal. The role of liver stem cells in regeneration has been controversial,[13–17] but many of the apparent inconsistencies can be reconciled by considering the different definitions used for these cells. Current evidence strongly suggests that different cell types and mechanisms are responsible for organ reconstitution depending on the type of liver injury. In addition, tissue

Handbook of Stem Cells
Volume 2

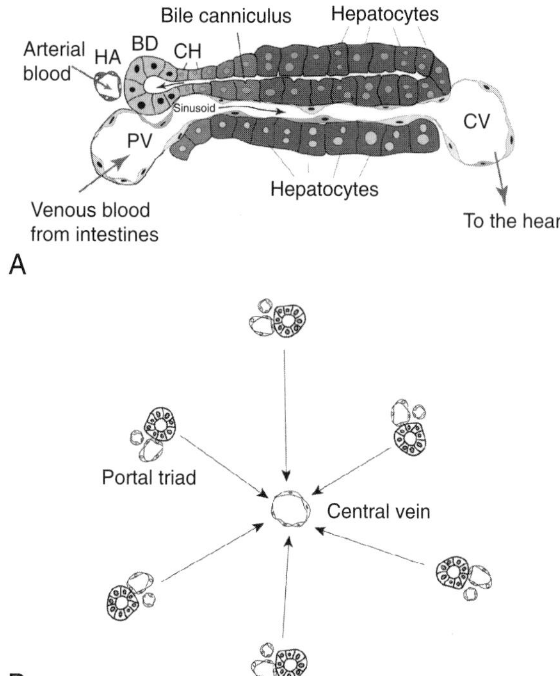

Figure 44–1. *Structure of the hepatic lobule.* (A) The portal triad consists of bile ducts (BD), hepatic artery (HA), and portal vein (PV). Mixed blood from the hepatic artery and portal vein flows past hepatocytes through the sinusoids, covered with fenestrated endothelial cells to the central vein (CV). Bile produced by the hepatocytes is collected in the bile canaliculus and flows toward the bile duct. The canal of Hering (CH) is the junction between the hepatic plate and the bile ducts. This is the region where oval cell precursors reside. (B) Each hepatic lobule consists of one central vein and six surrounding portal triads. (Please see CD-ROM for color version of figure.)

replacement by endogenous cells (regeneration) must be distinguished from reconstitution by transplanted donor cells (repopulation). Thus, the definition of liver stem cells includes: (1) cells responsible for normal tissue turnover, (2) cells that give rise to regeneration after partial hepatectomy, (3) cells responsible for progenitor-dependent regeneration, (4) transplantable liver-repopulating cells, and (5) cells that produce hepatocyte and bile duct epithelial phenotypes *in vitro*.

In the following sections, liver stem cells are described according to each of these definitions.

CELLS RESPONSIBLE FOR NORMAL LIVER TISSUE TURNOVER

The average life span of adult mammalian hepatocytes can be estimated to be between 200 and 300 days.[18] The mechanism by which these cells are replaced has been of interest for some time. One of the main models regarding normal liver turnover was termed the *streaming liver.*[19,20] According to this model, normal liver turnover is similar to regeneration in the intestine with young hepatocytes being born in the portal zone then migrating toward the central vein. The different patterns of gene expression periportal and pericentral hepatocytes were explained by the maturation process during this migration and thus represented a typical lineage progression. However, recent work has provided strong evidence against the streaming liver hypothesis. First, it has been shown that the gene expression pattern in hepatocytes is crucially dependent on the direction of blood flow.[21] If blood flow was reversed such that portal blood entered the lobule through the central vein and exited through the portal vein, the pattern inverted. Therefore, the lobular zonation is best explained by metabolite-induced gene regulation, not by lineage progression. Second, retroviral marking studies provide clear evidence against any hepatocyte migration during normal turnover.[22,23] These results have been confirmed using the mosaic pattern of X-inactivation in female mice to analyze patterns of hepatocyte growth.[24,25] Together, current evidence clearly indicates that normal liver turnover in adult animals is mediated primarily by *in situ* cell division of hepatocytes and bile duct epithelial cells themselves and not by stem cells.[26]

CELLS THAT GIVE RISE TO REGENERATION AFTER PARTIAL HEPATECTOMY

The process of liver regeneration after partial hepatectomy has been well studied and is the subject of several excellent reviews.[17,27] During partial hepatectomy, specific lobes are removed intact without damage to the lobes left behind. The residual lobes grow to compensate for the mass of the resected lobes, although the removed lobes never grow back. The process is completed within 1 week. Again, as in normal liver turnover, there is no evidence for the involvement or requirement for stem cells in this process. Classic thymidine-labeling studies show that virtually all hepatocytes in the remaining liver divide once or twice to restore the original cell number within 3–4 days.[11,12] The earliest labeled hepatocytes are seen 24 hours after partial hepatectomy, with the peak of thymidine incorporation occurring 24–48 hours depending on the species. Interestingly, there is zonal variation depending on how much tissue is removed. When only 15% of the liver is surgically removed, periportal (zone 1) hepatocytes divide preferentially, whereas cell division is seen equally in all three zones after 75% partial hepatectomy.[11] Following the hepatocytes, the other hepatic cell types undergo a wave of mitosis, thereby restoring the original number of all liver cells within 7 days.

Many positive and negative factors important for the initiation of regeneration after partial hepatectomy have been identified. The most important ones are HGF,[28] interleukin-6, tumor necrosis factor-alpha, transforming growth factor-alpha (TGF-α), and epidermal growth factor. Nonpeptide hormones also have a significant role in the regenerative response after liver injury. Triiodothyronine[29] and norepinephrine[30,31] can stimulate hepatocyte replication *in vivo*. It is unknown whether any of these factors are also important for progenitor-dependent liver regeneration or engraftment and expansion of liver stem cells (see the next section of this chapter).

Less knowledge exists about the mechanisms by which hepatocyte cell division and liver regeneration are stopped after the appropriate liver mass has been restored. In particular, the exogenous signals (endocrine, paracrine, or autocrine) involved in sensing the overall liver cell mass and negatively regulating its size are not known. Some evidence suggests that TGF-β1 may be important in termination of liver regeneration.[32]

CELLS RESPONSIBLE FOR PROGENITOR-DEPENDENT REGENERATION

Oval Cells

Although neither cell replacement during normal tissue turnover nor cell replacement after injury by partial hepatectomy requires stem cells for organ regeneration, this is not true for all types of liver injury. In some types of damage to liver, small cells with a high nuclear–cytoplasmic ratio emerge in the portal zone, proliferate extensively, and migrate into the lobule. These small cells, which eventually become differentiated hepatocytes, are termed *oval cells* because of their morphology.[33] Importantly, oval cells are not derived from hepatocytes; instead, they are the offspring of a cell in the canal of Hering (Fig. 44–1). Oval cell proliferation therefore represents an example of progenitor-dependent liver regeneration, and the cell that produces oval cells can be considered a "facultative liver stem cell."[34,35] In the rat, chronic liver injury by chemicals such as DL-ethionine, galactosamine, and azo dyes are examples of this type of liver damage (see Table 44–1). The toxic drugs are often combined with surgical partial hepatectomy. Many of the compounds that induce oval cell proliferation are DNA-damaging agents or carcinogens, and oval cells can therefore be considered precancerous. A common feature of progenitor-dependent liver regeneration is that the hepatocytes themselves cannot divide normally. Thus, progenitor-dependent regeneration may be used when parenchymal hepatocytes are severely damaged on a chronic basis, unable to regenerate efficiently, or both. Oval cells express markers of both bile duct epithelium (CK19) and hepatocytes (albumin). In addition, in the rat they express high levels of α-fetoprotein and are thus similar to fetal hepatoblasts in their gene expression profile.[33] Furthermore, oval cells are bipotential *in vitro* and retain the ability to differentiate into both the bile duct epithelial and hepatocyte lineages.[36,37] Because of their similarity to hepatoblasts and their bipotential capacity, oval cells have been considered early progenitors in analogy to committed hematopoietic progenitors. Thus, oval cell precursors located in the canal of Hering are likely candidates to be liver repopulating stem cells.[38]

In the rat, several monoclonal antibodies have been raised against oval cells and used to study lineage progression. The cell surface marker OV6 has found application in a variety of studies.[39] Generally, studies with these reagents have confirmed the similarity between oval cells and fetal hepatoblasts.

Until recently, it has been difficult to induce oval cell proliferation in the mouse and take advantage of the powerful genetics in this organism. Using transgenic mice, it would be possible to determine whether factors known to be important in liver regeneration after partial hepatectomy are also required for oval cell driven regeneration.

Recently, however, several protocols have been developed that result in progenitor dependent hepatocyte regeneration in the mouse.[40] One particularly useful regimen uses the chemical 3,5-diethoxycarbonyl-1,4-dihydrocollidine (DDC).[40] Mouse oval cells differ from their rat and human counterparts by not expressing α-fetoprotein. OV6 does also not react with murine oval cells, and to date only one oval cell–specific antibody, termed A6, has been developed for murine oval cells.[41] Nonetheless, work on the genetics of oval cell proliferation is now possible. An example is the recent discovery, using transgenic mice, that TGF-β1 inhibits oval cell proliferation.[40]

Table 44–1 lists conditions that result in oval cell proliferation in the rat and mouse. Oval cell proliferation has also been described in a variety of human liver diseases, indicating that progenitor-dependent regeneration can be found in multiple organisms. Oval cells are found in disorders associated with chronic liver injury and are located at the edges of nodules in liver cirrhosis. In both rats and humans, OV6 is a useful marker for these cells.[42]

Interestingly, rat oval cells induced by a classic carcinogen regimen express multiple genes typically associated with hematopoietic stem cells (HSCs).[54] The first of these to be identified were stem cell factor (SCF) and its cognate receptor, the c-kit tyrosine kinase. Isolation of HSCs by fluorescence-activated cell sorting (FACS) uses c-kit antigen as an important positive marker.[55] Both the *SCF* and the *c-kit* genes were expressed during the early stages of oval cell proliferation after partial hepatectomy in the 2-acetylaminofluorene (AAF)–partial hepatectomy model, but neither simple partial hepatectomy nor AAF administration alone induced a noticeable expression of the SCF–c-kit system. mRNA *in situ* hybridization revealed that the c-kit transcripts were restricted to oval cells,

TABLE 44–1
Induction of Progenitor-Dependent Liver Regeneration

Chemical–manipulation	Reference
Mouse	
Dipin	43
3,5-Diethoxycarbonyl-1,4-Dihydrocollidine (DDC)	40
Phenobarbital + cocaine + p.H.[a]	44
Choline-deficient diet + DL-ethionine	45
Rat	
2-Acetylaminofluorene (AAF)	46
Diethylnitrosamine (DEN)	47
Solt-Farber model (DEN + AAF + p.H.)	48
Modified Solt-Farber model (AAF + p.H.)	49
Choline-deficient diet + DL-ethionine	33
D-Galactosamine + p.H.	50
Lasiocarpine + p.H.	51
Retrorsine + p.H.	52, 53

[a]p.H. = partial hepatectomy.

whereas the SCF transcripts were expressed in both oval and stellate cells.

In addition, later work found that the Thy-1 marker used for sorting of HSCs in mouse was also highly expressed on rat oval cells.[55,56] Thy-1 staining clearly colocalized with classic oval cell markers such as α-fetoprotein.

The expression of HSC markers in oval cells is not unique to the rat. Human oval cells isolated from patients with chronic biliary diseases were found to express CD34 as well as the bile duct marker cytokeratin 19 (CK19). In addition, cells that are c-kit positive but are negative for hematopoietic markers have been identified in human pediatric liver disease.[57] Recently, very high levels of stem cell antigen-1 (Sca-1) were found to be expressed on murine oval cells induced by DDC.[58] Therefore, multiple independent studies support the concept that hepatic oval cells, but not regenerating hepatocytes, can express genes found in HSCs. These findings have resulted in the hypothesis that oval cell precursors may be bone marrow derived (see later sections of this chapter).

Other Hepatocyte Progenitors

Oval cells are defined by their morphologic appearance in the rat, but there is variability in the marker genes expressed at different times after induction of oval cell proliferation. In addition, the different induction regimens vary the phenotype. Therefore, it is not clear whether all oval cells are equal or whether subclasses of oval cells exist. Recently, another class of hepatocyte progenitors was described after treatment of rats with retrorsine and partial hepatectomy.[53] Retrorsine blocks the division of mature hepatocytes, but it does not result in the emergence of classic oval cells that are α-fetoprotein and OV6 positive. Instead, foci of small, hepatocyte-like cells emerge and eventually result in organ reconstitution. These small cells express both hepatocyte and bile duct markers. At this time, their origin (dedifferentiated hepatocytes, transitional cells in the canal of Hering, or bone marrow) is unknown.

TRANSPLANTABLE LIVER-REPOPULATING CELLS

One way to define stem cells is by their ability to repopulate the respective organ and restore its function. The HSC, for example, was defined by reconstitution of the blood lineages of lethally irradiated hosts.[55,59] In the 1990s, similar repopulation assays were developed for the liver in several animal models.[52,60,61] In liver repopulation, a small number of transplanted donor cells engrafts in the liver, the cells expand, and they replace >50% of the liver mass.[62] Thus, it has become possible to perform experiments analogous to those done in the hematopoietic system, including cell sorting, competitive repopulation, serial transplantation, and retroviral marking. Hepatic stem cells can now be defined by their ability to repopulate liver. It should be emphasized that liver repopulation refers to replacement of only the hepatocytes by transplanted cells. Efficient repopulation of the biliary system by transplanted cells has not yet been reported.

The main animal models for liver repopulation studies are summarized in Table 44–2. In all cases, liver repopulation by transplanted cells is based on a powerful selective advantage for the transplanted cells over the preexisting host hepatocytes. In many models, this selection is achieved by genetic differences (transgene–knockout), but DNA damage has also been used successfully, particularly in the rat.

The animals described previously have been used to determine the nature of transplantable liver repopulating cells and to determine whether undifferentiated stem cells are driving this process. The stem cell hypothesis was strengthened by the observation that liver repopulating cells could be serially transplanted for >100 cell doublings without loss of functionality.[68] Interestingly, the only donor-derived cells in this experiment were hepatocytes. No biliary epithelium or other cell types of donor origin were found, thus raising the possibility of a "unipotential" stem cell.

Hepatocytes as Liver-Repopulating Cells

It is reasonable to hypothesize that adult liver cells are not homogeneous in their capacity for cell division and that subpopulations with high repopulation capacity might exist. In the hematopoietic system, repopulation experiments with purified fractions of total bone marrow were used to identify subpopulations with high reconstitution activity. Similar experiments have recently been performed with liver cells and indicate that, in contrast to the hematopoietic system, differentiated hepatocytes have a high capacity for liver repopulation.

TABLE 44–2
Animals Models for Liver Repopulation

Animal	Model	Selective pressure	Reference
Mouse	Albumin-urokinase transgenic	Urokinase-mediated hepatocyte injury	61
Mouse	Fah knockout	Accumulation of toxic tyrosine metabolite	60
Mouse	Albumin-HSVTK transgenic	HSVTK-mediated conversion of ganciclovir to toxin	63
Mouse	Mdr3 knockout	Bile acid accumulation	64
Mouse	Bcl2-transgenic donor cells	Fas ligand (Jo2)-induced apoptosis in hepatocytes not expressing Bcl2	65
Rat–mouse	Retrorsine conditioning	Host hepatocytes inactivated by retrorsine (DNA damage)	52, 66
Rat	Radiation conditioning	Host hepatocytes inactivated by X-rays (DNA damage)	67

In the *Fah*-mutant mouse model, size fractionation, retroviral marking, and competitive repopulation between naïve liver cells and those that had been serially transplanted were performed.[69] All three experimental approaches indicated that large, binucleated hepatocytes representing ~70% of the population were primarily responsible for liver repopulation. Others confirmed this finding by transplanting hepatocytes that had been sorted based on their ploidy (DNA content). No differences in the repopulating ability of 2n, 4n, and 8n hepatocytes were found.[70] Thus, no evidence for a rare stem cell responsible for liver repopulation was detected. Together, these experiments strongly suggest that fully differentiated hepatocytes, which constitute most liver cells, are efficient in liver repopulation and have a stem cell-like capacity for cell division.

Nonhepatocytes as Liver-Repopulating Cells

Despite the evidence that hepatocytes are serially transplantable liver repopulating cells,[68,70] other cell types also capable of repopulating the liver. This finding is analogous to the situation in liver regeneration, where hepatocytes as well as undifferentiated hepatocyte progenitors are capable of reconstituting the organ. In the following sections, liver repopulation by several nonhepatocyte cell types will be described: (1) fetal hepatoblasts, (2) oval cells, (3) pancreatic liver progenitors, and (4) HSCs.

Liver Repopulation with Fetal Hepatoblasts. During embryonic development, the fetal liver bud contains hepatoblasts, cells that express α-fetoprotein as well as hepatocyte (albumin) and biliary (CK19) markers. These cells therefore may represent fetal liver stem cells capable of hepatocyte repopulation and potentially capable of reconstitution of the biliary system.

Two reports on transplantation of hepatoblasts have been published.[71,72] One study, using fetal rat liver cells in the retrorsine model, indicated that at least three distinct subpopulations of hepatoblasts between embryonic days (E) 12–14. One population appeared to be bipotential on the basis of histochemical markers, and the other two had either a unipotent hepatocyte or biliary epithelial cell phenotype.[71] After transplantation, the bipotential cells were able to proliferate in retrorsine-treated cell transplantation recipients, whereas the unipotent cells grew even in untreated rats. However, none of the fetal liver cell populations proliferated spontaneously. Partial hepatectomy or thyroid hormone treatment were required to augment proliferation of transplanted cells.[71] Nonetheless, fetal liver cells proliferated more readily than adult cells. Finally, the transplanted fetal cells produced both hepatocyte cords and mature bile duct structures. It was not formally proven, however, that both of these cell lineages originated from a clonal precursor.

Together, these results indicated that transplanted fetal hepatoblasts proliferate more readily than adult hepatocytes and that some fetal liver cells may remain bipotential.

Liver Repopulation with Oval Cells. Oval cells are similar to fetal hepatoblasts in that they are bipotential. These cells have therefore been of interest in liver repopulation experiments. Transplantation of either hepatic- or pancreatic-derived oval cells has been reported in the rat.[73] Upon transplantation, the oval cells proliferated modestly and differentiated into mature hepatocytes[73] even under nonselective conditions. However, because no *in vivo* selection model was used, the true capacity for liver repopulation was not demonstrated in these experiments. Recently, however, repopulation studies have been performed with purified murine oval cells induced by DDC.[74] These experiments clearly indicated that oval cells have extensive liver repopulation capacity and constitute a potential population for use in cell therapy.

Liver Repopulation with Pancreatic Progenitors. During embryogenesis, the main pancreatic cell types develop from a common endodermal precursor located in the ventral foregut, including ducts, ductules, acinar cells, and the endocrine α, β, and δ cells.[75,76] Importantly, the main epithelial cells of the liver, hepatocytes, and bile duct epithelium are thought to arise from the same region of the foregut endoderm.[77,78] This tight relationship between liver and pancreas in embryonic development has raised the possibility that a common hepatopancreatic precursor–stem cell may continue to persist in adult life in both the liver and the pancreas. Indeed, several independent lines of evidence suggest that adult pancreas contains cells that can generate hepatocytes. The earliest description of pancreatic hepatocytes was in hamsters treated with a pancreatic carcinogen, *N*-nitroso-*bis*(2-oxopropyl)amine in 1981.[79] Similarly, small, occasional clusters of hepatocyte-like cells were found in rats being treated with a peroxisome proliferator, Wy-14643.[80] Interestingly, some of the same carcinogens can be used to produce hepatic oval cells, particularly when combined with partial hepatectomy. The best known example is the emergence of hepatocytes in copper-depleted rats after refeeding of copper.[81,82] In this system, weanling rats are fed a copper-free diet for 8 weeks, which leads to complete acinar atrophy, and then are refed copper. Within weeks, cells with multiple hepatocellular characteristics emerge from the remaining pancreatic ducts. This work has been interpreted to suggest the presence of a pancreatic liver stem cell.[83] This notion is also supported by the appearance of hepatocellular markers in human pancreatic cancers.[84] More recently, a specific cytokine has been identified as a candidate to drive this process. Transgenic mice in which the keratinocyte growth factor gene is driven by an insulin promoter consistently develop pancreatic hepatocytes.[85,86] Thus, the existence of pancreatic liver precursors has been shown in several mammalian species and under multiple experimental conditions. There is also evidence for the reverse—that is, the existence of pancreatic precursors in the liver. Some cases of liver tumors, particularly cholangiocarcinomas, display expression of markers typical for pancreatic cell types.[84,87] In one small series of analyzed liver tumors, 61% of cholangiocarcinomas expressed pancreatic-type amylase.[87] Other tumors have been reported to produce lipase, another enzyme specific for pancreatic exocrine cells.[84] Similarly, cultured rat oval cell lines derived from the liver[88] could be differentiated *in vitro* into cells with regulated insulin secretion (i.e., properties similar to pancreatic β-cells). These cells were even able to rescue diabetic rats in transplantation experiments.[89] Others have demonstrated the emergence of insulin-secreting cells *in vivo* in the livers of animals treated with vectors expressing developmental pancreatic transcription factors.

Therefore, we can hypothesize that both adult liver and adult pancreas continue to harbor a small population of primitive hepatopancreatic stem cells with the potential to produce the same differentiated progeny as during embryogenesis.

Transplantation experiments have been conducted to verify the pancreatic liver stem cell hypothesis. As mentioned previously, pancreatic oval cells induced by copper depletion were shown to generate morphologically normal hepatocytes *in vivo*.[73] In addition, the Fah knockout model has been used to demonstrate the existence of hepatocyte progenitors in adult pancreas.[90] The pancreata of wild-type *Fah* mice were digested into single cells and then transplanted into *Fah*-mutant mice. Importantly, the cells used in these experiments were from normal adult pancreata, and no chemical treatments or oval cell induction regimens were used in the donor mice. Although only ~10% of pancreas cell-transplanted Fah-mutant mice survived long term and had extensive liver repopulation, >50% of recipients had donor-derived Fah$^+$ hepatocyte nodules.[91] Based on the number of hepatocyte nodules formed, it could be estimated that pancreatic liver precursors were rare (~1/5,000) in the donor cell population. Additional experiments showed that the pancreatic ducts did not generate hepatocytes in the liver repopulation assay. These findings are not inconsistent with the results obtained with the copper depletion model, because periductular, interstitial cells as well as the ducts themselves were considered candidates to be oval cell precursors.[92]

A model for the lineage relationships between hepatic and pancreatic cells is in Fig. 44–2. This model predicts the existence of an adult hepatopancreatic stem cell similar to the ventral foregut endodermal precursor that exists during embryonic development.

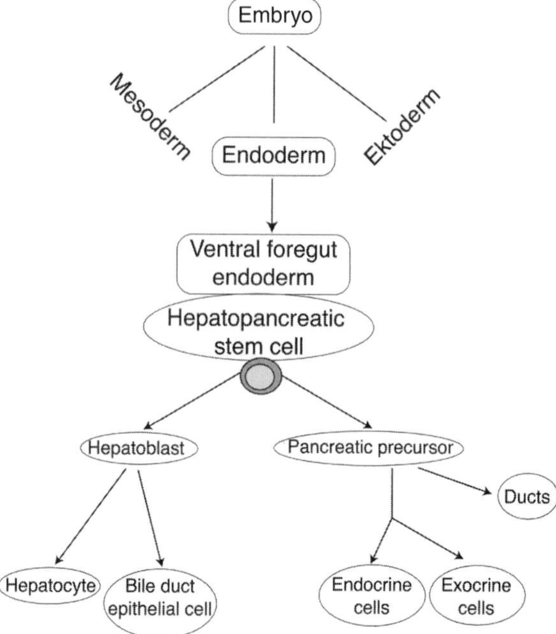

Figure 44–2. *Hypothetical embryonic lineage relationships between liver and pancreas.* The differentiation sequence from the totipotent endoderm to the liver and pancreatic lineages is depicted. The ventral foregut endoderm cell that produces both pancreas and liver during development may persist as a hepatopancreatic stem cell in adult life.

Liver Repopulation with Bone Marrow–Derived Progenitors. Recent work has documented that the adult bone marrow of mammals contains cells with a variety of differentiation capacities. The HSC generating all blood cell lineages has been known for many years to reside in this compartment. However, bone marrow also contains mesenchymal stem cells capable of differentiating into chondrocytes, osteoblasts, and other connective tissue cell types.[93–96] HSCs are nonadherent; mesenchymal stem cells adhere to plastic dishes in tissue culture and can be expanded there. A population of primitive, nonadherent cells characterized by their ability to pump the DNA-staining dye Hoechst can generate both muscle cells and hematopoiesis.[97,98] Thus, adult bone marrow had been shown to produce a variety of tissue types of mesodermal origin. In 1999, Petersen *et al.* first suggested that bone marrow also contained epithelial precursors.[99] Bone marrow and whole liver transplantation in genetically distinct animals were used to demonstrate that a portion of liver oval cells were donor derived after induction with AAF. Theise *et al.* showed that bone marrow derived hepatocytes also exist in the mouse and that oval cell induction was not required for this phenomenon.[100] More recently, several reports demonstrated that donor-derived epithelial cells are also in human patients that have undergone a gender-mismatched bone marrow transplantation.[101–103] In all these studies, the epithelial nature of the cells was demonstrated morphologically and by the expression of hepatocyte-specific markers.

HSCs as Hepatocyte Precursors Cell sorting experiments and the transplantation of purified HSCs of the c-kit^{high}Thy^{lo}Lin^{neg}Sca-1$^+$ (KTLS) phenotype and at limiting dilution showed that the primitive HSC was the bone marrow cell responsible for the donor-derived hepatocytes in *Fah* knockout mice.[104] This study also demonstrated extensive liver repopulation and a complete correction of the metabolic liver disease hereditary tyrosinemia,[104] thus demonstrating conclusively that bone marrow–derived hepatocytes function normally. The metabolic correction involved hepatocyte-specific parameters such as plasma amino acid levels, bilirubin conjugation, and excretion and serum transaminase levels.

By performing single-cell transplants, Krause *et al.* have showed that a single HSC not only could reconstitute the hematopoietic system of recipient mice but also could contribute to multiple tissues, including liver epithelium.[105] Interestingly, in this experiment, donor cell markers were found only in rare hepatic ducts, not hepatocytes. It should also be noted that the bone marrow stem cell type used was not isolated using the KTLS phenotype; instead, it used a very different protocol.[106] Therefore, it is not known whether the single-cell reconstitution with a KTLS stem cell would produce similar results.

Recently, it has been suggested that human HSCs, particularly those isolated from cord blood, can also produce hepatocyte-like cells in a xenotransplantation setting. Human CD34$^+$ cord blood cells were engrafted into nonobese diabetic severe-combined immunodeficiency (NOD-SCID) mice after low dose irradiation using the standard procedure.[107–111] If such animals were then exposed to liver injury—particularly carbon tetrachloride, human cells that produce albumin—a hepatocyte marker can be found at low frequency (<1/1,000). This finding suggests that human HSCs may also be able to produce hepatocytes, especially after injury. This finding has been reported independently by multiple groups.[107,111] It has been suggested that only a subpopulation of HSCs positive for the receptor for the complement molecule C1q (C1qR(p)) is capable of generating hepatocytes.[111] However, because of the rarity of the human albumin-producing cells, it is unknown whether these the cord blood–derived cells express only some hepatocyte markers or whether they are true hepatocytes with all requisite functions.

MAPCs as Hepatocyte Progenitors Despite the evidence that KTLS HSCs are the primary cell type responsible for the emergence of bone marrow–derived liver epithelial cells *in vivo,* they are not the only bone marrow–derived cells that can differentiate toward the hepatocytic lineage. Multipotent adult progenitor cells (MAPCs) are a unique population of adult stem cells that can be isolated from the marrow of multiple mammalian species, including human, rat, and mouse.[112–114] MAPCs are generated in culture by plating nonhematopoietic adherent cells and serial passaging. They are telomerase positive and grow stably in culture for many passages if kept at low density. These cells have properties similar to embryonic stem cells in that they can be differentiated toward many lineages *in vitro* under the appropriate conditions.[115] A protocol was developed that permitted the efficient induction of hepatocyte gene expression in human and murine MAPCs.[114] These conditions included culture on Matrigel and the use of fibroblast growth factor 4 (FGF-4) and HGF. Over two weeks, most MAPCs changed their phenotype and expressed multiple hepatocyte functions, including urea synthesis, albumin secretion, and phenobarbital-inducible cytochrome p450 induction.

MAPCs have also been transplanted *in vivo.* First, they were injected into blastocysts in a procedure similar to the one done with embryonic stem cells.[112] Embryos generated in this fashion had quantitative MAPC contribution to many tissues, including liver. When transplanted into adult mice, MAPC-derived cells were also found in liver and appeared to be hepatocytes. Although these MAPC-derived liver epithelial cells expressed hepatocyte markers, their ability to functionally correct liver disease has not yet been tested.

Physiologic Significance of Bone Marrow–Derived Hepatocytes Despite the unambiguous finding that fully functional bone marrow–derived hepatocytes exist, there has been considerable controversy regarding their functional importance in liver injury. In one model, illustrated in Fig. 44–3A, replenishment of liver cells from the bone marrow is an important injury response pathway, particularly in progenitor dependent regeneration (oval cell response). A hepatocyte would be generated either by direct differentiation of an HSC or by indirect differentiation through an oval cell intermediate. The opposing model, illustrated in Fig. 44–3B, suggests that oval cell precursors reside only in the liver (tissue resident stem cell) and that the bone marrow contributes few liver epithelial cells, even during injury. To determine whether liver damage enhances the transition of HSCs to hepatocytes, the degree of cell replacement after a bone marrow transplant in mice has been measured not only in healthy animals but also in the context of preexisting hepatocyte injury[116] or oval cell regeneration.[74] Importantly, the frequency of bone marrow-derived hepatocytes was not higher in the acute liver injury seen in Fah knockout mice than in healthy control livers.[116] In addition, no contribution from bone marrow precursors to the oval cell reaction induced by the chemical DDC was detected.[74,117] Together, these results indicate that HSCs do not serve as epithelial cell precursors in all forms of hepatic injury. It remains to be determined whether HSCs play a significant role in any clinically relevant hepatic injury models.

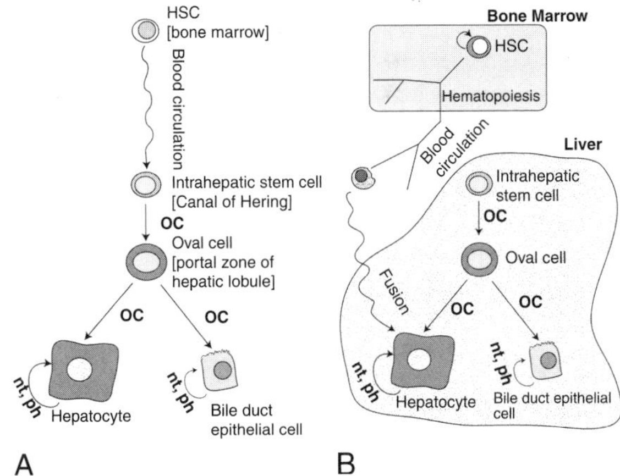

Figure 44–3. Models for the role of bone marrow resident stem cells in liver cell maintenance. The different kinds of liver regeneration (see text) are indicated. (A) Transdifferentiation model. The anatomic location of the cells is given in square brackets. HSCs generate hepatocytes by trafficking to the liver through the blood circulation to then engraft and differentiate into epithelial cell precursors (intrahepatic stem cells). These cells can become activated during progenitor-dependent liver regeneration (oval cell response) and produce oval cells. Oval cells differentiate into hepatocytes or bile ducts. (B) Fusion model. There is no direct lineage relationship between HSCs and liver epithelial cells. Cell fusion among circulating progeny of the HSCs and hepatocytes are responsible for the emergence of bone marrow–derived liver epithelial cells. Progenitor-dependent liver regeneration (oc) occurs by activation of intrahepatic liver stem cells, which are not derived from the bone marrow (nt: normal tissue turnover, ph: regeneration after partial hepatectomy, and oc: progenitor-dependent regeneration or oval cell response).

Mechanism for the Formation of Bone Marrow Stem Cell–Derived Hepatocytes Three basic mechanisms for the repopulation of liver by bone marrow–derived cells can be considered. First, bone marrow could theoretically harbor a specialized endodermal stem cell capable of producing hepatocytes and other epithelial cells. This cell would be analogous to the mesenchymal stem cell, which produces mesodermal derivatives such as muscle, cartilage, and fat.[93,118] Second, hepatocytes and blood cells could be derived from the same stem cell by hierarchical differentiation (Fig. 44–3A). Until recently, this has been the hypothesis favored by many in the field.[119] Third, bone marrow–derived hepatocytes could potentially be derived not from differentiation but from cell fusion (Fig. 44–3B). This possibility was raised by the observation that hematopoietic cells could spontaneously fuse with embryonic stem cells *in vitro* and then produce multiple tissues in chimeric mouse embryos.[120,121]

To address these hypotheses, transplantation experiments were designed in which genetic markers for both donor marrow and host hepatocytes were used in the *Fah* knockout model.[122] The results from this study were unambiguous: Most bone marrow–derived hepatocytes contained genetic information from both the donor and the host, indicating cell fusion. Cytogenetic analysis of female → male gender-mismatched transplants indicated a high frequency of tetraploid XXXY and hexaploid XXXXYY karyotypes, as predicted for fusion. Importantly, similar experiments were independently performed by another laboratory and confirmed that fusion was the predominant mechanism for the derivation of hepatocytes from bone marrow stem cells in the *Fah* knockout model.[122,123]

It remains to be seen whether functional hepatocytes can derive from bone marrow progenitors by a fusion-independent mechanism (i.e., proper differentiation). A recent study using xenotransplantation of human cord blood cells into NOD-SCID mice suggests that the observed cells producing human albumin did not derive by fusion.[108]

CELLS THAT PRODUCE IN HEPATOCYTE AND BILE DUCT EPITHELIAL PHENOTYPES *IN VITRO*

Several *in vitro* models for hepatic stem cell growth and differentiation have been developed. Two general approaches to the *in vitro* study of liver stem cells can be distinguished. First, cell sorting can be used to isolate putative liver stem cells by cell surface markers. These cells can then be cultured, and their growth and differentiation potential can be determined *in vitro*. Second, immortal cell lines can be derived from liver tissue by extensive *in vitro* manipulation and growth. To date, little work has been done on the prospective isolation of hepatic progenitors by cell sorting. In contrast, putative liver progenitor cell lines from several mammalian species have been isolated and propagated in tissue culture, including mouse, rat, pig, and human. These *in vitro* systems have scientific and potential medical uses. The medical purpose is to generate large numbers of hepatocytes *in vitro* for therapeutic transplantation. The scientific aims are to understand the factors that control the differentiation of these cells into hepatocytes and biliary duct epithelium. A common theme, applying to sorted primary cells as well as immortal progenitor cell lines, is that these cells can express markers typical for both pancreatic and hepatic cell fates.

In addition to the creation of hepatocyte progenitor cell lines, several investigators have devised strategies to conditionally immortalize differentiated hepatocytes for *in vitro* expansion and subsequent transplantation.[124] To date, the only cell lines that have had documented therapeutic effects in animal models have been these cell lines or primary cultures derived from hepatocytes.[125–128]

Prospective Isolation of Hepatocyte Progenitors by Cell Sorting

A recent report described elegant work in which fetal mouse liver cells were fractionated by FACS and analyzed for their proliferative as well as differentiation capacity.[129] A multipotent population of cells was identified in E13.5 mouse liver. These cells were characterized as c-kit$^-$, CD45$^-$, c-met$^+$, Ter119$^-$, and CD49f$^{+/low}$. *In vitro,* they proliferated extensively and could be differentiated into either hepatocytic or biliary lineages. However, the same cells could also express multiple pancreatic markers when cultured long term or transplanted into a pancreatic environment *in vivo*. The genes expressed *in vitro* included endocrine markers (preproinsulin and preproglucagon), pancreas-specific transcription factors (pdx-1 and pax6), and exocrine markers (amylase-2 and lipase). The same group has recently used a similar sorting approach in neonatal mouse pancreas.[130] The c-kit$^-$, CD45$^-$, c-met$^+$, Ter119$^-$, and CD49f$^{+/low}$ cells from the pancreas were able to be differentiated into hepatocytes *in vitro.*

Rat Cell Lines

WB-344 Cell Line This cell line was clonogenically derived from nonparenchymal rat liver cells[131] and is probably the most intensely studied liver stem cell line.[132–135] WB3-44 cells are likely derived from canal of Hering cells.[131] Although WB-344 cells can be cultured indefinitely *in vitro,* they retain the ability to differentiate into morphologically normal hepatocytes after transplantation without forming tumors.[133] To date, WB-344 cells are the only cells to fulfill this stringent criterion to represent a true liver stem cell line. Nonetheless, little is known about the molecular mechanisms regulating the stem cell → hepatocyte transition, and liver repopulation with this cell line has not yet been reported.

Rat Oval Cell Lines Multiple laboratories have isolated oval cell lines from carcinogen-treated rats.[136–139] Consistent with the proposed role of oval cells in the formation of hepatocarcinoma, these cell lines form tumors upon transplantation into immunodeficient recipients. The isolation, culture, and transplantation of these cells have been well reviewed.[37]

Mouse Cell Lines. Although it is normally difficult to establish permanent cell lines from mouse liver, such lines can be established routinely from transgenic mice that overexpress a constitutively active form of the HGF receptor c-met.[140,141] Two morphologically distinct types of cells emerge from such cultures. Both grow extensively in culture

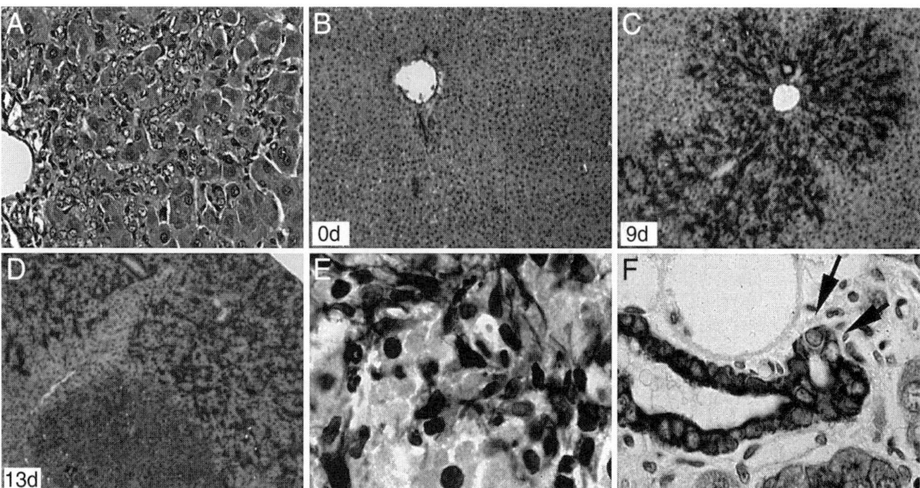

Figure 45–3. *Cellular events during the early stages of hepatic stem cell activation and differentiation.* (A) Infiltration of oval cells into the liver acinus (H&E staining). (B–D) Expansion of oval cells (GGT staining) during the 2 weeks following PH. Note the rapid expansion of the oval cells at 9 and 13 days as well as the appearance of a focus of basophilic hepatocytes that has lost the GGT staining at 13 days. (E) Example of the close association of desmin-positive stellate cells and oval cells during the early stages of oval cell expansions. (F) Early differentiation (marker: specific cytochrome P450 enzyme) of oval cells into a hepatocyte (arrows) (modified from Golding *et al.*[125] with permission). (Please see CD-ROM for color version of this figure.)

electron microscopy to evaluate the electron-dense periductular basement membrane, the luminal structure of biliary ductules and interhepatocytic canaliculi, and the hepatocyte-specific organelles (glycogen and peroxisomes)[9,24,25] (Fig. 45–6).

Oval cells, the immediate progeny of hepatic stem cells, first appear and accumulate most intensely in and near portal tracts; only later do they spread into the lobular parenchyma.[3,4,7] Numerous electron microscopic studies (sometimes coupled with the injection of electron-dense material into the biliary duct system) have shown that oval cells do not exist as individual cells isolated from one another; rather, they are organized into small ductules.[3,4,9,26] Oval cell ductules are surrounded by a basement membrane continuous with that of the preexisting biliary duct system, and they contain a lumen continuous with the lumens of both bile ducts and interhepatocytic bile canaliculi.[3,4,9,26] Oval cells, therefore, form uctules that are direct extensions of existing terminal biliary ductules, and the oval cell population is a great expansion of some or all of the cells that normally form the terminal biliary ductules. Periductular cells, which approximate the ductular basement membrane external to the terminal ductules, proliferate with the expansion of the population of oval cells, and most of the proliferating periductular cells are desmin-positive portal stellate cells[27] (Figs. 45–3E and 45–6D). Furthermore, although a few hematopoietic stem cells are known to reside in the adult liver[28] and some of them are undoubtedly located in portal tracts, there is little evidence that hematopoietic stem cells from bone marrow or resident in the liver are major cellular precursors of either oval cells or hepatocytes.[15–17] The evidence strongly supports the view that some or all of the epithelial cells of the terminal biliary ductules are the stem cells that generate oval cells and, through them, hepatocytes. The question remains as to whether only some or all of the cells in the canals of Hering are liver epithelial stem cells. Studies combining confocal and electron microscopy of terminal biliary ductules and oval cells that develop in rats exposed to the full Solt-Farber protocol (i.e., DEN+AAF+PH)[6] suggested that oval cells may be derived from a few "blast-like" cells embedded in the epithelium of small bile ductules without touching either the ductular basement membrane or the lumen.[24,25] These blast-like cells were hypothesized to be the stem cells from which oval cells arise.[24,25] However, subsequent studies using the modified Solt-Farber protocol (AAF+PH)[5] with low doses of AAF have not shown the blast-like cells[9]; rather, they suggest that most cells composing the canals of Hering are liver epithelial stem cells. Further studies on this point are necessary.

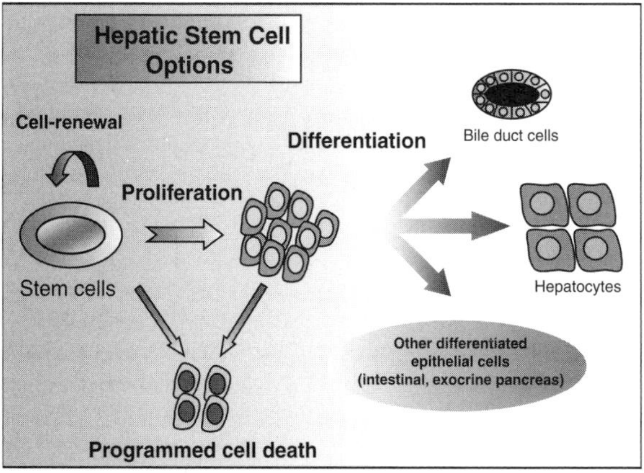

Figure 45–4. *Differentiation options for a liver stem cell.* (Please see CD-ROM for color version of this figure.)

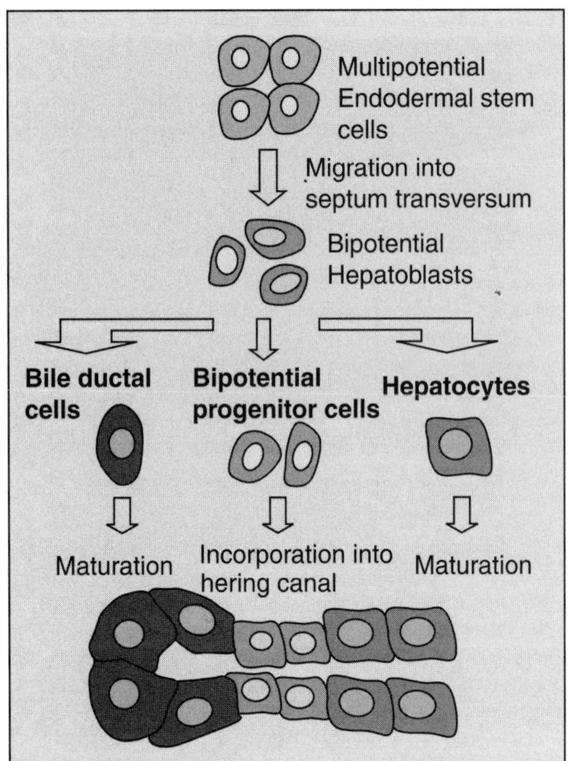

Figure 45–5. *General temporal sequence of the differentiation of hepatocytes and bile epithelial cells.* These cells are differentiating from the multipotential endodermal cells of the hepatic diverticulum through the development of the hepatoblasts with the bipotential differentiation option (modified from Grisham *et al.*[3] with permission). (Please see CD-ROM for color version of this figure.)

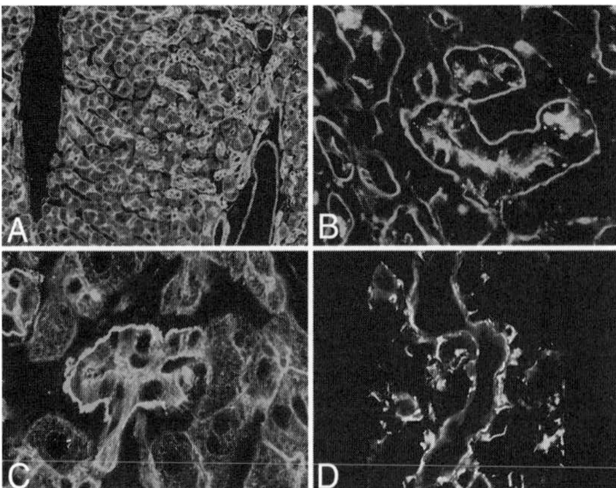

Figure 45–6. *Immunohistochemistry of the expanding oval cells 10 days after PH in the AAF+PH model.* Low power micrograph of the liver lobule stained for cytokeratin and laminin. (A) Numerous ductules surrounded by laminin are infiltrating the liver parenchyma toward the central vein. (B) High magnification of a ductule at the infiltration border showing an oval cell attached to a hepatocyte. Oval cell ductules in the liver lobule were stained for laminin and α-fetoprotein. (C) Note that α-fetoprotein is only observed inside the basement membrane. (D) Oval cell ductules were stained for laminin and desmin. Note the close association between the desmin-positive stellate cells and the expanding oval cell ductules (reproduced from Paku *et al.*[26] with permission). (Please see CD-ROM for color version of this figure.)

Sequential Cellular Events During Stem Cell Activation

The studies using confocal laser scanning microscopy and electron microscopy, with low doses of AAF in the AAF+PH model,[5] shed new light on the sequence of cellular events that follow stem cell activation.[9,26] Stem cell activation is followed by proliferation of biliary epithelial cells located in the canals of Hering, with subsequent elongation of terminal biliary ductules to generate the new population of oval cells, as noted previously[9,26] (Fig. 45–7). Adjacent stellate cells also proliferate and maintain their close association with the basement membrane that surrounds oval cells[9,26] (Figs. 45–3E and 45–6D). At low AAF doses, numerous small, basophilic, albumin-expressing hepatocytes emerge at the interface between oval cells and preexisting hepatocytes, and the new hepatocytes integrate smoothly into hepatic plates.[9] Acquisition of hepatocyte differentiation is temporally associated with the fragmentation of the periductular basement membrane and the disappearance of stellate cells.[9] Simultaneously, the lateral expansions of the ductular lumen form intercellular canaliculi (which express CD26), and the affected oval cells enlarge and develop stacks of endoplasmic reticulum; large, dense mitochondria; peroxisomes; and glycogen particles to form intermediate cells.[9] Intracellular organelles of intermediate cells gradually acquire the ultrastructural configurations typical of fully differentiated hepatocytes.[9,26]

Oval cell proliferation and hepatocyte differentiation differ from this pattern when high doses of AAF are administered in the AAF+PH model[8,9] or in the DEN+AAF+PH model.[24,25] Under these circumstances, the oval cell population expands greatly to form large masses of elongated, tortuous ductules that may penetrate deeply into the lobular parenchyma[3,4] (Fig. 45–3B through 45–3D). After high doses of AAF, differentiation of hepatocytes occurs focally, and foci of small, basophilic hepatocytes appear among the accumulated tangles of oval cells.[3,4,8,9] In either situation, hepatocytic differentiation always begins at the tips of expanded ductules where oval cells abut the preexisting hepatocytes in the lobular parenchyma.[9,25]

These observations suggest that both low and high doses of AAF activate stem cells and stimulate oval cell proliferation but that the accumulation of oval cells to large populations that expand into the lobular parenchyma is maximal at high AAF doses. In contrast, these studies show that hepatocyte differentiation from activated oval cells is most efficient at low doses of AAF. At high AAF doses, many oval cells undergo apoptosis,[8] suggesting a reciprocal relationship between differentiation and death of oval cells. High doses of AAF also favor aberrant differentiation of oval cells to form glands containing intestinal epithelium and pancreatic acinar epithelium.[5,29]

In optimal circumstances, hepatocytes may be so efficiently generated from stem cells in canals of Hering that oval cells are not morphologically noticeable. In fact, cells of the

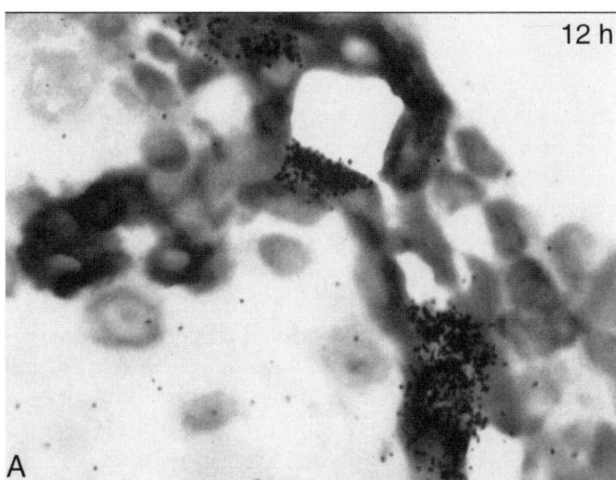

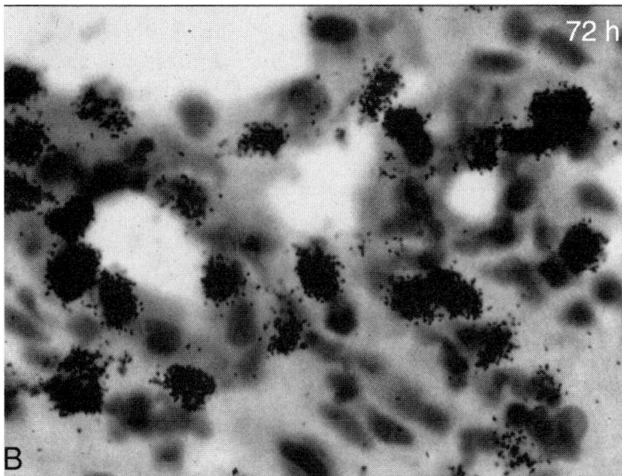

Figure 45–7. *Activation of liver stem cells in the AAF+PH model.* Activation is indicated by the proliferation of the small biliary cells. Results from a combination of immunohistochemistry with the OV-6 antibody (oval cell marker) and autoradiography following [3H]thymidine administration (A) 12 hours and (B) 72 hours after PH. Note that all thymidine-labeled cells are OV-6 positive at 12 hours. (Please see CD-ROM for color version of this figure.)

terminal biliary ductules transiently appear to start the program that leads to oval cell activation and proliferation by up-regulating c-kit expression even after PH alone (without AAF),[11] although this cellular process is overtaken by the rapid and extensive proliferation of residual hepatocytes in this circumstance.

Extracellular Matrix

Major components of the matrix of portal tracts are the basement membranes that enclose bile ducts, arteries, veins, and nerves. The periductular basement membrane is an electron-dense structure rich in laminins and containing type IV collagen, perlecan, entactin, tenascin, and dystroglycan (for reviews, see Martinez-Hernandez and Amenta[30,31]). Peribiliary basement membrane extends to the smallest ductules, but terminates sharply where the small ductular epithelial cells of the canals of Hering abut and form junctional complexes with hepatocytes at the portal ends of hepatic plates.[3,4,9,25,26] Visible basement membrane is lacking in the space of Disse of the hepatic lobular parenchyma, although some of the component molecules of basement membrane are present.[30] Numerous mesenchymal cells, closely related to interlobular stellate cells, which express desmin and α-smooth muscle actin, surround bile ducts in apposition to the external surface of the basement membrane.[9,25,26]

Activation of liver stem cells in the AAF+PH model is indicated by the proliferation of the small biliary epithelial cells and the expansion of the terminal segments of the biliary ducts, as noted previously, to produce the oval cell reaction[9,26] (Fig. 45–7). However, stem cell activation is first signaled by the up-regulation of the growth factor–receptor combination stem cell factor (SCF)–c-kit (see later sections of this chapter). Proliferation and elongation of the terminal ductules is initially accompanied by the proliferation of periductular stellate cells and the maintenance of a prominent basement membrane.[9,26] Subsequently, the basement membrane undergoes dissolution, as is evident both in confocal images in which the basement membrane is decorated with antilaminin antibody and in electron micrographs in which the electron-dense structure of the basement membrane is visible.[9] The levels of urokinase-type plasminogen activator (uPA) transcript and protein are up-regulated in periportal hepatocytes within a few minutes after PH (in the absence of AAF administration), remaining elevated for 4 days.[32] Up-regulation of urokinase-plasminogen activator receptor (uPAR) and plasminogen activator inhibitor-1 (PAI-1); the production of plasmin; and the degradation of fibrinogen, laminin, entactin, and fibronectin rapidly follow.[32] Expression of promatrix metalloprotein proteinases (MMP)-2 and -9 was also rapidly up-regulated in the immediate periportal hepatocytes after PH in the absence of AAF treatment.[33] In sharp contrast, exposure to AAF alone leads to the up-regulation of uPA, uPAR, and PAI-1 only in cells of the terminal bile ducts.[34] Subsequent PH in the AAF+PH model leads to heightened expression of the components of the plasmin-generating system in terminal biliary epithelial cells, associated with the production of plasmin and fibrin lysis.[34] *In situ* zymography on sections of tissue demonstrates that the breakdown of casein (in agarose) occurred only over accumulated oval cells and not over hepatocytes in the adjacent parenchyma.[34] Although activation of latent MMP was not analyzed in this study, the up-regulation of proteolysis in oval cells is temporally associated with the lysis of periductular basement membrane,[9,26] suggesting that MMPs are also involved. Furthermore, the central role of uPA expression in the amplification of oval cells is indicated by the observation that infusion of uPA into AAF-exposed rats enhances oval cell proliferation.[35]

Isolated–Cultured Liver Epithelial Cells with Stem-like Properties

Acquisition of hepatocyte differentiation after transplanting isolated cells into the liver of a recipient animal has been used to evaluate the stem cell properties of isolated cells.[10,36] In these studies, recipient animals may suffer from a lethal hepatic failure, the endpoint being the ability of the transplanted cells to rescue the recipient animals by repopulating the liver's hepatocyte population.[10,36] When transplanted into recipients with lethal hepatic failure, fully differentiated hepatocytes from healthy donors have excellent ability to rescue recipients.[36] Liver cell populations containing fully differentiated hepatocytes possess a major functional property of stem cells—the ability to cycle repeatedly and generate large populations of differentiated progeny, as is illustrated by a study in which hepatocytes were transplanted serially among recipients with lethal hepatic failure.[37] Interpretation of these results is complicated by the difficulty of isolating pure populations of hepatocytes. It is possible that the results of serial transplantation of hepatocytes could come from a minor population of contaminating stem cells, since the efficiency of long-term survival and proliferation of intrasplenically transplanted hepatocytes correlated with the proportion of oval cells in the transplanted population.[38]

Oval cells with phenotypic properties of liver stem or progenitor cells have been isolated from diseased livers, and the small oval cells can be separated from contaminating hepatocytes.[39] However, the first reported transplantation study employed a heterogeneous population of nonparenchymal liver cells enriched in oval cells (cells expressing the oval cell phenotype composed more than 75% of the population) recovered from livers of August Copenhagen Irish (ACI) rats fed a choline-deficient and AAF-supplemented diet.[40] Donor cells transplanted into the livers of male Lewis × ACI F1 rats fed a choline-deficient diet for 7 days and subjected to PH just prior to cell transplant were identified in frozen sections of livers receiving cell transplants by their lack of reactivity to ACI anti-LE alloantiserum.[40] Intrahepatic foci of cells derived from transplanted cells expressed immunophenotypes indicative of a mixture of both immature and mature hepatocytes, suggesting that the transplanted oval cells had acquired hepatocyte differentiation.[40] After transplantation into livers of dipeptidyl peptidase (DPP)-IV-deficient rats (which lack expression of DPP-IV on bile canalicular membranes of differentiated hepatocytes), oval cells recovered from the livers of galactosamine-treated, DPP-IV-proficient rats engrafted into hepatic plates, enlarged to the size of host hepatocytes, and acquired the ability to express canalicular DPP-IV (which allowed their distinction from host hepatocytes) and albumin but not α-fetoprotein.[41] These results indicate that the transplanted oval cells differentiated into hepatocytes *in vivo.* Oval cells recovered from livers of Long-Evans Cinnamon rats (which accumulate cytotoxic copper in hepatocytes because they carry a mutation in the *ATP7B* gene) differentiated into albumin-producing hepatocytes after they were transplanted into livers of Long-Evans Cinnamon × Nagase F1 analbuminemic rats (Nagase rats have a mutated *albumin* gene and do not synthesize albumin).[42] Hepatocyte differentiation of transplanted oval cells was associated with a mild elevation of serum albumin levels in recipients.[42] A highly purified population of oval cells recovered from the livers of mice treated with 3,5-diethoxycarbonyl-1,4-dihydrocollidine (DDC) rescued $FAH^{-/-}$ mice from lethal hepatic failure, indicating that the oval cells acquired hepatic differentiation and corrected the hepatic functional deficits.[43] Competitive repopulation studies showed that transplanted oval cells repopulated the diseased liver as efficiently as differentiated hepatocytes.[43] Intermediate cells (incompletely differentiated, small, hepatocyte precursor cells), recovered from nodular aggregates that develop in livers of rats exposed to retrorsine and subjected to PH, acquired complete hepatocyte differentiation (correlated with up-regulation of albumin and transferrin and down-regulation of α-fetoprotein) when they were transplanted into livers of syngeneic, DPP-IV-deficient, Fischer 344 rats.[44] In this situation, the fully differentiated hepatocytes that may have contaminated the isolated population of intermediate cells were not able to proliferate because of retrorsine-induced damage. Together, these results provide direct evidence for the derivation of hepatocyte lineages from oval cells and intermediate cells and, therefore, from liver stem cells.

The problem posed by the lack of purity of transplanted cell populations can be addressed using cloned lines of liver epithelial cells. Although it is not possible to establish cloned lines of normal, fully differentiated hepatocytes, cloned lines of small, poorly differentiated epithelial cells have been established both from the livers of healthy adult rats and from the livers of rats that are the site of the oval cell reaction.[3,4] Many of the cloned liver epithelial cell lines express phenotypic properties similar to the major phenotypic properties of oval cells *in vivo* irrespective of whether the cell lines were derived from livers of healthy animals or from livers in which oval cells had proliferated.[3,4] After tagging with a retroviral marker carrying the neomycin resistance gene and the gene for bacterial β-galactosidase, which distinguished transplanted and host cells, cells of the WB-344 line engrafted into hepatic plates and acquired differentiated properties identical to those of adjacent host hepatocytes when transplanted into livers of healthy Fischer 344 rats.[45,46] WB-F344 cells (derived from normal Fischer 344 rats) similarly engrafted and acquired hepatocyte differentiation when transplanted into livers of DPP-IV-deficient Fischer 344 rats; progeny of transplanted cells expressed DPP-IV on their bile canalicular membranes, but the host hepatocytes did not.[46] When transplanted into the livers of Nagase analbuminemic rats, WB-F344 cells formed clusters of albumin-producing hepatocytes among albumin-negative hepatocytes.[47] In contrast, RLEϕ13 rat liver epithelial cells, also derived from Fischer 344 rats and phenotypically similar to WB-F344 cells, integrated into hepatic plates but did not acquire hepatocyte differentiation after transplantation into the livers of syngeneic Fischer 344 rats.[48] Lack of *in vivo* differentiation of transplanted RLEϕ13 cells suggests that they may be less "activated" as oval cells than are WB-F344 cells.

RLEϕ13 cells stopped proliferating, enlarged with increased cytoplasmic area, and up-regulated transcripts for α-fetoprotein, albumin, multidrug resistance, and *c-myc* genes during a period of 72 hours after exposure to TGF-β1 *in vitro.*[49] When WB-F344 cells were cultured on collagen in a medium containing sodium butyrate, their proliferation was inhibited and the affected cells enlarged.[50] Cytoplasmic expansion was associated with reduced nuclear-cytoplasmic ratio and increased cytoplasmic complexity.[50] Cellular protein synthesis increased in the altered cells, and dexamethasone-inducible tyrosine aminotransferase activity, modulated by insulin and L-tyrosine in a manner specific for hepatocytes, was activated.[50] In contrast, when WB-F344 cells were cultured on Matrigel-coated plates, they responded to sodium butyrate exposure by forming duct-like structures that expressed cytokeratin 19, BDS7, γ-glutamyl transpeptidase, and aquaporin, phenotypic properties of cholangiocytes.[51] Exposure of cells of the RLEϕ13 line to medium containing 5′azadeoxycytidine; fibroblast growth factor (FGF) 1,2; oncostatin M (OSM); and hepatocyte growth factor (HGF), with or without dexamethasone, caused them to stop proliferating, enlarge, and develop increased cytoplasmic complexity.[52] Coordinately, the treated cells expressed multiple hepatocyte phenotypes, including albumin and tyrosine aminotransferase, and several hepatocyte-enriched transcription factors, including HNF-4. Cells of the hepatic stem-like (HSL) rat liver epithelial line express albumin, α-fetoprotein, cytokeratin, transferrin, tyrosine aminotransferase, and γ-glutamyl transpeptidase when co-cultured *in vitro* with isolated hepatic stellate cells.[53]

Cloned lines of epithelial cells isolated from livers of rats that were the site of oval cell proliferation react similarly to epithelial cells from healthy liver to *in vitro* stimuli to differentiate. Exposure of cells of the oval cell lines OC/CDE to sodium butyrate *in vitro* caused them to stop proliferating, increase in size, and express a few hepatocyte phenotypes (albumin was expressed in about 30% of the cells) and enhanced activities of glucose-6-phosphatase and γ-glutamyl transpeptidase but not of tyrosine transpeptidase.[54] When cultured in a three-dimensional matrix of gelled collagen I and supported by a fibroblast feeder layer, cells of the LE/2 and LE/6 oval cell lines slowly acquired hepatocyte features, including characteristic organellar ultrastructures and expression of albumin and cytokeratins 8 and 18.[55] The same cells yielded structures resembling bile ducts in cultures lacking a feeder layer but supplemented with HGF and keratinocyte growth factor.[55]

MOLECULAR FEATURES

Transcription Factors During Hepatogenesis

Much progress has been made in the understanding of the network of transcription factors that participate in liver development (for reviews, see Zaret[56] and Duncan[57]). Recent studies have provided important insight into the preferential requirement of certain transcription factors at each stage of hepatogenesis. For example, HNF-3β (foxa2) and Gata4 are necessary for the earliest stage of hepatic competency of the endoderm, whereas targeted disruption of Hex or Prox1 results in dramatic loss of parenchyma at early stages (specification and liver bud formation) of liver development.[58,59] Transcriptional regulation of hepatocyte-specific gene expression is, however, predominantly controlled by a set of transcription factors that includes HNF-3 (foxa), HNF-1, HNF-4, HNF-6, and CCAAT/enhancer-binding protein (C/EBP) (for reviews, see Cereghini[60] and Schrem *et al.*[61]). Genetic analyses in mice have shown that HNF-3β (foxa2), with HNF-3α and HNF-3γ (foxa2 and foxa3), is required for the full transcriptional activation of many liver-specific genes in addition to the development of the foregut endoderm from which both liver and pancreas are derived.[56,57,62] In addition, HNF-3β and HNF-3α regulate the expression of HNF-4α/HNF-1α.[63] However, HNF-3β (foxa2), HNF-3α, and HNF-3γ are dispensable for maintaining the differentiated state of the adult hepatocyte.[64–66] Although targeted disruption of C/EBPα or HNF-1α has no obvious effect on the development of the liver, the loss of the genes results in major hepatic dysfunctions.[67,68] These results emphasize the importance of C/EBPα and HNF-1α in maintaining the differentiated phenotype of adult hepatocytes. HNF-4α has traditionally been placed at the upper levels of the hierarchical order of the transcriptional factors controlling hepatocyte differentiation.[56,57] Targeted disruption of HNF-4α results in functional disruption of the visceral endoderm during gastrulation and in embryonal arrest prior to onset of hepatogenesis.[68,69] In experiments using tetraploid embryo complementation to provide wild-type extraembryonic endoderm, it was shown that embryos generated from HNF-4$\alpha^{-/-}$ ES cells were viable up to embryonic day 12 (E12).[70] Moreover, a comparison of livers derived from wild-type and HNF-4$\alpha^{-/-}$ ES cells revealed neither morphologic nor histologic differences. However, expression of genes characteristic for the hepatocytic lineage were either down-regulated or undetectable in hepatoblasts derived from HNF-4$\alpha^{-/-}$ ES cells when compared with those from the wild-type cells.[71] Similar results have been obtained in mice harboring conditional null alleles.[71–73] Together, these data support the central role of HNF-4α in hepatocyte differentiation, a function accomplished by activating a cascade of transcription factors that constitute the necessary network needed to define the gene expression profile of the adult hepatocyte.

In the mouse, hepatoblasts start to generate bile duct cells (cholangiocytes) around embryonic day 13.5.[74] Two transcription factors, HNF-6 and HNF-1β, are of central importance in biliary development.[75–77] The biliary epithelial cells form the intrahepatic and extrahepatic bile ducts and the gallbladder. Previous work has shown that the onecut transcription factor HNF-6 is expressed in hepatoblasts and in the gallbladder primordium.[68,78] Clotman *et al.*[77] showed that HNF-6 is also expressed in the biliary epithelial cells of the developing intrahepatic bile ducts and further investigated the effect of targeted disruption of the HNF-6 allele on biliary tract development by analyzing the phenotype of HNF-$6^{(-/-)}$ mice. In the HNF-$6^{-/-}$ mice, the gallbladder was absent, the extrahepatic bile ducts were abnormal, and the development of the intrahepatic bile ducts was disrupted in the prenatal period.[76] The morphology of the intrahepatic bile ducts in the HNF-$6^{-/-}$ mice was identical to that seen in mice in which the *HNF-1*β gene was conditionally inactivated in the liver.[78] Moreover, *HNF-1*β expression is down-regulated in the intrahepatic bile ducts of HNF-$6^{(-/-)}$ mice, and HNF-6 can stimulate the HNF-1β promoter.[76] These data are consistent with the notion that HNF-6 is essential for differentiation and morphogenesis of the biliary tract and that intrahepatic bile duct development is controlled by a HNF-6 → HNF-1β cascade.[76] Inactivation of the forkhead transcription factor *Foxf1* gene in the mesenchyme of septum transversum is decisive for the development of the extrahepatic bile ducts and the gallbladder, suggesting that this transcription factor may either directly or indirectly control the HNF-6 → HNF-1β cascade in the hepatoblasts.[79]

Transcription Factors and Liver Stem Cells

Compared to the extensive body of work on transcription factors in hepatogenesis, particularly in the mouse, knowledge about the role of these factors in hepatic stem cell biology is sparse. The first studies that attempted to characterize the sequential expression of liver-enriched transcription factors at the earliest stages of hepatic stem cell activation and expansion employed the AAF+PH model in the rat.[80,81] Expression of liver-enriched transcriptional factors (HNF-1α and -β; HNF-3α, -β and -γ; HNF-4; C/EBPα and -β; and DBP) was analyzed during oval cell proliferation and differentiation and compared to the expression of these factors during the late stages of hepatic ontogenesis. The steady-state mRNA levels of four liver-enriched transcriptional factors (HNF-1α, HNF-3α, HNF-4, and C/EBPβ) gradually decrease during the late period of embryonic liver development, and the levels of three factors (HNF-1β, HNF-3β, and DBP) increase. In the normal adult rat, liver expression of all of these transcription factors is restricted to hepatocytes. However, during early stages of oval cell proliferation, cells of both small and large bile ducts start to express HNF-1α, HNF-1β, HNF-3γ, C/EBP, and DBP but not HNF-4. Later, all of these factors are highly expressed in the proliferating oval cells. It is noteworthy that expression of HNF-4 is first observed when oval cells differentiate morphologically and functionally into hepatocytes (Fig. 45–8).

These data support the notion that the up-regulation of the "establishment" factors (HNF-1 and -3) may be an important step in oval cell activation. Furthermore, the data suggest that HNF-4 may be responsible for the final commitment of the oval cells to differentiate into hepatocytes, similar to the hepatoblast–hepatocyte transition. However, with the exception of HNF-4 and C/EBPβ, all of these transcription factors are expressed in mature bile ducts and ductules at the earliest stages of oval cell proliferation. This observation also suggests that a large fraction of the biliary epithelial cells can respond to a combination of loss of liver mass and impaired regenerative capacity of existing hepatocytes by expressing the "establishment transcriptional factors." In this context, it is important to note that available evidence suggests that oval cells are derived from the smallest branches, the terminal bile ductules, of the biliary tree.[3,9,26] It is, therefore, likely that molecules in addition to transcriptional factors determine the segment of the biliary ducts that constitute the hepatic stem cell compartment. It is not clear what these other components are, but the differential expression of growth factor–receptor systems, the capacity for extended proliferation, and the interactions with specific cell types (e.g., stellate cells) and extracellular matrix molecules may constitute significant determinants. However, it is possible to conclude that expression of a selective combination of transcription factors (e.g., HNF-1 and -3) is necessary but not sufficient for the activation of the hepatic stem cell compartment. In addition, the current data indicate that, in contrast to the continuous differentiation process of the parenchymal liver cells during ontogenesis, the differentiation of the liver stem cells into hepatocytes may occur in two discontinuous steps. The first step is the activation of the facultative stem cell compartment from which the oval cells arise as a distinct phenotype. Early oval cells form a multipotential population of amplifying cells (i.e., capable of differentiating into intestinal and exocrine pancreatic lineages in addition to hepatocytes and biliary epithelial cells). The second and possibly irreversible step in the differentiation of oval cells into hepatocytic lineage appears to be the "sudden" up-regulation of HNF-4. The molecular mechanism or mechanisms controlling the conversion of early oval cells into the hepatocytic lineage is not understood, underscoring the importance of further research in this area.

Cytokines and Growth Factors in Liver Stem Cell Activation and Expansion

Several growth factors and cytokines and their cognate receptors are centrally involved in the complex molecular pathways that regulate both the embryonic development of the liver[82] and the repair of the liver following injury (for reviews, see Michalopoulos and DeFrances,[1] Diehl,[83] and Galun and Axelrod [84]). Liver repair almost always occurs in the setting of the hepatic acute phase reaction, a central component of which is the elevated expression of tumor necrosis factor-α (TNF-α).[85]

In turn, TNF-α entrains a complex sequence of molecular changes in various liver cells, including hepatocytes and bile ductular epithelial cells, that can result either in their death or in their proliferation.

Activation of liver stem cells and proliferation of oval cells also appears to depend on the elevated expression of TNF-α and signaling through the type 1 TNF receptor (TNFR1). Both biliary epithelial cells and oval cells express TNFR1.[86] *In vitro* exposure of cells of the cloned oval cell line, LE/6, to TNF-α does not induce apoptosis; instead, it stimulates them to proliferate by sequentially activating NFκB and STAT3, resulting in the up-regulation of c-myc and interleukin-6 (IL-6).[87] Similarly, *in vitro* exposure of liver epithelial cells of the cloned RLEϕ13 line to TNF-α fails to induce them to undergo apoptosis[86] but does not significantly increase their rate of proliferation. Although TNF-α is up-regulated during the oval cell reaction in wild-type mice, the oval cell response is markedly reduced in mice in which the *TNFR1* gene is transgenically deleted.[88] Dexamethasone treatment inhibits oval cell proliferation in the AAF+PH model in rats,[89] possibly by inhibiting NFκB activation.[90] Cells, said to be proliferated oval cells, are diminished in bile duct-ligated rats when Kupffer cells are blocked by gadolinium chloride.[91] Cytokines of the IL-6 family, including leukemia inhibitory factor (LIF), its receptor (LIFR),[92] and OSM,[93] together with gp130, are up-regulated in oval cells proliferating in the AAF+PH model.

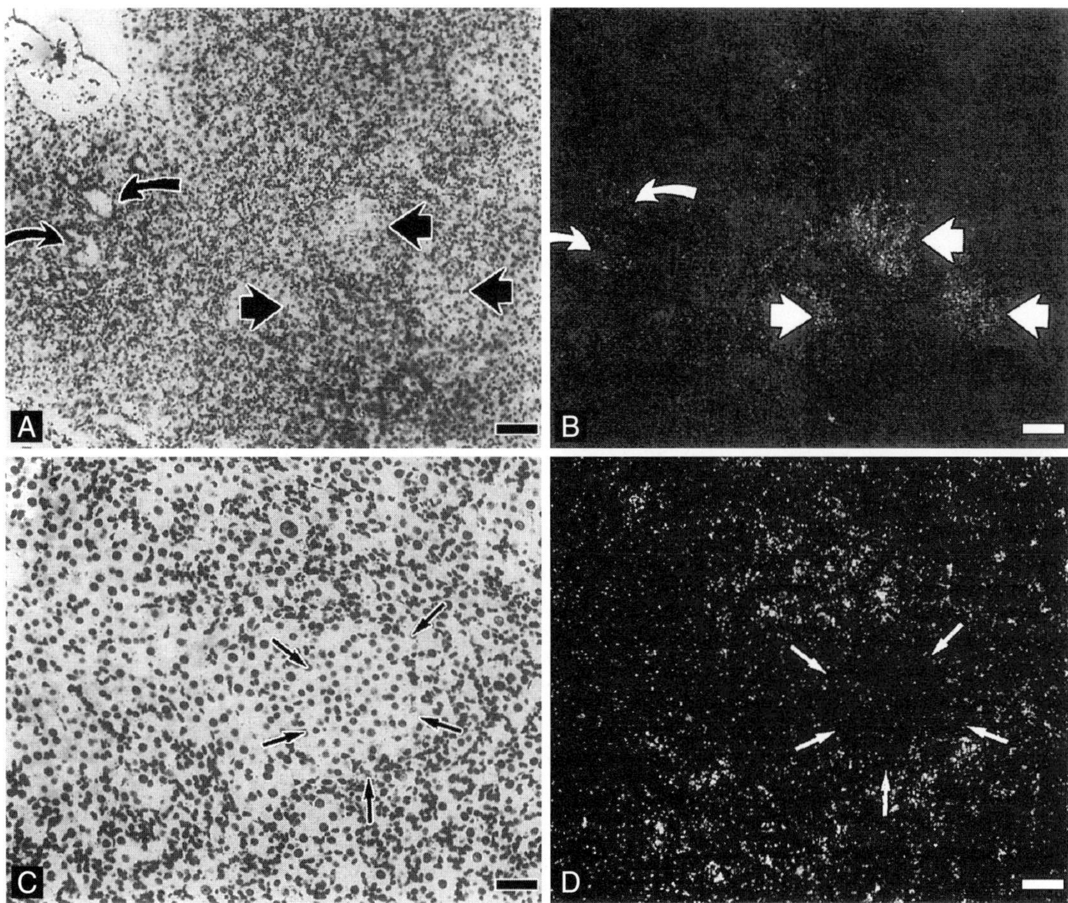

Figure 45–8. *HNF-4 and C/EBPβ expression during liver stem cell activation in the AAF+PH rat model.* (A and B) HNF-4 expression 9 days after PH. Thick arrows show small but positive basophilic foci; curved arrows mark positive intestinal type glands. (C and D) C/EBPβ expression 11 days after PH; a basophilic focus (arrows) lacks grains, and some of the surrounding oval cells are positive. Panels A and C are bright field; panels B and D show dark-field illumination. Bar = 28 μm. Reproduced from Nagy *et al.*[80] with permission).

LIF, LIFR, and gp130 are also up-regulated after PH alone, but this up-regulation is weaker than in the AAF+PH model[92] (Fig. 45–9).

Interferon-γ (IFN-γ) also appears to play a determinative role in oval cell activation and proliferation, since a complex network of genes (including IFN-γRα, IFN-γRβ, IL-1β, IL-18, gp91phox, IL-1β-converting enzyme, intercellular adhesion molecule-1, and uPAR) are up-regulated in oval cells in the AAF+PH model, but only IL-1β expression was transiently elevated after PH alone.[94] These results suggest that the IFN-γ–associated genes are related specifically to the generation of new hepatocyte lineages from stem cells. A gene for a molecule related to the ebnerin gene in rats, the *ductin* gene in mice and the deleted in malignant brain tumor 1 *(DMBT1)* gene in humans, is also highly up-regulated in oval cells in the AAF+PH model in rats.[94,95] This gene is also related to the opsonin receptor gene,[95] and its expression on mucosal surfaces may play a role in the innate immunity. The gene is highly expressed in oval cells proliferating in both retrorsine and AAF+PH models and in aberrantly differentiated intestinal epithelial cells in the AAF+PH model but not in basophilic hepatocytes (intermediate cells) of either the retrorsine or the AAF+PH model.[95] Expression of this gene appears to be involved in differentiation or fate decision of precursor cells that form ducts, suggesting that it may have a role in the differentiation of oval cells.[95]

SCF and its receptor, c-kit, are up-regulated during the oval cell reaction in rats subjected to the AAF+PH regimen.[96,97] Both SCF and c-kit are expressed in oval cells, but stellate cells express only SCF and hepatocytes express neither.[97] Since SCF–c-kit expression typifies other stem cells involved in lineage generation, as well as their immediate progeny,[98] this observation supports the opinion that oval cells are closely related to liver epithelial stem cells. The importance of SCF–c-kit in oval cell activation is corroborated by studies of the AAF+PH model that show that development of oval cells is markedly reduced in Ws/Ws rats, which contain a *c-kit* gene that is mutated in the tyrosine kinase domain and,

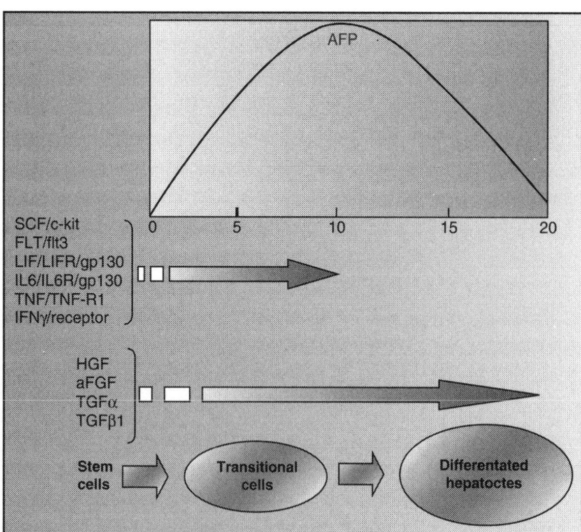

Figure 45–9. *Signaling pathways involved in activation, expansion, and differentiation of liver stem cells.* (Please see CD-ROM for color version of this figure.)

therefore, inactive in signal transduction.[99] The specific role of SCF–c-kit in activating latent liver stem cells is indicated by the few oval cells that develop in Ws/Ws rats being able to proliferate and differentiate in a manner comparable to oval cells in wild-type rats.[99]

Several mitogenic growth factors and their receptors are also up-regulated during the oval cell reaction and appear to play an essential role in the proliferation of oval cells to form an expanding population (Fig. 45–9). TGF-α/epidermal growth factor receptor (EGFR), HGF/c-met, and aFGF/bek/flg are all significantly elevated when oval cells are proliferating.[100] Transcripts for TGF-α/EGFR, aFGF/bek/flg, and c-met are clearly localized to oval cells, and HGF transcripts are confined to peribiliary stellate cells.[100–102] Stellate cells also synthesize TGF-α and acidic FGF (aFGF). HGF and TGF-α are elevated by PH alone, both are more strongly up-regulated within 4 hours after PH in the AAF+PH model, and they remain highly elevated for at least 96 hours.[27,103] Acidic FGF is increased within 24 hours after PH in AAF-treated rats and remains elevated for 96 hours.[27] FGFR *bek* is up-regulated at 12 hours after PH alone, and it is more strongly up-regulated within 2 days after PH in AAF-treated rats, remaining elevated for 15 to 20 days.[104] In contrast, FGFR *flg* is not expressed after PH alone but is strongly up-regulated within 2 days after PH in AAF-treated rats, remaining elevated for 15 days.[104] Both of these FGFRs are expressed by oval cells.[104] These results suggest that these mitogenic growth factors are responsible for the proliferation of oval cells to form an expanding population, following the activation of stem cells by up-regulation of SCF–c-kit. This opinion is corroborated by the infusion of AAF-treated rats (without PH) with either EGF or HGF for 7 days that results in extensive proliferation of oval cells with invasion into the lobular parenchyma as if PH had been performed.[35] *In vivo* transfer by adenoviral vector of the *HGF* gene, controlled by the CAG promoter, stimulated both SCF–c-kit expression and oval cell proliferation in AAF-treated rats.[105]

In the DEN+AAF+PH model, transcripts of TGF-β1 are expressed by oval cells and other nonparenchymal cells, including desmin-positive stellate cells, but not by small hepatocytes in nodular aggregates.[49] Latent and mature TGF-β1 proteins were also concentrated in oval and stellate cells, but they were missing from hepatocyte nodules. This finding was interpreted to suggest that TGF-β is involved in the acquisition of hepatocyte differentiation by oval cells, a suggestion strengthened by the observation that a cloned line of rat liver epithelial cells stopped proliferating; enlarged with increased cytoplasmic area; and up-regulated transcripts for α-fetoprotein, albumin, multidrug resistance, and *c-myc* genes during a period of 72 hours after exposure to TGF-β1 *in vitro*.[49] Expression of high levels of TGF-β1 protein in oval cells and stellate cells (positive for smooth muscle actin) was also found to occur in the AAF+PH model.[106] Highest expression of TGF-β1 by stellate cells was associated with apoptosis of oval cells, suggesting that the expression of this growth factor is also involved in the termination of oval cell proliferation. In keeping with this opinion, sustained transgenic overexpression of TGF-β1 prevented the accumulation of oval cells in DDC-treated mice.[107]

Summary

The biliary epithelial cells located in the canals of Hering have long been thought to be the source of liver epithelial stem cells.[108] The liver epithelial stem cell niche is posited to be located in the canals of Hering because of the location of these structures between the opposing differentiative microenvironments of the mature cholangiocytes–portal tract matrix and the mature hepatocytes–hepatic lobular matrix.[109] Biliary epithelial cells of the canals of Hering are thought to be the most undifferentiated epithelial cells in the liver. The AAF+PH model of hepatocyte lineage generation, in which the AAF dose is varied, provides unequivocal evidence for the presence of undifferentiated liver epithelial stem cells in the canals of Hering. Activation and proliferation of epithelial stem cells located in the canals of Hering yields an expanded population of stem cell progeny, the oval cells. The ductular epithelial stem cells are activated by low doses of AAF,[7–9] and even PH alone starts the process of activation.[11] The extent of oval cell proliferation is maximal at high doses of AAF,[7–9] but the efficiency and rapidity with which oval cells acquire hepatocyte differentiation is optimal at low AAF doses and is impeded by high doses of AAF.[7–9] Instead of differentiating appropriately into hepatocytes and cholangiocytes, at high AAF doses, some oval cells differentiate aberrantly to form intestinal and pancreatic acinar epithelium,[5,29] but most of the accumulated oval cells die by apoptosis when hepatocyte differentiation is blocked.[8] With the evidence that hematopoietic stem cells, either endogenous residents of the liver or those derived from bone marrow, are not major sources of stem cells that generate new lineages of hepatocytes and cholangiocytes,[15–17,19,20] these studies indicate that endogenous epithelial stem cells located in the canals of Hering are the major source of new hepatocyte and cholangiocyte lineages in adult animals, at least under experimental conditions. It is unclear whether only some or all of the biliary epithelial cells that compose the canals of Hering function as stem cells for the generation of new lineages of hepatocytes and cholangiocytes. We favor the hypothesis that all epithelial cells of the canals of Hering can be activated to function as stem cells, since the AAF+PH model provides no evidence for the existence of a more segregated population of stem cells.[9]

Hepatocyte lineage generation from stem cells is a highly ordered cellular process, and the studies reviewed suggest possible regulatory molecules and the outlines of signaling pathways that may be involved. For this analysis, the cellular process of hepatocyte lineage generation from oval cells may be divided into the following steps: (1) activation of stem cells to enable them to function as precursors of oval cells, (2) amplification of oval cell precursors and oval cells by repeated proliferative cycling, (3) differentiation of oval cells to form partially differentiated intermediate cells, (4) maturation of intermediate cells to form fully differentiated hepatocytes, (5) proliferation of the differentiated cells to yield a sufficient population to correct deficient hepatic function, and (6) termination of cell proliferation and remodeling of accumulated cell populations to produce a near-normal liver structure.

Activation of liver epithelial stem cells: Up-regulation of the expression of SCF–c-kit signals the activation of stem cell function by epithelial cells of the canals of Hering.[96,97] Oval cell proliferation is significantly reduced in Ws/Ws rats in which c-kit is mutated.[99] The plasminogen-activating system (uPA–uPAR and PAI-1) is also up-regulated quickly in the terminal biliary epithelial cells,[34] and SCF and uPA are simultaneously up-regulated in the adjacent peribiliary stellate cells.[34,97]

Nevertheless, these molecular changes may not represent the critical molecular event or events that *initiate* the activation of liver stem cells. The hepatic damage that leads to oval cell reaction stimulates the hepatic acute phase reaction, and hepatocyte lineage generation from stem cells always occurs in this setting. The hepatic acute phase reaction is associated with elevated levels of TNF-α and with altered expression of many hepatocyte transcription factors and proteins.[85] TNF-α is expressed by many cellular components of portal tracts, including biliary epithelial cells.[110] Terminal biliary epithelial cells express TNFR1,[86,87] suggesting that TNR-α signaling is involved in regulating stem cell activation and oval cell proliferation. Indeed, TNF-α stimulates the proliferation of a cultured oval cell line *in vitro,*[87] and it fails to induce apoptosis in another line of rat liver epithelial cells,[86] suggesting that TNF-α signaling through the TNFR1 may have a major role in initiating the activation of epithelial stem cells in terminal biliary ducts. In keeping with this possibility, oval cell proliferation is markedly inhibited in mice in which the TNFR1-gene is transgenically deleted.[88] Furthermore, members of the IL-6 cytokine family are up-regulated in oval cells,[92,93] and dexamethasone treatment inhibits oval cell proliferation.[89] These observations show that TNF-α-induced signaling has a central role in the activation of liver epithelial stem cells.

Amplification of stem and oval cells: Following their activation, hepatic stem cells and their progeny proliferate, leading to the accumulation of a population of oval cells. Increased cell cycling is associated temporally with the neo-expression or increased expression of several growth factors in oval and portal stellate cells and of the receptors for these growth factors in oval cells (Fig. 45–9). Among these growth factors and growth factor receptors are HGF/c-met, EGF and TGF-α/EGFR, and aFGF/bek/flt.[100–104] Infusion of AAF-exposed rats with any of the mitogenic growth factors—HGF, TGF-α, EGF, or aFGF—stimulates the proliferation and accumulation of oval cells.[35] Furthermore, pro-HGF may be cleaved to the active form by high ambient levels of plasmin that result from the up-regulation of uPA/uPAR,[111] which may also release other growth factors sequestered by binding to matrix molecules. These results indicate that the proliferation of activated stem cells and their progeny is driven by the coordinate up-regulation of the mitogenic growth factors and receptors in them and their progeny as well as by the up-regulation of growth factors in the adjacent stellate cells.

Differentiation of oval cells: The differentiation of oval cells into small, basophilic hepatocytes is temporally associated with the breakdown of the periductular basement membrane and the falloff of the stellate cells from their close association with the terminal ductules,[9,26] suggesting that a combination of alteration of the matrix and loss of paracrine growth support may be essential for hepatocyte differentiation to occur. Oval cells express OSM–OSMR as well as gp130.[93] OSM is an IL-6-type cytokine that induces fetal hepatoblasts to undergo hepatocyte differentiation (for review, see Kinoshita and Miyajima[82]). Exposure of animals to dexamethasone inhibits hepatocyte differentiation from oval cells in the AAF+PH model.[89] Differentiation of oval cells into hepatocytes is associated with the up-regulation of the hepatocyte-enriched transcription factors HNF-3, HNF-1, HNF-4, and C/EBP-β[80,81]; the up-regulation of TGF-β[49,106,112]; and the acquisition of morphological and functional properties of hepatocytes.[9,26] Heightened expression of HNF-4 appears to be a particularly important molecular event in the differentiation of hepatocytes from oval cells. Oval cells, but not intermediate cells or mature hepatocytes, express DMBT1 (or ductin–ebnerin),[94,95] which is also expressed by differentiated cholangiocytes and may be involved in the decision of oval cells to differentiate into cholangiocytes instead of hepatocytes,[95] since mature biliary epithelial cells of bile ducts also express this molecule.[95]

Maturation of intermediate cells: Intermediate cells, as exemplified by small hepatocyte precursor cells in the retrorsine model,[113,114] express phenotypic properties that overlap those of both oval cells and mature hepatocytes. Early intermediate cells express HNF-1, -3, -4, and -6; albumin; cytokeratin 18; and transferrin but not tyrosine aminotransferase, and expression of cytochrome P450 species typical of hepatocytes is incomplete.[113] Intermediate cells rapidly acquire the complete hepatocyte phenotype,[114] which is delayed by the treatment of animals with dexamethasone.[115] It seems likely that maturation of intermediate cells is directed by the cytokines and growth factors involved in the differentiation of oval cells.

Proliferation of intermediate and mature hepatocytes: Both intermediate cells and mature hepatocytes that develop from intermediate cells proliferate rapidly until the deficit in hepatic function is repaired.[7,113] The molecular regulation of proliferation of these cells has not been examined, and it may not differ from the regulation of hepatocyte proliferation following PH.[1]

Termination of proliferation and remodeling of accumulated hepatocytes: The molecular mechanism by which the termination of proliferation of oval cells, intermediate hepatocytes, and mature hepatocytes is regulated is poorly understood.[1] TGF-β and related inhibitory growth factors are believed to be involved.[1] Expression of TGF-β is up-regulated early in the process of oval cell proliferation and continues until the end.[49,106,112] That TGF-β is involved in suppressing or terminating oval cell production is suggested by the observation that infusion of TGF-β1 into rats treated on the AAF+PH model is followed by diminishing the expression of uPA/uPAR.[34] Furthermore, oval cell accumulation in the DDC model is suppressed in mice transgenically overexpressing TGF-β1.[107] Remodeling of the proliferated hepatocytes to form a normal liver structure is a complex cellular and molecular process that remains to be elucidated.

The evidence reviewed here suggests that the molecular regulation of lineage generation from liver epithelial stem cells and the proliferation of differentiated hepatocytes from residual differentiated hepatocytes share common elements. Recent experimental studies have partly elucidated the molecular mechanisms that regulate the proliferation of hepatocytes following simple removal of part of the liver (by PH or CCl_4-treatment).[1,116,117] Regulation of hepatocyte proliferation in this situation involves several distinct steps, including activation or priming, a process associated with switching residual hepatocytes from an out-of-cycle stage (G0) to an in-cycle stage (G1); amplification of the activated precursors by proliferation; and termination of proliferation.[1,116] Present evidence indicates that the regulation of hepatocyte proliferation–differentiation involves the molecular components of the acute phase reaction,[85] particularly the molecules produced by hepatic nonparenchymal cells, which then act on residual hepatocytes to stimulate them to reenter the proliferative cycle and generate sufficient cells to repair the functional deficit. Current insight is that the proinflammatory cytokine TNF-α has a pivotal role in entraining this process by binding to TNFR1 on hepatocytes and other liver cells to activate a series of intracellular signaling reaction.[116,117] The transcription factor NFκB is activated, and the production of IL-6 by macrophages and other cells is stimulated. IL-6 binds to the IL-6R/gp130 complex of residual hepatocytes to energize the JAK-STAT signal pathway, which eventuates in the phosphorylation of STAT3, converting affected hepatocytes from the G0 to the G1 stage of the cell cycle.[116,117] This molecular process appears to be further amplified by other acute phase cytokines, including soluble IL-6R (sIL-6R), which forms a complex with IL-6R/gp130 to amplify IL-6 binding.[118] IL-6R is cleaved from cell membranes to form sIL-6R partly by the action of C-reactive protein.[119] Complement factor 5 (C5) or its lytic product, C5a, is also required for the efficient hepatocyte proliferation, since hepatocyte replacement is severely impaired in mice deficient in C5 as a result of gene mutation[120]; the defect in hepatocyte replacement is corrected by infusing mutant mice with either C5 or C5a.[120] Furthermore, intrahepatic natural killer cells seem to have a role in efficient liver regeneration,[121,122] perhaps by binding to hepatocytes through Fas/Fas receptor to kill excess cells and regulate the size of the hepatocyte population or by producing cytokines, such as IFN-γ, that may promote parenchymal cell production. Amplification of the activated hepatocytes is driven by several mitogenic growth factors–receptors, including TGF-α/EGFR, HGF/c-met, and aFGF/FGFR.[1,111] Maturation of the proliferated hepatocytes may also involve another acute phase cytokine—OSM, a close relative of IL-6 that plays a role in the differentiation of hepatoblasts[82]—as well as negative growth factors, the TGF-βs and activins.[1] The latter growth factors may also regulate the cessation of cell proliferation.[1]

The data reviewed here suggest that the molecular regulation of hepatocyte lineage generation from stem cells and the proliferation of residual hepatocytes are generally similar, the regulation of both processes being based on various cytokines and growth factors activated during hepatic inflammation and on damage that stimulates the hepatic acute phase reaction. Nevertheless, parenchymal cells appear to be replaced in rodents by one of two cellular processes that seem to be mutually exclusive. Liver parenchyma is most commonly replaced after loss in rodents by the rapid proliferation of residual hepatocytes and cholangiocytes in the absence of stem cell activation. The generation of new lineages of hepatocytes and cholangiocytes from stem cells through the oval cell reaction seems to occur only when the residual parenchymal cells cannot proliferate.[3,4] If the molecular regulation of the two processes is so similar, then why do the cellular processes seem to be so distinct?

Evidence suggests that the distinction of the two processes may be more apparent than real. Even though the proliferation of residual hepatocytes is highly suppressed in both the AAF+PH[5,7] and retrorsine–PH[113] models in rats, new hepatocytes develop by the simultaneous proliferation of residual hepatocytes and by the generation of new hepatocyte lineages from stem cells in the galactosamine model in rats[123] and in the DDC model in mice,[107] although the process of stem cell activation predominates. Furthermore, a distinct biphasic pattern of liver parenchymal cell replacement does not typify all species of animals. In teleost fish, for example, hepatic defects of even a small magnitude are repaired by the proliferation of differentiated hepatocytes and cholangiocytes, and by the generation of new parenchymal cell lineages from stem cells located in terminal biliary ductules that take place concurrently.[124]

Whether damaged parenchyma is replaced by the proliferation of residual differentiated cells, by the generation from stem cells, or by both processes simultaneously may relate to the relative rapidity with which new hepatocytes are produced by the proliferation of residual differentiated cells and by the generation from stem cells. The generation of new parenchymal lineages is a slow process that involves the sequential activation, amplification, and differentiation of stem cells and their progeny, requiring several weeks in both rodents and fish, for example. Proliferation of residual differentiated hepatocytes and cholangiocytes is fast in rodents,[1] but residual hepatocytes cycle slowly in teleost fish after PH, and the formation of new hepatocytes appears to be produced in teleost fish with about equal speed from either epithelial stem cells or residual differentiated parenchymal cells.[124] Although liver stem cells appear to implement early activation steps following PH in rodents,[11] the slower process of generation of new parenchymal cells from stem cells is quickly overtaken by the more direct and rapid proliferation of residual differentiated cells. Rodents may have evolved a more rapid cellular mechanism to replace the loss of hepatic parenchyma from differentiated precursor cells because of multiple injurious agents in their environment. However, the rapid production of new differentiated parenchymal cells directly from residual differentiated parenchymal cells predominates in rodents only if the proliferation of the residual cells is unimpeded.

REFERENCES

1. Michalopoulos, G.K., and DeFrances, M.C. (1997). Liver regeneration. *Science* **276,** 60–66.
2. Columbano, A., and Ledda-Columbano, G.M. (2003). Mitogenesis by ligands of nuclear receptors: an attractive model for the study of the molecular mechanisms implicated in liver growth. *Cell Death Differ.* **10,** S19–S21.
3. Grisham, J.W., and Thorgeirsson, S.S. (1997). Liver stem cells. *In* "Stem Cells," (C.S. Potten, Ed.), pp. 233–282. Academic Press, London.
4. Coleman, W.B., and Grisham, J.W. (1998). Epithelial stem-like cells of the rodent liver. *In* "Liver Growth and Repair," (A.J. Strain *et al.,* Eds.), pp. 50–99. Chapman and Hall, London.
5. Tatematsu M., Ho, R.H., Kaku, T., Ekem, J.K., and Farber, E. (1984). Studies on the proliferation and fate of oval cells in the liver of rats treated with 2-acetylaminofluorene and partial hepatectomy. *Am. J. Pathol.* **114,** 418–430.
6. Solt, D.B., and Farber, E. (1976). New principle for the analysis of chemical carcinogenesis. *Nature* **263,** 701–703.
7. Evarts, R.P., Nagy, P., Nakatsukasa, H., Marsden, E., and Thorgeirsson, S.S. (1989). *In vivo* differentiation of rat liver oval cells into hepatocytes. *Cancer Res.* **49,** 1541–1547.
8. Alison, M., Golding, M., Lalani, E.N., Nagy, P., Thorgeirsson, S., and Sarraf, C. (1997). Wholesale hepatocytic differentiation in the rat from ductular oval cells, the progeny of biliary stem cells. *J. Hepatol.* **26,** 343–352.
9. Paku, S., Nagy, P., Kopper, L., and Thorgeirsson, S.S. (2004). AAF-dose-dependent differentiation of oval cells into hepatocytes: Confocal and electron microscopic studies. *Hepatology* **39,** 1353-1361.
10. Shafritz, D.A., and Dabeva, M.D. (2002). Liver stem cells and model systems for liver repopulation. *J. Hepatol.* **36,** 552–564.
11. Thorgeirsson, S.S. (1996). Hepatic stem cells in liver regeneration. *FASEB J.* **10,** 1249–1256.
12. Petersen, B.E., Bowen, W.C., Patrene, K.D., Mars, W.M., Sullivan, A.K., Murase, N., Boggs, S.S., Greenberger, J.S., and Goff, J.P. (1999). Bone marrow as a potential source of hepatic oval cells. *Science* **284,** 1168–1170.
13. Theise, N.D., Badve, S., Saxena, R., Henegariu, O., Sell, S., Crawford, J.M., and Krause, D.S. (2000). Derivation of hepatocytes from bone marrow cells in mice after radiation-induced myeloablation. *Hepatology* **31,** 235–240.
14. Schwartz, R.E., Reyes, M., Koodie, L., Jiang, Y., Blackstad, M., Lund, T., Lenvik, T., Johnson, S., Hu, W.S., and Verfaillie, C.M. (2002). Multipotent adult progenitor cells from bone marrow differentiate into functional hepatocyte-like cells. *J. Clin. Invest.* **109,** 1291–1302.
15. Mallet, V.O., Mitchell, C., Mezey, E., Fabre, M., Guidotti, J.E., Renia, L., Coulombel, L., Kahn, A., and Gilgenkrantz, H. (2002). Bone marrow transplantation in mice leads to a minor population of hepatocytes that can be selectively amplified *in vivo. Hepatology* **35,** 799–804.
16. Wagers, A.J., Sherwood, R.I., Christensen, J.L., and Weissman, I.L. (2002). Little evidence for developmental plasticity of adult hematopoietic stem cells. *Science* **297,** 2256–2259.
17. Wang, X., Montini, E., Al-Dhalimy, M., Lagasse, E., Finegold, M., and Grompe, M. (2002). Kinetics of liver repopulation after bone marrow transplantation. *Am. J. Pathol.* **161,** 565–574.
18. Lagasse, E., Connors, H., Al-Dhalimy, M., Reitsma, M., Dohse, M., Osborne, L., Wang, X., Finegold, M., Weissman, I.L., and Grompe, M. (2000). Purified hematopoietic stem cells can differentiate into hepatocytes *in vivo. Nat. Med.* **6,** 1229–1234.
19. Wang, X., Willenbring, H., Akkari, Y., Torimaru, Y., Foster, M., Al-Dhalimy, M., Lagasse, E., Finegold, M., Olson, S., and Grompe, M. (2003). Cell fusion is the principal source of bone marrow-derived hepatocytes. *Nature* **422,** 897–901.
20. Vassilopoulos G., Wang, P.R., and Russell, D.W. (2003). Transplanted bone marrow regenerates liver by cell fusion. *Nature* **422,** 901–904.
21. Sell, S. (2001). Heterogeneity and plasticity of hepatocyte lineage cells. *Hepatology* **33,** 738–750.
22. Theise, N.D., Saxena, R., Portmann, B.C., Thung, S.N., Yee, H., Chiriboga, L., Kumar, A., and Crawford, J.M. (1999). The canals of Hering and hepatic stem cells in humans. *Hepatology* **30,** 1425–1433.
23. Evarts, R.P., Hu, Z., Omori, N., Omori, M., Marsden, E.R., and Thorgeirsson, S.S. (1996). Precursor–product relationship between oval cells and hepatocytes: comparison between tritiated thymidine and bromodeoxyuridine as tracers. *Carcinogenesis* **17,** 2143–2151.
24. Novikoff, P.M., Yam, A., and Oikawa, I. (1996). Blast-like cell compartment in carcinogen-induced proliferating bile ductules. *Am. J. Pathol.* **148,** 1473–1492.
25. Novikoff, P.M., and Yam, A. (1998). Stem cells and rat liver carcinogenesis: contributions of confocal and electron microscopy. *J. Histochem. Cytochem.* **46,** 613–626.
26. Paku, S., Schnur, J., Nagy, P., and Thorgeirsson, S.S. (2001). Origin and structural evolution of the early proliferating oval cells in rat liver. *Am. J. Pathol.* **158,** 1313–1323.
27. Evarts, R.P., Hu, Z., Fujio, K., Marsden, E.R., and Thorgeirsson, S.S. (1993). Activation of hepatic stem cell compartment in the rat: role of transforming growth factor-α, hepatocyte growth factor, and acidic fibroblast growth factor in early proliferation. *Cell Growth Differ.* **4,** 555–561.
28. Taniguchi, H., Toyoshima, T., Fukao, K., and Nakauchi, H. (1996). Presence of hematopoietic stem cells in the adult liver. *Nat. Med.* **2,** 198–203.

29. Tatematsu, M., Kaku, T., Medline, A., and Farber, E. (1985). Intestinal metaplasia as a common option of oval cells in relation to cholangiofibrosis in liver of rats exposed to 2-acetylaminofluorene. *Lab. Invest.* **52,** 354–362.
30. Martinez-Hernandez, A., and Amenta, P.S. (1993). The hepatic extracellular matrix: I. Components and distribution in normal liver. *Virchows Arch. A. Pathol. Anat. Histopathol.* **423,** 1–11.
31. Martinez-Hernandez, A., and Amenta, P.S. (1995). The extracellular matrix in hepatic regeneration. *FASEB J.* **9,** 1401–1410.
32. Mars, W.M., Liu, M.L., Kitson, R.P., Goldfarb, R.H., Gabauer, M.K., and Michalopoulos, G.K. (1995). Immediate early detection of urokinase receptor after partial hepatectomy and its implications for initiation of liver regeneration. *Hepatology* **21,** 1695–1701.
33. Kim, T.H., Mars, W.M., Stolz, D.B., and Michalopoulos, G.K. (2000). Expression and activation of pro-MMP-2 and pro-MMP-9 during rat liver regeneration. *Hepatology* **31,** 75–82.
34. Bisgaard, H.C., Santoni-Rugiu, E., Nagy, P., and Thorgeirsson, S.S. (1998). Modulation of the plasminogen activator/plasmin system in rat liver regenerating by recruitment of oval cells. *Lab. Invest.* **78,** 237–246.
35. Nagy, P., Bisgaard, H.C., Santoni-Rugiu, E., and Thorgeirsson, S.S. (1996). *In vivo* infusion of growth factors enhances the mitogenic response of rat hepatic ductal (oval) cells after administration of 2-acetylaminofluorene. *Hepatology* **23,** 71–79.
36. Grompe, M., and Finegold, M.J. (2001). Liver stem cells. *In* "Stem Cell Biology," (D.R. Marshak *et al.,* Eds.), pp. 455–497. Cold Spring Harbor Press, Cold Spring Harbor, New York.
37. Overturf, K., Al-Dhalimy, M., Ou, C.N., Finegold, M., and Grompe, M. (1997). Serial transplantation reveals the stem cell-like regenerative potential of adult mouse hepatocytes. *Am. J. Pathol.* **151,** 1273–1280.
38. Matsusaka, S., Toyosaka, A., Nakasho, K., Tsujimura, T., Sugihara, A., Takanashi, T., Uematsu, K., Terada, N., and Okamoto, E. (2000). The role of oval cells in rat hepatocyte transplantation. *Transplantation* **70,** 441–446.
39. Yaswen, P., Hayner, N.T., and Fausto, N. (1984). Isolation of oval cells by centrifugal elutriation and comparison with other cell types purified from normal and preneoplastic livers. *Cancer Res.* **44,** 324–331.
40. Faris, R.A., and Hixson, D.C. (1989). Selective proliferation of chemically altered rat liver epithelial cells following hepatic transplantation. *Transplantation* **48,** 87–92.
41. Dabeva, M.D., Hwang, S.G., Vasa, S.R., Hurston, E., Novikoff, P.M., Hixson, D.C., Gupta, S., and Shafritz, D.A. (1997). Differentiation of pancreatic epithelial progenitor cells into hepatocytes following transplantation into rat liver. *Proc. Natl. Acad. Sci. U. S. A.* **94,** 7356–7361.
42. Yasui, O., Miura, N., Terada, K., Kawarada, Y., Koyama, K., and Sugiyama, T. (1997). Isolation of oval cells from Long–Evans Cinnamon rats and their transformation into hepatocytes *in vivo* in the rat liver. *Hepatology* **25,** 329–334.
43. Wang, X., Foster, M., Al-Dhalimy, M., Lagasse, E., Finegold, M., and Grompe, M. (2003). The origin and liver repopulating capacity of murine oval cells. *Proc. Natl. Acad. Sci. U. S. A.* **100,** 11,881–11,888.
44. Gordon, G.J., Butz, G.M., Grisham, J.W., and Coleman, W.B. (2002). Isolation, short-term culture, and transplantation of small hepatocyte-like progenitor cells from retrorsine-exposed rats. *Transplantation* **73,** 1236–1243.
45. Coleman, W.B., Wennerberg, A.E., Smith, G.J., and Grisham, J.W. (1993). Regulation of the differentiation of diploid and some aneuploid rat liver epithelial (stem-like) cells by the hepatic microenvironment. *Am. J. Pathol.* **142,** 1373–1382.
46. Coleman, W.B., McCullough, K.D., Esch, G.L., Faris, R.A., Hixson, D.C., Smith, G.J., and Grisham, J.W. (1997). Evaluation of the differentiation potential of WB-F344 rat liver epithelial stem-like cells *in vivo:* differentiation to hepatocytes after transplantation into dipeptidyl-peptidase-IV-deficient rat liver. *Am. J. Pathol.* **151,** 353–359.
47. Coleman, W.B., Butz, G.M., Howell, J.A., and Grisham, J.W. (2002). Transplantation and differentiation of rat liver epithelial stem-like cells. *In* "Hepatocyte Transplantation," (S. Gupta *et al.,* Eds.), pp. 38–50. Kluwer Academic Publishers, Dordrecht, the Netherlands.
48. Ott, M., Rajvanshi, P., Sokhi, R.P., Alpini, G., Aragona, E., Dabeva, M., Shafritz, D.A., and Gupta, S. (1999). Differentiation-specific regulation of transgene expression in a diploid epithelial cell line derived from the normal F344 rat liver. *J. Pathol.* **187,** 365–373.
49. Nagy, P., Evarts, R.P., McMahon, J.B., and Thorgeirsson, S.S. (1989). Role of TGF-β in normal differentiation and oncogenesis in rat liver. *Mol. Carcinog.* **2,** 345–354.
50. Coleman, W.B., Smith, G.J., and Grisham, J.W. (1994). Development of dexamethasone-inducible tyrosine aminotransferase activity in WB-F344 rat liver epithelial stem-like cells cultured in the presence of sodium butyrate. *J. Cell Physiol.* **161,** 463–469.
51. Couchie, D., Holic, N., Chobert, M.N., Corlu, A., and Laperche, Y. (2002). *In vitro* differentiation of WB-F344 rat liver epithelial cells into the biliary lineage. *Differentiation* **69,** 209–215.
52. Factor, V.M., Schroeder, I.S., Hironaka, K., Sanchez Munoz, A., Heo, J.H., and Thorgeirsson, S.S. (2002). *In vitro* differentiation of adult liver stem cells into the hepatocytic lineage. *Proc. Am. Assoc. Cancer Res.* **43,** 462.
53. Nagai, H., Terada, K., Watanabe, G., Ueno, Y., Aiba, N., Shibuya, T., Kawagoe, M., Kameda, T., Sato, M., Senoo, H., and Sugiyama, T. (2002). Differentiation of liver epithelial (stem-like) cells into hepatocytes induced by coculture with hepatic stellate cells. *Biochem. Biophys. Res. Commun.* **293,** 1420–1425.
54. Pack, R., Heck, R., Dienes, H.P., Oesch, F., and Steinberg, P. (1993). Isolation, biochemical characterization, long-term culture, and phenotype modulation of oval cells from carcinogen-fed rats. *Exp. Cell Res.* **204,** 198–209.
55. Lazaro, C.A., Rhim, J.A., Yamada, Y., and Fausto, N. (1998). Generation of hepatocytes from oval cell precursors in culture. *Cancer Res.* **58,** 5514–5522.
56. Zaret, K.S. (2002). Regulatory phases of early liver development: paradigms of organogenesis. *Nat. Rev. Genet.* **3,** 499–512.
57. Duncan, S.A. (2003). Mechanisms controlling early development of the liver. *Mech. Dev.* **120,** 19–33.
58. Keng, V.W., Yagi, H., Ikawa, M., Nagano, T., Myint, Z., Yamada, K., Tanaka, T., Sato, A., Muramatsu, I., Okabe, M., Sato, M., and Noguchi, T. (2000). Homeobox gene *Hex* is essential for onset of mouse embryonic liver development and differentiation of the monocyte lineage. *Biochem. Biophys. Res. Commun.* **276,** 1155–1161.
59. Sosa-Pineda, B., Wigle, J.T., and Oliver, G. (2000). Hepatocyte migration during liver development requires Prox1. *Nat. Genet.* **25,** 254–255.
60. Cereghini, S. (1996). Liver-enriched transcription factors and hepatocyte differentiation. *FASEB J.* **10,** 267–282.
61. Schrem, H., Klempnauer, J., and Borlak, J. (2002). Liver-enriched transcription factors in liver function and development: I. The hepatocyte nuclear factor network and liver-specific gene expression. *Pharmacol. Rev.* **54,** 129–158.

62. Kaestner, K.H. (2000). The hepatocyte nuclear factor 3 (HNF3 or FOXA) family in metabolism. *Trends Endocrinol. Metab.* **11,** 281–285.
63. Duncan S.A., Navas, M.A., Dufort, D., Rossant, J., and Stoffel, M. (1998). Regulation of a transcription factor network required for differentiation and metabolism. *Science* **281,** 692–695.
64. Kaestner, K.H., Hiemisch, H., and Schutz, G. (1998). Targeted disruption of the gene encoding hepatocyte nuclear factor 3-gamma results in reduced transcription of hepatocyte-specific genes. *Mol. Cell Biol.* **18,** 4245–4251.
65. Kaestner, K.H., Katz, J., Liu, Y., Drucker, D.J., and Schutz, G. (1999). Inactivation of the winged helix transcription factor HNF3α affects glucose homeostasis and islet glucagon gene expression *in vivo. Genes Dev.* **13,** 495–504.
66. Sund, N.J., Ang, S.L., Sackett, S.D., Shen, W., Daigle, N., Magnuson, M.A., and Kaestner, K.H. (2000). Hepatocyte nuclear factor 3β (Foxa2) is dispensable for maintaining the differentiated state of the adult hepatocyte. *Mol. Cell Biol.* **20,** 5175–5183.
67. Wang, N.D., Finegold, M.J., Bradley, A., Ou, C.N., Abdelsayed, S.V., Wilde, M.D., Taylor, L.R., Wilson, D.R., and Darlington, G.J. (1995). Impaired energy homeostasis in C/EBP-α knockout mice. *Science* **269,** 1108–1112.
68. Pontoglio, M., Barra, J., Hadchouel, M., Doyen, A., Kress, C., Bach, J.P., Babinet, C., and Yaniv, M. (1996). Hepatocyte nuclear factor 1 inactivation results in hepatic dysfunction, phenylketonuria, and renal Fanconi syndrome. *Cell* **84,** 575–585.
69. Chen, W.S., Manova, K., Weinstein, D.C., Duncan, S.A., Plump, A.S., Prezioso, V.R., Bachvarova, R.F., and Darnell, J.E. (1994). Disruption of the *HNF-4* gene, expressed in visceral endoderm, leads to cell death in embryonic ectoderm and impaired gastrulation of mouse embryos. *Genes Dev.* **8,** 2466–2477.
70. Duncan, S.A, Nagy, A., and Chan, W. (1997). Murine gastrulation requires *HNF-4*-regulated gene expression in the visceral endoderm: tetraploid rescue of *HNF-4(–/–)* embryos. *Development* **124,** 279–287.
71. Li, J., Ning, G., and Duncan, S.A. (2000). Mammalian hepatocyte differentiation requires the transcription factor HNF-4α. *Genes Dev.* **14,** 464–474.
72. Hayhurst, G.P., Lee, Y.H., Lambert, G., Ward, J.M., and Gonzalez, F.J. (2001). Hepatocyte nuclear factor 4α (nuclear receptor 2A1) is essential for maintenance of hepatic gene expression and lipid homeostasis. *Mol. Cell Biol.* **21,** 1393–1403.
73. Parviz, F., Li, J., Kaestner, K.H., and Duncan, S.A. (2002). Generation of a conditionally null allele of *hnf4α*. *Genesis* **32,** 130–133.
74. Shiojiri, N. (1984). Analysis of differentiation of hepatocytes and bile duct cells in developing mouse liver by albumin immunofluorescence. *Dev. Growth Differ.* **26,** 555–561.
75. Landry, C., Clotman, F., Hioki, T., Oda, H., Picard, J.J., Lemaigre, F.P., and Rousseau, G.G. (1997). HNF-6 is expressed in endoderm derivatives and nervous system of the mouse embryo and participates to the cross-regulatory network of liver-enriched transcription factors. *Dev. Biol.* **192,** 247–257.
76. Rausa, F., Samadani, U., Ye, H., Lim, L., Fletcher, C.F., Jenkins, N.A., Copeland, N.G., and Costa, R.H. (1997). The cut-homeodomain transcriptional activator HNF-6 is coexpressed with its target gene *HNF-3β* in the developing murine liver and pancreas. *Dev. Biol.* **192,** 228–246.
77. Clotman, F., Lannoy, V.J., Reber, M., Cereghini, S., Cassiman, D., Jacquemin, P., Roskams, T., Rousseau, G.G., and Lemaigre, F.P. (2002). The onecut transcription factor HNF6 is required for normal development of the biliary tract. *Development* **129,** 1819–1828.
78. Coffinier, C., Gresh, L., Fiette, L., Tronche, F., Schutz, G., Babinet, C., Pontoglio, M., Yaniv, M., and Barra, J. (2002). Bile system morphogenesis defects and liver dysfunction upon targeted deletion of HNF1β. *Development* **129,** 1829–1838.
79. Kalinichenko, V.V., Zhou, Y., Bhattacharyya, D., Kim, W., Shin, B., Bambal, K., and Costa, R.H. (2002). Haploinsufficiency of the mouse Forkhead Box *f1* gene causes defects in gall bladder development. *J. Biol. Chem.* **277,** 12,369–12,374.
80. Nagy, P., Bisgaard, H.C., and Thorgeirsson, S.S. (1994). Expression of hepatic transcription factors during liver development and oval cell differentiation. *J. Cell Biol.* **126,** 223–233.
81. Bisgaard, H.C., Nagy, P., Santoni-Rugiu, E., and Thorgeirsson, S.S. (1996). Proliferation, apoptosis, and induction of hepatic transcription factors are characteristics of the early response of biliary epithelial (oval) cells to chemical carcinogens. *Hepatology* **23,** 62–70.
82. Kinoshita, T., and Miyajima, A. (2002). Cytokine regulation of liver development. *Biochim. Biophys. Acta.* **1592,** 303–312.
83. Diehl, A.M. (2000). Cytokine regulation of liver injury and repair. *Immunol. Rev.* **174,** 160–171.
84. Galun, E., and Axelrod, J.H. (2002). The role of cytokines in liver failure and regeneration: potential new molecular therapies. *Biochim. Biophys. Acta.* **1592,** 345–358.
85. Moshage, H. (1997). Cytokines and the hepatic acute phase response. *J. Pathol.* **181,** 257–266.
86. Sanchez, A., Factor, V.M., Schroeder, I.S., Nagy, P., and Thorgeirsson, S.S. (2003). Activation of NF-κB and STAT3 in rat hepatic oval cells during 2-acetylaminofluorene/partial hepatectomy-induced liver regeneration. *Hepatology* **39,** 376–385.
87. Kirillova, I., Chaisson, M., and Fausto, N. (1999). Tumor necrosis factor induces DNA replication in hepatic cells through nuclear factor κB activation. *Cell Growth Differ.* **10,** 819–828.
88. Knight, B., Yeoh, G.C.T., Husk, K.L., Ly, T., Abraham, L.J., Yu, C., Rhim, J.A., and Fausto, N. (2000). Impaired preneoplastic changes and liver tumor formation in tumor necrosis factor receptor type 1 knockout mice. *J. Exp. Med.* **192,** 1809–1818.
89. Nagy, P., Kiss, A., Schnur, J., and Thorgeirsson, S.S. (1998). Dexamethasone inhibits the proliferation of hepatocytes and oval cells but not bile duct cells in rat liver. *Hepatology* **28,** 423–429.
90. Auphan, N., DiDonato J.A., Rosette, C., Helmsberg, A., and Karin, M. (1995). Immunosuppression by glucocorticoids: inhibition of NFκB activity through induction of IκB synthesis. *Science* **270,** 286–290.
91. Olynyk, J.K., Yeoh, G.C., Ramm, G.A., Clarke, S.L., Hall, P.M., Britton, R.S., Bacon, B.R., and Tracy, T.F. (1998). Gadolinium chloride suppresses hepatic oval cell proliferation in rats with biliary obstruction. *Am. J. Pathol.* **152,** 347–352.
92. Omori, N., Evarts, R.P., Omori, M., Hu, Z., Marsden, E.R., and Thorgeirsson, S.S. (1996). Expression of leukemia inhibitory factor and its receptor during liver regeneration in the adult rat. *Lab. Invest.* **75,** 15–24.
93. Hironaka, K., and Thorgeirsson, S.S. (Unpublished observations).
94. Bisgaard, H.C., Muller, S., Nagy, P., Rasmussen, L.J., and Thorgeirsson, S.S. (1999). Modulation of the gene network connected to interferon-γ in liver regeneration from oval cells. *Am. J. Pathol.* **155,** 1075–1085.
95. Bisgaard, H.C., Holmskov, U., Santoni-Rugiu, E., Nagy, P., Nielsen, O., Ott, P., Hage, E., Dalhoff, K., Rasmussen, L.J., and Tygstrup, N. (2002). Heterogeneity of ductular reactions in adult rat and human liver revealed by novel expression of deleted in malignant brain tumor 1. *Am. J. Pathol.* **161,** 1187–1198.

96. Fujio, K., Evarts, R.P., Hu, Z., Marsden, E.R., and Thorgeirsson, S.S. (1994). Expression of stem cell factor and its receptor, *c-kit,* during liver regeneration from putative stem cells in adult rat. *Lab. Invest.* **70,** 511–516.
97. Fujio, K., Hu, Z., Evarts, R.P., Marsden, E.R., Niu, C.H., and Thorgeirsson, S.S. (1996). Coexpression of stem cell factor and c-kit in embryonic and adult liver. *Exp. Cell Res.* **224,** 243–250.
98. Matthews, W., Jordan, C.T., Weigand, C.W., Pardoll, D., and Lemischka, I.R. (1991). A receptor tyrosine kinase specific to hematopoietic stem and progenitor cell-enriched populations. *Cell* **65,** 1143–1152.
99. Matsusaka, S., Tsujimura, T., Toyosaka, A., Nakasho, K., Sugihara, A., Okamoto, E., Uematsu, K., and Terada N. (1999). Role of *c-kit* receptor tyrosine kinase in development of oval cells in the rat 2-acetylaminofluorene/partial hepatectomy model. *Hepatology* **29,** 670–676.
100. Hu, Z., Evarts, R.P., Fujio, K., Omori, N., Omori, M., Marsden, E.R., and Thorgeirsson, S.S. (1996). Expression of transforming growth factor-alpha/epidermal growth factor receptor, hepatocyte growth factor/c-met, and acidic fibroblast growth factor/fibroblast growth factor receptors during hepatocarcinogenesis. *Carcinogenesis* **17,** 931–938.
101. Alison, M.R., Poulsom, R., Jeffrey, R., Anilkumar, T.V., Jagoe, R., and Sarraf, C.E. (1993). Expression of hepatocyte growth factor mRNA during oval cell activation in the rat liver. *J. Pathol.* **171,** 291–299.
102. Hu, Z., Evarts, R.P., Fujio, K., Marsden, E.R., and Thorgeirsson, S.S. (1993). Expression of hepatocyte growth factor and *c-met* genes during hepatic differentiation and liver development in the rat. *Am. J. Pathol.* **142,** 1823–1830.
103. Evarts, R.P., Nakatsukasa, H., Marsden, E.R., Hu, Z., and Thorgeirsson, S.S. (1992). Expression of transforming growth factor-alpha in regenerating liver and during hepatic differentiation. *Mol. Carcinog.* **5,** 25–31.
104. Hu, Z., Evarts, R.P., Fujio, K., Marsden, E.R., and Thorgeirsson, S.S. (1995). Expression of fibroblast growth factor receptors *flg* and *bek* during hepatic ontogenesis and regeneration in the rat. *Cell Growth Differ.* **6,** 1019–1025.
105. Shiota, G., Kunisada, T., Oyama, K., Udagawa, A., Nomi, T., Tanaka, K., Tsutsumi, A., Isono, M., Nakamura, T., Hamada, H., Sakatani, T., Sell, S., Sato, K., Ito, H., and Kawasaki, H. (2000). *In vivo* transfer of hepatocyte growth factor gene accelerates proliferation of hepatic oval cells in a 2-acetylaminofluorene/partial hepatectomy model in rats. *FEBS Lett.* **470,** 325–330.
106. Nakatsukasa, H., Evarts, R.P., Hsia, C.C., Marsden, E., and Thorgeirsson, S.S. (1991). Expression of transforming growth factor-beta 1 during chemical hepatocarcinogenesis in the rat. *Lab. Invest.* **65,** 511–517.
107. Preisegger, K.H., Factor, V.M., Fuchsbichler, A., Stumptner, C., Denk, H., and Thorgeirsson, S.S. (1999). Atypical ductular proliferation and its inhibition by transforming growth factor-β1 in the 3,5-diethoxycarbonyl-1,4-dihydrocollidine mouse model for chronic alcoholic liver disease. *Lab. Invest.* **79,** 103–109.
108. Wilson, J.W., and Leduc, E.H. (1958). Role of cholangioles in restoration of the liver of the mouse after dietary injury. *J. Pathol. Bacteriol.* **76,** 441–449.
109. Hixson, D.C., Faris, R.A., Yang, L., and Novikoff, P.M. (1992). Antigenic clues to liver development, renewal, and carcinogenesis. *In* "The Role of Cell Types in Hepatocarcinogenesis," (A.E. Sirica, Ed.), pp. 151–182. CRC Press, Boca Raton, FL.
110. Loffreda, S., Rai, R., Yang, S.Q., Lin, H.Z., and Diehl, A.M. (1997). Bile ducts and portal and central veins are major producers of tumor necrosis factor-α in regenerating rat liver. *Gastroenterology* **112,** 2089–2098.
111. Naldini, L., Tamagnone, L., Vigna, E., Sachs, M., Hartmann, G., Birchmeier, W., Daikuhara, Y., Tsubouchi, H., Blasi, F., and Comoglio, P.M. (1992). Extracellular proteolytic cleavage by urokinase is required for activation of hepatocyte growth factor/scatter factor. *EMBO J.* **11,** 4825–4833.
112. Park, D.Y., and Suh, K.S. (1999). Transforming growth factor-beta 1 protein, proliferation, and apoptosis of oval cells in acetylaminofluorene-induced rat liver regeneration. *J. Korean Med. Sci.* **14,** 531–538.
113. Gordon, G.J., Coleman, W.B., Hixson, D.C., and Grisham, J.W. (2000). Liver regeneration in rats with retrorsine-induced hepatocellular injury proceeds through a novel cellular response. *Am. J. Pathol.* **156,** 607–619.
114. Gordon, G.J., Coleman, W.B., and Grisham, J.W. (2000). Temporal analysis of hepatocyte differentiation by small hepatocyte-like progenitor cells during liver regeneration in retrorsine-exposed rats. *Am. J. Pathol.* **157,** 771–786.
115. Coleman, W.B. (Unpublished observations).
116. Fausto, N. (2000). Liver regeneration. *J. Hepatol.* **32** (Suppl. 1), 19–31.
117. Diehl, A.M. (2002). Liver regeneration. *Frontiers Biosci.* **7,** e301–e314.
118. Peters, M., Blinn, G., Jostock, T., Schirmacher, P., Meyer zum Buschenfelde, K.H., Galle, P.R., and Rose-John, S. (2000). Combined interleukin 6 and soluble interleukin 6 receptor accelerates murine liver regeneration. *Gastroenterology* **119,** 1663–1671.
119. Jones, S.A., Novick, D., Horiuchi, S., Yamamoto, N., Szalai, A.J., and Fuller, G.M. (1999). C-reactive protein: a physiological activator of interleukin 6 receptor shedding. *J. Exp. Med.* **189,** 599–604.
120. Mastellos, D., Papadimitriou, J.C., Franchini, S., Tsonis, P.A., and Lambris, J.D. (2001). A novel role of complement: mice deficient in the fifth component of complement (C5) exhibit impaired liver regeneration. *J. Immunol.* **166,** 2479–2486.
121. Vujanovic, N.L., Polimeno, L., Azzarone, A., Francavilla, A., Chambers, W.H., Starzl, T.E., Herberman, R.B., and Whiteside, T.L. (1995). Changes of liver-resident NK cells during liver regeneration in rats. *J. Immunol.* **154,** 6324–6338.
122. Minagawa, M., Oya, H., Yamamoto, S., Shimizu, T., Bannai, M., Kawamura, H., Hatakeyama, K, and Abo, T. (2000). Intensive expansion of natural killer T-cells in the early phase of hepatocyte regeneration after partial hepatectomy in mice and its association with sympathetic nerve activation. *Hepatology* **31,** 907–915.
123. Dabeva, M.D., and Shafritz, D.A. (1993). Activation, proliferation, and differentiation of progenitor cells into hepatocytes in the D-galactosamine model of liver regeneration. *Am. J. Pathol.* **143,** 1606–1620.
124. Okihiro, M.S., and Hinton, D.E. (2000). Partial hepatectomy and bile duct ligation in rainbow trout *(Oncorhynchus mykiss):* histologic, immunohistochemical, and enzyme histochemical characterization of hepatic regeneration and biliary hyperplasia. *Toxicol. Pathol.* **28,** 342–356.
125. Golding, M., Sarraf, C.E., Lalani, E.N., Anilkumar, T.V., Edwards, R.J., Nagy, P., Thorgeirsson, S.S., and Alison, M.R. (1995). Oval cell differentiation into hepatocytes in the acetylaminofluorene-treated regenerating rat liver. *Hepatology* **22,** 1243-1253.

46

Pancreatic Stem Cells

Yuval Dor and Douglas A. Melton

Introduction

From a clinical perspective, the pancreas is an important focus of stem cell research because it is an attractive target for cell replacement therapy. In type I diabetes, the insulin-producing β-cells that reside in the pancreatic islets of Langerhans are destroyed by autoimmune attack, and it is thought that self-renewing stem cells could provide an unlimited source of β-cells for transplantation. Such therapeutic efforts require the prospective isolation of stem cells with the potential to produce β-cells and the development of methods to direct their expansion and differentiation.

From a developmental biology perspective, the role of stem cells in the pancreas is a fascinating problem. New cells are produced during adulthood, but their origin is not clear. Much of the field is focused on the identification of β-cell progenitors and the characterization of their molecular requirements, but it is not known what role such cells play during pancreas maintenance and regeneration or whether the adult pancreas contains a population of true stem cells. Regardless, information about the specification of the β-cell fate from undifferentiated progenitors will certainly be important in eventually directing the differentiation of stem cells *in vitro*.

In this chapter, we review evidence for the existence and identity of pancreatic progenitor and stem cells and describe the criteria for experimental demonstration of such cells.

Definition of Stem Cells and of Progenitor Cells

The most rigorous definition of a stem cell is a cell that, upon proliferation, produces some progeny that have the same developmental potential (a process called self-renewal) as well as other progeny that have a more restricted developmental potential. Such cells may be present transiently during embryonic development or persistently during the entire life of the organism, but their defining property is self-renewal. A progenitor cell, on the other hand, is any cell that generates another differentiated cell type.[1]

Another important notion in stem cell biology with potential relevance to the pancreas is that of the facultative stem cell. These are thought to be functional, differentiated cells in an adult organ that can dedifferentiate in response to a specific signal (usually believed to be tissue damage) and then differentiate into another cell type. For example, the liver is thought to contain facultative stem cells that reside in the bile ducts and are capable of producing hepatocytes. Thus, the bile duct cells provide an effective reservoir of liver progenitors in case of tissue damage, although they may not meet the criteria of being stem cells at the single-cell level.

How can we demonstrate that a particular cell is a stem cell? Formally, such a demonstration must be based on clonal analysis: A single cell has to be followed over time, to show that it can produce more stem cells as well as differentiated cells. The gold standard for the identification of stem cells was set in the hematopoietic system, where clonal analysis has been carried out *in vitro* (by subcloning individual colonies) as well as *in vivo* (by serial transplantation of single stem cells into lethally irradiated mice). By contrast, the identification of progenitor cells is an easier task. It requires the demonstration using some sort of linage-tracing experiment that an undifferentiated cell population generates differentiated cells.

Even when stem cells cannot be identified or isolated in a particular organ, their existence may be inferred from kinetic studies of 5′-bromo-2′-deoxyuridine (BrdU) incorporation. Because stem cells are believed to be slowly dividing, the presence of label-retaining cells can identify the anatomical location of a stem cell niche. Such an analysis was carried out in self-renewing organ systems such as skin and hair.[2,3]

In light of these definitions, we provide in the next sections the evidence for stem cells and progenitors during pancreas development and adult life.

Progenitor Cells During Embryonic Development of the Pancreas

The adult pancreas contains three major cell types: exocrine cells, organized in acini, that secrete digestive enzymes; duct epithelial cells that flush these enzymes to the duodenum; and endocrine cells, organized in the islets of Langerhans, that secrete hormones to the blood. The islets, accounting for ~1% of the cells in the adult pancreas, contain four cell types that secrete different hormones: α-, β-, δ-, and pp-cells secreting glucagon, insulin, somatostatin, and pancreatic polypeptide, respectively.

In recent years, a detailed cellular and molecular understanding of pancreas development has emerged (Fig. 46–1). Although many questions remain, one recurring theme is the essential role played by progenitor cells in organogenesis. Early patterning of the gut tube generates a sheet of epithelial

Handbook of Stem Cells
Volume 2

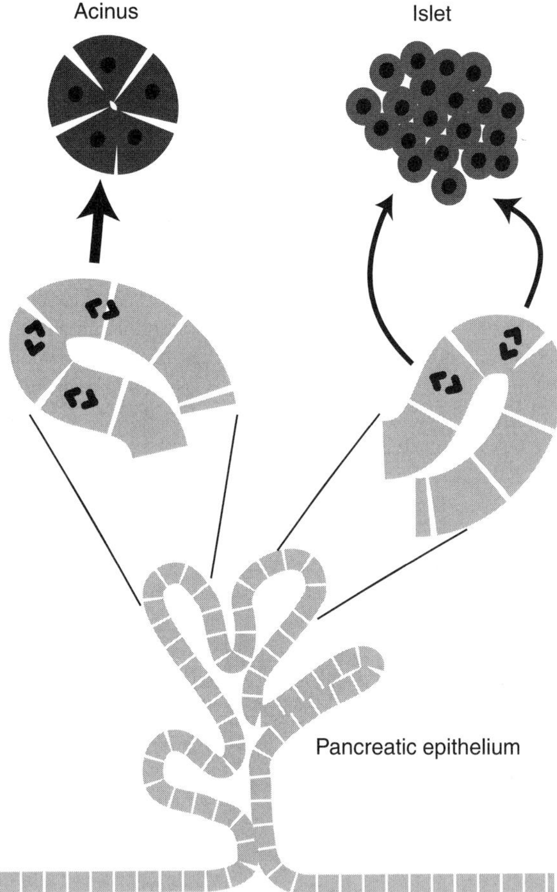

Figure 46–1. *Embryonic development of the pancreas and the plain of cell division.* Shown are Pdx1+ epithelial cells of the early pancreas (light squares), an acinus containing exocrine cells, and an islet of Langerhans composed of endocrine cells. The proposed plane of division of endocrine and exocrine progenitors is indicated. (Please see CD-ROM for color version of this figure.)

cells that express the homeobox gene *pdx1* around embryonic day 9 (E9) in the mouse. These epithelial cells bud from the gut tube, proliferate, and branch to form a tubular structure around E12.5 from which cells differentiate and organize into the exocrine and endocrine tissues of the mature pancreas.[4,5] Numerous experiments demonstrate that this process is based upon the proliferation and stepwise differentiation of progenitor cells. As shown by lineage-tracing experiments using tamoxifen-induced cre recombinase,[6] the early pdx1+ cells (which by E10.5 also express the transcription factor p48/ptf1)[7] produce all cell types in the adult pancreas. Later on, progenitors for duct, exocrine, and endocrine lineages segregate, proliferate, and differentiate. Endocrine progenitors migrate from the tubular structure of the early pancreas and coalesce to form the islets of Langerhans just before birth. During that period, they undergo further restrictions in their potential, marked by the transient expression of several genes. Most notably, neurogenin3 expression marks progenitor cells for all endocrine lineages.[6,8–10] Down-regulation of progenitor markers and expression of the hormone genes marks the terminal differentiation of endocrine cells. A similar mechanism of gradual commitment, although less well defined, is thought to act in the developing exocrine pancreas.

How do pancreatic progenitors choose their fates? A longstanding hypothesis is that the axis of mitosis in epithelial cells of the early pancreas correlates with, or even determines, the identity of daughter cells[11] (Fig. 46–1). When the plane of division is perpendicular to the lumen, both daughter cells remain epithelial (symmetric division) and may lobulate to form exocrine acini. When the plane of division is parallel to the lumen, one daughter cell detaches from the lumen and may become an endocrine progenitor cell (asymmetric division). This hypothesis, although untested, supports the popular view that adult pancreatic stem cells reside in the ducts. More recently, genetic evidence has suggested that cell–cell interactions mediated by the Notch pathway affect lateral specification of progenitor cells at multiple developmental junctions. Accordingly, mutations in Notch pathway genes can lead to accelerated, premature endocrine differentiation on the expense of the exocrine pancreas.[12,13] These two models for specification may be compatible, as the Notch pathway is known to affect the plane of division in neural progenitors.[14–17]

What is the relative contribution of progenitors and differentiated cells to proliferation of the embryonic pancreas? Although this question has not been addressed directly, the fate of hormone-expressing cells that appear early in pancreas development (E9.5–10.5) was recently examined.[18,19] These cells, many of which coexpress multiple endocrine hormones, where initially thought to replicate and generate the mature islets. However, lineage-tracing and ablation experiments suggest that the multiple-hormone-expressing cells do not contribute to the adult endocrine pancreas. Rather, mature endocrine cells appear to be derived from midgestation progenitors.

Following this progenitor-based formative stage, rapid growth of the pancreas in late gestation and early postnatal life is thought to involve gradually less differentiation of progenitor cells and more replication of fully differentiated cells (see later sections of this chapter).

Although the identity and importance of progenitors during pancreas development is clear, there is no indication for true self-renewal of cells during this period. The recent demonstration of heterogeneity among the pdx1+ cells of the early pancreas[20] suggests that lineage segregation occurs very early during pancreas organogenesis. Furthermore, no clonal analysis of the embryonic pancreas has been carried out *in vivo. In vitro* clonal analysis[21] demonstrated common origin of the exocrine and endocrine pancreas but not self-renewal. Therefore, it is fair to conclude that progenitor cells play a major role in pancreas formation. However, there is no evidence for pancreatic stem cells during embryonic development.

We now turn to the postnatal growth and maintenance of the pancreas, with special attention to β-cells. Do progenitor cells of the embryonic type persist in adult life in an active or latent form? Is there evidence for stem cells capable of generating new pancreatic cells in the adult?

Progenitor Cells in the Adult Pancreas

When describing stem/progenitor cells in the adult pancreas, it is important to deal separately with two questions: First, what is the turnover rate of the different components of the pancreas during postnatal growth, throughout adult maintenance, and in response to injury? Second, are the new cells derived from stem/progenitor cells (neogenesis) or from replicating differentiated cells? It must be remembered that an impressive capacity for homeostatic maintenance or even regeneration does not indicate neogenesis. For example, complete regeneration of the injured liver can occur solely by proliferation of differentiated hepatocytes without a requirement for stem cells.[22,23]

EVIDENCE FROM CELL DYNAMICS

After birth, the growth of the pancreas continues and slows significantly around 1 month of age in the mouse and rat. However, even in old animals there is a measurable rate of cell birth in all pancreatic compartments.[24,25] In the β-cell compartment, where most studies have been done, the replication rate falls from ~5% in 4-week-old animals[26,27] to ~0.1% in mice older than 3 months. Embryonic-type progenitors (based on expression patterns) are not seen in the normal adult animal (with the possible exception of rare islet cells generated from neurogenin3$^+$ progenitors).[6]

In spite of its low basal turnover rate, significant hyperplasia is seen in the adult pancreas under certain physiologic and pathologic conditions. For example, during, pregnancy the β-cell mass increases about twofold,[28] a response attributed to a combination of cell hypertrophy and cell proliferation. More dramatically, several reports have documented an ability of the β-cell compartment to recover from genetically programmed,[29–31] autoimmune,[32] surgical,[33] or chemical[34,35] damage.

Can the new cells, in normal homeostasis or in a regeneration setting, be fully accounted for by the replication of differentiated cells? Empirically, for the β-cell compartment, can the number of BrdU$^+$ pulse-labeled β-cells explain the accumulation of BrdU$^+$ β-cells following continuous administration of BrdU? If not, the presence of undifferentiated progenitors must be invoked. This type of analysis has, however, been proven difficult because it requires reliable values for several elusive parameters: What is the duration of the S phase and the total cell cycle in a specific compartment? What is the death rate, and how long does it take for a dying cell to be cleared? Furthermore, cell number is not easily inferred from total cell area as obtained by immunostaining because of cellular hypertrophy. Thus, a study of β-cell dynamics must include β-cell counting by sorting or by careful histological analysis across the whole pancreas, a criterion that is not always met.

The most comprehensive effort in this direction was carried out by Einegood *et al.*[26] who studied β-cell dynamics throughout the life span of the rat. Their results imply a significant contribution of progenitor cells to the β-cell mass in the first weeks after birth, then a shift to tissue maintenance by slow replication of β-cells. In addition, significant β-cell neogenesis was deduced in a similar study of chronic hyperglycemia in rats.[36] These kinetic studies suggest that adult pancreatic progenitors exist. However, they do not help in determining the molecular and anatomical origins of these cells.

Another argument for the existence of β-cell progenitors is the identification of single β-cells embedded in the adult exocrine tissue. These isolated cells are reportedly more frequent following insults, which led to the notion that they are newly generated from progenitors that reside in ducts or acini (see later sections of this chapter). The new β-cells are then believed to coalesce into islets in a mechanism resembling developmental islet morphogenesis.[36–38] However, careful analysis is required to distinguish this interpretation from other potential explanations (e.g., disintegration of existing islets).

A combination of BrdU pulse–chase experiments and genetic labeling of differentiated cells (for example, using an inducible cre recombinase) may allow a direct comparison between the contribution of progenitors and the contribution of differentiated cells to pancreas growth and maintenance.

Many experiments neglect the kinetic aspects of neogenesis and focus on histological identification of progenitors, based on expression markers, in certain anatomical locations. However, without lineage tracing, these studies cannot demonstrate the fate of the putative progenitors or determine their importance. In the next sections, we describe the most notable proposals for the identity of adult pancreatic stem–progenitor cells.

DUCTS

It is widely believed that adult pancreatic stem/progenitor cells are located in the duct epithelium. Indeed, cells expressing β-cell markers (insulin, glut-2, pax6, isl1, and HNF3β) can often be found embedded in or adjacent to adult ducts following an insult—diabetogenic or more general—to the pancreas.[34,37,39–41]

Moreover, duct cell replication (as assessed by BrdU incorporation) is increased after such insults.[33,34,42] In addition, adult duct preparations are claimed to be capable of endocrine differentiation *in vitro* (see later sections of this chapter). Conceptually, the appearance of endocrine cells in or near ducts is interpreted as recapitulation of embryonic pancreas morphogenesis, where endocrine progenitors bud from the epithelium. However, adult ducts are not necessarily identical in their genetic program to the embryonic tubes that should be referred to as "duct-like structures." Indeed, recent lineage experiments indicate that the definitive ductal and endocrine lineages are separated as early as E12.5.[6] With regard to endocrine cells seen budding from ducts, caution is required when suggesting dynamic interpretations to static histological snapshots (Fig. 46–2 and Fig. 46–3).

The preceding description shows the importance of specific duct markers for the assessment of the ductal origins of endocrine cells. Although several duct markers have been found (such as carbonic anhydrase, cystic fibrosis transmembrane-conductance regulator, and cytokeratin-19), so far none have been translated to a useful lineage marker in transgenic mice.

In summary, it seems that ducts can elicit a proliferative response to tissue damage and that endocrine markers are occasionally expressed in cells of the ductal epithelium.

However, the fate of these cells and their relative contribution to the endocrine or exocrine pancreas has yet to be demonstrated.

ACINI

Starting from the observation of isolated β-cells embedded in exocrine tissue, other investigators have proposed that acinar cells can transdifferentiate, with or without replication, into endocrine cells.[36,37] This possibility is supported by *in vitro* studies showing that an acinar cell line can adopt endocrine features under certain conditions (see later sections of this chapter). However, as in the case of duct-embedded progenitors, the lineage of these cells was not followed *in vivo;* therefore, their origin and fate could not be determined. In this case, though, good lineage markers exist, so the possible acinar origin of endocrine cells can be directly tested. Preliminary experiments with an Elastase promoter driven cre recombinase have suggested that under normal conditions, Elastase-expressing cells do not produce endocrine cells.[27] It remains to be tested, however, whether acinar cells contain "facultative" endocrine progenitors activated upon injury.

INTRAISLET PROGENITORS

Several groups have suggested the existence of intraislet progenitor cells capable of proliferation and differentiation to β-cells. These reports are based on the expression of putative stem–progenitor cell markers in islets. One such proposal is that the expression of Nestin, a marker of neuronal progenitors, labels intraislet endocrine progenitors with a potential for *in vitro* differentiation into several fates.[43,44] However, a recent lineage analysis using Cre recombinase driven by the Nestin promoter showed that pancreatic endocrine cells do not form by the differentiation of Nestin$^+$ cells.[44a–44c] In addition, Nestin was recently shown to be expressed in the mesenchymal but not in epithelial cells of the embryonic pancreas, further questioning its relevance for pancreatic lineages.[45]

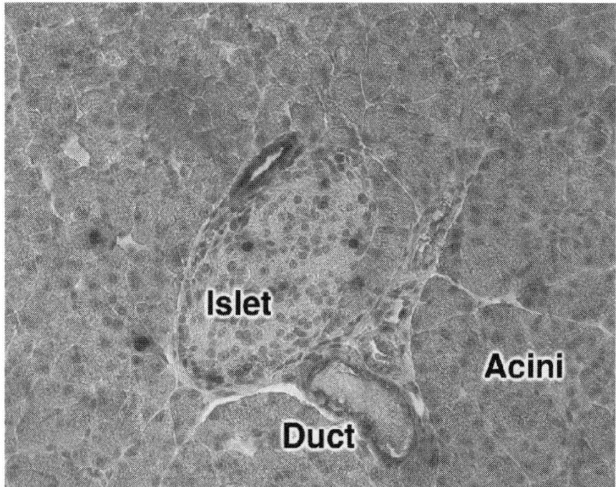

Figure 46–2. *Histology of adult pancreas.* Exocrine tissue (acini and ducts) and endocrine tissue (islet of Langerhans). Section from a 4-week-old mouse pancreas, pulse labeled with BrdU (darkest patches). Ducts are stained with the DBA (Dolichos Biflorus Agglutinin) lectin (dark staining). Note the close association between the ducts and the islet. Original magnification = 200X. (Please see CD-ROM for color version of this figure.)

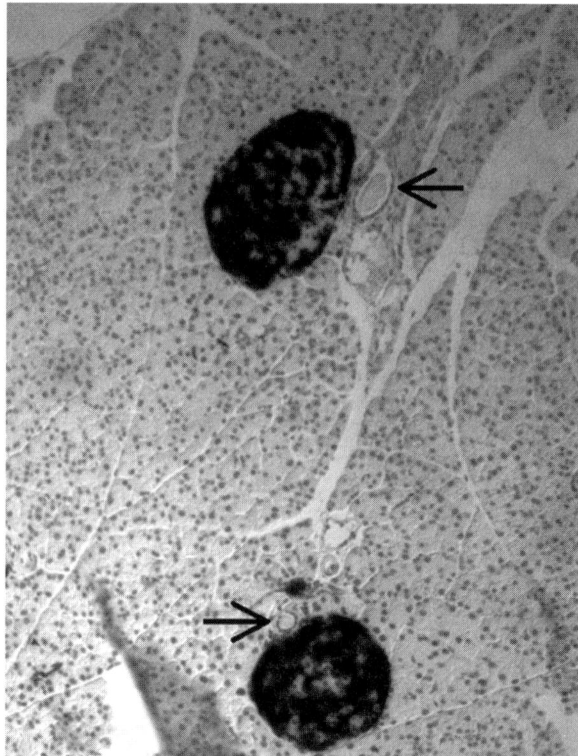

Figure 46–3. *Lineage labeling of the endocrine pancreas.* Section from the pancreas of a 4-week-old ngn3-cre, Z/AP, double-transgenic mouse, stained for alkaline phosphatase activity. In this mouse, cre-mediated recombination in *ngn3*$^+$ endocrine progenitor cells leads to heritable expression of the human placental alkaline phosphatase gene. Only islet cells are labeled, suggesting that ducts (arrows) and acini never expressed the *ngn3* gene. Original magnification = 100X. (Please see CD-ROM for color version of this figure.)

Others have documented the coexpression of pancreatic hormones in islets following a diabetogenic insult. For example, Guz *et al.*[35] have proposed that following streptozotocin treatment, somatostatin$^+$ cells and glucagon$^+$ cells generate β-cells by proliferation and differentiation through somatostatin$^+$/pdx1, and glucagon$^+$/glut-2$^+$ intermediate cell types. These proposals have yet to be confirmed by lineage analysis.

Finally, clinical transplantation of islets may provide important clues about islet cell dynamics. Islet grafts into the portal vein (as done with diabetic patients)[46] or under the kidney capsule (as done routinely with rodents)[47] survive for many months and provide glycemic control. Although it is clear that cells in the grafts die and proliferate,[48–51] it is not known if new endocrine cells in the graft are derived only from replicating differentiated cells or also from progenitors. Since purified islets with minimal exocrine tissue are used for transplantations, any indication for the existence of progenitors in the graft would point to an intraislet source.

BONE MARROW

A recent study found a significant contribution of bone marrow-derived cells to the β-cell compartment in the absence of tissue damage other than irradiation.[52] To facilitate the detection of

47

Stem Cells in the Gastrointestinal Tract

Sean Preston, Nicholas A. Wright, Natalie Direkze, and Mairi Brittan

Turnover of the epithelial cell lineages within the gastrointestinal tract is a constant process, occurring every 2 to 7 days under normal homeostasis and increasing after damage. This process is regulated by multipotent stem cells, which generate all gastrointestinal epithelial cell lineages and can regenerate whole intestinal crypts and gastric glands. The stem cells of the gastrointestinal tract are as yet undefined, although it is generally agreed that they are located within a "niche" in the intestinal crypts and gastric glands. Studies of allophenic, tetraparental chimaeric mice and targeted stem cell mutations suggest that a single stem cell undergoes an asymmetrical division to produce an identical daughter cell, thus replicating itself, and a committed progenitor cell, which further differentiates into an adult epithelial cell type. The discovery of stem cell plasticity in many tissues, including the ability of transplanted bone marrow to transdifferentiate into intestinal subepithelial myofibroblasts, provides a potential use of bone marrow cells to deliver therapeutic genes to damaged tissues, for example, in the treatment of mesenchymal diseases in the gastrointestinal tract, such as fibrosis and Crohn's disease. Studies are beginning to identify the molecular pathways that regulate stem cell proliferation and differentiation into adult gastrointestinal cell lineages, such as the Wnt and Notch–Delta signalling pathways, and to discover the importance of mesenchymal–epithelial interactions in normal gastrointestinal epithelium and in development and disease. Finally, despite some dispute, a strong case can be made for intestinal neoplasia arising as a result of a series of mutations in stem cells. The mechanism and direction of the spread of this mutated clone in the gastrointestinal mucosa is hotly disputed, and central to this argument is the position and nature of the gastrointestinal stem cell.

Introduction

There has been a tremendous increase in interest in stem cell biology and its potential applications in recent years. Although this has been galvanised by the exploitation of research in embryonic stem cells, it is interesting to note that what might be called the "intestinal stem cell community," albeit small, has been working productively for some 40 to 50 years. With stem cells now claiming considerable attention, in retrospect, many of the basic tenets that govern our understanding of organ-specific stem cells have come from studies in the gastrointestinal tract and the haematopoietic system.

In the gastrointestinal tract, there is a large body of evidence that multipotential stem cells are found in specific zones, or niches, within gastric glands and intestinal crypts, composed of and maintained by myofibroblasts in the adjacent lamina propria. In this chapter, we review evidence that these multipotential stem cells generate all gastrointestinal epithelial cell lineages through committed precursor cells housed in the proliferative compartments of intestinal crypts and gastric glands, a concept that has had a long and difficult gestation.[1] Notwithstanding their obvious significance, the gastrointestinal stem cells remain elusive and unidentified, mainly because of a lack of accepted morphological and functional markers at the single-cell level. We also explore concepts of stem cell number, location, and fate, and we touch on the ability of gastrointestinal stem cells to regenerate cell lineages of whole intestinal crypts and villi after damage. The luminal gut shows regional specialisations of function—the stomach primarily for absorption and the intestinal mucosa for both absorption and secretion. This is reflected by variation in the adult cell lineages native to each tissue, and it is thereby consistent that stem cell fate within each tissue is also different. We are beginning to understand the mechanisms that govern such variation. Controversial recent findings regarding stem cell plasticity in the gastrointestinal tract are examined in this chapter. Because of their longevity, putatively the same as that of the organism itself, stem cells are often viewed as the target cells for carcinogens and the cells of origin for spontaneous tumours. Recent thought on the location of stem cells in the colon has sparked debate concerning the possible pathways of morphological progression of transformed stem cells. This includes a *top-down* proliferation of mutated stem cells located within intercryptal zones on the mucosal surface, which spread downward into the adjacent crypts. Contrasting to this is a *bottom-up* theory of the upward proliferation of mutated stem cells in the crypt base to produce dysplastic crypts that replicate and expand by crypt fission. This brings other facets of gut biology into sharp focus—the mechanisms of crypt reproduction; the clonal architecture of normal and dysplastic gastric glands, intestinal crypts, and their derivative tumours; and the role that stem cells take in these events. Here, we propose that the stem cells accumulate the multiple genetic events leading to tumourigenesis, and we explore the manner by which such mutated clones spread in gastrointestinal epithelia. Many of these

Handbook of Stem Cells
Volume 2

concepts are being explored at the level of molecular regulatory pathways, including the signalling pathways of Wnt and transforming growth factor β (TGFβ).

This is quite a brief, since several of the most common tumours originate in the gastrointestinal tract and with increasing incidence in Barrett's oesophagus. Our concepts of stem cell biology impinge considerably on our understanding of how these tumours arise.

Gastrointestinal Mucosa Contains Multiple Lineages

In the small intestine, the epithelial lining forms numerous crypts and larger, finger-shaped projections called villi. In the colon there are many crypts, which vary in size throughout the colon; the shortest is in the ascending colon. Overall, four main epithelial cell lineages exist in the intestinal epithelium. These are the columnar cells, the mucin-secreting cells, the endocrine cells, and Paneth cells in the small intestine. Other less common cell lineages are also present, such as the caveolated cells and membranous or microfold cells. Columnar cells, with apical microvilli, are the most abundant epithelial cells, termed enterocytes in the small intestine and colonocytes in the large intestine. "Goblet" cells containing mucin granules—and thus producing swollen, goblet-shaped cells—are found throughout the colonic epithelium, secreting mucus into the intestinal lumen. Endocrine, "neuroendocrine," or "enteroendocrine" cells form an abundant cell population distributed throughout the intestinal epithelium; these cells secrete peptide hormones in an endocrine or paracrine manner from their contained dense core of neurosecretory granules. Paneth cells are located almost exclusively at the crypt base of the small intestine and ascending colon, contain large apical secretory granules, and express several proteins—including lysozyme, tumour necrosis factor, and the antibacterial cryptins (small molecular-weight peptides related to defensins).

In the stomach, the epithelial lining forms long, tubular glands divided into foveolus, isthmus, neck, and base regions. Gastric foveolar or surface mucus cells are located on the mucosal surface and in the foveola. They contain tightly packed mucous granules in the supranuclear cytoplasm and do not possess a theca. The mucus neck cells are situated within the neck and isthmus of the gastric glands and contain apical secretory mucin granules. The peptic–chief or zymogenic cells are located in the base of the glands in the fundic and body regions; they secrete pepsinogen from oval zymogenic granules. The parietal or oxyntic, acid-secreting cells are located in the body of the stomach in the base of the glands. These cells have many surface infoldings, or canaliculi, which form a network reaching almost to the base of the gland. Endocrine cell families include the enterochromaffin-like cells in the fundus or body that produce histamine; the gastrin-producing cells are a major component of the antral mucosa.

The intestinal crypts and gastric glands are enclosed within a fenestrated sheath of intestinal subepithelial myofibroblasts (ISEMFs). These cells exist as a syncytium that extends throughout the lamina propria and merges with the pericytes of the blood vessels. The ISEMFs are closely applied to the intestinal epithelium and play a vital role in epithelial–mesenchymal interactions. ISEMFs secrete hepatocyte growth factor (HGF), TGFβ,[2] and keratinocyte growth factor (KGF),[3] but the receptors for these growth factors are located on the epithelial cells. Thus, the ISEMFs are essential for the regulation of epithelial cell differentiation through the secretion of these and possibly other growth factors.[3] Platelet-derived growth factor-α (PDGF-A), expressed in the intestinal epithelium, acts by paracrine signalling through its mesenchymal receptor, PDGFR-α, to regulate epithelial–mesenchymal interactions during development. Studies of mice with targeted deletions in the PDGF-A or PDGFR-α genes have shown defects in normal proliferation and differentiation of PDGFR-α positive mesenchymal cells.[4] Typically, ISEMFs are α-smooth muscle actin-positive (αSMA+) and desmin–,[3] but some myofibroblasts also express myosin-heavy chains.[5] ISEMFs undergo proliferation despite this MyoD expression—unlike the skeletal muscle myoblast, which decycles once MyoD is expressed. It has been proposed that these cells form a renewing population, migrating upwards as they accompany the epithelial escalator.[6] Although they appear to proliferate and migrate, they move relatively slowly and then move off into the lamina propria to become polyploid.[7]

A second myofibroblast population in the intestine are the interstitial cells of Cajal. These cells are located close to neurones in the muscular layers; they act as pacemakers for gastrointestinal smooth muscle activity, propagate electrical events, and modulate neurotransmission.[8] They are said to be αSMA^+ and desmin+ and to immunostain for *c-kit* and CD45.[3]

Epithelial Cell Lineages Originate from a Common Precursor Cell

Little is known of the location and fate of the stem cells within the gastrointestinal tract because of the lack of distinctive and accepted stem cells markers, although they are usually said to appear undifferentiated and can be identified operationally by their ability to repopulate crypts and glands after damage.

The Unitarian hypothesis states that all the differentiated cell lineages within the gastrointestinal epithelium emanate from a common stem cell origin.[9] Although widely propounded, until very recently little definitive evidence existed to underpin this hypothesis.[10] Moreover, Pearse and Takor famously proposed that gastrointestinal endocrine cells derive from migrating neuroendocrine stem cells in the neural crest,[11] a concept that still has its adherents.[12] Although studies of quail neural crest cells transplanted into chick embryos,[13] or experiments where the neural crest is eradicated,[14] show gut endocrine cells to be of endodermal origin, Pearse[15] subsequently suggested that the endoderm is colonised by "neuroendocrine-programmed stem cells" from the primitive epiblast, which generate gut endocrine cells. This hypothesis was not ruled out by chick–quail chimaera experiments; therefore, other models must be used to ascertain the gut endocrine cell origins, such as the chimaeric mouse studies described later.

Several lines of evidence suggest that stem cells reside in the base of the crypts of Lieberkuhn in the small intestine, just superior to the Paneth cells (approximately the fourth or fifth cell position in mice). In the large intestine, they are presumed to be located in the midcrypt of the ascending colon and in the crypt base of the descending colon.[1] However, within the gastric glands, migration of cells is bidirectional from the neck–isthmus region to form the simple mucous epithelium of the foveolus or pit, and cells migrate downward to form parietal cells and chief cells. Therefore, the stem cells are believed to be within the neck–isthmus region of the gastric gland.[16] The unitarian hypothesis is now supported by a considerable body of research.

Single Intestinal Stem Cells Regenerate Whole Crypts Containing All Epithelial Lineages

The ability of intestinal stem cells to regenerate epithelial cell populations of entire intestinal crypts and villi following cytotoxic treatment has been demonstrated using the crypt microcolony assay.[17] Four days after irradiation, sterilised crypts undergo apoptosis and disappear, but they can be identified by remaining radio-resistant Paneth cells at the crypt base. At higher radiation dose levels, only single cells survive in each crypt, since a unit increase in radiation leads to unit reduction in crypt survival. Survival of one or more clonogenic cells in a crypt after radiation ensures crypt persistence, and there is regeneration of all epithelial cell populations of that crypt and, in the small intestine, of the overlying villi. Therefore, following cytotoxic damage, a single surviving stem cell can produce all cell types of the intestinal epithelium to reproduce a crypt.[18]

Mouse Aggregation Chimaeras Show That Intestinal Crypts Are Clonal Populations

Mouse embryo aggregation chimeras are readily made, wherein the two populations can be readily distinguished. The lectin *Dolichos biflorus* agglutinin (DBA) binds to sites on the B6-derived but not on the SWR-derived cells in C57BL/6J Lac (B6)↔SWR mouse embryo aggregation chimaeras, and it can be used to distinguish the two parental strains in gut epithelium. The intestinal crypts in each chimera studied were either positive or negative for DBA, and there were no mixed crypts in the tens of thousands studied[19] (Fig. 47–1A). Therefore, each crypt forms a clonal population. This is the case for Paneth, mucous, and columnar cells, although it was not possible to detect the markers in endocrine cells because of their inability to bind the lectin on their surface.[20] In neonatal C57BL/6J Lac (B6)↔SWR chimaeras, there were mixed (i.e., polyclonal) crypts for the first 2 weeks after birth, suggesting that multiple stem cells exist during development[21] (Fig. 47–1B through 47–1D). However all crypts ultimately become derived from a single stem cell between birth and postnatal day 14, so-called monoclonal conversion. This apparent cleansing or "purification" of crypts could be caused by the stochastic loss of one stem cell lineage or by the segregation of lineages because of an extremely active replication of crypts by fission, which occurs at this developmental period.[22,23] To exclude the possibility that crypts from distinct strains segregate differentially during organogenesis, Griffiths *et al.*[24] confirmed the findings in mice bearing an X-linked defective gene for glucose-6-phosphate dehydrogenase *(G6PD)* (Fig. 47–1E and later sections of this chapter).

In the stomach, the situation is similar although more complex. Epithelial cell lineages in the antral gastric mucosa of the mouse stomach, including the endocrine cells, derive from a common stem cell. Identification of the Y-chromosome by *in situ* hybridisation in XX–XY chimaeric mice showed that gastric glands were also clonal populations[21] (Fig. 47–1F) These findings were confirmed by Tatematsu *et al.*[25] in 1994 in CH3↔BALB/c chimaeric mice, where each gastric gland was composed of either CH3 or BALB/c cells; there were no mixed glands. Thus, we might advance the general hypothesis that gastric glands in the mouse, in addition to the intestinal crypts, are clonally derived. Additionally, by combining immunohistochemistry for gastrin, an endocrine cell marker, with *in situ* hybridisation to detect the Y-chromosome, the male regions of the gastric glands were shown to be almost exclusively Y-chromosome positive with gastrin-positive endocrine cells, whereas the female areas in the chimaeric stomach were gastrin positive and Y-chromosome negative[21] (Fig. 47–1D). These results finally negate the Pearse concept that gut endocrine cells originate from a separate stem cell pool.

Nomura *et al.*[26] used X-inactivation mosaic mice expressing a *lacZ* reporter gene to study clonality of gastric glands in the fundic and pyloric regions of the developing mouse stomach. As in the intestine, most glands are initially polyclonal, with three or four stem cells per gland, but they become monoclonal during the first 6 weeks of life—again either by purification of the glands, where division of one stem cell eventually overrides all other stem cells, or by gland fission. A population of approximately 5–10% of mixed, polyclonal glands persists into adulthood. The significance of these mixed glands with an increased stem cell number is not known, but it is possible that they do not undergo fission or have reduced fission rates; perhaps they even have an increased stem cell number during development and therefore maintain a higher number of stem cells after crypt fission.

Somatic Mutations in Stem Cells Reveal Stem Cell Hierarchy and Clonal Succession

Somatic mutations at certain loci allow us to study stem cell hierarchy and clonal succession within the gastrointestinal tract. Mutations in the *DLb-1* on chromosome 11 are one good example of this; C57BL/6J↔SWR F1 chimaeric mice show

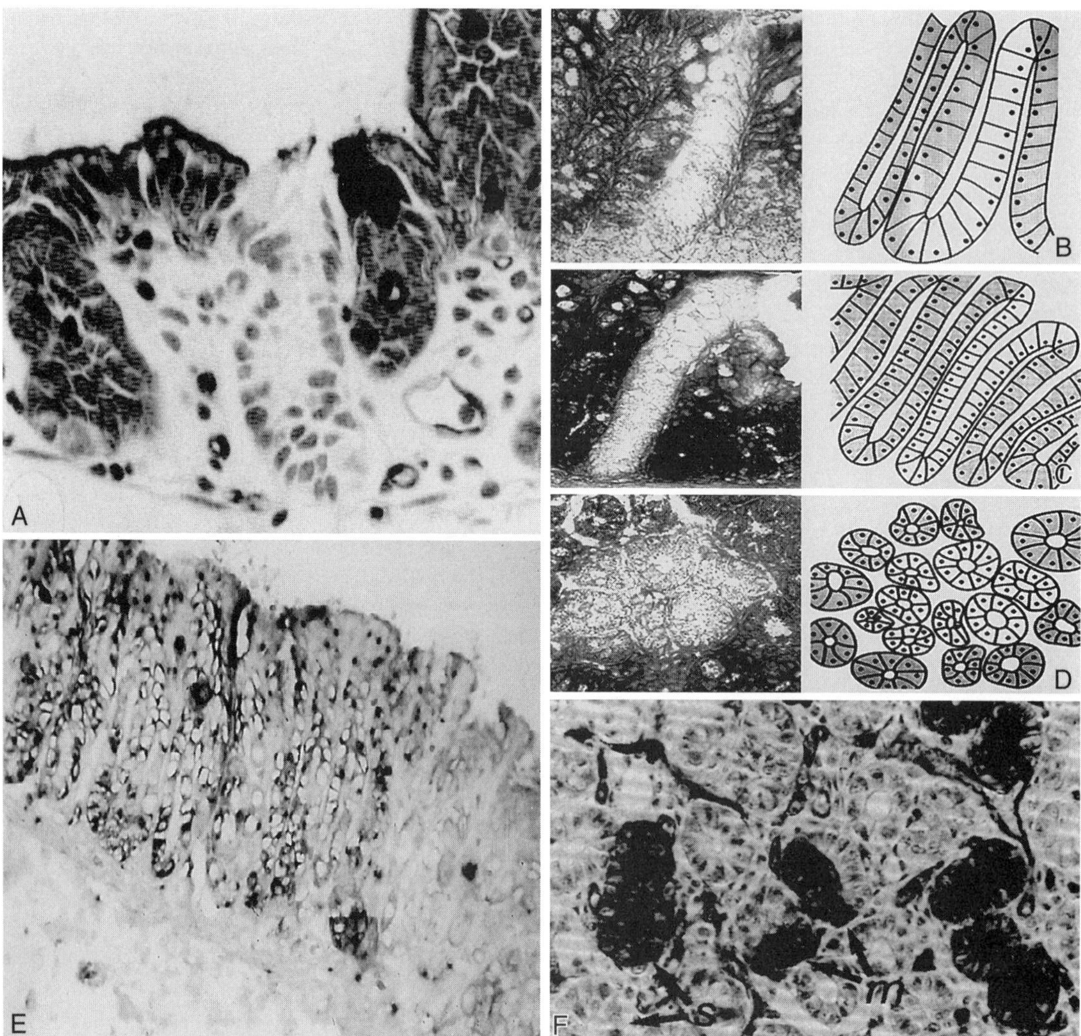

Figure 47–1. *Gastrointestinal clonality studies.* Mouse embryo aggregation chimaeras, XX–XY chimaeric mice, and X-inactivation mice. (A) DBA staining in the small intestine of ENU-treated (12 weeks) C57BL/6J-SWR F1 chimaeras showing entire negative and positive (black) crypts. (B–D) G6PD histochemistry in frozen sections of colonic mucosa in an ENU-treated C3H mouse: (B) partially negative crypt, (C) completely negative crypt, and (D) cross section of an eight-crypt patch at 21 weeks. (E) Y-spot pattern in the gastric mucosa and underlying tissues of an XX–XY chimaera. (F) Cross section through crypts in neonatal duodenum of B6-SWR chimaera stained with DBA (B6 = black staining, SWR = unstained). A balanced contribution to mixed crypts (m), and monoclonal crypts (s) is seen. Panel A reproduced with permission from Winton *et al.*,[102] panel B with permission from Park *et al.*,[22] panel E courtesy of E.M. Thompson, and panel F with permission from Schmidt *et al.*[21] (Please see CD-ROM for color version of this figure.)

heterozygous expression of a binding site on intestinal epithelial cells for the DBA lectin. This binding site can be abolished when the *Dlb-1* locus becomes mutated either spontaneously or by the chemical mutagen ethyl nitrosourea (ENU). After ENU treatment, crypts emerge that initially are partially and then are entirely negative for DBA staining.[27] Perhaps the simplest explanation for this phenomenon is that a mutation occurs at the *Dlb-1* locus in a stem cell within the small intestinal crypt. This mutated cell could expand stochastically to produce a clone of cells that cannot bind DBA and remain unstained[27] (Fig. 47–1E). If this is the case, then a single stem cell can generate all the epithelial lineages within an intestinal crypt of the small intestine.

A "knock-in" strategy at the *Dlb-1* locus can also be used to explain the preceding findings. If SWR mice do not express a DBA-binding site on their intestinal epithelial cells but can be induced to bind DBA by ENU treatment, wholly DBA+ or DBA− intestinal crypts would result. From the use of this model, Bjerknes and Cheng[23,28] propose that "committed epithelial progenitor" cells exist in mouse intestinal crypts by visualising the morphology, location, and longevity of mutant clones in crypts and villi of the mouse small intestine. These transitory committed progenitor cells—the columnar cell progenitors (C_0) and the mucus cell progenitors (M_0)—evolve from pluripotential stem cells and then differentiate further into adult intestinal epithelial cell types.

Not much is known about the mechanisms that regulate the proliferation of these progenitor cells, but administration of proglucagon-derived, glucagon-like peptide 2 (GLP-2) to SWR mice was found to induce intestinal epithelial growth and repair specifically by stimulating the columnar cell progenitors, resulting in increased crypt and villus size in the normal small intestine.[28] The receptor for GLP-2 (GLP2R) was recently shown to be located on enteric neurons[28] and not on the gut enteroendocrine cells and in the brain as previously thought.[29] GLP-2 activation of enteric neurons produces a rapid induction in *c-fos* expression, which signals growth of columnar epithelial cell progenitors and stem cells that generate adult columnar cell types. There is no stimulatory effect on the mucus cell lineage; instead, it is stimulated by KGF. Thus, the committed progenitor cells are involved in regeneration of damaged epithelia, possibly through a neural regulatory pathway (Fig. 47–2B).

There remains the possibility that cells from different parental strains of chimaeric animals segregate independently during development to produce *monophenotypic* crypts and not *monoclonal* crypts as we assumed earlier in this chapter. Mosaic expression of the electrophoretic isoenzymes PGK-1A and PGK-1B were analysed in colonic crypts of mice heterozygous for the X-linked alleles *Pgk-1^a^* and *Pgk-1^b^*.[19] In agreement with the results from the chimaeric studies, no mixed crypts were seen, thus eliminating the possibility that these crypts are monophenotypic and verifying that they are derived from a single progenitor cell. In a further model, mice that heterozygously express a defective *G6PD* gene have a crypt-restricted pattern of G6PD expression, thus confirming that the intestinal crypts are derived from a single stem cell.[24] Moreover, mice treated with the colon carcinogen dimethylhydrazine (DMH) or ENU also develop crypts that initially are partially and later are wholly negative for G6PD. The partially negative crypts could conceivably result from the mutation of a cell in the dividing transit population of the crypt that lacks stem cell properties. This is supported by the observation that these partially negative crypts are transient and decrease in frequency parallel to an increase in wholly negative crypts. Conversely such partially negative crypts could become wholly negative by stochastic expansion of a mutant stem cell. Wholly negative crypts would then be a clonal population derived from this mutant stem cell.

After administration of a mutagen, in both the *Dlb-1* and the G6PD models, the time taken for the decrease in partially mutated crypts and the emergence of entirely negative crypts to reach a plateau is approximately 4 weeks in the small intestine and up to 12 weeks in the large intestine (Fig. 47–2A). This difference is intriguing and was initially thought to be because of cell-cycle time differences between the colon and the small intestine. However, a favoured explanation can be found in the *stem cell niche hypothesis*. This hypothesis suggests that multiple stem cells occupy a crypt with random cell loss after stem cell division and was originally formulated as the stem cell zone hypothesis

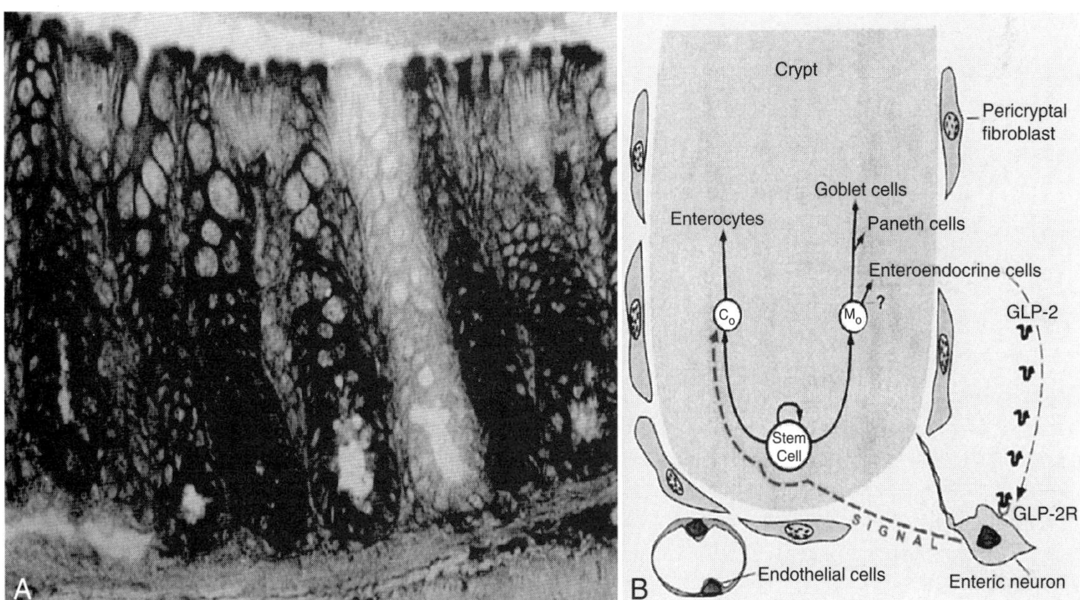

Figure 47–2. *Stem cell niche hypothesis.* (A) G6PD-stained frozen section of colonic mucosa from a CH3 mouse 14 days after a single dose of DMH, showing a single, wholly mutated crypt in which all cells have been replaced by a mutant phenotype. (B) Diagrammatic representation of the stem cell niche. An active, multipotent stem cell produces a daughter cell (C_o) generates enterocytic lineages and another that generates goblet, Paneth, and enteroendocrine cells (although it is not known whether all derive from M_o). GLP-2, produced by a subset of enteroendocrine cells, stimulates proliferation of the C_0 daughter through an interaction with enteric nervous system neurons that express the GLP-2 receptor (GLP-2R). Panel a reproduced with permission from Williams *et al.*,[35] and panel b reproduced with permission from Mills *et al.*[167] (Please see CD-ROM for color version of this figure.)

by Bjerknes and Cheng (see Wright[1] for review and Bjerknes *et al.*[30–34]). The numbers of stem cells may be larger in the small intestine than in the large intestine, causing the difference in time taken for phenotypic changes following mutagen treatment as the mutant stem cell expands stochastically[35] (Fig. 47–2A). An alternative hypothesis might lie in crypt fission: the rate of fission at the time of mutagen administration was higher in the colon than in the small intestine. During crypt fission, when crypts divide longitudinally, selective segregation of the two cell populations could occur, "cleansing" the partially mutated crypts by segregating the mutated and nonmutated cells and by duplicating the wholly negative crypts to create monoclonal crypts[22] (Fig. 47–3). First proposed as a concept by Park *et al.*,[22] this phenomenon was illustrated by Bjerknes and Cheng.[23]

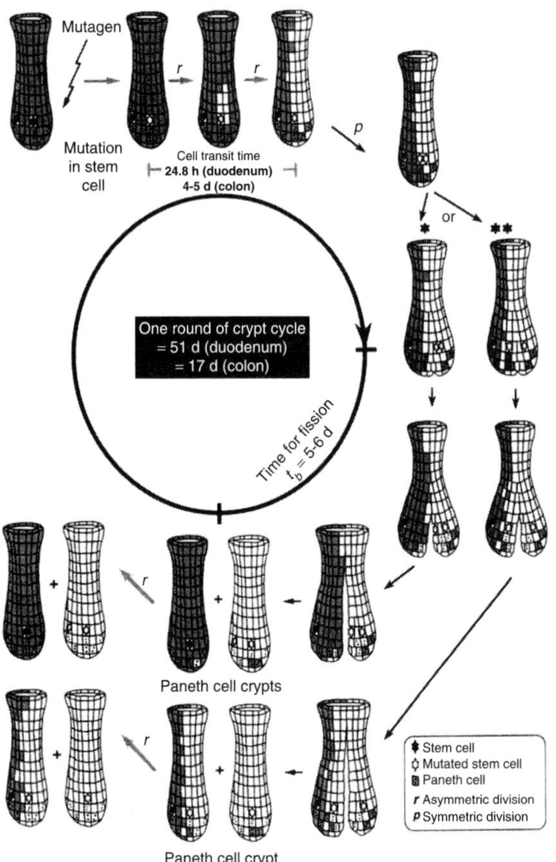

Figure 47–3. *Crypt cycle.* Emergence of transformed crypts after a single stem cell mutation. Crypt division is triggered by symmetric stem cell divisions (p), indicated by light-coloured arrows, whereas dark arrows show asymmetric stem cell divisions (r). This is independent of the crypt cycle and enables individual crypts to maintain a constant number of stem cells and to continuously replace differentiated progeny over a crypt cell turnover time, on average. Reproduced with permission from Park *et al.*[22] (Please see CD-ROM for color version of this figure.)

Human Intestinal Crypts Contain Multiple Epithelial Cell Lineages Derived from a Single Stem Cell

The investigation of gastrointestinal stem cells in humans has proved difficult. The human colorectal carcinoma cell line HRA19 was derived from a primary adenocarcinoma of the rectum. A colony of single morphology was cloned and grown as a monolayer *in vitro.*[36] When engrafted subcutaneously into nude mice, these clones produce tumours histologically identical to the original tumour and contain columnar, goblet, and neuroendocrine cells (Fig. 47–4A through 47-4D). These malignant epithelial cells are therefore multipotential and can produce all differentiated cell types in the human colorectal epithelium.[10] However, these results cannot definitively be applied to normal human gastrointestinal epithelia.

In most of the human population, the colonic goblet cells secrete O-acetylated mucin. However, approximately 9% of the human Caucasian population have a homozygous genetic mutation in the enzyme O-acetyl transferase *($OAT^{-/-}$)* and in goblet cells secreting this non–O-acetylated sialic acid; these are then positive when stained with mild periodic acid-Schiff (mPAS) stain.[37,38] In heterozygotes, which comprise approximately 42% of the population *(OAT^{-}/OAT^{+}),* O-acetylation proceeds, and crypts thereby stain negative for mPAS. Loss of the remaining active *OAT* gene converts the genotype to *OAT^{-}/OAT^{-}*, resulting in occasional, apparently randomly located positive mPAS-stained crypts with uniform staining of goblet cells from base to luminal surface, an effect that increases with age.[39] This could be because of a somatic mutation or nondisjunction in a single crypt stem cell and subsequent colonisation of the crypt by the mutated stem cell. The frequency of these events is racially determined[40] and increases after irradiation.[41] This has been interpreted as indicating an increased rate of stem cell mutation. Interestingly, there is no increase in the rate of apparent stem cell mutation in hereditary nonpolyposis carcinoma patients[42] nor in the background mucosa of left- and right-sided carcinomas.[43] However, just as in the mouse stem cell mutation models, when patients are followed by the mPAS method with time after irradiation, initially there is partial crypt staining, and then whole crypts appear where the goblet cells are mPAS+.[44] A *clonal stabilisation time* (defined as the period required for the emergence of most of such wholly stained crypts) in humans is approximately 1 year, a process we referred to previously as monoclonal crypt conversion.

These results have implications for the origins of goblet cell lineages in the gut: they indicate that they arise from crypt stem cells; however, they say little about the other cell lineages.

Perhaps the best evidence for the clonality of human intestinal crypts, and the stem cell derivation of all contained epithelial cell lineages, comes from studies of the colon of a rare XO–XY patient who received a prophylactic colectomy for familial adenomatous polyposis (FAP).[45,46] Nonisotopic *in situ* hybridisation (NISH) using Y-chromosome–specific probes showed the patient's normal intestinal crypts to be

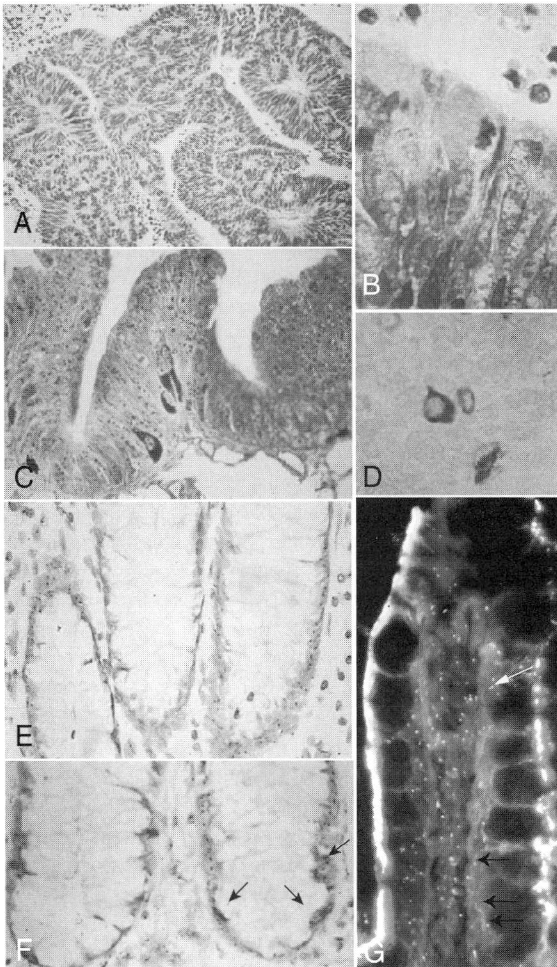

Figure 47–4. *Monoclonal origin of human clonic crypts.* (A) A tumour growing in a nude mouse derived from a single-cell cloned human colorectal carcinoma cell line, stained (B) with Alcian blue to show goblet cells, and with (C) Grimelius and (D) an antibody against chromogranin A to demonstrate endocrine cells. (E) Monoclonal origin of human colonic crypts: normal colonic mucosa in an XO–XY mosaic individual stained by *in situ* hybridisation for a Y-chromosome–specific probe showing an XO crypt (central) surrounded by two XY crypts. (F) Endocrine cells, highlighted by their chromogranin A content, also show clonality with the other crypt cell lineages in the same patient. (G) Villi, receiving cells from more than one crypt of different clonal derivation, show a polyclonal pattern in this XO–XY patient. Apart from the occasional Y-chromosome positive inflammatory cell (white arrow), most cells on the right of this villus are XO (black arrows); on the left side, the cells are XY. Panel A–D courtesy of S. Kirkland, panels E and F courtesy of M. Novelli, and panel G courtesy of R. Poulsom. (Please see CD-ROM for color version of this figure.)

composed almost entirely of either Y-chromosome positive or Y-chromosome negative cells (Fig. 47–4E), with about 20% of crypts being XO. Immunostaining for neuroendocrine specific markers and Y-chromosome NISH used in combination showed that crypt neuroendocrine cells shared the genotype of other crypt cells (Fig. 47–4F). In the small intestine, the villus epithelium was a mixture of XO and XY cells, in keeping with the belief that the villi derive from stem cells of more than one crypt (Fig. 47–4G). Of the 12,614 crypts examined, only 4 crypts were composed of XO and XY cells, which could be explained by nondisjunction with a loss of the Y-chromosome in a crypt stem cell. Importantly there were no mixed crypts at patch boundaries. These observations agree with previous findings using chimaeric mice that intestinal crypt epithelial cells, including neuroendocrine cells, are monoclonal and derive from a single multipotential stem cell. Consequently, the hypothesis that enteroendocrine cells and other differentiated cell types within the colorectal epithelium share a common cell of origin (the unitarian hypothesis) appears to apply to both mice and humans. These observations have recently been confirmed in Sardinian women heterozygous for a defective *G6PD* gene.[47]

It has been proposed that insight into stem cell organization can be gained from the study of the methylation pattern of nonexpressed genes in the colon. In the normal human colon, methylation patterns are somatically inherited endogenous sequences that randomly change and increase in occurrence with aging. Investigation of methylation patterns is a possible alternative to histological markers to investigate crypt histories and allow fate mapping. Examination of methylation tags of three neutral loci in cells from normal human colon showed variation in sequences between crypts and mosaic methylation patterns within single crypts. Multiple unique sites were present in morphologically identical crypts; for example, one patient had no identical methylation sequences of one gene within any of the crypts studied, even though all sequences were related.[48] This indicates that some normal human colonic crypts are quasi-clonal with multiple stem cells per crypt. Differences in methylation tags can highlight relationships among cells in a crypt where less closely related cells show greater sequence alterations and where closely related cells have similar methylation patterns. Sequence differences suggest that crypts are maintained by stem cells, which are randomly lost and replaced in a stochastic manner, eventually leading to a "bottleneck" effect in which all cells within a crypt are closely related to a single stem cell descendant. This reduction to the most recent common crypt progenitor is predicted to occur several times during life, superficially resembling the clonal succession of tumour progression.[49]

In situ analyses of glandular clonality in the human stomach have been more problematic. Nomura *et al.*[50] used X-chromosome–linked inactivation to study fundic and pyloric glands in human female stomachs. Studies using polymorphisms on X-linked genes, such as the androgen receptor (HUMARA) to distinguish between the two X-chromosomes revealed that, although pyloric glands appear homotypic and thus monoclonal, about half of the fundic glands studied were heterotypic for at the HUMARA locus and were consequently polyclonal. This finding suggests that a more complex situation occurs in humans than the studies of gastric gland clonality in chimaeric mice indicate. However, we have seen that some glands in the mouse remain polyclonal throughout life.[26]

Bone Marrow Stem Cells Contribute to Gut Repopulation After Damage

The haematopoietic bone marrow stem cell is of mesodermal origin, and its functionality and cell surface markers have been well characterised.[51] When transplanted into lethally irradiated animals and humans, as in clinical bone marrow transplantation, it has been long considered that the haematopoietic stem cell colonises host tissues to form only new erythroid, granulocyte–macrophage, megakaryocyte, and lymphoid lineages.[52] Although earlier studies suggest that vascular endothelium could derive from transplanted donor marrow, more recent studies not only have confirmed these earlier proposals concerning endothelial cells[53,54] but also have indicated that adult bone marrow stem cells possess a considerable degree of plasticity and can differentiate into different cell types, including hepatocytes,[55–59] biliary epithelial cells,[56] skeletal muscle fibres,[60] cardiomyocytes,[61] central nervous system cells,[62] and renal tubular epithelial cells.[63] These pathways can be bidirectional, as muscle[64] and neuronal stem cells[65] can also apparently form bone marrow. Furthermore, it appears that selection pressure induced by target organ damage can intensify the efficacy of this process as bone marrow stem cells differentiate into cardiomyocytes, endothelial cells, and smooth muscle cells in mice, with ischemic cell death following myocardial infarction and coronary artery occlusion.[61,66] Bone marrow stem cells have also been shown to differentiate into pancreatic β-cells,[67] and possibly more persuasively, fully differentiated cells can transdifferentiate into other adult cell types without undergoing cell division; for example, exocrine pancreatic cells can differentiate into hepatocytes *in vitro*.[68] Furthermore, isolated potential hepatic stem cells from fetal mouse livers, which differentiate into hepatocytes and cholangiocytes when transplanted into recipient animals, can form pancreatic ductal acinar cells and intestinal epithelial cells when transplanted directly into the pancreas or duodenal wall.[69] Thus, the conventional view that bone marrow stem cells generate cell types of a single lineage (i.e., all formed elements in the peripheral blood) has been rectified in favour of the findings that adult bone marrow stem cells are highly plastic and can differentiate into many cell types within various organs.

These observations have raised the possibility of regeneration of a failing organ by transplanting an individual's own bone marrow stem cells to colonise and repopulate the diseased tissue, thus avoiding the allograft reaction. In apparent proof of principle, fumarylacetoacetate hydrolase (FAH)-deficient mice, which resemble type 1 tyrosinaemia in humans, are rescued from liver failure by transplantation of purified haematopoietic stem cells that become morphologically normal hepatocytes, express the FAH enzyme, and therefore are functionally normal.[59]

There are now several reports that bone marrow cells can repopulate both epithelial and mesenchymal lineages in the gut. Brittan *et al.*[70] analysed colons and small intestines of female mice that received a bone marrow transplant from male mice donors and gastrointestinal biopsies from female patients with graft-versus-host disease following bone marrow transplant from male donors. Bone marrow cells frequently engraft into the mouse small intestine and colon and differentiate to form ISEMFs within the lamina propria. *In situ* hybridisation confirmed the presence of Y-chromosomes in these cells; their positive immunostaining for αSMA and negativity for desmin, the mouse macrophage marker F4/80, and the haematopoietic precursor marker CD34 determined their phenotype as pericryptal myofibroblasts in the lamina propria derived from transplanted bone marrow. This engraftment and transdifferentiation occurred as early as 1 week after bone marrow transplantation; almost 60% of ISEMFs were bone marrow–derived 6 weeks after the transplantation, indicating that transplanted bone marrow cells are capable of a sustained turnover of the ISEMF cells in the lamina propria (Fig. 47–5). Y-chromosome–positive ISEMFs were also seen in the human intestinal biopsy material.[70] Lethally irradiated female mice given a male bone marrow transplant and a subsequent foreign-body peritoneal implant formed granulation tissue capsules containing myofibroblast cells derived from the haematopoietic stem cells of the transplanted bone marrow.[71] This suggests that myofibroblasts may generally derive from bone marrow cells.

There are a growing number of reports that bone marrow cells can repopulate gastrointestinal epithelial cells in animals and man. Krause *et al.*[72] found bone marrow–derived epithelial cells in the lung, gastrointestinal tract, and skin 11 months after transplantation of a single haematopoietic bone marrow stem cell in the mouse. In the gastrointestinal tract, engrafted cells were present as columnar epithelial cells in the oesophageal lining, a small intestinal villus, colonic crypts, and gastric foveola. No apparent engraftment into the pericryptal myofibroblast sheath was reported, and as only a single haematopoietic stem cell was transplanted, it is possible that the ISEMFs derive from mesenchymal stem cells within transplanted whole bone marrow. It is, however, generally believed that stromal cell populations do not survive following bone marrow transplantation—although if an empty niche exists, as after irradiation in the gut, engraftment might occur. Two very recent reports have claimed that local application of bone marrow stem cells, either directly injected into the stomach and duodenum[73] or applied to the mucosa after the induction of experimental colitis,[74] can also apparently lead to epithelial transdifferentiation.

In biopsies from female patients who had undergone sex-mismatched haematopoietic bone marrow transplantation, *in situ* hybridisation for a Y-chromosome–specific probe with immunohistochemical staining for cytokeratins demonstrated mucosal cells of donor origin in the gastric cardia.[75] Moreover, Okamoto *et al.*[76] reported four long-term bone marrow transplant survivors with multiple engraftment of oesophageal, gastric, small intestinal, and colonic epithelial cells by donor bone marrow cells up to 8 years after transplantation, emphasising the long-term nature of this transdifferentiation.

It would be impossible to finish even such a short section on this topic without mentioning the mechanisms and significance

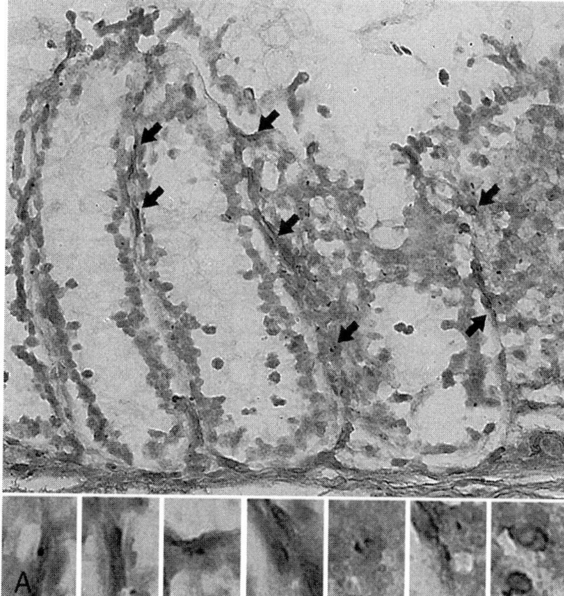

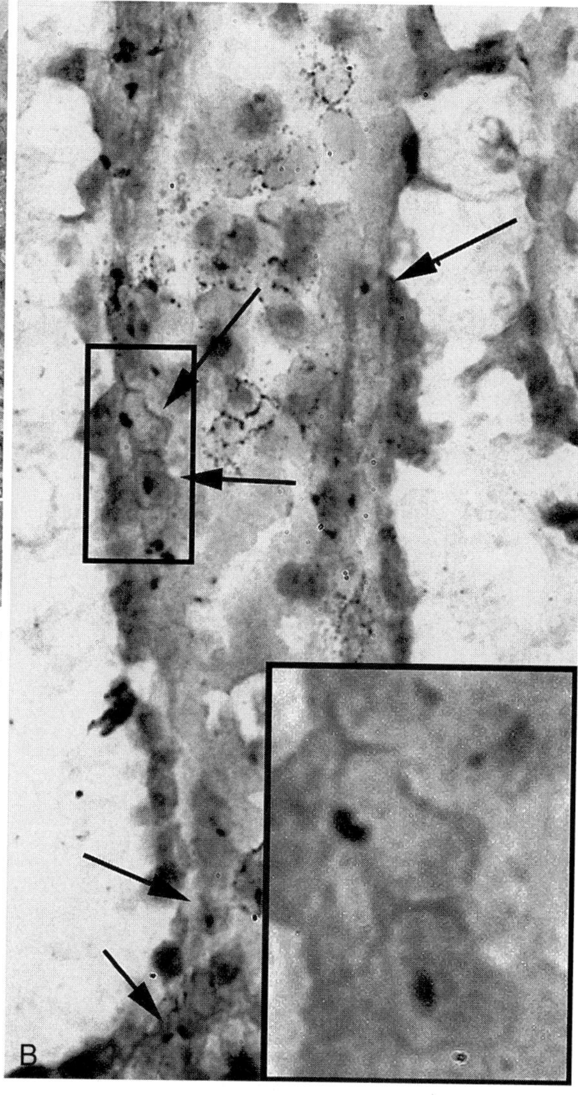

Figure 47–5. *Bone marrow-derived ISEMFs in the lamina propria of the mouse colon.* Female mouse colon following a male whole bone marrow transplant. Bone marrow-derived ISEMFs are present as Y-chromosome-positive cells, immunoreactive for α-SMA (A) 2 weeks after transplant (arrows and high-power inserts) and as columns reaching from crypt base to tip (B) 6 weeks after transplant (arrows and high-power inserts). The Y-chromosome is seen as a black punctate density, and cytoplasmic staining indicates immunoreactivity for α-SMA. Courtesy of M. Brittan. (Please see CD-ROM for color version of this figure.)

of such phenomena. At first considered to be caused by transdifferentiation or lack of lineage fidelity—commonly seen in invertebrates, during gastrulation, or during organogenesis—it is becoming clear that such changes are neither simple nor readily reproducible. Some labs have been unable to reproduce earlier findings,[77,78] and there are claims that adult tissues are contaminated with bone marrow precursors.[64] Finally, the fusion of a transplanted bone marrow cell with an indigenous adult cell has been proposed as the mechanism by which bone marrow stem cells acquire the phenotype of target cell lineages. Initially, cell fusion was seen as a rare event, occurring only *in vitro* and under circumstances of extreme selection.[79] In the FAH model described previously, cell fusion was recently shown to be common, and it cannot be ruled out as the main mechanism by which bone marrow stem cells transform to functional hepatocytes.[80,81] However, the genetic mechanisms whereby gene expression is switched off in the recipient cells—followed by clonal expansion to repopulate large areas of the liver, for example—are as yet unclear. We should also recall that several tissues in the mouse are polyploid, such as the liver and the acinar cells of the exocrine pancreas.[82] Other studies in which mixed-sex bone marrow transplants have been used to show plasticity have not reported evidence of cell fusion in animals or man: For example, bone marrow-engrafted cells in the human stomach, intestine, buccal mucosa, and pancreatic islet cells showed a normal complement of X- and Y-chromosomes.[67,75,76,83] Whatever the mechanism, it is clear that the most important criterion for altered lineage commitment, that of function,[84] has only been fulfilled in a few models, such as the FAH model and possibly postinfarction cardiomyocyte engraftment. The future in this field will prove interesting.

In inflammatory bowel diseases such as Crohn's disease, intestinal myofibroblasts are activated to proliferate and synthesize an extracellular matrix, and excessive collagen deposition causes fibrosis and postinflammatory scarring in the lamina propria and muscularis layers of the gut wall. Intestinal inflammation is believed to be mediated by luminal bacteria and bacterial wall polymers,[85] and tumour necrosis factor (TNF) plays a key role in the pathogenesis of intestinal inflammatory disease, since mice with targeted deletion of the AU-rich elements in TNF develop chronic ileitis resembling a Crohn's disease-like phenotype[86] (Fig. 47–6A through 47–6D). Moreover, a single dose of anti-TNF antibody to Crohn's disease patients can dramatically alleviate inflammation.[87] Other cytokines, including interleukin-10[88] and TGFβ[89] are implicated in the development of fibrosis in inflammatory bowel disease.

It has previously been concluded that fibrotic reactions, which occur in inflammatory bowel disease, and other diseases are caused by the local proliferation of myofibroblasts and fibroblasts.[90] Our recent data showing that transplanted bone marrow contributes to the intestinal subepithelial myofibroblast population implicates that extraintestinal cells may have a role in fibrosis. In this respect, we have shown that cells with a fibroblast–fibrocyte phenotype can derive from transplanted bone marrow and contribute to fibrotic reactions in and around the intestinal wall[91] (Fig. 47–6f). The concept that cells of the lamina propria, other than the lymphoid and myeloid lineages, exist in equilibrium with bone marrow precursors is an interesting one and could provide an opportunity for therapeutic delivery of cytokines to the intestine to prevent the development of fibrosis or even treat it. Further recent data[92] show that many of the myofibroblasts and fibroblasts recruited to, or expanding in, the lamina propria and submucosa of mice with induced TNBS colitis are bone marrow derived (Fig. 47–6g).

Gastrointestinal Stem Cells Occupy a Niche Maintained by ISEMFs in the Lamina Propria

Stem cells within many tissues are thought to reside within a niche formed by a group of surrounding cells and their

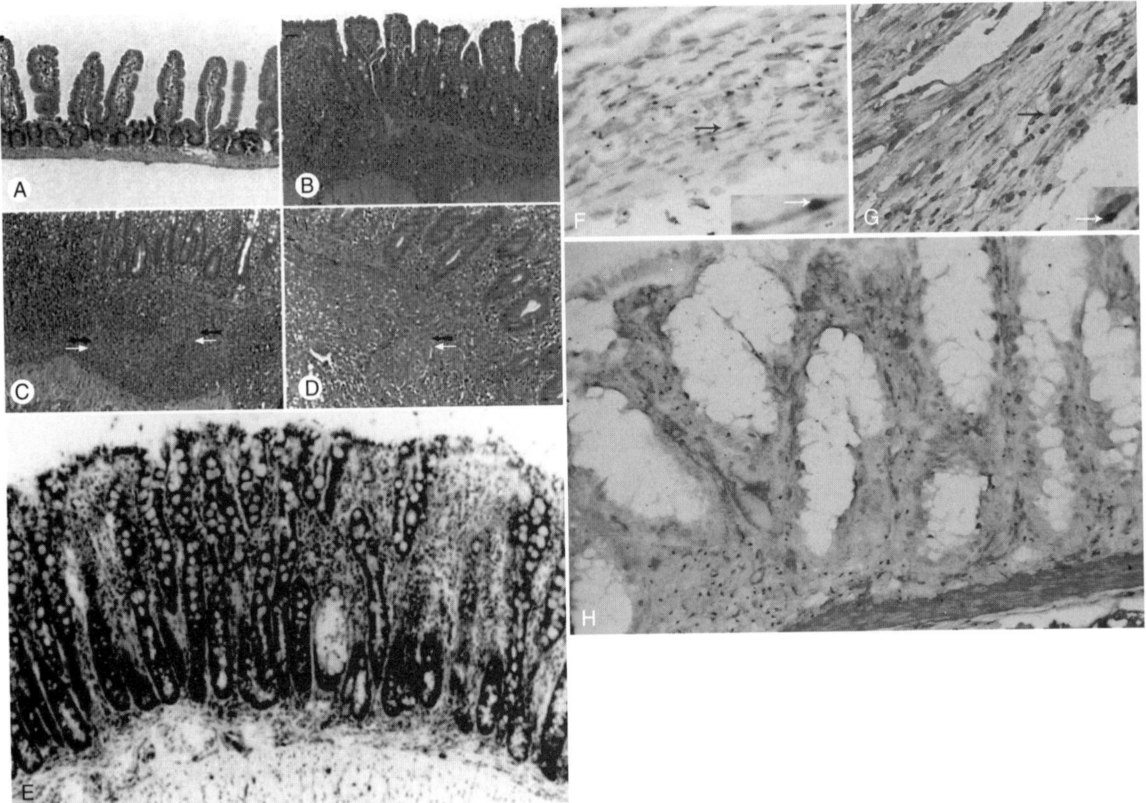

Figure 47–6. *Murine models of fibrosis.* Inflammatory bowel disease in $TNF^{\Delta ARE}$ and SAMP/Yit mouse ilea resembling human Crohn's disease. (A) Normal ileal morphology in an 8-week control mouse. (B) $TNF^{\Delta ARE}$ homozygous knockout at 7 weeks with blunt, distorted villi and increased inflammatory infiltrate. (C) $TNF^{\Delta ARE}$ heterozygote at 16 weeks with villus blunting and chronic inflammation. An ill-defined noncaseating granuloma is in the submucosa (arrows). (D) Ileocaecal region from a human patient with Crohn's disease demonstrating similar location and composition of granuloma compared with mouse model (arrow). (E) SAMP/Yit mouse at 20 weeks showing severe mucosal inflammation, crypt hyperplasia, elongation, and villous atrophy. (F) A fibrotic reaction in the serosal tissues of a paracetemol-treated male–female radiation chimaeric mouse, showing numerous spindle-shaped cells with Y-chromosomes revealing their bone marrow origin, which are also (G) vimentin-positive, confirming their fibroblast lineage. (H) Massive expansion of myofibroblasts of bone marrow origin in a male–female chimaeric mouse with colitis induced by TNBS. Panel d reproduced with permission from Kontoyiannis *et al.*,[86] panel e with permission from Matsumoto *et al.*,[168] panels f–g courtesy of N. Direkze, and panel H courtesy of M. Brittan. (Please see CD-ROM for color version of this figure.)

extracellular matrices, which provide an optimal microenvironment for the stem cells to function. The identification of a niche within any tissue involves knowledge of the location of the stem cells; as we have seen, this has proved problematical in the gastrointestinal tract. According to Spradling *et al.*,[93] to prove that a niche is present, the stem cells must be removed and subsequently replaced while the niche persists, providing support to the remaining exogenous cells. Although this has been accomplished in *Drosophila*,[94] such manipulations have not yet been possible in mammals. In this context, the survival of a single epithelial cell following cytotoxic damage to intestinal crypts in the microcolony assay is interesting, as many of the intestinal subepithelial myofibroblasts are also lost after irradiation,[95] although sufficient numbers may remain or be replaced by local proliferation or migration from the bone marrow to provide a supportive niche for the surviving stem cell or cells. The ISEMFs surround the base of the crypt and the neck–isthmus of the gastric gland, a commonly proposed location for the intestinal and gastric stem cell niches, respectively. It is proposed that ISEMFs influence epithelial cell proliferation and regeneration through epithelial–mesenchymal cross talk and that they ultimately determine epithelial cell fate.[3]

There has been a long quest for markers of stem cells in the intestine. The neural RNA-binding protein marker Musashi-1 (Msi-1) is a mammalian homologue of a *Drosophila* protein evidently required for asymmetrical division of sensory neural precursors. In the mouse, Msi-1 is expressed in neural stem cells[96,97] and has recently been proposed as the first intestinal stem cell marker because of its expression in developing intestinal crypts and specifically within the stem cell region of adult small intestinal crypts. This is further substantiated by its expanded expression throughout the entire clonogenic region in the small intestine after irradiation.[96,97]

The regulatory mechanisms of stem cell division within the niche to produce, on average, one stem cell and one cell committed to differentiation is as yet unknown, although there is no shortage of potential models.[98] In the stem cell zone hypothesis, the bottom few cell positions of the small intestinal crypt are occupied by a mixture of cell types: Paneth, goblet, and endocrine. The migration vector is toward the bottom of the crypt.[30–33] Above cell position 5, cells migrate upward, although only the cells that divide in the stem cell zone beneath are stem cells. Other models envisage the stem cells occupying a ring immediately above the Paneth cells,[99] although there is little experimental basis for such an assertion since "undifferentiated" cells of similar appearance are seen among the Paneth cells in thin sections.[31,32] Moreover, there is no difference in the expression of Msi-1 and Hes1—a transcriptional factor regulated by the Notch signalling pathway also required for neural stem cell renewal and neuronal lineage commitment—in undifferentiated cells located in either the stem cell zone or immediately above the Paneth cells.[100] This suggests that both populations may have the same potential as putative stem cells.

The number of stem cells in a crypt or a gland is presently unknown. Initially, all proliferating cells were believed to be stem cells.[101] Although clonal regeneration experiments using the microcolony assay indicated that intestinal crypts contained a multiplicity of stem cells, it was clear that this was less than the proliferative cellularity. Proposed stem cell numbers have varied from a single stem cell[102] to 16 or more.[103] Others have proposed that the number of stem cells per crypt varies throughout the crypt cycle, with the attainment of a *threshold number* of stem cells per crypt being the signal for fission to occur.[104] There is little experimental evidence to support these proposals. Although all cells in a crypt are initially derived from a single cell, as shown by the chimaeric and X-inactivation experiments discussed previously, mutagenesis studies such as those shown in Fig. 47–1e and Fig. 47–2a argue strongly for more than one stem cell per crypt, with stochastic clonal expansion of a mutant clone. A three stem cell colonic crypt has been suggested by Williams *et al.*[35] on this basis.

In organisms such as *Drosophila* and *Caenorhabditis elegans* stem cell divisions are known to be asymmetric. We have no such firm concept in the mammalian gut, although there is some evidence to support the proposal.[105,106] By labelling DNA template strands in intestinal stem cells with tritiated thymidine during development or tissue regeneration, and by labelling newly synthesized daughter strands with bromodeoxyuridine, segregation of the two markers can be studied. The template DNA strand labelled with tritiated thymidine is retained, but the newly synthesized strands labelled with bromodeoxyuridine become lost after the second division of the stem cell. This indicates not only that asymmetric stem cell divisions occur but also that by discarding the newly synthesized DNA, which is prone to mutation, into the daughter cell destined to differentiate, a mechanism of stem cell genome protection is afforded.[106]

When a stem cell divides, the possible outcomes are that two stem cells *(P)* are produced, that two daughter cells destined to differentiate *(Q)* cells are produced, or that there could be an asymmetric division resulting in one P and one Q cell. These are sometimes called p, q, and r divisions[104] or p and q divisions[107] (Fig. 47–7). If $p = 1$ and $q = 0$, then regardless of the number of stem cells per crypt, the cells are immortal and there will be no drift in the niche with time. Such a situation is called "deterministic."[48,107] However, if $p < 1$ and $Q > 0$ (i.e., a stochastic model), there will be eventual extinction of some stem cell lines and a drift toward a common stem cell from which all other cells derive. We previously described the variation in methylation patterns or "tags" that occur in human colonic crypts[48,107] and explained that crypts apparently show several unique tags. The variance of these unique tags was compared with those expected using a variety of models, including no drift with aging (the deterministic model), drift with immortal stem cells with divergence (the numbers of unique tags are proportional to the stem cell number), drift with one stem cell per crypt, and a stem cell niche with more recent divergence (with loss of stem cells occurring

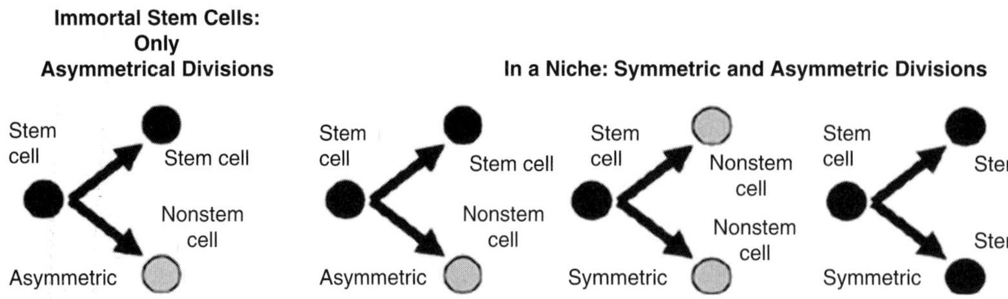

Figure 47–7. *How stem cells divide in a niche.* Classically, stem cells always replace themselves by asymmetrical division; therefore, their lineages never become extinct. However, although the stem cell number remains constant in a niche, both asymmetrical and symmetrical divisions occur. Symmetrical division can lead to one stem cell lineage becoming extinct as both daughters leave the niche, but to maintain a constant stem cell number in the niche, this loss is balanced by stem cell expansion, where both daughters remain in the niche as stem cells. Such stem cell loss with ensuing replacement can lead to the extinction of all lineages bar one, or *clonal succession.* Reproduced with permission from Kim *et al.*[161] (Please see CD-ROM for color version of this figure.)

proportional to the time since divergence). Multiple unique tags were found in some crypts, and the number of unique tags increased with the number of markers counted, which favours random tag drift and multiple stem cells per crypt. The variances were consistent with drift in immortal stem cells, where N (the number of stem cells) = 2, but favoured a model where $0.75 < P < 0.95$ and $N < 512$. Thus, the data supported a stochastic model with multiple stem cells per crypt. However, as in many such attempts, there are several major assumptions necessary, such as a constant stem cell number. It is clear that variation in both P and N occur in this model. However, this analysis is consistent with the results of Campbell *et al.*,[44] who deduced that the time taken for monoclonal conversion, or the "clonal stabilization time," of $OAT^{+/-}$ individuals to convert to $OAT^{-/-}$ cells following irradiation was found to be about 1 year. Assuming 64 stem cells per niche and $P = 0.95$, the mean time for conversion should be some 220 days. The same assumptions suggest a bottleneck, where all stem cells are related to the most recent common ancestral cell, occurring every 8.2 years.[106]

Multiple Molecules Regulate Gastrointestinal Development, Proliferation, and Differentiation

Although the molecular mechanisms by which pluripotent stem cells of the gastrointestinal tract produce differentiated cell types are not clearly understood, an increasing number of genes and growth factors have been identified that regulate development, proliferation, and differentiation as well as development of tumours. These are expressed by intestinal mesenchymal and epithelial cells and include members of the fibroblast growth factor family,[108] epidermal growth factor family, TGFβ (reviewed by Dignass *et al.*[109]), insulin-like growth factors 1 and 2,[110] HGF–scatter factor,[111] Sonic and Indian hedgehog,[112] and PDGF-α,[5] among others.

Wnt/β-catenin Signalling Pathway Controls Intestinal Stem Cell Function

The Wnt family of signalling proteins is critical during embryonic development and organogenesis in many species. There are 16 known mammalian *Wnt* genes, which bind to receptors of the frizzled *(Fz)* family, 8 of which have been identified in mammals. The multifunctional protein β-catenin normally interacts with a glycogen synthase kinase 3-β (GSK3-β), axin, and adenomatous polyposis coli (APC) tumour suppressor protein complex.[113] Subsequent serine phosphorylation of cytosolic β-catenin by GSK3-β leads to its ubiquitination and to its proteasomal degradation, thereby maintaining low levels of cytosolic and nuclear β-Catenin. Wnt ligand binding to its *Fz* receptor activates the cytoplasmic phosphoprotein *dishevelled,* which in turn initiates a signalling cascade resulting in increased cytosolic levels of β-catenin. β-Catenin then translocates to the cell nucleus, where it forms a transcriptional activator by combining with members of the T-cell factor/lymphocyte enhancer factor (Tcf/LEF) DNA-binding protein family. This activates specific genes, resulting in the proliferation of target cells, for example, in embryonic development (Fig. 47–8). In addition to its role in normal embryonic development, the Wnt/β-catenin pathway plays a key role in malignant transformation.[114,115] Mutations of the *APC* tumour suppression gene are present in up to 80% of human sporadic colorectal tumours.[116,117] This mutation prevents normal β-catenin turnover by the GSK3β/axin/APC complex. This results in increased nuclear *β-catenin/Tcf/LEF* gene transcription and a subsequent increase in β-catenin-induced Tcf/LEF transcription.[118,119] One of the main functions of *APC* appears to be the destabilisation of β-catenin. Free β-catenin is one of the earliest events, or perhaps even the initiating event, in tumorigenesis in the murine small intestine and in the human colon.[120] Many genes, including *c-myc, cyclin D1, CD44, c-Jun, Fra-1,* and urokinase-type plasminogen receptor have been identified as targets of the β-catenin/Tcf/LEF nuclear complex, although the precise mechanisms that lead to carcinogenesis are not entirely understood.[120–124]

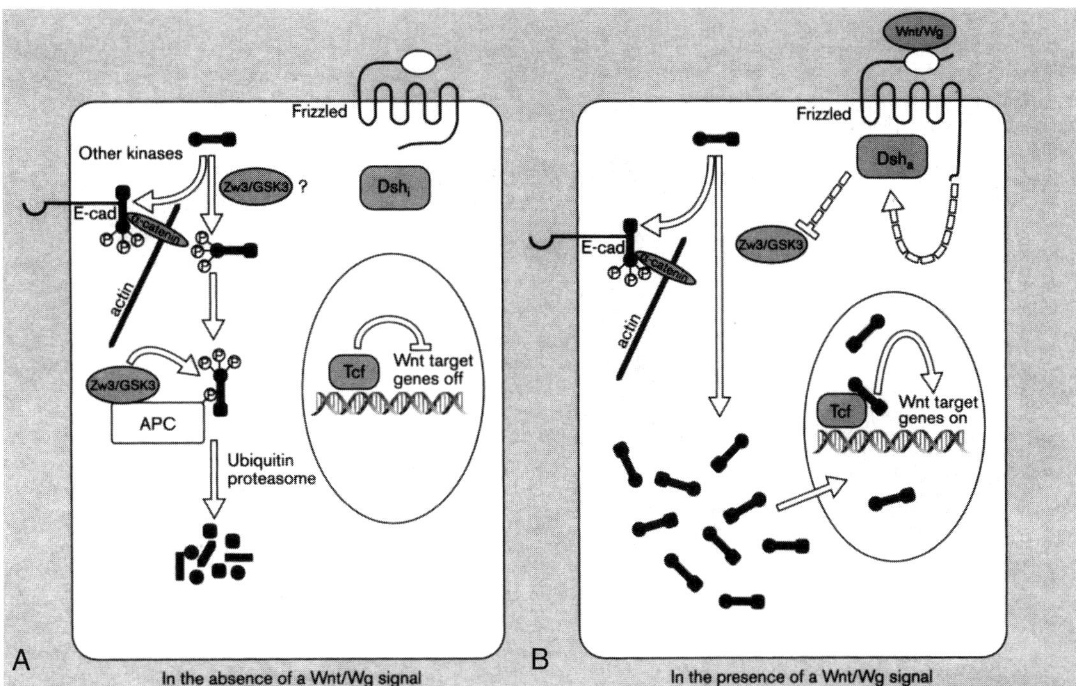

Figure 47–8. *Wnt signalling pathway.* (A) In the absence of Wnt signalling, *dishevelled* is inactive *(Dsh$_i$)*, and *Drosophila zeste*-white 3 or its mammalian homolog glycogen synthase kinase 3 (Zw3/GSK3) is active. β-Catenin (black dumbbell), through association with the APC–Zw3/GSK3 complex, undergoes phosphorylation and. degradation by the ubiquitin-proteasome pathway. Meanwhile, TCF is bound to its DNA-binding site in the nucleus, where it represses the expression of genes such as *Siamois* in *Xenopus*. (B) In the presence of a Wnt signal, *dishevelled* is activated *(Dsh$_a$)*, leading to inactivation of Zw3/GSK3 by an unknown mechanism. β-Catenin fails to be phosphorylated and is no longer targeted into the ubiquitin–proteasome pathway; instead, it accumulates in the cytoplasm and enters the nucleus by an unknown pathway, where it interacts with TCF to alleviate repression of the downstream genes and provide a transcriptional activation domain. Reproduced with permission from Willert *et al.*[115] (Please see CD-ROM for color version of this figure.)

The Tcf/LEF family of transcription factors has four members; Tcf-1, LEF1, Tcf-3, and Tcf-4. Tcf-4 is expressed in high levels in the developing intestine from embryonic day (E) 13.5 and in the epithelium of adult small intestine, colon, and colon carcinomas. When there is loss of function of APC or mutations in β-catenin, increased β-catenin/Tcf-4 complexes are formed that lead to uncontrolled transcription of target genes.[125,126] Mice with targeted disruption of the *Tcf-4* gene have no proliferating cells within their small intestinal crypts and lack a functional stem cell compartment[126] (Fig. 47–9A through Fig. 47–9F). This suggests that *Tcf-4* is responsible for establishing stem cell populations within intestinal crypts; this in turn is thought to be activated by a *Wnt* signal from the underlying mesenchymal cells in the stem cell niche. Chimaeric ROSA26 mice expressing a fusion protein containing the high mobility group box domain of Lef-1 linked to the transactivation domain of β-catenin (B6Rosa26<>129/Sv(Lef-1/β-cat) display increased intestinal epithelial apoptosis. This occurs specifically in 129/Sv cells throughout crypt morphogenesis, unrelated to enhanced cell proliferation. On completion of crypt formation and in adult mice, there is complete loss of all 129/Sv cells. Stem cell selection appears to be biased toward the unmanipulated ROSA26 cells in these chimeras, suggesting that "adequate threshold" levels of β-catenin during development permit sustained proliferation and selection of cells, establishing a stem cell hierarchy. Increased β-catenin expression appears to induce an apoptotic response, and thus the stem cell niche is unaffected by increased Lef-1/β-catenin during intestinal crypt development.[127]

Transcription Factors Define Regional Gut Specification and Intestinal Stem Cell Fate

HOX GENES DEFINE REGIONAL GUT SPECIFICATION

Mammalian homeobox genes *Cdx-1* and *Cdx-2* display specific regional expression in developing and mature colon and small intestine. During embryogenesis, *Cdx-1* localises to the proliferating cells of the crypts and maintains this expression during adulthood. The Tcf-4 knockout mouse does not express *Cdx-1* in the small intestinal epithelium, thus the Wnt/β-catenin complex appears to induce *Cdx-1* transcription in association with Tcf-4 during the development of intestinal crypts.[128] Mice heterozygous for a *Cdx-2* mutation develop colonic polyps composed of squamous, body, and antral gastric mucosa with small intestinal tissue (Fig. 47–9). Proliferation of *Cdx-2*–colonic cells with low *Cdx-2* levels can produce clones of cells phenotypically similar to epithelial cells of the stomach or small intestine.[129] This could indicate a possible homeotic shift in stem cell phenotype. Region-specific genes such as *Cdx-1, Cdx-2,* and *Tcf-4* appear to define the morphological features of differential regions of

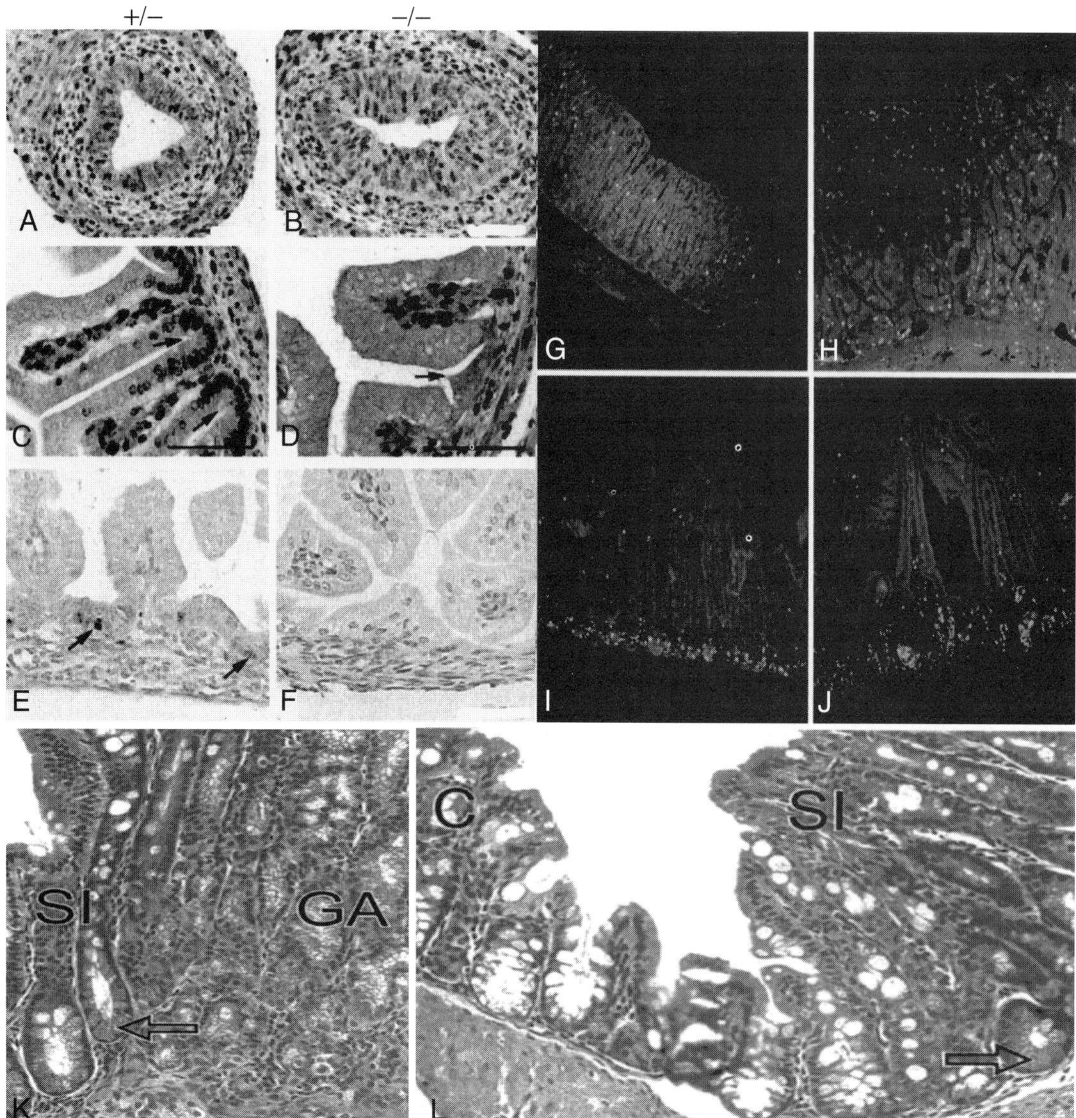

Figure 47–9. *Tcf-4 knockout mice, Foxl1 knockout mice, and Cdx-2 knockout mice.* (A–F) Small intestine from (A) E14.5 Tcf712$^{+/-}$ heterozygous, (B) Tcf712$^{-/-}$ homozygous, (C) E16.5 Tcf712$^{+/-}$, and (D) Tcf712$^{-/-}$ embryos stained with Ki-67 antibody. (E) E17 heterozygous and (F) homozygous bromodeoxyuridine-labelled embryos stained with antibromodeoxyuridine. Numerous proliferating cells are present (A and B) throughout the epithelium at E14.5 in heterozygotes and homozygotes, but are restricted (C) to intervillous regions in E16.5 heterozygotes and absent (D) in E16.5 homozygotes. bromodeoxyuridine-labelled cells are present in intervillous regions of the (E) Tcf712$^{+/-}$ embryos (arrows), but are absent from (F) Tcf712$^{-/-}$ embryos. (G–J) Horizontal bars indicate 0.1 mm. Epithelial proliferation is increased in Foxl1 mutant mice shown by injection of bromodeoxyuridine 1.5 hours before sacrifice (G and H) in the stomach and (I and J) jejunum of (G and I) wild-type and Foxl1-null mice in increased levels (H and J) shown by immunofluorescence, where labelled nuclei represent proliferating cells. (K–L) The lateral edge of a colonic polyp in Cdx-2$^{+/-}$ mouse encompassing the gastric antrum (GA), small intestine (SI), and colon (C). Bar indicates 5.55 mm. (k) Goblet cells in the villi and Paneth cells (arrow) in the crypts adjacent to the branched mucus-secreting cells of the gastric antrum. (l) Transition from SI to C shows stunted villi with goblet cells and Paneth cells (arrow) in the crypts between villi. Panels A–F reproduced with permission from Korinek *et al.*,[126] panels G–J with permission from Perreault *et al.*,[134] and panels K–L with permission from Beck *et al.*[129] (Please see CD-ROM for color version of this figure.)

the intestinal epithelium and regulate the proliferation and differentiation of the stem cells.

FORKHEAD FAMILY IS ESSENTIAL FOR INTESTINAL PROLIFERATION

The winged helix–forkhead family of transcription factors are essential for proper development of the ectodermal and endodermal regions of the gut. There are nine murine forkhead family members, which generate the forkhead box (Fox) proteins,[130] three homologues of the rat hepatic nuclear factor 3 gene (*HNF3*α, -β, and -γ), and six genes referred to as forkhead homologues (*fkh-1* through *fkh-6*).[131] *Fkh-6* is expressed in gastrointestinal mesenchymal cells[132] now reclassified as *Foxl1*.[130] *Foxl1* knockout mice have a dramatically altered gastrointestinal epithelium with branched and elongated glands in the stomach, elongated villi, hyperproliferative crypts, and goblet cell hyperplasia because of increased epithelial cell proliferation (Fig. 47–9G through 47–9J).[133] They show up-regulated levels of heparin sulfate proteoglycans (HSPGs), which increase *Wnt*-binding efficacy to the *Fz* receptors on gastrointestinal epithelial cells. This results in overactivation of the Wnt/β-catenin pathway and increased nuclear β-catenin.[134] The resultant β-catenin/Tcf/LEF complex activates target genes such as *cyclin D1* and *c-myc,* which increase epithelial cell proliferation. Therefore, *Foxl1* regulates the Wnt/β-catenin pathway in association with an increase in HSPGs, demonstrating epithelial cell regulation by mesenchymal factors during embryogenesis in the gastrointestinal tract. As *c-myc* is a known proto-oncogene, a mutation of *Foxl1* and the resultant increase in epithelial cell proliferation through inappropriate *c-myc* activation may lead to the development of colorectal cancers.[124]

E2F TRANSCRIPTION FAMILY IS ESSENTIAL FOR DEVELOPMENT OF THE CRYPT PROLIFERATIVE ZONE

The E2F family of transcription factors are regulators of cell proliferation, allowing transit from the G_1 to the S phase. E2F4 is expressed in the proliferative regions of embryonic intestine and in the adult small intestine and colon. In E2F4-knockout mice, intestinal crypts fail to develop, and the lamina propria appears thickened. E2F4 is thus essential for the development of the proliferative compartment of the intestinal epithelium, although the molecular pathways that influence E2F4 during development are unknown.[135]

Multiple Molecules Define Stem Cell Fate and Cell Position in the Villus–Crypt Axis

The colonic crypt and the villus–crypt axis offer a system in which the fate of stem cell progeny is defined. Their position within this axis can readily be determined. The goblet cell number normally remains relatively constant, and Paneth cells derive positional information and use it to remain in the crypt base. In mice, deletion of the *Math1* gene, a basic helix–loop–helix transcription factor and downstream component of the *Notch* signalling pathway, depletes goblet, Paneth, and enteroendocrine cell lineages in the small intestine. This indicates that Math1 is essential for stem cell commitment to one of three epithelial adult cell types. Math1 progenitors merely become enterocytes.[136] High levels of Notch switch on the Hes1 transcriptional repressor. This in turn blocks expression of Math1 so that cells remain progenitors and ultimately become enterocytes. Conversely, low Notch expression increases levels of its ligand Delta, which induces Math1 expression by blocking Hes1, causing cells to become goblet cells, Paneth cells, or enteroendocrine cells.[137] Hes1-null mice have elevated Math1 expression, with increased enteroendocrine and goblet cells and fewer enterocytes. This supports the evidence that Math1 regulates the determination of cell fate through a Notch–Delta signalling pathway[138] (Fig. 47–10).

Recent studies show that β-catenin and Tcf inversely control the expression of the EphB2/EphB3 receptors and their ligand ephrin-B1 in colorectal cancer and along the crypt–villus axis.[139] When *EphB2* and *EphB3* genes are disrupted, cell positioning within the crypt is also disrupted. For example Paneth cells do not migrate downward to their normal position at the bottom of the crypt but scatter along crypt and villus. This indicates that β-catenin and Tcf contribute to the sorting of cell populations through the EphB/ephrin-B system.

In the future, it is clear that functional genomics will have an increasing role to play in the study and identification of intestinal stem cells. Stappenbeck *et al.*[140] studied a consolidated population of stem cells isolated by laser-capture microdissection from germ-free transgenic mice lacking Paneth cells. There were no less than 163 transcripts enriched in these stem cells compared with normal crypt-base epithelium, which contains a predominance of Paneth cells. The profile showed prominent representation of genes involved in *c-myc* signalling, as well as in the processing, localisation, and translation of mRNAs. Similar studies in the mouse stomach showed that growth factor response pathways are prominent in gastric stem cells, examples including insulin-like growth factor.[141] A considerable fraction of stem cell transcripts encode products required for mRNA processing and cytoplasmic localisation. These include numerous homologues of *Drosophila* genes needed for axis formation during oogenesis.

Gastrointestinal Neoplasms Originate in Stem Cell Populations

We can use the development of colorectal carcinoma as a paradigm. The concept of the adenoma–carcinoma sequence, whereby adenomas develop into carcinomas, is now widely accepted,[142] and most colorectal carcinomas are believed to originate in adenomas. The initial genetic change in the development of most colorectal adenomas is thought to be at the *APC* locus, and the molecular events associated with these stages are clear: a second hit in the *APC* gene is sufficient to give microadenoma development, at least in FAP.[143] There are basically two models for adenoma morphogenesis, both of which closely involve basic concepts of stem cell biology in the colon: in the first, recently formulated, mutant cells appear in the *intracryptal zone* between crypt orifices, and as the clone expands, the cells migrate laterally and downward, displacing the normal epithelium of adjacent crypts.[144] A modification of this proposal is that a mutant cell in the crypt base, classically the site of the stem cell compartment,[1] migrates to the crypt apex where it expands. These proposals are based on findings in some early non-FAP adenomas, where dysplastic cells were seen exclusively at the orifices and on the luminal surface of colonic crypts[144]; measurement of loss of heterozygosity (LOH) for *APC* and nucleotide sequence analysis of the mutation cluster region of the *APC* gene carried out on microdissected, well-orientated histological sections of these adenomas showed that half the sample had LOH in the upper

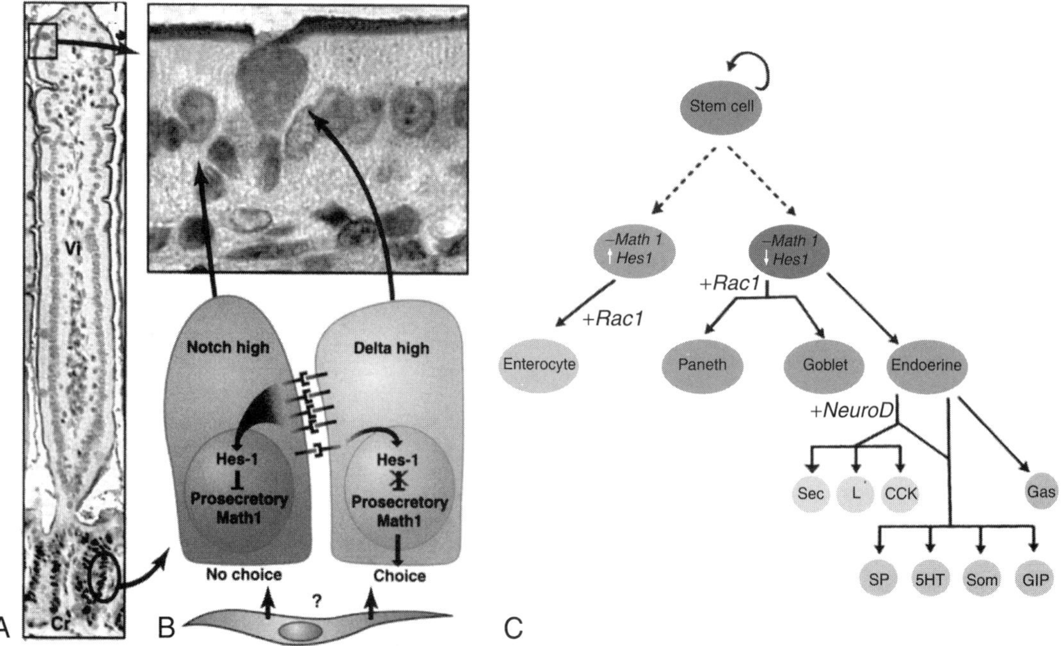

Figure 47–10. *Math1 signalling pathway.* (A) Low-power section of adult murine small intestine. Precursor cells are stained for cyclin proliferating cell nuclear antigen, enterocytes express intestinal alkaline phosphatase, and goblet cells secrete mucins. Inset shows high-power image of small intestinal enterocytes and goblet cells. (B) Math1, a component of the Notch signalling pathway, influences intestinal epithelial cell fate decisions. In crypt progenitor stem cells that express high levels of Notch, the Hes1 transcription factor is switched on, and the expression of Math1 and of other "prosecretory" genes is blocked. The result is that the precursor cells become enterocytes. In cells expressing low amounts of Notch, levels of Delta are high, production of Hes1 is blocked, and Math1 expression is induced. Production of the Math1 helix–loop–helix transcription factor allows precursor cells to make a choice: whether to become goblet cells, Paneth cells, or enteroendocrine cells (C) Math1 is essential for secretory cells. Whether Math1-expressing cells descend directly from stem cells or an intermediate progenitor remains unknown. (Vi: villus, Cr: crypt, Sec: secretin, L: glucagons–peptide YY, CCK: cholecystokinin, SP: substance P, 5HT: serotonin, Som: somatostatin, GIP: gastric inhibitory peptide, and Gas: gastrin). Panels A and B reproduced with permission from van Den Brink *et al.*,[137] and panel C reproduced with permission fromYang *et al.*[136] (Please see CD-ROM for color version of this figure.)

portion of the crypts, most with truncating *APC* mutations. Only these superficial cells showed prominent proliferative activity, with nuclear localisation of β-catenin indicating an *APC* mutation only in these apical cells (Fig. 47–11C). Earlier morphological studies have drawn attention to the same appearances.[145] This top-down morphogenesis has wide implications for concepts of stem cell biology in the gut. It is clear that most evidence indicates that crypt stem cells are found at the origin of the cell flux, near the crypt base.[23] These proposals, however, either re-establish the stem cell compartment in the intracryptal zone or make the intracryptal zone a favoured locus where stem cells, having acquired a second hit, clonally expand.

An alternative hypothesis proposes that the earliest lesion is the *unicryptal* or *monocryptal adenoma,* where the dysplastic epithelium occupies an entire single crypt. These lesions are common in FAP, and although they are rare in non-FAP patients, they have been described.[146] Here, a stem cell acquires the second hit, then it expands, stochastically or more likely because of a selective advantage, to colonise the whole crypt. Such monocryptal lesions thus should be clonal.[46] Similar crypt-restricted expansion of mutated stem cells has been well documented in mice after ENU treatment[22] and in humans heterozygous for the *OAT* gene, where after LOH, initially half then the whole crypt is colonised by the progeny of the mutant stem cell.[44] Interestingly, OAT^{+}/OAT^{-} individuals with FAP show increased rates of stem cell mutation with clustering of mutated crypts. Thus, in sharp contrast the mutated clone expands not by lateral migration but by *crypt fission* in which the crypt divides, usually symmetrically at the base (Fig. 47–12A) or by budding (Fig. 47–11B). Several studies have shown that fission of adenomatous crypts is the main mode of adenoma progression—predominantly in FAP, where such events are readily evaluated,[147,148] but also in sporadic adenomas.[149] The nonadenomatous mucosa in FAP, with only one *APC* mutation, shows a large increase in the incidence of crypts in fission.[147] Aberrant crypt foci, thought to be precursors of adenomas, grow by crypt fission,[150,151] as do hyperplastic polyps.[152] This concept does not exclude the possibility that the clone later expands by lateral migration and downward spread into adjacent crypts, but with the initial lesion the monocryptal adenoma, this model of morphogenesis is conceptually very different.

Recent work supporting the bottom-up spread of colorectal adenomas looked at a number of small (<3 mm) tubular adenomas. Here, nuclear accumulation of β-catenin (Fig. 47–11G) was seen, indicating loss of function of one of the genes in the *Wnt* pathway, most likely *APC,* with subsequent translocation of β-catenin to the nucleus. Serial sections

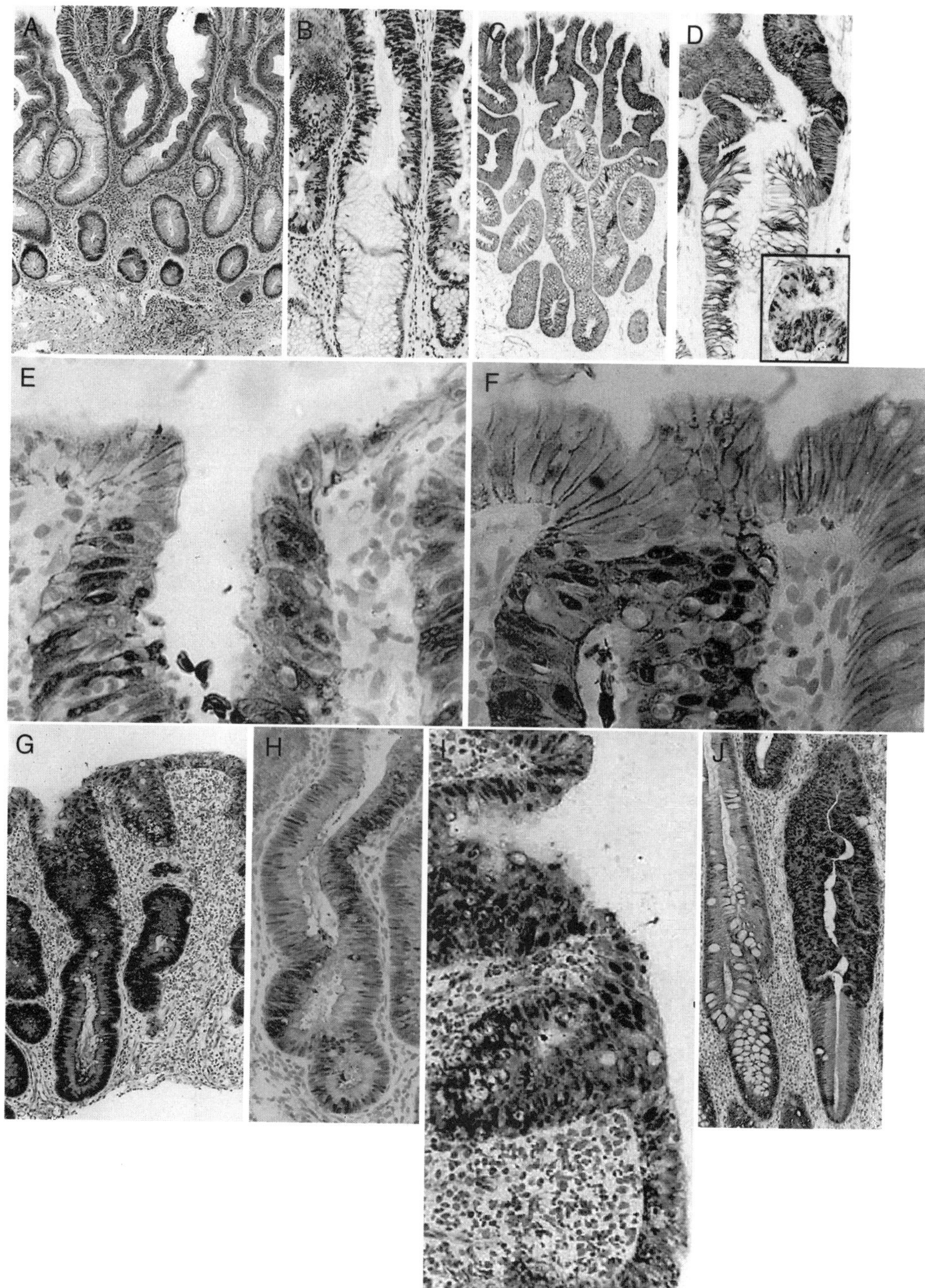

Figure 47–11. *Contrasting theories for the morphogenesis of adenomas and the part played by stem cells.* (A) Hematoxylin- and eosin-stained sections of a small tubular adenoma. Dysplastic epithelium is superficial within the crypts, with histologically normal underlying epithelium. (B) Abrupt transition between dysplastic and normal-appearing epithelial cells at the midpoint of this crypt. Proliferative activity assessed with the Ki-67 antibody, distributed throughout the dysplastic epithelium at the top of the crypts. (C) Nuclear β-catenin is highly expressed and distributed throughout the dysplastic epithelium at the top of the crypts but not in the crypt bases. (D) β-catenin in the nuclei of adenomatous crypts from a tiny tubular adenoma. (E) Nuclear β-catenin extends to the bottom of crypts in early adenomas, including the very bases of the crypts. (F) β-Catenin staining in nuclei of budding crypts. (G) Junction between early adenomatous crypts, showing a sharp junction on the surface with accumulation of nuclear β-catenin giving way sharply to membranous staining in the normal surface cells. (H) High-power serial sections, demonstrating the sharp junction between nuclear staining in the adenomatous cells and membranous staining in normal surface epithelial cells. (I) Surface continuity between crypts showing nuclear β-catenin staining. (J) Crypts from a larger adenoma stained for β-catenin, showing invasion of adjacent crypt territories in a top-down fashion. Panels A–D reproduced with permission from Shih *et al.*,[144] and panels E–J reproduced with permission from Preston *et al.*[154] (Please see CD-ROM for color version of this figure.)

(Fig. 47–11E and 47–11F) showed that the β-catenin nuclear staining extended to the bottom of the crypts and was present in crypts in the process of crypt fission (Fig. 47–11H). β-Catenin expression was particularly marked in the nuclei of buds. At the surface, there was a sharp cut-off between the adenomatous cells in the crypt that showed nuclear β-catenin and those surface cells that did not (Fig. 47–11E and 47–11F). The adjacent crypts were filled with dysplastic cells containing nuclear β-catenin, which were not confined to the upper portions of the crypts. In larger adenomas, there was unequivocal evidence of surface cells growing down and replacing the epithelium of normal-looking crypts (Fig. 47–11J). Crypt fission was rare in normal and noninvolved mucosa and usually began with basal bifurcation at the base of the gland (Fig. 47–12A), whereas in adenomas, fission was commonly asymmetrical (Fig. 47–12B) with budding from the superficial and mid-crypt (Fig. 47–12B). Multiple fission events were frequently observed in adenomas (Fig. 47–12C). The *crypt fission index* (the proportion of crypts in fission) in adenomas was significantly greater than that in noninvolved mucosa[152] (Fig. 47–2D).

It is usually stated that adenomas do not display a stem cell architecture, but recent observations[153,154] show that adenomatous crypts in early sporadic adenomas show superficial similarities to normal crypts in the distribution of their proliferative activity. Observations on possibly older adenomas have suggested that maximum proliferative activity is found towards the top of the crypts, indicating that that migration kinetics are reversed, with cells flowing toward the bottom of the crypt.[155,156] These observations are corroborated by the report of increased apoptosis at the bottom of adenomatous crypts.[157] Such a distribution could support a top-down mechanism. But there is evidence from examining the methylation histories of cells in adenomas for a discrete stem cell architecture;[158] moreover, although crypt mitotic scores are significantly greater in adenomas than in noninvolved mucosa and normal controls, the zonal distribution of mitoses in adenomatous crypts mitoses is evenly distributed throughout the crypt, which does not suggest a concentration of dysplastic cells in the tops of adenomatous crypts.

Examination of the adenomas of an XO–XY individual with FAP showed none exceeded 2.5 mm in diameter.[46] The monocryptal adenomas showed either the XO or the XY genotype and hence are clonal proliferations, as would be expected from the observation that crypts are clonal (Fig. 47–13A). Many microadenomas showed the XY genotype, and none of these early lesions showed mixture of XO and XY nuclei occupying the same crypt (Fig. 47–13B). It was shown that 76% of the microadenomas were polyclonal. There were also sharp boundaries at the surface between adjacent adenomatous crypt territories[154] (Fig. 47–3E).

What are the implications of these considerations upon our concepts of the single (stem) cell origin or clonality in colorectal adenomas? We have seen that crypts are clonal units; thus, these lesions would be polyclonal because of the mixture of clonal crypts and clonal adenoma—though in this instance, they have different clonal derivation. A study of both sporadic and FAP adenomas, using X-linked restriction fragment length polymorphisms, showed that such lesions were apparently monoclonal in origin.[45] On the other hand, the X-linked patch in the colon is large—and can be in excess of 450 crypts in diameter[47] (see Fig. 47–14). So, unless an adenoma grows

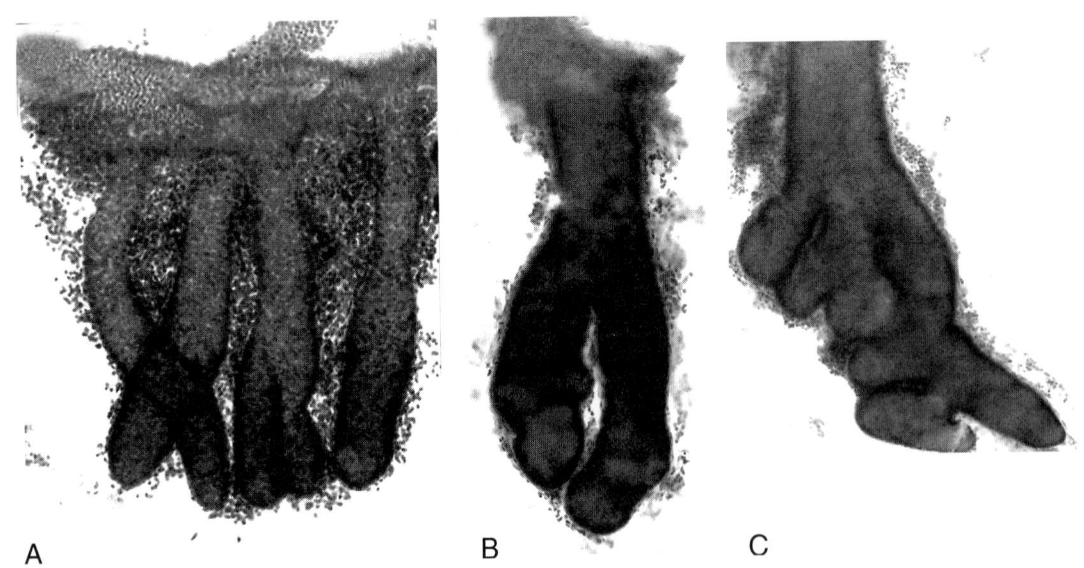

Figure 47–12. *Microdissected crypts from normal colonic mucosae and adenomas.* (A) Symmetrical fission of normal colonic crypts. (B) Isolated adenomatous crypt showing frequent crypt fission with atypical and asymmetrical branching. (C) Another crypt from an adenoma with bizarre shape, asymmetrical branching, and multiple budding. Reproduced with permission from Preston *et al.*[154] (Please see CD-ROM for color version of this figure.)

and space is intriguing (reviewed by Klein and Kyewski[100] and Kyewski *et al.*[101]). When analyzing the expression of "peripheral" antigens in the thymus medulla, Kyewski, Klein, and colleagues found very small clusters of medullary epithelial cells expressing an antigen in question.[102] A key regulator of this tolerogenic self-antigen expression is the transcription factor *Aire* (an autoimmune regulator). In humans, a defective form of AIRE is associated with multiorgan autoimmune disease. Likewise, mice lacking *Aire* expression in TECs show autoimmune diseases.[103] Ectopic transcription of some genes encoding peripheral antigens was reduced in $Aire^{-/-}$ medullary TECs. Hence, medullary TECs are of central importance for the establishment of T-cell tolerance and, thus, for the prevention of autoimmune disease.

In this context, a look at organogenesis of the medulla may be noteworthy. The medullary islets described previously range in diameter from 60 × 40 to 170 × 170 μm. My colleagues and I estimated that medullary islets include between 5 and 45 epithelial cells when analyzed in a two-dimensional lattice and more in three dimensions.[38] Thus, these putatively, clonally derived TEC clusters contain far higher cell numbers than the numbers of TECs expressing a given self-antigen. It is not known whether—and if yes, how—these two observations of the large numbers of clonally related TECs and the small numbers of antigen-expressing TECs within such islets are linked. One possibility would be to assume a further diversification of self-antigen expression within each islet (Fig. 49–2C). This could occur temporally or spatially.

A second implication of our finding that mTECs are composed of islets is related to the phenomenon of X-inactivation. A prediction based on the data described in this chapter is that expression of X-encoded self-antigens will vary from islet to islet in females but not in males. A given set of TEC islets would, according to this idea, express paternally inherited, X-encoded self-antigens, and another set would express maternally inherited, X-encoded self-antigens. It is not known how many contacts between immature thymocytes and TECs are required during negative and positive selection in the thymus. If a single "hit" is sufficient, some thymocytes may be selected on the basis of contact with one islet but may escape negative selection on the basis of the other islet. A similar idea has been proposed with regard to X-inactivation in thymic dendritic cells.[104] Whether genetic diversity, a cost of clonal TEC populations in the thymus, has a role in T-cell tolerance, and in its failure in autoimmunity, remains to be determined.

ACKNOWLEDGMENTS

I thank C. Blum, C. Haller, and Drs. S. Paul and H. Bluethmann for their contributions to the experiments discussed here.

I thank Drs. C. Waskow, H.J. Fehling, and N. Manley for comments on this manuscript. I am supported by a grant from the Deutsche Forschungsgemeinschaft (Sonderforschungsbereich 497-B5). Corresponding address: hans-reimer.rodewald@medizin.uni-ulm.de.

REFERENCES

1. Miller, J.F. (1961). Immunological function of the thymus. *Lancet* **2,** 748–749.
2. Rodewald, H.R., Kretzschmar, K., Takeda, S., Hohl, C., and Dessing, M. (1994). Identification of prothymocytes in murine fetal blood: T-lineage commitment can precede thymus colonization. *EMBO J.* **13,** 4229–4240.
3. Kawamoto, H., Ohmura, K., Hattori, N., and Katsura, Y. (1997). Hemopoietic progenitors in the murine fetal liver capable of rapidly generating T-cells. *J. Immunol.* **158,** 3118–3124.
4. Kondo, M., Weissman, I.L., and Akashi, K. (1997). Identification of clonogenic common lymphoid progenitors in mouse bone marrow. *Cell* **91,** 661–672.
5. Igarashi, H., Gregory, S.C., Yokota, T., Sakaguchi, N., and Kincade, P.W. (2002). Transcription from the RAG1 locus marks the earliest lymphocyte progenitors in bone marrow. *Immunity* **17,** 117–130.
6. Allman, D., Sambandam, A., Kim, S., Miller, J.P., Pagan, A., Well, D., Meraz, A., and Bhandoola, A. (2003). Thymopoiesis independent of common lymphoid progenitors. *Nat. Immunol.* **4,** 168–174.
7. Foss, D.L., Donskoy, E., and Goldschneider, I. (2001). The importation of hematogenous precursors by the thymus is a gated phenomenon in normal adult mice. *J. Exp. Med.* **193,** 365–374.
8. Moore, M.A.S., and Owen, J.J.T. (1967). Stem cell migration in developing myeloid and lymphoid systems. *Lancet* **2,** 658–659.
9. Berzins, S.P., Boyd, R.L., and Miller, J.F. (1998). The role of the thymus and recent thymic migrants in the maintenance of the adult peripheral lymphocyte pool. *J. Exp. Med.* **187,** 1839–1848.
10. Von Boehmer, H., Aifantis, I., Gounari, F., Azogui, O., Haughn, L., Apostolou, I., Jaeckel, E., Grassi, F., and Klein, L. (2003). Thymic selection revisited: how essential is it? *Immunol. Rev.* **191,** 62–78.
11. Starr, T.K., Jameson, S.C., and Hogquist, K.A. (2003). Positive and negative selection of T-cells. *Annu. Rev. Immunol.* **21,** 139–176.
12. Suniara, R.K., Jenkinson, E.J., and Owen, J.J. (1999). Studies on the phenotype of migrant thymic stem cells. *Eur. J. Immunol.* **29,** 75–80.
13. Kisielow, P., and von Boehmer, H. (1995). Development and selection of T-cells: Facts and puzzles. *Adv. Immunol.* **58,** 87–209.
14. Shortman, K., and Wu, L. (1996). Early T-lymphocyte progenitors. *Annu. Rev. Immunol.* **14,** 29–47.
15. Rodewald, H.R., and Fehling, H.J. (1998). Molecular and cellular events in early thymocyte development. *Adv. Immunol.* **69,** 1–112.
16. DiSanto, J.P., Radtke, F., and Rodewald, H.R. (2000). To be or not to be a pro-T? *Curr. Opin. Immunol.* **12,** 159–165.
17. Michie, A.M., and Zuniga-Pflucker, J.C. (2002). Regulation of thymocyte differentiation: pre-TCR signals and beta selection. *Semin. Immunol.* **14,** 311–323.
18. Ceredig, R., and Rolink, T. (2002). A positive look at double-negative thymocytes. *Nat. Rev. Immunol.* **2,** 888–897.
19. Borowski, C., Martin, C., Gounari, F., Haughn, L., Aifantis, I., Grassi, F., and Boehmer, H. (2002). On the brink of becoming a T-cell. *Curr. Opin. Immunol.* **14,** 200–206.
20. Flanagan, S.P. (1966). *Nude,* a new hairless gene with pleiotropic effects in the mouse. *Genet. Res.* **8,** 295–309.
21. Nehls, M., Pfeifer, D., Schorpp, M., Hedrich, H., and Boehm, T. (1994). New member of the winged-helix protein family disrupted in mouse and rat *nude* mutations. *Nature* **372,** 103–107.

22. Nehls, M., Kyewski, B., Messerle, M., Waldschutz, R., Schuddekopf, K., Smith, A.J., and Boehm, T. (1996). Two genetically separable steps in the differentiation of thymic epithelium. *Science* **272,** 886–889.
23. Greenberg, F. (1993). DiGeorge syndrome: a historical review of clinical and cytogenetic features. *J. Med. Genet.* **30,** 803–806.
24. Papaioannou, V.E. (2002). Embryonic stem cells and mouse models of human syndromes: Examples from the T-box gene family. *Reprod. Biomed. Online.* **4,** 68–71.
25. Perez, E., and Sullivan, K.E. (2002). Chromosome 22q11.2 deletion syndrome (DiGeorge and velo-cardio-facial syndromes). *Curr. Opin. Pediatr.* **14,** 678–683.
26. Packham, E.A., and Brook, J.D. (2003). T-box genes in human disorders. *Hum. Mol. Genet.* **12,** 37–44.
27. Kong, F.K., Chen, C.L., and Cooper, M.D. (2002). Reversible disruption of thymic function by steroid treatment. *J. Immunol.* **168,** 6500–6505.
28. Hendrickx, P., and Dohring, W. (1989). Thymic atrophy and rebound enlargement following chemotherapy for testicular cancer. *Acta Radiol.* **30,** 263–267.
29. Beschorner, W.E., Di Gennaro, K.A., Hess, A.D., and Santos, G.W. (1987). Cyclosporine and the thymus: Influence of irradiation and age on thymic immunopathology and recovery. *Cell. Immunol.* **110,** 350–364.
30. McCune, J.M. (1997). Thymic function in HIV-1 disease. *Semin. Immunol.* **9,** 397–404.
31. Gaulton, G.N. (1998). Viral pathogenesis and immunity within the thymus. *Immunol. Res.* **17,** 75–82.
32. Haynes, B.F., Markert, M.L., Sempowski, G.D., Patel, D.D., and Hale, L.P. (2000). The role of the thymus in immune reconstitution in aging, bone marrow transplantation, and HIV-1 infection. *Annu. Rev. Immunol.* **18,** 529–560.
33. Aspinall, R., and Andrew, D. (2000). Thymic involution in aging. *J. Clin. Immunol.* **20,** 250–256.
34. Lampert, I.A., and Ritter, M.A. (1988). The origin of the diverse epithelial cells of the thymus: Is there a common stem cell? *In* "Thymus Update," (M.D. Kendall *et al.,* eds.), pp. 5–25. Harwood Academic Publishers, London.
35. Ritter, M.A., and Boyd, R.L. (1993). Development in the thymus: it takes two to tango. *Immunol. Today* **14,** 462–469.
36. Ropke, C., van Soest, P., Platenburg, P.P., and van Ewijk, W. (1995). A common stem cell for murine cortical and medullary thymic epithelial cells? *Dev. Immunol.* **4,** 149–156.
37. Blackburn, C.C., Manley, N.R., Palmer, D.B., Boyd, R.L., Anderson, G., and Ritter, M.A. (2002). One for all and all for one: thymic epithelial stem cells and regeneration. *Trends Immunol.* **23,** 391–395.
38. Rodewald, H.R., Paul, S., Haller, C., Bluethmann, H., and Blum, C. (2001). Thymus medulla consisting of epithelial islets each derived from a single progenitor. *Nature* **414,** 763–768.
39. Gill, J., Malin, M., Hollander, G.A., and Boyd, R. (2002). Generation of a complete thymic microenvironment by $MTS24^+$ thymic epithelial cells. *Nat. Immunol.* **3,** 635–642.
40. Bennett, A.R., Farley, A., Blair, N.F., Gordon, J., Sharp, L., and Blackburn, C.C. (2002). Identification and characterization of thymic epithelial progenitor cells. *Immunity* **16,** 803–814.
41. Manley, N.R. (2000). Thymus organogenesis and molecular mechanisms of thymic epithelial cell differentiation. *Semin. Immunol.* **12,** 421–428.
42. Manley, N.R., and Blackburn, C.C. (2003). A developmental look at thymus organogenesis: Where do the nonhematopoietic cells in the thymus come from? *Curr. Opin. Immunol.* **15,** 225–232.
43. Rodewald, H.R. (2004) Epithelial Stem–progenitor cells in thymus organogenesis. *In* "Adult Stem Cells," (K. Turksen, ed.), pp. 83–100. Humana Press, Totowa.
44. Cordier, A.C., and Haumont, S.M. (1980). Development of thymus, parathyroids, and ultimobranchial bodies in *NMRI* and *nude* mice. *Am. J. Anat.* **157,** 227–263.
45. Janeway, C.A., and Travers, P. (1997) "Immunobiology: the Immune System in Health and Disease," 3rd ed. Current Biology, London.
46. Picker, L.J., and Siegelman, M.H. (1999) Lymphoid tissues and organs. *In* "Fundamental Immunology" (W. Paul, ed.), pp. 486–487. Lippincott-Raven, Philadelphia.
47. Le Douarin, N.M., and Jotereau, F.V. (1975). Tracing of cells of the avian thymus through embryonic life in interspecific chimeras. *J. Exp. Med.* **142,** 17–40.
48. Hetzer-Egger, C., Schorpp, M., Haas-Assenbaum, A., Balling, R., Peters, H., and Boehm, T. (2002). Thymopoiesis requires Pax9 function in thymic epithelial cells. *Eur. J. Immunol.* **32,** 1175–1181.
49. Anderson, G., Jenkinson, E.J., Moore, N.C., and Owen, J.J. (1993). MHC class II^+ epithelium and mesenchyme cells are both required for T-cell development in the thymus. *Nature* **362,** 70–73.
50. Bockman, D.E. (1997). Development of the thymus. *Microsci. Res. Tech.* **38,** 209–215.
51. Shinohara, T., and Honjo, T. (1996). Epidermal growth factor can replace thymic mesenchyme in induction of embryonic thymus morphogenesis *in vitro*. *Eur. J. Immunol.* **26,** 747–752.
52. Shinohara, T., and Honjo, T. (1997). Studies *in vitro* on the mechanism of the epithelial–mesenchymal interaction in the early fetal thymus. *Eur. J. Immunol.* **27,** 522–529.
53. Suniara, R.K., Jenkinson, E.J., and Owen, J.J. (2000). An essential role for thymic mesenchyme in early T-cell development. *J. Exp. Med.* **191,** 1051–1056.
54. Graf, D., Nethisinghe, S., Palmer, D.B., Fisher, A.G., and Merkenschlager, M. (2002). The developmentally regulated expression of Twisted gastrulation reveals a role for bone morphogenetic proteins in the control of T-cell development. *J. Exp. Med.* **196,** 163–171.
55. Varas, A., Hager-Theodorides, A.L., Sacedon, R., Vicente, A., Zapata, A.G., and Crompton, T. (2003). The role of morphogens in T-cell development. *Trends Immunol.* **24,** 197–206.
56. Nosaka, T., Morita, S., Kitamura, H., Nakajima, H., Shibata, F., Morikawa, Y., Kataoka, Y., Ebihara, Y., Kawashima, T., Itoh, T., Ozaki, K., Senba, E., Tsuji, K., Makishima, F., Yoshida, N., and Kitamura, T. (2003). Mammalian twisted gastrulation is essential for skeleto-lymphogenesis. *Mol. Cell. Biol.* **23,** 2969–2980.
57. Jiang, X., Rowitch, D.H., Soriano, P., McMahon, A.P., and Sucov, H.M. (2000). Fate of the mammalian cardiac neural crest. *Development* **127,** 1607–1616.
58. Ohnemus, S., Kanzler, B., Jerome-Majewska, L.A., Papaioannou, V.E., Boehm, T., and Mallo, M. (2002). Aortic arch and pharyngeal phenotype in the absence of BMP-dependent neural crest in the mouse. *Mech. Dev.* **119,** 127–135.
59. Owen, J.J., McLoughlin, D.E., Suniara, R.K., and Jenkinson, E.J. (2000). The role of mesenchyme in thymus development. *Curr. Top. Microbiol. Immunol.* **251,** 133–137.
60. Anderson, G., and Jenkinson, E.J. (2001). Lymphostromal interactions in thymic development and function. *Nature Rev. Immunol.* **1,** 31–40.
61. Revest, J.M., Suniara, R.K., Kerr, K., Owen, J.J., and Dickson, C. (2001). Development of the thymus requires signaling through the fibroblast growth factor receptor R2-IIIb. *J. Immunol.* **167,** 1954–1961.

62. Min, D., Taylor, P.A., Panoskaltsis-Mortari, A., Chung, B., Danilenko, D.M., Farrell, C., Lacey, D.L., Blazar, B.R., and Weinberg, K.I. (2002). Protection from thymic epithelial cell injury by keratinocyte growth factor: a new approach to improve thymic and peripheral T-cell reconstitution after bone marrow transplantation. *Blood* **99,** 4592–4600.
63. Rossi, S., Blazar, B.R., Farrell, C.L., Danilenko, D.M., Lacey, D.L., Weinberg, K.I., Krenger, W., and Hollander, G.A. (2002). Keratinocyte growth factor preserves normal thymopoiesis and thymic microenvironment during experimental graft-versus-host disease. *Blood* **100,** 682–691.
64. Anderson, G., Anderson, K., Tchilian, E.Z., Owen, J.J.T., and Jenkinson, E.J. (1997). Fibroblast dependency during early thymocyte development maps to the CD25⁺CD44⁺ stage and involves interactions with fibroblast matrix molecules. *Eur. J. Immunol.* **27,** 1200–1206.
65. von Freeden-Jeffry, U., Vieira, P., Lucian, L.A., McNeil, T., Burdach, S.E., and Murray, R. (1995). Lymphopenia in interleukin *(IL)*-7 gene-deleted mice identifies *IL-7* as a nonredundant cytokine. *J. Exp. Med.* **181,** 1519–1526.
66. Rodewald, H.R., Ogawa, M., Haller, C., Waskow, C., and DiSanto, J.P. (1997). Prothymocyte expansion by c-kit and the common cytokine receptor γ-chain is essential for repertoire formation. *Immunity.* **6,** 265–272.
67. Waskow, C., Paul, S., Haller, C., Gassmann, M., and Rodewald, H.R. (2002). Viable c-Kit$^{W/W}$ mutants reveal pivotal role for c-Kit in the maintenance of lymphopoiesis. *Immunity* **17,** 277–288.
68. Manley, N.R., and Capecchi, M.R. (1995). The role of Hoxa-3 in mouse thymus and thyroid development. *Development* **121,** 1989–2003.
69. Lindsay, E.A., Vitelli, F., Su, H., Morishima, M., Huynh, T., Pramparo, T., Jurecic, V., Ogunrinu, G., Sutherland, H.F., Scambler, P.J., Bradley, A., and Baldini, A. (2001). Tbx1 haploinsufficiency in the DiGeorge syndrome region causes aortic arch defects in mice. *Nature* **410,** 97–101.
70. Jerome, L.A., and Papaioannou, V.E. (2001). DiGeorge syndrome phenotype in mice mutant for the T-box gene, *Tbx1. Nat. Genet.* **27,** 286–291.
71. Xu, P.X., Zheng, W., Laclef, C., Maire, P., Maas, R.L., Peters, H., and Xu, X. (2002). Eya1 is required for the morphogenesis of mammalian thymus, parathyroid, and thyroid. *Development* **129,** 3033–3044.
72. Balciunaite, G., Keller, M.P., Balciunaite, E., Piali, L., Zuklys, S., Mathieu, Y.D., Gill, J., Boyd, R., Sussman, D.J., and Hollander, G.A. (2002). Wnt glycoproteins regulate the expression of *FoxN1,* the gene defective in *nude* mice. *Nat. Immunol.* **3,** 1102–1108.
73. Blackburn, C.C., Augustine, C.L., Li, R., Harvey, R.P., Malin, M.A., Boyd, R.L., Miller, J.F., and Morahan, G. (1996). The *nu* gene acts cell autonomously and is required for differentiation of thymic epithelial progenitors. *Proc. Natl. Acad. Sci. U. S. A.* **93,** 5742–5746.
74. Bleul, C.C., and Boehm, T. (2001). Laser capture microdissection-based expression profiling identifies PD1 ligand as a target of the *nude* locus gene product. *Eur. J. Immunol.* **31,** 2497–2503.
75. Bleul, C.C., and Boehm, T. (2000). Chemokines define distinct microenvironments in the developing thymus. *Eur. J. Immunol.* **30,** 3371–3379.
76. Dietrich, S., and Gruss, P. (1995). Undulated phenotypes suggest a role of Pax-1 for the development of vertebral and extravertebral structures. *Dev. Biol.* **167,** 529–548.
77. Su, D.M., and Manley, N.R. (2000). Hoxa3 and pax1 transcription factors regulate the ability of fetal thymic epithelial cells to promote thymocyte development. *J. Immunol.* **164,** 5753–5760.
78. Su, D., Ellis, S., Napier, A., Lee, K., and Manley, N.R. (2001). Hoxa3 and pax1 regulate epithelial cell death and proliferation during thymus and parathyroid organogenesis. *Dev. Biol.* **236,** 316–329.
79. Peters, H., Neubuser, A., Kratochwil, K., and Balling, R. (1998). Pax9-deficient mice lack pharyngeal pouch derivatives and teeth and exhibit craniofacial and limb abnormalities. *Genes Dev.* **12,** 2735–2747.
80. Jenkinson, E.J., and Owen, J.J. (1990). T-cell differentiation in thymus organ cultures. *Semin. Immunol.* **2,** 51–58.
81. Anderson, G., Moore, N.C., Owen, J.J.T., and Jenkinson, E.J. (1996). Cellular interactions in thymocyte development. *Annu. Rev. Immunol.* **14,** 73–99.
82. Oosterwegel, M.A., Haks, M.C., Jeffry, U., Murray, R., and Kruisbeek, A.M. (1997). Induction of *TCR* gene rearrangements in uncommitted stem cells by a subset of IL-7-producing, class II-expressing thymic stromal cells. *Immunity* **6,** 351–360.
83. Muller, K.M., Luedecker, C.J., Udey, M.C., and Farr, A.G. (1997). Involvement of E-cadherin in thymus organogenesis and thymocyte maturation. *Immunity* **6,** 257–264.
84. Anderson, K.L., Moore, N.C., McLoughlin, D.E., Jenkinson, E.J., and Owen, J.J. (1998). Studies on thymic epithelial cells *in vitro. Dev. Comp. Immunol.* **22,** 367–377.
85. Merkenschlager, M., and Fisher, A.G. (1992). Human postnatal thymocytes generate phenotypically immature CD3dim, CD5dim, CD1a bright progeny in organ culture. *J. Immunol.* **148,** 1012–1015.
86. Poznansky, M.C., Evans, R.H., Foxall, R.B., Olszak, I.T., Piascik, A.H., Hartman, K.E., Brander, C., Meyer, T.H., Pykett, M.J., Chabner, K.T., Kalams, S.A., Rosenzweig, M., and Scadden, D.T. (2000). Efficient generation of human T-cells from a tissue-engineered thymic organoid. *Nat. Biotechnol.* **18,** 729–734.
87. Kendall, M.D., Schuurman, H.J., Fenton, J., Broekhuizen, R., and Kampinga, J. (1988). Implantation of cultured thymic fragments in congenitally athymic *(nude)* rats. *Cell Tiss. Res.* **254,** 283–294.
88. Pyke, K.W., Bartlett, P.F., and Mandel, T.E. (1983). The *in vitro* production of chimeric murine thymus from nonlymphoid embryonic precursors. *J. Immunol. Methods.* **58,** 243–254.
89. Rodewald, H.R. (1996). Reconstitution of selective hematopoietic lineages and hematopoietic environments *in vivo. In* "Human Disease: From Genetic Cause to Biochemical Effects (Proceedings of the Symposium 'The Genetic Basis of Human Disease')." Basel, Switzerland.
90. Rodewald, H.R. (2000). Thymus epithelial cell reaggregate grafts. *Curr. Top. Microbiol. Immunol.* **251,** 101–108.
91. Rodewald, H.R. (Unpublished).
92. Kirberg, J., Baron, A., Jakob, S., Rolink, A., Karjalainen, K., and von Boehmer, H. (1994). Thymic selection of CD8⁺ single positive cells with a class II major histocompatibility complex-restricted receptor. *J. Exp. Med.* **180,** 25–34.
93. Petrie, H.T., and Van Ewijk, W. (2002). Thymus by numbers. *Nat. Immunol.* **3,** 604–605.
94. Couzin, J. (2002). Immunology: plant a few cells, sprout a thymus. *Science* **296,** 2120–2121.
95. Kontgen, F., Suss, G., Stewart, C., Steinmetz, M., and Bluethmann, H. (1993). Targeted disruption of the MHC class II *Aa* gene in C57BL/6 mice. *Int. Immunol.* **5,** 957–964.
96. Boyd, R.L., Tucek, C.L., Godfrey, D.I., Izon, D.J., Wilson, T.J., Davidson, N.J., Bean, A.G., Ladyman, H.M., Ritter, M.A., and Hugo, P. (1993). The thymic microenvironment. *Immunol. Today.* **14,** 445–459.

97. Gosgrove, D., Gray, D., Dierich, A., Kaufman, J., Lemeur, M., Benoist, C., and Mathis, D. (1991). Mice lacking MHC class II molecules. *Cell* **66,** 1051–1066.
98. Grusby, M.J., Johnson, R.S., Papaioannou, V.E., and Glimcher, L.H. (1991). Depletion of CD4+ T-cells in major histocompatibility complex class II-deficient mice. *Science* **253,** 1417–1420.
99. Till, J.E., and McCullouch, E.A. (1961). A direct measurement of the radiation sensitivity of normal mouse bone marrow cells. *Radiat. Res.* **14,** 213–222.
100. Klein, L., and Kyewski, B. (2000). Self-antigen presentation by thymic stromal cells: a subtle division of labor. *Curr. Opin. Immunol.* **12,** 179–186.
101. Kyewski, B., Derbinski, J., Gotter, J., and Klein, L. (2002). Promiscuous gene expression and central T-cell tolerance: more than meets the eye. *Trends Immunol.* **23,** 364–371.
102. Derbinski, J., Schulte, A., Kyewski, B., and Klein, L. (2001). Promiscuous gene expression in medullary thymic epithelial cells mirrors the peripheral self. *Nat. Immunol.* **2,** 1032–1039.
103. Anderson, M.S., Venanzi, E.S., Klein, L., Chen, Z., Berzins, S.P., Turley, S.J., von Boehmer, H., Bronson, R., Dierich, A., Benoist, C., and Mathis, D. (2002). Projection of an immunological self shadow within the thymus by the aire protein. *Science* **298,** 1395–1401.
104. Stewart, J.J. (1998). The female X-inactivation mosaic in systemic lupus erythematosus. *Immunol. Today.* **19,** 352–357.

50

Bladder Progenitor Cells and Their Use for Tissue Engineering

Anthony Atala

Introduction

Gastrointestinal segments are commonly used as tissues for bladder replacement or repair. However, when gastrointestinal tissue is in contact with the urinary tract, multiple complications may ensue, such as infection, metabolic disturbances, urolithiasis, perforation, increased mucous production, and malignancy.[1–4] Because of the problems encountered with the use of gastrointestinal segments, numerous investigators have attempted to use alternative materials and tissues for bladder replacement or repair. These include matrices for tissue regeneration and tissue engineering using cell transplantation.

Engineering tissue using selective cell transplantation provides the means to create functional, new bladder segments.[5] Tissue-engineering technologies have already been clinically applied to the bladder by the use of injectable cells for the treatment of vesicoureteral reflux and urinary incontinence.[6–10] The approach, which my colleagues and I have followed to bioengineer bladder tissue, involves the eventual use of autologous cells, thus avoiding rejection: A biopsy of tissue is obtained from the host, and the cells are dissociated and expanded *in vitro,* reattached to a matrix, and implanted into the same host.[5,10–27]

The success of using cell transplantation strategies for bladder reconstruction depends on the ability to use donor tissue efficiently and to provide the right conditions for long-term survival, differentiation, and growth. We have achieved an approach to bladder tissue regeneration by patching isolated cells to a support structure, which would have suitable surface chemistry for guiding the reorganization and growth of the cells. The supporting matrix is composed of biodegradable artificial or natural polymers, which can allow cell survival by diffusion of nutrients across short distances once the cell-support matrix is implanted. The cell-support matrix becomes vascularized with expansion of the cell mass following implantation.

Adult Bladder Progenitor Cells

One of the initial limitations of applying tissue-engineering techniques to the bladder had been the previously encountered inherent difficulty of growing genitourinary-associated cells in large quantities. In the past, it was believed that urothelial cells had a natural senescence that was hard to overcome. Normal urothelial cells could be grown in the laboratory setting but with limited expansion. A system of harvesting adult urothelial progenitor cells was created in our laboratory; it does not use enzymes or serum and has a large expansion potential.[18]

The mitotic index of the bladder is low, less than 0.03. However, when the bladder is injured, the mitotic index increases markedly to more than 0.3. Therefore, it was evident that an undifferentiated cell population was activated upon injury. To determine the location of the adult progenitor cell population, a laser injury model was created in mice previously injected with bromodeoxyuridine (BrdU), a thymidine analog incorporated into the cells DNA during replication. Bladder tissue sections were obtained at different time points following injury, from 1 hour to 7 days. By 24 hours after injury, the entire bladder epithelial layer had been repopulated to a normal level. A few hours after the bladder injury was created, some of the basal layer cells showed BrdU uptake (Fig. 50–1). My colleagues and I thereafter targeted the basal cell population for isolation and possible expansion. Nonetheless, even when the basal cell layer was isolated, it could not be expanded to large numbers, and senescence was evident. We then turned our attention to the cell media and its additives. The cells were exposed to different media, growth factors, cytokines, and other additives in a controlled manner. The cells were then probed for differentiation, using E-cadherin and zona occludens-1 antibodies under confocal microscopy (Fig. 50–2). It became evident that some of the common media additives at that time (1990) would terminally differentiate the cells. Thereafter, only media components that had no effect on urothelial cell differentiation were used. Using the techniques described, urothelial cells could be readily expanded until the desired cell numbers were obtained.

It is now possible to expand a urothelial strain from a single specimen that initially covers a surface area of 1 cm^2 to one covering a surface area of 4202 m^2 (the equivalent area of one football field) within 8 weeks.[18] The bladder muscle cells are processed by the tissue explant technique and are expanded in a similar manner. My colleagues and I have shown that normal human bladder epithelial and muscle cells can be efficiently harvested from surgical material, that they can be extensively expanded in culture, and that their

Handbook of Stem Cells
Volume 2

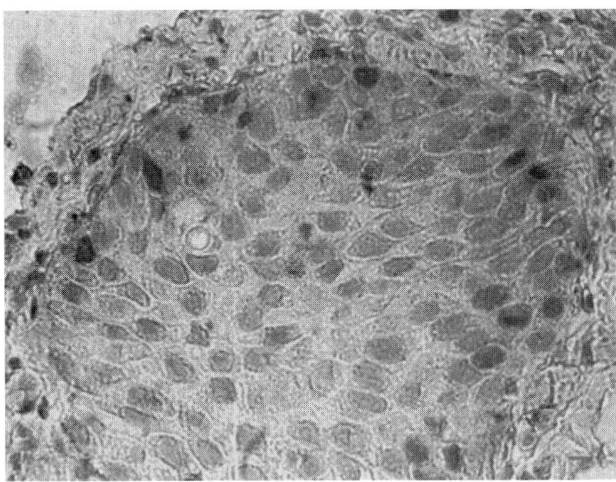

Figure 50–1. Bromodeoxyuridine uptake after bladder injury shows that the replicating cells are in the basal layers of bladder tissue. (Please see CD-ROM for color version of this figure.)

differentiation characteristics, growth requirements, and other biological properties can be studied.[11,16–20,22–31]

Bladder Tissue Engineering Using Committed Progenitor Cells

Cell delivery vehicles: As described initially by Folkman[32] in 1973, cells or tissue cannot be implanted in volumes greater than 3 mm^3. This maximum diffusion distance limits nutrition and gas exchange. The cell delivery vehicles, which my colleagues and I have used, are designed for cell attachment and capillary infiltration to the interstitial spaces after implantation *in vivo.*[12,13,16,17,19,20,22–27] In this manner, large numbers of cells can be implanted with maximal survival.

Both synthetic and natural biodegradable materials have been used as cell delivery vehicles.[12,13,16,17,19,20,22–27] We have used resorbable biodegradable polymers, which are preferable because permanent polymers, such as silicone and Teflon, carry the risk of infection, calcification, and unfavorable connective tissue responses.[5] The cell delivery scaffolds used experimentally in our laboratory include polyglycolic acid polymer scaffolds alone and with copolymers of poly-l-lactic acid and poly-DL-lactide-co-glycolide.[12,13,22] These polymers have many desirable features: They are biocompatible and processible. Degradation occurs by hydrolysis, and the time sequence can be varied from weeks to more than a year by manipulating the ratio of monomers and by varying the processing conditions. We have also used processed collagen derived from allogeneic donor bladder submucosa and small intestinal submucosa (SIS).[25] These biodegradable matrices, both natural and artificial, can be readily modified depending on their intended application into a variety of shapes and structures, including small-diameter fibers and porous films, various levels of rigidity or elasticity, and different time sequences for degradation.

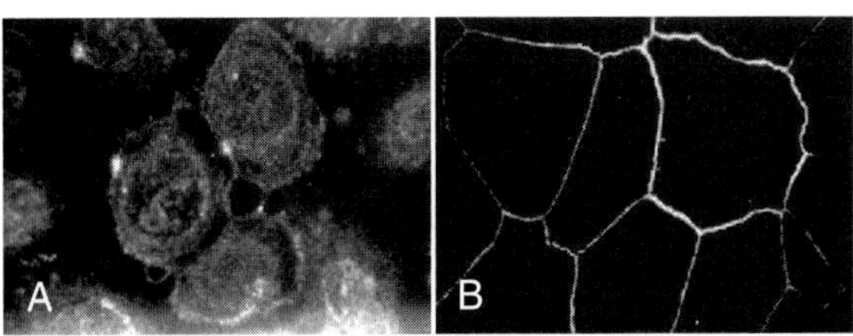

Figure 50–2. Confocal microscopy of urothelial probed with zona occludens-1 localized (A) to the cell cytoplasm in the undifferentiated state and (B) in the cell wall in the differentiated state.

The porosity, pore size distribution, and continuity dictate the interaction of the biomaterials and transplanted cells with the host tissue. The appropriate porosity and branching pattern of the matrix results in the formation of a capillary network in the developing tissue.[12,13,16,17,19,20,22–27] Vascularization of the engineered tissue is required to meet the metabolic requirements of the tissue and to integrate it with the surrounding host.

Formation of bladder tissue ex situ: Urothelial and muscle cells can be expanded *in vitro,* seeded onto the polymer scaffold, and allowed to attach and form sheets of cells. The cell–polymer scaffold can then be implanted *in vivo.* My colleagues and I have performed a series of *in vivo* urologic associated cell–polymer experiments. Histologic analysis of human urothelial, bladder muscle, and composite urothelial and bladder muscle–polymer scaffolds, implanted in athymic mice and retrieved at different time points, indicated that viable cells were evident in all three experimental groups.[13] Implanted cells oriented themselves spatially along the polymer surfaces. The cell populations appeared to expand from one layer to several layers of thickness with progressive cell organization with extended implantation times. Cell–polymer composite implants of urothelial and muscle cells, retrieved at extended times (50 days), showed extensive formation of multilayered sheet-like structures and well-defined muscle layers. Polymers seeded with cells and manipulated into a tubular configuration showed layers of muscle cells lining the multilayered epithelial sheets. Cellular debris appeared reproducibly in the luminal spaces, suggesting that epithelial cells lining the lumina are sloughed into the luminal space. Cell polymers implanted with human bladder muscle cells alone showed almost complete replacement of the polymer with sheets of smooth muscle at 50 days. This experiment demonstrated, for the first time, that composite tissue-engineered structures could be created *de novo.* Prior to this study, only single-cell type tissue-engineered structures had been created.

Formation of bladder tissue: To determine the effects of implanting engineered tissues in continuity with the urinary tract, an animal model of bladder augmentation was used.[25] Partial cystectomies, which involved removing approximately 50% of the native bladders, were performed in 10 beagles. In 5, the retrieved bladder tissue was microdissected and the mucosal and muscular layers were separated. The bladder urothelial and muscle cells were cultured using the techniques described previously. Both urothelial and smooth muscle cells were harvested and expanded separately. A collagen-based matrix, derived from allogeneic bladder submucosa, was used for cell delivery. This material was chosen for these experiments because of its native elasticity. Within 6 weeks, the expanded urothelial cells were collected as a pellet. The cells were seeded on the luminal surface of the allogeneic bladder submucosa and incubated in serum-free keratinocyte growth medium for 5 days. Muscle cells were seeded on the opposite side of the bladder submucosa and subsequently placed in Dulbecco's modified Eagle's medium supplemented with 10% fetal calf serum for an additional 5 days. The seeding density on the allogeneic bladder submucosa was approximately 1×10^7 cells/cm^2.

Preoperative fluoroscopic cystography and urodynamic studies were performed in all animals. Augmentation cystoplasty was performed with the matrix with cells in one group (n = 5) and with the matrix without cells in the second group (n = 5). The augmented bladders were covered with omentum to facilitate angiogenesis to the implant. Cystostomy catheters were used for urinary diversion for 10 to 14 days. Urodynamic studies and fluoroscopic cystography were performed at 1, 2, and 3 months after operation. Augmented bladders were retrieved 2 (n = 6) and 3 (n = 4) months after surgery and examined grossly, histologically, and immunocytochemically.

Bladders augmented with the matrix seeded with cells showed a 99% increase in capacity, whereas bladders augmented with the cell-free matrix showed only a 30% increase in capacity (Fig. 50–3). Functionally, all animals showed normal bladder compliance as evidenced by urodynamic studies; however, the remaining native bladder tissue may have accounted for these results. Histologically, the retrieved engineered bladders contained a cellular organization consisting of urothelial-lined lumen surrounded by submucosal tissue

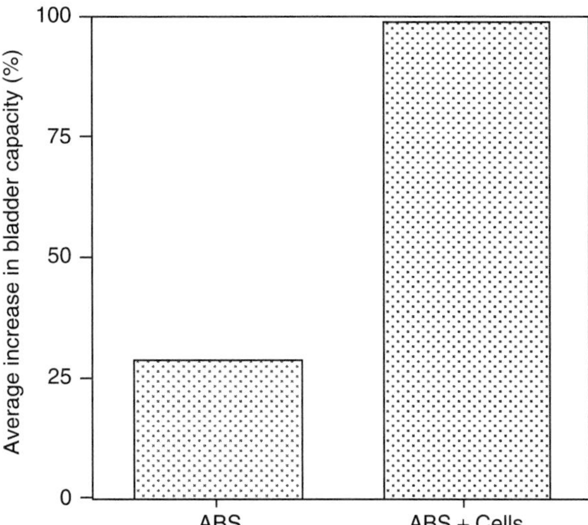

Figure 50–3. Bladders augmented with a collagen matrix seeded with urothelial and smooth muscle cells showed a 99% increase in capacity compared to bladders augmented with the cell-free matrix, which showed only a 30% increase in capacity within three months after implantation (ABS: allogeneic bladder submucosa). (Please see CD-ROM for color version of this figure.)

and smooth muscle. However, the muscular layer was more prominent in the cell-reconstituted scaffold.[25]

Most of the free grafts (without cells) used for bladder replacement in the past have been able to show adequate histology in terms of a well-developed urothelial layer; however, they have been associated with an abnormal muscular layer that varies in its full development.[14,15] It has been well established for decades that the bladder is able to regenerate generously over free grafts. Urothelium is associated with a high reparative capacity.[33] Bladder muscle tissue is less likely to regenerate normally. Both urothelial and muscle ingrowth are believed to be initiated from the edges of the normal bladder toward the region of the free graft.[34,35] Usually, however, contracture or resorption of the graft has been evident. The inflammatory response toward the matrix may contribute to the resorption of the free graft.

We hypothesized that building the three-dimensional structure construct *in vitro,* prior to implantation, would facilitate the eventual terminal differentiation of the cells after implantation *in vivo* and would minimize the inflammatory response toward the matrix, thus avoiding graft contracture and shrinkage. This study demonstrated a major difference between matrices used with autologous cells (tissue engineered) and matrices used without cells.[25] Matrices implanted with cells for bladder augmentation retained most of their implanted diameter; in matrices implanted without cells for bladder augmentation, graft contraction and shrinkage occurred. The histomorphology demonstrated a marked paucity of muscle cells and a more aggressive inflammatory reaction in the matrices implanted without cells. Of interest is that the urothelial cell layers appeared normal even though its underlying matrix was significantly inflamed. My colleagues and I further hypothesized that having an adequate urothelial layer from the outset would limit the amount of urine contact with the matrix and would therefore decrease the inflammatory response. We also suggested that the muscle cells were necessary for bioengineering, since native muscle cells are less likely to regenerate over the free grafts. Further studies performed in our laboratory confirmed these hypotheses.[22] Thus, both the urothelial and the muscle cells on the matrices we used for bladder replacement appear to be important for successful tissue bioengineering.

Bladder replacement using tissue engineering: The results of our initial studies showed that the creation of artificial bladders may be achieved *in vivo;* however, it could not be determined whether the functional parameters noted were because of the augmented segment or the intact native bladder tissue. To better address the functional parameters of tissue-engineered bladders, an animal model was designed that required a subtotal cystectomy and subsequent replacement with a tissue-engineered organ.[22]

A total of 14 beagle dogs underwent a trigone-sparing cystectomy. The animals were randomly assigned to one of three groups. Group A (n = 2) underwent closure of the trigone without a reconstructive procedure. Group B (n = 6) underwent reconstruction with a cell-free bladder-shaped biodegradable polymer. Group C (n = 6) underwent reconstruction using a bladder-shaped biodegradable polymer that delivered autologous urothelial cells and smooth muscle cells. The cell populations had been separately expanded from a previously harvested autologous bladder biopsy. Preoperative and postoperative urodynamic and radiographic studies were performed serially. Animals were sacrificed at 1, 2, 3, 4, 6, and 11 months postoperatively. Gross, histological, and immunocytochemical analyses were performed.[22]

The cystectomy-only controls and the polymer-only grafts maintained average capacities of 22% and 46% of preoperative values, respectively. An average bladder capacity of 95% of the original precystectomy volume was achieved in the tissue-engineered bladder replacements. These findings were confirmed radiographically (Fig. 50–4). The subtotal cystectomy reservoirs, which were not reconstructed, and the polymer-only reconstructed bladders showed a marked decrease in bladder compliance (10% and 42%, respectively). The compliance of the tissue-engineered bladders showed almost no difference from preoperative values measured when the native bladder was present (106%). Histologically, the polymer-only bladders presented a pattern of normal urothelial cells with a thickened fibrotic submucosa and a thin layer of muscle fibers. The retrieved tissue-engineered bladders showed a normal cellular organization, consisting of a trilayer of urothelium, submucosa, and muscle (Fig. 50–5). Immunocytochemical analyses for desmin, alpha-actin, cytokeratin 7, pancytokeratins AE1/AE3, and uroplakin III confirmed the muscle and urothelial phenotype. S-100 staining indicated the presence of neural structures. The results from this study showed that it is possible to tissue engineer bladders that are anatomically and functionally normal.[22]

Fetal bladder tissue engineering: The prenatal diagnosis of patients with bladder disease is now more prevalent. Prenatal ultrasonography allows a thorough survey of fetal anatomy. The absence of bladder filling, a mass of echogenic tissue on the lower abdominal wall, or a low set umbilicus during prenatal sonographic examination may suggest the diagnosis of bladder exstrophy. These findings and the presence of intraluminal intestinal calcifications suggest the presence of a cloacal malformation.

The natural consequence of the evolution in prenatal diagnosis led to the use of intervention before birth to reverse potentially life-threatening processes. However, the concept of prenatal intervention is not limited to this narrow group of indications. A prenatal rather than a postnatal diagnosis of exstrophy may be beneficial under certain circumstances. There is a renewed interest in performing a single-stage reconstruction in some patients with bladder exstrophy.

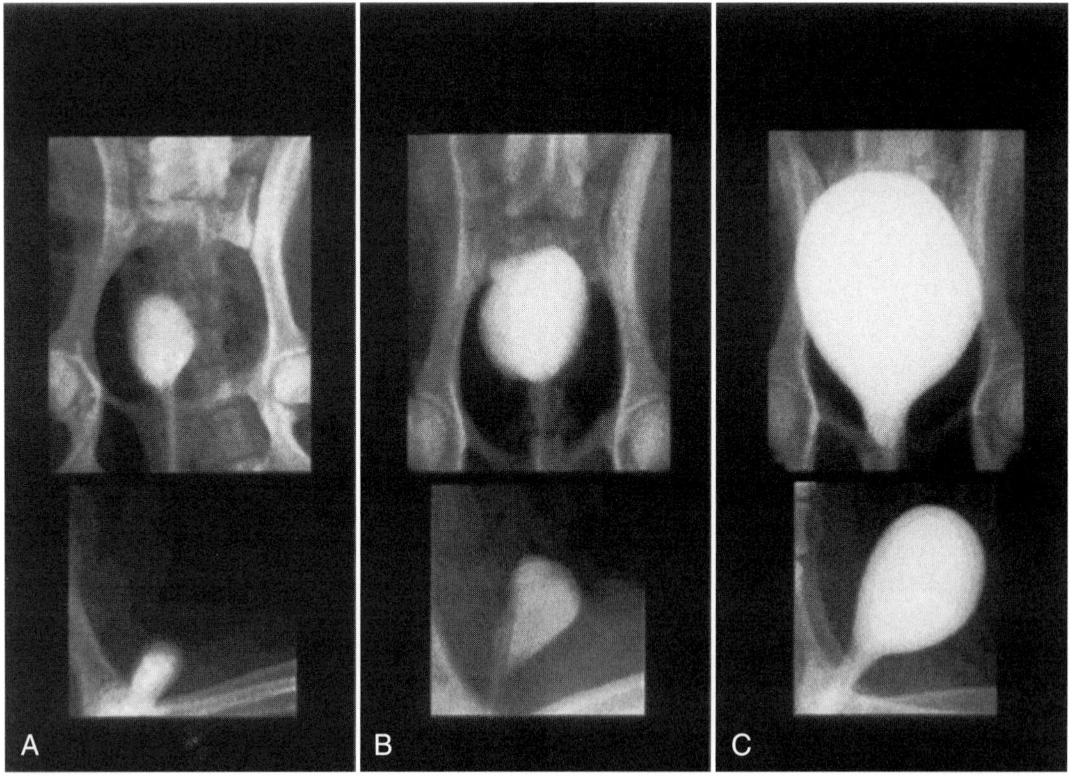

Figure 50–4. (A) Radiographic cystograms in beagles 11 months after subtotal cystectomy without reconstruction, (B) with reconstruction using a polymer scaffold without cells, and (C) with reconstruction with a cell-seeded polymer scaffold. Trigone-sparing cystectomy organs retained a small reservoir. Bladders replaced with the polymer scaffold alone (without cells) showed a small, noncompliant reservoir. Tissue-engineered neobladders showed normal configuration and capacity.

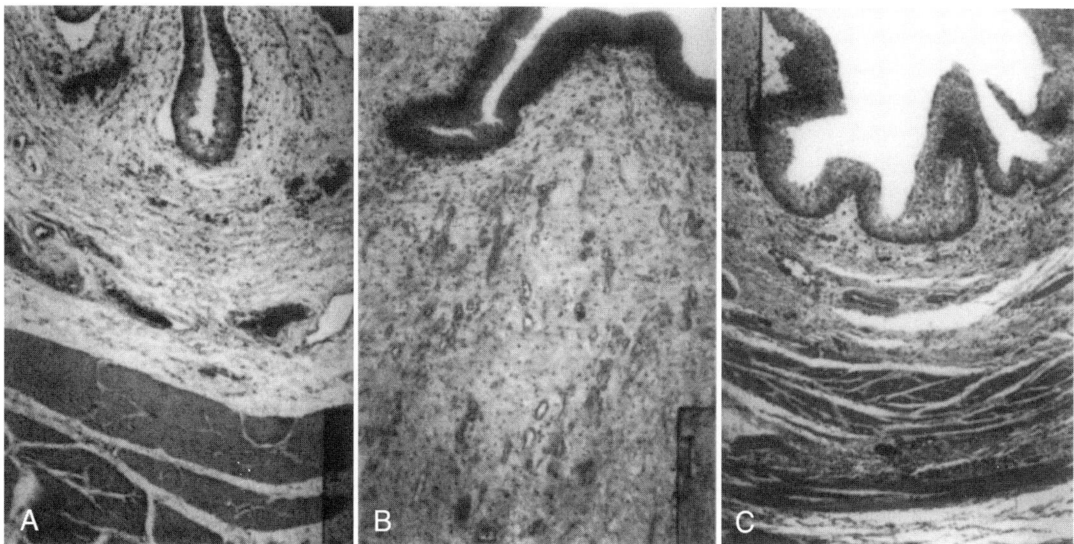

Figure 50–5. *Hematoxylin and Eosin histological results 6 months after surgery.* (A) Normal canine bladder. (B) The dome of the bladder replaced with the polymer scaffold alone (without cells). The histological section shows a thickened layer of fibrotic tissue with urothelium but with only scarce muscle fibers. (C) The tissue-engineered neoorgan, constructed with a polymer scaffold seeded with cells, shows a histomorphologically normal appearance. A trilayered architecture consisting of urothelium, submucosa, and smooth muscle is evident. Original magnification = 250 ×.

Limiting factors for following a single-stage or multistage approach may include the findings of a small, fibrotic bladder patch, without either elasticity or contractility, or a hypoplastic bladder.

There are several strategies that may be pursued, using today's technological and scientific advances, and may facilitate prenatal management of patients with bladder disease. Having a ready supply of urologic-associated tissue for surgical reconstruction at birth may be advantageous. Theoretically, once the diagnosis of bladder exstrophy is confirmed prenatally, a small bladder and skin biopsy could be obtained using ultrasound guidance. These biopsy materials could then be processed and the different cell types could be expanded *in vitro*. Using the tissue-engineering techniques developed at our center and described previously, reconstituted bladder and skin structures *in vitro* could then be available at the time of birth for a one-stage reconstruction, allowing adequate anatomic and functional closure.

Toward this end, my colleagues and I conducted a series of experiments using fetal lambs.[17,19,20] Bladder exstrophy was created surgically in 10 fetal lambs between 90–95 days of gestation. The lambs were randomly divided into two groups of 5. In group I, a small fetal bladder specimen was harvested using fetoscopy. The bladder specimen was separated and muscle and urothelial cells were harvested and expanded separately under sterile conditions in a humidified 5% CO_2 chamber, as previously described. Seven to 10 days prior to delivery, the expanded bladder muscle cells were seeded on one side and the urothelial cells were seeded on the opposite side of a 20-cm^2 biodegradable polyglycolic acid polymer scaffold. After delivery, all lambs in group I had surgical closure of their bladder using the tissue-engineered bladder tissue. No fetal bladder harvest was performed in the group II lambs, and bladder exstrophy closure was performed using only the native bladder. Cystograms were performed 3 and 8 weeks after surgery. The engineered bladders were more compliant ($p = 0.01$) and had a higher capacity ($p = 0.02$) than the native bladder closure group. Histologic analysis of the engineered tissue showed a normal histological pattern indistinguishable from native bladder at 2 months.[19] Similar prenatal studies were performed in lambs, engineering skin for reconstruction at birth.[20]

The preceding studies show that there is potential for replicating this technology in humans. Certainly, other tissues, such as cartilage, corpora cavernosa, and bowel can be harvested and expanded in the same manner. Similar studies addressing these tissues are in progress in our laboratory.

In addition to being able to manage the bladder exstrophy complex *in utero* with tissue-engineering techniques, we could manage patients after birth in a similar manner, whenever a prenatal diagnosis is not assured. In these instances, bladder tissue biopsies could be obtained at the time of the initial surgery. Different tissues could be harvested and stored for future reconstruction, if necessary. A tissue bank for exstrophy complex patients could preserve different cell types indefinitely. Gene therapy could also be achieved by transfecting the cells prior to seeding and implantation.[24]

Summary

It is evident from experimental studies that matrices implanted in bladders without cells, including bladder submucosa, SIS, or artificial biodegradable polymer scaffolds, contract with time and lead to diminished bladder capacities, whereas matrices implanted with cells are able to achieve normal bladder functional characteristics over time. Clinical trials are being arranged for the use of engineered bladder tissues for augmentation. The next several years will be important in determining the long-term clinical validity of these techniques.

REFERENCES

1. Atala, A., Hendren, H., Bauer, S., and Retik, A. (1993). The effect of gastrocystoplasty on bladder function. *J. Urol.* **149,** 1099.
2. Kaefer, M., Tobin, M.S., Hendren, W.H., Bauer, S.B., Peters, C.A., Atala, A., Colodny, A.H., Mandell, J., and Retik, A.B. (1997). Continent urinary diversion: The Children's Hospital experience. *J. Urol.* **157,** 1394–1399.
3. Kaefer, M., Hendren, H., Bauer, S., Goldenblatt, P., Peters, C., Atala, A., and Retik, A. (1998). Reservoir calculi: a comparison of reservoirs constructed from stomach and other enteric segments. *J. Urol.* **160,** 2187–2190.
4. McDougal, W.S. (1992). Metabolic complications of urinary intestinal diversion. *J. Urol.* **147,** 1199–1208.
5. Atala, A. (1997). Tissue engineering in the genitourinary system. *In* "Tissue Engineering," (A. Atala *et al.,* eds.), p. 149. Birkhauser Press, Boston.
6. Atala, A., Cima, L.G., Kim, W.S., Page, K.T., Vacanti, J.P., Retik, A.B., and Vacanti, C.A. (1993). Injectable polymers seeded with chondrocytes as a therapeutic approach. *J. Urol.* **150,** 745–747.
7. Atala, A., Kim, W.S., Paige, K.T., Vacanti, C.A., and Retik, A.B. (1994). Endoscopic treatment of vesicoureteral reflux with a chondrocyte-alginate suspension. *J. Urol.* **152,** 641–643.
8. Diamond, D.A., and Caldamone, A.A. (1999). Endoscopic correction of vesicoureteral reflux in children using autologous chondrocytes: preliminary results. *J. Urol.* **162,** 1185–1188.
9. Bent, A.E., Tutrone, R.T., McLennan, M.T., Lloyd, K., Kennelly, M.J., and Badlani, G. (2001). Treatment of intrinsic sphincter deficiency using autologous ear chondrocytes as a bulking agent. *Neurourol. Urodyn.* **20,** 157–165.
10. Kershen, R.T., and Atala, A. (1999). New advances in injectable therapies for the treatment of incontinence and vesicoureteral reflux. *Urol. Clin. North Am.* **26,** 81–94.
11. Amiel, G.E., and Atala, A. (1999). Current and future modalities for functional renal replacement. *Urol. Clin. North Am.* **26,** 235–246.
12. Atala A., Vacanti J.P., Peters C.A., Mandell J., Retik A.B., and Freeman, M.R. (1992). Formation of urothelial structures *in vivo* from dissociated cells attached to biodegradable polymer scaffolds *in vitro. J. Urol.* **48,** 658–662.
13. Atala A., Freeman, M.R., Vacanti, J.P., Shepard, J., and Retik, A.B. (1993). Implantation *in vivo* and retrieval of artificial structures consisting of rabbit and human urothelium and human bladder muscle. *J. Urol.* **150,** 608–612.
14. Atala, A. (1995). Commentary on the replacement of urologic associated mucosa. *J. Urol.* **156,** 338–339.
15. Atala, A. (1998). Autologous cell transplantation for urologic reconstruction. *J. Urol.* **159,** 2–3.
16. Atala, A. (1999). Future perspectives in reconstructive surgery using tissue engineering. *Urol. Clin. North Am.* **26,** 157–165.
17. Atala, A. (In press). Tissue-engineering techniques for closure of bladder exstrophy: An experimental animal model. *In* "The Exstrophy–Epispadias Complex," (J. Gearhart, ed.), pp. 63–64. Plenum Press, New York.
18. Cilento, B.G., Freeman, M.R., Schneck, F.X., Retik, A.B., and Atala, A. (1994). Phenotypic and cytogenetic characterization of human bladder urothelia expanded *in vitro. J. Urol.* **152,** 655–670.
19. Fauza, D.O., Fishman, S., Mehegan, K., and Atala, A. (1998). Videofetoscopically assisted fetal tissue engineering: bladder augmentation. *J. Pediatr. Surg.* **33,** 7–12.
20. Fauza, D.O., Fishman, S., Mehegan, K., and Atala, A. (1998). Videofetoscopically assisted fetal tissue engineering: skin replacement. *J. Pediatr. Surg.* **33,** 357–361.
21. Machlouf, M., and Atala, A. (1998). Emerging concepts for tissue and organ transplantation. *Graft* **1,** 31–37.
22. Oberpenning, F.O., Meng, J., Yoo, J., and Atala, A. (1999). *De novo* reconstitution of a functional urinary bladder by tissue engineering. *Nat. Biotech.* **17,** 149–155.
23. Park, H.J., Kershen, R., Yoo, J., and Atala, A. (1999). Reconstitution of human corporal smooth muscle and endothelial cells *in vivo. J. Urol.* **162,** 1106–1109.
24. Yoo, J.J., and Atala, A. (1997). A novel gene delivery system using urothelial tissue-engineered neoorgans. *J. Urol.* **158,** 1066–1070.
25. Yoo, J.J., Meng, J., Oberpenning, F., and Atala, A. (1998). Bladder augmentation using allogeneic bladder submucosa seeded with cells. *Urology* **51,** 221–225.
26. Yoo, J.J., Lee, I., and Atala, A. (1998). Cartilage rods as a potential material for penile reconstruction. *J. Urol.* **160,** 1164–1168.
27. Yoo, J., Park, H.J., Lee, I., and Atala, A. (1999). Autologous engineered cartilage rods for penile reconstruction. *J. Urol.* **162,** 1119–1121.
28. Freeman, M.R., Yoo, J.J., Raab, G., Soker, S., Adam, R.M., Schneck, F.X., Renshaw, A.A., Klagsbrun, M., and Atala, A. (1997). Heparin-binding EGF-like growth factor is an autocrine factor for human urothelial cells and is synthesized by epithelial and smooth muscle cells in the human bladder. *J. Clin. Invest.* **99,** 1028–1036.
29. Nguyen, H.T., Park, J.M., Peters, C.A., Adam, R.A., Orsola, A., Atala, A., and Freeman, M.R. (1999). Cell-specific activation of the *HB-EGF* and *ErbB1* genes by stretch in primary human bladder cells. *In Vitro Cell. Dev. Biol.* **35,** 371–375.
30. Tobin, M.S., Freeman, M.R., and Atala, A. (1994). Maturational response of normal human urothelial cells in culture is dependent on extracellular matrix and serum additives. *Surg. For.* **45,** 786–789.
31. Tsuji, I., Ishida, H., and Fujieda, J. (1961). Experimental cystoplasty using preserved bladder graft. *J. Urol.* **85,** 42.
32. Folkman, J., and Hochberg, M.M. (1973). Self-regulation of growth in three dimensions. *J. Exp. Med.* **138,** 745.
33. De Boer, W.I., Schuller, A.G., Vermay, M., and van der Kwast, T.H. (1994). Expression of growth factors and receptors during specific phases in regenerating urothelium after acute injury *in vivo. Am. J. Pathol.* **145,** 1199–1207.
34. Baker, R., Kelly, T., Tehan, T., Putnam, C., and Beaugard, E. (1958). Subtotal cystectomy and total bladder regeneration in treatment of bladder cancer. *J. Am. Med. Assoc.* **168,** 1178–1185.
35. Gorham, S.D., French, D.A., Shivas, A.A., and Scott, R. (1989). Some observations on the regeneration of smooth muscle in the repaired urinary bladder of the rabbit. *Eur. Urol.* **16,** 440–443.

51

Isolation and Characterization of Myogenic Stem Cells from Adult Skeletal Muscle

Zipora Yablonka-Reuveni

Introduction

This chapter discusses the methodologies commonly used in my laboratory for the isolation, culturing, and characterization of myogenic stem cells from adult skeletal muscle. The main focus of the chapter is on the isolation and characterization of myogenic progenitors from adult mice. The methods are also suitable for the isolation of myogenic stem cells from a variety of species, including rat[1] and chicken (discussed briefly in this chapter). The procedures have been modified from our initial studies on myogenic stem cells from fetal and adult chickens.[2–4]

Myoblasts in the adult muscle are classically considered to be derived from quiescent cells located on the surface of the myofiber.[5] These myofiber-associated cells were originally defined on the basis of their location beneath the myofiber basement membrane and thus termed satellite cells.[6] However, it was not until the introduction of single myofiber cultures that direct evidence has been provided that the myofiber unit can yield myogenic cells, capable of fusing into myotubes, and that the source of these myogenic cells are the satellite cells.[7–10]

Satellite cells provide the adult muscle with a reserve capacity to replace differentiated, postmitotic cells required for maintaining myofiber integrity and muscle function—as such, the satellite cells have been considered tissue-specific stem cells.[11] The terms *myogenic stem cell, myogenic precursor cell,* and *myogenic progenitor* have often been used interchangeably to refer to the satellite cell. Studies of myogenic precursors extracted from postnatal muscle have often referred to the isolated cells and their progeny as *satellite cells.* However, the assignment of satellite cell identity is based strictly on the location of the cell beneath the myofiber basement membrane.[6] Moreover, it now appears that some myogenic progenitors in populations of cells isolated from whole muscle could potentially be derived from sources other than satellite cells.[12] Therefore, in this chapter, the term *myogenic stem cells* is used as a general term for myogenic precursors isolated from the adult skeletal muscle regardless of their *in vivo* location in the muscle tissue, and the term *satellite cells* refers only to those cells situated within the myofiber unit.

Investigating the Presence of Myogenic Stem Cells in Cell Isolates from Adult Skeletal Muscle

The presence of myogenic precursors in cell preparations from adult skeletal muscle has been investigated at the morphologic level based on the emergence of multinucleated myotubes in cultures prepared from these cell isolates. The presence of myogenic progenitors in cell preparations can further be determined by analyzing the cultured cells for the expression of muscle-specific proteins, characteristic of the proliferative and differentiative phases of myogenesis. Proliferating progeny of satellite cells, or of myogenic precursors isolated from whole muscle, express the muscle-specific transcription factors MyoD and Myf5 and the paired box transcription factor Pax7.[1,8,13–16] The transition of skeletal myoblasts from proliferation to differentiation is associated with the onset of expression of the muscle-specific transcription factor myogenin.[1,8,10,13,14] Coinciding with or soon after the onset of myogenin expression, differentiating progeny of myogenic progenitors initiate the expression of various muscle structural genes, including sarcomeric myosin.[1,13,17,18]

Our collective immunocytochemical studies of myogenic progenitors from growing and adult skeletal muscle of mice, rats, and chickens[1,13,17–19] have prompted us to investigate the capacity of cell preparations to undergo myogenesis by analyzing the progression of the cultured cells through the following multistep program: $Pax7^+ \rightarrow Pax7^+/MyoD^+ \rightarrow MyoD^+/myogenin^+ \rightarrow MyoD^+/myogenin^+/myosin^+ \rightarrow$ Fusion into myotubes. This schematic is based on our detection of both $Pax7^+/MyoD^-$ cells and $Pax7^+/MyoD^+$ cells in culture; myogenin$^+$ cells, which appear later in culture, are negative for Pax7 but positive for MyoD. Single cells positive for sarcomeric myosin appear in culture following the emergence of myogenin$^+$ cells and are negative for Pax7 but positive for both

Handbook of Stem Cells
Volume 2

TABLE 51–1
Mouse Monoclonal Antibodies Frequently Used in Our Studies for Analyzing Myogenesis

Antibody[a]	Clone	Isotype[b]	Source	Refs.
Anti-MyoD	5.8A	IgG1	Commercial[c]	13,14,24
Anti-myogenin	F5D	IgG1	DSHB[d]	13,14,25,26
Anti-Pax7	Pax7	IgG1	DSHB	11,19,27
Anti-sarcomeric myosin	MF20	IgG2b	DSHB	17,18,28
Anti-desmin[e]	D3	IgG2a	DSHB	13,17,23,29

[a]All antibodies detailed in the table are suitable for immunocytochemical detection of mouse and rat proteins. The antibodies against Pax7, desmin, and sarcomeric myosin were prepared originally against chicken antigens[27–29] and can be used to study myogenesis in the chicken.[18,19,23] The antibody against sarcomeric myosin recognizes an epitope shared by all isoforms of sarcomeric myosin heavy chain in skeletal and cardiac muscle in a wide range of species. The antibodies against MyoD and myogenin described in this table do not react with chicken proteins; appropriate rabbit polyclonal antibodies against chicken MyoD and myogenin have been described.[18,19]

[b]The isotype of each antibody is provided to help in designing double-immunostaining studies. We routinely perform such studies using the anti-sarcomeric myosin in combination with the antibodies against MyoD, myogenin, and Pax7. Isotype-specific secondary antibodies are available from a variety of commercial sources. We obtain such antibodies from Molecular Probes.

[c]Various commercial sources carry this antibody. We obtain it from BD Biosciences.

[d]The Developmental Studies Hybridoma Bank (DSHB), at the University of Iowa, is under the auspices of the National Institute of Child Health and Human Development (http://www.uiowa.edu/~dshbwww). The monoclonal antibody against myogenin is also available through various commercial sources.

[e]For consistent immunostaining with this antibody, we use a general secondary antibody that recognizes all IgG isotypes. We have been unable to obtain reproducible immunostaining with the desmin antibody when employing an isotype-specific secondary antibody to visualize desmin in mouse myogenic cultures. Also, for consistent results, mouse cultures should be fixed with methanol and not with paraformaldehyde when working with this antibody. An alternative mouse monoclonal antibody against human desmin that reacts well with desmin in paraformaldehyde-fixed mouse myogenic cultures is available from Dako (clone D33).

MyoD and myogenin.[a] Multinucleated myotubes, whose cytoplasm is positive for sarcomeric myosin and whose nuclei are positive for MyoD and myogenin (but negative for Pax7), appear after the emergence of single cells positive for sarcomeric myosin+.[b]

Desmin, an intermediate filament protein expressed by skeletal, smooth, and cardiac muscle, has also been used extensively to monitor "myogenicity" (i.e., the presence and frequency of myogenic cells) in cell isolates prepared from mouse, rat, and human skeletal muscle. In myogenic cultures from these three species, desmin is expressed by both proliferating and differentiating myoblasts.[13,20–22] In contrast, proliferating myoblasts from bovine and chicken do not uniformly express desmin; in these cases, the main increase in desmin expression correlates with terminal differentiation and myotube formation.[21,23] Hence, when using desmin antibodies to analyze myogenicity, it is advisable to first establish the suitability of this approach for the species being studied. Desmin is also expressed in vascular smooth muscle cells, and such vasculature-derived cells could potentially be present in primary myogenic preparations from skeletal muscle. It is therefore important to determine that the desmin-expressing cells are indeed of skeletal muscle origin (e.g., expressing MyoD) when investigating the presence of myogenic stem cells based on desmin expression.

[a]Under certain culture conditions, the expression of MyoD is drastically reduced upon the transition of the cells into the myogenin+ state.[8,10,13,14]

[b]Myotubes in long-term cultures (e.g., 30 days and older) continue to express sarcomeric myosin at a high level, but the expression of MyoD and myogenin is drastically reduced and becomes less apparent when analyzing cultures using immunocytochemistry.

Myf5 expression in proliferating myogenic precursors has also been investigated using immunocytochemsitry.[13] However, well-characterized antibodies against Myf5 are not widely available, and the use of commercially available antibodies against Myf5 has remained controversial because of lot-to-lot variations.

The presence of myogenic cells in primary cell isolates can be additionally analyzed at the RNA level by determining the expression of a collection of muscle-specific genes using reverse transcription–polymerase chain reaction (RT-PCR).[1] Although RT-PCR studies can indicate whether myogenic stem cells were in the initial cell isolates, this approach cannot provide specific feedback regarding the purity of the cell preparation. Ideally, RT-PCR studies should be performed along with direct cell analysis, using immunocytochemistry when antibodies are available.

Table 51–1 summarizes the source and characteristics of a set of easily obtainable monoclonal antibodies frequently used in our laboratory for the analysis of myogenesis in cultures prepared from mouse and rat skeletal muscle. Figs. 51–1 through 51–3 depict representative micrographs of myogenic cultures from adult mouse skeletal muscle immunostained with the monoclonal antibodies described in Table 51–1. The antibody against Pax7 reacts only with mononucleated cells (nuclear stain, Fig. 51–1A), and the antibodies against MyoD and myogenin react with both mononucleated cells and myotubes (nuclear stain, Fig. 51–1B and 51–1C). The mononucleated MyoD+ cells consist of both proliferating (Pax7+) and differentiating (Pax7−) myoblasts.[19] The mononucleated myogenin+ myoblasts have already initiated the differentiation program and are typically negative for Pax7.[19] The antibody against sarcomeric myosin recognizes both

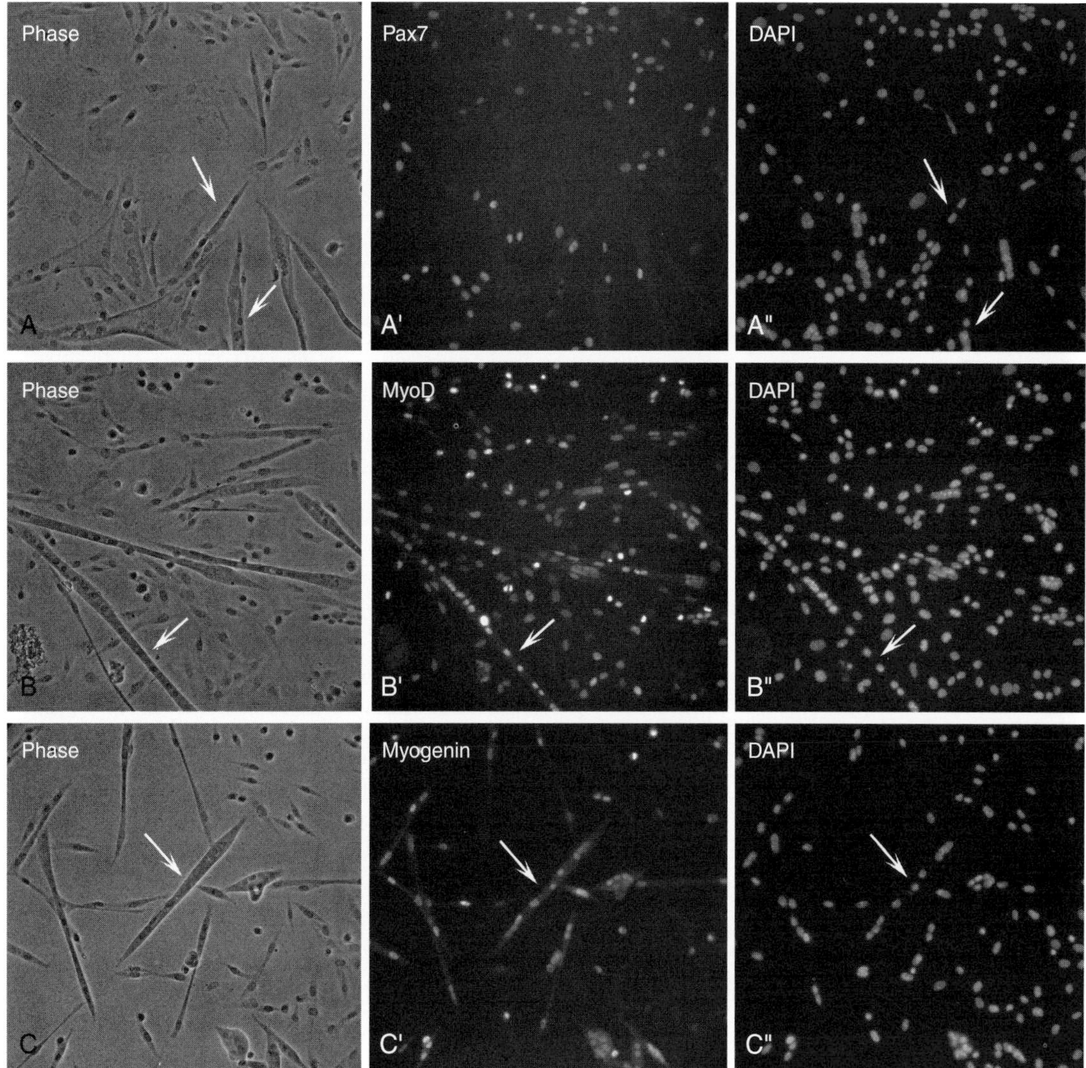

Figure 51–1. *Parallel phase and fluorescent micrographs of immunolabeled mouse cultures.* Cultures were reacted with mouse monoclonal antibodies against (A) Pax7, (B) MyoD, and (C) myogenin. The secondary antibody was Alexa Fluor 488 goat anti-mouse IgG. For all three antibodies, cultures were stained with DAPI to visualize all nuclei. Arrows point to myotubes. Micrographs were taken using a 20X objective. Cells were isolated from the hind limb muscles of a 3-month-old mouse using Pronase and cultured in DMEM-based growth medium using our standard conditions. Tissue culture plates were coated with gelatin. Cultures were harvested on day 7, fixed with paraformaldehyde, and processed for immunofluorescence according to stndard protocols.

mononucleated cells and myotubes (Fig. 51–2; please see CD-ROM for color version of this figure). In accordance with the multistep schematic detailed above, the nuclei in myosin$^+$ mononucleated cells (i.e., differentiated myoblasts) and myotubes are negative for Pax7 but positive for myogenin, as shown by double immunostaining (Fig. 51–2). The antibody against desmin recognizes both mononucleated cells and myotubes (Fig. 51–3).

Fig. 51–4 depicts chicken myogenic cultures reacted using double immunofluorescence with the monoclonal antibody against Pax7 and a rabbit polyclonal antibody against chicken MyoD (Fig. 51–4A) or a rabbit polyclonal antibody against chicken myogenin (Fig. 51–4B). Note that each panel represents merged images of double-labeled cultures (please see CD-ROM for color version of this figure). The antibodies against chicken MyoD and myogenin were described in our previous publications[18,19] Similar to the mouse studies, in the chicken cultures Pax7 is coexpressed with MyoD in mononucleated cells (arrows, Fig. 51–4A), and Pax7 expression is diminished in myogenin$^+$ mononucleated cells and myotubes (Fig. 51–4B). Many of the MyoD$^+$ cells in the culture shown in Fig. 51–4A are no longer positive for Pax7, as the cells have already differentiated and fused into myotubes. Pax7$^+$ cells negative for MyoD are also seen in these differentiating cultures (Fig. 51–4A). In accordance with the schematic steps of myogenesis detailed above, these

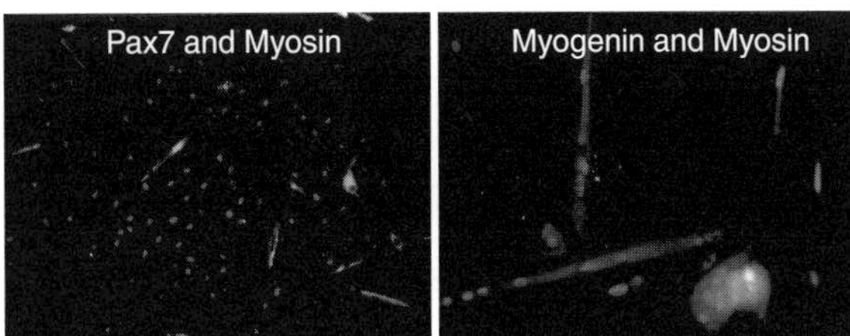

Figure 51-2. *Merged images of double immunofluorescent cultures prepared from mouse muscles.* Cultures were reacted with a mouse monoclonal antibody against sarcomeric myosin and (A) a monoclonal antibody against Pax7 or (B) a monoclonal antibody against myogenin. The secondary antibodies were Alexa Fluor 488 goat anti-mouse IgG2b (to detect reactivity with anti-myosin) and Alexa Fluor 568 goat anti-mouse IgG1 (to detect reactivity with anti-Pax7 or anti-myogenin). The micrograph in panel A was taken with a 20X objective; the one in panel B was taken with a 40X objective to show details of myogenin$^+$ nuclei within myotubes. Cells were isolated, cultured, and fixed as in Fig. 51–1. (Please see CD-ROM for color version of this figure.)

Pax7$^+$/MyoD$^-$ cells represent cells that have not yet entered MyoD expression.

Isolation of Myogenic Stem Cells from Adult Mouse

For routine myogenic cultures we typically isolate cells from one C57BL/6 mouse (2–3 months old). The tibialis anterior, extensor digitorum longus (EDL), and gastrocnemius muscles from both hind limbs are generally used as the source for cells. Myogenic stem cells can be isolated from other muscles, including the diaphragm, using a similar approach. However, the contribution of connective tissue and vasculature varies from muscle to muscle, and the isolation procedure should be modified accordingly to minimize cells derived from such structures. The purity of the resultant myogenic stem cell preparation is dependent on the amount of effort spent cleaning the muscle of these additional structures.

The method we use for the isolation of myogenic stem cells from adult mouse muscle is essentially the same we described in a previous article for rat muscle.[1] All procedures are performed sterilely and carried out at room temperature unless otherwise noted. The muscle is harvested into Dulbecco's Modified Eagle's Medium (DMEM), high glucose, with L-glutamin, 110-mg/L sodium pyruvate, and pyridoxine hydrochloride, supplemented with 50-U/ml penicillin and 50-mg/ml streptomycin (DMEM and antibiotics are from Gibco-Invitrogen). The muscle is then rinsed several times with additional DMEM, cleaned as much as possible of connective tissue and tendons, cut into small pieces (about 2 mm^3), and digested with 0.1% Pronase (Calbiochem, Product No. 53702, reconstituted in DMEM). Digestion is carried out inside the tissue culture incubator (37.5°C, 5% CO_2) for 1 hour with continuous gentle agitation using a standard, small rotator. The digested muscle pieces are collected in a 15-ml conical tube by low-speed centrifugation (~500 × g, 3 minutes) and resuspended in 3 ml of DMEM containing 10% horse serum. To release single cells, the suspension is triturated vigorously by repetitive passages, first through a 5-ml pipette and then through a 9-inch Pasteur pipette. The remaining tissue pieces are allowed to settle in the 15-ml conical tube, and the supernatant containing the cells is transferred to a new tube. The tissue pieces are subjected to two additional rounds of trituration and settling. The pooled cell suspension from the three triturations is then passed through a double-layered lens paper filter to remove large debris. To perform this step, a 5-ml syringe is connected to an autoclaved Millipore Swinney filter holder unit with double-layered lens paper as the filter, and the cell suspension is allowed to drip through into a new tube; for maximal cell recovery, allow an additional 1 ml DMEM to drip through the filter to recover the residual cell suspension trapped in the filter unit; apply gentle pressure with the syringe plunger if needed. The cells are harvested from the filtered suspension by a low-speed centrifugation (~1000 × g, 10 minutes) and resuspended in 1 ml of physiologic medium. The number of cells in the suspension is determined with the aid of a hematocytometer.

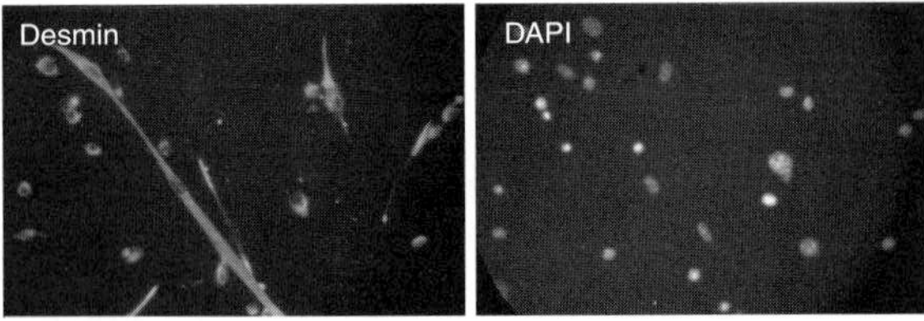

Figure 51-3. *Parallel fluorescent micrographs of a mouse culture reacted with a monoclonal antibody against desmin and stained with DAPI to label nuclei.* Micrographs were taken using 40X objective. Cells were isolated, cultured, and stained as in Fig. 51–1 except that methanol was used to fix the culture.

Primary Cultures of Myogenic Stem Cells from Adult Mouse

STANDARD CONDITIONS

The cell pellet harvested from the final filtered suspension as described in the previous section is resuspended in 1 ml of a DMEM-based growth medium (DMEM fortified with penicillin and streptomycin and supplemented with 20% fetal calf serum, 10% horse serum, and 1% chicken embryo extract).[c] For standard cultures, the cells are plated at a density of $1 - 2 \times 10^5$ cells per plate in 35-mm tissue culture dishes (Corning) coated with 2% gelatin (denatured collagen type I, Sigma-Aldrich).[d]

[c]The specific source for fetal calf serum and horse serum varies, based on the outcome of testing multiple lots. We purchase a large volume of sera found to be optimal to ensure consistent availability of the same sera for multiple years. Details regarding culture conditions for testing optimal lots of sera and preparation of chicken embryo extract can be found in our earlier publications.[30,31]

[d]Gelatin is reconstituted in tissue culture-grade water (2 g in 100 ml H_2O) and the suspension is autoclaved to dissolve the gelatin and sterilize the preparation. The solution is divided into aliquots while still warm and stored at 4°C. To liquefy the preparation prior to coating the plates, the gelatin aliquot should be warmed to 37°C and kept at room temperature. The remaining gelatin solution can be stored at 4°C for future use.

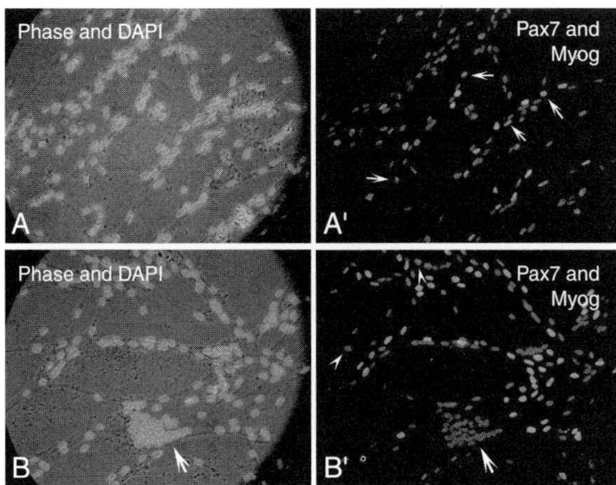

Figure 51–4. *Parallel micrographs of merged phase-DAPI images and merged double immunofluorescent images of chicken myogenic cultures.* Cultures were reacted with a mouse monoclonal antibody against Pax7 and (A) a rabbit antibody against chicken MyoD or (B) a rabbit antibody against chicken myogenin. The secondary antibodies were Alexa Fluor 488 goat anti-mouse IgG and Alexa Fluor 568 goat anti-rabbit IgG. Cultures were additionally stained with DAPI to visualize all nuclei. Arrows in panel A point to nuclei double stained with the antibodies against Pax7 and MyoD. Arrowheads in panel B point to paired nuclei, one of which is positive for Pax7 and the other one for myogenin; a partial overlap in the position of the two nuclei produces an impression of a double-stained nucleus. The arrow in panel B points to a myotube with many nuclei. Micrographs were taken using a 40X objective. Cells were isolated from the breast muscle of a 10-day-old chicken (White Leghorn) using Pronase as described in the section "Isolation of Myogenic Stem Cells from Adult Mouse" for mouse myoblasts. Cells were cultured in our standard MEM-based medium for chicken myoblasts.[3,18] This medium contains 10% horse serum and 5% chicken embryo extract. Cultures were harvested and processed for immunofluorescence as in Fig. 51–1. (Please see CD-ROM for color version of this figure.)

A cell suspension prepared from one mouse as described above typically yields 3–4 parallel 35-mm plates. Alternatively, cells are plated at a density of $1 - 2 \times 10^4$/well (standard density) or $1 - 2 \times 10^3$/well (low density) into 24-well trays (Falcon) coated with 2% gelatin. In all cases, the cultures are left undisturbed for three days; the medium is then replaced with fresh medium followed by medium changes every other day.[e]

[e] *The initial cell suspension contains residual debris derived from the digested muscle. This debris is especially prominent when isolating cells from adult muscle and is less apparent in cell preparations from newborn muscle. Repetitive rinse cycles of the final cell preparation by resuspending the cells in a rinse medium followed by a centrifugation to recover the cells is discouraged as there is significant cell loss when this approach is employed. If cells have to be separated from debris immediately upon cell isolation (e.g., when the isolated cells are subjected immediately to biochemical or molecular analysis), then our recommended approach is to further fractionate the isolated cells by Percoll density centrifugation (additional details are in the section "Fractionation of Myogenic Stem Cells Using Percoll Density Centrifugation"). If, on the other hand, the cells are maintained in culture, then it is advisable to rinse the cultures 1–2 times with DMEM or medium (~1 ml) at the first medium change to reduce the debris. The cultures should be rinsed very gently to minimize cell detachment.*

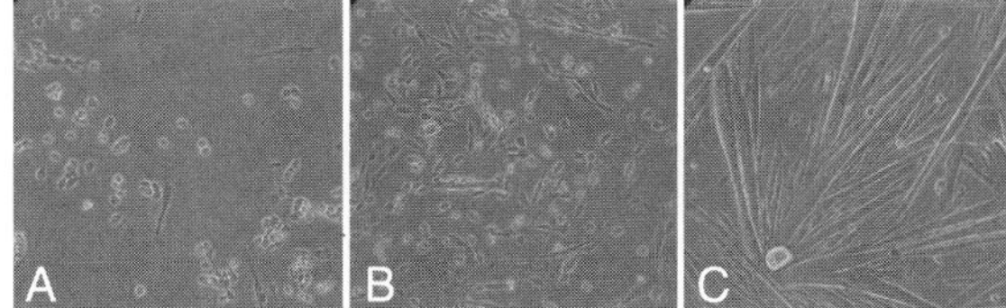

Figure 51–5. *Phase micrographs depicting the morphology of mouse myogenic cultures at different times following cell isolation.* Panels A, B, and C depict cultures on days 4, 5, and 18, respectively. Live cultures were photographed using a 20X objective. Cells were isolated and cultured as in Fig. 51–1.

The DMEM-based serum-rich medium used for our standard cultures supports both proliferation and differentiation of myoblasts (Fig. 51–5). We allow the cells to undergo spontaneous differentiation in this medium and do not employ special media to induce differentiation. Primary cultures prepared as detailed above display ~90% myogenic purity. Myogenic purity can be determined by the number of nuclei positive for Pax7 combined with the total number of nuclei in cells positive for sarcomeric myosin (i.e., nuclei in single cells and multinucleated myotubes). Early, on, the number of myosin$^+$ cells is minimal; later, the number of Pax7$^+$ cells is reduced and the number of myosin$^+$ cells increases. As described in the introduction, nuclei in differentiated mononucleated cells and myotubes (i.e., myosin$^+$ cells) are negative for Pax7.

Our approach for determining myogenicity by double immunostaining with antibodies against Pax7 and sarcomeric myosin provides a means to investigate the pool of proliferating myoblasts based on the number of Pax7$^+$ cells as well as to determine the differentiation potential of the cell preparation based on the number of myosin$^+$ cells. A residual number of cells that have already transited into the Pax7$^-$/myogenin$^+$ state but have not yet entered the myosin$^+$ state are not included in the myogenic cell pool when measuring myogenicity with antibodies against Pax7 and sarcomeric myosin. As an alternative, an analysis of myogenicity and differentiation potential in mouse cultures can be performed by double immunostaining with the antibodies against MyoD and sarcomeric myosin listed in Table 51–1.

NONSTANDARD CONDITIONS

Myogenic cultures from adult mouse muscle, maintained in our standard conditions described above, differentiate spontaneously regardless of the high level of serum in the growth medium. Myotubes are easily detected by the end of the first week in culture and the onset of myogenin expression is detected in rare cells as early as culture day 4 followed by a continuous increase in the number of myogenin$^+$ cells on days 5 and 6. Although differentiation can be delayed if the initial cell density is reduced, it cannot be prevented when primary mouse myoblasts are maintained in our standard DMEM-based growth medium. Various laboratories have adapted a different approach for the isolation and culture of myoblasts from postnatal mouse muscle, using a protocol developed by Rando and Blau.[32] Under these conditions, the initial cell isolate is cultured in Ham's F10-based medium containing 20% fetal bovine serum and fibroblast growth factor (FGF2, 5 ng/ml). The cell isolate is subjected to an initial step of preplating to reduce the contribution of nonmyogenic cells present in the initial preparation. Such nonmyogenic cells tend to adhere to the tissue culture plate before the myogenic cells. Following the initial preplating step, the nonadhering cells are transferred to a secondary culture plate where they are allowed to adhere and grow until reaching semi-confluence. This is followed by expansion of the cell preparation using serial passaging. For each passaging round, semi-confluent cells are lifted by enzymatic digestion and subjected to the preplating-plating protocol as described for the first round of cell plating. The continuous preplating steps minimize the contribution of nonmyogenic cells. Following several preplating-plating rounds the cultures are further expanded without preplating. To induce differentiation, cultures derived by cell passaging are transferred into a DMEM-based medium containing 2–5% horse serum. In some laboratories, the cell stock expanded from the initial cell isolate is divided into aliquots and kept frozen until needed. Despite the common referral to the cells resulting from this procedure as primary myoblasts, it is unclear if such passaged cells indeed represent primary myoblasts or whether the procedure results in progeny derived from a subpopulation of expandable myoblasts. In addition, it is important to note that the protocol for expansion of freshly isolated myoblasts by passaging has been introduced in studies of cells isolated from the musculature of juvenile mice; this protocol is not necessarily appropriate for expanding myoblasts from older mice.

To investigate the kinetics of myogenesis of primary mouse myoblasts maintained in DMEM- versus F10-based medium, we isolated cells from adult mouse muscle using our standard cell isolation conditions described previously in this chapter. The initial cell isolate was then divided into two parallel aliquots. One aliquot was cultured in our standard DMEM-based growth medium (DMEM fortified with antibiotics and containing 20% fetal bovine serum, 10% horse serum, and 1% chicken embryo extract). The second aliquot was cultured under the same conditions, except DMEM in the growth medium was replaced with Ham's F10 (Gibco-Invitrogen). Since the matrix used to coat the tissue culture plastic can also influence myogenesis, we further investigated the myogenicity of the primary cell preparation when cells were cultured in plates coated with 2% gelatin (as in our routine cultures described earlier in this chapter) versus diluted Matrigel (a basement membrane preparation from BD Biosciences; for further details, see Table 51–2). Myogenicity of the cultures was determined through double immunofluorescence using the antibodies against Pax7 and sarcomeric

TABLE 51–2
Effect of Medium and Substratum on Myogenicity of Primary Myogenic Cultures from Adult Mouse Skeletal Muscle[a]

		% of the total number of cells analyzed			
Medium	Matrix	Pax7$^+$/myosin$^-$ mononucleated cells	Pax7$^-$/myosin$^+$ mononucleated cells	Nuclei in myotubes	% myogenicity[b,c]
DMEM	Gelatin	30.8 ± 7.6	6.6 ± 2.7	49.5 ± 12.2	86.8 ± 3.5
F10	Gelatin	19.4 ± 10.1	12.0 ± 6.6	25.1 ± 9.5	56.5 ± 12.4
DMEM	Matrigel	38.1 ± 14.5	9.4 ± 1.2	38.7 ± 16.8	86.2 ± 4.8
F10	Matrigel	44.6 ± 19.8	4.2 ± 1.4	4.3 ± 5.0	53.1 ± 21.5

[a]Cells were isolated using our standard protocol and cultured into one 24-well tissue culture plate at a density of 10^3 cells per well. Twelve wells were coated with gelatin (2%, reconstituted in water) and 12 wells were coated with Matrigel (1 mg/ml, diluted with DMEM; further details regarding Matrigel handling are described in our recent publication).[30] Within each set of gelatin- and Matrigel-coated wells, cells in one set of 6 wells were maintained in DMEM-based medium and cells in the parallel set of 6 wells were maintained in F10-based medium. DMEM- and F10-based media each contained 20% fetal bovine serum, 10% horse serum, and 1% chicken embryo extract. The medium was changed 3 days following culture establishment and every other day thereafter. Cultures were harvested 12 days following the initial culturing, fixed, processed using double immunofluorescence with Pax7 and MF20 antibodies, and counterstained with DAPI to visualize all nuclei in the culture (i.e., in mononucleated cells and myotubes = total number of cells) as described in the legend to Fig. 51–1. Five wells from each group were used for double immunostaining with the antibodies against Pax7 and sarcomeric myosin, and the results represent the average per the 5 wells. Each well was analyzed by quantifying 11 arbitrary fields using a 40X objective. The average number of cells per well (i.e., per 11 microscopic fields) in each of the flour groups was as follows: 714 (DMEM/gelatin), 1130 (F10/gelatin), 429 (DMEM/Matrigel), and 502 (F10/Matrigel).

[b]The degree of myogenicity is significantly reduced in F10-based culturing medium compared to the DMEM-based medium ($F_{1,8} = 54.36$; $p < 0.0001$) but is not affected by the matrix used to coat the tissue culture plates. For statistics, two-way analysis of variance without repeated measures was applied (within subject factor: DMEM or F-10 media; between subject factor: gelatin or Matrigel matrixes). Data calculated as proportions were transformed to the arcsine of the square-root transformed raw data. Tukey HSD post hoc test was then applied to reveal differences among specific groups. Alfa level was set to 0.05.

[c]A residual population of myogenin$^+$ cells that has not yet entered the myosin$^+$ state but has terminated Pax7 expression is not accounted for when analyzing myogenicity according to the procedure described in this section. Double immunostaining with the monoclonal antibodies against myogenin and sarcomeric myosin of cultures parallel to those used for the analysis summarized in this table showed that 3–5% of the total cells were myogenin$^+$/myosin$^-$.

Myogenin and Alpha Smooth Muscle Actin

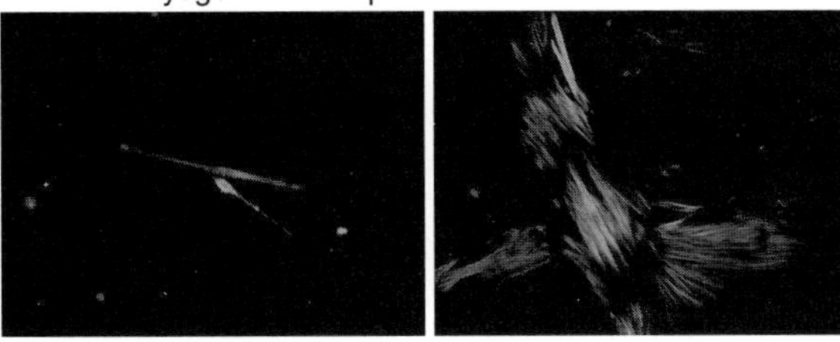

Figure 51–6. *Merged Images of Double Immunostained Mouse Cultures Depicting the Expression of α-Smooth Muscle Actin by Myogenin⁺ and Myogenin⁻ Cells.* (A) Differentiated myoblasts and myotubes and (B) nonmyogenic cells in a mouse myogenic culture maintained in F10-based medium. Cells were isolated and cultured as in Fig. 51–1 except that the growth medium was F10 based and the culture plate was coated with Matrigel. Double immunofluorescence was performed with a mouse monoclonal antibody against α-smooth muscle actin (IgG2A, clone 1A4 from Sigma-Aldrich)[34] and the mouse monoclonal antibody against myogenin (IgG1, described in Table 51–1). The secondary antibodies were Alexa Fluor 488 goat anti-mouse IgG2A and Alexa Fluor 568 goat anti-mouse IgG1. Micrographs were taken with a 20X objective. (Please see CD-ROM for color version of this figure.)

myosin described in Table 51–1. The results of this investigation are summarized in Table 51–2. The data indicate that fusion into myotubes is drastically suppressed when cells are cultured in plates coated with Matrigel and receive F10-based growth medium. The overall myogenicity of cultures maintained in F10-based medium is also significantly reduced regardless of the matrix used ($p < 0.0001$; see Table 51–2). This reduced myogenicity in F10 medium is caused by the increased presence of nonmyogenic cells (i.e., cells negative for all skeletal myogenic markers described in Table 51–1). The growth of such nonmyogenic cells is suppressed in DMEM-based medium, but F10-based medium supports a more robust growth of these cells. Employing immunocytochemistry, we found that many of these nonmyogenic cells are positive for alpha smooth muscle actin (αSMA). Although αSMA is expressed by differentiating myoblasts and myotubes in mouse and rat myoblasts, such differentiated myoblasts express skeletal myogenic markers as well.[8,33,f] Figure 51–6 depicts micrographs of αSMA^+ cells in a mouse myogenic culture maintained in F10-based medium. The culture was double stained with antibodies against αSMA[34] and myogenin (Table 51–1). Myogenic cells ($myogenin^+/\alpha SMA^+$) and nonmyogenic cells ($myogenin^-/\alpha SMA^+$) are shown in panels A and B, respectively, in Figure 51–6. Note that both panels depict merged images of myogenin and αSMA immunolabling; please see CD-ROM for the original color version. Because the nonmyogenic αSMA^+ cells are large and flat, they are often not recognized when examining myogenic cultures by standard phase microscopy. The nonmyogenic cells resemble in their morphology and expression of αSMA, contractile cells named myofibroblasts that are related to smooth muscle cells and have been isolated from a variety of tissues.[35]

We are presently investigating the possibility that the αSMA^+ nonmyogenic cells appearing in cultures prepared from mouse skeletal muscle are in fact descendants of myogenic progenitors (i.e., satellite cells) that can enter a nonmyogenic route and that this alternative program is further enhanced in F10 medium.[37]

Sequential Preplating of Primary Cell Isolates from Skeletal Muscle to Enrich Long-Term, Proliferating, Multipotential Stem Cells

Recent studies have used repetitive preplating cycles, performed over several days, to separate a population of late-adhering cells from primary preparations isolated from skeletal muscle of juvenile mice.[38] The resultant late-adhering cell population was reported to contain long-term proliferating myogenic progenitors capable of supporting muscle regeneration *in vivo* far better than early-adhering myogenic cells. The late-adhering cells were also shown to be able generate other cell phenotypes in addition to myogenic cells. These studies have led to the conclusion that the late-adhering cell population contains multipotential stem cells.[38]

Our series of cell culture studies using the sequential preplating approach, have not identified unique cells in the late-adhering cells in comparison with the early-adhering cells.[39] The primary cell isolates were prepared from the hind limb muscles of 3-month-old mice employing our standard cell isolation procedure discussed previously in this chapter. We examined the cell preparations in DMEM- and F10-based growth media. The cells were sequentially preplated in 35-mm tissue culture plates coated with 2% gelatin or diluted Matrigel (for details, see Table 51–2). Sequential preplatings were performed every 24 hours following culturing and carried out for 7–10 days. In our hands, the remaining cells in the late preplate cultures underwent a limited number of proliferative rounds and either differentiated into $myosin^+$ cells or withdrew from the cell cycle without differentiating.

Further studies are required to resolve the differences between our approach and the aforementioned published study regarding the ability of the sequential preplating methodology to separate long-term, proliferating, multipotential cells from cell isolates prepared from skeletal muscle.[38] It is possible that the number of late-adhering cells in skeletal muscle is drastically reduced in the older mice used in our studies. We routinely work with 3-month-old mice, and the study reporting the isolation of multipotential cells from mouse skeletal muscle was performed with 3- to 5-day-old mice.[38] It is also possible that our extensive removal of connective tissue and vasculature elements of the muscle prior to the enzymatic digestion step eliminates such presumptive stem cells from our primary cell isolate.

[f] *Differentiating myoblasts and myotubes in cell cultures derived from fetal, posthatch, and adult chicken muscle do not express αSMA, although the protein is expressed in chicken muscle during early embryogenesis.*[37]

Fractionation of Myogenic Stem Cells Using Percoll Density Centrifugation

Cell preparations isolated from adult skeletal muscle using our standard conditions contain some leftover tissue debris resulting from the enzymatic digestion step. Under our current pronase digestion procedures, the level of residual debris is greatly reduced compared to that seen in our initial study on the isolation of myogenic progenitors from adult chicken muscle.[3] This residual debris does not interfere with our ability to monitor the cells and determine their number in the final cell preparation. Nevertheless, the removal of such residual debris can be important when preparing freshly isolated cells for transplantation into a host animal or when analyzing gene expression in the initial cell population.

To efficiently reduce the debris in the final cell preparation, we have developed conditions for fractionation of the cells by Percoll density centrifugation.[3,4] In our early studies, the cells were recovered from the interface between 20 and 70% Percoll fractions, and the debris was distributed within the 20% fraction. Additionally, this approach has allowed us to separate nonmyogenic and myogenic cell populations from cell isolates prepared from developing and adult muscle.[2,40] The separated nonmyogenic and myogenic cells could be further analyzed by 1- and 2-D gel electrophoresis to identify cell type–specific proteins.[40] Modification of the initial Percoll fractionation procedure to a five-step Percoll gradient has enabled us to isolate myogenic and nonmyogenic cell populations from adult mouse and rat muscle and to further analyze such cell populations by RT-PCR.[1] Our initial Percoll density protocol has also been adopted for studies on the isolation of side population cells from mouse skeletal muscle.[41] In-depth details regarding Percoll density centrifugation and the recovery of cells from the Percoll fractions can be found in our original publications.[1–4,40] A somewhat similar approach for isolating myogenic cell populations employing Percoll density centrifugation has been reported independently of our studies.[42]

Clonal Analysis of Myogenic Progenitors

Various studies have recently reported the isolation of multipotential stem cells from skeletal muscle. In these studies, cells were dissociated from the muscle tissue by enzymatic digestion and then subjected to various enrichment protocols to isolate progenitor cells subsequently shown, under various cell culture and *in vivo* tests, to produce different cell phenotypes.[12,38,43,44] Only in some of these studies, the multipotential cells were clonally derived to ensure that a single progenitor is generating the multiple cell phenotypes.

Here, I review our methods for obtaining clonally derived myogenic cells from skeletal muscle. In one approach, the initial cell preparation is isolated from whole muscle tissue using our standard cell isolation conditions discussed in the section "Isolation of Myogenic Stem Cells from Adult Mouse." In a second approach, the cells are cloned from individual myofibers.

DERIVATION OF CLONES FROM CELL ISOLATES PREPARED FROM WHOLE MUSCLE

The cells in the initial cell preparation isolated from whole muscle are serially diluted; each dilution round lowers the cell density 10-fold until a concentration of 100 cells per 1 ml of growth medium is reached. Aliquots of 0.5 ml are dispensed into 60-mm tissue culture plates precoated with 2% gelatin.[g] The cultures receive an additional 2. 5 ml of growth medium and are given a gentle swirl to ensure even distribution of cells and medium. Cultures are maintained undisturbed for 3–4 days followed by microscopic inspection and the marking of individual clones. The medium is typically replenished for the first time 5 days following culture establishment and every 3–4 days thereafter by replacing about 50% of the medium. Clones prepared this way can be followed morphologically as well as fixed and analyzed by immunocytochemistry.[2,3,17,45] Individual clones, well separated from each other, can be further expanded to obtain cultures derived from individual progenitors.[46] We typically maintain clones in the original culture plate for no longer than 10–14 days prior to clonal expansion.

To expand clones, the medium is removed from the culture plate, the culture is rinsed once with a serum-free medium (i.e., DMEM), and cloning rings (Fisher Scientific) are placed around individual clones. A seal is generated between the cloning ring and the culture plate by coating the periphery of the cloning ring with a sterile silica gel before placing it over the clone. Each clone receives a small volume of 0.1% trypsin for 10–15 minutes, and the clonal cell suspension is then harvested using a Pasteur pipette. The harvested cell aliquot is placed into a test tube containing 1 ml of growth medium. The trypsinized clone (still encircled by a cloning ring) is rinsed with a small volume of growth medium, and the rinse is pooled with the original sample. The cell suspension is triturated with a 9-inch Pasteur pipette and cultured into a single well of a 24-well culture plate precoated with 2% gelatin (or diluted Matrigel if desired). When this clonal culture becomes semi-confluent, the cells can be trypsinized and transferred into a 35-mm culture plate to allow clonal expansion. Clonal cultures that continue to grow well can be expanded further into larger culture plates. At all stages, the expanded cultures should be kept sparse during clonal expansion. Clonally expanded cell stocks can be used for a variety of parallel studies.[46] It should be noted that not all myogenic progenitors can be successfully expanded for a long period. Also, special attention must be given to characterizing the clonally expanded population to ensure that cells have not lost their original phenotype during the prolonged culturing. This can be done by analyzing an aliquot of the cells for the degree of myogenicity using immunocytochemistry as described earlier

[g] *The matrix used for coating the tissue culture dish can be modified to enhance cell attachment and growth as necessary. Native collagen type I and Matrigel have been used by various laboratories to support the attachment of myogenic cells. In some instances, we replace gelatin with Matrigel (diluted to 1 mg/ml in DMEM) to enhance cell attachment when culturing highly diluted cells.*

in this chapter. The final cell stock can be recloned if necessary to ensure clonality of the culture.

To bypass the use of cloning rings, clones can be prepared from the initial cell preparation by limited dilution. The cell preparation that has been dissociated from the muscle tissue is serially diluted 10-fold each round as described above to a final concentration of 1 cell per 1 ml of growth medium. This diluted cell preparation is then dispensed into 24-well tissue culture plates, precoated with gelatin (or Matrigel), aliquoting 0.5 ml of cell suspension per well. Each well receives an additional 0.5 ml of fresh medium. The cultures are left undisturbed for 5 days, followed by microscopic analysis and clonal expansion using trypsin as described above without the need for cloning rings.

DERIVATION OF CLONES FROM SINGLE MUSCLE FIBERS

More recently, we have begun to clone myogenic stem cells from individual muscle fibers to study the proliferative and lineage potential of satellite cells.[37] Individual myofibers can be isolated from a variety of muscles using collagenase.[8,9,13,30,37] The fibers are then individually transferred into 1 ml of medium and triturated with a 21-gauge needle; the suspension is dispensed into 24-well trays precoated with Matrigel. The number of wells into which a fiber suspension is divided depends on the number of satellite cells present on the fiber. Preparations from the EDL muscle are divided into 12 wells[36] based on reports that EDL fibers from an adult mouse contain an average of 7–8 satellite cells per fiber.[37,47] Further details regarding the maintenance and analysis of clonal cultures are as described in the previous section.

Conclusion

In recent years there has been a continuous increase in the number of publications that report the ability of a variety of nonmuscle tissues to produce skeletal myogenic cells. Additional studies have proposed that multipotent cells present in skeletal muscle but reside in locations different from that of satellite cells can generate myogenic cells.[48] Such studies are at times difficult to evaluate, especially when the original progenitor cells have not actually been cloned and the final cell preparation used to demonstrate multipotentialities might contain multiple cell types. It is hoped that standardized approaches for the isolation and characterization of myogenic stem cells are likely to improve our understanding of the capacity of satellite cells and multipotential stem cells to contribute toward cell-based therapies of muscular dystrophy and enhancement of muscle function in aging muscle.

ACKNOWLEDGMENTS

I thank Monika Wleklinski-Lee for excellent research support and helpful comments during the preparation of this manuscript. I am additionally grateful to Dr. Gavriela Shefer for helpful discussions.

The studies described in this chapter were supported by grants from the National Institute of Health (AG13798 and AG21566); the Cooperative State Research, Education, and Extension Service–U.S. Department of Agriculture (National Research Initiative Agreements 99-35206-7934 and 2003-35206-12843); and the Nathan Shock Center of Excellence in the Basic Biology of Aging, University of Washington. I additionally thank the American Heart Association for supporting my initial research on myogenic stem cells.

REFERENCES

1. Kastner, S., Elias, M.C., Rivera, A.J., and Yablonka-Reuveni, Z. (2000). Gene expression patterns of the fibroblast growth factors and their receptors during myogenesis of rat satellite cells. *J. Histochem. Cytochem.* **48,** 1079–1096.
2. Yablonka-Reuveni, Z., and Nameroff, M. (1987). Skeletal muscle cell populations: separation and partial characterization of fibroblast-like cells from embryonic tissue using density centrifugation. *Histochemistry* **87,** 27–38.
3. Yablonka-Reuveni, Z., Quinn, L.S., and Nameroff, M. (1987). Isolation and clonal analysis of satellite cells from chicken pectoral muscle. *Dev. Biol.* **119,** 252–259.
4. Yablonka-Reuveni, Z. (1989). Application of density centrifugation and flow cytometry for the isolation and characterization of myogenic and fibroblast-like cells from skeletal muscle. *In* "Cellular and Molecular Biology of Muscle Development," (L.H. Kedes *et al.*, Eds.), UCLA Symposia on Molecular and Cellular Biology, New Series, Vol. 93, pp. 869–879. Alan R. Liss, New York.
5. Hawke, T.J., and Garry, D.J. (2001). Myogenic satellite cells: Physiology to molecular biology. *J. Appl. Physiol.* **91,** 534–551.
6. Mauro, A. (1961). Satellite cell of skeletal muscle fibers. *J. Biophys. Biochem. Cytol.* **9,** 493–495.
7. Bischoff, R. (1975). Regeneration of single skeletal muscle fibers *in vitro*. *Anat. Rec.* **182,** 215–235.
8. Yablonka-Reuveni, Z., and Rivera, A.J. (1994). Temporal expression of regulatory and structural muscle proteins during myogenesis of satellite cells on isolated adult rat fibers. *Dev. Biol.* **164,** 588–603.
9. Rosenblatt, J.D., Lunt, A.I., Parry, D.J., and Partridge, T.A. (1995). Culturing satellite cells from living single muscle fiber explants. *In Vitro Cell. Dev. Biol. Anim.* **31,** 773–779.
10. Yablonka-Reuveni, Z., and Rivera, A.J. (1997). Proliferative dynamics and the role of FGF2 during myogenesis of rat satellite cells on isolated fibers. *Basic App. Myol. (BAM)* **7,** 176–189.
11. Zammit, P., and Beauchamp, J. (2001). The skeletal muscle satellite cell: stem cell or son of stem cell? *Differentiation* **68,** 193–204.
12. Asakura, A., Seale, P., Girgis-Gabardo, A., and Rudnicki, M.A. (2002). Myogenic specification of side population cells in skeletal muscle. *J. Cell Biol.* **159,** 123–134.
13. Yablonka-Reuveni, Z., Rudnicki, M.A., Rivera, A.J., Primig, M., Anderson, J.E., and Natanson, P. (1999). The transition from proliferation to differentiation is delayed in satellite cells from mice lacking MyoD. *Dev. Biol.* **210,** 440–455.
14. Yablonka-Reuveni, Z., Seger, R., and Rivera, A.J. (1999). Fibroblast growth factor promotes recruitment of skeletal muscle satellite cells in young and old rats. *J. Histochem. Cytochem.* **47,** 23–42.
15. Cooper, R.N., Tajbakhsh, S., Mouly, V., Cossu, G., Buckingham, M., and Butler-Browne, G.S. (1999). *In vivo* satellite cell activation via Myf5 and MyoD in regenerating mouse skeletal muscle. *J. Cell Sci.* **112,** 2895–2901.
16. Seale, P., Sabourin, L.A., Girgis-Gabardo, A., Mansouri, A., Gruss, P., and Rudnicki, M.A. (2000). Pax7 is required for the specification of myogenic satellite cells. *Cell* **102,** 777–786.

17. Yablonka-Reuveni, Z., and Rivera, A.J. (1997). Influence of PDGF-BB on proliferation and transition through the MyoD-myogenin-MEF2A expression program during myogenesis in mouse C2 myoblasts. *Growth Factors* **15,** 1–27.
18. Yablonka-Reuveni, Z., and Paterson, B.M. (2001). MyoD and myogenin expression patterns in cultures of fetal and adult chicken myoblasts. *J. Histochem. Cytochem.* **49,** 455–462.
19. Halevy, O., Piestun, Y., Allouh, M.Z., Rosser, B.W.C, Rinkevitch, Y., Reshef, R., Wleklinski-Lee, M., and Yablonka-Reuveni, Z. The pattern of Pax7 expression during myogenesis in the posthatch chicken establishes a model for satellite cell differentiation and renewal. (Submitted).
20. Kaufman, S.J., and Foster, R.F. (1988). Replicating myoblasts express a muscle-specific phenotype. *Proc. Natl. Acad. Sci. U. S. A.* **85,** 9606–9610.
21. Allen, R.E., Rankin, L.L., Greene, E.A., Boxhorn, L.K., Johnson, S.E., Taylor, R.G., and Pierce, P.R. (1991). Desmin is present in proliferating rat muscle satellite cells but not in bovine muscle satellite cells. *J. Cell. Physiol.* **149,** 525–535.
22. Renault, V., Piron-Hamelin, G., Forestier, C., DiDonna, S., Decary, S., Hentati, F., Saillant, G., Butler-Browne, G.S., and Mouly, V. (2000). Skeletal muscle regeneration and the mitotic clock. *Exp. Gerontol.* **35,** 711–719.
23. Yablonka-Reuveni, Z., and Nameroff, M. (1990). Temporal differences in desmin expression between myoblasts from embryonic and adult chicken skeletal muscle. *Differentiation* **45,** 21–28.
24. Dias, P., Parham, D.M., Shapiro, D.N., Tapscott, S.J., and Houghton, P.J. (1992). Monoclonal antibodies to the myogenic regulatory protein MyoD1: Epitope mapping and diagnostic utility. *Cancer Res.* **52,** 6431–6439.
25. Wright, W.E, Binder, M., and Funk, W. (1991). Cyclic amplification and selection of targets (CASTing) for the myogenin consensus binding site. *Mol. Cell. Biol.* **11,** 4104–4110.
26. Wright, W.E, Dac-Korytko, I., and Farmer, K. (1996). Monoclonal antimyogenin antibodies define epitopes outside the bHLH domain where binding interferes with protein–protein and protein–DNA interactions. *Dev. Genet.* **19,** 131–138.
27. Kawakami, A., Kimura-Kawakami, M., Nomura, T., and Fujisawa, H. (1997). Distributions of PAX6 and PAX7 proteins suggest their involvement in both early and late phases of chick brain development. *Mech. Dev.* **66,** 119–130.
28. Danto, S.I., and Fischman, D.A. (1984). Immunocytochemical analysis of intermediate filaments in embryonic heart cells with monoclonal antibodies to desmin. *J. Cell Biol.* **98,** 2179–2191.
29. Bader, D., Masaki, T., and Fischman, D.A. (1982). Immunochemical analysis of myosin heavy chain during avian myogenesis *in vivo* and *in vitro. J. Cell Biol.* **95,** 763–770.
30. Shefer, G., and Yablonka-Reuveni, Z. (Submitted). Isolation and culture of skeletal muscle myofibers as a means to analyze satellite cells. *In* "Basic Cell Culture Protocols," (C. Helgason *et al.,* Eds.). Humana Press, Totowa, NJ.
31. Yablonka-Reuveni, Z. (1995). Myogenesis in the chicken: the onset of differentiation of adult myoblasts is influenced by tissue factors. *Basic App. Myolo. (BAM)* **5,** 33–42.
32. Rando, T.A., and Blau, H.M. (1994). Primary mouse myoblast purification, characterization, and transplantation for cell-mediated gene therapy. *J. Cell Biol.* **125,** 1275–1287.
33. Springer, M.L., Ozawa, C.R., and Blau, H.M. (2002). Transient production of alpha-smooth muscle actin by skeletal myoblasts during differentiation in culture and following intramuscular implantation. *Cell Motil. Cytoskel.* **51,** 177–186.
34. Skalli, O., Ropraz, P., Treciak, A., Benzonana, G., Gillessen, D., and Gabbiani, G. (1986). A monoclonal antibody against alpha-smooth muscle actin: a new probe for smooth muscle differentiation. *J. Cell Biol.* **103,** 2787–2796.
35. Serini, G., and Gabbiani, G. (1999). Mechanisms of myofibroblast activity and phenotypic modulation. *Exp. Cell Res.* **250,** 273–283.
36. Yablonka-Reuveni, Z., and Christ, B. (Unpublished).
37. Shefer, G., Wleklinski, M., and Yablonka-Reuveni, Z. Skeletal muscle satellite cells can spontaneously go MAD. (Submitted).
38. Qu-Petersen, Z., Deasy, B., Jankowski, R., Ikezawa, M., Cummins, J., Pruchnic, R., Mytinger, J., Cao, B., Gates, C., Wernig, A., and Huard, J. (2002). Identification of a novel population of muscle stem cells in mice: Potential for muscle regeneration. *J. Cell Biol.* **157,** 851–864.
39. Yablonka-Reuveni, Z. and Wleklinski-Lee, M. (Unpublished studies).
40. Yablonka-Reuveni, Z., Anderson, S.K., Bowen-Pope, D.F., and Nameroff, M. (1988). Biochemical and morphological differences between fibroblasts and myoblasts from embryonic chicken skeletal muscle. *Cell Tissue Res.* **252,** 339–348.
41. McKinney-Freeman, S.L., Jackson, K.A., Camargo, F.D., Ferrari, G., Mavilio, F., and Goodell, M.A. (2002). Muscle-derived hematopoietic stem cells are hematopoietic in origin. *Proc. Natl. Acad. Sci. U. S. A.* **99,** 1341–1346.
42. Morgan, J.E. (1988). Myogenicity *in vitro* and *in vivo* of mouse muscle cells separated on discontinuous Percoll gradients. *J. Neurol. Sci.* **85,** 197–207.
43. Torrente, Y., Tremblay, J.P., Pisati, F., Belicchi, M., Rossi, B., Sironi, M., Fortunato, F., El Fahime, M., D'Angelo, M.G., Caron, N.J., Constantin, G., Paulin, D., Scarlato, G., and Bresolin, N. (2001). Intra-arterial injection of muscle-derived CD34(+)Sca-1(+) stem cells restores dystrophin in mdx mice. *J. Cell Biol.* **152,** 335–348.
44. Tamaki, T., Akatsuka, A., Ando, K., Nakamura, Y., Matsuzawa, H., Hotta, T., Roy, R.R., and Edgerton, V.R. (2002). Identification of myogenic–endothelial progenitor cells in the interstitial spaces of skeletal muscle. *J. Cell Biol.* **157,** 571–577.
45. Hartley, R.S., Bandman, E., and Yablonka-Reuveni, Z. (1992). Skeletal muscle satellite cells appear during late chicken embryogenesis. *Dev. Biol.* **153,** 206–216.
46. Yablonka-Reuveni, Z., and Seifert, R.A. (1993). Proliferation of chicken myoblasts is regulated by specific isoforms of platelet-derived growth factor: evidence for differences between myoblasts from mid and late stages of embryogenesis. *Dev. Biol.* **156,** 307–318.
47. Zammit, P.S., Heslop, L., Hudon, V., Rosenblatt, J.D., Tajbakhsh, S., Buckingham, M.E., Beauchamp, J.R., and Partridge, T.A. (2002). Kinetics of myoblast proliferation show that resident satellite cells are competent to fully regenerate skeletal muscle fibers. *Exp. Cell Res.* **281,** 39–49.
48. Grounds, M.D., White, J.D., Rosenthal, N. and Bogoyevitch, M.A. (2002). The role of stem cells in skeletal and cardiac muscle repair. *J. Histochem. Cytochem.* **50,** 589-610.

52

Isolation and Characterization of Stem Cells from the Nervous System

Siddharthan Chandran and Maeve A. Caldwell

Introduction

Neural stem cell (NSC) biology has generated considerable interest over the last decade. Improved understanding of the biology of NSC describes the mechanisms underlying cell diversity, and application of such knowledge raises the prospect of interventional reparative therapies for a variety of human neurologic diseases. The capacity of NSCs to generate enriched and expanded defined populations is particularly attractive in the field of applied neurobiology. Cells can now be isolated from the developing or adult rodent central nervous system (CNS) and expanded in culture, while retaining the capacity for differentiation into a variety of cellular phenotypes. Similar cells may also be isolated from human tissues. Ethical and practical constraints on the procurement of viable human tissue emphasizes the worth of NSCs in providing an alternative plentiful source of human neural cells.

No absolute standards for growing NSCs exist; this partly reflects the definition of NSCs on the basis of potential and in relation to other cells. There are no unique morphologic criteria or markers, and experimental manipulation is required to examine potential. NSCs are largely identified retrospectively contingent on their phenotypic and self-renewal potential.[1,2] A consensual definition of what constitutes a stem cell remains elusive. A plural definition of an NSC requires the ability to self-renew and to generate differentiated progeny. This definition is in some ways arbitrary and avoids issues such as how extensive does self-renewal and how multipotent does a cell need be to qualify as a stem cell. This matter is further influenced by whether one is studying populations or single cells; the latter requires demonstration that a single cell can self-renew and generate neurons, astrocytes, and oligodendrocytes. In contrast, a lineage-restricted cell with the capacity for self-renewal is classified as a progenitor cell. Clonal analysis, whether in isolated single-cell or population culture systems, is central to such definitions. Where this has been done, stem cells have been shown to exist in various regions of the developing and adult brain (Table 52–1).

The paucity of distinct stage-specific markers in general and NSC markers in particular is a major problem in NSC biology. Antibodies to nestin (neuroepithelial stem cell marker) will label NSCs but also will cross-react with glial cells under certain conditions.[30,31] Recent studies have identified musashi and Sox as putative markers of immature neuro-epithelial-derived cells.[32–34] The absence of cell surface markers has led to cells being characterized largely on their response to epidermal and fibroblast growth factor-2 (EGF and FGF-2), the primary mitogens for NSCs.

Isolation and Expansion

NSCs have been isolated from many regions of the developing brain and specific regions of the adult brain in rodent and human systems (Table 52–1). It has become increasingly clear that age and region influence the characteristics of the NSC in terms of proliferative, trophic requirement and phenotypic potential.[35,36] The difficulty of prospective *in vivo* studies of cell fate and potential in the normal and pathologic context have meant that much of what we have learnt in terms of stem cell biology is derived from *in vitro* studies. Nonetheless, *in vitro* studies are invaluable in studying cell potential and generating expanded cell populations; they also are self-evidently prerequisite for the *in vivo* functional studies collectively required to make clinical translation a possibility.

The common method for *in vitro* NSC studies is to use dissociated plated or cell suspension cultures, dissected from an anatomically defined region, either singly or in dense culture in the presence of FGF-2, EGF, or both (Fig. 52–1). Withdrawal of mitogen and plating upon substrate leads to differentiation. Refinements of the basic method are nearly endless and commonly include the use of different substrates and defined versus serum-containing media. This system is selective in that it allows the elimination of primary differentiated cells shortly after starting the culture. In contrast, the undifferentiated cells enter active proliferation in response to growth factors (mitogens), namely, EGF and FGF-2.

In addition, extended growth of neural precursor cell (NPC) lines has been achieved using gene transfer techniques. These have been achieved by retroviral transduction of an immortalizing gene such as the temperature-sensitive mutant of Simian virus 40 (SV40) Large-T or oncogenes such as myc (c or v) (see Table 52–2 for a summary). This process of immortalization arrests cells at defined stages of development and has allowed the means to generate cell lines from cell types that are not abundant or have a short life span in culture.

Handbook of Stem Cells
Volume 2

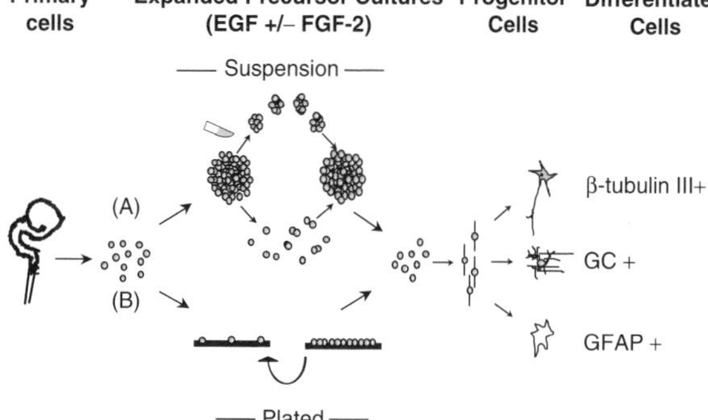

Figure 52–1. NPCs can be isolated from various regions of CNS and induced to divide in culture using the mitogens EGF and FGF-2. Cells can be grown in (A) substrate-free suspension or (B) adherent conditions. Irrespective of culture method, cells are maintained and propagated (passaged) by enzymatic methods, mechanical methods, or both. Attention is drawn to the use of mechanical cleavage by "chopping" (see text for further details) for long-term propagation of human-derived neurospheres. Withdrawal of mitogen and the provision of a substrate induces differentiation of cells within the spheres into neurons, astrocytes, and oligodendrocytes that can be readily identified by standard immunochemistry. (Please see CD-ROM for color version of this figure.)

Immunochemical characterization of progeny permits classification of the lineage potential of the starting cell population into multipotent cells, neuroblasts, or glioblasts. Common to many *in vitro* potential studies of lineage is the culture of single cells allowing clonal analyses to demonstrate monoclonal derivation of differentiated progeny.[47] An alternative method for clonal analysis is to use a limiting titer of a retrovirus to follow the fate of a single cell within a dense culture.[12]

Collection and Preparation of Primary Embryonic and Adult Tissue

Historically, *in vitro* studies have demonstrated that the developmental stage of tissue is crucial with regard to the yield and characteristics of NSCs contained within. In general, stem cells isolated from early rat (<E14) or mouse (<E12) primary embryonic tissue from any brain region respond to FGF-2, and stem cells derived from older embryonic tissue, or the adult, respond to both FGF-2 and EGF.[48,49] The exact relationship among cells that respond to these mitogens is unclear; there is some evidence that FGF-dependent precursors generate EGF-responsive precursors.[50] Developmental stage is also important for human tissues. A limited or absent response is generally observed in EGF-only cultures in embryos under 10 weeks, although it can be difficult to establish the exact age of samples in many cases.[18,51]

Neurogenesis occurs throughout the life of the organism in discrete regions of the adult brain, namely the hippocampus,[52,53] the cortex,[54–56] and the olfactory bulb.[57–59] Emerging neurons in the adult olfactory bulb are derived from ongoing proliferation in the periventricular region including the ependymal and subependymal layers of the forebrain lateral ventricles. Multipotent NSCs have been isolated from the subependymal layer and are responsive to EGF, FGF-2, or both.[26,60] Similarly, adult hippocampal NSCs can be grown in FGF-2, EGF, serum, or a combination of these (see Table 52–1).

In contrast to human studies, rodent cultures can be precisely aged, the presence of a vaginal plug following overnight mating generally being regarded as E0. Pregnant dams are terminally anaesthetized, and the fetuses are removed and placed in chilled phosphate-buffered saline (0.1%)–glucose (0.6%). Human tissues are collected in accordance with local ethical committee guidelines and only following appropriate approval of the project. Individual brain regions are dissected[61] and incubated in 0.1% trypsin for 20 minutes at 37°C. Following 3 minutes in a trypsin inhibitor and 0.01% DNase, the tissue pieces are suspended in 1 ml of final plating medium (or an appropriate volume to have approximately 1000 cells/μl) and are gently dissociated to a single-cell suspension using a fine-polished glass pipette.

In contrast to embryonic tissue, it is necessary to use an alternative enzymatic method to adequately digest adult tissue. The enzyme of choice is generally papain-DNase (for the exact method, see Palmer *et al.*[27] and Gritti *et al.*[62]). Tissue is incubated in papain-DNase for 30-60 minutes or in trypsin for 30 minutes.[24–28]

Culture Media

The basic formulation is generally serum free, although some groups use serum for the first few days to increase survival and then switch to a serum-free cocktail. The standard formulation is Dulbecco's modified Eagle's medium (DMEM) with high glucose and lactate mixed 3:1 with HAMS F12, which contains a range of amino acids and other supplements. This medium is supplemented typically with the Bottenstein- and Sato-type hormone mix termed N2, which is commercially available, and an antifungal and antibiotic agent (PSF). To increase the survival of primary precursor cells (which are especially vulnerable in the absence of serum over the first few days in culture), we recommend using B27 supplement. B27 contains, in addition to N2, a range of antioxidants and other compounds, which significantly enhance the survival of proliferating cells.[63] Mitogens commonly used are EGF, FGF-2 alone, or FGF-2 in combination. Leukemia inhibitory factor (LIF) can also be added for long-term propagation of human-derived NSCs.[20] The effects of FGF-2 can be greatly enhanced by adding heparin (5 μg/ml) to the medium.[64] Once the NSC cultures are established (i.e., passage 1), there is no advantage to using B27 over N2 supplement for further expansion of the cells.

For differentiation studies, following withdrawal of mitogen, we generally use serum-free media supplemented with B27. Serum (<1%) can be used to aid attachment but is often unnecessary, particularly when an extracellular matrix such as laminin is used as a substrate.

Methods of Growing NPCs

There are essentially two methods for growing NPCs (Fig. 52–1).

TABLE 52–1
Culture Conditions for Stem and Progenitor Cells from Embryonic and Adult CNS

Species	Age	Region	Substrate	Medium embryonic	Supplement	Mitogens	Ref.
Mouse	E10	Mesencephalon or telencephalon	Plastic	DMEM + 1% FBS	N2	FGF-2 (50 ng/ml) and heparin (8 mg/ml)	3, 4
Mouse	E10	Mesencephalon or telencephalon	Plastic	DMEM + 10% FBS	None	FGF-2 (50 ng/ml) and heparin (8 mg/ml)	5
Mouse	E14	Striatum	PORN	DMEM/F12	N2	EGF (20 ng/ml)	6, 7
Rat	E13–14	Cerebral hemispheres or spinal cord	PLL	DMEM	N2	FGF-2 (5 ng/ml)	8, 9
Rat	E15	Cortex	Astrocyte monolayer	DMEM + 10% FBS	None	None	10
Rat	E13.5–14.5	Striatum	PORN	DMEM/F12	N2	FGF-2 (5 ng/ml), NGF (150 ng/ml), or FGF-2 to NGF	11
Rat	E12–18	Cortex	Astrocyte monolayer	DMEM + 0.5% FBS	None	None	12
Rat	E10.5	Neural crest	Fibronectin	L-15	N2	EGF (100 ng/ml), FGF-2 (4 ng/ml), and NGF (20 ng/ml)	13
Rat	E10.5	Spinal cord	PDL–fibronectin	DMEM/F12	B27, CEE	FGF-2	14
Rat	E16–18	Hippocampus or spinal cord	PORN and laminin	DMEM/F12	N2	FGF-2 (20 ng/ml)	15, 16
Rat	E16	Hippocampus	PORN and fibronectin	DMEM/F12	N2	FGF-2 (10 ng/ml)	17
Human	6–8 weeks	Ventral forebrain	Plastic	DMEM/F12 + 5% horse serum	N2	EGF (20 ng/ml) and/or IGF-1 (100 ng/ml)	18
Human	7–21 weeks	Cortex, mesencephalon, and spinal cord	Plastic	DMEM/F12	B27	EGF (20 ng/ml), FGF-2 (20 ng/ml), and heparin (5 μg/ml) or FGF-2 alone after 35 days	19

Continued

TABLE 52-1—cont'd
Culture Conditions for Stem and Progenitor Cells from Embryonic and Adult CNS

Species	Age	Region	Substrate	Medium embryonic	Supplement	Mitogens	Ref.
Human	5–11 weeks	Forebrain	Plastic	DMEM/F12	N2	EGF (20 ng/ml), FGF-2 20 ng/ml), heparin (2 mg/ml), and LIF (10 ng/ml)	20
Human	6–12 weeks	Cortex, telencephalon, spinal cord, whole brain, and brainstem	Plastic	NSA basal serum free	N2	EGF (20 ng/ml) and FGF-2 (10 ng/ml)	21
Human	18–22 weeks	Brain	PLL–laminin	DMEM/F12	N2	FGF-2 (25 ng/ml) and NT3 (1 ng/ml)	22
Human	15–23 weeks	Telencephalic ventricular zone (musashi or nestin promoter)	None	DMEM/F12	N2	FGF-2(20 ng/ml) and EGF (10 ng/ml)	23
				Adult			
Mouse		Whole brain	Plastic	DMEM + 10% FBS	No	FGF-2 (20 ng/ml), EGF (20 ng/ml) or Ast-1 CM	24
Mouse	3–18 months	Striatum	Plastic	DMEM/F12	N2	EGF (20 ng/ml)	25
Mouse	3–8 months	Striatum	Plastic	DMEM/F12	N2	FGF-2 (20 ng/ml) and heparin 2 μg/ml)	26
Rat	Adult (160–170 g)	Hippocampus	PORN–laminin	DMEM/F12	N2	10% FBS (1 day), then FGF-2 (20 ng/ml)	27
Rat	Adult (225 g)	Subventricular zone	E-C-L, PORN, fibronectin, or laminin	DMEM/F12	N2	FGF-2 (10 ng/ml) and/or EGF	28
Human	11 weeks and 27 years	Hippocampus, ventricular zone, cortex, and corpus callosum	Fibronectin	DMEM/F12, 10% FBS	BSA, insulin, and transferrin	FGF-2 (20 ng/ml), EGF (20 ng/ml), PDGF-AB (20 ng/ml)	29

TABLE 52–2
Culture Conditions for Immortalized Stem and Progenitor Cells from Embryonic and Postnatal CNS

Species	Age	Region	Oncogene	Substrate	Medium	Supplement	Mitogens	Ref.
				Embryonic				
Mouse	E10	Mesencephalon	c-myc and N-myc	Plastic	DMEM +10% FBS	No	No	37, 38
Rat	E10.5	Neural tube	v-myc	Fibronectin	L-15 +10% FBS	No	No	39
Rat	E16	Hippocampus	tsSV40 A58	PORN	DMEM +10% FBS	No	No	40
Rat	E15	Medullary raphe	tsSV40 A58	Collagen and PLL	DMEM/F12 + 10% FBS	No	No	41
Human	10–10.5	Diencephalon and telencephalon	v-myc	Plastic– PLL	DMEM/F12 +1% FBS	N2	FGF-2 (20 ng/ml) and EGF (20 ng/ml)	42
				Neonatal				
Mouse	Newborn	Olfactory bulb	v-myc	PLL	DMEM + 20% FBS	No	No	43
Mouse	Newborn	Striatum	SV40 large-T	Plastic	DMEM + 10% FBS	No	No	44
Mouse	P4	Cerebellum	v-myc	PLL	DMEM + 20% FBS	No	No	43
Rat	P2	Cerebellum	tsSV40 A58	PORN	DMEM + 10% FBS	No	No	45
Rat	P2	Cerebellum	tsSV40 A58	PORN and laminin	DMEM + 10% FBS	No	No	46

MONOLAYER GROWTH OF PRECURSORS

This method requires the surface of the culture flask to be coated with polyornithine followed by laminin (5–10 μg/ml).[15] Following coating, the laminin is washed twice with plating media. It is important that the laminin is not allowed to dry out before the addition of cells. Cells are seeded into FGF-2–supplemented media (20 ng/ml) (as described previously) and attach to the substrate, forming a dividing monolayer. Upon confluence, cells are gently trypsinized with 0.1% trypsin for 10 minutes. Tapping the flask will dislodge the cells, which can then be collected by washing with 10 ml of chilled growth medium. Following centrifugation (1000 g, 5 minutes) the pellet can be resuspended in trypsin inhibitor followed by DNase as described previously for primary tissues. The resulting cell suspension can be reseeded in fresh media with subsequent passaging at confluence with trypsin to propagate cultures (see Ray *et al.*[65] for details of this method). An alternative method to generating monolayer cultures is to use serum and FGF-2[3,4] or serum and EGF[66,67] under substrate-free conditions.

EGF- OR FGF-2-RESPONSIVE PRECURSORS GROWN AS NEUROSPHERES

Cells are seeded into uncoated culture flasks at 200×10^3 per ml with the mitogens EGF, FGF-2, or both (each at 20 ng/ml). FGF-2 is critically dependent on heparin in the medium when cells are grown in suspension as "neurospheres."[64] Many single cells will die, but after a few days small adherent clusters (neurospheres) appear; they increase in size and detach over time (Fig. 52–1). In rodents, it will take approximately a week until the neurospheres are large enough to passage, whereas human tissues can often take 2 to 4 weeks.

At passaging, the spheres are collected, centrifuged, and then treated in one of three ways. The first method involves digesting the spheres in trypsin, counting, and subsequently reseeding. Although this can produce encouraging results for one or two passages, we have consistently seen increased amounts of spontaneous differentiation using enzyme digestion, such that by the third passage little division can be found. The second method involves mechanical dissociation of the spheres with a fine-polished pipette. This technique results in the death of approximately 50% of the cells, and although significant growth of mouse EGF-responsive neurospheres can be achieved, it only allows the short-term expansion of rat or human neurospheres.[68] The reasons underlying this are not clear, although it is possible that the action of breaking the cells to a single-cell suspension (1) induces spontaneous differentiation into a postmitotic cell, (2) causes so much trauma that the cell no longer divides rapidly, or (3) removes the extracellular matrix or cell–cell contact necessary for division. The third method for passaging is to simply section the neurospheres into segments using the McIlwain tissue chopper.[19] This method involves rapidly cutting the neurospheres with a razor blade at 250-μm intervals, rotating 90 degrees, and then cutting again. This results in numerous sphere segments that can be reseeded. This method avoids the use of trypsin and maintains cell–cell contact at all times. It is especially effective for enabling long-term propagation of human-derived NPCs. Rodent neurospheres will expand using this sectioning method, but they still appear to enter senescence between 4 and 6 weeks and appear far more liable to spontaneously differentiate even in a substrate-free environment.

Although neurospheres can be grown from either EGF- or FGF-2-treated conditions, the respective mitogen can influence the behavior of the NPC. We have consistently noticed an increased number of neurons in FGF-2, both within spheres and upon plating. Human neurospheres grown for long periods show increased expansion rates in EGF (in comparison to FGF-2) at later times and show less spontaneous differentiation. Finally, recent studies suggest that LIF added to the medium can mimic the effects seen when cell–cell contact is maintained and allow long-term growth of human NPCs.[20]

Assessing Growth Patterns

Knowledge of the growth rates of NPC cultures is useful for several reasons, including objective quantitative demonstration that the cultures are increasing in cell number, a requirement if the cells are to be used in transplantation paradigms or to compare the effect of culture conditions on the total cell number. One method of assessing cell division rates is to use thymidine or bromodeoxyuridine (BrdU) incorporation assays. In the thymidine assay, cells are grown in the presence of [^{3}H] thymidine for a defined time and subsequently assessed for radioactivity using a scintillation counter.[64] Alternatively, cells can be exposed to BrdU (1 μm for 24 hours), which is incorporated into the nuclei of dividing cells. These cultures can then be immunostained to assess positive nuclei. Both of these methods will give an index of the rate of proliferation at any time point but will not establish total cell growth. This is because cells could be dividing rapidly but dying at the same rate, the net effect being no increase in cell number but a high percentage of thymidine or BrdU incorporation. A more direct method is to simply seed a defined number of cells at the start of each culture period and count the total cells at the end of the culture period. Here, 96-well plate assays can be established and combined with the MTT survival assay to allow a high number of samples to be processed simultaneously. However, different plastic substrates can affect the growth of NPCs, and appropriate controls should be included. Where whole spheres are sectioned there is an obvious problem with counting individual cells at the start and end of a culture period. One method is to take several aliquots from the flask prior to passage and obtain a representative pro rata cell count using trypsin digestion to allow an estimate of the total cells within the flask. However, this is an imprecise and variable method. A more accurate alternative is to remove an aliquot of spheres one day after sectioning and grow them in parallel to the bulk flask cultures, but in 24-well plates permitting serial measurement. Measuring the sphere diameters at the start and end of the growth period enables researchers to calculate the total increase in cell number over the growth period—there is a linear relationship between sphere size and the number of cells within the sphere.[19]

Single-Cell Growth Factor Response Detected Using p.CREB Immunoreactivity

Nuclear phosphorylation of the transcription factor cAMP-response element-binding (CREB) protein on serine 133 represents a relatively simple method for detecting immunohistochemically the single-cell response to growth factors within a mixed population of cells. Phosphorylation of CREB (p.CREB) can be detected immunohistochemically.[50,69] p.CREB is a well-characterized intracellular response following ligand receptor tyrosine kinase activation (relevant ligands include EGF, FGF-2, and PDGF).[70] Plated cells are immediately fixed 7–10 minutes after ligand stimulation. Double labeling with phenotypic markers allows determination of which cell type is responding to the growth factor.

Differentiation of Expanded NPCs

During the growth phase, it is critical to maintain as many of the cells within the NPC culture in the undifferentiated state. Cell propagation is, however, finite, with senescence occurring at different times contingent on species, region, and mitogen.[71,72] The continual presence of the mitogens EGF or FGF-2 is often sufficient to prevent differentiation. Therefore, one key determinant of inducing differentiation is mitogen withdrawal. For FGF-2–responsive cultures grown as monolayers, differentiation can also take place through density arrest if the cells are not passaged when they reach confluence. Following the onset of differentiation, proliferation slows, many cells pass into the postmitotic state, and these cells begin to adopt mature phenotypes. This can sometimes take weeks, and it is advisable to analyze cultures at varying times up to 5 weeks, particularly if there is a major interest in mature neuronal phenotypes. Attention is drawn to the importance of live staining for certain cell surface markers, especially for those of the early oligodendrocyte lineage and appropriate fixation for intracellular markers (see Table 52–3).

There is considerable variation in the literature with regard to the percentage of neurons, astrocytes, and oligodendrocytes generated from FGF-2-responsive cultures grown as monolayers. In some cases, almost pure populations of neurons have been found;[15] in others, albeit in adult, only a small percentage produce neurons.[73] The numbers of astrocytes and oligodendrocytes also vary contingent on the brain region and culture conditions. These parameters should be established for each culture system using the markers suggested in Table 52–3.

For EGF- or FGF-2–responsive suspension cultures, growth will continue in the presence of mitogens. Differentiation can be induced by plating single-cell suspension (following trypsin digestion) onto poly-L-lysine and laminin-coated coverslips in the absence of mitogens. The second method is to plate whole spheres in otherwise identical conditions. Cells rapidly migrate radially from the core of the sphere to form a monolayer culture over a period of 1–5 weeks. For rat neurospheres grown in EGF, we have consistently seen a decrease in the number of neurons generated at each passage such that by 5 weeks less than 5% of the differentiated cells are neurons, the majority being glial.[35] Similar findings have been reported for mouse neurospheres that produce <5% neurons spontaneously in culture and predominantly produce glia following transplantation into the developing brain.[92,93] Human neurospheres grown in either EGF or FGF-2 continue to generate large numbers of neurons provided that they are plated as whole spheres.[19] These appear to migrate along radially oriented glial cells. When sister spheres are dissociated to a single-cell suspension and plated, few neurons develop and most of the cells are astrocytes. This supports several observations suggesting that cell–cell contact is vital for neuronal induction from noncommitted precursor cells.[94]

Clonal Analysis of NPCs

Clonal analysis, though technically challenging and difficult, is essential to characterize the potential of any given cell. A minimal requirement of a stem cell is monoclonal derivation of all neural cell types. A variety of methods exist in the literature, each of which is briefly described.

1. Two methods exist for establishing single-cell cultures, limiting dilution and micromanipulation of single cells using a micromanipulator. The former requires serial dilution of a starting dissociated cell suspension to a final concentration of approximately 200 cells per clonal grid dish, coated as described previously. Four hours after plating, single- cell grids are identified and followed thereon. An adaptation of this method is to use cloning rings to isolate single cells plated onto a Petri dish.[60] Terasaki 96-well plates have also been successfully used for single-cell cultures. Simply following single cells plated on a Petri dish is not adequate for clonal analysis, as the migration of cell–progeny can confound subsequent analysis. A limitation of single-cell isolate cultures is the high degree of cell death in the absence of cell–cell contact, amplified by serum-free conditions. Optimal culture media for these cultures are varied and complex. The presence of astrocyte- and meningeal-conditioned media with membrane homogenate facilitates single-cell cultures.[47] A simpler cocktail of defined media (DMEM/F12 + N2 supplement) containing 10% chick embryo extract (CEE), in addition to FGF-2 is sufficient to allow single-cell proliferation of embryonic cultures.[13,14] Withdrawal of CEE after 7–10 days allows the clones to differentiate with subsequent immunohistochemical characterization for markers of neurons, astrocytes, and oligodendrocytes. The clones will produce neurons only, glia only, or a mixture of both, thus allowing classification of the starting cell as multipotent or phenotypically restricted. Confirmation of this cell as a stem cell requires subcloning to demonstrate self-renewal.

TABLE 52–3
Markers Commonly Used to Label Stem Cells, Precursor Cells, and Their Differentiated Progeny

Antigenic markers	Nature of antigen	Cells labeled	Ref.
	Embryonic and adult		
Nestin	Intermediate filament	Stem and progenitor	45
Musashi	RNA-binding protein	Stem and progenitor	74
Vimentin	Intermediate filament	Precursor	75
A2B5	Surface ganglioside	Precursor	76
O4	Sulfatide	Immature oligodendrocyte	77
Gal C	Galactosphingolipid	Mature oligodendrocyte	78
GFAP	Intermediate filament	Astrocyte	79
L1	Cell-adhesion molecule	Premigratory neuron	80
Hu	Early neurogenic cells	Neuron	81
β-tubulin III	Cytoskeletal protein	Neuron	82
Map 2ab	Microtubule-associated protein	Mature neuron found in dendrites	83
Map 2c	Microtubule-associated protein	Precursor and neuron	84
NSE	Neuron-specific enolase	Neuron	85
NeuN	Neuronal nuclear antigen A60	Neuron	86
Neurofilament	Intermediate filament	Neuron	87
Tau	Microtubule-associated protein	Neuron found in axons	88
Synaptophysin	Presynaptic vesicle	Neuron	89
	Adult		
LeX/ssea	Carbohydrate	Stem	90
Peanut agglutinin and heat-stable antigen	Degree of binding to peanut agglutinin and heat-stable antigen	Stem	91

2. Clonal analysis can also be undertaken in high-density cultures with modified retroviral vectors. This system in a sense more accurately reflects the *in situ* environment than single-cell cultures. Retroviruses are ideal vehicles for the stable introduction of genes into a host cell because of the innate property of retroviruses to integrate into host DNA of proliferating cells. Other means of gene transfer such as adenovirus vectors and nonviral methods such as liposomes are largely unsuitable for clonal analysis because of transient gene expression; these are not discussed further. A dense culture of cells plated in the conventional manner is exposed to a low titer suspension of amphipathic, replication-defective, recombinant retrovirus containing a reporter gene (β-*Gal* or green fluorescent protein). The exact titer has been previously determined in control cultures such that on average a single cell within the starting density of 1×10^5 cells will be infected (for further details, see Cepko *et al.*[95]). A refinement of retroviral clonal analysis is the use of a selection gene such as *neo,* which offers a further method for the isolation of the retroviral-containing cell population. Differentiation of the cell population upon mitogen withdrawal permits identification of the progeny of the starting cell by coexpression of the reporter product with differentiated phenotypic markers. In the case of a fluorescent marker, the cell–progeny can be easily identified and isolated. Clonality within a presumed monoclonal-derived progeny population can be confirmed by Southern analysis—seeking a unique initial insertion site within the progeny of a given clone.[27]
3. Clonal single-cell cultures or high-density cultures containing an easily identifiable marker such as green fluorescent protein can be observed by continuous time-lapse video microscopy. This innovation allows the examination of cell–cell spatial relationships within a clonal population and, if combined with immunohistochemistry, the construction of genealogic "lineage trees" (for a review, see Shen *et al.*[96]). Furthermore, researchers can observe cell death in addition to cell proliferation and differentiation. Ideally, such video recording needs to be within a humidified incubator with 6% CO_2 in otherwise identical conditions to those described earlier. However, short-term video monitoring is possible in ambient conditions using L-15 rather than DMEM. These culture conditions are nonetheless far from ideal and only viable, at least in our hands, in dense clonal cultures over 24–72 hours.

53

Hematopoietic Stem Cell Mobilization and Homing

Ruth Seggewiss, Cynthia E. Dunbar, and Donald Orlic

Hematopoietic stem cells (HSCs) circulate from the extraembryonic yolk sac (YS), the intraembryonic aorta–gonad–mesonephros (AGM) region, and the liver during murine embryonic and fetal development as they colonize organs active in postnatal hematopoiesis. In adult life the ability of HSCs to enter the circulation, even in low numbers, may be an important aspect of hematopoietic homeostasis. We are beginning to understand many of the mechanisms by which therapeutic agents interrupt stem and progenitor cell tethering to matrix molecules and stromal cells in the bone marrow (BM) environment. Once released from its attachment, a stem cell undergoes transmural migration through openings in the basement membrane and endothelial lining of a blood sinus and enters the circulation. Although normally low, the number of circulating HSCs can be increased in response to treatment with drugs, chemokines, and cytokines. Mobilization has been achieved in both laboratory and clinical settings. In several well-defined examples, stem and progenitor cells are released from their attachment to stromal cells when a cytokine–receptor axis such as c-kit–stem cell factor (SCF) or CXCR4-stromal derived factor-1 is interrupted. In other instances the action of the mobilizing agent may be indirect. For example, one cytokine, granulocyte colony-stimulating factor (G-CSF), activates neutrophils by targeting the G-CSF receptor resulting in the release of the enzymes elastase and cathepsin G. The down-regulation of stem cell surface adherent molecules that precedes mobilization must be reversed with the reappearance of VLA-4 and CXCR4 in order for circulating stem cells to home to marrow niches where adhesion will occur.

A recently investigated, highly contested function of BM stem cells involves the concept of plasticity. According to this hypothesis, circulating stem cells traffic to sites of tissue injury leading to infiltration of the damaged tissue and generation of nonhematopoietic cell types. Ischemic areas in the eye, heart, and lower limb are candidate sites of stem cell transdifferentiation. Because clinical trials are underway, there is need for a clearer understanding of the mechanisms involved in stem cell mobilization and homing to all tissues. It also is incumbent on scientists to discover more effective mechanisms for stem cell mobilization without the accompanying increase in circulating white blood cells (WBCs) and platelets. We believe that improvements in quantity and quality of mobilized stem cell populations will lead to better outcomes.

Handbook of Stem Cells
Volume 2

Historical Perspective

HEMATOPOIETIC STEM CELLS CIRCULATE TO ESTABLISH HEMATOPOIESIS DURING ONTOGENY

Hemangioblasts are thought to be the earliest cells committed to hematopoiesis and vasculogenesis. They reportedly originate from embryonic stem cells (ESCs) and can be derived *in vitro* from embryoid bodies.[1] The dual developmental fate of hemangioblasts leads to the generation of HSCs and endothelial progenitor cells (EPCs).

Hematopoietic activity emerges early in embryonic development as HSCs are distributed, via the circulation, to fetal organs where they establish sites of hematopoiesis. The extraembryonic YS blood islands are one of several independent sources of early hematopoietic and angiogenic activity. HSC activity is established in the YS by day 9 (E9) of embryonic development in mice.[2] The $CD34^+$ $c\text{-}kit^+$ phenotype of YS HSCs[3] and their ability to support definitive hematopoiesis in newborn mice[2] argues for their characterization as definitive HSCs. At nearly the same time, E10.5, $CD34^+$ $c\text{-}kit^+$ $CD31^+$ adult-repopulating HSCs can be isolated from the intraembryonic AGM region in mice.[4,5] Thus, the YS and AMG region in embryonic mice provide cells that initially colonize the vascular system and establish hematopoiesis in the fetal liver. Later in development, blood-borne HSCs seed the thymus and BM to complete the development of the primary hematopoietic organs.

Similar ontogenic events have been identified in the human embryo during the first month of development. Hematopoietic activity is established in the extraembryonic YS mesoderm[6] followed by the emergence of aorta-associated intraembryonic $CD34^+$ cells at day E27.[7] Taken together these studies assume a circulation-based dispersal of colonizing HSCs, but none provide direct evidence to support this assumption. The probable need for migration of HSCs during fetal development may result in a residual migratory and homing capability that can be carried over into neonatal and adult life.

SEVERAL STEM CELL POPULATIONS EXIST IN BONE MARROW AND BLOOD

The HSCs in BM and blood are the ancestors of all mature blood cells. They have been enriched based on specific phenotypic markers.[8–11] Their direct progeny are the common lymphocytic progenitors (CLPs) that are responsible for formation of B and T lymphocytes[12] and the common myelocytic progenitors (CMPs) that generate erythrocytes, granulocytes, monocytes, and platelets.[13] The latter are similar in their pattern of development to the earlier described colony-forming units–spleen (CFU-S) that home to the irradiated spleen following intravenous infusion and establish discrete multilineage colonies.[14,15]

The EPCs, also referred to as angioblasts, reside in BM and circulate to a limited extent in blood.[16] Their role in vessel repair in normal individuals and persons at risk for cardiovascular disease is currently under investigation.[17] Two additional primitive cell populations in BM, stromal cells,[18,19] and multipotent adult progenitor cells (MAPCs),[20] have vast developmental potential. Single MAPCs or stromal cells can be coaxed to differentiate *in vitro* into cells of multiple embryonic germ layers. There is little evidence, however, that stromal cells and MAPCs can be mobilized from BM into the circulation. Therefore, unlike HSCs and EPCs, there appears to be little potential for stromal cells and MAPCs to function in cell or tissue renewal under acute injury or steady-state conditions.

ADULT CIRCULATING HEMATOPOIETIC STEM CELLS

After years of speculation, several key experiments in the 1940s, 1950s, and early 1960s demonstrated the existence of HSCs in the circulation. The initial report found that bovine fraternal twins sharing a common placenta and blood supply were each endowed with chimeric BM and thus lymphohematopoietic cells from its sibling after birth.[21] This observation of a natural phenomenon was soon followed by experiments to test the hypothesis that HSCs circulated in the blood of adult animals and humans. It was learned that shielding of the spleen, a source of HSCs in mice, protected against a lethal dose of whole-body radiation by reconstituting the BM.[22] Although it is now clear that survival was achieved by HSCs circulating from the protected spleen, at the time the experiments were done, the authors proposed that survival was due to a secreted hormone produced by the spleen. In a later extension of this approach, HSCs from the lead-shielded hind limbs of one member of a parabiotic pair of mice circulated to the total body irradiated member and reconstituted its ablated BM.[23] These studies and others involving transplantation of blood leukocytes into irradiated recipients to reconstitute BM function showed that HSCs circulate in the blood and can home to appropriate niches in BM following radiation ablation of hematopoietic tissue.[24] These pioneering experiments eventually provided the basis for clinical HSC transplantation via intravenous infusion, initially using BM as the HSC source in patients with hematologic disorders such as leukemia.

The impetus for considering peripheral blood as a source of primitive hematopoietic cells for clinical applications was a report in 1971 documenting the presence of a low concentration of CFU in the blood of humans.[25] Patients with chronic myelogenous leukemia (CML) were noted to have much higher concentrations of circulating progenitors, which stimulated a group of clinical researchers to collect and cryopreserve these cells from the blood buffy coat fraction of CML patients during chronic phase. They found that these cells could contribute to hematopoietic recovery, restoring a second chronic phase, when infused following very high-dose chemotherapy for blastic transformation.[26,27] However, it was unclear whether this approach would be relevant in other clinical situations, because the concentration of primitive cells in the blood was much lower in patients with disorders other than CML.

As the benefits of chemotherapeutic dose-intensification supported by autologous marrow rescue became more apparent for patients with lymphoma in the mid-1980s, investigation of peripheral blood as a stem cell source intensified. Lymphoma patients with fibrosis precluding adequate marrow harvesting underwent as many as 12 apheresis procedures to collect steady-state circulating mononuclear cells (MNCs). The ability of these cells to rescue patients following high-dose chemotherapy or chemoradiotherapy was demonstrated by four groups concurrently in 1985–1986.[28–31] However, there was concern that these peripheral blood stem cell (PBSC) grafts did not contain sufficient repopulating cells for long-term engraftment but instead served only as hematopoietic bridge until return of endogenous hematopoiesis, because some patients in these early trials had suboptimal hematopoietic recovery.[32] Formal demonstration of long-term engraftment with autologous PBSCs came from early retroviral gene transfer trials in patients with myeloma or breast cancer.[33] The initial allogeneic transplant using steady-state peripheral blood cells was reported in 1989 when a sibling donor refused marrow harvest but consented to 10 collections of peripheral blood cells via apheresis. The recipient engrafted rapidly following infusion of the T-cell depleted peripheral blood cells but died from infectious complications after 1 month.[34]

In the 1990s, with the realization that the yield of circulating primitive hematopoietic cells could be greatly increased during recovery from chemotherapy and/or following treatment with hematopoietic cytokines, mobilized peripheral blood progenitor cells replaced BM as the preferred source of stem cells for autologous transplantation and their use with allogeneic donors increased. These changes were due to the relative ease of collection of peripheral blood progenitor cells, faster hematologic recovery compared with BM transplantation, lower levels of tumor cell contamination, fewer complications, and lower costs for the patients.[35,36] By 1998, 95% of autologous transplants and 25% of allogeneic transplants were performed with peripheral blood progenitor cells (PBPC) instead of BM cells, and this percentage has continued to increase.[37]

Stem Cell Mobilization: Experimental Models

CYCLOPHOSPHAMIDE-INDUCED STEM CELL MOBILIZATION

Since the demonstration that cyclophosphamide (CY) could induce CD34$^+$ stem and progenitor cell mobilization from BM of cancer patients,[38] this drug has been tested extensively in experimental animals. Cells mobilized into the peripheral blood of mice following a single injection of CY have the capacity to rescue lethally irradiated BM.[39] The number of long-term reconstituting HSCs mobilized by a single dose of CY alone or CY plus G-CSF was estimated, using a competitive repopulation assay, to be nearly equal to the number of HSCs in total BM, but their stay in the circulation is temporary.[40] In response to CY and G-CSF treatment, the HSCs in BM undergo a series of cell divisions and increase their number 12-fold. However, when the newly generated HSCs enter the circulation they revert to the quiescent G_0/G_1 phase of the cell cycle.[41]

CYTOKINE-INDUCED STEM CELL MOBILIZATION

Under normal conditions there are few circulating HSCs, approximately 10 to 30 per total blood volume in adult mice.[42] When compared with the estimated 2600 HSCs in BM, as few as 0.01% of the total HSCs in an adult mouse exist in the blood at any moment. Although it is questionable whether such low numbers of circulating HSCs can have a role in hematopoietic homeostasis, there is some evidence that suggests there may be a high rate of turnover of circulating HSCs on a daily basis,[43] and it has been hypothesized that steady-state egress of HSCs into the blood may represent a death pathway.[44] However, the ultimate distribution of circulating HSCs is not exclusively in the BM, spleen, or other hematopoietic tissues. Several studies found that skeletal muscle is a repository of significant numbers of itinerant HSCs originating in BM.[45–47] Interestingly, even after a long residence in skeletal muscle, these migrating HSCs retain the capacity to generate blood cells if harvested and transplanted following myeloablation.

It is well documented that large numbers of HSCs can be induced to enter the circulation. This is achieved using various perturbations such as cytokines and is now routine practice in both animal and clinical settings. One measure of successful HSC mobilization in mice involves an increase in the number of cells with the c-kit$^+$ Sca1$^+$ Lin$^-$ phenotype. In primates, including humans, HSC and progenitor cell mobilization is measured on the basis of the number of CD34$^+$ Lin$^-$ cells in the circulation. It follows that a clearer understanding of the mechanism and magnitude of BM HSC mobilization and homing may provide insight into steady-state renewal of hematopoietic tissue and contribute to a better clinical outcome in BM transplant recipients.

Studies in adult mice have provided substantial insights into HSC mobilization. In one experiment, recombinant rat stem cell factor (rrSCF) was injected into adult mice for 7 days.[48] HSC content in blood MNCs from rrSCF-treated C57BL/6J mice was compared with HSC activity in BM cells from untreated congenic B6.CH-1^b/ByJ (HW80) mice, a strain that differs in one allele at the β-globin locus and allows analysis of HSC contributions to hematopoiesis via globin allelic quantitation. The rrSCF induced a 10-fold increase in the absolute number of HSCs in total blood volume from a baseline value of 10 to 100, a 16-fold increase in HSCs in spleen from 500 to 8000, and a decrease in the number of HSCs in marrow from 2400 to 900. The overall increase in HSC was three-fold. From this it appeared that the spleen functioned as a "sink" for HSCs mobilized from BM and any derived through self-renewal within the spleen. Mice were splenectomized in a subsequent experiment to obtain a more accurate estimate of the effectiveness of cytokine treatment in mobilization of HSCs from BM to blood and to better mimic the human situation, in which the spleen does not function as a hematopoietic organ under most circumstances. When mice were injected with recombinant human granulocyte-colony stimulating factor (rhG-CSF) and rrSCF for 5 consecutive days there was a 250-fold increase in circulating HSCs, from 29 to 7200.[42] Similar experiments were done based on CD34$^+$ progenitor cell mobilization in nonhuman primate studies. Baboons were injected with rhG-CSF alone or with a combination of recombinant human stem cell factor (rhSCF) plus rhG-CSF for 5 days and mobilized progenitor cells were harvested by apheresis. Both treatments resulted in an increase in circulating WBCs and primitive colony-forming cells (CFCs).[49,50] The combination of rhSCF and rhG-CSF mobilized 14-fold more CFC than rhG-CSF alone. These striking increases in total HSCs in the blood of adult mice and baboons created new research opportunities in the area of stem cell biology.

Gene transfer efficiency into HSCs from large animal and human BM is extremely low when using vectors that must enter cells via amphotropic retroviral receptors, because of low concentrations of these receptors on primitive cells.[51] This inefficiency is also attributed to the quiescent G_0 status of HSCs because retroviral insertion into the nuclear DNA requires that the cells be in cycle.[52] Several studies suggest that cytokine mobilized circulating HSCs may be good candidates for improved gene therapy. Human stem and progenitor cells (CD34$^+$ CD38$^-$ Lin$^-$), mobilized by five daily injections of rhG-CSF, show a four-fold higher level of amphotropic retrovirus receptor mRNA compared with cells of the same phenotype in steady-state BM.[53] A corresponding high level of receptor mRNA in rhG-CSF and rhSCF mobilized rhesus macaque CD34$^+$ cells could explain their 10–15% gene marking efficiency.[54,55] However, cells mobilized with G-CSF alone appear to be much less desirable targets for retroviral gene transfer, indicating that different mobilization regimens may result in release of cells with very different characteristics.[56]

CHEMOKINE-INDUCED STEM CELL MOBILIZATION

Interleukin-8 (IL-8) is a chemokine that belongs to the CXC family.[57,58] It is an autocrine factor, produced by normal hematopoietic progenitors, mature blood cells, and leukemic cells, that promotes cell survival and proliferation in response to hematopoietic cytokines, functions as a chemoattractant, and activates neutrophils. Inhibition of the IL-8 pathway results in reduction of CD34⁺ proliferation and colony formation.[59] As a single agent, IL-8 induces progenitor cell mobilization in primates and mice within a few hours; however, the total number of mobilized CD34⁺ cells is low compared with G-CSF–induced mobilization.[57] IL-8 also results in immediate mobilization of mature granulocytes.[60] Recently, it was demonstrated that polymorphonuclear cells serve as key regulators in IL-8 induced hematopoietic progenitor cell mobilization, because the mobilization capacity of IL-8 was severely reduced in neutropenic mice but reappeared with neutrophil reconstitution.[61]

The Complementary Processes of Mobilization and Homing

Postnatal hematopoiesis occurs in a very specific three-dimensional BM microenvironment made up of supportive nonhematopoietic cell populations, including mesenchymal stromal cells, adipocytes, endothelial cells, and an extracellular matrix (ECM) produced by these stromal elements consisting of fibronectin, collagen, proteoglycans, heparins, and other molecules that provide structure, an adhesive surface, and binding sites for cytokines that are present at high concentrations focally, especially adjacent to the endosteum[62,63] (Fig. 53–1A). These cellular and matrix components of the microenvironment supply cytokines and cell–cell signals critical to maintenance of steady-state hematopoiesis and to a rapid response to hematopoietic demand. Tight control of self-renewal and differentiation depends on these interactions, with both positive and negative signals supplied by interactions of HSCs with microenvironmental components.[64]

Clarification of the interactions between HSCs and progenitor cells and the components of the marrow microenvironment are central to an understanding of stem cell mobilization and the converse process of "homing." Homing is defined as migration of HSCs and progenitor cells specifically from the blood to the BM followed by "engraftment" in permissive niches of the microenvironment where they survive, proliferate, and differentiate into multilineage cells. Homing is assumed to be a multistep process with similarities to the migration of leukocytes to inflammatory sites and movement of lymphocytes within lymph nodes.[65,66] Mobilization and homing can be considered as mirror images, that is, the interactions that must be severed to release stem and progenitor cells from the marrow into the circulation must be reestablished to retain these cells within marrow niches after intravenous infusion (Fig. 53–1B and C). Teleologically, these processes appear to be central to the shift of hematopoietic activity from YS to fetal liver to marrow during *in utero* development and may act as adaptive mechanisms in response to overwhelming injury in distant marrow spaces or other organs or tissues in which marrow cells may influence regeneration.[67–69] A recent study in a mouse model described endotoxins as cofactors in cytokine and chemokine induced mobilization.[70]

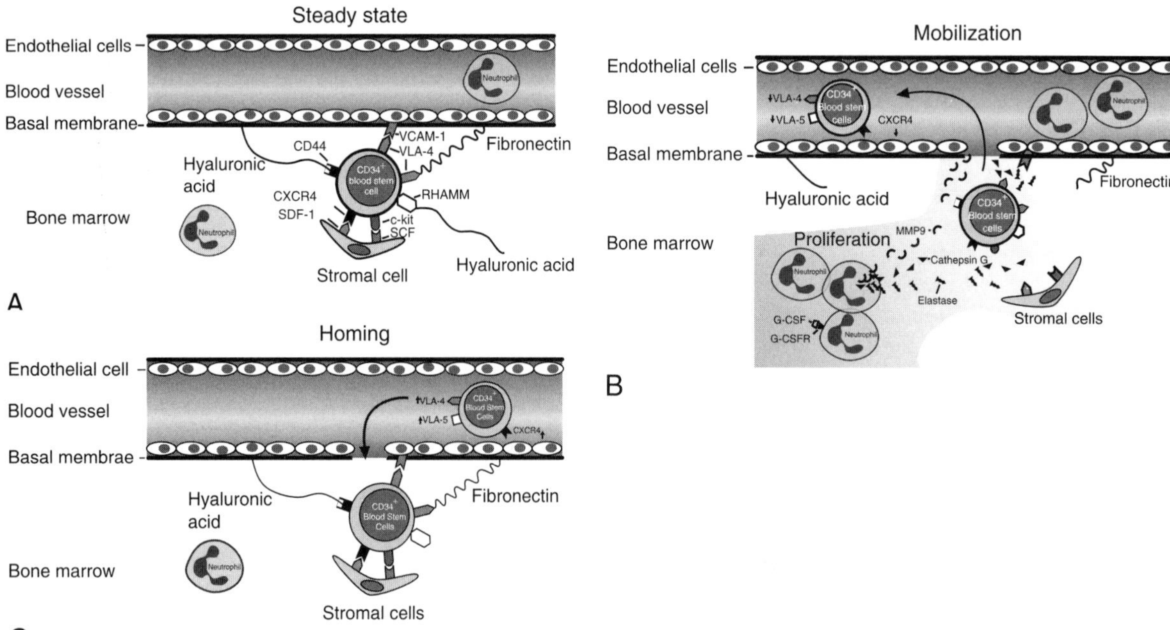

Figure 53-1. These figures indicate some proposed interactions of hematopoietic stem cells with microenvironment of the bone marrow in (A) the steady state, (B) during mobilization, and (C) during homing. Additional details regarding the role of the different cellular elements as well as matrix components are given in the text in the section. The Complementary Process of Mobilization and Homing.

Cords of hematopoietic cells are interspersed within an extensive network of venous sinuses in the marrow space. The barrier to HSC migration from the cords to the lumen of the vessels consists of an incomplete layer of adventitial cells, a basement membrane, and endothelial cells.[71] There are frequent interruptions within the highly attenuated endothelial cell lining. These fenestrations are the sites of blood cell migration as demonstrated for mature neutrophils.[72] Presumably, mobilized stem and progenitor cells use this same transmural pathway following their release from tethering within the marrow stroma.

Over the past 5 years, significant progress has been made toward identifying the interactions between receptors on HSCs and progenitor cells and components of the microenvironment and some of the proteolytic processes that are central to mobilization and homing. However, the relative importance of these findings remains unclear because significant redundancy of function exists as previously encountered with cytokine signaling pathways. These ambiguities complicate interpretation of results from elegant experiments using mouse knockout technology.[73] *In vitro* assays that measure adhesion and migration of hematopoietic progenitors across purified stromal cells or ECM proteins have yielded valuable insights, but these models lack the complex three-dimensional structure, diversity of cellular components, and gradients of nutrients, cytokines, and gases that would characterize the marrow parenchyma.[74,75]

It has been difficult to separate the events of *in vivo* homing and engraftment. When stem/progenitor cells were labeled with membrane dyes such as CSFE and reinfused, their homing pattern to marrow and other sites could be assessed by flow cytometry, but precise localization could not be determined.[76] Recent advances in techniques for labeling cells with light-emitting proteins or iron particles may allow much more precise *in vivo* visualization by sophisticated optical cameras or magnetic resonance imaging.[77,78]

In vivo analysis of homing of primitive human hematopoietic cells has relied in part on the use of xenograft models including immunodeficient mice and preimmune fetal sheep. Intravenous injection of human stem and progenitor cells into nonobese-diabetic severe-combined immunodeficient (NOD/SCID) mice results in a generally low, 10% maximum homing efficiency.[79,80] This low efficiency may be due to cross-species differences in receptor–ligand interactions, with resultant disruption of the complex processes involved in homing such as recognition and penetration of the marrow vascular endothelium and migration to a supportive microenvironment.[43,81,82] A prolonged period in the circulation may render these xenogenic stem/progenitor cells vulnerable to capture and destruction in other organs. This raises questions regarding the limitations of these representative models for the study of human HSC homing and engraftment. In recent efforts to overcome difficulties with interspecies cell–cell or cell–matrix recognition, two groups described improved engraftment after direct injection of human hematopoietic cells into the marrow space of NOD/SCID immunodeficient mice, thereby allowing a separation of HSC function from limitations of vascular homing defects.[83,84]

We summarize the interactions between receptors on primitive hematopoietic cells and their ligands present on or secreted by cells in the microenvironment. These ligands are found to be central both to retaining primitive cells within the marrow microenvironment and to their homing following transplantation. These interactions must be disrupted for HSC release and mobilization, and we describe experimental models implicating several active enzymatic processes in response to cytokines, chemokines, and other agents introduced previously.

ROLE OF VERY LATE ANTIGEN 4 (VLA-4) AND OTHER INTEGRINS IN MOBILIZATION AND HOMING

VLA-4 is an integrin ($\alpha4\beta1$) expressed on HSCs and progenitor cells and is perhaps the most intensively studied hematopoietic adhesion molecule.[85] VLA-4 binds the ECM component, fibronectin, and the cell surface molecule vascular cell adhesion molecule-1 (VCAM-1 or CD106) that is constitutively expressed on stromal and endothelial cells. Engagement of VLA-4 results in inhibition of cycling and maintenance of viability and engraftment potential of cultured CD34$^+$ HSCs.[86,87] Interruption of VLA-4 interactions using monoclonal antibodies against either VLA-4 or VCAM-1 inhibits adhesion of stem and progenitor cells to stromal cell layers *in vitro*. *In vivo* administration of these antibodies to mice or primates results in the release of progenitors into the peripheral blood. These findings indicate a central role for VLA-4 in marrow retention of hematopoietic precursors.[85,88–90] Normal mobilization after VLA-4/VCAM-1 interruption requires an intact c-kit signaling pathway as demonstrated by defective mobilization in c-kit–deficient W/Wv mice.[92]

Clearly, the VLA-4/VCAM-1 interaction is not the only important tethering mechanism. Interruption of interactions involving the beta-2 integrins, leukocyte function associated-antigen-1 (LFA-1) or CD18, results in enhanced mobilization in response to anti-VLA-4. Also, primitive cells express a second fibronectin-binding $\beta1$ integrin (VLA-5, $\alpha5\beta1$).[92]

The expression of VLA-4 is consistently lower on peripheral blood CD34$^+$ cells compared with those in BM, both in steady-state hematopoiesis and in response to mobilization, suggesting that cells with decreased VLA-4 expression may be preferentially released.[93–95] Levels of the related integrins VLA-5 and LFA-1 were also decreased in mobilized CD34$^+$ cells compared with BM.[96] In non-Hodgkin's lymphoma (NHL) patients, successful mobilization was associated with a less pronounced decrease in VLA-4 expression on circulating CD34$^+$ cells compared with marrow CD34$^+$ cells.[97] The mechanism of release from VLA-4 tethering seems to involve actual cleavage of VCAM-1, mediated by neutrophil proteases.[98]

The role of VLA-4 in homing was initially demonstrated in 1991. *In vitro* blocking of VLA-4 inhibited the binding of hematopoietic cells to fibronectin and inhibited engraftment of murine multipotent CFU-S cells.[99] Beta-1 integrin knockout animals lacking intact VLA-4 and VLA-5 exhibit abnormal patterns of HSC migration and colonization during fetal development and fail to contribute to hematopoiesis in transplantation chimeras, again suggesting a homing defect.[100,101] Beta-2 integrin (CD18/CD11) deficient cells retain engraftment potential, but blocking VLA-4 on these cells almost completely inhibits homing to a greater degree than blockade of VLA-4 on wild-type progenitors, thus providing evidence for synergism between these cell surface receptors in the homing process.[91,92] Because mobilized primitive cells express lower levels of VLA-4 and adhesion receptors compared with cells in marrow, it might be expected that homing of PBSCs is less efficient than bone marrow stem cells (BMSCs). This was confirmed in a mouse model and was demonstrated by inefficient engraftment of PBSCs compared with BMSCs in a xenograft model.[102–104] The more rapid hematopoietic recovery obtained in recipients of PBSCs compared with BMSCs may reflect a higher stem cell dose using peripheral blood, thus overcoming any impact of a relative homing defect or differences in time required to initiate proliferation. Mobilized stem cells may also rapidly regain VLA-4 expression, allowing enhanced homing after reinfusion. CD34$^+$ cells with high levels of VLA-4 result in faster engraftment in patients as assessed by platelet recovery following transplantation.[105]

ROLE OF CD44 AND OTHER HYALURONAN AND SELECTIN RECEPTORS

Hyaluronic acid (HA) is a glycosaminoglycan that is a major component of the ECM, and primitive hematopoietic cells express two cell surface receptors that bind HA, CD44 and RHAMM. Both are decreased on circulating CD34$^+$ cells following cytokine mobilization.[106] CD44 also binds E-selectin expressed by marrow endothelial cells.[107] Anti-CD44 antibodies can mobilize murine HSCs, although not as efficiently as anti-VLA-4.[90] Mice deficient in CD44 do not mobilize normal numbers of stem and progenitor cells; however, it is not clear whether this is due to baseline abnormal localization of primitive cells or some requirement for CD44 signaling during mobilization.[108] It is interesting that E-selectin deficient mice have marked leukocytosis and increased numbers of circulating stem cells, suggesting that an intact CD44–E-selectin interaction is necessary to retain primitive cells within the marrow space.[109] Homing of wild-type stem and progenitor cells to the marrow is defective in mice lacking both E-selectin as well as P-selectin, a second family member expressed on endothelial cells and platelets.[110] Fucoidin, a sulfated polysaccharide that rapidly mobilizes HSCs, was initially used because it binds to and inhibits selectin function, but because the agent can also mobilize HSC in selectin-deficient mice, an alternative mechanism for mobilization involving SDF-1 is more likely (see later).[111,112]

ROLE OF C-KIT AND STEM CELL FACTOR

Elucidation of a wide variety of processes in hematopoiesis has been facilitated by the availability of the mutant anemic W (for white spotted) and Steel mouse strains with very similar phenotypes.[113] Transplantation experiments more than 30 years ago demonstrated that the W mutants had endogenous HSC defects, because marrow cells from these animals could not engraft normally in wild-type animals. Conversely, Steel mutants were postulated to have a marrow microenvironmental defect because their marrow cells could engraft in wild-type mice, but transplantation of wild-type marrow into Steel recipients was unsuccessful. The defects in W strains were identified in the c-kit proto-oncogene, a tyrosine kinase cell surface receptor, whereas the Steel mutants were defective in the ligand for this receptor SCF.[114,115] Both soluble and transmembrane forms of SCF exist and are expressed by marrow stromal cells. A fascinating related strain, Steel-Dickie, has a mutation that results in production of normal amounts of soluble SCF but no cell-associated SCF.[116] These mice have a phenotype almost as severe as animals lacking both forms of SCF, suggesting that interactions between HSCs and marrow stromal elements via c-kit/membrane-bound SCF are very important for homing following transplantation and for maintenance of HSCs within the marrow microenvironment in steady-state hematopoiesis. Disruption of the interaction between c-kit and SCF by matrix metalloproteinase-9[117] may be important in mobilization because PBSCs have a lower level of c-kit expression compared with BMSCs.

THE ROLE OF CXCR4 INTERACTIONS IN MOBILIZATION AND HOMING

Perhaps the most extensively studied cell–cell interaction involved in mobilization and homing is the binding of the chemokine receptor CXCR4 to its ligand, stromal-derived factor 1 (SDF-1). Conditioned media from a murine stromal cell line MS-5 was found to contain a potent chemoattractant for HSCs, and on purification the active substance was identical to the previously isolated protein SDF-1.[118–120] SDF-1 is the only known chemokine to act as a chemoattractant, for purified murine HSCs.[121] The maintenance of a specific SDF-1 concentration gradient seems to be necessary for the retention and homing of HSCs and progenitor cells.[118,122] SDF-1 not only acts as a chemoattractant, it also stimulates migration through endothelial cell layers.[123,124] Mice completely deficient in SDF-1 do not survive to birth and have defects consistent with impaired migration of HSCs from fetal liver to BM.[125]

CXCR4 was initially identified as a co-receptor for HIV-1 entry into T cells and was only later found to be expressed on HSCs and progenitor cells.[126] Mice deficient in CXCR4 have a lethal phenotype, although fetal liver cells from these mice can engraft inefficiently in the marrow of conditioned adult mice.[73,127] Blockade of CXCR4 on human CD34$^+$ cells markedly reduces homing and engraftment in NOD/SCID mice.[128] There has been some controversy regarding the role of CXCR4 in homing because of reports indicating that sorted CXCR4$^-$/CD34$^+$ cells from the peripheral blood can engraft. Recent investigations show that cells initially negative for surface CXCR4 can rapidly transfer intracellular CXCR4 to the cell surface, suggesting that CXCR4$^-$ cells can gain homing ability in an oscillatory manner.[129,130] Local injection of SDF-1 can attract transplanted CD34$^+$ cells to sites outside the BM.[131] Transgenic mice expressing CXCR4 on their CD4$^+$ T lymphocytes show an increase in CD4$^+$ cells in the BM and reduced numbers of circulating CD4$^+$ cells.[132]

The role of CXCR4–SDF-1 interaction during HSC mobilization is being elucidated. BM CD34$^+$ cells migrate more actively toward SDF-1 than peripheral blood CD34$^+$ cells, and CD34$^+$ cells within the marrow of G-CSF-treated mice have increased levels of CXCR4.[118,133] However, mobilized CD34$^+$ cells express lower levels of CXCR4, thus the magnitude of mobilization is directly related to the percentage of CD34$^+$ cells expressing CXCR4.[134] Blocking either CXCR4 or SDF-1 with neutralizing antibodies decreased mobilization in response to G-CSF, suggesting that active signaling via the CXCR4–SCF-1 complex is required for egress of primitive cells out of the marrow into the blood.[133] Investigators have hypothesized that a critical determinant in mobilization is the creation of an increasing SDF-1 gradient extending from the extravascular hematopoietic foci to the lumen of the sinus vessels. Mobilization by various agents results in decreased concentrations of SDF-1 within the marrow microenvironment (see later for potential mechanisms), and HSCs enter the circulation in response to the resulting SDF-1 gradient. Mobilizing agents were not found to alter blood SDF-1 concentrations to the same degree as in marrow.[133,135] To date, it has not been determined whether the disruption of SDF-1–CXCR4 or VLA4–VCAM-1 interactions are both necessary or whether disturbance of either one results in mobilization of HSCs and progenitor cells.

INVOLVEMENT OF PROTEASES IN THE PROCESSES OF MOBILIZATION AND HOMING

The interactions between VLA-4 and VCAM-1, c-kit and SCF, CD44 and HA, CXCR-4 and SDF-1, or other yet to be discovered contact points between HSCs and components of the marrow microenvironment must be disrupted to initiate HSC mobilization and enable the stem and progenitor cells to traverse the basement membrane and endothelial cell layer of venous sinuses during entry into the circulation. Clues for the processes of mobilization came from elegant studies in mice lacking the granulocyte-colony stimulating factor receptor (G-CSFR). These G-CSFR-mice have a baseline neutropenia and decreased numbers of marrow myeloid precursors.[136] Mobilization with G-CSF was, not surprisingly, deficient, but mobilization following CY or IL-8 treatments was also impaired.[137] In transplantation chimeras, expression of the G-CSFR on HSCs was not required for mobilization, and, in mice reconstituted with both wild-type and G-CSFR-deficient HSCs, treatment with G-CSF mobilized both populations equally, suggesting an indirect effect of G-CSF on mobilization. Further clues came from the apparent requirement for granulocyte proliferation or activation induced by G-CSF or IL-8 before mobilization. From these studies, it became clear that neutrophil secretion of the proteases, elastase, and cathepsin G was required to cleave both VCAM-1 and SDF-1, resulting in release of HSCs from adhesive interactions.[98,134,138] These proteases can also cleave CXCR4, leading to an impaired response to SDF-1.[139]

Matrix metalloproteinases (MMPs) are zinc-dependent endopeptidases that can degrade the components of the ECM and vascular basement membranes. They are produced by various connective tissue, epithelial, endothelial, and hematopoietic cells.[140] The MMPs participate in many physiologic processes and in tumor invasion and metastasis.[141–143] Investigations of this important class of proteases, required for HSC trafficking through the subendothelial basement membrane, were stimulated by the observation that anti-MMP-9 antibodies significantly reduced mobilization in mice.[144,145] MMP-9 is stored in granules of neutrophils and immediately released on stimulation with tumor necrosis factor alpha (TNF-α) or IL-8.[146,147] The action of MMP-9 is balanced by complex interactions with natural tissue inhibitors of metalloproteinases (TIMPs) thus regulating ECM turnover. The TIMPs bind to the catalytic sites of the activated form of secreted MMP-9.[148]

IL-8-induced HSC mobilization is achieved in MMP-9$^{-/-}$ mice. Therefore, MMP-9 is not an indispensable protease for mobilization.[61] In BM, MMP-9 and TIMP are involved in SDF-1–induced chemotaxis of stem and progenitor cells and their subsequent migration across the vascular basement membranes.[148] Several reviews deal with the growing evidence for the regulatory role of cytokines, chemokines, and growth factors in the synthesis and secretion of MMPs.[149] Circulating CD34$^+$ cells strongly express MMP-9 and MMP-2 in contrast to steady-state BM CD34$^+$ cells. A clear positive correlation between MMP-expression levels and CD34$^+$ cell migration was shown, with a 50% inhibition of migration in the presence of MMP-9 and MMP-2 antibodies.[150] In addition to degrading the basement membrane, MMP-9 is also involved in the interruption of cell–cell interactions in the marrow space, with a recent report showing release of SCF (c-kit ligand) from stromal cells.[117] Recently, the importance of proteases as potential key mediators of hematompoietic stem and progenitor cell mobilization was questioned by studies in mice deficient in MMP-9, neutrophil elastase and cathepsin G or dipeptidyl peptidase since G-CSF–induced mobilization was normal in these enzyme deficient mice.[151]

Novel Applications of Bone Marrow and Circulating Stem Cells

CIRCULATING BONE MARROW STEM CELLS COLONIZE DISTANT ORGANS

One of the more remarkable and controversial recent claims in stem cell biology relates to the possible ability of circulating BM-derived stem cells to home to nonhematopoietic organs and give rise to diverse lineages by transdifferentiation. The reader is referred to several excellent reviews on this topic.[152–155] For clinicians, interest in the concept of transdifferentiation derives largely from reports that show a Y chromosome in nonhematopoietic cells in female patients after transplantation of sex-mismatched allogeneic BM. Y-positive organs include skin,[156] brain,[157] heart,[158] gastrointestinal tract,[156,159] and liver.[160] Likewise, female donor organs in male recipients could be shown to have recipient-type nonhematopoietic cells in the liver[160] and heart.[161–163] These findings suggest that one or several populations of BM cells can enter the circulation and home to nonhematopoietic organs where they either undergo transdifferentiation or fuse with endogenous cells to generate diverse cell lineages. However, the donor-type cells were generally few and so scattered as to raise doubt regarding functional significance.

As with any novel finding, controversy arose regarding the proposed phenomenon of stem cell plasticity and transdifferentiation. Cell clones derived *in vitro* by cell–cell fusion of BM MNCs with ESCs expressed genomic DNA of both cell types.[164] It was concluded that the BM cells involved in fusion were monocytes and/or macrophages but not stem cells. Macrophages were also reported to fuse *in vivo* with genetically impaired hepatocytes.[165,166] Although there is a need to clarify the issue of cell fusion versus what was first described as transdifferentiation to correct a genetic disorder,[167] therapeutically either mechanism could be potentially harnessed and exploited using circulating BM cells.

CIRCULATING STEM CELLS TARGET EXPERIMENTALLY INJURED TISSUES

Occlusion of the left coronary artery (LCA) induces myocardial ischemia distal to the site of the ligature. Cardiomyocytes die and the affected area undergoes fibrosis as healing progresses. Evidence that BMSCs can circulate and home to the site of myocardial infarction and initiate regeneration derives from several experiments in mice. When mice were treated with rrSCF and rhG-CSF to mobilize BMSCs followed by LCA occlusion, the mobilized BMSCs were recruited to the site of infarction leading to myocardial regeneration and improved left ventricular function and survival.[168] In a similar study involving LCA occlusion in chimeric mice,[169] enhanced green fluorescent protein positive (eGFP$^+$) BM cells circulated to the site of infarction and generated eGFP$^+$ cardiomyocytes and endothelial cells in the zone of myocardial infarction. A recent study[170] supports these findings while others either fail to demonstrate regeneration[171,172] or propose cell–cell fusion as an alternate explanation for transdifferentiation.[173]

Additional evidence that BMSCs circulate and home to sites of injury and regenerate nonhematopoietic tissues was reported in several other murine studies that involved reconstituted chimeric BM. In one study, BM stem cells from male donors circulated to a number of nonhematopoietic organs and gave rise to Y-positive epithelial cells.[174] In a similar protocol, following argon laser beam destruction of focal retinal capillaries and induced ischemia, eGFP$^+$ stem cells circulated from the chimeric BM to the site of injury and initiated neovasculogenesis restoring blood flow.[175] In contrast to the previously described studies, others have shown that circulating GFP$^+$ stem cells from the transgenic mouse of a parabiotic pair repopulated the BM in the opposite member but did not infiltrate its other organs.[176] Failure to induce tissue damage in the nontransgenic parabiont or failure to mobilize large numbers of GFP$^+$ BMSCs may account for the lack of detectable stem cell transdifferentiation or cell fusion.

CIRCULATING STEM AND PROGENITOR CELLS IN CLINICAL TRIALS

Mobilized human stem and progenitor cells were harvested from the circulation by leukapheresis, enriched for CD34$^+$ cells, and labeled with Dil, a fluorescent marker. At 48 hours after ligation of the LCA in immune-incompetent adult rats, Dil-labeled human CD34$^+$ cells were infused via the tail vein.[177] The transplanted human CD34$^+$ cells engaged in neovasculogenesis at the site of the myocardial infarction. This laboratory demonstration that circulating human CD34$^+$ cells have the capacity to home to the site of an experimentally induced myocardial infarction and to regenerate blood vessels has led to several clinical investigations in heart patients.

A clinical trial is underway to test the hypothesis that autologous, circulating and BM-derived MNCs can improve left ventricular function in patients with acute ischemic myocardial disease.[178] The MNCs were infused into the infarct-related coronary artery using a balloon catheter and the patients were monitored for 3 months or more. The procedure appeared to be safe and feasible. There was no reported difference in myocardial response to circulating versus BM MNCs. Another trial involving the use of autologous peripheral blood or BM MNCs in wound healing was undertaken in patients with bilateral lower extremity ischemia-induced ulcers.[179] When BM-derived MNCs were injected into the gastrocnemius muscle of one leg in patients with bilateral ischemia, open ulcers were partially healed and there was significant neovasculogenesis while no improvement was observed in the opposite leg. Treatment with peripheral blood MNCs did not prove efficacious. The authors hypothesized this discrepancy was due to the 500-fold lower frequency of CD34$^+$ cells in the MNC fraction of peripheral blood compared with BM. These initial clinical trials establish a rationale for future use of granulocyte-macrophage colony-stimulating factor (GM-CSF), G-CSF, and/or SCF therapy to mobilize primitive BM cells for therapeutic purposes.

Requirements for Improved Stem Cell Mobilization

Although there are a number of reagents that can mobilize HSCs and progenitor cells, it is not clear which drugs, cytokines, or cytokine combinations are most effective. The commonly used cytokines GM-CSF, G-CSF, and SCF are individually able to mobilize BM stem and progenitor cells and can act in a synergistic manner. Several aspects of HSCs and progenitor cell mobilization have become the focus of intense clinical interest, especially as related to understanding and overcoming barriers to adequate HSC collection from so-called poor mobilizers, patients and donors who despite lack of prior marrow-toxic therapy mobilize suboptimally in response to G-CSF treatment. These include genetic factors affecting mobilization and novel mobilization agents such as the specific CXCR4 antagonist AMD3100, the specific CXCR2 antagonist SB-251353, and other agents that could bypass any barriers to mobilization in these individuals.

In murine models, the search for a genetic locus linked to poor mobilization has been hindered by the fact that strains with a mobilization defect also appear to have reduced numbers of HSCs in the marrow. It is unclear if this is a cause or an effect of a mobilization or homing defect. These animals and human poor mobilizers have normal blood counts and no clear propensity to leukemia. In mice, mobilization seems to be controlled at least in part by loci on chromosomes 2 and 11.[180] Interestingly, seven different quantitative trait loci that affect longevity and the quantity of HSCs were linked on mouse chromosomes 2, 4, 7, and 11.[181,182]

In an effort to better understand the crucial interaction of CXCR4 with its ligand SDF-1 in mobilization, 63 patients were analyzed for the correlation between SDF-1 gene polymorphisms and mobilization capacity.[183] It was determined that the presence of the SDF-1 3′-A allele was predictive for a high level of circulating CD34$^+$ cells, although the SDF-1 genotype was not absolutely predictive for moderate or poor mobilization. Therefore, other yet unknown genetic factors may be involved in mobilization capacity such as certain human leukocyte antigen (HLA) genotypes. Thus, genetic determinants affecting marrow stem cell numbers may preclude increasing HSC mobilization in human poor mobilizers.[184]

Several new agents have been developed for HSC mobilization, based on available knowledge of the involved receptor interactions. AMD3100 is a small molecule initially developed as a highly potent and selective inhibitor of human immunodeficiency virus (HIV)-1 and HIV-2 replication.[185,186] Later, the binding-specificity of AMD3100 to CXCR4 was documented.[187] In a phase I study, AMD3100-induced leukocytosis was noted as a side effect with WBC counts 1.5- to 3.1-fold above baseline in healthy volunteers, well below the counts seen with G-CSF treatment.[188] Preliminary results in a human phase I–II trial show a rapid five-fold increase in circulating CD34$^+$ cells and an 18-fold increase in colony forming unit–granulocyte-macrophage (CFU-GM) in volunteers after a single injection of AMD 3100.[189] Thus far perioral paresthesia, nausea, and vomiting are the only side effects reported.[188] Meanwhile, it has been shown in a clinical phase I trial that AMD3100 led to sufficient HSC mobilization in multiple myeloma and non-Hodgkin's lymphoma patients 4 and 6 hours after injection.[190]

SB-251353 is a truncated form of the human chemokine GROB that binds specifically to the CXCR2 receptor.[191] In mice and rhesus monkey models it has been demonstrated that a single injection of SB-251353 alone or in combination with G-CSF can mobilize primitive hematopoietic cells with long-term repopulating ability within 15 minutes. Furthermore, cells positive for CD34, a surrogate marker for HSCs and progenitor cells, increased in the circulation after combined treatment with G-CSF and SB-251353 compared with G-CSF alone. Although the mechanism is unclear, SB-251353 apparently synergizes with G-CSF to increase the yield of CD34$^+$ cells. Preliminary data in a mouse model suggest a role for MMP-9 in SB-251353-induced mobilization.[192] There are also many other new agents under development.

It is clear there is need for improved methods for mobilization of stem and progenitor cells. This may require discovery of novel factors responsible for the amplification and release of stem and progenitor cells from their BM niches into the circulation where they can be harvested by apheresis. Realization of this goal will greatly enhance our ability to use mobilized stem and progenitor cells for gene and cell therapy.

REFERENCES

1. Choi, K., Kennedy, M., Kazarov, A., Papadimitriou, J.C., and Keller, G. (1998). A common precursor for hematopoietic and endothelial cells. *Development* **125,** 725–732.
2. Yoder, M.C., and Hiatt, K. (1997). Engraftment of embryonic hematopoietic cells in conditioned newborn recipients. *Blood* **89,** 2176–2183.
3. Yoder, M.C., Hiatt, K., Dutt, P., Mukherjee, P., Bodine, D.M., and Orlic, D. (1997). Characterization of definitive lymphohematopoietic stem cells in the day 9 murine yolk sac. *Immunity* **7,** 335–344.
4. de Bruijn, M.F., Speck, N.A., Peeters, M.C., and Dzierzak, E. (2000). Definitive hematopoietic stem cells first develop within the major arterial regions of the mouse embryo. *EMBO J.* **19,** 2465–2474.
5. Medvinsky, A., and Dzierzak, E. (1996). Definitive hematopoiesis is autonomously initiated by the AGM region. *Cell* **86,** 897–906.
6. Luckett, W.P. (1978). Origin and differentiation of the yolk sac and extraembryonic mesoderm in presomite human and rhesus monkey embryos. *Am. J. Anat.* **152,** 59–97.
7. Tavian, M., Coulombel, L., Luton, D., Clemente, H.S., Dieterlen-Lievre, F., and Peault, B. (1996). Aorta-associated CD34+ hematopoietic cells in the early human embryo. *Blood* **87,** 67–72.
8. Civin, C.I., Strauss, L.C., Brovall, C., Fackler, M.J., Schwartz, J.F., and Shaper, J.H. (1984). Antigenic analysis of hematopoiesis: III. A hematopoietic progenitor cell surface antigen defined by a monoclonal antibody raised against KG-1a cells. *J. Immunol.* **133,** 157–165.
9. Ogawa, M., Matsuzaki, Y., Nishikawa, S., Hayashi, S., Kunisada, T., Sudo, T., Kina, T., and Nakauchi, H. (1991). Expression and function of c-kit in hemopoietic progenitor cells. *J. Exp. Med.* **174,** 63–71.
10. Orlic, D., Fischer, R., Nishikawa, S., Nienhuis, A.W., and Bodine, D.M. (1993). Purification and characterization of heterogeneous pluripotent hematopoietic stem cell populations expressing high levels of c-kit receptor. *Blood* **82,** 762–770.
11. Spangrude, G.J., Heimfeld, S., and Weissman, I.L. (1988). Purification and characterization of mouse hematopoietic stem cells. *Science* **241,** 58–62.
12. Kondo, M., Weissman, I.L., and Akashi, K. (1997). Identification of clonogenic common lymphoid progenitors in mouse bone marrow. *Cell* **91,** 661–672.
13. Akashi, K., Traver, D., Miyamoto, T., and Weissman, I.L. (2000). A clonogenic common myeloid progenitor that gives rise to all myeloid lineages. *Nature* **404,** 193–197.
14. Till, J.E.M., and McCulloch, E.A. (1961). A direct measurement of the radiation sensitivity of normal mouse bone marrow cells. *Radiat. Res.* **14,** 1419–1430.
15. Wu, A.M., Till, J.E., Siminovitch, L., and McCulloch, E.A. (1967). A cytological study of the capacity for differentiation of normal hemopoietic colony-forming cells. *J. Cell Physiol.* **69,** 177–184.
16. Lin, Y., Weisdorf, D.J., Solovey, A., and Hebbel, R.P. (2000). Origins of circulating endothelial cells and endothelial outgrowth from blood. *J. Clin. Invest.* **105,** 71–77.
17. Hill, J.M., Zalos, G., Halcox, J.P., Schenke, W.H., Waclawiw, M.A., Quyyumi, A.A., and Finkel, T. (2003). Circulating endothelial progenitor cells, vascular function, and cardiovascular risk. *N. Engl. J. Med.* **348,** 593–600.
18. Prockop, D.J. (1997). Marrow stromal cells as stem cells for non-hematopoietic tissues. *Science* **276,** 71–74.

19. Prockop, D.J. (2002). Adult stem cells gradually come of age. *Nat. Biotechnol.* **20,** 791–792.
20. Jiang, Y., Jahagirdar, B.N., Reinhardt, R.L., Schwartz, R.E., Keene, C.D., Ortiz-Gonzalez, X.R., Reyes, M., Lenvik, T., Lund, T., Blackstad, M., Du, J., Aldrich, S., Lisber, A., Low, W.C., Largaespada, D.A., and Verfaillie, C.M. (2002). Pluripotency of mesenchymal stem cells derived from adult marrow. *Nature* **418,** 41–49.
21. Owen, R.D. (1945). Immunogenetic consequences of vascular anastomoses between bovine twins. *Science* **102,** 400–401.
22. Jacobson, L.O., Marks, E.K., and Gaston, E. (1955). Observations on the effect of spleen shielding and the injection of cell suspensions on survival following irradiation. *In* "Radiobiology Symposium" (Z.M.A. Bacq, and Alexander P., ed), pp. 122–133, Academic Press, New York.
23. Tyler, R.W., and Everett, N.B. (1966). A radioautographic study of hemopoietic repopulation using irradiated parabiotic rats: relation to the stem cell problem. *Blood* **28,** 872–890.
24. Goodman, J.H., and Hodgson G.S., (1962). Evidence for stem cells in the peripheral blood of mice. *Blood* **19,** 702–714.
25. McCredie, K.B., Hersh, E.M., and Freireich, E.J. (1971). Cells capable of colony formation in the peripheral blood of man. *Science* **171,** 293–294.
26. Goldman, J.M., Catovsky, D., and Galton, D.A. (1978). Reversal of blast-cell crisis in C.G.I. by transfusion of stored autologous buffy-coat cells. *Lancet* **1,** 437–438.
27. Goldman, J.M., Catovsky, D., Goolden, A.W., Johnson, S.A., and Galton, D.A. (1981). Buffy coat autografts for patients with chronic granulocytic leukaemia in transformation. *Blut* **42,** 149–155.
28. Juttner, C.A., L.B., T., Haylock, D.N., Branford, A., and Kimber, R.J. (1985). Circulating autologous stem cells collected in very early remission from acute non-lymphoblastic leukaemia produce prompt but incomplete haemopoietic reconstitution after high dose melphalan or supralethal chemoradiotherapy. *Br. J. Haematol.* **61,** 739–745.
29. Kessinger, A., Armitage, J.O., Landmark, J.D., and Weisenburger, D.D. (1986). Reconstitution of human hematopoietic function with autologous cryopreserved circulating stem cells. *Exp. Hematol.* **14,** 192–196.
30. Korbling, M., Dorken, B., Ho, A.D., Pezzutto, A., Hunstein, W., and Fliedner, T.M. (1986). Autologous transplantation of blood-derived hemopoietic stem cells after myeloablative therapy in a patient with Burkitt's lymphoma. *Blood* **67,** 529–532.
31. Reiffers, J., Bernard, P., David, B., Vezon, G., Sarrat, A., Marit, G., Moulinier, J., and Broustet, A. (1986). Successful autologous transplantation with peripheral blood hemopoietic cells in a patient with acute leukemia. *Exp. Hematol.* **14,** 312–315.
32. Kessinger, A. (1995). Do autologous peripheral blood cell transplants provide more than hematopoietic recovery? *Stem Cells* **13,** 351–354.
33. Dunbar, C.E., Cottler-Fox, M., O'Shaughnessy, J.A., Doren, S., Carter, C., Berenson, R., Brown, S., Moen, R.C., Greenblatt, J., and Stewart, F.M. (1995). Retrovirally marked CD34-enriched peripheral blood and bone marrow cells contribute to long-term engraftment after autologous transplantation. *Blood* **85,** 3048–3057.
34. Kessinger, A., Smith, D.M., Strandjord, S.E., Landmark, J.D., Dooley, D.C., Law, P., Coccia, P.F., Warkentin, P.I., Weisenburger, D.D., and Armitage, J.O. (1989). Allogeneic transplantation of blood-derived, T cell-depleted hemopoietic stem cells after myeloablative treatment in a patient with acute lymphoblastic leukemia. *Bone Marrow Transplant* **4,** 643–646.
35. Bensinger, W.I., Martin, P.J., Storer, B., Clift, R., Forman, S.J., Negrin, R., Kashyap, A., Flowers, M.E., Lilleby, K., Chauncey, T.R., Storb, R., and Appelbaum, F.R. (2001). Transplantation of bone marrow as compared with peripheral-blood cells from HLA-identical relatives in patients with hematologic cancers. *N. Engl. J. Med.* **344,** 175–181.
36. To, L.B., Haylock, D.N., Simmons, P.J., and Juttner, C.A. (1997). The biology and clinical uses of blood stem cells. *Blood* **89,** 2233–2258.
37. Goldman, J.M., and Horowitz, M.M. (2002). The international bone marrow transplant registry. *Int. J. Hematol.* **76** (Suppl 1), 393–397.
38. Siena, S., Bregni, M., Brando, B., Ravagnani, F., Bonadonna, G., and Gianni, A.M. (1989). Circulation of CD34+ hematopoietic stem cells in the peripheral blood of high-dose cyclophosphamide-treated patients: enhancement by intravenous recombinant human granulocyte-macrophage colony-stimulating factor. *Blood* **74,** 1905–1914.
39. Craddock, C.F., Apperley, J.F., Wright, E.G., Healy, L.E., Bennett, C.A., Evans, M., Grimsley, P.G., and Gordon, M.Y. (1992). Circulating stem cells in mice treated with cyclophosphamide. *Blood* **80,** 264–269.
40. Neben, S., Marcus, K., and Mauch, P. (1993.) Mobilization of hematopoietic stem and progenitor cell subpopulations from the marrow to the blood of mice following cyclophosphamide and/or granulocyte colony-stimulating factor. *Blood* **81,** 1960–1967.
41. Morrison, S.J., Wright, D.E., and Weissman, I.L. (1997). Cyclophosphamide/granulocyte colony-stimulating factor induces hematopoietic stem cells to proliferate prior to mobilization. *Proc. Natl. Acad. Sci. U. S. A.* **94,** 1908–1913.
42. Bodine, D.M., Seidel, N.E., Gale, M.S., Nienhuis, A.W., and Orlic, D. (1994). Efficient retrovirus transduction of mouse pluripotent hematopoietic stem cells mobilized into the peripheral blood by treatment with granulocyte colony-stimulating factor and stem cell factor. *Blood* **84,** 1482–1491.
43. Wright, D.E., Wagers, A.J., Gulati, A.P., Johnson, F.L., and Weissman, I.L. (2001). Physiological migration of hematopoietic stem and progenitor cells. *Science* **294,** 1933–1936.
44. Abkowitz, J.L., Robinson, A.E., Kale, S., Long, M.W., and Chen, J. (2003). The mobilization of hematopoietic stem cells during homeostasis and after cytokine exposure. *Blood.* **102,** 867–872.
45. Issarachai, S., Priestley, G.V., Nakamoto, B., and Papayannopoulou, T. (2002). Cells with hemopoietic potential residing in muscle are itinerant bone marrow-derived cells. *Exp. Hematol.* **30,** 366–373.
46. Kawada, H., and Ogawa, M. (2001). Bone marrow origin of hematopoietic progenitors and stem cells in murine muscle. *Blood* **98,** 2008–2013.
47. McKinney-Freeman, S.L., Jackson, K.A., Camargo, F.D., Ferrari, G., Mavilio, F., and Goodell, M.A. (2002). Muscle-derived hematopoietic stem cells are hematopoietic in origin. *Proc. Natl. Acad. Sci. U. S. A.* **99,** 1341–1346.
48. Bodine, D.M., Seidel, N.E., Zsebo, K.M., and Orlic, D. (1993). In vivo administration of stem cell factor to mice increases the absolute number of pluripotent hematopoietic stem cells. *Blood* **82,** 445–455.
49. Andrews, R.G., Briddell, R.A., Knitter, G.H., Opie, T., Bronsden, M., Myerson, D., Appelbaum, F.R., and McNiece, I.K. (1994). In vivo synergy between recombinant human stem cell factor and recombinant human granulocyte colony-stimulating factor in baboons enhanced circulation of progenitor cells. *Blood* **84,** 800–810.

50. Andrews, R.G., Briddell, R.A., Knitter, G.H., Rowley, S.D., Appelbaum, F.R., and McNiece, I.K. (1995). Rapid engraftment by peripheral blood progenitor cells mobilized by recombinant human stem cell factor and recombinant human granulocyte colony-stimulating factor in nonhuman primates. *Blood* **85,** 15–20.
51. Orlic, D., Girard, L.J., Jordan, C.T., Anderson, S.M., Cline, A.P., and Bodine, D.M. (1996). The level of mRNA encoding the amphotropic retrovirus receptor in mouse and human hematopoietic stem cells is low and correlates with the efficiency of retrovirus transduction. *Proc. Natl. Acad. Sci. U. S. A.* **93,** 11097–11102.
52. Mulligan R.C. (1993). The basic science of gene therapy. *Science* **260**, 926–932.
53. Horwitz, M.E., Malech, H.L., Anderson, S.M., Girard, L.J., Bodine, D.M., and Orlic, D. (1999). Granulocyte colony-stimulating factor mobilized peripheral blood stem cells enter into G1 of the cell cycle and express higher levels of amphotropic retrovirus receptor mRNA. *Exp. Hematol.* **27,** 1160–1167.
54. Kim, H.J., Tisdale, J.F., Wu, T., Takatoku, M., Sellers, S.E., Zickler, P., Metzger, M.E., Agricola, B.A., Malley, J.D., Kato, I., Donahue, R.E., Brown, K.E., and Dunbar, C.E. (2000). Many multipotential gene-marked progenitor or stem cell clones contribute to hematopoiesis in nonhuman primates. *Blood* **96,** 1–8.
55. Wu, T., Kim, H.J., Sellers, S.E., Meade, K.E., Agricola, B.A., Metzger, M.E., Kato, I., Donahue, R.E., Dunbar, C.E., and Tisdale, J.F. (2000). Prolonged high-level detection of retrovirally marked hematopoietic cells in nonhuman primates after transduction of CD34+ progenitors using clinically feasible methods. *Mol. Ther.* **1,** 285–293.
56. Hematti, P., Sellers, S.E., Agricola, B.A., Metzger, M.E., Donahue, R.E., and Dunbar, C.E. (2003). Retroviral transduction efficiency of G-CSF+SCF-mobilized peripheral blood CD34+ cells is superior to G-CSF or G-CSF+Flt3-L-mobilized cells in nonhuman primates. *Blood* **101,** 2199–2205.
57. Laterveer, L., Lindley, I.J., Hamilton, M.S., Willemze, R., and Fibbe, W.E. (1995). Interleukin-8 induces rapid mobilization of hematopoietic stem cells with radioprotective capacity and long-term myelolymphoid repopulating ability. *Blood* **85,** 2269–2275.
58. Laterveer, L., Lindley, I.J., Heemskerk, D.P., Camps, J.A., Pauwels, E.K., Willemze, R., and Fibbe, W.E. (1996). Rapid mobilization of hematopoietic progenitor cells in rhesus monkeys by a single intravenous injection of interleukin-8. *Blood* **87,** 781–788.
59. Corre, I., Pineau, D., and Hermouet, S. (1999). Interleukin-8: an autocrine/paracrine growth factor for human hematopoietic progenitors acting in synergy with colony stimulating factor-1 to promote monocyte-macrophage growth and differentiation. *Exp. Hematol.* **27,** 28–36.
60. Vetillard, J., Drouet, M., Neildez-Nguyen, T.M., Mestries, J.C., Mathieu, J., Thierry, D., and Herodin, F. (1999). Interleukine-8 acts as a strong peripheral blood granulocyte-recruiting agent rather than as a hematopoietic progenitor cell-mobilizing factor. *J. Hematother. Stem Cell Res.* **8,** 365–379.
61. Pruijt, J.F., Verzaal, P., van Os, R., de Kruijf, E.J., van Schie, M.L., Mantovani, A., Vecchi, A., Lindley, I.J., Willemze, R., Starckx, S., Opdenakker, G., and Fibbe, W.E. (2002). Neutrophils are indispensable for hematopoietic stem cell mobilization induced by interleukin-8 in mice. *Proc. Natl. Acad. Sci. U. S. A.* **99,** 6228–6233.
62. Gong, J.K., (1978). Endosteal marrow: a rich source of hematopoietic stem cells. *Science* **199,** 1443–1445.
63. Yoder, M.C., and Williams, D.A. (1995). Matrix molecule interactions with hematopoietic stem cells. *Exp. Hematol.* **23,** 961–967.
64. Verfaillie, C.M. (1998). Adhesion receptors as regulators of the hematopoietic process. *Blood* **92,** 2609–2612.
65. Butcher, E.C., and Picker, L.J. (1996). Lymphocyte homing and homeostasis. *Science* **272,** 60–66.
66. Springer, T.A. (1994). Traffic signals for lymphocyte recirculation and leukocyte emigration: the multistep paradigm. *Cell* **76,** 301–314.
67. Krause, D.S. (2002). Plasticity of marrow-derived stem cells. *Gene Ther.* **9,** 754–758.
68. Lemischka, I. (2002). A few thoughts about the plasticity of stem cells. *Exp. Hematol.* **30,** 848–852.
69. Tisdale, J.F., and Dunbar, C.E. (2002). Plasticity and hematopoiesis: Circe's transforming potion? *Curr. Opin. Hematol.* **9,** 268–273.
70. Velders, G.A., Van Os, R., Hagoort, H., Versaal, P., Guiot, H.F., Lindley, I.J., Willemze, R., Opdenakker, G., and Fibbe, W.E. (2004). Reduced stem cell mobilization in mice receiving antibiotic modulation of the intestinal flora: involvement of endotoxins as cofactors in mobilization. *Blood* **103,** 340–346.
71. Campbell, F.R. (1972). Ultrastructural studies of transmural migration of blood cells in the bone marrow of rats, mice and guinea pigs. *Am. J. Anat.* **135,** 521–535.
72. Weiss, L. (1970). Transmural cellular passage in vascular sinuses of rat bone marrow. *Blood* **36,** 189–208.
73. Ma, Q., Jones, D., and Springer, T.A. (1999). The chemokine receptor CXCR4 is required for the retention of B lineage and granulocytic precursors within the bone marrow microenvironment. *Immunity* **10,** 463–471.
74. Mohle, R., Moore, M.A., Nachman, R.L., and Rafii, S. (1997). Transendothelial migration of CD34+ and mature hematopoietic cells: an in vitro study using a human bone marrow endothelial cell line. *Blood* **89,** 72–80.
75. van der Loo, J.C., Xiao, X., McMillin, D., Hashino, K., Kato, I., and Williams, D.A. (1998). VLA-5 is expressed by mouse and human long-term repopulating hematopoietic cells and mediates adhesion to extracellular matrix protein fibronectin. *J. Clin. Invest.* **102,** 1051–1061.
76. Nilsson, S.K., Johnston, H.M., and Coverdale, J.A. (2001). Spatial localization of transplanted hemopoietic stem cells: inferences for the localization of stem cell niches. *Blood* **97,** 2293–2299.
77. Edinger, M., Cao, Y.A., Verneris, M.R., Bachmann, M.H., Contag, C.H., and Negrin, R.S. (2003). Revealing lymphoma growth and the efficacy of immune cell therapies using in vivo bioluminescence imaging. *Blood* **101,** 640–648.
78. Hinds, K.A., Hill, J.M., Shapiro, E.M., Laukkanen, M.O., Silva, A.C., Combs, C.A., Varney, T.R., Balaban, R.S., Koretsky, A.P., and Dunbar, C.E. (2003). Highly efficient endosomal labeling of progenitor and stem cells with large magnetic particles allows magnetic resonance imaging of single cells. *Blood* **102,** 867–872.
79. Cashman, J.D., and Eaves, C.J. (2000). High marrow seeding efficiency of human lymphomyeloid repopulating cells in irradiated NOD/SCID mice. *Blood* **96,** 3979–3981.
80. van Hennik, P.B., de Koning, A.E., and Ploemacher, R.E. (1999). Seeding efficiency of primitive human hematopoietic cells in nonobese diabetic/severe combined immune deficiency mice: implications for stem cell frequency assessment. *Blood* **94,** 3055–3061.
81. Cui, J., Wahl, R.L., Shen, T., Fisher, S.J., Recker, E., Ginsburg, D., and Long, M.W. (1999). Bone marrow cell trafficking following intravenous administration. *Br. J. Haematol.* **107,** 895–902.
82. Jetmore, A., Plett, P.A., Tong, X., Wolber, F.M., Breese, R., Abonour, R., Orschell-Traycoff, C.M., and Srour, E.F. (2002). Homing efficiency, cell cycle kinetics, and survival of quiescent

and cycling human CD34(+) cells transplanted into conditioned NOD/SCID recipients. *Blood* **99,** 1585–1593.

83. Wang, J., Kimura, T., Asada, R., Harada, S., Yokota, S., Kawamoto, Y., Fujimura, Y., Tsuji, T., Ikehara, S., and Sonoda, Y. (2003a). SCID-repopulating cell activity of human cord blood-derived CD34- cells assured by intra-bone marrow injection. *Blood* **101,** 2924–2931.
84. Yahata, T., Ando, K., Sato, T., Miyatake, H., Nakamura, Y., Muguruma, Y., Kato, S., and Hotta, T. (2003). A highly sensitive strategy for SCID-repopulating cell assay by direct injection of primitive human hematopoietic cells into NOD/SCID mice bone marrow. *Blood* **101,** 2905–2913.
85. Simmons P.J., Masinovsky, B., Longenecker, B.M., Berenson, R., Torok-Storb, B., and Gallatin, W.M. (1992). Vascular cell adhesion molecule-1 expressed by bone marrow stromal cells mediates the binding of hematopoietic progenitor cells. *Blood* **80,** 388–395.
86. Hurley, R.W., McCarthy, J.B., and Verfaillie, C.M. (1995). Direct adhesion to bone marrow stroma via fibronectin receptors inhibits hematopoietic progenitor proliferation. *J. Clin. Invest.* **96,** 511–519.
87. Takatoku, M., Sellers, S., Agricola, B.A., Metzger, M.E., Kato, I., Donahue, R.E., and Dunbar, C.E. (2001). Avoidance of stimulation improves engraftment of cultured and retrovirally transduced hematopoietic cells in primates. *J. Clin. Invest.* **108,** 447–455.
88. Papayannopoulou, T., Craddock, C., Nakamoto, B., Priestley, G.V., and Wolf, N.S. (1995). The VLA4/VCAM-1 adhesion pathway defines contrasting mechanisms of lodgement of transplanted murine hemopoietic progenitors between bone marrow and spleen. *Proc. Natl. Acad. Sci. U. S. A.* **92,** 9647–9651.
89. Papayannopoulou, T., and Nakamoto, B. (1993). Peripheralization of hemopoietic progenitors in primates treated with anti-VLA4 integrin. *Proc. Natl. Acad. Sci. U. S. A.* **90,** 9374–9378.
90. Vermeulen, M., Le Pesteur, F., Gagnerault, M.C., Mary, J.Y., Sainteny, F., and Lepault, F. (1998). Role of adhesion molecules in the homing and mobilization of murine hematopoietic stem and progenitor cells. *Blood* **92,** 894–900.
91. Papayannopoulou, T., Priestley, G.V., and Nakamoto, B. (1998). Anti-VLA4/VCAM-1-induced mobilization requires cooperative signaling through the kit/mkit ligand pathway. *Blood* **91,** 2231–2239.
92. Papayannopoulou, T., Priestley, G.V., Nakamoto, B., Zafiropoulos, V., Scott, L.M., and Harlan, J.M. (2001). Synergistic mobilization of hemopoietic progenitor cells using concurrent beta1 and beta2 integrin blockade or beta2-deficient mice. *Blood* **97,** 1282–1288.
93. Bellucci, R., De Propris, M.S., Buccisano, F., Lisci, A., Leone, G., Tabilio, A., and de Fabritiis, P. (1999). Modulation of VLA-4 and L-selectin expression on normal CD34+ cells during mobilization with G-CSF. *Bone Marrow Transplant* **23,** 1–8.
94. Dercksen, M.W., Gerritsen, W.R., Rodenhuis, S., Dirkson, M.K., Slaper-Cortenbach, I.C., Schaasberg, W.P., Pinedo, H.M., von dem Borne, A.E., and van der Schoot, C.E. (1995). Expression of adhesion molecules on CD34+ cells: CD34+ L-selectin+ cells predict a rapid platelet recovery after peripheral blood stem cell transplantation. *Blood* **85,** 3313–3319.
95. Prosper, F., Stroncek, D., McCarthy, J.B., and Verfaillie, C.M. (1998). Mobilization and homing of peripheral blood progenitors is related to reversible downregulation of alpha4 beta1 integrin expression and function. *J. Clin. Invest.* **101,** 2456–2467.
96. Watanabe, T., Dave, B., Heimann, D.G., Lethaby, E., Kessinger, A., and Talmadge, J.E. (1997). GM-CSF-mobilized peripheral blood CD34+ cells differ from steady-state bone marrow CD34+ cells in adhesion molecule expression. *Bone Marrow Transplant* **19,** 1175–1181.
97. Gazitt, Y., and Liu, Q. (2001). Plasma levels of SDF-1 and expression of SDF-1 receptor on CD34+ cells in mobilized peripheral blood of non-Hodgkin's lymphoma patients. *Stem Cells* **19,** 37–45.
98. Levesque, J.P., Takamatsu, Y., Nilsson, S.K., Haylock, D.N., and Simmons, P.J. (2001). Vascular cell adhesion molecule-1 (CD106) is cleaved by neutrophil proteases in the bone marrow following hematopoietic progenitor cell mobilization by granulocyte colony-stimulating factor. *Blood* **98,** 1289–1297.
99. Williams, D.A., Rios, M., Stephens, C., and Patel, V.P. (1991). Fibronectin and VLA-4 in haematopoietic stem cell-microenvironment interactions. *Nature* **352,** 438–441.
100. Hirsch, E., Iglesias, A., Potocnik, A.J., Hartmann, U., and Fassler, R. (1996). Impaired migration but not differentiation of haematopoietic stem cells in the absence of beta1 integrins. *Nature* **380,** 171–175.
101. Potocnik, A.J., Brakebusch, C., and Fassler, R. (2000). Fetal and adult hematopoietic stem cells require beta1 integrin function for colonizing fetal liver, spleen, and bone marrow. *Immunity* **12,** 653–663.
102. Lapidot, T., and Kollet, O. (2002). The essential roles of the chemokine SDF-1 and its receptor CXCR4 in human stem cell homing and repopulation of transplanted immune-deficient NOD/SCID and NOD/SCID/B2m(null) mice. *Leukemia* **16,** 1992–2003.
103. Plett, P.A., Frankovitz, S.M., Wolber, F.M., Abonour, R., and Orschell-Traycoff, C.M. (2002). Treatment of circulating CD34(+) cells with SDF-1alpha or anti-CXCR4 antibody enhances migration and NOD/SCID repopulating potential. *Exp. Hematol.* **30,** 1061–1069.
104. Szilvassy, S.J., Meyerrose, T.E., Ragland, P.L., and Grimes, B. (2001). Differential homing and engraftment properties of hematopoietic progenitor cells from murine bone marrow, mobilized peripheral blood, and fetal liver. *Blood* **98,** 2108–2115.
105. Spencer, A., Jackson, J., and Baulch-Brown, C. (2001). Enumeration of bone marrow 'homing' haemopoietic stem cells from G-CSF-mobilised normal donors and influence on engraftment following allogeneic transplantation. *Bone Marrow Transplant* **28,** 1019–1022.
106. Pilarski, L.M., Pruski, E., Wizniak, J., Paine, D., Seeberger, K., Mant, M.J., Brown, C.B., and Belch, A.R. (1999). Potential role for hyaluronan and the hyaluronan receptor RHAMM in mobilization and trafficking of hematopoietic progenitor cells. *Blood* **93,** 2918–2927.
107. Dimitroff, C.J., Lee, J.Y., Rafii, S., Fuhlbrigge, R.C., and Sackstein, R. (2001). CD44 is a major E-selectin ligand on human hematopoietic progenitor cells. *J. Cell Biol.* **153,** 1277–1286.
108. Schmits, R., Filmus, J., Gerwin, N., Senaldi, G., Kiefer, F., Kundig, T., Wakeham, A., Shahinian, A., Catzavelos, C., Rak, J., Furlonger, C., Zakarian, A., Simard, J.J., Ohashi, P.S., Paige, C.J., Gutierrez-Ramos, J.C., and Mak, T.W. (1997). CD44 regulates hematopoietic progenitor distribution, granuloma formation, and tumorigenicity. *Blood* **90,** 2217–2233.
109. Frenette, P.S., Mayadas, T.N., Rayburn, H., Hynes, R.O., and Wagner, D.D. (1996). Susceptibility to infection and altered hematopoiesis in mice deficient in both P- and E-selectins. *Cell* **84,** 563–574.
110. Frenette, P.S., Subbarao, S., Mazo, I.B., von Andrian, U.H.,and Wagner, D.D. (1998). Endothelial selectins and vascular cell

adhesion molecule-1 promote hematopoietic progenitor homing to bone marrow. *Proc. Natl. Acad. Sci. U. S. A.* **95,** 14423–14428.

111. Frenette, P.S., and Weiss, L. (2000). Sulfated glycans induce rapid hematopoietic progenitor cell mobilization: evidence for selectin-dependent and independent mechanisms. *Blood* **96,** 2460–2468.
112. Sweeney, E.A., Priestley, G.V., Nakamoto, B., Collins, R.G., Beaudet, A.L., and Papayannopoulou, T. (2000). Mobilization of stem/progenitor cells by sulfated polysaccharides does not require selectin presence. *Proc. Natl. Acad. Sci. U. S. A.* **97,** 6544–6549.
113. Russell, E.S. (1979). Hereditary anemias of the mouse: a review for geneticists. *Adv. Genet.* **20,** 357–459.
114. Chabot, B., Stephenson, D.A., Chapman, V.M., Besmer, P., and Bernstein, A. (1988). The proto-oncogene c-kit encoding a transmembrane tyrosine kinase receptor maps to the mouse W locus. *Nature* **335,** 88–89.
115. Huang, E., Nocka, K., Beier, D.R., Chu, T.Y., Buck, J., Lahm, H.W., Wellner, D., Leder, P., and Besmer, P. (1990). The hematopoietic growth factor KL is encoded by the Sl locus and is the ligand of the c-kit receptor, the gene product of the W locus. *Cell* **63,** 225–233.
116. Brannan, C.I., Lyman, S.D., Williams, D.E., Eisenman, J., Anderson, D.M., Cosman, D., Bedell, M.A., Jenkins, N.A., and Copeland, N.G. (1991). Steel-Dickie mutation encodes a c-kit ligand lacking transmembrane and cytoplasmic domains. *Proc. Natl. Acad. Sci. U. S. A.* **88,** 4671–4674.
117. Heissig, B., Hattori, K., Dias, S., Friedrich, M., Ferris, B., Hackett, N.R., Crystal, R.G., Besmer, P., Lyden, D., Moore, M.A., Werb, Z., and Rafii, S. (2002). Recruitment of stem and progenitor cells from the bone marrow niche requires MMP-9 mediated release of kit-ligand. *Cell* **109,** 625–637.
118. Aiuti, A., Webb, I.J., Bleul, C., Springer, T., and Gutierrez-Ramos, J.C. (1997). The chemokine SDF-1 is a chemoattractant for human CD34+ hematopoietic progenitor cells and provides a new mechanism to explain the mobilization of CD34+ progenitors to peripheral blood. *J. Exp. Med.* **185,** 111–120.
119. Nagasawa, T., Kikutani, H., and Kishimoto, T. (1994.) Molecular cloning and structure of a pre-B-cell growth-stimulating factor. *Proc. Natl. Acad. Sci. U. S. A.* **91,** 2305–2309.
120. Tashiro, K., Tada, H., Heilker, R., Shirozu, M., Nakano, T., and Honjo, T. (1993). Signal sequence trap: A cloning strategy for secreted proteins and type I membrane proteins. *Science* **261,** 600–603.
121. Wright, D.E., Bowman, E.P., Wagers, A.J., Butcher, E.C., and Weissman, I.L. (2002). Hematopoietic stem cells are uniquely selective in their migratory response to chemokines. *J. Exp. Med.* **195,** 1145–1154.
122. Kim, C.H., and Broxmeyer, H.E. (1998). In vitro behavior of hematopoietic progenitor cells under the influence of chemoattractants: stromal cell-derived factor-1, steel factor, and the bone marrow environment. *Blood* **91,** 100–110.
123. Peled, A., Grabovsky, V., Habler, L., Sandbank, J., Arenzana-Seisdedos, F., Petit, I., Ben-Hur, H., Lapidot, T., and Alon, R. (1999a). The chemokine SDF-1 stimulates integrin-mediated arrest of CD34(+) cells on vascular endothelium under shear flow. *J. Clin. Invest.* **104,** 1199–1211.
124. Peled, A., Kollet, O., Ponomaryov, T., Petit, I., Franitza, S., Grabovsky, V., Slav, M.M., Nagler, A., Lider, O., Alon, R., Zipori, D., and Lapidot, T. (2000). The chemokine SDF-1 activates the integrins LFA-1, VLA-4, and VLA-5 on immature human CD34(+) cells: Role in transendothelial/stromal migration and engraftment of NOD/SCID mice. *Blood* **95,** 3289–3296.
125. Nagasawa, T., Hirota, S., Tachibana, K., Takakura, N., Nishikawa, S., Kitamura, Y., Yoshida, N., Kikutani, H., and Kishimoto, T. (1996). Defects of B-cell lymphopoiesis and bone-marrow myelopoiesis in mice lacking the CXC chemokine PBSF/SDF-1. *Nature* **382,** 635–638.
126. Mohle, R., Bautz, F., Rafii, S., Moore, M.A., Brugger, W., and Kanz, L. (1998). The chemokine receptor CXCR-4 is expressed on CD34+ hematopoietic progenitors and leukemic cells and mediates transendothelial migration induced by stromal cell-derived factor-1. *Blood* **91,** 4523–4530.
127. Kawabata, K., Ujikawa, M., Egawa, T., Kawamoto, H., Tachibana, K., Iizasa, H., Katsura, Y., Kishimoto, T., and Nagasawa, T. (1999). A cell-autonomous requirement for CXCR4 in long-term lymphoid and myeloid reconstitution. *Proc. Natl. Acad. Sci. U. S. A.* **96,** 5663–5667.
128. Peled, A., Petit, I., Kollet, O., Magid, M., Ponomaryov, T., Byk, T., Nagler, A., Ben-Hur, H., Many, A., Shultz, L., Lider, O., Alon, R., Zipori, D., and Lapidot, T. (1999b). Dependence of human stem cell engraftment and repopulation of NOD/SCID mice on CXCR4. *Science* **283,** 845–848.
129. Kollet, O., Petit, I., Kahn, J., Samira, S., Dar, A., Peled, A., Deutsch, V., Gunetti, M., Piacibello, W., Nagler, A., and Lapidot, T. (2002). Human CD34(+)CXCR4(−) sorted cells harbor intracellular CXCR4, which can be functionally expressed and provide NOD/SCID repopulation. *Blood* **100,** 2778–2786.
130. Rosu-Myles, M., Gallacher, L., Murdoch, B., Hess, D.A., Keeney, M., Kelvin, D., Dale, L., Ferguson, S.S., Wu, D., Fellows, F., and Bhatia, M. (2000). The human hematopoietic stem cell compartment is heterogeneous for CXCR4 expression. *Proc. Natl. Acad. Sci. U. S. A.* **97,** 14626–14631.
131. Kollet, O., Spiegel, A., Dar, A., Samira, S., Chen, Y., Shafritz, D., Suriawinata, J., Thung, S., Seis-Dedos, F., Nagler, A., Revel, M., and Lapidot, T. (2001). Involvement of SDF-1/CXCR4 Interactions in the migration of immature human CD34+ cells into the liver of transplanted NOD/SCID mice. *Blood* **98,** 2297a.
132. Sawada, S., Gowrishankar, K., Kitamura, R., Suzuki, M., Suzuki, G., Tahara, S., and Koito, A. (1998). Disturbed CD4+ T cell homeostasis and in vitro HIV-1 susceptibility in transgenic mice expressing T cell line-tropic HIV-1 receptors. *J. Exp. Med.* **187,** 1439–1449.
133. Petit, I., Szyper-Kravitz, M., Nagler, A., Lahav, M., Peled, A., Habler, L., Ponomaryov, T., Taichman, R.S., Arenzana-Seisdedos, F., Fujii, N., Sandbank, J., Zipori, D., and Lapidot, T. (2002). G-CSF induces stem cell mobilization by decreasing bone marrow SDF-1 and up-regulating CXCR4. *Nat. Immunol.* **3,** 687–694.
134. Gazitt, Y., Shaughnessy, P., and Liu, Q. (2001). Expression of adhesion molecules on CD34(+) cells in peripheral blood of non-Hodgkin's lymphoma patients mobilized with different growth factors. *Stem Cells* **19,** 134–143.
135. Lapidot, T., and Petit, I. (2002). Current understanding of stem cell mobilization: the roles of chemokines, proteolytic enzymes, adhesion molecules, cytokines, and stromal cells. *Exp. Hematol.* **30,** 973–981.
136. Liu, F., Wu, H.Y., Wesselschmidt, R., Kornaga, T., and Link, D.C. (1996). Impaired production and increased apoptosis of neutrophils in granulocyte colony-stimulating factor receptor-deficient mice. *Immunity* **5,** 491–501.
137. Liu, F., Poursine-Laurent, J., and Link, D.C. (1997). The granulocyte colony-stimulating factor receptor is required for the mobilization of murine hematopoietic progenitors into peripheral blood by cyclophosphamide or interleukin-8 but not flt-3 ligand. *Blood* **90,** 2522–2528.

138. Levesque, J.P., Bendall, L.J., Hendy, J., Takamatsu, Y., and Simmons, P.J. (2002). Neutrophil enzymes degrade CXCR4 on CD34+ progenitors: Implications for progenitor cell mobilization. *Blood* **100,** 107a.
139. Levesque, J.P., Hendy, J., Takamatsu, Y., Simmons, P.J., and Bendall, L.J. (2003). Disruption of the CXCR4/CXCL12 chemotactic interaction during hematopoietic stem cell mobilization induced by GCSF or cyclophosphamide. *J. Clin. Invest.* **111,** 187–196.
140. Nagase, H., and Woessner, J.F., Jr. (1999). Matrix metalloproteinases. *J. Biol. Chem.* **274,** 21491–21494.
141. Chambers, A.F., and Matrisian, L.M. (1997). Changing views of the role of matrix metalloproteinases in metastasis. *J. Natl. Cancer Inst.* **89,** 1260–1270.
142. Stetler-Stevenson, W.G., Hewitt, R., and Corcoran, M. (1996). Matrix metalloproteinases and tumor invasion: from correlation and causality to the clinic. *Semin. Cancer Biol.* **7,** 147–154.
143. Stetler-Stevenson, W.G., and Yu, A.E. (2001). Proteases in invasion: matrix metalloproteinases. *Semin. Cancer Biol.* **11,** 143–152.
144. Fibbe, W.E., Pruijt, J.F., van Kooyk, Y., Figdor, C.G., Opdenakker, G., and Willemze, R. (2000). The role of metalloproteinases and adhesion molecules in interleukin-8-induced stem-cell mobilization. *Semin. Hematol.* **37,** 19–24.
145. Pruijt, J.F., Fibbe, W.E., Laterveer, L., Pieters, R.A., Lindley, I.J., Paemen, L., Masure, S., Willemze, R., and Opdenakker, G. (1999). Prevention of interleukin-8-induced mobilization of hematopoietic progenitor cells in rhesus monkeys by inhibitory antibodies against the metalloproteinase gelatinase B (MMP-9). *Proc. Natl. Acad. Sci. U. S. A.* **96,** 10863–10868.
146. Borregaard, N., and Cowland, J.B. (1997). Granules of the human neutrophilic polymorphonuclear leukocyte. *Blood* **89,** 3503–3521.
147. Masure, S., Proost, P., Van Damme, J., and Opdenakker, G. (1991). Purification and identification of 91-kDa neutrophil gelatinase. Release by the activating peptide interleukin-8. *Eur. J. Biochem.* **198,** 391–398.
148. Janowska-Wieczorek, A., Marquez, L.A., Dobrowsky, A., Ratajczak, M.Z., and Cabuhat, M.L. (2000). Differential MMP and TIMP production by human marrow f126.and peripheral blood CD34(+) cells in response to chemokines. *Exp. Hematol.* **28,** 1274–1285.
149. Ries, C., and Petrides, P.E. (1995). Cytokine regulation of matrix metalloproteinase activity and its regulatory dysfunction in disease. *Biol. Chem. Hoppe Seyler* **376,** 345–355.
150. Janowska-Wieczorek, A., Marquez, L.A., Nabholtz, J.M., Cabuhat, M.L., Montano, J., Chang, H., Rozmus, J., Russell, J.A., Edwards, D.R., and Turner, A.R. (1999). Growth factors and cytokines upregulate gelatinase expression in bone marrow CD34(+) cells and their transmigration through reconstituted basement membrane. *Blood* **93,** 3379–3390.
151. Levesque, J.P., Liu, F., Simmons, P.J., Betsuyaku, T., Senior, R., Pham, C., and Link, D.C. (2004). Characterization of hematopoietic progenitor mobilization in protease deficient mice. *Blood* March 9 Epub, (in press).
152. Anderson, D.J., Gage, F.H., and Weissman, I.L. (2001). Can stem cells cross lineage boundaries? *Nat. Med.* **7,** 393–395.
153. Blau, H.M., Brazelton, T.R., and Weimann, J.M. (2001). The evolving concept of a stem cell: Entity or function? *Cell* **105,** 829–841.
154. Graf, T., (2002). Differentiation plasticity of hematopoietic cells. *Blood* **99,** 3089–3101.
155. Wells, W.A. (2002). Is transdifferentiation in trouble? *J. Cell Biol.* **157,** 15–18.
156. Korbling, M., Katz, R.L., Khanna, A., Ruifrok, A.C., Rondon, G., Albitar, M., Champlin, R.E., and Estrov, Z. (2002). Hepatocytes and epithelial cells of donor origin in recipients of peripheral-blood stem cells. *N. Engl. J. Med.* **346,** 738–746.
157. Weimann, J.M., Charlton, C.A., Brazelton, T.R., Hackman, R.C., and Blau, H.M. (2003). Contribution of transplanted bone marrow cells to Purkinje neurons in human adult brains. *Proc. Natl. Acad. Sci. U. S. A.* **100,** 2088–2093.
158. Deb, A., Wang, S., Skelding, K.A., Miller, D., Simper, D., and Caplice, N.M. (2003). Bone marrow-derived cardiomyocytes are present in adult human heart: a study of gender-mismatched bone marrow transplantation patients. *Circulation* **107,** 1247–1249.
159. Okamoto, R., Yajima, T., Yamazaki, M., Kanai, T., Mukai, M., Okamoto, S., Ikeda, Y., Hibi, T., Inazawa, J., and Watanabe, M. (2002). Damaged epithelia regenerated by bone marrow-derived cells in the human gastrointestinal tract. *Nat. Med.* **8,** 1011–1017.
160. Theise, N.D., Nimmakayalu, M., Gardner, R., Illei, P.B., Morgan, G., Teperman, L., Henegariu, O., and Krause, D.S. (2000). Liver from bone marrow in humans. *Hepatology* **32,** 11–16.
161. Laflamme, M.A., Myerson, D., Saffitz, J.E., and Murry, C.E. (2002). Evidence for cardiomyocyte repopulation by extracardiac progenitors in transplanted human hearts. *Circ. Res.* **90,** 634–640.
162. Muller, P., Pfeiffer, P., Koglin, J., Schafers, H.J., Seeland, U., Janzen, I., Urbschat, S., and Bohm, M. (2002). Cardiomyocytes of noncardiac origin in myocardial biopsies of human transplanted hearts. *Circulation* **106,** 31–35.
163. Quaini, F., Urbanek, K., Beltrami, A.P., Finato, N., Beltrami, C.A., Nadal-Ginard, B., Kajstura, J., Leri, A., and Anversa, P. (2002). Chimerism of the transplanted heart. *N. Engl. J. Med.* **346,** 5–15.
164. Terada, N., Hamazaki, T., Oka, M., Hoki, M., Mastalerz, D.M., Nakano, Y., Meyer, E.M., Morel, L., Petersen, B.E., and Scott, E.W. (2002). Bone marrow cells adopt the phenotype of other cells by spontaneous cell fusion. *Nature* **416,** 542–545.
165. Vassilopoulos, G., Wang, P.R., and Russell, D.W. (2003). Transplanted bone marrow regenerates liver by cell fusion. *Nature* **422,** 901–904.
166. Wang, X., Willenbring, H., Akkari, Y., Torimaru, Y., Foster, M., Al-Dhalimy, M., Lagasse, E., Finegold, M., Olson, S., and Grompe, M. (2003). Cell fusion is the principal source of bone-marrow-derived hepatocytes. *Nature* **422,** 897–901.
167. Lagasse, E., Connors, H., Al-Dhalimy, M., Reitsma, M., Dohse, M., Osborne, L., Wang, X., Finegold, M., Weissman, I.L., and Grompe, M. (2000). Purified hematopoietic stem cells can differentiate into hepatocytes in vivo. *Nat. Med.* **6,** 1229–1234.
168. Orlic, D., Kajstura, J., Chimenti, S., Limana, F., Jakoniuk, I., Quaini, F., Nadal-Ginard, B., Bodine, D.M., Leri, A., and Anversa, P. (2001). Mobilized bone marrow cells repair the infarcted heart, improving function and survival. *Proc. Natl. Acad. Sci. U. S. A.* **98,** 10344–10349.
169. Jackson, K.A., Majka, S.M., Wang, H., Pocius, J., Hartley, C.J., Majesky, M.W., Entman, M.L., Michael, L.H., Hirschi, K.K., and Goodell, M.A. (2001). Regeneration of ischemic cardiac muscle and vascular endothelium by adult stem cells. *J. Clin. Invest.* **107,** 1395–1402.
170. Lanza, R., Moore, M.A., Wakayama, T., Perry, A.C., Shieh, J.H., Hendrikx, J., Leri, A., Chimenti, S., Monsen, A., Nurzynska, D., West, M.D., Kajstura, J., and Anversa, P. (2004). Regeneration of the infarcted heart with stem cells derived by nuclear transplantation. *Circ. Res.* **94,** 820–827.

171. Murry, C.E., Soonpaa, M.H., Reinecke, H., Nakajima, H., Nakajima, H.O., Rubart, M., Pasumarthi, K.B., Virag, J.I., Bartelmez, S.H., Poppa, V., Bradford, G., Dowell, J.D., Williams, D.A., and Field, L.J. (2004). Haematopoietic stem cells do not transdifferentiate into cardiac myocytes in myocardial infarcts. *Nature* **428,** 664–668.
172. Balsam, L.B., Wagers, A.J., Christensen, J.L., Kofidis, T., Weissman, I.L., and Robbins, R.C. (2004). Haematopoietic stem cells adopt mature haematopoietic fates in ischaemic myocardium. *Nature* **428,** 668–673.
173. Alvarez-Dolado, M., Pardal, R., Garcia-Verdugo, J.M., Fike, J.R., Lee, H.O., Pfeffer, K., Lois, C., Morrison, S.J., and Alvarez-Buylla, A. (2003). Fusion of bone-marrow-derived cells with Purkinje neurons, cardiomyocytes, and hepatocytes. *Nature* **425,** 968–973.
174. Krause, D.S., Theise, N.D., Collector, M.I., Henegariu, O., Hwang, S., Gardner, R., Neutzel, S., and Sharkis, S.J. (2001). Multi-organ, multi-lineage engraftment by a single bone marrow-derived stem cell. *Cell* **105,** 369–377.
175. Grant, M.B., May, W.S., Caballero, S., Brown, G.A., Guthrie, S.M., Mames, R.N., Byrne, B.J., Vaught, T., Spoerri, P.E., Peck, A.B., and Scott, E.W. (2002). Adult hematopoietic stem cells provide functional hemangioblast activity during retinal neovascularization. *Nat. Med.* **8,** 607–612.
176. Wagers, A.J., Sherwood, R.I., Christensen, J.L., and Weissman, I.L. (2002). Little evidence for developmental plasticity of adult hematopoietic stem cells. *Science* **297,** 2256–2259.
177. Kocher, A.A., Schuster, M.D., Szabolcs, M.J., Takuma, S., Burkhoff, D., Wang, J., Homma, S., Edwards, N.M., and Itescu, S. (2001). Neovascularization of ischemic myocardium by human bone-marrow-derived angioblasts prevents cardiomyocyte apoptosis, reduces remodeling and improves cardiac function. *Nat. Med.* **7,** 430–436.
178. Assmus, B., Schachinger, V., Teupe, C., Britten, M., Lehmann, R., Dobert, N., Grunwald, F., Aicher, A., Urbich, C., Martin, H., Hoelzer, D., Dimmeler, S., and Zeiher, A.M. (2002). Transplantation of progenitor cells and regeneration enhancement in acute myocardial infarction (TOPCARE-AMI). *Circulation* **106,** 3009–3017.
179. Tateishi-Yuyama, E., Matsubara, H., Murohara, T., Ikeda, U., Shintani, S., Masaki, H., Amano, K., Kishimoto, Y., Yoshimoto, K., Akashi, H., Shimada, K., Iwasaka, T., and Imaizumi, T. (2002). Therapeutic angiogenesis for patients with limb ischaemia by autologous transplantation of bone-marrow cells: a pilot study and a randomised controlled trial. *Lancet* **360,** 427–435.
180. Hasegawa, M., Baldwin, T.M., Metcalf, D., and Foote, S.J. (2000). Progenitor cell mobilization by granulocyte colony-stimulating factor controlled by loci on chromosomes 2 and 11. *Blood* **95,** 1872–1874.
181. de Haan, G., Bystrykh, L.V., Weersing, E., Dontje, B., Geiger, H., Ivanova, N., Lemischka, I.R., Vellenga, E., and Van Zant, G. (2002). A genetic and genomic analysis identifies a cluster of genes associated with hematopoietic cell turnover. *Blood* **100,** 2056–2062.
182. Geiger, H., True, J.M., de Haan, G., and Van Zant, G. (2001). Age- and stage-specific regulation patterns in the hematopoietic stem cell hierarchy. *Blood* **98,** 2966–2972.
183. Benboubker, L., Watier, H., Carion, A., Georget, M.T., Desbois, I., Colombat, P., Bardos, P., Binet, C., and Domenech, J. (2001). Association between the SDF1-3′A allele and high levels of CD34(+) progenitor cells mobilized into peripheral blood in humans. *Br. J. Haematol.* **113,** 247–250.
184. Geiger, H., and Van Zant, G. (2002). The aging of lympho-hematopoietic stem cells. *Nat. Immunol.* **3,** 329–333.
185. De Clercq, E., Yamamoto, N., Pauwels, R., Balzarini, J., Witvrouw, M., De Vreese, K., Debyser, Z., Rosenwirth, B., Peichl, P., Datema, R., Thornton, D., Skerlj, R., Gaul, F., Padmanabhan, S., Bridger, G., Henson, G., and Abrams, M. (1994). Highly potent and selective inhibition of human immunodeficiency virus by the bicyclam derivative JM3100. *Antimicrob. Agents Chemother.* **38,** 668–674.
186. De Vreese, K., Reymen, D., Griffin, P., Steinkasserer, A., Werner, G., Bridger, G.J., Este, J., James, W., Henson, G.W., Desmyter, J., Anne, J., and De Clercq, I. (1996). The bicyclams, a new class of potent human immunodeficiency virus inhibitors, block viral entry after binding. *Antiviral Res.* **29,** 209–219.
187. Hatse, S., Princen, K., Bridger, G., De Clercq, E., and Schols, D. (2002). Chemokine receptor inhibition by AMD3100 is strictly confined to CXCR4. *FEBS Lett.* **527,** 255–262.
188. Hendrix, C.W., Flexner, C., MacFarland, R.T., Giandomenico, C., Fuchs, E.J., Redpath, E., Bridger, G., and Henson, G.W. (2000). Pharmacokinetics and safety of AMD-3100, a novel antagonist of the CXCR-4 chemokine receptor, in human volunteers. *Antimicrob. Agents Chemother.* **44,** 1667–1673.
189. Liles, W.C., Broxmeyer, H.E., Rodger, E., Wood, B., Hubel, K., Cooper, S., Hangoc, G., Bridger, G.J., Henson, G.W., Calandra, G., and Dale, D.C. (2003). Mobilization of hematopoietic progenitor cells in healthy volunteers by AMD3100, a CXCR4 antagonist. *Blood* **102,** 2728–2730.
190. Devine, S.M., Flomenberg, N., Vesole, D.H., Liesvold, J., Weisdorf, D., Badel, K., Calandra, G., and DiPersio, J.F. (2004). Rapid mobilization of CD34+ cells following administration of the CXCR4 antagonist AMD3100 to patients with multiple myeloma and non-Hodgkin's lymphoma. *J. Clin. Oncol.* **22,** 95–102.
191. King, A.G., Horowitz, D., Dillon, S.B., Levin, R., Farese, A.M., MacVittie, T.J., and Pelus, L.M. (2001). Rapid mobilization of murine hematopoietic stem cells with enhanced engraftment properties and evaluation of hematopoietic progenitor cell mobilization in rhesus monkeys by a single injection of SB-251353, a specific truncated form of the human CXC chemokine GRObeta. *Blood* **97,** 1534–1542.
192. Pelus, L.M., Bian, H., King, A.G., and Fukuda, S. (2004). Neutrophil-derived MMP-9 mediates synergistic mobilization of hematopoietic stem and progenitor cells by the combination of G-CSF and the chemokines GROβ/CXCL2 and GROβT/CXCL2δ4. *Blood* **1**(103), 110–119.

54

Isolation and Characterization of Hematopoietic Stem Cells

Gerald J. Spangrude and William B. Slayton

Central to the development of methods for stem cell isolation is the availability of quantitative techniques for assessment of stem cell function. In this regard, any approach to identification and isolation of adult stem cells can be no better than the assay used to detect function. This is a critical issue with blood stem cells, because the robust nature of hematopoiesis requires massive expansion of very few stem cells to provide a continual source of replacements for mature cells that die every day. The degree of expansion that occurs from stem cell to progenitor cell to mature cell is vast enough to prevent absolute distinction between the most primitive stem cells and the differentiating progeny of these cells. Methods for hematopoietic stem cell (HSC) isolation described here include approaches that minimize co-isolation of non–stem cells, while also providing techniques to isolate populations of progenitor cells possessing remarkable proliferative potential in the absence of stem cell activity. Comparison of primitive HSCs with early progenitor cells provides interesting insights into the early stages of hematopoietic development.

Isolation of Hematopoietic Stem Cells from Mice

HISTORICAL PERSPECTIVE

Although transplantation experiments conducted in the 1950s established the ability of cells derived from bone marrow and spleen to reverse hematopoietic failure after radiation exposure,[1] HSCs were studied mainly on a morphologic basis before the 1960s. A major breakthrough came in 1961, when Till and McCulloch[2] published an article describing the spleen colony-forming assay. This marked the first attempt to describe and quantitate stem cell activity *in vivo*. Shortly after this, tissue culture systems were developed that allowed the assay of hematopoietic progenitor cells *in vitro*.[3,4] Both assays provided quantitative results because of their clonal nature, whereby single cells proliferate to form a colony of differentiating progeny. The mouse became the animal of choice for the early studies of HSCs, because of the ability to obtain bone marrow easily and inexpensively and to perform transplant studies in which the behavior of primitive cells could be studied *in vivo*. In addition, the development of inbred strains of mice had already allowed the definition of the role of the major histocompatibility complex in determining graft acceptance or rejection. This animal model, in combination with the ability of clonal assays to determine enrichment factors for the colony-forming cells, provided the basis for approaches to the characterization and isolation of HSCs.

Till and McCulloch demonstrated that the subset of cells able to form spleen colonies was heterogeneous. When spleen colonies were harvested from animals and transplanted into a second set of irradiated recipients, only a subset of colonies could give rise to secondary colonies.[5] This group of cells was also capable of reconstituting lethally irradiated animals. For approximately 20 years, the spleen colony-forming unit was equated with HSC activity. However, in the early 1980s it became clear that this assay measured the behavior of a number of cell types that were not by definition HSCs.[6] Conversely, populations of cells that fit the definition of HSCs but did not make colonies in the colony-forming unit–spleen (CFU-S) assay were also identified.[7] Prospective isolation of defined cell populations from the mixture of cell types found in normal bone marrow was required to resolve the differences between true HSCs and other types of blood progenitors.

Some of the earliest attempts to isolate stem and progenitor cell subsets from bone marrow involved separating cells based on size, density, and cell cycle characteristics. These experiments demonstrated that the cells that produced splenic colonies were largely separable from those that made colonies *in vitro*[8] and that many spleen colony-forming cells were sensitive to killing by cycle-active drugs, whereas HSCs were largely spared.[7] It soon became clear that the only definitive means by which HSCs could be distinguished from later stages of development was to evaluate the ability of a transplanted population of cells to maintain production of multiple types of blood cells over many months *in vivo*. Even by this assessment, false indications of stem cell function are possible. Because of the extensive proliferative potential of true stem cells, a single cell remaining within the bone marrow after radiation-induced ablation will proliferate and self-renew sufficiently to dominate long-term hematopoiesis. Although transplanted progenitor cells may provide sufficient

Handbook of Stem Cells
Volume 2

hematopoietic function to rescue animals from hematopoietic failure after radiation conditioning, it is necessary to use markers to distinguish blood cells derived from the donor graft from those of recipient origin to definitively demonstrate HSC function. Examples of such markers include chromosomal abnormalities induced by radiation[9]; retroviral insertion sites[10]; and allelic forms of enzymes,[11] intracellular molecules,[12] and cell-surface antigens.[13] Using these tools, it has been possible to demonstrate that progenitor cells can be radioprotective without providing the long-term chimerism that is characteristic of HSCs.[14,15] Furthermore, researchers using these tools have shown that a single transplanted or endogenous HSC is sufficient to maintain life-long hematopoiesis.[16,17]

The development of fluorescence-activated cell sorting (FACS) allowed isolation of distinct cell populations that were too similar in physical characteristics to be separated by size or density. Flow cytometry uses fluorescent tags to detect surface proteins that are differentially expressed at particular stages of development, allowing fine distinctions to be made among physically homogeneous populations of cells. Although a number of surface proteins are expressed by HSCs, there is no single marker that absolutely defines HSCs in any species. This makes a multiparameter approach, using positive and negative selection for expression of a variety of markers, a necessary component of any enrichment scheme.

METHODS FOR ENRICHMENT OF MOUSE HEMATOPOIETIC STEM CELLS

A method using a combination of negative selection for proteins not expressed by HSCs with positive selection for proteins that are expressed has proven to be extremely useful for definition and isolation of HSCs from both mouse[13] and human[18] tissue. In the first applications of this technology, both positive and negative selections were applied using FACS. In more recent years, both types of selection have been adapted to magnetic technology. This advance in the field makes crude methods of HSC enrichment accessible to investigators who lack access to sophisticated FACS instruments. However, isolation of true HSCs from primitive progenitor cells requires FACS technology because of the application of intracellular fluorescent probes that indicate cellular quiescence[15] or efflux pump activity.[19] In addition, although magnetic isolation usually maximizes yields at the expense of purity, FACS isolations provide high purity with acceptable yields. A combination of magnetic and FACS selection allows isolation of HSCs in a routine manner.

Magnetic Selection Techniques

Regardless of the specific technology used for HSC enrichments, the most critical parameter to be considered is the specific markers to be used in negative and positive selections. For negative selections, a conventional approach has evolved that uses panels of antibodies specific for proteins expressed by most bone marrow cells. Caution must be exercised to select antibodies that do not react with HSCs, because this would result in the loss of the HSCs during negative selection. It is particularly important to note that developmental stages and activation-specific responses can change the antigenic profile of HSCs. For example, the CD34 antigen fluctuates on and off in HSCs during development, as well as during a period of time following the administration of chemotherapy.[20] Other antigens are also known to fluctuate in a similar manner.[21,22] Therefore, negative selection protocols must be tailored to match the known phenotype of HSCs in the particular tissue of interest. If the investigator wishes to work with tissues for which the antigenic phenotype of HSCs has not been described, appropriate assays should be used to evaluate the HSC content of populations fractionated into positive and negative cells to identify antibodies that will be useful in depleting significant numbers of cells without affecting the recovery of HSCs. As discussed previously, the most appropriate assay for this analysis would be a long-term engraftment study rather than one of the more rapid techniques such as spleen colony formation or *in vitro* culture systems.

Magnetic selections can be accomplished by two general approaches. The first approach, which is best suited for negative selections, involves mixing a cell population marked by the antibodies of interest with a suspension of paramagnetic particles that bind to the antibody tag. Application of a magnetic field will then separate bead-cell aggregates from the unmarked cells, which can be collected by simple aspiration. This technique is rapid and has the advantage of not perturbing the cells of interest through association with antibody molecules or magnetic particles. Because of this, the magnetic particles of choice will be relatively large (1–5 μm) to facilitate the rapid migration of the labeled cells in the magnetic field.[23]

The second approach to magnetic selection is positive selection of the cells of choice. In this case, particles of a much smaller size (50 nm) are used to minimize potential effects of the antibody–particle complexes on the biology of the selected cells. The small size of the magnetic particles used in positive selection decreases the effectiveness of the magnetic field in attracting the labeled cells. To overcome this limitation, commercial positive selection systems use a flow column packed with a fibrous metal, into which the magnetic field is introduced by induction. This creates a high-flux magnetic field with very short distances between the labeled cells and the magnetized column matrix and results in the retention of labeled cells in the column. Once the unlabeled cells are passed through the column and washed out, the column is removed from the magnetic field and the selected cells can be collected.[24]

The combination of negative with positive magnetic selection is a powerful technique for crude enrichment of a mixture of hematopoietic stem and progenitor cells. These cells may be used directly in studies evaluating hematopoietic function *in vivo* or *in vitro* or may be further processed to achieve higher purity of functionally distinct subsets of HSCs or progenitor cells (see later discussion). A specific method, originally reported using negative and positive selection by FACS,[25] can be easily modified to substitute magnetic selections using the same combinations of antibodies as originally described (Table 54–1). Unconjugated rat antibodies are used in combination with magnetic beads conjugated to anti-rat immunoglobulin for negative selection, whereas avidin-biotin selection systems work very well for positive selection using biotinylated antibodies followed by avidin-conjugated microbeads. HSCs and progenitor cells can be enriched routinely by a factor of 1000 using this technique.

Fluorescence-activated Cell Sorting Selection

Although magnetic enrichment strategies are sufficient when mixed populations of cells are an adequate product, the more refined approaches to HSC and progenitor cell characterization require FACS selection. Modern commercial FACS instruments can separate populations of cells based on 15 parameters, allowing the simultaneous application of positive and negative selection for a variety of surface markers. High-speed sorting improves the yield of cells obtained from this approach, and purity is very high. Workers in the field often use a negative selection before FACS sorting, because a good negative selection reduces the cellularity of the sample and thus the time needed for sorting by a factor of 50 to 100 without adversely affecting the yield of HSCs. Samples subjected to positive magnetic selection can subsequently be processed to isolate specific cellular subsets by FACS. Pre-enrichment of target populations before FACS can have a significant impact on the final purity of the isolated cell populations.

Selection Based on Cell Surface Antigen Expression. Recent studies have described antigenic profiles of a variety of progenitor cell subsets in the mouse. Progenitors restricted to lymphoid,[26] myeloid,[27] and erythroid[28] lineages have been characterized for prospective isolation using FACS technology. In addition, the hierarchy of HSCs, which includes cell populations possessing more or less potential for self-renewal, has been fractionated based on surface antigen expression.[29]

Selection Based on Supravital Stains. The combination of multiple cell surface markers with supravital fluorescent dyes that indicate cell function has become a method of choice for isolating HSCs. Baines and Visser[30] first used the fluorescent DNA probe Hoescht-33342 to separate quiescent cells from the bone marrow. More recently, red and blue emissions from Hoescht-33342 have been used to define a small subset of bone marrow cells, called the side population, which comprise approximately 0.07% of the whole bone marrow, and are highly enriched for long-term reconstituting HSCs.[31] Recently, the molecular basis for the ability of Hoescht-33342 to identify HSCs has been suggested to be due to its role as a substrate for the multidrug resistance pump ABCG2.[19] Interestingly, expression of ABCG2 is a characteristic also observed in embryonic stem cells, suggesting that expression of this protein may represent a general marker of stem cells.

Bertoncello *et al.*[32] pioneered the use of a second supravital fluorescent probe, rhodamine-123 (Rh-123), to subset primitive stem cells. Although Rh-123 is most widely used as a substrate to evaluate multidrug resistance pump activity, a second characteristic of the probe is its affinity for the inner mitochondrial membrane. Hence, the intensity of Rh-123 staining reflects a balance between efflux by specific molecular pumps and accumulation in mitochondrial membranes. Because Rh-123 is a charge-sensitive probe for mitochondria, accumulation of the probe is directly proportional to cellular activation state and inversely proportional to cellular efflux activity. In combination, these two selective criteria achieve a remarkable segregation of stem and progenitor cells previously isolated by negative/positive selection based on antigen expression. Primitive HSCs, which express high levels of efflux pump activity and contain few activated mitochondria, accumulate very little Rh-123 during a 30-minute labeling period. In contrast, progenitor cells which have become activated by the differentiation process contain many activated mitochondria and have downregulated efflux activity.[33]

The combination of cell surface and metabolic markers provides a means to enrich HSCs to the point that fewer than 10 cells are required to reconstitute hematopoiesis in irradiated mice.[34,35] In addition, enrichments based on antigenic expression combined with Rh-123 allows simultaneous isolation of Rh-123^{low} HSCs and Rh-123^{high} primitive progenitor cells, allowing for direct comparisons of the functions[36] and molecular signatures[37] of these two closely related populations of cells.

TABLE 54–1
Antibody Specificities for Use in a Negative–Positive Magnetic Enrichment Protocol

Antigen	Antibody	Lineage
Negative selection		
CD11b	M1/70	Myeloid[a]
Ly6-G	RB6-8C5	Myeloid
CD45(B220 isoform)	RA3-6B2	Lymphoid
CD2	RM2.2	Lymphoid
CD3	KT3	Lymphoid
CD5	53-7.3	Lymphoid
CD8	53-6.7	Lymphoid
TER-119	TER-119	Erythroid
Positive selection		
Ly6A/E	E13 161-7	Various[b]

[a]CD11b is expressed by mouse fetal liver stem cells[22] and, thus, should not be included in negative selections from this tissue.

[b]Ly6A/E is expressed by lymphoid lineage cells and by hematopoietic stem and progenitor cells. Depletion of the lymphoid lineage cells during negative selection allows positive selection based on Ly6A/E to yield a highly enriched population of stem and progenitor cells.

Isolation of Hematopoietic Stem Cells from Humans

HISTORICAL PERSPECTIVE

In contrast to the mouse, in which HSC behavior can be defined in transplant experiments, defining and quantifying human HSCs has been difficult because transplantation experiments using limiting dilution or competitive repopulation approaches are impossible to perform in humans. *In vitro* colony-forming assays were once used routinely to estimate the number of HSCs in a bone marrow or peripheral blood stem cell harvest. However, with the recognition that these assays fail to distinguish different classes of primitive stem cells that have distinct functions on transplantation,[38] other assays were developed. Several *in vitro* assays, including the long-term culture-initiating cell assay[39] and the cobblestone area forming cell assay,[40] have been used to measure human stem cell number and behavior.

Researchers have addressed the inability to study HSC engraftment behavior in humans by developing xenogeneic transplant models. Several models that use immunodeficient mice as transplant recipients have been developed to measure engraftment and self-renewal of human HSCs *in vivo.* The nonobese diabetic/severe combined immunodeficiency (NOD/SCID) mouse model has emerged as a standard assay that allows engraftment of human cells in mouse bone marrow.[41] Ultimately, however, studies that depend on xenogeneic transplantation rely on inference, and stem cells may behave differently in systems that are more genetically compatible.

The first attempts to separate human HSCs from bone marrow mirrored earlier studies in mouse.[42] The recognition that primate hematopoietic progenitor cells expressed CD34[43] provided a way for scientists to study the HSC compartment in humans. Using techniques pioneered in the mouse, researchers used negative selection against lineage antigens and positive selection for CD34.[18,44] The $CD34^+$ subset was found to be heterogeneous, with most of the cells being progenitors for the erythroid, lymphoid, or myeloid lineages. Further enrichment of HSCs was obtained by positive selection for additional surface antigens in combination with metabolic markers.[45]

CD34 AS THE PRIMARY MARKER OF HUMAN HEMATOPOIETIC STEM CELLS

Recently, a controversy has evolved regarding the utility of CD34 as a general marker of HSCs in human tissue.[46] The controversy arose as a result of studies in the mouse, in which various groups published conflicting results regarding the isolation of mouse HSCs based on CD34 expression.[47–49] A large number of monoclonal antibodies have been developed to different epitopes on the human CD34 antigen. In contrast, the CD34 molecule in the mouse has been characterized only by one rabbit polyclonal antiserum that is monospecific and one monoclonal antibody directed against a CD34 epitope. These reagents provide contrasting results: the $CD34^+$ but not the $CD34^-$ cells in mouse bone marrow contained HSCs based on the polyclonal serum, whereas the mouse-specific monoclonal antibody RAM34 showed variable expression on HSCs defined by other markers. This issue was resolved in a series of experiments by Ogawa *et al.*, in which the expression of mouse CD34 was shown to be modulated from negative to positive depending on the proliferative state of the HSC population under analysis. Thus, although most HSCs found under normal steady-state conditions in adult mouse bone marrow lack CD34 expression, stimulation *in vivo* by 5-fluorouracil (5-FU) injection or *in vitro* by cytokine stimulation resulted in recovery of most HSC activity among $CD34^+$ cells.[20] The expression of CD34 was again lost as the cells engrafted in marrow and returned to steady-state conditions. Similar observations were reported in an analysis of mouse ontogeny. Further experiments showed that CD38, which is absent from human HSCs but present on mouse HSCs under steady-state conditions, also modulates during recovery from 5-FU or during mobilization induced by granulocyte colony-stimulating factor (G-CSF).[50] Thus, in the mouse the expression of CD34 and CD38 reflect the activation state of the HSCs. Interestingly, an analysis of the expression of human CD34 in a transgenic mouse model demonstrated that the human and mouse genes are differentially regulated, suggesting that the current practice of human bone marrow transplantation using only $CD34^+$ cells is justified despite the mouse data.[51] Because the initial data from the mouse model could be interpreted to indicate that human patients receiving $CD34^+$ transplants are missing an important subset of HSCs, it is important to learn that CD34 expression is a characteristic of most HSCs in humans.[52]

The question of lineage-marker fidelity between mouse and human is biologically interesting, because it might imply important functions for these molecules in the behavior of HSC subsets. The functions of these molecules in mice and humans must be identified so that the gene program that specifies HSCs and their functions can be better understood. Enriched populations of $CD34^+$ cells have been used clinically for transplantation in humans following chemotherapy. Enriching marrow progenitors and purging T cells has been used to prevent graft versus host disease in allogeneic transplantation[53] and as a means to enrich human HSCs for gene therapy applications.[54]

Hematopoietic Stem Cells as a Paradigm for Stem Cell Biology

Robust production of blood is essential for survival, because of the critical roles blood plays in oxygenation of tissues, control of vascular integrity, and distribution of cells responsible for immunity to infection. Furthermore, the large total number of blood cells coupled with relatively short cellular life span results in a need for ongoing replacement of senescent cells. The sustained daily rate of blood cell production reflects the potential of the stem cells that drive the process of hematopoiesis. These extreme demands of proliferation and differentiation, coupled with a long history of successful transplantation in humans, make the HSC a gold standard for all forms of stem cell therapy. The development of methods to enrich this class of stem cells serves as a robust paradigm by which other applications of stem cell therapy might be measured. It is entirely possible that organ systems such as the central nervous system, while harboring cells with stem cell-like characteristics, have not been subjected to evolutionary pressure favoring rapid replacement of dying cells. It will, therefore, be critical to understand more of the regulatory control over self-renewal, proliferation, and differentiation of HSCs to facilitate the application of stem cell therapies for tissues lacking the demands of blood production.

ACKNOWLEDGMENT

This work was supported by grants DK57899 (G.J.S.) and HL03962 (W.B.S.) from the National Institutes of Health.

REFERENCES

1. Ford, C.E., Hamerton, J.L., Barnes, D.W.H., and Loutit, J.F. (1956). Cytological identification of radiation-chimaeras. *Nature* **177,** 452–454.
2. Till, J.E., and McCulloch, E.A. (1961). A direct measurement of the radiation sensitivity of normal mouse bone marrow cells. *Radiat. Res.* **14,** 213–222.
3. Pluznik, D.H., and Sachs, L. (1965). The cloning of normal "mast" cells in tissue culture. *J. Cell Physiol.* **66,** 319–324.
4. Bradley, T.R., and Metcalf, D. (1966). The growth of mouse bone marrow cells in vitro. *Aust. J. Exp. Biol. Med. Sci.* **44,** 287–299.
5. Siminovitch, L., McCulloch, E.A., and Till, J.E. (1963). The distribution of colony-forming cells among spleen colonies. *J. Cell Comp. Physiol.* **62,** 327–336.
6. Magli, M.C., Iscove, N.N., and Odartchenko, N. (1982). Transient nature of early haematopoietic spleen colonies. *Nature* **295,** 527–529.
7. Hodgson, G.S., and Bradley, T.R. (1979). Properties of haematopoietic stem cells surviving 5-fluorouracil treatment: evidence for a pre-CFU-S cell? *Nature* **281,** 381–382.
8. Worton, R.G., McCulloch, E.A., and Till, J.E. (1969). Physical separation of hemopoietic stem cells from cells forming colonies in culture. *J. Cell Physiol.* **74,** 171–182.
9. Becker, A.J., McCulloch, E.A., and Till, J.E. (1963). Cytological demonstration of the clonal nature of spleen colonies derived from transplanted mouse marrow cells. *Nature* **197,** 452–454.
10. Keller, G., and Snodgrass, R. (1990). Life span of multipotential hematopoietic stem cells in vivo. *J. Exp. Med.* **171,** 1407–1418.
11. Watt, D.J., Lambert, K., Morgan, J.E., Partridge, T.A., and Sloper, J.C. (1982). Incorporation of donor muscle precursor cells into an area of muscle regeneration in the host mouse. *J. Neurol. Sci.* **57,** 319–331.
12. Russell, E.S., and McFarland, E.C. (1974). Genetics of mouse hemoglobins. *Ann. NY Acad. Sci.* **241,** 25–38.
13. Spangrude, G.J., Heimfeld, S., and Weissman, I.L. (1988). Purification and characterization of mouse hematopoietic stem cells. *Science* **241,** 58–62.
14. Jones, R.J., Celano, P., Sharkis, S.J., and Sensenbrenner, L.L. (1989). Two phases of engraftment established by serial bone marrow transplantation in mice. *Blood* **73,** 397–401.
15. Spangrude, G.J., and Johnson, G.R. (1990). Resting and activated subsets of mouse multipotent hematopoietic stem cells. *Proc. Natl. Acad. Sci. U. S. A.* **87,** 7433–7437.
16. Smith, L.G., Weissman, I.L., and Heimfeld, S. (1991). Clonal analysis of hematopoietic stem-cell differentiation in vivo. *Proc. Natl. Acad. Sci. U. S. A.* **88,** 2788–2792.
17. Benveniste, P., Cantin, C., Hyam, D., and Iscove, N.N. (2003). Hematopoietic stem cells engraft in mice with absolute efficiency. *Nat. Immunol.* **4,** 708–713.
18. Baum, C.M., Weissman, I.L., Tsukamoto, A.S., Buckle, A., and Peault, B. (1992). Isolation of a candidate human hematopoietic stem-cell population. *Proc. Natl. Acad. Sci. U. S. A.* **89,** 2804–2808.
19. Zhou, S., Schuetz, J.D., Bunting, K.D., Colapietro, A.M., Sampath, J., Morris, J.J., Lagutina, I., Grosveld, G.C., Osawa, M., Nakauchi, H., and Sorrentino, B.P. (2001). The ABC transporter Bcrp1/ABCG2 is expressed in a wide variety of stem cells and is a molecular determinant of the side-population phenotype. *Nat. Med.* **7,** 1028–1034.
20. Ogawa, M., Tajima, F., Ito, T., Sato, T., Laver, J.H., and Deguchi, T. (2001). CD34 expression by murine hematopoietic stem cells. Developmental changes and kinetic alterations. *Ann. NY Acad. Sci.* **938,** 139–145.
21. Randall, T.D., and Weissman, I.L. (1997). Phenotypic and functional changes induced at the clonal level in hematopoietic stem cells after 5-fluorouracil treatment. *Blood* **89,** 3596–3606.
22. Morrison, S.J., Hemmati, H.D., Wandycz, A.M., and Weissman, I.L. (1995). The purification and characterization of fetal liver hematopoietic stem cells. *Proc. Natl. Acad. Sci. U. S. A.* **92,** 10302–10306.
23. Dynal. (2003). Dynal Biotech Web site (http://www.dynal.no/).
24. Miltenyi. (2003). Miltenyi Biotech Web site (http://www.miltenyibiotec.com/index.php).
25. Spangrude, G.J., and Scollay, R. (1990). A simplified method for enrichment of mouse hematopoietic stem cells. *Exp. Hematol.* **18,** 920–926.
26. Kondo, M., Weissman, I.L., and Akashi, K. (1997). Identification of clonogenic common lymphoid progenitors in mouse bone marrow. *Cell* **91,** 661–672.
27. Akashi, K., Traver, D., Miyamoto, T., and Weissman, I.L. (2000). A clonogenic common myeloid progenitor that gives rise to all myeloid lineages. *Nature* **404,** 193–197.
28. Nicola, N.A., Metcalf, D., von Melchner, H., and Burgess, A.W. (1981). Isolation of murine fetal hemopoietic progenitor cells and selective fractionation of various erythroid precursors. *Blood* **58,** 376–386.
29. Morrison, S.J., Wandycz, A.M., Hemmati, H.D., Wright, D.E., and Weissman, I.L. (1997). Identification of a lineage of multipotent hematopoietic progenitors. *Development* **124,** 1929–1939.
30. Baines, P., and Visser, J.W.M. (1983). Analysis and separation of murine bone marrow stem cells by H33342 fluorescence-activated cell sorting. *Exp. Hematol.* **11,** 701–708.
31. Goodell, M.A., Brose, K., Paradis, G., Conner, A.S., and Mulligan, R.C. (1996). Isolation and functional properties of murine hematopoietic stem cells that are replicating in vivo. *J. Exp. Med.* **183,** 1797–1806.
32. Bertoncello, I., Hodgson, G.S., and Bradley, T.R. (1985). Multiparameter analysis of transplantable hemopoietic stem cells: I. The separation and enrichment of stem cells homing to marrow and spleen on the basis of rhodamine-123 fluorescence. *Exp. Hematol.* **13,** 999–1006.
33. Kim, M.J., Cooper, D.D., Hayes, S.F., and Spangrude, G.J. (1998). Rhodamine-123 staining in hematopoietic stem cells of young mice indicates mitochondrial activation rather than dye efflux. *Blood* **91,** 4106–4117.
34. Wolf, N.S., Kone, A., Priestley, G.V., and Bartelmez, S.H. (1993). In vivo and in vitro characterization of long-term repopulating primitive hematopoietic cells isolated by sequential Hoechst 33342-rhodamine 123 FACS selection. *Exp. Hematol.* **21,** 614–622.

35. Spangrude, G.J., Brooks, D.M., and Tumas, D.B. (1995). Long-term repopulation of irradiated mice with limiting numbers of purified hematopoietic stem cells: in vivo expansion of stem cell phenotype but not function. *Blood* **85,** 1006–1016.
36. Slayton, W.B., Georgelas, A., Pierce, L.J., Elenitoba-Johnson, K.S., Perry, S.S., Marx, M., and Spangrude, G.J. (2002). The spleen is a major site of megakaryopoiesis following transplantation of murine hematopoietic stem cells. *Blood* **100,** 3975–3982.
37. Phillips, R.L., Ernst, R.E., Brunk, B., Ivanova, N., Mahan, M.A., Deanehan, J.K., Moore, K.A., Overton, G.C., and Lemischka, I.R. (2000). The genetic program of hematopoietic stem cells. *Science* **288,** 1635–1640.
38. Li, C.L., and Johnson, G.R. (1992). Rhodamine123 reveals heterogeneity within murine Lin-, Sca-1+ hemopoietic stem cells. *J. Exp. Med.* **175,** 1443–1447.
39. Sutherland, H.J., Eaves, C.J., Eaves, A.C., Dragowska, W., and Lansdorp, P.M. (1989). Characterization and partial purification of human marrow cells capable of initiating long-term hematopoiesis in vitro. *Blood* **74,** 1563–1570.
40. Breems, D.A., Blokland, E.A., Neben, S., and Ploemacher, R.E. (1994). Frequency analysis of human primitive haematopoietic stem cell subsets using a cobblestone area forming cell assay. *Leukemia* **8,** 1095–1104.
41. Wermann, K., Fruehauf, S., Haas, R., and Zeller, W.J. (1996). Human-mouse xenografts in stem cell research. *J. Hematother.* **5,** 379–390.
42. Morstyn, G., Nicola, N.A., and Metcalf, D. (1980). Purification of hemopoietic progenitor cells from human marrow using a fucose-binding lectin and cell sorting. *Blood* **56,** 798–805.
43. Berenson, R.J., Andrews, R.G., Bensinger, W.I., Kalamasz, D., Knitter, G., Buckner, C.D., and Bernstein, I.D. (1988). Antigen CD34+ marrow cells engraft lethally irradiated baboons. *J. Clin. Invest.* **81,** 951–955.
44. Andrews, R.G., Singer, J.W., and Bernstein, I.D. (1989). Precursors of colony-forming cells in humans can be distinguished from colony-forming cells by expression of the CD33 and CD34 antigens and light scatter properties. *J. Exp. Med.* **169,** 1721–1731.
45. Srour, E.F., Leemhuis, T., Brandt, J.E., vanBesien, K., and Hoffman, R. (1991). Simultaneous use of rhodamine 123, phycoerythrin, Texas red, and allophycocyanin for the isolation of human hematopoietic progenitor cells. *Cytometry* **12,** 179–183.
46. Goodell, M.A. (1999). CD34(+) or CD34(–): does it really matter? *Blood* **94,** 2545–2547.
47. Krause, D.S., Ito, T., Fackler, M.J., Smith, O.M., Collector, M.I., Sharkis, S.J., and May, W.S. (1994). Characterization of murine CD34, a marker for hematopoietic progenitor and stem cells. *Blood* **84,** 691–701.
48. Morel, F., Galy, A., Chen, B., and Szilvassy, S.J. (1998). Equal distribution of competitive long-term repopulating stem cells in the CD34+ and CD34– fractions of Thy-1lowLin-/lowSca-1+ bone marrow cells. *Exp. Hematol.* **26,** 440–448.
49. Osawa, M., Hanada, K., Hamada, H., and Nakauchi, H. (1996). Long-term lymphohematopoietic reconstitution by a single CD34-low/negative hematopoietic stem cell. *Science* **273,** 242–245.
50. Tajima, F., Deguchi, T., Laver, J.H., Zeng, H., and Ogawa, M. (2001). Reciprocal expression of CD38 and CD34 by adult murine hematopoietic stem cells. *Blood* **97,** 2618–2624.
51. Okuno, Y., Iwasaki, H., Huettner, C.S., Radomska, H.S., Gonzalez, D.A., Tenen, D.G., and Akashi, K. (2002). Differential regulation of the human and murine CD34 genes in hematopoietic stem cells. *Proc. Natl. Acad. Sci. U. S. A.* **99,** 6246–6251.
52. Ishikawa, F., Livingston, A.G., Minamiguchi, H., Wingard, J.R., and Ogawa, M. (2003). Human cord blood long-term engrafting cells are CD34+ CD38–. *Leukemia* **17,** 960–964.
53. Briones, J., Urbano-Ispizua, A., Lawler, M., Rozman, C., Gardiner, N., Marin, P., Salgado, C., Feliz, P., McCann, S., and Montserrat, E. (1998). High frequency of donor chimerism after allogeneic transplantation of CD34+-selected peripheral blood cells. *Exp. Hematol.* **26,** 415–420.
54. Piacibello, W., Bruno, S., Sanavio, F., Droetto, S., Gunetti, M., Ailles, L., de Sio, F. S., Viale, A., Gammaitoni, L., Lombardo, A., Naldini, L., and Aglietta, M. (2002). Lentiviral gene transfer and ex vivo expansion of human primitive stem cells capable of primary, secondary, and tertiary multilineage repopulation in NOD/SCID mice. Nonobese diabetic/severe combined immunodeficient. *Blood* **100,** 4391–4400.

55

Approaches to Hematopoietic Stem Cell Separation and Expansion

David N. Haylock and Paul J. Simmons

Introduction

During the last decade, there has been great interest in the development of methods for manipulating the growth and development of human hemopoietic stem cells (HSCs) and progenitor stem cells for therapy.[1,2] These initiatives include the generation of committed progenitor cells and myeloid precursors for transplantation,[3–5] expansion of HSCs from hemopoietic tissues such as umbilical cord blood (CB) to increase the safety and applicability of hemopoietic cell transplantation,[6,7] and the use of HSCs as vehicles for gene therapy.[8,9] Optimal methods for manipulating human HSCs and their progeny for any therapeutic application will arise from a comprehensive understanding of the molecular regulatory mechanisms that control stem cell fate and hemopoietic cell differentiation. However, at present, very little is known about the most fundamental aspect of stem cell biology (i.e., the decision to self-renew or to commit to differentiation). Even though it is well recognized that the hemopoietic microenvironment plays a key role in these processes,[10–13] the exact molecules responsible for these non–cell autonomous aspects of HSC regulation remain to be elucidated. Accordingly, a major challenge for the field is to define the molecular "parts lists" for both stem and progenitor cell populations and the supporting microenvironment and moreover to establish how these individual components interact to form regulatory pathways and networks.[11,12,14] With this knowledge it might be possible to develop *ex vivo* culture systems that replicate *in vivo* hemopoiesis and truly harness the potential of human HSCs and their progeny for application in a range of cellular therapies. Thus, identification and isolation of hemopoietic cells at all stages of the developmental hierarchy is an essential prerequisite to defining their genomic and proteomic profile and, in the long-term, developing methods for *ex vivo* manipulation of hemopoiesis. The first section of this chapter focuses on strategies for identification and separation of human HSCs and lineage-committed progenitors. The second section discusses approaches to HSC expansion and the recent clinical experience with *ex vivo* manipulated hemopoietic cells.

Handbook of Stem Cells
Volume 2

Human Hemopoietic Stem Cells: From Function to Cellular Entity

The concept of a hierarchy of blood cells arising from multipotent, self-renewing HSCs that give rise to progeny with progressively diminishing potential for self-renewal, proliferation, and differentiation is a well-established paradigm of hemopoiesis. Initial evidence for this model emerged primarily through transplantation experiments performed in the mouse model.[15–17] Subsequently, a large number of similar studies, particularly those involving retroviral marking of candidate HSCs identified and isolated by fluorescence-activated cell sorting (FACS) demonstrated that a single HSC is both necessary and sufficient to sustain life-long, multilineage hemopoiesis in both primary and secondary recipients.[18–21] Although equivalent experiments have not been performed with single primitive human hemopoietic progenitor cells (HPCs), there is abundant clinical transplantation data demonstrating that populations that are highly enriched for HSCs can sustain human hemopoiesis.

In humans, the HSC pool is estimated to represent a very small fraction (probably <0.01%) of the nucleated cells within the bone marrow (BM).[22] However, the identification and quantitation of primitive human HPCs with marrow repopulating ability has been problematic and remains a contentious issue. Until recently there was consensus that human HSCs were restricted to the CD34 antigen positive ($CD34^+$) subfraction of human adult BM.[23] Autologous[24,25] and allogeneic transplantation[26,27] with $CD34^+$ cells has produced stable lymphohemopoietic repopulation for more than 6 years in humans and 10 years in nonhuman primates[28] suggesting that some $CD34^+$ cells have long-term marrow repopulating ability. Although these studies strongly suggest that long-term repopulating HSCs reside within the $CD34^+$ fraction of adult BM, they do not yield any definitive information on the identity of cells that exhibit this function. Many investigators have addressed this issue using a range of methods that, in general terms, seek to isolate candidate human HSCs according to (1) physical characteristics, (2) function and biologic responses, and (3) cell surface antigen expression. These strategies, either alone or collectively, enable subfractions of cells to be isolated and tested in a range of surrogate *in vitro* and *in vivo* assays of hemopoiesis.

Hemopoietic Stem Cells: Isolation Based on Physical Characteristics

Developing and mature granulocytic blood cells exhibit relatively greater buoyant density than lymphocytes and monocytes, which facilitates their separation by centrifugation on Percoll or Ficoll density gradients.[29,30] However, isolation of highly enriched fractions of HPCs and HSCs from lymphocytes and monocytes by this approach is not feasible given their overlapping densities. Nevertheless, subtle differences in cell size and buoyant density between HSCs, HPCs, and mature lymphoid cells is exploited in counterflow centrifugal elutriation (CCE)[31] for enrichment of murine HSCs.[32] Although this approach results in isolation of purified populations of cells with long-term repopulating ability, it requires precise instrument calibration and stringent process control. Therefore, CCE is not an easily transferred methodology and is likely to yield different cell fractions in different laboratories; consequently, it has not been adopted widely as technique for isolation of human HSCs.

Hemopoietic Stem Cells: Isolation Based on Function and Biologic Responses

As described later, monoclonal antibodies directed against cell surface and integral membrane proteins are frequently used for isolation of HSCs. An inherent concern with this approach is that labeling could also lead to activation or modulation of cell function via antibody-mediated antigen cross-linking. For example, monoclonal antibodies that recognize growth factor receptors (e.g., CD117, flt3) or sialomucins (e.g., CD34) may induce signaling and change the function or hemopoietic potential of the isolated candidate HSCs in subsequent assays.[33] This concern with antibody-mediated HSC isolation may be alleviated by methods that exploit the different biologic responses of HSCs and their progeny.

HSCs can be discriminated from their progeny by their ability to efflux fluorescent dyes such as rhodamine-123 and Hoechst 33342[34–36] and their relative quiescence.[37] Although isolation of primitive HPCs according to dye efflux is a well-established and proven tool for the research laboratory, the attendant risk of genetic change mediated by RNA/DNA binding dyes makes it unlikely that this approach will ever be used for isolation of cells for clinical purposes. The relative quiescence of HSCs can be exploited experimentally by exposing cells to cell-cycle-specific antimetabolites such as 5-fluorouracil (5-FU) and hydroxyperoxycyclophosphamide.[38,39] This approach is most powerful when used in conjunction with culture conditions that induce division of committed HPCs but not candidate HSCs.[40] In this respect, one feature that distinguishes HSCs from their progeny is their requirement for simultaneous stimulation by combinations of early-acting, synergistic cytokines to induce cell division. As shown in Fig. 55–1, single human BM CD34$^+$CD38$^-$ cells may be hierarchically ordered according to their hemopoietic growth factor (HGF) requirements. We have previously proposed that candidate HSCs within the CD34$^+$CD38$^-$ fraction of adult BM require simultaneous exposure to multiple HGFs including stem cell factor (SCF), fetal liver tyrosine kinase-ligand (Flt3L), and megakaryocyte growth and development factor (MGDF) to induce cell division whereas less primitive HPCs are able to divide in HGF combinations lacking either Flt3L or MGDF.[41,42] A logical extension of this hierarchical model is that it may provide a means for the functional isolation of the candidate HSCs within the CD34$^+$CD38$^-$ subpopulation. This could be achieved by stimulating CD34$^+$CD38$^-$ cells with a minimal combination of factors (e.g., IL-3, IL-6, granulocyte colony-stimulating factor [G-CSF], SCF) and then incubation with a cell-cycle–specific antimetabolite such as 5-FU as previously described by Beradi *et al.*[40] The cells spared by 5-FU would, therefore, contain the most primitive HPCs within the CD34$^+$CD38$^-$ fraction. Clearly, such an approach would need to be validated in a suitable *in vivo* model of human hemopoiesis.

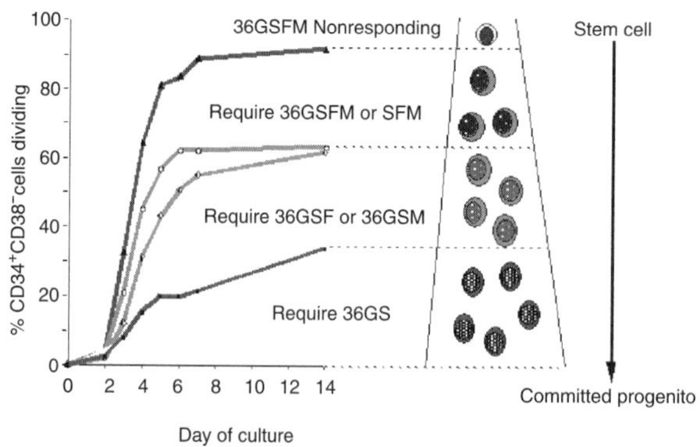

Figure 55–1. *Functional hierarchy within the CD34$^+$CD38$^-$ fraction of bone marrow.* In this model, hemopoietic progenitor cells (HPCs) within the CD34$^+$CD38$^-$ fraction of cells can be discriminated according to the combinations of hemopoietic growth factor (HGF) required to initiate cell division.[41,42] The most primitive HPCs reside at the top of the hierarchy and require simultaneous stimulation with combinations of early-acting HGF including IL-3$^+$IL-6$^+$G-CSF$^+$SCF$^+$FLT3L$^+$TPO/MGDF(36GSFM) or SFM to induce cell division. It is proposed that these ancestral HPCs will not divide in lesser combinations of HGF that do not include these three HGFs. In contrast, committed HPCs are located at the bottom of the hierarchy and will divide in combinations that do not contain each or all of these early-acting HGFs. Thus, HPCs dividing in the combination of 36GS are considered hierarchically more committed than those cells dividing in HGF combinations such as 36GSF or 36GST.

Hemopoietic Stem Cells: Isolation Based on Cell Surface Antigen Expression

The most extensively used approaches for prospective isolation of HSCs from murine and human hemopoietic tissues are those based on monoclonal antibodies directed against cell surface antigens. These methods have been underpinned by development of fluorochromes, improvements in monoclonal antibody conjugation processes, innovations in flow cytometry, and generation of inert particles for solid phase selection of tagged cells. These advances, together with improved *in vitro* and *in vivo* assays for testing potential of isolated HPC fractions, have lead to a better definition of hemopoietic cells with stem cell activity.

Surrogate *in vitro* assay systems for testing candidate HSCs include the standard semisolid clonogenic assays performed in agar, agarose, or methycellulose[43,44]; long-term bone marrow (LTBM) culture[13,45–47]; the CFU-blast assay[48,49]; and the pre-CFU assay.[50,51] The latter three assays detect primitive hemopoietic cells by their ability to generate committed progenitor cells (as determined by clonogenic assays) and/or the production of mature cells of multiple lineages. In addition, *in vivo* transplantation experiments with immunodeficient animals[52–54] have proved to be extremely useful for investigating the hemopoietic potential of defined populations of human HPCs.

Results from these various *in vivo* and *in vitro* assay systems suggest that primitive human HPCs (perhaps HSCs) can be discriminated from lineage-committed progenitors by the expression or absence of particular cell surface antigens. A composite phenotype for adult human HSCs could be CD34$^+$c-kit$^+$HLA-DR$^-$CD38$^-$CD71$^-$CD45RA$^-$Rhodamine-123^{dull}, whereas committed progenitor cells would be CD34$^+$ but express lineage (e.g., CD33, CD10, CD19, CD2, CD7) or activation (e.g., HLA-DR, CD38) antigens. In addition, human clinical transplant trials, performed with cells isolated by FACS, demonstrate that CD34$^+$ cells expressing Thy-1 result in rapid and sustained hemopoietic engraftment.[55] Even though simultaneous labeling with such a large panel of cell surface markers, including Thy-1, might lead to isolation of an enriched population of HSCs there is still considerable heterogeneity within this fraction. For example, approximately 1 in every 600 CB CD34$^+$CD38$^-$ cells display repopulating activity in non-obese diabetic/severe combined immune deficient (NOD/SCID) mice,[56] which clearly highlights the need for additional cell surface markers or approaches that identify long-term repopulating HSCs.

One such candidate marker that facilitates further enrichment of HSCs is the ATP-binding cassestte (ABC) transporter Bcrp1/ABCG2[57,58]; a molecular determinant of the side population (SP) phenotype that is expressed in a wide variety of somatic stem cells.[59] Expression of ABCG2 can be exploited by virtue of conferring ability to efflux fluorescent dyes such as Hoescht 33342, thus facilitating sorting of the Hoescht negative or SP fraction. The need for incubation of cells in an avid DNA binding dye such as Hoescht 33342, and its attendant potential risk for DNA damage is likely to prevent this strategy from being used for isolation of human cells for therapy. However, antibodies to ABCG2 could be used for direct isolation of this fraction of HSCs by FACS and/or immunomagnetic bead systems.

The five-transmembrane antigen CD133 also provides a valuable means for identification and isolation of primitive human HPCs.[60] A subtractive immunization approach involving alternate contralateral footpad injections of mature hemopoietic cells and CD34$^+$ cells lead to identification of AC133, an antibody with specificity for CD34$^+$ bright cells in fetal liver, cord blood (CB), BM, and mobilized peripheral blood (MPB).[61] Notably, CD34$^+$CD133$^+$ but not CD34$^+$ CD133$^-$ cells were able to sustain human hemopoiesis in secondary transplants in the pre-immune fetal sheep model, providing initial evidence that long-term repopulating cells expressed CD133.[61] Subsequent studies confirmed that NOD/SCID repopulating cells (SRC) reside almost exclusively within the CD133$^+$CD34$^+$CD38$^-$ fraction of BM[61,62] and the CD133$^+$ CD34$^+$CD38$^-$Lin$^-$CD7$^-$ fraction of MPB and umbilical CB.[63,64]

We have recently identified a further antibody BB9, which recognizes a cell surface glycoprotein with restricted expression by primitive human HPCs within BM, MPB, and CB.[65] This antibody was generated following immunization of mice with human BM stromal cells, a strategy based on the knowledge that although phenotypically distinct, BM stromal cells and primitive human HPCs nevertheless share expression of several cell surface antigens including CD34,[66,67] CD90,[68] and CD164.[69] The antigen recognized by BB9 is expressed throughout hemopoietic ontogeny and can be found at high levels as early as 24 days of human development where it is present on rare cells in mesoderm of the splanchnopleura.[70] At later stages BB9 antigen is present on hemopoietic precursors emerging on the ventral side of the aorta and the surrounding endothelium. Notably, these BB9$^+$ cells do not express CD34 or CD45, suggesting that they represent emergence of cells with blood-forming potential in the para-aortic splanchnopleura. The utility of BB9 as a marker of HSCs in adult hemopoietic tissues is currently being investigated.

In addition to the BB9 antigen, members of the sialomucin family, including CD34, podocalyxin-like protein,[71] and endoglycan,[72] are also expressed on primitive hemopoietic cells and may serve as additional markers of HSCs in adult hemopoietic tissues.

Hemopoietic Stem Cells: CD34$^+$ or CD34$^-$?

Despite the vast amount of experimental data supporting the hypothesis that CD34 expression can be used to define HSCs this must be re-examined in light of studies investigating the hemopoietic potential of CD34$^{low/-}$ cells.[64,73–83] The first report of hemopoietic reconstitution potential of CD34$^{low/-}$ cells was made by Owasa *et al.*,[73] who performed transplantation into Ly5.2 recipient mice with low numbers of c-Kit$^+$ Sca-1$^+$ Lin$^-$ CD34$^{low/-}$ cells isolated from Ly5.1 donors. These data were confirmed and extended by Morel *et al.*, who used a similar transplantation strategy to compare the contribution made by CD34$^+$ and CD34$^-$ cells to hemopoiesis in primary and secondary recipient mice. These studies suggested that primitive competitive repopulating cells were distributed equally between CD34$^+$ and CD34$^-$, c-Kit$^+$Sca-1$^+$Lin$^-$ cells.[75] In contrast, competitive repopulation experiments have demonstrated that CD34$^+$Lin$^-$ HPCs are better able to engraft BM than CD34$^-$ cells: the CD34$^+$Lin$^-$ cells providing both short- and long-term engraftment but CD34$^-$Lin$^-$ cells being capable of only long-term engraftment.[79,80] Furthermore, analysis of CD34 expression on murine HSCs at different developmental stages show that antigen expression on murine HSCs declines with age and is more akin to an activation marker: long-term repopulating HSCs from BM, liver, and spleen in fetal and neonatal mice are $CD34^+$ whereas $CD34^-$ HSCs emerge around 7 weeks and increase thereafter.[84,85]

Evidence for an equivalent $CD34^-$ HSC fraction in human hemopoietic tissues comes from analysis of Hoechst 33342 effluxing SP cells[74] and transplants in NOD/SCID mice[78] and pre-immune fetal sheep.[76,86] Despite these findings, the utility of human $CD34^-$ cells for *ex vivo* manipulation remains controversial. Culture of human Lin^-CD34^- umbilical CB cells on the murine marrow stromal cell line HESS-5 in the presence of exogenous TPO, FLT3L, SCF, G-CSF, IL-3, and IL-6 results in the acquisition of CD34 by up to 12% of cells during 7 days of culture.[82] Although, the long-term multilineage repopulating ability of these cultured cells was demonstrated by transplantation into irradiated NOD/SCID mice, there was no direct evidence that repopulation could be attributed to nascent $CD34^+$ cells. A small fraction (approximately 1%) of $CD34^-Lin^-$ cells isolated from normal adult BM and G-CSF mobilized blood have also been shown to divide and differentiate in serum-free liquid suspension cultures stimulated by FLT3L, TPO, SCF, IL-3, and hyper-IL-6.[81] These cultures supported a 28-fold increase in total cells within 10 days and 5% of generated cells were $CD34^+$. Notably, transplantation of up to 1.7×10^5 Lin^-CD34^- adult BM cells failed to engraft sublethally irradiated NOD/SCID-$\beta_2M^{-/-}$ mice, contrasting with the demonstrated efficacy of the same population in contributing to human hemopoiesis in the NOD/SCID and pre-immune fetal sheep transplant models.[76–78] The conflicting results of these studies may in part be explained by the use of NOD/SCID-$\beta_2M^{-/-}$ mice rather than NOD/SCID recipients or by the subtle difference in the panel of monoclonal antibodies used to remove or discriminate cells expressing lineage-associated antigens. Furthermore, the conflicting data from these studies suggest that further investigations are required to more accurately assess the potential of human Lin^-CD34^- cells. In this regard, the recent identification and purification of a rare human stem cell population with hemopoietic and hepatic potential based on the expression of a receptor for the complement molecule C1q (C1qR(p)) may be extremely useful. C1qR(p) appears to be a positive marker of all BM-repopulating stem cells because it is expressed on both $CD34^-$ and $CD34^+$ stem cells from umbilical CB and adult BM. In addition, highly purified $lineage^-$, $CD45^+CD38^-CD34^{+or-}$ $C1qR(p)^+$ cells not only have BM-repopulating capacity but also can differentiate into human hepatocytes *in vivo*.[87]

Despite these recent findings, the extremely low incidence of such cells in adult BM and umbilical CB that exhibit NOD/SCID repopulating ability[64] and the low proportion that can be stimulated in *ex vivo* cultures suggest that the clinical use of $CD34^-$ HPCs may not be feasible. Accordingly, because the greatest numbers of adult human HSCs are found within the $CD34^+lin^-CD38^-CD133^+Thy\text{-}1^+$ fraction of BM, MPB, and CB, the protocols for *ex vivo* manipulation of these cells for clinical transplantation are based mainly on selection of cells expressing CD34.

Separation of Human Hemapoietic Progenitor Cells for the Clinic

Although peripheral blood progenitor cell collections and BM harvests are widely used for transplantation, there are a number of reasons for selecting HPCs from these sources before transplantation. These include, T-cell depletion of allografts, tumor cell depletion of autologous grafts, and enrichment of primitive HPCs for use in *ex vivo* expansion or gene transduction protocols. With regard to the former, direct and indirect cell selection strategies have been used for depletion of T cells from BM or mobilized blood. Initial clinical studies were conducted with grafts depleted of T cells by sheep red blood cell rosetting,[88] lectins,[89] CCE,[90,91] anti–T-cell monoclonal antibodies including Campath-1,[92] and immunotoxins.[93]

However, an increasing proportion of T-cell depleted grafts are achieved by positive selection of HPCs according to expression of CD34 or more recently CD133. As described later a number of clinical-scale commercial devices have been successfully used for $CD34^+$ cell selection and as an attendant feature provide 2–5 log of T-cell depletion from BM or mobilized blood collections.[94–96] Moreover in the autologous setting, where tumor cells do not express cell surface CD34, the graft may be depleted of tumor as a consequence of $CD34^+$ cell selection.[97–99] Analysis of $CD34^+$ enriched mobilized blood by immunocytochemistry with combinations of epithelial-specific anti-cytokeratin monoclonal antibodies has demonstrated removal of contaminating breast cancer cells[100–102] and more than 2 log depletion of neuroblastoma cells.[103] Although $CD34^+$ selection reduces tumor load of a graft, even as shown by molecular analysis[97,104] there is no clear evidence that this manipulation results in increased disease-free survival or overall survival of patients following high-dose chemotherapy and stem cell rescue.[99,105]

Berenson *et al.* at the Fred Hutchinson Cancer Centre pioneered transplantation with positively selected $CD34^+$ cells.[106] Their laboratory and clinical scale (CEPRATE) devices relied on labeling of $CD34^+$ cells with a biotinylated anti-CD34 monoclonal antibody and subsequent capture of cells by immunoadsorption on a column of avidin-coated beads. $CD34^+$ cells retained in the column were released following gentle agitation and washing, a process facilitated by the low binding affinity and avidity of the primary monoclonal, 12.8, which was of the IgM isotype.[107] Autologous[108] and allogeneic[96,109] transplants performed with $CD34^+$ cells purified by the CEPRATE device confirmed that these cells could reconstitute human hemopoiesis. Baxter and Miltenyi Biotec subsequently developed similar devices and closed systems for positive selection of $CD34^+$ cells. A notable difference between these later two approaches is the different composition and size of particles used for capture of cells coated by CD34 monoclonal antibodies. The Isolex and Isolex300i devices are based on 0.45 micron super-paramagnetic particles produced by Dynal[110] that are detached from captured cells by either chymopapain[111] as with the Isolex or by incubation with a specific peptide release agent[112] as used in the current Isolex300i platform. In contrast, the CliniMACS device is based on magnetic capture of CD34+ cells by very small ferrous/ferric dextran microbeads that have a diameter similar to that of the cytoplasmic membrane.[113] In the CliniMACS, microbeads are not removed from CD34+ cells and are presumably degraded in culture or *in vivo* following transplantation. Both devices have been widely used for isolation of CD34+ cells from MPB, BM, and umbilical CB and give similar levels of performance. Combined results from clinical trials indicate that the median yield and purity of CD34+ cells from the Isolex and CliniMACS are, 54 and 71%, and 83 and 85%, respectively.[96,114–123] A feature of these clinical studies is the large variation in both yield (30–80%) and purity of CD34+ cells (51–98%) obtained, irrespective of the selection device. The reasons for such variable performance remain unclear.[124]

A study of 240 mobilized blood cell products selected on the Isolex300i suggests that red blood cell concentration, platelet concentration, total white blood cells selected, and time until processing have little effect on either yield and purity.[114] In contrast, the study by Hilbrandt *et al.*[117] suggests that red blood cell volume of the starting product has the highest predictive impact on yield and purity of CD34+ cells selected on the Isolex300i. Studies within our own institution[124] are in accord with data published by Gryn *et al.* but highlight that optimum purity with CliniMACS is obtained when the number of white blood cells loaded are kept below 6×10^{10}.[125] Of some concern, however, was our observation that CD34+ cells selected by the CliniMACS, but not the Isolex300i, may have a qualitative defect and lead to delayed neutrophil and platelet recovery.[124,125] An increased proportion of apoptotic cells and significantly reduced clonogenic capacity has also been reported for CD34+ cells selected on the CliniMACS[119] and may, in part, explain the delay in hemopoietic recovery observed in our clinical trial. In addition, QBEND10-induced homotypic aggregation of CD34+ cells and subsequent inhibition of proliferation may also contribute to this clinical outcome.[126]

A concern for all cell selection devices is recovery of CD34+ cells, especially because the dose of CD34+ cells transplanted correlates with the rate and extent of hemopoietic recovery. This is especially relevant to CB transplantation and for clinical protocols that use CD34+ cells to support multiple rounds of high-dose therapy[124] or for *ex vivo* expansion or genetic manipulation of CD34+ cells. There is a need to improve the efficiency of CD34+ cell selection, given that at best the commercial devices presently available recovery on average 55–70% of CD34+ cells. It is likely that HPC recovery with these systems is a function of their underlying engineering and design features rather than the properties of monoclonal antibodies and immunomagnetic particles. In this respect, selection of CD133+ cells from G-CSF MPB on the CliniMacs device results in similar yields (69%) to that observed for CD34+ cells.[127]

Selection of purified human HPCs for transplantation can also be performed by high-speed FACS; this approach requires pre-enrichment of HPCs from the source tissue and is absolutely dependent on dedicated, highly skilled operators and instrument stability for many hours.[55] Accordingly, even though this technology can provide a highly purified fraction of HPCs, and potentially extremely low levels of T-cell or tumor contamination, it is no longer used in the clinic.

Ex Vivo Expansion of Hemopoietic Progenitor Cells

In general, *ex vivo* expansion of human hemopoietic cells for therapy has involved culture of unfractionated BM, mobilized blood, or CB or CD34+ cells selected from these tissues, in either stromal-dependent or stromal-free conditions. Stromal-cell–dependent systems are based on the premise that an *ex vivo* generated adherent stromal layer represents a microenvironment that mimics that of the BM and thus will recapitulate the complex regulatory system that normally controls HSC proliferation and differentiation. In contrast, stromal-cell–free systems depend exclusively on provision of purified recombinant HGFs to promote HPC/HSC proliferation and differentiation. Both systems have been used with the objective of expanding HSCs or for generation of committed progenitors and differentiated cells that could be used for enhancing hemopoietic recovery (HR) posttransplant. At present, there are no convincing data in either system to demonstrate that long-term repopulating human HSCs can be expanded sufficiently to have a clinical impact in those situations in which a greater number of such cells are required. In contrast, as described in the following, both stromal-based and stromal-free systems have been used successfully for generation of committed HPCs and differentiated progeny that result in improved HR.

Clinical Trials with *Ex Vivo* Expanded Hemopoietic Progenitor Cells

As described previously, advances in clinical-scale systems for safe and reproducible isolation of HPCs and HSCs from BM, CB, and MPB together with production of clinical-grade recombinant human cytokines has resulted in significant interest in the use of *ex vivo* cultured cells for therapy. However, although many laboratories have performed preclinical studies to optimize hemopoietic cell expansion, only a relative small number of clinical trials have been conducted. An excellent review by Devine *et al.* discusses the clinical application for HPC expansion, current pitfalls, and the key issues regarding the future use of this technology.[128]

Since 1992 there have been 21 published reports of patients transplanted or infused with *ex vivo* cultured HPCs.[5,129–149] Collectively, these studies, listed in Table 55–1, record 299 patients receiving cultured cells with no reports of toxicity or serious adverse events. However, there is a wide discrepancy in the documented effects on HR attributed to the infused cells. Eleven of these studies were performed with mobilized blood cells with the majority ($n = 8$) involving cultures initiated with CD34+-selected cells.[5,131–134,136,143,144] Other clinical trials used unmanipulated mononuclear cells

TABLE 55–1
Clinical Studies Performed with *Ex Vivo* Cultured Human Hemopoietic Progenitor Cells

Author/Year/ Ref	Cell Source	Culture Conditions	Patient Group	Outcome
Naparstek 1992/128	Allo BM	GM-CSF/IL3	Leukemia	No improvement in neutrophil or platelet recovery
Gluck 1995/129	Apheresis MNC	IL-3, IL-6, G-CSF, GM-CSF, SCF, 20% FCS	3 with CaBr	NAE No improvement in HR
Brugger 1995/5	Autologous PBPC, selected CD34+	IL-1, IL-3, IL-6, SCF, EPO, autologous plasma	10 with advanced cancer	NAE No improvement in HR
Alcorn 1996/131	Autologous PBPC Selected CD34+	IL-1, IL-3, IL-6, SCF, EPO, 5–10% autologous serum	10 with nonhemopoietic malignancies	NAE No improvement in HR
Williams 1996/132	Autologous PBPC Selected CD34+	PIXY321, XVIVO-10 + 1% human serum albumin	8 with CaBr	NAE 2 patients with improved neutrophil recovery
Holyoake 1997/133	Autologous PBPC Selected CD34+	IL-1, IL-3, IL-6, SCF, EPO, 5–10% autologous serum	4 patients; (2 MM, 2 NHL) conditioned with CY/TBI and Bu/Melph	Graft failure Infusion of unmanipulated MNC
Bertolini 1997/134	Autologous PBPC Selected CD34+	IMDM + 5% AB serum, IL-3, IL-6, IL-11, SCF, FLT3L, MGDF, and MIP-1α	10 patients (8 with CaBr, 2 NHL) infused	NAE Prompt HR Reduced platelet support
Kogler 1999/135	UCB	XVIVO-10, 10% CB plasma, G-CSF, TPO, FLT3L	1 child with c-ALL	ANC of 410 at day 14, delayed platelet recovery
Reiffers 1999/136	Autologous Selected CD34+ PBPC	G-CSF, SCF, MGDF	14 patients with MM	Median duration of severe neutropenia 1.5 days, median <20,000 platelets of 1 day
Bachier 1999/137	BM MNC	Aastrom device, EPO, PIXY321, FLT3L	5 patients with high-risk stage II or MBC	Equivalent HR to unmanipulated BM
Chabannon 1999/138	Autologous BM	Aastrom device, EPO, PIXY321, FLT3L	6 patients with CaBr	Equivalent HR to unmanipulated BM
Pecora 2000/139	Unrelated UCB	Aastrom device	2 adults with CML	Engrafted with NAE
McNiece 2000/140	UCB unrelated donors	Stericell Flask, G-CSF, SCF, MGDF	19 patients; 17 hemopoietic malignancies, 2 with CaBr	500 ANC in 25 days Delayed platelet recovery (58 days to 20,000)
Koc 2000/141	Mobilized PB MNC	20–50 days for MSC	28 patients with advanced and CaBr	NAE; ANC of 500 on day 8; 20,000 platelets on 8.5 days
Stiff 2000/142	BM	Aastrom device, EPO + PIXY321 + FLT3L	19 adults CaBr	500 ANC at 16 days
McNiece 2000/143	Autologous PB CD34+ cells	G-CSF, SCF, MGDF	21 patients with CaBr	Improved neutrophil recovery, no change in platelet recovery
Zimmerman 2000/144	Auto MBPC CD34+ cells	SFM and PIXY321	21 patients with CaBr	Equivalent HR to unmanipulated PBPC
Paquette 2000/145	Unselected, PBPC	G-CSF, SCF, MGDF	24 patients with CaBr	Significantly improved neutrophil, platelet, and red cell recovery
Engelhardt 2001/146	Auto BM	Aastrom device, EPO, PIXY321, FLT3L	10 patients with CaBr	Equivalent HR to unmanipulated BM

TABLE 55–1
Clinical Studies Performed with *Ex Vivo* Cultured Human Hemopoietic Progenitor Cells—cont'd

Author/Year/ Ref	Cell Source	Culture Conditions	Patient Group	Outcome
Sphall 2002/147	Allo UCB	10 days, G-CSF, SCF, MGDF	37 patients, 34 hematologic malignancies and 3 CaBr	NAE; No improvement in rate of HR
Jaroscak 2003/148	Allo UCB	Aastrom device	27 patients, various	NAE; No improvement in early HR

Allo, allogeneci; ANC, absolute neutrophil count; auto, autologous; BM, bone marrow; CaBr, cancer of the breast; c-ALL, common acute lymphoblastic leukemia; CB, cord blood; CML, chronic myeloid leukemia; CY/TBI, cytoxan/total body irradiation; EPO, erythropoietin; FCS, fetal calf serum; G-CSF, granulocyte colony-stimulating factor; GM-CSF, granulocyte monocyte colony-stimulating factor; HR, hemopoietic recovery; IMDM, Iscoves modification of Dulbecco's media; MBC, metastatic breast cancer; MGDF, megakaryocyte growth and development factor; MM, multiple myeloma; MNC, mononuclear cells; MSC, mesenchymal stem cells; NAE, no adverse events; NHL, non-Hodgkin's lymphoma; PBPC, peripheral blood progenitor cells; SCF, stem cell factor; SFM, serum free medium; TPO, thrombopoietin.

collected by apheresis, BM ($n = 5$),[128,137,138,142,146] or umbilical CB ($n = 5$).[135,139,140,147–149]

A common feature of these studies is use of combinations of recombinant human HGFs to stimulate growth and proliferation of cells. In this respect, IL-1, IL-3, IL-6, IL-11, G-CSF, granulocyte-monocyte colony-stimulating factor (GM-CSF), SCF, Flt3L, MGDF, EPO, MIP1-alpha, and the IL-3/GM-CSF fusion molecule Pixy321 have been used either alone or in various combinations. Notably, 15 of the 21 published studies are based on *ex vivo* culture of HPCs in flasks or bags under static conditions and the remaining 6 use the Aastrom perfusion bioreactor[137–139,142,146,148,149] in which cell growth is dependent on the generation of an adherent stromal layer.[149,150] The main objective for *ex vivo* expansion in each of these published reports was to generate a cellular product that would enhance the rate of neutrophil or platelet recovery posttransplant or after high-dose chemotherapy.

The first clinical transplant with *ex vivo* expanded cells was performed in 1992 and involved expansion of a proportion of allogeneic BM in GM-CSF and IL-3.[128] No improvement in the rate of neutrophil and platelet recovery was reported and few data were given on composition of the *ex vivo* expanded cellular product, which was a common problem for the majority of subsequent clinical studies with expanded cells. Three more years elapsed before three patients with breast cancer received apheresis mononuclear cells expanded for 7 days in a combination of IL-3, IL-6, G-CSF, GM-CSF, SCF, and 20% fetal calf serum. An average of 3.5×10^9 cells were infused without toxicity or improved HR.[129] A similar study was performed with purified autologous CD34+ cells cultured for 12 days in IL-1, IL-3, IL-6, SCF, EPO, and autologous plasma. Ten patients were infused with the cultured cells but HR was equivalent to that observed with unmanipulated peripheral blood progenitor cells (PBPC).[5] In retrospect, the study of the group from Chicago[132] was ground breaking, in that it provided the first indication that infusion of sufficient *ex vivo* generated neutrophil precursors could improve the rate of neutrophil recovery in patients following chemotherapy; this was a remarkable outcome given that cells were stimulated with only the IL-3/GM-CSF fusion protein PIXY321. Of the eight patients transplanted with *ex vivo* cultured cells, two received almost 1×10^{10} cells and these patients showed a slight reduction in the period of neutropenia.

Until this stage no attempt had been made to use *ex vivo* culture cells following intensive myeloablative conditioning therapy. However, this was tested in four patients following cyclophosphamide/total body irradiation or busulphan/melphalan conditioning.[133] Autologous CD34+ cells were cultured for 8 days under stromal-free conditions and infused without unmanipulated PBPC. Unfortunately these patients failed to engraft and the unmanipulated, backup mobilized blood had to be infused, highlighting the possibility that HPCs cultured under stroma-free conditions may be insufficient to support maintenance of cells with short- and long-term engrafting potential.

The first study designed specifically to improve platelet recovery by infusion of *ex vivo* generated cells was reported in 1997 and involved culture of mobilized blood CD34+ cells in the combination of IL-3, IL-6, IL-11, SCF, FLT3L, MGDF, and MIP-1alpha supplemented with 5% AB serum.[134] A total of 10 patients received unmanipulated cells then 3 hours later the *ex vivo* generated cells. No adverse events were recorded, and, although HR was prompt in all patients, the rate of platelet recovery was not improved.

Convincing evidence that infusion of *ex vivo* generated myeloid postprogenitor cells could significantly improve the rate of neutrophil and possibly platelet recovery was provided by the group in Bordeaux.[136] Autologous CD34+ cells isolated from patients mobilized by chemotherapy and G-CSF were cultured for 12 days in large plastic tissue culture flasks containing 1 L of a proprietary medium, supplemented with G-CSF, SCF, and MGDF each at 100 ng/ml. Fourteen newly diagnosed patients with multiple myeloma were infused with *ex vivo* expanded cells on day 0 then unmanipulated cells 1 day later. Patients were conditioned with 200 mg/m^2 melphalan or 140 mg/m^2 melphalan plus 8–10 Gy of total body irradiation. G-CSF was administered following infusion of cells until the neutrophil count returned to safe levels. Hemopoietic recovery was compared with an age- and sex-matched historical control group of patients treated with an identical conditioning regimen and infusion of unmanipulated mobilized blood progenitor cells.

Patients receiving the *ex vivo* expanded cells had a median duration of severe neutropenia of 1.5 days as compared with 9.5 days in the historical control group transplanted with mobilized blood progenitors. In addition, there was only 1 day where the median platelet count was less than 20,000 per μL. Apart from demonstrating that neutropenia could be abrogated by infusion of *ex vivo* expanded neutrophil postprogenitors, this landmark study also provided evidence of a cell-dose effect in predicting the rate of HR. As evidenced by their data, it was suggested that at least 1×10^{10} expanded maturing neutrophil and megakaryocytic precursors were required to affect enhanced neutrophil and platelet recovery. This proposed cell dose is in accord with an hypothesis made some 7 years earlier[3] and with that predicted in a computer simulation of HR based on blood progenitor cell transplantation.[151]

Subsequent studies based on culture of CD34$^+$ cells with G-CSF, SCF, and MGDF have since confirmed and extended the data published by Reiffers *et al.*[140,143] Notably, infusion of *ex vivo* expanded cells without unmanipulated mobilized blood progenitors has been shown to restore hemopoiesis following high-dose myelosuppressive chemotherapy.[143] Infusion of *ex vivo* generated hemopoietic cells has also been tried to improve the rate of neutrophil and platelets recovery in patients being transplanted with umbilical CB cells. Although CB is a rich source of primitive HPC, the limited volume obtained from a single CB collection has resulted in it being used predominantly for transplantation of children and small adults. Even then, transplantation with CB is typically associated with prolonged periods of neutropenia and thrombocytopenia post engraftment.[152] *Ex vivo* expansion of CB CD34$^+$ cells could thus be performed with two objectives in mind: first, to generate an increased number of long-term repopulating cells, thus enabling the tissue to be used for transplantation of larger recipients and second to generate progenitors and post progenitor cells capable of contributing to rapid neutrophil and platelet recovery. At present, there are no convincing data demonstrating an increase in long-term repopulating HSCs following *ex vivo* culture of CB cells: this remains as a major objective for the proponents of *ex vivo* cellular therapy. In respect of the second of these objectives, infusion of *ex vivo* expanded CB CD34$^+$ cells has resulted in only a slight improvement in neutrophil recovery without a concomitant improvement in platelet recovery.[135,140,147,148] Accordingly, prolonged pancytopenia remains as a major problem for CB transplantation that limits the use of this tissue for transplantation to children or small adults. In this respect, CB represents a paradoxical source of cells for transplantation. There are abundant laboratory data demonstrating that CB CD34$^+$ cells as compared with BM or mobilized blood CD34$^+$ cells exhibit increased HSC potential as assessed by a greater expansion of hemopoietic progenitors and nucleated cells in cultures with combinations of early acting cytokines[153] and by their superior ability to engraft in xenogenic models.[154,155] However, CB CD34$^+$ cells are significantly inferior to BM or MPB at reconstituting hemopoiesis after transplantation. This outcome might simply reflect the log fewer nucleated CB and CD34$^+$ cells transplanted. Alternatively, it might reflect an inherent limitation of an ontogenetically primitive HSC population being forced to reside within the postnatal hemopoietic microenvironment. In addition, there is a limited understanding of which HSC and HPC populations contribute to HR during the first 1–2 months after CB transplantation. Until this is better defined, it will be difficult to generate by *ex vivo* culture cell mixtures that result in improved HR.

Collectively, the clinical studies performed with *ex vivo* generated hemopoietic cells demonstrate that infusion of neutrophil precursor cells can improve neutrophil recovery following myelosuppressive chemotherapy. However, the mechanism(s) responsible for this improved HR remains to be elucidated. Although infused *ex vivo* expanded CD34$^+$ cells contains a mixture of maturing myeloid cells, it is uncertain which cell types within this mix is responsible for the enhanced rate of neutrophil recovery. Unfortunately, none of the published studies include a comprehensive analysis of cells generated in *ex vivo* culture and infused into patients. For example, by combining immunophenotyping with morphologic examination of stained cytocentrifuge preparations the number of CD34$^+$ cells, myeloblasts, or promyelocytes could have been determined and correlated to neutrophil recovery. Furthermore, it is uncertain what proportion of infused cells actually lodge in the marrow, although one recent study indicates that after an initial transient residence within the lung an increasing proportion are located within femoral heads 1 hour post infusion.[144] This issue may be particularly relevant when expanded cells are being cultured specifically for generation of platelet precursors. In this case, megakaryocytes or their precursors may be trapped within small blood vessels, never lodge at endothelial surfaces within the BM, and thus not contribute to platelet production.

Ex Vivo Expansion of Hemopoietic Stem Cells

In vivo, HSC numbers are maintained by self-renewal, a process that results in generation of at least one daughter with hemopoietic potential identical to that of the parent HSC. The challenge for *ex vivo* expansion of HSCs is to culture cells under conditions that promote division in which both daughter cells retain long-term hemopoietic reconstituting potential. Only then will there be an increase in the absolute number of HSCs. Conditions that do not achieve this goal will at best result in maintenance of HSC numbers or at worst lead to HSC depletion as a result of irreversible lineage commitment by both daughter cells. The interactions between cell autonomous (intrinsic) and non–cell-autonomous (extrinsic) mechanisms that regulate stem cell fate decisions and self-renewal *in vivo* remain to be elucidated; thus, it is premature to speculate how these processes can be faithfully recreated *in vitro* so that HSCs can be "expanded."

Nevertheless, it is evident that HSC growth and development *in vivo* is influenced by the interactions that these cells have with stromal cells and their biosynthetic products that constitute the BM microenvironment.[10,11] For example, key HGFs such as SCF and flt3-ligand that exhibit potent biologic effects on primitive HPCs as soluble recombinant molecules *in vitro* are expressed within the hemopoietic microenvironment as integral membrane proteins at the surface of stromal cells.[156,157] The importance of membrane-bound SCF for hemopoiesis is clearly demonstrated by the severe macrocytic anemia observed in Sl^d mice that are able to secrete soluble SCF but lack the membrane form. Efforts to take advantage of these cellular interactions for expansion of human HSCs have lead to the generation of stromal cell lines from murine fetal liver, the aorto–gonad–mesonephros region,[158] and murine BM.[159,160] Notably, the murine AFT024 line exhibits an ability to at least maintain, if not increase, numbers of multipotent human HPCs during culture.[11,161–165] However, it is most unlikely that nonhuman lines such as AFT024 will ever be used for generation of human cells for the clinic, because of the risks associated with transplantation of nonhuman cells or xenogeneic proteins. This limitation could be overcome by the use of autologous stromal cell lines that have been engineered to express a repertoire of membrane-bound factors that promote HSC proliferation yet restrict differentiation. Moreover, the imposed restrictions that may be placed on the use of nonhuman or human-derived stromal lines for HSC expansion have lead to continued interest in culture systems that seek to expand HSCs with purified recombinant cytokines alone.

Under stromal-cell–free systems HPC proliferation and differentiation is absolutely dependent on provision of endogenous recombinant HGFs. However, despite the range of cytokines available and the flexibility and control afforded by such systems, identification of conditions that promote self-renewal of human HSCs has proven to be a challenge. Nevertheless, cultures containing combinations of early-acting synergistic cytokines such as SCF, flt3-ligand, and thrombopoietin suggest that this might be possible.[166–169] Furthermore, these studies indicate that initiation of cultures at relatively low concentrations of enriched HSCs, frequent replacement of cytokines and media, and/or the use of relatively high concentrations of cytokines favor HSC amplification. The molecular mechanisms responsible for this outcome remain to be defined, although the use of high concentrations of cytokines may lead to maintenance of critical signaling pathways above thresholds that favor self-renewal over differentiation.[170] Culture of HSCs on immobilized ligands[171] or in bioreactors, where concentrations of cytokines are continually monitored and maintained at high levels, may result in even greater levels of stem cell expansion.

Further recent studies demonstrate that interactions between cytokine receptor signaling pathways, bone morphogenic proteins,[172] members of the Hedgehog family of proteins[173] and activation of the Notch receptors[174,175] regulate proliferation and differentiation of HSCs and may play a role in regulation of self-renewal. In this respect, identification of other genes that regulate stem cell fate decisions will be critical to developing methods for *ex vivo* expansion of HSCs. Activation of the wnt signaling pathway[176,177] and expression of the Bmi-1 gene[178] appear to be critical players in this process. The impact of these recent findings on the clinic depends on extensive preclinical studies with HSCs isolated from different human hemopoietic tissues. The most challenging clinical area for testing the efficacy of *ex vivo* expanded HSCs is umbilical CB transplantation where delayed hemopoietic recovery remains as a major cause of morbidity.

REFERENCES

1. Emerson, S.G. (1996). Ex vivo expansion of hematopoietic precursors, progenitors, and stem cells: the next generation of cellular therapeutics. *Blood* **87,** 3082–3088.
2. Haylock, D.N., Makino, S., Dowse, T.L., Trimboli, S., Niutta, S., To, L.B., Juttner, C.A., and Simmons, P.J. (1994). Ex vivo hematopoietic progenitor cell expansion. *Immunomethods* **5,** 217–225.
3. Haylock, D.N., To, L.B., Dowse, T.L., Juttner, C.A., and Simmons, P.J. (1992). Ex vivo expansion and maturation of peripheral blood CD34+ cells into the myeloid lineage. *Blood* **80,** 1405–1412.
4. Brugger, W., Heimfeld, S., Berenson, R.J., Mertelsmann, R., and Kanz, L. (1995). Reconstitution of hematopoiesis after high-dose chemotherapy by autologous progenitor cells generated ex vivo. *N. Engl. J. Med.* **333,** 283–287.
5. Williams, S.F., Lee, W.J., Bender, J.G., Zimmerman, T., Swinney, P., Blake, M., Carreon, J., Schilling, M., Smith, S., Williams, D.E., Oldham, F., and Van Epps, D. (1996). Selection and expansion of peripheral blood CD34+ cells in autologous stem cell transplantation for breast cancer. *Blood* **87,** 1687–1691.
6. Gluckman, E. (2000). Current status of umbilical cord blood hematopoietic stem cell transplantation. *Exp. Hematol.* **28,** 1197–1205.
7. McNiece, I., Kubegov, D., Kerzic, P., Shpall, E.J., and Gross, S. (2000). Increased expansion and differentiation of cord blood products using a two-step expansion culture. *Exp. Hematol.* **28,** 1181–1186.
8. Cassel, A., Cottler-Fox, M., Doren, S., and Dunbar, C.E. (1993). Retroviral-mediated gene transfer into CD34 enriched human peripheral blood stem cells. *Exp. Hematol.* **21,** 585–591.
9. Nolta, J.A., Smogorzewska, E.M., and Kohn, D.B. (1995). Analysis of optimal conditions for retroviral-mediated transduction of primitive human hematopoietic cells. *Blood* **86,** 101–110.
10. Simmons, P.J., Levesque, J.-P., and Zannettino, A.C.W. (1997). Cell adhesive molecules and their roles in regulating hemopoiesis. *Bailleres Clin. Hematol.* **10,** 485–505.
11. Hackney, J.A., Charbord, P., Brunk, B.P., Stoeckert, C.J., Lemischka, I.R., and Moore, K.A. (2002). A molecular profile of a hematopoietic stem cell niche. *Proc. Natl. Acad. Sci. U. S. A.* **99,** 13061–13066.
12. Ivanova, N.B., Dimos, J.T., Schaniel, C., Hackney, J.A., Moore, K.A., and Lemischka, I.R. (2002). A stem cell molecular signature. *Science* **298,** 601–604.
13. Dexter, T.M., Allen, T.D., and Lajitha, L.G. (1977). Conditions controlling the proliferation of hematopoietic stem cells in vitro. *J. Cell Physiol.* **91,** 335–344.

14. Phillips, R.L., Ernst, R.E., Brunk, B., Ivanova, N., Mahan, M.A., Deanehan, J.K., Moore, K.A., Overton, G.C., and Lemischka, I.R. (2000). The genetic program of hematopoietic stem cells. *Science* **288,** 1635–1640.
15. Lorenz, E., Uphoff, D., Reid, T.R., and Shelton, E. (1951). Modification of irradiation injury in mice and guinea pigs by bone marrow injections. *J. Natl. Cancer Inst.* **12,** 197–201.
16. Lindsley, D.L., Odell, T.T., and Tausche, F.G. (1955). Implantation of functional erythropoietic elements following total body irradiation. *Proc. Soc. Exp. Biol. Med.* **90,** 512–515.
17. Ford, C.E., Hamerton, J.L., Barnes, D.W.H., and Loutit, J.F. (1956). Cytological identification of radiation chimeras. *Nature* **177,** 452–454 .
18. Lemischka, I.R., Raulet, D.H., and Mulligan, R.C. (1986). Developmental potential and dynamic behaviour of hematopoietic stem cells. *Cell* **45,** 917–927.
19. Snodgrass, R., and Keller, G. (1987). Clonal fluctuation within the heamatopoietic system of mice reconstituted with retrovirus-infected stem cells. *EMBO J.* **6,** 3955–3600.
20. Capel, B., Hawley, R., Covarrubias, L., Hawley, T., and Mintz, B. (1989). Clonal contributions of small numbers of retrovirally marked hematopoietic stem cells engrafted in unirradiated neonatal *W/W*^{v} mice. *Proc. Natl. Acad. Aci. U. S. A.* **86,** 4564–4568.
21. Spangrude, G.J., Heimfeld, S., and Weissman, I.L. (1988). Purification and characterization of mouse hematopoietic stem cells. *Science* **241,** 58–62.
22. Harrison, D.E., Astle, C.M., and Lerner, C. (1988). Number and continuous proliferative pattern of transplanted primitive imunohematopoietic stem cells. *Proc. Natl. Acad. Sci. U. S. A.* **85,** 822–826.
23. Sutherland, D.R., and Keating, A. (1992). The CD34 antigen: structure, biology, and potential clinical applications. *J. Hematother.* **1,** 115–129.
24. Berenson, R.J., Bensinger, W.I., Hill, R.S., Andrews, R.G., Garcia-Lopez, J., Kalamasz, D.F., Still, B.S., Spitzer, G., Buckner, C.D., Bernstein, I.D., and Thomas, E.D. (1991). Engraftment after infusion of CD34+ marrow cells in patients with breast cancer or neuroblastoma. *Blood* **77,** 1717–1722.
25. Shpall, E.J., Jones, R.B., Bearman, S.I., Franklin, W.A., Archer, P.G., Curiel, T., Bitter, M., Claman, H.N., Stemmer, S.M., and Purdy, M. (1994). Transplantation of enriched CD34 positive autologous marrow into breast cancer patients following high dose chemotherapy: influence of CD34$^+$ peripheral blood progenitors and growth factors on engraftment. *J. Clin. Oncol.* **12,** 28–36.
26. Link, H., Arseniev, L., Bahre, O., Kadar, J.G., Diedrich, H., and Poliwoda, H. (1996). Transplantation of allogeneic CD34+ blood cells. *Blood* **87,** 4903–4909.
27. Bensinger, W.I., Buckner, C.D., Rowley, S., Demirer, T., Storb, R., and Appelbaum, F.A. (1996). Transplantation of allogeneic CD34+ peripheral blood stem cells (PBSC) in patients with advanced hematologic malignancy. *Bone Marrow Transplant Suppl.* **2,** S38–39.
28. Andrews, R.G., Bryant, E.M., Bartelmez, S.H., Muirhead, D.Y., Knitter, G.H., Bensinger, W., Strong, D.M., and Bernstein, I.D. (1992). CD34$^+$ marrow cells devoid of T and B lymphocytes reconstitute stable lymphopoiesis and myelopoiesis in lethally irradiated allogeneic baboons. *Blood* **80,** 1693–16701.
29. Guenechea, G., Gan, O.I., Dorrell, C., and Dick, J.E. (2001). Distinct classes of human stem cells that differ in proliferative and self-renewal potential. *Nat. Immunol.* **2,** 75–82.
30. Thomas, T.E., Abraham, S.J., Phillips, G.L., and Lansdorp, P.M. (1992). A simple procedure for large-scale density separation of bone marrow cells for transplantation. *Transplantation* **53,** 1163–1165.
31. Wagner, J.E., Donnenberg, A.D., Noga, S.J., Cremo, C.A., Gao, I.K., Yin, H.J., Vogelsang, G.B., Rowley, S., Saral, R., and Santos, G.W. (1988). Lymphocyte depletion of donor bone marrow by counterflow centrifugal elutriation: Results of a phase I clinical trial. *Blood* **72,** 1168–1176.
32. Jones, J., Wagner, J.E., Celano, P., Zicha, M.S., and Sharkis, S.J. (1990). Separation of pluripotent haematopoietic stem cells from spleen colony-forming cells. *Nature* **347,** 188–189.
33. Gordon, M.Y., Marley, S.B., Davidson, R.J., Grand, F.H., Lewis, J.L., Nguyen, D.X., Lloyd, S., and Goldman, J.M. (2000). Contact-mediated inhibition of human haematopoietic progenitor cell proliferation may be conferred by stem cell antigen, CD34. *Hematol. J.* **1,** 77–86.
34. Bertoncello, I., Hodgson, G.S., and Bradley, T.R. (1985). Multiparameter analysis of transplantable hemopoietic stem cells: I. The separation and enrichment of stem cells homing to marrow and spleen on the basis of rhodamine-123 fluorescence. *Exp. Hematol.* **13,** 999–1006.
35. Spangrude, G.J., and Johnson, G.R. (1990). Resting and activated subsets of mouse multi-potent hematopoietic stem cells. *Proc. Natl. Acad. Sci. U. S. A.* **87,** 7433–7437.
36. Wolf, N.S., Kone, A., Priestly, G.V., and Bartelmez, S.H. (1993). In vivo and in vitro characterization of long-term repopulating primitive hematopoietic cells isolated by sequential Hoechst 33342-rhodamine 123 FACS selection. *Exp. Hematol.* **21,** 614–622.
37. Bradford, G.B., Williams, B., Rossi, R., and Bertoncello, I. (1997). Quiescence, cycling, and turnover in the primitive hematopoietic stem cell compartment. *Exp. Hematol.* **25,** 445–453.
38. Ottmann, O.G., Stella, C.C., Eder, M., Reutzel, P., Strocker, S., Hoelzer, D., and Ganser, A. (1991). Regulation of early hematopoiesis in serum-deprived cultures of mafosfamide-treated and untreated CD34-enriched bone marrow cells. *Exp. Hematol.* **19,** 773–778.
39. Winton, E.F., and Colenda, K.W. (1987). Use of long-term human marrow cultures to demonstrate progenitor cell precursors in marrow treated with 4-hydroperoxycyclophosphamide. *Exp. Hematol.* **15,** 710–714.
40. Beradi, A.C., Wang, A., Levine, J.D., Lopez, P., and Scadden, D.T. (1995). Functional isolation and characterisation of hematopoietic stem cells. *Science* **267,** 104–108.
41. Haylock, D.N., Horsfall, M., Dowse, T.L., Ramshaw, H.S., Niutta, S., Protopsaltis, S., Peng, L., Burrell, C., Rappold, I., Buhring H.-J., and Simmons, P. (1997). Increased recruitment of hematopoietic progenitor cells underlies the ex vivo expansion potential of FLT3 ligand. *Blood* **90,** 2260–2272.
42. Haylock, D.N., Niutta, S., Levesque, J.-P., To, L.B., and Simmons, P.J. (1997). Megakaryocyte growth and development factor (MGDF) preferentially promotes survival and is essential for maximal recruitment 1997 of adult bone marrow CD34+CD38- cells into division. *Blood* **90** (Suppl. 1), 474.
43. Metcalf, D., and Burgess, A.W. (1982). Clonal analysis of progenitor cell commitment to granulocyte or macrophage production. *J. Cell Physiol.* **111,** 275–282.
44. Metcalf, D. (1984). "The Hemopoietic Colony Stimulating Factors." Elsevier, Amsterdam.
45. Moore, M.A.S., Sheridan, A.P.C., Allen, T.D., and Dexter, T.M. (1979). Prolonged hematopoiesis in a primate bone marrow culture system: Characterisation of stem cell production and the hematopoietic microenvironment. *Blood* **54,** 775–793.

46. Gordon, M.Y., Riley, G.P., and Greaves, D.R. (1987). Plastic adherent progenitor cells in human bone marrow. *Exp. Hematol.* **15,** 772–778.
47. Sutherland, H.J., Eaves, C.J., Eaves, A.C., Dragowska, W., and Lansdorp, P.M. (1989). Characterisation and partial purification of human marrow cells capable of initiating long-term hematopoiesis in vitro. *Blood* **74,** 1563–1570.
48. Leary, A.G., and Ogawa, M. (1987). Blast cell colony assay for umbilical cord blood and adult bone marrow progenitors. *Blood* **69,** 953–956.
49. Rowley, S.D., Sharkis, S.J., and Hattenburg, C. (1987). Culture from human bone marrow of blast cell progenitor cell with an extensive proliferative capacity. *Blood* **69,** 804–808.
50. Iscove, N.N., Shaw, A.R., and Keller, G. (1989). Net increase of pluripotential hematopoietic precursors in suspension culture in response to IL-1 and IL-3. *J. Immunol.* **142,** 2332–2337.
51. Smith, C., Gasparetto, C., Collins, N., Gillio, A., Muench, M., O'Reilly, R.J., and Moore, M.A.S. (1991). Purification and partial characterization of a human hematopoietic precursor population. *Blood* **77,** 2122–2128.
52. Srour, E.F., Hoffman, R., and Zanjani, E.D. (1992). Animal models for human hematopoiesis. *J. Hematother.* **1,** 143–153.
53. McCune, J.M., Namikawa, R., Kaneshima, H., Shultz, L.D., Lieberman, M., and Weissman, I.L. (1988). The SCID-hu mouse: murine model for the analysis of human hematolymphoid differentiation and function. *Science* **241,** 1632–1639.
54. Namikawa, R., Weilbacher, K.N., and Kaneshima, H. (1990). Long-term human hematopoiesis in the SCID hu mouse. *J. Exp. Med.* **172,** 1055–1063.
55. Negrin, R.S., Atkinson, K., Leemhuis, T., Hanania, E., Juttner, C., Tierney, K., Hu, W.W., Johnston, L.J., Shizurn, J.A., Stockerl-Goldstein, K.E., Blume, K.G., Weissman, I.L., Bower, S., Baynes, R., Dansey, R., Karanes, C., Peters, W., and Klein, J. (2000). Transplantation of highly purified CD34+Thy-1+ hematopoietic stem cells in patients with metastatic breast cancer. *Biol. Blood Marrow Transplant.* **6,** 262–271.
56. Bhatia, M., Wang, J.C., Kapp, U., Bonnet, D., and Dick, J.E. (1997). Purification of primitive human hematopoietic cells capable of repopulating immune-deficient mice. *Proc. Natl. Acad. Sci. U. S. A.* **94,** 5320–5325.
57. Zhou, S., Schuetz, J.D., Bunting, K.D., Colapietro, A.-M., Sampath, J., Morris, J.J., Lagutina, I., Grosveld, G.C., Osawa, M., Nakauchi, H., and Sorrentino, B.P. (2001).The ABC transporter Bcrpl/ABCG2 is expressed in a wide variety of stem cells and is a molecular determinant of the side-population phenotype. *Nat. Med.* **7,** 1028–1034.
58. Scharenberg, C.W., Harkey, M.A., and Torok-Storb, B. (2002). The ABCG2 transporter is an efficient Hoechst 33342 efflux pump and is preferentially expressed by immature human hematopoietic progenitors. *Blood* **99,** 507–512.
59. Goodell, M.A., Brose, K., Paradis, G., Conner, A.S., and Mulligan, R.C. (1996). Isolation and functional properties of murine hematopoietic stem cells that are replicating in vivo. *J. Exp. Med.* **183,** 1797–1806.
60. Miraglia, S., Godfrey, W., Yin, A.H., Arkins, K., Warnke, R., Holden, J.T., Bray, R.A., Waller, E.K., and Buck, D.W. (1997). A novel five-transmembrane hematopoietic stem cell antigen: isolation, characterization, and molecular cloning. *Blood* **90,** 5013–5021.
61. Yin, A.H., Miraglia, S., Zanjani, E.D., Almeida-Porada, G., Ogawa, M., Leary, A.G., Olweus, J., Kearney, J., and Buck, D.W. (1997). AC133, a novel marker for human hematopoietic stem and progenitor cells. *Blood* **90,** 5002–5012.
62. de Wynter, E.A., Buck, D., Hart, C., Heywood, R., Coutinho, L.H., Clayton, A., Rafferty, J.A., Burt, D., Guenechea, G., Bueren, J.A., Gagen, D., Fairbairn, L.J., Lord, B.I., and Testa, N.G. (1998). CD34+AC133+ cells isolated from cord blood are highly enriched in long-term culture-initiating cells, NOD/SCID-repopulating cells and dendritic cell progenitors. *Stem Cells* **16,** 387–396.
63. Gordon, P.R., Leimig, T., Babarin-Dorner, A., Houston, J., Holladay, M., Mueller, I., Geiger, T., and Handgretinger, R. (2003). Large-scale isolation of CD133+ progenitor cells from G-CSF mobilized peripheral blood stem cells. *Bone Marrow Transplant* **31,** 17–22.
64. Gallacher, L., Murdoch, B., Wu, D.M., Karanu, F.N., Keeney, M., and Bhatia, M. (2000). Isolation and characterization of human CD34(–)Lin(–) and CD34(+)Lin(–) hematopoietic stem cells using cell surface markers AC133 and CD7. *Blood* **95,** 2813–2820.
65. Ramshaw, H.S., Haylock, D., Swart, B., Gronthos, S., Horsfall, M.J., Niutta, S., and Simmons, P.J. (2001). Monoclonal antibody BB9 raised against bone marrow stromal cells identifies a cell-surface glycoprotein expressed by primitive human hemopoietic progenitors. *Exp. Hematol.* **29,** 981–992.
66. Simmons, P.J., and Torok-Storb, B. (1991). CD34 expression by stromal precursors in normal human adult bone marrow. *Blood* **78,** 2848–2853.
67. Waller, E.K., Olweus, J., Lund-Johansen, F., Huang, S., Nguyen, M., Guo, G.R., and Terstappen, L. (1995). The "common stem cell" hypothesis reevaluated: human fetal bone marrow contains separate populations of hematopoietic and stromal progenitors. *Blood* **85,** 2422–2435.
68. Gronthos, S., and Simmons, P.J. (1996). The biology and application of human bone marrow stromal cell precursors. *J. Hematother.* **5,** 15–23.
69. Zannettino, A.C., Berndt, M.C., Butcher, C., Butcher, E.C., Vadas, M.A., and Simmons, P.J. (1995). Primitive human hematopoietic progenitors adhere to P-selectin (CD62P). *Blood* **85,** 3466–3477.
70. Tavian, M., Brouard, N., Noel, F., Haylock, D.N., Simmons, P.J., and Peault, B. (2002). BB9, a surface molecule of adult bone marrow stromal cells, marks candidate multipotent Pre-HSC within the para-aortic splanchnopleura in the human embryo. *Blood* **100,** 506.
71. Li, J., Li, Y., Brophy, P.D., and Kershawt, D.B. (2001). Gene structure and alternative splicing of murine podocalyxin: a member of the CD34 sialomucin family. *DNA Seq.* **12,** 407–412.
72. Sassetti, C., Van Zante, A., and Rosen, S.D. (2000). Identification of endoglycan, a member of the CD34/podocalyxin family of sialomucins. *J. Biol. Chem.* **275,** 9001–9010.
73. Owasa, M., Hanada, K., Hamada, H., and Nakauchi, H. (1996). Long-term lymphohematopoietic reconstitution by a single CD34-low/negative hematopoietic stem cell. *Science* **273,** 242–245.
74. Goodell, M.A., Rosenweig, M., Kim, H., Marks, D.F., DeMaria, M., Paradis, G., Grupp, S.A., Sieff, C.A., Mulligan, R.C., and Johnson, R.P. (1997). Dye efflux studies suggest that hematopoietic stem cells expressing low or undetectable levels of CD34 antigen exist in multiple species. *Nat. Med.* **3,** 1337–1345.
75. Morel, F., Galy, A., Chen, B., and Szilvassy, S.J. (1998). Equal distribution of competitive long-term repopulating stem cells in the CD34+ and CD34- fractions of Thy-1lowLin-/lowSca-1+ bone marrow cells. *Exp. Hematol.* **26,** 440–448.
76. Zanjani, E.D., Almeida-Porada, G., Livingston, A.G., Flake, A.W., and Ogawa, M. (1998). Human bone marrow CD34- cells engraft

in vivo and undergo multilineage expression that includes giving rise to CD34+ cells. *Exp. Hematol.* **26,** 353–360.

77. Zanjani, E.D., Almeida-Porada, G., Livingston, A.G., Porada, C.D., and Ogawa, M. (1999). Engraftment and multilineage expression of human bone marrow CD34- cells in vivo. *Ann. N. Y. Acad. Sci.* **872,** 220–231.
78. Bhatia, M., Bonnet, D., Murdoch, B., Gan, O.I., and Dick, J.E. (1998). A newly discovered class of human hematopoietic cells with SCID-repopulating activity. *Nat. Med.* **4,** 1038–1045.
79. Donnelly, D.S., Zelterman, D., Sharkis, S., and Krause, D.S. (1999). Functional activity of murine CD34+ and CD34– hematopoietic stem cell populations. *Exp. Hematol.* **27,** 788–796.
80. Sato, T., Laver, J.H., and Ogawa, M. (1999). Reversible expression of CD34 by murine hematopoietic stem cells. *Blood* **94,** 2548–2554.
81. Fujisaki, T., Berger, M.G., Rose-John, S., and Eaves, C.J. (1999). Rapid differentiation of a rare subset of adult human Lin$^-$CD34$^-$CD38$^-$ cells stimulated by multiple growth factors in vitro. *Blood* **94,** 1926–1932.
82. Nakamura, Y., Ando, K., Chargui, J., Kawada, H., Sato, T., Tssuji, T., Hotta, T., and Kato, S. (1999). Ex vivo generation of CD34$^+$ cells from CD34$^-$ hematopoietic cells. *Blood* **94,** 4053–4059.
83. Andrews, R.G., Peterson, L.J., Morris, J., Potter, J., Heyward, S., Gough, M., Bryant, E., Kiem, H. (2000). Differential engraftment of genetically modified CD34(+) and CD34(–) hematopoietic cell subsets in lethally irradiated baboons. *Exp. Hematol.* **28,** 508–518.
84. Ito, T., Tajima, F., and Ogawa, M. (2000). Developmental changes of CD34 expression by murine hematopoietic stem cells. *Exp. Hematol.* **28,** 1269–1273.
85. Matsuoka, S., Ebihara, Y., Xu, M., Ishii, T., Sugiyama, D., Yoshino, H., Ueda, T., Manabe, A., Tanaka, R., Ikeda, Y., Nakahata, T., and Tsuji, K. (2001). CD34 expression on long-term repopulating hematopoietic stem cells changes during developmental stages. *Blood* **97,** 419–425.
86. Verfaillie, C.M., Almeida-Porada, G., Wissink, S., and Zanjani, E.D. (2000). Kinetics of engraftment of CD34(–) and CD34(+) cells from mobilized blood differs from that of CD34(–) and CD34(+) cells from bone marrow. *Exp. Hematol.* **28,** 1071–1079.
87. Danet, G.H., Luongo, J.L., Butler, G., Lu, M.M., Tenner, A.J., Simon, M.C., and Bonnet, D.A. (2002). C1qRp defines a new human stem cell population with hematopoietic and hepatic potential. *Proc. Natl. Acad. Sci. U. S. A.* **99,** 10441–10445.
88. Reisner, Y., Kapoor, N., Kirkpatrick, D., Pollack, M.S., Cunningham-Rundles, S., Dupont, B., Hodes, M.Z., Good, R.A., and O'Reilly, R.J. (1983). Transplantation for severe combined immunodeficiency with HLA-A,B,D,DR incompatible parental marrow cells fractionated by soybean agglutinin and sheep red blood cells. *Blood* **61,** 341–348.
89. Reisner, Y., Kapoor, N., O'Reilly, R.J., and Good, R.A. (1980). Allogeneic bone marrow transplantation using stem cells fractionated by lectins: VI, *in vitro* analysis of human and monkey bone marrow cells fractionated by sheep red blood cells and soybean agglutinin. *Lancet* **2**(8208,8209), 1320–1324.
90. Noga, S.J., Donnenberg, A.D., Schwartz, C.L., Strauss, L.C., Civin, C.I., and Santos, G.W. (1986). Development of a simplified counterflow centrifugation elutriation procedure for depletion of lymphocytes from human bone marrow. *Transplantation* **41,** 220–229.
91. Noga, S.J. (1999). Engineering hematopoietic grafts using elutriation and positive cell selection to reduce GVHD. *Cancer Treat. Res.* **101,** 311–330.
92. Waldmann, H., Polliak, A., Hale, G., Or, R., Cividalli, G., Weiss, L., Weshler, Z., Samuel, S., Manor, D., and Brautbar, C. (1984). Elimination of graft-versus-host disease by in-vitro depletion of alloreactive lymphocytes with a monoclonal rat anti-human lymphocyte antibody (CAMPATH-1). *Lancet* **2**(8401), 483–486.
93. Frame, J.N., Collins, N.H., Cartagena, T., Waldmann, H., O'Reilly, R.J., Dupont, B., and Kernan, N.A. (1989). T cell depletion of human bone marrow. Comparison of Campath-1 plus complement, anti-T cell ricin A chain immunotoxin, and soybean agglutinin alone or in combination with sheep erythrocytes or immunomagnetic beads. *Transplantation* **47,** 984–988.
94. Dreger, P., Viehmann, K., Steinmann, J., Eckstein, V., Muller-Ruchholtz, W., Loffler, H., and Schmitz N. (1995). G-CSF-mobilized peripheral blood progenitor cells for allogeneic transplantation: Comparison of T cell depletion strategies using different CD34+ selection systems or CAMPATH-1. *Exp. Hematol.* **23,** 147–154.
95. Polouckova, A., Vodvarkova, A., Kobylka, P., Hruba, A., Gasova, Z., Marinov, I., Fales, I., Sedlacek, P., Kozak, T., and Stary, J. (2001). Comparison of two different methods for CD34+ selection and T cell depletion in peripheral blood stem cell grafts—our experiences with CellPro, E rosetting and CliniMACS technique. *Neoplasma* **48,** 374–381.
96. Urbano-Ispizua, A., Solano, C., Brunet, S., de la Rubia, J., Odriozola, J., Zuazu, J., Figuera, A., Caballero, D., Martinez, C., Garcia, J., Sanz, G., Torrabadella, M., Alegre, A., Perez-Oteiza, J., Jurado, M., Oyonarte, S., Sierra, J., Garcia-Conde, J., and Rozman, C. (1998). Allogeneic transplantation of selected CD34+ cells from peripheral blood: experience of 62 cases using immunoadsorption or immunomagnetic technique. Spanish Group of Allo-PBT. *Bone Marrow Transplant* **22,** 519–525.
97. Voso, M.T., Hohaus, S., Moos, M., Pforsich, M., Cremer, F.W., Schlenk, R.F., Martin, S., Hegenbart, U., Goldschmidt, H., and Haas, R. (1999). Autografting with CD34+ peripheral blood stem cells: retained engraftment capability and reduced tumour cell content. *Br. J. Haematol.* **104,** 382–391.
98. Burgess, J., Mills, B., Griffith, M., Mansour, V., Weaver, C.H., Schwartzberg, L.S., Snyder, E.L., Krause, D.S., Yanovich, S., Prilutskaya, M., Umiel, T., and Moss, T.J. (2001). Breast tumor contamination of PBSC harvests: Tumor depletion by positive selection of CD34(+) cells. *Cytotherapy* **3,** 285–294.
99. Stewart, A.K., Vescio, R., Schiller, G., Ballester, O., Noga, S., Rugo, H., Freytes, C., Stadtmauer, E., Tarantolo, S., Sahebi, F., Stiff, P., Meharchard, J., Schlossman, R., Brown, R., Tully, H., Benyunes, M., Jacobs, C., Berenson, R., White, M., DiPersio, J., Anderson, K.C., and Berenson, J. (2001). Purging of autologous peripheral-blood stem cells using CD34 selection does not improve overall or progression-free survival after high-dose chemotherapy for multiple myeloma: results of a multicenter randomized controlled trial. *J. Clin. Oncol.* **19,** 3771–3779.
100. Hohaus, S., Pforsich, M., Murea, S., Abdallah, A., Lin, Y.S., Funk, L., Voso, M.T., Kaul, S., Schmid, H., Wallwiener, D., and Haas, R. (1997). Immunomagnetic selection of CD34+ peripheral blood stem cells for autografting in patients with breast cancer. *Br. J. Haematol.* **97,** 881–888.
101. Farley, T.J., Ahmed, T., Fitzgerald, M., and Preti, R.A. (1997). Optimization of CD34+ cell selection using immunomagnetic beads: implications for use in cryopreserved peripheral blood stem cell collections. *J. Hematother.* **6,** 53–60.
102. Preti, R.A., Lazarus, H.M., Winter, J., Stadtmauer, E.A., Nadasi, S., McMannis, J., Karandish, S., Jennis, A., Goldberg,

post-prigenitor cells have to be transplanted to competely abrogate neutropenia after peripheral blood transplantation? Results of a computer simulation. *Exp. Hematol.* **27,** 956–965.

152. Rubinstein, P., Carrier, C., Scaradavou, A., Kurtzberg, J., Adamson, J., Migliaccio, A.R., Berkowitz, R.L., Cabbad, M., Dobrila, N.L., Taylor, P.E., Rosenfield, R.E., and Stevens, C.E. (1998). Outcomes among 562 recipients of placental-blood transplants from unrelated donors. *N. Engl. J. Med.* **339,** 1565–1577.
153. Piacibello, W., Sanavio, F., Severino, A., Dane, A., Gammaitoni, L., Fagioli, F., Perissinotto, E., Cavalloni, G., Kollet, O., Lapidot, T., and Aglietta, M. (1999). Engraftment in nonobese diabetic severe combined immunodeficient mice of human CD34(+) cord blood cells after ex vivo expansion: Evidence for the amplification and self-renewal of repopulating stem cells. *Blood* **93,** 3736–3749.
154. Hogan, C.J., Shpall, E.J., McNiece, I., and Keller, G. (1997). Multilineage engraftment in NOD/LtSz-scid/scid mice from mobilized human CD34+ peripheral blood progenitor cells. *Biol. Blood Marrow Transplant.* **3,** 236–246.
155. Zanjani, E.D., Almeida-Porada, G., Ascensao, J.L., MacKintosh, F.R., and Flake, A.W. (1997). Transplantation of hematopoietic stem cells in utero. *Stem Cells* **1,** 79–92.
156. Anderson, D.M., Lyman, S.D., Baird, A., Wignall, J.M., Eisenman, J., Rauch, C., March, C.J., Boswell, H.S., Gimpel, S.D., and Cosman, D. (1990). Molecular cloning of mast cell growth factor, a hematopoietin that is active in both membrane bound and soluble forms. *Cell* **63,** 235–243.
157. Lyman, S.D., James, L., Johnson, L., Brasel, K., de vries, P., Escobar, S.S., Downey, H., Spett, R.R., Beckman, M.P., and McKenna, H.J. (1994). Cloning of the human homologue of the murine flt3 ligand: a growth factor for early hematopoietic progenitor cells. *Blood* **15,** 2795–2801.
158. Xu, M.J., Tsuji, K., Ueda, T., Mukouyama, Y.S., Hara, T., Yang, F.C., Ebihara, Y., Matsuoka, S., Manabe, A., Kikuchi, A., Ito, M., Miyajima, A., and Nakahata, T. (1998). Stimulation of mouse and human primitive hematopoiesis by murine embryonic aorta-gonad-mesonephros-derived stromal cell lines. *Blood* **92,** 2032–2040.
159. Shih, C.C., Hu, M.C., Hu, J., Medeiros, J., and Forman, S.J. (1999). Long-term ex vivo maintenance and expansion of transplantable human hematopoietic stem cells. *Blood* **94,** 1623–1636.
160. Ohneda, O., Fennie, C., Zheng, Z., Donahue, C., La, H., Villacorta, R., Cairns, B., and Lasky, L.A. (1998). Hematopoietic stem cell maintenance and differentiation are supported by embryonic aorta-gonad-mesonephros region-derived endothelium. *Blood* **92,** 908–919.
161. Moore, K.A., Ema, H., and Lemischka, I.R. (1997). In vitro maintenance of highly purified, transplantable hematopoietic stem cells. *Blood* **89,** 4337–4347.
162. Thiemann, F.T., Moore, K.A., Smogorzewska, E.M., Lemischka, I.R., and Crooks, G.M. (1998). The murine stromal cell line AFT024 acts specifically on human CD34+CD38-progenitors to maintain primitive function and immunophenotype in vitro. *Exp. Hematol.* **26,** 612–619.
163. Punzel, M., Moore, K.A., Lemischka, I.R., and Verfaillie, C.M. (1999). The type of stromal feeder used in limiting dilution assays influences frequency and maintenance assessment of human long-term culture initiating cells. *Leukemia* **13,** 92–97.
164. Lewis, I.D., Almeida-Porada, G., Du, J., Lemischka, I.R., Moore, K.A., Zanjani, E.D., and Verfaillie, C.M. (2001). Umbilical cord blood cells capable of engrafting in primary, secondary, and tertiary xenogeneic hosts are preserved after ex vivo culture in a noncontact system. *Blood* **97,** 3441–3449.
165. Nolta, J.A., Thiemann, F.T., Arakawa-Hoyt, J., Dao, M.A., Barsky, L.W., Moore, K.A., Lemischka, I.R., and Crooks, G.M. (2002). The AFT024 stromal cell line supports long-term ex vivo maintenance of engrafting multipotent human hematopoietic progenitors. *Leukemia* **16,** 352–361.
166. Cashman, J.D., and Eaves, C.J. (1999). Human growth factor-enhanced regeneration of transplantable human hematopoietic stem cells in nonobese diabetic/severe combined immunodeficient mice. *Blood* **93,** 481–487.
167. Yagi, M., Ritchie, K.A., Sitnicka, E., Storey, C., Roth, G.J., and Bartelmez, S. (1999). Sustained ex vivo expansion of hematopoietic stem cells mediated by thrombopoietin. *Proc. Natl. Acad. Sci. U. S. A.* **96,** 8126–8131.
168. Bhatia, M., Bonnet, D., Kapp, U., Wang, J.C., Murdoch, B., and Dick, J.E. (1997). Quantitative analysis reveals expansion of human hematopoietic repopulating cells after short-term ex vivo culture. *J. Exp. Med.* **186,** 619–624.
169. Gammaitoni, L., Bruno, S., Sanavio, F., Gunetti, M., Kollet, O., Cavalloni, G., Falda, M., Fagioli, F., Lapidot, T., Aglietta, M., and Piacibello, W. (2003). Ex vivo expansion of human adult stem cells capable of primary and secondary hemopoietic reconstitution. *Exp. Hematol.* **31,** 261–270.
170. Zandstra, P.W., Lauffenburger, D.A., and Eaves, C.J. (2000). A ligand-receptor signaling threshold model of stem cell differentiation control: a biologically conserved mechanism applicable to hematopoiesis. *Blood* **96,** 1215–1222.
171. Erben, U., Thiel, E., and Notter, M. (1999). Differential effects of a stem cell factor-immunoglobulin fusion protein on malignant and normal hematopoietic cells. *Cancer Res.* **15,** 2923–2930.
172. Bhatia, M., Bonnet, D., Wu, D., Murdoch, B., Wrana, J., Gallacher, L., and Dick, J.E. (1999). Bone morphogenetic proteins regulate the developmental program of human hematopoietic stem cells. *J. Exp. Med.* **189,** 1139–1148.
173. Bhardwaj, G., Murdoch, B., Wu, D., Baker, D.P., Williams, K.P., Chadwick, K., Ling, L.E., Karanu, F.N., and Bhatia, M. (2001). Sonic hedgehog induces the proliferation of primitive human hematopoietic cells via BMP regulation. *Nat. Immunol.* **2,** 172–180.
174. Karanu, F.N., Murdoch, B., Miyabayashi, T., Ohno, M., Koremoto, M., Gallacher, L., Wu, D., Itoh, A., Sakano, S., and Bhatia, M. (2001). Human homologues of Delta-1 and Delta-4 function as mitogenic regulators of primitive human hematopoietic cells. *Blood* **97,** 1960–1967.
175. Karanu, F.N., Murdoch, B., Gallacher, L., Wu, D.M., Koremoto, M., Sakano, S., and Bhatia, M. (2000). The notch ligand jagged-1 represents a novel growth factor of human hematopoietic stem cells. *J. Exp. Med.* **192,** 1365–1372.
176. Reya, T., Duncan, A.W., Ailles, L., Domen, J., Scherer, D.C., Willert, K., Hintz, L., Nusse, R., and Weissman, I.L. (2003). A role for Wnt signalling in self-renewal of haematopoietic stem cells. *Nature* **423,** 409–414.
177. Willert, K., Brown, J.D., Danenberg, E., Duncan, A.W., Weissman, I.L., Reya, T., Yates, J.R., and Nusse, R. (2003). Wnt proteins are lipid-modified and can act as stem cell growth factors. *Nature* **423,** 448–452.
178. Park, I.K., Qian, D., Kiel, M., Becker, M.W., Pihalja, M., Weissman, I.L., Morrison, S.J., and Clarke, M.F. (2003). Bmi-1 is required for maintenance of adult self-renewing haematopoietic stem cells. *Nature* **423,** 302–305.

Figure 56–3. Arabidopsis *shoot apical meristem (SAM) mutants.* (A) Wild-type SAM growing outward as a point and initiating lateral organs on the flanks. (B) Enlarged *clv3-2* SAM growing as a mound (arrow) and producing many extra flowers. (C) An *stm-11* seedling that lacks a functional SAM and forms cotyledons but no other lateral organs. (D) A *wus-1* adventitious SAM that has formed a reduced number of flowers. These flowers lack the inner organs, often terminating in a single stamen (arrowhead). (Reprinted with permission from (2002). *Annu. Rev. Plant Biol.* 53.)

limited number of lateral organs before prematurely terminating.[22] A few adventitious meristems ultimately undergo the transition to flowering and generate a reduced number of floral meristems that also fail to form the full complement of organs. Targeted misexpression of *STM* in developing leaves suppresses cell differentiation and instead maintains the competency of the cells to form lateral outgrowths and express the cell cycle regulatory genes *CycB1*;1[23] and *CycD3*.[24] From these data it is inferred that *STM* is required to prevent the differentiation of *Arabidopsis* SAM cells, including the stem cell reservoir, during both embryonic and postembryonic development.

STM and other KNOX proteins comprise a plant-specific clade of the Three Amino acid Loop Extension (TALE) superclass of homeodomain transcription factors.[25] Animals and fungi also contain TALE proteins, indicating a common ancestral origin for the superclass.[25,26] TALE class proteins are characterized by the presence of a conserved homeodomain that acts as a sequence-specific DNA binding domain and two motifs termed the ELK and MEINOX domains that may be involved in protein–protein interactions.[25,27] Phylogenetic and gene expression analysis distinguishes two classes of *knox* genes[28]: class I genes such as *STM* from *Arabidopsis* and *KNOTTED1* from *Zea mays* are characterized by meristem-specific mRNA accumulation, while class II genes are expressed more broadly throughout the plant.

STM is first expressed in one or two cells of the late globular stage embryo, in the region that is predicted to develop into the SAM.[29] *STM* acts very early during embryogenesis, because it is required for expression of the *UNUSUAL FLORAL ORGANS (UFO)* gene at the early heart stage.[20] After germination, *STM* is transcribed in all of the cells of vegetative and flowering meristems, but it is down-regulated in developing leaf and floral primordia. *STM* expression is thus associated with and is a marker for meristem activity throughout *Arabidopsis* development. Ectopic expression of *STM* is sufficient to induce the expression of the class I *knox* genes *KNAT1* and *KNAT2* but not the stem cell marker *CLV3,* revealing that *STM* is capable of inducing some meristem-expressed genes but not ectopic stem cell identity.[23]

Recent evidence indicates that a key function for *STM* is to repress the expression of the *ASYMMETRIC LEAVES1 (AS1)* gene in the SAM. *AS1* encodes a Myb domain putative transcription factor that is expressed only in lateral organ primordia, in a reciprocal domain to *STM*.[30] Plants carrying loss-of-function *as1* mutations form lobed leaves, which occasionally bear ectopic shoots, in which several class I *knox* genes are ectopically expressed.[31,32] Exclusion of *knox* gene activity from organ founder cells by *AS1* is, therefore, instrumental in the acquisition of differentiated cell fates.[33,34] *STM* negatively regulates *AS1* in the meristem apex,[30] preserving the stem cells and their immediate descendants in an uncommitted state. Thus, *stm* mutant embryos fail to establish a functional SAM because misexpression of *AS1* across the shoot apex causes the cells to assume the identities of differentiated cells. This pathway of mutual negative interactions between *Myb* and *knox* genes distinguishes organ founder cells from SAM cells, enabling spatial separation and tightly controlled regulation of lateral organ cell fate. The basic features of this pathway have also been well documented in maize *(Zea mays)* and snapdragon *(Antirrhinum majus)*.[35–37]

The *ZWILLE/PINHEAD (ZLL/PNH)* and *ARGONAUTE1 (AGO1)* genes are required for the correct specification of stem cells during *Arabidopsis* embryo development. Most *zll/pnh* mutant embryos fail to establish a functional SAM, and instead the shoot apex differentiates into a pin-like organ or a single leaf.[38–40] Subsequently, the *zll/pnh* seedlings form adventitious meristems *de novo* from the axils of the cotyledons and terminal leaf. These later-arising meristems develop relatively normally, bearing slightly defective but fertile flowers. Thus, *ZLL/PNH* is required primarily during embryogenesis to prevent the differentiation of stem cells in the center of the embryonic shoot apex. Expression of the SAM marker *STM* is correctly induced in *zll/pnh* embryonic SAMs, but it is not properly maintained at high levels later in embryogenesis.[39] The adventitious meristems that arise after *zll/pnh* seedling germination do not misregulate *STM,* suggesting that *ZLL/PNH* does not play an important regulatory role in postembryonic meristems. Thus, the main requirement for *ZLL/PNH* appears to be to transiently sustain high levels of *STM* expression during the late stages of embryo formation to preserve the stem cell population in an uncommitted, proliferative state.

Loss-of-function *ago1* mutations cause pleiotropic effects on overall plant architecture, affecting both lateral organs and the SAM.[41] Occasionally an *ago1* mutant will form a pin-like terminal structure at its shoot apex, although the penetrance of this phenotype is low. The *zll/pnh* SAM phenotype is also not completely penetrant, even among plants carrying null alleles of the locus,[40] which suggested that *ZLL/PNH* and *AGO1* might partially compensate for one another during *Arabidopsis* development. Indeed, the *zll/pnh ago1* double mutants have more severe embryo phenotypes than either single mutant and fail to accumulate STM protein in the SAM.[40] The *ago1* mutation also behaves dominantly when *zll/pnh* is homozygous, and vice versa, indicating that the severity of each mutant phenotype is sensitive to the dose of the other. Thus *ZLL/PNH* and *AGO1* have overlapping functions in the maintenance of *Arabidopsis* embryonic stem cells.

ZLL/PNH and *AGO1* are members of the Argonaute gene family.[39,41] Members of this family, which are found throughout eukaryotes (see reference 42 for review), encode ~100–120 kDa highly basic proteins. Argonaute proteins contain two highly conserved domains, a PAZ domain and a PIWI domain.[43] The 130 amino acid PAZ domain, which is believed to mediate protein–protein interactions such as homodimerization and heterodimerization,[43] is also found in Dicer, an RNase III-like dsRNA endonuclease.[44] The 300 amino acid C-terminal PIWI domain has as yet no defined function. The *Arabidopsis* genome encodes 10 putative Argonaute proteins, the other eight of which are uncharacterized. However, a rice homolog of *ZLL/PNH* called *OsPNH1* has been identified that is likewise required for stem cell maintenance and encodes a cytosolic protein.[45]

Argonaute family proteins have been grouped into two subclasses based on phylogenetic analysis. Members of one subclass resemble AGO1 and the rabbit translation initiation factor eIF2C, whereas members of the other more closely resemble *Drosophila* Piwi.[42] The *piwi* gene is necessary for mediating stem cell fate decisions in the fruit fly, because adult flies carrying loss-of-function *piwi* mutations completely lack germline stem cells.[46] The *piwi* gene is expressed in the germline stem cells themselves and also in the surrounding somatic cells of the ovary, and *piwi* transcription in the ovary maintains the self-renewing, asymmetric stem cell divisions through a somatic signaling mechanism.[47] Similarly, the Piwi-related PRG-1 and PRG-2 proteins are required for stem cell proliferation and fertility in *Caenorhabditis elegans,*[47] indicating that Argonaute family members may play evolutionarily conserved roles in germline stem cell maintenance.

AGO1 and *ZLL/PNH* are widely expressed during *Arabidopsis* development, consistent with their pleiotropic effects on plant growth. *AGO1* is transcribed throughout the plant at all stages of development.[41] *ZLL/PNH* expression is first detected in embryos at the four-cell stage, throughout the embryo proper.[39,40] As embryogenesis proceeds, *ZLL/PNH* expression is gradually lost from the protoderm and becomes concentrated in the center of the embryo. After germination, high levels of *ZLL/PNH* expression are found in the provascular tissues, whereas much lower levels are detected throughout the SAM and on the adaxial side of the cotyledon primordia.

Although the precise biochemical mechanism of AGO1 and ZLL/PNH function is not yet understood, recent studies have revealed a role for AGO1 in posttranscriptional gene silencing (PTGS).[48] PTGS is an RNA silencing phenomenon related to RNA interference and quelling, processes through which the generation of double-stranded RNA (dsRNA) induces the homology-dependent degradation of the cognate mRNA (reviewed in reference 49). The *Drosophila* ago2 protein is a component of the RNA-induced silencing complex (RISC), which contains processed small interfering RNAs (siRNAs) and associates with the cognate mRNA to target it for cleavage.[50] The *ago1* null alleles are impaired in the PTGS of transgenes and also in disease resistance.[51] ZLL/PNH, on the other hand, does not participate in PTGS[51] and consequently may function in a related, but separable, pathway of gene regulation from AGO1.

WUSCHEL (WUS) gene activity is required for renewal of the stem cell population in the *Arabidopsis* SAM. Plants carrying loss-of-function *wus* mutations do not organize a functional SAM during embryogenesis, forming an aberrant flat apex instead of a tiered dome of cells between the cotyledons.[52] After germination, *wus* mutants sporadically generate adventitious meristems at multiple foci, but these meristems are transient and produce only a few organs before terminating prematurely. Unlike wild-type plants, which initiate lateral organs from the flanks of the SAM, *wus* mutant plants initiate organ primordia randomly across the entire shoot apex. Repeated creation and premature termination of *wus* meristems eventually produces bushy plants with multiple rosettes. Some *wus* meristems enter the reproductive phase and form abnormal flowering meristems (Fig. 56–3D). These flowering meristems often develop aerial rosettes of leaves and terminate prematurely after producing a reduced number of flowers that lack the inner organ types. These phenotypes reveal that *WUS* activity is necessary to maintain the pool of undifferentiated stem cells in the SAM.[52]

WUS encodes a homeodomain protein, of a novel subtype that is distantly related to STM, and is localized to the nucleus.[53] *WUS* expression is initiated in the 16-cell stage of embryo development, in the inner cells of the apical region above the O′ line.[53] During subsequent cell divisions, *WUS* expression gradually becomes restricted to a small domain of subepidermal cells in the center of the embryonic shoot apex. Following germination, the *WUS* expression domain consists of a small group of cells in the interior layers of the SAM, beneath the stem cell population.[53] *WUS* and *STM* are activated independently of one another, but *STM* expression is eventually lost in *wus* mutant seedlings and vice versa. Strong *stm* alleles are epistatic to *wus* alleles, indicating that *STM* most likely establishes the embryonic stem cell reservoir on which *WUS* acts. However, *wus* mutations enhance intermediate and weak *stm* phenotypes,[54] which demonstrates that the limited postembryonic meristematic activity displayed by weaker *stm* alleles requires *WUS* function. *WUS,* therefore, acts downstream of *STM* to maintain stem cells once they are formed. Maintenance of the *WUS* expression domain also requires the activity of *FASCIATED1 (FAS1)* and *FAS2,* which encode components of *Arabidopsis* chromatin assembly factor-1.[55] FAS1 and FAS2 are, therefore, likely to facilitate the appropriate chromatin conformation to promote stable *WUS* gene transcription.

Finally, experiments in petunia *(Petunia hybrida)* have identified a requirement for the *HAIRY MERISTEM (HAM)* gene in SAM maintenance. The *ham* mutant SAMs generate a variable number of leaves and then terminate, differentiating into stem tissue that fails to respond to activity of the meristem genes *PhSTM* and *PhWUS.*[56] *HAM* encodes a putative transcription factor of the GRAS family that is expressed in stem provasculature and lateral organ primordia (i.e., in differentiating cells outside the stem cell domain). Analysis of unstable *ham* alleles shows that *HAM* acts in a non–cell autonomous manner to promote stem cell identity and that it functions in parallel with *PhWUS.* It is proposed that *HAM* represents a means through which cells that depart the stem cell domain actively sustain a field of uncommitted cells in their wake, preventing the uncommitted cells from entering a default pathway of differentiation into stem tissue.[56]

Intercellular Signaling Is Required for Stem Cell Maintenance

In *Arabidopsis,* three *CLAVATA* genes (*CLV1, 2,* and *3*) encode key regulators of the stem cell reservoir in shoot and floral meristems. Recessive loss-of-function *clv1, clv2,* or *clv3* mutants form enlarged SAMs, which contain more stem cells than wild-type SAMs, beginning during embryogenesis.[57–60] The stem cell reservoir in *clv* mutant SAMs enlarges progressively throughout development,[19,60] such that by the time the plant undergoes the transition to flowering the SAM becomes massively overgrown (Fig. 56–3B). The *clv* mutants also generate enlarged floral meristems, which produce flowers containing extra organs including up to four times the normal number of carpels that fuse to form a club-shaped ("clavata") fruit. In addition, the floral meristems of plants carrying strong *clv* alleles often fail to terminate on carpel formation and accumulate stem cells in the center of the mature fruit. These phenotypes indicate that the wild-type function of *CLV1, CLV2,* and *CLV3* is to restrict stem cell accumulation in shoot and floral meristems. Mutants with enlarged SAM phenotypes resembling those of the *clv* mutants have also been reported in tomato,[61,62] maize,[63] and soybean.[64]

The *clv1, clv2,* and *clv3* mutant phenotypes are very similar to one another, and genetic analysis has revealed that the *CLV* genes act together in the same pathway to regulate stem cell fate.[59,60] Double mutants carrying weak *clv1* and *clv3* alleles display severe *clv* mutant phenotypes, whereas those carrying strong *clv1* and *clv3* alleles have phenotypes indistinguishable from either single mutant.[59] Furthermore, doubly heterozygous *clv1/+ clv3/+* plants display an intermediate *clv* phenotype. The *clv2* mutants display slightly weaker stem cell phenotypes than *clv1* and *clv3* mutants, and strong *clv1* and *clv3* alleles are epistatic to *clv2* with regard to these traits.[60] However, although *clv1* and *clv3* mutations solely affect stem cells, *clv2* mutations cause more pleiotropic phenotypes. Thus *CLV1, CLV2,* and *CLV3* act in the same genetic pathway in shoot and floral meristems, but *CLV2* also functions more broadly to regulate other aspects of development.

The cloning of the *CLV* genes revealed that they encode key components of a meristem signal transduction pathway. The *CLV1* gene encodes a receptor kinase composed of 21 extracellular leucine-rich repeats (LRRs), a transmembrane domain, and an intracellular serine/threonine kinase domain.[65] The CLV1 kinase domain has been shown to autophosphorylate and transphosphorylate serines and threonine residues, indicating that it is capable of intracellular signal transduction.[66] The *CLV2* gene encodes a receptor-like protein composed of extracellular LRRs, a transmembrane domain, and a short cytoplasmic tail.[67] Both CLV1 and CLV2 are members of large families of receptor proteins found in higher plants. More than 200 putative CLV1-like LRR receptor-like kinases (LRR-RLKs) and at least 50 CLV2-like LRR receptor-like proteins have been identified in the *Arabidopsis* genome.[68] Mutations in a maize orthologue of *CLV2,* called *FEA2,* cause enlargement of tassel and ear meristems,[63] indicating that CLV pathway functions may be conserved among higher plants. Members of the LRR-RLK family function in various plant signaling processes, including development,[69,70] immune response,[71] and hormone perception.[72] However, the functions of the vast majority of the *Arabidopsis* LRR receptor-like proteins are unknown. The LRR motif is commonly found in protein–protein interaction domains of both animal and plant proteins,[73] which suggests that the CLV1 and CLV2 receptors might bind protein or peptide ligands through their extracellular LRR domains.

CLV3 is a founding member of a plant-specific family of putative signaling molecules called the CLV3/ESR-related (CLE) proteins. The *CLV3* gene encodes a 96 amino acid polypeptide with an N-terminal signal sequence.[19] The signal peptide directs CLV3 through the secretory pathway, and CLV3 functions in the extracellular space as is characteristic of diffusible signaling proteins.[74] The CLV3 protein also contains a C-terminal 14 amino acid motif that is highly conserved among three maize Embryo Surrounding Region (ESR) proteins, the products of two dozen *Arabidopsis CLE* genes, and ESTs from various other plants.[75] The *ESR* genes are expressed in a restricted region of the maize endosperm surrounding the developing embryo, where they are proposed to mediate interactions between the two tissues.[76,77] The function of the other *Arabidopsis CLE* genes, which are expressed in diverse tissues,[78] is not known.

CLV1, CLV2, and CLV3 are components of a multimeric signaling complex (Fig. 56–4). CLV1 (a 105-kDa monomeric protein) is associated with two discrete protein complexes in plant extracts, a 185-kDa complex and a more abundant 450-kDa complex, as a disulfide-linked multimer.[79] A functional CLV1 kinase domain is required for formation of the 450-kDa complex, indicating that this complex contains the active form of CLV1 and that the 185-kDa complex is inactive. The 450-kDa complex is not detected in *clv3* mutant plants, indicating that the presence of CLV3 is required for the

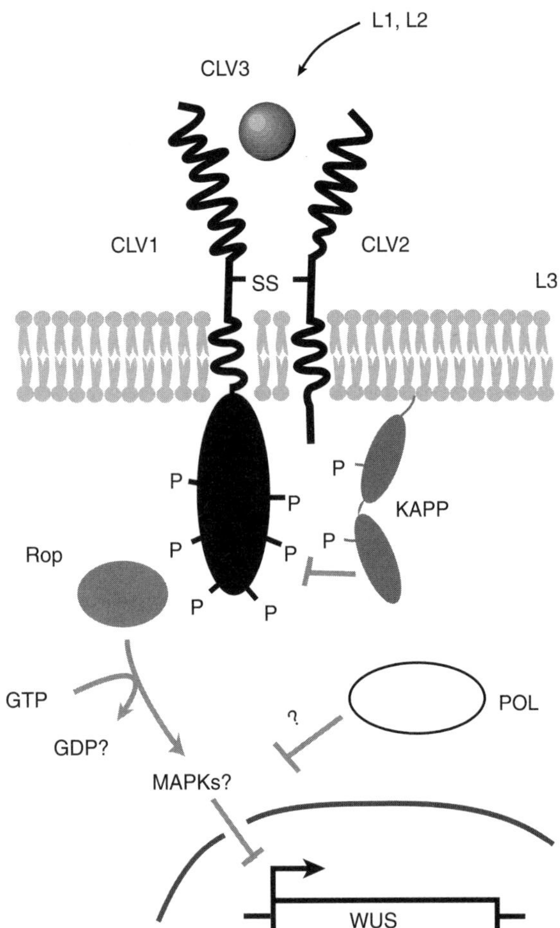

Figure 56–4. *Schematic representation of the CLV signal transduction complex.* CLV3 is secreted from the stem cells (L1, L2) and moves through the extracellular space to the underlying cells (L3). The CLV1 receptor kinase forms a heteromeric complex with the CLV2 receptor-like protein at the plasma membrane of the underlying cells. Binding of CLV3 to the extracellular LRR domains of CLV1 and CLV2 is proposed to stimulate the assembly of an active intracellular signaling complex that includes the KAPP type 2C protein phosphatase and a Rop GTPase. The signal is relayed to the nucleus via as yet unidentified factors, potentially components of a MAP kinase (MAPK) cascade, to limit *WUS* transcription. POL is proposed to function either as a negative regulator of the CLV signaling pathway or as a positive regulator of *WUS* that is downregulated by CLV signaling.

formation of an active signaling complex.[79] CLV2 is likely to be a member of both the 185-kDa and the 450-kDa complexes, because their accumulation is significantly reduced in *clv2* mutants.[67] CLV1 and CLV2 proteins both contain paired cysteines in their extracellular domains, flanking the LRRs, that potentially allow for homodimerization or heterodimerization through the formation of disulfide bridges. The remaining CLV1 protein in *clv2* mutant extracts is found in a novel ~600-kDa complex. This complex may retain some function *in vivo,* which could account for why the phenotypes of *clv2* null mutants are less severe than those of *clv1* and *clv3* mutants. These data are consistent with the proposal that CLV3 acts as the ligand for a plasma membrane-bound receptor complex containing both CLV1 and CLV2.[19,79] Alternatively, CLV3 may be required for the production or release of the ligand or as a ligand cofactor.

Activity of the CLV signaling complex requires the SHEPHERD (SHD) protein. The *shd* mutants, like the *clv* mutants, have enlarged shoot and floral meristems and produce extra carpels and gynoecium tissue.[80] The *shd* phenotypes are similar to the *clv* mutant phenotypes, and *clv1* and *clv3* alleles are epistatic to *shd* in genetic tests. The *wus* mutations are also epistatic to *shd,* confirming that SHD functions in the CLV stem cell maintenance pathway. However, *shd* mutants also have other defects; thus, the requirement for *SHD* is not limited to shoot and floral meristems. *SHD* encodes the *Arabidopsis* orthologue of glucose regulated protein 94 (GRP94), an ER-resident HSP90-like molecular chaperone protein found in mammals.[81] Secreted proteins (e.g., CLV3) and the extracellular domains of membrane-spanning proteins (e.g., CLV1 and CLV2) are synthesized on the membrane of the endoplasmic reticulum (ER). Once properly folded and assembled, the proteins are transported to the plasma membrane by the vesicular transport machinery. GRP94 and other molecular chaperones have protein-binding properties and are associated with the folding intermediates of a number of oligomeric proteins under stress and nonstress conditions.[82,83] *SHD,* which is expressed throughout shoot and floral meristems and in other tissues, may therefore be required for the correct folding of one or more CLV proteins, and/or for assembly of the receptor complex.

Signal transduction via cell surface receptors generally requires association with and activation of downstream signaling components or regulatory factors. Although a complete intracellular signaling cascade has not been identified for the CLV pathway, several proteins have been identified that interact with the active form of the CLV1 complex in the cytosol. One is a kinase-associated protein phosphatase (KAPP), which contains a type I signal anchor, a forkhead-associated (FHA) domain that binds phospho-serine motifs, and a type 2C protein phosphatase domain.[84] *KAPP* is expressed in meristems in a region encompassing the CLV1 expression domain.[66,85,86] The KAPP protein is a component of the 450 kDa CLV1 active complex, but the association of CLV1 and KAPP *in vitro* requires both CLV1 kinase activity and KAPP phosphorylation.[79] The FHA domain is contained within the KAPP kinase interaction domain, suggesting that KAPP may bind the CLV1 kinase domain by recognizing its phosphoserine residues. Overexpression of KAPP in wild-type plants causes a weak *clv* mutant phenotype, and, therefore, KAPP is proposed to dephosphorylate CLV1 and act as a negative regulator of the CLV pathway.[66,86]

KAPP is a shared component of multiple signal transduction pathways and interacts with a number of *Arabidopsis* receptor-like kinases.[85,87] A plasma membrane–localized LRR-RLK called AtSERK1 has been shown to become sequestered in intracellular vesicles when transiently co-expressed with KAPP.[88] KAPP dephosphorylation of threonine residues in the AtSERK1 kinase domain A-loop was found to play an active role in the receptor internalization.

These results suggest that KAPP is an integral part of an endocytosis mechanism that internalizes AtSERK1, and possibly other LRR-RLKs such as CLV1, during receptor-mediated signaling.

Finally, at least one member of the Rop subfamily of small GTPase-related proteins is also associated with the CLV active complex.[89] The *Arabidopsis* Rop GTPases (for Rho-related proteins from plants) cluster in phylogenetic trees with animal Rho GTPases and appear to be members of a unique subfamily that has so far only been identified in plants.[90] Rho GTPases are members of the Ras GTPase superfamily of cytosolic GTP-binding proteins. In animals and fungi, Ras GTPases have been shown to mediate many different receptor tyrosine kinase signaling events by activating intracellular protein kinase cascades.[91,92] Ras GTPases have not been found in plants;[68] thus, Rop GTPases are thought to play functionally analogous roles in plant signal transduction to Ras GTPases in animals. There are 11 Rop family members in *Arabidopsis,* many of which are expressed in shoots,[89] and they participate in a variety of developmental processes in addition to stem cell maintenance.[93] Based on the mechanism of Ras and Rho GTPase activity as it is understood in animals, it has been proposed that Rop GTPases may participate in SAM signaling by activating a mitogen-activated protein kinase (MAPK)-like cascade in response to CLV1 kinase activation.[79]

A Negative Feedback Loop Maintains Stem Cell Homeostasis

Stem cells at the *Arabidopsis* shoot apex are maintained by inductive signals they receive from their local environment. One such signal is mediated by *WUS. WUS* encodes a homeodomain-containing putative transcription factor that acts to promote stem cell fate,[53] and genetic tests show that *WUS* is a component of the CLV signal transduction pathway.[94] *WUS* is expressed in a small domain in the interior of the SAM, but it is sufficient to induce stem cell fate in the overlying cells. When *WUS* is misexpressed under the control of a promoter that drives *WUS* transcription in all initiating organ primordia on the flanks of the SAM,[94] the resulting transgenic seedlings do not form any lateral organs. Instead, the shoot apex consists entirely of undifferentiated stem cells. *CLV3* mRNA can be detected on the periphery of the meristematic cell mass, indicating that *WUS* activity is also sufficient to induce *CLV3* transcription. Furthermore, transgenic plants that express *WUS* in an enlarged domain under the control of the *CLV1* promoter accumulate excess *CLV3*-expressing stem cells and resemble *clv* mutants.[94] *WUS* is therefore a key component of a stem cell-promoting pathway that preserves the *CLV3*-expressing stem cell reservoir at the shoot apex. Because *WUS* mRNA and protein are not detected in the stem cells themselves, stem cell activity is most likely maintained by an inductive signal regulated by *WUS.* Interestingly, misexpression of *WUS* throughout the plant does not cause widespread induction of *CLV3* expression, indicating that most likely only cells at the apex of established meristems are competent to respond to a *WUS*-derived signal.[95]

Expression of the ligand-encoding *CLV3* gene and the receptor-encoding *CLV1* gene is also restricted to specific domains of the meristem. *CLV3* and *CLV1* are initially transcribed in heart stage embryos, in a small group of cells between the cotyledons where the SAM is organized. Following germination, *CLV3* mRNA accumulates in a few cells at the shoot apex corresponding to the stem cell reservoir, predominantly in the superficial L1 and L2 cells.[19] *CLV3* transcripts are not detected on the periphery of the SAM or in initiating lateral organ primordia. However, *CLV3* mRNA reappears in the stem cells of the floral meristem shortly after its separation from the SAM. *CLV3* continues to be expressed in the floral meristem stem cells until the initiation of the central carpel primordia. *CLV3* mRNA is therefore associated with the stem cell population throughout *Arabidopsis* development. Initiation of *CLV3* expression in the embryonic shoot apex depends on the activity of *WUS,* which is required for stem cell maintenance.[95] Later in development, *WUS* functions together with *STM* to sustain the appropriate level of *CLV3* expression in stem cells. Like *CLV3, CLV1* is expressed specifically in shoot and floral meristems, but *CLV1* transcripts are localized in the deeper regions of the SAM, largely beneath the stem cell reservoir.[65] Thus, the *CLV3* expression domain overlies the *CLV1* expression domain, indicating that the stem cells and cells underlying them communicate with one another via the CLV signaling pathway. *CLV2* transcripts are detected in shoots, developing flowers, and other tissues, consistent with its pleiotropic mutant phenotypes.[67]

The *Arabidopsis DORNROSCHEN/ENHANCER OF SHOOT REGENERATION1 (DRN/ESR1)* gene, which is defined by a gain-of-function mutation *drn-D,* is required for the correct spatial expression of *CLV3* and for SAM maintenance.[96] The shoot apex of *drn-D* mutants is massively enlarged compared with the wild type but arrests prematurely, and *CLV3* and *WUS* become co-expressed in an enlarged domain in the interior of the SAM. Furthermore, *STM* expression is abolished in enlarging *drn-D* meristems, but it reappears later in a crescent shape across the arrested apex. *DRN/ESR1* encodes a plant-specific AP2/ERF-type putative transcription factor. The *DRN/ESR1* expression pattern is dynamic in embryos, but following germination the transcripts are consistently detected in the stem cell population of shoot and floral meristems and in lateral organ primordia. Increased *DRN/ESR1* expression in enlarged *drn-D* apices leads to cellular differentiation at the shoot tip, suggesting that under normal circumstances the gene may play a role in promoting the transition of stem cell daughters into pathways leading to differentiation.[96]

The mRNA expression domains of *CLV1* and *CLV3* enlarge coordinately in *clv1, 2,* or *3* mutant plants.[19,67] Thus *CLV1, CLV2,* and *CLV3* all act to limit the number of *CLV3*-expressing stem cells. The coordinated expansion of the *CLV* expression domains therefore depends on a positive, stem cell-promoting pathway, which is negatively regulated by the stem cell-restricting CLV pathway. The two pathways were uncoupled by overexpressing *CLV3* ectopically in transgenic *Arabidopsis* plants.[97] Transgenic plants constitutively expressing high levels of *CLV3* generate several leaves and then terminate meristem activity, indicating that stem cell identity is not maintained in the presence of elevated levels of *CLV3*. Transgenic plants expressing lower levels of constitutive *CLV3* retain some stem cell activity but generate reduced numbers of flowers and floral organs, demonstrating an inability to fully renew the stem cell population. The abundance of the CLV3 ligand is therefore the critical factor that determines the size of the stem cell pool and, consequently, the extent of organ formation from shoot and floral meristems. Constitutive expression of the *CLV3* transgene in *clv1* or *clv2* mutant plants does not rescue the *clv* mutant phenotype.[97] Thus, CLV3 signaling requires the function of both CLV1 and CLV2, and the terminal meristem phenotypes observed in the transgenic *CLV3* plants are due to enhanced CLV3 signaling through the CLV1/CLV2 receptor complex.

The CLV pathway controls stem cell fate by regulating the size of the *WUS* expression domain.[97] In *clv3* mutant plants the *WUS* expression domain, which is restricted under normal circumstances to the deepest layers of the meristem, expands both laterally and also upward into the subepidermal L2 cell layer. Conversely, *WUS* mRNA is not detected in the arrested meristems of transgenic plants that overexpress *CLV3*, indicating that elevated CLV3 signaling causes down-regulation of *WUS* transcription and loss of stem cells. Signaling through the CLV pathway thus limits WUS activity by restricting its expression to a small domain of cells beneath the stem cell reservoir. When the *CLV3* transgene is introduced into a *wus* null mutant background the resulting plants resemble *wus*, indicating that *WUS* is likely to be the primary target of negative regulation by the stem cell-restricting CLV pathway.

A protein phosphatase encoded by the *POLTERGEIST (POL)* gene is also a target of the CLV stem cell regulatory pathway. Several recessive *pol* mutants were identified as suppressors of weak *clv* mutant phenotypes.[98] *pol* single-mutant plants are nearly identical to wild-type plants, but *POL* is proposed to promote stem cell fate on the grounds that *pol clv* double mutants accumulate fewer stem cells in their shoot and floral meristems than *clv* single mutants. *POL* encodes a novel protein phosphatase 2C subtype, containing a functional phosphatase domain as well as a unique N-terminal region that may play a regulatory role *in vivo*.[99] *POL* mRNA is present in all *Arabidopsis* tissues, and is detected throughout shoot and floral meristems. Genetic evidence indicates that *POL* is a negative regulator of CLV signaling that acts downstream of the receptor complex, because *pol* alleles suppress most *clv* mutant phenotypes in a semidominant fashion but have no effect on CLV1 receptor activation.[98] Because *pol* mutations enhance the *wus* stem cell termination phenotypes, *POL* may act in parallel with *WUS* to specify stem cells. However, the lack of a meristem phenotype in *pol* mutants indicates that, although *WUS* can almost completely compensate for the absence of *POL* activity, *POL* is not able to effectively compensate for the loss of *WUS*. Interestingly, analysis of *pol wus* double mutants and *pol clv wus* triple mutants shows that *POL* functions in both the *WUS*-dependent CLV pathway and a novel, *WUS*-independent CLV pathway to regulate stem cell identity.[99]

Conclusion

Although the picture is far from complete, our current understanding of stem cell activity in *Arabidopsis* SAMs is that it is mediated by mutual regulation and signaling between the stem cells and their local environment, which involves both positive and negative interactions (Fig. 56–5). *WUS* is transcribed in a small group of cells in the interior of the SAM. *WUS* activity induces stem cell fate and *CLV3* expression within the stem cell population in the overlying cells via a cell non-autonomous mechanism. *STM* does not play a direct role in stem cell specification, but it is required throughout the SAM to repress the *AS1* expression and cell differentiation. This allows the meristem cells, including the stem cell reservoir, to maintain a proliferative state. CLV3 signal originating from the stem cells is then perceived by the underlying, *CLV1*-expressing cells. Negative signaling through the CLV pathway targets *POL* and *WUS*, limiting the extent of *WUS* activity by restricting its expression to the deeper regions of the meristem. Activity of the positive pathway mediated by *WUS* promotes the expression of *CLV3*, and the persistence of the *CLV3*-expressing stem cell reservoir.

Perturbation of the stem cell feedback loop causes an imbalance between stem cell renewal and organ formation, dramatically affecting development. Disruption of the negative pathway in *clv* mutants causes the *WUS* expression domain to expand laterally and upward, and the resultant increase in *WUS* activity stimulates excess stem cell accumulation and meristem overgrowth. Conversely, disruption of the positive pathway in *wus* mutants causes the specification of insufficient numbers of stem cells, leading to premature meristem termination. When *CLV3* is overexpressed, constitutive signaling through the CLV1/CLV2 receptor complex enhances the negative pathway, abolishing *WUS* transcription and causing the complete loss of stem cells.

The flow of stem cell maintenance information in *Arabidopsis* plants via a ligand-receptor signal transduction pathway is critical for normal plant growth and development. The mutual regulation of *WUS* by the stem cell-restricting

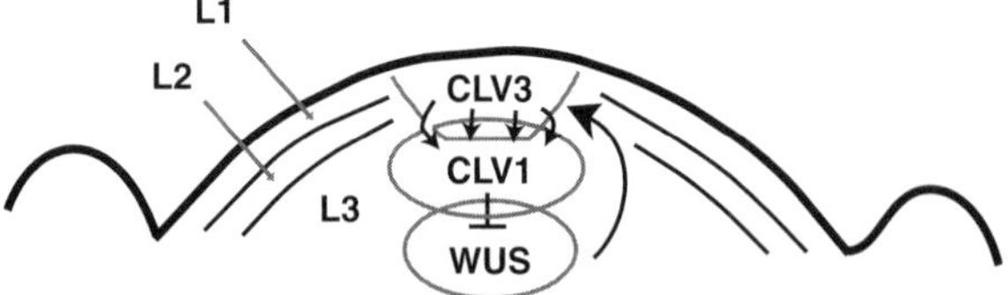

Figure 56–5. *Negative feedback loop regulating stem cell fate in the Arabidopsis shoot apex. CLV3, CLV1 and WUS are expressed in overlapping domains of the meristem. WUS is expressed in the deepest region of the meristem. WUS induces stem cell fate in the overlying L1 and L2 cells and promotes the expression of CLV3 in these cells. CLV3 signaling through the CLV1 receptor complex in underlying cells restricts WUS to its narrow expression domain in the L3.*

pathway and of *CLV3* by the stem cell-promoting pathway maintains a homeostatic feedback system that tends toward equilibrium. These interactions stabilize the distinct identities of neighboring cellular domains within the SAM and sustain an appropriately sized stem cell reservoir over extended periods of time. The stem cell feedback loop elegantly compensates for fluctuations in stem cell number that occur as cells depart the meristem during organ formation, enabling plants to continuously grow and develop in response to environmental stimulus throughout their life cycles.

ACKNOWLEDGMENTS

My laboratory's work on plant development is supported by the U.S. Department of Agriculture and the National Science Foundation.

REFERENCES

1. Steeves, T.A., and Sussex, I.M. (1989). "Patterns in Plant Development." New York: Cambridge University Press.
2. Eiges, R., and Benvenisty, N. (2002). A molecular view on pluripotent stem cells. *FEBS Lett.* **529,** 135–141.
3. Skoog, F., and Miller, C.O. (1957). Chemical regulation of growth and organ formation in plant tissues cultured in vitro. *Soc. Exp. Biol. Symp.* **11,** 118–131.
4. Ruth, J., Klekowski Jr., E.J., and Stein, O.L. (1985). Impermanent initials of the shoot apex and diplontic selection in a juniper chimera. *Am. J. Bot.* **72,** 1127–1135.
5. Newman, I.V. (1965). Patterns in the meristems of vascular plants. III. Pursuing the patterns where no cell is a permanent cell. *J. Linn. Soc. Bot.* **59,** 185–214.
6. Satina, S., Blakeslee, A.F., and Avery, A.G. (1940). Demonstration of the three germ layers in the shoot apex of Datura by means of induced polyploidy in periclinical chimeras. *Am. J. Bot.* **27,** 895–905.
7. Poethig, R.S. (1987). Clonal analysis of cell lineage patterns in plant development. *Am. J. Bot.* **74,** 581–194.
8. Stewart, R.N. (1978). Ontogeny of the primary body in chimeral forms in higher plants. *In* "The Clonal Basis of Development" (Subtelny, S., and Sussex, I.M., eds.). pp. 131–160. Academic Press, New York.
9. Furner, I.J., and Pumfrey, J.E. (1992). Cell fate in the shoot apical meristem of *Arabidopsis thaliana. Development* **115,** 755–764.
10. Irish, V.F., and Sussex, I.M. (1992). A fate map of the Arabidopsis embryonic shoot apical meristem. *Development* **115,** 745–753.
11. Poethig, R.S., Coe, E.H.J., and Johri, M.M. (1986). Cell lineage patterns in maize Zea mays embryogenesis: a clonal analysis. *Dev. Biol.* **117,** 392–404.
12. Tilney-Bassett, R.A.E. (1986). "Plant Chimeras." E. Arnold, London.
13. Poethig, R.S., and Sussex, I.M. (1985). The cellular parameters of leaf development in tobacco: a clonal analysis. *Planta* **165,** 170–184.
14. Poethig, R.S., and Sussex, I.M. (1985). The developmental morphology and growth dynamics of the tobacco leaf. *Planta* **165,** 158–169.
15. Meyerowitz, E.M. (1997). Genetic control of cell division patterns in developing plants. *Cell* **88,** 299–308.
16. West, M.A.L., and Harada, J.J. (1993). Embryogenesis in higher plants: an overview. *Plant Cell* **5,** 1361–1369.
17. Barton, M.K., and Poethig, R.S. (1993). Formation of the shoot apical meristem in *Arabidopsis thaliana*: an analysis of development in the wild type and in the shoot meristemless mutant. *Development* **119,** 823–831.
18. Takada, S., and Tasaka, M. (2002). Embryonic shoot apical meristem formation in higher plants. *J. Plant Res.* **115,** 411–417.
19. Fletcher, J.C., Brand, U., Running, M.P., Simon, R., and Meyerowitz, E.M. (1999). Signaling of cell fate decisions by CLAVATA3 in Arabidopsis shoot meristems. *Science* **283,** 1911–1914.
20. Long, J.A., and Barton, M.K. (1998). The development of apical embryonic pattern in Arabidopsis. *Development* **125,** 3027–3035.
21. Reiser, L., Sanchez-Baracaldo, P., and Hake, S. (2000). Knots in the family tree: evolutionary relationships and functions of knox homeobox genes. *Plant Mol. Biol.* **42,** 151–166.
22. Clark, S.E., Jacobsen, S.E., Levin, J.Z., and Meyerowitz, E.M. (1996). The CLAVATA and SHOOTMERISTEMLESS loci competitively regulate meristem activity in Arabidopsis. *Development* **122,** 1567–1575.
23. Lenhard, M., Jurgens, G., and Laux, T. (2002). The WUSCHEL and SHOOTMERISTEMLESS genes fulfill complementary roles in Arabidopsis shoot meristem regulation. *Development* **129,** 3195–3206.
24. Gallois, J.-L., Woodward, C., Reddy, G.V., and Sablowski, R. (2002). Combined SHOOTMERISTEMLESS and WUSCHEL trigger ectopic organogenesis in Arabidopsis. *Development* **129,** 3207–3217.
25. Burglin, T.R. (1997). Analysis of TALE superclass homeobox genes (MEIS, PBC, Iriquois, TGIF) reveals a novel domain conserved between plants and animals. *Nucleic Acids Res.* **25,** 4173–4180.
26. Bharanthan, G., Janssen, B.J., Kellogg, E.A., and Sinha, N. (1997). Did homeodomain proteins duplicate before the origin of angiosperms, fungi, and metazoa? *Proc. Natl. Acad. Sci. U. S. A.* **94,** 13749–13753.
27. Burglin, T.R. (1998). The PBC domain contains a MEINOX domain: coevolution of Hox and TALE homeobox genes. *Dev. Genes Evol.* **208,** 113–116.
28. Kerstetter, R., Volbrecht, E., Lowe, B., Veit, B., Yamaguchi, J., and Hake, S. (1994). Sequence analysis and expression patterns divide the maize knotted1-like homeobox genes into two classes. *Plant Cell* **6,** 1877–1887.
29. Long, J.A., Moan, E.I., Medford, J.I., and Barton, M.K. (1996). A member of the KNOTTED class of homeodomain proteins encoded by the STM gene of Arabidopsis. *Nature* **379,** 66–69.
30. Byrne, M.E., Barley, R., Curtis, M., Arroyo, J.M., Dunham, M., Hudson, A., and Martienssen, R.A. (2000). Asymmetric leaves1 mediates leaf patterning and stem cell function in Arabidopsis. *Nature* **408,** 967–971.
31. Ori, N., Eshed, Y., Chuck, G., Bowman, J.L., and Hake, S. (2000). Mechanisms that control knox gene expression in the Arabidopsis shoot. *Development* **127,** 5523–5532.
32. Semiarti, E., Ueno, Y., Tsukaya, H., Iwakawa, H., Machida, C., and Machida, Y. (2001). The ASYMMETRIC LEAVES2 gene of *Arabidopsis thaliana* regulates formation of a symmetric lamina, establishment of venation and repression of meristem-related homeobox genes in leaves. *Development* **128,** 1771–1783.
33. Smith, L.G., and Hake, S. (1992). The initiation and determination of leaves. *Plant Cell* **4,** 1017–1027.
34. Jackson, D., Veit, B., and Hake, S. (1994). Expression of maize KNOTTED1 related homeobox genes in the shoot apical meristem

predicts patterns of morphogenesis in the vegetative shoot. *Development* **120,** 405–413.
35. Waites, R., Selvadurai, H.R.N., Oliver, I.R., and Hudson, A. (1998). The PHANTASTICA gene encodes a MYB transcription factor involved in growth and dorsoventrality of lateral organs in Antirrhinum. *Cell* **93,** 779–789.
36. Timmermans, M.C.P., Hudson, A., Becraft, P.W., and Nelson, T. (1999). ROUGH SHEATH2: a Myb protein that represses knox homeobox genes in maize lateral organ primordia. *Nature* **284,** 151–153.
37. Tsiantis, M., Schneeburger, R., Golz, J.F., Freeling, M., and Langdale, J.A. (1999). The maize rough sheath2 gene and leaf development programs in monocot and dicot plants. *Nature* **284,** 154–156.
38. McConnell, J.R., and Barton, M.K. (1995). Effect of mutations in the PINHEAD gene of Arabidopsis on the formation of shoot apical meristems. *Dev. Genet.* **16,** 358–366.
39. Moussian, B., Schoof, H., Haecker, A., Jurgens, G., and Laux, T. (1998). Role of the ZWILLE gene in the regulation of central shoot meristem cell fate during Arabidopsis embryogenesis. *EMBO J.* **17,** 1799–1809.
40. Lynn, K., Fernandez, A., Aida, M., Sedbrook, J., Tasaka, M., Masson, P., and Barton, M.K. The PINHEAD/ZWILLE gene acts pleiotropically in Arabidopsis development and has overlapping functions with the ARGONAUTE1 gene. (1999). *Development* **126,** 469–481.
41. Bohmert, K., Camus, I., Bellini, C., Bouchez, D., Caboche, M., and Benning, C. (1998). AGO1 defines a novel locus of Arabidopsis controlling leaf development. *EMBO J.* **17,** 170–180.
42. Carmell, M.A., Xuan, Z., Zhang, M.Q., and Hannon, G.J. (2002). The Argonaute family: tentacles that reach into RNAi, developmental control, stem cell maintenance, and tumorigenesis. *Genes Dev.* **16,** 2733–2742.
43. Cerutti, L., Mian, N., and Bateman, A. (2000). Domains in gene silencing and cell differentiation proteins: the novel PAZ domain and redefinition of the Piwi domain. *Trends Biochem. Sci.* **25,** 481–482.
44. Bernstein, E., Caudy, A.A., Hammond, S.M., and Hannon, G.J. (2001). Role for a bidentate ribonuclease in the initiation step of RNA interference. *Nature* **409,** 363–366.
45. Nishimura, A., Ito, M., Kamiya, N., Sato, Y., and Matsuoka, M. (2002). OsPNH1 regulates leaf development and maintenance of the shoot apical meristem in rice. *Plant J.* **30,** 189–201.
46. Lin, H., and Spradling, A.C. (1997). A novel groups of pumilio mutations affects the asymmetric division of germline stem cells in the Drosophilia ovary. *Development* **124,** 2463–2476.
47. Cox, D.N., Chao, A., Baker, J., Chang, L., Qiao, D., and Lin, H. (1998). A novel class of evolutionarily conserved genes defined by piwi are essential for stem cell self-renewal. *Genes Dev.* **12,** 3715–3727.
48. Fagard, M., Boutet, S., Morel, J.-B., Bellini, C., and Vaucheret, H. (2000). AGO1, QDE-2, and RDE-1 are related proteins required for post-transcriptional gene silencing in plants, quelling in fungi, and RNA interference in animals. *Proc. Natl. Acad. Sci. U. S. A.* **97,** 11650–11654.
49. Carthew, R.W. (2001). Gene silencing by double-stranded RNA. *Curr. Opin. Cell Biol.* **13,** 244–248.
50. Hammond, S.M., Boettcher, S., Caudy, A.A., Kobayashi, R., and Hannon, G.J. (2001). Argonaute2, a link between genetic and biochemical analysis of RNAi. *Science* **293,** 1146–1150.
51. Morel, J.-B., Godon, C., Beclin, C., Boutet, S., Feuerbach, F., Proux, F., and Vaucheret, H. (2002). Fertile hypomorphic ARGONAUTE (ago1) mutants impaired in post-transcriptional gene silencing and virus resistance. *Plant Cell* **14,** 629–639.
52. Laux, T., Mayer, K.F.X., Berger, J., and Jurgens, G. (1996). The WUSCHEL gene is required for shoot and floral meristem integrity in Arabidopsis. *Development* **122,** 87–96.
53. Mayer, K.F.X., Schoof, H., Haecker, A., Lenhard, M., Jurgens, G., and Laux, T. (1998). Role of WUSCHEL in regulating stem cell fate in the Arabidopsis shoot meristem. *Cell* **95,** 805–815.
54. Endrizzi, K., Moussian, B., Haecker, A., Levin, J.Z., and Laux, T. (1996). The SHOOTMERISTEMLESS gene is required for maintenance of undifferentiated cells in Arabidopsis shoot and floral meristems and acts at a different regulatory level than the meristem genes WUSCHEL and ZWILLE. *Plant J.* **10,** 967–79.
55. Kaya, H., Shibahara, K.-i., Taoka, K.-i., Iwabuchi, M., Stillman, B., and Araki, T. (2000). FASCIATA genes for chromatin assembly factor-1 in Arabidopsis maintain the cellular organization of apical meristems. *Cell* **104,** 131–142.
56. Stuurman, J., Jaggi, F., and Kuhlemeier, C. (2002). Shoot meristem maintenance is controlled by a GRAS-gene mediated signal from differentiating cells. *Genes Dev.* **16,** 2213–2218.
57. Leyser, H.M.O., and Furner, I.J. (1992). Characterisation of three shoot apical meristem mutants of *Arabidopsis thaliana. Development* **116,** 397–403.
58. Clark, S.E., Running, M.P., and Meyerowitz, E.M. (1993). CLAVATA1, a regulator of meristem and flower development in Arabidopsis. *Development* **119,** 397–418.
59. Clark, S.E., Running, M.P., and Meyerowitz, E.M. (1995). CLAVATA3 is a specific regulator of shoot and floral meristem development affecting the same processes as CLAVATA1. *Development* **121,** 2057–2067.
60. Kayes, J.M., and Clark, S.E. (1998). CLAVATA2, a regulator of meristem and organ development in Arabidopsis. *Development* **125,** 3843–3851.
61. Merton, T.R., and Burdick, A.B. (1954). The morphology, anatomy and genetics of a stem fasciation in *Lycopersicon esculentum. Am. J. Bot.* **41,** 726–732.
62. Szymkowiak, E.J., and Sussex, I.M. (1992). The internal meristem layer (L3) determines floral meristem size and carpel number in tomato periclinical chimeras. *Plant Cell* **4,** 1089–1100.
63. Taguchi-Shiobara, F., Yuan, Z., Hake, S., and Jackson, D. (2001). The fasciated ear2 gene encodes a leucine-rich repeat receptor-like protein that regulates shoot meristem proliferation in maize. *Genes Dev.* **15,** 2755–2766.
64. Yamamoto, E., Karakaya, H.C., and Knap, H.T. (2000). Molecular characterization of two soybean homologs of *Arabidopsis thaliana* CLAVATA1 from the wild type and fasciation mutant. *Biochim. Biophys. Acta* **1491,** 333–340.
65. Clark, S.E., Williams, R.W., and Meyerowitz, E.M. (1997). The CLAVATA1 gene encodes a putative receptor kinase that controls shoot and floral meristem size in Arabidopsis. *Cell* **89,** 575–585.
66. Williams, R.W., Wilson, J.M., and Meyerowitz, E.M. (1997). A possible role for kinase-associated protein phosphatase in the Arabidopsis CLAVATA1 signaling pathway. *Proc. Natl. Acad. Sci. U. S. A.* **94,** 10467–10472.
67. Jeong, S., Trotochaud, A.E., and Clark, S.E. (1999). The Arabidopsis CLAVATA2 gene encodes a receptor-like protein required for the stability of the CLAVATA1 receptor-like kinase. *Plant Cell* **11,** 1925–1933.
68. Initiative, A.G. (2000). Analysis of the genome sequence of the flowering plant *Arabidopsis thaliana. Nature* **408,** 796–814.
69. Torii, K.U., Mitsukawa, N., Oosumi, T., Matsuura, Y., Yokoyama, R., Whittier, R.F., and Komeda, Y. (1996). The Arabidopsis ERECTA gene encodes a putative receptor protein

kinase with extracellular leucine-rich repeats. *Plant Cell* **8,** 735–746.

70. Jinn, T.-L., Stone, J.M., and Walker, J.C. (2000). HAESA, an Arabidopsis leucine-rich repeat receptor kinase, controls floral organ abcission. *Genes Dev.* **14,** 108–117.
71. Gomez-Gomez, L., and Boller, T. (2000). FLS2: A LRR receptor-like kinase involved in recognition of of the flagellin elicitor in Arabidopsis. *Mol. Cell* **5,** 1–20.
72. Li, J., and Chory, J. (1997). A putative leucine-rich repeat receptor kinase involved in brassinosteroid signal transduction. *Cell* **90,** 929–938.
73. Buchanan, S.G.S.C., and Gay, N.J. (1996). Structural and functional diversity in the leucine-rich repeat family of proteins. *Prog. Biophys. Mol. Biol.* **65,** 1–12.
74. Rojo, E., Sharma, V.K., Kovaleva, V., Raikhel, N.V., and Fletcher, J.C. (2002). CLV3 is localized to the extracellular space, where it activates the Arabidopsis CLAVATA stem cell signaling pathway. *Plant Cell* **14,** 969–977.
75. Cock, J.M., and McCormick, S. (2001). A large family of genes that share homology with CLAVATA3. *Plant Physiol.* **126,** 939–942.
76. Bonello, J.-F., Opsahl-Ferstad, H.-G., Perez, P., Dumas, C., and Rogowsky, P.M. Esr genes show different levels of expression in the same region of maize endosperm. (2000). *Gene* **246,** 219–227.
77. Opsahl-Ferstad, H.-G., Le Deunff, E., Dumas, C., and Rogowsky, P.M. (1997). ZmEsr, a novel endosperm-specific gene expressed in a restricted region around the maize embryo. *Plant J.* **12,** 235–246.
78. Sharma, V.K., Ramirez, J., and Fletcher, J.C. (2003). The Arabidopsis CLV3-like (CLE) genes are expressed in diverse tissues and encode secreted proteins. *Plant Mol. Biol.* **51,** 415–425.
79. Trotochaud, A.E., Hao, T., Wu, G., Yang, Z., and Clark, S.E. (1999). The CLAVATA1 receptor-like kinase requires CLAVATA3 for its assembly into a signaling complex that includes KAPP and a Rho-related protein. *Plant Cell* **11,** 393–405.
80. Ishiguro, S., Watanabe, Y., Ito, N., Nonaka, H., Takeda, N., Sakai, T., Kanaya, H., and Okada, K. (2002). SHEPHERD is the Arabidopsis GRP94 responsible for the formation of functional CLAVATA proteins. *EMBO J.* **21,** 898–908.
81. Argon, Y., and Simen, B.B. (1999). GRP94, an ER chaperone with protein and peptide binding properties. *Semin. Cell Dev. Biol.* **10,** 495–505.
82. Melnick, J., Aviel, S., and Argon, Y. (1992). The endoplasmic reticulum protein GRP94, in addition to BIP, associates with unassembled immunoglobulin chains. *J. Biol. Chem.* **267,** 21303–21306.
83. Ferreira, L.R., Norris, K., Smith, T., Hebert, C., and Sauk, J.J. (1994). Association of Hsp47, Grp78 and Grp94 with procollagen supports the successive or coupled action of molecular chaperones. *J. Cell Biochem.* **56,** 518–526.
84. Li, J., Smith, G.P., and Walker, J.C. (1999). Kinase interaction domain of kinase-associated protein phosphatase, a phosphoprotein-binding domain. *Proc. Natl. Acad. Sci. U. S. A.* **96,** 7821–7826.
85. Stone, J.M., Collinge, M.A., Smith, R.D., Horn, M.A., and Walker, J.C. (1994). Interaction of a protein phosphatase with an Arabidopsis serine-threonine receptor kinase. *Science* **266,** 793–795.
86. Stone, J.M., Trotochaud, A.E., Walker, J.C., and Clark, S.E. (1998). Control of meristem development by CLAVATA1 receptor kinase and kinase-associated phosphatase interactions. *Plant Physiol.* **117,** 1217–1225.
87. Braun, D.M., Stone, J.M., and Walker, J.C. (1997). Interaction of maize and Arabidopsis kinase interaction domains with a subset of receptor-like kinases: implications for transmembrane signaling in plants. *Plant J.* **12,** 83–95.
88. Shah, K., Russinova, E., Gadella, J.T.W.J., Willemse, J., and de Vries, S.C. (2002). The Arabidopsis kinase-associated protein phosphatase controls internalization of the somatic embryogenesis receptor kinase 1. *Genes Dev.* **16,** 1707–1720.
89. Li, H., Wu, G., Ware, D., Davis, K.R., and Yang, Z. (1998). Arabidopsis Rho-related GTPases: differential gene expression in pollen and polar localization in fission yeast. *Plant Physiol.* **118,** 407–417.
90. Vernoud, V., Horton, A.C., Yang, Z., and Nielsen, E. (2003). Analysis of the small GTPase gene superfamily of Arabidopsis. *Plant Physiol.* **131,** 1191–1208.
91. Chant, J., and Stowers, L. (1995). GTPase cascades choreographing cellular behavior: movement, morphogenesis, and more. *Cell* **81,** 1–4.
92. Nagata, K.-i., and Hall, A. (1996). The Rho-GTPase regulates protein kinase activity. *BioEssays* **18,** 529–531.
93. Li, H., Shen, J.-J., Zheng, Z.-L., Lin, Y., and Yang, Z. (2001). The Rop GTPase switch controls multiple developmental processes in Arabidopsis. *Plant Physiol.* **126,** 670–684.
94. Schoof, H., Lenhard, M., Haecker, A., Mayer, K.F.X., Jurgens, G., and Laux, T. (2000). The stem cell population of Arabidopsis shoot meristems is maintained by a regulatory loop between the CLAVATA and WUSCHEL genes. *Cell* **100,** 635–644.
95. Brand, U., Grunewald, M., Hobe, M., and Simon, R. (2002). Regulation of CLV3 expression by two homeobox genes in Arabidopsis. *Plant Physiol.* **129,** 565–575.
96. Kirch, T., Simon, R., Grunewald, M., and Werr, W. (2003). The DORNROSCHEN/ENHANCER OF SHOOT REGENERATION1 gene of Arabidopsis acts in the control of meristem cell fate and lateral organ development. *Plant Cell* **15,** 694–705.
97. Brand, U., Fletcher, J.C., Hobe, M., Meyerowitz, E.M., and Simon, R. (2000). Dependence of stem cell fate in Arabidopsis on a feedback loop regulated by CLV3 activity. *Science* **289,** 617–619.
98. Yu, L.P., Simon, E.J., Trotochaud, A.E., and Clark, S.E. (2000). POLTERGEIST functions to regulate meristem development downstream of the CLAVATA loci. *Development* **127,** 1661–1670.
99. Yu, L.P., Miller, A.K., and Clark, S.E. (2003). POLTERGEIST encodes a protein phosphatase 2C that regulates the CLAVATA pathways controlling stem cell identity at Arabidopsis shoot and floral meristems. *Curr. Biol.* **13,** 179–188.

57

Microarray Analysis of Stem Cells and Differentiation

Howard Y. Chang, James A. Thomson, and Xin Chen

Introduction

For the past several decades, biologists have only been able to tackle the analysis of one or a few genes at a time. However, the advent of complete genomic sequences of more than 800 organisms (including the human and mouse genomes) and the development of microarray technology have revolutionized molecular biology. Microarrays enable biologists to perform global analysis on the expression of tens of thousands of genes simultaneously, and they have been widely used in gene discovery, biomarker determination, disease classification, and studies of gene regulation.[1–4] Expression profiling using microarrays is generally considered "discovery research," although it can also be a powerful approach to test defined hypotheses. One advantage of microarray experiments is that at the outset, microarray experiments need not be hypothesis driven. Instead, it allows biologists a means to gather gene expression data on an unbiased basis and can help to identify genes that may be further tested as the targets in hypothesis-driven studies.

Overview of Microarray Technology

There are two major microarray platforms that have been widely used: cDNA microarrays and oligonucleotide microarrays.

cDNA MICROARRAYS

The principle of cDNA microarray is illustrated in Fig. 57–1. In brief, cDNA clones, which generally range from several hundred base pairs to several kilobases, are printed on a glass surface, either by mechanical or ink jet microspotting. Sample RNA and a reference RNA are differentially labeled with fluorescent Cy5 or Cy3 dyes, respectively, using reverse transcriptase. The subsequent cDNAs are hybridized to the arrays overnight. The slides are washed and scanned with a fluorescence laser scanner. The relative abundant of the transcripts in the samples can be determined by the red/green ratio on each spotted array element.

Handbook of Stem Cells
Volume 2

One of the limitations of cDNA microarray has been that it required relatively large amount of total RNA ($\geq$10 μg) for hybridization. However, significant progress has been made recently for linear amplification of RNA, generally based on Eberwine's protocol.[5] In this case, RNA is converted into cDNA with oligo dT primers that contains a T7 RNA polymerase promoter sequence at its 5′ end. The cDNA can be subsequently used as the template for T7 RNA polymerase to transcribe into antisense RNA. The linear amplification protocol can produce 10^6 fold of amplification. Therefore, only very small amount of samples are required in modern microarray experiments.

There are several advantages to cDNA microarrays. The two-color competitive hybridization can reliably measure the difference between two samples because variations in spot size or amount of cDNA probe on the array will not affect the signal ratio. The cDNA microarrays are relatively easy to produce. In fact, the arrayer can be easily built, and microarrays can be manufactured in university research labs. Also, cDNA microarrays are in general much cheaper compared with oligonucleotide arrays and are quite affordable to most research biologists.

There are also some disadvantages for this system. One is that the production of the cDNA microarray requires the collection of a large set of sequenced clones. The clones, however, may be misidentified or contaminated. Second, genes with high sequence similarity may hybridize to the same clone and generate cross-hybridization. To avoid this problem, clones with 3′ end untranslated regions, which in general are much more divergent compared with the coding sequences, should be used in producing the microarrays.

OLIGONUCLEOTIDE ARRAYS

The most widely used oligonucleotide arrays are GeneChips produced by Affymetrix, which use photolithography-directed synthesis of oligonucleotides on glass slides. The Affymetrix GeneChip measures the absolute levels for each transcript in the sample. The principle of the Affymetrix GeneChip is shown in Fig. 57–2. In general, for each transcript, approximately 20 distinct and minimal overlapped 25-mer oligonucleotides are selected and synthesized on the array. For each oligonucleotide, there is also a paired mismatch control oligonucleotide, which differs from the perfect match probe by one nucleotide in the central position. Comparison of the

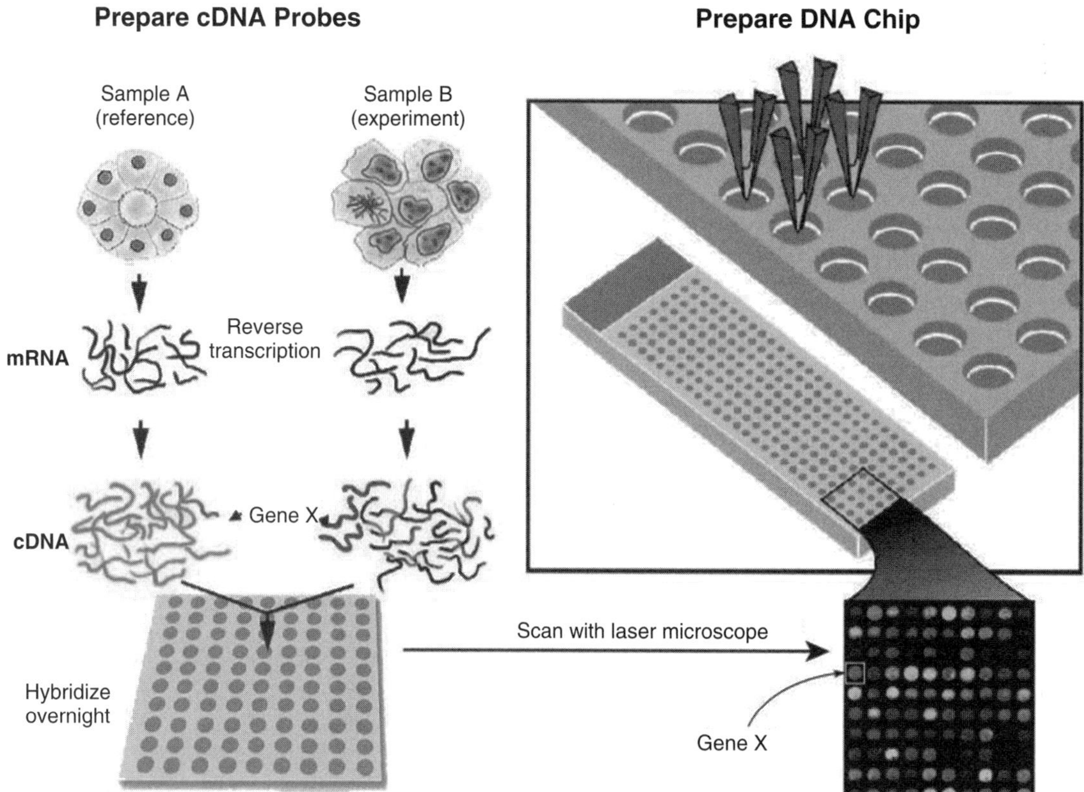

Figure 57–1. *Principle of cDNA microarrays.* Polymerase chain reaction (PCR) products are printed onto glass slides to produce high-density cDNA microarrays. RNA is extracted from experimental samples and reference samples and differentially labeled with Cy5 and Cy3, respectively, by reverse transcriptase. The subsequent cDNA probes are mixed and hybridized to cDNA microarray overnight. The slides are washed and scanned with a fluorescence laser scanner. The relative red/green ratio of gene X indicates the relative abundance of gene X in experimental samples versus reference.

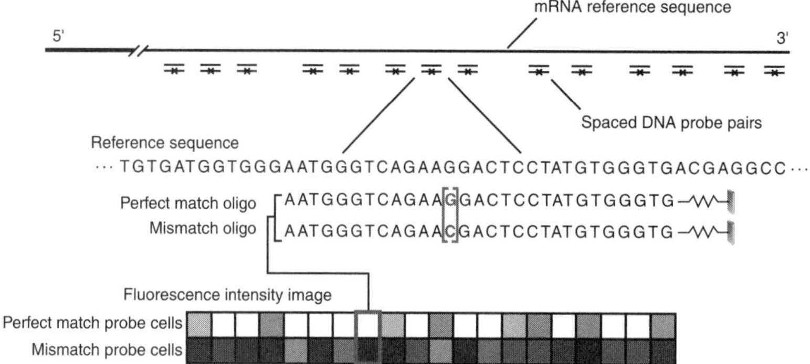

Figure 57–2. *Principle of the Affymetrix GeneChip.* For each gene, approximately 20 distinct and minimally overlapped 25-mer oligonucleotides are selected and synthesized on the array. For each oligonucleotide, there is also a paired mismatch control oligonucleotide probe, which differs from the perfect match probe by one nucleotide in the central position. Comparison of the hybridization signals from perfect match oligonucleotide with the paired mismatch oligonucleotide allows automatic subtraction of background. (Provided by Affymetrix, Santa Clara, CA.)

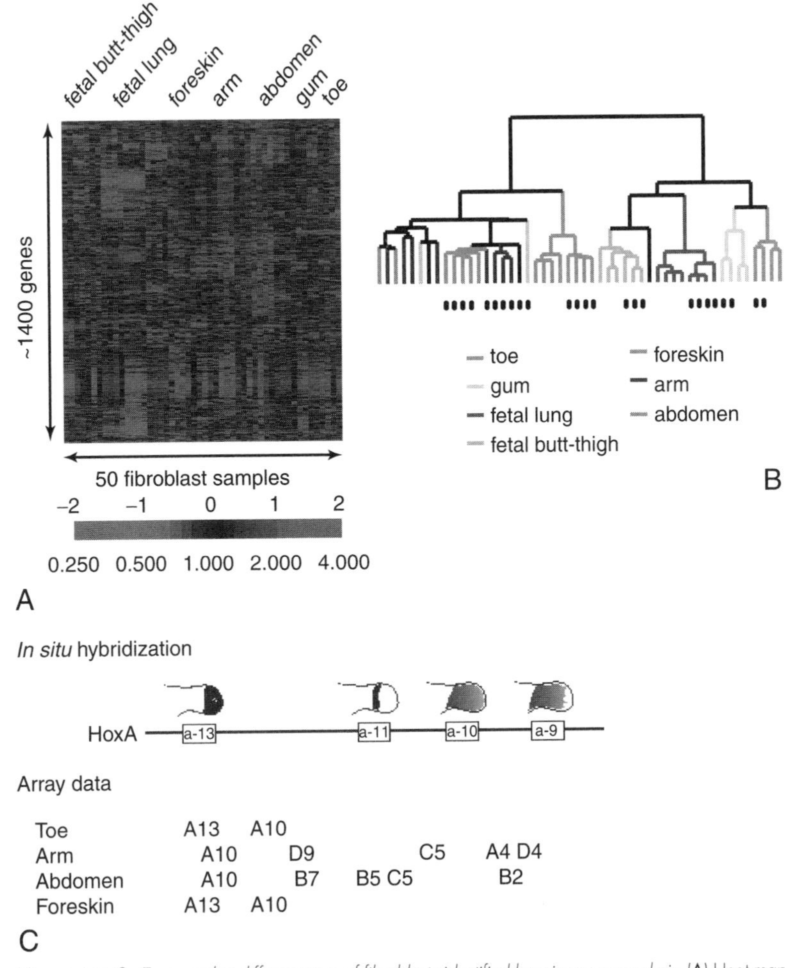

Figure 57–3. *Topographic differentiation of fibroblasts identified by microarray analysis.* (**A**) Heat map of fibroblast gene expression patterns. Fibroblasts from several anatomic sites were cultured, and their mRNAs were analyzed by cDNA microarray hybridization.[29] Approximately 1400 genes varied by at least three-fold in two samples. The fibroblast samples were predominantly grouped together based on site of origin. (**B**) Supervised hierarchical clustering revealed the relationship of fibroblast cultures to one another. Site of origin is indicated by the color code, and high or low serum culture condition is indicated by the absence (high) or presence (low) of the black square below each branch. Because fibroblasts from the same site were grouped together irrespective of donor, passage number, or serum condition, topographic differentiation appeared to be the predominant source of gene expression variation among these cells. (**C**) HOX expression in adult fibroblasts recapitulates the embryonic Hox code. In a comparison of HOX expression pattern in secondary axes, schematic of expression domains of 5′ HoxA genes in the mouse limb bud at approximately 11.5 days postcoitus is shown on top. The HOX genes up regulated in fibroblasts from the indicated sites are shown below. HoxC5 is expressed in embryonic chick forelimbs, and HoxD9 functions in proximal forelimb morphogenesis. (Discussed in detail in reference 29).

microarray analysis is likely to become one of the main work horses of the stem cell biologist.

REFERENCES

1. Brown, P.O., and Botstein, D. (1999). Exploring the new world of the genome with DNA microarrays. *Nat. Genet.* **21** (1 Suppl), 33–37.
2. Gerhold, D.L., Jensen, R.V., and Gullans, S.R. (2002). Better therapeutics through microarrays. *Nat. Genet.* **32** (Suppl), 547–551.
3. Chung, C.H., Bernard, P.S., and Perou, C.M. (2002). Molecular portraits and the family tree of cancer. *Nat. Genet.* **32** (Suppl), 533–540.
4. Butte, A. (2002). The use and analysis of microarray data. *Nat. Rev. Drug Discov.* **1,** 951–960.
5. Wang, E., Miller, L.D., Ohnmacht, G.A., Liu, E.T., and Marincola, F.M. (2000). High-fidelity mRNA amplification for gene profiling. *Nat. Biotechnol.* **18,** 457–459.
6. Perou, C.M., Sorlie, T., Eisen, M.B., van de Rijn, M., Jeffrey, S.S., Rees, C.A., Pollack, J.R., Ross, D.T., Johnsen, H., Akslen, L.A., Fluge, O., Pergamenschikov, A., Williams, C., Zhu, S.X., Lonning, P.E., Borresen-Dale, A.L., Brown, P.O., and Botstein, D. (2000).

Molecular portraits of human breast tumours. *Nature* **406,** 747–752.

7. Diehn, M., Alizadeh, A.A., Rando, O.J., Liu, C.L., Stankunas, K., Botstein, D., Crabtree, G.R., and Brown, P.O. (2002). Genomic expression programs and the integration of the CD28 costimulatory signal in T cell activation. *Proc. Natl. Acad. Sci. U. S. A.* **99,** 11796–11801.
8. Boldrick, J.C., Alizadeh, A.A., Diehn, M., Dudoit, S., Liu, C.L., Belcher, C.E., Botstein, D., Staudt, L.M., Brown, P.O., and Relman, D.A. Stereotyped and specific gene expression programs in human innate immune responses to bacteria. *Proc. Natl. Acad. Sci. U. S. A.* **99,** 972–977.
9. Sherlock, G. (2001). Analysis of large-scale gene expression data. *Brief Bioinform.* **2,** 350–362.
10. Slonim, D.K. (2002). From patterns to pathways: gene expression data analysis comes of age. *Nat. Genet.* **32** (Suppl), 502–508.
11. Dudoit, S., and Fridlyand, J. (2002). A prediction-based resampling method for estimating the number of clusters in a dataset. *Genome Biol.* **3** (7), RESEARCH0036.
12. Troyanskaya, O.G., Garber, M.E., Brown, P.O., Botstein, D., and Altman R.B. (2002). Nonparametric methods for identifying differentially expressed genes in microarray data. *Bioinformatics* **18,** 1454–1461.
13. Park, P.J., Pagano, M., and Bonetti, M. (2001). A nonparametric scoring algorithm for identifying informative genes from microarray data. *Pac. Symp. Biocomput.* 52–63.
14. Tusher, V.G., Tibshirani, R., and Chu, G. (2001). Significance analysis of microarrays applied to the ionizing radiation response. *Proc. Natl. Acad. Sci. U. S. A.* **98,** 5116–5121.
15. Eisen, M.B., Spellman, P.T., Brown, P.O., and Botstein, D. (1998). Cluster analysis and display of genome-wide expression patterns. *Proc. Natl. Acad. Sci. U. S. A.* **95,** 14863–14868.
16. Tamayo, P., Slonim, D., Mesirov, J., Zhu, Q., Kitareewan, S., Dmitrovsky, E., Lander, E.S., and Golub, T.R. (1999). Interpreting patterns of gene expression with self-organizing maps: methods and application to hematopoietic differentiation. *Proc. Natl. Acad. Sci. U. S. A.* **96,** 2907–2912.
17. Toronen, P., Kolehmainen, M., Wong, G., and Castren, E. (1999). Analysis of gene expression data using self-organizing maps. *FEBS Lett.* **451,** 142–146.
18. Alter, O., Brown, P.O., and Botstein, D. (2000). Singular value decomposition for genome-wide expression data processing and modeling. *Proc. Natl. Acad. Sci. U. S. A.* **97,** 10101–10106.
19. Raychaudhuri, S., Stuart, J.M., and Altman, R.B. (2000). Principal components analysis to summarize microarray experiments: application to sporulation time series. *Pac. Symp. Biocomput.* 455–466.
20. Ivanova, N.B., Dimos, J.T., Schaniel, C., Hackney, J.A., Moore, K.A., and Lemischka, I.R. (2002). A stem cell molecular signature. *Science* **298,** 601–604.
21. Ramalho-Santos, M., Yoon, S., Matsuzaki, Y., Mulligan, R.C., and Melton, D.A. (2002). "Stemness": transcriptional profiling of embryonic and adult stem cells. *Science* **298,** 597–600.
22. Roy, P.J., Stuart, J.M., Lund, J., and Kim, S.K. (2002). Chromosomal clustering of muscle-expressed genes in *Caenorhabditis elegans. Nature* **418,** 975–979.
23. Spellman, P.T., and Rubin, G.M. (2002). Evidence for large domains of similarly expressed genes in the Drosophila genome. *J. Biol.* **1,** 5.
24. Xu, R.H., Chen, X., Li, D.S., Li, R., Addicks, G.C., Glennon, C., Zwaka, T.P., and Thomson, J.A. (2002). BMP4 initiates human embryonic stem cell differentiation to trophoblast. *Nat. Biotechnol.* **20,** 1261–1264.
25. Diehn, M., Eisen, M.B., Botstein, D., and Brown, P.O. (2000). Large-scale identification of secreted and membrane-associated gene products using DNA microarrays. *Nat. Genet.* **25,** 58–62.
26. LaBarge, M.A., and Blau, H.M. (2002). Biological progression from adult bone marrow to mononucleate muscle stem cell to multinucleate muscle fiber in response to injury. *Cell* **111,** 589–601.
27. Watt, F.M., and Hogan, B.L. (2000). Out of Eden: stem cells and their niches. *Science* **287,** 1427–1430.
28. Hackney, J.A., Charbord, P., Brunk, B.P., Stoeckert, C.J., Lemischka, I.R., and Moore, K.A. (2002). A molecular profile of a hematopoietic stem cell niche. *Proc. Natl. Acad. Sci. U. S. A.* **99,** 13061–13066.
29. Chang, H.Y., Chi, J.T., Dudoit, S., Bondre, C., van de Rijn, M., Botstein, D., and Brown, P.O. (2002). Diversity, topographic differentiation, and positional memory in human fibroblasts. *Proc. Natl. Acad. Sci. U. S. A.* **99,** 12877–128782.
30. Gasch, A.P., and Eisen, M.B. (2002). Exploring the conditional coregulation of yeast gene expression through fuzzy k-means clustering. *Genome Biol.* **3,** RESEARCH0059.
31. Iyer, V.R., Horak, C.E., Scafe, C.S., Botstein, D., Snyder, M., and Brown P.O. (2001). Genomic binding sites of the yeast cell-cycle transcription factors SBF and MBF. *Nature* **409,** 533–538.
32. Lieb, J.D., Liu, X., Botstein, D., and Brown, P.O. (2001). Promoter-specific binding of Rap1 revealed by genome-wide maps of protein-DNA association. *Nat. Genet.* **28,** 327–334.

58

High Resolution Clonal Marking–Analysis

Joby L. McKenzie and John E. Dick

Introduction

Homeostasis of the hematopoietic system is maintained by the hematopoietic stem cell (HSC) compartment through an intricate balance between self-renewal and differentiation cell divisions. Thus, insight into the developmental fate of stem cells will enhance our understanding of the regulation of the entire blood system. HSCs are challenging to study because they are rare, rendering HSC analysis the equivalent to looking for a needle in a haystack. Most stem cell assays are geared toward cell population studies. However, to gain a detailed analysis of the functional capacity of the entire HSC pool, analysis must be done at the level of the individual cell. An individual HSC can be studied by transplantation with a single purified HSC or with a population of uniquely marked HSCs. The field of stem cell biology has evolved greatly since the early 1960s, when Till and McCulloch developed the first quantitative assay for individual stem cells.[1] During this time, technologic advances in both purifying and tagging HSCs have enabled an exponential progression of our level of understanding of the hematopoietic system and an appreciation of the complexity of the HSC compartment.

HSC evaluation can only take place in the context of an *in vivo* assay system since current *in vitro* assays are unable to maintain intrinsic stem cell characteristics. The murine model was a convenient system to begin analysis of the HSC; thus, there is a marked difference is our knowledge of the murine HSC in comparison to the human HSC. As discussed in this chapter, an *in vivo* repopulation assay for human HSCs was only recently developed. Human HSCs must be uniquely tagged to track stem cell behavior at the single-cell level. By contrast, murine HSCs can be purified and transplanted at the single-cell level.[2] The obvious complication in purifying stem cells is the ability to distinguish cells based on their immunophenotype and functionally assay these cells *in vivo*. Previously, when individual stem cells were transplanted, only one-fifth of them could be later detected.[3–5] This could be because of a problem in HSC homing to the appropriate niche in the bone marrow (BM) or because the phenotype defining a "pure" HSC population was in fact heterogeneous. Using a modified transplant protocol, a recent study determined that a high proportion of transplanted single murine stem cells can engraft; however, only a limited number possess sufficient self-renewal capacity to sustain a long-term graft.[6] Using a slightly different HSC purification strategy, another group further confirmed that murine HSC can be isolated as a pure HSC population.[7] Functional tests from these single HSCs demonstrate nearly absolute efficiency for donor engraftment.[7] The capability of purifying individual murine HSCs is a relatively new advancement. Historically, individual HSCs were studied using some form of clonal tracking where a genetic marker was introduced into a population of HSCs and then transplanted. Thus, individual or marked cells are tracked temporally and spatially following transplantation through a retrospective analysis of the mature cells of the blood system, as the progeny from each HSC carries the same unique tag. Consequently, the stem cell and its subsequent progeny define a distinguishable clone that can be assayed for life span, lineage commitment, and proliferative potential as well as a quantitative evaluation of the clonal composition maintaining hematopoiesis. Clonal tracking also permits an investigation into the effects of experimental manipulations on these individual HSCs, including *in vitro* culture, cytokine stimulation, and radiation on intrinsic stem cell properties. Tracking stem cells has also aided the determination of the characteristics and interaction among the various stem cell classes and their contribution to the hematopoietic system. A greater understanding of the composition of the entire HSC compartment and the molecular and cellular regulation of HSCs will be required to bring future HSC-based therapies to the clinic.

First Attempts to Characterize Individual Murine Stem Cells

Early endeavors in murine stem cell marking used sublethal irradiation of the donor to generate chromosomal abnormalities.[8–10] Marked donor bone marrow was then injected into syngeneic mice, and the contribution of clones were monitored over time. Important conclusions about stem cells were drawn from these cytologic studies. Most importantly, these studies were the first to prove that the colony-forming unit–spleen (CFU-S) was clonal. Wu *et al.*[9] set the stage in 1968 by hypothesizing that the CFU-S and lymphoid cells have a common progenitor. In 1977, Abramson and colleagues[10] published data that supported the 1968 hypothesis. Experimentally, W/W^v mice received lightly irradiated bone marrow from syngeneic W/W mice and were given 8 to 12 months to establish a graft. Subsequently, the bone marrow,

Handbook of Stem Cells
Volume 2

thymus, and spleen were harvested and the cells were analyzed for chromosomal aberrations induced by radiation. The cells derived from the spleen were also analyzed in independent lipopolysaccharide (LPS) and phytohemagglutinin (PHA) cultures that assay for abnormal B- and T-lymphocyte karyotypes, respectively. Additionally, bone marrow was injected into secondary recipients and the day-12 CFU-S cells underwent karyotypic analysis. Stem cells were classified as those cells that generated CFU-S, PHA blasts, and LPS blasts that carried the same chromosomal aberration; unusual karyotypes present only in the LPS cultures represented B-lymphocyte–restricted stem cells. From this work, it was concluded that myeloid and lymphoid cells were derived from a common stem cell but that another class of stem cells could be restricted in its differentiation capacity. However, the low marking frequency and potential for altering intrinsic stem cell function by irradiation meant that it was difficult to establish whether such HSC classes were experimentally induced artifacts or they truly existed. New techniques to track individual stem cells needed to be developed.

Murine Studies Employing Retroviral Vectors

New attempts at tagging stem cells used the newly developed approach of introducing marker genes by DNA or viral transduction. As a first effort, DNA-mediated transfer of genes into mouse bone marrow cells was reported; however, the efficiency was poor.[11,12] In 1983, Joyner *et al.*[13] achieved successful gene transfer into murine hematopoietic progenitor cells through retroviral vectors. A retrovirus enters the cell by recognition of a specific receptor and subsequently integrates at a semirandom position[14–16] in the replicating genome. The specific site of integration is therefore a unique marker for each stem cell and its progeny.[13,17,18] Compared to radiation marking, retroviruses can infect a wide range of cells with high efficiency, are stably integrated, have a low proviral copy number per host cell, have a defined proviral structure,[19] and were theoretically considered to not alter the intrinsic properties of HSCs. These initial experiments set the foundation for the clonal assessment of stem cells for the next two decades.

Williams *et al.*[17] were able to transduce CFU-S using a Moloney murine sarcoma virus-based retroviral vector that encoded the neomycin resistance gene. This system provided a means of tracking clones and characterizing their developmental program. Using a similar murine leukemia virus and an altered transduction protocol, Dick *et al.*[20] and Keller *et al.*[21] achieved highly efficient transduction of primitive long-term repopulating stem cells. These studies provided the first conclusive evidence for the existence of a single cell able to generate all blood lineages for a mouse lifetime. Pretreatment of bone marrow with 5-fluorouracil to eliminate actively replicating cells induced the subsequent proliferation of quiescent stem cells, thus permitting their transduction.[22] In addition, cytokines were employed to stimulate HSCs into cycle during *in vitro* culture. Given that retroviruses can only infect cycling cells,[23,24] these modification led to a substantial increase in gene transfer efficiency. The marked stem cells were injected into either lethally conditioned recipients or genetically deficient W/W^v mice and given 6–17 weeks to expand within the host and commit to differentiation. The value of W/W^v recipients was that all potential stem cell classes could engraft since there was no selective pressure against stem cells that only repopulated specific lineages or were required to function rapidly to rescue a lethally irradiated recipient. W/W^v mice did not require donor engraftment for survival in contrast to the situation with lethally irradiated mice. To track the clones following transplantation, DNA was extracted from the hematopoietic tissues of mice sacrificed at different endpoints and digested with a restriction endonuclease that had a single site in the vector. Each clone is therefore represented by a single restriction fragment length polymorphism (RFLP) containing a proviral sequence assessed using Southern blot analysis as depicted in Fig. 58–1A.[25] The potential of each marked stem cell was characterized based on the presence of bands and their relative intensities in the BM, spleen, and thymus. Stem cells were classified as pluripotent or restricted to the lymphoid or myeloid lineages. In some cases, mice were repopulated by a single detectable clone that contributed to all hematopoietic tissues, providing conclusive proof for the existence of a pluripotential HSC and showing the dramatic proliferative potential of the individual HSC. A further analysis of the fractionated lineages following murine reconstitution was performed by Lemischka and colleagues.[26] Similar to previous studies, it was concluded that different classes of stem cells exist. However, through serial transplantations, these authors demonstrated that a stem cell clone with no detectable contribution to hematopoiesis in the primary recipient could be activated upon secondary transplantation. Therefore, a stem cell can replicate in a manner sufficient to allow retroviral insertion then can return to a quiescent state. Snodgrass and Keller[27] in 1987 saw clones that appeared early and were present later as well as a flux in the clonal composition over time when sampling spleen at two different times. Thus, researchers needed to be cautious when interpreting data supporting restricted stem cells since the absence of a band in one lineage at one time did not prove that a contribution had not been made at another time. This study challenged the widely accepted theory that HSC dynamics were controlled by clonal succession.[28–30] The clonal succession theory proposes that there are many clones with the potential to repopulate the hematopoietic system; however, only a subset of these are active at any time. This analysis suggested that clonal stability may be the more likely state: that the graft is dominated by fluctuating clones at early time points but is maintained by long-lived clones. These opposing theories of clonal succession versus clonal stability are still debated in the literature today.

Murine Long-Term Clonal Analysis

Although a picture of the dynamics of the murine HSC compartment was emerging by the late 1980s, long-term studies to assess the clonal composition of the stem cell pool that more

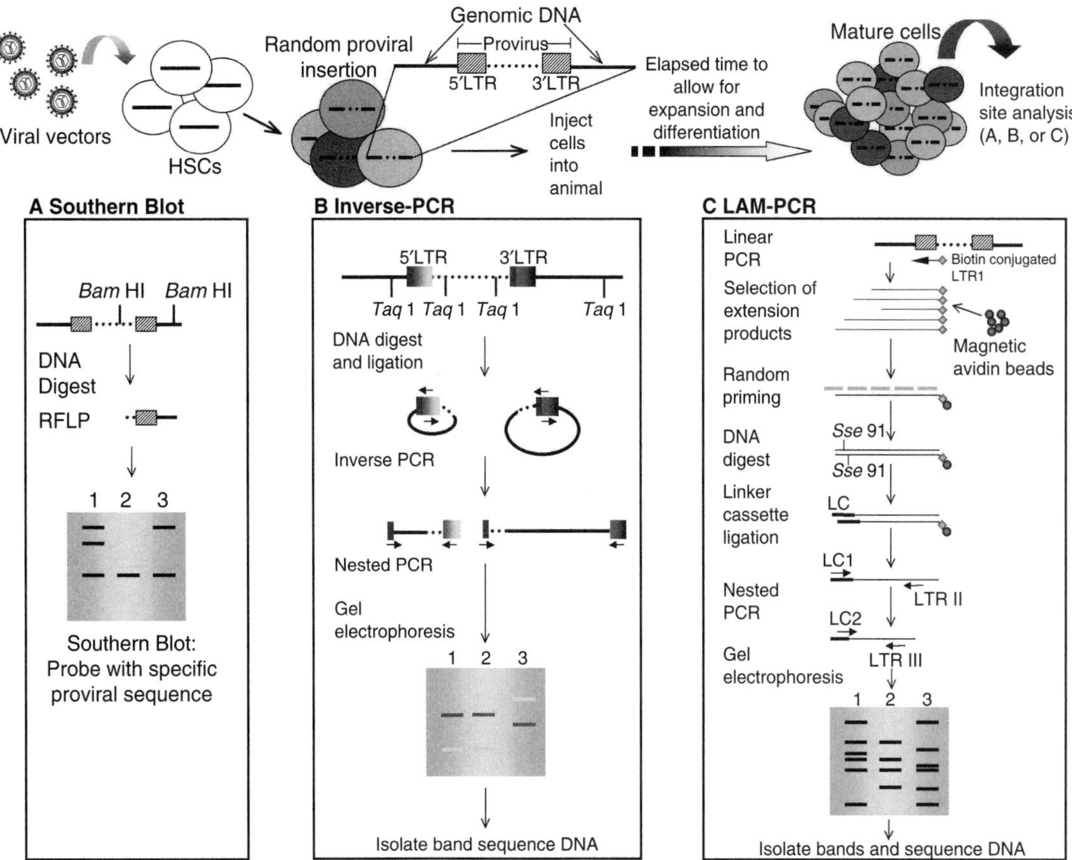

Figure 58–1. *Integration site analysis techniques used on transduced HSCs and their progeny.* Retroviral or lentiviral vectors are used to transduce HSCs resulting in a unique proviral insertion for each stem cell; thus, each stem cell is distinctively marked. A given number of months after transplant, the hematopoietic tissue is sampled for mature progeny that carry the same unique insertion site as the stem cell from which it originated, thus enabling the tracking of HSCs. Each clone is represented in a different shade of gray. The DNA from the mature cell population is then used for integration site analysis by one of three methods: (A) Southern blot, (B) inverse PCR, or (C) LAM-PCR. (A) Southern blot[25]: DNA digestion using a restriction enzyme that cuts once in the proviral sequence and again in the genomic DNA of sampled tissue is electrophoresed to separate the RFLP based on their unique mobility within the gel. The DNA is then immobilized by transferring to a membrane and probing with a proviral-specific sequence labeled with a radioactive isotope. Bands are visualized by exposing the film to the radioactive membrane. (B) Inverse PCR:[58] After DNA digestion with a restriction enzyme that cuts twice in the provirus and in the flanking genomic DNA, two variable-sized fragments are liberated that represent one clone. The two bands containing either the 3′LTR or the 5′LTR are then self-ligated and followed by two rounds of PCR. The first round is performed using the circular DNA as a template for linear amplification employing two LTR-specific primers. The second, nested PCR, uses nested primers also specific to LTR sequence. These bands are then size fractionated by gel electrophoresis and subsequently extracted from the gel and sequenced. (C) LAM-PCR:[60] The first round of PCR involves linear amplification using only one primer that is biotinylated (diamonds) and specific to the 5′LTR (LTR1). Following the linear PCR, there is a selection of the biotinylated extension fragments by incubating the PCR reaction with avidin-coated magnetic beads. A second strand for each enriched fragment is synthesized using random hexanucleotide priming (represented by the broken line). The double-stranded DNA is then digested and subsequently ligated to a linker cassette (LC). The ligation product is subjected to an addition PCR using LTR- and LC-specific primers (LTRII and LC1). The last PCR step uses additional nested LTR and LC primers (LTRIII and LC2). The PCR products are visualized on a high-resolution gel followed by an option of sequencing the fragments by excising, amplifying, and cloning the bands. (Please see CD-ROM for color version of this figure.)

closely mimicked the steady state were required for a complete understanding of HSC dynamics. The data collected were limited in that analysis was never taken beyond the time required for the hematopoietic system to recover from the stress of transplantation and reach a point that would reflect the intrinsic stem cell state. Jordan and Lemischka[31] evaluated 142 stem cell clones from 63 reconstituted mice, analyzing four major peripheral blood lineages at regular intervals over 4–16 months. Like the previous studies, clonal analysis was made possible through retroviral vectors and Southern analysis. One important modification was the deletion of the U3 region in the 3′ long-terminal repeat (LTR) of the retroviral vector, rendering the virus replication incompetent and precluding the emergence of new clones caused by secondary viral insertions. Based on this thorough analysis, a model was proposed whereby clonal flux characterized the first 4–6 months posttransplantation, followed by maintenance of the stem cell pool by a small number of clones that remain stable for the life of the mouse.

Large Animal Studies as a Transition to Humans

Contrasting the widely demonstrated ability to transduce murine pluripotent stem cells in a highly efficient manner, when applied to larger animal models and human gene therapy trials, this ability was diminished.[32,33] Whereas the murine system has been a valuable resource for HSC biology, there is not always a correlation between the murine and the primate systems; thus, it is imperative that the primate system, both human and nonhuman, be extensively studied. Gene transfer experiments using nonprimate models as hosts applied conditions similar to those used successfully in the murine setting. Gene transfer was barely detectable into HSCs, and the maintenance of gene expression was often short lived.[34–37] Unbeknownst to investigators paving the way in large animal studies, the optimizations of transduction procedures leading to high gene transfer efficiency in the mouse could not simply be translated to other animal systems. As well, the combinations of cytokines that led to high gene transfer frequencies in the murine model were not as beneficial in the primate model, and as such, the cytokine combinations needed to be amended.[35] Additionally, the retroviral receptor expression profile in primates varies from that in mice; therefore, the envelope proteins encoded in the retroviral vectors had to be optimized.[38] Also, efficient murine retroviral transduction was favored by culturing the targeted bone marrow cells over a layer of retrovirus-producing cells. When this protocol was employed with rhesus monkey cells, the producer cells had a deleterious effect on the bone marrow cells and the animals subsequently died because of graft failure.[33,34,39] Whereas the murine system guided the new field of primate gene therapy, the initial prospects were bleak and the gap between murine and primate HSC knowledge was vast.

Optimizing Gene Transfer Protocols

The prospect of applying gene marking methodology for future gene therapy protocols prompted many technical improvements. The transduction culture media was enhanced with various combinations of cytokines including interleukin-3, interleukin-6, stem cell factor,[40] granulocyte colony-stimulating factor,[41] and Flt-3 ligand.[42] CH-296, a fragment of the extracellular matrix molecule fibronectin, was also demonstrated to improve the transduction efficiency of primitive hematopoietic cells, allowing the retroviral particles to bind the chymotryptic fragments of fibronectin. Thus, retroviruses were colocalized with the adherent hematopoietic cells.[43,44] An added advantage of the CH-296 fragment was that during the transduction procedure, cells were protected from apoptosis.[45]

Although the use of retroviruses led to important insights into the biology of mammalian HSCs, the prerequisite for cells to be in cycle for retroviral infection to occur was a severe limitation of this vector system. Thus, alternative marking methods were necessary. Replication-defective human immunodeficiency virus type 1 (HIV-1)-based lentiviral vectors offer a distinct advantage of integration into the genome of nonproliferating cells,[46,47] consequently negating the requirement for extensive cell culture and cytokines to induce cell cycling. This mechanism of integration is mediated by karyophilic determinants encoded in the HIV genome that allow the viral preintegration complex to enter the nonmitotic host cell chromosome.[47] Thus, quiescent stem cells can be transduced without the need for proliferative stimuli that can alter the intrinsic stem cell character.

Transduction efficiency was augmented by improving the vector construct. Modifications of the vector construct by adding the woodchuck hepatitis virus posttranscriptional regulatory element (WPRE) resulted in enhanced gene expression facilitated by an increase in the nuclear export of transcripts containing WPRE.[48] Second, transduction efficiency was further optimized by broadening the tropism of viral vectors through the use of novel envelope proteins. Naldini *et al.*[49] tested a vesicular stomatitis virus-G (VSV-G) envelope protein encoded on a second plasmid[48] (see also Rebel *et al.*),[50] thus enabling an expansive range of host-cell types to be infected by binding ubiquitous cell membrane phospholipids.[51] Because of the higher expression levels of the gibbon ape leukemia virus (GALV) receptor on primate cells, the GALV envelope was used as another means of pseudotyping retroviral vectors employed in primate cell transduction.[52]

In moving from the murine system to large animal models and humans, only moderate transduction rates were reported in studies using retroviral vectors.[35,36] Investigators studying the HSCs of primates encountered barriers using retroviral vectors, which may be explained by the fact that primate pluripotent HSCs have a prolonged cycling period during steady-state hematopoiesis and, as a population, are largely quiescent in comparison to those of rodents.[53] Additionally, most of the transplantations in rodents to characterize HSCs were performed with bone marrow that had been treated with 5-fluorouracil, thus initiating HSCs to proliferate. By employing a lentivector pseudotyped with VSV-G or a retrovector pseudotyped with GALV, higher transduction efficiencies were made possible in human HSCs.[54,55] Sequential optimization of lentiviral vectors, such as the insertion of the DNA flap containing the central polypurine tract has enhanced transduction efficiency of human cells.[56] Thus, lentiviral vectors are paving the way in the new century for higher gene transfer rates, which will equate to more marked stem cells.

Novel Integration Site Analysis Techniques

Like any investigation, results reflect the sensitivity of the analysis tool employed. Although Southern blot analysis enables a comprehensive examination of the murine HSC compartment, these results were limited to a compilation of clones that each contributed at least 10^5 cells at the time of collection.[57] Hence, a more sensitive technique to assess the developmental and proliferative capacity of all the stem cell clones, regardless of their size, would be essential to gain further insight into the understanding of HSC biology.

Nolta *et al.*[58] in 1996 employed a technique, inverse polymerase chain reaction (PCR), in which the retroviral LTR was used as an anchor to identify and subsequently amplify each unique clonal insertion site. As outlined in Fig. 58–1B, inverse PCR is reminiscent of Southern blot analysis in that it exploits the unique location of a proviral integration within the host genome. Using this technique, Nolta *et al.*[58] were able to formally show for the first time that pluripotential human HSCs could be transduced with retroviruses. However, the amplification from the 3′ and 5′ ends are biased in that the number of informative bands from the 3′ end are more frequent, which could lead to an underestimation of the number of clones in the assayed hematopoietic tissue.[59]

Concomitant with the birth of inverse PCR was the development of our ability to follow human stem cell clones in *in vivo* settings. Likewise, linear amplification-mediated (LAM)-PCR devised by Schmidt *et al.*[60] enabled a more sensitive method for insertion site analysis than both Southern blot analysis and inverse PCR, with the potential of identifying multiple clones in one pass. LAM-PCR is based on the presence of unique retroviral insertion sites relative to restriction sites for each clone. Furthermore, each RFLP can be reliably amplified, thus enabling a complete clonal analysis of any sample notwithstanding DNA quantity. The steps for LAM-PCR are illustrated in Fig. 58–1C.

Since the advent of LAM-PCR, several groups have established similar protocols to determine the clonal makeup of reconstituted recipients but also to use as a tool for insertional mutagenesis. Lenvik *et al.*[61] used the blockerette-capture, T7-amplified (BCT-)RT-PCR to determine flanking sequences and achieved sensitivity comparable to that of the LAM-PCR. Laufs *et al.*[16] used a modification of the ancestor of LAM-PCR, ligation-mediated PCR,[62] to perform a thorough analysis of integration sites of retroviruses into preferred human genomic targets. As a direct comparison of the sensitivities of the outlined integration site analysis techniques, Southern blot analysis can determine one clone that contributes a total of 10^5 cells;[57] LAM-PCR can detect multiple clones in a population of 10^3 cells[60], inverse PCR can identify a clone from colony of 200 cells,[58,59] and BCT-RT-PCR can identify a clone from as little as one transduced cell in a population of 1000 untransduced cells.[61] Although Southern analysis is less sensitive, it has not lost its place as the mainstay for clonal analysis, as it is able to reliably detect the major clones without detecting the clones that may be considered contaminants if there is only in one copy in the total graft. Thus, Southern analysis is ideal for assessing key clonal contributions, and the extreme sensitivity of the PCR-based techniques permits clonal tracking of even the rarest stem cell subpopulations, as will be required for a comprehensive understanding of the HSC compartment.

Clonal Analysis of HSCs in Large Animal Models

By implementing the optimized protocols for gene transfer and novel integration site analysis techniques, clonal analysis was made possible for HSCs in large animals. Advances in the protocols for retroviral transduction such as the use of CH-296 and stromal cells with cytokines eventually permitted long-term marking of multiple lineages at levels between 10 and 15% in primate HSCs.[63] Recently, Kim *et al.*[59] formally demonstrated the pluripotential differentiation of HSCs in rhesus macaques by showing that marked HSCs could contribute to both myeloid and lymphoid lineages. A subset of these pluripotent clones was present at both early and late time points, thus indicating clonal stability. The enhanced sensitivity of inverse PCR and improved gene transfer conditions allowed detailed analysis of the clonal dynamics in the rhesus macaques that had previously been precluded by low levels of proviral-containing hematopoietic cells. These results were reminiscent of those achieved in murine studies, and given that gene transfer was long-lived in multipotent clones, the implication for successful human gene therapy was imminent.

LAM-PCR allowed Dunbar and colleagues to further investigate the nature of long-term pluripotent nonprimate stem cells.[60] Using LAM-PCR as a sensitive technique, a composite picture of the stem cell compartment of the rhesus macaque and baboon could be derived. Their study provided a longer-term follow-up period of 23 to 33 months and demonstrated a complex polyclonal composition of stem cells maintaining the hematopoietic system with reconstitution of the blood system from both short-term and long-term repopulating cells. However, long-term hematopoiesis was maintained through clonal stability.

Transition to Humans: Clonal Analysis Using X-Chromosome Inactivation

Another stream of clonal analysis pioneered by Fialkow in 1977 and used by Abkowitz and colleagues employs population studies of the X-linked enzyme glucose-6-phosphate dehydrogenase (G6PD).[64–68] Because G6PD resides on the X-chromosome, X-inactivation of this enzyme can be exploited as a means of statistically calculating the clonal makeup of recipients at a population level. X-inactivation is a method of dosage compensation whereby somatic cells have one X-chromosome randomly repressed, or inactivated, at an early embryonic stage in development. All descendents from this initially inactivated cell will carry the same inactivated X-chromosome. Thus, the female is composed of a mosaic of paternal and maternal expressing X-chromosomes. Individuals that are heterozygous at the G6PD locus carry two alleles, for example, Gd^B and Gd^A. Fialkow *et al.*[64] were able to show that in eight female patients with chronic myelocytic leukemia (CML) each had a single enzyme type in all leukemic granulocytes but were heterogeneous in nonleukemic granulocytes, indicating that CML had a clonal origin in a stem cell. Abkowitz exploited these population studies using Safari cats that were derived from a cross between Geoffroy *(Leopardus geoffroyi)* and domestic *(Felis catus)* cats, yielding electrophoretically distinct G6PD isoforms, Geoffroy-G6PD (G-G6PD), and domestic-G6PD[69] (d-G6PD).[69]

Previous studies from this group demonstrated that the heterozygous makeup of the d-G6PD and G-G6PD in hematopoietic progenitor cells of Safari cats was both random and stable over a 5-year period.[70] This G6PD ratio was measured by the CFU assay that assessed the contribution of d-G6PD and G-G6PD in burst-forming units–erythroid and the granulocyte–macrophage CFUs. To follow the clonal dynamics of HSCs from autologous bone marrow transplantations into Safari cats, a stochastic model was developed to estimate the number of active stem cells and their mean life span. This stochastic model was premised on the facts that there is a d- or G-G6PD stem cell reserve and that the active stem cells contributing to hematopoiesis have a constant death risk. Preliminary studies with the Safari cat transplantation experiments assessed the number of clones contributing to hematopoiesis and concluded clonal succession based on the number of estimated stem cells present, which fluctuated over the 1.5 years in which bone marrow samples were acquired.[65] However, in a thorough 6-year analysis, it was observed that the number of clones stabilized between 1–4.5 years, similar to the situation in mice.[66] Whereas the mouse experienced only a 4- to 6-month period of clonal fluctuation before the hematopoietic system returned to steady-state conditions; the larger hematopoietic demands of the cat perhaps extended this time period.[31,66] Although these computer simulations need to be supported with further clonal studies at the level of individual stem cells, the effect of these results on our understanding of large animal stem cell biology is valuable.

Clonal Analysis of Human HSCs

The study of human HSCs was hampered by the protracted development of the appropriate system in which to assay the cells. Several xenotransplantation models have been developed that employ murine or sheep recipients. Mice that have a suppressed immune system facilitate human cell engraftment upon intravenous transplantation of primitive hematopoietic cells, thus allowing human HSC development. The first studies involving transplantation of human hematopoietic cells into mouse recipients used immunodeficient *bg/nu/xid* mice.[71] The *bg/nu/xid* mice are athymic, prevent T-cell maturation (nude, *Hfh11*^{nu}, or *nu,* mutation), have a reduced number of natural killer (NK) cells (beige, or *bg,* mutation), and have a reduced number of lymphokine-activated killer cells required for host response to foreign cells (*xid* mutation).[72,73] Other immunodeficient mice used in this era of xenotransplantation were severe-combined immunodeficiency (SCID) C.B-17 *scid/scid* mice, nonobese diabetic SCID (NOD-SCID) NOD/LtSz-*scid/scid* mice, and NOD-SCID-β_2-microglobulin-null (NOD-SCID-$\beta_2m^{-/-}$) mice.[74–76] To some extent, these mice lack functional lymphoid cells including NK cells, have less mature macrophages, and do not have serum hemolytic complement activity. Alternative means of assaying human cells in the mouse xenogeneic microenvironment are by using a SCID-hu model in which human fetal thymus, liver, lymph node, and spleen are introduced into SCID mice surgically or through IV injection.[77] Although all of these murine models enabled human cell engraftment, the stem cell assayed was dependent on the model used. Moreover, different types of cells could engraft in different animal hosts. As such, the quest for alternative animal models to assay human HSCs continued beyond the mouse. Zanjani *et al.*[78] developed a preimmune sheep model which exploits the naïve immune system of the fetal sheep. This xenogeneic environment supports the ability to respond to human cytokines, can engraft secondary recipients, and allows human graft levels to be followed serially over time by aspiration of host bone marrow. Moreover, the large size means that the proliferative stress on the human HSC will more closely approximate the human. The drawback to the preimmune sheep model is that it is technically challenging and not practical for most investigators.[78] Common to all of the models are the ability of human HSCs to repopulate the bone marrow, maintain long-term proliferation, and produce multilineage progeny. It is clear that each model offers its own advantages and disadvantages.

Following the establishment of the various xenotransplantation models, the next several years were dominated by characterization of HSCs at the population level.[71,77,79–81] The identification of a cell population that was more primitive than previously defined progenitor cell populations assayed *in vitro* (long-term culturing-initiating cells and colony-forming cells) was identified in 1996 by Larochelle *et al.*[82] to be exclusively present in the CD34$^+$CD38$^-$ fraction of human cord blood (CB) and BM[82] (see also Bhatia *et al.*[83]). This human cell population was assayed in NOD-SCID mice and thus was coined the SCID-repopulating cell (SRC). In later years, however, expression of CD34 on the cell surface no longer defined the most primitive cell type; rather, cells lacking CD34 expression as well as lineage antigens were considered more primitive than some CD34$^+$ cells.[84–87] The diversity of the potential stem cell populations in the human hematopoietic system was emerging. Several groups were able to identify a more committed stem cell by employing murine models that had further immune defects, including NOD-SCID-$\beta_2m^{-/-}$ mice and NOD-SCID mice treated with an anti-NK antibody.[88–90] Cells expressing CD34 and CD38 surface markers defined a population of cells that contributed to the engraftment of murine recipients at early time points after transplantation but were unable to maintain the human graft at later time points and lacked self-renewal potential.[89] Aside from purifying cell populations based on a composite expression of surface molecules, it was possible to assay HSC frequency in xenotransplant models using limiting dilution assays. Using the NOD-SCID mouse, the frequency of the SRC was found to be 1 in 9.3×10^5 human CB cells, 1 in 3.0×10^6 bone marrow cells, and 1 in 6.0×10^6 mobilized peripheral blood cells.[91,92] It was also determined that the CD34$^-$CD38$^-$ stem cell population was present at a lower frequency in the human hematopoietic system than CD34$^+$CD38$^-$ stem cells, indicating expansion of cell populations as they mature.[93] These studies were important in assessing stem cells as a population.

These fractionation studies led to important conclusions about the stem cell compartment. First, immunophenotypically distinct populations had different engraftment kinetics highlighted by early and long-term contributions, suggesting that the hematopoietic system was structured as a hierarchy. This hierarchy was proposed to consist of cells that became more restricted in their lineage commitment in parallel to acquiring a shortened life span as they differentiated from stem cells to multipotent progenitor cell, to unilineage progenitor cells, and finally to the bulk of the blood system, the mature cells. The concept of heterogeneity within the human stem cell compartment also arose from these studies. The more primitive stem cell populations had a characteristic delay in engraftment accompanied by long-term contribution to hematopoietic reconstitution, whereas less primitive stem cell populations were able to reconstitute the donor hematopoietic system more quickly but could maintain the graft for only a short period. However, clonal analysis of individual human HSC was required to prove that the hematopoietic hierarchy was comprised of distinct stem cell classes. In 1996, the application of inverse PCR to stem cell studies was reported by Nolta *et al.*[58] and Larochelle *et al.*[82] These studies were made possible because of optimized retroviral transduction procedures. These two plenary papers were able to show, for the first time in humans, that stem cells were pluripotent and that oligoclonal stem cell contribution could maintain hematopoiesis in a xenograft model.

With improvements in transduction efficiency because of the use of the CH-296, the optimization of cytokine combinations, and the modifications of vector constructs,[43,50,94–97] clonal analysis of human HSCs was achieved using conventional Southern blot analysis because of the large percentage of marked cells within the human graft of NOD-SCID mice. In 2000, Barquinero *et al.*[98] observed an oligoclonal repopulation pattern of human stem cells in NOD-SCID mice and found that there are generally one to four clones that make both dominant and subordinate contributions to the overall graft. In closing the gap between murine HSC and human HSC knowledge, Guenechea *et al.*[57] demonstrated that the human HSC compartment was comprised of distinct classes of stem cells, using Southern blot analysis to follow clones temporally in NOD-SCID mice transplanted with human CB cells that were first transduced with a retrovirus containing green fluorescent protein. In this study, two distinctive clonal populations were present in the repopulated mice: There were clones present at early time points that were lost at later time points, and there were clones that persisted. Although the clonal analysis in this study was only performed over 12 weeks, the data seemed to support the conclusions drawn from the murine and nonhuman primate models in which clonal stability maintains the hematopoietic system.

The ability of a stem cell to maintain the balance of mature cells in the hematopoietic system is regulated by self-renewal divisions, whereby a stem cell makes a replica copy of itself without differentiating. Self-renewal of human HSCs was demonstrated by Ailles *et al.*,[99] who performing secondary transplants in NOD-SCID-$\beta_2m^{-/-}$ mice. These experiments demonstrated polyclonal engraftment as well as propagation of a subset of the clones in the primary graft to the secondary recipient.

More recently, an intrafemoral (IF) injection technique has proved to be a more sensitive way of assaying rare stem cell populations, like the CD34$^-$-SRC. As opposed to IV injection, direct delivery of these cells into the bone marrow cavity may prevent the loss associated with blood circulation prior to homing to the bone marrow microenvironment.[100–102] This technique also offers another means of assaying HSCs, thus enabling the discovery of new classes of stem cells.[100] Applying this technique, the rapid-SRC (R-SRC) was identified as those hematopoietic cell within the Lin$^-$CD34$^+$CD38^{lo}CD36$^-$ subpopulation that were able to rapidly generate a myeloerythroid graft, a cell population not efficiently detected in the conventional IV NOD/SCID assay.[100] Because engraftment levels are higher using this technique, integration site analysis will also be facilitated.

Although our understanding of the human HSC compartment has grown immensely over the last decade, many questions remain. Through the employment of lentiviral vectors to achieve higher gene transfer rates, the more sensitive IF transplantation assay, and newer integration site analysis techniques to achieve a more complete picture of the clonal composition of stem cell populations, answers regarding stem cell classes and their relationship within the human hematopoietic system are now attainable.

Insertional Mutagenesis

The application of retroviral vectors to transduce hematopoietic cells began in 1983, at which time the risk of insertional mutagenesis in murine gene transfer protocols was considered to be low. By applying the highly sensitive integration site analysis techniques combined with genomic sequence information, it is now possible to sequence the contiguous DNA into which the provirus had inserted. In 2002, a string of reports was published confirming insertional mutagenesis into known oncogenes, causing heightened awareness of the danger of employing viral vectors for gene therapy or other uses. In experimental mice, leukemia was induced by a retroviral vector integrating into the transcription factor *Evi1*.[103] A recent gene therapy trial in France, involving 11 boys that were born with SCID syndrome as a result of a mutation in their X-linked common gamma-c chain (γc) gene, restored immunity in 9 of the 11 patients.[104] In this trial, CD34$^+$ bone marrow cells from the patients were transduced with a retroviral vector expressing the γc transgene. Approximately 3 years later, 2 of these 9 patients developed acute leukemia because of insertion of the provirus into *LMO2*, a known leukemic oncogene.[105,106]

Although lentiviruses are able to more efficiently mark stem cells, several groups have reported multiple insertions per cell and thus an increased risk of insertional mutagenesis.[15,99,107] In an experiment designed to evaluate the integration efficiency of lentiviral vectors into individual human hematopoietic cells, it was determined that one integration site was located in the *BRCA1* tumor-suppressor gene.[107]

Particular caution must therefore be exercised when developing gene therapy protocols using lentiviruses since they have the capacity for a high frequency of integration at multiple sites within the genome. Moreover, attention must be warranted for clonal HSC analysis since at some low frequency some detected clones could contain some abnormality. However, complication of data from hundreds of human xenografts have not detected abnormalities in proliferation or differentiation.[108,109]

Summary

Through the years, the HSC has gone from being a mysterious entity hypothesized to exist to being a powerful tool used in clinical practice. Clonal tracking and analysis of stem cells has evolved from the first work by Wu *et al.*[8] and Abramson *et al.*,[10] using radiation-induced chromosome marking, to the present day, whereby lentiviral transduction coupled with LAM-PCR has the potential to follow all clones temporally and spatially. Endeavors to perfect transduction procedures and integration site analysis in the murine system have paved the way for all applications in large animal models.

Not only were techniques optimized, but preexisting theories were challenged. For decades there was the debate over clonal succession and clonal stability. Although the early studies of Lemischka and Abkowitz suggested that clonal succession defined stem cell homeostasis, with longer period of analysis, they concluded that the initial clonal flux was caused by the stress induced by total body irradiation and was dominated over time by a stable subset of clones.[26,65] Nevertheless, some experimental data still can be interpreted as supporting clonal succession.[110,111]

Over the decades, the systems under analysis have become more complex, marking methods more intricate, and integration site analysis techniques more sensitive. In combination, this has enabled the evolution of HSC characterization. Although scientists continue to challenge the field in what is known, the boundaries into the unknown are being extended. Perhaps one day tracking stem cells *in vivo* and having a thorough understanding of their intrinsic stem cell properties will be elementary.

ACKNOWLEDGMENTS

This work was supported by grants to J.E. Dick from The Stem Cell Network of the National Centres of Excellence, the National Cancer Institute of Canada with funds from the Canadian Cancer Society, the Canadian Genetic Diseases Network of the National Centres of Excellence, the Canadian Institutes for Health Research, and a Canada Research Chair.

REFERENCES

1. Till, J.E., and McCulloch, E.A. (1961). A direct measurement of the radiation sensitivity of normal mouse bone marrow cells. *Radiat. Res.* **14,** 213–222.
2. Osawa, M., Hanada, K., Hamada, H., and Nakauchi, H. (1996). Long-term lymphohematopoietic reconstitution by a single CD34$^{low/-}$ hematopoietic stem cell. *Science* **273,** 242–245.
3. Spangrude, G.J., Brooks, D.M., and Tumas, D.B. (1995). Long-term repopulation of irradiated mice with limiting numbers of purified hematopoietic stem cells: *in vivo* expansion of stem cell phenotype but not function. *Blood* **85,** 1006–1016.
4. Osawa, M., Nakamura, K., Nishi, N., Takahasi, N., Tokuomoto, Y., Inoue, H., and Nakauchi, H. (1996). *In vivo* self-renewal of c-Kit$^+$Sca-1$^+$Lin$^{low/-}$ hemopoietic stem cells. *J. Immunol.* **156,** 3207–3214.
5. Domen, J., and Weissman, I.L. (2000). Hematopoietic stem cells need two signals to prevent apoptosis; BCL-2 can provide one of these, Kitl/c-Kit signaling the other. *J. Exp. Med.* **192,** 1707–1718.
6. Benveniste, P., Cantin, C., Hyam, D., and Iscove, N.N. (2003). Hematopoietic stem cells engraft in mice with absolute efficiency. *Nat. Immunol.* **4,** 708–713.
7. Matsuzaki, Y., Kinjo, K., Mulligan, R.C., and Okano, H. (2004). Unexpectedly efficient homing capacity of purified murine hematopoietic stem cells. *Immunity* **20,** 87–93.
8. Wu, A.M., Till, J.E., Siminovitch, L., and McCulloch, E.A. (1967). A cytological study of the capacity for differentiation of normal hemopoietic colony-forming cells. *J. Cell Physiol.* **69,** 177–184.
9. Wu, A.M., Till, J.E., Siminovitch, L., and McCulloch, E.A. (1968). Cytological evidence for a relationship between normal hemopoietic colony-forming cells and cells of the lymphoid system. *J. Exp. Med.* **127,** 455–463.
10. Abramson, S., Miller, R.G., and Phillips, R.A. (1977). The identification in adult bone marrow of pluripotent and restricted stem cells of the myeloid and lymphoid systems. *J. Exp. Med.* **145,** 1567–1579.
11. Cline, M.J., Stang, H., Mercola, K., Morse, L., Ruprecht, R., Brown, J., and Salser, W. (1980). Gene transfer in intact animals. *Nature* **284,** 422–425.
12. Mercola, K.E., Stang, H.D., Browne, J., Salser, W., and Cline, M.J. (1980). Insertion of a new gene of viral origin into bone marrow cells of mice. *Science* **208,** 1033–1035.
13. Joyner, A., Keller, G., Phillips, R.A., and Bernstein, A. (1983). Retrovirus transfer of a bacterial gene into mouse hematopoietic progenitor cells. *Nature* **305,** 556–558.
14. Kitamura, Y., Lee, Y.M., and Coffin, J.M. (1992). Nonrandom integration of retroviral DNA *in vitro*: effect of CpG methylation. *Proc. Nat. Acad. Sci. USA* **89,** 5532–5536.
15. Schroder, A.R., Shinn, P., Chen, H., Berry, C., Ecker, J.R., and Bushman, F. (2002). HIV-1 integration in the human genome favors active genes and local hotspots. *Cell* **110,** 521–529.
16. Laufs, S., Gentner, B., Nagy, K.Z., Jauch, A., Benner, A., Naundorf, S., Kuehlcke, K., Schiedlmeier, B., Ho, A.D., Zeller, W.J., and Fruehauf, S. (2003). Retroviral vector integration occurs in preferred genomic targets of human bone marrow-repopulating cells. *Blood* **101,** 2191–2198.
17. Williams, D.A., Lemischka, I.R., Nathan, D.G., and Mulligan, R.C. (1984). Introduction of new genetic material into pluripotent hematopoietic stem cells of the mouse. *Nature* **310,** 476–480.
18. Miller, A.D., Eckner, R.J., Jolly, D.J., Friedmann, T., and Verma, I.M. (1984). Expression of a retrovirus encoding human HPRT in mice. *Science* **225,** 630–632.
19. Miller, A.D. (1996). Cell-surface receptors for retroviruses and implications for gene transfer. *Proc. Natl. Acad. Sci. U. S. A.* **93,** 11,407–11,413.

20. Dick, J.E., Magli, M.C., Huszar, D., Phillips, R.A., and Bernstein, A. (1985). Introduction of a selectable gene into primitive stem cells capable of long-term reconstitution of the hemopoietic system of W/W^v mice. *Cell* **42,** 71–79.
21. Keller, G., Paige, C., Gilboa, E., and Wagner, E. (1985). Expression of a foreign gene in myeloid and lymphoid cells derived from multipotent hemopoietic precursors. *Nature* **318,** 149–154.
22. Hodgson, G.S., and Bradley, T.R. (1979). Properties of hematopoietic stem cells surviving 5-fluorouracil treatment: evidence for a pre-CFU-S cell? *Nature* **281,** 381–382.
23. Miller, D.G., Adam, M.A., and Miller, A.D. (1990). Gene transfer by retrovirus vectors occurs only in cells that are actively replicating at the time of infection. *Mol. Cell Biol.* **10,** 4239–4242.
24. Roe, T., Reynolds, T.C., Yu, G., and Brown, P.O. (1993). Integration of murine leukemia virus DNA depends on mitosis. *EMBO J.* **12,** 2099–2108.
25. Southern, E.M. (1975). Detection of specific sequences among DNA fragments separated by gel electrophoresis. *J. Mol. Biol.* **98,** 503–517.
26. Lemischka, I.R., Raulet, D.H., and Mulligan, R.C. (1986). Developmental potential and dynamic behavior of hematopoietic stem cells. *Cell* **45,** 917–927.
27. Snodgrass, R., and Keller, G. (1987). Clonal fluctuation within the hematopoietic system of mice reconstituted with retrovirus-infected stem cells. *EMBO J.* **6,** 3955–3960.
28. Kay, H.E.M. (1965). How many cell generations? (Hypothesis). *Lancet.* **1,** 418–419.
29. Micklem, H.S. (1984). Hemopoiesis by clonal succession? A commentary. *Blood Cells* **10,** 487–492.
30. Mintz, B., Anthony, K., and Litwin, K. (1984). Monoclonal derivation of mouse myeloid and lymphoid lineages from totipotent hematopoietic stem cells experimentally engrafted in fetal hosts. *Proc. Natl. Acad. Sci. U. S. A.* **81,** 7835–7839.
31. Jordan, C.T., and Lemischka, I.R. (1990). Clonal and systemic analysis of long-term hematopoiesis in the mouse. *Genes Dev.* **4,** 220–232.
32. Brenner, M. (1996). Gene marking. *Hum. Gene Ther.* **7,** 1927–1936.
33. Van Beusechem, V.W., and Valerio, D. (1996). Gene transfer into hematopoietic stem cells of nonhuman primates. *Hum. Gene Ther.* **7,** 1649–1668.
34. Kantoff, P.W., Gillio, A.P., McLachlin, J.R., Bordignon, C., Eglitis, M.A., Kernan, N.A., Moen, R.C., Kohn, D.B., Yu, S.F., Karson, E., Zwiebel, J.A., Gilboa, E., Blaese, R.M., Nienhuis, A., O'Reilly, R.J., and Anderson, W.F. (1987). Expression of human adenosine deaminase in nonhuman primates after retrovirus-mediated gene transfer. *J. Exp. Med.* **166,** 219–234.
35. Bodine, D.M., McDonagh, K.R., Brandt, S.J., Ney, P.A., Agricola, B., Byrne, E., and Nienhuis, A.W. (1990). Development of a high-titer retrovirus producer cell line capable of gene transfer in rhesus monkey hematopoietic stem cells. *Proc. Natl. Acad. Sci. U. S. A.* **87,** 3738–3742.
36. Van Beusechem, V., Kukler, A., Heidt, P., and Valerio, D. (1992). Long-term expression of human adenosine deaminase in rhesus monkeys transplanted with retrovirus-infected bone marrow cells. *Proc. Natl. Acad. Sci. U. S. A.* **89,** 7640–7644.
37. Schuening, F., Kawahara, K., Miller, A., To, R., Goehle, S., Stewart, D., Mullally, K., Fisher, L., Graham, T., Applebaum, F., Hackman, R., Osborne, W., and Storb, R. (1991). Retrovirus-mediated gene transduction into long-term repopulating marrow cells of the dog. *Blood* **78,** 2568–2576.
38. Orlic, D., Girard, L.J., Jordan, C.T., Anderson, S.M., Cline, A.P., and Bodine, D.M. (1996). The level of mRNA encoding the amphotropic retrovirus receptor in mouse and human hematopoietic stem cells is low and correlates with the efficiency of retrovirus transduction. *Proc. Natl. Acad. Sci. U. S. A.* **93,** 11,097–11,102.
39. Cornetta, K., Wieder, R., and Anderson, W.F. (1989). Gene transfer into primates and prospects for gene therapy in humans. *Prog. Nucleic Acid Res. Mol. Biol.* **36,** 311–322.
40. Luskey, B.D., Rosenblatt, M., Zsebo, K., and Williams, D.A. (1992). Stem cell factor, interleukin-3, and interleukin-6 promote retroviral-mediated gene transfer into murine hematopoietic stem cells. *Blood* **80,** 396–402.
41. Bodine, D.M., Seidel, N.E., Gale, M.S., Nienhuis, A.W., and Orlic, D. (1994). Efficient retrovirus transduction of mouse pluripotent hematopoietic stem cells mobilized into the peripheral blood by treatment with granulocyte colony-stimulating factor and stem cell factor. *Blood* **84,** 1482–1491.
42. Petzer, A.L., Hogge, D.E., Landsdorp, P.M., Reid, D.S., and Eaves, C.J. (1996). Self-renewal of primitive human hematopoietic cells (long-term culture-initiating cells) *in vitro* and their expansion in defined medium. *Proc. Natl. Acad. Sci. U. S. A.* **93,** 1470–1474.
43. Hanenberg, H., Xiao, X.L., Dilloo, D., Hashino, K., Kato, I., and Williams, D. (1996). Colocalization of retrovirus and target cells on specific fibronectin adhesion domains increases genetic transduction of mammalian cells. *Nat. Med.* **2,** 876–882.
44. Moritz, T., Dutt, P., Xiao, X.L., Carstanjen, D., Vik, T., Hanenberg, H., and Williams, D. (1996). Fibronectin improves transduction of reconstituting hematopoietic stem cells by retroviral vectors: Evidence for direct viral binding to chymotryptic carboxy-terminal fragments. *Blood* **88,** 855–862.
45. Donahue, R.E., Sorrentino, B.P., Hawley, R.G., An, D.S., Chen, I.S., and Wersto, R.P. (2001). Fibronectin fragment CH-296 inhibits apoptosis and enhances *ex vivo* gene transfer by murine retrovirus and human lentivirus vectors independent of viral tropism in nonhuman primate CD34$^+$ cells. *Mol. Ther.* **3,** 359–367.
46. Gallay, P., Swingler, S., Aiken, C., and Trono, D. (1995). HIV-1 infection of nondividing cells: C-terminal tyrosine phosphorylation of the viral matrix protein is a key regulator. *Cell* **80,** 379–388.
47. Gallay, P., Swingler, S., Song, J., Bushman, F., and Trono, D. (1995). HIV nuclear import is governed by the phosphotyrosine-mediated binding of matrix to the core domain of integrase. *Cell* **83,** 569–576.
48. Zufferey, R., Donello, J.E., Trono, D., and Hope, T.J. (1999). Woodchuck hepatitis virus posttranscriptional regulatory element enhances expression of transgenes delivered by retroviral vectors. *J. Virol.* **73,** 2886–2892.
49. Naldini, L., Blomer, U., Gallay, P., Ory, D., Mulligan, R., Gage, F.H., Verma, I.M., and Trono, D. (1996). *In vivo* gene delivery and stable transduction of nondividing cells by a lentiviral vector. *Science* **272,** 263–267.
50. Rebel, V.I., Tanaka, M., Lee, J.S., Hartnett, S., Pulsipher, M., Nathan, D.G., Mulligan, R.C., and Sieff, C.A. (1999). One-day *ex vivo* culture allows effective gene transfer into human nonobese-diabetic severe-combined immune-deficient repopulating cells using high-titer vesicular stomatitis virus-G protein pseudotyped retrovirus. *Blood* **93,** 2217–2224.
51. Burns, J.C., Friedmann, T., Driever, W., Burrascano, M., and Yee, J.K. (1993). Vesicular stomatitis virus-G glycoprotein pseudotyped retroviral vectors: concentration to very high titer and efficient gene transfer into mammalian and nonmammalian cells. *Proc. Natl. Acad. Sci. U. S. A.* **90,** 8033–8037.

52. Kiem, H.P., Heyward, S., Winkler, A., Potter, J., Allen, J.M., Miller, A.D., and Andrews, R.G. (1997). Gene transfer into marrow repopulating cells: comparison between amphotropic and gibbon ape leukemia virus pseudotyped retroviral vectors in a competitive repopulation assay in baboons. *Blood* **90,** 4638–4645.
53. Mahmud, N., Devine, S.M., Weller, K.P., Parmar, S., Sturgeon, C., Nelson, M.C., Hewett, T., and Hoffman, R. (2001). The relative quiescence of hematopoietic stem cells in nonhuman primates. *Blood* **97,** 3061–3068.
54. Guenechea, G., Gan, O., Inamitsu, T., Dorrell, C., Pereira, D., Kelly, M., Naldini, L., and Dick, J. (2000). Transduction of human $CD34^{+}CD38^{-}$ bone marrow and cord blood-derived SCID-repopulating cells with third-generation lentiviral vectors. *Mol. Ther.* **1,** 452–459.
55. Horn, P.A., Topp, M.S., Morris, J.C., Riddell, S.R., and Kiem, H.P. (2002). Highly efficient gene transfer into baboon marrow repopulating cells using GALV-pseudotype oncoretroviral vectors produced by human packaging cells. *Blood* **100,** 3960–3967.
56. Sirven, A., Pflumio, F., Zennou, V., Titeux, M., Vainchenker, W., Coulombel, L., Dubart-Kupperschmitt, A., and Charneau, P. (2000). The human immunodeficiency virus type-1 central DNA flap is a crucial determinant for lentiviral vector nuclear import and gene transduction of human hematopoietic stem cells. *Blood* **96,** 4103–4110.
57. Guenechea, G., Gan, O.I., Dorrell, C., and Dick, J.E. (2001). Distinct classes of human stem cells that differ in proliferative and self-renewal potential. *Nat. Immunol.* **2,** 75–82.
58. Nolta, J., Dao, M., Wells, S., Smogorzewska, E., and Kohn, D. (1996). Transduction of pluripotent human hematopoietic stem cells demonstrated by clonal analysis after engraftment in immune deficient mice. *Proc. Natl. Acad. Sci. U. S. A.* **93,** 2414–2419.
59. Kim, H.J., Tisdale, J.F., Wu, T., Takatoku, M., Sellers, S.E., Zickler, P., Metzger, M.E., Agricola, B.A., Malley, J.D., Kato, I., Donahue, R.E., Brown, K.E., and Dunbar, C.E. (2000). Many multipotential gene-marked progenitor or stem cell clones contribute to hematopoiesis in nonhuman primates. *Blood* **96,** 1–8.
60. Schmidt, M., Zickler, P., Hoffmann, G., Haas, S., Wissler, M., Muessig, A., Tisdale, J.F., Kuramoto, K., Andrews, R.G., Wu, T., Kiem, H.P., Dunbar, C.E., and von Kalle, C. (2002). Polyclonal long-term repopulating stem cell clones in a primate model. *Blood* **100,** 2737–2743.
61. Lenvik, T., Lund, T.C., and Verfaillie, C.M. (2002). Blockerette-ligated capture T7-amplified RT-PCR, a new method for determining flanking sequences. *Mol. Ther.* **6,** 113–118.
62. Schmidt, M., Glimm, H., Lemke, N., Muessig, A., Speckmann, C., Haas, S., Zickler, P., Hoffmann, G., and Von Kalle, C. (2001). A model for the detection of clonality in marked hematopoietic stem cells. *Ann. NY Acad. Sci.* **938,** 146–155; discussion 155–146.
63. Wu, T., Kim, H.J., Sellers, S.E., Meade, K.E., Agricola, B.A., Metzger, M.E., Kato, I., Donahue, R.E., Dunbar, C.E., and Tisdale, J.F. (2000). Prolonged high-level detection of retrovirally marked hematopoietic cells in nonhuman primates after transduction of $CD34^{+}$ progenitors using clinically feasible methods. *Mol. Ther.* **1,** 285–293.
64. Fialkow, P., Jacobson, R., and Papayannopoulou, T. (1977). Chronic myelocytic leukemia: clonal origin in a stem cell common to the granulocyte, erythrocyte, platelet, and monocyte–macrophage. *Am. J. Med.* **63,** 125–130.
65. Abkowitz, J.L., Linenberger, M.L., Newton, M.A., Shelton, G.H., Ott, R.L., and Guttorp, P. (1990). Evidence for the maintenance of hematopoiesis in a large animal by the sequential activation of stem cell clones. *Proc. Natl. Acad. Sci. U. S. A.* **87,** 9062–9066.
66. Abkowitz, J.L., Persik, M.T., Shelton, G.H., Ott, R.L., Kiklevich, J.V., Catlin, S.N., and Guttorp, P. (1995). Behavior of hematopoietic stem cells in a large animal. *Proc. Natl. Acad. Sci. U. S. A.* **92,** 2031–2035.
67. Abkowitz, J.L., Golinelli, D., Harrison, D.E., and Guttorp, P. (2000). *In vivo* kinetics of murine hemopoietic stem cells. *Blood* **96,** 3399–3405.
68. Abkowitz, J.L., Catlin, S.N., McCallie, M.T., and Guttorp, P. (2002). Evidence that the number of hematopoietic stem cells per animal is conserved in mammals. *Blood* **100,** 2665–2667.
69. O'Brien, S.J., Haskins, M.E., Winkler, C.A., Nash, W.G., and Patterson, D.F. (1986). Chromosomal mapping of β-globin and albino loci in the domestic cat: a conserved mammalian chromosome group. *J. Hered.* **77,** 374–378.
70. Guttorp, P., Newton, M.A., and Abkowitz, J.L. (1990). A stochastic model for hematopoiesis in cats. *IMA J. Math. Appl. Med. Biol.* **7,** 125–143.
71. Kamel-Reid, S., and Dick, J.E. (1988). Engraftment of immune-deficient mice with human hematopoietic stem cells. *Science* **242,** 1706–1709.
72. Dorshkind, K., Pollack, S.B., Bosma, M.J., and Phillips, R.A. (1985). Natural killer (NK) cells are present in mice with severe-combined immunodeficiency (SCID). *J. Immunol.* **134,** 3798–3801.
73. Andriole, G.L., Mule, J.J., Hansen, C.T., Linehan, W.M., and Rosenberg, S.A. (1985). Evidence that lymphokine-activated killer cells and natural killer cells are distinct based on an analysis of congenitally immunodeficient mice. *J. Immunol.* **135,** 2911–2913.
74. Greiner, D.L., Hesselton, R.A., and Shultz, L.D. (1998). SCID mouse models of human stem cell engraftment. *Stem Cells* **16,** 166–177.
75. Shultz, L., Schweitzer, P., Christianson, S., Gott, B., Schweitzer, I., Tennent, B., McKenna, S., Mobraaten, L., Rajan, T., Greiner, D., and Leiter, E. (1995). Multiple defects in innate and adaptive immunological function in NOD/LtSz-scid mice. *J. Immunol.* **154,** 180–191.
76. Christianson, S.W., Greiner, D.L., Hesselton, R.A., Leif, J.H., Wagar, E.J., Schweitzer, I.B., Rajan, T.V., Gott, B., Roopenian, D.C., and Shultz, L.D. (1997). Enhanced human CD4+ T-cell engraftment in β2-microglobulin-deficient NOD-SCID mice. *J. Immunol.* **158,** 3578–3586.
77. McCune, J.M., Namikawa, R., Kaneshima, H., Shultz, L.D., Lieberman, M., and Weissman, I.L. (1988). The SCID-hu mouse: murine model for the analysis of human hematolymphoid differentiation and function. *Science* **241,** 1632–1639.
78. Zanjani, E.D., Almeida-Porada, G., and Flake, A.W. (1996). The human–sheep xenograft model: a large animal model of human hematopoiesis. *Int. J. Hematol.* **63,** 179–192.
79. Mosier, D.E., Gulizia, R.J., Baird, S.M., and Wilson, D.B. (1988). Transfer of a functional human immune system to mice with severe-combined immunodeficiency. *Nature* **335,** 256–259.
80. Flake, A.W., Harrison, M.R., and Zanjani, E.D. (1991). *In utero* stem cell transplantation. *Exp. Hematol.* **19,** 1061–1064.
81. Zanjani, E.D., Flake, A.W., Rice, H., Hedrick, M., and Tavassoli, M. (1994). Long-term repopulating ability of xenogeneic transplanted human fetal liver hematopoietic stem cells in sheep [see comments]. *J. Clin. Invest.* **93,** 1051–1055.

82. Larochelle, A., Vormoor, J., Hanenberg, H., Wang, J., Bhatia, M., Lapidot, T., Moritz, T., Murdoch, B., Xiao, X., Kato, I., Williams, D., and Dick, J. (1996). Identification of primitive human hematopoietic cells capable of repopulating NOD-SCID mouse bone marrow: implications for gene therapy. *Natl. Med.* **2,** 1329–1337.
83. Bhatia, M., Wang, J.C.Y., Kapp, U., Bonnet, D., and Dick, J.E. (1997). Purification of primitive human hematopoietic cells capable of repopulating immune-deficient mice. *Proc. Natl. Acad. Sci. U. S. A.* **94,** 5320–5325.
84. Bhatia, M., Bonnet, D., Murdoch, B., Gan, O.I., and Dick, J.E. (1998). A newly discovered class of human hematopoietic cells with SCID-repopulating activity. *Nat. Med.* **4,** 1038–1045.
85. Zanjani, E.D., Almeida-Porada, G., Livingston, A.G., Flake, A.W., and Ogawa, M. (1998). Human bone marrow $CD34^-$ cells engraft *in vivo* and undergo multilineage expression that includes giving rise to $CD34^+$ cells. *Exp. Hematol.* **26,** 353–360.
86. Nakamura, Y., Ando, K., Chargui, J., Kawada, H., Sato, T., Tsuji, T., Hotta, T., and Kato, S. (1999). *Ex vivo* generation of $CD34^+$ cells from $CD34^-$ hematopoietic cells. *Blood* **94,** 4053–4059.
87. Gallacher, L., Murdoch, B., Wu, D.M., Karanu, F.N., Keeney, M., and Bhatia, M. (2000). Isolation and characterization of human $CD34^-Lin^-$ and $CD34^+Lin^-$ hematopoietic stem cells using cell surface markers AC133 and CD7. *Blood* **95,** 2813–2820.
88. Glimm, H., Eisterer, W., Lee, K., Cashman, J., Holyoake, T.L., Nicolini, F., Shultz, L.D., von Kalle, C., and Eaves, C.J. (2001). Previously undetected human hematopoietic cell populations with short-term repopulating activity selectively engraft NOD-SCID-β2-microglobulin-null mice. *J. Clin. Invest.* **107,** 199–206.
89. Hogan, C.J., Shpall, E.J., and Keller, G. (2002). Differential long-term and multilineage engraftment potential from subfractions of human $CD34^+$ cord blood cells transplanted into NOD-SCID mice. *Proc. Natl. Acad. Sci. U. S. A.* **99,** 413–418.
90. Kerre, T.C., De Smet, G., De Smedt, M., Offner, F., De Bosscher, J., Plum, J., and Vandekerckhove, B. (2001). Both $CD34^+38^+$ and $CD34^+38^-$ cells home specifically to the bone marrow of NOD/LtSZ scid/scid mice but show different kinetics in expansion. *J. Immunol.* **167,** 3692–3698.
91. Wang, J.C., Doedens, M., and Dick, J.E. (1997). Primitive human hematopoietic cells are enriched in cord blood compared with adult bone marrow or mobilized peripheral blood as measured by the quantitative *in vivo* SCID-repopulating cell assay. *Blood* **89,** 3919–3924.
92. Conneally, E., Cashman, J., Petzer, A., and Eaves, C. (1997). Expansion *in vitro* of transplantable human cord blood stem cells demonstrated using a quantitative assay of their lymphomyeloid repopulating activity in nonobese diabetic-scid/scid mice. *Proc. Natl. Acad. Sci. U. S. A.* **94,** 9836–9841.
93. Bhatia, M., Bonnet, D., Kapp, U., Wang, J.C., Murdoch, B., and Dick, J.E. (1997). Quantitative analysis reveals expansion of human hematopoietic repopulating cells after short-term *ex vivo* culture. *J. Exp. Med.* **186,** 619–624.
94. Conneally, E., Eaves, C.J., and Humphries, R.K. (1998). Efficient retroviral-mediated gene transfer to human cord blood stem cells with *in vivo* repopulating potential. *Blood* **91,** 3487–3493.
95. Marandin, A., Dubart, A., Pflumio, F., Cosset, F.L., Cordette, V., Chapel-Fernandes, S., Coulombel, L., Vainchenker, W., and Louache, F. (1998). Retrovirus-mediated gene transfer into human $CD34^+38^{low}$ primitive cells capable of reconstituting long-term cultures *in vitro* and nonobese diabetic-severe combined immunodeficiency mice *in vivo. Hum. Gene Ther.* **9,** 1497–1511.
96. Schilz, A.J., Brouns, G., Knoss, H., Ottmann, O.G., Hoelzer, D., Fauser, A.A., Thrasher, A.J., and Grez, M. (1998). High-efficiency gene transfer to human hematopoietic SCID-repopulating cells under serum-free conditions. Blood 92, 3163–3171.
97. Van Hennik, P.B., Verstegen, M.M., Bierhuizen, M.F., Limon, A., Wognum, A.W., Cancelas, J.A., Barquinero, J., Ploemacher, R.E., and Wagemaker, G. (1998). Highly efficient transduction of the green fluorescent protein gene in human umbilical cord blood stem cells capable of cobblestone formation in long-term cultures and multilineage engraftment of immunodeficient mice. *Blood* **92,** 4013–4022.
98. Barquinero, J., Segovia, J.C., Ramirez, M., Limon, A., Guenechea, G., Puig, T., Briones, J., Garcia, J., and Bueren, J.A. (2000). Efficient transduction of human hematopoietic repopulating cells generating stable engraftment of transgene-expressing cells in NOD-SCID mice. *Blood* **95,** 3085–3093.
99. Ailles, L., Schmidt, M., Santoni de Sio, F.R., Glimm, H., Cavalieri, S., Bruno, S., Piacibello, W., Von Kalle, C., and Naldini, L. (2002). Molecular evidence of lentiviral vector-mediated gene transfer into human self-renewing, multipotent, long-term NOD-SCID repopulating hematopoietic cells. *Mol. Ther.* **6,** 615–626.
100. Mazurier, F., Doedens, M., Gan, O.I., and Dick, J.E. (2003). Rapid myeloerythroid repopulation following intrafemoral transplantation of NOD-SCID mice reveals a new class of human stem cells. *Nat. Med.* **9,** 959–963.
101. Wang, J., Kimura, T., Asada, R., Harada, S., Yokota, S., Kawamoto, Y., Fujimura, Y., Tsuji, T., Ikehara, S., and Sonoda, Y. (2003). SCID-repopulating cell activity of human cord blood-derived $CD34^-$ cells assured by intrabone marrow injection. *Blood* **101,** 2924–2931.
102. Yahata, T., Ando, K., Sato, T., Miyatake, H., Nakamura, Y., Muguruma, Y., Kato, S., and Hotta, T. (2003). A highly sensitive strategy for SCID: repopulating cell assay by direct injection of primitive human hematopoietic cells into NOD-SCID mice bone marrow. *Blood* **101,** 2905–2913.
103. Li, Z., Dullmann, J., Schiedlmeier, B., Schmidt, M., von Kalle, C., Meyer, J., Forster, M., Stocking, C., Wahlers, A., Frank, O., Ostertag, W., Kuhlcke, K., Eckert, H.G., Fehse, B., and Baum, C. (2002). Murine leukemia induced by retroviral gene marking. *Science* **296,** 497.
104. Cavazzana-Calvo, M., Hacein-Bey, S., de Saint Basile, G., Gross, F., Yvon, E., Nusbaum, P., Selz, F., Hue, C., Certain, S., Casanova, J.L., Bousso, P., Deist, F.L., and Fischer, A. (2000). Gene therapy of human severe combined immunodeficiency (SCID)-X1 disease. *Science* **288,** 669–672.
105. Kaiser, J. (2003). Gene therapy: seeking the cause of induced leukemias in X-SCID trial. *Science* **299,** 495.
106. Gansbacher, B. (2003). Report of a second serious adverse event in a clinical trial of gene therapy for X-linked severe-combined immune-deficiency (X-SCID): position of the European Society of Gene Therapy (ESGT). *J. Gene Med.* **5,** 261–262.
107. Woods, N.B., Muessig, A., Schmidt, M., Flygare, J., Olsson, K., Salmon, P., Trono, D., von Kalle, C., and Karlsson, S. (2003). Lentiviral vector transduction of NOD-SCID repopulating cells results in multiple vector integrations per transduced cell: risk of insertional mutagenesis. *Blood* **101,** 1284–1289.
108. Mazurier, F., Gan, O.I., McKenzie, J., Doedens, M., and Dick, J.E. (2003). Lentivector-mediated clonal tracking reveals intrinsic heterogeneity in the human hematopoietic stem cell compartment and culture-induced stem cell impairment. *Blood* **103,** 545–542.

109. Dao, M.A., Scott, S.C., Bauer, G., Arevalo, J., Wang, X., Csik, S., Skelton, D., Crooks, G.M., Kohn, D.B., and Nolta, J.A. (2003). *In vivo* model to assess biosafety: testing the risk of RCR and insertional mutagenesis from retroviral and lentiviral vectors. *Mol. Ther.* **7,** 2.

110. Drize, N.J., Keller, J.R., and Chertkov, J.L. (1996). Local clonal analysis of the hematopoietic system shows that multiple small short-living clones maintain lifelong hematopoiesis in reconstituted mice. *Blood* **88,** 2927–2938.

111. Drize, N.J., Olshanskaya, Y.V., Gerasimova, L.P., Manakova, T.E., Samoylina, N.L., Todria, T.V., and Chertkov, J.L. (2001). Lifelong hematopoiesis in both reconstituted and sublethally irradiated mice is provided by multiple sequentially recruited stem cells. *Exp. Hematol.* **29,** 786–794.

59

Systematic Approach to the Development of Stem Cell Expansion Cultures

Gerard J. Madlambayan, Dolores Baksh, and Peter W. Zandstra

New paradigms are required to overcome recognized bottlenecks in the expansion of adult stem cell numbers. The interactive nature of parameters that affect stem cell growth *in vitro* suggests the need for a systematic understanding, such as that starting to be used in other biological applications, to optimize stem cell growth. In this chapter, we outline a systematic approach for the design and optimization of stem cell–based bioprocesses. This approach requires (1) that culture parameters and networks of parameter interactions governing stem cell self-renewal and differentiation be defined and characterized, (2) that robust assays of stem cell developmental potential be used, (3) that an assessment of how perturbations in parameter values that affect stem cell growth be performed, and (4) that a quantitative understanding of how dynamic changes in biologic and microenvironmental conditions that affect stem cell growth be developed. Examples of the use of this new systematic approach to the development of bioprocesses to expand hematopoietic stem cell (HSC) and mesenchymal stem cell (MSC) numbers are described.

Introduction

Stem cells have generated a great deal of excitement as a potential source of cells for cell-based therapeutic strategies because of their ability to self-renew and differentiate into functional cells. Stem cells can be derived from multiple stages of development as well as from numerous adult tissues. Adult tissues are an attractive and readily accepted source of stem cells because such cells have demonstrated efficacy in multiple types of cellular therapeutics and may be directly obtained from individual patients, thereby eliminating difficulties associated with tissue rejection. Despite their enormous potential, the use of adult stem cells has been limited (both in numbers of patients treated and in scope of application), primarily because of our inability to reliably and reproducibly identify and isolate these rare cells from the heterogeneous populations in which they typically reside and, perhaps more importantly, to grow populations of cells that retain stem cell properties over multiple cell divisions.

Handbook of Stem Cells
Volume 2

Designing stem cell–based technologies requires insight into the culture parameters that govern stem cell self-renewal and differentiation, an appreciation of how these parameters interact with one another, and an understanding of how dynamic and kinetic changes in biologic and microenvironmental conditions affect stem cell growth. This chapter identifies some of the main bioprocess engineering considerations for the development of such technologies and begins to define systematic approaches for the optimization of these cultures. Our goal is to provide a framework for the development of stem cell–based bioprocesses, in particular with the purpose of designing systems with the ability to manipulate the self-renewal and differentiation of adult stem cells in a predictable manner. It is recognized that not all parameters will be applicable to all cell types; thus, selected examples are used to illustrate specific points and should not be considered an exhaustive review of the literature.

Multiparametric Optimization of Stem Cell–Based Bioprocesses

Stem cell–based bioprocesses can be compartmentalized into input *(I)*, culture *(C)*, and output *(O)* phases (Fig. 59–1A). The goal of developing these processes is to achieve an optimal output (O_{opt}) by controlling a set of input (I_p) and culture parameters *(P)* that affect stem cell growth. Table 59–1 provides a list of parameters to be considered in each compartment as well as a brief description of the parameter and a comment on at least one of its potential effects on stem cell culture development.

Importantly, although understanding the effects of individual culture parameters has contributed significantly to the development of improved stem cell cultures[1–4] (Fig. 59–1B), this analysis is only a first step in the design of stem cell bioprocesses. A review of the literature reveals that significant confusion exists regarding the effects of culture parameters both for distinct tissue-specific stem cells and among different stem cell systems. This confusion can be attributed at least partly to the fact that the effects of individual parameters are not typically considered in the context of interactions between parameters (both positive and negative); nor are changes taken into account of the effects of these parameters with time (as a consequence of changes in cellular composition [because of cell proliferation, differentiation, apoptosis, etc.], microenvironment [as molecules are added, generated, and degraded], and media composition [glucose, lactate, oxygen, and pH levels]). Ultimately, the effects of different combinations or

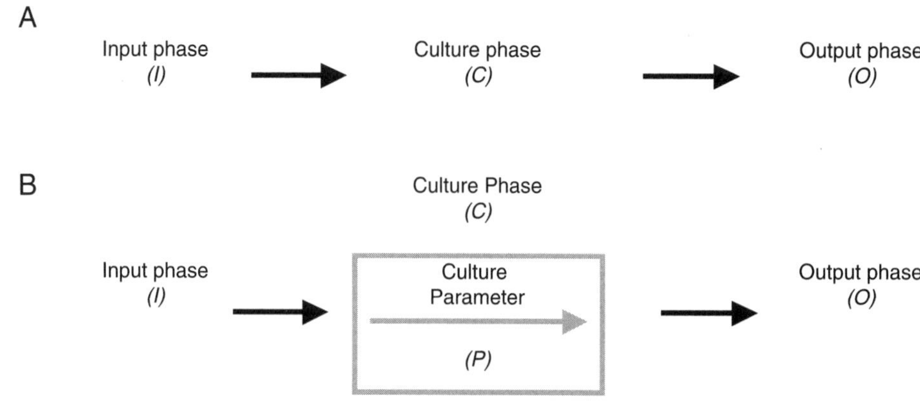

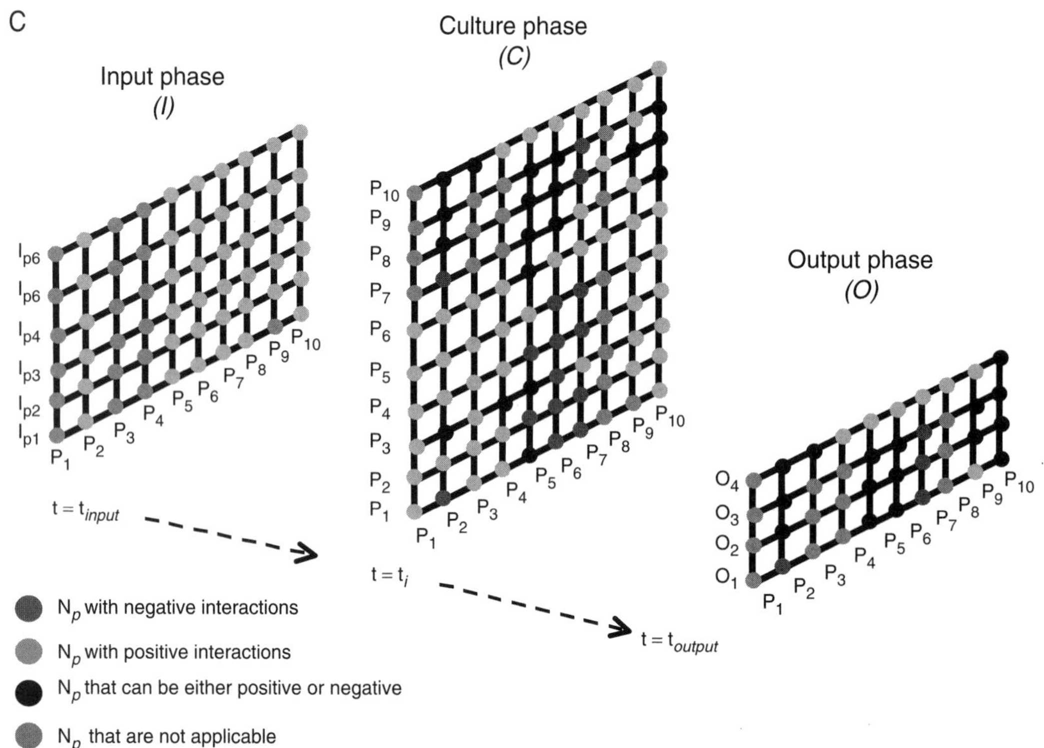

Figure 59–1. *Representation of stem cell bioprocess development.* (A) Stem cell expansion cultures can be categorized into input *(I)*, culture *(C)*, and output *(O)* phases. (B) The effects of individual culture parameters *(P)* have provided valuable insight into the processes that govern stem cell expansion and have led to improved stem cell culture configurations. (C) An illustration of the evolution of parameter interactions (depicted with two-parameter interactions only) as a function of time throughout culture is provided. The two-dimensional plane at $t = t_{input}$ describes the possible input (I_p) and culture parameters *(P)*, such as those enumerated in Table 59–1, that may have the greatest effect at the start of culture. As the culture progresses (i.e., $t = t_i$), there is an emergence of new parameter interactions that affect culture output. Finally, at $t = t_{output}$, parameters that specifically affect product quality are identified. *Continued*

networks of parameters (N_p) that define relationships between input and culture conditions need to be incorporated into culture optimization strategies. For example, Fig. 59–1C illustrates dynamic changes in N_p as a function of time throughout culture. Each grid line in the two-dimensional planes represents an individual parameter. An interaction occurs where lines cross; it is represented as a node (circle). These interactions can have positive effects, negative effects, both effects, or no effects on stem cell output. Fig. 59–1D shows that the optimal "pathway" through the culture phase (dashed line) starts at the time $t = t_{input}$ with a set of I_p and P values, connects N_p values that positively affect O at each time point (dark circles), and through a series of steps (changes in N_p) moves toward an optimized stem cell output.

Defining these networks of culture parameters is a daunting task. However, methodologies for multiparameter optimization

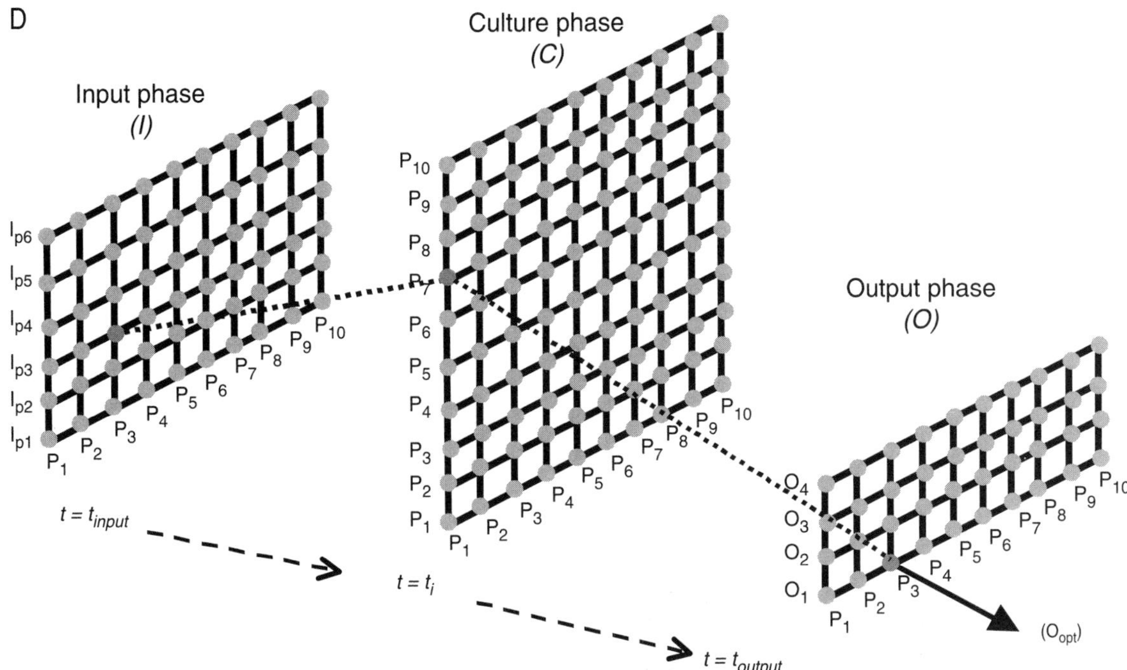

Figure 59-1, cont'd (D) Optimal expansion conditions result when N_p values (dark circles connected by the dotted line) are found for each time point, which moves the culture toward optimal stem cell output (O_{opt}). Individual culture parameters are symbolized by black grid lines making up each plane. Each point (filled circle) in the plane represents N_p values defined by the interaction between two parameters. An optimized culture system is represented by a dashed line that connects parameter network nodes that have positive effects on stem cell expansion. References exist for many of these two-parameter interactions and are reviewed in the specific examples given in the text. Where specific references cannot be found, interactions are inferred. Multiple parameter interactions would occur in the same manner. Specific input, culture, and output parameter types are listed with a corresponding number value in Table 59–1. (Please see CD-ROM for color version of this figure.)

and the analysis of interacting systems in biology is developing rapidly.[5–7] Strategies for elucidating the interactions between sets of input and culture parameter types generally require several iterative steps. Governing parameters must be defined and characterized (Table 59–1), and robust approaches to quantitatively measure O values (stem cell numbers and properties) need to be developed and incorporated. At this point, experiments can be performed to assess how each parameter or parameter network responds to perturbations that affect O values. Finally, an understanding of the interactions between parameters, and their effects on O can lead to predictive models of culture performance. Described in the next sections are some of the basic requirements for the development of a systematic approach to stem cell-based bioprocess design.

Critical Aspects in the Development of Predictive Networks of Culture Parameters

ROBUST, QUANTITATIVE, AND PREDICTIVE ASSAYS OF STEM CELL DEVELOPMENTAL POTENTIAL

Under most conditions, *in vitro* culture will compromise the developmental potential of the input stem cell population. Robust monitoring of the expanding cell population using standardized functional (both *in vitro* and *in vivo*) and phenotypic assays should be, and often is, implemented as a standard practice to test the effect of culture conditions on stem cell growth.

In general, *in vivo* functional assays offer the best indication of the developmental potential of a stem cell population. This is because they directly test the potential for a stem cell population to contribute to the development or redevelopment of a particular organ or tissue (for human stem cells, these are typically preformed in appropriate animal models). A good example of this type of assay is the ability of human HSCs to serially (and at limiting dilution) reconstitute hematopoiesis in immunocompromised recipients. Although many animal models have been developed,[8–10] the most widely used involves the use of nonobese-diabetic severe-combined immunodeficient (NOD-SCID) mice.[11,12] Similarly, acceptable *in vivo* models have been designed to test MSC potential, specifically for their capacity to generate a bone phenotype in nonskeletal[13] and skeletal sites.[14] Transplanted MSCs have also been shown to form both bone and cartilage in ectopic sites.[15] An *in vivo* assay that rigorously tests the broad differentiation potential (i.e., bone, cartilage, muscle, fat, etc.) of transplanted MSCs, a property that has been clearly demonstrated *in vitro*,[16] remains to be developed. Unfortunately, despite their evident biologic relevance, *in vivo* functional

TABLE 59–1
Key Parameters That Affect Stem Cell Bioprocess Design and Optimization

Compartment	Type	Definition	Example Considerations
Input parameters (I_p)	1. Ontogenic source	Biologic fluid (e.g., cord blood and peripheral blood) or tissue type	Tissue type may affect relative stem cell numbers as well as their developmental potential
	2. Source state	Fresh vs frozen	May affect stem cell purity and viability
	3. Stem cell frequency and absolute number	Number of assay defined cells per total cell number	An inverse relationship exists between cell frequency and the number of cells required for a given stem cell input
	4. Types and numbers of accessory cells	Stromal cells (for HSCs) and differentiated cells	Accessory cells may influence stem cell expansion through direct and indirect signals
	5. Inoculum cell density	Cells per milliliter or cells per area	May be a function of stem cell frequency and absolute number
	6. Developmental potential of input cells	Toti- and pluripotent vs multi- and unipotent	Determines the numbers and types of cells that may be formed
Culture parameters *(P)*	1. Exogenously added factors	Growth factors, cytokines, chemokines, etc.	Concentration, stability *in vitro*, downstream signaling interactions, and direct vs indirect effects
	2. Endogenously produced factors	Growth factors, cytokines, chemokines, etc.	Production rates may be influenced by accessory cells or exogenous factors, inhibitory or stimulatory
	3. Culture configuration	Static (T-flask), stirred suspension, perfusion cultures, etc.	Influences scalability and the growth of adherent vs nonadherent cells
	4. Operating conditions	Magnetic stir bar, baffles, and mixing speed (rpm)	Appropriate mixing speed (e.g., 40 rpm) prevents shear stress on cells
	5. pH	Physiologic ranges are typically 7.0–7.5	May affect growth factor-binding efficiency, cell survival, differentiation, etc.
	6. Oxygen	Dissolved oxygenated content	May regulate endogenous production of growth factors through hypoxic response mechanisms
	7. Metabolic products	Lactate, CO_2, etc.	Affects cell viability and intracellular reactions
	8. Feeding protocol	Medium exchange rate, medium exchange regimen (cell retention vs partial removal of cells), and perfusion	Controls culture microenvironment
	9. Medium components	Serum vs serum-free and type (i.e., animal vs human)	Use of animal serum may provide regulatory hurdles, defined vs undefined
	10. Time	Culture length	Depends on culture performance and required yield of stem cells
Output *(O)*	1. Stem cell frequency and absolute number	Number (i.e., colony number and phenotypic expression) per total cell number expanded	Provides indication of culture performance with respect to increased frequency
	2. Cell cycling state	G_0, G_1, and $S/G_2/M$	Determining cycling state (i.e., S phase) may predict the relative success in an *in vivo* application (e.g., homing to the bone marrow microenvironment
	3. Developmental potential	Multidifferentiation capacity (i.e., multi-, tri-, and bipotential)	Culture manipulation may compromise mulitpotentiality
	4. *In vivo* potential	*In vivo* animal model (e.g., NOD-SCID mouse)	Assess homing and engraftment capabilities

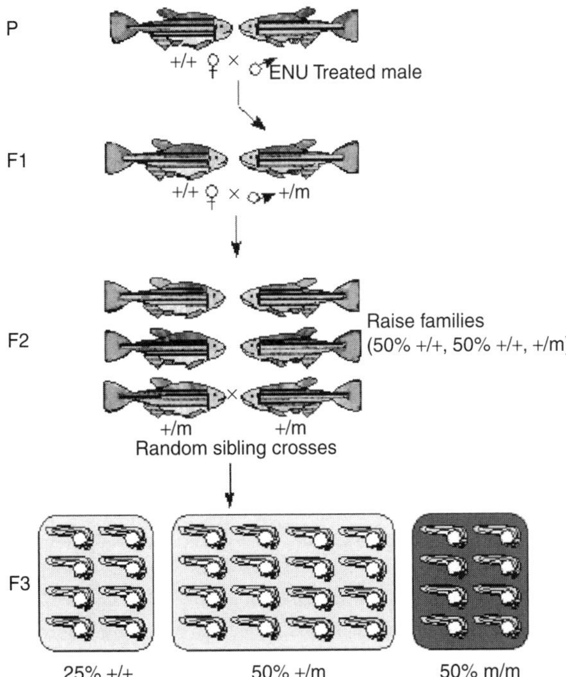

Figure 60–2. *GATA-1 promoter driving GFP in transgenic zebra fish embryo at 24 hpf.* (A) The transgenic embryo as seen under a dissecting scope. (B) Under fluorescence, the GATA-1 driving GFP expression localizes to the ICM. (GATA-1 GFP line courtesy of S. Lin; photos courtesy of R. Wingert). (Please see CD-ROM for color version of this figure.)

Disease Models in Zebra Fish

Zebra fish mutants have been shown to resemble human diseases including hematopoietic, cardiovascular, and kidney disorders. Although other organisms such as *Caenorhabditis elegans* and *Drosophila* have been extensively studied with respect to developmental processes and may be used in screens, they do not address many of the morphologic aspects unique to vertebrates. The zebra fish, however, is a vertebrate system and thus may be used to address developmental processes in the kidney, in multilineage hematopoiesis, in notochord, as well as in neural crest cells, among others.[31] Zebra fish mutants have played an important role not only in clarifying vertebrate-specific developmental processes but also as models for specific human disorders.

The hematopoietic mutant known as sauternes *(sau)* exhibits delayed maturation of erythroid cells and abnormal globin expression.[39] The *sau* mutant fish develops a microcytic hypochromic anemia. Cloning of the *sau* gene revealed the gene product to be aminolevulinate synthase (ALAS2), an enzyme required for the first step of heme biosynthesis. Mirroring the fish genetic disease, humans with a mutation in *ALAS2* gene have been found to have congenital sideroblastic anemias.[40] *Sau* is the first animal model of this disease.

Another hematopoietic mutant acting as a model of a human disease is yquem *(yqe)*.[29,41] The mutant yqe^{tp61} is homozygous for a mutation in the gene encoding uroporphyrinogen decarboxylase (UROD), an enzyme involved in the heme biosynthetic pathway.[41] Humans with homozygous deficiencies of UROD develop hepatoerythropoietic porphyria. The yqe^{tp61} zebra fish develop a photosensitive porphyria syndrome.

The zebra fish mutant known as retsina *(ret)* has recently been shown to exhibit an erythroid-specific mitotic defect with dyserythropoiesis comparable to human congenital dyserythropoietic anemia.[42] This work identifies a gene *(slc4a1)* encoding an erythroid-specific cytoskeletal protein necessary for correct mitotic divisions of erythroid cells. In addition to modeling a human disease, this study demonstrates the notion of cell-specific mitotic adaptation.

Positional cloning of the zebra fish mutant *wiessherbst* identified the gene *ferroportin1,* a transmembrane protein responsible for the transport of iron from maternal yolk stores into circulation, solving the puzzle of the elusive iron exporter.[30] This gene was first identified in zebra fish. Later research determined that humans with mutations in ferroportin1 develop the human disease type IV hemachromatosis.[43]

Further studies are being conducted in zebra fish to tie mutant phenotypes to known as well as undocumented human disorders. The use of the zebra fish system to gain understanding of human disease states has been proved and evolves as technologies advance. Screens continue to uncover mutant phenotypes with specific developmental abnormalities, many of which will play roles in deciphering human disease states.

Future of the System

In a recent study, transgenic zebra fish lines were created that resulted in acute T-cell leukemia in the fish.[44] In this investigation, transgenic fish were created with the lymphoid-specific RAG2 promoter driving mouse c-*myc,* a gene known to function in the pathogenesis of leukemias and lymphomas. Additionally, a chimeric transgene consisting of *myc* fused to GFP allowed the visualization of the spread of tumors from the thymus of affected fish. Tumors in these transgenic fish spread from origins in the thymus to skeletal muscle and abdominal organs. The leukemic transgenic fish from this study may be used for suppressor–enhancer genetic screens to identify components either lessening or worsening the leukemic progress.

Another recent body of work focused on zebra fish regeneration.[45] The zebra fish is able to regenerate fins, a unique characteristic of some lower vertebrates. Little is known about the molecular and cellular processes involved in regeneration, and genetic screens have recently been employed to investigate the molecular mechanism. Because many of the genes involved in regeneration are necessary for embryonic development, temperature-sensitive mutants have been screened for and successfully identified.[46,47] In addition, transgenic lines expressing GFP have been used as a visual tool and stand to aid the purification of specific cell populations involved in regeneration events.[45] In addition to the fin regeneration

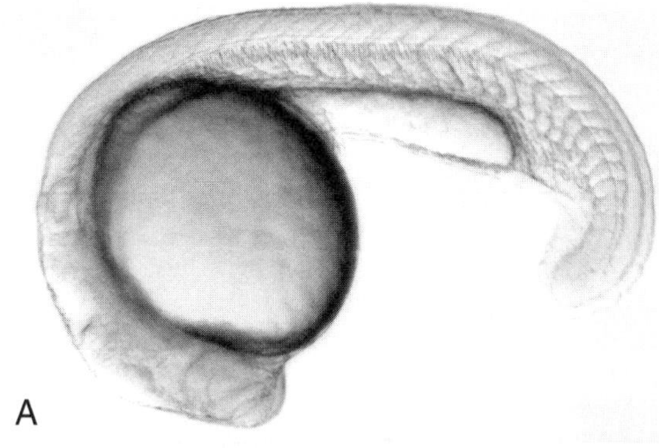

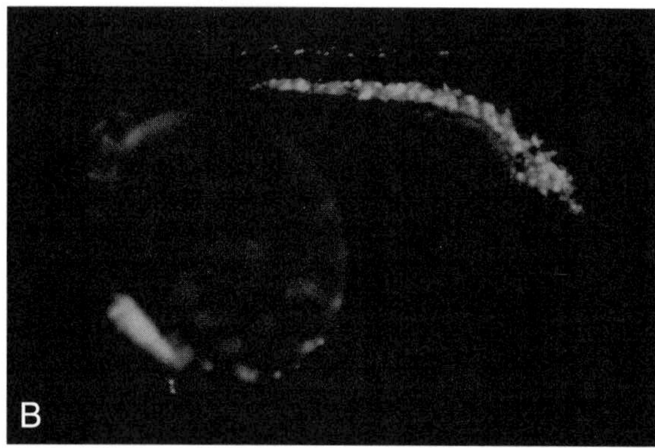

Figure 60-3. *Transgenic zebra fish with GFP expressed from the GATA-1 promoter.* (A) Embryonic morphology. (B) Transient GFP expression in the intermediate cell mass of zebra fish embryos. (Adapted from reference 36.) (Please see CD-ROM for color version of this figure.)

studies, heart regeneration has been examined in zebra fish.[48] The processes of dedifferentiation, patterning, and proliferation, as well as the existence of pluripotent cells in adult tissues, are being examined in zebra fish and remain extremely compelling for the field of stem cell biology. Although at a very early stage, regeneration studies may also address human tissue repair, stem cell transplantation, and even tissue engineering.[49]

Pioneering studies have been and are being conducted that reveal an exciting future for the zebra fish system. Large-scale genetic screens, cell-sorting techniques, and transgenic technologies have been used in elegant investigations into hematopoiesis and stem cell biology. Further dissection of developmental processes and their connections to human disease will surely benefit from the utility of this model organism.

ACKNOWLEDGMENTS

We thank Caroline Erter for providing (Fig. 60–1) and Rebecca Wingert and Shou Lin for providing (Fig. 60–2). We thank David Traver, James Amatruda, and Elizabeth Patton for critical review of this manuscript and Trista North, Jenna Galloway, Alan Davidson, and Noelle Paffet-Lugasy for beneficial discussions. K. Rose Finley and is supported by grants from the National Institutes of Health and the Howard Hughes Medical Institute. L.I. Zon is an associate investigator of the Howard Hughes Medical Institute.

REFERENCES

1. Thisse, C., and Zon, L.I. (2002). Organogenesis: heart and blood formation from the zebra fish point of view. *Science* **295,** 393–572.
2. Bahary, N., and Zon, L.I. (1998). Use of the zebra fish *(Danio rerio)* to define hematopoiesis. *Stem Cells* **16,** 89–98.
3. Driever, W., Solnica-Krezel, L., Schier, A.F., Neuhass, S.C., Malicki, J., Stemple, D.L., Stainier, D.Y., Zwartkruis, F., Abdelilah, S., Rangini, Z., Belak, J., Boggs, C. (1996). A genetic screen for mutations affecting embryogenesis in zebra fish. *Development* **123,** 37-46.
4. Haffter, P., Granato, M., Brand, M., Mullins, M.C., Hammerschmidt, M., Kane, D.A., Odenthal, J., van Eeden, F.J., Jiang, Y.J., Heisenberg, C.P., Kelsh, R.N., Furutani-Seiki,, M., Vogelsang, E., Beuchle, D., Schach, U., Fabian, C., Nusslein-Volhard, C. (1996). The identification of genes with unique and essential functions in the development of the zebra fish, *Danio rerio. Development* **123,** 1-36.
5. Barbazuk, W.B., Korf, I., Kadavi, C., Heyen, J., Tate, S., Wun, E., Bedell, J.A., McPherson, J.D., Johnson, S.L. (2000). The syntenic relationship of the zebra fish and human genomes. *Genome Research* **10**(9), 11351–11358.
6. Wingert, R.A., Zon, L.I. (2003). Genetic dissection of hematopoiesis using the zebra fish. *In* "Hematopoietic Stem Cells" 1st Ed. (Godin and A. Cumano, eds.), Landes Bioscience.
7. Davidson, A.J., Zon, L.I. (2000). Turning mesoderm into blood: the formation of hematopoietic stem cells during embryogenesis. *Curr. Top. Dev. Biol.* **50,** 45–60.
8. Mullins, M., Hammerschmidt, M., Kane, D.A., Odenthal, J., Brand, M, van Eeden, F.J., Furutani-Seiki, M., Granato, M., Haffter, P., Heisenberg, C.P., Jiang, Y.J., Kelsh, R.N., Nusslein-Volhard, C. (1996) Genes establishing dorsoventral pattern formation in the zebra fish embryo: the ventral specifying genes. *Development* **123,** 81–93.
9. Gering, M., Rodaway, A.R.F., Gottgens, B., Patient, R.K., Green, A.R.l. (1998). The SCL gene specifies hemangioblast development from early mesoderm. *EMBO J.* **17,** 4029–4045.
10. Amatruda, J.F., Zon, L.I. (1999). Dissecting hematopoiesis and disease using the zebra fish. *Dev. Bio.* **216,** 1–15.
11. Liao, W., Bisgrove, B.W., Sawyer, H., Hug, B., Bell, B., Peters, K., Grunwald, D.J., Stainier, D.Y. (1997). The zebra fish gene cloche acts upstream of a flk-1 homologue to regulate endothelial cell differentiation. *Development* **124,** 381–389.
12. Thompson, M.A., Ransom, D.G., Pratt, S.J., MacLennan, H., Kieran, M.W., Detrich, H.W., Vail, B., Huber, T.L., Paw, B., Brownlie, A.J., Oates, A.C., Fritz, A., Gates, M.A., Amores, A., Bahary, N., Talbot, W.S., Her. H., Beier, D.R., Postlethwait, J.H., Zon L.I. (1998). The cloche and spadetail genes differentially affect hematopoiesis and vasculogenesis. *Dev. Bio.* **197,** 248–269.
13. Detrich, H.W. 3rd, Kieran, M.W., Chan, F.Y., Barone, L.M., Yee, K., Rundstadler, J.A., Pratt, S., Ransom, D., Zon, L.I. (1995). Intraembryonic hematopoietic cell migration during vertebrate development. *PNAS* **92,** 10713–10717.
14. Galloway. J.L., Zon, L.I. (2003). Ontogeny of hematopoiesis: examining the emergence of hematopoietic cells in the vertebrate embryo. *Curr Top Dev Biol* **53,** 139–58.
15. Traver, D., Herbomel, P., Patton, E.E., Murphey, R.D., Yoder, J.A., Litman, G.W., Catic, A. Amemiya, C.T., Zon, L.I., Trede N.S. (2003). The zebra fish as a model organism to study development of the immune system. *Adv Immunol.* **81,** 253–330.

16. Traver, D., Zon, L.I. (2002). Walking the walk: migration and other common themes in blood and vascular development. *Cell* **108,** 731–734.
17. Patton, E.E., Zon, L.I. (2001). The art and design of genetic Screens: zebra fish. *Nat Gen Rev* **2,** 956–966.
18. Solnica-Krezel, L., Schier, A.F., Driever, W. (1994). Efficient recovery of ENU-induced mutations from the zebra fish germline. *Genetics* **136,** 1401–1420.
19. Mullins, M.C., Hammerschmidt, M., Haffter, P., Nusslein-Volhard, C. (1994). Large-scale mutagenesis in the zebra fish: in search of genes controlling development in a vertebrate. *Curr Biol* **4,** 189–202.
20. Walker, C. (1999). Haploid screens and gamma-ray mutagenesis. *Methods Cell Biol* **60,** 43–70.
21. Amsterdam, A., Burgess, S., Golling, G., Chen, W., Sun, Z., Townsend, K., Farrington, S., Haldi, M., Hopkins, N. (1999). A large-scale insertional mutagenesis screen in zebra fish. *Genes Dev* **13,** 2713–2724.
22. Golling, G., Amsterdam, A, Sun, Z., Antonelli, M., Maldonado, E., Chen, W., Burgess, S., Haldi, M., Artzt, K., Farrington, S., Lin, S.Y., Nissen, R.M., Hopkins, N. (2002). Insertional mutagenesis in zebra fish rapidly identifies genes essential for early vertebrate development. *Nat Genet* **31,** 135–140.
23. Gaiano, N., Amsterdam, A., Kawakami, K., Allende, M., Becker, T., Hopkins, N. (1996). Insertional mutagenesis and rapid cloning of essential genes in zebra fish. *Nature* **383,** 829–832.
24. Streisinger, G., Walker, C., Dower, N., Knauber, D., Singer, F. (1981). Production of clones of homozygous diploid clones of homozygous diploid zebra fish (*Brachydanio rerio*). *Nature* **291,** 293–296.
25. Beattie, C.E., Raible, D.W., Henion, P.D., Eisen, J.S. (1999). Early pressure screens. *Methods. Cell. Biol.* **60,** 71–86.
26. Weinstein, B.M., Schier, A.F., Abdeliah, S., Malicki, J., Solnica-Krezel, L., Stemple, D.L., Stainier, D.Y.R., Zwartkruis, F., Driever, W., Fishman, M.C. (1996). Hematopoietic mutations in the zebra fish. *Development* **123,** 303–309.
27. Ransom, D.G., Haffter, P., Odenthal, J., Brownlie, A., Vogelsang, E., Kelsh, R.N., Brand, M., van Eeden, F.J.M., Furutani-Seiki, M., Granato, M., Hammerschmidt, M., Heisenberg, C. P., Jiang, Y. J., Kane, D.A., Mullins, M.C., Nusslein-Volhard, C. (1996). Characterization of zebra fish mutants with defects in embryonic hematopoiesis. *Development* **123,** 311–319.
28. Donovan, A., Brownlie, A., Zhou, Y., Shepard, J., Pratt, S.J., Moynihan, J., Paw, B.H., Drejer, A., Barut, B., Zapata, A., Law, T.C., Brugnara, C., Lux, S.E., Pinkus, G.S., Pinkus, J.L., Kingsley, P.D., Palis, J., Fleming, M.D., Andrews, N.C., Zon, L.I. (2000). Positional cloning of zebra fish ferroportin1 identifies a conserved vertebrate iron exporter. *Nature* **403,** 776–781.
29. Dooley, K., Zon, L.I. (2000). Zebra fish: a model system for the study of human disease. Curr *Opin. Genet. Dev.* **10,** 252–256.
30. Kimmel, C.B., Kane, D.A., Walker, C., Warga, R.M., Rothman, M.B. (1989). A mutation that changes cell movement and cell fate in the zebra fish embryo. *Nature* **337,** 358–362.
31. Griffin, K.J.P., Amacher, S.L., Kimmel, C.B., Kimelman, D. (1998). Molecular identification of spadetail: regulation of zebra fish trunk and tail mesoderm formation by T-box genes. *Development* **125,** 3379–3388.
32. Davidson, A.J., Ernst, P., Wang, Y., Dekens, M.P.S., Kingsley, P.D., Palis, J., Korsmeyer, S.J., Daley, G.Q., Zon, L.I. (2003). Cdx4 mutants fail to specify blood progenitors and can be rescued by multiple hox genes. *Nature* **425,** 300–306.
33. Stainier, D.Y.R., Weinstein, B.M., Detrich, H.W., Zon, L.I., Fishman, M.C. (1995). Cloche, an early acting zebra fish gene, is required by both the endothelial and hematopoietic lineages. *Development* **121,** 3141–3150.
34. Liao, E.C., Paw, B.H., Oates, A.C., Pratt, S.J., Postlethwait, J.H., Zon, L.I. (1998). SCL/Tal-1 transcription factor acts downstream of cloche to specify hematopoietic and vascular progenitors in the zebra fish. *Genes. Dev.* **12,** 621–626.
35. Liao, L.C., Trede, N.S., Ransom, D., Zapata, A., Kieran, M., Zon, L.I. (2002). Non cell autonomous requirement for the bloodless gene in primitive hematopoiesis of zebra fish. *Development* **129,** 649–659.
36. Long, Q., Meng, A., Wang, H., Jessen, R., Farrell, M.J., Lin, S. (1997). GATA-1 expression pattern can be recapitulated in living transgenic zebra fish using GFP reporter gene. *Development* **124,** 4105–4111.
37. Traver, D., Paw, B.H., Poss, K.D., Penberthy, W.T., Lin, S., Zon, L.I. (2003). Transplantation and in vivo imaging of multilineage engraftment in zebra fish bloodless mutants. *Nat. Immunol.* **4**(12), 1238–1246.
38. Thisse, C., Degrave, A., Kryukov, G.V., Gladyshev, V.N., Obrecht-Pflumio, S., Krol, A., Thisse, B., Lescure, A. (2003). Spatial and temporal expression patterns of selenoprotein genes during embryogenesis in zebra fish. *Gene. Expr. Patterns.* **3(4),** 525–532.
39. Brownlie, A., Donovan, A., Pratt, S.J., Paw, B.H., Oates, A.C., Grugnara, D., Witkowska, H.E., Sassa, S., Zon, L.I. (1998). Positional cloning of the zebra fish sauternes gene: a model for congenital sederoblastic anemia. *Nat. Genet.* **20,** 244–250.
40. Edgar, A.S., Wickramasinge, S.N. (1998). Hereditary sideroblastic anemia due to a mutation in exon 10 of the erythroid 5-aminolaevulinate synthase gene. *Br. J. Haematol.* **100**(2), 389–392.
41. Wang, H., Long, Q., Marty, S.D., Sassa, S., Lin, S. (1998). A zebra fish model for hematoerythropoietic porphyria. *Nat. Genet.* **20,** 239–243.
42. Paw, B., Davidson, A.J., Zhou, Y., Li, R., et. al. (2003). Cell-specific mitotic defect and dyserythropoiesis associated with erythroid band 3 deficiency. *Nat Genet.* **34,** 59–64.
43. Njajou, O.T., Vaessen, N., Josse, M., Berghuis, B., van Dongen, J.W., Breuning, M.H., Snijders, P.J., Rutten, W.P., Sandkuijl, L.A., Oostra, B.A., van Duijn, C.M., Heutink, P. (2001). A mutation in SLC11A3 is associated with autosomal dominant heochromatosis. *Nat. Gen.* **28,** 213–214.
44. Langenau, D.M., Traver, D., Ferrando, A.A., Kutok, J.L., Aster, J.C., Kanki, J.P., Lin, S., Prochownik, E., Trede, N.S., Zon, L.I., Look, A.T. (2003). Myc-induced t cell leukemia in transgenic zebra fish. *Science* **299,** 887–890.
45. Poss, K., Keating, M.T., Nechiporuk, A. (2003). Tales of regeneration in zebra fish. *Dev. Dyn. Rev.* **226,** 202–210.
46. Johnson, S.L., and Weston, J.A. (1995). Temperature-sensitive mutations that cause stage-specific defects in Zebrafish fin regeneration. *Genetics* **141,** 1583–1595.
47. Poss, K., Nechiporuk, A., Hillam, A.M., Johnson, S.L., Keating, M.T. (2002). Mps1 defines a proximal blastemal proliferative compartment essential for zebra fish fin regeneration. *Development* **129,** 5141–5149.
48. Poss. K., Wilson, L.G., Keating, M.T. (2002). Heart regeneration in Zebrafish. *Science* **298,** 2188–2190.
49. Slack, J.M.W. (2003). Regeneration research today. *Dev. Dyn.* **226,** 162–166.

61

Circulating Hematopoietic Stem Cell Transplantation

Anne Kessinger and J. Graham Sharp

The circulating blood normally contains a subpopulation of self-renewing, pluripotent hematopoietic stem cells. These cells will durably reverse bone marrow aplasia when transplanted. The numbers of these cells in the circulation are usually quite low, but if they are increased deliberately with mobilizing therapies, they can be harvested efficiently in sufficient numbers for transplantation using apheresis techniques. Transplantation of mobilized hematopoietic stem cells derived from the blood in both the autologous and allogeneic settings provides faster marrow function recovery than transplantation of nonmobilized blood-derived stem cells or marrow-derived stem cells. Whether they offer clinical benefits in addition to restoring marrow function following transplantation is unknown.

Hematopoietic Stem Cell Transplantation

Restoring hematopoiesis in patients whose bone marrows have been obliterated by disease, by administration of marrow-ablative therapies, or both requires the transplantation of hematopoietic stem cells. The transplant is performed by infusing the stem cells intravenously. If the donor and the recipient of the stem cells are the same individual, the process is termed an autologous transplant. Autologous transplants are generally used in the management of malignant diseases. Patients whose malignancies cannot be eradicated with standard doses of cytotoxic chemotherapeutic agents or radiation therapy are treated with higher doses. These doses are marrow ablative, and infusion of hematopoietic stem cells is required after the therapy has been completed to restore vital marrow function. If the donor and the recipient of hematopoietic stem cells are identical twins, the process is called a syngeneic transplant. If the donor and the recipient of the hematopoietic stem cells are different individuals and not identical twins, an allogeneic transplant has been performed. In this case, the donor and recipient must be closely human leukocyte antigen (HLA) matched to prevent rejection of the graft by the recipient because the cells are recognized as "nonself." Matching is less critical if the hematopoietic stem cells are derived from umbilical cord blood. There is approximately a 1 in 4 chance that a sibling will be HLA identical to the patient. In the general population, depending on the HLA type, there is approximately a 1 in 50,000 chance that an unrelated individual will be an HLA match to the patient. Allogeneic transplants are performed if the recipient's marrow is malignant, as in myelogenous leukemia, and needs to be replaced or if a patient with genetic disorder such as an immune deficiency requires a new immune system generated from a new bone marrow for survival. Marrow-derived hematopoietic stem cell transplantation had been successfully established as a method to restore marrow function in patients decades before blood was discovered to be a useful source of transplantable cells. Hematopoietic transplants are also sometimes used to "reset" (autologous) or change (allogeneic) immune systems, function, or both for patients with acquired or inherited immune disorders.

Circulating Hematopoietic Stem Cells

The presence of hematopoietic stem cells in the circulation of humans was suspected as early as 1909,[1] although this notion was contrary to the dogma of that time. Through the 1950s, hematology textbooks taught that hematopoietic stem cells normally existed only in the bone marrow.[2] In the 1960s, a series of animal studies identified stem cells in the circulation,[3,4] and in the 1970s, hematopoietic stem–progenitor cells were discovered as a constant subpopulation of the cells that normally circulate in the human blood stream.[5,6]

Their initial discovery in the blood raised questions as to whether circulating hematopoietic stem cells were identical to their marrow counterparts and whether they could restore hematopoiesis when transplanted. Early studies of blood-derived stem–progenitor cell transplantation to lethally irradiated animal models were successful,[3,7–9] but clinical investigations required the development of techniques to collect the cells in the large numbers previously identified as necessary for successful marrow-derived hematopoietic stem cell transplantation. During hematopoietic steady state, few hematopoietic stem–progenitor cells normally circulate.[10] A solution was found in 1977 when Weiner *et al.*[11] reported that large numbers of human progenitor cells could be collected with a blood cell separator. Apheresis procedures repeated daily

Handbook of Stem Cells
Volume 2

during steady-state hematopoiesis and cryopreservation and storage of the harvested cells permitted the accrual of sufficient numbers of cells for successful human transplantation.[12]

Clinical Autologous Circulating Hematopoietic Stem Cell Transplantation

The first series of patients reported to receive blood-derived hematopoietic stem cell transplants was reported in Great Britain. Fifty patients with accelerated phase chronic myeloid leukemia (CML) were treated with high-dose therapy and autologous nonmobilized circulating stem–progenitor cell transplantation between 1977 and 1983.[10] Because the peripheral blood of patients with newly diagnosed CML contains many times the usual number of hematopoietic stem–progenitor cells that circulate during the steady state,[13] harvesting enough cells for a successful transplant was accomplished with 2 to 4 apheresis procedures. The stem cells, known to be leukemic, were collected soon after diagnosis and cryopreserved. Later, when the CML transformed to a more aggressive, accelerated phase, the patients were treated with marrow-ablative high-dose therapy designed to eradicate the leukemia and then transplanted with their cryopreserved cells in hopes of returning the disease to the more indolent chronic phase. Of the 50 patients, 47 recovered hematopoietic function with chronic phase disease following transplant, although the usefulness of the transplants was negated by the short duration of the second chronic phase.

Encouraged by the report that circulating leukemic stem–progenitor cells could be used to restore hematopoiesis, two syngeneic transplants were attempted using normal nonleukemic blood stem cells in 1979[14] and 1980.[15] The cells were collected during steady state and infused on the same days they were collected. Cells were infused over 14 days[14] in the first transplant and over 8 days[15] in the second. After 56–60 days with no evidence of hematopoietic recovery, syngeneic marrow transplants from the same donors restored hematopoiesis, resulting in admonitions regarding the use of normal circulating hematopoietic stem cells for transplantation is clinical settings. Some years later, infusion of cryopreserved blood stem cells, collected during steady state containing fewer colony-forming unit granulocyte–macrophage (CFU-GM) progenitors in fewer mononuclear cells than the failed syngeneic transplants and administered over 2–4 hours rather than several days, typically resulted in hematopoietic recovery by 30 days.[12] Thus, the protracted infusion times may have influenced the reported engraftment failures in the two attempted syngeneic transplants. Nonetheless, these negative reports understandably delayed the emergence of circulating hematopoietic stem cell transplantation into the clinic.

Five years passed before the next report of clinical attempts at blood-derived stem–progenitor cell transplantation using nonleukemic cells appeared. Two autologous transplants were reported, and the outcomes of these transplants were more encouraging.[16] The following year, descriptions of successful autologous transplants from six institutions throughout the world appeared.[17–22] From this beginning, circulating hematopoietic stem cells have become the most commonly used autograft product.

Clinical Allogeneic Circulating Hematopoietic Stem Cell Transplantation

Although the investigations that resulted in the success and acceptance of autologous circulating hematopoietic stem cell transplants were under way, concurrent clinical studies of allogeneic circulating hematopoietic stem cell transplantation were conspicuously absent. At issue were three concerns unique to allogeneic transplants. First was that the presence of human circulating pluripotent, self-renewing hematopoietic stem cells capable of providing sustained hematopoietic function when transplanted had not yet been unequivocally identified. In the mid-1970s, animal studies suggested that blood-derived stem cells were far less effective that bone marrow cells and had a limited capacity for self-renewal.[23] The concern from those early experiments was that the few stem cells observed in the blood stream were a result of clonal senescence in the marrow and had been expelled as waste products into the blood stream. The observation that transplanted human autologous circulating hematopoietic stem cell apheresis products restored sustained hematopoiesis did not provide definitive evidence that pluripotent stem cells had been transplanted. If the patients received marrow-suppressive but not marrow-lethal therapy prior to the autologous transplant, the transplanted progenitors could have provided early hematopoiesis but the long-term marrow function could have resulted from surviving marrow hematopoietic stem cells. There was no marker to distinguish between the progeny of transplanted autologous circulating hematopoietic stem cells and the recovered autochthonous marrow stem cells, so the origin (graft versus marrow) of long-term hematopoiesis was uncertain. Successful animal studies of allogeneic circulating hematopoietic stem cell transplantation permitted identification of donor origin hematopoiesis (e.g., male recipients and female donors),[24] and lent some credence to the possibility that self-renewing stem cells were present in the human circulation. However, since no assay short of transplantation existed for human self-renewing stem cells, clinical investigators were reluctant to risk the possibility that circulating hematopoietic stem cells did not exist. Allogeneic human bone marrow transplantation had already been established as a reliable entity, and transplanting human allogeneic circulating stem cells was problematic.

A second concern that slowed the development of allogeneic circulating hematopoietic stem cell transplantation was the presence of much larger numbers of T-lymphocytes in blood-derived apheresis products than in marrow harvests.[25] Graft-versus-host disease (GVHD), which results from an immunologic assault by the intact immune cells in the graft product on the immunocompromised recipient, is a morbid and sometimes fatal consequence of allogeneic transplantation. In preclinical models, the incidence of GVHD is higher when larger numbers of T-cells are infused.[26] If T-lymphocytes are depleted from human allogeneic marrow prior to transplantation, less GVHD is encountered; higher numbers of T-cells in transplanted allograft products correlate with an increased incidence of chronic GVHD.[27] A higher incidence and more severe GVHD was anticipated after allogeneic circulating hematopoietic stem cell transplantation than would be encountered following allogeneic marrow-derived hematopoietic stem cell transplantation.

The third concern focused on donor safety and convenience during circulating hematopoietic stem cell collections. Before hematopoietic cytokines became available for human use in 1991, only nonmobilized cells could be collected from normal donors. Collecting a sufficient number of cells for allografting required multiple apheresis procedures, an unwieldy and time-consuming prospect for the donor.

The first clinical, allogeneic blood-derived hematopoietic stem cell transplant was reported in 1989.[28] The clinical situation was unique, because the matched sibling donor was unwilling to donate marrow but agreed to undergo multiple (10) apheresis procedures. The collections were manipulated so as to reduce the number of T-cells in the graft to approximate the number in allogeneic bone marrow graft products. A marrow biopsy 3 weeks after the transplant revealed good cellularity and the presence of all three blood cell lineages (erythrocytes, leukocytes, and megakaryocytes), which were proved to be of donor origin. Because the patient died of an infection 32 days after the transplant, the presence of pluripotent self-renewing stem cells in the graft product could not be confirmed. Severe GVHD did not occur.

No further allogeneic blood-derived stem cell transplant attempts were reported until 1993.[29] Again, the clinical situation was unusual. The patient had been treated with high-dose therapy for acute lymphocytic leukemia and received a second bone marrow transplant from the same donor after the first one failed to engraft. When the second marrow transplant also failed, collecting marrow from the donor a third time in a short period was problematic, so granulocyte colony-stimulating factor (G-CSF) was administered to this donor and mobilized blood stem cells were collected and infused (see the section "Mobilization of Hematopoietic Stem Cells to the Circulation"). Soon thereafter, rapid hematopoietic reconstitution of donor origin was identified in the recipient. The blood-derived stem cells were considered responsible for the success, but because the recipient had received two prior marrow infusions, the precise origin of the engrafted cells (blood versus marrow) could not be determined. Later that same year, a report of a successful allogeneic blood stem cell transplant appeared.[30] The length of follow-up of this patient was sufficient[31] to show that pluripotent stem cells capable of providing long-term hematopoiesis had been collected from blood and transplanted.

In early 1995, three reports, describing a total of 25 successful allogeneic blood-derived stem cell transplantations, appeared simultaneously.[31–33] From that time forward, the use of blood rather than marrow for allogeneic transplantation became more common. Recovery of circulating red blood cell, white blood cell, and platelet counts is faster than seen following allogeneic bone marrow transplantation.[34]

Mobilization

MOBILIZATION OF HEMATOPOIETIC STEM CELLS TO THE CIRCULATION

If the numbers of circulating hematopoietic stem–progenitor cells in the circulation could be deliberately increased while the cells were being collected for transplantation, the number of apheresis procedures required to harvest a target number of cells could be reduced. In 1976, administration of myelosuppressive chemotherapy was reported to increase the numbers of hematopoietic progenitors in the circulation by fourfold 2–3 weeks later.[35] In 1984, a 25-fold increase in the number of circulating CFU-GM was observed in patients with acute myelocytic leukemia (AML) as they recovered from induction chemotherapy.[36] Whether these cells, collected while they were mobilized into the circulation, could be used for successful transplantation was initially addressed in 1985 when the first two reported transplants of chemotherapy-mobilized stem cells in patients with AML met with partial success. The first patient experienced a fatal relapse 21 days after transplant, and the second patient was recovering hematopoiesis 12 weeks after transplant when relapse occurred.[16] These results encouraged the investigators to perform additional chemotherapy-mobilized autologous circulating stem cell transplants, and complete restoration of long-term hematopoiesis was observed.[37]

Between 1986 and 1991, autologous, peripheral blood stem cell graft products were collected either in steady state or following chemotherapy-induced mobilization. As expected, fewer apheresis procedures were required to collect mobilized versus steady-state stem cells, but mobilized cells provided an unanticipated additional benefit: faster hematopoietic recovery.[38] Circulating blood cells recovery is a week or more faster after transplantation of mobilized blood stem cell collections than after transplantation of nonmobilized blood- or marrow-derived stem cells. This advantage was responsible for the eventual shift from bone marrow to blood as the preferred source of autologous hematopoietic stem cells for transplantation.

In 1988, two hematopoietic cytokines, GM-CSF[39] and G-CSF[40] were reported to mobilize hematopoietic stem–progenitor cells into the blood stream. If the cytokines were given after administration of myelosuppressive chemotherapy, the mobilization effect was even greater.[39] As a result, in clinical practice today, chemotherapy is combined with cytokines for mobilization and is no longer used alone. The mobilizing chemotherapy is either cyclophosphamide in doses of 1.5–7 g/M^2 or a chemotherapeutic agent or agents specific for the underlying malignancy. In those situations in which administration of a chemotherapeutic agent or agents is not appropriate (e.g., allogeneic normal donors and some autologous donors in complete remission), cytokines alone are used to induce mobilization.[41]

MOBILIZATION EFFICIENCY AND OUTCOME

Whether identifying the most efficient mobilization therapy among the several demonstrated effective strategies is important or even necessary is an intriguing question. If one mobilization strategy routinely produces sufficient numbers of cells in a single apheresis procedure to ensure rapid and reliable hematopoietic recovery, is a second mobilization strategy that provides twice as many cells preferable? The second strategy might be chosen if higher doses of circulating mobilized stem–progenitor cells provide added benefit beyond rapid durable engraftment and result in no additional toxicity.

Although transplantation of 5×10^6 autologous stem–progenitor cells expressing the protein CD34 per kilogram of recipient weight provides optimal circulating red and white blood cell recovery following transplantation,[42] the rate of circulating platelet recovery increases with higher doses of $CD34^+$ cells. At least 15×10^6 autologous $CD34^+$ cells/kg recipient weight resulted in the recovery of circulating platelet counts of 50×10^6/L a median of 11 days after transplant as compared with 14 days for patients receiving fewer $CD34^+$ cells but at least 2.3×10^6/kg.[43] However, platelet transfusion is rarely administered to nonbleeding patients if counts are $> 20 \times 10^9$/L, and the patients receiving the higher numbers of $CD34^+$ cells maintained this count a median of 8 days after transplant compared to 10 days for those receiving lower number of $CD34^+$ cells. The benefits of recovery of circulating platelet counts earlier than 10 days after transplant may not be outweighed by the increased resources required to collect more than 2.5 to 5×10^6 autologous $CD34^+$ cells/kg.

For allogeneic transplants, some indirect evidence exists for an added benefit of transplantation of more blood-derived stem–progenitor cells than required for rapid hematopoietic recovery. When allogeneic bone marrow doses were correlated with outcomes following transplantation, transplant-related mortality, overall survival, and disease-free survival were statistically better in patients who received higher rather than lower doses of nucleated cells.[44] A randomized prospective study comparing mobilized blood-derived stem cell versus marrow-derived stem cell transplants resulted in better disease-free survival and overall survival for patients receiving blood-derived stem cells.[34] Whether this benefit was a result of the larger number of stem–progenitor cells in a blood stem cell versus a marrow stem cell graft product[45] is unknown. A second, smaller randomized study of allogeneic marrow versus mobilized blood stem cell transplantation found that patients who received fewer than 2×10^6/kg $CD34^+$ cells, regardless of the cell source, experienced higher mortality and poorer survival.[46] Transplantation of higher stem cell doses in the allogeneic setting has been associated with more complete recovery of circulating lymphocytes,[47] although no clinical benefit associated with this finding has been identified.

In regards to any additional toxicities associated with transplantation of more cells than required for rapid hematopoietic recovery, increasing allogeneic $CD34^+$ cell doses have been correlated with a higher likelihood of clinical extensive chronic GVHD, suggesting that increasing the CD34 cell numbers in mobilized allogeneic graft products may be counterproductive.[48] In another study, transfusion of lower doses of $CD34^+$ cells selected from the apheresis collection, thereby eliminating many of the immune cells in the transplanted product, was associated with increased survival compared with higher doses.[49] Together, these studies have not established whether transplantation of higher doses of hematopoietic stem–progenitor cells provides any additional advantage, but higher doses may be a disadvantage in the allogeneic setting.

MOBILIZATION OF MALIGNANT CELLS

In addition to mobilizing autologous hematopoietic stem–progenitor cells, cytokines[50] and chemotherapy plus cytokines[51] have mobilized tumor cells to the blood stream, although tumor cell mobilization was not identified in every studied autologous collection.[52,53] Autologous hematopoietic stem cell donors with follicular non-Hodgkin's lymphoma (NHL) were more likely to have detectable tumor cells in their apheresis products if they mobilized CD34+ cells poorly (42%) rather than well (17%), regardless of the mobilizing therapy used.[54] In another study, poor mobilizers were more likely to experience lymphoma relapse after transplant, but the reason is unclear since the infused products were not assayed for tumor cells.[55] In contrast, other investigators[56] found no differences in event-free survival, overall survival, or relapse between good mobilizers and poor mobilizers who had NHL and were treated with high-dose therapy and autologous transplantation. These results support an earlier finding that patients with low-grade NHL who received either mobilized or steady-state blood stem–progenitor cells following high-dose therapy had similar event-free and overall survivals.[57] Although avoiding increased tumor cell contamination in autologous mobilized blood stem cell collections seems intuitively desirable, no evidence exists to suggest that infusion of mobilized tumor cells in the graft product increases the incidence of relapse of NHL,[57] multiple myeloma,[58] or breast cancer[59] following transplant. In contrast, infusions of tumor-contaminated bone marrow harvests have been associated with poorer outcomes in lymphoma[60,61] and breast cancer.[62] These observations suggest that the characteristics of tumor cells in the circulation may differ from those in the bone marrow, perhaps because of microenvironmental influences on patterns of gene expression.

POOR RESPONSE TO MOBILIZATION THERAPY

The response of individual autologous donors to administration of mobilizing therapies is variable and incompletely predictable.[63] Of patients with NHL, 21 to 48% have exhibited poor mobilization after administration of chemotherapy and G-CSF.[55,56,64] Of these donors, 16 to 33% were unable to mobilized a sufficient number of collectable stem–progenitor cells for transplant use.[55,64] Factors predicting a higher likelihood of poor mobilization include prior antitumor chemotherapy,[65] prior radiation therapy,[65,66] follicular rather than diffuse NHL as the underlying disease,[67] and the presence of overt marrow metastases.[68] Low circulating-platelet counts on the first day of autologous blood stem–progenitor cell collection from donors with lymphoma have predicted for poor mobilization.[69] Older age was associated with poor autologous mobilization in some patient groups[67,70] but not in others.[71,72] Even though some donors with predictors of poor mobilization responded well to mobilizing therapies,[73] poorly mobilizing autologous donors were assumed to have sustained an injury to the hematopoietic stem cell system that was responsible for the poor effect. In support of this premise, autologous donors with breast cancer who had received more chemotherapy and radiation or had tumor metastases in the marrow also had fewer stem–progenitor cells in apheresis products collected during steady state than donors who were less heavily pretreated and had no marrow metastases.[74] However, studies of normal blood stem cell donors suggest that marrow damage probably does not account for all of the poor mobilization encountered in autologous donors.

Beginning in the mid-1990s, normal donors with no history of cancer were treated with mobilizing cytokines to facilitate the collection of allogeneic circulating stem–progenitor cells.[75] Between 4 and 20% of allogeneic cell donors have been identified as poor mobilizers.[76–79] This observation suggests that a damaged marrow is not the only explanation for poor mobilization, and animal studies have pointed toward genetic factors playing a role.[80,81]

Patient Outcome After Blood Stem Cell Transplantation

Transplantation of blood-derived hematopoietic stem cells is primarily a method to restore hematopoietic and immune function following administration of marrow-lethal doses of therapy, but some investigators have raised the possibility that the cells included in a blood stem cell apheresis product may also provide a therapeutic advantage for the patient. A prospective randomized study compared the outcomes of patients with hematologic malignancies who received marrow- versus blood-derived allogeneic transplants and found that disease-free survival and overall survival was better in the patients who received blood-derived graft products.[34] A retrospective comparison of HLA-identical, unrelated donor allogeneic blood-derived versus marrow stem cell transplants to patients with CML also revealed improved disease-free survival and overall survival in the blood-derived stem cell group.[82] Although immune reconstitution measured with a variety of laboratory parameters has been identified as faster and more complete following blood-derived versus marrow stem cell transplants in the autologous,[83] unrelated allogeneic,[82] and related allogeneic[84] settings, the reason for the better patient outcomes in these trials could not be identified. One possible clinical outcome of improved immune reconstitution is a reduction in infectious episodes following neutrophil recovery. In a pediatric population, the incidence of herpes zoster infection was similar following blood-derived versus marrow autologous transplantation.[85] However, the risk of cytomegalovirus-induced interstitial pneumonitis was reduced in patients receiving allogeneic blood-derived versus marrow-derived hematopoietic stem cells.[86] A randomized prospective trial of autologous marrow- versus blood-derived transplants for patients with NHL found better overall survival and complete response rates in those patients receiving blood-derived graft products, although the differences were not statistically significant.[87]

Not all retrospective studies have identified therapeutic advantages to patients receiving blood-derived hematopoietic stem cell transplants, so this issue is far from resolved. Stem cells in the circulation could have different potentials for differentiation, perhaps as a result of the different environments provided by the marrow and the circulation. The existence of plasticity in somatic or adult stem cells, as contrasted with embryonic or fetal stem cells, is controversial.[88] Some plasticity of circulating hematopoietic stem cells may have been demonstrated in sex-mismatched, allogeneic, blood-derived stem cell human transplants[89] when biopsies taken weeks or months after the transplant revealed cells of donor origin in skin, liver, and gut. What role these play in therapeutic outcome and whether they are present in greater or lesser numbers in blood- versus marrow-derived allograft products are unknown.

Summary

Self-renewing pluripotent hematopoietic stem cells normally circulate in the human blood stream and can be used to durably reverse bone marrow aplasia. If these cells are mobilized into the circulation at the time of collection, they can be harvested efficiently in sufficient numbers for transplantation using apheresis techniques. Transplantation of mobilized blood-derived hematopoietic stem cells in both the autologous and the allogeneic settings provides faster marrow recovery than transplantation of nonmobilized blood-derived stem cells or marrow-derived stem cells. Whether they offer benefits including significant contributions of progeny to multiple tissues in addition to restoring marrow function is unknown.

REFERENCES

1. Maximow, A. (1909). Der lymphozyt als gemeinesame stamzelle der verscheiden blutelemente in der embryobalen entwicklung und in post fetalen lieben der saugetiere. *Folia Haematol* **8,** 125–134.
2. Wintrobe, M., ed. (1961). "Clinical Hematology," 5th ed. Lea and Febinger, Philadelphia.
3. Perry, V.P., Malinin, T.I., Kerby, C.C., and Dolan, M.F. (1965). Protection of lethally irradiated guinea pigs with fresh and frozen homologous peripheral blood leukocytes. *Cryobiology* **1,** 233–239.
4. Cavins, J.A., Scheer, S.C., Thomas, E.D., and Feerebee, J.W. (1965). The recovery of lethally irradiated dogs given infusions of autologous leukocytes preserved at −80°C. *Blood* **23,** 38–42.
5. Rubin, S.H., and Cowan, D.H. (1973). Assay of granulocytic progenitor cells in human peripheral blood. *Exp. Hematol.* **1,** 127–131.
6. Barr, R.D., Whang-Peng, J., and Perry, S. (1975). Hematopoietic stem cells in human peripheral blood. *Science* **190,** 284–285.
7. Debalak-Fehir, K.M., and Epstein, R.B. (1975). Restoration of hematopoiesis in dogs by infusion of cryopreserved autologous peripheral white cells following busulfan-cyclophosphamide treatment. *Transplantation* **20,** 63–67.
8. Calvo, W., Fliedner T.M., Herbst, E., Hugl, E., and Bruch, C. (1976). Regeneration of blood-forming organs after autologous leukocyte transfusion in lethally irradiated dogs: II—Distribution and cellularity of the marrow in irradiated and transfused animals. *Blood* **47,** 593–601.

9. Storb, R., Graham, T.C., Epstein, R.B., Sale, G.E., and Thomas, E.D. (1977). Demonstration of hemopoietic stem cells in the peripheral blood of baboons by cross circulation. *Blood* **50,** 537–542.
10. McCarthy, D.M., and Goldman, J.M. (1984). Transfusion of circulating stem cells. *CRC Crit. Rev. Clin. Lab. Sci.* **20,** 1–24.
11. Weiner, R.S., Richman, C.M, and Yankee, R.A. (1977). Semicontinuous flow centrifugation of the pheresis of immunocompetent cells and stem cells. *Blood* **49,** 391–397.
12. Kessinger, A., Vose, J.M., Bierman, P.J., and Armitage, J.O. (1991). High-dose therapy and autologous peripheral stem cell transplantation for patients with bone marrow metastases and relapsed lymphoma: an alternative to marrow purging. *Exp. Hematol.* **19,** 1013–1016.
13. Goldman, J.M., Th'ng, K.H., and Lowenthal, R.M. (1974). *In vitro* colony-forming cells and colony-stimulating factor in chronic granulocytic leukaemia. *Br. J. Cancer* **30,** 1–12.
14. Hershko, C., Gale, R.P., Ho, W.G., and Cline, M.J. (1979). Cure of aplastic anemia in paroxysmal nocturnal hemoglobinuria by marrow infusion from identical twin: failure of peripheral leukocyte transfusion to correct marrow aplasia. *Lancet* **1,** 945–947.
15. Abrams, R.A., Glaubiger, D., Appelbaum, F.R., and Deisseroth, A.B. (1980). Result of attempted hematopoietic reconstitution using isologous peripheral blood mononuclear cells: a case report. *Blood* **56,** 516–520.
16. Juttner, C.A., To, L.B., Haylock, D.N, Branfore, A., and Kimber, R.J. (1985). Circulating autologous stem cells collected in very early remission from acute nonlymphoblastic leukemia produce prompt but incomplete hemopoietic reconstitution after high-dose melphalan or supralethal chemoradiotherapy. *Br. J. Haematol.* **61,** 739–745.
17. Castaigne, S., Calvo, F., Douay, L., Thomas, F., Benbunan, M., Gerota, J., and Degos, L. (1986). Successful hematopoietic reconstitution using autologous peripheral blood mononucleated cells in a patient with acute promyelocytic leukaemia. *Br. J. Haematol.* **62,** 209–211.
18. Tilly, H., Bastit, D., Lucet, J.C., Esperou, H., Monconduit, M., and Puguet, H. (1986). Hemopoietic reconstitution after autologous peripheral blood stem cell transplantation in acute leukemia. *Lancet* **2,** 154–155.
19. Bell, A.J., Figes, A., Oscier, D.G., and Hamblin, T.J. (1986). Peripheral blood stem cell autografting. *Lancet* **1,** 1027.
20. Korbling, M., Dorken, B., Ho, A.D., Pezzutto, A., Hunstein, W., and Fliedner, T.M. (1986). Autologous transplantation of blood-derived hemopoietic stem cells after myeloablative therapy in a patient with Burkitt's lymphoma. *Blood* **67,** 529–532.
21. Reiffers, J., Vezon, G., David, B., Bernard, P., Moulinier, J., and Broustet, A. (1986). Hemopoietic recovery with Philadelphia negative cells in a patient treated with autografting for Ph[1] positive chronic granulocytic leukemia in transformation. *Br. J. Haematol.* **55,** 382–383.
22. Kessinger, A., Armitage, J.O., Landmark, J.D., and Weisenburger, D.D. (1986). Reconstitution of human hematopoietic function with autologous, cryopreserved, circulating stem cells. *Exp. Hematol.* **14,** 192–196.
23. Micklem, H.S., Anderson, N., and Ross, E. (1975). Limited potential of circulating hemopoietic stem cells. *Nature* **256,** 41–43.
24. Korbling, M., Fliedner, T.M., Calvo, W., Ross, W.M., Nothdurft, W., and Steinbach, I. (1979). Albumin density gradient purification of canine hemopoietic blood stem cells: long-term allogeneic engraftment without GVH reaction. *Exp. Hematol.* **7,** 277–288.
25. Weaver, C.H., Longin, K., Buckner, C.D., and Bensinger, W. (1994). Lymphocyte content in peripheral blood mononuclear cells collected after the administration of recombinant human granulocyte colony-stimulating factor. *Bone Marrow Transplant.* **13,** 411–415.
26. Owens, A.H., and Santos, G.W. (1968). The induction of graft-versus-host disease in mice treated with cyclophosphamide. *J. Exp. Med.* **128,** 277–291.
27. Kernan, N.A., Collins, N.H., Juliano, L., Cartagena, T., Dupont, B., and O'Reilly, R.J. (1986). Clonable T-lymphocytes in T-cell-depleted bone marrow transplants correlate with development of graft-versus-host disease. *Blood* **68,** 770–773.
28. Kessinger, A., Smith, D.M., Strandjord, S.E., Landmark, J.D., Dooley, D.C., Law, P., Coccia, P.F., Warkentin, P.I., Weisenburger, D.D., and Armitage, J.O. (1989). Allogeneic transplantation of blood-derived, T-cell-depleted hemopoietic stem cells after myeloablative treatment in a patient with acute lymphoblastic leukemia. *Bone Marrow Transplant.* **4,** 643–646.
29. Dreger, P., Suttorp, M., Haferlach, T., Loffler, H., Schmitz, N., and Schroyens, W. (1993). Allogeneic granulocyte colony-stimulating factor-mobilized peripheral blood progenitor cells for treatment of engraftment failure after bone marrow transplantation. *Blood* **81,** 1404–1407.
30. Russell, N.H., Hunter, A., Rogers, S., Hanley, J., and Anderson, D. (1993). Peripheral blood stem cells as an alternative to marrow for allogeneic transplantation. *Lancet* **341,** 1492.
31. Schmitz, N., Dreger, P., Suttorp, M., Rohwedder, E.B., Haferlach, T., Loffler, H., Hunter, A., and Russell, N.H. (1995). Primary transplantation of allogeneic peripheral blood progenitor cells mobilized by filgrastim (granulocyte colony-stimulating factor). *Blood* **85,** 1666–1672.
32. Korbling, M., Przepiorka, D., Huh, Y.O., Engel, H., van Besien, K., Giralt, S., Andersson, B., Kleine, H.D., Seong, D., Deisseroth, A.B., and Champlin, R. (1995). Allogeneic blood stem cell transplantation for refractory leukemia and lymphoma: potential advantage of blood over marrow allografts. *Blood* **85,** 1659–1665.
33. Bensinger, W.I., Weaver, C.H., Appelbaum, F.R., Rowley, S., Demirer, T., Sanders, J., Storb, R., and Buckner, C.D. (1995). Transplantation of allogeneic peripheral blood stem cells mobilized by recombinant human granulocyte colony-stimulating factor. *Blood* **85,** 1655–1658.
34. Bensinger, W.I., Martin, P.J., Storer, B., Clift, R., Forman, S.J., Negrin, R., Kashyap, A., Flowers, M.E.D., Lilleby, K., Chauncey, T.R., Storb, R., and Appelbaum, F.R. (2001). Transplantation of bone marrow as compared with peripheral blood cells from HLA-identical relatives in patients with hematologic cancers. *N. Engl. J. Med.* **344,** 175–181.
35. Richman, C.M., Weiner, R.S., and Yankee, R.A. (1976). Increase in circulating stem cells following chemotherapy in man. *Blood* **47,** 1031–1039.
36. To, L.B., Haylock, D.N, Kimber, R.J., and Juttner, C.A. (1984). High levels of circulating hemopoietic stem cells in very early remission form acute nonlymphoblastic leukemia and their collection and cryopreservation. *Br. J. Haematol.* **58,** 399–410.
37. Juttner, C.A., To, L.B., Ho, J.Q.K., Bardy, P.G., Dyson, P.G., Haylock, D.N., Kimber, R.J. (1988). Early lymphohematopoietic recovery after autografting using peripheral blood stem cells in acute nonlymphoblastic leukemia. *Transplant. Proc.* **20,** 40–43.
38. Beyer, J., Schwella, M., Zingsem, J., Strohsheer, I., Schwaner, I., Oettle, H., Serke, S., Huhn, D., and Steiger, W. (1995).

Hematopoietic rescue after high-dose chemotherapy using autologous peripheral-blood progenitor cells or bone marrow: A randomized comparison. *J. Clin. Oncol.* **13,** 1328–1335.

39. Socinski, M.A., Cannistra, S.A., Cannistra, S.A., Elias, A., Antman, K.H., Schnipper, L., and Griffin, J.D. (1988). Granulocyte–macrophage colony-stimulating factor expands the circulating hemopoietic progenitor cell compartment in man. *Lancet* **1,** 1194–1198.
40. Duhrsen, U., Villeval, J.L., Boyd, J., Kannourakis, G., Morstyn, G., and Metcalf, D. (1988). Effects of recombinant human granulocyte colony-stimulating factor on hematopoietic progenitor cells in cancer patients. *Blood* **72,** 2074–2081.
41. Russell, N.H., McQuaker, G., Stainer, C., Byrne, J.L., and Haynes, A.P. (1998). Stem cell mobilization in lymphoproliferative diseases. *Bone Marrow Transplant.* **22,** 935–940.
42. Siena, S., Schiavo, R., Pedrazzoli, P., and Carlo-Stella, C. (2000). Therapeutic relevance of CD34 cell dose in blood cell transplantation for cancer therapy. *J. Clin. Oncol.* **18,** 1360–1377.
43. Kletterer, N., Salles, G., Raba, M., Espinouse, D., Sonet, A., Tremisi, P., Dumonet, C., Moullet, I., Eljaafari-Corbin, A., Neidhardt-Beard, E.M., Bouaria, F., and Coffier, B. (1998). High CD34+ cell counts decrease hematologic toxicity of autologous peripheral blood progenitor cell transplantation. *Blood* **91,** 3148–3155.
44. Dominietto, A., Lamparelli, T., Raiola, A.M., Van Lint, M.T., Gualandi, F., Berisso, G., Bregante, S., di Grazia, C., Soracco, M., Pitto, A., Frassoni, F., and Bacigalupo, A. (2002). Transplant-related mortality and long-term graft function are significantly influenced by cell dose in patients undergoing allogeneic marrow transplantation. *Blood* **100,** 3930–3934.
45. Singhal, S., Powles, R., Kulkarni, S., Treleaven, J., Sirohi, B., Millar, B., Shepherd, V., Saso, R., Rowland, A., Long, S., Cabral, S., Horton, C., and Mehta, J. (2000). Comparison of marrow and blood cell yields from the same donors in a double-blind, randomized study of allogeneic marrow versus blood stem cell transplantation. *Bone Marrow Transplant.* **26,** 489–496.
46. Singhal, S., Powles, R., Treleaven, J., Kulkarni, S., Sirohi, B., Horton, C., Millar, B., Shepherd, V., Tait, D., Saso, R., Rowland, A., Long, S., and Mehta, J. (2000). A low CD34+ cell dose results in higher mortality and poorer survival after blood or marrow stem cell transplantation from HLA-identical siblings: should 2×10^6 CD34+ cells/kg be considered the minimum threshold? *Bone Marrow Transplant.* **26,** 489–496.
47. Sharp, J.G., Kessinger, A., Lynch, J.C., Pavletic, Z.S., and Joshi, S.S. (2000). Blood stem cell transplantation: an effect mediated by a circulating factor. *J. Hematother.* **7,** 343–349.
48. Zaucha, J.M., Gooley, T., Bensinger, W.I., Heimfeld, S., Chauncey, T.R., Zaucha, R., Martin, P.J., Flowers, M.E., Storek, J., Georges, G., Storb, R., and Torok-Storb, B. (2001). CD34 cell dose in granulocyte colony-stimulating factor-mobilized peripheral blood mononuclear cell grafts affects engraftment kinetics and development of extensive chronic graft-versus-host disease after human leukocyte antigen-identical sibling transplantation. *Blood* **98,** 3221–3227.
49. Urbano-Ispizua, A., Carreras, E., Marin, P., Rovira, M., Martinez, C., Fernandez-Aviles, F., Xicoy, B., Hernandez-Boluda, J.C., and Montserrat, E. (2001). Allogeneic transplantation of CD34+ selected cells from peripheral blood from human leukocyte antigen-identical siblings: detrimental effect of a high number of donor CD34+ cells? *Blood* **98,** 2352–2357.
50. Vora, A.J., Toh, C.H., Pel, J., and Greaves, M. (1994). Use of granulocyte colony-stimulating factor (G-CSF) for mobilizing peripheral blood stem cells: Risk of mobilizing clonal myeloma cells in patients with bone marrow infiltration. *Br. J. Haematol.* **86,** 180–182.
51. Brugger, W., Bross, K.J., Glatt, M., Weber, F., Mertelsmann, R., and Kranz, L. (1994). Mobilization of tumor cells and hematopoietic progenitor cells into peripheral blood of patients with solid tumors. *Blood* **83,** 636–640.
52. Lemoli, R.M., Fortuna, A., Motta, M.R., Rizzi, S., Giudice, V., Nannetti, A., Martinelli, G., Cavo, M., Amabile, M., Mangianti, S., Fogli, M., Conte, R., and Tura, S. (1996). Concomitant mobilization of plasma cells and hematopoietic progenitors into peripheral blood of multiple myeloma patients: positive selection and transplantation of enriched CD34+ cells to remove circulating tumor cells. *Blood* **87,** 1625–1634.
53. Franklin, W.A., Glaspy, J., Pflaumer, S.M., Sones, R.B., Hami, L., Martinez, C., Murphy, J.R., and Shpall, E.J. (1999). Incidence of tumor–cell contamination in leukapheresis products of breast cancer patients mobilized with stem cell factor and granulocyte colony-stimulating factor (G-CSF) or with G-CSF alone. *Blood* **94,** 340–347.
54. Gazitt, Y., Shaughnessy, P., and Liu, Q. (2001). Differential mobilization of CD34+ cells and lymphoma cells in non-Hodgkin's lymphoma patients mobilized with different growth factors. *J. Hematother. Stem Cell Res.* **9,** 737–748.
55. Sugrue, M.W., Williams, K., Pollock, B.H., Khan, S., Peracha, S., Wingard, J.R., and Moreb, J.S. (2000). Characterization and outcome of "hard to mobilize" lymphoma patients undergoing autologous stem cell transplantation. *Leuk. Lymph.* **39,** 509–519.
56. Stockerl-Goldstein, K.E., Reddy, S.A., Horning, S.F., Blume, K.G., Chao, N.F., Hu, W.W., Johnston, L.F., Long, G.D., Strober, S., Wong, R.M., Feiner, R.H., Kobler, S., and Negrin, R.S. (2000). Favorable treatment outcome in non-Hodgkin's lymphoma patients with "poor" mobilization of peripheral blood progenitor cells. *Biol. Blood Marrow Transplant.* **6,** 506–512.
57. Kessinger, A., Bierman, P.J., Cowles, M.K., Anderson, J.R., Armitage, J.O., Bishop, M.R., and Vose, J.M. (1998). Mobilized versus nonmobilized peripheral stem cell transplantation after high-dose therapy for low-grade non-Hodgkin lymphoma. *Cancer Res. Ther. Contr.* **5,** 113–119.
58. Boccadoro, M., Omede, P., Dominietto, A., Palumbo, A., Bringhen, S., Giaretta, F., Ortolano, B., Triolo, S., and Pileri, A. (2000). Multiple myeloma: the number of reinfused plasma cells does not influence outcome of patients treated with intensified chemotherapy and PBPC support. *Bone Marrow Transplant.* **25,** 25–29.
59. Cooper, B.W., Moss, T.H., Ross, A.A., Ybanez, J., and Lazarus, J.M. (1998). Occult tumor contamination of hematopoietic stem cell products does not affect clinical outcome of autologous transplantation in patients with metastatic breast cancer. *J. Clin. Oncol.* **16,** 3509–3517.
60. Sharp, J.G., Joshi, S.S., Armitage, J.O., Bierman, P.J., Coccia, P.F., Harrington, D.S., Kessinger, A., Crouse, D.A., Mann, S.L., and Weisenburger, D.D. (1992). Significance of detection of occult non-Hodgkin's lymphoma in histologically uninvolved marrow by a culture technique. *Blood* **79,** 1074–1080.
61. Sharp, J.G., Kessinger, A., Mann, S., Crouse, D.A., Armitage, J.O., Bierman, P., and Weisenburger, D.D. (1996). Outcome of high-dose therapy and autologous transplantation in non-Hodgkin's lymphoma based on the presence of tumor in the marrow or infused hematopoietic harvest. *J. Clin. Oncol.* **14,** 214–219.

62. Sharp, J.G. (2000). Minimal disease: Detection and significance. *In* "High-Dose Cancer Therapy: Pharmacology, Hematopoietins, Stem Cells," (J.O. Armitage *et al.,* Eds.), 3rd Ed., pp. 301–330. Lippincott, Williams & Wilkins, Philadelphia.
63. Watts, M.J., Ings, S.J., Flynn, M., Dodds, D., Goldstone, A.H., and Linch, D.C. (2000). Remobilization of patients who fail to achieve minimal progenitor thresholds at the first attempt is clinically worthwhile. *Br. J. Haematol.* **111,** 287–291.
64. Perry, A.R., Watts, M.J., Peniket, A.J., Goldstone, A.H., and Linch, D.C. (1998). Progenitor cells yields are frequently poor in patients with histologically indolent lymphomas especially when mobilized within 6 months of previous chemotherapy. *Bone Marrow Transplant.* **21,** 1201–1205.
65. Brugger, W., Bross, K., Frisch, J., Dern, P., Weber, B., Mertelsmann, R., and Kranz, L. (1992). Mobilization of peripheral blood progenitors by sequential administration of interleukin-3 and granulocyte–macrophage colony-stimulating factor following polychemotherapy with etoposide, ifosfamide, and cisplatin. *Blood* **79,** 1193–1200.
66. Haas, R., Mohle, R., Fruehauf, S., Goldschmidt, H., Witt, B., Flentje, M., Wannenmacher, M., and Hunstein, W. (1994). Patient characteristics associated with successful mobilizing and autografting of peripheral blood progenitor cells in malignant lymphoma. *Blood* **83,** 3787–3794.
67. Gazitt, Y., Callander, N., Freytes, C.O., Shaughnessy, P., Liu, Q., Tsai, T.W., and Devore, P. (2000). Peripheral blood stem cell mobilization with cyclophosphamide in combination with G-CSF, GM-CSF, or sequential FM-CSF–G-CSF in non-Hodgkin's lymphoma patients: A randomized prospective study. *J. Hematother. Stem Cell Res.* **9,** 737–748.
68. Bensinger, W., Appelbaum, F., Rowley, S., Storb, R., Sanders, J., Lilleny, K., Gooley, T., Demirer, T., Schiffman, K., Weaver, C., Clift, R., Chauncey, T., Klarnet, J., Montgomery, P., Petersdorf, S., Weiden, P., Witherspoon, R., and Buckner, C.D. (1995). Factors that influence collection and engraftment of autologous peripheral-blood stem cells. *J. Clin. Oncol.* **13,** 2547–2555.
69. Zimmerman, T.M., Michelson, G.C., Mick, R., Grinblatt, D.L., and Williams, S.F. (1999). Timing of platelet recovery is associated with adequacy of leukapheresis product yield after cyclophosphamide and G-CSF in patients with lymphoma. *J. Clin. Apheresis* **14,** 31–34.
70. Koumakis, G., Vassilomanolakis, M., Hazichristou, H., Barbounis, V., Fillis, J., Papanastasiou, K., Moraki, M., Kritsioti, M., Plataniotis, G., Stamatelou, M., and Efremidis, A.P. (1996). Predictive factors affecting mobilization and peripheral blood stem cell (PBSC) collection using single apheresis (SA) for rescuing patients after high-dose chemotherapy (HD.CHE) in various malignancies. *Bone Marrow Transplant.* **18,** 1065–1072.
71. Kotasek, D., Shepherd, K.M., Sage, R.E., Dale, B.M., Norman, J.E., Charles, P., Gregg, A., Pillow, A., and Bolton, A. (1992). Factors affecting blood stem cell collections following high-dose cyclophosphamide mobilization in lymphoma, myeloma, and solid tumors. *Bone Marrow Transplant.* **9,** 11–17.
72. Canales, M.A., Fernandez-Jimenez, M.C., Martin, A., Arrieta, R., Caballero, M.D., Diez, J., Wuevedo, E., Garcia-Bustos, J., San Migues, J.F., and Hernandez-Navarro, F. (2001). Identification of factors associated with poor peripheral blood progenitor cell mobilization in Hodgkin's disease. *Haematologica* **86,** 494–498.
73. Fruehauf, S., Haas, R., Conradt, C., Murea, S., Witt, B., Mohle, R., and Hunstein, W. (1995). Peripheral blood progenitor cell (PBPC) counts during steady-state hematopoiesis allow to estimate the yield of mobilized PBPC after filgrastim (R-metHuG-CSF) supported cytotoxic chemotherapy. *Blood* **85,** 2619–2626.
74. Demirkazik, A., Kessinger, A., Lynch, J., Reed, E., Tarantolo, S., and Sharp, J.G. (2002). Effect of prior therapy and bone marrow metastases on progenitor cell content of blood stem cell harvests in breast cancer patients. *Biol. Blood Marrow Transplant.* **8,** 268–272.
75. Bensinger, W.I, Clift, R.A., Anasetti, C., Appelbaum, F.A., Demirer, T., Rowley, S., Sandmaier, B.M., Torok-Storb, B., and Buckner, C.D. (1996). Transplantation of allogeneic peripheral blood stem cells mobilized by recombinant human granulocyte colony-stimulating factor. *Stem Cells* **14,** 90–105.
76. Wiesneth, M., Schreiner, T., Friedrich, A., Bunjes, D., Krug, E., Maccari, B., Muller, S., Nowak, S., and Kubanek, B. (1998). Mobilization and collection of allogeneic peripheral blood progenitor cells for transplantation. *Bone Marrow Transplant.* **21 (Suppl. 3),** 21–24.
77. Bishop, M.R., Tarantolo, S.R., Bierman, P.J., Vose, J.M., Armitage, J.O., Pavletic, Z.S., Lynch, J., Kollath, J., Reddy, R.L, Warkentin, P.I., and Kessinger, A. (1997). Predictive factors for the identification of allogeneic blood stem cell donors as "poor mobilizers" prior to stem cell collection. *Blood* **90 (Suppl. 1),** 592a.
78. Anderlini, P., and Korbling, M. (1997). The use of mobilized peripheral blood stem cells from normal donors for autografting. *Stem Cells* **15,** 9–17.
79. Holm, M., and Hokland, P. (1998). Not all healthy donors mobilized hematopoietic progenitor cells sufficiently after G-CSF administration to allow for subsequent CD34 purification of the leukapheresis product. *J. Hematother.* **7,** 111–113.
80. Roberts, A.W., Foote, S., Alexander, W.S., Scott, C., Robb, L., and Metcalf, D. (1997). Genetic influences determining progenitor cell mobilization and leukocytosis induced by granulocyte colony-stimulating factor. *Blood* **89,** 2736–2744.
81. Kessinger, A., Mann, S., O'Kane Murphy, B., Jackson, J.D., and Sharp, J.G., (2001). Circulating factors may be responsible for murine strain-specific responses to mobilizing cytokines. *Exp. Hematol.* **29,** 775–778.
82. Elmaagacli, A.H., Basogllu, S., Peceny, R., Trenschel, R., Ottinger, H., Lollert, A., Runde, V., Grosse-Wilde, H., Beelen, D.W., and Schaefer, U.W. (2002). Improved disease-free survival after transplantation of peripheral blood stem cells as compared with bone marrow from HLA-identical unrelated donors in patients with first chronic phase chronic myeloid leukemia. *Blood* **99,** 1130–1135.
83. Scheid, C., Pettengell, R., Ghielmini, M., Radford, J.A., Morgenstern, G.R., Stern, P.L., and Crowther, D. (1995). Time course of the recovery of cellular immune function after high-dose chemotherapy and peripheral blood progenitor cell transplantation for high-grade non-Hodgkin's lymphoma. *Bone Marrow Transplant.* **15,** 901–906.
84. Ottinger, H.D., Beelen, D.W., Scheulen, B., Schaefer, U.W., and Grosse-Wilde, H. (1996). Improved immune reconstitution after allotransplantation of peripheral blood stem cells instead of bone marrow. *Blood* **88,** 2775–2779.
85. Takaue, Y., Okamoto, Y., Kawano, Y., Suzue, T., Abe, T., Saito, S.I., Hirao, A., Makimoto, A., Kawahito, M., Watanabe, T., Shimokawa, T., and Kuroda, Y. (1994). Regeneration of immunity and varicella-zoster virus infection after high-dose chemotherapy and peripheral blood stem cell autografts in children. *Bone Marrow Transplant.* **14,** 219–223.
86. Trenschel, R., Ross, S., Husing, J., Ottinger, H., Elmaagacli, A., Roggendorf, M., Schaefer, U.W., and Runde, V. (2000).

Reduced risk of persisting cytomegalovirus pp65 antigenemia following allogeneic PBSCT. *Bone Marrow Transplant.* **25,** 665–672.
87. Vose, J.M., Sharp, G., Chan, W.C., Nichols, C., Loh, K., Inwards, D., Rifkin, R., Bierman, P.J., Lynch, J.C., Weisenburger, D.D., Kessinger, A., and Armitage, J.O. (2002). Autologous transplantation for aggressive non-Hodgkin's lymphoma: results of a randomized trial evaluating graft source and minimal residual disease. *J. Clin. Oncol.* **20,** 2344–2352.
88. Orkin, S.H., and Zon, L.I. (2002). Hematopoiesis and stem cells:plasticity versus developmental heterogeneity. *Nat. Immunol.* **3,** 323–328.
89. Korbling, M., Katz, R.L., Khanna, A., Ruifrok, A.C., Rondon, G., Albitar, M., Champlin, R.E., and Estrov, Z. (2002). Hepatocytes and epithelial cells of donor origin in recipients of peripheral blood stem cells. *N. Engl. J. Med.* **346,** 738–746.

62

Neurologic Diseases

Ferdinando Rossi and Elena Cattaneo

Following injury or degeneration, spontaneous replacement of dead cells occurs in several tissues characterized by a high physiologic turnover. Such compensatory mechanisms are extremely poor in the mature CNS, and the loss of neural cells, and particularly neurons, usually leads to permanent anatomic damage and functional disability. Because of the increased life expectancy and the improvement of therapeutic procedures that prolong the survival of patients, the incidence of neurologic disorders has greatly increased in Western countries, and the development of efficient treatments for brain injury and neurodegenerative diseases has become an urgent priority for biomedical research.

Repair strategies for neurodegeneration have been primarily based on transplantation of exogenous cells.[1] Recently, however, the discovery that stem or progenitor cells reside in the adult CNS, and that neurogenic processes persist in some adult brain regions,[2,3] has disclosed the possibility of promoting regeneration by mobilizing endogenous elements. Both approaches assume that undifferentiated cells are able to acquire mature phenotypes and become specifically integrated in the adult CNS environment. Although this can be achieved in tissues with a rather simple structure, such as muscle or skin, the task becomes extremely difficult when new elements must be functionally integrated into highly complex neural networks. Thus, a major challenge in brain repair research is to understand the cell–environment interactions that may allow the rewiring of disrupted circuits.

The last 30 years have seen major advancements in the field of neural transplantation, and several clinical trials have been prompted. In these procedures, fetal cells were grafted to the brain of patients with neurologic disorders, including Parkinson's or Huntington's disease.[1] Despite some controversial results,[4,5] there is general agreement that this approach yields significant benefits to the patients.[6] However, the application of fetal cell transplantation as a large-scale therapy is seriously hampered by ethical and methodological constraints related to the use of human abortive material. Consequently, strong efforts have been devoted to the search for alternative sources of donor cells. Stem cells, defined as self-renewing multipotent cells,[7] are expected to be a potentially definitive solution to most of these difficulties. Nevertheless, besides the ethical issues that hinder stem cell research,[8] many problems have to be solved before these cells can be safely and efficaciously used for clinical application.[9] Rather than prompting their premature entry into surgical rooms, careful scientific (and economic) effort should be devoted to answering basic questions: What type of donor cells do we need? Where are they? What is their fate? How do we integrate them into neural networks? What would they deliver?

Requirements for Efficient Brain Repair by Cell Replacement

The conditions that have to be met to obtain successful cell replacement in the CNS are different in different types of disease.[9] It must be emphasized that cell replacement may repair brain damage, but it does not counteract the underlying pathogenic mechanisms. Hence, treatment is indicated when degeneration is induced by intrinsic defects of specific cell populations (e.g., genetic diseases) or extrinsic agents that are no more active (e.g., MPTP intoxication or traumatic–vascular injuries). In contrast, beneficial outcome may be strongly hampered when degeneration is caused by persistent environmental toxicity (e.g., demyelinating diseases) that would also affect newly added elements. In general, cell replacement procedures should be only applied after noxious agents have been neutralized or removed and the progression of the disease has been arrested. In spite of the slow progression of some neurologic disorders with delayed neuronal loss, it is now known that early molecular dysfunctions are present that may precociously affect implanted cells.

Also relevant is the spatiotemporal distribution and evolution of the disease. For instance, significant remyelination has been obtained by the transplantation of different cell types, including oligodendroglial progenitors,[10] bone marrow stromal cells,[11] neural,[12] or embryonic stem cells.[13,14] Although these reports indicate that cell therapy may be successfully applied to cure demyelinating diseases, the focal progressive nature of these disorders would require multiple transplantation procedures, which may prove hardly practicable on patients. Mobilization of endogenous progenitors might be a suitable alternative that would circumvent this problem. However, most precursor cells that can be recruited reside in the subventricular zone of the lateral ventricles, and they are only able to colonize adjacent white matter tracts.[15,16] Thus, alternative procedures have to be designed to boost intrinsic potentialities for myelin repair or to deliver donor cells to disseminated focal injuries.

Handbook of Stem Cells
Volume 2

Even more challenging is the reconstruction of functional circuits disrupted after neuronal degeneration. Easiest to approach are conditions in which cell death affects circumscribed neuronal populations with a well-defined connectivity. Hence, in Parkinson's disease, dopaminergic cells transplanted to the striatum are able to reestablish a regulated release of dopamine,[17] accompanied by significant improvement of motor symptoms.[1] Similarly, a certain degree of anatomic repair and functional recovery have been obtained for Huntington's disease in both experimental models[18,19] and clinical trials.[20] In contrast, requirements are more demanding when precisely patterned long-distance connections have to be rewired, as in the case of Alzheimer's disease, lateral amyotrophic sclerosis, cerebellar degeneration, or vascular–traumatic injuries. Studies on experimental models of such disorders indicate that newly added cells can establish afferent connections with host neurons, rewire local circuits, and provide trophic support to neighboring cells, but they generally fail to restore long-distance connections.[21,22] It is unclear whether this is because of the lack of efficient guidance cues in the adult CNS environment or because of an intrinsic inability of immature neurons to sustain long-distance neuritic navigation.

The reestablishment of specific connection patterns also requires new neurons to be targeted to precise host sites, such as cortical layers. Appropriate homing of transplanted cells is usually achieved in the immature brain[23,24] and in certain regions of the adult CNS, most notably those that retain neurogenic activity.[25,26] In contrast, cells grafted to other regions of the adult CNS usually remain in ectopic positions, favoring the formation of aberrant connections. A major obstacle for the correct targeting of grafted cells is the disruption of cytoarchitecture induced by the disease or even the transplantation procedure. Tissue damage and interruption of the blood–brain barrier may modify the host microenvironment perturbing the migration of donor cells. Not surprisingly, a more efficient integration of new elements is achieved with endogenous progenitors[27,28] or after transplantation in conditions with minimal tissue damage.[29] However, even when the local architecture is preserved, the correct positioning of donor cells can only be achieved if specific migratory cues are active, which is not always the case. For instance, transplanted Purkinje cells acquire their typical position in the developing cerebellum[30] but remain ectopic in the adult molecular layer[21] even in the absence of injury or degeneration.[31] In this context, the development of techniques that allow the visualization of grafted cells *in vivo* will be most useful to improve the delivery and targeting of donor cells to specific host sites.[32]

Finally, it is worth emphasizing that anatomic repair alone may be not sufficient to obtain functional recovery. Clinical improvement of transplanted parkinsonian patients progresses long after the full maturation of the graft.[33] Similarly, laboratory animals that received neural grafts to repair experimental injuries have to relearn specific behavioral tasks.[34] These observations suggest that significant functional benefits can be only achieved if cell replacement therapies are associated with targeted training and rehabilitation paradigms that help the patient to use newly wired connections to produce adaptive behavior.

Sources of Stem Cells for Brain Repair

Stem cells can be obtained from a variety of sources, including blastocysts, fetal tissues, and adult tissues. Nevertheless, each type of stem cell has distinctive properties and drawbacks that have to be carefully evaluated and taken in consideration when planning a cell replacement approach.

Embryonic stem cells, derived from the inner cell mass of preimplantation embryos, have the widest developmental potential. They can participate fully in fetal development when reintroduced into the embryo, and their capacity for multilineage differentiation can be reproduced in culture.[35] After *ex vivo* exposure to specific signals, these cells can be induced to generate specific neuron types[36] or oligodendrocytes, which can be implanted in the adult CNS to remyelinate focal lesions.[13,14] In addition, when grafted to the 6-hydroxydopamine (6-OHDA)-lesioned adult striatum, embryonic stem cells spontaneously produce a significant fraction of dopaminergic and serotonergic neurons leading to amelioration of motor defects.[37] Although embryonic stem cells are endowed with remarkable capacities for self-renewal and phenotypic plasticity, their tumorigenic behavior is a major obstacle to their use. In addition, the development of therapeutic approaches based on human embryonic stem cells is severely hampered by the well-known ethical constraints related to the production of human blastocysts to generate new embryonic stem cell lines. Although alternatives are offered in some countries that have authorized the use of public funds to obtain new embryonic stem cell lines from the surplus of frozen blastocysts derived from *in vitro* fertilization procedures, other countries are awaiting clearer legislation and have to rely on the use of preexisting cell lines.

Tissue-specific somatic stem cells, derived from adult tissues, may be a valid alternative that can circumvent these problems. In principle, self-renewing multipotent cells can be easily isolated from some peripheral organs (e.g., skin or bone marrow) and used for autotransplantation in patients. These cells have proven records of successful engraftment into the tissue type from which they were originating. Bone marrow transplant is the current treatment for various hematopoietic disorders, including leukemia. Skin transplant, by itself or through epidermal stem cells, has been used for years to heal skin burnings. A major question that has emerged in the last few years is whether such tissue-specific stem cells can generate phenotypes other than those of origin. The possibility that an adult stem cell can change its fate would have a tremendous scientific affect on tissues like the brain, given that the extraction of neural stem cells would remain technically challenging and currently suffers from a lack of technologies for their identification and homogenous propagation *in vitro*.

An approach that uses stem cells from another tissue district is based on the assumption that these cells can cross lineage boundaries and acquire phenotypes characteristic of the recipient tissue, including the nervous system. However, although different kinds of somatic stem cells can be induced to express neural markers *in vitro,* their capability of adopting neuronal identities is a matter of debate. For instance, transdifferentiation of bone marrow stem cells to neural phenotypes has been claimed by several recent reports[38–40] that included postmortem analysis of patients that underwent bone marrow transplantation.[41,42] Most results, however, have been obtained in extreme experimental conditions (e.g., total body irradiation). In addition, the number of cells that acquire neuronal identities is too low to be of clinical relevance, and the plasticity of the tissue-specific stem cells is suggested to result from the fusion of donor cells with host neurons.[42] If this is the mechanism, the therapeutic benefit may derive from conveying wild-type DNA to a genetically damaged host cell[43,44] and may not depend on the unexpected plasticity of the donor stem cells. Thus, these observations need to be replicated, and the underlying mechanisms must be elucidated. Most importantly, it remains to be established whether nonneural stem cells can generate significant amounts of new neurons in an injured brain.

Finally, neural stem cells have been isolated from different regions of the adult CNS, including neurogenic and nonneurogenic sites.[2,45] However, because of the lack of efficient and validated procedures to prospectively identify and isolate neural stem cells, cultured neurospheres contain bona fide stem cells as well as other cells at various stages of differentiation and endowed with diverse developmental potentialities. Thus, the current methods applied to expand proliferating cells derived from the CNS (exposure to growth factors) are not specific for neural cells and do not allow the enrichment of cell populations with homogenous properties that may be efficiently used for clinical application. Again, the potentialities of these cells have to be ascertained. Stem cells isolated from the adult mouse brain contribute to the formation of different germ layers when implanted in early-stage chick or mouse embryos.[46] On the other hand, several reports indicate that neural stem cells acquire both temporal and positional information and their neurogenic capacity may be different according to their age and site of origin.[3,47–49] Nonetheless, these cells may be amenable to *ex vivo* manipulations aimed at inducing specific neural lineages and generating site-specific neuronal phenotypes in the recipient brain.[50] On the whole, the available evidence does not allow us to decide whether a particular type of stem cell or progenitor is most suitable to treat neurodegenerative disorders, and stem cell application to regenerative medicine should proceed in multiple directions to find the best donors for each condition.

Isolation and Manipulation of Stem Cells for Cell Replacement in the CNS

The acquisition of mature phenotypes and their functional integration into adult CNS circuits depend on the intrinsic potentialities of the newly added cells and on the presence of specific extrinsic signals. To date, most transplantation experiments have been carried out with fetal cells, which are already committed to specific identities and differentiate according to cell-autonomous mechanisms. By contrast, stem cells are multipotent; hence, their phenotypic choice must be directed by the inductive information present in their microenvironment. Driving multipotent cells to generate precise phenotypic repertoires is a primary prerequisite for successful cell replacement. To obtain the desired phenotypes, stem cells can be instructed *ex vivo* before transplantation. Alternatively, as described in the section "Inductive Signals in the Adult CNS Environment," they will have to rely on instructive–selective cues active in the recipient CNS.

The procedures applied to isolate and characterize stem cells are determinant for the outcome of the subsequent therapeutic application. In most instances, however, the cultures of these cells, and particularly those derived from the CNS, are not homogeneous, and genuine stem cells can only be identified retrospectively. Prospective isolation of neural stem cells has been reported,[51–53] but widely accepted standard procedures that can be used on a large scale are still unavailable. In addition, stem cells derived from different CNS regions[48,49] or at different ages[3,47] do not share the same properties. Consequently, cells from distinct sources most likely have diverse developmental potentialities, implying that different neurodegenerative diseases cannot be treated with the same cell type.

Ex vivo specification of stem cells can be obtained by exposure to inductive environmental signals or by activating specific gene programs. Several conditions have been found that promote the generation of specific neural phenotypes *in vitro,* including low-oxygen concentration[54] or application of different growth factors or hormones.[55] Human neural stem cells exposed to a priming molecular cocktail preferentially generate neurons *in vitro* and acquire cholinergic phenotype in a site-specific manner when transplanted to the adult rat CNS.[50] In addition, differentiation of spinal motor neurons has been induced by exposing embryonic stem cells to a specific sequence of environmental stimuli, known to regulate motor neuron generation *in situ.*[36]

The proliferation and differentiation of stem cells can be also modulated by targeted gene manipulation. The expression of key molecules that regulate cell response to external stimuli, such as growth factor receptors or transducer proteins,[56,57] can be modified to adjust the proliferation–differentiation properties of stem cells. In addition, the induction of population-specific gene programs may be applied to generate desired phenotypic repertoires. For instance, Neurogenin (Ngn1) has been shown to induce neuronal differentiation but inhibit gliogenesis.[58] In addition, overexpression of the *Nurr-1* gene drives multipotent cells to generate large quantities of dopaminergic neurons *in vitro* and after transplantation to adult hosts.[59,60] Despite these remarkable results, our understanding of the molecular cascades that underlie the development of specific neural phenotypes is still inadequate to effectively control the fate of newly added cells. In this respect, information derived from basic developmental neurobiology will be most important to understand the potentialities of the cells used for therapy and to replicate step-by-step differentiation pathways, as done for spinal motor neurons.[36] This information will be most promptly derived through the study of how stem cells are programmed during embryonic life and in the blastocysts.

Inductive Signals in the Adult CNS Environment

If stem cells are placed into the CNS without prior specification, their fate will be determined by local signals provided by the recipient milieu. Multipotent cells grafted to neurogenic regions of the developing brain are able to acquire site-specific phenotypes,[23,24,61] suggesting that efficient instructive cues are in the immature CNS environment. However, most therapeutic strategies for neurodegenerative diseases have to be applied to the mature CNS. Hence, it is crucial to establish whether the same cues are available after the end of development or whether they can be reactivated after injury or degeneration.

In the adult CNS, neurogenic processes continue in the olfactory bulb and hippocampal dentate gyrus.[2,45] The addition of neurons has been reported in several other regions,[62,63] but this evidence remains controversial.[64,65] The subventricular zone–olfactory bulb and the dentate gyrus provide peculiar environmental niches in which specific cellular–molecular interactions direct the differentiation of multipotent progenitors toward restricted repertoires of local neuron phenotypes.[66–68] Transplantation experiments show that stem or progenitor cells placed in these regions adopt local neuronal identities.[25,26,69,70] In contrast, when the same cells are implanted in nonneurogenic regions, such as the cerebellum or the spinal cord, they only generate glia.[25,70] Thus, in the normal adult CNS, efficient inductive signals to generate local neurons are only in neurogenic regions.

The situation may be different in the injured brain. A growing body of evidence shows that neurogenic processes in the subventricular zone–olfactory bulb and hippocampal dentate gyrus are regulated by different stimuli[71,72] and that the rate of neuronal production is increased to compensate for neuronal loss following different types of insult, including mechanical damage,[73] ischemia,[74] or excitotoxicity.[75,76] Most interestingly, several recent reports indicate that after injury new neurons can be also generated in nonneurogenic regions, such as neocortex,[27] hippocampal CA1,[28] and striatum.[77] Although these findings suggest that compensatory mechanisms may be reactivated after injury in nonneurogenic sites, most of the newly born neurons derive from the subventricular zone of lateral ventricles; thus, it remains to be elucidated whether similar self-repair mechanisms can be elicited throughout the neuraxis.

The CNS reaction to injury or degeneration induces the activation of signaling mechanisms that may hamper the replacement of lost neurons. In most instances, multipotent cells transplanted to experimental brain injuries generate mostly glia and only a few nerve cells.[26,78–81] The latter are consistently located a distance from the lesion site, where normal cytoarchitecture is preserved and many host neurons survived. This suggests that the injured tissue activates strong gliogenic signals that overcome neurogenic cues in directing the phenotypic choices of transplanted or endogenous multipotent cells. In this respect, the transplantation procedure, which is inevitably associated with some tissue damage and disruption of the blood–brain barrier, may contribute to diverting a significant fraction of donor cells toward glial identities. Cell replacement strategies should take into account these constraints and aim at potentiating the self-repair properties of the adult CNS, counteracting other influences that would drive multipotent cells toward undesired identities.

Strategies to Promote the Intrinsic Neurogenic Potential of the Adult CNS

The discovery that neurogenic processes continue in some regions of the adult CNS and, most importantly, that they can be reinitiated in other ones after injury has opened new perspectives for cell replacement. Indeed, mobilization of resident progenitor cells might become a valid alternative to transplantation, since it could reduce invasive procedures and facilitate the appropriate targeting of newly generated neurons to wide CNS regions. However, if pathologic degeneration can be effectively compensated in normally neurogenic sites, the spontaneous regeneration observed in other regions is not adequate to achieve significant repair. The number of neogenerated nerve cells is very low, and they often survive for a limited period.[77] Consequently, targeted manipulations must be applied to exploit latent self-repair potentialities of the mature CNS.

Stimulation of neurogenic processes in the adult brain has been attempted by infusion of different bioactive molecules known to modulate proliferation and differentiation of stem cells *in vitro*. Long-lasting infusion of epidermal growth factor (EGF) and basic fibroblast growth factor (bFGF) enhance the proliferation of resident progenitors in the subventricular zone of the lateral ventricles.[82,83] These factors also exert some influence on the phenotypic choice of newly born elements: EGF promotes neuronal production in the olfactory bulb, whereas bFGF increases gliogenesis in both the olfactory bulb and the dentate gyrus. Some newly born cells, colabeled with neuronal markers, have been observed in the neocortex and striatum, but their phenotype and degree of integration have not been characterized further.[83] Infusion of the same factors in the fourth ventricle also enhances the proliferation of progenitor cells in the brainstem and spinal cord.[84] Here, however, these cells exclusively differentiate into glia, further corroborating the idea that neurogenic potentialities may be not homogeneously distributed throughout the CNS.

Application of brain-derived neurotrophic factor, through viral vectors[85] or long-lasting infusion,[86,87] also promotes proliferation in the subventricular zone and neuronal incorporation in the olfactory bulb. In addition, numerous proliferating cells appear in several regions surrounding the cerebral ventricles. Some such newly born cells, which express features of medium-sized spiny neurons, are present in the striatum,[85] whereas cells labeled with markers for immature neurons occur in several other regions.[87] Thus, the application of bioactive molecules can effectively enhance the proliferation of endogenous progenitor cells. However, the evidence that these cells can acquire mature neuron phenotypes and become stably incorporated in adult circuits is still scant.

Similar approaches have been attempted to promote spontaneous repair after injury. In one report, transforming growth factor-alpha has been infused to the striatum after 6-OHDA-induced degeneration of the nigrostriatal projection.[88] The treatment produced a robust increase of proliferation in the adjacent subventricular zone, accompanied by massive migration into the denervated striatum where some cells expressed tyrosine hydroxylase. In another elegant study,[28] EGF and bFGF where infused during a precise window after hippocampal ischemia, which induced massive neuronal degeneration in CA1. After several weeks, the authors observed regeneration of about 40% pyramidal neurons. Remarkably, the newly born cells acquired appropriate positions and established specific and functional connections with adult partners. The treated mice also showed significant behavioral recovery in spatial learning tasks. These striking observations indicate that spontaneous compensatory mechanisms may be effectively boosted to obtain significant anatomic repair and functional recovery. It remains to be elucidated whether a similar treatment can be equally successful on other neuron types from different CNS regions. It is likely that different neuron populations will require specific molecular cocktails and administration schedules.

Concluding Remarks

The exciting breakthroughs obtained during the last few years show that stem cell research is a solid prospect for obtaining repair after brain injury or neurodegenerative diseases. Nevertheless, a long road must be run before these cells can be efficiently used for clinical application. Reliable standardized procedures have to be established to prospectively isolate stem cells from developing and adult tissues and particularly from the CNS. The basic biologic properties of these cells, in terms of proliferation and differentiation potential, have to be thoroughly characterized to obtain adequate amounts of donor cells with stable homogeneous characteristics. Standards for safety should be also established by monitoring cell properties to avoid transformation or loss of viability and developmental potential. In addition, the molecular pathways underlying the generation of specific phenotypes have to be elucidated to design targeted manipulations that allow the generation of desired cell types in the required quantities. Finally, the fine nature of the adult CNS environment and the peculiar features related to different pathologic conditions have to be clarified to develop strategies that optimize the adaptive integration of newly added elements. Most likely, therapeutic applications of stem cells will not yield miraculous results in the near future. However, upcoming controlled clinical trials must be pursued in continuous cross talk with basic biologic experimentation to progressively improve cell replacement procedures and to develop targeted protocols for each disease. These protocols will likely require a combination of cell and drug therapy and include rehabilitation paradigms. Successful application of stem cells to treat neurodegenerative diseases is a reachable goal, but it will require time, patience, and painstaking dedication of numerous basic and clinical scientists. The field offers hopes but not promises.

Summary

Anatomical repair and functional recovery after injury or degeneration in the central nervous system (CNS) require specific integration of novel elements into complex neural circuitries. Because of the poor capability for spontaneous regeneration of the mature nervous tissue, cell replacement approaches primarily rely on transplantation of exogenous cells. Recent reports, however, indicate that significant recovery may be also obtained by mobilization of undifferentiated cells that reside in the adult brain. Because of their strong proliferative capabilities and supposedly broad developmental potential, stem cells are a suitable tool for developing cell-based therapies for neurologic diseases. However, successful strategies for cell replacement in the adult CNS require a profound knowledge of the basic biologic properties of stem cells and of the cell–environment interactions needed for their functional integration in the recipient neural networks. This chapter reviews recent advances in the isolation and characterization of stem cells that may be used for neurologic therapy, including procedures that enhance their ability to generate mature neural elements. In addition, we describe experiments aimed at promoting repair of brain injury by stem cell transplantation or by mobilization of endogenous progenitor cells.

ACKNOWLEDGMENTS

Our work is supported by grants to F. Rossi from the Ministry of Research and University (Italy, MIUR 2001055212-001), Ministero della Sanità-Progetto Alzheimer (Italy, 300RFA00/01-05), University of Turin and to E. Cattaneo from the Ministry of Research and University (MIUR 2001055212-004 and MM06278849-005), Ministero della Sanità-Progetto Alzheimer (300RFA00/01-02), Telethon (No. 840), Associazione Italiana Ricerca sul Cancro (Italy), the Huntington's Disease Society of America (New York) and the Hereditary Disease Foundation (Los Angeles).

REFERENCES

1. Björklund, A., and Lindvall, O. (2000). Cell replacement therapies for central nervous system disorders. *Nat. Neurosci.* **3,** 537–544.
2. Temple, S., and Alvarez-Buylla, A. (1999). Stem cells in the adult mammalian central nervous system. *Curr. Opin. Neurobiol.* **9,** 135–141.
3. Temple, S. (2002). The development of neural stem cells. *Nature* **414,** 112–117.

4. Freed, C.R., Greene, P.E., Breeze, R.E., Tsai, W.Y., DuMouchel, W., Kao, R., Dillon, S., Winfield, H., Culver, S., Trojanowski, J.Q., Eidelberg, D., and Fahn, S. (2001). Transplantation of embryonic dopamine neurons for severe Parkinson's disease. *N. Engl. J. Med.* **344,** 710–719.
5. Hauser, R.A., Furtado, S., Cimino, C.R., Delgado, H., Eichler, S., Schwartz, S., Scott, D., Nauert, G.M., Soety, E., Sossi, V., Holt, D.A., Sanberg, P.R., Stoessl, A.J., and Freeman, T.B. (2002). Bilateral human fetal striatal transplantation in Huntington's disease. *Neurology* **58,** 682–695.
6. Dunnett, S.B., Björklund, A., and Lindvall, O. (2001). Cell therapy in Parkinson's disease: stop or go? *Nat. Rev. Neurosci.* **2,** 365–369.
7. Weissman, I., Anderson, D.J., and Gage, F. (2001). Stem and progenitor cells: origin, phenotypes, lineage commitments, and transdifferentiations. *Annu. Rev. Cell Dev. Biol.* **17,** 387–403.
8. Mc Laren, A. (2001). Ethical and social considerations of stem cell research. *Nature* **414,** 129–131.
9. Rossi, F., and Cattaneo, E. (2002). Neural stem cell therapy for neurological diseases: dreams and reality. *Nat. Rev. Neurosci.* **3,** 401–409.
10. Jeffery, N.D., Crang, A.J., O'Leary, M.T., Hodge, S.J., and Blakemore, W.F. (1999). Behavioral consequences of oligodendrocyte progenitor cell transplantation into experimental demyelinating lesions in the rat spinal cord. *Eur. J. Neurosci.* **11,** 1508–1514.
11. Akiyama, Y., Radtke, C., and Kocsis, J.D. (2002). Remyelination of the rat spinal cord by transplantation of identified bone marrow stromal cells. *J. Neurosci.* **22,** 6623–6630.
12. Akiyama, Y, Honmou, O., Kato, T., Uede, T., Hashi, K., and Kocsis, J.D. (2001). Transplantation of clonal neural precursor cells derived from adult human brain establishes functional peripheral myelin in the rat spinal cord. *Exp. Neurol.* **167,** 27–39.
13. Brüstle, O., Jones, K.N., Learish, L.D., Karram, K., Choudhary, K., Wiestler, O.D., Duncan, I.D., and McKay, R.D.G. (1999). Embryonic stem cell-derived glial precursors: a source of myelinating transplants. *Science* **285,** 754–756.
14. Liu, S., Steward, T.J., Howard, M.J., Chakrabortty, S., Holekamp, T.F., and McDonald, J.W. (2000). Embryonic stem cells differentiate into oligodendrocytes and myelinate in culture and after spinal cord transplantation. *Proc. Natl. Acad. Sci. U. S. A.* **97,** 6126–6131.
15. Nait-Oumesmar, B., Decker, L., Lachapelle, F., Avellana-Adalid, V., Bachelin, C., and Baron Van-Evercooren, A. (1999). Progenitor cells of the adult mouse subventricular zone proliferate, migrate, and differentiate into oligodendrocytes after demyelination. *Eur. J. Neurosci.* **11,** 4357–4366.
16. Picard-Riera, N., Decker, L., Delarasse, C., Goude, K., Nait-Oumesmar, B., Pham-Dinh, D., and Baron Van-Evercooren, A. (2002). Experimental autoimmune encephalomyelitis mobilizes neural progenitors from the subventricular zone to undergo oligodendrogenesis in adult mice. *Proc. Natl. Acad. Sci. U. S. A.* **99,** 13,211–13,216.
17. Piccini, P., Brooks, D.J., Björklund, A., Gunn, R.N., Grasby, P.M., Rimoldi, O., Brundin, P., Hagell, P., Rehnchrona, S., Widner, H., and Lindvall, O. (1999). Dopamine release from nigral transplants visualized *in vivo* in a Parkinson's patient. *Nat. Neurosci.* **2,** 1136–1140.
18. Kendall, A.L., Rayment, F.D., Torres, E.M., Baker, H.F., Ridley, R.M., and Dunnett, S.B. (1998). Functional integration of striatal allografts in a primate model of Huntington's disease. *Nat. Med.* **4,** 727–729.
19. Palfi, S.P., Conde, F., Riche, D., Brouillet, E., Dautry, C., Mittoux, V., Chibois, A., Peschanski, M., and Hantraye, P. (1998). Fetal striatal allografts reverse cognitive deficits in a primate model of Huntington's disease. *Nat. Med.* **4,** 963–966.
20. Bachoud-Levi, A.C., Remy, P., Nguyen, J.P., Brugieres, P., Lefaucheur, J.P., Bourdet, C., Baudic, S., Gaura, V., Maison, P., Haddad, B., Boisse, M.F., Grandmougin, T., Jeny, R., Bartolomeo, P., Dalla Barba, G., Degos, J.D., Lisovoski, F., Ergis, A.M., Pailhous, E., Cesaro, P., Hantraye, P., and Peschanski, M. (2000). Motor and cognitive improvements in patients with Huntington's disease after neural transplantation. *Lancet* **356,** 1945–1946.
21. Sotelo, C., and Alvarado-Mallart, R.M. (1991). The reconstruction of cerebellar circuits. *Trends Neurosci.* **14,** 350–355.
22. Grabowski, M., Johansson, B.B., and Brundin, P. (1995). Neocortical grafts placed in the infarcted brain of adult rats: few or no efferent fibers grow from transplant to host. *Exp. Neurol.* **134,** 273–276.
23. Campbell, K., Olsson, M., and Björklund, A. (1995). Regional incorporation and site-specific differentiation of striatal precursors transplanted to the embryonic forebrain ventricle. *Neuron* **15,** 1259–1273.
24. Brüstle, O., Maskos, U., and McKay, R.D.G. (1995). Host-guided migration allows targeted introduction of neurons into the embryonic brain. *Neuron* **15,** 1275–1285.
25. Suhonen, J.O., Peterson, D.A., Ray, J., and Gage, F.H. (1996). Differentiation of adult hippocampus-derived progenitors into olfactory neurons *in vivo. Nature* **383,** 624–627.
26. Herrera, D.G., Garcia-Verdugo, J.M., and Alvarez-Buylla, A. (1999). Adult-derived neural precursors transplanted into multiple regions in the adult brain. *Annu. Neurol.* **46,** 867–877.
27. Magavi, S.S., Leavitt, B.R., and Macklis, J.D. (2000). Induction of neurogenesis in the neocortex of adult mice. *Nature* **405,** 951–955.
28. Nakatomi, H., Kuriu, T., Okabe, S., Yamamoto, S., Hatano, O., Kawashara, N., Tamura, A., Kirino, T., and Nakafuku, M. (2002). Degeneration of hippocampal pyramidal neurons after ischemic brain injury by recruitment of endogenous neural progenitors. *Cell* **110,** 429–441.
29. Macklis, J.D. (1993). Transplanted neocortical neurons migrate selectively in regions of neuronal degeneration produced by chromophore-targeted laser photolysis. *J. Neurosci.* **13,** 3848–3863.
30. Carletti, B., Grimaldi, P., Magrassi, L., and Rossi, F. (2002). Specification of cerebellar progenitors following heterotopic–heterochronic transplantation to the embryonic CNS *in vivo* and *in vitro. J. Neurosci.* **22,** 7132–7146.
31. Rossi, F., Borsello, T., and Strata, P. (1994). Embryonic Purkinje cells grafted on the surface of the adult uninjured rat cerebellum migrate in the host parenchyma and induce sprouting of intact climbing fibers. *Eur. J. Neurosci.* **6,** 121–136.
32. Hoehn, M., Küstermann, E., Blunk, J., Wiedermann, D., Trapp, T., Wecker, S., Föcking, M., Arnold, H., Hescheler, J., Fleischmann, B.K., Schwindt, W., and Bührle, C. (2002). Monitoring of implanted stem cell migration *in vivo:* a highly resolved, *in vivo* magnetic resonance imaging investigation of experimental stroke in rat. *Proc. Natl. Acad. Sci. U. S. A.* **99,** 16,267–16,272.
33. Piccini, P., Lindvall, O., Björklund, A., Brundin, P., Hagell, P., Ceravolo, R., Oertel, W., Niall, Q., Samuel, M., Rehncrona, S., Widner, H., and Brooks, D.J. (2000). Delayed recovery of movement-related cortical function in Parkinson's disease after striatal dopaminergic grafts. *Ann. Neurol.* **48,** 689–695.

34. Döbrössy, M.D., and Dunnett, S.B. (2001). The influence of environment and experience of neural grafts. *Nat. Rev. Neurosci.* **2,** 871–879.
35. Smith, A.G. (2001). Embryo-derived stem cells: of mice and men. *Annu. Rev. Cell Dev. Biol.* **17,** 435–462.
36. Wichterle, H., Lieberman, I., Porter, J., and Jessell, T.M. (2002). Directed differentiation of embryonic stem cells into motor neurons. *Cell* **110,** 385–397.
37. Björklund, L., Sanchez-Pernaute, R., Chung, S., Andersson, T., Chen, I.Y.C., McNaught, K.S., Brownell A.L., Jenkins, B.J., Wahlestedt, C., Kim, K.S., and Isacson, O. (2002). Embryonic stem cells develop into functional dopaminergic neurons after transplantation in a Parkinson's rat model. *Proc. Natl. Acad. Sci. U. S. A.* **99,** 2344–2349.
38. Brazelton, T.R., Rossi, F.M.V., Keshet, G.I., and Blau, H.M. (2000). From marrow to brain: Expression of neuronal phenotypes in adult mice. *Science* **290,** 1775–1779.
39. Mezey, E., Chandross, K.J., Harta, G., Maki, R.A., and McKercher, S.R. (2000). Turning blood into brain: cells bearing neuronal antigens generated *in vivo* from bone marrow. *Science* **290,** 1779–1782.
40. Priller, J., Persons, D.A., Klett, F.F., Kempermann, G., Kreutzberg, G.W., and Dirnagl, U. (2001). Neogenesis of cerebellar Purkinje neurons from gene-marked bone marrow cells *in vivo. J. Cell Biol.* **155,** 733–738.
41. Mezey, E., Key, S., Vogelsang, G., Szalayova, I., Lange, G.D., and Crain, B. (2003). Transplanted bone marrow generates new neurons in human brains. *Proc. Natl. Acad. Sci. U. S. A.* **100,** 1364–1369.
42. Weimann, J.M., Charlton, C.A., Brazelton, T.R., Hackman, R.C., and Blau, H.M. (2003). Contribution of transplanted bone marrow cells to Purkinje neurons in human adult brains. *Proc. Natl. Acad. Sci. U. S. A.* **100,** 2088–2093.
43. Vassilopoulos, G., Wang, P.., and Russell, D.W. (2003). Transplanted bone marrow regenerates liver by cell fusion. *Nature* **422,** 901–904.
44. Wang, X., Willenbring, H., Akkari, Y., Torimaru, Y., Foster, M., Al-Dhalimy, M., Lagasse, E., Finegold, M., Olson, S., and Grompe, M. (2003). Cell fusion is the principal source of bone-marrow-derived hepatocytes. *Nature* **422,** 897–901.
45. Gage, F.H. (2000). Mammalian neural stem cells. *Science* **287,** 1433–1438.
46. Clarke, D.L., Johansson, C.B., Wilbertz, J., Veress, B., Nilsson, E., Karlström, H., Lendhal, U., and Frisén, J. (2000). Generalized potential of adult neural stem cells. *Science* **288,** 1660–1663.
47. Morrison, S.J. (2001). Neuronal potential and lineage determination by neural stem cells. *Curr. Opin. Cell Biol.* **13,** 666–672.
48. Zappone, M.V., Galli, R., Catena, R., Meani, N., De Biasi, S., Mattei, E., Tiveron, C., Vescovi, A.L., Lovell-Badge, M., Ottolenghi, S., Nicolis, S.K. (2000). Sox2 regulatory sequences direct expression of a b-geo transgene to telencephalic neural stem cells and precursors of the mouse embryo, revealing regionalization of gene expression in CNS stem cells. *Development* **127,** 2367–2382.
49. Hitoshi, S., Tropepe, V., Ekker, M., and van der Kooy, D. (2002). Neural stem cell lineages are regionally specified, but not committed, within distinct compartments of the developing brain. *Development* **129,** 233–244.
50. Wu, P., Tarasenko, Y.I., Gu, Y., Huang, L.Y.M., Coggeshall, R.E., and Yu, Y. (2002). Region-specific generation of cholinergic neurons from human neural stem cells grafted in adult rat. *Nat. Neurosci.* **12,** 1271–1278.
51. Morrison, S.J., White, P.M., Zock, C., and Anderson, D.J. (1999). Prospective identification, isolation by flow cytometry, and *in vivo* self-renewal of multipotent mammalian neural crest stem cells. *Cell* **96,** 737–749.
52. Keyoung, H.M., Roy, N.S., Benraiss, A., Louissaint, A., Jr., Suzuki. A., Hashimoto, M., Rashbaum, W.K., Okano, H., and Goldman, S.A. (2001). High-yield selection and extraction of two promoter-defined phenotypes of neural stem cells from the fetal human brain. *Nat. Biotechnol.* **19,** 843–850.
53. Rietze, R.L., Valcanis, H., Brooker, G.F., Thomas, T., Voss, A.K., and Bartlett, P.F. (2001). Purification of a pluripotent neural stem cell from the adult mouse brain. *Nature* **412,** 736–739.
54. Studer, L., Csete, M., Lee, S.H., Kabbani, N., Walikonis, J., Wold, B., and McKay, R.D.G. (2000). Enhanced proliferation, survival, and dopaminergic differentiation of CNS precursors in lowered oxygen. *J. Neurosci.* **20,** 7377–7383.
55. Panchision, D., Hazel, T., and McKay, R.D.G. (1998). Plasticity and stem cells in the vertebrate nervous system. *Curr. Biol.* **10,** 727–733.
56. Cattaneo, E., and Pelicci, P.G. (1998). Emerging roles for SH2/PTB-containing Shc adapter proteins in the developing mammalian brain. *Trends Neurosci.* **21,** 476–481.
57. Conti, L., Sipione, S., Magrassi, L., Bonfanti, L., Rigamonti, D., Pettirossi, V., Peschanski, M., Haddad, B., Pelicci, P.G., Milanesi, G., Pelicci, G., and Cattaneo, E. (2001). Shc signaling in differentiating neural progenitor cells. *Nat. Neurosci.* **4,** 579–586.
58. Sun, Y., Nadal-Vicens, M., Misono, S., Lin, M.Z., Zubiaga, A., Hua, X., Fan, G., and Greenberg, M.E. (2001). Neurogenin promotes neurogenesis and inhibits glial differentiation by independent mechanisms. *Cell* **104,** 365–376.
59. Wagner, J., Åkerud, P., Castro, D.S., Holm, P.C., Canals, J.M., Snyder, E.Y., Perlmann, T., and Arenas, E. (1999). Induction of a midbrain dopaminergic phenotype in *Nurr1*-overexpressing neural stem cells by type 1 astrocytes. *Nat. Biotechnol.* **17,** 653–659.
60. Kim, J.H., Auerbach, J.M., Rodriguez-Gomez, J.A., Velasco, I., Gavin, D., Lumelsky, N., Lee, S.H., Nguyen, J., Sanchez-Pernaute, R., and McKay, R.D.G. (2002). Dopamine neurons derived from embryonic stem cells function in an animal model of Parkinson's disease. *Nature* **418,** 50–56.
61. Lim, D.A., Fishell, G.A., and Alvarez-Buylla, A. (1997). Postnatal mouse subventricular zone neuronal precursors can migrate and differentiate within multiple levels of the developing neuraxis. *Proc. Natl. Acad. Sci. U. S. A.* **94,** 14,832–14,836.
62. Gould, E., Reeves, A.J., Graziano, M.S.A., and Gross, C.G. (1999). Neurogenesis in the neocortex of adult primates. *Science* **286,** 548–552.
63. Bernier, P., Bédard, A., Vinet, J., Lévesque, M., Parent, A. (2002). Newly generated neurons in the amygdala and adjoining cortex of adult primates. *Proc. Natl. Acad. Sci. U. S. A.* **98,** 11,464–11,469.
64. Kornack, D.R., and Rakic, P. (2001). Cell proliferation without neurogenesis in the adult primate neocortex. *Science* **294,** 2127–2130.
65. Koketsu, D., Mikami, A., Miyamoto, Y., and Hisatune, T. (2003). Nonrenewal of neurons in the cortex of adult macaque monkeys. *J. Neurosci.* **23,** 937–942.
66. Lim, D.A., Tramontin, A.D., Trevejo, J.M., Herrera, D.G., Garcia-Verdugo, J.M., and Alvarez-Buylla, A. (2000). Noggin antagonizes BMP signaling to create a niche for adult neurogenesis. *Neuron* **28,** 713–726.
67. Song, H., Stevens, C.F., and Gage, F.H. (2002). Astroglia induces neurogenesis from adult neural stem cells. *Nature* **417,** 39–44.

68. Doetsch, F., Petreanu, L., Caille, I., Garcia-Verdugo, J.M., and Alvarez-Buylla, A. (2002). EGF converts transit-amplifying neurogenic precursors in the adult brain into multipotent stem cells. *Neuron* **36,** 1021–1034.
69. Vicario-Abejón, C., Cunningham, M.G., and McKay, R.D.G. (1995). Cerebellar precursors transplanted to the neonate dentate gyrus express features characteristic of hippocampal neurons. *J. Neurosci.* **15,** 6351–6363.
70. Shihabuddin, L.S., Horner, P.J., Ray, J., and Gage, F.H. (2000). Adult spinal cord stem cells generate neurons after transplantation in the adult dentate gyrus. *J. Neurosci.* **20,** 8727–8735.
71. McEwen, B.S. (1999). Stress and hippocampal plasticity. *Annu. Rev. Neurosci.* **22,** 105–122.
72. Gould, E., Tanapat, P., Rydel, T., and Hastings, N. (2000). Regulation of hippocampal neurogenesis in adulthood. *Biol. Psych.* **48,** 715–720.
73. Gould, E., and Tanapat, P. (1997). Lesion-induced proliferation of neuronal progenitors in the dentate gyrus of the adult rat. *Neuroscience* **80,** 427–436.
74. Jin, K., Minami, M., Lan, J.Q., Mao, X.O., Batteur, S., Simon, R.P., and Greenberg, D.A. (2001). Neurogenesis in dentate subgranular zone and rostral subventricular zone after focal cerebral ischemia in the rat. *Proc. Natl. Acad. Sci. U. S. A.* **98,** 4710–4715.
75. Bengzon, J., Kokaia, Z., Elmér, E., Nanobashvili, A., Kokaia, M., and Lindvall, O. (1997). Apoptosis and proliferation of dentate gyrus neurons after single and intermittent limbic seizures. *Proc. Natl. Acad. Sci. U. S. A.* **94,** 10,432–10,437.
76. Parent, J.M., Yu, T.W., Leibowitz, R.T., Geshwind, D.H., Slowiter, R.S., and Lowenstein, D.H. (1997). Dentate granule cell neurogenesis is increased by seizures and contributes to aberrant network reorganization in the adult rat hippocampus. *J. Neurosci.* **17,** 3727–3738.
77. Arvidsson, A., Collin, T., Kirik, D., Kokaia, Z., and Lindvall, O. (2002). Neuronal replacement from endogenous precursors in the adult brain after stroke. *Nat. Med.* **8,** 963–970.
78. Gage, F.H., Coates, P.W., Palmer, T.D., Kuhn, H.G., Fisher, L.J., Suhonen, J.O., Peterson, D.A., Suhr, S.T., and Ray, J. (1995). Survival and differentiation of adult neuronal progenitor cells transplanted to the adult brain. *Proc. Natl. Acad. Sci. U. S. A.* **92,** 11,879–11,883.
79. Shihabuddin, L.S., Holets, V.R., and Whittemore, S.R. (1996). Selective hippocampal lesions differentially affect the phenotypic fate of transplanted neuronal precursors. *Exp. Neurol.* **139,** 61–72.
80. Lundberg, C., Winkler, C., Whittemore, S.R., and Björklund, A. (1996). Conditionally immortalized neural progenitor cells grafted to the striatum exhibit site-specific neuronal differentiation and establish connections with the host globus pallidus. *Neurobiol. Dis.* **3,** 33–50.
81. Lundberg, C., Martinez-Serrano, A., Cattaneo, E., McKay, R.D.G., and Björklund, A. (1997). Survival, integration, and differentiation of neural stem cell lines after transplantation to the adult rat striatum. *Exp. Neurol.* **145,** 342–360.
82. Kuhn, G.H., Winkler, J., Kempermann, G., Thal, L.J., and Gage, F.H. (1997). Epidermal growth factor and fibroblast growth factor-2 have different effects on neural progenitors in the adult rat brain. *J. Neurosci.* **17,** 5820–5829.
83. Craig, C.G., Tropepe, V., Morshead, C.M., Reynolds, B.A., Weiss, S., and van der Kooy, D. (1996). *In vivo* growth factor expansion of endogenous subependymal neural precursor cell populations in the adult mouse brain. *J. Neurosci.* **16,** 2649–2658.
84. Martens, D.J., Seaberg, R.M., and van der Kooy, D. (2002). *In vivo* infusions of exogenous growth factors into the fourth ventricle of the adult mouse brain increase the proliferation of neural progenitors around the fourth ventricle and the central canal of the spinal cord. *Eur. J. Neurosci.* **16,** 1045–1057.
85. Benraiss, A., Chmielnicki, E., Lerner, K., Roh, D., and Goldman, S.A. (2001). Adenoviral brain-derived neurotrophic factor induces both neostriatal and olfactory neuronal recruitment from endogenous progenitor cells in the adult forebrain. *J. Neurosci.* **21,** 6718–6731.
86. Zigova, T., Pencea, V., Wiegand, S.J., and Luskin, M.B. (1998) Intraventricular administration of BDNF increases the number of newly generated neurons in the adult olfactory bulb. *Mol. Cell. Neurosci.* **11,** 234–245.
87. Pencea, V., Bingaman, K.D., Wiegand, S.J., and Luskin, M.B. (2001). Infusion of brain-derived neurotrophic factor into the lateral ventricle of the adult rat leads to new neurons in the parenchyma of the striatum, septum, thalamus, and hypothalamus. *J. Neurosci.* **21,** 6706–6717.
88. Fallon, J., Reid, S., Kinyamu, R., Opole, I., Opole, R., Baratta, J., Kork, M., Endo, T.L., Duong, A., Nguyen, G., Kerkhehabadi, M., Twardzik, D., and Loughlin, S. (2000). *In vivo* induction of massive proliferation, directed migration, and differentiation of neural cells in the adult mammalian brain. *Proc. Natl. Acad. Sci. U. S. A.* **97,** 14,686–14,691.

63

Restoration of Vision

Pamela A. Raymond

Introduction

EMBRYONIC ORIGIN OF THE EYE

Although eyes are located at the body surface (a necessary requirement for detection of light and formation of visual images), the sensory neural component of the eye (the retina) is an extension of the brain. At an early stage in embryonic development, the bilaterally paired optic primordia (optic vesicles), which later in development produce retinal neurons, grow laterally from the forebrain. As the optic primordia contact the overlying surface ectoderm, they induce the formation of specialized epithelial structures—the lens and cornea—essential to create a functional eye.[1] The mature vertebrate eye has a complex anatomy and a diverse embryologic origin, including tissue components that derive from the epidermis, mesoderm, and neural crest as well as the central nervous system (CNS). The CNS component is critical, since in the absence of the bilateral optic primordia, the eyes fail to develop.[1]

In addition to the neural retina, other tissue derivatives of the optic primordia include the retinal pigmented epithelium (RPE), the ciliary and iris epithelia, and the optic nerves. The partitioning of the optic primordia into distinct tissue components involves complex morphogenetic movements and inductive interactions with surrounding tissues, including the ventral midline of the neural tube, the head mesenchyme, and the overlying surface ectoderm. Several homeobox-containing genes are essential for normal eye development, including *Otx2, Pax6, Six3,* and *Rx/Rax,* and the regionalized expression of these regulatory genes is the earliest indication of which progenitor cells in the presumptive brain are fated to generate the optic primordia.[1,2] These molecular determinants of eye formation show a remarkable and unexpected degree of evolutionary conservation of function.[3]

The presumptive neural retina in the embryo is in all respects analogous to the neuroepithelium (also called the ventricular zone) that generates the rest of the brain. As the primitive optic vesicle collapses to form an optic cup, its outer surface differentiates into the RPE and the inner surface becomes specialized as the neural retina. The former ventricular surface is thus interposed between the presumptive RPE and the presumptive neural retina. During the next stage of morphogenesis, the RPE thins to a monolayer epithelium and becomes pigmented, whereas the neural retina thickens into a pseudostratified epithelium.[4] Nuclei in the presumptive neural retina undergo interkinetic migration with mitotic figures confined to the former ventricular surface,[5] the outer limiting membrane (OLM) of the retina. The epithelium at the rim of the optic cup later differentiates as the bilayered ciliary and iris epithelia, and the latter encloses the pupil of the eye.

RETINAL NEUROGENESIS

Formation of the mature retinal structure is essentially a process of delamination of the pseudostratified epithelium of the proliferative ventricular zone forming the inner wall of the optic cup. Two generalizations about the order of neurogenesis in the retina seem to be valid for all species studied.[1,6–8] First, differentiation of neurons begins near the optic stalk, which connects the optic primordium to the brain. Production of neurons then proceeds in a centripetal wave toward the retinal margin. Second, the first cells to become postmitotic are always retinal ganglion cells, the neurons (at the inner surface of the retina) from which the fibers of the optic nerve originate. Among the last neurons to cease dividing are the photoreceptors, in particular the rods, which remain at the OLM and differentiate to produce a modified ciliated appendage that projects into the subretinal space (former ventricle) and that contains the visual transduction machinery, including opsin protein. The order of differentiation of retinal neurons thus defines an inside-out gradient with respect to the center of the optic globe superimposed on a centripetal gradient of maturation, which initiates at the optic stalk and then sweeps across the hemispheric retinal anlagen.

Retinal neurogenesis proceeds over a relatively prolonged period, which in most species extends into postnatal life.[6,9–11] In teleost fish and amphibians, only a small fraction of the retina is generated by delamination of the primitive retinal epithelium in the embryo; a much larger proportion is produced postembryonically from a narrow annulus of proliferating retinal neuroepithelial cells, called the circumferential germinal zone or ciliary marginal zone.[12–18] These cells represent a remnant of the embryonic ventricular zone at the far peripheral rim of the hemispheric retina, which was the destination of the traveling wave of differentiation. From this persistent germinal zone, annuli of new retina are added as the eye continues to grow postembryonically. The regulation of

Handbook of Stem Cells
Volume 2

mitotic activity in the circumferential germinal zone is under the control of the growth hormone–insulin-like growth factor-I axis, which allows for coordination of somatic and retinal growth (reviewed by Reh and Fischer[18]).

An additional source of neurogenesis exists in teleost fish retinas, apparently uniquely among vertebrates. In many fish, rod photoreceptors accumulate with growth as the eye (and body) enlarges. The new rod photoreceptors are generated from proliferating progenitor cells in the inner retina associated with the radial fibers of the Müller glial cells; these progenitors divide slowly to generate a population of rapidly proliferating rod precursors with limited potential for cell division, which migrate to the outer retina and differentiate exclusively as rod (not cone) photoreceptors.[19–26] The interstitial addition of rod photoreceptors into the mature retinal mosaic serves to maintain scotopic visual sensitivity despite continued ocular growth and expansion of the retinal surface caused by stretching as a consequence of intraocular pressure in the fluid-filled globe.[27–29]

NEUROGENESIS IN THE CENTRAL VISUAL TARGETS

The optic stalk, which formed the primitive connection between the optic primordium and the brain, later provides a conduit along which the optic nerve fibers grow to reach their central targets. Optic axons from the retinal ganglion cells travel to the midbrain optic tectum, their major target in fish, amphibians, and birds. In mammals, the homologue of the optic tectum, the superior colliculus, is one target for optic fibers, but another important visual pathway is via the lateral geniculate nucleus of the thalamus to the visual cortex.

Development of the optic tectum–superior colliculus follows a similar pattern in all vertebrate species that have been studied. In general, maturation proceeds from the anterior–ventral–lateral edge to the posterior–dorsal–medial pole.[14–16,30–34] This gradient of maturation precisely reflects the pathway followed by the ingrowing optic fibers, and abundant evidence suggests that the optic fibers stimulate neurogenesis of tectal neurons.[35–38] The optic fibers from the retina terminate on tectal neurons in a precise topographic arrangement (forming the retinotectal map). However, postembryonic neurogenesis in the enlarging retina and optic tectum are topologically discordant: New retinal ganglion cells are added in the circumferential germinal zone at the retinal periphery, whereas the tectal germinal zone is U-shaped and surrounds only the posterior–dorsal–medial edges. Thus, as new optic fibers grow into the tectum, the terminals of the extant optic fibers must shift (i.e., break and remake their postsynaptic connections) to continually readjust the topographic map, with calculated rates of terminal arbor movement up to 5 μm per day in juvenile goldfish.[16,39]

Synaptic plasticity is now a well-recognized phenomenon in the brain, even in adult mammals, but the concept of postembryonic neurogenesis, and the existence of adult neural stem cells, has been embraced only more recently. This rediscovery has triggered an explosion of new research.[40] In contrast, ongoing neurogenesis in adult fish and amphibians, which is related to continued growth in body size, has been an established principle for decades, although this phenomenon has received scant experimental attention in recent years. With postembryonic neurogenesis, the visual system of juvenile–adult fish and amphibians exhibits a vigorous capacity for regeneration, which includes not only fiber regeneration (regrowth of the severed optic nerve and restoration of functional vision)[41–45] but also replacement of neurons in the retina and optic tectum following injury. This latter topic is described in the next section.

Neural Stem Cells and Injury-Induced Regeneration of Neurons

WHY STUDY NEURAL STEM CELLS IN FISH?

The phenomenon of postembryonic neurogenesis and the associated continuing capacity to regenerate neurons in the mature CNS is provoking a renewed interest awakened by the revelation that neural stem cells, defined as proliferating progenitors with the capacity to generate neurons, are present in the adult mammalian brain.[40,46,47] Understanding the growth and regenerative ability of the classic vertebrate (anamniote) models of neuronal regeneration might provide clues to unlocking the latent capabilities for regeneration of adult CNS that are normally dormant in adult mammals, including humans.

RETINAL REGENERATION

Classic Model: Urodele Amphibian Retina Regenerates by Transdifferentiation of the RPE

The urodele amphibians (newt–salamander) are the acknowledged champions of vertebrate tissue regeneration, as they have the ability to regenerate limbs, tails, jaws, hearts,[48] and in the eye, the lens and neural retina.[49,50] Studies of retinal regeneration in urodele amphibians began in the late eighteenth century (reviewed by Stone[51,52]). In the classic model, the eye was enucleated and then replaced in the orbit, causing the devascularized neural retina to degenerate, but after a few weeks, the retina regenerated and vision was restored (reviewed by Raymond and Hitchcock[53]). Neurogenesis in the ciliary marginal zone contributes to the functional recovery, by quickly generating an annulus of new retina, in an exaggeration of the normal growth process; this is not considered regeneration. However, in the central retina, differentiated RPE cells undergo transdifferentiation or metaplasia, involving several rounds of mitotic division, to recreate a neuroepithelium from which regenerated neural retina arises.[54] Numerous laboratories have provided convincing cellular and molecular evidence that RPE cells have the capacity to transdifferentiate and produce retinal neurons, although this capacity decreases with age of the animal (reviewed by Raymond and Hitchcock[53]). Transdifferentiation of the RPE into neural retinal tissue that expresses retinal-specific markers has also been described in chick in response to fibroblast growth factor-2, but the retinal regenerate in this instance is improperly polarized (the retinal ganglion cells are at the outer surface and the photoreceptors project into the vitreous); therefore, it is not likely to be functional (reviewed by Raymond and Hitchcock[53]).

Retinal Stem Cells in Teleost Fish

Like amphibians, teleost fish have the ability to regenerate a functional retina following surgical or chemical injury,[55–60] but replacement of retinal neurons is not through transdifferentiation of RPE.[61] Recent work has demonstrated that residual neuronal progenitor cells sequestered in the inner retina, which in the intact retina are restricted to the rod photoreceptor lineage, have the latent ability to produce all types of retinal neurons, and this capacity is unleashed following retina injury (reviewed by Otteson and Hitchcock,[26] Raymond and Hitchcock,[53,64] Raymond,[62] and Hitchcock and Raymond[63]).

Following retinal injury, mitotic activity is enhanced in the differentiated regions of the retina as well as in the circumferential germinal zone at the retinal margin.[55–57,60–61,65–69] In the case of surgical lesions or laser-induced photocoagulation of defined areas within the laminated retina, a blastema formed at the wound margins is derived from a local source of proliferating cells and not from the germinal zone at the margin, which is hundreds of micrometers away.[70] Following widespread cytochemical or photopic retinal destruction, foci of mitotic cells in the inner nuclear layer (INL) associated with radial Müller glial fibers appear across the retina.[57–60,65,71–76] The injury-induced mitogenic response of the intrinsic retinal progenitors in trout retinas is mimicked by intraocular injection of ciliary neurotrophic factor.[75] The proliferating neurogenic clusters in the injured retina have the cytoarchitecture and gene expression patterns of the retinal progenitors in the circumferential germinal zone and in the embryonic neuroepithelium, including *Vsx1, Pax6,* and *Notch3.*[75,77–79] Over the next several weeks, the missing neurons are regenerated in an orderly progression that mimics embryonic development.[60,72,76]

Certain constraints limit retinal regeneration in fish, and an analysis of these limitations provides clues to the underlying cellular mechanisms. If the damage includes the layer of photoreceptors, then retinal neurons are restored, but if specific cytotoxic agents are used at doses that selectively target certain types of retinal neurons (e.g., 6-hydroxydopamine to destroy dopaminergic neurons), then the deleted cells are not replaced.[73,74,80] However, if the lesion is confined to the layer of photoreceptors (accomplished with a photocoagulating laser burn in which heat radiates from the primary site of photon absorption in the RPE), then cone photoreceptors are replaced followed by rod photoreceptors (normally added by proliferating rod precursors even in the intact retina).[72,76] These observations are consistent with the inference that the injury-induced neurogenic clusters recreate a focal site of undifferentiated neuroepithelium (comparable to the retinal anlagen in the embryonic retina or the circumferential germinal zone) and that the progenitor cells require contact with the OLM (equivalent to the ventricular surface) to adopt a multipotent lineage—in other words, a primitive ventricular zone is reestablished to recreate the sequence of retinal neurogenesis.

The slowly proliferating cells in the INL associated with Müller glia in the fish retina have all the characteristics of retinal stem cells.[22,26,53] They are rare, mitotically quiescent, or slowly dividing cells; they generate rapidly proliferating progeny (often referred to as transit amplifying cells) with limited mitotic capacity and restricted cell lineage; they have a latent multipotent capacity to generate all the cell types in the tissue in response to injury; and they have a molecular profile similar to multipotent progenitors in the embryonic tissue.[40,46,47,81–84]

An intriguing possibility under investigation is that the radial Müller glia of the teleost fish retina function as stem cells.[76] A few reports describe persistent proliferating cells in the INL of larval *Xenopus laevis,*[85] which express cell surface molecules *(Notch* and *Delta)* important for determining the cell fate choice of retinal progenitors—that is, whether to differentiate as Müller glia or as retinal neurons.[86,87] These cells have been implicated in the regeneration of the retina in *Xenopus* tadpoles following small surgical lesions.[88] Müller glia are among the last retinal cells to differentiate, and in all vertebrate retinas they retain the capacity for mitotic activity in response to injury.[89–98] The recent realization that neural stem cells in embryonic and adult mammalian brains express molecular and cytologic characteristics of radial glia or astrocytes[46,99–103] suggests that Müller glia should be considered retinal stem cell candidates.

REGENERATION OF THE OPTIC TECTUM

Beginning in the 1960s, a series of papers described sites of proliferation, called *matrixzonen,* in the brains of juvenile and adult fish.[104–106] These sites of cell proliferation were presumed to be remnants of the so-called matrix layer[107] of the embryonic neuroepithelium that persisted in localized regions of the adult brain, always adjacent to the ventricle, after neuronal differentiation was essentially completed. These sites of cell proliferation (now called germinal zones) are implicated in the regeneration of brain structures, a capacity present in all animals during embryonic stages, lost in most animals as development progresses, but retained in some adult animals (fish and urodele amphibians).[108–113]

Several studies in teleost fish have shown that mitotic activity in the germinal zones of the optic tectum is enhanced after traumatic lesions of the adjacent brain tissue. In many cases, the lesion was a stab wound in central tectum, and reconstitution of the normal cytoarchitecture was preceded by the appearance of a column of undifferentiated cells arising from the deep layers of the tectum.[108,109,111,112] These proliferating cells displaced the phagocytic cells and degenerating debris that initially filled the wound; over several months the column of cells gradually dispersed, and the normal cytoarchitecture was eventually reestablished. In some cases, regeneration occurred following more extensive lesions that removed parts of the tectum, but the regenerative response required that the germinal zone located at the posterior–dorsal–medial borders of the optic tectum remained intact.[108,109] Regeneration was always associated with an increase in the rate of mitotic activity in the germinal zone.[108,109,111,112] Even in fish, the capacity for regeneration of brain structures diminishes greatly with increased age,[108,109] and this is associated with shrinkage of and decreased proliferative activity in the germinal zones.[111–113]

Recovery of Function Following Retinal and Optic Tectum Regeneration

RESTORATION OF VISION BY THE REGENERATED RETINA

The cellular and synaptic anatomy of the regenerated fish retina has been examined quantitatively in several studies, which showed that the normal cytoarchitecture is largely restored, including synaptic density and the regular mosaic pattern of dopaminergic retinal neurons.[114–116] The only feature of retinal organization that is not recreated is the regular spatial pattern of the spectral types of cone photoreceptors.[66,67,72,117–119]

Few studies have examined the recovery of functional vision following retinal regeneration, and these have all used the adult goldfish as a model system. The optic tectum is reinnervated by optic fibers from regenerated retinal ganglion cells, and a visuomotor reflex (optokinetic nystagmus) returns within a few months.[120,121] Components of the electroretinogram reappear sequentially as the retina regenerates, and although the waveform and spectral sensitivity approached normal values after several months, the amplitude remained below normal.[122,123] The pattern of recovery of electroretinogram function was similar to that described previously for the regenerated newt retina.[124,125]

BEHAVIORAL RECOVERY FOLLOWING TECTAL REGENERATION

Following lesions to the optic tectum in goldfish, various motor disturbances were seen, typically associated with sustained body flexure, circling movements, or both.[108] The progress of histologic regeneration (described previously) was correlated with a return of behavioral function, and the abnormal movements generally diminished in severity as the volume of the regenerate increased. It is unclear whether any of these behaviors required visual input.

Summary

The brevity of the preceding description on the functional recovery of vision following regeneration of the retina and the central visual targets in fish and amphibians, and the lack of current references, reveals this to be a largely neglected area of research. This is unfortunate, as the historic evidence clearly demonstrates that much could be learned from more detailed studies of neuronal regeneration in the CNS of fish and amphibians using modern techniques of molecular biology and genetics. This information could provide important insights into the potentials and limitations for future therapeutic applications of regenerative medicine.

ACKNOWLEDGMENTS

Some parts of the preceding text were adapted from an unpublished manuscript written several years ago in collaboration with the late W. Maxwell Cowan. Stephen S. Easter, Jr., provided translations from Italian of publications by F. Lombardo, and Karen Chalmers and Roswitha Lugauer provided translations from German of publications by W. Kirsche, H. Müller, H. Rahmann, and W. Richter. The author has published previously as P.R. Johns.

REFERENCES

1. Chow, R.L., and Lang, R.A. (2001). Early eye development in vertebrates. *Annu. Rev. Cell Dev. Biol.* **17,** 255–296.
2. Chuang, J.C., and Raymond, P.A. (2002). Embryonic origin of the eyes in teleost fish. *Bioessays* **24,** 519–529.
3. Arendt, D., and Wittbrodt, J. (2001). Reconstructing the eyes of Urbilateria. *Philos. Trans. R. Soc. Lond. B. Biol. Sci.* **356,** 1545–1563.
4. Meller, K., and Tetzlaff, W. (1976). Scanning electron microscopic studies on the development of the chick retina. *Cell Tiss. Res.* 145–170.
5. Fujita, S., and Hori, M. (1963). Analysis of cytogenesis in chick retina by 3H-thymidine autoradiography. *Arch. Histol. Cytol.* **23,** 359–366.
6. Sidman, R.L. (1960). Histogenesis of mouse retina studied with thymidine-H3. *In* "The Structure of the Eye," (G.K. Smelser, ed.), pp. 487–506. Academic Press, New York.
7. Easter, S.S., Jr. (2000). Let there be sight. *Neuron* **27,** 193–195.
8. Livesey, F.J., and Cepko, C.L. (2001). Vertebrate neural cell-fate determination: lessons from the retina. *Nat. Rev. Neurosci.* **2,** 109–118.
9. Johns, P.R. (1977). Growth of the adult goldfish eye: III—Source of the new retinal cells. *J. Comp. Neurol.* **176,** 343–358.
10. Johns, P.R., Rusoff, A.C., and Dubin, M.W. (1979). Postnatal neurogenesis in the kitten retina. *J. Comp. Neurol.* **187,** 545–555.
11. Fischer, A.J., and Reh, T.A. (2000). Identification of a proliferating marginal zone of retinal progenitors in postnatal chickens. *Dev. Biol.* **220,** 197–210.
12. Müller, H. (1952). Bau und wachstum der netzhaut des guppy *(Lebistes reticulatus).* [Growth and development of the retina in the guppy *(Lebistes reticulatus).*] [In German]. *Zool. Jb.* **63,** 275–324.
13. Gaze, R., and Watson, W.E. (1968). Cell division and migration in the brain after optic nerve lesions. *In* "Growth of the Nervous System," (G.E.W. Wolstenholme *et al.,* eds.), pp. 53–67. Churchill, London.
14. Meyer, R. (1978). Evidence from thymidine labeling for continuing growth of retina and tectum in juvenile goldfish. *Exp. Neurol.* **59,** 99–111.
15. Easter, S.S. (1983). Postnatal neurogenesis and changing connections. *Trends Neurosci.* **6,** 53–56.
16. Raymond, P.A. (1986). Movement of retinal terminals in goldfish optic tectum predicted by analysis of neuronal proliferation. *J. Neurosci.* **6,** 2479–2488.
17. Perron, M., and Harris, W.A. (2000). Retinal stem cells in vertebrates. *Bioessays* **22,** 685–688.
18. Reh, T.A., and Fischer, A.J. (2001). Stem cells in the vertebrate retina. *Brain Behav. Evol.* **58,** 296–305.
19. Johns, P.R., and Fernald, R.D. (1981). Genesis of rods in teleost fish retina. *Nature* **293,** 141–142.
20. Johns, P.R. (1982). The formation of photoreceptors in larval and adult goldfish. *J. Neurosci.* **2,** 179–198.
21. Raymond, P.A. (1985). The unique origin of rod photoreceptors in the teleost retina. *Trends Neurosci.* **8,** 12–17.

22. Raymond, P.A., and Rivlin, P.K. (1987). Germinal cells in the goldfish retina that produce rod photoreceptors. *Dev. Biol.* **122,** 120–138.
23. Fernald, R.D. (1989). Retinal rod neurogenesis. *In* "Development of the Vertebrate Retina," (B.L. Finlay *et al.,* eds.), pp. 31–42. Plenum, New York.
24. Julian, D., Ennis, K., and Korenbrot, J.I. (1998). Birth and fate of proliferative cells in the inner nuclear layer of the mature fish retina. *J. Comp. Neurol.* **394,** 271–282.
25. Otteson, D.C., D'Costa, A.R., and Hitchcock, P.F. (2001). Putative stem cells and the lineage of rod photoreceptors in the mature retina of the goldfish. *Dev. Biol.* **232,** 62–76.
26. Otteson, D.C., and Hitchcock, P.F. (2003). Stem cells in the teleost retina: persistent neurogenesis and injury-induced regeneration. *Vis. Res.* **43,** 927–936.
27. Easter, S.S., Johns, P.R., and Baumann, L.R. (1977). Growth of the adult goldfish eye: I—Optics. *Vis. Res.* **17,** 469–477.
28. Raymond, P.A., Hitchcock, P.F., and Palopoli, M.F. (1988). Neuronal cell proliferation and ocular enlargement in Black Moor goldfish. *J. Comp. Neurol.* **276,** 231–238.
29. Powers, M.K., Bassi, C.J., Rone, L.A., and Raymond, P.A. (1988). Visual detection by the rod system in goldfish of different sizes. *Vis. Res.* **28,** 211–221.
30. LaVail, J., and Cowan, W.M. (1971). The development of the chick optic tectum: II—Autoradiographic studies. *Brain Res.* **28,** 421–441.
31. Straznicky, K., and Gaze, R. (1972). Development of the optic tectum in *Xenopus laevis:* an autoradiographic study. *J. Embryol. Exp. Morphol.* **26,** 87–115.
32. Currie, J., and Cowan, W.M. (1974). Some observations on the early development of the optic tectum in the frog *(Rana pipiens)* with special reference to the effects of early eye removal on mitotic activities in the larval tectum. *J. Comp. Neurol.* **156,** 123.
33. Crossland, W., and Uchwat, C. (1982). Neurogenesis in the central visual pathways of the golden hamster. *Dev. Brain Res.* **5,** 99–103.
34. Raymond, P.A., and Easter, S.S., Jr. (1983). Postembryonic growth of the optic tectum in goldfish: I—Location of germinal cells and numbers of neurons produced. *J. Neurosci.* **3,** 1077–1091.
35. Cowan, W.M., Martin, A.H., and Wenger, E. (1968). Mitotic patterns in the optic tectum of the chick during normal development and after early removal of the optic vesicle. *J. Exp. Zool.* **169,** 71, 92.
36. Eichler, V. (1971). Neurogenesis in the optic tectum of larval *Rana pipiens* following unilateral enucleation. *J. Comp. Neurol.* **141,** 375, 396.
37. Schmatolla, F., and Erdmann, G. (1973). Influence of retinotectal innervation on cell proliferation and cell migration in the embryonic teleost tectum. *J. Embryol. Exp. Morphol.* **29,** 697–712.
38. Raymond, P.A., Easter, S.S., Burnham, J.A., and Powers, M.K. (1983). Postembryonic growth of the optic tectum in goldfish: II—Modulation of cell proliferation by retinal fiber input. *J. Neurosci.* **3,** 1092–1099.
39. Easter, S.S., and Stuermer, C.A. (1984). An evaluation of the hypothesis of shifting terminals in goldfish optic tectum. *J. Neurosci.* **4,** 1052–1063.
40. Temple, S. (2001). The development of neural stem cells. *Nature* **414,** 112–117.
41. Sperry, R.W. (1955). Functional regeneration in the optic system. *In* "Regeneration in the CNS," (W.F. Windle, ed.), p. 66–76. Thomas, Springfield, IL.
42. Aurora, H.L., and Sperry, R.W. (1963). Color discrimination after optic nerve regeneration in the fish, *Astronotus ocellatus. Dev. Biol.* **7,** 234–243.
43. Sperry, R.W. (1963). Chemoaffinity in the orderly growth of nerve fiber patterns and connections. *Proc. Natl. Acad. Sci. U. S. A.* **50,** 703–710.
44. Sperry, R.W. (1974). Optic nerve regeneration with return of vision in anurans. *J. Neurophysiol.* **7,** 57–69.
45. Easter, S.S., Jr. (1986). Rules of retinotectal mapmaking. *Bioessays* **5,** 158–162.
46. Alvarez-Buylla, A., Garcia-Verdugo, J.M., and Tramontin, A.D. (2001). A unified hypothesis on the lineage of neural stem cells. *Nat. Rev. Neurosci.* **2,** 287–293.
47. Panchision, D.M., and McKay, R.D. (2002). The control of neural stem cells by morphogenic signals. *Curr. Opin. Genet. Dev.* **12,** 478–487.
48. Tanaka, E.M. (2003). Regeneration: if they can do it, why can't we? *Cell* **113,** 559–562.
49. Kodama, R., and Eguchi, G. (1995). From lens regeneration in the newt to *in vitro* transdifferentiation of vertebrate pigmented epithelial cells. *Semin. Cell Biol.* **6,** 143–149.
50. Mitashov, V.I. (1996). Mechanisms of retina regeneration in urodeles. *Int. J. Dev. Biol.* **40,** 833–844.
51. Stone, L.S. (1950). The role of retinal pigment cells in regenerating neural retinae of adult salamander eyes. *J. Exp. Zool.* **113,** 9–31.
52. Stone, L.S. (1950). Neural retina degeneration followed by regeneration from surviving pigment cells in grafted adult salamander eyes. *Anat. Rec.* **106,** 89–110.
53. Raymond, P.A., and Hitchcock, P.F. (2000). How the neural retina regenerates. *In* "Vertebrate Eye Development," (M.E. Fini, ed.), Vol. 31, pp. 197–218. Springer-Verlag, Berlin.
54. Okada, T.S. (1980). Cellular metaplasia or transdifferentiation as a model for retinal cell differentiation. *Curr. Top. Dev. Biol.* **16,** 349–380.
55. Lombardo, F. (1968). La rigenerazione della retina negli adulti di un teleosteo. [Regeneration of the retina in an adult teleost.] [In Italian]. *Accad. Lincei-Rendi. Sci. Fisic. Matemat. e Nat., Series 8* **45,** 631–635.
56. Lombardo, F. (1972). Andamento e localizzazione della mitosi durante la rigenerazione della retina di un teleosteo adulto. [Time course and localization of mitoses during regeneration of the retina in an adult teleost.] [In Italian]. *Accad. Lincei-Rendi. Sci. Fisic. Matemat. e Nat., Series 8* **53,** 323–327.
57. Maier, W., and Wolburg, H. (1979). Regeneration of the goldfish retina after exposure to different doses of ouabain. *Cell Tiss. Res.* **202,** 99–118.
58. Kurz-Isler, G., and Wolburg, H. (1982). Morphological study on the regeneration of the retina in the rainbow trout after ouabain-induced damage: evidence for dedifferentiation of photoreceptors. *Cell Tiss. Res.* **225,** 165–178.
59. Negishi, K., Teranishi, T., Kato, S., and Nakamura, Y. (1988). Immunohistochemical and autoradiographic studies on retinal regeneration in teleost fish. *Neurosci. Res. Suppl.* **8,** S43–S57.
60. Raymond, P.A., Reifler, M.J., and Rivlin, P.K. (1988). Regeneration of goldfish retina: rod precursors are a likely source of regenerated cells. *J. Neurobiol.* **19,** 431–463.
61. Knight, J., and Raymond, P. (1994). Retinal pigmented epithelium does not transdifferentiate in adult goldfish. *J. Neurobiol.* **27,** 447–456.
62. Raymond, P.A. (1991). Retinal regeneration in teleost fish. *Ciba Found. Symp.* **160,** 171–186.

63. Hitchcock, P.F., and Raymond, P.A. (1992). Retinal regeneration. *Trends Neurosci.* **15,** 103–108.
64. Raymond, P.A., and Hitchcock, P.F. (1997). Retinal regeneration: common principles but a diversity of mechanisms. *Adv. Neurol.* **72,** 171–184.
65. Negishi, K., Teranishi, T., Kato, S., and Nakamura, Y. (1987). Paradoxical induction of dopaminergic cells following intravitreal injection of high doses of 6-hydroxydopamine in juvenile carp retina. *Dev. Brain Res.* **33,** 67–79.
66. Cameron, D.A., and Easter, S.S. (1995). Cone photoreceptor regeneration in adult fish retina: phenotypic determination and mosaic pattern formation. *Vis. Neurosci.* **15,** 2255–2271.
67. Cameron, D.A. (2000). Cellular proliferation and neurogenesis in the injured retina of adult zebra fish. *Vis. Neurosci.* **17,** 789–797.
68. Negishi, K., Sugawara, K., Shinagawa, S., Teranishi, T., Kuo, C.H., and Takasaki, Y. (1991). Induction of immunoreactive proliferating cell nuclear antigen (PCNA) in goldfish retina following intravitreal injection with tunicamycin. *Dev. Brain Res.* **63,** 71–83.
69. Negishi, K., Stell, W.K., Teranishi, T., Karkhanis, A., Owusu-Yaw, V., and Takasaki, Y. (1991). Induction of proliferating cell nuclear antigen (PCNA)-immunoreactive cells in goldfish retina following intravitreal injection with 6-hydroxydopamine. *Cell. Mol. Neurobiol.* **11,** 639–659.
70. Hitchcock, P.F., Lindsey Myhr, K.J., Easter, S.S., Mangione-Smith, R., and Jones, D.D. (1992). Local regeneration in the retina of the goldfish. *J. Neurobiol.* **23,** 187–203.
71. Vihtelic, T.S., and Hyde, D.R. (2000). Light-induced rod and cone cell death and regeneration in the adult albino zebra fish *(Danio rerio)* retina. *J. Neurobiol.* **44,** 289–307.
72. Braisted, J.E., Essman, T.F., and Raymond, P.A. (1994). Selective regeneration of photoreceptors in goldfish retina. *Development* **120,** 2409–2419.
73. Braisted, J.E., and Raymond, P.A. (1992). Regeneration of dopaminergic neurons in goldfish retina. *Development* **114,** 913–919.
74. Braisted, J.E., and Raymond, P.A. (1993). Continued search for the cellular signals that regulate regeneration of dopaminergic neurons in goldfish retina. *Dev. Brain Res.* **76,** 221–232.
75. Faillace, M.P., Julian, D., and Korenbrot, J.I. (2002). Mitotic activation of proliferative cells in the inner nuclear layer of the mature fish retina: regulatory signals and molecular markers. *J. Comp. Neurol.* **451,** 127–141.
76. Wu, D.M., Schneiderman, T., Burgett, J., Gokhale, P., Barthel, L., and Raymond, P.A. (2001). Cones regenerate from retinal stem cells sequestered in the inner nuclear layer of adult goldfish retina. *Invest. Ophthalmol. Vis. Sci.* **42,** 2115–2124.
77. Levine, E.M., Hitchcock, P.F., Glasgow, E., and Schechter, N. (1994). Restricted expression of a new paired-class homeobox gene in normal and regenerating adult goldfish retina. *J. Comp. Neurol.* **348,** 596–606.
78. Hitchcock, P.F., Macdonald, R.E., VanDeRyt, J.T., and Wilson, S.W. (1996). Antibodies against *pax6* immunostain amacrine and ganglion cells and neuronal progenitors, but not rod precursors, in the normal and regenerating retina of the goldfish. *J. Neurobiol.* **29,** 399–413.
79. Sullivan, S.A., Barthel, L.K., Largent, B.L., and Raymond, P.A. (1997). A goldfish Notch-3 homologue is expressed in neurogenic regions of embryonic, adult, and regenerating brain and retina. *Dev. Genet.* **20,** 208–223.
80. Negishi, K., Teranishi, T., and Kato, S. (1985). Growth rate of a peripheral annulus defined by neurotoxic destruction in the goldfish retina. *Dev. Brain Res.* **20,** 291–295.
81. Gage, F.H. (1998). Stem cells of the central nervous system. *Curr. Opin. Neurobiol.* **8,** 671–676.
82. Alvarez-Buylla, A., and Temple, S. (1998). Stem cells in the developing and adult nervous system. *J. Neurobiol.* **36,** 105–110.
83. Momma, S., Johansson, C.B., and Frisén, J. (2000). Get to know your stem cells. *Curr. Opin. Neurobiol.* **10,** 45–49.
84. Tsai, R.Y., Kittappa, R., and McKay, R.D. (2002). Plasticity, niches, and the use of stem cells. *Dev. Cell* **2,** 707–712.
85. Taylor, J.S.H., Jack, J.L., and Easter, S.S. (1989). Is the capacity for optic nerve regeneration related to continued retinal ganglion cell production in the frog? A test of the hypothesis that neurogenesis and axon regeneration are obligatorily linked. *Eur. J. Neurosci.* **1,** 626–638.
86. Dorsky, R.I., Chang, W.S., Rapaport, D.H., and Harris, W.A. (1997). Regulation of neuronal diversity in the *Xenopus* retina by Delta signaling. *Nature* **385,** 67–70.
87. Perron, M., and Harris, W.A. (2000). Determination of vertebrate retinal progenitor cell fate by the Notch pathway and basic helix–loop–helix transcription factors. *Cell. Mol. Life Sci.* **57,** 215–223.
88. Levine, R.L. (1981). La régénérescence de la rétine chez *Xenopus laevis* [Regeneration of the retina in *Xenopus laevis.*] [In French]. *Rev. Can. Biol.* **40,** 19–27.
89. Laqua, H., and Machemer, R. (1975). Glial cell proliferation in retinal detachment (massive periretinal proliferation). *Am. J. Ophthalmol.* **80,** 602–618.
90. Bignami, A., and Dahl, D. (1979). The radial glia of Müller in the rat retina and their response to injury: an immunofluorescence study with antibodies to the glial fibrillary acidic (GFA) protein. *Exp. Eye Res.* **28,** 63–69.
91. Turner, D.L., and Cepko, C.L. (1987). A common progenitor for neurons and glia persists in rat retina late in development. *Nature* **328,** 131–136.
92. Ikeda, T., and Puro, D.G. (1995). Regulation of retinal glial cell proliferation by antiproliferative molecules. *Exp. Eye Res.* **60,** 435–443.
93. Seigel, G.M., Mutchler, A.L., and Imperato, E.L. (1996). Expression of glial markers in a retinal precursor cell line. *Mol. Vis.* **2,** 2 (April 24).
94. Ohnuma, S., Philpott, A., Wang, K., Holt, C.E., and Harris, W.A. (1999). p27Xic1, a Cdk inhibitor, promotes the determination of glial cells in *Xenopus* retina. *Cell* **99,** 499–510.
95. Dyer, M.A., and Cepko, C.L. (2000). Control of Muller glial cell proliferation and activation following retinal injury. *Nat. Neurosci.* **3,** 873–880.
96. Furukawa, T., Mukherjee, S., Bao, Z.Z., Morrow, E.M., and Cepko, C.L. (2000). Rax, Hes1, and Notch1 promote the formation of Muller glia by postnatal retinal progenitor cells. *Neuron* **26,** 383–394.
97. Hojo, M., Ohtsuka, T., Hashimoto, N., Gradwohl, G., Guillemot, F., and Kageyama, R. (2000). Glial cell fate specification modulated by the bHLH gene *Hes5* in mouse retina. *Development* **127,** 2515–2522.
98. Vetter, M.L., and Moore, K.B. (2001). Becoming glial in the neural retina. *Dev. Dyn.* **221,** 146–153.
99. Hartfuss, E., Galli, R., Heins, N., and Gotz, M. (2001). Characterization of CNS precursor subtypes and radial glia. *Dev. Biol.* **229,** 15–30.
100. Noctor, S.C., Flint, A.C., Weissman, T.A., Dammerman, R.S., and Kriegstein, A.R. (2001). Neurons derived from radial glial cells establish radial units in neocortex. *Nature* **409,** 714–720.

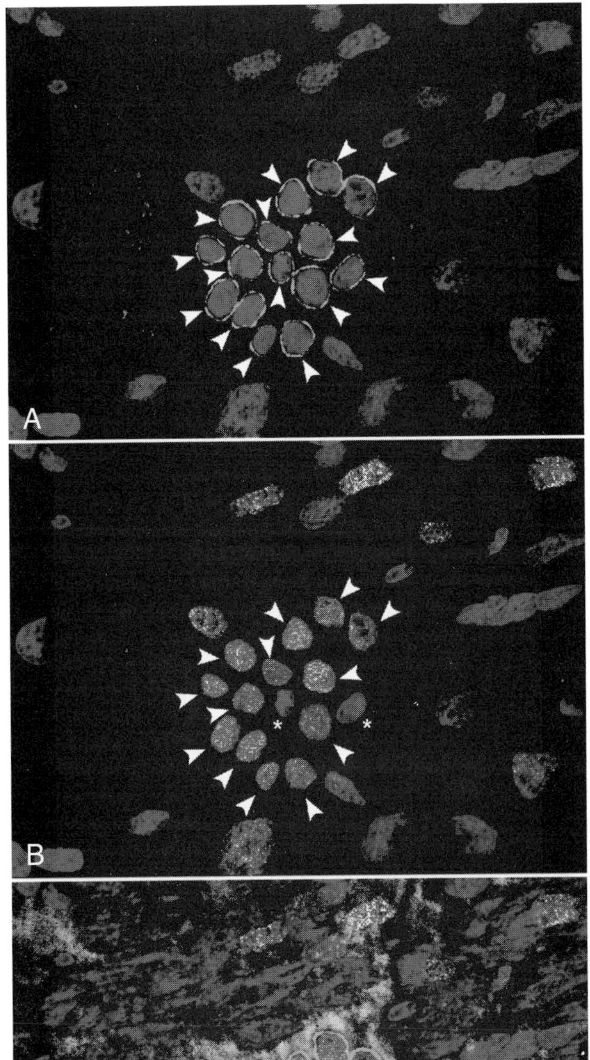

Figure 64–3. *Atrial niche in the adult rat heart.* (A) A cluster of 15 c-kit^{POS} cells (arrowheads), (B) 13 of which express GATA-4 (white). Asterisks indicate two GATA-4^{-} cells. (C) These cells are nested in fibronectin (white). Myocytes are identified by α-sarcomeric actin antibody staining (dark gray). Nuclei are labeled by propidium iodide (gray area inside cells). Confocal microscopy; scale bar = 10 μm. (Please see CD-ROM for color version of this figure.)

the renewal of the epidermis.[22] This region ensures good physical protection and is rich in melanin to prevent DNA damage induced by ultraviolet light.[22] Niches are present in all self-renewing organs.[21] Whether CSCs are dispersed in the myocardium or are nested in pockets with a structural organization typical of niches is an important question that was recently answered.[12] Qualitative and quantitative results indicate that CSCs are stored in niches, preferentially located in the atria and apex but also detectable in the ventricle (Fig. 64–3). The recognition that stem cells are clustered in specific regions of the heart exposed to moderate and minimal mechanical forces and that they are stored in niches favors the notion that these cells are organ specific. This possibility would speak against the view that stem cells in the myocardium are replenished by cells of bone marrow origin, which migrate chronically to the heart.

The concept of niches was introduced in 1978 by Schofield, who defined a niche as "a stable microenvironment that might control hematopoietic stem cell behavior."[23] Recently, the niche has been viewed as "a subset of tissue cells and extracellular substrates that can indefinitely house one or more stem cells and control their self-renewal and progeny production *in vivo*."[21] Stem cells, progenitors, precursors, and early differentiating cells are clustered in the niche and may be coupled through the expression of gap junctions.[24] Gap junctions are intercellular channels formed by individual structural units called connexins.[25] Gap junctions allow cells to communicate with each other and to exchange small molecules. In a manner similar to HSCs, CSCs may use gap junctions to transmit and receive signals for cell survival, proliferation, or differentiation.[24,25] Gap junctions could couple the CSCs among them with myocytes or adjacent cells that exert a support function similar to that of stromal cells in the bone marrow.[24] Data from our laboratory support this contention in the heart (Fig. 64–4). In summary, the localization of primitive cells in the myocardium is inversely related to the distribution of stress in the anatomic components of the heart.

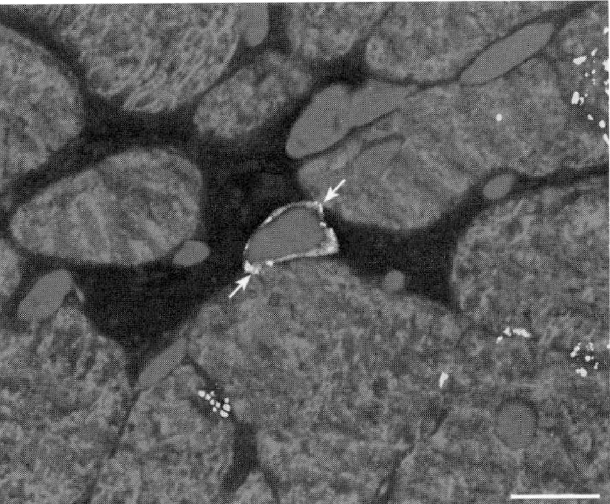

Figure 64–4. *C-kit^{POS} cell shows on the surface connexin 43.* C-kit^{POS} cell (light gray of membrane); connexin 43 (white spots). Connexin 43 is located between the primitive cell and a myocyte (arrows). Myocytes are identified by α-sarcomeric actin antibody staining (gray). Nuclei are labeled by propidium iodide (e.g., the dark area inside the c-kit). Confocal microscopy; scale bar = 10 μm. (Please see CD-ROM for color version of this figure.)

Repair of Myocardial Damage by Nonresident Primitive Cells

Major discoveries have been made concerning the biology of adult stem cells: First, they can differentiate into cell lineages distinct from the organ in which they reside and into cells derived from a different germ layer.[26–30] These properties were considered to be restricted to embryonic stem cells.[31] Second, adult stem cells can migrate to sites of injury, repairing damage in various organs.[30,32–35] Neural stem cells have been identified in selective regions of the brain[19,36,37] that, like the heart, was considered a postmitotic organ. Thus, adult stem cells may exist in other unexpected organs, and stem cell behavior is not dictated by the source.[35–38] HSCs can replace bone marrow and lymphoid organs by migrating to these sites across the vascular endothelium and along stromal pathways.[39] Moreover, HSCs regenerate skeletal muscle, and skeletal muscle stem cells can repopulate the bone marrow.[27,40,41] However, these particular skeletal muscle stem cells are of bone marrow origin.[40] HSCs can also differentiate in functioning hepatocytes.[30,42] Hematopoietic precursors, injected intravenously, reach the brain where they divide, infiltrate the entire organ, and produce the cell types of the CNS.[26,29,43,44] Conversely, CNS stem cells, which derive from the ectoderm, can transdifferentiate into blood cells, which generate from the mesoderm; HSCs can assume the characteristics of CNS cells. Together, this information supports the notion that injury to a target organ promotes alternate stem cell differentiation emphasizing the plasticity of these cells.[35,36,39,45] Recently, this became a controversial issue; it will be addressed later in this section. The controversy is because the early belief in stem cell transdifferentiation has prompted the use of bone marrow cells for the reconstitution of the infarcted myocardium. Additionally, this approach was considered superior to other forms of cellular therapy of the damaged heart.

In the last few years, effort has been made to restore function in the infarcted myocardium by transplanting cultured fetal myocytes or tissue, neonatal and adult myocytes, skeletal myoblasts, and bone marrow-derived immature cardiomyocytes.[3,6–8,12] When incorporation of the engrafted cells or tissue was successful, some improvement in ventricular performance occurred. However, these interventions failed to reconstitute healthy myocardium, integrated structurally and functionally with the spared portion of the wall. This defect was particularly evident with skeletal myoblasts, which did not express connexin 43, a surface protein responsible for the formation of ion channels and electric coupling between cells.[46,47] Moreover, the vascularization of the implants remained an unresolved issue. These problems pointed to the identification of new therapeutic strategies for the regeneration of dead myocardium. The generalized growth potential and differentiation of adult HSCs injected in the circulation or locally delivered in areas of injury suggested that these primitive cells sense signals from the lesion foci, migrating to these sites of damage. Subsequently, homed HSCs proliferate and differentiate, initiating growth processes resulting in the formation of all cellular components of the originally destroyed tissue. On this basis, a population of bone marrow cells enriched with Lin^{-}c-kit^{POS} cells was implanted into the viable myocardium in the proximity of an acute infarct.[48] This was done to facilitate the translocation of these cells to the necrotic region of the left ventricular wall, to reconstitute myocardium, and to interfere with healing and cardiac decompensation. In 9 days, numerous small cardiomyocytes and vascular structures developed within the infarcted zone and partially replaced the dead tissue (Fig. 64–5). The newly formed young myocardium expressed transcription factors required for myogenic differentiation, cardiac myofibrillar proteins, and connexin 43.[48] Coronary arterioles and capillaries were distributed within the regenerated portion of the left ventricle; these vessels were functionally connected with the primary coronary circulation. For the first time, bone marrow cells were shown to develop myocardium *in vivo,* reducing infarct size and ameliorating cardiac performance.

We now describe the role of cytokines and growth factors in the mobilization of stem cells and their translocation to damaged organs and to the heart in particular.[33,49] This issue is highly relevant clinically because its understanding may permit the application of strategies that do not require local implantation of exogenous stem cells or their preventive storage from the recipient patient. Two critical determinants seem to be necessary to obtain the maximal activation of the therapeutic potential of undifferentiated cells in organs from which they are not derived: organ damage and high levels of primitive cells in the circulation.[39,50] It has been shown that these two conditions are not always essential. Cell fate transition also has been observed in uninjured organs and following the

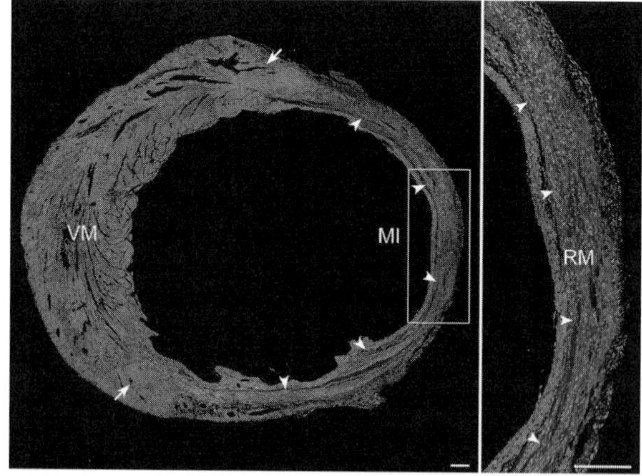

Figure 64–5. *Transverse section of an extensive myocardial infarct.* (A) Infarct was treated with the injection of bone marrow cells in the border zone (arrows). Nine days later, a band of regenerating myocardium was identified (arrowheads). (B) A portion of this band, included in the rectangle, is illustrated at higher magnification. Cardiac myosin heavy-chain labeling of myocyte cytoplasm and propidium iodide staining of nuclei are shown (VM: viable myocardium, MI: myocardial infarct, and RM: regenerating myocardium). Confocal microscopy; scale bar = 300 μm. From Orlic *et al.*,[48] with permission. (Please see CD-ROM for color version of this figure.)

use of a single bone marrow cell.[29,39,43,51] However, the degree of engraftment of individual cells is much lower and decreases further in unaffected tissues.[29,39,43,51] It is well established that stem cell factor and granulocyte colony-stimulating factor are powerful cytokines that markedly increase the number of circulating HSCs.[33] These mobilized cells can reconstitute the lymphohematopoietic system of lethally irradiated recipient mice, raising the likely possibility that, in the presence of myocardial infarction, they may home to the heart and follow a differentiation pathway that includes myocytes and coronary vessels. As anticipated, this protocol was very successful; tissue reconstitution included parenchymal cells and vascular profiles. Again, *de novo* myocardium was obtained and the repaired area of the wall was functionally competent, improving cardiac pump function and significantly attenuating the negative remodeling of the postinfarcted heart.[33]

Our results on myocardial regeneration after infarction using bone marrow cell implantation or cytokine administration do not address the critical issues of HSC plasticity and transdifferentiation.[35,37,52] Importantly, the hypothesis has been advanced that the donor stem cells might fuse with the parenchymal cells of the host tissue, giving the wrong appearance of transdifferentiation.[53–57] So far, the accumulated data indicate that the bone marrow contains cells capable of regenerating dead tissue, but the cell or cells in the bone marrow or the cytokine-mobilized cell or cells that have the potential of triggering a reparative response within the infarct has not been determined. Additionally, the contribution of cell fusion cannot be excluded. However, the size of newly formed myocytes is only 1/15 to 1/20 of the surrounding spared myocytes, and this factor argues against cell fusion. Similarly, the donor-derived cells divide rapidly, but tetraploid cells divide slowly and might not divide if the partner cell is a terminally differentiated cardiomyocyte.[3]

Repair of Myocardial Damage by Resident Primitive Cells

An important question to be raised concerns whether HSCs have to be considered the stem cells of choice for cardiac repair or whether resident CSCs could be selectively mobilized and, ultimately, employed to replace damaged myocardium. CSCs can be expected to be more effective than HSCs in rebuilding dead ventricular tissue. This is because HSCs have to reprogram themselves to produce progeny differentiating into cardiac cell lineages.[39,58] Such an intermediate phase is avoided by the direct activation and migration of CSCs to the site of injury. Moreover, CSCs may be capable of reaching in a short time functional competence and structural characteristics typical of mature myocytes and coronary vessels. It is intuitively apparent that the attraction of this concept and approach is its simplicity. Cardiac repair might be accomplished by merely enhancing the normal turnover of myocardial cells. Although this is a gray area, results in our laboratory have demonstrated that cell regeneration occurs throughout the life span of the heart and the organism.[1,59] This process continuously replaces old dying cells with new, younger, better-functioning units. Cell renewal is not restricted to parenchymal cells but involves all the cell populations of the heart. For example, the presence of CSCs has provided a logical explanation for the wide heterogeneity among myocytes in the adult ventricular myocardium.[59] Old hypertrophied myocytes are mixed with smaller, fully differentiated cells and cycling, amplifying myocytes.[1,3,59] The latter group of cells can create significant amounts of new myocardium by dividing rapidly and differentiating simultaneously until the adult phenotype has been reached.

Stem cells divide rarely, and committed transient amplifying cells are the actual group of replicating cells in self-renewing organs. The less primitive amplifying cells possess a unique property: They undergo rounds of doublings and simultaneously differentiate. Stem cells can divide symmetrically and asymmetrically. When stem cells divide symmetrically, two self-renewing daughter cells are formed. The purpose of this division is cell proliferation (i.e., expansion of the stem cell pool). When stem cells engage themselves in asymmetric division, one daughter-stem cell and one daughter-amplifying cell are obtained.[9] The objective of this division is cell differentiation (i.e., the production of committed progeny). Stem cells can also divide symmetrically into two committed amplifying cells, decreasing the number of primitive cells.[9]

CSCs undergo lineage commitment, and myocytes, smooth muscle cells, and endothelial cells are generated.[3,6,8,10,11–14,16] CSCs express c-Met and insulin-like growth factor-1 receptors (IGF-1R) and, thereby, can be activated and mobilized by hepatocyte growth factor (HGF) and IGF-1 (Fig. 64–6). *In vitro* mobilization and invasion assays have documented that the c-Met–HGF system is responsible for most of the locomotion of these primitive cells. However, the IGF-1–IGF-1R system is implicated in cell replication, differentiation, and survival.[13,60,61] These differential effects of HGF and IGF-1 on CSC motility and growth have been confirmed in *ex vivo,* oxygenated Tyrode's solution preparations of nonfixed, perfused, living myocardium by two-photon microscopy.[15] These observations have promoted a series of experiments in which primitive and progenitor cells have been mobilized from the site of storage in the atria to the infarcted ventricular myocardium in rodents.[13] The intense myocardial regeneration induced by this novel form of cellular therapy has been able to rescue animals with infarcts incompatible with life in any species studied so far. This includes mice, rats, dogs, and unquestionably humans.[11,13,14,62] The reconstituted infarcted ventricular wall is composed of contracting cells and blood-supplying coronary vessels, resembling the composition and characteristics of early postnatal myocardial tissue. Since the period for regeneration was very short, it is reasonable to assume that the formed parenchymal cells would develop with time into mature myocytes.[11,13,14]

As explained later in the section "Myocardial Regeneration in Humans," the transition from putative CSCs to cardiac progenitors, myocyte progenitors, precursors, and ultimately amplifying myocytes has been seen, with aspects resembling clonogenic growth, in the hypertrophied heart of patients with chronic aortic stenosis.[17] The identification of these forms of

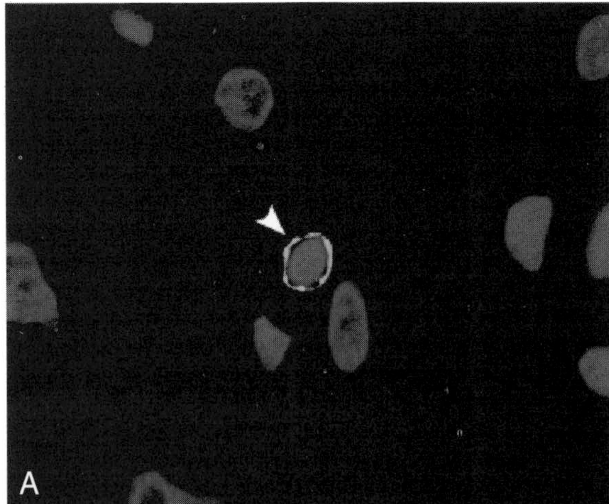

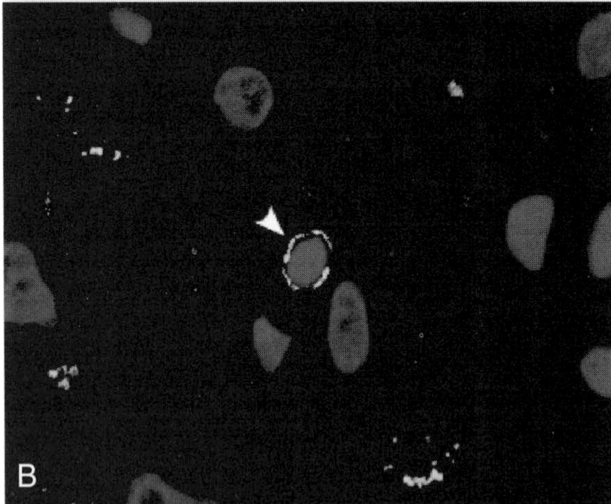

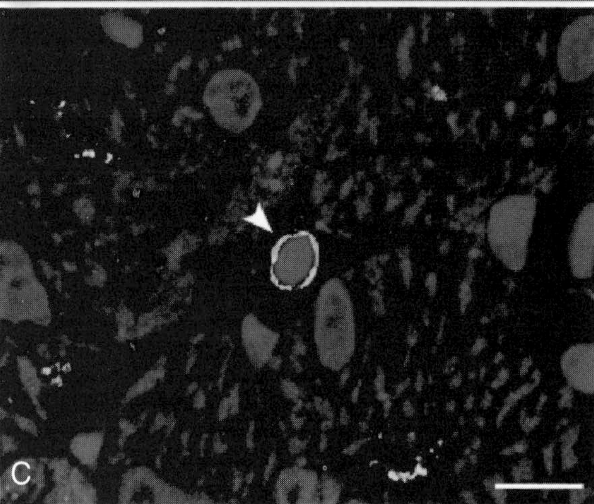

Figure 64–6. *C-kit^{POS} cell expresses IGF-1R. (A) C-kit^{POS}* cell (arrowhead), (B) IGF-1R (arrowhead), and (C) colocalization of c-kit and IGF-1R on the same cell (arrowhead). Myocytes are identified by α-sarcomeric actin antibody staining in panel C (gray). Nuclei are labeled by propidium iodide (e.g., the dark area inside the c-kit and IGF-1R). Confocal microscopy; scale bar = 10 μm. (Please see CD-ROM for color version of this figure.)

growth in humans was critical for the significance of the observations made in animal models.[63,64] The magnitude of growth in the pressure overloaded left ventricle exceeds the extent of cardiac regeneration detected in rodents and provides us with the first demonstration that the human heart can repair itself.[17] Thus, the heart is a self-renewing organ in which the replenishment of its parenchymal and nonparenchymal cells has to be regulated by a stem cell compartment and by the ability of these primitive cells to self-renew and differentiate. This is because regeneration conforms to a hierarchic archetype in which slowly dividing stem cells produce highly proliferating, lineage-restricted progenitor cells, which then become committed precursors that, eventually, reach growth arrest and terminal differentiation.[9]

In summary, primitive cells resident in the heart can be activated and translocated to damaged portions of the ventricle where, after homing, they initiate an extensive reparative process leading to the reconstitution of functioning myocardium supplied by newly formed vessels connected with the primary coronary circulation. This approach is superior to that obtained by the use of bone marrow cells because of its simplicity and immediate accessibility to the sites of stem cell storage in the heart. Additionally, the differentiation of cardiac primitive cells is rapid and does not require the reprogramming necessary for cells used to make blood into a state that would allow them to generate cardiac cell lineages.

Myocardial Regeneration in Humans

According to the dogma, ventricular myocytes in human beings are terminally differentiated cells and their life span corresponds to that of the individual. The number of myocytes reaches an adult value a few months after birth,[65] and the same myocytes are believed to contract 70 times per minute throughout life. Because a certain fraction of the population reaches 100 years of age or more, an inevitable consequence of the dogma is that cardiac myocytes are immortal functionally and structurally. This assumption contradicts the concept of cellular aging and programmed cell death and the logic of a slow turnover of cells with the progression of life in the mammalian heart. Conversely, several reports have provided unequivocal evidence that myocytes die and new ones constantly form in the normal human heart at all ages. Both processes are markedly enhanced in pathologic states, and the imbalance between cell growth (Fig. 64–7) and cell death may be an important determinant of the onset of ventricular dysfunction and its evolution to terminal failure and death of the organism.[3,7,8,59] Recent observations have indicated that the human heart contains a population of primitive cells prevalently located in the atria,[16] mimicking the results in rodents.[12,13] Through growth and differentiation, primitive cells contribute to the remodeling of the stressed heart by generating myocytes, coronary arterioles, and capillary profiles. These newly formed structures acquire the adult phenotype, are well integrated in the existing myocardium, and become indistinguishable from the preexisting tissue components. Such a phenomenon has been carefully

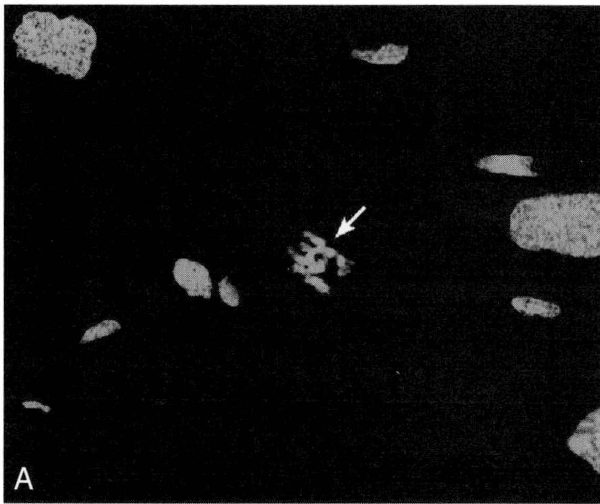

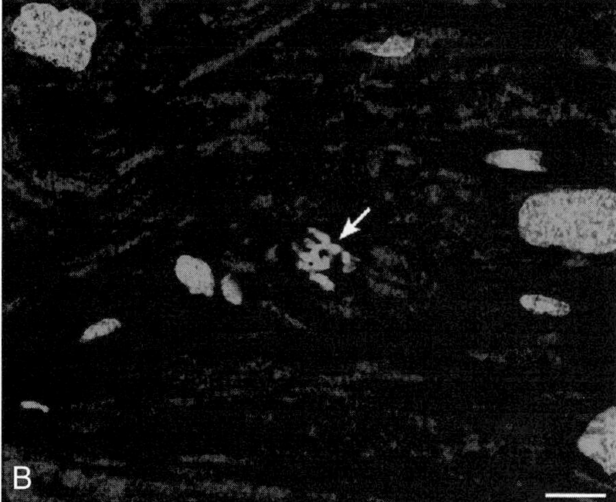

Figure 64–7. *Dividing myocyte in the left ventricle of a human heart affected by idiopathic dilated cardiomyopathy.* (A) Metaphase chromosomes are shown by propidium iodide (arrow and large gray structures). (B) The myocyte cytoplasm is stained by α-sarcomeric actin antibody (gray). Confocal microscopy; scale bar = 10 μm. (Please see CD-ROM for color version of this figure.)

documented in cardiac chimerism caused by the migration of primitive cells from the recipient to the grafted heart.[16]

A relevant issue is that the growth potential of the diseased human heart decreases in relation to the duration of the overload,[62] suggesting that primitive cells undergo lineage commitment and this process reduces the stem cell pool size. For example, a myocyte mitotic index of nearly 0.08% is detected in the surviving myocardium of the border zone acutely after infarction.[62,66] However, in postinfarction end-stage failure, this parameter becomes 0.015%.[67] Concurrently, myocyte death, apoptotic and necrotic in nature, markedly increases exceeding cell multiplication.[3,7,8,59] Therefore, the question concerns whether interventions can be applied locally to expand the stem cell compartment or whether this amplification has to be performed outside of the organ in culture systems. The latter is a less favorable strategy because it requires time and interferes with the urgency of therapy in most patients with advanced cardiac decompensation.

REFERENCES

1. Anversa, P., and Kajstura, J. (1998). Ventricular myocytes are not terminally differentiated in the adult mammalian heart. *Circ. Res.* **183,** 1–14.
2. MacLellan, W.R., and Schneider, M.D. (2000). Genetic dissection of cardiac growth control pathways. *Annu. Rev. Physiol.* **62,** 289–319.
3. Nadal-Ginard, B., Kajstura, J., Leri, A., and Anversa, P. (2003). Myocyte death, growth, and regeneration in cardiac hypertrophy and failure. *Circ. Res.* **92,** 139–150.
4. Oh, H., and Schneider, M.D. (2002). The emerging role of telomerase in cardiac muscle cell growth and survival. *J. Mol. Cell Cardiol.* **34,** 717–724.
5. Chien, K.R., and Olson, E.N. (2002). Converging pathways and principles in heart development and disease. *Cell* **110,** 153–162.
6. Anversa, P., Kajstura, J., Nadal-Ginard, B., and Leri, A. (2003). Primitive cells and tissue regeneration. *Circ. Res.* **92,** 579–582.
7. Nadal-Ginard, B., Kajstura, J., Anversa, P., and Leri A. (2003). A matter of life and death: cardiac myocyte apoptosis and regeneration. *J. Clin. Invest.* **111,** 1457–1459.
8. Anversa, P., and Leri, A. (2003). Myocardial regeneration. *In* "Heart Diseases." WB Saunders, Philadelphia. (In press).
9. Kondo, M., Wagers, A.J., Manz, M.G., Prohaska, S.S., Scherer, D.C., Beilhack, G.F., Shizuru, J.A., and Weissman, I.L. (2003). Biology of hematopoietic stem cells and progenitors: implications for clinical application. *Annu. Rev. Immunol.* **21,** 759–806.
10. Anversa, P., and Nadal-Ginard, B. (2002). Myocyte renewal and ventricular remodeling. *Nature* **415,** 240–243.
11. Beltrami, A.P., Barlucchi, L., Torella, D., Baker, M., Limana, F., Chimenti, S., Kasahara, H., Rota, M., Musso, E., Urbanek, K., Leri, A.; Kajstura, J., Nadal-Ginard, B., and Anversa, P., (2003). Adult cardiac stem cells are multipotent and support myocardial regeneration. *Cell* **144,** 763–776.
12. Cesselli, D., Kajstura, J., Jakoniuk, I., Urbanek, U., Kasahara, I., Nadal-Ginard, B., Quaini, F., Anversa, P., and Leri, A. (2002). Cardiac stem cells are nested in niches of the adult mouse heart and possess the ability to divide and differentiate in the various cardiac lineages. *Circulation* **106(Suppl II),** II-286.
13. Chimenti, S., Barlucchi, L., Limana, F., Jakoniuk, I., Cesselli, D., Beltrami, A.P., Mancarella, S., Castaldo, C., Nadal-Ginard, B., Leri, A., Kajstura, J., and Anversa, P. (2002). Local mobilization of resident cardiac primitive cells by growth factors repairs the infarcted heart. *Circulation* **106(Suppl II),** II-14.
14. Linke, A., Castaldo, C., Chimenti, S., Leri, A., Kajstura, J., Hintze, T.H., and Anversa, P. (2002). Mobilization of cardiac stem cells by growth factors promotes repair of infarcted myocardium improving regional and global cardiac function in conscious dogs. *Circulation* **106 (Suppl. 2),** 11–52.
15. Anversa, P. (2004). (Unpublished results).
16. Quaini, F., Urbanek, K., Beltrami A.P., Finato, N., Beltrami, C.A., Nadal-Ginard, B., Kajstura, J., Leri, A., and Anversa, P. (2002). Chimerism of the transplanted heart. *N. Engl. J. Med.* **346,** 5–15.
17. Urbanek, K., Quaini, F., Tasca, G., Torella, D., Castaldo, C., Nadal-Ginard, B., Leri, A., Kajstura, J., Quaini, E., and Anversa, P. (2003). Intense myocyte formation from cardiac stem cells in human cardiac hypertrophy. *Proc. Natl. Acad. Sci. U. S. A.* **100,** 10,440–10,445.

18. Ma, X., Ling, K.W., and Dzierzak, E. (2001). Cloning of the *Ly-6A (Sca-1)* gene locus and identification of a 3′ distal fragment responsible for high-level gamma-interferon-induced expression *in vitro*. *Br. J. Haematol.* **114,** 724–730.
19. Van Praag, H., Schinder, A.F., Christie, B.R., Toni, N., Palmer, T.D., and Gage, F.H. (2002). Functional neurogenesis in the adult hippocampus. *Nature* **415,** 1030–1034.
20. Suslov, O.N., Kukekov, V.G., Ignatova, T.N., and Steindler, D.A. (2002). Neural stem cell heterogeneity demonstrated by molecular phenotyping of clonal neurospheres. *Proc. Natl. Acad. Sci. U. S. A.* **99,** 14,506–14,511.
21. Spradling, A., Drummond-Barbosa, D., and Kai, T. (2001). Stem cells find their niche. *Nature* **414,** 98–104.
22. Watt, F.M., and Hogan, B.L.M. (2000). Out of Eden: stem cells and their niches. *Science* **287,** 1427–1438.
23. Schovfield, R. (1978). The relationship between the spleen colony-forming cell and the hemopoietic stem cells. *Blood Cell* **4,** 7–25.
24. Cancelas, J.A., Koevoet, W.L.M., de Koning, A.E., Mayen, A.E.M., Rombouts, E.J.C., and Ploemacher, R.E. (2000). Connexin-43 gap junctions are involved in multiconnexin-expressing stromal support of hemopoietic progenitors and stem cells. *Blood* **96,** 498–505.
25. Kumar, N.M., and Gilula, N.B. (1996). The gap junction communication channel. *Cell* **84,** 381–388.
26. Eglitis, M.A., and Mezey, E. (1997). Hematopoietic cells differentiate into both microglia and macroglia in the brains of adult mice. *Proc. Natl. Acad. Sci. U. S. A.* **94,** 4080–4085.
27. Ferrari, G., Cusella-DeAngelis, G., Coletta, M., Paolucci, E., Stornaiuolo, A., Cossu, G., and Mavilio, F. (1998). Muscle regeneration by bone marrow-derived myogenic progenitors. *Science* **279,** 1528–1530.
28. Bjornson, C.R., Rietze, R.L., Reynolds, B.A., Magli, M.C., and Vescovi, A.L. (1999). Turning brain into blood: a hematopoietic fate adopted by adult neural stem cells *in vivo*. *Science* **283,** 534–537.
29. Brazelton, T.R., Rossi, F.M., Keshet, G.I., and Blau, H.M. (2000). From marrow to brain: expression of neuronal phenotypes in adult mice. *Science* **290,** 1775–1779.
30. Lagasse, E., Connors, H., Al-Dhalimy, M., Reitsma, M., Dohse, M., Osborne, L., Wang, X., Finegold, M., Weissman, I.L., and Grompe, M. (2000). Purified hematopoietic stem cells can differentiate into hepatocytes *in vivo*. *Nat. Med.* **6,** 1229–1234.
31. Gepstein, L. (2002) Derivation and potential applications of human embryonic stem cells. *Circ. Res.* **91,** 866–876.
32. Fallon, J., Reid, S., Kinyamu, R., Opole, I., Opole, R., Baratta, J., Korc, M., Endo, T.L., Duong, A., Nguyen, G., Karkehabadhi, M., Twardzik, D., and Loughlin, S. (2000). *In vivo* induction of massive proliferation, directed migration, and differentiation of neural cells in the adult mammalian brain. *Proc. Natl. Acad. Sci. U. S. A.* **97,** 14,686–14,691.
33. Orlic, D., Kajstura, J., Chimenti, S., Limana, F., Jakoniuk, I., Quaini, F., Nadal-Ginard, B., Bodine, D.M., Leri, A., and Anversa, P. (2001). Mobilized bone marrow cells repair the infarcted heart, improving function and survival. *Proc. Natl. Acad. Sci. U. S. A.* **98,** 10,344–10,349.
34. Kocher, A.A., Schuster, M.D., Szabolcs, M.J., Takuma, S., Burkhoff, D., Wang, J., Homma, S., Edwards, N.M., and Itescu, S. (2001). Neovascularization of ischemic myocardium by human bone marrow-derived angioblasts prevents cardiomyocyte apoptosis, reduces remodeling, and improves cardiac function. *Nat. Med.* **7,** 430–436.
35. Avots, A., Harder, F., Schmittwolf, C., Petrovic, S., and Muller, A.M. (2002). Plasticity of hematopoietic stem cells and cellular memory. *Immunol. Rev.* **187,** 9–21.
36. Galli, R., Gritti, A., Bonfanti, L., and Vescovi, A.L. (2003). Neural stem cells: an overview. *Circ. Res.* **92,** 598–608.
37. Horner, P.J., and Gage, F.H. (2000). Regenerating the damaged central nervous system. *Nature* **407,** 963–970.
38. Forbes, S.J., Vig, P., Poulsom, R., Wright, N.A., and Alison, M.R. (2002). Adult stem cell plasticity: new pathways of tissue regeneration become visible. *Clin. Sci. (Lond).* **103,** 355–369.
39. Blau, H.M., Brazelton, T.R., and Weimann, J.M. (2001). The evolving concept of a stem cell: entity or function? *Cell* **105,** 829–841.
40. Jackson, K.A., Tiejuan, M., and Goodell, M.A. (1999). Hematopoietic potential of stem cells isolated from murine skeletal muscle. *Proc. Natl. Acad. Sci. U. S. A.* **96,** 14,482–14,486.
41. Mckinney-Freeman, S.L., Jackson, K.A., Camargo, F.D., Ferrari, G., Mavillo, F., and Goodell, M.A. (2002). Muscle-derived hematopoietic stem cells are hematopoietic in origin. *Proc. Natl. Acad. Sci. U. S. A.* **99,** 1341–1346.
42. Theise, N.D., Badve, S., Saxena, R., Henegariu, O., Sell, S., Crawford, J.M., and Krause, D.S. (2000). Derivation of hepatocytes from bone marrow cells in mice after radiation-induced myeloablation. *Hepatology* **31,** 235–240.
43. Mezey, E., Chandross, K.J., Harta, G., Maki, R.A., and McKercher, S.R. (2000). Turning blood into brain: cells bearing neuronal antigens generated *in vivo* from bone marrow. *Science* **290,** 1779–1782.
44. Mahmood, A., Lu, D., Wang, L., Li, Y., Lu, M., and Chopp, M. (2001). Treatment of traumatic brain injury in female rats with intravenous administration of bone marrow stromal cells. *Neurosurgery* **49,** 1196–1203.
45. LaBarge, M.A., and Blau, H. (2002). Biological progression from adult bone marrow to mononucleate muscle stem cell to multinucleate muscle fiber in response to injury. *Cell* **111,** 589–601.
46. Murray, C.E., Wiseman, R.W., Schwartz, S.M., and Hauschka, S.D. (1996). Skeletal myoblast transplantation for repair of myocardial necrosis. *J. Clin. Invest.* **98,** 2512–2523.
47. Taylor, D.A., Atkins, B.Z., Hungspreug, P., Jones, T.R., Reedy, M.C., Hutcheson, K.A., Glower, D.D., and Kraus, W.E. (1998). Regenerating functional myocardium: improved performance after skeletal myoblast transplantation. *Nat. Med.* **4,** 929–933.
48. Orlic, D., Kajstura, J., Chimenti, S., Jakoniuk, I., Anderson, S.M., Li, B., Pickel, J., McKay, R., Nadal-Ginard, B., Bodine, D.M., Leri, A., and Anversa, P. (2001). Bone marrow cells regenerate infarcted myocardium. *Nature* **410,** 701–705.
49. Gill, S.S., Patel, N.K., Hotton, G.R., O'Sullivan, K., McCarter, R., Bunnage, M., Brooks, D.J., Svendsen, C.N., and Heywood, P. (2003). Direct brain infusion of glial cell line-derived neurotrophic factor in Parkinson's disease. *Nat. Med.* **9,** 589–595.
50. Studer, L., Csete, M., Lee, S.H., Kabbani, N., Walikonis, J., Wold, B., and McKay, R. (2000). Enhanced proliferation, survival, and dopaminergic differentiation of CNS precursors in lowered oxygen. *J. Neurosci.* **20,** 7377–7383.
51. Krause, D.S., Theise, N.D., Collector, M.I., Henegariu, O., Hwang, S., Gardner, R., Neutzel, S., and Sharkis, S.J. (2001). Multiorgan, multilineage engraftment by a single bone marrow-derived stem cell. *Cell* **105,** 369–377.
52. Theise, N.D., and Krause, D.S. (2002). Toward a new paradigm of cell plasticity. *Leukemia* **16,** 542–548.

53. Terada, N., Hamazaki, T., Oka, M., Hoki, M., Mastalerz, D.M., Nakano, Y., Meyer, E.M., Morel, L., Petersen, B.E., and Scott, E.W. (2002). Bone marrow cells adopt the phenotype of other cells by spontaneous cell fusion. *Nature* **416,** 542–545.
54. Ying, Q.L., Nichols, J., Evans, E.P., and Smith, A.G. (2002). Changing potency by spontaneous fusion. *Nature* **416,** 545–548.
55. Spees, J.L., Olson, S.D., Ylostalo, J., Lynch, P.J., Smith, J., Perry, A., Peister, A., Wang, M.Y., and Prockop, D.J. (2003). Differentiation, cell fusion, and nuclear fusion during *ex vivo* repair of epithelium by human adult stem cells from bone marrow stroma. *Proc. Natl. Acad. Sci. U. S. A.* **100,** 2397–2402.
56. Vassilopoulos, G., Wang, P.R., and Russell, D.W. (2003). Transplanted bone marrow regenerates liver by cell fusion. *Nature* **422,** 901–904.
57. Wang, X., Willenbring, H., Akkari, Y., Torimaru, Y., Foster, M., Al-Dhalimy, M., Lagasse, E., Finegold, M., Olson, S., and Grompe, M. (2003). Cell fusion is the principal source of bone marrow-derived hepatocytes. *Nature* **422,** 897–901.
58. Lassar, A.B., and Orkin, S. (2001). Plasticity and commitment, developmental decisions in the life of a cell. *Curr. Opin. Cell. Biol.* **13,** 659–661.
59. Anversa, P., and Olivetti, G., (2002). Cellular basis of physiological and pathological myocardial growth. *In* "Handbook of Physiology," pp. 75–144. Oxford University Press, New York.
60. Li, Q., Li, B., Wang, X., Leri, A., Jana, K.P., Liu, Y., Kajstura, J., Baserga, R., and Anversa, P. (1997). Overexpression of insulin-like growth factor-1 in mice protects from myocyte death after infarction, attenuating ventricular dilation, wall stress, and cardiac hypertrophy. *J. Clin. Invest.* **100,** 1991–1999.
61. Li, B., Setoguchi, M., Wang, X., Andreoli, A.M., Leri, A., Malhotra, A., Kajstura, J., and Anversa, P. (1999). Insulin-like growth factor-1 attenuates the detrimental impact of nonocclusive coronary artery constriction on the heart. *Circ. Res.* **84,** 1007–1019.
62. Urbanek, K., Quaini, F., Bussani, R., Silvestri, F., Jakoniuk, I., Beltrami, A.P., Chimenti, C., Beltrami, C.A., Nadal-Ginard, B., Leri, A., Kajstura, J., and Anversa P. 2002. Cardiac stem cell growth and death differs in acute and chronic ischemic heart failure in humans. *Circulation* **106,** II–382.
63. Del Monte, F., Butler, K., Boecker, W., Gwathmey, J.K., and Hajjar, R.J. (2002). Novel technique of aortic banding followed by gene transfer during hypertrophy and heart failure. *Physiol. Genomics* **9,** 49–56.
64. Sadoshima, J., Montagne, O., Wang, Q., Yang, G., Warden, J., Liu, J., Takagi, G., Karoor, V., Hong, C., Johnson, G.L., Vatner, D.E., and Vatner, S.F. (2002). The MEKK1-JNK pathway plays a protective role in pressure overload but does not mediate cardiac hypertrophy. *J. Clin. Invest.* **110,** 271–279.
65. Arai, S., and Machida, A. (1972). Myocardial cell in left ventricular hypertrophy. *Tohoku J. Exp. Med.* **108,** 361–367.
66. Beltrami, A.P., Urbanek, K., Kajstura, J., Yan, S.M., Finato, N., Bussani, R., Nadal-Ginard, B., Silvestri, F., Leri, A., Beltrami, C.A., and Anversa, P. (2001). Evidence that human cardiac myocytes divide after myocardial infarction. *N. Engl. J. Med.* **344,** 1750–1757.
67. Kajstura, J., Leri, A., Finato, N., Di Loreto, C., Beltrami, C.A., and Anversa, P. (1998). Myocyte proliferation in end-stage cardiac failure in humans. *Proc. Natl. Acad. Sci. U. S. A.* **95,** 8801–8805.

65

Stem Cells for the Treatment of Muscular Dystrophy: More Than Wishful Thinking?

Maurilio Sampaolesi, M. Gabriella Cusella De Angelis, and Giulio Cossu

This chapter deals with the use of stem cells to treat muscular dystrophy. It reviews previous attempts at cell therapy in animal models and patients through the use of donor myoblasts, explaining the likely reasons for their failure. It then reports the identification of myogenic progenitors in the bone marrow and the related trials, this time in mice only, to treat dystrophy by bone marrow transplantation. It proceeds to describe recently identified stem cells in relationship to their ability to home within a dystrophic muscle and to differentiate into skeletal muscle cells. Different known features of various stem cells are compared in this perspective, and the few available examples of their use in murine models of dystrophy reported. On the basis of current knowledge and waiting for a rapid advance in stem cell biology, an audacious prediction of clinical translation for these cell therapy protocols is outlined.

Introduction

Muscular dystrophies are caused by progressive degeneration of skeletal muscle fibers. Lack of one of several proteins either at the plasma membrane[1] or, less frequently, within internal membranes[2] increases the probability of damage during contraction and eventually leads to fiber degeneration, although the molecular mechanisms are not yet understood in detail.[3,4] Fiber degeneration is counterbalanced by regeneration of new fibers at the expense of resident myogenic cells, located underneath the basal lamina and termed satellite cells.[5] Although satellite cells were considered the only cell endowed with myogenic potential,[6] evidence has accumulated showing that other progenitor cells may participate to muscle regeneration.[7] These latter cells are probably derived from distinct anatomic sites, such as the microvascular niche of the bone marrow, and reach skeletal muscle through the circulation and possibly with the incoming vessels. Balance between fiber degeneration and fiber regeneration dictates the cellular and the clinical outcome. In the most severe forms, such as Duchenne muscular dystrophy, regeneration is exhausted and skeletal muscle is progressively replaced by fat and fibrous tissue. This condition leads the patient to progressive weakness and eventual death by respiratory failure, cardiac failure, or both.

Current therapeutic approaches involve steroids and result in modest beneficial effects.[8] Novel experimental approaches[9] can be schematically grouped in three major areas. The first is gene therapy aiming at the production of new viral vectors (mainly Adeno, Adeno-associated, lenti, and herpes vectors) less antigenic and more efficient in transducing adult muscle fibers. Second, novel pharmacologic approaches focus on high-throughput screens for molecules that may interfere with pathogenetic pathways. The search should identify molecules that cause the skipping of the mutated exon[10] or up-regulate utrophin synthesis, a cognate protein that compensates for dystrophin absence when overexpressed in dystrophic mice.[11] The final group is cell therapy, based initially on myoblast transplantation and more recently on the transplantation of stem–progenitor cells. The recent identification of novel types of stem cells opens new perspectives for cell therapy, the topic of this chapter; however, the limited knowledge of stem cell biology is an obstacle that must be overcome to devise protocols with a significant prospect of clinical improvement in patients affected by severe forms of muscular dystrophy.

Myoblast Transplantation: Reasons for Failure

This field was opened by a pioneer study by Partridge *et al.*, who showed that intramuscular injection of C2C12 cells, an immortal myogenic cell line derived from adult satellite cells, would reconstitute with high efficiency dystrophin-positive, apparently normal fibers in dystrophic *mdx* mice.[12] This result caused immediate hopes for therapy that within few months led to several clinical trials in the early 1990s. Myogenic cells were isolated from immune-compatible donors, expanded *in vitro,* and injected in a specific muscle of the patient. These clinical trials failed (for a review, see Partridge[13]) for several reasons, some of which may have been predicted (at variance with C2, human myogenic cells do not have an unlimited life span and are not syngeneic between donor and host); others became apparent long after the start of the trials. For example, most injected cells (up to 99%) succumb first to an inflammatory response and then to an immune reaction[14] against donor cell antigens. Cells that survive do not migrate more than few millimeters from the injection site, indicating that innumerable injections should be performed to provide a homogeneous distribution

Handbook of Stem Cells
Volume 2

of donor cells. Even though donor myogenic cells can survive for a decade in the injected muscle,[15] the overall efficiency of the process soon made it clear that, although biologically interesting, this approach would have been clinically hopeless.

In the following years, the laboratory of Tremblay focused on these problems and in a stepwise manner produced a progressive increase in the survival success of injected myoblasts and in their colonization efficiency. Immune suppression and injection of neutralizing antibodies (directed against surface molecules of infiltrating cells such as LFA-1), pretreatment of myoblasts *in vitro* with growth factors, and modification of the muscle-connective tissue all contributed to this improvement.[16,17] Extension of this protocol to primates[18] has lead to a new clinical trial whose initial results have just been published.[18] On a parallel route, several laboratories, including our own, developed strategies to expand *in vitro* myoblasts from the patients, transduce them with viral vectors encoding the therapeutic gene, and inject them back in at least a few life-essential muscles of the patients from which they were initially derived. This approach would solve the problem of donor cell rejection but not that of an immune reaction against the vector and the therapeutic gene, a new antigen in genetic diseases. In this case, however, it soon became clear that it was difficult to produce an integrating vector that would accommodate the enormous cDNA of dystrophin. The generation of a microdystrophin (containing both protein ends but missing most of the internal exons) appears to have recently solved at least part of this problem.[19] However, the limited life span of myogenic cells isolated from dystrophic patients appeared as an even worse problem, and all the attempts to solve it, ranging from immortalization with oncogenes or telomerase to myogenic conversion of nonmyogenic cells, again produced biologically interesting but clinically inadequate results.[20–22]

Myogenic Stem Cells in the Bone Marrow and Bone Marrow Transplantation

The search for cells that may be converted to a myogenic phenotype led us to identify a cryptic myogenic potential in a large number of cells within the mesoderm, including the bone marrow. For these studies, we took advantage of a transgenic mouse expressing a nuclear *lacZ* under the control of muscle-specific regulatory elements (MLC3F-n*lacZ*) only in striated muscle.[23] Since direct injection into the muscle tissue is an inefficient and impractical cell delivery route, bone marrow–derived progenitors immediately appeared as a potential alternative to myoblasts and satellite cells, since they could be systemically delivered to a dystrophic muscle. To test this possibility, we transplanted MLC3F-n*lacZ* bone marrow into lethally irradiated *scid/bg* mice and, when reconstitution by donor bone marrow had occurred, induced muscle regeneration by cardiotoxin injection into a leg muscle *(tibialis anterior)*. Histochemical analysis unequivocally showed the presence of β-gal-staining nuclei at the center and periphery of regenerated fibers, demonstrating for the first time that murine bone marrow contains transplantable progenitors that can be recruited to an injured muscle through the peripheral circulation and can participate in muscle repair by undergoing differentiation into mature muscle fibers.[24] The publication of this report raised new interest in myogenic progenitors and in their possible clinical use. It was reasoned that, although the frequency of the phenomenon was low, in a chronically regenerating, dystrophic muscle, myogenic progenitors would have found a favorable environment and consequently would have contributed significantly to regeneration of dystrophin-positive normal fibers. This, however, turned out not to be the case. In the following year, the groups of Kunkel and Mulligan showed that *mdx* mice transplanted with the bone marrow side population, or SP (a fraction of the total cells separated by die exclusion and containing stem–progenitor cells able to repopulate the hematopoietic system upon transplantation[25]), of syngeneic C57BL/10 mice develop, within several weeks, a small number of dystrophin-positive fibers containing genetically marked (Y-chromosome) donor nuclei.[26] Even many months after the transplantation, the number of fibers carrying dystrophin and the Y-chromosome never exceeded 1% of the total fibers in the average muscle, thus precluding a direct clinical translation for this protocol. Similar results were later obtained in a slightly different animal model, the *mdx4cv* mutant by Ferrari *et al.*[27] Recently, retrospective analysis in a Duchenne patient that had undergone bone marrow transplantation confirmed the persistence of donor-derived skeletal muscle cells over many years, again at a low frequency.[28]

Reasons for this low efficiency may be: (1) the paucity of myogenic progenitors in the bone marrow; (2) inadequate transplantation, a procedure optimized for hematopoietic reconstitution; (3) insufficient signals to recruit myogenic progenitors from the bone marrow; (4) inadequate environment to promote survival, proliferation, differentiation, or a combination of these for these progenitors because of competition by resident satellite cells (that sustain regeneration for most of the *mdx* mouse life span) or because of an unfavorable environment created by inflammatory cells; and (5) difficulties in reaching regenerating fibers because of the increased deposition of fibrous tissue and the reduced vascular bed of the dystrophic muscle. Although in Duchenne muscular dystrophy patients regeneration by endogenous satellite cells is exhausted much earlier in life than in the mouse, and therefore muscle colonization by blood-borne progenitors may be different, the data by Gussoni *et al.*[28] suggests that in any case the process occurs with low frequency.

Multipotent Stem Cells in the Bone Marrow: What Can Be Expected from Them?

The bone marrow hosts several multipotent cells, which include hematopoietic stem cells (HSCs), mesenchymal stem cells (MSCs) and, recently added to the list, multipotent adult progenitor cells (MAPCs), endothelial progenitor cells (EPCs) and mesoangioblasts.

These cells are described in detail in different chapters of this book; here, we briefly review their features concerning their myogenic potential and consequently their possible use in preclinical models of muscular dystrophy.

HEMATOPOIETIC STEM CELLS

Up to very recently no data were available on the ability of purified HSC to differentiate into skeletal muscle, save the evidence presented by Gussoni *et al.* Of the myogenic potential of bone marrow SP cells, certainly not a pure population.[28]

When bone marrow was fractionated into CD45 positive and negative fractions, the muscle forming activity after bone marrow transplantation was associated with the $CD45^+$ fraction[29] suggesting that a myogenic potential is present in the hematopoietic stem cell itself or in a yet to be identified cell that however expresses several markers in common with true HSC. In the following 2 years, several reports have convincingly demonstrated that bone marrow SP cells can be recruited to dystrophic or regenerating muscle and differentiate into skeletal muscle cells upon exposure to differentiating muscle cells or in response to Wnt molecules secreted by recruiting cells; moreover a fraction of SP cells localizes in a position (between the basal lamina and the sarcolemma) typical of satellite cells and indeed expresses markers of satellite cells.[30–32] Moreover, circulating human AC133 positive cells differentiate into skeletal muscles *in vitro* and *in vivo* when injected into dystrophic immunodeficient mice.[33] Two papers recently provided final evidence that a single hematopoietic stem cell is able to reconstitute the hematopoietic system of a recipient mouse upon BMT and at the same time gives rise to a progeny that differentiates into skeletal muscle *in vivo*.[34,35] The two papers, however, disagree on the mechanism of such phenomenon: one, in agreement with previous data, identifies donor cells also as bona fide "satellite cells,"[34] the other fails to identify donor derived satellite cells and claims fusion of a myeloid intermediate progenitor to be the cause of differentiation. While further work will be required to solve this issue, the presence of a cryptic myogenic potential in true hematopoietic stem cells suggest that it should be possible to import a huge amount of knowledge from both experimental and clinical hematology toward the design of clinical protocols for muscular dystrophy. Still additional steps would have to be devised since we already know that bone marrow transplantation is likely to be insufficient to ameliorate the dystrophic phenotype. Specifically, homing of progenitor cells to muscle would have to be stimulated since HSC naturally home to the bone marrow and, equally important, HSC would have to be directed to a myogenic fate with much higher efficiency than what is currently observed. Transient expression of leukocyte adhesion proteins and inducible expression of MyoD may be steps in this direction.

MESENCHYMAL STEM CELLS

Initially identified by Friedenstein *et al.*,[36] MSCs, mainly originating from pericytes, are located in the perivascular district of the bone marrow stroma and are the natural precursors of bone, cartilage, and fat, the constituent tissues of the bone.[37]

Although MSCs were reported to produce myotubes in culture upon induction with 5-azacytidine,[38] they do not differentiate into muscle under normal conditions.[39] When transplanted in sheep fetus *in utero,* human MSCs colonized most tissues, including skeletal muscle, although their effective muscle differentiation was not demonstrated.[40] Even though MSCs can be easily expanded *in vitro,* they are not currently considered among the best candidates in protocols aimed at reconstituting skeletal muscle in primary myopathies.

ENDOTHELIAL PROGENITOR CELLS

Initially identified as $CD34^+$, Flk-1^+ circulating cells,[41] EPCs were shown to be transplantable and to participate actively to angiogenesis in a variety of physiologic and pathologic conditions.[42] *In vitro* expansion of EPCs is still problematic, and few laboratories have succeeded in optimizing this process. The clear advantage of EPCs would be their natural homing to the site of angiogenesis that would target them to the site of muscle regeneration. However, their ability to differentiate into skeletal muscle has not been tested.

MULTIPOTENT ADULT PROGENITOR CELLS

The group of Verfaillie[43] recently identified a rare cell within MSC cultures from human or rodent bone marrow: the MAPC. This cell can be expanded for more than 150 population doublings and differentiates not only into mesenchymal lineage cells but also endothelium, neuroectoderm, and endoderm. Similar cells can be selected from mouse muscle and brain, suggesting that they may be associated with the microvascular niche of probably many if not all tissues of the mammalian body.[44] Furthermore, when injected into a blastocyst, MAPCs colonize all the tissues of the embryo, with a frequency comparable to that of ES cells.[45] Because of their apparently unlimited life span and multipotency, MAPCs appear to be obvious candidates for many cell replacement therapies, although complete differentiation into the desired cell type still needs to be optimized. As concerns skeletal muscle, neither the frequency at which MAPCs differentiate into skeletal muscle cells after azacytidine treatment nor attempts to optimize this process have been reported. In addition, the ability of MAPCs to travel through the body using the circulatory route has not been formally demonstrated, although the general features of these cells strongly suggest this to be the case. It will be interesting to see whether MAPCs may restore a normal phenotype in mouse models of muscular dystrophy.

MESOANGIOBLASTS

Searching for the origin of the bone marrow cells that contribute to muscle regeneration,[24] we identified, by clonal analysis, a progenitor cell derived from the embryonic aorta that shows similar morphology to adult satellite cells and expresses several myogenic and endothelial markers expressed by satellite cells. *In vivo* aorta-derived myogenic progenitors participate in muscle regeneration and fuse with resident satellite cells.[46] The transient expression of endothelial markers in satellite cells (VE-cadherin, VEGFR2, etc.) was unpredicted at the time, but later, clonal analysis *in vivo* by retroviral labeling confirmed the existence of bipotent endothelial–skeletal myogenic progenitors in the avian embryos.[47] To test the role of these progenitors *in vitro,* we grafted quail or mouse embryonic aorta into host chick embryos. Donor cells, initially incorporated into the host vessels, were later integrated into mesoderm tissues, including bone marrow, cartilage, bone, smooth, skeletal, and cardiac muscle. When expanded on a feeder layer of embryonic fibroblasts, the clonal progeny of a single cell from the mouse dorsal aorta acquires unlimited life span, expresses hemangioblastic markers (CD34, Sca-1, and Thy-1), and maintains multipotency in culture or when transplanted into a chick embryo. We concluded that these newly identified, vessel-associated stem cells, the mesoangioblasts, participate in postembryonic development of the mesoderm, and we speculated that postnatal mesodermal stem cells may be rooted in a vascular developmental origin.[48]

In as much as mesoangioblasts can be expanded indefinitely, are able to circulate, and are easily transduced with lentiviral vectors, they appeared as a potential novel strategy for the cell therapy of genetic diseases. In principle, mesoangioblasts can be derived from the patient, expanded and transduced *in vitro,* and then reintroduced into the arterial circulation leading to colonization of the downstream tissues. In the past few months, we succeeded in isolating mesoangioblasts from juvenile tissues of the mouse and from human fetal vessels. Attempts to isolate the same cells from postnatal human vessels are in progress.

When injected into the blood circulation, mesoangioblasts accumulate in the first capillary filter they encounter and are able to migrate outside of the vessel, but only in the presence of inflammation, as in the case of dystrophic muscle. We thus reasoned that if these cells were injected into an artery, they would accumulate in the capillary filter and from there in the interstitial tissue of downstream muscles. Indeed, intra-arterial delivery of wild-type mesoangioblasts in the α-sarcoglycan knockout mouse, a model for limb-girdle muscular dystrophy,[49] corrects morphologically and functionally the dystrophic phenotype of all the muscle downstream of the injected vessel (Fig. 65–1).

Furthermore, mesoangioblasts, isolated from small vessels of juvenile (P15) α-sarcoglycan null mice, were transduced with a lentiviral vector expressing the α-sarcoglycan–enhanced green fluorescent protein fusion protein, injected into the femoral artery of null mice, and reconstituted skeletal muscle similarly to wild-type cells. These data represent the first successful attempt to treat a murine model of limb-girdle myopathy with a novel class of autologous stem cells. Widespread distribution through the capillary network is the distinct advantage of this strategy over alternative approaches of cell or gene therapy.[50]

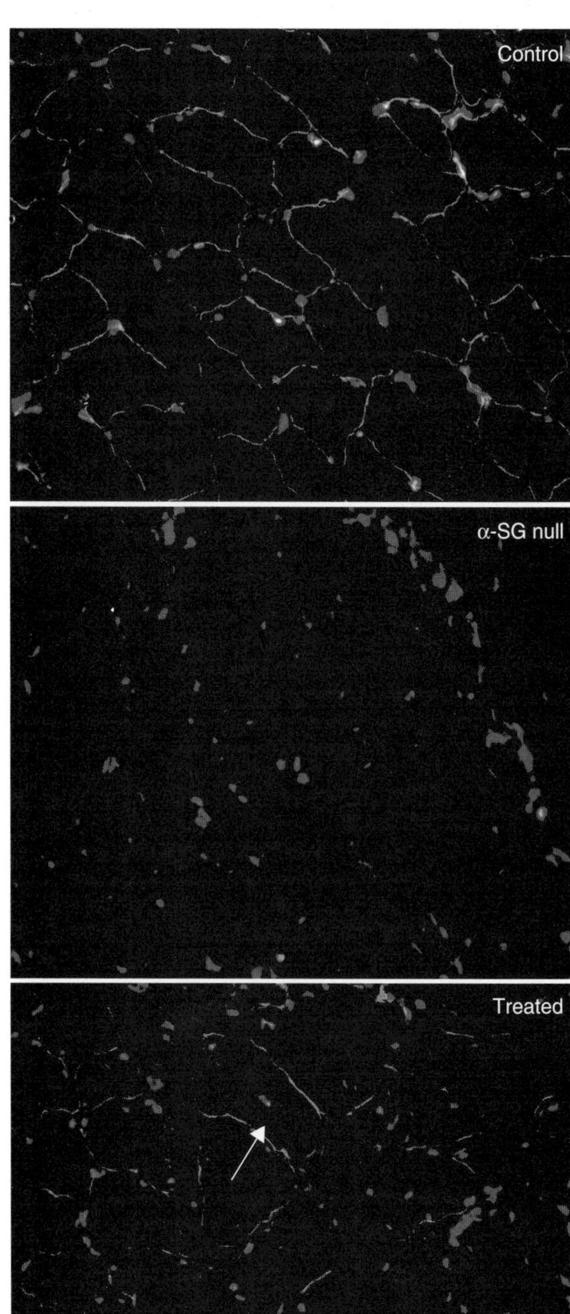

Figure 65–1. *Expression of α-sarcoglycan in α-sarcoglycan null mice after intra-arterial delivery of wild-type mesoangioblasts.* (A) A control quadriceps (CTR) from a wild-type mouse, (B) a dystrophic quadriceps, and (C) a dystrophic quadriceps injected with wild-type mesoangioblasts two months before sacrifice were stained with anti-α-sarcoglycan polyclonal antibody (white lines) and Dapi (white blotches). Large areas of the treated muscle expressed α-sarcoglycan at the fiber plasma membrane; the arrow shows a centrally located nucleus of a regenerating fiber. (Please see CD-ROM for color version of this figure.)

majority of quiescent adult skeletal muscle satellite cells. *J. Cell Biol.* **151,** 1221–1234.

56. Qu-Petersen, Z., Deasy, B., Jankowski, R., Ikezawa, M., Cummins, J., Pruchnic, R., Mytinger, J., Cao, B., Gates, B., Wernig, A., and Huard, J. (2002). Identification of a novel population of muscle stem cells in mice: Potential for muscle regeneration. *J. Cell Biol.* **157,** 851–864.
57. Tamaki, T., Akatsuka, A., Ando, K., Nakamura, Y., Matsuzawa, H., Hotta, T., Roy, R.R., and Edgerton, V.R. (2002). Identification of myogenic–endothelial progenitor cells in the interstitial spaces of skeletal muscle. *J. Cell Biol.* **157,** 571–577.
58. Cao, B., Zheng, B., Jankowski, R.J., Kimura, S., Ikezawa, M., Deasy, B., Cummins, J., Epperly, M., Qu-Petersen, Z., and Huard, J. (2003). Muscle stem cells differentiate into hematopoietic lineages but retain myogenic potential. *Nat. Cell Biol.* **5,** 640–646.
59. Cossu, G., and Mavilio, F. (2000). Myogenic stem cells for the therapy of primary myopathies: wishful thinking or therapeutic perspective? *J. Clin. Invest.* **105,** 1669–1674.
60. Daley, G.Q. (2002). Prospects for stem cell therapeutics: myths and medicines. *Curr. Opin. Genet. Dev.* **12,** 607–613.

insulin followed by the constitutive release by a cell such as the hepatocyte. An example of this approach employed adeno-associated virus to transduce liver with the L-type pyruvate kinase promoter that responds to glucose to induce the production of single-chain insulin.[67] The advantage of single-chain insulin is that it does not need to be cleaved by the convertases normally needed for proinsulin to become biologically active insulin. It was shown that high plasma glucose levels could stimulate increases of plasma insulin sufficient to bring glucose levels of diabetic mice into the normal range. Important questions have been raised, however, about whether this approach could be clinically useful. A recent perspective article pointed out that the timing of insulin release by a gene-dependent constitutive secretory mechanism seems highly unlikely to be useful for type 1 or even type 2 diabetes, in which more rapid insulin delivery or suppression will be needed to cope with the normal dynamics of metabolism found with eating, fasting, and exercise.[68]

Summary

The quest to find insulin-producing cells that might be used for transplantation is intense. Rapid improvements in our understanding of the mechanisms of cellular development and an array of potential stem or precursor cell candidates provide fuel for optimism that adult cells could solve the problem of diabetes.

REFERENCES

1. Weir, G.C., and Bonner-Weir, S. (1997). Scientific and political impediments to successful islet transplantation. *Diabetes* **46,** 1247–1256.
2. Shapiro, A.M., Lakey, J.R., Ryan, E.A., Korbutt, G.S., Toth, E., Warnock, G.L., Kneteman, N.M., and Rajotte, R.V. (2000). Islet transplantation in seven patients with type 1 diabetes mellitus using a glucocorticoid-free immunosuppressive regimen. *N. Engl. J. Med.* **27,** 230–238.
3. Hanahan, D. (1998). Peripheral antigen-expressing cells in thymic medulla: factors in self-tolerance and autoimmunity. *Curr. Opin. Immunol.* **10,** 656–662.
4. Devaskar, S.U., Giddings, S.J., Rajakumar, P.A., Carnaghi, L.R., Menon, R.K., and Zahm, D.S. (1994). Insulin gene expression and insulin synthesis in mammalian neuronal cells. *J. Biol. Chem* **269,** 8445–8454.
5. Giddings, S.J., King, C.D., Harman, K.W., Flood, J.F., and Carnaghi, L.R. (1994). Allele specific inactivation of insulin 1 and 2, in the mouse yolk sac, indicates imprinting. *Nat. Genet.* **6,** 310–313.
6. Hubner, K., Fuhrmann, G., Christenson, L.K., Kehler, J., Reinbold, R., De La Fuente, R., Wood, J., Strauss, J.F., 3rd, Boiani, M., and Scholer, H.R. (2003). Derivation of oocytes from mouse embryonic stem cells. *Science* **300,** 1251–1256.
7. Petersen, B.E., Bowen, W.C., Patrene, K.D., Mars, W.M., Sullivan, A.K., Murase, N., Boggs, S.S., Greenberger, J.S., and Goff, J.P. (1999). Bone marrow as a potential source of hepatic oval cells. *Science* **284,** 1168–1170.
8. Block, G.D., Locker, J., Bowen, W.C., Petersen, B.E., Katyal, S., Strom, S.C., Riley, T., Howard, T.A., and Michalopoulos, G.K. (1996). Population expansion, clonal growth, and specific differentiation patterns in primary cultures of hepatocytes induced by HGF/SF, EGF, and TGF† in a chemically defined (HGM) medium. *J. Cell. Biol.* **132,** 1133–1149.
9. Bonner-Weir, S. (2000). Islet growth and development in the adult. *J. Mol. Endocrinol.* **24,** 1–6.
10. Bonner-Weir, S. (2000). Life and death of the pancreatic β-cells. *Trends Endoc. Metab.* **11,** 375–378.
11. Bonner-Weir, S., and Sharma, A. (2002). Pancreatic stem cells. *J. Pathol.* **197,** 519–526.
12. Scaglia, L., Cahill, C.J., Finegood, D.T., and Bonner-Weir, S. (1997). Apoptosis participates in the remodeling of the endocrine pancreas in the neonatal rat. *Endocrinology* **138,** 1736–1741.
13. Finegood, D.T., Scaglia, L., and Bonner-Weir, S. (1995). (Perspective) Dynamics of B-cell mass in the growing rat pancreas: estimation with a simple mathematical model. *Diabetes* **44,** 249–256.
14. Bonner-Weir, S., Trent, D.F., and Weir, G.C. (1983). Partial pancreatectomy in the rat and subsequent defect in glucose-induced insulin release. *J. Clin. Invest.* **71,** 1544–1553.
15. Xu, G., Stoffers, D.A., Habener, J.F., and Bonner-Weir, S. (1999). Exendin-4 stimulates both β-cell replication and neogenesis, resulting in increased β-cell mass and improved glucose tolerance in diabetic rats. *Diabetes* **48,** 2270–2276.
16. Bruning, J.C., Winnay, J., Bonner-Weir, S., Taylor, S.I., Accili, D., and Kahn, C.R. (1999). Development of a novel polygenic model of NIDDM in mice heterozygous for IR and IRS-1 null alleles. *Cell* **88,** 561–572.
17. Butler, A.E., Janson, J., Bonner-Weir, S., Ritzel, R., Rizza, R.A., and Butler, P.C. (2003). β-cell deficit and increased β-cell apoptosis in humans with type 2 diabetes. *Diabetes* **52,** 102–110.
18. Yoon, K.H., Ko, S.H., Cho, J.H., Lee, J.M., Ahn, Y.B., Song, K.H., Yoo, S.J., Kang, M.I., Cha, B.Y., Lee, K.W., Son, H.Y., Kang, S.K., Kim, D.G., Lee, I.K., and Bonner-Weir, S. (2003). Selective β-cell loss and α-cell expansion in patients with type 2 diabetes mellitus in Korea. *J. Clin. Endocrinol. Metab.* **88,** 2300–2308.
19. Bonner-Weir, S. (Unpublished).
20. Bonner-Weir, S., Deery, D., Leahy, J.L., and Weir, G.C. (1989). Compensatory growth of pancreatic β-cells in adult rats after short-term glucose infusion. *Diabetes* **38,** 49–53.
21. Scaglia, L., Smith, F.E., and Bonner-Weir, S. (1995). Apoptosis contributes to the involution of β-cell mass in the postpartum rat pancreas. *Endocrinol.* **136,** 5461–5468.
22. Jonas, J.C., Sharma, A., Hasenkamp, W., Ilkova, H., Patane, G., Laybutt, R., Bonner-Weir, S., and Weir, G.C. (1999). Chronic hyperglycemia triggers loss of pancreatic β-cell differentiation in an animal model of diabetes. *J. Biol. Chem.* **274,** 14,112–14,121.
23. Sharma, A., Zangen, D.H., Reitz, P., Taneja, M., Lissauer, M.E., Miller, C.P., Weir, G.C., Habener, J.F., and Bonner-Weir, S. (1999). The homeodomain protein IDX-1 increases after an early burst of proliferation during pancreatic regeneration. *Diabetes* **48,** 507–513.
24. Gu, G., Dubauskaite, J., and Melton, D.A. (2002). Direct evidence for the pancreatic lineage: NGN3+ cells are islet progenitors and are distinct from duct progenitors. *Development* **129,** 2447–2457.
25. Bonner-Weir, S., Baxter, L.A., Schuppin, G.T., and Smith, F.E. (1993). A second pathway for regeneration of the adult exocrine and endocrine pancreas: a possible recapitulation of embryonic development. *Diabetes* **42,** 1715–1720.

26. Pictet, R., and Rutter, W.J. (1972). The endocrine pancreas. *In* "Handbook of Physiology," (D. Steiner *et al.,* Eds.), pp. 25–66. Williams & Wilkins, Baltimore.
27. Dudek, R.W., Lawrence, I.E., Jr., Hill, R.S., and Johnson, R.C. (1991). Induction of islet cytodifferentiation by fetal mesenchyme in adult pancreatic ductal epithelium. *Diabetes* **40,** 1041–1048.
28. Gu, D., and Sarvetnick, N. (1993). Epithelial cell proliferation and islet neogenesis in IFN-γ transgenic mice. *Development* **118,** 33–46.
29. Yoon, K.H., Quickel, R.R., Tatarkiewicz, K., Ulrich, T.R., Hollister-Lock, J., Trivedi, N., Bonner-Weir, S., and Weir, G.C. (1999). Differentiation and expansion of β-cell mass in porcine neonatal pancreatic cell clusters transplanted into nude mice. *Cell Transplant.* **8,** 673–689.
30. Toschi, E., Gaudet, J., Sharma, A., Weir, G.C., Sgroi, D., and Bonner-Weir, S. (2003). Delineation of phenotypic differences between new and old β-cells. *Diabetes* **52 (Suppl. 1.),** A363.
31. Bonner-Weir, S., Taneja, M., Weir, G.C., Tatarkiewicz, K., Song, K.H., Sharma, A., and O'Neil, J.J. (2000). *In vitro* cultivation of human islets from expanded ductal tissue. *Proc. Natl. Acad. Sci. USA* **97,** 7999–8004.
32. Gao, R., Ustinov, J., Pulkkinen, M.A., Lundin, K., Korsgren, O., and Otonkoski, T. (2003). Characterization of endocrine progenitor cells and critical factors for their differentiation in human adult pancreatic cell culture. *Diabetes* **52,** 2007–2015.
33. Hardikar, A.A., Marcus-Samuels, B., Geras-Raaka, E., Raaka, B.M., and Gershengorn, M.C. (2003). Human pancreatic precursor cells secrete FGF2 to stimulate clustering into hormone-expressing islet-like cell aggregates. *Proc. Natl. Acad. Sci. USA* **100,** 7117–7122.
34. Ramiya, V.K., Marraist, M., Arfors, K.E., Schatz, D.A., Peck, A.B., and Cornelius, J.C. (2000). Reversal of insulin-dependent diabetes using islets generated *in vitro* from pancreatic stem cells. *Nat. Med.* **6,** 278–282.
35. Sachs, D.H., and Bonner-Weir, S. (2000). New islets from old. *Nature* **6,** 278–282.
36. Deltour, L., Leduque, P., Paldi, A., Ripoche, M.A., Dubois, P., and Jami, J. (1991). Polyclonal origin of pancreatic islets in aggregation mouse chimaeras. *Development* **112,** 1115–1121.
37. Guz, Y., Nasir, I., and Teitelman, G. (2001). Regeneration of pancreatic β-cells from intraislet precursor cells in an experimental model of diabetes. *Endocrinology* **142,** 4956–4968.
38. Lumelsky, N., Blondel, O., Laeng, P., Velasco, I., Ravin, R., and McKay, R. (2001). Differentiation of embryonic stem cells to insulin-secreting structures similar to pancreatic islets. *Science* **292,** 1389–1393.
39. Rajagopal, J., Anderson, W.J., Kume, S., Martinez, O.I., and Melton, D.A. (2003). Insulin staining of ES cell progeny from insulin uptake. *Science* **299,** 363.
40. Zulewski, H., Abraham, E.J., Gerlach, M.J., Daniel, P.B., Moritz, W., Muller, B., Vallejo, M., Thomas, M.K., and Habener, J.F. (2001). Multipotential nestin-positive stem cells isolated from adult pancreatic islets differentiate *ex vivo* into pancreatic endocrine, exocrine, and hepatic phenotypes. *Diabetes* **50,** 521–533.
41. Delacour, A., Nepote, V., Trumpp, A., and Herrera, P.L. (2004). Nestin expression in pancreatic exocrine cell lineages. *Mech. Dev.* **121,** 3–14.
42. Klein, T., Ling, Z., Heimberg, H., Madsen, O.D., Heller, R.S., and Serup, P. (2003). Nestin is expressed in vascular endothelial cells in the adult human pancreas. *J. Histochem. Cytochem.* **51,** 697–706.
43. Lardon, J., Rooman, I., and Bouwens, L. (2002). Nestin expression in pancreatic stellate cells and angiogenic endothelial cells. *Histochem. Cell Biol.* **117,** 535–540.
44. Selander, L., and Edlund, H. (2002). Nestin is expressed in mesenchymal and not epithelial cells of the developing mouse pancreas. *Mech. Dev.* **113,** 189–192.
45. Oie, H.K., Gazdar, A.F., Minna, J.D., Weir, G.C., and Baylin, S.B. (1983). Clonal analysis of insulin and somatostatin secretion and L-dopa decarboxylase expression by a rat islet cell tumor. *Endocrinology* **112,** 1070–1075.
46. Mashima, H., Shibata, H., Mine, T., and Kojima, I. (1996). Formation of insulin-producing cells from pancreatic acinar AR42J cells from pancreatic acinar AR42J cells by hepatocyte growth factor. *Endocrinol.* **137,** 3969–3976.
47. Ishiyama, N., Kanzaki, M., Seno, M., Yamada, H., Kobayashi, I., and Kojima, I. (1998). Studies on the betacellulin receptor in pancreatic AR42J cells. *Diabetologia* **41,** 623–628.
48. Dabeva, M.D., Hwang, S.G., Vasa, S.R., Hurston, E., Novikoff, P.M., Hixson, D.C., Gupta, S., and Shafritz, D.A. (1997). Differentiation of pancreatic epithelial progenitor cells into hepatocytes following transplantation into rat liver. *Proc. Natl. Acad. Sci. USA* **94,** 7356–7361.
49. Grompe, M. (2003). Pancreatic-hepatic switches *in vivo*. *Mech. Dev.* **120,** 99–106.
50. Rooman, I., Lardon, J., and Bouwens, L. (2002). Gastrin stimulates β-cell neogenesis and increases islet mass from transdifferentiated but not from normal exocrine pancreas tissue. *Diabetes* **51,** 686–690.
51. Lipsett, M., and Finegood, D.T. (2002). β-cell neogenesis during prolonged hyperglycemia in rats. *Diabetes* **51,** 1834–1841.
52. Herzog, E.L., Chai, L., and Krause, D.S. (2003). Plasticity of marrow-derived stem cells. *Blood* **102,** 3483–3493.
53. Wagers, A.J., Sherwood, R.I., Christensen, J.L., and Weissman, I.L. (2002). Little evidence for developmental plasticity of adult hematopoietic stem cells. *Science* **297,** 2256–2259.
54. Wang, X., Willenbring, H., Akkari, Y., Torimaru, Y., Foster, M., Al-Dhalimy, M., Lagasse, E., Finegold, M., Olson, S., and Grompe, M. (2003). Cell fusion is the principal source of bone marrow-derived hepatocytes. *Nature* **422,** 897–901.
55. Ianus, A., Holz, G.G., Theise, N.D., and Hussain, M.A. (2003). *In vivo* derivation of glucose-competent pancreatic endocrine cells from bone marrow without evidence of cell fusion. *J. Clin. Invest.* **111,** 843–850.
56. Jiang, Y., Jahagirdar, B.N., Reinhardt, R.L., Schwartz, R.E., Keene, C.D., Ortiz-Gonzalez, X.R., Reyes, M., Lenvik, T., Lund, T., Blackstad, M., Du, J., Alrich, S., Lisberg, A., Low, W.C., Largaespada, D.A., and Verfaillie, C.M. (2002). Pluripotency of mesenchymal stem cells derived from adult marrow. *Nature* **418,** 41–49.
57. Hess, D., Li, L., Martin, M., Sakano, S., Hill, D., Strutt, B., Thyssen, S., Gray, D.A., and Bhatia, M. (2003). Bone marrow-derived stem cells initiate pancreatic regeneration. *Nat. Biotechnol.* **21,** 763–770.
58. Ferber, S., Halkin, A., Cohen, H., Ber, I., Einav, Y., Goldberg, I., Barshack, I., Seijffers, R., Kopolovic, J., Kaiser, N., and Karasik, A. (2000). Pancreatic and duodenal homeobox gene 1 induces expression of insulin genes in liver and ameliorates streptozotocin-induced hyperglycemia. *Nat. Med.* **6,** 505–506.
59. Ber, I., Shternhall, K., Perl, S., Ohanuna, Z., Goldberg, I., Barshack, I., Benvenisti-Zarum, L., Meivar-Levy, I., and Ferber, S. (2003). Functional, persistent, and extended liver to pancreas transdifferentiation. *J. Biol. Chem.* **278,** 31,950–31,957.

60. Kojima, H., Fujimiya, M., Matsumura, K., Younan, P., Imaeda, H., Maeda, M., and Chan, L. (2003). NeuroD-betacellulin gene therapy induces islet neogenesis in the liver and reverses diabetes in mice. *Nat. Med.* **9,** 596–603.
61. Yang, L., Li, S., Hatch, H., Ahrens, K., Cornelius, J.G., Petersen, B.E., and Peck, A.B. (2002). *In vitro* transdifferentiation of adult hepatic stem cells into pancreatic endocrine hormone-producing cells. *Proc. Natl. Acad. Sci. USA* **99,** 8078–8083.
62. Zalzman, M., Gupta, S., Giri, R.K., Berkovich, I., Sappal, B.S., Karnieli, O., Zern, M.A., Fleischer, N., and Efrat, S. (2003). Reversal of hyperglycemia in mice by using human expandable insulin-producing cells differentiated from fetal liver progenitor cells. *Proc. Natl. Acad. Sci. USA* **100,** 7253–7258.
63. Antinozzi, P.A., Berman, H.K., O'Doherty, R.M., and Newgard, C.B. (1999). Metabolic engineering with recombinant adenoviruses. *Annu. Rev. Nutr.* **19,** 511–544.
64. Lipes, M.A., Cooper, E.M., Skelly, R., Rhodes, C.J., Boschetti, E., Weir, G.C., and Davalli, A.M. (1996). Insulin-secreting nonislet cells are resistant to autoimmune destruction. *Proc. Natl. Acad. Sci. USA* **93,** 8596–8600.
65. Cheung, A.T., Dayanandan, B., Lewis, J.T., Korbutt, G.S., Rajotte, R.V., Bryer-Ash, M., Boylan, M.O., Wolfe, M.M., and Kieffer, T.J. (2000). Glucose-dependent insulin release from genetically engineered K-cells. *Science* **290,** 1959–1962.
66. Yoshida, S., Kajimoto, Y., Yasuda, T., Watada, H., Fujitani, Y., Kosaka, H., Gotow, T., Miyatsuka, T., Umayahara, Y., Yamasaki, Y., and Hori, M. (2002). PDX-1 induces differentiation of intestinal epithelioid IEC-6 into insulin-producing cells. *Diabetes* **51,** 2505–2513.
67. Lee, H.C., Kim, S.J., Kim, K.S., Shin, H.C., and Yoon, J.W. (2000). Remission in models of type 1 diabetes by gene therapy using a single-chain insulin analogue. *Nature* **408,** 483–488.
68. Halban, P.A., Kahn, S.E., Lernmark, A., and Rhodes, C.J. (2001). Gene and cell-replacement therapy in the treatment of type 1 diabetes: how high must the standards be set? *Diabetes* **50,** 2181–2191.

67

Hematopoietic Stem Cell Transplantation for Solid Tumors

Yoshiyuki Takahashi, Ramaprasad Srinivasan, and Richard W. Childs

Introduction

Allogeneic hematopoietic stem cell transplantation (HCT) was initially devised as a means of regenerating hematopoiesis rendered defunct as a consequence of high-dose chemotherapy given to patients with hematologic malignancies. The concept that allogeneic HCT is merely a method for providing hematopoietic sustenance has undergone significant revision following the recognition that graft-versus-leukemia (GVL) or graft-versus-solid tumor (GVT) effects occur in patients with cancer undergoing the procedure. With the realization that GVL alone is sufficient to eradicate some hematologic malignancies, investigators developed reduced-intensity or "nonmyeloablative" HCT in an attempt to minimize transplant-related toxicity and exploit the beneficial effects of GVL. The recent demonstration of GVT effects in patients with metastatic renal cell carcinoma (RCC) following nonmyeloablative HCT sparked interest in exploring for similar beneficial, donor immune-mediated, antitumor effects after allogeneic HCT in other solid tumors. This chapter outlines the development of nonmyeloablative HCT as an evolving investigational strategy in the management of metastatic solid tumors.

HCT as Allogeneic Immunotherapy

Allogeneic HCT was introduced into clinical practice as a means of immunohematopoietic reconstitution following bone marrow ablation by high-dose chemotherapy administered as "definitive" treatment for certain hematologic malignancies. Graft-versus-host disease (GVHD), the most visible manifestation of alloimmunity following transplantation, was largely regarded as an undesirable accompaniment. A landmark analysis published in the late 1970s[1] noted that recipients of syngeneic or human lymphocyte antigen (HLA)-matched sibling transplants who developed moderate to severe acute GVHD or chronic GVHD had a 2.5 times lower probability of disease relapse than recipients who developed mild or no acute GVHD. This association between GVHD and freedom from disease relapse suggested the existence of a beneficial allogeneic GVL effect. Subsequent studies demonstrated that the risk of chronic myeloid leukemia (CML) relapse was higher in recipients of T-cell-depleted as opposed to T-cell-intact allografts, suggesting that donor T-cells were involved in the eradication of leukemia following HCT.[2,3] A higher risk of CML relapse in recipients of HCT from syngeneic versus HLA-matched nonidentical twin donors suggests that the degree of donor–host antigen disparity influences disease outcome after allogeneic HCT.[4] Perhaps the most conclusive evidence for the existence of a T-cell–mediated alloimmune effect against leukemia comes from studies demonstrating the ability of donor lymphocyte infusions to reinduce remission in CML patients who have relapsed after transplantation.[5] A heightened awareness of the curative potential of GVL has led to the design of novel clinical strategies that rely largely on the generation of donor antihost alloimmunity to eradicate malignant disease. The major difference between these newer strategies and more conventional transplant approaches is the reliance of the former on minimally myelosuppressive but strongly immunosuppressive conditioning regimens. Several studies, using a variety of nonmyeloablative or "reduced intensity" conditioning strategies, have demonstrated the efficacy of this approach in eradicating hematologic malignancies known to be susceptible to GVL.[6–8] Early results showing low rates of transplant mortality (10–20% in nonmyeloablative HCT versus 30–40% in myeloablative, HLA-matched sibling transplants) suggest that nonmyeloablative procedures may be safer than conventional, allogeneic HCT. The improved toxicity profile observed with nonmyeloablative HCT has extended the gamut of allogeneic immunotherapy to older and debilitated patients hitherto ineligible for transplantation. In addition, it has provided the basis for exploring the potential of allogeneic immunotherapy to induce GVT effects in patients with treatment-refractory solid tumors.

Allogeneic Immunotherapy for Solid Tumors

Animal models of carcinogenesis and clinical experience with human immune deficiency states strongly suggest a role for the immune system in protecting against carcinogenesis.[9,10] An inevitable corollary of these observations is the finding that patients with cancer have a weakened or dysfunctional immune system. Consequently, a variety of interventions directed at augmenting antitumor immune responses have been explored in clinical trials. Nonspecific stimulation of innate immunity using cytokine-based therapy has resulted in well-defined clinical responses in tumors such as melanoma and metastatic renal cell cancer.[11–13] These trials have provided the impetus for the development of tumor-specific vaccines and adoptive T-cell-based strategies.[14–17] Although attractive and informative from an immunologic perspective, few patients have achieved a tangible clinical benefit from these strategies. The reliance on an autologous immune system, often ravaged by tumor-related factors or prior chemotherapy, may partly explain the limited efficacy of immunotherapy regimens based on boosting innate immunity. This disadvantage is further compounded by host immune tolerance to tumors. The premise that these limitations might be overcome by providing the host with a new, healthy, and "nontolerized" immune system forms the primary rationale underlying trials of HCT in solid tumors. Early evidence that allogeneic HCT could induce regression of metastatic solid tumors was mostly anecdotal, based on a handful of case reports or on small case series.[18–20] Beginning in the late 1990s, a systematic evaluation designed to answer whether GVT effects could be induced against metastatic RCC, melanoma, and other treatment-refractory solid tumors was undertaken by investigators at the National Institutes of Health (NIH) and other transplant medical centers; the preliminary findings from these studies are outlined in the following sections.

NONMYELOABLATIVE HCT FOR RCC

The ability of interleukin-2 and interferon therapy to induce clinical remissions of metastatic RCC has led to its characterization as an "immunoresponsive" tumor and hence a potential candidate for experimental alloimmune therapy. For patients with metastatic disease, a dismal 5-year survival probability and limited therapeutic options make the risks associated with allogeneic HCT acceptable. The first clinical trial evaluating GVT effects against metastatic RCC was initiated at the NIH in 1998.[21,22] The strategy, as outlined in Fig. 67–1, involved nonmyeloablative conditioning with a cyclophosphamide- and fludarabine-based regimen designed to induce maximal host immunosuppression followed by infusion of a granulocyte colony-stimulating factor-mobilized peripheral blood stem cell graft from an HLA-matched sibling donor. Cyclosporine A, administered either alone or with mycophenolate mofetil or low-dose methotrexate were used as GVHD prophylaxis. Since rapid donor T-cell chimerism is likely to expedite the generation of GVT effects, immunosuppression withdrawal and donor lymphocyte infusions were incorporated into the treatment to promote early and complete donor T-lymphocyte engraftment. More than 50 patients with metastatic RCC have undergone nonmyeloablative HCT at the NIH. Of 50 evaluable patients, 22 (44%) have had evidence of a GVT effect, including 4 complete responses (8%) and 18 partial responses. Many of the responses have proved durable, including the 5 patient transplanted who remains in complete remission 5 years posttransplant. GVHD was the most common complication, with approximately two thirds of the patients experiencing acute grade II–IV GVHD and approximately 50% developing chronic (mostly limited) GVHD. Despite the advanced disease status of patients enrolled on this pilot trial, transplant-related mortality was relatively low, with 6 patients (12%) succumbing to nonrelapse mortality.

Several clinical observations supported the notion that disease responses reflected GVT activity (Table 67–1).

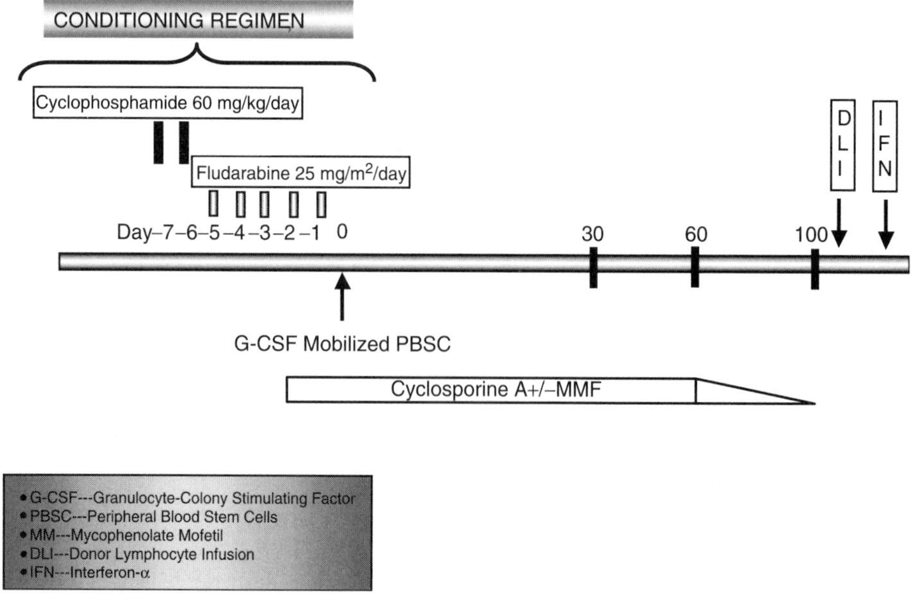

Figure 67–1. *Cyclophosphamide- and fludarabine-based nonmyeloablative HCT protocol for RCC.* GVHD prophylaxis is accomplished by cyclosporine with or without mycophenolate mofetil or low-dose methotrexate. Withdrawal of immunosuppression and administration of donor lymphocyte infusions are used to favor transition to complete donor T-cell chimerism or induce tumor regression in the absence of GVHD. Immunomodulatory cytokines such as interferon-α can be used to promote tumor regression under some circumstances.

TABLE 67–1
Tumor Response Patterns Consistent with a GVT Effect After Nonmyeloablative HCT

Delayed onset of response (>100 days posttransplant)
Response following donor lymphocyte infusions
Response following withdrawal of immunosuppression
Response following or concomitant with GVHD
Prolonged duration of response in tumors previously treatment refractory

First, responses were typically delayed until several months after transplantation and occurred only after predominant donor T-lymphoid chimerism had been achieved. Second, although GVHD was not necessary for tumor regression, responses occurred frequently in the context of acute GVHD. Third, clinical remission could be induced in some patients with donor lymphocyte infusions or following the withdrawal of immunosuppression. Finally, donor-derived T-cell populations that are tumor cytotoxic have been isolated from some responding patients, implying a role for cell-mediated alloimmune responses in tumor regression. Fig. 67–2 illustrates clinical responses seen in two patients with metastatic RCC following nonmyeloablative HCT and highlights the temporal relationship between disease response and posttransplant events, such as conversion to complete donor T-cell chimerism, immunosuppression withdrawal, and administration of donor lymphocyte infusions.

Several groups have subsequently confirmed the ability to induce graft-versus-RCC effects following HCT. Using cyclophosphamide and fludarabine for pretransplant conditioning, Rini *et al.*[23] achieved complete donor engraftment in 12/15 metastatic RCC patients undergoing an HLA-matched sibling transplant. Of the 12 patients who engrafted, 4 demonstrated partial tumor regression. As would be expected, none of the patients who rejected their allografts demonstrated meaningful clinical responses. Bregni *et al.*[24] used a thiotepa- and fludarabine-based conditioning regimen in 7 patients with metastatic RCC undergoing HCT, 4 of whom experienced a partial disease remission compatible with a GVT effect.

Allogeneic HCT remains an experimental therapeutic modality in the management of metastatic RCC. The primary outcome of the aforementioned trials was to establish incontrovertible evidence of GVT effects against this malignancy. In addition, these studies suggest that certain characteristics of the patient and tumor herald a better outcome, such as small to moderate tumor burden, slow rate of tumor growth, clear cell histology, and good patient performance status. Larger trials in progress may help to identify those RCC patients who are most likely to benefit from allogeneic HCT as well as define the role transplantation will ultimately play in their management.

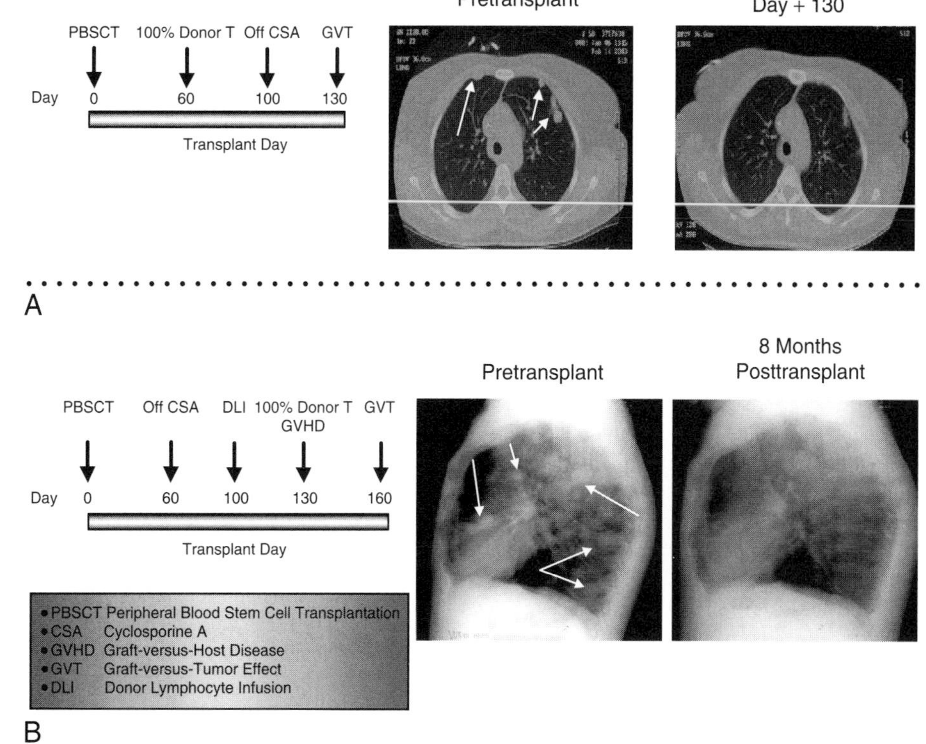

Figure 67–2. *Regression of metastatic RCC resions following nonmyeloablative HCT.* (A) Near complete regression of multiple pulmonary metastases in a patient with RCC. Clinical response followed transition to complete donor chimerism and complete withdrawal of immunosuppression (cyclosporine A). (B) Regression of multiple pulmonary metastases in another patient 8 months following the administration of a donor lymphocyte infusion and the development of GVHD. By day 130, 100% donor T-cell chimerism was noted.

NONMYELOABLATIVE HCT FOR MELANOMA

Malignant melanoma shares several features with RCC that would potentially make it a good candidate tumor to investigate for GVT effects. Unfortunately, most studies have failed to demonstrate clinically meaningful graft-versus-melanoma responses following HCT. A recent report described a poor outcome in 25 patients treated with one of three nonmyeloablative allogeneic HCT approaches at several transplant centers.[25] Of the patients, 4 (16%) had transient tumor regression at one or more sites immediately following transplant conditioning, probably representing a response to chemotherapy. Only 1 patient had delayed tumor regression consistent with a GVT effect. Median survival was less than 4 months, with most deaths attributable to disease progression. Of concern, several patients exhibited rapid tumor growth early in the course of transplant. It is unclear if this rapid progression following conditioning occurred as a consequence of suppressing host immunity or merely represented a phase in the natural history of the malignancy. Regardless, the bulk of evidence to date suggests allogeneic HCT, at least in its current form, is unlikely to benefit most patients with metastatic melanoma.

NONMYELOABLATIVE HCT FOR OTHER SOLID TUMORS

Experience with HCT in other solid tumors is limited (Table 67–2). Among those tumors studied, data to support the existence of a GVT effect is greatest among women with breast cancer receiving an allogeneic HCT. One of the earliest suggestions of a GVT effect came from a case report of a woman with metastatic breast cancer who received a transplant from an HLA-identical sibling following myeloablative conditioning.[19] Regression of liver metastases coincident with acute GVHD supported the notion that a GVT effect had occurred in this patient. Subsequently, a pilot trial reported clinical responses in 6/10 metastatic breast cancer patients undergoing myeloablative HCT with at least two of these responses attributable to a GVT effect.[20] Bregni *et al.*[24] reported 2 partial responses among 6 metastatic breast cancer patients undergoing nonmyeloablative HCT. The temporal association of GVHD and donor lymphocyte infusion administration to response argues strongly for an alloimmune-mediated antitumor effect. Case reports detailing possible GVT effects in patients with ovarian carcinoma,[26] colon cancer,[27] and osteosarcoma[28] were recently published, but larger numbers of patients are needed to conclusively establish that allogeneic immune effects mediate tumor regression in these malignancies.

TABLE 67–2
Susceptibility of Various Solid Tumors to GVT Effects

Malignancy	Susceptibility to GVT	Reference
Renal cell cancer	Yes	21–24
Melanoma	No	25
Breast cancer	Yes	19, 20, 24
Ovarian cancer	Possible	26
Osteosarcoma	Possible	28
Colon adenocarcinoma	Possible	27

Summary

Nonmyeloablative allogeneic HCT is a novel therapeutic approach in the management of metastatic RCC and other incurable malignancies. Even though results from early clinical trials are encouraging, this treatment modality should be considered experimental. Although unequivocal evidence of solid tumor susceptibility to a GVT effect has been demonstrated in only a few malignancies, ongoing studies are likely to broaden the spectrum of disease that may benefit from allogeneic HCT.

REFERENCES

1. Weiden, P.L., Flournoy, N., Thomas, E.D, Prentice, R., Fefer, A., Buckner, C.D., and Storb, R. (1979). Antileukemic effects of graft-versus-host disease in human recipients of allogeneic marrow grafts. *N. Engl. J. Med.* **300,** 1068–1073.
2. Apperley, J.F., Jones, L., Hale, G., Waldmann, H., Hows, J., Rombos, Y., Tsatalas, C., Marcus, R.E., Goolden, A.W., Gordon-Smith, E.C., *et al.* (1986). Bone marrow transplantation for patients with chronic myeloid leukemia: T-cell depletion with Campath-1 reduces the incidence of graft-versus-host disease but may increase the risk of leukemic relapse. *Bone Marrow Transplant.* **1,** 53–68.
3. Goldman, J.M., Gale, R.P., Horowitz, M.M., Biggs, J.C., Champlin, R.E., Gluckman, E., Hoffmann, R.G., Jacobsen, S.J., Marmont, A.M., McGlave, P.B., *et al.* (1988). Bone marrow transplantation for chronic myelogenous leukemia in chronic phase: increased risk of relapse associated with T-cell depletion. *Ann. Int. Med.* **108,** 806–814.
4. Horowitz, M.M., Gale, R.P., Sondel, P.M., Goldman, J.M., Kersey, J., Kolb, H.J., Rimm, A.A., Ringden, O., Rozman, C., Speck, B., *et al.* (1990). Graft-versus-leukemia reactions after bone marrow transplantation. *Blood* **75,** 552–562.
5. Kolb, H.J., Mittermueller, J., Clemm, C., Holler, E., Ledderose, G., Brehm, G., Heim, M., and Wilmanns, W. (1990). Donor leukocyte transfusions for treatment of recurrent chronic myelogenous leukemia in marrow transplant patients. *Blood* **76,** 2462–2465.
6. Khouri, I.F., Keating, M., Korbling, M., Przepiorka, D., Anderlini, P., O'Brien, S., Giralt, S., Ippoliti, C., von Wolff, B., Gajewski, J., Donato, M., Claxton, D., Ueno, N., Andersson, B., Gee, A., and Champlin, R. (1998). Tansplant-lite: Induction of graft versus malignancy using fludarabine-based nonablative chemotherapy and allogeneic blood progenitor-cell transplantation as treatment for lymphoid malignancies. *J. Clin. Oncol.* **16,** 2817–2824.
7. McSweeney, P.A., Niederwieser, D., and Shiruzu, J.A. (2001). Hematopoietic cell transplantation in older patients with hematologic malignancies: replacing high-dose cytotoxic therapy with graft-versus-tumor effects. *Blood* **97,** 3390–3400.
8. Slavin, S., Nagler, A., Naparastek, E., Kapelushnik, Y., Aker, M., Cividalli, G., Varadi, G., Kirschbaum, M., Ackerstein, A. Samuel, S., Amar, A., Brautbar, C., Ben-Tal, O., Eldor, A., and Or, R.

(1998). Nonmyeloablative stem cell transplantation and cell therapy as an alternative to conventional bone marrow transplantation with lethal cytoreduction for the treatment of malignant and nonmalignant hematologic diseases. *Blood* **91,** 756–763.

9. Holland, J.M., Mitchell, T.J., Gipson, L.C., and Whitaker, M.S. (1978). Survival and cause of death in aging germ-free athymic nude and normal inbred C3Hf/He mice. *J. Nat. Cancer Inst.* **61,** 1357–1361.
10. Kinlein, L.J. (1996). Immunologic factors including AIDS. *In* "Cancer Epidemiology and Prevention," (D. Schottenfield *et al.,* eds.), pp. 532–545. Oxford University Press, New York.
11. Negrier, S., Escudier, B., Lasset, C., Douillard, J.Y., Savary, J., Chevreau, C, Ravaud, A. Mercatello, A. Peny, J., Mousseau, M., Philip, T., and Tursz, T. (1998). Recombinant human interleukin-2, recombinant human interferon alfa-2a, or both in metastatic renal-cell carcinoma. *N. Engl. J. Med.* 1272–1278.
12. Quesada, J.R., Swanson, D.A., and Trindade, A. (1983). Renal cell carcinoma: antitumor effects of leukocyte interferon. *Cancer Res.* **43,** 940.
13. Rosenberg, S.A., Yang, J.C., Topalian, S.L., Schwartzentruber, D.J., Weber, J.S., Parkinson, D.R., Seipp, C.A., Einhorn, J.H., and White, D.E. (1994). Treatment of 283 consecutive patients with metastatic melanoma or renal cell carcinoma using high-dose bolus interleukin-2. *JAMA* **271,** 907–913.
14. Rosenberg, S.A. (1999). A new era for cancer immunotherapy based on the genes that encode cancer antigens. *Immunity* **10,** 281–287.
15. Ada, G. (1999). The coming of age of tumor immunotherapy. *Immunol. Cell Biol.* **77,** 180–185.
16. Rosenberg, S.A., Lotze, M.T., Muul, L.M., Chang, A.E., Avis, F.P., Leitman, S., Linehan, W.M., Robertson, C.N., Lee, R.E., Rubin, T.J., *et al.* (1987). A progress report on the treatment of 157 patients with advanced cancer using lymphokine-activated killer cells and interleukin-2 or high-dose interleukin-2 alone. *N. Engl. J. Med.* **316,** 889–897.
17. Rosenberg, S.A., Yang, J.C., Schwartzentruber, D.J., Hwu, P., Marincola, F.M., Topalian, S.L., Restifo, N.P., Dudley, M.E., Schwartz, S.L., Spiess, P.J., Wunderlich, J.R., Parkhurst, M.R., Kawakami, Y., Seipp, C.A., Einhorn, J.H., and White, D.E. (1998). Immunologic and therapeutic evaluation of a synthetic peptide vaccine for the treatment of patients with metastatic melanoma. *Nat. Med.* **4,** 321–327.
18. Ben-Yosef, R., Or, R., Nagler, A., and Slavin, S. (1996). Graft-versus-tumor and graft-versus-leukemia effect in patient with concurrent breast cancer and acute myelocytic leukemia. *Lancet* **348,** 1242–1243.
19. Eibl, B., Schwaighofer, H., Nachbaur, D., Marth, C., Gachter, A., Knapp, R., Bock, G., Gassner, C., Schiller, L., Petersen, F., and Niederwieser, D. (1996). Evidence of a graft-versus-tumor effect in a patient treated with marrow ablative chemotherapy and allogeneic bone marrow transplantation for breast cancer. *Blood* **88,** 1501–1508.
20. Ueno, N.T., Rondon, G., Mirza, N.Q., Geisler, D.K., Anderlini, P., Giralt, S.A., Andersson, B.S., Claxton, D.F., Gajewski, J.L., Khouri, I.F., Korbling, M., Mehra, R.C., Przepiorka, D., Rahman, Z, Samuels, B.I. van Beisen, K., Hortobagyi, G.N., and Champlin, R.E. (1998). Allogeneic peripheral-blood progenitor-cell transplantation for poor-risk patients with metastatic breast cancer. *J. Clin. Oncol.* **16,** 986–993.
21. Childs, R., Clave, E., Tisdale, J., Plante, M., Hensel, N., Barrett, J. (1999). Successful treatment of metastatic renal cell carcinoma with a nonmyeloablative allogeneic peripheral blood progenitor cell transplant: evidence for a graft-versus-tumor effect. *J. Clin. Oncol.* **17,** 2044–2051.
22. Childs, R., Chernoff, A., Contentin, N., Bahceci, E., Schrump, D., Leitman, S., Read, E.J., Tisdale, J., Dunbar, C., Linehan, W.M., Young, N.S., and Barrett, A.J. (2000). Regression of metastatic renal-cell carcinoma after nonmyeloablative allogeneic peripheral-blood stem-cell transplantation. *N. Engl. J. Med.* **343,** 750–758.
23. Rini, B.I., Zimmerman, T., Stadler, W.M., Gajewski, T.F., and Vogelzang, N.J. (2002). Allogeneic stem cell transplantation of renal cell cancer after nonmyeloablative chemotherapy: Feasibility, engraftment, and clinical results. *J. Clin. Oncol.* **20,** 2017–2024.
24. Bregni, M., Dodero, A., Peccatori, J., Pescarollo, A., Bernardi, M., Sassi, I., Voena, C., Zaniboni, A., Bordignon, C., and Corradini, P. (2002). Nonmyeloablative conditioning followed by hematopoietic cell allografting and donor lymphocyte infusions for patients with metastatic renal and breast cancer. *Blood* **99,** 4234–4236.
25. Childs, R., Bradstock, K.F., Gottlieb, D., Blaise, D., Leifer, E., Geller, N., Mohty, M., Faucher, C., Srinivasan, R., Kefford, R., Hegenbart, U., Niederwieser, D., and Barrett, A.J. (2002). Nonmyeloablative allogeneic stem cell transplantation (NST) for metastatic melanoma: nondurable chemotherapy responses without clinically meaningful graft-versus-tumor (GVT) effects. *Blood* **100,** (abstract #1661).
26. Bay, J.O., Fleury, J., Choufi, B., Tournilhac, O., Vincent, C., Bailly, C., Dauplat, J., Viens, P., Faucher, C., and Blaise, D. (2002). Allogeneic hematopoietic stem cell transplantation in ovarian carcinoma: Results of five patients. *Bone Marrow Transplant* **30,** 95–102.
27. Hentschke, P., Barkholt, L., Uzunel, M., Mattsson, J., Wersall, P., Pisa, P., Martola, J., Albiin, N., Wernerson, A., Soderberg, M., Remberger, M., Thorne, A., and Ringden, O. (2003). Low-intensity conditioning and hematopoietic stem cell transplantation in patients with renal and colon carcinoma. *Bone Marrow Transplant* **31,** 253–261.
28. Makimoto, A., Mineishi, S., Tanosahi, R., Kanda, Y., Saito, T., Nakai, K., Matsubara, H., Ohira, M., Fujimoto, H., Tobisu, K., Yamamoto, A., Takaue, Y., and Kakizoe, T. (2001). Nonmyeloablative stem cell transplantation (NST) for refractory solid tumors. *Proc. Am. Soc. Clin. Oncol.* **20,** 12a.

68

Immune Reconstitution

Richard K Burt and Larissa Verda

Introduction

Qualitative and quantitative changes occur within the immune system during aging. Normal age-related T-cell alterations include a decline in CD4+ cells, loss of naive (antigenic virgin) cells, increase in memory (antigen experienced) cells, decline in T-cell proliferative responses, and narrowing of the T-cell receptor repertoire. T-cell age-associated alterations are secondary to increased extrathymic T-cell reconstitution following postpuberty thymic involution combined with peripheral antigen-driven T-cell maturation and expansion. Age-related B-cell changes are predominately qualitative and include loss of high-affinity antibodies, increase in low-affinity antibodies and autoantibodies, impaired isotype switching, and hindered antibody responses to vaccination. B-cell–related changes appear secondary to age-related impairment of T-cell function. Immune reconstitution after hematopoietic stem cell transplantation (HSCT), whether from autologous or allogeneic stem cells, initially arises by means of extrathymic reconstitution. It is, therefore, at onset dominated by changes similar to those of an aged immune system. After HSCT, it may take 1 to 2 or more years for thymic reconstitution of a T- and B-cell phenotype and function normal for the recipient's age. The younger the recipient, the more rapid thymic reconstitution occurs. The health of the graft and patient survival appears to correlate with the rapidity of shift from extrathymic to thymic T-cell reconstitution following HSCT.

Innate Versus Adaptive Immunity

Two types of immune system, innate and adaptive, coexist in humans. The evolutionarily more primitive innate immune system consists of cells using germline genes to express receptors that recognize specific bacterial, viral, or otherwise foreign antigens. These cells include granulocytes, macrophages, and natural killer (NK) cells, as well as proteins such as C3-like complement. There are approximately 33,000 genes in the human genome.[1] Therefore, although specific for nonself determinants, the innate immune system has limited diversity. Receptors for cells of adaptive immunity (T and B lymphocytes) arises by somatic recombination of germ line variable (V), joining (J) and diversity (D) genes leading to a highly diverse number (10^{14} to 10^{19}) of possible T- and B-cell receptors from a limited number of V(J)D genes. This provides adaptive immunity with diversity but also allows for generation of self-reactive repertoires.

Handbook of Stem Cells
Volume 2

Phylogeny of Adaptive Immunity

The most primitive living vertebrates such as modern jawless fish (agnathans like hagfish and lampreys) generally lack T-cell receptors (TCRs), immunoglobulin (Ig) receptors, and major histocompatibility complex (MHC) molecules. Some hagfish and lampreys have been reported to have lymphocytes and plasma cells despite absence of an identifiable thymus, spleen, or lymph nodes. These arise within lymphoid clusters in the pronephros (kidney) and intestinal lamina propria that may be phylogenetic precursors of a thymus and spleen, respectively.[2,3]

Cartilaginous fish (chondrichthyans) such as sharks are the first vertebrates to have adaptive immunity. They have demonstrable lymphocytes with TCR, MHC class I and II molecules, and Igs.[4] Although lymph nodes are absent, the primary lymphoid organ or thymus appears for the first time in evolution with chondrichthyans. The thymus arises with occurrence of jawed fish as a part of the pharyngeal pouch. The major site of T-cell production is the thymus. In comparison, the major site of hematopoietic and B-cell production is the bone marrow. Early primitive vertebrates may have no bone marrow. In these animals, hematopoietic cell and B-cell production occurs in various organs (liver, kidney, gonads, meninges) in which there is a stromal environment similar to marrow. Compared with the thymus and bone marrow, secondary lymphoid structures such as the spleen and lymph nodes are later developments of evolution.[3]

Generation of T Cells

THYMUS

T-cell differentiation occurs within the thymus and is characterized by ordered expression of various CD surface molecules and V, D, and J gene rearrangements. Progenitor cells originating in the bone marrow migrate to the thymus. These early pre-T cells are $CD3^-CD4^-CD8^-$ triple negative (TN) cells. TN cells differentiate into $CD3^-CD4^+CD8^-$ intrathymic T progenitor (ITTP) cells. ITTP subsequently differentiate into $CD3^+CD4^+CD8^+$ double positive (DP) T cells. DP thymocytes undergo apoptosis if their TCR fails to recognize an antigen. Negative selection or apoptosis also occurs if the antigen binding avidity is too strong. Positive selection or survival appears to occur only if antigen binding is of moderate avidity. Along with positive and negative selection, DP thymocytes differentiate into single positive (SP) cells either $CD3^+CD4^+CD8^-$ (CD4 SP) or $CD3^+CD4^-CD8^+$($CD8^+$ SP) and exit the thymus as recent thymic emigrants into the blood and lymphoid tissues. Via their TCRs, $CD4^+$ SP and $CD8^+$ SP T cells recognize peptide bound to MHC class II and I molecules, respectively.[5–7]

The TCR is usually composed of an alpha (α) beta (β) heterodimer (TCRαβ). In a minority of peripheral blood T lymphocytes the TCR receptor is composed of a gamma (γ) delta (δ) heterodimer (TCRγδ). Either the TCRγδ or TCRαβ heterodimer is coupled to the CD3 molecule, which is composed of epsilon (ε), gamma (γ), delta (δ), and zeta (ξ) chains (CD3γδεξ). The TCR recognizes antigen by binding to peptide bound within the cleft of an MHC molecules on the surface of cells. Following TCR engagement signal transduction begins with phosphorylation of CD3 chains at their immunoreceptor tyrosine activation motifs (ITAM). Each CD3 γ, δ, and ε chain contains one ITAM, whereas the ξ chain contains three ITAM (Fig. 68–1).[8–10]

Using the membrane protein CD45 to differentiate naive (CD45RA) from memory (CD45RO) T-cells, thymic-dependent T-cell production appears to diminish markedly after puberty presumably because of thymic atrophy.[11,12] If the thymus involutes, new adult T-cells would then be derived exclusively from peripheral expansion of existing memory cells. However, cells with a CD45RO phenotype may revert to CD45RA and vise versa.[13] Despite the existence of CD45 phenotype switch between RA and RO isotypes, $CD4^+CD45RA^+$ remains a common surrogate marker for naive $CD4^+$ cells.[13–15] Memory $CD4^+$ T cells may be denoted by a $CD4^+$ $CD29^+$ rather than $CD4^+CD45RO^+$ phenotype.[16] Because cord blood is enriched for $CD8^+CD11a^{low}$ T-cells, this phenotype may be used as a marker for naive $CD8^+$ T-cells.[17,18] Alternatively, newer DNA assays of T-cell receptor excision circles (TRECs) are being used as an assay for recent thymic emigrants (RTE).

T-CELL RECEPTOR EXCISION CIRCLES

There is no cell surface phenotypic marker uniquely specific for recent thymic emigrants. A DNA assay may be used to help separate recent thymic emigrants from the rest of the pool of naive T cells. TRECs are extra-chromosomal excision DNA segments generated within the thymus during rearrangement of V, D, and J genes to generate TCRδ and TCRβ chains or V and J genes to generate TCRγ and TCRα chains. TRECs cannot replicate and are diluted during peripheral T-cell expansion. Peripheral blood TREC level is, therefore, dependent on both thymic output and longevity of naive T-cells that in turn is dependent on T-cell division and death.[19,20] The order and segments of TCR genes rearranged is tightly regulated. TCRδ chain rearrangement occurs first followed by TCRγ, then TCRβ and finally TCRα. The TCRβ chain is rearranged during the stage of DN thymocytes ($CD3^+CD4^-CD8^-$).[21] TCRα chain rearrangement occurs in DP thymocytes.[22]

TCR gene rearrangement to generate the αβ TCR creates two episomal circular DNA fragments, a signal joint TREC (sjTREC) and a coding joint TREC (cjTREC) (Fig. 68–2). The δ locus is located within the α locus and is excised in the process of α gene recombination. The first recombination event to remove Dδ and Jδ segments leads to the sjTREC. The second recombination to unite Vα and Jα genes leads to the cjTREC (Fig. 68–2). For Vβ gene rearrangement, there is no intervening δ locus to excise. Similar to the α chain, Dβ and Jβ recombination results in a sjTREC, whereas Vβ recombined with the prior DJ rearrangement results in a cjTREC (Fig. 68–2). If gene rearrangement occurs within both alleles, then a maximum of two sjTREC and two cjTREC may be present for each α and β chain rearrangement for each αβ TCR-positive T-cell. In addition to the type of signal or coding TREC joint analyzed, polymerase chain reaction (PCR) methodology and measurements units vary. TREC concentrations have been reported as TREC per million peripheral

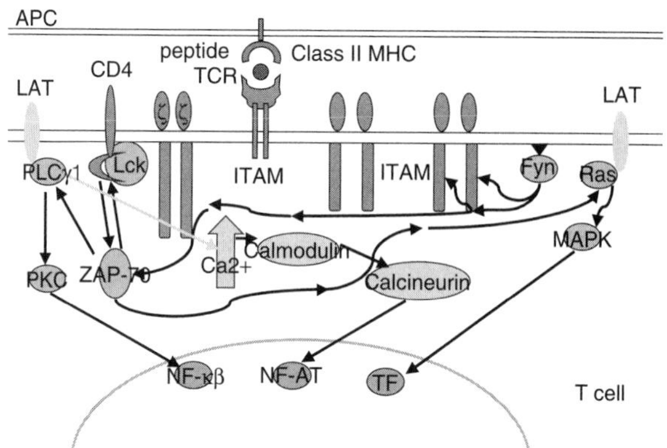

Figure 68–1. *Scheme of signaling pathways during T-cell activation.* The TCR-mediated signal results in the activation of various signal transduction pathways with consequent activation of transcription factors as NF-κB, NF-AT, and TF. Phosphorylation of tyrosines in the ITAMs by Fyn and Lck is an early consequence of crosslinking the TCR and results in the rapid phosphorylation and activation of ZAP-70. Another substrates for Fyn and Lck are ITAMs themselves, thus provide the recruitment of ZAP-70 to the TCR-CD3 signaling complex. In one pathway, ZAP-70 activates PLCγ1 that lead finally to the Ca^{2+} release, activation of calcineurin, and translocation of NF-AT to the nucleus. In another pathway, activated ZAP-70 phosphorylates LAT resulting in Ras activation and the initiation of MAPK pathway distal events and via the activation of PKC causing the release of NF-κB. ζ (zeta), γ (gamma), ε (epsilon), δ (delta)–invariant polypeptide chains of CD3 complex; APC, antigen presenting cell; Fyn, Fgr yes novel protein; ITAM, immunoreceptor tyrosine-based activation motif; LAT, linker for activation of T cells; Lck, lymphocyte specific tyrosine kinase; MAPK, mitogen activated protein kinase; NF-AT, nuclear factor of activated T cells; PKC, protein kinase C; PLCγ1, phospholipase C; Ras, from raus sarcoma virus oncogene, here: small G protein Ras; NF-κB, nuclear factor κB; TCR, T-cell receptor; TF, transcription factor; ZAP-70, zeta associated protein of 70 kDa. (Modified from Clements, J.L., Boerth, N.J., Lee, J.R., and Koretzky, G.A. [1999]. Integration of T cell receptor-dependent signaling pathways by adapter proteins. *Annu. Rev. Immunol.* **17,** 89–108.) (Please see CD-ROM for color version of this figure.)

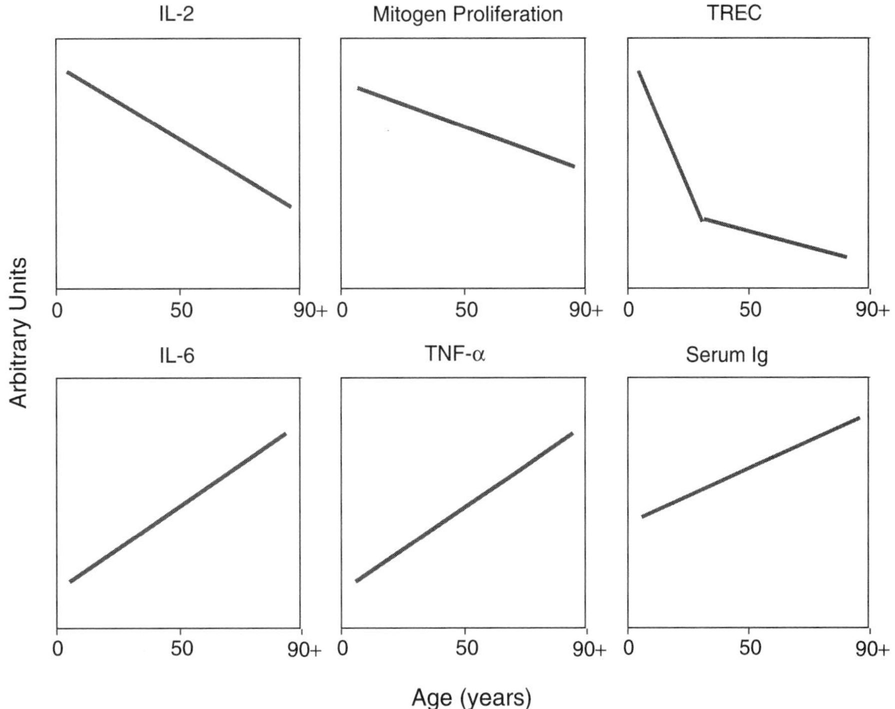

Figure 68–6. *Age-related changes.* Ig, immunoglobulin; IL-2, interleukin-2; IL-6, interleukin-6; TNFα, tumor necrosis factor α; TREC, T-cell receptor excision circle. (Modified from Franceschi, C., Monti, D., Sansoni, P., and Cossarizza, A. [1995]. The immunology of exceptional individuals: The lesson of centenarians. *Immunol. Today* **16,** 12–16.) (Please see CD-ROM for color version of this figure.)

numbers of B-cells. Chronic antigenic stimulation of terminal B-cells results in age-related Ig repertoire skewing that may contribute to oligoclonality.[118,119]

T-cell changes resulting from diminished thymic function play a dominant role in age-related T- and B-cell changes. However, many areas merit further investigation including differential gene expression, signal transduction and co-stimulatory molecule alterations and changes in suppressor or regulatory T cells, and anti-idiotypic antibody networks between the lymphocytes of young and old individuals.

Immune Reconstitution after Hematopoietic Stem Cell Transplantation

Immune reconstitution in adults occurs after retroviral therapy for human immunodeficiency virus (HIV) infection and following high-dose chemotherapy or chemoradiotherapy with or without autologous or allogeneic HSCT. Although the trends are similar, this chapter does not discuss immune reconstitution in patients with HIV infection. There are multiple factors that could theoretically influence immune reconstitution after HSCT including type of graft (cord blood, bone marrow, peripheral blood, T-cell depleted, unmanipulated), disease, conditioning regimen, graft-versus-host disease (GVHD), recipient or donor age, cytokines, posttransplant immune suppressive or immune-modulating medications, and infections. Of these conditions, the factors that influence development of healthy immune reconstitution are factors that affect thymic function. For autologous HSCT, the dominant factor is patient age. For allogeneic HSCT, the predominant factors are recipient age, GVHD, and number of T-cells infused in the graft.

AUTOLOGOUS HEMATOPOIETIC STEM CELL TRANSPLANTATION

Posttransplant recovery is the inverse of aging with initial expansion of memory T-cells and delayed recovery from naive T-cells. Immune reconstitution after autologous HSCT is not affected by GVHD or immune suppressive medications and is reviewed first. NK cells, which regenerate independent of a thymus, recover normal number and function within 1 month of autologous bone marrow transplantation (BMT) or peripheral blood stem cell transplant (PBSCT).[120–126] After autologous BMT $CD3^+$ T cell number normalizes within 3 months.[127] The number of $CD4^+$ cells is decreased for 12 or more months.[128,129] $CD4^+CD45RA^+$ naive T-cells may take 1 to 2 years to reach normal numbers. By 3 months, $CD8^+$ cell numbers usually return to normal, leading to an inverted CD4/CD8 ratio for 12 or more months.[128,129] The $CD8^+$ cells tend to be $CD28^-$ consistent with expansion of memory T cells.[124,127,130–132]

Autologous PBSCT grafts contain 1-log greater T-cells than BM grafts and may be expected to hasten lymphopoiesis.[133]

However, CD4+ T-cell recovery and T-cell proliferative responses to mitogens are similar between autologous PBSCT and BMT and between unmanipulated PBSCT and CD34+ selected (i.e., T-cell depleted) PBSCT.[124,131,134] There is, however, a statistically significant correlation between CD4+ cell count reconstitution and age at time of transplant. The younger the patient, the more rapid the recovery of the CD4+ T-cell count.[124,130,134–136]

B-cell number is normal by 3 months, and IgM returns to normal in 6 months.[124,128,137–140] T-cell proliferative responses to mitogens may be reduced for 12 or more months[139,141,142] indicating lack of effective T-cell help in germinal center class switch rearrangements that results in subnormal IgG and IgA for 12 and 24 months, respectively.[131,138,139] The patient's disease and type of conditioning regimen particularly total body irradiation (TBI) versus non-TBI has not been reported to influence immune reconstitution. Radiation could cause more damage to thymic epithelium than chemotherapy, but little is available in the literature for comparison.

ALLOGENEIC HEMATOPOIETIC STEM CELL TRANSPLANTATION

Allogeneic grafts may be unmanipulated, T-cell depleted, or from cord blood and may be from a human leukocyte antigen (HLA)-matched sibling; a one, two, or three (haploidentical) antigen mismatched related donor; or an unrelated donor. The posttransplant course is often complicated by immunosuppressive medications and GVHD. TREC assays have confirmed T-cell regeneration after allogeneic HSCT. Both age and extensive chronic GHVD are associated with thymic involution and are strongly correlated with lower TREC recovery.[143–147] TREC recovery is more rapid and higher for younger patients (age <19 years old) (Fig. 68–7) and correlates with CD4+CD45RA+ T-cell recovery.[143] One manifestation of extensive chronic GVHD is lymphoid and thymic atrophy and low TREC values are associated with extensive chronic GVHD (Fig. 68–7).[144,148,149] TREC values and naive CD4+CD45RA+ T-cell recovery may also be delayed early after HSCT with T-cell depletion (TCD) allografts compared with unmanipulated allografts although differences diminish by 9 months after HSCT.[144,150] When corrected for GVHD and age, TREC recovery is not affected by whether the donor is HLA identical or HLA mismatched.[123,143,148] Low TREC values correlate with both a decrease in TCR diversity and increase in opportunistic infections.[144] Absent, monoclonal, or oligoclonal profiles for most Vβ TCR repertoires persists up to 6 months after allogeneic BMT, when normalization of TCR complexity starts.[151]

As mentioned previously for autologous transplants, immune reconstitution occurs at a similar pace for both BMT and PBSCT. In contrast for allogeneic HSCT, immune reconstitution for adults is faster with PBSCT compared with BMT (Fig. 68–8).[152,153] Peripheral blood provides a 10 times greater inoculum of lymphocytes with the graft compared with a marrow graft.[152] It may be during the first year after an allogeneic HSCT that most immune reconstitution arises from the T-cells infused with the graft. De novo generation of new T-cells from the stem cell compartment is hindered by thymic atrophy from clinical or subclinical GVHD and chronic immune suppressive therapy (i.e., cyclosporine).[154–157] Total CD4+ number and naive CD4+CD45RA+ T-cells recover more rapidly after PBSCT compared with BMT (Fig. 68–8). Similarly when compared with marrow total CD8+ and naive CD8+CD11a^{low} cells recover more rapidly with PBSCT (Fig. 68–8).[152,153] Independent of graft (marrow or blood), total CD4+ and CD4+CD45RA+ numbers remain depressed at 12 months after transplantation (Fig. 68–8).[120,121,152,153,158,159] Similar to an autologous HSCT, CD8+ cell numbers, most of which are infused memory cells, reach normal levels after day 100 (Fig. 68–8).[121] Thus, the thymic pathway may appear more important for CD4+ T-cells than CD8+ T-cell regeneration. However, most of the CD8+ T-cells are expanded graft-derived memory cells because naive CD8+CD11a^{low} cells that depend on thymic reconstitution remain low for more than 12 months.[153] Monocytes and NK cells arise extrathymically and are within normal range by 30 days independent of marrow or blood stem cell transplantation (Fig. 68–8).[120,122,123,145,152,153] Total B-cell numbers and naive B-cells (IgD+) normalize before 1 year with no difference between marrow and peripheral blood stem cell (PBSC) B-cell number after day 100 (Fig. 68–8).[122,153,160]

Lymphocyte dose in the graft has also been reported to be important for immune reconstitution when T-cell depleted grafts are compared with unmanipulated donor grafts.[122,150,161]

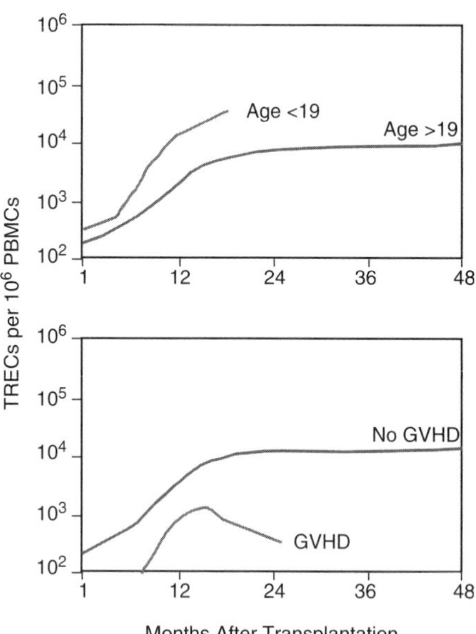

Figure 68–7. *Influence of age and graft-versus-host disease (GVHD) on T-cell receptor excision circle (TREC) reconstitution after allogeneic stem cell transplantation.* PBMCs, peripheral blood mononuclear cells. (Modified from Lewin, S.R., Heller, G., Zhang, L., Rodrigues, E., Skulsky, E., van den Brink, M.R.M., Small, T.N., Kernan, N.A., O'Reilly, R.J., Ho, D.D., and Young, J.W. [2002]. Direct evidence for new T-cell generation by patients after either T-cell–depleted or unmodified allogeneic hematopoietic stem cell transplantation. *Blood* **100,** 2235–2241.) (Please see CD-ROM for color version of this figure.)

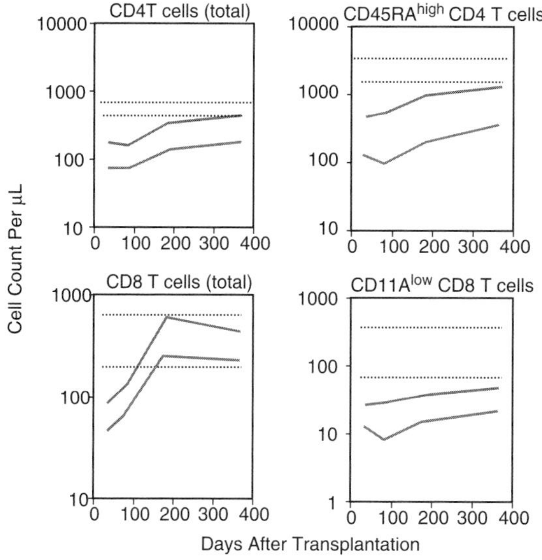

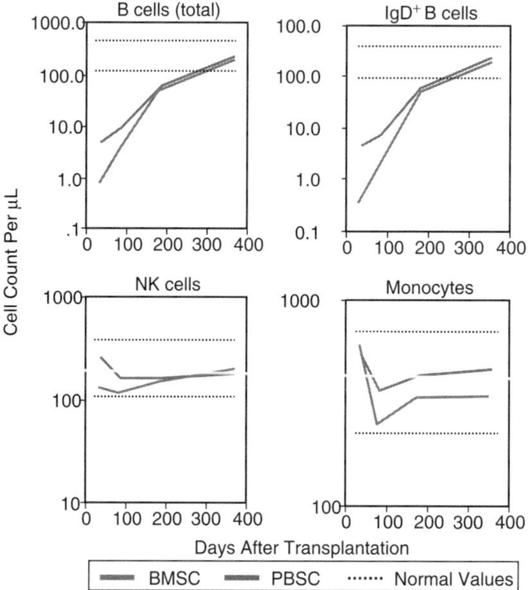

Figure 68–8. *Schematic diagrams of immune reconstitution after allogeneic bone marrow or allogeneic peripheral blood stem cell transplantation.* CD4 T cells, T helper (Th) cells; CD8 T cells, T cytotoxic (Tc) cells; CD11^{low}CD8 cells, naive T cytotoxic (Tc) cells; CD45^{high} CD4 T cells, naive T helper cells; IgD$^+$ B cells, naive B cells; NK cells, natural killer cells. (Modified from Storek, J., Dawson, M.A., Storer, B., Stevens-Ayers, T., Maloney, D.G., Marr, K.A., Witherspoon, R.P., Bensinger, W., Flowers, M.E.D., Martin, P., Storb, R., Appelbaum, F.R., and Boeckh, M. [2001]. Immune reconstitution after allogeneic marrow transplantation compared with blood stem cell transplantation. *Blood* **97,** 3380–3389.) (Please see CD-ROM for color version of this figure.)

T-cell spectratypes analysis showed delayed T-cell repertoire normalization after T-cell depleted allogeneic BMT compared with unmanipulated BMT.[162,163] For pediatric and adult patients receiving unrelated donor transplants, T-cell depleted marrow grafts manifest slower recovery of CD3$^+$, CD4$^+$, and CD4$^+$CD45RA$^+$ T-cells compared with unmanipulated grafts from an unrelated donor.[123,164] Immune reconstitution has been reported to be similarly slower in unrelated or mismatched related HSCT that received higher doses of lymphocyte depleting anti-thymocyte globulin compared with those receiving lower doses.[123,165] It has been observed in one study that immune recovery seemed to be more effective in highly CD34$^+$ purified haploidentical allografts compared with the CD34$^+$ selected matched unrelated.[166] However, although age, chronic GVHD, and the number of lymphocytes in the allograft affect immune reconstitution, in general HLA-match–mismatch related or unrelated grafts appear to have similar recovery of CD3$^+$, CD4$^+$, and CD8$^+$ T-cells.[167,168]

Because of limited number of cells, cord blood is generally restricted to children or young adults and is generally thought to have a lower risk of GVHD (both factors may be favorable for immune reconstitution). In general, immune reconstitution after unrelated cord blood stem cell transplantation has been reported to be similar to other allogeneic stem cell sources.[149,158] NK, CD19$^+$, and CD4$^+$ cell numbers are normal by 2 months, 6 months, and 12 months, respectively. Mitogen responses are normal by 6 to 9 months. The exception is that CD8$^+$ T-cell recovery may be more delayed than other stem cell sources with normal counts delayed until 9 months. Consequently, the CD4/CD8 ratio may be normal as early as 6 months after cord blood transplantation. Delayed CD8$^+$ cells recovery may be secondary to fewer CD8$^+$ antigen-stimulated memory T cells in cord blood.[149,160,169]

In general, the disease for which a stem cell recipient undergoes HSCT does not affect immune reconstitution. The exception is severe combined immune deficiency (SCID). SCID is marked by an absence of T cells. B cells may (B$^+$ SCID) or may not (B$^-$ SCID) be present. Patients with B$^+$ SCID have faster T- and B-cell reconstitution than B$^-$ SCID following HSCT. B$^+$ SCID may engraft without a conditioning regimen. NK cells are absent in B$^+$ SCID but are present in B$^-$ SCID. The presence of host NK cells increases the risk of graft rejection unless an immune suppressive conditioning regimen is used. Therefore, patients with B$^-$ SCID often receive an immune suppressive conditioning regimen before stem cell infusion. Conditioning regimens may damage the thymus and impair T-cell regeneration in B$^-$ SCID.[146,148,170,171] Evaluating immune responses for the first 3 months after HSCT, a study compared miniconditioning regimens (also known as nonmyeloablative transplant [NST] regimens) to intense myeloablative conditioning regimens. The myeloablative regimen markedly diminished T-cell mitogen responses. In contrast, early after a NST, the mitogen response was maintained.[172] The type (e.g., TBI) or intensity of the conditioning regimen's effect on immune reconstitution has generally not been investigated or reported, perhaps because the intensity of the different regimens have been basically similar. Minor differences in conditioning regimen-related thymic injury may be overshadowed by more important factors such as recipient age and presence or absence of GVHD.[162,172–176]

Although $CD19^+$ or $CD20^+$ B-cell number generally normalizes within the first few months after HSCT, B-cell function appears to be largely dependent on recovery of T-cell helper function. B-cell Ig production is diminished in patients with chronic GVHD compared with those without GVHD.[121,137,138,177] Antigen-specific titers after immunization are diminished or absent if GVHD is present. For this reason, after an allogeneic HSCT, reimmunization to childhood vaccines is delayed until the patient is off immune suppression without GVHD.[130,178]

Cytokines (predominately granulocyte colony-stimulating factor [G-CSF]) are used to mobilize PBSCs and to shorten the duration of postconditioning neutropenia. G-CSF promotes IL-4 and IL-10 Th2 cytokine production.[179] In addition, G-CSF preferentially mobilizes lymphoid dendritic (DC2) cells.[180,181] G-CSF mobilized PBSCs contain higher doses of DC2 compared with myeloid dendritic (DC1) cells. DC1 cells produce IL-12 and promote Th1-cell differentiation. DC2 cells promote Th2-cell differentiation.[182,183] It has been suggested that adoptive transfer of DC2 cells in the PBSC graft diminishes the risk of acute GVHD.[184,185] However, it is possible that DC2 cells may also increase the risk of chronic GVHD that may offset any potential immune reconstitution benefit. The role of cytokines and/or adoptive cell transfer in posttransplant immune reconstitution has yet to be fully appreciated. For example, IL-7 and oncostatin M are thymic cytokines that may be beneficial in posttransplant immune reconstitution.[41,42] In murine models, posttransplant IL-7 accelerated memory $CD4^+$ and $CD8^+$ T-cell regeneration without worsening GVHD. However, IL-7 had little effect on naive $CD4^+$ or $CD8^+$ T-cells.[186,187] As mentioned earlier Oncostatin M appears to induce extrathymic T-cell lymphogenesis in animal models and may be beneficial for naive $CD4^+$ and $CD8^+$ recovery following HSCT.

Autoimmune Diseases

Autologous HSCT is being performed for an increasing number of autoimmune diseases. The rationale is reviewed elsewhere.[188] The principles of immune reconstitution that affect autologous and allogeneic HSCT for malignancies (i.e., thymic recovery) probably apply equally well to autoimmune diseases. To date little data have been reported on immune reconstitution after autologous HSCT for autoimmune diseases. However, the same slow recovery of $CD4^+$, rapid return of $CD8^+$ cells, and inverted CD4/CD8 ratio has been reported.[141,189] Autoimmune diseases often have pretransplant disease-related immune abnormalities. It has been anticipated, but for the most part unstudied, that HSCT will correct these abnormalities.[190] Severe systemic lupus erythematosus manifests Th2 cytokine and TCR CDR3 spectratype receptor skewing. These abnormalities have been reported to normalize after autologous HSCT.[191] The autoantigen for most autoimmune diseases is unknown but, if known, HSCT will allow determination of autoantigen receptor clone frequency and correlation with disease symptoms. Alternatively, by following T-cell autoantigen specific clones for occurrence, frequency, and phenotype and correlating with disease manifestation, HSCT may allow determination of disease-specific initiating and spread epitopes.

Both autologous and allogeneic HSCT studies are currently ongoing throughout the world. Table 68-1 is a brief summary of benchmarks in clinical HSCT for autoimmune diseases. For autologous HSCT, autologous stem cells are similar to a blood transfusion in that they are supportive care and not treatment. The efficacy and toxicity lies entirely with the conditioning regimen. Therefore, the immune suppressive conditioning regimen should (1) be designed for immune ablation not myeloablation, (2) be based on dose escalation of immune suppressive agents that work as conventional therapy, (3) avoid conditioning regimen agents that may cause injury to already disease affected and damaged tissue, (4) avoid injury to tissue specific stem cell compartments that may be important for organ repair, and (5) have a regimen intensity that is justified for the risk of the disease being treated. For allogeneic HSCT, a graft versus autoimmune (GVA) effect that protects against disease relapse may be obtained from the disease resistant donor stem cell compartment. The risk benefit of an allogeneic HSCT can only be justified if graft versus host disease (GVHD) is eliminated. Therefore, allogeneic HSCT should be directed toward achieving stable mixed chimerism in which GVHD is avoided by lymphocyte depletion of the donor graft either *ex vivo* through positive or negative cell selection or *in vivo* with a potent T, B, and dendritic cell depleting agent such as CAMPATH-1H (Alemtuzumab). Otherwise, the principles of conditioning regimen design for allogeneic HSCT are the same as for autologous HSCT of autoimmune diseases.

Summary

Lymphopoiesis changes with age from thymic production to dependence on extrathymic mechanisms. After HSCT, the reverse occurs with early extrathymic lymphopoiesis followed by thymic regeneration of naive T-cells. The ultimate health of the graft is determined by the ability of the thymus to regenerate naive T-cells. After autologous HSCT, immune reconstitution is predominately affected by recipient age. Following an allogeneic HSCT, immune reconstitution correlates with recipient age, GVHD, and number of infused donor T-cells, all of which are related to thymic reconstitution. In general, immune reconstitution is not affected by donor age, type of graft, or disease. Conditioning regimen intensity may result in thymic injury and affect immune reconstitution, although this needs further investigation. Patient survival is associated with a healthy graft, which correlates with return of thymic reconstitution of T-cells. Poor thymic reconstitution as demonstrated by low TRECs, correlates with diminished T-cell receptor diversity, opportunistic infections, and lower patient survival. Future trials may be designed to improve immune reconstitution by using post-transplant cytokines such as IL-7 or Oncostatin M. The importance of thymic regeneration of T regulatory cells such as $CD4^+CD25^+$ T-cells following HSCT is unclear. Control of GVHD or autoimmune disease by $CD4^+CD25^+$ T-cells offers new opportunities for posttransplant

TABLE 68–1
Time Line of First Reported Hematopoietic Stem Cell Transplantation for Autoimmune Diseases

1993	Marmont, A.M. (1993). *Lupus* **2,** 151–156.	First editorial suggesting that HSCT should be used as treatment for SLE
1995	Burt, R.K. (1995). *Bone Marrow Transplant.* **16,** 1–6.	First editorial suggesting that HSCT should be used as treatment for MS
1995	Committee Chair, Alan Tyndall.	European Group for Blood and Marrow Transplantation (EBMT) and European League Against Rheumatism (EULAR) establish a working committee on stem cell transplant for autoimmune diseases for Europe and Asia
1995	Committee Chair, Richard Burt.	International Bone Marrow Transplantation Registry (IBMTR) and Autologous Blood and Marrow Transplant Registry (ABMTR) establish a working committee on stem cell transplant for autoimmune diseases for the Americas
1997	Fassas, A. (1997). *Bone Marrow Transplant.* **20,** 631–638.	First report of HSCT for MS in the world
1997	Marmont, A.M. (1997). *Lupus* **6,** 545–548.	First report of autologous HSCT for SLE in the world
1997	Burt, R.K. (1997). *N. Engl. J. Med.* **337,** 1777–1778.	First report of autologous HSCT for SLE in America
1997	Joske, D.J. (1997). *Lancet* **350,** 337.	First report of autologous HSCT for RA in the world
1997	Tyndall, A. (1997). *Lancet* **349,** 254.	First report of autologous HSCT for scleroderma
1998	Burt, R.K. (1998). *Bone Marrow Transplant.* **21,** 537–541.	First report of autologous HSCT for MS in America
1999	Wulffraat, N. (1999). *Lancet* **353,** 550–553.	First report of autologous HSCT for juvenile chronic arthritis in the world
1999	Burt, R.K. (1999). *Arthritis Rheum.* **42,** 2281–2285.	First report of autologous HSCT for RA in America
1999	Burt, R.K., Burns, W.H., and Sullivan, K. (Contract principal investigators).	National Institutes of Health (NIH) awards three contracts to develop phase III trials of HSCT for autoimmune diseases
2000	Slavin, S. (2000). *Exp. Hematol.* **28,** 853–857.	First clinical evidence of allogeneic graft versus autoimmunity (GVA) effect
2001	Snowden, J. (Principal investigator).	EBMT/EULAR opens phase III trial of autologous HSCT for RA
2001	van Laar J. (Principal investigator).	EBMT/EULAR opens phase III trial of autologous HSCT for scleroderma
2002	Burt, R.K. (2003). *Blood* **101,** 2064–2066.	First report of autologous HSCT for Crohn's disease in the world
2004	Burt, R.K. (2004). *Arthritis Rheum.* (In press).	First report of allogeneic HSCT for the indication of rheumatoid arthritis in the world

EBMT, European Bone Marrow Transplant Registry; EULAR, European League Against Rheuamtism; HSCT, hematopietic stem cell transplantation; MS, multiple sclerosis; RA, rheuamtoid arthritis; SLE, systemic lupus erythematosus.

adoptive immunotherapy and/or preservation and cytokine enhancement of thymic function.

REFERENCES

1. Venter, J.C., Adams, M.D., Myers, E.W., Li, P.W., Mural, R.J., Sutton, G.G., Smith, H.O., Yandell, M., Evans, C.A., Holt, R.A., *et al.* (2001). The sequence of the human genome. *Science* **291,** 1304–1351.
2. Tomanaga, S., Hirokane, H., and Awaya, K. (1973). The primitive spleen of the hagfish. *Zool. Mag.* **82,** 215–217.
3. Zapata, A., and Amemiya, C.T. (2000). Phylogeny of lower vertebrates and their immunological structures. *Curr. Top. Microbiol. Immunol.* **248,** 67–107.
4. Du Pasquier, L., and Flajnik, M. (1999). Origin and evolution of the vertebrate immune system. *In* "Fundamental Immunology," 4th ed. (W.J. Paul, Ed.), pp. 605–650. Lippincott-Raven Publishers, Philadelphia.
5. Sprent, J, and Webb, S.R. (1995). Intrathymic and extrathymic clonal deletion of T cells. *Curr. Opin. Immunol.* **7,** 196–205.
6. Von Boehmer, H. (1994). Positive selection of lymphocytes. *Cell* **76,** 219–228.
7. Nossal, G.J.V. (1994). Negative selection of lymphocytes. *Cell* **76,** 229–240.

8. Nel, A.E. (2002). T-cell activation through the antigen receptor. Part 1: Signaling components, signaling pathways, and signal integration at the T-cell antigen receptor synapse. *J. Allergy Clin. Immunol.* **109,** 758–770.
9. Nel, A.E., and Slaughter, N. (2002). T-cell activation through the antigen receptor. Part 2: Role of signaling cascades in T-cell differentiation, anergy, immune senescence, and development of Immunotherapy. *J. Allergy Clin. Immunol.* **109,** 901–915.
10. Sebzda, E., Mariathasan, S., Ohteki, T., Jones, R., Bachmann, M.E., and Ohashi, P.S. (1999). Selection of the T cell repertoire. *Annu. Rev. Immunol.* **17,** 829–874.
11. Kay, M.M., Mendoza, J., Diven, J., Denton, T., Union, N., and Lajiness, M. (1979). Age-related changes in the immune system of mice of eight medium and long-lived strains and hybrids. *Mech. Ageing Dev.* **11,** 295–346.
12. de Vries, E., de Groot, R., de Bruin-Versteeg, S., Comans-Bitter, W.M., and van Dongen, J.J. (1999). Analyzing the developing lymphocyte system of neonates and infants. *Eur. J. Pediatr.* **158,** 611–617.
13. Bell, E.B., and Sparshott, S.M. (1990). Interconversion of CD45R subsets of CD4 T cells in vivo. *Nature* **348,** 163–166.
14. Brod, S.A., Rudd, C.E., Purvee, M., and Hafler, D.A. (1989). Lymphokine regulation of CD45R expression on human T cell clones. *J. Exp. Med.* **170,** 2147–2152.
15. Steffens, C.M., Al-Harthi, L., Shott, S., Yogev, R., and Landay, A. (2000). Evaluation of thymopoiesis using T cell receptor excision circles (TRECs): differential correlation between adult and pediatric TRECs and naive phenotypes. *Clin. Immunol.* **97,** 95–101.
16. Utsuyama, M., Hirokawa, K., Kurashima, C., Fukayama, M., Inamatsu, T., Suzuki, K., Hashimoto, W., and Sato, K. (1992). Differential age-change in the numbers of $CD4^{+}CD45RA^{+}$ and $CD4+CD29^{+}$ T cell subsets in human peripheral blood. *Mech. Ageing Dev.* **63,** 57–68.
17. Reason, D.C., Ebisawa, M., Saito, H., Nagakura, T., and Iikira Y. (1990). Human cord blood lymphocytes do not simultaneously express CD4 and CD8 cell surface markers. *Biol. Neonate* **58,** 87–90.
18. Griffiths-Chu, S., Patterson, J.A.K., Berger, C.L., Edelson, R.L., and Chu, A.C. (1984). Characterization of immature T cell subpopulations in neonatal blood. *Blood* **64,** 296–300.
19. McFarland, R.D., Douek, D.C., Koup, R.A., and Picker, L.J. (2000). Identification of a human recent thymic emigrant phenotype. *Proc. Natl. Acad. Sci. U. S. A.* **97,** 4215–4220.
20. Sempowski, G.D., Thomasch, J.R., Gooding, M.E., Hale, L.P., Edwards, L.J., Ciafaloni, E., Sanders, D.B., Massey, J.M., Douek, D.C., Koup, R.A., and Haynes BF. (2001). Effect of thymectomy on human peripheral blood T cell pools in myasthenia gravis. *J. Immunol.* **166,** 2808–2817.
21. Reimann, J. (1991). Double-negative (CD4-CD8-), TCRαβ-expressing, peripheral T cells. *Scand. J. Immunol.* **34,** 679–688.
22. Hazenberg, M.D., Verschuren, M.C.M., Hamann, D., Miedema, F., and van Dongen, J.J.M. (2001). T cell receptor excision circles as markers for recent thymic emigrants: basic aspects, technical approach, and guidelines for interpretation. *J. Mol. Med.* **79,** 631–640.
23. Douek, D.C., McFarland, R.D., Keiser, P.H., Gage, E.A., Massey, J.M., Haynes, B.F., Polis, M.A., Haase, A.T., Feinberg, M.B., Sullivan, J.L., Jamieson, B.D., Zack, J.A., Picker, L.J., and Koup, R.A. (1998). Changes in thymic function with age and during the treatment of HIV infection. *Nature* **396,** 690–695.
24. Ye, P., and Kirschner, D.E. (2002). Reevaluation of T cell receptor excision circles as a measure of human recent thymic emigrants. *J. Immunol.* **169,** 4968–4979.
25. Hazenberg, M.D., Borghans, J.A.M., de Boer, R.J., and Miedema, F. (2003). Thymic output: a bad TREC record. *Nat. Immunol.* **4,** 97–99.
26. Howie, D., Spencer, J., DeLord, D., Pitzalis, C., Wathen, N.C., Dogan, A., Akbar, A., and MacDonald, T.T. (1998). Extrathymic T cell differentiation in the human intestine early in life. *J. Immunol.* **161,** 5862–5872.
27. Guy-Grand, D., Azogui, O., Celli, S., Darche, S., Nussenzweig, M.C., Kourilsky, P., and Vassalli, P. (2003). Extrathymic T cell lymphopoiesis: ontogeny and contribution to gut intraepithelial lymphocytes in athymic and euthymic mice. *J. Exp. Med.* **197,** 333–341.
28. Lary, K., Lefrancois, L., Lingenheld, E.G., Ishikawa, H., Lewis, J.M., Olson, S., Suzuki, K., Tigelaar, R.E., and Puddington, L. (2000). Enterocyte expression of Il-7 induces development of γδ T cell and Peyer's patches. *J. Exp. Med.* **191,** 1569–1580.
29. Peschon, J.J., Morrissey, P.J., Grabstein, K.H., Ramsdell, F.J., Maraskovsky, E., Gliniak, B.C., Park, L.S., Ziegler, S.F., Williams, D.E., and Ware, C.B. (1994). Early lymphocyte expansion is severely impaired in interleukin 7 receptor-deficient mice. *J. Exp. Med.* **180,** 1955–1960.
30. Rocha, B., Guy-Grand, D., and Vassalli, P. (1995). Extrathymic T cell differentiation. *Curr. Opin. Immunol.* **7,** 235–242.
31. Mowat, A.M.I., and Viney, J.L. (1997). The anatomical basis of intestinal immunity. *Immunol. Rev.* **156,** 145–166.
32. Guy-Grand, D., Cerf-Bensussan, N., Malissen, B., Malasis-Seris, M., Briotet, C., and Vassalli, P. (1991). Two gut intraepithelial CD8+ lymphocyte populations with different T cell receptors: A role for the gut epithelium in T cell differentiation. *J. Exp. Med.* **173,** 471–481.
33. Poussier, P., and Julius, M. (1994). Thymus independent T cell development and selection in the intestinal epithelium. *Annu. Rev. Immunol.* **12,** 521–553.
34. Konno, A., Okada, K., Mizuno, K., Nagaoki, S., Toma, T., Uehara, T., Ohta, K., Kasahara, Y., Seki, H., Yachie, A., and Koizumi, S. (2002). CD8αα memory effector T cells descend directly from clonally expanded $CD8\alpha+\beta^{low}$ TCRαβ T cells in vivo. *Blood* **100,** 4090–4097.
35. Kennedy, J.D., Pierce, C.W., and Lake, J.P. (1992). Extrathymic T cell maturation. *J. Immunol.* **148,** 1620–1629.
36. Antica, M., and Scollay, R. (1999). Development of T lymphocytes at extrathymic sites. *J. Immunol.* **163,** 206–211.
37. Maleckar, J.R., and Sherman, L.A. (1987). The composition of the T cell receptor repertoire in nude mice. *J. Immunol.* **138,** 3873–3876.
38. Collard, H.R., Boeck, A., Mc Maughlin, T.M., Watson, T.J., Schiff, S.E., Hale, L.P., and Markert, M.L. (1999). Possible extrathymic development of nonfunctional T cells in a patient with complete DiGeorge syndrome. *Clin. Immunol.* **91,** 156–162.
39. Wang, X., Dao, M.A., Kuo, I., and Nolta, J.A. (2001). Phenotypic comparison of extrathymic human bone-marrow-derived T cells with thymic-selected T cells recovered from different tissues. *Clin. Immunol.* **100,** 339–348.
40. Pawelec, G., Muller, R., Rehbein, A., Hahnel, K., and Ziegler, B.L. (1998). Extrathymic T cell differentiation in vitro from human CD34+ stem cells. *J. Leukocyte Biol.* **64,** 733–739.
41. Boileau, C., Houde, M., Dulude, G., Clegg, C.H., and Perreault, C. (2000). Regulation of extrathymic T cell development and turnover by oncostatin M. *J. Immunol.* **164,** 5713–5720.
42. Clegg, C.H., Rulffes, J.T., Wallace, P.M., and Haugen, H.S. (1996). Regulation of an extrathymic T-cell development pathway by oncostatin M. *Nature* **384,** 261–263.

43. Clegg, C.H., Haugen, H.S., Rulffes, J.T., Friend, S.L., and Farr, A.G. (1999). Oncostatin M transforms lymphoid tissue function in transgenic mice by stimulating lymph node T-cell development and thymus autoantibody production. *Exp. Hematol.* **27,** 712–725.
44. Terra, R., Labrecque, N., and Perreault, C. (2002). Thymic and extrathymic T cell development pathways follow different rules. *J. Immunol.* **169,** 684–692.
45. Tsark, E.C., Dao, M.A., Wang, X., Weinberg, K., and Nolta, J.A. (2001). IL-7 enhances the responsiveness of human T cells that develop in the bone marrow of athymic mice. *J. Immunol.* **166,** 170–181.
46. Wilson, S.B., Kent, S.C., Patton, K.T., Orban, T., Jackson, R.A., Exley, M., Porcelli, S., Schatz, D.A., Atkinson, M.A., Balk, S.P., Strominger, J.L., and Hafler, D.A. (1998). Extreme Th1 bias of invariant Vα25JαQ T cells in type 1 diabetes. *Nature* **391,** 177–181.
47. Bendelac, A., Killeen, N., Littman, D., and Schwartz, R.H. (1994). A subset of CD4+ thymocytes selected by MHC class I molecules. *Science 263,* 1774–1778.
48. Godfrey, D.I., Hammond, K.J.L., Poulton, L.D., and Baxter, A.G. (2000). NKT cells: facts, functions and fallacies. *Immunol. Today* **21,** 573–583.
49. Lee, P.T., Benlagha, K., Teyton, L., and Bendelac, A. (2002). Distinct functional lineages of human Vα24 natural killer T cells. *J. Exp. Med.* **195,** 637–641.
50. Bendelac, A., Rivera, M.N., Park, S.-H., and Roark, J.H. (1997). Mouse CD1-specific NK1 T cells: development, specificity, and function. *Annu. Rev. Immunol.* **15,** 535–562.
51. Abo, T., Kawamura, T., and Watanabe, H. (2000). Physiological responses of extrathymic T cells in the liver. *Immunol. Rev.* **174,** 135–149.
52. Makino, Y., Yamagata, N., Sasho, T., Adachi, Y., Kanno, R., Koseki, H., Kanno, M., and Taniguchi, M. (1993). Extrathymic development of V[alpha]14-positive cells. *J. Exp. Med.* **177,** 1399–1408.
53. Taniguchi, M., Makino, Y., Cui, J., Masuda, K., Kawano, T., Sato, H., Kondo, E., and Koseki, H. (1996). V[alpha]14+ NKT cells: a novel lymphoid cell lineage with regulatory function. *J. Allergy Clin. Immunol.* **98,** 263–269.
54. Roncarolo, M.G., and Levings, M.K. The role of different subsets of T regulatory cells in controlling autoimmunity. *Curr. Opin. Immunol.* **12,** 676–683.
55. Shevach, E.M. (2000). Regulatory T cells in autoimmunity. *Annu. Rev. Immunol.* **18,** 423–449.
56. Jordan, M.S., Boesteanu, A., Reed, A.J., Petrone, A.L., Holenbeck, A.E., Lerman, M.A., Naji, A., and Caton, A.J. (2001). Thymic selection of $CD4^+CD25^+$ regulatory cells induced by an agonist self-peptide. *Nat. Immunol.* **2,** 301–306.
57. Thornton, A.M., and Shevach, E.M. (2000). Suppressor effector function of $CD4^+CD25^+$ immunoregulatory T cells is antigen nonspecific. *J. Immunol.* **164,** 183–190.
58. Levings, M.K., Sangregorio, R., and Roncarolo, M.G. (2001). Human $CD25^+CD4^+$ T regulatory cells suppress naive and memory T-cell proliferation and can be expanded *in vitro* without loss of function. *J. Exp. Med.* **193,** 1295–1302.
59. Dieckmann, D., Plottner, H., Berchtold, S., and Berger, T. (2001). Ex vivo isolation and characterization of $CD4^+CD25^+$ T cells with regulatory properties from human blood. *J. Exp. Med.* **193,** 1303–1310.
60. Ng, W.F., Duggan, P.J., Ponchel, F., Matarese, G., Lombardi, G., Edwards, A.D., Isaacs, J.D., and Lechler, R.I. (2001). Human CD4(+)CD25(+) cells: a naturally occurring population of regulatory T cells. *Blood* **98,** 2736–2744.
61. Baecher-Allan, C., Brown, J.A., Freeman, G.J., and Hafler, D.A. (2001). $CD4^+CD25$ high regulatory cells in human peripheral blood. *J. Immunol.* **167,** 1245–1253.
62. Shevach, E.M. (2001). Certified professionals: CD4(+)CD25(+) suppressor T cells. *J. Exp. Med.* **193,** F41–46.
63. Sakaguchi, S. (2000). Regulatory T cells: key controllers of immunologic self-tolerance. *Cell* **101,** 455–458.
64. Salomon, B., Lenschow, D.J., Rhee, L., Ashourian, N., Singh, B., Sharpe, A., and Bluestone, J.A. (2000). B7/CD28 costimulation is essential for the homeostasis of the $CD4^+CD25^+$ immunoregulatory T cells that control autoimmune diabetes. *Immunity* **12,** 431–440.
65. Longo, N.S., and Lipsky, P.E. (2001). Somatic hypermutation in human B cell subsets. *Springer Semin. Immunopathol.* **23,** 367–385.
66. Hasler, P., and Zouali, M. (2001). B cell receptor signaling and autoimmunity. *FASEB J.* **14,** 2085–2098.
67. Rajewsky, K. (1996). Clonal selection and learning in the antibody system. *Nature* **381,** 751–758.
68. Reth, M. (1992). Antigen receptors on B lymphocytes. *Annu. Rev. Immunol.* **10,** 97–121.
69. Kurosaki, T., Johnson, S.A., Pao, L., Sada, K., Yamamura, H., and Cambier, J.C. (1995). Role of Syk autophosphorylation site and SH2 domains in B cell receptor signaling. *J. Exp. Med.* **182,** 1815–1823.
70. Gold, M.R., Matsuuchi, L., Kelly, R.B., and DeFranco, A.L. (1991). Tyrosine phosphorylation of components of the B-cell antigen receptors following receptor crosslinking. *Proc. Natl. Acad. Sci. U. S. A.* **88,** 3436–3440.
71. Honjo, T., Kinoshita, K., and Muramatsu, M. (2002). Molecular mechanism of class switch recombination: linkage with somatic hypermutation. *Annu. Rev. Immunol.* **20,** 165–196.
72. Diaz, M, and Casali, P. (2002). Somatic immunoglobulin hypermutation. *Curr. Opin. Immunol.* **14,** 235–240.
73. Flajnik, M.F. (2002). Comparative analyses of immunoglobulin genes: surprises and portents. *Nat. Rev. Immunol.* **2,** 688–698.
74. Papavasiliou, F.N., and Schtaz, D.G. (2002). Somatic hypermutation of immunoglobulin genes: merging mechanisms for genetic diversity. *Cell* **109,** S35–S44.
75. Jacobs, H., and Bross, L. (2001). Towards an understanding of somatic hypermutation. *Curr. Opin. Immunol.* **13,** 208–218.
76. Arpin, C., Dechanet, J., Van Kooten, C., Merville, P., Grouard, G., Briere, F., Banchereau, J., and Liu, Y.-J. (1995). Generation of memory B cells and plasma cells in vitro. *Science* **268,** 720–722.
77. Clark, E.A., and Ledbetter, J.A. (1994). How B and T cells talk to each other. *Nature* **367,** 425–428.
78. Kuppers, R., Klein, U., Hansmann, M.L., and Rajewsky, K. (1999). Cellular origin of human B-cell lymphomas. *N. Engl. J. Med.* **341,** 1520–1529.
79. de Vries, E., de Bruin-Versteeg, S., Comans-Bitter, W.M., de Groot, R., Hop, W.C.J., Boerma, G.J.M., Lotgering, F.K., and van Dongen, J.J.M. (2000). Longitudinal survey of lymphocyte subpopulations in the first year of life. *Pediatr. Res.* **47,** 528–537.
80. Comans-Bitter, M.W., de Groot, R., van den Beemd, R., Neijens, H., Hop, W.S.J., Groeneveld, K., Hooijkaas, H., and van Dongen, J.J.M. (1997). Immunophenotyping of blood lymphocytes in childhood: reference values for lymphocyte subpopulations. *J. Pediatr.* **130,** 388–393.
81. Erkeller-Yuksel, F.M., Deneys, V., Hannet, I., Hulstaert, F., Hamilton, C., Mackinnon, H., Stokes, L.T., Munhyeshuli, V., and Vanlangendonck, F. (1991). Age-related changes in human blood lymphocyte subpopulations. *J. Pediatr.* **120,** 216–222.

82. Ben-Yehuda, A., and Weksler, M.E. (1992). Immune senescence: mechanisms and clinical implications. *Cancer Invest.* **10,** 525–531.
83. Cossarizza, A., Ortolani, C., Monti, D., and Franceschi, C. (1997). Cytometric analysis of immunosenescence. *Cytometry* **27,** 297–313.
84. Tarazona, R., Solana, R., Ouyang, Q., and Pawelec, G. (2002). Basic biology and clinical impact of immunosenescence. *Exp. Gerontol.* **37,** 183–189.
85. Thoman, M.L., and Weigle, W.O. (1989). The cellular and subcellular bases of immunosenescence. *Adv. Immunol.* **46,** 221–261.
86. Ferguson, F.G., Wikby, A., Maxson, P., Olsson, J., and Johansson, B. (1995). Immune parameters in a longitudinal study of a very old population of Swedish people: a comparison between survivors and nonsurvivors. *J. Gerontol.* **50A,** B378–B382.
87. Ginaldi, L., De Martinis, M., D'Ostilio, A., Marini, L., Loreto, F., Modesti, M., and Quanglino, D. (2001). Changes in the expression of surface receptors on lymphocyte subsets in the elderly: quantitative flow cytometric analysis. *Am. J. Hematol.* **67,** 63–72.
88. Thoman, M.L. (1997). Early steps in T cell development are affected by aging. *Cell Immunol.* **178,** 117–123.
89. Mackall, C.L., and Gress, R.E. (1997). Thymic aging and T-cell regeneration. *Immunol. Rev.* **160,** 91–102.
90. LeMaoult, J., Messaoudi, I., Manavalan, J.S., Potvin, H., Nikolich-Zugich, D., Dyall, R., Szabo, P., Weksler, M.E., and Nikolich-Zulich, J. (2000). Age-related dysregulation in CD8 T cell homeostasis: kinetics of a diversity loss. *J. Immunol.* **165,** 2367–2373.
91. Pannetier, C., Even, J., and Kourilsky, P. (1995). T-cell repertoire diversity and clonal expansions in normal and clinical samples. *Immunol. Today* **16,** 176–181.
92. Franceschi, C., Monti, D., Sansoni, P., and Cossarizza, A. (1995). The immunology of exceptional individuals: the lesson of centenarians. *Immunol. Today* **16,** 12–16.
93. Song, H., Price, P.W., and Cerny, J. (1997). Age-related changes in antibody repertoire: contribution from T cells. *Immunol. Rev.* **160,** 55–62.
94. Liu, Y.J., de Bouteiller, O., and Fugier-Vivier, I. (1997). Mechanisms of selection and differentiation in germinal centers. *Curr. Opin. Immunol.* **9,** 256–262.
95. Mackall, C.L., Punt, J.A., Morgan, P., Farr, A.G., and Gress, R.E. (1998). Thymic function in young/old chimeras: substantial thymic T cell regenerative capacity despite irreversible age-associated thymic involution. *Eur. J. Immunol.* **28,** 1886–1893.
96. Douziech, N., Seres, I., Larbi, A., Szikszay, E., Roy, P.M., Arcand, M., Dupuis, G., and Fulop, Jr., T. Modulation of human lymphocyte proliferative response with aging. *Exp. Gerontol.* **37,** 369–387.
97. Huang, Y.-P., Pechere, J.-C., Michel, M., Gauthey, L., Loreto, M., Curran, J.A., and Michel, J.-P. (1992). In vivo T cell activation, in vitro defective IL-2 secretion, and response to Influenza vaccination in elderly women. *J. Immunol.* **148,** 715–722.
98. Guidi, L., Bartoloni, C., Frasca, D., Antico, L., Pili, R., Cursi, F., Tempesta, E., Rumi, C., Menini, E., Carbonin, P., Doria, G., and Gambassi, G. (1991). Impairment of lymphocyte activities in depressed aged subjects. *Mech. Ageing Dev.* **60,** 13–24.
99. McNerlan, S.E., Rea, I.M., and Alexander, H.D. (2002). A whole blood method for measurement of intracellular TNF-α, IFN-γ and Il-2 expression in stimulated $CD3^+$ lymphocytes: Differences between young and elderly subjects. *Exp. Gerontol.* **37,** 227–234.
100. Wayne, S.J., Rhyne, R.L., Garry, P.J., and Goodwin, J.S. (1990). Cell-mediated immunity as a predictor of morbidity and mortality in subjects over 60. *J. Gerontol.* **45,** M45–48.
101. Dennett, N.S., Barcia, R.N., and McLeod, J.D. (2002). Age associated decline in CD25 and CD28 expression correlate with an increased susceptibility to CD95 mediated apoptosis in T cells. *Exp. Gerontol.* **37,** 271–283.
102. Pahlavani, M.A., Harris, M.D., and Richardson, A. (1995). The age-related decline in the induction of the IL-2 transcription is correlated to changes in the transcription factor NFAT. *Cell Immunol.* **165**, 84–91.
103. Colonna-Romano, G., Potestio, M., Aquino, A., Candore, G., Lio, D., and Caruso, C. (2001). Gamma/delta T lymphocytes are affected in the elderly. *Exp. Gerontol.* **37,** 205–211.
104. Kawakami, T., Kawakami, Y., Aaronson, S.A., and Robins, K.C. (1988). Acquisition of transforming properties by FYN, a normal SRC-related human gene. *Proc. Natl. Acad. Sci. U. S. A.* 85, 3870–3874.
105. Guidi, L., Antico, L., Bartoloni, C., Costanzo, M., Errani, A., Tricerri, A., Vangeli, M., Doria, G., Gatta, L., Goso, C., Mancino, L., and Frasca, D. (1998). Changes in the amount and level of phosphorylation of p56(lck) in PBL from aging humans. *Mech. Ageing Dev.* **102,** 177–186.
106. Pawelec, G., Hirokawa, K., and Fulop, T. (2001). Altered T cell signalling in ageing. *Mech. Ageing Dev.* **122,** 1613–1637.
107. Miller, R.A. (1996). The aging immune system: Primer and prospectus. *Science* **273,** 70–74.
108. Tamir, A., Eisenbraun, M.D., Garcia, G.G., and Miller, R.A. (2000). Age-dependent alterations in the assembly of signal transduction complexes at the site of T cell/APC interaction. *J. Immunol.* **165,** 1243–1253.
109. Fernandez-Gutierrez, B., Jover, J.A., De Miguel, S., Hernandez-Garcia, C., Vidan, M.T., Ribera, J.M., Banares, A., and Serra, J.A. (1999). Early lymphocyte activation in elderly humans: impaired T and T-dependent B cell responses. *Exp. Gerontol.* **34,** 217–229.
110. Klinman, N.R., and Kline, G.H. (1997). The B-cell biology of aging. *Immunol. Rev.* **160,** 103–114.
111. LeMaoult, J., Szabo, P., and Weksler, M.E. (1997). Effect of age on humoral immunity, selection of the B-cell repertoire and B-cell development. *Immunol. Rev.* **160,** 115–126.
112. Waldschmidt, T.J., Panoskaltsis-Mortaro, A., McElmurry, R.T., Tygrett, L.T., Taylor, P.A., and Blazar, B.R. (2002). Abnormal T-cell dependent B-cell responses in SCID mice receiving allogeneic bone marrow in utero. Severe combined immune deficiency. *Blood* **100,** 4557–4564.
113. Hinkley, K.S., Chiasson, R.J., Prior, T.K., and Riggs, J.E. (2002). Age-dependent increase of peritoneal B-1b B cells in SCID mice. *Immunology* **105,** 196–203.
114. Weksler, M.E., Russo, C., and Siskind, G.W. (1989). Peripheral T cells select the B cell repertoire in old mice. *Immunol. Rev.* **110,** 173–185.
115. Gottesman, S.R., Walford, R.L., and Thorbecke, G.J. (1984). Proliferative and cytotoxic immune function in aging mice. II. Decreased generation of specific suppressor cells in alloreactive cultures. *J. Immunol.* **133,** 1782–1787.
116. Gottesman, S.R., Walford, R.L., and Thorbecke, G.J. (1985). Proliferative and cytotoxic immune function in aging mice. III. Exogenous interleukin-2 rich supernatant only partially restores alloreactivity in vitro. *Mech. Ageing Dev.* **31,** 103–113.
117. Thoman, M.L., and Weigle, W.O. (1983). Deficiency in suppressor T cell activity in aged animals. Reconstitution of this activity by interleukin 2. *J. Exp. Med.* **157,** 2184–2189.

118. Wang, X., and Stollar, B.D. (1999). Immunoglobulin VH gene expression in human aging. *Clin. Immunol.* **93,** 132–142.
119. Banerjee, M., Mehr, R., Belelovsky, A., Spencer, J., and Dunn-Walters, D.K. (2002). Age- and tissue-specific differences in human germinal center B cell selection revealed by analysis of IgV_H gene hypermutation and lineage trees. *Eur. J. Immunol.* **32,** 1947–1957.
120. Shenoy, S., Mohanakumar, T., Todd, G., Westhoff, W., Dunnigan, K., Adkins, D.R., Brown, R.A., and DiPersio, J.F. (1999). Immune reconstitution following allogeneic peripheral blood stem cell transplants. *Bone Marrow Transplant.* **23,** 335–346.
121. Fujimaki, K., Maruta, A., Yoshida, M., Kodama, F., Matsuzaki, M., Fujisawa, S., Kanamori, H., and Ishigatsubo, Y. (2001). Immune reconstitution assessed during five years after allogeneic bone marrow transplantation. *Bone Marrow Transplant.* **27,** 1275–1281.
122. Novitzky, N., Davison, G.M., Hale, G., and Waldmann, H. (2002). Immune reconstitution at 6 months following T-cell depleted hematopoietic stem cell transplantation is predictive for treatment outcome. *Transplantation* **74,** 1551–1559.
123. Small, T.N., Papadopoulos, E.B., Boulad, F., Black, P., Castro-Malaspina, H., Childs, B.H., Collins, N., Gillio, A., George, D., Jakubowski, A., Heller, G., Fazzari, M., Kernan, N., MacKinnon, S., Szabolics, P., Young, J.W., and O'Reilly, R.J. (1999). Comparison of immune reconstitution after unrelated and related T-cell depleted bone marrow transplantation: effect of patient age and donor leukocyte infusions. *Blood* **93,** 467–480.
124. Hoepfner, S., Haut, P.R., O'Gorman, M., and Kletzel, M. (2003). Rapid immune reconstitution following autologous hematopoietic stem cell transplantation in children: a single institution experience. *Bone Marrow Transplant.* **31,** 285–290.
125. Lamb, Jr., L.S., Gee, A.P., Henslee-Downey, P.J., Geier, S.S., Hazlett, L., Pati, A.R., Godder, K., Abhyankar, S.A., Turner, M.W., Lee, C., Harris, W.G., and Parrish, R.S. (1998). Phenotypic and functional reconstitution of peripheral blood lymphocytes following T-cell depleted bone marrow transplantation from partially mismatched related donors. *Bone Marrow Transplant.* **21,** 461–471.
126. Moretta, A., Maccario, R., Fagioli, F., Giraldi, E., Busca, A., Montagna, D., Miniero, R., Comoli, P., Giorgiani, G., Zecca, M., Pagani, S., and Locatelli, F. (2001). Analysis of immune reconstitution in children undergoing cord blood transplantation. *Exp. Hematol.* **29,** 371–379.
127. Sugita, K., Soiffer, R.J., Murray, C., Schlossman, S.F., Ritz, J., and Morimoto, C. (1994). The phenotype and reconstitution of immunoregulatory T cell subsets after T-cell-depleted allogeneic and autologous bone marrow transplantation. *Transplantation* **57,** 1465–1473.
128. Anderson, K.C., Ritz, J., Takvorian, T., Coral, F., Daley, H., Gorgone, B.C., Freedman, A.S., Canellos, G.P., Schlossman, S.F., and Nadler, L.M. (1987). Hematologic engraftment and immune reconstitution posttransplantation with anti-B1 purged autologous bone marrow. *Blood* **69,** 597–604.
129. Schlenke, P., Sheikhzadeh, S., Weber, K., Wagner, T., and Kirchner, H. (2001). Immune reconstitution and production of intracellular cytokines in T lymphocyte populations following autologous peripheral blood stem cell transplantation. *Bone Marrow Transplant.* **28,** 251–257.
130. Guillaume, T., Rubinstein, D.B., and Symann, M. (1998). Immune reconstitution and immunotherapy after autologous hematopoietic stem cell transplantation. *Blood* **92,** 1471–1490.
131. Mackall, C.L., Stein, D., Fleisher, T.A., Brown, M.R., Hakim, F.T., Bare, C.V., Leitman, S.F., Read, E.J., Carter, C.S., Wexler, L.H., and Gress, R.E. (2000). Prolonged CD4 depletion after sequential autologous peripheral blood progenitor cell infusions in children and young adults. *Blood* **96,** 754–762.
132. Leblond, V., Othman, T.B., Blanc, C., Theodorou, I., Choquet, S., Sutton, L., Debre, P., and Autran, B. (1997). Expansion of $CD4^+CD7^-$ T cells, a memory subset with preferential interleukin-4 production, after bone marrow transplantation. *Transplantation* **64,** 1453–1459.
133. Weaver, C.H., Longin, K., Buckner, C.D., and Bensinger, W. (1994). Lymphocyte content in peripheral blood mononuclear cells collected after the administration of recombinant human granulocyte colony-stimulating factor. *Bone Marrow Transplant.* **13,** 411–415.
134. Bomberger, C., Singh-Jairam, M., Rodey, G., Guerriero, A., Yeager, A.M., Fleming, W.H., Holland, H.K., and Waller, E.K. (1998). Lymphoid reconstitution after autologous PBSC transplantation with FACS-sorted $CD34^+$ hematopoietic progenitors. *Blood* **91,** 2588–2600.
135. Rutella, S., Pierelli, L., Bonanno, G., Mariotti, A., Sica, S., Sora, F., Chiusolo, P., Scambia, G., Rumi, C., and Leone, G. (2001). Immune reconstitution after autologous peripheral blood progenitor cell transplantation: Effect of interleukin-15 on T-cell survival and effector functions. *Exp. Hematol.* **29,** 1503–1516.
136. Mackall, C.L., Fleisher, T.A., Brown, M.R., Andrich, M.P., Chen, C.C., Feuerstein, I.M., Horowitz, M.E., Magrath, I.T., Shad, A.T., Steinberg, S.M., Wexler, L.H., and Gress, R.E. (1995). Age, thymopoiesis, and $CD4^+$ T-lymphocyte regeneration after intensive chemotherapy. *N. Engl. J. Med.* **332,** 143–149.
137. Storek, J., Ferrara, S., Ku, N., Giorgi, J.V., Champlin, R.E., and Saxon, A. (1993). B cell reconstitution after human bone marrow transplantation: recapitulation of ontogeny? *Bone Marrow Tranpslant.* **12,** 387–398.
138. Small, T.N., Keever, C.A., Weiner-Fedus, S., Heller, G., O'Reilly, R.J., and Flomenberg, N. (1990). B-cell differentiation following autologous, conventional, or T-depleted bone marrow transplantation: a recapitulation of normal B-cell ontogeny. *Blood* **76,** 1647–1656.
139. Akpek, G., Lenz, G., Lee, S.M., Sanchorawala, V., Wright, D.G., Colarusso, T., Waraska, K., Lerner, A., Vosburgh, E., Skinner, M., and Comenzo, R.L. (2001). Immunologic recovery after autologous blood stem cell transplantation in patients with AL-amyloidosis. *Bone Marrow Transplant.* **28,** 1105–1109.
140. Avigan, D., Wu, Z., Joyce, R., Elias, A., Richardson, P., McDermont, D., Levine, J., Kennedy, L., Giallombardo, N., Hurley, D., Gong, J., and Kufe, D. (2000). Immune reconstitution following high-dose chemotherapy with stem cell rescue in patients with advanced breast cancer. *Bone Marrow Transplant.* **26,** 169–176.
141. Wulffraat, N.M., and Kuis, W. (1999). Autologous stem cell transplantation: a possible treatment for refractory juvenile chronic arthritis? *Rheumatology* **38,** 764–766.
142. Heitger, A., Winklehner, P., Obexer, P., Eder, J., Zelle-Rieser, C., Kropshofer, M., Thurnher, M., and Holter, W. (2002). Defective T-helper cell function after T-cell-depleting therapy affecting naive and memory populations. *Blood* **99,** 4053–4062.
143. Storek, J., Ansamma, J., Dawson, M.A., Douek, D.C., Storer, B., and Maloney, D.G. (2002). Factors influencing T-lymphopoiesis after allogeneic hematopoietic cell transplantation. *Transplantation* **73,** 1154–1158.

144. Lewin, S.R., Heller, G., Zhang, L., Rodrigues, E., Skulsky, E., van den Brink, M.R.M., Small, T.N., Kernan, N.A., O'Reilly, R.J., Ho, D.D., and Young, J.W. (2002). Direct evidence for new T-cell generation by patients after either T-cell-depleted or unmodified allogeneic hematopoietic stem cell transplantation. *Blood* **100,** 2235–2241.
145. Savage, W.J., Bleesing, J.J.H., Douek, D., Brown, M.R., Linton, G.M., Malech, H.L., and Horwitz, M.E. (2001). Lymphocyte reconstitution following non-myeloablative hematopoietic stem cell transplantation follows two patterns depending on age and donor/recipient chimerism. *Bone Marrow Transplant.* **28,** 463–471.
146. Myers, L.A., Patel, D.D., Puck, J.M., and Buckley, R.H. (2002). Hematopoietic stem cell transplantation for severe combined immunodeficiency in the neonatal period leads to superior thymic output and improved survival. *Blood* **99,** 872–878.
147. Hochberg, E.P., Chillemi, A.C., Wu, C.J., Neuberg, D., Canning, C., Hartman, K., Alyea, E.P., Soiffer, R.J., Kalams, S.A., and Ritz, J. (2001). Quantitation of T-cell neogenesis in vivo after allogeneic bone marrow transplantation in adults. *Blood* **98,** 1116–1121.
148. Haddad, E., Landais, P., Friedrich, W., Gerritsen, B., Cavazzana-Calvo, M., Morgan, G., Bertrand, Y., Fasth, A., Porta, F., Cant, A., Espanol, T., Muller, S., Veys, P., Vossen, J., and Fischer, A. (1998). Long-term immune reconstitution and outcome after HLA-nonidentical T-cell-depleted bone marrow transplantation for severe combined immunodeficiency: a European retrospective study of 116 patients. *Blood* **91,** 3646–3653.
149. Weinberg, K., Blazar, B.R., Wagner, J.E., Agura, E., Hill, B.J., Smogorzewska, M., Koup, R.A., Betts, M.R., Collins, R.H., and Douek, D.C. (2001). Factors affecting thymic function after allogeneic hematopoietic stem cell transplantation. *Blood* **97,** 1458–1466.
150. Lowdell, M.W., Craston, R., Ray, N., Koh, M., Galatowicz, G., and Prentice, H.G. (1998). The effect of T cell depletion with Campath-1M on immune reconstitution after chemotherapy and allogeneic bone marrow transplant as a treatment for leukaemia. *Bone Marrow Transplant.* **21,** 679–686.
151. Wu, C.J., Chillemi, A., Alyea, E.P., Orsini, E., Neuberg, D., Soiffer, R.J., and Ritz, J. (2000). Reconstitution of T-cell receptor repertoire diversity following T-cell depleted allogeneic bone marrow transplantation is related to hematopoietic chimerism. *Blood* **95,** 352–359.
152. Ottinger, H.D., Beelen, D.W., Scheulen, B., Schaefer, U.W., and Grosse-Wilde, H. (1996). Improved immune reconstitution after allotransplantation of peripheral blood stem cells instead of bone marrow. *Blood* **88,** 2775–2779.
153. Storek, J., Dawson, M.A., Storer, B., Stevens-Ayers, T., Maloney, D.G., Marr, K.A., Witherspoon, R.P., Bensinger, W., Flowers, M.E.D., Martin, P., Storb, R., Appelbaum, F.R., and Boeckh, M. (2001). Immune reconstitution after allogeneic marrow transplantation compared with blood stem cell transplantation. *Blood* **97,** 3380–3389.
154. Beschorner, W.E., Di Gennaro, K.A., Hess, A.D., and Santos, G.W. (1987). Cyclosporine and the thymus: influence of irradiation and age on thymus immunopathology and recovery. *Cell Immunol.* **110,** 350–364.
155. Dulude, G., Roy, D.-C., and Perreault, C. (1999). The effect of graft-versus-host disease on T cell production and homeostasis. *J. Exp. Med.* **189,** 1329–1341.
156. Rondelli, D., Re, F., Bandini, G., Raspadori, D., Arpinati, M., Senese, B., Stanzani, M., Bonifazi, F., Falcioni, S., Chirumbolo, G., and Tura, S. (2000). Different immune reconstitution in multiple myeloma, chronic myeloid leukemia and acute myeloid leukemia patients after allogeneic transplantation of peripheral blood stem cells. *Bone Marrow Transplant.* **26,** 1325–1331.
157. Lum, L.G., Seigneuret, M.C., Storb, R.F., Witherspoon, R.P., and Thomas, E.D. (1981). In vitro regulation of immunoglobulin synthesis after marrow transplantation. I. T-cell and B-cell deficiencies in patients with and without chronic graft-versus-host disease. *Blood* **58,** 431–439.
158. Talvensaari, K., Clave, E., Douay, C., Rabian, C., Garderet, L., Busson, M., Garnier, F., Douek, D., Gluckman, E., Charron, D., and Toubert, A. (2002). A broad T-cell repertoire diversity and an efficient thymic function indicate a favorable long-term immune reconstitution after cord blood stem cell transplantation. *Blood* **99,** 1458–1464.
159. Honda, K., Takada, H., Nagatoshi, Y., Akazawa, K., Ohga, S., Ishii, E., Okamura, J., and Hara, T. (2000). Thymus-dependent expansion of T lymphocytes in children after allogeneic bone marrow transplantation. *Bone Marrow Transplant.* **25,** 647–652.
160. Abu-Ghosh, A., Goldman, S., Slone, V., van de Ven, C., Suen, Y., Murphy, L., Sender, L., and Cairo, M.S. (1999). Immunological reconstitution and correlation of circulating serum inflammatory mediators/cytokines with the incidence of acute graft-versus-host disease during the first 100 days following unrelated umbilical cord blood transplantation. *Bone Marrow Transplant.* **24,** 535–544.
161. Roux, E., Durmont-Girard, F., Starobinski, M., Siegrist, C.-A., Helg, C., Chapuis, B., and Roosnek, E. (2000). Recovery of immune reactivity after T-cell-depleted bone marrow transplantation depends on thymic activity. *Blood* **96,** 2299–2303.
162. Verfuerth, S., Peggs, K., Vyas, P., Barnett, L., O'Reilly, J., and Mackinnon, S. (2000). Longitudinal monitoring of immune reconstitution by CDR3 size spectratyping after T-cell-depleted allogeneic bone marrow transplant and the effect of donor lymphocyte infusions on T-cell repertoire. *Blood* **95,** 3990–3995.
163. Roux, E., Helg, C., Dumont-Girard, F., Chapuis, B., Jeannet, M., and Roosnek, E. (1996). Analysis of T-cell repopulation after allogeneic bone marrow transplantation: significant differences between recipients of T-cell depleted and unmanipulated grafts. *Blood* **87,** 3984–3992.
164. Godthelp, B.C., van Tol, M.J.D., Vossen, J.M., and van den Elsen, P.J. (1999). T-cell immune reconstitution in pediatric leukemia patients after allogeneic bone marrow transplantation with T-cell-depleted or unmanipulated grafts: evaluation of overall and antigen-specific T-cell repertoires. *Blood* **94,** 4358–4369.
165. Duval, M., Pedron, B., Rohrlich, P., Legrand, F., Faye, A., Lescocur, B., Bensaid, P., Larchee, R., Sterkers, G., and Vilmer, E. (2002). Immune reconstitution after haematopoietic transplantation with two different doses of pre-graft antithymocyte globulin. *Bone Marrow Transplant.* **30,** 421–426.
166. Handgretinger, R., Lang, P., Schumm, M., Pfeiffer, M., Gottschling, S., Demirdelen, B., Bader, P., Kuci, S., Klingebiel, T., and Niethammer, D. (2001). Immunological aspects of haploidentical stem cell transplantation in children. *Ann. N. Y. Acad. Sci.* **938,** 340–357.
167. Beelen, D.W., Ottinger, H.D., Elmaagacli, A., Scheulen, B., Basu, O., Kremens, B., Havers, W., Grosse-Wilde, H., and

Schaefer, U.W. (1997). Transplantation of filgrastim-mobilized peripheral blood stem cells from HLA-identical sibling or alternative family donors in patients with hematologic malignancies: a prospective comparison on clinical outcome, immune reconstitution, and hematopoietic chimerism. *Blood* **90,** 4725–4735.

168. Paloczi, K. (2000). Immune reconstitution: an important component of a successful allogeneic transplantation. *Immunol. Lett.* **74,** 177–181.
169. Thomson, B.G., Robertson, K.A., Gowan, D., Heilman, D., Broxmeyer, H.E., Emanuel, D., Kotylo, P., Brahmi, Z., and Smith, F.O. (2000). Analysis of engraftment, graft-versus-host disease, and immune recovery following unrelated donor cord blood transplantation. *Blood* **96,** 2703–2711.
170. Dror, Y., Gallagher, R., Wara, D.W., Colombe, B.W., Merino, A., Benkerrou, M., and Cowan, M.J. (1993). Immune reconstitution in severe combined immunodeficiency disease after lectin-treated, T-cell depleted haplocompatible bone marrow transplantation. *Blood* **81,** 2021–2030.
171. Brugnoni, D., Airo, P., Pennacchio, M., Carella, G., Malagoli, A., Ugazio, A.G., Porta, F., and Cattaneo, R. (1999). Immune reconstitution after bone marrow transplantation for combined immunodeficiencies: down-regulation of Bcl-2 and high expression of CD95/Fas account for increased susceptibility to spontaneous and activation-induced lymphocyte cell death. *Bone Marrow Transplant.* **23,** 451–457.
172. Morecki, S., Gelfand, Y., Nagler, A., Or, R., Naparstek, E., Varadi, G., Engelhard, D., Akerstein, A., and Slavin, S. (2001). Immune reconstitution following allogeneic stem cell transplantation in recipients conditioned by low intensity vs myeloablative regimen. *Bone Marrow Transplant.* **28,** 243–249.
173. Roberts, M.M., To, L.B., Gillis, D., Mundy, J., Rawling, C., Ng, K., and Juttner, C.A. (1993). Immune reconstitution following peripheral blood stem cell transplantation, autologous bone marrow transplantation and allogeneic bone marrow tranplantation. *Bone Marrow Transplant.* **12,** 469–475.
174. Lum, L.G., Seigneuret, M.C., Storb, R.F., Witherspoon, R.P., and Thomas, E.D. (1981). In vitro regulation of immunoglobulin synthesis after marrow transplantation. I. T-cell and B-cell deficiencies in patients with and without chronic graft-versus-host disease. *Blood* **58,** 431–439.
175. Parra, C., Roldan, E., Rodriguez, C., Perez de Oteyza, J., Otheo, E., Lopez, J., Maldonado, M.S., Garcia Larana, J., Munoz, A., Odmozola, J., and Brieva, J.A. (1996). Immunologic reconstitution of peripheral blood lymphocytes in patients treated by bone marrow transplantation. *Med. Clin.* **106,** 169–173.
176. Steingrimsdottir, H., Gruber, A., Bjorkholm, M., Svensson, A., and Hansson, M. (2000). Immune reconstitution after autologous hematopoietic stem cells transplantation in relation to underlying disease, type of high-dose therapy and infectious complications. *Haematologica* **85,** 832–838.
177. Paulin, T., Ringden, O., and Nilsson, B. (1987). Immunological recovery after bone marrow transplantation: role of age, graft-versus-host disease, prednisolone treatment and infections. *Bone Marrow Transplant.* **1,** 317–328.
178. Li Volti, S.L., Di Gregorio, F., Romeo, M.A., Cannella, A., Pizzarelli, G., Sciacca, A., and Russo, G. (1997). Immune status and the immune response to hepatitis B virus vaccine in thalassemic patients after allogeneic bone marrow transplantation. *Bone Marrow Transplant.* **19,** 157–160.
179. Singh, R.K., Ino, K., Varney, M.L., Heimann, D.G., and Talmadge, J.E. (1999). Immunoregulatory cytokines in bone marrow and peripheral blood stem cell products. *Bone Marrow Transplant.* **23,** 53–62.
180. Klangsinsirikul, P., and Russell, N.H. (2002). Peripheral blood stem cell harvests from G-CSF-stimulated donors contain a skewed Th2 CD4 phenotype and a predominance of type 2 dendritic cells. *Exp. Hematol.* **30,** 495–501.
181. Volpi, I., Perruccio, K., Tosti, A., Capanni, M., Ruggeri, L., Posati, S., Aversa, F., Tabilio, A., Romani, L., Martelli, M.F., and Velardi, A. (2001). Postgrafting administration of granulocytes colony-stimulating factor impairs functional immune recovery in recipients of human leukocyte antigen haplotype-mismatched hematopoietic transplants. *Blood* **97,** 2514–2520.
182. Arpinati, M., Green, C.L., Heimfeld, S., Heuser, J.E., and Anaseti, C. (2000). Granulocyte-colony stimulating factor mobilizes T helper 2-inducing dendritic cells. *Blood* **95,** 2484–2490.
183. Rissoan, M.-C., Soumelis, V., Kadowaki, N., Grouard, G., Briere, F., de Waal Malefyt, R., and Liu, Y.-J. (1999). Reciprocal control of T helper cell and dendritic cell differentiation. *Science* **283,** 1183–1186.
184. Pan, L., Delmonte, Jr., J., Jalonen, C.K., and Ferrara, J.L. (1995). Pretreatment of donor mice with granulocytes colony-stimulating factor polarizes donor T lymphocytes toward type-2 cytokine production and reduces severity of experimental graft-versus-host disease. *Blood* **86,** 4422–4429.
185. Rondelli, D., Raspadori, D., Anasetti, C., Bandini, G., Re, F., Arpinati, M., Stanzani, M., Morelli, A., Baccini, C., Zaccaria, A., Lemoli, R.M., and Tura, S. (1998). Alloantigen presenting capacity, T cell alloreactivity and NK function of G-CSF-mobilized peripheral blood cells. *Bone Marrow Transplant.* **22,** 631–637.
186. Alpdogan, O., Schmaltz, C., Muriglan, S.J., Kappel, B.J., Perales, M.-A., Rotolo, J.A., Halm, J.A., Rich, B.E., and van den Brink, M.R.M. (2001). Administration of interleukin-7 after allogeneic bone marrow transplantation improves immune reconstitution without aggravating graft-versus-host disease. *Blood* **98,** 2256–2265.
187. Schluns, K.S., Kieper, W.C., Jameson, S.C., and Lefrancois, L. (2000). Interleukin-7 mediates the homeostasis of naive and memory T cells in vivo. *Nat. Immunol.* **1,** 426–432.
188. Burt, R.K., Slavin, S., Burns, W.H., and Marmont, A.M. (2002). Induction of tolerance in autoimmune diseases by hematopoietic stem cell transplantation: getting closer to a cure? *Blood* **99,** 768–784.
189. Leng, X., Zhao, Y., Zhou, D., Li, T., Tang, F., Zeng, X., Zhang, F., Dong, Y., Zhao, Y., and Shen, T. (2002). Study of treatment of refractory rheumatoid arthritis with autologous peripheral blood stem cell transplantation. *Chung-Hua I Hsueh Tsa Chin.* **82,** 748–751.
190. Hahn, B.H., Bagdy, M.K., and Osterland, C.K. (1973). Abnormalities of delayed type hypersensitivity in systemic lupus erythematosus. *Am. J. Med.* 55, 25–31.
191. Traynor, A.E., Schroeder, J., Rosa, R.M., Cheng, D., Stefka, J., Mujais, S., Baker, S., and Burt, R.K. (2000). Treatment of severe systemic lupus erythematosus with high-dose chemotherapy and haemopoietic stem-cell transplantation: a phase I study. *Lancet* **356,** 701–707.

fibrin,[41,42] bovine, or human collagen[43,44]; hyaluronic acid[45]; shark proteoglycans;[46] and polymers.[47,48,49] Therefore, it is crucial to thoroughly evaluate the effects of each of these matrices on the growth of the keratinocyte stem cells, since suboptimal culture conditions may result in enhanced clonal conversion, a reduced keratinocyte life span, and an irreversible degradation of the quality of the graft. This is best accomplished by clonal analysis and by the transplantation of the cultured cells onto athymic or severe-combined immune deficient mice using reference strains of keratinocytes, the performances of which are well known.[22,35] Using this approach, we have demonstrated that fibrin matrices alleviate the need for the detachment of the grafts, eliminate shrinkage, and hence have considerable advantages over plastic for the culture of epidermal stem cells for grafting. The use of a fibrin matrix considerably shortens the duration of cultivation required to generate many CEAs, making it possible to transplant the entire body area of an adult human with CEAs as soon as 15 days after injury.[35] Most importantly, the long-term regeneration of human epidermis on third-degree burns transplanted with autologous, cultured epithelium grown on a fibrin matrix has been demonstrated.[22,35] Fibrin matrices are also extremely useful in the transplantation of autologous limbal stem cells to restore a corneal epithelium.[50] The transplantation of small colonies of keratinocytes (preconfluent cultures) grown on fibrin matrices or of individual keratinocytes suspended in fibrin gels has been proposed.[51] This may be useful to quickly transplant small full-thickness burns or to enhance healing of superficial burn wounds. However, it remains to be demonstrated that individual cells or small colonies generate an epidermal barrier faster than confluent and organized cultures when directly exposed to the hostile environment of the grafting bed in large full-thickness burns. Composite grafts combining autologous keratinocytes and fibroblasts embedded in a collagen gel, a fibrin matrix, or polymers may also be useful to generate closer-to-normal skin by enhancing the formation of dermis.[52] However, with today's technology, the population of fibroblasts in a small skin biopsy cannot be sufficiently expanded in a time frame compatible with the transplantation of acute burn wounds. This is why composite grafts associating autologous fibroblasts and keratinocytes are reserved for chronic wounds.[53] Many groups have proposed using allogeneic fibroblasts, large stocks of which can be prepared in advance. However, allogeneic fibroblasts do not permanently engraft, despite contradictory claims in the literature.[54] To our knowledge, composite grafts may be efficient to treat chronic skin defects like leg ulcers, but they have not proved useful for the successful treatment of extensive burn wounds. Hopefully, progress in the cultivation of human fibroblasts will be made; then, composite grafting will have a major effect.[55]

Transplantation of Keratinocyte Stem Cells

Various surgical procedures have been developed over the years to transplant cultured keratinocytes. CEAs were initially transplanted directly on the granulation tissue that spontaneously forms after full-thickness burns were excised to fascia.[16] Success was then variable, ranging from excellent to poor, and surgeons quickly stressed that the quality of the wound bed was crucial. In that regard, one of the most appreciated procedures is known as Cuono's, in which full-thickness burns are excised to fascia and temporarily covered with meshed, expanded fresh or cryopreserved split-thickness human allografts obtained from organ donors.[56] At grafting time, which usually occurs two to three weeks after the initial biopsy was taken for expansion of stem cells, allografts are dermabraded or tangentially excised and a careful hemostasis is performed. Cultured epithelium grafts, with the basal cells oriented toward the grafting bed, are then gently applied and covered with petroleum gauze dressings to prevent desiccation (Fig. 69-4). Sliding and displacement of the graft should be strictly avoided. CEAs are then overlaid with bridal veil gauze, sterile dry compresses, and elastic bandage.[34] Skin substitutes like Integra® or Biobrane® are useful alternatives to cadaver skin when the latter is not available or cannot be used for religious reasons. Cuono's procedure has greatly increased the rate of CEA engraftment, which is best appreciated clinically. At the time of the first dressing ("takedown"), the engrafted epithelium appears shiny and translucid. With time, the regenerated epithelium matures to resemble a normal epidermis (Figs. 69-4, 69-5). CEAs perform best in areas in which shear forces or frictions are minimal and in non–weight-bearing surfaces. Successful engraftment now averages 70% of the transplanted area, but it is not unusual to obtain a 100% take.[22,34,35] In a recent study, younger age was significantly associated with better CEAs take, possibly reflecting clonal type differences between young and old people.[21,34] Most importantly, the transplantation of CEAs necessitates a highly trained surgical and nursing staff. For instance, four to six nurses require from 60 to 90 minutes to perform each dressing change following CEA application at the Percy Burn Center in France, which has one of the largest and most successful records in CEA transplantation. Infection of the grafting bed is the enemy of CEAs and provokes a quick disappearance of the grafts. The fight of infection relies on systemic antibiotics and local antiseptics, which are clinically efficient and usually not harmful to the CEAs, despite an alleged toxicity *in vitro*.[34] Fragility and blistering of CEAs are also commonly observed during the weeks following transplantation, most likely as a consequence of a delayed maturation of the anchoring fibrils.[57,58] In some cases, lysis of CEAs, which had otherwise nicely engrafted, occurs after a few weeks with no rational explanation. Bleeding of the grafting bed can also result in the loss of CEAs, further emphasizing the importance of thorough hemostasis at grafting time. Another complication of CEAs is epidermal hyperkeratosis, which may need repeated treatment with moisturizing and keratolytic ointments.[34] Wound contracture is also a problem, as in all patients with large burns, but there seems to be less hypertrophic scarring with CEAs than with conventional split-thickness autografts.[34]

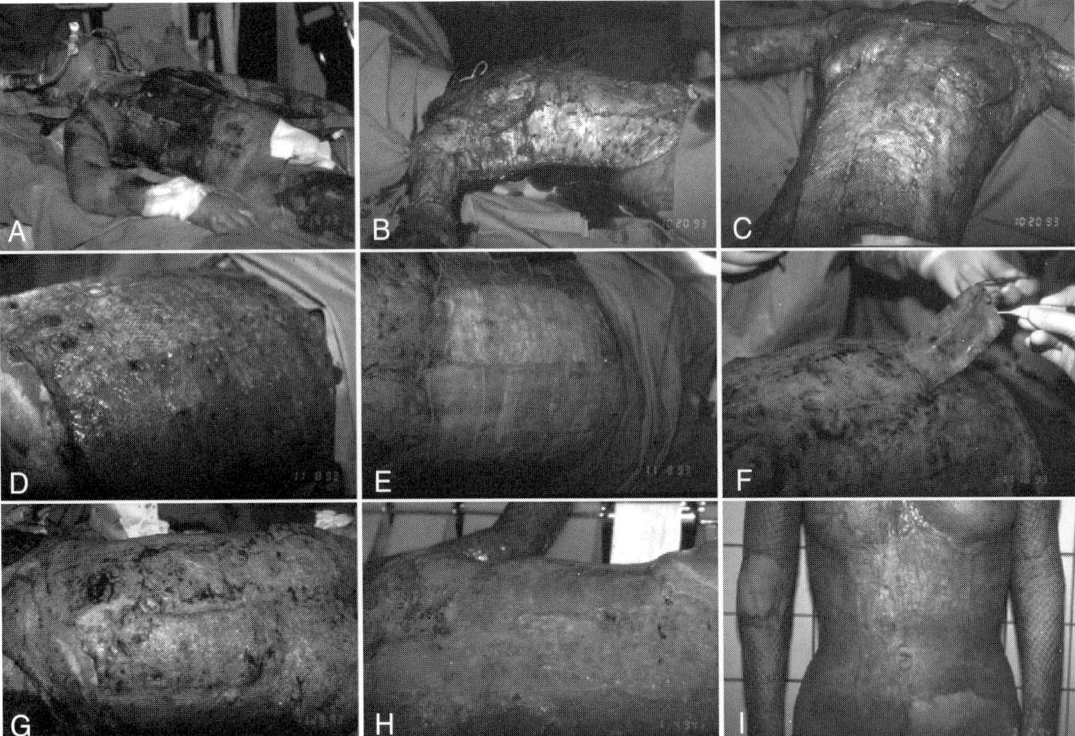

Figure 69–4. *Transplantation of human cultured epithelium autografts.* A 35-year-old woman was burned by flames; over 50% of her body has third-degree burns. (A) Admission. (B) Excision to fascia of full-thickness thoracic and abdominal burn wounds the day after injury. (C) Temporary coverage of the excised area with split-thickness meshed human cadaver allografts. (D) Appearance of the dermabraded grafting bed. (E) Transplantation of control-cultured epithelia (top) and cultured epithelia grown on fibrin matrices (bottom). (F) Appearance of the transplanted area 8 days later (takedown). (G) Appearance of the same area 21 days later. Note the excellent take of both control (bottom) and experimental (top) cultured epithelia (the photograph was taken from the opposite side to that shown in panels E, H, and I). Appearance of the same transplanted area (H) 57 days and (I) 4 months later. Reproduced with permission from Ronfard *et al.*[35] (Please see CD-ROM for color version of this figure.)

Regeneration of Epidermis

Cultured epithelia prepared according to the methods of Green and colleagues are stratified but lack the uppermost-differentiated epidermal layers necessary for barrier function. However, the horny layers mature rapidly once the CEAs are transplanted, indicating that the cells adequately express their program of differentiation.[35,58] This epidermis always contains suprabasal Langerhans cells and may contain melanocytes, although at a variable density in the basal layer. The presence of Merkel cells has been reported.[59] The most surprising observation is the presence of rete ridges, vascular arcades, and elastic fibers, which are not observed during normal wound healing.[1,35,58] However, the formation of a neodermis that closely resembles the papillary dermis is a slow process that takes years (see Fig. 69-5). This extremely intriguing observation suggests that mesenchymal stem cells may have been transplanted with the epidermal stem cells and that epidermal–mesenchymal interactions reminiscent of fetal wound healing have occurred. This awaits confirmation. Most importantly, hair follicles and sweat glands are not regenerated. There are several explanations for this: multipotent epithelial stem cells are not present in CEAs, possibly because current culture conditions favor the epidermal lineage or because multipotent stem cells are absent in adult skin, and the inductive signals necessary for appendage morphogenesis are missing. However, recent results from our laboratory indicate that the skin of adult mammals contains multipotent epithelial cells with the capacity to generate epidermis, sebaceous glands, and all follicular lineages.[7] Other groups have demonstrated that dermal papilla cells obtained from adult hair follicles have inductive capacities.[60] These are important findings that open the path to the reconstruction of hair follicles and other epidermal appendages.

The long-term self-renewal of epidermis generated from CEAs is a concern in view of recent findings demonstrating a shortening of telomeres in keratinocytes obtained from transplanted patients.[61] This further illustrates that cells should be cultivated according to state-of-the-art technology and that cell culture, as good as it can be, is a stress to cells. It is impossible as yet to distinguish between the consequences of clonal conversion, which can occur quickly in relation to poor cultivation and independently of the mitotic clock, and the shortening of telomeres, a difference expressed in a recent review as mitotic clock or culture shock.[62] The expansion of the epidermal stem cells in culture represents, at the most,

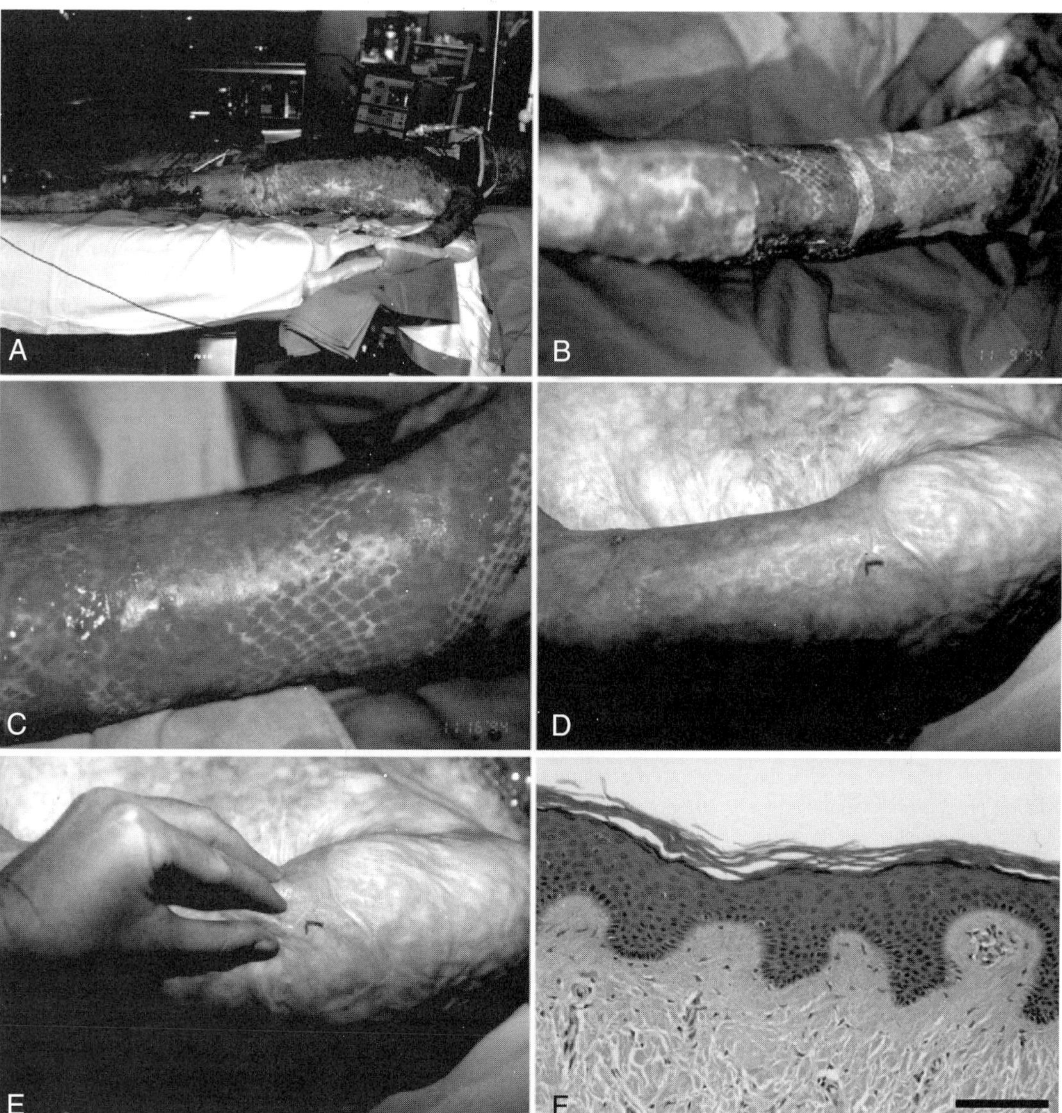

Figure 69–5. *Long-term follow-up of cultured epithelia transplanted on a fibrin matrix.* A 9-year-old boy was burned by flames; over 95% of his body has third-degree burns. (A) Admission at Percy Burn Centre a month after injury. (B) Transplantation of cultured epithelia grown on a fibrin matrix on the left arm. (C) Appearance of the transplanted area at takedown. (D and E) Clinical appearance of the skin 3.5 years after the transplantation. The skin is elastic when pinched and has a smoother appearance than the neighboring split-thickness skin autografts. (F) Histologic appearance of the skin 3.5 years after transplantation. The epidermis is histologically normal. Note the presence of rete ridges and a superficial neodermis with vascular arcades. Similar results were obtained with cultured epithelia grown in absence of fibrin. Bar = 100 μm. Reproduced with permission from Ronfard *et al.*[35] (Please see CD-ROM for color version of this figure.)

22 cell doublings, a small number when holoclones can undergo at least 180 doublings, meaning that holoclones and early meroclones have plenty of growth potential left to renew their share of epidermis for a long time. The number of stem cells (holoclones) or cells with significant growth potential (meroclones) in the CEAs that can engraft and self-renew the epidermis becomes important. Surprisingly, there are no data in the literature on this subject even though hundreds of patients have been transplanted. Nevertheless, clinical follow-up indicates that epidermis generated from CEAs self-renews for years, suggesting that holoclones and meroclones are present in sufficient number. However, this should be thoroughly investigated.

Indications of CEAs

Indications of CEAs have been extensively reviewed.[14] The main indication of CEAs is full-thickness burns over 60% of TBSA in which CEAs are highly beneficial and lifesaving. CEAs can also be useful in reconstructive surgery to enhance healing of donor sites, to prevent recurrence of cheloids, and to cover wounds made by the excision of giant congenital nevi and of tattoos. CEAs may be useful in urology and oral surgery. But one of the most impressive use of CEAs is in ophthalmology.[50] Pellegrini and colleagues have beautifully demonstrated that limbal stem cells (limbal holoclones) can be cultivated on a fibrin matrix and transplanted to restore the integrity of the corneal epithelium.[50,63,64] This approach, coupled with elective keratoplasty, has restored vision to patients whose sight was impaired because of corneal burn wounds. Gene therapy of skin-disabling diseases or of hereditary diseases of the corneal epithelium will also certainly benefit from the experience gained with the treatment of large burns. Indeed, epidermal stem cells or limbal stem cells can be successfully transduced by defective retroviral or lentiviral vectors and engineered to express a protein of medical interest.[65–67] For instance, transduction of a cDNA encoding laminin 5 or collagen VII in epidermal stem cells of patients with junctional epidermolysis bullosa or dystrophic epidermolysis bullosa, respectively, should permit the treatment of elective areas to enhance the quality of life of those patients.[67–69]

Fragility, lack of dermal components, and high costs have significantly limited the use of CEAs. As an example, a commercial CEA (Epicel®) manufactured according to good manufacturing practices costs $14 per cm^2 (including biopsy kit, culture, and shipping), which prices the transplantation of a square meter of CEA at $140,000.[34] However, the transplantation of keratinocyte stem cells is lifesaving, and its cost should be compared to that of other transplantation procedures. Furthermore, progress has been made. For instance, the use of a fibrin matrix diminishes the fragility of the CEA and is user friendly. Moreover, it should reduce costs as the number of CEAs necessary to cover an area is two times less, the duration of cultivation is significantly shortened, and there are no large personnel requirements to prepare the grafts.[22,35] Composite grafts including autologous mesenchymal and keratinocyte stem cells are also foreseen, but they are more complex to manufacture.[55] Their cost will certainly be higher than that of CEAs.

Summary

A challenge in *ex vivo* skin cell therapy is to obtain a massive expansion of the stem cells from a small skin biopsy in the shortest time as possible while preserving stemness. The method of cultivation described by Rheinwald and Green in 1975 achieves this goal and has not been matched.[11] Cell therapy using autologous keratinocyte stem cells cultivated according to the preceding method has saved the lives of hundreds of burned patients[16,22,26–35] and has restored sight to vision-impaired patients.[50,63] But progress can be made, such as improving the cultivation technology both for keratinocytes stem cells and for mesenchymal stem cells, reconstructing hair follicles and sweat glands, and improving the mechanical properties and the aesthetic of the regenerated skin. The answer to those challenges lies in a better understanding of the cellular and molecular events involved in skin renewal and morphogenesis as well as in a better understanding of fetal and adult wound healing. In that regard, the use of embryonic stem cell lines will be extremely helpful.[70] But the skin experience clearly indicates that scientific knowledge is not enough and that it is necessary to adapt the requirements of the stem cells to the preoccupations of the regulatory agencies. Moreover, high manufacturing costs are a major preoccupation of biotechnology and pharmaceutical companies as well as of health insurance providers. This economical aspect should not be underestimated; it can adversely affect stem cell therapy, as illustrated by the recent difficulties of several biotechnology companies specialized in skin cell therapy.[71]

ACKNOWLEDGMENTS

We are grateful to Daniel Littman for proofreading the manuscript. This work was supported by funds from the Swiss Federal Institute Lausanne (EPFL) and from the Lausanne University Hospital (CHUV) to Y. Barrandon and by a grant from the Swiss National Foundation to A. Rochat.

REFERENCES

1. Brouard, M., and Barrandon, Y. (2003). Controlling skin morphogenesis: hope and despair. *Curr. Opin. Biotechnol.* **14,** 520–525.
2. Gambardella, L., and Barrandon, Y. (2003). The multifaceted adult epidermal stem cell. *Curr. Opin. Cell Biol.* **15,** 771–777.
3. Lajtha, L.G. (1979). Stem cell concepts. *Differentiation* 14, 23–34.
4. Watt, F.M. (2001). Stem cell fate and patterning in mammalian epidermis. *Curr. Opin. Genet. Dev.* **11,** 410–417.
5. Ghazizadeh, S., and Taichman, L.B. (2001). Multiple classes of stem cells in cutaneous epithelium: a lineage analysis of adult mouse skin. *EMBO J.* **20,** 1215–1222.
6. Taylor, G., Lehrer, M.S., Jensen, P.J., Sun, T.T., and Lavker, R.M. (2000). Involvement of follicular stem cells in forming not only the follicle but also the epidermis. *Cell* **102,** 451–461.
7. Oshima, H., Rochat, A., Kedzia, C., Kobayashi, K., and Barrandon, Y. (2001). Morphogenesis and renewal of hair follicles from adult multipotent stem cells. *Cell* **104,** 233–245.
8. Miller, S.J., Burke, E.M., Rader, M.D., Coulombe, P.A., and Lavker, R.M. (1998). Re-epithelialization of porcine skin by the sweat apparatus. *J. Invest. Dermatol.* **110,** 13–19.
9. Argyris, T. (1976). Kinetics of epidermal production during epidermal regeneration following abrasion in mice. *Am. J. Pathol.* **83,** 329–340.
10. Al-Barwari, S.E., and Potten, C.S. (1976). Regeneration and dose-response characteristics of irradiated mouse dorsal epidermal cells. *Int. J. Radiat. Biol.* **30,** 201–216.
11. Rheinwald, J.G., and Green, H. (1975). Serial cultivation of strains of human epidermal keratinocytes: the formation of keratinizing colonies from single cells. *Cell* **6,** 331–343.
12. Barrandon, Y., and Green, H. (1987). Cell migration is essential for sustained growth of keratinocyte colonies: the roles of transforming growth factor-alpha and epidermal growth factor. *Cell* **50,** 1131–1137.
13. Rochat, A., Kobayashi, K., and Barrandon, Y. (1994). Location of stem cells of human hair follicles by clonal analysis. *Cell* **76,** 1063–1073.
14. Pellegrini, G., Bondanza, S., Guerra, L., and De Luca, M. (1998). Cultivation of human keratinocyte stem cells: current and future clinical applications. *Med. Biol. Eng. Comput.* **36,** 778–790.

15. O'Connor, N.E., Mulliken, J.B., Banks-Schlegel, S., Kehinde, O., and Green, H. (1981). Grafting of burns with cultured epithelium prepared from autologous epidermal cells. *Lancet* **1,** 75–78.
16. Gallico, G.G., 3rd, O'Connor, N.E., Compton, C.C., Kehinde, O., and Green, H. (1984). Permanent coverage of large burn wounds with autologous cultured human epithelium. *N. Engl. J. Med.* **311,** 448–451.
17. Bickenbach, J.R. (1981). Identification and behavior of label-retaining cells in oral mucosa and skin. *J. Dent. Res.* **60,** S1611–S1620.
18. Lavker, R.M., and Sun, T.T. (1983). Epidermal stem cells. *J. Invest. Dermatol.* **81,** 121S–127S.
19. Jones, P.H., and Watt, F.M. (1993). Separation of human epidermal stem cells from transit amplifying cells on the basis of differences in integrin function and expression. *Cell* **73,** 713–724.
20. Tani, H., Morris, R.J., and Kaur, P. (2000). Enrichment for murine keratinocyte stem cells based on cell surface phenotype. *Proc. Natl. Acad. Sci. U. S. A.* **97,** 10,960–10,965.
21. Barrandon, Y., and Green, H. (1987). Three clonal types of keratinocyte with different capacities for multiplication. *Proc. Natl. Acad. Sci. U. S. A.* **84,** 2302–2306.
22. Pellegrini, G., Ranno, R., Stracuzzi, G., Bondanza, S., Guerra, L., Zambruno, G., Micali, G., and De Luca, M. (1999). The control of epidermal stem cells (holoclones) in the treatment of massive full-thickness burns with autologous keratinocytes cultured on fibrin. *Transplantation* **68,** 868–879.
23. Rochat, A., and Barrandon, Y. (Unpublished data).
24. Green, H., Kehinde, O., and Thomas, J. (1979). Growth of cultured human epidermal cells into multiple epithelia suitable for grafting. *Proc. Natl. Acad. Sci. U. S. A.* **76,** 5665–5668.
25. Banks-Schlegel, S., and Green, H. (1980). Formation of epidermis by serially cultivated human epidermal cells transplanted as an epithelium to athymic mice. *Transplantation* **29,** 308–313.
26. Kumagai, N., Nishina, H., Tanabe, H., Hosaka, T., Ishida, H., and Ogino, Y. (1988). Clinical application of autologous cultured epithelia for the treatment of burn wounds and burn scars. *Plast. Reconstr. Surg.* **82,** 99–110.
27. Munster, A.M., Weiner, S.H., and Spence, R.J. (1990). Cultured epidermis for the coverage of massive burn wounds: a single center experience. *Ann. Surg.* **211,** 676–679.
28. Teepe, R.G., Kreis, R.W., Koebrugge, E.J., Kempenaar, J.A., Vloemans, A.F., Hermans, R.P., Boxma, H., Dokter, J., Hermans, J., Ponec, M., and Vermeer, B.J. (1990). The use of cultured autologous epidermis in the treatment of extensive burn wounds. *J. Trauma* **30,** 269–275.
29. Haith, L.R., Jr., Patton, M.L., and Goldman, W.T. (1992). Cultured epidermal autograft and the treatment of the massive burn injury. *J. Burn Care Rehabil.* **13,** 142–146.
30. Hickerson, W.L., Compton, C., Fletchall, S., and Smith, L.R. (1994). Cultured epidermal autografts and allodermis combination for permanent burn wound coverage. *Burns* **20** (Suppl. 1), S52–S55.
31. Paddle-Ledinek, J.E., Cruickshank, D.G., and Masterton, J.P. (1997). Skin replacement by cultured keratinocyte grafts: an Australian experience. *Burns* **23,** 204–211.
32. Rue, L.W., 3rd, Cioffi, W.G., McManus, W.F., and Pruitt, B.A., Jr. (1993). Wound closure and outcome in extensively burned patients treated with cultured autologous keratinocytes. *J. Trauma* **34,** 662–667; discussion 667–668.
33. Meuli, M., and Raghunath, M. (1997). Burns (Part 2): tops and flops using cultured epithelial autografts in children. *Pediatr. Surg. Int.* **12,** 471–477.
34. Carsin, H., Ainaud, P., Le Bever, H., Rives, J., Lakhel, A., Stephanazzi, J., Lambert, F., and Perrot, J. (2000). Cultured epithelial autografts in extensive burn coverage of severely traumatized patients: a five-year single-center experience with 30 patients. *Burns* **26,** 379–387.
35. Ronfard, V., Rives, J.M., Neveux, Y., Carsin, H., and Barrandon, Y. (2000). Long-term regeneration of human epidermis on third-degree burns transplanted with autologous cultured epithelium grown on a fibrin matrix. *Transplantation* **70,** 1588–1598.
36. Oshima, H., Inoue, H., Matsuzaki, K., Tanabe, M., and Kumagai, N. (2002). Permanent restoration of human skin treated with cultured epithelium grafting—wound healing by stem cell-based tissue engineering. *Hum. Cell* **15,** 118–128.
37. Perez-Losada, J., and Balmain, A. (2003). Stem cell hierarchy in skin cancer. *Nat. Rev. Cancer* **3,** 434–443.
38. Owens, D.M., and Watt, F.M. (2003). Contribution of stem cells and differentiated cells to epidermal tumors. *Nat. Rev. Cancer* **3,** 444–451.
39. Green, H. (1991). Cultured cells for the treatment of disease. *Sci. Am.* 265, 96–102.
40. Germain, L., Rouabhia, M., Guignard, R., Carrier, L., Bouvard, V., and Auger, F.A. (1993). Improvement of human keratinocyte isolation and culture using thermolysin. *Burns* **19,** 99–104.
41. Kaiser, H.W., Stark, G.B., Kopp, J., Balcerkiewicz, A., Spilker, G., and Kreysel, H.W. (1994). Cultured autologous keratinocytes in fibrin glue suspension, exclusively and combined with STS allograft (preliminary clinical and histological report of a new technique). *Burns* **20,** 23–29.
42. Ronfard, V., Broly, H., Mitchell, V., Galizia, J.P., Hochart, D., Chambon, E., Pellerin, P., and Huart, J.J. (1991). Use of human keratinocytes cultured on fibrin glue in the treatment of burn wounds. *Burns* **17,** 181–184.
43. Shahabeddin, L., Berthod, F., Damour, O., and Collombel, C. (1990). Characterization of skin reconstructed on a chitosan-cross-linked collagen-glycosaminoglycan matrix. *Skin Pharmacol.* **3,** 107–114.
44. Hansbrough, J.F., Boyce, S.T., Cooper, M.L., and Foreman, T.J. (1989). Burn wound closure with cultured autologous keratinocytes and fibroblasts attached to a collagen–glycosaminoglycan substrate. *JAMA* **262,** 2125–2130.
45. Myers, S.R., Grady, J., Soranzo, C., Sanders, R., Green, C., Leigh, I.M., and Navsaria, H.A. (1997). A hyaluronic acid membrane delivery system for cultured keratinocytes: clinical "take" rates in the porcine keratodermal model. *J. Burn Care Rehabil.* **18,** 214–222.
46. Yannas, I.V., Lee, E., Orgill, D.P., Skrabut, E.M., and Murphy, G.F. (1989). Synthesis and characterization of a model extracellular matrix that induces partial regeneration of adult mammalian skin. *Proc. Natl. Acad. Sci. U. S. A.* **86,** 933–937.
47. Hansbrough, J.F., Morgan, J.L., Greenleaf, G.E., and Bartel, R. (1993). Composite grafts of human keratinocytes grown on a polyglactin mesh-cultured fibroblast dermal substitute function as a bilayer skin replacement in full-thickness wounds on athymic mice. *J. Burn Care Rehabil.* **14,** 485–494.
48. Meana, A., Iglesias, J., Madrigal, B., and Sanchez, J. (1997). Use of cyanoacrylate glue to prepare cultured keratinocyte sheets for grafting. *Burns* **23,** 645–646.
49. Yamato, M., Utsumi, M., Kushida, A., Konno, C., Kikuchi, A., and Okano, T. (2001). Thermo-responsive culture dishes allow the intact harvest of multilayered keratinocyte sheets without dispase by reducing temperature. *Tiss. Eng.* **7,** 473–480.

50. Rama, P., Bonini, S., Lambiase, A., Golisano, O., Paterna, P., De Luca, M., and Pellegrini, G. (2001). Autologous fibrin-cultured limbal stem cells permanently restore the corneal surface of patients with total limbal stem cell deficiency. *Transplantation* **72,** 1478–1485.
51. Horch, R.E., Bannasch, H., Kopp, J., Andree, C., and Stark, G.B. (1998). Single-cell suspensions of cultured human keratinocytes in fibrin glue reconstitute the epidermis. *Cell Transplant.* **7,** 309–317.
52. Boyce, S.T., and Warden, G.D. (2002). Principles and practices for treatment of cutaneous wounds with cultured skin substitutes. *Am. J. Surg.* **183,** 445–456.
53. Limat, A., and Hunziker, T. (2002). Use of epidermal equivalents generated from follicular outer root sheath cells *in vitro* and for autologous grafting of chronic wounds. *Cells Tissues Organs* **172,** 79–85.
54. Briscoe, D.M., Dharnidharka, V.R., Isaacs, C., Downing, G., Prosky, S., Shaw, P., Parenteau, N.L., and Hardin-Young, J. (1999). The allogeneic response to cultured human skin equivalent in the hu-PBL-SCID mouse model of skin rejection. *Transplantation* **67,** 1590–1599.
55. Llames, S.G., Del Rio, M., Larcher, F., Garcia, E., Garcia, M., Escamez, M.J., Jorcano, J.L., Holguin, P., and Meana, A. (2004). Human plasma as a dermal scaffold for the generation of a completely autologous bioengineered skin. *Transplantation* **77,** 350–355.
56. Cuono, C., Langdon, R., and McGuire, J. (1986). Use of cultured epidermal autografts and dermal allografts as skin replacement after burn injury. *Lancet* **1,** 1123–1124.
57. Woodley, D.T., Peterson, H.D., Herzog, S.R., Stricklin, G.P., Burgeson, R.E., Briggaman, R.A., Cronce, D.J., and O'Keefe, E.J. (1988). Burn wounds resurfaced by cultured epidermal autografts show abnormal reconstitution of anchoring fibrils. *Jama.* **259,** 2566–2571.
58. Compton, C.C., Gill, J.M., Bradford, D.A., Regauer, S., Gallico, G.G., and O'Connor, N.E. (1989). Skin regenerated from cultured epithelial autografts on full-thickness burn wounds from 6 days to 5 years after grafting: a light, electron microscopic and immunohistochemical study. *Lab. Invest.* **60,** 600–612.
59. Compton, C.C., Regauer, S., Seiler, G.R., and Landry, D.B. (1990). Human Merkel cell regeneration in skin derived from cultured keratinocyte grafts. *Lab. Invest.* **63,** 233–241.
60. Reynolds, A.J., Lawrence, C., Cserhalmi-Friedman, P.B., Christiano, A.M., and Jahoda, C.A. (1999). Transgender induction of hair follicles. *Nature* **402,** 33–34.
61. Counter, C.M., Press, W., and Compton, C.C. (2003). Telomere shortening in cultured autografts of patients with burns. *Lancet* **361,** 1345–1346.
62. Sherr, C.J., and DePinho, R.A. (2000). Cellular senescence: mitotic clock or culture shock? *Cell* **102,** 407–410.
63. Pellegrini, G., Traverso, C.E., Franzi, A.T., Zingirian, M., Cancedda, R., and De Luca, M. (1997). Long-term restoration of damaged corneal surfaces with autologous cultivated corneal epithelium. *Lancet* **349,** 990–993.
64. Pellegrini, G., Golisano, O., Paterna, P., Lambiase, A., Bonini, S., Rama, P., and De Luca, M. (1999). Location and clonal analysis of stem cells and their differentiated progeny in the human ocular surface. *J. Cell Biol.* **145,** 769–782.
65. Mathor, M.B., Ferrari, G., Dellambra, E., Cilli, M., Mavilio, F., Cancedda, R., and De Luca, M. (1996). Clonal analysis of stably transduced human epidermal stem cells in culture. *Proc. Natl. Acad. Sci. U. S. A.* **93,** 10,371–10,376.
66. Morgan, J.R., Barrandon, Y., Green, H., and Mulligan, R.C. (1987). Expression of an exogenous growth hormone gene by transplantable human epidermal cells. *Science* **237,** 1476–1479.
67. Chen, M., Kasahara, N., Keene, D.R., Chan, L., Hoeffler, W.K., Finlay, D., Barcova, M., Cannon, P.M., Mazurek, C., and Woodley, D.T. (2002). Restoration of type VII collagen expression and function in dystrophic epidermolysis bullosa. *Nat. Genet.* **32,** 670–675.
68. Dellambra, E., Vailly, J., Pellegrini, G., Bondanza, S., Golisano, O., Macchia, C., Zambruno, G., Meneguzzi, G., and De Luca, M. (1998). Corrective transduction of human epidermal stem cells in laminin-5-dependent junctional epidermolysis bullosa. *Hum. Gene Ther.* **9,** 1359–1370.
69. Ortiz-Urda, S., Thyagarajan, B., Keene, D.R., Lin, Q., Fang, M., Calos, M.P., and Khavari, P.A. (2002). Stable nonviral genetic correction of inherited human skin disease. *Nat. Med.* **8,** 1166–1170.
70. Coraux, C., Hilmi, C., Rouleau, M., Spadafora, A., Hinnrasky, J., Ortonne, J.P., Dani, C., and Aberdam, D. (2003). Reconstituted skin from murine embryonic stem cells. *Curr. Biol.* 13, 849–853.
71. Bouchie, A. (2002). Tissue engineering firms go under. *Nat. Biotechnol.* **20**, 1178–1179.

70

Orthopaedic Applications of Stem Cells

Jerry I. Huang, Jung U. Yoo, and Victor M. Goldberg

Introduction

More than 33 million musculoskeletal injuries occur in the United States each year.[1] Bone is capable of regeneration, and defects often heal spontaneously. However, cartilage, tendon, and ligament injuries usually result in replacement of the site by organized scar tissue, which is inferior to the native tissue. An increased understanding of cell biology and various tissue types may lead to the future possibility of using tissue engineering techniques to recapitulate the embryonic events that result in the development of native tissue. The goal of tissue engineering is to generate biologic substitutes for repair and/or replacement of injured tissue. Three basic elements are required. First, appropriate cells must be present to give rise to the structural tissue. Second, appropriate growth factors and differentiation stimuli must exist for the cells to proceed down the proper lineage. Third, a scaffolding matrix must act as a building block for cellular attachment, differentiation, and maturation into the desired tissue. The generated construct must be site specific and integrate well at the host–graft interface.

Technologic advances have resulted in the advent of a wide array of biomaterials and synthetic growth factors. Clinicians and scientists face the enormous task of generating biologic constructs that emulate the interaction between cells and the complex extracellular matrix they secrete and encapsulate them. A thorough understanding of the biology of each tissue type (material properties, ratio of extracellular matrix components, and cellular profile) is essential to construction of functional tissue. The first element of tissue engineering is the use of cells. Different approaches include the use of differentiated lineage-specific cells (osteoblasts, chondrocytes, tenocytes, meniscal fibrochondrocytes, etc.) or the use of progenitor cells.

Pluripotent mesenchymal stem cells (MSCs) with the ability to differentiate into multiple mesodermal lineages have been isolated from bone marrow, adipose tissue, and synovium.[2–4] Stem cells have the advantage that they are unlimited in supply, easily harvested, and can be expanded in tissue culture to large numbers. Moreover, it is postulated that induction of stem cells down various mesodermal lineages will result in tissue that more closely resembles native tissue and recapitulates embryonic development. MSCs isolated from human bone marrow aspirates have been shown to retain pluripotentiality and proliferative ability through long-term passaging.[4] Another advantage of using MSCs for tissue engineering strategies is that they can be used in allogeneic transplantation. Human MSCs cells do not induce a mixed lymphocyte reaction when incubated with allogeneic donor lymphocytes and have the ability to suppress an ongoing mixed lymphocyte reaction.[5] Allogeneic MSC-based tissue constructs would be limitless in supply and have enormous economic advantages.

A number of growth factors have been described that enhance angiogenesis, promote cell proliferation, and induce differentiation of cells down various mesodermal lineages. The delivery of single doses of recombinant growth factors has been demonstrated to be effective in the healing of segmental bone defects and articular cartilage defects.[6,7] Similarly, the structural properties of ligaments during the repair process can be improved by the application of growth factors.[8,9] However, there are many clinical situations in which a sustained exposure to growth factors is necessary. Moreover, leakage of supraphysiologic doses to adjacent sites can pose huge problems such as heterotopic ossification from osteoinductive factors.

In addition to being a powerful tool in cell-based therapy, MSCs may also be useful as a delivery vehicle for growth factors through genetic manipulation. Cells can be transduced with a retrovirus so that the target gene can be integrated into the cell's DNA. This allows for propagation of gene expression when the cell replicates so that long-term expression of the target gene would occur. Alternatively, gene therapy strategies using adenoviral vectors would be useful in clinical situations where only transient gene expression is desired. *In vivo* gene therapy in which the viral vector is introduced to a tissue by direct injection has many disadvantages. A host response to the virus may result in immunologic rejection. Moreover, transduction efficiencies are often low especially if the target tissue contains slowly growing cells. Diffusion of the vector to adjacent areas may also lead to potential complications. *Ex vivo* gene therapy using MSCs overcomes some of these potential problems. Use of autologous cells as delivery vehicles would prevent the host immune response. In addition, cells can be seeded onto matrix scaffolds customized to the shapes and sizes required at the target tissue.

This chapter provides a brief summary of the biology and properties of various musculoskeletal tissue types, highlights the present tissue engineering strategies, and draws speculations as

Handbook of Stem Cells
Volume 2

to the future direction of the application of MSCs in tissue engineering as it applies to each tissue. MSCs can serve as the building blocks for tissue regeneration by their ability to differentiate down various lineages. They also hold great promise as delivery vehicles for sustained release of growth factors to injured tissue sites. The growth factors may enhance tissue repair by promoting migration of MSCs, inducing differentiation of progenitor cells, and enhancing vascularization of the newly formed tissue.

Bone

Bone has the ability to regenerate itself with functional tissue with properties similar to the original tissue. However, bone tissue engineering still has many clinical applications, including fracture nonunion, congenital malformations requiring bone-lengthening, tumors, and bone loss secondary to trauma or osseous infections. Moreover, bone regeneration in the setting of bony ingrowth is important in joint arthrodesis for osteoarthritis, spinal fusion, and more rigid fixation of prosthetic implants.

The extracellular matrix of bone is primarily type I collagen and calcium phosphate. Osteoblasts line the periphery and are active in matrix deposition. In the clinical setting, autogenous bone grafts harvested from the iliac crest and fibular grafts are often used in fracture repair. However, some of the disadvantages of harvesting autogenous bone graft are donor-site morbidity and their limited supply.[10–13] Clearly, there is a need for alternative methods of harvesting autologous bone substitutes. Connolly *et al.*[14] harvested autologous marrow aspirates from the posterior iliac crests as a graft substitute for patients with tibial nonunions and injected them into fracture sites. A considerable amount of new bone was evident and the patient was able to fully weight bear at 5 months. Percutaneous harvest of bone marrow aspirates is less invasive and bone marrow suspensions may serve as useful bone graft substitutes.

MSCs isolated from bone marrow aspirates and processed lipoaspirate (PLA) cells from adipose tissue differentiate into osteoblasts when cultured in the presence of dexamethasone, ascorbic acid, and beta-glycerophosphate.[2,15] Bone marrow-derived MSCs have also shown the ability to form heterotopic bone in animal models. MSCs seeded onto hydroxyapatite (HA) and tricalcium phosphate (TCP) ceramic discs implanted into subcutaneous pockets show evidence of bone formation within the pores of the ceramic scaffolds.[16,17] Yoshikawa *et al.* demonstrated that preincubation of human MSCs in a porous ceramics in the presence of osteoinductive medium followed by intraperitoneal implantation into athymic nude mice resulted in the formation of thick layers of lamellar bone and active osteoblasts that line the ceramic surface.

Another preclinical animal study showed the ability of autologous MSCs loaded into HA/TCP carriers to heal a critical-sized segmental defect in a canine model.[18] Significant bone formation occurred at the host–implant interface and a continuous span of bone was seen across the defect. Evidence of both woven and lamellar bone was seen. Periosteal calluses formed around the implant. During the 16-week period of the study, the callus remodeled and resulted in healing of the defect with bone that was similar in shape and size to the original segment of bone that was resected. Human MSCs loaded onto HA/TCP carriers were implanted into femoral defects in athymic rats in a study similar to the one described previously.[19] Radiographic and histologic evidence of new bone formation was seen at 8 weeks. Biomechanical testing showed that cell-loaded ceramic implants had more than twice the stiffness and torque to failure as ceramic implants that had no cells.

Growth factors in the bone morphogenetic protein (BMP) family including BMP-2 and BMP-7 also induce progenitor cells to differentiate down the osteogenic lineage. Current strategies for bone tissue engineering include the use of osteoconductive matrix devices that promote bony ingrowth and the delivery of osteoinductive growth factors to bony defect sites. Matrix materials include calcium HA, type I collagen gel, polylactic acid polymers, and demineralized bone matrix. Yasko *et al.*[7] demonstrated histologic and radiographic evidence of healing in segmental bone defects using demineralized bone matrices implanted with recombinant human bone morphogenetic protein-2 *(rhBMP-2)*. In a study involving a larger animal model, a sheep femoral defect model was used to show the efficacy of *BMP-2* in healing critical-sized long bone defects in a large animal model.[20] A prospective, randomized trial of 450 patients looking at the safety and efficacy of *rhBMP-2* in improving the outcome of open tibial fractures showed that patients treated with intramedullary nailing and *rhBMP-2* had significantly lower risks of delayed union and need for more invasive intervention such as bone grafting and nail exchange.[21] Moreover, they tend to have significantly faster fracture healing and lower risks of infection and need for hardware removal. Gene therapy using genetically manipulated MSCs is an attractive alternative method for delivery of growth factors. Not only can they safely deliver sustained release of growth factors to anatomic sites but their osteogenic potential allows them to serve as substrates for osteoinductive factors and building blocks for newly formed bone.

Regional gene therapy using MSCs as a vehicle for localized expression of osteoinductive proteins has shown promising results in animal models. Human bone marrow stromal cells transfected with adenoviral-*BMP-2* leads to more robust, trabecular bone in an athymic rat femoral defect model compared with the thin, lacelike bone that formed in defects filled with matrix carrying localized recombinant human *BMP-2* *(rhBMP-2)*.[22] Moreover, the femurs from the adenoviral *BMP-2* showed no statistically significant difference in biomechanical strength with respect to ultimate torque to failure and energy to failure compared with control femurs. The difference in characteristics of the healing response may be related to the increased efficacy from sustained release of *BMP-2* from the adenovirally transfected bone marrow cells compared with the single-dose response seen in the *rhBMP-2* group. Moreover, the implanted bone marrow stromal cells may themselves contribute to osteogenesis in the defect site. Dragoo *et al.*[23] successfully transfected stem cells isolated from adipose tissue with the *BMP-2* gene and showed rapid induction of the cells into the osteoblast phenotype in *in vitro* cell cultures. Collagen matrices seeded with the transduced cells were able to produce heterotopic bone in the hind limbs of SCID mice. Adipose tissue is plentiful and easily accessible and may well serve as another alternative bone graft substitute in an orthopaedic surgeon's armamentarium.

Vascular invasion is a vital step in endochondral ossification. Vascular endothelial growth factor (VEGF) is one of the best-characterized angiogenic factors. Studies have also shown that it is essential during embryogenesis, skeletal development, and endothelial function.[24–27] Muscle-derived MSCs transduced with retroviral *VEGF* was found to work synergistically with cells transfected with BMP-4 to enhance bone healing in critical-sized calvarial defects.[28] VEGF was found to be important for endochondral bone formation through enhancement of angiogenesis, cell recruitment, improved cartilage formation, and accelerated cartilage resorption. This study demonstrated another strategy for use of stem cells in gene therapy-based treatment of skeletal defects.

Several applications of MSCs in the repair of local bone defects have been described previously. Bone marrow–derived MSCs may also hold great potential for treatment of diffuse musculoskeletal disease. Osteoporosis and osteogenesis imperfecta (OI) are two of the more attractive candidates. OI is a genetic disorder of MSCs characterized by a defect in the type I collagen gene that results in children with growth retardation, short stature, and numerous fractures secondary to fragile bone. Six children have already been enrolled in a clinical trial at St. Jude Children's Research Hospital that involve the intravenous administration of unmanipulated bone marrow from human leukocyte antigen (HLA)-identical or single-antigen–mismatched siblings.[29] Five of the six patients showed engraftment in one or more sites, including bone, skin, and stroma. More importantly, these five patients all showed acceleration of growth velocity during the 6 months postinfusion. The authors attributed the increase in growth to the generation of normal osteoblasts from the MSCs that engrafted in skeletal sites.

Cartilage

Osteoarthritis is currently one of the most prevalent chronic conditions in the United States, accounting for as many as 39 million physician visits a year.[30] According to a National Health Interview Survey, it is estimated that approximately 70% of the population older than 65 years will have activity limitation or require medical attention because of osteoarthritis.[31] Moreover, a significant number of adolescents and young adults suffer from chondral defects secondary to trauma, sports-related injuries, and osteochondritis dissecans. Of 31,516 knee arthroscopies in a survey conducted by Curl *et al.*,[32] 63 % of the knees had chondral lesions, with an average of 2.7 hyaline cartilage lesions per knee. Cartilage has poor intrinsic healing ability, and superficial defects typically do not heal spontaneously.[33] This is related to both the lack of vascular supply and the poor proliferative ability of chondrocytes. When the lesion extends into the subchondral bone, mesenchymal cell recruitment occurs from the synovium and subchondral marrow and a healing response ensues in which the defect is filled with repair tissue resembling fibrocartilage.[34,35] Unfortunately, this tissue is structurally inferior to the native cartilage.

Articular cartilage is highly acellular with cell volume averaging only approximately 2% of the total cartilage volume in adults.[36] The extracellular matrix is composed of a highly complex network of collagen fibrils and proteoglycans. Type II collagen is the dominant collagen subtype found in cartilage. The molecule is a triple helix composed of three $\alpha 1$ chains and with multiple cross-links. The collagen fibrils contribute to the tensile strength of cartilage. Load-transmission capacity and compressive strength mainly arise from the proteoglycans, the other main constituent of the extracellular matrix of articular cartilage. The core protein of aggrecan contains a large number of chondroitin sulfate and keratin sulfate side chains that become highly hydrated. Aggrecan molecules also contain a hyaluronic acid–binding region.

Clinically, current treatment options for cartilage defects can be categorized into cartilage stimulation and cartilage replacement strategies. Cartilage stimulation techniques include abrasion arthroplasty, subchondral drilling, and the microfracture technique.[37–39] However, the repair tissue never achieves the hyaline architecture of the native tissue. Osteochondral autografts and allografts represent the other spectrum where the defect is filled with plugs taken from normal regions of articular cartilage.[40–43] The main disadvantages associated with use of autografts are paucity of tissue and donor-site morbidity and the possible long-term complications. Allografts, on the other hand, face the risk of donor rejection from immunogenicity and disease transmission. Joint prosthesis remains the mainstay for symptomatic relief of pain and improvement of daily function of patients suffering from severe articular cartilage defects. In 1999 alone, more than 244,000 total knee arthroplasties were performed.[29]

An exciting development has been the introduction of tissue engineering strategies for cartilage defects. Cell-based therapy for treatment of cartilage defects is already in use clinically with the use of autologous chondrocytes.[44] Chondrocytes are isolated and culture expanded from arthroscopically harvested cartilage and reimplanted into deep articular cartilage defects. Since 1987, more than 950 patients have been treated with this technique.[45] Long-term (mean 7.5 years) follow-up of patients showed good to excellent rating with the Cincinnati rating score. Biopsy specimen resembled hyaline cartilage with extracellular matrices that consisted primarily of type II collagen and aggrecan.[45] Some of the disadvantages of this technology include a limited supply and donor site morbidity associated with the initial cartilage harvest.

MSCs capable of chondrogenesis are present in bone marrow, periosteum, synovium, and adipose tissue.[2,46–50]

Human MSCs can be culture expanded more than 1 billion-fold and retain their multilineage potential.[4] Moreover, they proliferate rapidly and have the advantage that they can recapitulate the embryonic events present in chondrogenesis. The importance of MSCs in cartilage repair is illustrated by the lack of a repair response in defects that do not penetrate subchondral bone. On penetration, recruitment of pluripotential marrow mesenchymal cells ensues. The influence of local cytokines from inflammatory cells and synovial fluid results in differentiation of the progenitor cells into chondrocytes and filling of the space with fibrocartilage.

The ability of MSCs to heal full-thickness articular cartilage defects was shown to be possible in a rabbit femoral condyle model.[51] Wakitani *et al.* isolated bone marrow–derived and periosteum-derived MSCs from New Zealand White rabbits and embedded them into a collagen-based scaffold. The cellular constructs were implanted into 6 mm long × 3 mm wide × 3 mm deep full-thickness cartilage defects in the weight-bearing portion of the medial femoral condyle. Healing of the defect by hyaline cartilage was evident as early as 2 weeks with filling of the subchondral space with dense highly vascularized new bone. After 4 weeks, the neocartilage was thicker and excellent integration was noted at the interface between the new subchondral bone and the host tissue. Moreover, further analysis of the histologic specimen at the various time points showed that the formation of subchondral bone resulted from a recapitulation of the embryonic process of enchondral ossification with progression of chondrocytes to a hypertrophic state, followed by vascular invasion and ossification.[35] No evidence of osteoarthrosis was noted in any of the knees. At later time points, however, significant remodeling of the cartilage occurred with loss of metachromatic staining. Genetic modification of the MSCs may enhance the healing response and allow for better long-term repair tissue.

In another study, periosteal cells transfected with a retroviral vector containing *BMP-7* showed *in vitro* and *in vivo* gene expression for at least 8 weeks after seeding onto polymer grafts.[52] When the cell-based constructs were placed into 3-mm circular osteochondral defects in the intertrochlear grooves of rabbit knees, the defects were completely filled with predominantly hyaline-like tissue that persisted for as along as 12 weeks after implantation. The subchondral portion of the defects showed rapid reconstitution of bone. Restoration of the tidemark and formation of subchondral bone were also seen in articular cartilage defects treated with collagen scaffolds containing another member of the transforming growth factor *(TGF)* superfamily *BMP-2*.[6]

As we reach a better understanding of the biology and biomechanical properties of articular cartilage and its response to different growth factors, gene-modified tissue engineering can become a more powerful tool for cartilage resurfacing. A number of growth factors have been described that enhance chondrocyte proliferation and chondrogenic differentiation including fibroblast growth factor-2 (FGF-2), insulin-like growth factor-I (IGF-I), TGF-1, growth hormone (GH), BMP-7 (also known as osteogenic protein-1), and BMP-2.[48,50,53–59] Induction of chondrogenesis using growth factors can be accomplished by direct injection into the defect site and application of gene therapy techniques.

With direct injections, single supraphysiologic doses of growth factors may often be insufficient for proper healing. Degradation of the proteins may occur as a result of an inflammatory reaction and the recruitment of macrophages and neutrophils. Moreover, dilution and clearance of growth factors by the surrounding synovial fluid occurs over time.[60] Prolonged exposure to growth factors may be necessary for chondrogenic differentiation of resident progenitor cells. In addition, by using chondrocytes or MSCs as a delivery vehicle for growth factors via gene therapy, the cells can in turn be the building blocks for the regenerated cartilage and respond to autocrine and paracrine growth factors. The newly formed cartilage can be a chimera of the original cell construct and new mesenchymal progenitor cells from the recruitment and migration that occurs from the actions of the cytokines secreted by the transduced cells.

Mandel *et al.*[61] demonstrated the feasibility of successful transduction of bone marrow–derived mesenchymal progenitor cells with both retroviral and adenoviral *TGFβ-1* vectors. These genetically modified progenitor cells were able to undergo chondrogenesis *in vitro* with and without exogenous *TGFβ-1* addition. Nixon *et al.*[62] constructed a replication-incompetent adenovirus vector expressing IGF-I and successfully transfected chondrocytes, MSCs, and synoviocytes. Significant increases in proteoglycan production in the extracellular matrix secondary to *IGF-1* induction were noted. Moreover, cells expressed high levels of the *IGF-1* for up to 28 days in culture. Both of these studies verify the possibility of genetically modifying MSCs so that they have the ability to secrete chondroinductive growth factors over sustained time periods.

Animal models for *ex vivo* gene therapy of articular cartilage defects using MSCs have already been carried out. Gelse *et al.*[63] investigated the ability of adenoviral-mediated expression of perichondrial MSCs to heal an articular cartilage defect in a rat model. The effects of *AdBMP-2* and *AdIGF-1* transfected cells suspended in fibrin glue were evaluated with respect to their ability to heal the defects and integrate with the host tissue. The partial thickness lesions healed in both the *AdBMP-2* and *AdIGF-1* groups with repair cartilage exhibiting hyaline morphology that were composed of type II collagen in the extracellular matrix but no type I collagen. The defects in the nontransfected cell group primarily filled with fibrous tissue rich in type I collagen. Again, this is consistent with the observations seen in the natural repair process in which MSCs from marrow cavity progress to repair subchondral cartilage defects with fibrocartilage-like tissue. A complication of the *AdBMP-2* group that was not seen in the *AdIGF-1* group was osteophyte formation secondary to leakage of cells outside the construct.

Chondroprotective approaches to preservative of articular cartilage have also been explored by several groups. Instead of trying to stimulate cartilage repair and replace cartilage defects, an alternative is prophylactic treatment and cessation of disease progression in its earlier stages. Interleukin-1 receptor antagonists (IL-1Ra), tumor necrosis factor (TNF) blockers, and interleukin-4 (IL-4) have all been described to protect against degenerative changes in articular cartilage.[64] The anti-inflammatory drugs infliximab (Remicade) and etanercept (Enbrel), both inhibitors of TNF, have both been approved by the Food and Drug Administration for patients suffering from rheumatoid arthritis.[30] Animal models have already shown the suppression of osteoarthritic changes using gene therapy to effect delivery of IL-1Ra.[65–68] Transduced MSCs expressing IL-1Ra or antagonists of TNF may both enhance the reparative process through their inherent chondrogenic potential and retard the degradative process in cartilage lesions.

Meniscus

The annual incidence of meniscal tears is approximately 60 to 70 per 100,000.[69,70] The menisci of the knee are semilunar fibrocartilaginous structures that are integral to the normal function of the knee. The extracellular matrix consists of collagenous fibers that are mostly oriented circumferentially, with interspersing of radial fibers that contribute to its structural integrity.[71] The circumferential fibers help disperse compressive forces while the radial fibers protect against tearing from tensile forces. The matrix contains mainly type I, II, and III collagens, with type I collagen being the most prevalent. The cells of the meniscus are fibrochondrocytes because of their chondrocyte-like appearance and synthesis of fibrocartilaginous matrices. The main function of the meniscus is load transmission during weight-bearing. In extension, approximately 50% of the load in the knee is transmitted to the menisci. At 90 degrees of flexion, this increases to almost 90% of the total load.[72] The medial meniscus also acts as an important secondary restraint to anteroposterior translation, especially in the anterior cruciate ligament (ACL) deficient knee.[73] Finally, the meniscus is important in shock absorption and joint lubrication.

Early in prenatal development, the menisci are very cellular and highly vascularized.[74] After skeletal maturity, the vascular zone is generally confined to the peripheral one third of the meniscus. Longitudinal tears in the peripheral zone can generally be repaired, whereas radial tears are usually not amenable to repair. Defects that can not be repaired are usually debrided to avoid the irritation from loose meniscal flaps. Total meniscectomy is usually contraindicated because it leads to number of osteoarthritic changes originally described by Fairbank.[75] Long-term follow-up studies showed that a high percentage of patients with a history of meniscectomy go on to develop knee instability and considerable amounts of radiographic degenerative changes in the knee.[76–79]

Clearly, there is a need for new treatment options. Currently, meniscal allograft transplantation is one of the few alternatives for replacement of large meniscal defects. Unfortunately, there is a risk of rejection and disease transmission with allograft tissue. Moreover, the graft size of the donor must match the recipient which can sometimes be difficult. Long-term problems with meniscal allografts include graft shrinkage, decreased cellularity, and loss of normal biologic activity.[80,81] Other experimental methods for meniscal repair include the use of fibrin clots, collagen-based polymers, and a number of polyurethane-based meniscal prostheses.[82–86]

MSCs may provide novel treatment strategies in both growth-factor based and cell-based treatment options for meniscal tears. A number of cytokines including platelet-derived growth factor (PDGF), BMP-2, hepatocyte growth factor (HGF), epidermal growth factor (EGF), IGF-I, and endothelial cell growth factor have been implicated in the proliferation and migration of meniscal cells within the different zones.[87,88] Single doses of growth factors may not provide adequate stimulus in the repair tissue. Successful adenoviral-mediated expression of *BMP-2, PDGF, EGF,* and *IGF-1* have already been demonstrated in culture systems of MSCs and fibroblasts.[22,62,89] MSCs can serve as delivery vehicles for sustained release of growth factors that contribute to cell proliferation, recruitment, and differentiation and an increase in localized vascularization. Martinek *et al.*[90] demonstrated the feasibility of gene therapy in tissue-engineered meniscal tissue by showing evidence of transduced gene expression in meniscal allografts at 4 weeks. In another study, bovine meniscal cells were transfected with an adenovirus vector encoding *HGF,* seeded onto polyglycolic acid scaffolds, and placed into subcutaneous pouches of athymic mice.[91] Gene expression of *HGF* was associated with a significant increase in neovascularization.

The repair of meniscal defects by fibrocartilage has been advocated by some authors. Lesions in the avascular zone of canine menisci repaired by implantation of polyurethane polymers showed evidence of fibrocartilaginous tissue compared with only fibrous tissue in the control group.[86] In a small clinical series, Rodkey *et al.*[83] implanted resorbable collagen scaffolds into medial meniscus lesions and showed preservation of the joint surfaces and evidence of regeneration of tissue regeneration 2 years postoperatively. The chondrogenic potential of bone marrow–derived MSCs has been well-characterized.[48,50] An alternative strategy in meniscal repair would be a prefabrication of a cartilage-like construct using stem cells and a biodegradable matrix. Data from a rabbit partial meniscectomy model showed that MSCs embedded in a collagen sponge can enhance the formation of fibrocartilage tissue at the defect site.[92] Although the tissue would not have the identical properties of native menisci, it would serve a similar function in joint surface preservation and load transmission across the knee joint.

Ligaments and Tendons

Ligaments and tendons are bands of dense connective tissue that lend stability and provide movement of joints. Injury that leads to inflammation or tear of these structures can result in significant functional deficits and development of degenerative joint disease. During the normal healing process, various growth factors such as PDGF, FGF, and TGFβ are released by macrophages and platelets to stimulate fibroblast proliferation and tissue remodeling.[93] These growth factors contribute to proliferation, extracellular matrix secretion, and recruitment of cells. Tissue engineered cellular constructs and delivery of growth factors via gene therapy offers great potential in augmenting the healing process.

In general, most of the dry weight of skeletal ligaments is made up of collagen. Greater than 90% of this is type I with a small percentage of type III.[94] Glycosaminoglycans and elastin also make up a small proportion of the biochemical makeup. Ligaments are oriented to resist tensile forces along their long axes. The diameter of collagen fibril diameters and the number of collagen pyridinoline cross-links correlate with the tensile strength of the healed ligament.[95,96] Ligaments work in conjunction with muscle-tendon forces, bony intra-articular constraints, and other soft tissues to help stabilize joints and prevent nonphysiologic movements. There are differences in the intrinsic healing capacity of various ligaments. After injury, ligaments heal in a series of stages: hemorrhagic, inflammatory, proliferation, and remodeling.[93] Clinically, medial collateral ligament (MCL) injuries heal reliably without surgical intervention, whereas ACL tears usually do not heal spontaneously.[97] Histologic studies of human ACL tears show that, unlike extrasynovial ligaments, no evidence of bridging occurs between remnants of the ACL from the femoral and tibial sides.[98] Typically, ACL ruptures are treated with a variety of different tendon autografts and allografts. Unfortunately, autograft harvest involves damage to previously healthy tissue, and allografts carry the risk of disease transmission. Moreover, although isolated MCL tears do well with nonoperative treatment, biochemical analysis shows that untreated MCL scar has a higher than normal proportion of type III collagen, higher collagen turnover rates, and increases in total glycosaminoglycan. Histologically, the extracellular matrix never completely approaches the highly organized appearance of normal ligament substance.[94] Studies have also shown that MCL fibroblasts migrate more rapidly and repopulate cell free areas more rapidly than those from ACLs.[99,100] Structural differences exist between cells of the MCL and the ACL.[100–102]

Growth factors play a large role in healing and remodeling of musculoskeletal tissue. Schmidt *et al.*[103] showed exposure to EGF and basic FGF leads to a significantly higher rate of proliferation in fibroblasts from the MCL and ACL. Fibroblast proliferation is a major component of the normal ligament healing process. Similarly, Marui *et al.*[104] showed that FGF and EGF treatment of ligament fibroblast cultures leads to increased collagen synthesis. IGF-I also stimulates type I collagen synthesis in fibroblasts.[105] However, complex interactions exist between different growth factors because some act synergistically, whereas others antagonize one another.[106] The structural and functional properties of tissues are largely dependent on the composition of the extracellular matrix.

The use of MSCs in gene therapy strategies for ligamentous and tendon injuries has many potential clinical uses. Growth factors can be delivered locally to injury sites that can promote each of the four stages of normal healing. Increased fibroblast proliferation effected by FGF and EGF can be promoted through adenoviral-mediated gene expression. Short bursts of growth factors will enable the healing process to occur more rapidly in the initial stages. TGFβ-1 promotes wound healing in many animal models.[107,108] Its ability to augment cellular proliferation and increase secretion of collagen in the extracellular matrix hold great promises as a useful target gene for regional growth factor delivery. Animal studies have already shown that MCLs exposed to PDGF leads to stiffness and breaking energy similar to their respective controls.[8,109] Moreover, combination treatment with IGF-I and FGF further enhances these structural properties.[9] In a canine model, basic FGF leads to increased neovascularization and better orientation of collagen fibers in a partially ruptured ACL.[110] The feasibility of using cells as a delivery vehicle of growth factors into the knee joint was confirmed by a study showing cell-seeded collagen scaffolds that remained viable for up to 4 weeks when implanted in the knee joint.[111]

In addition to the use of autografts and allografts, current treatment options that have been proposed for tendon defects include use of synthetic polymers and acellular biodegradable scaffolds.[112–116] Scaffolds serve as a conduit for recruitment of cells during the initial healing process. As they degrade over time, the mechanical loading forces are transferred to the new repair tissue. Despite the promising data regarding repair strength and biomechanical properties, the immunogenicity and biocompatibility of the materials over time are not well understood. It would be ideal to use autologous sources of cells in combination with biodegradable matrices as a tissue-engineered construct to reconstruct ligaments or tendons.

Fibroblasts generate tension and change their orientation along tensile forces when cultured in three-dimensional collagen gels.[117] MSCs display a similar fibroblastic property. The combination of MSCs with biodegradable scaffolds could be useful for bridging of large tendon defects. Autologous cell-based tendon repair was performed in a hen flexor tendon model in which tenocytes seeded onto polyglycolic acid scaffolds were able to heal a 3- to 4-cm defect.[118] The healed tissue resembled native tendon grossly and histologically. Biomechanically, the experimental group had 83% of the breaking strength of the normal tendon. Similarly, MSC-based repairs of Achilles tendon in animal models showed improvement of the biomechanics and function of the tendon. However, the histologic appearance and biomechanical strength are inferior to normal tendon controls.

In one study, collagen gels were seeded with MSCs in a full-thickness patellar tendon defect model to compare its effectiveness compared with the natural repair process. At 26 weeks after the original implantation, composite constructs showed significantly higher moduli and maximum stresses compared with the natural repair group.[119] When compared with native tissue, however, the maximum stress was only one fourth of the control. Moreover, 28% of the cell–matrix constructs formed bone in the tendon repair site

Young *et al.*[120] seeded rabbit MSCs onto a pretensioned polyglyconate suture to create a contracted construct. At 40 hours, cell nuclei were spindle shaped and a cell viability of approximately 75% was noted in the constructs. Repair tissue treated with MSCs had a significantly larger cross-sectional area at the repair site than the contralateral control (suture only) and untreated native tissue. Cell-seeded repairs showed superior biomechanical properties with a two-fold increase in load-related properties. Compared with native tissue, the treated tendons had almost two thirds of the structural properties at 12 weeks. A rapid rate of increase in load-related material properties may reflect the remodeling stage of healing mediated by the MSCs. Histologically, increases in tenocytes and collagen crimping pattern also occurred over time.

The two studies reviewed previously demonstrate the potential of MSCs to help augment the tendon repair process. Tissue-engineered constructs combining stem cells with biodegradable scaffolds enhance the biomechanical properties of the repair tissue and remodels over time to more closely resemble the complex organization of normal tendon. Pre-incubation of the constructs *in vitro* with growth factors may produce better biologic substitutes. Moreover, transfection of MSCs with genes such as *TGFβ-1, EGF,* and *FGF* may lead to a synergistic effect and lead to stronger structural repair tissue. Successful transfection of myoblasts and ACL fibroblasts with adenovirus and subsequent introduction into the rabbit ACL have been demonstrated.[121] Expression of the *lacZ* reporter gene was noted at 7 days and persisted for as long as 6 weeks. *BMP-12* gene transfer into lacerated chicken tendon resulted in augmentation of ultimate force and stiffness of the repaired tissue.[122] The same group previously demonstrated that mesenchymal progenitor cells form tendon-like tissue ectopically when transfected with the *BMP-12* gene.[123]

Spine

Posterolateral lumbar intertransverse process fusions are very commonly performed for spinal disorders secondary to degenerative changes and trauma. However, the nonunion rates have been reported to be as high as 40% with single-level fusions and even higher in multiple-level procedures.[124] Currently, nonunions are prevented by application of instrumentation such as pedicle screws, rods or plates, and various interbody fusion devices to achieve better correction of deformities and biomechanical stability during the healing period. However, a significant number of nonunions and pseudoarthrosis still exists in fusions with instrumentation, and some have shown no statistically significant decrease in nonunions with use of screw fixation.[125–127]

More recently, a large number of clinical studies have compared the efficacy of osteoinductive proteins with autogenous iliac crest bone graft in lumbar fusions. Johnsson *et al.*[128] showed in a small randomized clinical series that osteogenic protein-1 (OP-1), also known as BMP-7, was as effective as autogenous bone graft in achieving single-level lumbar fusions. In a rabbit model, *BMP-7* was found to overcome the inhibitory effects of nicotine on spinal fusion.[129] In a prospective, randomized, clinical trial, Boden *et al.*[130] compared Texas Scottish Rite Hospital (TSRH) pedicle screw instrumentation with rhBMP-2 with TSRH pedicle screw instrumentation and rhBMP-2 without instrumentation and showed that the groups with rhBMP-2 had 100% fusion rates compared with only 40% (2/5) fusion in the TSRH pedicle screw instrumentation only group. Improvement of the Oswetry score at follow-up was highest in the rhBMP-2 only group. The use of *rhBMP-2* as an adjunct in fusion using lumbar interbody devices was demonstrated by Sandhu *et al.*[131] in a sheep model. Recombinant BMP-2 was shown to be superior to autogenous bone graft. Minimally invasive spinal fusion and relief of discogenic back pain was possible in a series of 22 patients undergoing laparoscopic placement of *rhBMP-2.*[132]

Direct introduction of growth factors into the intervertebral space for spinal fusion, however, does have its risks. Heterotopic bone formation could occur from leakage of osteoinductive proteins outside its carrier into the surrounding tissue. This could be devastating, especially in the setting of dural tears. Moreover, most osteoinductive growth factors are rapidly metabolized so that single-bolus injections may not achieve ideal efficacy in clinical settings. Gene therapy using MSCs offers the ability to deliver sustained release of growth factors to a local site. Successful spinal fusion has been shown in rats using bone marrow cells transfected with a novel osteoinductive protein, LIM mineralization protein-1 *(LMP-1).*[133] LMP-1 is thought to be a soluble osteoinductive factor that induces expression of other BMPs and their receptors.[124] Adenoviral-mediated regional gene therapy using MSCs expressing *BMP-2* achieved radiographic evidence of fusion in a rat model by 4 weeks postoperatively.[134] Moreover, the group receiving *AdBMP-2*-transfected cells showed repair with coarse trabecular bone compared with thin, lacelike bone in the rhBMP-2 group. The long-term sustained release of osteoinductive proteins was perhaps more effective in producing a stronger biologic response than a single supraphysiologic dose. Another possibility could be that the MSCs differentiated down the osteogenic lineage and are now contributing to the new bone in the fusion mass.

Similar to cartilage repair strategies, another potential strategy in the treatment of spinal disorders would be the suppression of disc degeneration. Fraying, splitting, and loss of collagen fibers in the intervertebral discs and calcification of the cartilage in the endplates occur with age.[135,136] Matrix metalloproteinases and aggrecanases are also thought to be important in extracellular matrix degradation in the disc.[137] Proteoglycans are important for maintenance of disc height and its compressive ability and their preservation is essential for the load-bearing capacity of intervertebral discs. Thompson *et al.*[138] studied the effect of various growth factors on proliferation and proteoglycan synthesis of annular pulposus and nuclear pulposus cells isolated from canine intervertebral discs and found that TGFβ-1 and EGF induced a five-fold increase in proteoglycan production. Retardation of programmed cell death in annulus cells and a dose-dependent increase in proteoglycan synthesis have been shown in discs exposed to IGF-1.[139,140] Delivery of *TGFβ-1* and/or *IGF-1* to intervertebral discs using MSCs as a vehicle for gene therapy, therefore, represent two possible strategies in the treatment of disc disorders.

Successful retroviral-mediated gene transfer of *lacZ* and *IL-1Ra* of cultured chondrocytes has been performed by Wehling *et al.*[141] The authors suggested the harvest of endplate tissue cartilage from patients with degenerative discs and the subsequent reintroduction of genetically modified cells into the disc space. This same strategy can be applied using MSCs that can be easily isolated from the iliac crest. As mentioned previously, adenoviral-mediated expression of *IGF-I* by MSCs has already been successfully shown.[63] Gruber *et al.* showed the efficacy of *in vivo TGFβ-1* gene transfer to intervertebral discs and its ability to increase the level of proteoglycan synthesis.

Summary

MSCs hold great potential for the development of new treatment strategies for a host of orthopaedic conditions. Animal models have demonstrated the wide spectrum of clinical situations in which MSCs could have therapeutic effects. Clinical application of the principles of cell-based tissue engineering is already seen with the Carticel (Genzyme, Cambridge, MA) program that uses culture-expanded autologous chondrocytes in the repair of articular cartilage defect. The multilineage potential and plasticity of MSCs allow them to be building blocks for a host of nonhematopoietic tissues including bone, cartilage, tendon, and ligament. Advances in fabrication of biodegradable scaffolds that serve as beds for MSC implantation will hopefully lead to better biocompatibility and host tissue integration. Minimal toxicity has been observed in animal models involving genetically manipulated stem cells transduced with retroviral and adenoviral vectors. Gene therapy using stem cells as delivery vehicles is a powerful weapon that can be used in a plethora of clinical situations that would benefit from the osteoinductive, chondroinductive, proliferative, and angiogenic effects of growth factors.

REFERENCES

1. Praemer, A.F.S., and Rice, D.P. (1992). "Musculoskeletal Conditions in the United States," pp. 85–113. American Academy of Orthopaedic Surgeons, Park Ridge, IL.
2. Zuk, P.A., Zhu, M., Mizuno, H., Huang, J., Futrell, J.W., Katz, A.J., Benhaim, P., Lorenz, H.P., and Hedrick, M.H. (2001). Multilineage cells from human adipose tissue: implications for cell-based therapies. *Tiss. Eng.* **7,** 211–228.
3. De Bari, C., Dell'Accio, F., Tylzanowski, P., and Luyten, F.P. (2001). Multipotent mesenchymal stem cells from adult human synovial membrane. *Arthritis Rheum.* **44,** 1928–1942.
4. Pittenger, M.F., Mackay, A.M., Beck, S.C., Jaiswal, R.K., Douglas, R., Mosca, J.D., Moorman, M.A., Simonetti, D.W., Craig, S., and Marshak, D.R. (1999). Multilineage potential of adult human mesenchymal stem cells. *Science* **284,** 143–147.
5. Caplan, A.I., and Mosca, J.D. (2000). Orthopaedic gene therapy. Stem cells for gene delivery. *Clin. Orthop.* **379(Suppl),** S98–100.
6. Sellers, R.S., Peluso, D., and Morris, E.A. (1997). The effect of recombinant human bone morphogenetic protein-2 (rhBMP-2) on the healing of full-thickness defects of articular cartilage. *J. Bone Joint Surg. Am.* **79,** 1452–1463.
7. Yasko, A.W., Lane, J.M., Fellinger, E.J., Rosen, V., Wozney, J.M., and Wang, E.A. (1992). The healing of segmental bone defects, induced by recombinant human bone morphogenetic protein (rhBMP-2). A radiographic, histological, and biomechanical study in rats. *J. Bone Joint Surg. Am.* **74,** 659–670.
8. Hildebrand, K.A., Woo, S.L., Smith, D.W., Allen, C.R., Deie, M., Taylor, B.J., and Schmidt, C.C. (1998). The effects of platelet-derived growth factor-BB on healing of the rabbit medial collateral ligament. An in vivo study. *Am. J. Sports Med.* **26,** 549–554.
9. Letson, A.K., and Dahners, L.E. (1994). The effect of combinations of growth factors on ligament healing. *Clin. Orthop.* **308,** 207–212.
10. Silber, J.S., Anderson, D.G., Daffner, S.D., Brislin, B.T., Leland, J.M., Hilibrand, A.S., Vaccano, A.R., and Albert, T.J. (2003). Donor site morbidity after anterior iliac crest bone harvest for single-level anterior cervical discectomy and fusion. *Spine* **28,** 134–139.
11. Heary, R.F., Schlenk, R.P., Sacchieri, T.A., Barone, D., and Brotea, C. (2002). Persistent iliac crest donor site pain: independent outcome assessment. *Neurosurgery* **50,** 510–516; discussion 516–517.
12. Sasso, R.C., Williams, J.I., Dimasi, N., and Meyer, Jr., P.R. (1998). Postoperative drains at the donor sites of iliac-crest bone grafts. A prospective, randomized study of morbidity at the donor site in patients who had a traumatic injury of the spine. *J. Bone Joint Surg. Am.* **80,** 631–635.
13. Arrington, E.D., Smith, W.J., Chambers, H.G., Bucknell, A.L., and Davino, N.A. (1996). Complications of iliac crest bone graft harvesting. *Clin. Orthop.* **329,** 300–309.
14. Connolly, J.F., Guse, R., Tiedman, J., and Dehne, R. (1991). Autologous marrow injection as a substitute for operative grafting of tibial nonunions. *Clin. Orthop.* **266,** 259–270.
15. Jaiswal, N., Haynesworth, S.E., Caplan, A.I., and Bruder, S.P. (1997). Osteogenic differentiation of purified, culture-expanded human mesenchymal stem cells in vitro. *J. Cell Biochem.* **64,** 295–312.
16. Ohgushi, H., Okumura, M., Tamai, S., Shors, E.C., and Caplan, A.I. (1990). Marrow cell induced osteogenesis in porous hydroxyapatite and tricalcium phosphate: a comparative histomorphometric study of ectopic bone formation. *J. Biomed. Mater. Res.* **24,** 1563–1570.
17. Ohgushi, H., Goldberg, V.M., and Caplan, A.I. (1989). Heterotopic osteogenesis in porous ceramics induced by marrow cells. *J. Orthop. Res.* **7,** 568–578.
18. Bruder, S.P., Kraus, K.H., Goldberg, V.M., and Kadiyala, S. (1998). The effect of implants loaded with autologous mesenchymal stem cells on the healing of canine segmental bone defects. *J. Bone Joint Surg. Am.* **80,** 985–996.
19. Bruder, S.P., Kurth, A.A., Shea, M., Hayes, W.C., Jaiswal, N., and Kadiyala, S. (1998). Bone regeneration by implantation of purified, culture-expanded human mesenchymal stem cells. *J. Orthop. Res.* **16,** 155–162.
20. Gerhart, T.N., Kirker-Head, C.A., Kriz, M.J., Holtrop, M.E., Hennig, G.E., Hipp, J., Schelling, S.H., and Wang, E. (1993). Healing segmental femoral defects in sheep using recombinant human bone morphogenetic protein. *Clin. Orthop.* **293,** 317–326.
21. Govender, S., Csimma, C., Genant, H.K., Valentin-Opran, A., Amit, Y., Arbel, R., Aro, H., Atar, D., Bishay, M., Borner, M.G., Chiron, P., Choong, P., Cinats, J., Courtenay, B., Feibel, P., Holt, M., Josten, C., Ketterl, R.L., Lindeque, B., Lob, G., Mathevon, H., McCoy, G., Marsh, D., Miller R., Munting, E., Oevre, S., Nordsletten, L., Patel, A., Pohl, A., Rennie, W., Reynders, P.,

Rommens, P.M., Rondia, J., Rossouw, W.C., Daneel, P.J., Ruff, S., Ruter, A., Santavirta, S., Schildhauer, T.A., Gekle, C., Schnettler, R., Segal, D., Seiler, H., Snowdowne, R.B., Stapert, J., Taglang, G., Verdonk, R., Vogels, L., Weckbach, A. Wentzensen, A., and Wisniewski, T. (2002). Recombinant human bone morphogenetic protein-2 for treatment of open tibial fractures: a prospective, controlled, randomized study of four hundred and fifty patients. *J. Bone Joint Surg. Am.* **84-A,** 2123–2134.

22. Lieberman, J.R., Daluiski, A., Stevenson, S., Wu, L., McAllister, P., Lee, Y.P., Kabo, J.M., Finerman, G.A., Berk, A.J., and Witte, D.N. (1999). The effect of regional gene therapy with bone morphogenetic protein-2-producing bone-marrow cells on the repair of segmental femoral defects in rats. *J. Bone Joint Surg. Am.* **81,** 905–917.
23. Dragoo, J.L., Choi, J.Y., Lieberman, J.R., Huang, J., Zuk, P.A., Zhang, J., Hedrick, M.H., and Berhaim, P. (2003). Bone induction by BMP-2 transduced stem cells derived from human fat. *J. Orthop. Res.* **21,** 622–629.
24. Ferrara, N., and Gerber, H.P. (2001). The role of vascular endothelial growth factor in angiogenesis. *Acta. Haematol.* **106,** 148–156.
25. Ferrara, N., Chen, H., Davis-Smyth, T., Gerber, H.P., Nguyen, T.N., Peers, D., Chisholm, V., Millar, K.J., and Schwall, R.H. (1998). Vascular endothelial growth factor is essential for corpus luteum angiogenesis. *Nat. Med.* **4,** 336–340.
26. Giordano, F.J., Gerber, H.P., Williams, S.P., VanBruggen, N., Bunting, S., Ruiz-Lozano, P., Gu, Y., Nath, A.K., Huang, Y., Hickey, R., Dalton, N., Peterson, K.L., Ross, J., Jr., Chien, K.R., and Ferrara, N. (2001). A cardiac myocyte vascular endothelial growth factor paracrine pathway is required to maintain cardiac function. *Proc. Natl. Acad. Sci. U. S. A.* **98,** 5780–5785.
27. Gerber, H.P., Vu, T.H., Ryan, A.M., Kowalski, J., Werb, Z., and Ferrara, N. (1999). VEGF couples hypertrophic cartilage remodeling, ossification and angiogenesis during endochondral bone formation. *Nat. Med.* **5,** 623–628.
28. Peng, H., Wright, V., Usas, A., Gearhart, B., Shen, H.C., Cummins, J., and Huard, J. (2002). Synergistic enhancement of bone formation and healing by stem cell-expressed VEGF and bone morphogenetic protein-4. *J. Clin. Invest.* **110,** 751–759.
29. Horwitz, E.M., Gordon, P.L., Koo, W.K., Marx, J.C., Neel, M.D., McNall, R.Y., Muul, R., and Hofmann, T. (2002). Isolated allogeneic bone marrow-derived mesenchymal cells engraft and stimulate growth in children with osteogenesis imperfecta: implications for cell therapy of bone. *Proc. Natl. Acad. Sci. U. S. A.* **99,** 8932–8937.
30. Jackson, D.W., Simon, T.M., and Aberman, H.M. (2001). Symptomatic articular cartilage degeneration: the impact in the new millennium. *Clin. Orthop.* **391(Suppl.),** S14–25.
31. Jackson, D.W., and Simon, T.M. (1999). Tissue engineering principles in orthopaedic surgery. *Clin. Orthop.* **367(Suppl.),** S31–45.
32. Curl, W.W., Krome, J., Gordon, E.S., Rushing, J., Smith, B.P., and Poehling, G.G. (1997). Cartilage injuries: a review of 31,516 knee arthroscopies. *Arthroscopy* **13,** 456–460.
33. Ghadially, F.N., Thomas, I., Oryschak, A.F., and Lalonde, J.M. (1977). Long-term results of superficial defects in articular cartilage: a scanning electron-microscope study. *J. Pathol.* **121,** 213–217.
34. Hunziker, E.B., and Rosenberg, L.C. (1996). Repair of partial-thickness defects in articular cartilage: cell recruitment from the synovial membrane. *J. Bone Joint Surg. Am.* **78,** 721–733.
35. Caplan, A.I., Elyaderani, M., Mochizuki, Y., Wakitani, S., and Goldberg, V.M. (1997). Principles of cartilage repair and regeneration. *Clin. Orthop.* **342,** 254–269.
36. Poole, A.R., Kojima, T., Yasuda, T., Mwale, F., Kobayashi, M., and Laverty, S. (2001). Composition and structure of articular cartilage: A template for tissue repair. *Clin. Orthop.* **391(Suppl.),** S26–33.
37. Beiser, I.H., and Kanat, I.O. (1990). Subchondral bone drilling: a treatment for cartilage defects. *J. Foot Surg.* **29,** 595–601.
38. Johnson, L.L. (2001). Arthroscopic abrasion arthroplasty: a review. *Clin. Orthop.* **391(Suppl.),** S306–317.
39. Steadman, J.R., Rodkey, W.G., and Rodrigo J.J. (2001). Microfracture: surgical technique and rehabilitation to treat chondral defects. *Clin. Orthop.* **391(Suppl.),** S362–369.
40. Jakob, R.P., Franz, T., Gautier, E., and Mainil-Varlet, P. (2002). Autologous osteochondral grafting in the knee: indication, results, and reflections. *Clin. Orthop.* **401,** 170–184.
41. Hangody, L., and Fules, P. (2003). Autologous osteochondral mosaicplasty for the treatment of full-thickness defects of weight-bearing joints: ten years of experimental and clinical experience. *J. Bone Joint Surg. Am.* **85-A** (Suppl 2), 25–32.
42. Garrett, J.C. (1998). Osteochondral allografts for reconstruction of articular defects of the knee. *Instr. Course Lect.* **47,** 517–522.
43. Bugbee, W.D., and Convery, F.R. (1999). Osteochondral allograft transplantation. *Clin. Sports. Med.* **18,** 67–75.
44. Brittberg, M., Lindahl, A., Nilsson, A., Ohlsson, C., Isaksson, O., and Peterson, L. (1994). Treatment of deep cartilage defects in the knee with autologous chondrocyte transplantation +AFs-see comments+AF0. *N. Engl. J. Med.* **331,** 889–895.
45. Brittberg, M., Tallheden, T., Sjogren-Jansson, B., Lindahl, A., and Peterson, L. (2001). Autologous chondrocytes used for articular cartilage repair: An update. **391(Suppl.),** *Clin. Orthop.* S337–448.
46. Nakahara, H., Bruder, S.P., Goldberg, V.M., and Caplan, A.I. (1990). In vivo osteochondrogenic potential of cultured cells derived from the periosteum. *Clin. Orthop.* **259,** 223–232.
47. Nishimura, K., Solchaga, L.A., Caplan, A.I., Yoo, J.U., Goldberg, V.M., and Johnstone, B. (1999). Chondroprogenitor cells of synovial tissue. *Arthritis Rheum.* **42,** 2631–2637.
48. Johnstone, B., Hering, T.M., Caplan, A.I., Goldberg, V.M., and Yoo, J.U. (1998). In vitro chondrogenesis of bone marrow-derived mesenchymal progenitor cells. *Exp. Cell Res.* **238,** 265–272.
49. Erickson, G.R., Gimble, J.M., Franklin, D.M., Rice, H.E., Awad, H., and Guilak, F. (2002). Chondrogenic potential of adipose tissue-derived stromal cells in vitro and in vivo. *Biochem. Biophys. Res. Commun.* **290,** 763–769.
50. Yoo, J.U., Barthel, T.S., Nishimura, K., Solchaga, L., Caplan, A.I., Goldberg, V.M., Johnstone, B. (1998). The chondrogenic potential of human bone-marrow-derived mesenchymal progenitor cells. *J. Bone Joint Surg. Am.* **80,** 1745–1757.
51. Wakitani, S., Goto, T., Pineda, S.J., Young, R.G., Mansour, J.M., Caplan, A.I., Goldberg, V.M. (1994). Mesenchymal cell-based repair of large, full-thickness defects of articular cartilage. *J. Bone Joint Surg. Am.* **76,** 579–592.
52. Grande, D.A., Breitbart, A.S., Mason, J., Paulino, C., Laser, J., and Schwartz, R.E. (1999). Cartilage tissue engineering: Current limitations and solutions. *Clin. Orthop.* **369(Suppl.),** S176–185.
53. Maor, G., Hochberg, Z., von der Mark, K., Heinegard, D., and Silbermann, M. (1989). Human growth hormone enhances chondrogenesis and osteogenesis in a tissue culture system of chondroprogenitor cells. *Endocrinology* **125,** 1239–1245.
54. Schofield, J.N., and Wolpert, L. (1990). Effect of TGF-beta 1, TGF-beta 2, and bFGF on chick cartilage and muscle cell differentiation. *Exp. Cell Res.* **191,** 144–148.

55. Denker, A.E., Nicoll, S.B., and Tuan, R.S. (1995). Formation of cartilage-like spheroids by micromass cultures of murine C3H10T1/2 cells upon treatment with transforming growth factor-beta 1. *Differentiation* **59,** 25–34.
56. Denker, A.E., Haas, A.R., Nicoll, S.B., and Tuan, R.S. (1999). Chondrogenic differentiation of murine C3H10T1/2 multipotential mesenchymal cells: I. Stimulation by bone morphogenetic protein-2 in high-density micromass cultures. *Differentiation* **64,** 67–76.
57. Klein-Nulend, J., Semeins, C.M., Mulder, J.W., Winters, H.A., Goei, S.W., Ooms, ME., Burger, E.H. (1998). Stimulation of cartilage differentiation by osteogenic protein-1 in cultures of human perichondrium. *Tiss. Eng.* **4,** 305–313.
58. Martin, I., Vunjak-Novakovic, G., Yang, J., Langer, R., and Freed, L.E. (1999). Mammalian chondrocytes expanded in the presence of fibroblast growth factor 2 maintain the ability to differentiate and regenerate three-dimensional cartilaginous tissue. *Exp. Cell Res.* **253,** 681–688.
59. Asahina, I., Sampath, T.K., and Hauschka, P.V. (1996). Human osteogenic protein-1 induces chondroblastic, osteoblastic, and/or adipocytic differentiation of clonal murine target cells. *Exp. Cell Res.* **222,** 38–47.
60. Yoo, J.U., Mandell, I., Angele, P., and Johnstone, B. (2000). Chondrogenitor cells and gene therapy. *Clin. Orthop.* **379(Suppl.),** S164–170.
61. Mandell, I., Yoo, J.U., and Johnstone, B. (1999). Gene delivery to mesenchymal cells. *Trans. Orthop. Res. Soc.* **24,** 112.
62. Nixon, A.J., Brower-Toland, B.D., Bent, S.J., Saxer, R.A., Wilke, M.J., Robbins, P.D., et al. (2000). Insulinlike growth factor-I gene therapy applications for cartilage repair. *Clin. Orthop.* **379(Suppl.),** S201–213.
63. Gelse, K., von der Mark, K., Aigner, T., Park, J., and Schneider, H. (2003). Articular cartilage repair by gene therapy using growth factor-producing mesenchymal cells. *Arthritis Rheum.* **48,** 430–441.
64. Evans, C.H., Ghivizzani, S.C., Smith, P., Shuler, F.D., Mi, Z., and Robbins, P.D. (2000). Using gene therapy to protect and restore cartilage. *Clin. Orthop.* **379(Suppl.),** S214–219.
65. Baragi, V.M., Renkiewicz, R.R., Jordan, H., Bonadio, J., Hartman, J.W., and Roessler, B.J. (1995). Transplantation of transduced chondrocytes protects articular cartilage from interleukin 1-induced extracellular matrix degradation. *J. Clin. Invest.* **96,** 2454–2460.
66. Caron, J.P., Fernandes, J.C., Martel-Pelletier, J., Tardif, G., Mineau, F., Geng, C., Pelletier, J.P. (1996). Chondroprotective effect of intraarticular injections of interleukin-1 receptor antagonist in experimental osteoarthritis. Suppression of collagenase-1 expression. *Arthritis Rheum.* **39,** 1535–1544.
67. Fernandes, J., Tardif, G., Martel-Pelletier, J., Lascau-Coman, V., Dupuis, M., Moldovan, F., Sheppard, M., Krishnar, B.R., and Pelletier, J.P. (1999). In vivo transfer of interleukin-1 receptor antagonist gene in osteoarthritic rabbit knee joints: prevention of osteoarthritis progression. *Am. J. Pathol.* **154,** 1159–1169.
68. Pelletier, J.P., Caron, J.P., Evans, C., Robbins, P.D., Georgescu, H.I., Jovanovic, D., Fernandes, J.C., and Martin-Pelletier, J. (1997). In vivo suppression of early experimental osteoarthritis by interleukin-1 receptor antagonist using gene therapy. *Arthritis Rheum.* **40,** 1012–1019.
69. Nielsen, A.B., and Yde, J. (1991). Epidemiology of acute knee injuries: a prospective hospital investigation. *J. Trauma* **31,** 1644–1648.
70. Hede, A., Hempel-Poulsen, S., and Jensen, J.S. (1990). Symptoms and level of sports activity in patients awaiting arthroscopy for meniscal lesions of the knee. *J. Bone Joint Surg. Am.* **72,** 550–552.
71. Bullough, P.G., Munuera, L., Murphy, J., and Weinstein, A.M. (1970). The strength of the menisci of the knee as it relates to their fine structure. *J. Bone Joint Surg. Br.* **52,** 564–567.
72. McCarty, E.C., Marx, R.G., and DeHaven, K.E. (2002). Meniscus repair: considerations in treatment and update of clinical results. *Clin. Orthop.* **402,** 122–134.
73. Shoemaker, S.C., and Markolf, K.L. (1986). The role of the meniscus in the anterior-posterior stability of the loaded anterior cruciate-deficient knee. Effects of partial versus total excision. *J. Bone Joint Surg. Am.* **68,** 71–79.
74. Clark, C.R., and Ogden, J.A. (1983). Development of the menisci of the human knee joint. Morphological changes and their potential role in childhood meniscal injury. *J. Bone Joint Surg. Am.* **65,** 538–547.
75. Fairbank, T.J. (1948). Knee joint changes after meniscectomy. *J. Bone Joint Surg. Br.* **30,** 664–670.
76. Veth, R.P. (1985). Clinical significance of knee joint changes after meniscectomy. *Clin. Orthop.* **198,** 56–60.
77. Wroble, R.R., Henderson, R.C., Campion, E.R., el-Khoury, G.Y., and Albright, J.P. (1992). Meniscectomy in children and adolescents. A long-term follow-up study. *Clin. Orthop.* **279,** 180–189.
78. Sonne-Holm, S., Fledelius, I., and Ahn, N.C. (1980). Results after meniscectomy in 147 athletes. *Acta Orthop. Scand.* **51,** 303–309.
79. McNicholas, M.J., Rowley, D.I., McGurty, D., Adalberth, T., Abdon, P., Lindstrand, A., Lohmander, L.S. (2000). Total meniscectomy in adolescence. A thirty-year follow-up. *J. Bone Joint Surg. Br.* **82,** 217–221.
80. Rath, E., Richmond, J.C., Yassir, W., Albright, J.D., and Gundogan, F. (2001). Meniscal allograft transplantation. Two- to eight-year results. *Am. J. Sports Med.* **29,** 410–414.
81. Stollsteimer, G.T., Shelton, W.R., Dukes, A., and Bomboy, A.L. (2000). Meniscal allograft transplantation: a 1- to 5-year follow-up of 22 patients. *Arthroscopy* **16,** 343–347.
82. Messner, K., and Gillquist, J. (1993). Prosthetic replacement of the rabbit medial meniscus. *J. Biomed. Mater. Res.* **27,** 1165–1173.
83. Rodkey, W.G., Steadman, J.R., and Li, S.T. (1999). A clinical study of collagen meniscus implants to restore the injured meniscus. *Clin. Orthop.* **367(Suppl.),** S281–292.
84. Arnoczky, S.P., Warren, R.F., and Spivak, J.M. (1988). Meniscal repair using an exogenous fibrin clot. An experimental study in dogs. *J. Bone Joint Surg. Am.* **70,** 1209–1217.
85. van Trommel, M.F., Simonian, P.T., Potter, H.G., and Wickiewicz, T.L. (1998). Arthroscopic meniscal repair with fibrin clot of complete radial tears of the lateral meniscus in the avascular zone. *Arthroscopy* **14,** 360–365.
86. Klompmaker, J., Veth, R.P., Jansen, H.W., Nielsen, H.K., de Groot, J.H., Pennings, A.J., Kuijer, R. (1996). Meniscal repair by fibrocartilage in the dog: characterization of the repair tissue and the role of vascularity. *Biomaterials* **17,** 1685–1691.
87. Bhargava, M.M., Attia, E.T., Murrell, G.A., Dolan, M.M., Warren, R.F., and Hannafin, J.A. (1999). The effect of cytokines on the proliferation and migration of bovine meniscal cells. *Am. J. Sports Med.* **27,** 636–643.
88. Hashimoto, J., Kurosaka, M., Yoshiya, S., and Hirohata, K. (1992). Meniscal repair using fibrin sealant and endothelial cell growth factor. An experimental study in dogs. *Am. J. Sports Med.* **20,** 537–541.
89. Lieberman, J.R., Le, L.Q., Wu, L., Finerman, G.A., Berk, A., Witte, O.N., Stevenson, S. (1998). Regional gene therapy with a BMP-2-producing murine stromal cell line induces heterotopic and orthotopic bone formation in rodents. *J. Orthop. Res.* **16,** 330–339.

90. Martinek, V., Usas, A., Pelinkovic, D., Robbins, P., Fu, F.H., and Huard, J. (2002). Genetic engineering of meniscal allografts. *Tiss. Eng.* **8,** 107–117.
91. Hidaka, C., Ibarra, C., Hannafin, J.A., Torzilli, P.A., Quitoriano, M., Jen, S.S., Warren, R.F., and Crystal, R.G. (2002). Formation of vascularized meniscal tissue by combining gene therapy with tissue engineering. *Tiss. Eng.* **8,** 93–105.
92. Walsh, C.J., Goodman, D., Caplan, A.I., and Goldberg, V.M. (1999). Meniscus regeneration in a rabbit partial meniscectomy model. *Tiss. Eng.* **5,** 327–337.
93. Woo, S.L., Hildebrand, K., Watanabe, N., Fenwick, J.A., Papageorgiou, C.D., and Wang, J.H. (1999). Tissue engineering of ligament and tendon healing. *Clin. Orthop.* **367(Suppl.),** S312–323.
94. Frank, C., Amiel, D., Woo, S.L., and Akeson, W. (1985). Normal ligament properties and ligament healing. *Clin. Orthop.* **196,** 15–25.
95. Frank, C., McDonald, D., Bray, D., Bray, R., Rangayyan, R., Chimich, D., and Shrive, N. (1992). Collagen fibril diameters in the healing adult rabbit medial collateral ligament. *Connect Tiss. Res.* **27,** 251–263.
96. Frank, C., McDonald, D., Wilson, J., Eyre, D., and Shrive, N. (1995). Rabbit medial collateral ligament scar weakness is associated with decreased collagen pyridinoline crosslink density. *J. Orthop. Res.* **13,** 157–165.
97. O'Donoghue, D.H., Rockwood, Jr., C.A., Frank, G.R., Jack, S.C., and Kenyon, R. (1966). Repair of the anterior cruciate ligament in dogs. *J. Bone Joint Surg. Am.* **48,** 503–519.
98. Murray, M.M., Martin, S.D., Martin, T.L., and Spector, M. (2000). Histological changes in the human anterior cruciate ligament after rupture. *J. Bone Joint Surg. Am.* **82,** 1387–1397.
99. Geiger, M.H., Green, M.H., Monosov, A., Akeson, W.H., and Amiel, D. (1994). An in vitro assay of anterior cruciate ligament (ACL) and medial collateral ligament (MCL) cell migration. *Connect Tiss. Res.* **30,** 215–224.
100. Nagineni, C.N., Amiel, D., Green, M.H., Berchuck, M., and Akeson, W.H. (1992). Characterization of the intrinsic properties of the anterior cruciate and medial collateral ligament cells: an in vitro cell culture study. *J. Orthop. Res.* **10,** 465–475.
101. Lyon, R.M., Akeson, W.H., Amiel, D., Kitabayashi, L.R., and Woo, S.L. (1991). Ultrastructural differences between the cells of the medical collateral and the anterior cruciate ligaments. *Clin. Orthop.* **272,** 279–286.
102. Ross, S.M., Joshi, R., and Frank, C.B. (1990). Establishment and comparison of fibroblast cell lines from the medial collateral and anterior cruciate ligaments of the rabbit. *In Vitro Cell Dev. Biol.* **26,** 579–584.
103. Schmidt, C.C., Georgescu, H.I., Kwoh, C.K., Blomstrom, G.L., Engle, C.P., Larkin, L.A., Evans, C.H., and Woo, S.L. (1995). Effect of growth factors on the proliferation of fibroblasts from the medial collateral and anterior cruciate ligaments. *J. Orthop. Res.* **13,** 184–190.
104. Marui, T., Niyibizi, C., Georgescu, H.I., Cao, M., Kavalkovich, K.W., Levine, R.E., and Woo, S.L. (1997). Effect of growth factors on matrix synthesis by ligament fibroblasts. *J. Orthop. Res.* **15,** 18–23.
105. Gillery, P., Leperre, A., Maquart, F.X., and Borel, J.P. (1992). Insulin-like growth factor-I (IGF-I) stimulates protein synthesis and collagen gene expression in monolayer and lattice cultures of fibroblasts. *J. Cell. Physiol.* **152,** 389–396.
106. DesRosiers, E.A., Yahia, L., and Rivard, C.H. (1996). Proliferative and matrix synthesis response of canine anterior cruciate ligament fibroblasts submitted to combined growth factors. *J. Orthop. Res.* **14,** 200–208.
107. Schultz, G.S., White, M., Mitchell, R., Brown, G., Lynch, J., Twardzik, D.R., Todaro, G.J. (1987). Epidermal wound healing enhanced by transforming growth factor-alpha and vaccinia growth factor. *Science* **235,** 350–352.
108. Mustoe, T.A., Pierce, G.F., Thomason, A., Gramates, P., Sporn, M.B., and Deuel, T.F. (1987). Accelerated healing of incisional wounds in rats induced by transforming growth factor-beta. *Science* **237,** 1333–1336.
109. Batten, M.L., Hansen, J.C., and Dahners, L.E. (1996). Influence of dosage and timing of application of platelet-derived growth factor on early healing of the rat medial collateral ligament. *J. Orthop. Res.* **14,** 736–741.
110. Kobayashi, D., Kurosaka, M., Yoshiya, S., and Mizuno, K. (1997). Effect of basic fibroblast growth factor on the healing of defects in the canine anterior cruciate ligament. *Knee Surg. Sports Traumatol. Arthrosc.* **5,** 189–194.
111. Bellincampi, L.D., Closkey, R.F., Prasad, R., Zawadsky, J.P., and Dunn, M.G. (1998). Viability of fibroblast-seeded ligament analogs after autogenous implantation. *J. Orthop. Res.* **16,** 414–420.
112. Lieberman, J.R., Lozman, J., Czajka, J., and Dougherty, J. (1988). Repair of Achilles tendon ruptures with Dacron vascular graft. *Clin. Orthop.* **234,** 204–208.
113. Goldstein, J.D., Tria, A.J., Zawadsky, J.P., Kato, Y.P., Christiansen, D., and Silver, F.H. (1989). Development of a reconstituted collagen tendon prosthesis. A preliminary implantation study. *J. Bone Joint Surg. Am.* **71,** 1183–1191.
114. Aragona, J., Parsons, J.R., Alexander, H., and Weiss, A.B. (1981). Soft tissue attachment of a filamentous carbon-absorbable polymer tendon and ligament replacement. *Clin. Orthop.* **160,** 268–278.
115. Rodkey, W.G., Cabaud, H.E., Feagin, J.A., and Perlik, P.C. (1985). A partially biodegradable material device for repair and reconstruction of injured tendons. Experimental studies. *Am. J. Sports Med.* **13,** 242–247.
116. Kato, Y.P., Dunn, M.G., Zawadsky, J.P., Tria, A.J., and Silver, F.H. (1991). Regeneration of Achilles tendon with a collagen tendon prosthesis. Results of a one-year implantation study. *J. Bone Joint Surg. Am.* **73,** 561–574.
117. Takakuda, K., and Miyairi, H. (1996). Tensile behaviour of fibroblasts cultured in collagen gel. *Biomaterials* **17,** 1393–1397.
118. Cao, Y., Liu, Y., Liu, W., Shan, Q., Buonocore, S.D., and Cui, L. (2002). Bridging tendon defects using autologous tenocyte engineered tendon in a hen model. *Plast. Reconstr. Surg.* **110,** 1280–1289.
119. Awad, H.A., Boivin, G.P., Dressler, M.R., Smith, F.N., Young, R.G., and Butler, D.L. (2003). Repair of patellar tendon injuries using a cell-collagen composite. *J. Orthop. Res.* **21,** 420–431.
120. Young, R.G., Butler, D.L., Weber, W., Caplan, A.I., Gordon, S.L., and Fink, D.J. (1998). Use of mesenchymal stem cells in a collagen matrix for Achilles tendon repair. *J. Orthop. Res.* **16,** 406–413.
121. Menetrey, J., Kasemkijwattana, C., Day, C.S., Bosch, P., Fu, F.H., Moreland, M.S., and Huard, J. (1999). Direct-, fibroblast- and myoblast-mediated gene transfer to the anterior cruciate ligament. *Tiss. Eng.* **5,** 435–442.
122. Lou, J., Tu, Y., Burns, M., Silva, M.J., and Manske, P. (2001). BMP-12 gene transfer augmentation of lacerated tendon repair. *J. Orthop. Res.* **19,** 1199–1202.

123. Lou, J., Xu, F., Merkel, K., and Manske, P. (1999). Gene therapy: adenovirus-mediated human bone morphogenetic protein-2 gene transfer induces mesenchymal progenitor cell proliferation and differentiation in vitro and bone formation in vivo. *J. Orthop. Res.* **17,** 43–50.
124. Boden, S.D., Zdeblick, T.A., Sandhu, H.S., and Heim, S.E. (2000). The use of rhBMP-2 in interbody fusion cages. Definitive evidence of osteoinduction in humans: a preliminary report. *Spine* **25,** 376–381.
125. Ivanic, G.M., Pink, T.P., Achatz, W., Ward, J.C., Homann, N.C., and May, M. (2003). Direct stabilization of lumbar spondylolysis with a hook screw: mean 11-year follow-up period for 113 patients. *Spine* **28,** 255–259.
126. West, 3rd, J.L., Bradford, D.S., and Ogilvie, J.W. (1991). Results of spinal arthrodesis with pedicle screw-plate fixation. *J. Bone Joint Surg. Am.* **73,** 1179–1184.
127. France, J.C., Yaszemski, M.J., Lauerman, W.C., Cain, J.E., Glover, J.M., Lawson, K.J., Coe, J.D., and Topper, S.M. (1999). A randomized prospective study of posterolateral lumbar fusion. Outcomes with and without pedicle screw instrumentation. *Spine* **24,** 553–560.
128. Johnsson, R., Stromqvist, B., and Aspenberg, P. (2002). Randomized radiostereometric study comparing osteogenic protein-1 (BMP-7) and autograft bone in human noninstrumented posterolateral lumbar fusion: 2002 Volvo Award in clinical studies. *Spine* **27,** 2654–2661.
129. Patel, T.C., Erulkar, J.S., Grauer, J.N., Troiano, N.W., Panjabi, M.M., and Friedlaender, G.E. (2001). Osteogenic protein-1 overcomes the inhibitory effect of nicotine on posterolateral lumbar fusion. *Spine* **26,** 1656–1661.
130. Boden, S.D., Kang, J., Sandhu, H., and Heller, J.G. (2002). Use of recombinant human bone morphogenetic protein-2 to achieve posterolateral lumbar spine fusion in humans: a prospective, randomized clinical pilot trial: 2002 Volvo Award in clinical studies. *Spine* **27,** 2662–2673.
131. Sandhu, H.S., Toth, J.M., Diwan, A.D., Seim, 3rd, H.B., Kanim, L.E., Kabo, J.M., and Turner, A.S. (2002). Histologic evaluation of the efficacy of rhBMP-2 compared with autograft bone in sheep spinal anterior interbody fusion. *Spine* **27,** 567–575.
132. Kleeman, T.J., Ahn, U.M., and Talbot-Kleeman, A. (2001). Laparoscopic anterior lumbar interbody fusion with rhBMP-2: a prospective study of clinical and radiographic outcomes. *Spine* **26,** 2751–2756.
133. Boden, S.D., Titus, L., Hair, G., Liu, Y., Viggeswarapu, M., Nanes, M.S., and Baranowski, C. (1998). Lumbar spine fusion by local gene therapy with a cDNA encoding a novel osteoinductive protein (LMP-1). *Spine* **23,** 2486–2492.
134. Wang, J.C., Kanim, L.E., Yoo, S., Campbell, P.A., Berk, A.J., Lieberman, J.R. (2003). Effect of regional gene therapy with bone morphogenetic protein-2-producing bone marrow cells on spinal fusion in rats. *J. Bone Joint Surg. Am.* **85,** 905–911.
135. Bernick, S., and Cailliet, R. (1982). Vertebral end-plate changes with aging of human vertebrae. *Spine* **7,** 97–102.
136. Bernick, S., Walker, J.M., and Paule, W.J. (1991). Age changes to the anulus fibrosus in human intervertebral discs. *Spine* **16,** 520–524.
137. Gruber, H.E., Hanley, Jr., E.N. (2003). Recent advances in disc cell biology. *Spine* **28,** 186–193.
138. Thompson, J.P., and Oegema, Jr., T.R., and Bradford, D.S. (1991). Stimulation of mature canine intervertebral disc by growth factors. *Spine* **16,** 253–260.
139. Gruber, H.E., Norton, H.J., and Hanley, Jr., E.N. (2000). Anti-apoptotic effects of IGF-1 and PDGF on human intervertebral disc cells in vitro. *Spine* **25,** 2153–2157.
140. Osada, R., Ohshima, H., Ishihara, H., Yudoh, K., Sakai, K., Matsui, H., and Tsuji, H. (1996). Autocrine/paracrine mechanism of insulin-like growth factor-1 secretion, and the effect of insulin-like growth factor-1 on proteoglycan synthesis in bovine intervertebral discs. *J. Orthop. Res.* **14,** 690–699.
141. Wehling, P., Schulitz, K.P., Robbins, P.D., Evans, C.H., and Reinecke, J.A. (1997). Transfer of genes to chondrocytic cells of the lumbar spine. Proposal for a treatment strategy of spinal disorders by local gene therapy. *Spine* **22,** 1092–1097.

71

Stem Cells in Tissue Engineering

Pamela Gehron Robey and Paolo Bianco

Introduction

In its first inception, tissue engineering was based on the use of natural or synthetic scaffolds seeded with organ-specific cells *ex vivo.* This approach was somewhat distinct from guided tissue regeneration, which used scaffolds and/or bioactive factors to encourage local cells to repair a defect *in situ.* These two approaches are now merged in the current field of tissue engineering that encompasses multiple and diverse disciplines to use cells, materials, and bioactive factors in various combinations to restore and even improve tissue structure and function. Stem-cell–based tissue engineering represents a major turn in the conceptual approach to reconstruction of tissues. By expanding the repertoire of available cells, of envisioned targets, and of technologic means of generating functional tissues *ex vivo,* and above all by making it possible (or promising) to engineer tissues otherwise not engineerable, advances in stem cell biology have a profound impact on tissue engineering at large. In many cases, tissue engineering seems to have more use for stem cells than nature itself. This is especially apparent in the case of stem cells derived from tissues with low turnover or no apparent turnover at all. If neural stem cells were able to repair the loss of dopaminergic neurons in the intact brain *in vivo,* there would be no Parkinson's disease for which to envision stem-cell–based therapies. Dental pulp stem cells do not regenerate primary dentin *in vivo,* but enough dentin can be made from the pulp of a single extracted tooth to generate *ex vivo* the amount of dentin required to fabricate dentures for a marine platoon. Current definitions of stem cells in fact include, in many cases, a technologic dimension (a cell that can be expanded and bent to generation of differentiating cells *ex vivo*). Importantly, the two neighboring fields of cell therapy (reconstruction of functional tissues *in vivo* using cells) and tissue engineering proper (reconstruction of functional tissues using cells and something else) merge significantly once a stem cell angle is adopted for either, not only with respect to the ultimate goals but also to several biotechnologic aspects.

The Reservoirs of Postnatal Stem Cells

Both for ethical constraints and for ease of harvest and control, current approaches to tissue engineering using stem cells largely rely on the use of postnatal stem cells. Once restricted to a handful of constantly (and rapidly) self-renewing tissues, the repertoire of stem cells has expanded to include perhaps every single tissue in the body, regardless of rate of tissue turnover.[1–3] Not all of these tissue-specific stem cells, however, are equally accessible for safe harvest or available in sufficient quantity (or amenable for *ex vivo* expansion) to generate the number of cells needed for tissue regeneration. However, lessons on the dynamics of tissue homeostasis (growth, turnover) that can be learned from these cells have an obvious impact in the design of future tissue-engineering strategies nonetheless. In addition, mechanisms whereby postnatal cells maintain differentiated functions in tissues and organs are relevant even to future embryonic stem-cell–based approaches and can only be learned from postnatal cells.

Handbook of Stem Cells
Volume 2

Do Not Be Rigid About Plasticity

The recent clamor about the potential "plasticity" of certain classes of postnatal stem cells unquestionably adds further questions, once the perspective of use for tissue reconstruction is directly addressed. It would be impractical, to say the least, to use neural stem cells for bone marrow transplantation, and a tissue engineer's enthusiasm for this unexpected finding may remain lukewarm. In contrast, deciding whether liver regeneration is successfully accomplished using previously unknown "hepatogenic" stem cells or by reprogramming of a donor lymphocyte nucleus following cell fusion may not disrupt a tissue engineer's sleep, as long as the goal is met. Unquestionably, some examples of effective tissue reconstruction *in vivo* based on "unorthodox" differentiation of postnatal stem cells have been given.[4,5] However, further investigation is needed to confirm not only the concept of postnatal stem cell plasticity but specifically the technologic aspects of its effective translation into clinical application once proof of principle has been given.

"BREAK UP THE BONES AND SUCK THE SUBSTANTIVE MARROW"[6]

It has long been known that bone marrow is the home of at least two different types of stem cells—the hematopoietic stem cell (HSC) and the bone marrow stromal stem cell (BMSSC) (also known as the mesenchymal stem cell), each able to reconstitute the hematopoietic and skeletal system, respectively. Both systems are thought to be able to contribute differentiated cell types outside of their physiologic progeny.

Highly purified HSCs were reported to give rise to cardiomyocytes,[7] hepatocytes,[4] and a host of epithelial tissues.[8] BMSSCs have been reported to generate functional cardiomyocytes *in vitro* (murine)[9] and to be capable of neural differentiation.[10] A rare subset of murine BMSSCs (multipotential adult progenitor cells [MAPCs]) have been reported to almost be as multipotent as embryonal stem (ES) cells.[11] AC133 (CD133) positive endothelial progenitors are found in the marrow,[12] and endothelial cells themselves may generate cardiomyocytes *in vitro.*[13] Circulating, marrow-derived cells contribute to regeneration of skeletal muscle in response to injury[14] and in mouse models of muscular dystrophy.[15,16] Donor-derived cells have also been detected in neuronal tissue, in newly formed vasculature, in the kidney, and even in the oral cavity following bone marrow or mobilized peripheral blood transplantation.[17] Ideally, the identification of a single accessible site that would contain reservoirs of cells with pluripotentiality and multipotentiality that are easily harvested in large quantities would mark a major advantage in tissue engineering. If substantiated, this wealth of observations would make the bone marrow the central organ of tissue engineering and stem cell therapy (Fig. 71–1).

Current Approaches to Tissue Engineering

Tissue engineering approaches to the regeneration of functional tissue using postnatal stem cells can be envisioned by three different scenarios: (1) expansion of a population *ex vivo* before transplantation into the host; (2) re-creation of a tissue or organ *ex vivo* for transplantation; and (3) design of substances and/or devices for *in vivo* activation of stem cells, either local or distant, to induce appropriate tissue repair (Fig. 71–2). In all of these cases, considerable knowledge of the stem cell population's dynamics is required to predict and control their activity under a variety of different circumstances.

EX VIVO CULTURE OF POSTNATAL STEM CELLS

Ex vivo expansion of tissue- or organ-specific cells, used either alone or added to carriers or scaffoldings at the time of transplantation, has been the primary approach in tissue engineering to date. However, *ex vivo* expansion of postnatal stem cells, in a fashion that maintains an appropriate proportion of stem cells within the population, is a significant hurdle that must be overcome. For example, despite enormous effort, the culture conditions for maintaining HSCs (let alone expanding their number) are as yet undefined. It is perhaps for this very reason that currently there are only a handful of examples in which *ex vivo* expanded postnatal stem cells are used successfully to restore structure and function. The key to successful expansion will lie in understanding cell proliferation kinetics (asymmetrical vs symmetrical division).[18] The efficacy achieved by the use of *ex vivo*-expanded populations, whether stem or more committed in character, may also depend, at least in part, on the nature of the tissue under reconstruction. Within this context, the rate of tissue turnover most likely defines the rate of success. In tissues with a high rate of turnover, such as blood and skin, it is clear that long-term success depends on the persistence of a stem cell within the transplanted population. More committed progenitors may provide some short-term advantage, but, without a self-renewing population, failure is ultimate. However, in tissues that turn over

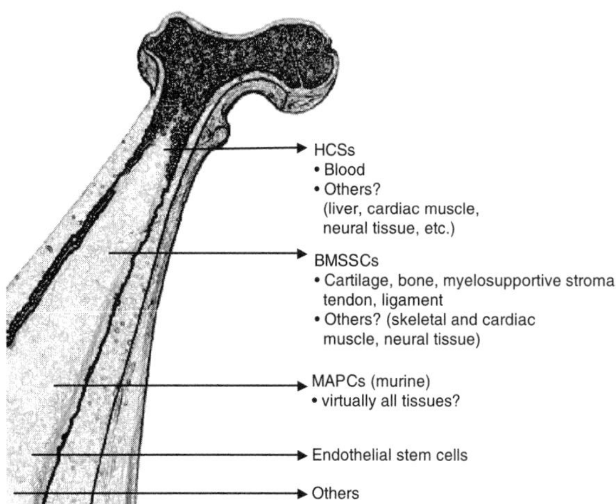

Figure 71–1. *Bone marrow as a central source of postnatal stem cells.* Bone marrow consists of at least two well-defined populations of postnatal stem cells, the hematopoietic stem cell (HSC) and the bone marrow stromal stem cell (BMSSC), both of which form numerous phenotypes within their cellular system but may also form cells outside of them. Multipotential adult progenitor cells (MAPCs) are a subset of BMSSCs and have been reported to form virtually all cell types in mouse. Endothelial precursors (AC133+) have recently been identified, and other types, such as an hepatocyte-like stem cell, may also exist. These remarkable findings, if verified, place bone marrow high on the list of tissues that are easily accessible in sufficient quantity for use in tissue engineering.

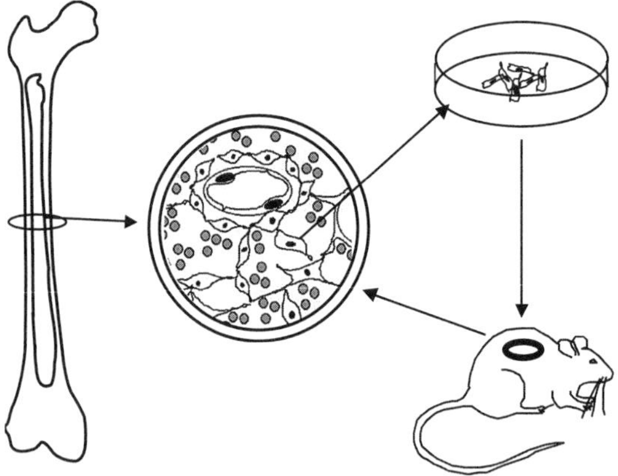

Figure 71–2. *Current applications of postnatal stem cells in tissue engineering.* Although virtually all tissues in the body have cells with some regenerative capabilities, current postnatal stem cell–based strategies, or ones in the foreseeable future, rely on a relatively limited number of source tissues. Autologous bone marrow is currently in trial for myocardial regeneration. Most approaches use *ex vivo* expanded cell populations that are then delivered orthotopically in various combinations with bioactive factors and scaffolds and with skeletal and muscle regeneration. Generation of two-dimensional and three-dimensional structures *ex vivo* requires the use of bioreactors in which cells are seeded onto scaffoldings and subjected to nutrient flow, bioactive factors, and mechanical forces to induce formation of functional tissue for transplantation.

In analyzing these models, stringent criteria must be defined to determine efficacy, and we must remain principled in assessing them. This is an exciting time, but this is also a time for due diligence to bring what started off as a scientific curiosity into medical reality.

ACKNOWLEDGMENTS

The support of Telethon Fondazione Onlus Grant E1029 (to P.B.) is gratefully acknowledged.

REFERENCES

1. Stocum, D.L. (2001). *Wound Repair Regen.* **9,** 429–442.
2. Tsonis, P.A. (2002). *Differentiation* **70,** 397–409.
3. Preston, S.L., Alison, M.R., Forbes, S.J., Direkze, N.C., Poulsom, R., and Wright, N.A. (2003). *Mol. Pathol.* **56,** 86–96.
4. Lagasse, E., Connors, H., Al-Dhalimy, M., Reitsma, M., Dohse, M., Osborne, L., Wang, X., Finegold, M., Weissman, I.L., and Grompe, M. (2000). *Nat. Med.* **6,** 1229–1234.
5. Sampaolesi, M., Torrente, Y., Innocenzi, A., Tonlorenzi, R., D'Antona, G., Pellegrino, M.A., Barresi, R., Bresolin, N., De Angelis, M.G., Campbell, K.P., Bottinelli, R., and Cossu, G. (2003). *Science* **301,** 487–492.
6. Rabelais, F. (1991). "Gargantua and Pantagruel" (B. Raffel, Translation). Norton, New York.
7. Orlic, D., Kajstura, J., Chimenti, S., Limana, F., Jakoniuk, I., Quaini, F., Nadal-Ginard, B., Bodine, D.M., Leri, A., and Anversa, P. (2001). *Proc. Natl. Acad. Sci. U. S. A.* **98,** 10344–10349.
8. Krause, D.S., Theise, N.D., Collector, M.I., Henegariu, O., Hwang, S., Gardner, R., Neutzel, S., and Sharkis, S.J. (2001). *Cell* **105,** 369–377.
9. Makino, S., Fukuda, K., Miyoshi, S., Konishi, F., Kodama, H., Pan, J., Sano, M., Takahashi, T., Hori, S., Abe, H., Hata, J., Umezawa, A., and Ogawa, S. (1999). *J. Clin. Invest.* **103,** 697–705.
10. Azizi, S.A., Stokes, D., Augelli, B.J., DiGirolamo, C., and Prockop, D.J. (1998). *Proc. Natl. Acad. Sci. U. S. A.* **95,** 3908–3913.
11. Jiang, Y., Jahagirdar, B. N., Reinhardt, R.L., Schwartz, R.E., Keene, C.D., Ortiz-Gonzalez, X.R., Reyes, M., Lenvik, T., Lund, T., Blackstad, M., Du, J., Aldrich, S., Lisberg, A., Low, W.C., Largaespada, D.A., and Verfaillie, C.M. (2002). *Nature* **418,** 41–49.
12. Gehling, U.M., Ergun, S., Schumacher, U., Wagener, C., Pantel, K., Otte, M., Schuch, G., Schafhausen, P., Mende, T., Kilic, N., Kluge, K., Schafer, B., Hossfeld, D. K., and Fiedler, W. (2000). *Blood* **95,** 3106–3112.
13. Badorff, C., Brandes, R.P., Popp, R., Rupp, S., Urbich, C., Aicher, A., Fleming, I., Busse, R., Zeiher, A.M., and Dimmeler, S. (2003). *Circulation* **107,** 1024–1032.
14. Ferrari, G., Cusella-De Angelis, G., Coletta, M., Paolucci, E., Stornaiuolo, A., Cossu, G., and Mavilio, F. (1998). *Science* **279,** 1528–1530.
15. Gussoni, E., Soneoka, Y., Strickland, C.D., Buzney, E.A., Khan, M.K., Flint, A.F., Kunkel, L.M., and Mulligan, R.C. (1999). *Nature* **401,** 390–394.
16. Bittner, R.E., Schofer, C., Weipoltshammer, K., Ivanova, S., Streubel, B., Hauser, E., Freilinger, M., Hoger, H., Elbe-Burger, A., and Wachtler, F. (1999). *Anat. Embryol. (Berl.)* **199,** 391–396.
17. Poulsom, R., Alison, M.R., Forbes, S.J., and Wright, N.A. (2002). *J. Pathol.* **197,** 441–456.
18. Sherley, J.L. (2002). *Stem Cells* **20,** 561–572.
19. Weissman, I.L. (2000). *Science* **287,** 1442–1446.
20. Bianco, P., and Robey, P.G. (2001). *Nature* **414,** 118–121.
21. Ringe, J., Kaps, C., Burmester, G.R., and Sittinger, M. (2002). *Naturwissenschaften* **89,** 338–351.
22. Quarto, R., Mastrogiacomo, M., Cancedda, R., Kutepov, S.M., Mukhachev, V., Lavroukov, A., Kon, E., and Marcacci, M. (2001). *N. Engl. J. Med.* **344,** 385–386.
23. Mankani, M.H., Krebsbach, P.H., Satomura, K., Kuznetsov, S.A., Hoyt, R., and Robey, P.G. (2001). *Arch Surg* **136,** 263–270.
24. Halvorsen, Y.D., Franklin, D., Bond, A.L., Hitt, D.C., Auchter, C., Boskey, A.L., Paschalis, E.P., Wilkison, W.O., and Gimble, J.M. (2001). *Tissue Eng.* **7,** 729–741.
25. Zuk, P.A., Zhu, M., Ashjian, P., De Ugarte, D.A., Huang, J.I., Mizuno, H., Alfonso, Z.C., Fraser, J.K., Benhaim, P., and Hedrick, M.H. (2002). *Mol. Biol. Cell* **13,** 4279–4295.
26. Brittberg, M., Lindahl, A., Nilsson, A., Ohlsson, C., Isaksson, O., and Peterson, L. (1994). *N. Engl. J. Med.* **331,** 889–895.
27. Risbud, M.V., and Sittinger, M. (2002). *Trends Biotechnol.* **20,** 351–356.
28. Gronthos, S., Mankani, M., Brahim, J., Robey, P.G., and Shi, S. (2000). *Proc. Natl. Acad. Sci. U. S. A.* **97,** 13625–13630.
29. Miura, M., Gronthos, S., Zhao, M., Lu, B., Fisher, L.W., Robey, P.G., and Shi, S. (2003). *Proc. Natl. Acad. Sci. U. S. A.* **100,** 5807–5812.
30. Asakura, A. (2003). *Trends Cardiovasc. Med.* **13,** 123–128.
31. Cossu, G., and Mavilio, F. (2000). *J. Clin. Invest.* **105,** 1669–1674.
32. Menasche, P., Hagege, A.A., Vilquin, J.T., Desnos, M., Abergel, E., Pouzet, B., Bel, A., Sarateanu, S., Scorsin, M., Schwartz, K., Bruneval, P., Benbunan, M., Marolleau, J. P., and Duboc, D. (2003). *J. Am. Coll. Cardiol.* **41,** 1078–1083.
33. Leobon, B., Garcin, I., Menasche, P., Vilquin, J.T., Audinat, E., and Charpak, S. (2003). *Proc. Natl. Acad. Sci. U. S. A.* **100,** 7808–7811.
34. Itescu, S., Schuster, M.D., and Kocher, A.A. (2003). *J. Mol. Med.* **81,** 288–296.
35. Perin, E.C., Dohmann, H.F., Borojevic, R., Silva, S.A., Sousa, A.L., Mesquita, C.T., Rossi, M.I., Carvalho, A.C., Dutra, H.S., Dohmann, H.J., Silva, G.V., Belem, L., Vivacqua, R., Rangel, F.O., Esporcatte, R., Geng, Y.J., Vaughn, W.K., Assad, J.A., Mesquita, E.T., and Willerson, J.T. (2003). *Circulation* **107,** 2294–2302.
36. Stamm, C., Westphal, B., Kleine, H.D., Petzsch, M., Kittner, C., Klinge, H., Schumichen, C., Nienaber, C.A., Freund, M., and Steinhoff, G. (2003). *Lancet* **361,** 45–46.
37. Badylak, S.F. (2002). *Semin. Cell Dev. Biol.* **13,** 377–383.
38. Hench, L.L., and Polak, J.M. (2002). *Science* **295,** 1014–1017.
39. Niklason, L.E., Gao, J., Abbott, W.M., Hirschi, K.K., Houser, S., Marini, R., and Langer, R. (1999). *Science* **284,** 489–493.
40. Griffith, L.G., and Naughton, G. (2002). *Science* **295,** 1009–1014.
41. Green, H. (1989). *Lab. Invest.* **60,** 583–584.
42. Barrandon, Y., and Green, H. (1987). *Proc. Natl. Acad. Sci. U.S.A.* **84,** 2302–2306.
43. Pellegrini, G., Ranno, R., Stracuzzi, G., Bondanza, S., Guerra, L., Zambruno, G., Micali, G., and De Luca, M. (1999). *Transplantation* **68,** 868–879.

44. Dellambra, E., Pellegrini, G., Guerra, L., Ferrari, G., Zambruno, G., Mavilio, F., and De Luca, M. (2000). *Hum. Gene Ther.* **11,** 2283–2287.
45. Robbins, P.B., Lin, Q., Goodnough, J.B., Tian, H., Chen, X., and Khavari, P.A. (2001). *Proc. Natl. Acad. Sci. U. S. A.* **98,** 5193–5198.
46. Limat, A., and Hunziker, T. (2002). *Cells Tissues Organs* **172,** 79–85.
47. Rama, P., Bonini, S., Lambiase, A., Golisano, O., Paterna, P., De Luca, M., and Pellegrini, G. (2001). *Transplantation* **72,** 1478–1485.
48. Schwab, M.E. (2002). *Science* **295,** 1029–1031.

72

Stem Cell Gene Therapy

Brian R. Davis and Nicole L. Prokopishyn

This volume surveys the biologic properties and potential clinical uses of various classes of adult stem cells. In this chapter, we focus specifically on *ex vivo* gene therapeutic modification of autologous stem cells from patients with genetic disease and discuss the elements crucial for successful clinical application of these therapies. In particular, we contrast gene addition and genome editing approaches for stem cell gene therapy, highlighting the particular challenges that each approach faces to achieve therapeutic benefit.

Introduction

Primitive stem cells capable of self-renewing proliferation and single or multiple cell lineage progeny generation have been identified in several human and mouse tissues. For example, various stem cells individually capable of producing hematopoietic, mesenchymal, endothelial, or liver cells have been identified in adult bone marrow. Although the biologic characterization of various nonhematopoietic stem cells is still in its early stages (e.g., extent of plasticity, *ex vivo* expansion, and cues *in vitro* and/or *in vivo* required to activate stem cells to produce progeny of a particular type), laboratory and therapeutic clinical experience with hematopoietic stem cells (HSCs) suggest that other stem cell types will likely have successful clinical application.

The HSC has exhibited the ability to establish a normal, healthy blood system in patients following transplantation of normal blood stem cells from closely matched individuals–treating disorders of the blood system including immune deficiency, thalassemia, and leukemia. HSC gene therapy offers significant promise for treatment of various hematopoietic diseases because genetic correction of autologous HSCs could result in long-term correction of blood system cells while avoiding the immune system complications resulting from nonidentical transplantation. For example, thalassemia and sickle cell anemia, the most common genetic diseases of blood, could potentially be treated either by delivery of the globin transgene to HSCs (provided that there is appropriate, erythroid-specific expression of the globin transgene in the progeny red blood cells) or by direct repair of a specific globin gene mutation in the HSCs.[1,2]

Significant attention has been devoted to the isolation, culture, and genetic modification of human bone marrow–derived mesenchymal stem cells (MSCs), because they generate cells of cartilage, bone, adipose, marrow stroma, and possibly muscle.[3–6] Provided that these genetically modified cells or their differentiated progeny can be efficiently delivered to the required tissues *in vivo,* genetic modification of these cells is a potential treatment for various genetic diseases affecting mesenchymal cells such as osteogenesis imperfecta, Marfan's syndrome, and muscular dystrophy.[7] Identification of somatic stem cells giving rise to liver,[8,9] pancreas,[10] and brain[11] raises the possibilities of future application of *ex vivo* stem cell gene therapy to treatment of diseases affecting these organ systems. Furthermore, recent identification and isolation of multipotential adult progenitor cells (MAPCs) capable of significant *ex vivo* expansion and differentiation to multiple lineages including neurons, hepatocytes, and endothelial cells potentially makes these cells ideal targets for *ex vivo* stem cell gene therapy.[12,13]

Although one day it may be possible to specifically target various stem cells *in vivo* (e.g., based on a stem cell–specific surface phenotype), this possibility is not available today. Instead, it is more likely that the relevant autologous stem cells will first be isolated from tissues of affected individuals and genetically modified *ex vivo.* The ability to isolate stem cells (hematopoietic and nonhematopoietic) from patients with genetic disease, genetically correct the stem cells, possibly expand them *ex vivo,* and transplant them back into patients with the goal of producing genetically corrected cells *in vivo* offers significant potential for the genetic treatment of human disease.

Genetic modification in stem cells will be designed to either completely correct the genetic defect or at least compensate for the genetic defect. Gene defects occur in a variety of forms, ranging from a simple base pair mutation (e.g., resulting in an amino acid change, a frame shift, the introduction of a stop codon, or a splicing defect) to complete absence of a gene. Two general approaches can be used to correct defective genes within cells: gene addition and genome editing (outlined in Fig. 72–1).

Gene Addition

Gene addition involves the delivery of corrective DNA (usually composed of the entire coding region of a gene and appropriate regulatory sequences) that compensates for or overrides the defective gene (Fig. 72–1). The defective gene,

Handbook of Stem Cells
Volume 2

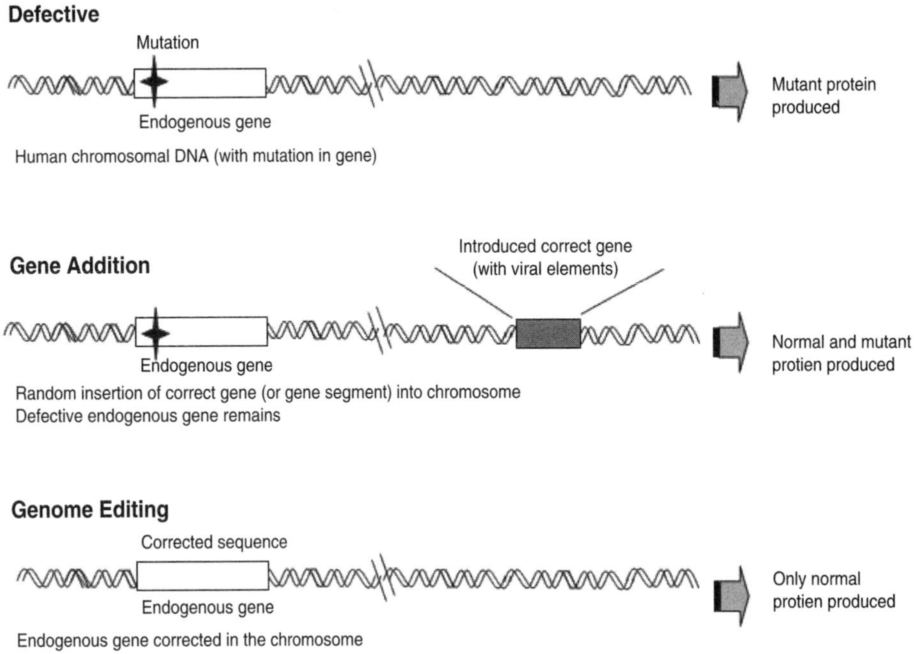

Figure 72–1. Schematic comparison of gene addition and genome editing approaches to stem cell gene therapy.

unless it is completely absent, remains in the affected cells. This approach is particularly applicable when the endogenous gene product is not expressed (e.g., because of extensive deletion of the gene, a silencing mutation in the transcriptional regulatory sequences, or introduction of a stop codon near the start of the coding sequence).

Successful application of stem cell gene therapy requires that therapeutic genes delivered to stem cells persist in the self-renewing stem cells and in their mature and differentiated progeny. This requirement for transgene persistence is critical because (1) transgenes present only transiently in stem cells undergoing self-renewing proliferation will only be of short-term therapeutic benefit and (2) expression of the corrective gene likely exerts its effect in the differentiated progeny, which may be numerous cell divisions downstream of the genetically modified stem cell. Transgene persistence can be accomplished, in principle, either by integration into one of the existing chromosomes or by incorporation of the transgene in a synthetic human microchromosome.

VIRAL VECTORS

Over the past two decades significant attention has been devoted to the development of viral vectors and transduction protocols capable of stable introduction of genetic information into stem cells. Retrovirus, lentivirus, and adeno-associated virus (AAV) vectors are the most common vectors used in transduction of HSCs[14–20] (reviewed in references 21 and 22). Recent applications using foamy virus suggest that these vector systems are also capable of marking engrafting stem cells as assayed in NOD/SCID mice.[23,24] After several years of disappointing results, recent reports in humans[25] and other primates,[26,27] most particularly the French report of successful treatment of X-linked severe combined immune deficiency (SCID),[28] indicate that viral approaches can be successful in treating specific HSC-based diseases; however, a number of potential difficulties must be overcome to make this a safe and effective approach for stem cell gene therapy (discussed later).

NONVIRAL INTEGRATION STRATEGIES

Other approaches have recently been developed that allow for integration into the genome without use of viral vectors. Stable integration of large DNA sequences into specific "attP sites" in the genome can be accomplished using integrase from bacteriophage phiC31.[29–31] This method for introducing large DNA, including needed regulatory elements, may allow genetic correction of inherited diseases caused by mutations in large genes. As well, transposon-based systems have been designed to allow for the insertion of transgenes into the human genome without the use of integrating viral vectors. Indeed, studies with human somatic stem cells *in vitro* and murine models *in vivo* indicate that Sleeping Beauty transposable elements may be able to correct certain genetic diseases.[32,33] However, optimal transposon size may prevent the inclusion of larger genes or necessary regulatory elements.[32]

SYNTHETIC MICROCHROMOSOMES

Synthetic microchromosomes (SMCs), containing centromeric and telomeric sequences derived from functional human chromosomes, demonstrate significantly increased persistence and regulation of copy number in comparison with episomal constructs based on Epstein-Barr virus. SMCs have been shown to be mitotically and cytogenetically stable and segregated appropriately in a cycling human tumor cell line.[34] SMCs accommodate insertion of genetic regions that are sufficient to house therapeutic transgenes together with crucial intron/exon structure and regulatory sequences conferring appropriate transgene regulation. Whether transgene sequences maintained on SMCs are subject to the dysregulated expression and silencing that affect integrated sequences remains to be determined. Crucial issues with application of these SMCs to stem cell gene therapy will be the efficient delivery of single-copy SMCs to target cells and persistence of these SMCs during cell division and differentiation.

Genome Editing

The second approach, genome editing, uses DNA repair and/or homologous recombination processes to correct an existing defective gene sequence so that the defective or mutated area of the gene is restored to a corrected normal state. Genome editing (as shown in Fig. 72–1) involves the delivery of small DNA fragments, hybrid DNA/RNA molecules, and/or modified DNA polymers that are homologous to the target gene sequence with the exception of the base or bases intended for alteration. The genome editing process is directed by endogenous cellular machinery (potentially including mismatch repair and homologous recombination) acting at these target bases and the sequence mismatches created. The target bases are exchanged for the bases present on the introduced DNA fragment–correcting or repairing the gene. The genetic alterations exacted are specific, targeted, and permanent. Repairing the defective sequence itself maintains the corrected genetic material within its normal chromatin environment, ensuring appropriate genetic regulation and expression in the cell. Genetic diseases resulting from well-defined, limited alterations in the DNA sequence, such as sickle cell disease, are ideal candidates for genome editing based gene therapy strategies. As well, genome editing may be the only suitable strategy in situations in which mutant gene product exercises a dominant negative influence over the normal gene product. For example, overexpression of normal collagen can not surmount the harmful effects of mutant collagen chains produced in the disease osteogenesis imperfecta.[35]

Several classes of genome editing molecules display conversion frequencies significantly higher than traditional gene targeting methodologies in mammalian cells and have potential for clinical benefit.[36–42] As well, recent advances in AAV vector development suggest these constructs may be capable of gene repair at frequencies sufficient for therapy.[43] Recently, a report suggested that increased homologous recombination and gene correction can be obtained by combining triplex homing molecules and DNA or RNA–DNA hybrids–a technology called guided homologous recombination (GOREC).[44]

RNA–DNA HYBRIDS

These molecules, containing a central stretch of DNA bases (typically five bases) with the "correcting" sequence flanked by short stretches of RNA that form hairpin loops at the molecule ends, have demonstrated repair of both single base-pair substitutions and deletions. The gene correction mechanism is believed to involve mismatch repair.[39,40,45] RNA–DNA hybrid molecules have been shown able to mediate correction of the sickle cell mutation in lymphoblastoid cell lines[39] and introduce the sickle cell mutation into $CD34^+$ cells from normal individuals.[40,45]

SINGLE-STRANDED DNA OLIGONUCLEOTIDES

Modified synthetic single-stranded DNA oligonucleotides, approximately 25 to 74 bases in length, have also been found capable of single nucleotide exchange in a variety of organisms.[46–48] Studies in yeast suggest that these molecules act by creating a single mismatched base pair on hybridization with the complementary sequence in the chromosome, which is then recognized and corrected by endogenous DNA repair machinery.[46] Successful application of these molecules to genome editing in mammalian cells has recently been reported.[49]

SMALL FRAGMENT HOMOLOGOUS REPLACEMENT (SFHR)

SFHR uses short (typically 50 to 800 nucleotides) single- or double-stranded DNA fragments (SDFs) to alter one or more nucleotides of a specific sequence in the chromosome of a living cell.[36–38,50,51] The SDFs typically span the exon targeted for correction, with the terminal DNA sequences extending into non-exon regions. The precise cellular mechanism(s) responsible for SFHR-mediated genome editing remains to be elucidated. SDFs have been shown to efficiently (~0.1 to 10%) correct or modify specific sequences in genes known to be responsible for disease in several human and mouse transformed and primary cell lines.[36,38,51–54] Recent reports describing the targeting of the *CFTR* gene in mouse lung epithelial cells and the β-globin gene in human hematopoietic stem/progenitor cells (HSPCs) suggest therapeutic potential for this technology.[50,55] Furthermore, studies have demonstrated that SFHR-mediated genome editing can exact the modification of up to five bases within a given region.[56]

TRIPLEX FORMING OLIGONUCLEOTIDES (TFOS)

Triplex DNA can be used to introduce mutations or genetic modifications in certain gene sequences.[57] Triple helices, formed when the TFOs bind in the major groove of duplex DNA at polypurine–polypyrimidine sequences, have the ability to induce mutations in mammalian cells. A major limitation of this technology is the requirement for specific GC-rich repeats for sequence recognition.

ADENO-ASSOCIATED VIRUS VECTORS

Although initial attempts to use appropriately constructed linear single-stranded AAV vectors in gene repair resulted in low levels of targeted gene repair, recent improvements have provided for targeted replacement of up to 1 kb into human chromosomes without additional mutation to the genome.[43,58–60] AAV vectors have also demonstrated efficient correction of single-base mutations in marker genes including HPRT and alkaline phosphatase.[61] The random integration of AAV vectors into chromosomal DNA represents a potential drawback to this approach.

Addition of accessory molecules may also provide for increased genome editing rates. For example, up to 100-fold increases in gene targeting mediated by AAV have been observed following the introduction of DNA double-strand breaks with sequence specific nuclease.[62,63] Indeed, induced DNA double-strand breaks using sequence specific nucleases have also been shown effective in increasing the efficiency of non-AAV targeted gene repair in human cells.[64]

Much debate surrounds the reported efficiencies of genome editing by many of the previously listed molecules. For example, it is well recognized that the residual presence of significant quantities of genome editing molecules for several days posttransfection can result in polymerase chain reaction (PCR) artifacts, giving false evidence for conversion. Indeed, application of these technologies to stem cell gene therapy will require definitive proof of their merit in genome editing of chromosomal targets. Required demonstration of efficacy includes molecular evidence for genome editing at later times posttransfection, phenotypic demonstration of genome editing, Southern blot confirmation of the genome editing event, and demonstration of the absence of nonspecific gene conversion and absence of random integration of genome editing molecules in target cells. Such evidence will allow for further application of these powerful tools.

Requirements for Successful Stem Cell Gene Therapy

GENETIC MODIFICATION DIRECTLY IN STEM CELLS

For long-term therapeutic benefit, it will typically be insufficient to modify only progenitor or differentiated cells; instead, direct genetic modification in stem cells will be required for sustained availability and production of corrected progeny cells. It is also essential that this genetic modification be accomplished without loss of stem cell activity.

Gene Addition

Since the mid-1980s, retrovirus vectors have been the ehicles of choice for delivering transgenes (typically cDNAs together with limited transcriptional regulatory sequence) to cells, because they facilitate efficient transgene delivery and integration into the chromosomal DNA of proliferating target cells. For example, efficient transduction of MAPCs and MSCs with standard retroviral vectors has been reported.[12,13,65–67] The particular challenge of transducing quiescent HSCs was a primary impetus for significant improvements in transduction technology, optimization of *in vitro* transduction conditions including choice of cytokines and use of retronectin, use of various viral envelopes, and development of lentivirus vectors and AAV vectors (although there is controversy regarding the AAV integration efficiency in HSCs[68]). The limited packaging size of retroviral, lentiviral, and AAV vectors precludes packaging of certain cDNAs (e.g., the complete dystrophin cDNA [14-kb cDNA] is too large to be incorporated into the previously mentioned vectors). The packaging of cDNAs means that only one gene product will typically be expressed, as opposed to the possible expression of alternatively spliced forms from the normal genomic configuration.

These transduction methods allow for delivery without loss of stem cell activity. However, questions still remain as to the ability of these constructs to maintain long-term expression in the stem cells and their differentiated progeny, especially because the limited packing size of the vectors often precludes inclusion of key regulatory elements, exon/intron structure, and necessary insulator sequences (see the section on physiologically appropriate expression levels of the corrected gene product in the relevant cells).

Genome Editing

Stem cell genome editing requires delivery of genome editing molecules to stem cells without loss of stem cell function and successful editing of genomic sequences directly in the stem cells. Ideally, one would want efficient, quantitative delivery of genomic editing molecules to the nuclei of stem cells. Typical nonviral macromolecule delivery methodologies face inherent and/or potential limitations in human stem cells. For example, electroporation or liposome-mediated transfection conditions have not yet been reported that allow for the efficient delivery of macromolecules to HSCs without significant loss of viability or stem cell function.[69,70] In addition, these methods typically give rise to cells having significant cell-to-cell variation in the number of DNA molecules transfected. The microinjection technology described in the section on genome editing of human HSPCs was developed for delivery of macromolecules to both human HSCs and MSCs in an effort to alleviate the problems inherent to traditional nonviral methods.

It is not presently known whether the efficiency of editing chromosomal sequences is affected by the cycling status of stem cells. Although not an issue for those stem cells that can apparently be maintained in a proliferative state *in vitro* without loss of stem cell function (e.g., MAPCs and MSCs), the question of whether replication of the target gene chromosomal DNA is required for successful genome editing is important for quiescent HSCs. It is perhaps important to note that the various genome editing molecules summarized previously may use different mechanisms for genome editing and may, therefore, exhibit different requirements for cycling. It also remains to be determined whether efficient genome editing requires active transcription and/or an open chromatin conformation of the target gene. Although some genes requiring modification will already be expressed in stem cells (e.g., housekeeping genes), there are other target genes that would normally not be expressed until a certain state of differentiation or activation has been reached. Although it is assumed that stem cells in a quiescent state normally perform ongoing surveillance and repair of chromosomal mutations in both transcriptionally active and inactive genes, to our knowledge this has not been directly examined.

GENETICALLY CORRECTED STEM CELLS AND THEIR RELEVANT DIFFERENTIATED PROGENY CONSISTENTLY PRESENT AT SUFFICIENT FREQUENCY *IN VIVO*

A critical issue in stem cell gene therapy is achieving and maintaining a level of corrected stem cells and/or their progeny *in vivo* sufficient to achieve the desired therapeutic effect. Transplanted genetically modified stem cells and their progeny will exist *in vivo* in a background of transplanted unmodified cells and endogenous, unmodified stem cells and their progeny. The percentage of "corrected" cells required for therapeutic value will differ for various diseases. Factors that will influence the percentage of genetically modified cells *in vivo* are (1) the percentage and number of genetically modified stem cells *ex vivo* before transplantation; (2) the ability to expand the stem cells *ex vivo;* (3) the ability to selectively expand or select for the genetically modified stem cells *ex vivo* or *in vivo* (at the expense of the endogenous, defective stem cells); and (4) whether the genetically modified cells (either stem cells or their differentiated progeny) have a proliferative, survival, or functional advantage *in vivo.*

If there was a capability for significant *ex vivo* expansion of stem cells, without loss of stem cell biologic activity (including self-renewal and differentiation capability), the number of genetically modified stem cells delivered to the patient could be significantly increased, potentially increasing the frequency of genetically corrected versus endogenous defective stem cells *in vivo* following transplant. In addition, if there existed the ability to obtain, *ex vivo,* expanded populations of cells all derived from a single stem cell clone, cells for transplantation could be prepared that were precharacterized for their site of retroviral integration (to eliminate clones with problematic insertional mutagenesis sites or to identify integrants likely to demonstrate appropriately regulated transgene expression) or for successful genome editing (i.e., only delivering appropriately corrected stem cells). Studies performed with human MSCs or human MAPCs suggest that these classes of stem cells may be capable of significant *ex vivo* expansion.[3,4,12,13,71]

Gene Addition

Inclusion of a selectable marker gene, in addition to the therapeutic transgene, in the same viral vector will, in principle, permit *ex vivo* or *in vivo* selection of genetically modified stem cells and their progeny. For example, various groups have examined the ability to specifically select *in vivo* for HSCs and progeny transduced with a retroviral vector expressing either normal O^6 methylguanine methyltransferase (MGMT) that confers resistance to nitrosoureas, such as BCNU, or a mutant MGMT (e.g., P140K) resistant to the combination of O^6-benzylguanine plus BCNU.[72–77] Other selectable genes have included dihydroxyfolate reductase (DFHR) and multiple drug resistance (MDR).[78] Although these studies have demonstrated excellent *in vivo* selection for the genetically modified cell, a concern remains with regard to potential *in vivo* toxicity at time of chemotherapeutic treatment or incidence of cancer in later years because of the chemotherapeutic treatment(s).

Genome Editing

Genome editing will most likely first find application when there is a natural *in vivo* selective advantage for genetically corrected stem cells and/or their progeny (e.g., Wiskott Aldrich syndrome [WAS], Fanconi's anemia, or X-SCID). There should be a strong selective advantage *in vivo* for the corrected HSCs and their T-lymphocyte progeny in WAS as evidenced by studies of X-chromosome inactivation patterns in female WAS carriers[79–81] and the selective reversion to a corrected WASP allele in a patient with WAS.[82] These data strongly suggest that even the correction of a small number of HSCs with the capability of differentiating into gene-corrected T-cell progenitors and mature T lymphocytes may lead to significant clinical benefit in WAS. This suggestion is supported by recent efforts to treat X-SCID via stem cell gene therapy.[83,84] It is believed that strong *in vivo* selective pressure for T and B cells expressing the gamma chain of the interleukin (IL)-2 receptor contributed to the success of the X-SCID trial in France.[28]

For those diseases in which the genome edited stem cells and/or their progeny do not have a selective advantage *in vivo,* successfully genome edited stem cells could be subsequently transduced with constructs having selectable genes (e.g., P140K MGMT) as described previously. Use of systems such as Cre-Loc could facilitate excision of drug selection constructs following *in vivo* selection.

PHYSIOLOGICALLY APPROPRIATE EXPRESSION LEVELS OF THE CORRECTED GENE PRODUCT IN THE RELEVANT CELLS

Correction of genetic deficiencies will typically require that the therapeutic gene be expressed at the appropriate level in the relevant cells for the life of the patient. Genetic treatment of some diseases will have less stringent requirements for either the level of required expression (e.g., chronic granulomatous disease) or the ability to tolerate indiscriminate expression (e.g., adenosine deaminase deficiency, Gaucher disease). In contrast, successful treatment of other diseases (e.g., hemoglobinopathies, X-linked agammaglobulinemia) will likely require expression that is both of sufficient level and cell-type specific.[85] For example, it is expected that clinical benefit in hemoglobinopathies will require that nonerythroid cells remain absent of globin expression and that most erythrocytes will express the inserted gene at greater than 10 to 20% of normal globin levels for thalassemia and 20 to 40% of HbF levels for sickle cell disease.[1] Finally, ectopic constitutive expression of therapeutic transgenes may be harmful in cases in which expression of the endogenous gene is tightly regulated (e.g., with respect to the cell's activation state). For example, although ectopic expression of the CD40L transgene corrected a CD40L deficiency in mice it also caused a thymic lymphoproliferative disease.[86]

Gene Addition

Significant problems have been encountered in satisfying the requirement for long-term, cell type-specific transgene expression. For example, the expression of retrovirus-transduced transgenes is frequently silenced in the progeny of transduced human or primate progenitors.[85,87,88] Furthermore, even in those cells demonstrating some expression, there may be significant variability in the level of expression from cell to cell. The difficulty in achieving appropriate expression (proper level, regulation, and cell-type specificity) is due to integration position effects, uneven distribution of the number of integrated gene copies per cell, and the inability to package sufficient regulatory sequences within the viral vector. As a consequence of this dysregulated expression, cells, although genetically modified with corrective genes, may not efficiently display the corrected phenotype. The variation in level of transgene expression from cell to cell is determined, to a large extent, by the site of proviral integration. For retroviral and lentiviral vectors, the site of integration is essentially random, although there is a preference for active or "bent" chromatin. Several recent studies have reported that multiple retroviral or lentiviral integration events per cell were required for adequate levels of transgene expression. For example, Woods *et al.*[89] reported an average of 5.6 ± 3.3 integration events per cell under efficient transduction conditions, and several groups have reported that multiple proviral integrations per cell were required for consistent therapeutic expression presumably because some of the integration events are "silent" or expressed at only very low level.[90–93] The requirement for multiple integration events creates at least two problems: (1) increased likelihood of insertion mutagenesis (see later) and (2) a potential for inappropriately high expression of transgene in the cells (e.g., an overexpression of β globin may be manifest as α-thalassemia).

Interestingly, these same features of dysregulated transgene expression were also observed in the early transgenic mouse expression studies.[94] Subsequent studies demonstrated that long-term, position-independent, copy number–dependent, cell-type specific expression required strong promoter/enhancer elements, sufficient genomic sequences to dominantly confer the appropriate chromatin configuration (i.e., an open chromatin conformation in expressing cells; e.g., inclusion of locus control region [LCR]-like elements),[94–96] and sufficient intron/exon structure and sequences for high-level expression.[85] The strict packaging requirements for retrovirus, lentivirus, and AAV vectors may preclude inclusion of sufficient regulatory sequences and/or intron/exon structure for therapeutic applications requiring highly regulated gene expression. Strong splicing signals (i.e., intron/exon structure) or cryptic splicing signals in transgene sequences (e.g., when inserted in reverse orientation) may interfere with packaging of the desired unspliced full-length construct.[97] Certain position effects may be overcome via use of insulator sequences; whether their inclusion will suffice to ensure accurate and regulated expression is under active investigation.[98,99]

The complex and coordinate regulation of globin gene expression *in vivo* raises significant challenges for treating sickle cell anemia or β-thalassemia by addition of a normal or specially designed globin gene using retroviral, lentiviral, or AAV vectors. Much effort has been dedicated to identifying and including in viral vectors the regulatory sequences that are necessary and sufficient for appropriately regulated transgene expression. Recently, use of optimized vector constructs have yielded significant improvements in long-term, erythroid-specific globin expression in mouse models.[15,90–93,99–103] Whether these very promising results will be confirmed in human clinical trials remains to be determined.

A significant challenge for achieving appropriately regulated transgene expression via stem cell gene therapy is that the transgene, together with regulatory sequences, is delivered into a chromatin environment (specifically, stem cell) that may be significantly different from the chromatin environment in which the transgene expression is ultimately required (e.g., erythroid for globin expression; T-cell for WASP expression). For example, a transgene may integrate into an active chromatin locus in stem cells that may subsequently become an inactive chromatin locus in the differentiated cell type(s). Furthermore, it is not known whether transcriptional regulatory sequences directly incorporated into stem cell chromatin will show the same loading of chromatin remodeling and transcription factors as when the transcriptional regulatory sequences are present in the chromatin from the stage of embryonic stem cell onward. In other words, is chromatin structure (including histones, transcription factors, etc.) a consequence of sequential steps of factor addition and removal, originating in the fertilized egg or embryonal stem cell? Or can it be created *de novo* from factors present in the HSC? For example, Vassilopoulos *et al.*[104] reported that appropriate activity of the β-globin regulatory sequences required passage through a nonerythroid environment.

Genome Editing

Repairing the mutation itself within the defective gene (e.g., β-globin gene) would maintain the correct genetic material within its normal chromatin environment and in principle ensure appropriate genetic regulation and expression in the progeny differentiated cells (e.g., erythroid cells). This is one of the primary advantages of the genome editing approach for genes in which the transcriptional regulatory sequences are intact.

AB SENCE OF INTERFERENCE FROM ENDOGENOUS DEFECTIVE GENE PRODUCT ON THE ACTIVITY OF THE CORRECTED GENE PRODUCT

For those situations in which there is ongoing expression of the endogenous defective gene, a critical issue is whether this mutant gene product will interfere with the function of the introduced correct transgene. For example, it is possible that endogenous expression of a truncated or mutant protein could interfere with the functioning of an introduced normal protein in a dominant negative manner (e.g., collagen or WASP). Persistence of the mutant protein may be a particular problem in cases in which the gene product normally forms homodimers or heterodimers or trimers (e.g., CD40L).

Gene Addition

Addition of a normal gene into a stem cell means that the defective gene is still present within that cell and capable of action. If ongoing expression of the endogenous defective gene is detrimental to the cell, it may be necessary to either express a specific transgene product that is designed to specifically counteract the activity of the mutant gene (e.g., expression of an anti-sickling gene) or to overexpress the normal transgene product at a level sufficient to dilute out the effect of the mutant gene product. These approaches may not be possible in all cases because overexpression of the normal gene product may itself generate negative side effects or unexpected results.

Genome Editing

Genome editing may be the only suitable genetic modification in situations in which the mutant gene product exercises a dominant negative influence over the normal gene product, because this approach would convert the endogenous gene to a normal form, ablating the detrimental mutant gene.

ABSENCE OF ADVERSE EFFECTS

Of critical importance in any therapy is minimization of side effects or adverse effects caused by the treatment itself. A partial listing of potential adverse effects from stem cell gene therapy would include insertional mutagenesis from transgene integration, nonspecific gene editing introducing untoward mutations, and inadvertent carcinogenesis from the *in vivo* selection method for corrected cells. Although a complete absence of any adverse effects is clearly the goal of any genetic therapy, the potential risks of any treatment must be assessed in concert with the potential benefits. For some of the diseases potentially amenable to stem cell gene therapy, the current prognosis is very poor with no other therapy available. It should also be remembered that the introduction of other groundbreaking therapies (e.g., heart transplantation, marrow transplantation) resulted in numerous initial failures, including death of patients. In addition, even today, therapies such as allogenic marrow transplantation for primary immunodeficiency disease are only 90% successful.

Gene Addition

A difficulty of the gene addition approach is the potential leukemogenicity resulting from random integration of the introduced viral vector into chromosomal DNA (e.g., either activating oncogenes or disabling tumor suppressor genes). This possibility has been reported both in retroviral transduction of mouse stem cells[105] and in the otherwise successful X-SCID human trial in France.[28] Furthermore, Woods *et al.*[89] reported that efficient lentiviral vector transduction of human NOD-SCID repopulating cells yielded multiple integrations per cell—increasing the chance of insertional mutagenesis. In fact, one of the characterized integrants was localized in the *BRCA1* tumor suppressor gene.

Genome Editing

One of the crucial criteria for genome editing is the specificity of the editing event. A balance between specific and nonspecific genome editing may occur and as such it is imperative to develop methods that favor specific actions. As well, use of methods that introduce double-strand DNA breaks (believed to increase the rates of repair) requires strict regulation to ensure that these breaks are limited and specific to the target sequence (e.g., through engineering of site-specific nucleases). Some of the molecules used in genome editing also have the potential for random integration within the genome and, therefore, possess the potential to disrupt genes and or cause mutagenesis. Assessment of this risk or application of molecules that do not randomly integrate into the genome will be necessary for therapeutic application.

Genome Editing of Human Hematopoietic Stem/Progenitor Cells

One of the current limitations to development of genome editing strategies in human adult stem cells, and particularly HSPCs, has been the difficulty in achieving efficient delivery of genome editing molecules to the nucleus of stem cells without loss of stem cell activity. This section summarizes our development of a novel method for delivering macromolecules to the nuclei of HSPCs and MSCs and our experience, in particular, with genome editing of HSPCs.

MICROINJECTION-MEDIATED DELIVERY OF MACROMOLECULES TO ADULT STEM CELLS

Although therapeutic application will likely require the correction of a large number of HSPCs (given current identification procedures for engrafting cells) and, therefore, a robust method for bulk delivery of macromolecules to the patient's cells, microinjection provides an ideal experimental tool for quantitative delivery of macromolecules to the nuclei of HSPCs.[106,107] With the development of strategies for attachment of HSPCs to extracellular matrix-coated dishes without affecting cell function and the development of injection needles with very small outer tip diameters (OTDs) (~0.2 μ) that do not damage these relatively small cells (~6 μ diameter for stem cells[108]), glass needle–mediated microinjection technology has been successfully applied to HSPCs.[106,107] Importantly, macromolecule delivery is accomplished with high postinjection cell viability (up to 87% postinjection viabilities in $CD34^+/CD38^-$ cells), no discernible impact on stem/progenitor cell proliferation or biologic activity, and a high frequency of cells expressing injected transgenes.[107]

Microinjection can deliver macromolecules into cells irrespective of whether the cells are in a quiescent or cycling state, and by regulating concentration of DNA injected, flow rate, and injection time per cell, the number of molecules delivered to a cell can be approximately controlled. Microinjection has been demonstrated to be a well-tolerated method for the delivery of various genome editing molecules to HSPCs.[45,50] These microinjection technologies have been expanded to MSCs with postinjection viability and short-term *GFP* gene expression greater than 60%.[109]

GENOME EDITING OF THE β-GLOBIN GENE IN HEMATOPOIETIC STEM/PROGENITOR CELLS

Genome editing strategies have been used to introduce the sickle cell disease lesion, a single base-pair transversion (A → T), in codon 6 of the β-globin gene in normal HSPCs. Targeted modification of the β-globin gene has been assessed following delivery via microinjection of both RNA–DNA hybrids[45] and SFHR molecules.[50,55]

RNA–DNA Hybrids

Liu *et al.*[45] recently described the application of RNA–DNA hybrids to site-specific nucleotide exchange in the human globin gene in primitive human blood cells.[45] RNA–DNA hybrids delivered via microinjection to $CD34^+$ and Lin^-CD38^- cells resulted in the A to T nucleotide exchange in 23% of experiments analyzed. Furthermore, conversion of the β-globin gene was detected in the erythroid progeny of Lin^-CD38^- cells at the mRNA level. Interestingly, conversion rates as high as 10 to 15% were seen in some experimental samples, suggesting that levels of conversion may be sufficient to achieve therapeutic benefit in patients with sickle cell disease.

Small Fragment Homologous Replacement

The feasibility of using SFHR in the modification of normal human β ($β^A$)-globin sequences was assessed in engrafting normal HSPCs. Short DNA fragments ($β^S$ SDF, 559 bp) made up of sickle β ($β^S$)-globin sequence were microinjected into the nuclei of $Lin^-/CD38^-$ cells. Site-specific conversion ($β^A \rightarrow β^S$-globin) was observed in 42% of the experiments (70 experiments total) as determined by DNA and RNA analysis at 2 to 7 weeks postinjection. The percent fraction of β-globin alleles that were converted in each experiment ranged between 1 to 13%.[50,55]

$Lin^-/CD38^-$ cells, microinjected with $β^S$ SDF, were also transplanted into irradiated NOD/SCID/$β_2$ microglobulin knockout mice to assess whether $β^A$ to $β^S$ conversion had actually occurred in cells capable of engrafting the bone marrow of these mice. Successful engraftment of genetically modified primitive human blood cells in immune-deficient mice was observed with significant conversion of the β-globin gene ($β^A$ to $β^S$).[50,55] Evidence for the presence of sickle globin protein in modified cells and/or demonstration of genome editing of HSPCs isolated from sickle cell patients will provide further support for application of genome editing technologies in *ex vivo* stem cell gene therapy.

Conclusion

Gene addition and genome editing approaches as applied to human stem cells offer significant therapeutic potential. It is most likely that clinical benefit will be initially demonstrated in diseases in which there is a clear selective advantage (e.g., proliferative, functional, or survival) for the corrected stem cells or their progeny and/or in which the requirements for regulation of gene expression are less stringent. Significant improvements in both technologies will be required to bring about therapeutic benefit to a wider range of inherited genetic diseases.

REFERENCES

1. McInerney, J.M., Nemeth, M.J., and Lowrey, C.H. (2000). Erythropoiesis: review article—slow and steady wins the race? Progress in the development of vectors for gene therapy of beta-thalassemia and sickle cell disease. *Hematology* **4,** 437–455.
2. McCune, S.L., Reilly, M.P., Chomo, M.J., Asakura, T., and Townes, T.M. (1994). Recombinant human hemoglobins designed for gene therapy of sickle cell disease. *Proc. Natl. Acad. Sci. U. S. A.* **91,** 9852–9856.
3. Pittenger, M.F., Mackay, A.M., Beck, S.C., Jaiswal, R.K., Douglas, R., Mosca, J.D., Moorman, M.A., Simonetti, D.W., Craig, S., and Marshak, D.R. (1999). Multilineage potential of adult human mesenchymal stem cells. *Science* **284,** 143–147.
4. Bruder, S.P., Jaiswal, N., and Haynesworth, S.E. (1997). Growth kinetics, self-renewal, and the osteogenic potential of purified human mesenchymal stem cells during extensive subcultivation and following cryopreservation. *J. Cell. Biochem.* **64,** 278–294.
5. Prockop, D.J. (1998). Marrow stromal cells as stem cells for continual renewal of nonhematopoietic tissues and as potential vectors for gene therapy. *J. Cell Biochem. Suppl.* **30–31,** 284–285.
6. Gronthos, S., Zannettino, A.C., Hay, S.J., Shi, S., Graves, S.E., Kortesidis, A., and Simmons, P.J. (2003). Molecular and cellular characterisation of highly purified stromal stem cells derived from human bone marrow. *J. Cell Sci.* **116,** 1827–1835.
7. Van Damme, A., Vanden Driessche, T., Collen, D., and Chuah, M.K. (2002). Bone marrow stromal cells as targets for gene therapy. *Curr. Gene Ther.* **2,** 195–209.
8. Petersen, B.E., Bowen, W.C., Patrene, K.D., Mars, W.M., Sullivan, A.K., Murase, N., Boggs, S.S., Greenberger, J.S., and Goff, J.P. (1999). Bone marrow as a potential source of hepatic oval cells. *Science* **284,** 1168–1170.
9. Theise, N.D., Badve, S., Saxena, R., Henegariu, O., Sell, S., Crawford, J.M., and Krause, D.S. (2000). Derivation of hepatocytes from bone marrow cells in mice after radiation-induced myeloablation. *Hepatology* **31,** 235–240.
10. Ramiya, V.K., Maraist, M., Arfors, K.E., Schatz, D.A., Peck, A.B., and Cornelius, J.G. (2000). Reversal of insulin-dependent diabetes using islets generated in vitro from pancreatic stem cells. *Nat. Med.* **6,** 278–282.
11. Johansson, C.B., Momma, S., Clarke, D.L., Risling, M., Lendahl, U., and Frisen, J. (1999). Identification of a neural stem cell in the adult mammalian central nervous system. *Cell* **96,** 25–34.
12. Jiang, Y., Vaessen, B., Lenvik, T., Blackstad, M., Reyes, M., and Verfaillie, C.M. (2002). Multipotent progenitor cells can be isolated from postnatal murine bone marrow, muscle, and brain. *Exp. Hematol.* **30,** 896–904.
13. Reyes, M., Dudek, A., Jahagirdar, B., Koodie, L., Marker, P.H., and Verfaillie, C.M. (2002). Origin of endothelial progenitors in human postnatal bone marrow. *J. Clin. Invest.* **109,** 337–346.
14. Bradfute, S.B., and Goodell, M.A. (2003). Adenoviral transduction of mouse hematopoietic stem cells. *Mol. Ther.* **7,** 334–340.
15. May, C., Rivella, S., Callegari, J., Heller, G., Gaensler, K. M., Luzzatto, L., and Sadelain, M. (2000). Therapeutic haemoglobin synthesis in beta-thalassaemic mice expressing lentivirus-encoded human beta-globin. *Nature* **406,** 82–86.

16. Guenechea, G., Gan, O.I., Inamitsu, T., Dorrell, C., Pereira, D.S., Kelly, M., Naldini, L., and Dick, J.E. (2000). Transduction of human CD34+. *Mol. Ther.* **1**(6), 566–573.
17. Uchida, N., Sutton, R.E., Friera, A.M., He, D., Reitsma, M.J., Chang, W.C., Veres, G., Scollay, R., and Weissman, I.L. (1998). HIV, but not murine leukemia virus, vectors mediate high efficiency gene transfer into freshly isolated G0/G1 human hematopoietic stem cells. *Proc. Natl. Acad. Sci. U. S. A.* **95,** 11939–11944.
18. Larochelle, A., Vormoor, J., Hanenberg, H., Wang, J. C., Bhatia, M., Lapidot, T., Moritz, T., Murdoch, B., Xiao, X.L., Kato, I., Williams, D.A., and Dick, J.E. (1996). Identification of primitive human hematopoietic cells capable of repopulating NOD/SCID mouse bone marrow: implications for gene therapy. *Nat. Med.* **2,** 1329–1337.
19. Miller, D.G., Adam, M.A., and Miller, A.D. (1990). Gene transfer by retrovirus vectors occurs only in cells that are actively replicating at the time of infection. *Mol. Cell Biol.* **10,** 4239–4242.
20. Sutton, R.E., Wu, H.T., Rigg, R., Bohnlein, E., and Brown, P.O. (1998). Human immunodeficiency virus type 1 vectors efficiently transduce human hematopoietic stem cells. *J. Virol.* **72,** 5781–5788.
21. Baum, C., Dullmann, J., Li, Z., Fehse, B., Meyer, J., Williams, D.A., and von Kalle, C. (2003). Side effects of retroviral gene transfer into hematopoietic stem cells. *Blood* **101,** 2099–2114.
22. Hawley, R.G. (2001). Progress toward vector design for hematopoietic stem cell gene therapy. *Curr. Gene Ther.* **1,** 1–17.
23. Zucali, J.R., Ciccarone, T., Kelley, V., Park, J., Johnson, C.M., and Mergia, A. (2002). Transduction of umbilical cord blood CD34+ NOD/SCID-repopulating cells by simian foamy virus type 1 (SFV-1) vector. *Virology* **302,** 229–235.
24. Hirata, R.K., Miller, A.D., Andrews, R.G., and Russell, D.W. (1996). Transduction of hematopoietic cells by foamy virus vectors. *Blood* **88,** 3654–3661.
25. Aiuti, A., Slavin, S., Aker, M., Ficara, F., Deola, S., Mortellaro, A., Morecki, S., Andolfi, G., Tabucchi, A., Carlucci, F., Marinello, E., Cattaneo, F., Vai, S., Servida, P., Miniero, R., Roncarolo, M.G., and Bordignon, C. (2002). Correction of ADA-SCID by stem cell gene therapy combined with nonmyeloablative conditioning. *Science* **296**(5577), 2410–2413.
26. Horn, P.A., Topp, M.S., Morris, J.C., Riddell, S.R., and Kiem, H.P. (2002). Highly efficient gene transfer into baboon marrow repopulating cells using GALV-pseudotype oncoretroviral vectors produced by human packaging cells. *Blood* **100,** 3960–3967.
27. Horn, P.A., Morris, J.C., Bukovsky, A.A., Andrews, R.G., Naldini, L., Kurre, P., and Kiem, H.P. (2002). Lentivirus-mediated gene transfer into hematopoietic repopulating cells in baboons. *Gene Ther.* 1464–1471. *Gene Ther.* **9**(21), 1464–1471.
28. Cavazzana-Calvo, M., Hacein-Bey, S., de Saint, B.G., Gross, F., Yvon, E., Nusbaum, P., Selz, F., Hue, C., Certain, S., Casanova, J.L., Bousso, P., Deist, F.L., and Fischer, A. (2000). Gene therapy of human severe combined immunodeficiency (SCID)-X1 disease. *Science* **288,** 669–672.
29. Ortiz-Urda, S., Thyagarajan, B., Keene, D.R., Lin, Q., Fang, M., Calos, M.P., and Khavari, P.A. (2002). Stable nonviral genetic correction of inherited human skin disease. *Nat. Med.* **8,** 1166–1170.
30. Olivares, E.C., Hollis, R.P., Chalberg, T.W., Meuse, L., Kay, M.A., and Calos, M.P. (2002). Site-specific genomic integration produces therapeutic Factor IX levels in mice. *Nat. Biotechnol.* **20,** 1124–1128.
31. Sclimenti, C.R., Thyagarajan, B., and Calos, M.P. (2001). Directed evolution of a recombinase for improved genomic integration at a native human sequence. *Nucleic Acids Res.* **29,** 5044–5051.
32. Ortiz-Urda, S., Lin, Q., Yant, S.R., Keene, D., Kay, M.A., and Khavari, P.A. (2003). Sustainable correction of junctional epidermolysis bullosa via transposon-mediated non-viral gene transfer. *Gene Ther.* **10,** 1099–1104.
33. Montini, E., Held, P.K., Noll M., Morcinek, N., Al-Dhalimy, M., Finegold, M., Yant, S.R., Kay, M.A., and Grompe, M. (2002). In vivo correction of murine tyrosinemia type I by DNA-mediated transposition. *Mol. Ther.* **6,** 759–769.
34. Harrington, J.J., Van Bokkelen, G., Mays, R.W., Gustashaw, K., and Willard, H.F. (1997). Formation of de novo centromeres and construction of first-generation human artificial microchromosomes. *Nat. Genet.* **15,** 345–355.
35. Gajko-Galicka, A. (2002). Mutations in type I collagen genes resulting in osteogenesis imperfecta in humans. *Acta Biochim. Pol.* **49,** 433–441.
36. Goncz, K.K., Kunzelmann, K., Xu, Z., and Gruenert, D.C. (1998). Targeted replacement of normal and mutant CFTR sequences in human airway epithelial cells using DNA fragments. *Hum. Mol. Genet.* **7,** 1913–1919.
37. Goncz, K.K., and Gruenert, D.C. (2000). Site-directed alteration of genomic DNA by small-fragment homologous replacement. *Methods Mol. Biol.* **133,** 85–99.
38. Kunzelmann, K., Legendre, J.Y., Knoell, D.L., Escobar, L.C., Xu, Z., and Gruenert, D.C. (1996). Gene targeting of CFTR DNA in CF epithelial cells. *Gene Ther.* **3,** 859–867.
39. Cole-Strauss, A., Yoon, K., Xiang, Y., Byrne, B.C., Rice, M.C., Gryn, J., Holloman, W.K., and Kmiec, E.B. (1996). Correction of the mutation responsible for sickle cell anemia by an RNA- DNA oligonucleotide. *Science* **273,** 1386–1389.
40. Xiang, Y., Cole-Strauss, A., Yoon, K., Gryn, J., and Kmiec, E.B. (1997). Targeted gene conversion in a mammalian CD34+-enriched cell population using a chimeric RNA/DNA oligonucleotide. *J. Mol. Med.* **75,** 829–835.
41. Bandyopadhyay, P., Ma, X., Linehan-Stieers, C., Kren, B.T., and Steer, C.J. (1999). Nucleotide exchange in genomic DNA of rat hepatocytes using RNA/DNA oligonucleotides: targeted delivery of liposomes and polyethylenimine to the asialoglycoprotein receptor. *J. Biol. Chem.* **274,** 10163–10172.
42. Kren, B.T., Parashar, B., Bandyopadhyay, P., Chowdhury, N.R., Chowdhury, J.R., and Steer, C.J. (1999). Correction of the UDP-glucuronosyltransferase gene defect in the gunn rat model of Crigler-Najjar syndrome type I with a chimeric oligonucleotide. *Proc. Natl. Acad. Sci. U. S. A.* **96,** 10349–10354.
43. Russell, D.W., Hirata, R.K., and Inoue, N. (2002). Validation of AAV-mediated gene targeting. *Nat. Biotechnol.* **20,** 658.
44. Maurisse, R., Feugeas, J.P., Biet, E., Kuzniak, I., Leboulch, P., Dutreix, M., and Sun, J.S. (2002). A new method (GOREC) for directed mutagenesis and gene repair by homologous recombination. *Gene Ther.* **9,** 703–707.
45. Liu, H., Agarwal, S., Kmiec, E., and Davis, B.R. (2002). Targeted beta-globin gene conversion in human hematopoietic CD34(+) and Lin(-)CD38(-)cells. *Gene Ther.* **9,** 118–126.
46. Brachman, E.E., and Kmiec, E.B. (2003). Targeted nucleotide repair of cyc1 mutations in Saccharomyces cerevisiae directed by modified single-stranded DNA oligonucleotides. *Genetics* **163,** 527–538.
47. Parekh-Olmedo, H., Czymmek, K., and Kmiec, E.B. (2001). Targeted gene repair in mammalian cells using chimeric RNA/DNA oligonucleotides and modified single-stranded vectors. *Sci. STKE.* 2001 Mar 13; 2001(73):PL1.
48. Liu, L., Rice, M.C., and Kmiec, E.B. (2001). *In vivo* gene repair of point and frameshift mutations directed by chimeric RNA/DNA

oligonucleotides and modified single-stranded oligonucleotides. *Nucleic Acids Res.* **29,** 4238–4250.

49. Liu, L., Brachman, E.E., Drury, M.D., Sonntag, J.M., Maquire, K.K., and Kmiec, E.B. (2003). Regulation of gene repair directed by synthetic end-modified oligonucleotides. *Mol. Ther.* **7,** S308.
50. Goncz, K.K., Prokopishyn, N.L., Chow, B.L., Davis, B.R., and Gruenert, D.C. (2002). Application of SFHR to gene therapy of monogenic disorders. *Gene Ther.* **9,** 691–694.
51. Goncz, K.K., Colosimo, A., Dallapiccola, B., Gagne, L., Hong, K., Novelli, G., Papahadjopoulos, D., Sawa, T., Schreier, H., Wiener-Kronish, J., Xu, Z., and Gruenert, D.C. (2001). Expression of DeltaF508 CFTR in normal mouse lung after site-specific modification of CFTR sequences by SFHR. *Gene Ther.* **8,** 961–965.
52. Bruscia, E., Sangiuolo, F., Sinibaldi, P., Goncz, K.K., Novelli, G., and Gruenert, D.C. (2002). Isolation of CF cell lines corrected at DeltaF508-CFTR locus by SFHR-mediated targeting. *Gene Ther.* **9,** 683–685.
53. Goncz, K.K., Feeney, L., and Gruenert, D.C. (1999). Differential sensitivity of normal and cystic fibrosis airway epithelial cells to epinephrine. *Br. J. Pharmacol.* **128,** 227–233.
54. Kapsa, R.M., Quigley, A.F., Vadolas, J., Steeper, K., Ioannou, P.A., Byrne, E., and Kornberg, A.J. (2002). Targeted gene correction in the mdx mouse using short DNA fragments: towards application with bone marrow-derived cells for autologous remodeling of dystrophic muscle. *Gene Ther.* **9,** 695–699.
55. Davis, B.R., Prokopishyn, N.L., Goncz, K.K., and Gruenert, D.C. (2002). Sequence specific genomic editing of the beta-globin gene in human blood stem/progenitor cells. *Blood* **100,** 183a.
56. Colosimo, A., Goncz, K.K., Holmes, A.R., Kunzelmann, K., Novelli, G., Malone, R.W., Bennett, M.J., and Gruenert, D.C. (2000). Transfer and expression of foreign genes in mammalian cells. *Biotechniques* **29,** 314–318, 320–322, 324.
57. Wang, G., Seidman, M.M., and Glazer, P.M. (1996). Mutagenesis in mammalian cells induced by triple helix formation and transcription-coupled repair. *Science* **271,** 802–805.
58. Hirata, R., Chamberlain, J., Dong, R., and Russell, D.W. (2002). Targeted transgene insertion into human chromosomes by adeno-associated virus vectors. *Nat. Biotechnol.* **20,** 735–738.
59. Russell, D.W., and Hirata, R.K. (1998). Human gene targeting by viral vectors. *Nat. Genet.* **18,** 325–330.
60. Inoue, N., Hirata, R.K., and Russell, D.W. (1999). High-fidelity correction of mutations at multiple chromosomal positions by adeno-associated virus vectors. *J. Virol.* **73,** 7376–7380.
61. Inoue, N., Dong, R., Hirata, R.K., and Russell, D.W. (2001). Introduction of single base substitutions at homologous chromosomal sequences by adeno-associated virus vectors. *Mol. Ther.* **3,** 526–530.
62. Porteus, M.H., Cathomen, T., Weitzman, M.D., and Baltimore, D. (2003). Efficient gene targeting mediated by adeno-associated virus and DNA double-strand breaks. *Mol. Cell Biol.* **23,** 3558–3565.
63. Miller, D.G., Petek, L.M., and Russell, D.W. (2003). Human gene targeting by adeno-associated virus vectors is enhanced by DNA double-strand breaks. *Mol. Cell Biol.* **23,** 3550–3557.
64. Porteus, M.H., and Baltimore, D. (2003). Chimeric nucleases stimulate gene targeting in human cells. *Science* **300,** 763.
65. Baxter, M.A., Wynn, R.F., Deakin, J.A., Bellantuono, I., Edington, K.G., Cooper, A., Besley, G.T., Church, H.J., Wraith, J.E., Carr, T.F., and Fairbairn, L.J. (2002). Retrovirally mediated correction of bone marrow-derived mesenchymal stem cells from patients with mucopolysaccharidosis type I. *Blood* **99,** 1857–1859.
66. Evans, C.H., Ghivizzani, S.C., Smith, P., Shuler, F.D., Mi, Z., and Robbins, P.D. (2000). Using gene therapy to protect and restore cartilage. *Clin. Orthop.* **379**(Suppl), S214–S219.
67. Lou, J., Xu, F., Merkel, K., and Manske, P. (1999). Gene therapy: adenovirus-mediated human bone morphogenetic protein-2 gene transfer induces mesenchymal progenitor cell proliferation and differentiation in vitro and bone formation in vivo. *J. Orthop. Res.* **17,** 43–50.
68. Srivastava, A. (2002). Obstacles to human hematopoietic stem cell transduction by recombinant adeno-associated virus 2 vectors. *J. Cell Biochem. Suppl.* **38,** 39–45.
69. Harrison, G.S., Wang, Y., Tomczak, J., Hogan, C., Shpall, E.J., Curiel, T.J., and Felgner, P.L. (1995). Optimization of gene transfer using cationic lipids in cell lines and primary human CD4+ and CD34+ hematopoietic cells. *Biotechniques* **19,** 816–823.
70. Toneguzzo, F., and Keating, A. (1986). Stable expression of selectable genes introduced into human hematopoietic stem cells by electric field-mediated DNA transfer. *Proc. Natl. Acad. Sci. U.S.A.* **83,** 3496–3499.
71. Qi, H., Aguiar, D.J., Williams, S.M., La Pean, A., Pan, W., and Verfaillie, C.M. (2003). Identification of genes responsible for osteoblast differentiation from human mesodermal progenitor cells. *Proc. Natl. Acad. Sci. U. S. A.* **100,** 3305–3310.
72. Zielske, S.P., and Gerson, S.L. (2002). Lentiviral transduction of P140K MGMT into human CD34(+) hematopoietic progenitors at low multiplicity of infection confers significant resistance to BG/BCNU and allows selection in vitro. *Mol. Ther.* **5,** 381–387.
73. Lee, K., Gerson, S.L., Maitra, B., and Koc, O.N. (2001). G156A MGMT-transduced human mesenchymal stem cells can be selectively enriched by O6-benzylguanine and BCNU. *J. Hematother. Stem Cell Res.* **10(5),** 691–701.
74. Davis, B.M., Koc, O.N., and Gerson, S.L. (2000). Limiting numbers of G156A O(6)-methylguanine-DNA methyltransferase-transduced marrow progenitors repopulate nonmyeloablated mice after drug selection. *Blood* **95,** 3078–3084.
75. Koc, O.N., Reese, J.S., Szekely, E.M., and Gerson, S.L. (1999). Human long-term culture initiating cells are sensitive to benzylguanine and 1,3-bis(2-chloroethyl)-1-nitrosourea and protected after mutant (G156A) methylguanine methyltransferase gene transfer. *Cancer Gene Ther.* **6,** 340–348.
76. Allay, J.A., Koc, O.N., Davis, B.M., and Gerson, S.L. (1996). Retroviral-mediated gene transduction of human alkyltransferase complementary DNA confers nitrosourea resistance to human hematopoietic progenitors. *Clin. Cancer Res.* **2,** 1353–1359.
77. Davis, B.M., Reese, J.S., Koc, O.N., Lee, K., Schupp, J.E., and Gerson, S.L. (1997). Selection for G156A O6-methylguanine DNA methyltransferase gene- transduced hematopoietic progenitors and protection from lethality in mice treated with O6-benzylguanine and 1,3-bis(2-chloroethyl)-1- nitrosourea. *Cancer Res.* **57**(22), 5093–5099.
78. Sellers, S.E., Tisdale, J.F., Agricola, B.A., Metzger, M.E., Donahue, R.E., Dunbar, C.E., and Sorrentino, B.P. (2001). The effect of multidrug-resistance 1 gene versus neo transduction on ex vivo and in vivo expansion of rhesus macaque hematopoietic repopulating cells. *Blood* **97,** 1888–1891.
79. Wengler, G., Gorlin, J.B., Williamson, J.M., Rosen, F.S., and Bing, D.H. (1995). Nonrandom inactivation of the X chromosome in early lineage hematopoietic cells in carriers of Wiskott-Aldrich syndrome. *Blood* **85,** 2471–2477.
80. Greer, W.L., Kwong, P.C., Peacocke, M., Ip, P., Rubin, L.A., and Siminovitch, K.A. (1989). X-chromosome inactivation in the Wiskott-Aldrich syndrome: a marker for detection of the carrier

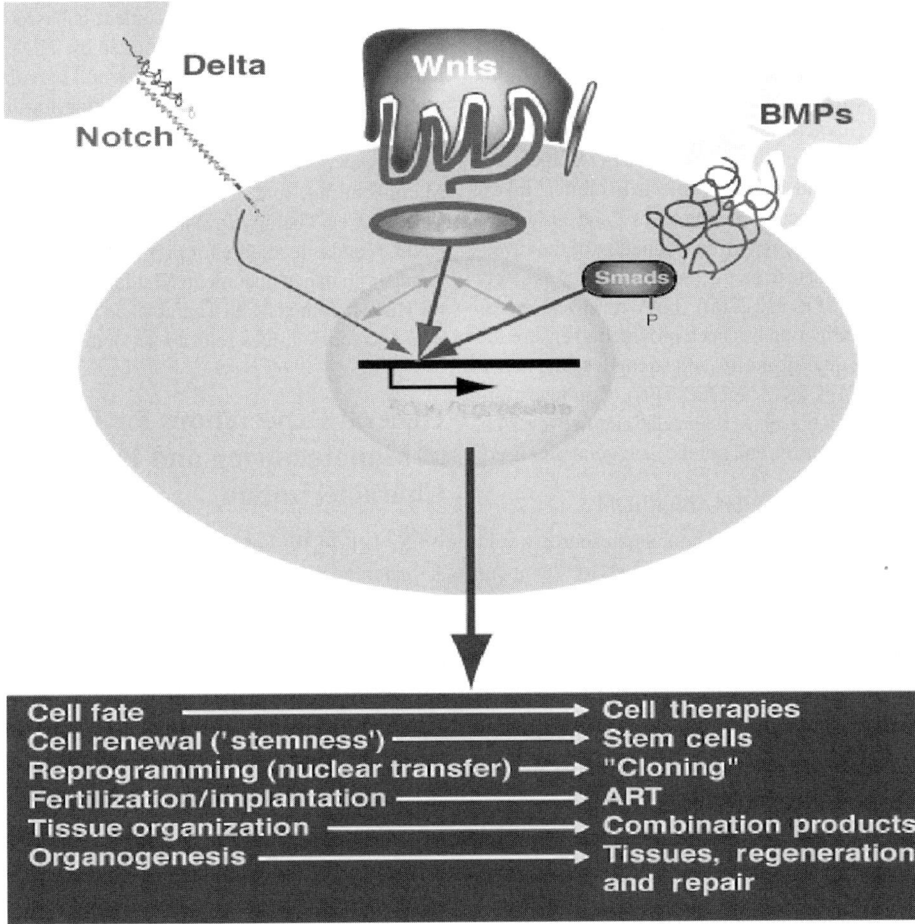

Figure 73–1. *Illustration of three crucial cellular signaling pathways that are active research areas within CBER's Division of Cellular and Gene Therapies.* The *Notch-Delta* pathway, the *BMP* pathway, and the *Wnt* pathway each influence cell fate specification within a variety of medically significant cellular lineages. Some direct examples of relevance to stem cell biology and related cellular therapies are listed at the bottom of the illustration. (Please see CD-ROM for color version of this figure.)

Regulatory Approaches for Stem Cell Products

CORD BLOOD, PERIPHERAL BLOOD, AND BONE MARROW–DERIVED STEM CELLS

Several different regulatory approaches can be applied to hematopoietic stem cells (HSCs) such as those derived from cord blood, peripheral blood, and bone marrow. The regulatory approach taken for a specific product is determined by the clinical use and method of manufacturing of the HSC product. For both umbilical cord blood and unrelated allogeneic peripheral blood stem cells, the FDA has called for data to determine the feasibility of regulating some of the lower risk uses of HSCs through a standards-based approach.[2] This proposed approach requires cell-processing establishments to register, ensure that they meet standards for safety, and use FDA-approved donor screening test kits. Finally, autologous or allogeneic cord blood, peripheral blood, or bone marrow stem cell products will be regulated under IND if more than minimal manipulation occurs, the cell product is combined with a drug or device, or the intended use is considered to be nonhomologous. Although the field of stem cell biology has produced evidence that stem cell activity for a variety of lineages can be demonstrated in cord blood, peripheral blood, or bone marrow cell preparations, the FDA will regard use of these products for anything beyond hematopoietic reconstitution as nonhomologous use until a clearer scientific picture emerges.

STEM CELL INVESTIGATIONAL NEW DRUG REGULATION

The remainder of this chapter discusses stem cell products that will be regulated under IND. These are products that are more than minimally manipulated, combined with a drug or device, metabolically active, or nonhomologous in their intended use. When an IND application or pre-IND information package is reviewed in the OCTGT, reviewers from three disciplines are assigned including (1) a product expert, (2) a pharmacology/toxicology expert, and (3) a clinical expert. However, the information in this chapter focuses on product issues such as manufacturing and characterization of stem cell products.

In the review of IND applications, primary FDA objectives are to ensure the safety and rights of subjects in clinical investigations. An additional objective during phases 2 and 3 is to help ensure that the quality of the scientific evaluation of the investigational product is adequate to permit an evaluation of its safety and effectiveness (21 CFR 312.22(a)). FDA reviewers assess whether sufficient information has been provided to ensure the proper identification, quality, purity, and strength of the investigational product (21 CFR 312.23(a)(7)(i)). For investigational cell therapy products such as stem cells, alternative terms, such as safety, identity, purity, and potency are generally used.

STEM CELLS AND XENOTRANSPLANTATION

Any stem cell product derived from a nonhuman source would be considered a xenotransplantation product. Also, therapeutic use of stem cell products grown on feeder layers of nonhuman origin falls into the category of xenotransplantation. The FDA has a regulatory framework in place to regulate such products and has no policy or intent to prohibit use of stem cells grown under such conditions. The Guidance to Industry document "Source Animal, Product, Preclinical, and Clinical Issues Concerning the Use of Xenotransplantation Products in Humans"[3] includes human body fluids, cells, tissues, or organs that have had *ex vivo* contact with nonhuman animal cells, tissues, or organs as xenotransplant products. The major issue is to ensure that the human stem cell line is free from infectious agents of nonhuman origin. The possible presence of xenozoonotic infectious agents is a concern that would not necessarily apply to stem cell products grown under conditions that exclude contact with nonhuman feeder cells.

COMBINATION PRODUCTS

One area of intense development is the use of stem cells in combination with drugs, recombinant proteins, or devices. Examples include combinations of stem cells with devices such as scaffolds for bone or organ replacement or for extracorporeal liver or kidney assist devices. Such applications fall under the category of combination products (defined in 21CFR 3.2(e)). The regulatory path for these applications can involve experts from several FDA centers using mechanisms of consultative or collaborative review. The center responsible for organizing the review will be assigned based on a determination of the primary mode of action of the combined product. The FDA's newly formed Office of Combination Products will serve to facilitate the review process and ensure quality, clarity, and efficiency of application reviews that involve multiple FDA centers.

CHEMISTRY, MANUFACTURING, AND CONTROL REVIEWER GUIDANCE FOR CELL THERAPY PRODUCTS

CBER has issued a guidance document intended to facilitate consistency and efficiency of review of cell therapy products, including stem cells.[4] This document is based on current best review practices and can be consulted by IND sponsors to gain a thorough perspective on the types and organization of information that CBER reviewers are looking for during review of a cell therapy IND. The document is entitled "Draft Guidance for Reviewers: Instructions and Template for Chemistry, Manufacturing, and Control (CMC) Reviewers of Human Somatic Cell Therapy Investigational New Drug Applications (INDs)" and is available for public examination and comment. Another guidance document "Guidance for Industry: Guidance for Human Somatic Cell Therapy and Gene Therapy" discusses many scientific issues relevant to stem cell therapies.[5]

General Expectations for Control of Manufacturing and Product Characterization

SAFETY, IDENTITY, PURITY, AND POTENCY

A major goal of FDA oversight of cellular therapies is to ensure safety of patients who receive an investigational product. Careful attention to the details of manufacturing and product characterization are key factors in ensuring safety. These are also important factors in assessment of purity of the final product that will be administered to patients. Assessment of identity and purity is a challenge for cellular products, especially stem cells. Identity or purity assessments can involve biologic, biochemical, and functional characterization and should be designed to determine how well the characteristics of the cell population conform to the expected and desired properties.

Another important and challenging goal of stem cell product characterization is assessment of the potency of the final product. Potency is the "specific ability of the product, as indicated by appropriate laboratory tests...to effect a given result" (21CFR 600.3). Although the mechanism of action is not necessarily known, the outcome of a laboratory test for potency should correlate very well with the desired clinical effect. Because stem cells are intended to undergo differentiation before mediating their clinical effect, the problem of what to measure and how to correlate the measurement with a final outcome is a great challenge. Because direct measurement of stem cell potency may be challenging because of lack of appropriate *in vitro* or *in vivo* assays, use of other means to demonstrate potency could be adequate for initiation of clinical trials. However, development of a valid potency assay for stem cell product lot release will be required for FDA licensure. It is generally expected that a potency assay will be in place before phase 3. An expanded discussion of this important topic is presented in the subsection on potency in the section on testing of stem cell products.

In summary, as with all biologic therapeutic products, assessments of safety, purity, and potency of stem cell products is crucial in product development.

CONTROL OF PROCESS AND PRODUCT

As with all complex biologic products, regulation of the manufacturing process is as important as characterization and testing of the final product in ensuring the safety, purity, and potency of stem cell products. Thus, thorough characterization of starting materials and manufacturing intermediates is required to ensure that the final cellular product is acceptable for administration to humans.

The first step of stem cell product manufacture is acquisition of stem cells from a suitable donor source. Whether human or animal donors are used, the principles of donor suitability are similar and rely on detailed knowledge of medical status and history of the donor. Infectious adventitious agents are of primary concern in terms of safety. For nonhuman stem cells, Public Health Service (PHS) and FDA guidance documents[3,6] put forth extensive recommendations for animal husbandry, health surveillance, disease screening, and veterinary care of donor animals. For human sources the FDA advises medical history screening and infectious agent testing and may recommend genetic screening or testing depending on patient populations, donor pool, and evolution of genetic testing technology. Details of donor suitability and screening are described in more detail in the subsection on donor screening in the section on manufacturing and characterization issues for stem cell products.

Other important factors include genetic status of donor cells, especially those that may cause adverse events in recipients. This consideration is often of concern for human donors but could be important for both sources. Elimination of undesirable genetic traits in donor stem cells will help ensure that the recipient does not develop a donor-derived medical condition.

CURRENT GOOD MANUFACTURING PRACTICE

The principles of cGMP, set forth in 21 CFR 210 and 211, apply to stem cell products and encompass both the manufacturing facility and the specific product prepared within the facility. Although full implementation of cGMP is expected by licensure, incorporation of cGMPs at earlier stages of product development is expected but can be staged in a manner consistent with the phase of product development. For example, cGMP includes appropriate written protocols for each stage of product manufacturing and characterization. At later stages of product development, standard operating procedures (SOPs) that document all significant information relating to stem cell production should be used. Quality oversight by the sponsor is important for each stage of development and involves both quality control (QC) and quality assurance (QA) mechanisms. This means that the person(s) responsible for assurance that the production and characterization testing have all been performed properly and have met specified criteria (QA) are separate from and not direct subordinates of the person(s) responsible for conducting these tests and filing these reports (QC).

The cGMPs also stipulate development of validated assays that must be in place by product licensure. Data regarding assay performance (specificity, sensitivity, and reliability) should be submitted to the FDA as part of the validation process.

Manufacturing and Characterization Issues for Stem Cell Products

This section describes in detail, the various recommendations currently used by FDA reviewers to ensure that safe, pure, and potent cell products are administered to patients in clinical investigations. Figure 73–2 illustrates some of the complexities of stem cell biology and summarizes some of the challenges associated with development of stem cell therapies.

COMPONENTS AND CHARACTERIZATION

Although the goal of stem cell manufacturing is to produce a safe, pure, and efficacious product, the complexity of the process necessitates careful control of the entire manufacturing procedure and of the components used. Thus, all components used to manufacture the cellular product should be carefully described. This includes the source of each component and a summary of testing performed on each component.

Donor Screening

Donor screening is an important consideration in ensuring safety of stem cell products. The description of stem cell sources should include tissue of origin and type of cell, such as hematopoietic, neuronal, or embryonic stem cells and such details as whether or not donor cells are mobilized or activated *in vivo* in the donor. The collection method and use of any devices during collection are also important details.

Appropriate infectious disease screening procedures must be performed. The FDA has issued several draft guidances or proposed rules for industry on donor screening that should be consulted.[7–9] If autologous cells are used, screening is relevant if the tissue culture methods used during the manufacture of

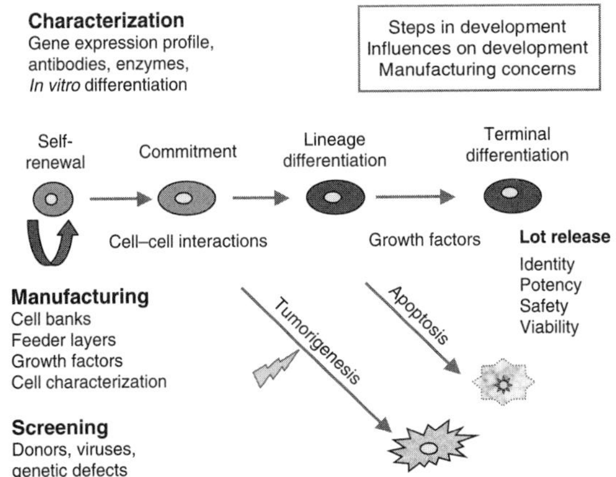

Figure 73–2. *A hypothetical cellular differentiation pathway is used to illustrate the complexity of regulatory oversight of stem cell products.* Mechanisms that control biologic processes such as self-renewal or lineage commitment include changes in gene and protein expression that lead to differentiation (steps in development, blue text) and interactions with the host through microenvironmental cell–cell interactions or growth factors (influences on development, green text). Regulatory concerns that are associated with these processes during *in vitro* stem cell manufacture are shown (black text). (Please see CD-ROM for color version of this figure.)

the product could propagate or spread viruses or other adventitious agents (e.g., human immunodeficiency virus-1 [HIV-1], cytomegalovirus [CMV]). For allogeneic stem cell products, there are many specific agents of concern and tests are designed for specific and nonspecific pathogen detection. Donor screening and testing should be performed for adventitious agents, such as HIV-1, HIV-2, hepatitis B virus (HBV) (surface and core antigen), hepatitis C virus (HCV), human T-lymphotropic virus types 1 and 2 (HTLV-1, HTLV-2), CMV, Epstein-Barr virus (EBV), and others, as appropriate. FDA-licensed or FDA-approved test kits should be used in these detection assays, when available.

In addition to infectious agent screening, an IND application should include a description of other serologic, diagnostic, and clinical history data obtained from the donor. It may be important to conduct other characterizations such as typing for genetic polymorphisms and major histocompatability complex (MHC) loci. If cord blood or other maternally derived tissue is used but not banked, one should document testing performed on donor mothers.

For embryonic stem cell sources, the donor screening could include the following: (1) screening of egg/sperm donors for infectious diseases (HIV-1 and HIV-2, HTLV-1 and HTLV-2, HBV, HCV, CMV, and other agents of concern); (2) evaluation of egg/sperm donors' medical histories; and (3) genetic testing for selected, relevant disorders. In addition, archiving of donor blood or tissue samples could be important for later testing if adverse events are later associated with a stem cell therapy.

Derivation of Stem Cell Lines

The origin of the stem cells including the source tissue, collection methods, and methods of propagation are all important details that should be reported to the FDA. If stem cell products are derived from nonhuman sources, they fall under the definition of xenotransplantation products. The draft guidances on "Source Animal, Product, Preclinical, and Clinical Issues Concerning the Use of Xenotransplantation Products in Humans"[3] and the "PHS Guideline on Infectious Disease Issues in Xenotransplantation"[6] describe additional steps that may be necessary to address the infectious disease risks that may be posed by the use of xenotransplantation products. Animal husbandry, herd health surveillance, adventitious agent testing of stem cell products, and archiving of animal and patient materials are all important issues associated with use of xenotransplantation products.

For embryonic stem cell lines, procedures used to acquire donor eggs and sperm, to perform *in vitro* fertilization, and to isolate cleavage-stage embryos should be described in detail. Details regarding origin and characterization of feeder layers should be included and cover species of origin, whether feeders are primary cultures or established cell lines, maintenance of the feeder layers, stability of feeder lines (if established lines), details regarding any cell banks, and passage numbers of cells in the banks and in production. If murine feeders are used, details should include the mouse strain, a description of animal husbandry and housing, mouse colony health status, tissue of origin, and the method of feeder harvest and propagation should be provided.

A description of the assessments used to characterize stem cell lines should be provided and could include but is not restricted to the following: (1) a demonstration of pluripotency, (2) karyotype and chromosomal analysis, (3) growth and proliferation characteristics, (4) expression of molecular markers indicative of undifferentiated stem cells, and (5) stability of cell lines over time in tissue culture and following extended periods of cryopreservation. Chapter 77 of Volume 1 gives greater details regarding important information for FDA evaluation of embryonic stem cell products.

If human feeder cells are used during propagation of any stem cell product, donor screening and adventitious agent testing of the feeder layers are also important to ensure the safety of the cell lines grown in contact with the feeders.

If cell lines are used as feeders for propagation of stem cells, the sections on cell banks (discussed later) are applicable to both the stem cells and the feeder cell lines.

Cell Bank System

For some types of stem cells and feeder cell lines, cell banks will be established to ensure that a well-characterized, safe source for manufacturing is available for as long as the product is intended to be available. In these cases, there should be detailed information relating to the cell bank system used in product manufacture, such as history, source, derivation, characterization, and frequency of testing for each master cell bank (MCB) and working cell bank (WCB), if used. Several guidance documents regarding establishment and characterization of cell banks are available and should be consulted.[10,11] For some stem cell products cell banks may not be established and not all of the testing described in the following sections may be possible.

Master Cell Bank. MCB characterization should include sufficient testing to establish the safety, identity, purity, and stability of the cells. MCB testing should establish microbiologic safety including sterility, freedom from mycoplasma, freedom from the presence of specific pathogens, and *in vivo* and *in vitro* testing for adventitious viral agents as appropriate. Cells of human origin, unless autologous, should be tested for human viruses such as CMV, HIV-1 and HIV-2, HTLV-1 and HTLV-2, EBV, HBV, and HCV, as appropriate. Cell lines that are exposed to bovine or porcine components (e.g., serum, serum components, trypsin) should be tested (9CFR113.47). *In vitro* and *in vivo* adventitious agent tests are nonspecific screens designed to detect the presence of a wide spectrum of viruses that could be introduced during manufacturing or were present in the starting stem cell population. The *in vitro* adventitious virus assay can sometimes be used to identify certain viruses. The *in vivo* and *in vitro* virus tests detect complimentary virus types (Table 73–1).

Identity is an important characteristic of the MCB and should include tests to unambiguously distinguish the specified cells through physical or chemical characteristics of the cell line

TABLE 73–1
Tests to Detect Adventitious Viruses

In Vivo Adventitious Virus Testing	*In Vitro* Adventitious Virus Testing
Picornaviruses: e.g., influenza, coxsackie A and B, poliovirus	Picornaviruses: e.g., poliovirus, coxsackie B, echovirus, rhinovirus
Bunyavirus: e.g., lymphocytic choriomeningitis virus (LCMV), hantavirus	Togavirus: e.g., rubella
	Paramyxovirus: e.g., parainfluenza, mumps measles, respiratory syncytial virus (RSV)
Herpesvirus: e.g., herpes simplex virus-1 (HSV-1)	
Paramyxovirus: e.g., mumps	Orthomyxovirus: e.g., influenza
Coronavirus	Adenovirus
Flavivirus	Herpesvirus

From references 15 and 16.

such as cell surface marker phenotype, genotype, or other markers. Purity of bank cells should also be established and include identification and quantification of any contaminating cells.

Finally, activity of cells should be characterized by some criteria related to the proposed use of the stem cells. For example, committed stem cells in a given lineage should be demonstrated to express lineage and developmental stage specific genes or generate appropriate progeny in *in vitro* assays. For a licensed product or one in phase 3 trials, lot release testing of final product requires a demonstration of potency. Therefore, a useful MCB activity assay would be related to the lot release assay used for final product.

In addition to the previously mentioned criteria, other information about the establishment of the MCB and critical to product safety should be described. This includes details of culture conditions used and documentation of all media, reagents, and components used during production. Certificates of analysis (COA) are important documents for such manufacturing details. In addition, details related to cryopreservation, storage, and thawing of the MCB, including information pertaining to cell density, number of vials frozen, storage temperature, viability of cells after thaw, and cell bank location are also important.

Finally, a particularly challenging but important issue for stem cells is functional, genetic, and phenotypic stability of the MCB after thaw and after multiple passages.

Working Cell Bank. The amount of information needed to characterize a WCB is usually less extensive than for the MCB. Details about the WCB should include the number of MCB vials used to establish the WCB. If a MCB is not established, more extensive testing of the WCB is necessary and would include all testing described previously for MCBs, including testing for adventitious viral agents. If a MCB is used, less WCB characterization is necessary and testing could be limited to tests for bacterial and fungal sterility, mycoplasma, and appropriate identity testing.

MANUFACTURING COMPONENTS AND PROCEDURES

The CBER approach to regulation of biologics involves scrutiny of the manufacturing process and the final products, because many steps of the process can affect safety, purity, and potency, especially by introducing adventitious agents. CBER reviewers will examine details of all reagents used to manufacture stem cell products including reagents that are not intended to be part of the final product. Examples include components that are essential for cellular growth, differentiation, selection, purification, or other critical manufacturing steps such as fetal bovine serum, trypsin, growth factors, cytokines, monoclonal antibodies, antibiotics, cell separation devices, and media and media components. These reagents can affect the safety, potency, and purity of the final product.

If the reagent is not FDA approved, additional testing may be needed to ensure its safety and quality. Appropriate testing will depend on how and when during the manufacturing scheme the specific reagent is used. Additional testing may include safety testing (sterility, endotoxin, mycoplasma, and adventitious agents) and functional analysis, purity, and other assays to demonstrate absence of potentially harmful substances. In addition, there should be a description of test procedures for detection of residual levels of reagents in the final product.

CBER reviewers will also examine all procedures used during the production, purification, and harvest of the cellular therapy product. Details of the methods of cell collection, processing, and culture condition including mechanical or enzymatic dispersion, cell selection methods, and description of cell culture systems are all important. Finally, any in-process testing for identity, sterility, purity, or function should be described. If cells are cryopreserved or cultured long term before injection into patients, stability studies should be initiated.

Details regarding formulation of the final product should include whether any excipients such as growth factors or human serum albumin are included in the final formulation and details regarding their source, concentration, and characteristics.

TESTING OF STEM CELL PRODUCTS

Testing of stem cell products includes, but is not limited to, microbiologic testing (sterility, mycoplasma, and adventitious viral agents) and assessments of other product characteristics such as identity, purity (including endotoxin), viability, and potency. Such testing should be performed throughout manufacturing, including manufacture of cell banks, to evaluate the manufacturing process itself and to ensure the quality and consistency of the product lots. Control of the manufacturing process is crucial to consistently produce an equivalent product from lot to lot. Consistency is needed to identify the critical parameters necessary to ensure the desired clinical effect.

Product testing is designed to determine how well the product meets the specifications used for intermediate and final product release criteria. Specifications are the quality standards such as tests, analytical procedures, and acceptance criteria, which confirm the quality of products and other materials used in the production of a product. Acceptance criteria mean numerical limits, ranges, or other criteria for the tests described. The proposed specifications should be appropriate to the stage of product development keeping in mind that release criteria should be refined and tightened as product development progresses toward licensure.

Release tests and specifications for stem cell products should include, but are not limited to, microbiologic testing, identity, purity, potency, viability, and cell number. Criteria for each is discussed in the following sections.

Microbiologic Testing

Microbiologic testing should be performed on stem cell banks, feeder cells, in-process cell cultures, and the final product, as appropriate. Sterility testing on the final product should be performed as described in 21 CFR 610.12 or as described in *United States Pharmacopoeia* (USP) <71> Sterility Testing (under 21 CFR 610.9).[12] Alternative test methods can be proposed and, if found to be adequate, may be used but must be validated to be equivalent to the prescribed testing before product licensing.

If antibiotics are used in product manufacturing, they should be removed before sterility testing. If the antibiotics cannot be removed, the bacteriostasis and fungistasis testing as described in USP <71> Sterility Tests may be necessary to ensure that any residual antibiotic present in the product does not interfere with the results of sterility testing.

Results of sterility testing are part of required final product specifications. If the final product is frozen before use, sterility testing should be performed immediately before cryopreservation and acceptable results should be confirmed before administration. If a stem cell product undergoes further manufacturing after thawing (e.g., as washing, culturing, combination with a device), further sterility testing may be necessary. In certain circumstances, stem cell products can be administered to patients before completion of 14-day sterility tests. If cells must be administered before obtaining the results from 14-day sterility testing, sterility testing should be initiated on a sample taken 48 to 72 hours before final harvest or after the last refeeding of the cultures and the sterility test cultures should be negative before release of the product. This test should be continued for the full 14 days even after the product has been given to the patients. Also, a Gram stain should be performed and be negative before administration and a sterility test on the final formulated product should be initiated and continued for the entire 14 days. In these cases, sterility lot release criteria should be a no-growth result from the 48- to 72-hour sterility test and a negative Gram stain. In addition, contingency procedures should be developed in case the more extended sterility tests show that the product the patient received was contaminated. Contingency procedures should include contacting the treating physician, the patient, the FDA, and the institutional review board (IRB). In addition, plans to determine the type of contamination should be in place.

In-process sterility testing at critical points during manufacturing is encouraged to ensure safety of stem cell products. Routine testing during extended culture periods and after critical points in manufacturing, such as when cells have undergone activation or other modification, adds an additional margin of safety and tests the robustness of the manufacturing process. Appropriate in-process testing is based on the manufacturing scheme and the test method used for in-process sterility testing is at the discretion of the sponsor.

Mycoplasma testing should be performed on the product when there is the best chance of detecting contamination, such as after pooling of cultures but before cell washing. Mycoplasma testing should include both cells and supernatant. Results from culture-based mycoplasma tests are sometimes unavailable before administration of cellular products. In this case the use of polymerase chain reaction (PCR)-based mycoplasma assays is acceptable during the investigational phases of product development. However, before product licensing, the PCR test must be shown equivalent to recommended assays as described in §610.9.

Adventitious virus testing is necessary for stem cell lines and feeder cells, when these are used. *In vitro* viral testing should be conducted on the stem cell MCB and end of production cells (one-time test), when appropriate. *In vivo* viral assays should also be conducted on the MCB.

For human stem cell products, there should also be selected species-specific testing for adventitious viruses. Selection of the virus-specific tests is dependent on the origin of the stem cells and any feeder layer cells used. Whenever FDA-approved tests are available, these tests should be used. When human cell lines are used as the therapeutic product, there should be testing for human pathogens. PCR-based test tests for CMV, HIV-1 and HIV-2, HTLV-1 and HTLV-2, EBV, HBV, HCV, and other human viral agents should be included, as appropriate.

For more information on adventitious agent testing, one should refer to reference 10 and ICH guidance Q5A: "Guidance on Viral Safety Evaluation of Biotechnology Products Derived From Cell Lines of Human or Animal Origin."[13]

Identity

The identity of the stem cell MCB and the final product should be determined by established assays. These assays should be able to distinguish the MCB or final product from cell products being manufactured in the same facility (21 CFR 610.14). If the final product consists of one or more differentiated or undifferentiated cell types, tests should be in place to distinguish between the cell types that might be present. If feeder layers were used to propagate a stem cell product, tests that distinguish the stem cell and feeder cells should be used. Identity testing for the MCB should also include testing to distinguish between multiple cell lines used to produce a single final product. Appropriate tests might include assays for cell surface markers or genetic polymorphisms. Identity acceptance criteria for MCBs and final products should be established and based on measurements of different cell types in a stem cell product. These measures reflect on the reliability, reproducibility, and robustness of the manufacturing process and may be important measures in terms of safety and efficacy of stem cell products.

Purity

The purity of a stem cell product could be defined as freedom from extraneous material and cells, except that which is unavoidable in the manufacturing process (21 CFR 610.13). In addition to unintended cell types such as feeder cells or undesirable differentiated cells, testing for purity should include assays for endotoxin and for reagents or components used during manufacture, such as cytokines, growth factors, antibodies, and serum. Further information is available in ICH Q3 on "Impurities."[14]

The ability of stem cells to adopt a variety of cell fates makes determination of purity a challenge. However, unwanted, unintended differentiated cell types could affect the function, efficacy, and safety of a stem cell product. In addition, although a determination of the purity of a stem cell product may not currently be correlated with safety or efficacy outcomes, reproducibility of manufacturing conditions can be assessed by this measurement. Accumulation of this data will allow correlation of clinical outcomes with purity assessments.

Viability

Viability of the final product is an important measurement that impacts safety and efficacy of stem cell products and indicates the robustness of the manufacturing process. Drastically reduced viability of individual lots can be an important warning regarding manufacturing conditions or presence of toxic impurities. Great variability in viability can potentially indicate problems with the manufacturing process. For somatic cellular therapies, the minimum acceptable viability specification of the final product is generally set at 70%. If this level cannot be achieved, data should be generated to justify the lower viability specification by demonstrating that dead cells and cell debris do not affect the safe administration or therapeutic effect of the stem cell product.

Cell Number and Dose

For stem cell products, there should be specifications for the minimum number of viable and functional cells as part of the product testing and lot release. The number of viable cells administered to a patient or in preclinical studies is important in following the safety and efficacy of stem cell products. Determination of a suitable dose in terms of both safety and efficacy is a challenge due to the ability of stem cells to self-renew and to differentiate. However, every attempt should be made to design appropriate preclinical studies to address this challenge. Such studies, as well as any applicable clinical experience, should be used in setting the specifications for cell number in stem cell product doses.

Potency

A major challenge with regard to stem cells is assessing biologic activity or potency. A suitable potency assay should measure relative biologic function of the product and should be useful in establishing a safe and efficacious dose for administration to patients. However, determination of the specific biologic functions of a stem cell that predict its useful and safe cell fate is a challenging necessity. Depending on the specific stem cell product, a variety of possible approaches can be envisioned. The FDA does not have specific requirements for particular potency assessments and will consider the merits of individual proposals in the context of overall risk–benefit considerations depending on the disease indication and the patient population. Potency can be established using several assays, which should include a quantitative assay but may also include qualitative biologic assays. In terms of product development, potency assays should be in place by the end of IND phase 2 and should consists of *in vivo* or *in vitro* tests that measure an appropriate biologic activity. This assay should be validated by licensure.

For embryonic stem cells, assays that display desirable activities could include demonstration of *in vitro* differentiation such as demonstration of pluripotency by ability to generate the three different embryonic tissues. For stem cells with a more restricted lineage potential, *in vitro* differentiation into known progeny lineages such as lymphoid and myeloid differentiation from HSCs or adipogenesis, chondrogenesis, and osteogenesis from mesenchymal stem cells are significant ways to demonstrate maintenance of desirable biologic activity. Other approaches to indicate maintenance of biologic activity could include expression of cell surface markers, proteins, or gene expression profiles using reverse transcriptase (RT)-PCR, microarrays, or proteomics techniques.

Summary

Stem cells are among the most complex biologics to date. FDA recommendations for stem cell–based product manufacture and characterization incorporate the tremendous experience gained in many cell therapy clinical trials and from experience with the entire field of stem cell research. In advising sponsors about their stem cell development program, the FDA recognizes the need for flexibility in its recommendations and will consider many factors, including the intended target population, the seriousness of the disease under study, and the potential benefits and risks from the investigational product. The agency continually updates and reassesses recommendations for stem cell production and testing based on the growing experience and on feedback from a variety of sources.

It is important to note that the information in this chapter represents guiding principles and general information and should be used in conjunction with consultation from FDA staff. The FDA encourages new investigators to consult with FDA staff before submission of an IND. The formal process for FDA consultation is a pre-IND meeting. Sponsors may request information about the pre-IND and IND process through CBER's Office of Communication, Training, and Manufacturers Assistance (OCTMA) at 301-827-2000.

ACKNOWLEDGMENTS

The author would like to thank numerous colleagues in the Office of Cellular, Tissue, and Gene Therapies for their support and thoughtful commentary. Special thanks are extended to Dr. Malcolm Moos for his contribution of Fig. 73–1 and to Drs. Darin Weber and Donald Fink for reading and critique of the manuscript.

REFERENCES

1. BRMAC Meeting #27, July 13, 2000. Transcript available at http://www.fda.gov/ohrms/dockets/ac/cber00.htm#Biological (accessed April 14, 2004).
2. Federal Register Notice. (2000). Request for proposed standards for unrelated allogeneic peripheral and placental/umbilical cord blood hematopoietic stem/progenitor cell products; reopening of comment period. *Federal Register* **65 (75),** 20825. Available at http://www.fda.gov/cber/genadmin/cord2.txt (accessed April 14, 2004).
3. Guidance for Industry: Source Animal, Product, Preclinical and Clinical Issues Concerning the Use of Xenotransplantation Products in Humans. April 2003. Available at http://www.fda.gov/cber/gdlns/clinxeno.pdf (accessed April 14, 2004).
4. Draft Guidance for Reviewers: Instructions and Template for Chemistry, Manufacturing, and Control (CMC) Reviewers of Human Somatic Cell Therapy Investigational New Drug Applications (INDs). 8/15/2003. Available at http://www.fda.gov/cber/guidelines.htm#somcell (accessed April 14, 2004).
5. Guidance for Industry: Guidance for Human Somatic Cell Therapy and Gene Therapy. March 1998. Available at http://www.fda.gov/cber/gdlns/somgene.pdf (accessed April 14, 2004).
6. PHS Guideline on Infectious Disease Issues in Xenotransplantation. January 19, 2001. Available at http://www.fda.gov/cber/gdlns/xenophs0101.htm (accessed April 14, 2004).
7. Class II Special Controls Guidance Document: Human Dura Mater; Draft Guidance for Industry and FDA. October 22, 2002. Available at http://www.fda.gov/cdrh/ode/guidance/054.html (accessed April 14, 2004).
8. Draft Guidance for Industry: Preventive Measures to Reduce the Possible Risk of Transmission of Creutzfeldt-Jakob Disease (CJD) and Variant Creutzfeldt-Jakob Disease (vCJD) by Human Cells, Tissues, and Cellular and Tissue-Based Products (HCT/Ps). June 2002. Available at http://www.fda.gov/cber/gdlns/cjdvcjd0602.htm (accessed April 14, 2004).
9. Proposed Rule: Suitability Determination for Donors of Human Cellular and Tissue-Based Products. September 30, 1999. 64 (FR 52696). Available at http://www.fda.gov/cber/rules/suitdonor.pdf (accessed April 14, 2004).
10. Points to Consider in the Characterization of Cell Lines Used to Produce Biologicals. July 12, 1993. Available at http://www.fda.gov/cber/gdlns/ptccell.pdf (accessed April 14, 2004).
11. ICH Guideline Q5D: Derivation and Characterisation of Cell Substrates Used for Production of Biotechnological/Biological Products. July 1997. Available at httpL//www.ich.org/pdfICH/q5d.pdf (accessed April 14, 2004).
12. USP Topic. (2003). Sterility Tests. *In* "United States Pharmacopoeia (USP)," 27th revision. Available at www.usp.org (accessed April 14, 2004).
13. ICH Guideline Q5A: Guidance on Viral Safety Evaluation of Biotechnology Products Derived from Cell Lines of Human or Animal Origin. March 1997. Available at http://www.ich.org (accessed April 14, 2004).
14. ICH Topic Q3: Impurities. (Including guidelines on "Impurities in New Drug Substances," "Impurities in New Drug Products," and "Impurities: Residual Solvents"). Available at http://www.ich.org (accessed April 14, 2004).
15. McIntosh, K. (1990). Diagnostic virology. *In* "Fields Virology," 2nd ed. (B.N. Fields, D.M. Knipe, eds.), pp. 383–410. Raven Press, New York.
16. Wagner, R. (1990). Rhabdoviridae and their replication. *In* "Fields Virology," 2nd ed. (B.N. Fields, D.M. Knipe, eds.), pp. 867–883. Raven Press, New York.

74

Commercial Development of Stem Cell Technology

Michael J. Lysaght and Anne L. Hazlehurst

Just under 30 biotechnology startup firms in 11 countries are pursuing commercial development of stem cell technology and therapeutic cloning. These firms employ 950–1000 scientists and support staff and spend just under $200 million on research and development each year. The field has the look and feel of a high-tech cottage industry, with close to half the startups employing less than 15 full-time equivalents (FTEs). Funding is mostly from venture capitalists and private investors. Participants are geographically disperse with about 40% of the activity outside the United States. Focus is slightly weighted toward adult stem cells as compared with embryonic stem cells. Taken as a whole, both the structure and scope of private sector activity in stem cells seems appropriate to the promise and development time-frames of this important new technology.

Introduction

In the past 5 years, stem cells have emerged from condign obscurity to remarkable levels of prominence in both the scientific literature and lay consciousness. Reports in peer-reviewed journals are prominently covered as front page news in the *New York Times* and are summarized on nightly national network news. *Time, Newsweek, Business week, The Atlantic Monthly,* and many of their peer journals have all carried in-depth cover stories on stem cells. C-Span broadcast the full 2-day National Academy of Sciences Workshop on the topic. Stem cells can fairly be said to have provided many scientists with their "15 minutes of fame."

Why all the attention, all of sudden? First, of course, was Dolly and the paradigmatic revelation that a fully differentiated adult cell could be reprogrammed back to totipotent stem cell status.[1] So far, the technologies for cloning and stem cell biology are inseparable: it is not yet possible to create a clone without first creating a stem cell by nuclear transfer. Furthermore, advances in the understanding of basic stem cell biology have potential relevance to therapeutic or reproductive cloning. Not long after Wilmut's announcement of Dolly came the techniques for isolating and culturing human embryonic stem cells and the capability to begin teasing the cultured cells down defined lineage pathways.[2,3] Working largely with murine models, other investigators demonstrated that embryonic stem cells could be converted into tissue with functional utility in animal models of diabetes and Parkinson's disease.[4,5] Other groups pursued adult stem cells, demonstrating a hitherto unsuspected capacity for transdifferentation.[6–8] However, concerns about separation, identification, proliferation, and cell fusion leave the plasticity of adult stem cells somewhat ambiguous. More controversial but certainly attention-getting were the reports of the cloning of an early stage human embryo by nuclear transfer[9] and the claim that parthenogenesis may eventually compete with nuclear transfer as a technique for cloning adult mammals.[10] This dramatic progress was well summarized in a recent editorial in *Nature* by C. DeWitt[11]:

> Stem Cells are truly remarkable. They bridge the gulf between the fertilized egg that is our origin and the architecture that we become. They supply the cells that construct our bodies and, as we age, replenish worn out, damaged, and diseased tissues. They renew themselves, resisting the powerful pull toward differentiation that overcomes more prosaic cells. Scientists now face the formidable task of… bringing stem cell therapies to the clinic.

The potential therapeutic applications of stem cells span virtually every facet of regenerative medicine. Scientists have hailed them as the key to future cures for neurodegenerative diseases, diabetes, heart failure, and countless other disorders. With such strong claims come large expectations, and consequently, stem cells have a long way to go in living up to their reputation. The time and resources required to validate the clinical importance of the technology will not be insignificant but are justified by the potential therapeutic importance of this technology.

The Study

Stem cell science and technologies are being pursued by the National Institutes of Health (NIH) and other government research agencies and in the private sector. Our study concerns the latter and is intended to quantify and discuss current commercial involvement in the development of stem cell technology: How many scientists and support staff are involved? How many firms? With what sorts of financing? And what patterns of activity and organization? Consideration of the

Handbook of Stem Cells
Volume 2

impact of regulatory mechanisms and the status of clinical studies will help shed light on the complex issues facing the industry. No attempt is made to pick eventual winners and losers among the various companies or even to review and assess the validity of the underlying science. The analysis in this chapter is a revised and updated version of an earlier survey appearing in the journal *Tissue Engineering*.[12] Data presented here are correct and valid as of December 31, 2002. However, the field is evolving rapidly, and, thus, this report is best regarded as a snapshot of a single point in time.

To be eligible for inclusion in this study, firms needed to be significantly vested in stem cell technology. Typical focus areas included embryonic or adult stem cells, nuclear transfer and therapeutic cloning, banking of cord blood, and development or sale of enabling equipment and supplies. All firms identified by the NIH as custodians of "approved" stem cell lines were included. Not-for-profit organizations were excluded, as were firms involved in reproductive cloning of pets and livestock animals. Conventional bone marrow transplantation did not qualify. Firms that were peripherally or incidentally involved in stem cells were not included.

A list of qualifying firms was compiled from general awareness of the field, from keyword Web searches, from companies whose scientists presented at relevant technical or investor conferences (PTEI, Society for Regenerative Medicine, Techvest), and from the trade literature.[13] Once compiled, the list was circulated to and vetted by individuals knowledgeable in the field. The compilation is believed to be reasonably complete, although some smaller and newer firms will inevitably be missed in a field growing as rapidly as this.

A profile on each firm was then developed, including principle technical focus; date of founding; number of employees; source of funding; and, where appropriate, the fraction of the firm's efforts that were dedicated to stem cells.

For public firms, this information was available from annual reports and Securities and Exchange Commission (SEC) filings. For private firms, the information was obtained from the firm's Web site or by contacting the chief executive officer (CEO) or chief financial officer (CFO). Firms conducting operations in more than one country were asked for a breakdown of employees by geographical region. In a few cases, only a range of the number of FTEs was available; here, the midvalue of the range is reported. Wherever possible, information was double-checked against information available from proprietary databases.[13,14]

Private firms were generally unwilling to disclose their annual spending rate. Accordingly, where not directly available, this number was estimated from a lumped sum correlation of $200,000 in total annual company expenditure per employee per year. This correlation had been validated in earlier surveys of the tissue engineering field.[15,16]

Capital value for public companies was calculated as the product of the number of shares times individual share value, as of December 31, 2002. Number of shares were obtained from company financial statements and share values from online listings. Share values denominated in foreign currencies were converted to dollars at the exchange rates prevailing on December 31, 2002. For firms involved in activities other than stem cells, the capital value was prorated according to the estimated fraction of the firm's activity devoted to stem cells. This implicitly assumes that all of a firm's activities contribute equally to its capital value.

A Snapshot of the Field

At the close of 2002, private sector research and development in stem cells was conducted by just under 1000 scientists and support staff in 31 firms, operating in 11 countries. Aggregate spending was $194 million. Four of the 29 firms are public, the remaining are private. Capital value of the public companies, prorated for their involvement in stem cells, is $98.7 million.

A list of the firms, their location, their Web site, and a thumbnail sketch of each of the firm's activities is given in Table 74–1. Twelve firms employ fewer than 15 FTEs and spend a combined ~$22 million per year; 10 firms have between 15 and 35 FTEs and spend in aggregate ~$50 million per year; and 8 have more than 35 employees and spend an aggregate of ~$122 million per year (Table 74–2). Approximately 37% of the firms use embryonic stem cells and 57% rely on adult stem cells. Thirteen percent of the firms provide cell banking services (Fig. 74–1). The United States constitutes about half of the global resources devoted to stem cells (Fig. 74–2). Firms serving as repositories for approved human stem cell lines, that is, those that can be used in federally funded U.S. research, can be found in Table 74–3. Table 74–4 summarizes the total and prorated capital value, as of the close of 2002, for the 4 (of 31) firms that are public.

Perspectives

The 1000 FTEs and their associated costs are a substantial commitment but the net involvement of the private sector is nevertheless quite modest. Aggregate stem cell activity in the private sector is three times smaller than the total funds devoted to tissue engineering research and development in 2002. It is approximately the size of the staff that a pharmaceutical company would deploy for a single drug for each of the 12 years required to bring a lead compound to markets. It represents less than 1.5% of the annual research budget of Pfizer, a single drug company.

The size distribution of the individual firms in Table 74–2 is also telling. Companies with less than 15 employees, (just under half of all stem cell companies) are really just getting started. By the time a firm has 15–35 employees it can conduct discovery-level science and highly productive firms of this size can certainly affect a field and create increments in shareholder value through intellectual property. However, the actual discovery, definition, development, and regulatory management of a product is extremely labor intensive. It would be highly unusual for a company to be successful at these latter activities with fewer than 100–150 employees.

There is only a weak correlation between company size and company age. Such a pattern is unusual for biotech startups

TABLE 74–1
Stem Cell Firms (as of December 31, 2002)

Company	Web Address	FTEs	Cell Type	Description
Advanced Cell Technology Worcester, MA	www.advancedcell.com	12	ESC	Therapeutic cloning
Befutur Technologies Case Postale, Switzerland	www.befutur.com	12	Both	Tissue regeneration
BresaGen, Inc. Adelaide, Aus/Athens, GA	www.bresagen.com.au	35 (60)	ESC	Neuronal SCs for Parkinson's disease
Cardion Ag Erkath, Germany/Boston, MA	www.cardion-ag.de	14 (50)	ESC	Pancreatic islet cells for diabetes
Celgene Warren, NJ	www.celgene.com	90	Adult	Human SCs from the placenta for cell therapy and banking
CyThera, Inc. San Diego, CA	www.cytheraco.com	12	ESC	Tissue/organ repair, diabetes
Develogen Göttingen, Germany	www.develogen.com	60 (114)	?	Differentiation pathways—diabetes
ES Cell International Melbourne, Australia	www.escellinternational.com	40	ESC	Tissue/organ regeneration
Gamida Cell, Ltd Israel	www.gamida.com	28	Adult	Hematopoietic stem cell therapy, regenerative medicine
Genzyme Biosurgery Cambridge, MA	www.genzymebiosurgery.com	22	Adult	Expansion and transplantation of myoblasts for heart function
Geron Menlo Park, CA	www.geron.com	50 (142)	Both	Therapeutic cloning, drug discovery, xenotransplantation
Infigen Deforest, WI	www.infigen.com	10 (35)	N/A	Cloning, xenotransplantation
Ixion Biotechnology Alachua, FL	www.ixion-biotech.com	6 (18)	Adult	Islet cell production for diabetes
Kaleidos Pharma Seattle, WA	www.kaleidospharma.com	6	Adult	Tissue/organ regeneration
Kourion Therapeutics Duesseldorf, Germany	www.kouriontx.com	19	Adult	Neural, cardiac, osteogenic, chondrogenic therapy
Maria Biotech Company, Ltd Soeul, Korea	www.mariabiotech.co.kr	22	ESC	Heart disease, diabetes, banking
NeuralStem Biopharmaceuticals Gaithersburg, MD	www.neuralstem.com	21	Adult	Neurodegenerative disease/ damage–neural SCs
NeuroNova Stockholm, Sweden	www.neuronova.com	20	Adult	Neurologic disease/damage–neural SCs
Neuronyx Malvern, PA	www.neurononyx.com	42	Adult	CNS disorders, bone marrow SCs
Osiris Baltimore, MD	www.osiristx.com	80	Adult	Tissue/organ regeneration—hMSCs
Primegen Santa Ana, CA	www.primegenbiotech.com	20	?	SC therapy to counter aging
Reliance Life Sciences Bombay, India	—	25	ESC	Tissue/organ regeneration; banking
Reneuron Surrey, UK	www.reneuron.com	25	Adult	Neurologic disease/damage; drug discovery

Continued

TABLE 74–1—cont'd
Stem Cell Firms (as of December 31, 2002)

Company	Web Address	FTEs	Cell Type	Description
SCS KK Kobe, Japan	—	3	ESC	SC therapy; gene and drug discovery
Stem Cell Sciences (SCS) Melbourne, Australia	www.stemcellsciences.com.au	13	ESC	Neurologic disease/damage; gene and drug discovery
Stem Cell, Inc. Palo Alto, CA	www.stemcellsinc.com	33	Adult	Tissue/organ regeneration; drug discovery; gene therapy
StemCell Technologies Vancouver, Canada	www.stemcell.com	110	N/A	SC isolation, proliferation, differentiation
Stemron Gaithersburg, MD	www.stemron.com	6	Adult	Tissue/organ regeneration
StemSource Inc. Thousand Oaks, CA	www.stemsource.com	10	Adult	Banking, SCs from fat
ViaCell Boston, MA	www.viacellinc.com	138 (160)	Adult	Cord blood SC therapy; banking
VistaGen, Inc. Burlingame, CA	www.vistagen-inc.com	6	Both	Drug development; CNS, cardiovascular, cancer

CNS, central nervous system; ESC, embryonal stem cell; FTEs, full-time equivalents; hMSC, human mesenchymal stem cell; SC, stem cell.

that usually grow linearly for their first several years. For example, most tissue engineering startups were found to add about five employees per year for each of their first 5 years.[15] The different behavior of stem cell companies may result from funding limitations, or it may just be that the industry is in early stages with many firms not yet far enough along to prudently and profitably spend at a more rapid rate.

Given their size and resources, most stem cell firms are developing technology rather than products. The rationale is that such technology will have realizable value as the field grows and matures. Companies are also investing is "squatter sovereignty" with the intention of developing infrastructure, experience and, trade skills that will allow them to participate in, or even dominate, a potentially explosive area of future biomedicine. Although high risk, these business models appear sound. In the absence of defined products a "small is beautiful" approach to stem cell startups may be appropriate.

A few firms do have defined products; others are selling services such as neonatal stem cell banking, and still others make and sell the specialized equipment needed for nuclear transfer. Although most activity is centered in pure-play technology-development, a select number of firms appear to be moving products into clinical trials. An Israeli company, Gamida Cell, Ltd., has entered Phase I FDA clinical trials with StemEx, a stem and progenitor cell proliferation technology designed to enhance immune reconstitution in patients undergoing intensive chemotherapy. The product is likely to compete with Osiris' human mesenchymal stem cells (hMSCs) transplant support system that is currently in FDA Phase II clinical trials. The established success of hematopoietic cell transplants makes these therapy formats a logical area for establishing the credibility of stem cell therapies. In addition, in the first FDA-sanctioned trials of stem cell therapy for nonhematopoietic tissue regeneration, Genzyme Biosurgery is co-sponsoring an investigation into the use of myoblasts (muscle stem cells) to improve heart function in patients who have suffered a myocardial infarction. The trial, which will take place primarily at European hospitals, represents a joint effort between government funded research from the Hopital European Georges Pompidos in France and the privately funded, U.S.-based Genzyme Biosurgery.

Funding, Market Value, and Regulatory Issues

Most of the stem cell startups are private and thus funded by capital from angels, venture groups, and mezzanine financiers. Four are public, that is, listed on National Association of Securities Dealers Automated Quotation System (NASDAQ) or an equivalent national exchange (Table 74–3). Three went public as stem cell firms (BresaGen, Geron, Renouron) and one (Stem Cell Inc.) raised funds under a different persona and subsequently moved its activities wholly into stem cells. Given the current condition of the stock market, not too much can be read into the current capital value of public stem cell companies. The soundest conclusion is that the market appears to be lumping these companies together with other biotech startups and that stem cell firms trade neither at a premium or discount over early-stage biotech startups. The constant calliope of publicity about stem cells has not lead to a rash of IPOs which is probably a good thing. More disturbing is the lack of corporate partnerships or other flow of resources from

TABLE 74–2
Stem Cell Companies Listed by Size (as of December 31, 2002)

	Number of FTEs	Estimated Spending (Million/yr)
Firms with <15 FTEs ACT, Befutur Technologies, Cardion, Cythera, Infigen,* Ixion,* Kaleidos Pharma, SCS KK, Stem Cell Sciences, Stemron, StemSource, Inc., Vistagen, Inc.	110	$22
Firms with 15–35 FTEs Bresagen,* Gamida Cell, Kourion, Maria Biotech, NeuralStem, NeuroNova, Primegen, Reliance, Reneuron, Stem Cells, Inc.	248	$50
Firms with more than 35 FTEs Celgene,, Developen,, ES Cell International, Geron, Neuronyx, Osiris, StemCell Technologies, ViaCell,	610	$122

FTE refers to full-time equivalent supporting stem cell technology. Firms indicated with an asterisk have additional employees working in other areas.

big pharma or big med-devices into stem cells. This source of revenue has been critical to the success of biotechnology in the past and will likely prove necessary for stem cells in the future.

Stem cell firms are highly diversified in both their technology approaches and geographical bases. There is a tilt toward focus on adult cells as compared with embryonic cells, at least in the number of firms working on each (see Fig. 74–1). This is move away from the almost 50–50 split between the two in mid-2002[12] and may reflect the ethical controversies over the use of embryonic cells. The dependence of future research and clinical applications on regulatory laws causes the broad geographical base of the industry to be very telling. Some countries are distinctly more hospitable to embryonic stem cells and therapeutic cloning than others. Among those countries that have thus far established policies, the United Kingdom, Sweden, Israel, and Japan are the most permissive, whereas Germany and the United States are the most constraining. In December of 2002, Australia's senate passed a bill allowing the use of previously created frozen embryos for embryonic cell harvesting, a legislative decision that is expected to promote the expansion of the country's demonstrated interest in stem cell technology. Meanwhile, the U.S. House of Representatives has voted to ban therapeutic cloning altogether in a decision mirroring one made in 2001. The Senate is believed likely to table or defeat the bill, as it did in 2001, but the U.S. government's continued examination of the issue is predictive of future regulatory battles and ethical disputes related to therapeutic cloning. As of yet, private sector firms in the United States seem relatively undeterred by potential legislative constraints. However, capital and scientists are likely to gravitate toward the region or environment where they can best flourish. Hence, the existence of a geographically dispersed industry ensures that restrictive legislation in one region will not stop the science from advancing.

TABLE 74–3
Firms Serving as Custodians for National Institutes of Health (NIH)-approved Embryonic Stem Cell Lines

Company	Number of Approved Cell Lines
Bresagen, Inc.	4
CyThera, Inc.	9
ES Cell International	9
Geron	7
Maria Biotech Ltd	3
Reliance Life Sciences	7

The private sector is just one of many sources of stem cell research and development. Government agencies both perform work in their own laboratories and fund research in universities and research institutes. Foundations and non-for-profit laboratories also support stem cell research. No summary data on public sector spending on stem cells seems to be available. Based on the number and impact of publications in the peer-reviewed literature, it would appear that publicly supported stem cell research equals or exceeds that of the private sector. This pattern differs from that in classical tissue engineering, where support has always come almost entirely from the private sector.[15,16] Because the public and private sectors have different goals, different priorities, different time frames, and different constraints, a balance between the two seems very sensible. Furthermore, several companies such as BresaGen, Maria Biotech, and NeuroNova maintain working collaborations with government-funded research that is being conducted at nearby universities and research institutes. Such partnerships reflect a pooling of resources that may not occur between companies vying for future market share in a particular area. The field of genomics represents a good example of how a combination of critical mass research in both the public and private can accelerate development.

Conclusion

Private sector activity in stem cells has emerged as a small, clearly identifiable, high-tech cottage industry. If past history of biotech startups is a guide, these firms are attended by zeal, focus, high-energy, excitement, enthusiasm, and instability. Their relatively small size is likely an advantage at the current stage of development. If, and when, the field of stem cells achieves a clinically important role in twenty-first century health care, the commitment and belief of these early pioneers will be amply rewarded.

TABLE 74–4
Capital Value of Public Firms

	Shares Outstanding (Millions)	Share Price Where Listed	Share Price U.S. Dollars	Capital Value U.S. Dollars (Millions)	Prorated Capital Value (Millions of Dollars)
BresaGen (35%)	46	Aus $0.44	$0.26	$11.8	$5.9
Geron (100%)	24	U.S. $3.60	$3.60	$88	$88
Reneuron (100%)	39	£0.08	$0.13	$5.0	$5.0
Stem Cells Inc. (100%)	24	$1.09	$1.09	$26.4	$26.4

Data is for December 31, 2002.
Conversion rates: 0.58 Australian Dollar = 1 U.S. Dollar; 1.60 Pounds = 1 U.S. Dollar.
In column 1, number in parenthesis represents fraction of company activities committed to stem cells. The prorated capital value is the total value times this fraction (see text)

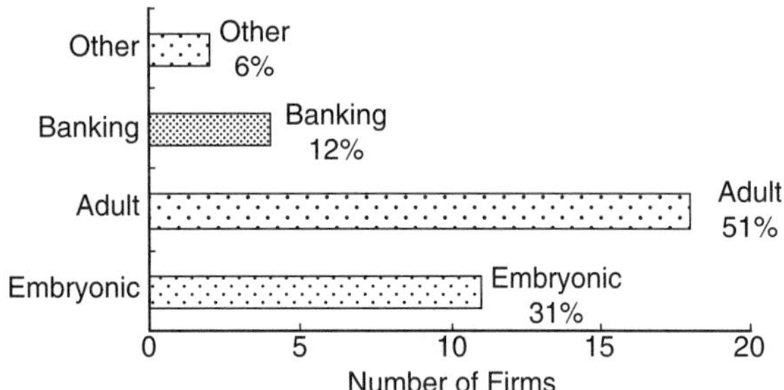

Figure 74–1. *Principle activity of private sector, stem cell firms.* The adult stem cell is the largest segment of this field but activity is well diversified across other areas of activity. Some companies have multiple activities and were included in more than one category.

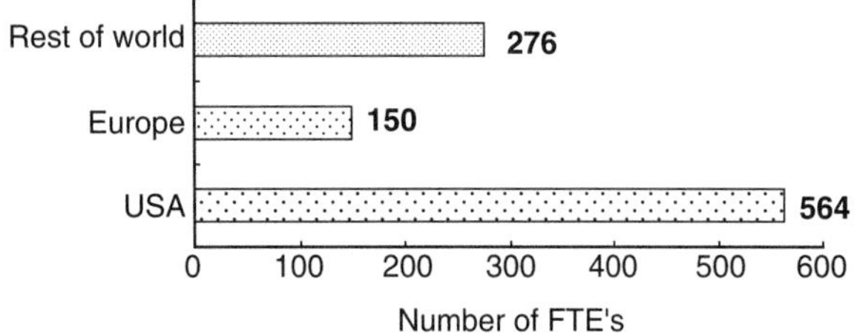

Figure 74–2. *Location of full-time equivalents (FTEs) by geographical area.* About half the commercial activity in this field is taking place in the United States. Europe is the least represented sector.

REFERENCES

1. Campbell, K.H., McWhir, J., Ritchie, W.A., and Wilmut, I. (1996). Sheep cloned by nuclear transfer from a cultured cell line. *Nature* **380,** 64–66.
2. Thomson, J.A., Itskovitz-Eldor, J., Shapiro, S.S., Waknitz, M.A., Swoergoe, K.K., Marshall, V.V., and Jones, J.M. (1998). Embryonic stem cell lines derived from human blastocysts. *Science* **282,** 1145–1147.
3. Shamblott, M.J., Axelman, J., Wang, S., Bugg, E.M., Littlefield, J.W., Donovan, P.J., Blumenthal, P.D., Huggins, G.R., and Gearhart, J.D. (1998). Derivation of pluripotent stem cells from cultured human primordial germ cells. *Proc. Natl. Acad. Sci. U. S. A.* **95,** 13726–13731.
4. Lumelsky, N., Blondel, O., Laeng, P., Velasco, I., Ravin, R., and McKay, R. (2001). Differentiation of embryonic stem cells to insulin-secreting structures similar to pancreatic islets. *Science* **292,** 1389–1394.
5. Kim, J.H., Auerbach, J.M., Rodriguez, G., Jose, A., Velasco, A., Gavin, D., Lumelsky, N., Lee, S.N., Nguyen, J., Sanchez-Pernuate, R., Bankiewicz, K., and McKay, R. (2002). Dopamine neurons derived from embryonic stem cells function in an animal model of Parkinson's disease. *Nature* **418,** 50–66.
6. Zuk, P.A., Zhu, M., Mizuno, H., Huang, J., Futrell, J.W., Katz, A.J., Benhaim, P., Lorenz, H.P., and Hedrick, M.H. (2001). Multilineage cells from human adipose tissue: Implications for cell-based therapies. *Tissue Eng.* 211–228.
7. Jiang, B., Jahagirdar, R., Reinhardt, L., Schwartz, R.E., Keene, C.D., Ortiz-Gonzalez, X.R., Reyes, M., Lenvik, T., Lund, T., Blackstad, M., Du, J., Aldrich, S., Lisberg, A., Low, W.C., Largaespada, D.A., and Verfaillie, C.M. (June 2002). Pluripotency of mesenchymal stem cells derived from adult marrow. *Nature* (advance online publication) DOI: **10.**1038.
8. Orlic, D., Kajstura, J., Chimenti, S., Jakoniuk, I., Anderson, S.M., Li, B., Pickel, J., and Mckay, R. (2001). Bone marrow cells regenerate infracted myocardium *Nature* **410,** 701–705.
9. Cibelli, J.B., Lanza, R.P., West, M.D., and Ezzell, C. (2002). The first cloned embryo. *Sci. Am.* **286,** 44–51.
10. Cibelli, J.B., Grant, K.A., Chapman, K.B., Cunniff, K., Worst, T., Green, J.L., Walker, S.J., Gutin, P.H., Vilner, L., Tabar, V., Dominko, T., Kane, J., Wettstein, P.J., Lanza, R.P., Studer, L., Vrana-Kent, E., and West, M.D. (2002). Parthenogenetic stem cells in nonhuman primates. *Science* **195,** 819.
11. DeWitt, N. (2001). Stem cells. *Nature* **414,** 87.
12. Lysaght, M.J., and Hazlehurst, A. (2003). Private sector support of stem cell technology and therapeutic cloning. *Tissue Eng.* **9** (in press).
13. "Stem Cell Research News." Data Trends Publication Inc., Leesburg VA. Available at http://www.stemcellresearchnews.com (accessed).
14. VentureOne, San Francisco, CA. Available at http://www.-venturesource.com (accessed).
15. Lysaght, M.J., Nguy, N., and Sullivan, K. (1998). An economic survey of the emerging tissue engineering industry. *Tissue Eng.* **4,** 231.
16. Lysaght, M.J., and Reyes, J. (2001). The growth of tissue engineering. *Tissue Eng.* **7,** 485–493.

Index

Page numbers followed by "t" denote tables; those followed by "f" denote figures.

N